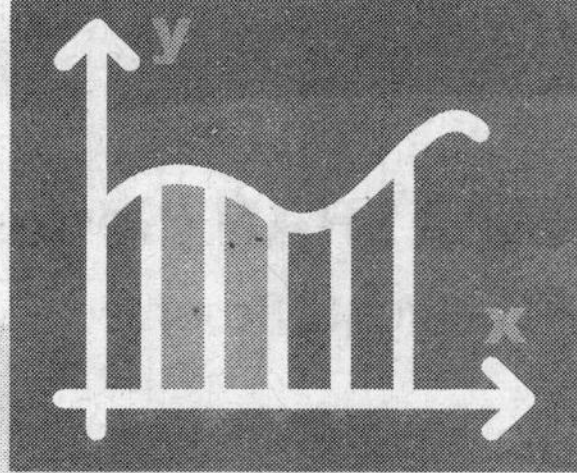

Skills in Mathematics for

JEE Main & Advanced

Algebra

With Sessionwise Theory & Exercises

Dr. SK Goyal

ARIHANT PRAKASHAN (Series), MEERUT

ARIHANT PRAKASHAN (Series), MEERUT

卐 Administrative & Production Offices

Regd. Office

'Ramchhaya' 4577/15, Agarwal Road, Darya Ganj, New Delhi -110002
Tele: 011- 47630600, 43518550

卐 Head Office

Kalindi, TP Nagar, Meerut (UP) - 250002 Tel: 0121-7156203, 7156204

卐 Sales & Support Offices

Agra, Ahmedabad, Bengaluru, Bareilly, Chennai, Delhi, Guwahati, Hyderabad, Jaipur, Jhansi, Kolkata, Lucknow, Nagpur & Pune.

卐 **ISBN** : 978-93-25298-63-7

卐 **PRICE** : ₹695.00

Published by Arihant Publications (India) Ltd.

For further information about the books published by Arihant, log on to www.arihantbooks.com or e-mail at info@arihantbooks.com

Follow us on   

PREFACE

"THE ALGEBRAIC SUM OF ALL THE TRANSFORMATIONS OCCURRING IN A CYCLICAL PROCESS CAN ONLY BE POSITIVE, OR, AS AN EXTREME CASE EQUAL TO NOTHING"

MEANS IF YOU CONTINUOUSLY PUT YOUR EFFORTS ON AN ASPECT YOU HAVE VERY GOOD CHANCE OF POSITIVE OUTCOME i.e. SUCCESS

It is a matter of great pride and honour for me to have received such an overwhelming response to the previous editions of this book from the readers. In a way, this has inspired me to revise this book thoroughly as per the changed pattern of JEE Main & Advanced. I have tried to make the contents more relevant as per the needs of students, many topics have been re-written, a lot of new problems of new types have been added in etcetc. All possible efforts are made to remove all the printing errors that had crept in previous editions. The book is now in such a shape that the students would feel at ease while going through the problems, which will in turn clear their concepts too.

A Summary of changes that have been made in Revised & Enlarged Edition

- Theory has been completely updated so as to accommodate all the changes made in JEE Syllabus & Pattern in recent years.
- The most important point about this new edition is, now the whole text matter of each chapter has been divided into small sessions with exercise in each session. In this way the reader will be able to go through the whole chapter in a systematic way.
- Just after completion of theory, Solved Examples of all JEE types have been given, providing the students a complete understanding of all the formats of JEE questions & the level of difficulty of questions generally asked in JEE.
- Along with exercises given with each session, a complete cumulative exercises have been given at the end of each chapter so as to give the students complete practice for JEE along with the assessment of knowledge that they have gained with the study of the chapter.
- Last 13 Years questions asked in JEE Main & Adv, IIT-JEE & AIEEE have been covered in all the chapters.

However I have made the best efforts and put my all Algebra teaching experience in revising this book. Still I am looking forward to get the valuable suggestions and criticism from my own fraternity i.e. the fraternity of JEE teachers.

I would also like to motivate the students to send their suggestions or the changes that they want to be incorporated in this book.

All the suggestions given by you all will be kept in prime focus at the time of next revision of the book.

Dr. SK Goyal

CONTENTS

1. COMPLEX NUMBERS 1-102

LEARNING PART

Session 1
- Integral Powers of Iota (i)
- Switch System Theory

Session 2
- Definition of Complex Number
- Conjugate Complex Numbers
- Representation of a Complex Number in Various Forms

Session 3
- amp (z)– amp (–z)=± p, According as amp (z) is Positive or Negative
- Square Root of a Complex Number
- Solution of Complex Equations
- De-Moivre's Theorem
- Cube Roots of Unity

Session 4
- nth Root of Unity
- Vector Representation of Complex Numbers
- Geometrical Representation of Algebraic Operation on Complex Numbers
- Rotation Theorem (Coni Method)
- Shifting the Origin in Case of Complex Numbers
- Inverse Points
- Dot and Cross Product
- Use of Complex Numbers in Coordinate Geometry

PRACTICE PART
- JEE Type Examples
- Chapter Exercises

2. THEORY OF EQUATIONS 103-206

LEARNING PART

Session 1
- Polynomial in One Variable
- Identity
- Linear Equation
- Quadratic Equations
- Standard Quadratic Equation

Session 2
- Transformation of Quadratic Equations
- Condition for Common Roots

Session 3
- Quadratic Expression
- Wavy Curve Method
- Condition for Resolution into Linear Factors
- Location of Roots (Interval in which Roots Lie)

Session 4
- Equations of Higher Degree
- Rational Algebraic Inequalities
- Roots of Equation with the Help of Graphs

Session 5
- Irrational Equations
- Irrational Inequations
- Exponential Equations
- Exponential Inequations
- Logarithmic Equations
- Logarithmic Inequations

PRACTICE PART
- JEE Type Examples
- Chapter Exercises

3. SEQUENCES AND SERIES 207-312

LEARNING PART

Session 1
- Sequence
- Series
- Progression

Session 2
- Arithmetic Progression

Session 3
- Geometric Sequence or Geometric Progression

Session 4
- Harmonic Sequence or Harmonic Progression

Session 5
- Mean

Session 6
- Arithmetico-Geometric Series (AGS)
- Sigma (S) Notation
- Natural Numbers

Session 7
- Application to Problems of Maxima and Minima

PRACTICE PART
- JEE Type Examples
- Chapter Exercises

4. LOGARITHMS AND THEIR PROPERTIES 313-358

LEARNING PART

Session 1
- Definition
- Characteristic and Mantissa

Session 2
- Principle Properties of Logarithm

Session 3
- Properties of Monotonocity of Logarithm
- Graphs of Logarithmic Functions

PRACTICE PART
- JEE Type Examples
- Chapter Exercises

5. PERMUTATIONS AND COMBINATIONS 359-436

LEARNING PART

Session 1
- Fundamental Principle of Counting
- Factorial Notation

Session 2
- Divisibility Test
- Principle of Inclusion and Exclusion
- Permutation

Session 3
- Number of Permutations Under Certain Conditions
- Circular Permutations
- Restricted Circular Permutations

Session 4
- Combination
- Restricted Combinations

Session 5
- Combinations from Identical Objects

Session 6
- Arrangement in Groups
- Multinomial Theorem
- Multiplying Synthetically

Session 7
- Rank in a Dictionary
- Gap Method
[when particular objects are never together]

PRACTICE PART
- JEE Type Examples
- Chapter Exercises

6. BINOMIAL THEOREM 437-518

LEARNING PART

Session 1
- Binomial Theorem for Positive Integral Index
- Pascal's Triangle

Session 2
- General Term
- Middle Terms
- Greatest Term
- Trinomial Expansion

Session 3
- Two Important Theorems
- Divisibility Problems

Session 4
- Use of Complex Numbers in Binomial Theorem
- Multinomial Theorem
- Use of Differentiation
- Use of Integration
- When Each Term is Summation Contains the Product of Two Binomial Coefficients or Square of Binomial Coefficients
- Binomial Inside Binomial
- Sum of the Series

PRACTICE PART
- JEE Type Examples
- Chapter Exercises

7. DETERMINANTS 519-604

LEARNING PART

Session 1
- Definition of Determinants
- Expansion of Determinant
- Sarrus Rule for Expansion
- Window Rule for Expansion

Session 2
- Minors and Cofactors
- Use of Determinants in Coordinate Geometry
- Properties of Determinants

Session 3
- Examples on Largest Value of a Third Order Determinant
- Multiplication of Two Determinants of the Same Order
- System of Linear Equations
- Cramer's Rule
- Nature of Solutions of System of Linear Equations
- System of Homogeneous Linear Equations

Session 4
- Differentiation of Determinant
- Integration of a Determinant
- Walli's Formula
- Use of S in Determinant

PRACTICE PART
- JEE Type Examples
- Chapter Exercises

8. MATRICES 605-690

LEARNING PART

Session 1
- Definition
- Types of Matrices
- Difference Between a Matrix and a Determinant
- Equal Matrices
- Operations of Matrices
- Various Kinds of Matrices

Session 2
- Transpose of a Matrix
- Symmetric Matrix
- Orthogonal Matrix
- Complex Conjugate (or Conjugate) of a Matrix
- Hermitian Matrix
- Unitary Matrix
- Determinant of a Matrix
- Singular and Non-Singular Matrices

Session 3
- Adjoint of a Matrix
- Inverse of a Matrix
- Elementary Row Operations
- Equivalent Matrices
- Matrix Polynomial
- Use of Mathematical Induction

Session 4
- Solutions of Linear Simultaneous Equations Using Matrix Method

PRACTICE PART
- JEE Type Examples
- Chapter Exercises

9. PROBABILITY 691-760

LEARNING PART

Session 1
- Some Basic Definitions
- Mathematical or Priori or Classical Definition of Probability
- Odds in Favours and Odds Against the Event

Session 2
- Some Important Symbols
- Conditional Probability

Session 3
- Total Probability Theorem
- Baye's Theorem or Inverse Probability

Session 4
- Binomial Theorem on Probability
- Poisson Distribution
- Expectation
- Multinomial Theorem
- Uncountable Uniform Spaces

PRACTICE PART
- JEE Type Examples
- Chapter Exercises

10. MATHEMATICAL INDUCTION 761-784

LEARNING PART
- Introduction
- Statement
- Mathematical Statement

PRACTICE PART
- JEE Type Examples
- Chapter Exercises

11. SETS, RELATIONS AND FUNCTIONS 785-836

LEARNING PART

Session 1
- Definition of Sets
- Representation of a Set
- Different Types of Sets
- Laws and Theorems
- Venn Diagrams (Euler-Venn Diagrams)

Session 2
- Ordered Pair
- Definition of Relation
- Ordered Relation
- Composition of Two Relations

Session 3
- Definition of Function
- Domain, Codomain and Range
- Composition of Mapping
- Equivalence Classes
- Partition of Set
- Congruences

PRACTICE PART
- JEE Type Examples
- Chapter Exercises

SYLLABUS

JEE MAIN

Unit I Sets, Relations and Functions
Sets and their representation, Union, intersection and complement of sets and their algebraic properties, Power set, Relation, Types of relations, equivalence relations, functions, one-one, into and onto functions, composition of functions.

Unit II Complex Numbers
Complex numbers as ordered pairs of reals, Representation of complex numbers in the form a+ib and their representation in a plane, Argand diagram, algebra of complex numbers, modulus and argument (or amplitude) of a complex number, square root of a complex number, triangle inequality.

Unit III Matrices and Determinants
Matrices, algebra of matrices, types of matrices, determinants and matrices of order two and three. Properties of determinants, evaluation of deter-minants, area of triangles using determinants. Adjoint and evaluation of inverse of a square matrix using determinants and elementary transformations, Test of consistency and solution of simultaneous linear equations in two or three variables using determinants and matrices.

Unit IV Permutations and Combinations
Fundamental principle of counting, permutation as an arrangement and combination as selection, Meaning of P(n,r) and C (n,r), simple applications.

Unit V Mathematical Induction
Principle of Mathematical Induction and its simple applications.

Unit VI Binomial Theorem and its Simple Applications
Binomial theorem for a positive integral index, general term and middle term, properties of Binomial coefficients and simple applications.

Unit VII Sequences and Series
Arithmetic and Geometric progressions, insertion of arithmetic, geometric means between two given numbers. Relation between AM and GM Sum upto n terms of special series: $\sum n, \sum n^2, \sum n^3$. Arithmetico - Geometric progression.

Unit VIII Probability
Probability of an event, addition and multiplication theorems of probability, Baye's theorem, probability distribution of a random variate, Bernoulli and Binomial distribution.

JEE ADVANCED

Algebra
Algebra of complex numbers, addition, multiplication, conjugation, polar representation, properties of modulus and principal argument, triangle inequality, cube roots of unity, geometric interpretations.

Quadratic equations with real coefficients, relations between roots and coefficients, formation of quadratic equations with given roots, symmetric functions of roots.

Arithmetic, geometric and harmonic progressions, arithmetic, geometric and harmonic means, sums of finite arithmetic and geometric progressions, infinite geometric series, sums of squares and cubes of the first n natural numbers.

Logarithms and their Properties
Permutations and combinations, Binomial theorem for a positive integral index, properties of binomial coefficients.

Matrices as a rectangular array of real numbers, equality of matrices, addition, multiplication by a scalar and product of matrices, transpose of a matrix, determinant of a square matrix of order up to three, inverse of a square matrix of order up to three, properties of these matrix operations, diagonal, symmetric and skew-symmetric matrices and their properties, solutions of simultaneous linear equations in two or three variables.

Addition and multiplication rules of probability, conditional probability, independence of events, computation of probability of events using permutations and combinations.

CHAPTER

01

Complex Numbers

Learning Part

Session 1

- Integral Powers of Iota (i)
- Switch System Theory

Session 2

- Definition of Complex Number
- Conjugate Complex Numbers
- Representation of a Complex Number in Various Forms

Session 3

- $\text{amp}(z) - \text{amp}(-z) = \pm\pi$, According as amp ($z$) is Positive or Negative
- Square Root of a Complex Number
- Solution of Complex Equations
- De-Moivre's Theorem
- Cube Roots of Unity

Session 4

- nth Root of Unity
- Vector Representation of Complex Numbers
- Geometrical Representation of Algebraic Operation on Complex Numbers
- Rotation Theorem (Coni Method)
- Shifting the Origin in Case of Complex Numbers
- Inverse Points
- Dot and Cross Product
- Use of Complex Numbers in Coordinate Geometry

Practice Part

- JEE Type Examples
- Chapter Exercises

Arihant on Your Mobile !
Exercises with the symbol can be practised on your mobile. See inside cover page to activate for free.

The square of any real number, whether positive, negative or zero, is always non-negative i.e. $x^2 \geq 0$ for all $x \in R$. Therefore, there will be no real value of x, which when squared, will give a negative number.

Thus, the equation $x^2 + 1 = 0$ is not satisfied for any real value of x. 'Euler' was the first Mathematician to introduce the symbol i (read 'Iota') for the square root of -1 with the property $i^2 = -1$. The theory of complex number was later on developed by Gauss and Hamilton. According to Hamilton, "Imaginary number is that number whose square is a negative number". Hence, the equation $x^2 + 1 = 0$

$$\Rightarrow \quad x^2 = -1$$

$$\text{or} \quad x = \pm\sqrt{-1}$$

(in the sense of arithmetic, $\sqrt{-1}$ has no meaning).

Symbolically, $\sqrt{-1}$ is denoted by i (the first letter of the word 'Imaginary').

$\therefore$ Solutions of $x^2 + 1 = 0$ are $x = \pm i$.

Also, i is the unit of complex number, since i is present in every complex number. Generally, if a is positive quantity, then

$$\begin{aligned}\sqrt{-a} \times \sqrt{-a} &= \sqrt{(-1) \times a} \times \sqrt{(-1) \times a} \\ &= \sqrt{-1} \times \sqrt{a} \times \sqrt{-1} \times \sqrt{a} \\ &= i\sqrt{a} \times i\sqrt{a} \\ &= i^2 a = -a\end{aligned}$$

Remark

$\sqrt{-a} = i\sqrt{a}$, where a is positive quantity. Keeping this result in mind, the following computation is correct

$$\sqrt{-a}\sqrt{-b} = i\sqrt{a} \cdot i\sqrt{b} = i^2\sqrt{ab} = -\sqrt{ab}$$

where, a and b are positive real numbers.

But the computation, $\sqrt{-a}\sqrt{-b} = \sqrt{(-a)(-b)} = \sqrt{|a||b|}$ is wrong. Because the property, $\sqrt{a}\sqrt{b} = \sqrt{ab}$ is valid only when atleast one of a and b is non-negative.

If a and b are both negative, then $\sqrt{a}\sqrt{b} = -\sqrt{|a||b|}$.

Example 1. Is the following computation correct? If not, give the correct computation.

$$\sqrt{-2}\sqrt{-3} = \sqrt{(-2)(-3)} = \sqrt{6}$$

Sol. No,

If a and b are both negative real numbers, then $\sqrt{a}\sqrt{b} = -\sqrt{ab}$

Here, $a = -2$ and $b = -3$.

$$\therefore \quad \sqrt{-2}\sqrt{-3} = -\sqrt{(-2)(-3)} = -\sqrt{6}$$

Example 2. A student writes the formula $\sqrt{ab} = \sqrt{a}\sqrt{b}$. Then, he substitutes $a = -1$ and $b = -1$ and finds $1 = -1$. Explain, where he is wrong.

Sol. Since, a and b are both negative, therefore $\sqrt{ab} \neq \sqrt{a}\sqrt{b}$.

Infact a and b are both negative, then we have $\sqrt{a}\sqrt{b} = -\sqrt{ab}$.

Example 3. Explain the fallacy

$$-1 = i \times i = \sqrt{-1} \times \sqrt{-1} = \sqrt{(-1) \times (-1)} = \sqrt{1} = 1.$$

Sol. If a and b are both negative, then

$$\sqrt{a}\sqrt{b} = -\sqrt{|a||b|}$$

$$\therefore \quad \sqrt{-1} \times \sqrt{-1} = -\sqrt{|-1||-1|} = -1$$

Session 1

Integral Powers of Iota (i), Switch System Theory

Integral Powers of Iota (i)

(i) If the index of i is whole number, then

$$i^0 = 1, i^1 = i, i^2 = (\sqrt{-1})^2 = -1,$$

$$i^3 = i \cdot i^2 = -i, i^4 = (i^2)^2 = (-1)^2 = 1$$

To find the value of i^n ($n > 4$) First divide n by 4. Let q be the quotient and r be the remainder.

i.e.

$$4\overline{)\,n\,}(q$$
$$\underline{-4q}$$
$$r$$

$$\Rightarrow \quad n = 4q + r$$

When, $0 \leq r \leq 3$

$$\therefore \quad i^n = i^{4q+r} = (i^4)^q (i)^r = (1)^q \cdot (i)^r = i^r$$

In general, $i^{4n} = 1$, $i^{4n+1} = i$, $i^{4n+2} = -1$, $i^{4n+3} = -i$ for any whole number n.

(ii) If the index of i is a negative integer, then

$$i^{-1} = \frac{1}{i} = \frac{i}{i^2} = \frac{i}{-1} = -i, \; i^{-2} = \frac{1}{i^2} = -1,$$

$$i^{-3} = \frac{1}{i^3} = \frac{i}{i^4} = i, \; i^{-4} = \frac{1}{i^4} = \frac{1}{1} = 1, \text{ etc.}$$

Example 4. Evaluate.

(i) i^{1998}

(ii) i^{-9999}

(iii) $(-\sqrt{-1})^{4n+3}, n \in N$

Sol. (i) 1998 leaves remainder 2, when it is divided by 4.

i.e. $4\overline{)1998}(499$, $\quad 1996$, $\quad 2$

$\therefore \quad i^{1998} = i^2 = -1$

Aliter

$$i^{1998} = \frac{i^{2000}}{i^2} = \frac{1}{-1} = -1$$

(ii) 9999 leaves remainder 3, when it is divided by 4.

i.e. $4\overline{)9999}(2499$, $\quad 9996$, $\quad 3$

$$\therefore \quad i^{-9999} = \frac{1}{i^{9999}} = \frac{1}{i^3} = \frac{i}{i^4} = \frac{i}{1} = i$$

Aliter

$$i^{-9999} = \frac{1}{i^{9999}} = \frac{i}{i^{10000}} = \frac{i}{1} = i$$

(iii) $4n+3$ leaves remainder 3, when it is divided by 4.

i.e., $4\overline{)4n+3}(n$, $\quad 4n$, $\quad 3$

$\therefore \quad i^{4n+3} = i^3 = -i$

Now, $(-\sqrt{-1})^{4n+3} = (-i)^{4n+3} = -(i)^{4n+3}$

$= -(-i)$

$= i$

Aliter $(-\sqrt{-1})^{4n+3} = (-i)^{4n+3} = -i^{4n+3}$

$= -(i^4)^n \cdot i^3$

$= -(1)^n(-i) = i$

Example 5. Find the value of $1 + i^2 + i^4 + i^6 + \ldots + i^{2n}$, where $i = \sqrt{-1}$ and $n \in N$.

Sol. $\because \quad 1 + i^2 + i^4 + i^6 + \ldots + i^{2n} = 1 - 1 + 1 - 1 + \ldots + (-1)^n$

***Case* I** If n is odd, then

$$1 + i^2 + i^4 + i^6 + \ldots + i^{2n} = 1 - 1 + 1 - 1 + \ldots + 1 - 1 = 0$$

***Case* II** If n is even, then

$$1 + i^2 + i^4 + i^6 + \ldots + i^{2n} = 1 - 1 + 1 - 1 + \ldots + 1 = 1$$

Example 6. If $a = \dfrac{1+i}{\sqrt{2}}$, where $i = \sqrt{-1}$, then find the value of a^{1929}.

Sol. $\because \quad a^2 = \left(\dfrac{1+i}{\sqrt{2}}\right)^2 = \left(\dfrac{1+i^2+2i}{2}\right)$

$$= \left(\frac{1-1+2i}{2}\right) = i$$

$\therefore \quad a^{1929} = a \cdot a^{1928} = a \cdot (a^2)^{964} = a(i)^{964}$

$= a(i)^{4 \times 241} = a \cdot (i^4)^{241} = a$

Example 7. Dividing $f(z)$ by $z - i$, where $i = \sqrt{-1}$, we obtain the remainder i and dividing it by $z + i$, we get the remainder $1 + i$. Find the remainder upon the division of $f(z)$ by $z^2 + 1$.

Sol. $z - i = 0 \Rightarrow z = i$

Remainder, when $f(z)$ is divided by $(z - i) = i$

i.e. $\quad f(i) = i \quad \ldots$(i)

and remainder, when $f(z)$ is divided by $(z + 1) = 1 + i$

i.e. $\quad f(-i) = 1 + i \quad [\because z + i = 0 \Rightarrow z = -i] \ldots$(ii)

Since, $z^2 + 1$ is a quadratic expression, therefore remainder when $f(z)$ is divided by $z^2 + 1$, will be in general a linear expression. Let $g(z)$ be the quotient and $az + b$ (where a and b are complex numbers) be the remainder, when $f(z)$ is divided by $z^2 + 1$.

Then, $\quad f(z) = (z^2 + 1)g(z) + az + b \quad \ldots$(iii)

$\therefore \quad f(i) = (i^2 + 1)g(i) + ai + b = ai + b$

or $\quad ai + b = i \quad$ [from Eq. (i)] ... (iv)

and $\quad f(-i) = (i^2 + 1)g(-i) - ai + b = -ai + b$

or $\quad -ai + b = 1 + i \quad$ [from Eq. (ii)] ...(v)

From Eqs. (iv) and (v), we get

$$b = \frac{1}{2} + i \text{ and } a = \frac{i}{2}$$

Hence, required remainder $= az + b$

$$= \frac{1}{2}iz + \frac{1}{2} + i$$

The Sum of Four Consecutive Powers of *i* (Iota) is Zero

If $n \in I$ and $i = \sqrt{-1}$, then

$$i^n + i^{n+1} + i^{n+2} + i^{n+3} = i^n(1 + i + i^2 + i^3)$$
$$= i^n(1 + i - 1 - i) = 0$$

Remark

1. $\displaystyle\sum_{r=p}^{m} f(r) = \sum_{r=1}^{m-p+1} f(r+p-1)$
2. $\displaystyle\sum_{r=-p}^{m} f(r) = \sum_{r=1}^{m+p+1} f(r-p-1)$

Example 8. Find the value of $\sum_{n=1}^{13}(i^n+i^{n+1})$ (where, $i=\sqrt{-1}$)

Sol. $\because \sum_{n=1}^{13}(i^n+i^{n+1})=\sum_{n=1}^{13}i^n+\sum_{n=1}^{13}i^{n+1}=(i+0)+(i^2+0)$

$$=i-1\left[\because \sum_{n=2}^{13}i^n=0 \text{ and } \sum_{n=2}^{13}i^{n+1}=0 \text{ (three sets of four consecutive powers of } i)\right]$$

Example 9. Find the value of $\sum_{n=0}^{100}i^{n!}$ (where, $i=\sqrt{-1}$).

Sol. $n!$ is divisible by 4, $\forall\ n\geq 4$.

$$\therefore \sum_{n=4}^{100}i^{n!}=\sum_{n=1}^{97}i^{(n+3)!}$$

$$=i^0+i^0+i^0+\dots 97 \text{ times }=97 \quad \dots\text{(i)}$$

$$\therefore \sum_{n=0}^{100}i^{n!}=\sum_{n=0}^{3}i^{n!}+\sum_{n=4}^{100}i^{n!}$$

$$=i^{0!}+i^{1!}+i^{2!}+i^{3!}+97 \quad \text{[from Eq. (i)]}$$

$$=i^1+i^1+i^2+i^6+97=i+i-1-1+97$$

$$=95+2i$$

Example 10. Find the value of $\sum_{r=1}^{4n+7}i^r$ (where, $i=\sqrt{-1}$).

Sol. $\sum_{r=1}^{4n+7}i^r=i^1+i^2+i^3+\sum_{r=4}^{4n+7}i^r=i-1-i+\sum_{r=1}^{4n+4}i^{r+3}$

$$=-1+0 \quad [(n+1) \text{ sets of four consecutive powers of } i]$$

$$=-1$$

Example 11. Show that the polynomial $x^{4p}+x^{4q+1}+x^{4r+2}+x^{4s+3}$ is divisible by x^3+x^2+x+1, where $p,q,r,s\in N$.

Sol. Let $f(x)=x^{4p}+x^{4q+1}+x^{4r+2}+x^{4s+3}$

and $x^3+x^2+x+1=(x^2+1)(x+1)$

$$=(x+i)(x-i)(x+1),$$

where $i=\sqrt{-1}$

Now, $f(i)=i^{4p}+i^{4q+1}+i^{4r+2}+i^{4s+3}=1+i+i^2+i^3=0$

[sum of four consecutive powers of i is zero]

$$f(-i)=(-i)^{4p}+(-i)^{4q+1}+(-i)^{4r+2}+(-i)^{4s+3}$$

$$=1+(-i)^1+(-i)^2+(-i)^3=1-i-1+i=0$$

and $f(-1)=(-1)^{4p}+(-1)^{4q+1}+(-1)^{4r+2}+(-1)^{4s+3}$

$$=1-1+1-1=0$$

Hence, by division theorem, $f(x)$ is divisible by x^3+x^2+x+1.

Switch System Theory

(Finding Digit in the Unit's Place)

We can determine the digit in the unit's place in a^b, where $a,b\in N$. If last digit of a are 0, 1, 5 and 6, then digits in the unit's place of a^b are 0, 1, 5 and 6 respectively, for all $b\in N$.

Powers of 2

$2^1,2^2,2^3,2^4,2^5,2^6,2^7,2^8,2^9,\dots$ the digits in unit's place of different powers of 2 are as follows :

2, 4, 8, 6, 2, 4, 8, 6, 2,… (period being 4)
↑ ↑ ↑ ↑ ↑ ↑ ↑ ↑ ↑
①②③⓪①②③⓪①… (switch number)

(The remainder when b is divided by 4, can be 1 or 2 or 3 or 0). Then, press the switch number and then we get the digit in unit's place of a^b (just above the switch number) i.e. 'press the number and get the answer'.

Example 12. What is the digit in the unit's place of $(5172)^{11327}$?

Sol. Here, last digit of a is 2.

The remainder when 11327 is divided by 4, is 3. Then, press switch number 3 and then we get 8.

Hence, the digit in the unit's place of $(5172)^{11327}$ is 8.

Powers of 3

$3^1,3^2,3^3,3^4,3^5,3^6,3^7,3^8,\dots$ the digits in unit's place of different powers of 3 are as follows:

3, 9, 7, 1, 3, 9, 7, 1,… (period being 4)
↑ ↑ ↑ ↑ ↑ ↑ ↑ ↑
①②③⓪①②③⓪ … (switch number)

The remainder when b is divided by 4, can be 1 or 2 or 3 or 0. Now, press the switch number and get the unit's place digit (just above).

Example 13. What is the digit in the unit's place of $(143)^{86}$?

Sol. Here, last digit of a is 3.

The remainder when 86 is divided by 4, is 2.

Then, press switch number 2 and then we get 9.

Hence, the digit in the unit's place of $(143)^{86}$ is 9.

Powers of 4

$4^1, 4^2, 4^3, 4^4, 4^5, \ldots$ the digits in unit's place of different powers of 4 are as follows:

4, 6, 4, 6, 4, ... (period being 2)

↑ ↑ ↑ ↑ ↑

① ⓪ ① ⓪ ① ... (switch number)

The remainder when b is divided by 2, can be 1 or 0. Now, press the switch number and get the unit's place digit (just above the switch number).

Example 14. What is the digit in unit's place of $(1354)^{22222}$?

Sol. Here, last digit of a is 4.

The remainder when 22222 is divided by 2, is 0. Then, press switch number 0 and then we get 6.

Hence, the digit in the unit's place of $(1354)^{22222}$ is 6.

Powers of 7

$7^1, 7^2, 7^3, 7^4, 7^5, 7^6, 7^7, 7^8, \ldots$ the digits in unit's place of different powers of 7 are as follows:

7, 9, 3, 1, 7, 9, 3, 1,... (period being 4)

↑ ↑ ↑ ↑ ↑ ↑ ↑ ↑

① ② ③ ⓪ ① ② ③ ⓪ ... (switch number)

(The remainder when b is divided by 4, can be 1 or 2 or 3 or 0). Now, press the switch number and get the unit's place digit (just above).

Example 15. What is the digit in the unit's place of $(13057)^{941120579}$?

Sol. Here, last digit of a is 7.

The remainder when 941120579 is divided by 4, is 3. Then, press switch number 3 and then we get 3.

Hence, the digit in the unit's place of $(13057)^{941120579}$ is 3.

Powers of 8

$8^1, 8^2, 8^3, 8^4, 8^5, 8^6, 8^7, 8^8, \ldots$ the digits in unit's place of different powers of 8 are as follows:

8, 4, 2, 6, 8, 4, 2, 6,... (period being 4)

↑ ↑ ↑ ↑ ↑ ↑ ↑ ↑

① ② ③ ⓪ ① ② ③ ⓪ ... (switch number)

The remainder when b is divided by 4, can be 1 or 2 or 3 or 0.

Now, press the switch number and get the unit's place digit (just above the switch number).

Example 16. What is the digit in the unit's place of $(1008)^{786}$?

Sol. Here, last digit of a is 8.

The remainder when 786 is divided by 4, is 2. Then, press switch number 2 and then we get 4.

Hence, the digit in the unit's place of $(1008)^{786}$ is 4.

Powers of 9

$9^1, 9^2, 9^3, 9^4, 9^5, \ldots$ the digits in unit's place of different powers of 9 are as follows:

9, 1, 9, 1, 9,... (period being 2)

↑ ↑ ↑ ↑ ↑

① ⓪ ① ⓪ ① ... (switch number)

The remainder when b is divided by 2, can be 1 or 0.

Now, press the switch number and get the unit's place digit (just above the switch number).

Example 17. What is the digit in the unit's place of $(2419)^{111213}$?

Sol. Here, last digit of a is 9.

The remainder when 111213 is divided by 2, is 1. Then, press switch number 1 and then we get 9.

Hence, the digit in the unit's place of $(2419)^{111213}$ is 9.

Exercise for Session 1

1 If $(1+i)^{2n}+(1-i)^{2n}=-2^{n+1}$ (where, $i=\sqrt{-1}$) for all those n, which are

(a) even
(b) odd
(c) multiple of 3
(d) None of these

2 If $i=\sqrt{-1}$, the number of values of i^n+i^{-n} for different $n \in I$ is

(a) 1
(b) 2
(c) 3
(d) 4

3 If $a>0$ and $b<0$, then $\sqrt{a}\,\sqrt{b}$ is equal to (where, $i=\sqrt{-1}$)

(a) $-\sqrt{a\cdot|b|}$
(b) $\sqrt{a\cdot|b|}\,i$
(c) $\sqrt{a\cdot|b|}$
(d) None of these

4 Consider the following statements.

$S_1: -6=2i\times 3i=\sqrt{(-4)}\times\sqrt{(-9)}$ (where, $i=\sqrt{-1}$)
$S_2: \sqrt{(-4)}\times\sqrt{(-9)}=\sqrt{(-4)\times(-9)}$
$S_3: \sqrt{(-4)\times(-9)}=\sqrt{36}$
$S_4: \sqrt{36}=6$

Of these statements, the incorrect one is

(a) S_1 only
(b) S_2 only
(c) S_3 only
(d) None of these

5 The value of $\sum_{n=0}^{50} i^{(2n+1)!}$ (where, $i=\sqrt{-1}$) is

(a) i
(b) $47-i$
(c) $48+i$
(d) 0

6 The value of $\sum_{r=-3}^{1003} i^r$ (where $i=\sqrt{-1}$) is

(a) 1
(b) -1
(c) i
(d) $-i$

7 The digit in the unit's place of $(153)^{98}$ is

(a) 1
(b) 3
(c) 7
(d) 9

8 The digit in the unit's place of $(141414)^{12121}$ is

(a) 4
(b) 6
(c) 3
(d) 1

Session 2

Definition of Complex Number, Conjugate Complex Numbers, Representation of a Complex Number in Various Forms

Definition of Complex Number

A number of the form $a + ib$, where $a, b \in R$ and $i = \sqrt{-1}$, is called a **complex number.** It is denoted by z i.e. $z = a + ib$.

A complex number may also be defined as an ordered pair of real numbers; and may be denoted by the symbol (a, b). If we write $z = (a, b)$, then a is called the real part and b is the imaginary part of the complex number z and may be denoted by Re (z) and Im (z), respectively i.e., $a = \text{Re}(z)$ and $b = \text{Im}(z)$.

Two complex numbers are said to be equal, if and only if their real parts and imaginary parts are separately equal.

Thus, $a + ib = c + id$

$\Leftrightarrow$ $a = c$ and $b = d$

where, $a, b, c, d \in R$ and $i = \sqrt{-1}$.

i.e. $z_1 = z_2$

$\Leftrightarrow$ $\text{Re}(z_1) = \text{Re}(z_2)$ and $\text{Im}(z_1) = \text{Im}(z_2)$

Important Properties of Complex Numbers

1. The complex numbers do not possess the property of order, i.e., $(a + ib) >$ or $< (c + id)$ is not defined. *For example*, $9 + 6i > 3 + 2i$ makes no sense.
2. A real number a can be written as $a + i \cdot 0$. Therefore, every real number can be considered as a complex number, whose imaginary part is zero. Thus, the set of real numbers (R) is a proper subset of the complex numbers (C) i.e. $R \subset C$. Hence, the complex number system is $N \subset W \subset I \subset Q \subset R \subset C$
3. A complex number z is said to be purely real, if $\text{Im}(z) = 0$; and is said to be purely imaginary, if $\text{Re}(z) = 0$. The complex number $0 = 0 + i \cdot 0$ is both purely real and purely imaginary.
4. In real number system, $a^2 + b^2 = 0 \Rightarrow a = 0 = b$.

   But if z_1 and z_2 are complex numbers, then $z_1^2 + z_2^2 = 0$ does not imply $z_1 = z_2 = 0$.

   For example, $z_1 = 1 + i$ and $z_2 = 1 - i$

   Here, $z_1 \neq 0, z_2 \neq 0$

   But $z_1^2 + z_2^2 = (1 + i)^2 + (1 - i)^2 = 1 + i^2 + 2i + 1 + i^2 - 2i$
   $= 2 + 2i^2 = 2 - 2 = 0$

   However, if product of two complex numbers is zero, then atleast one of them must be zero, same as in case of real numbers.

   If $z_1 z_2 = 0$, then $z_1 = 0, z_2 \neq 0$ or $z_1 \neq 0, z_2 = 0$

   or $z_1 = 0, z_2 = 0$

Algebraic Operations on Complex Numbers

Let two complex numbers be $z_1 = a + ib$ and $z_2 = c + id$, where $a, b, c, d \in R$ and $i = \sqrt{-1}$.

1. Addition $z_1 + z_2 = (a + ib) + (c + id)$
$= (a + c) + i(b + d)$

2. Subtraction $z_1 - z_2 = (a + ib) - (c + id)$
$= (a - c) + i(b - d)$

3. Multiplication $z_1 \cdot z_2 = (a + ib) \cdot (c + id)$
$= ac + iad + ibc + i^2 bd$
$= ac + i(ad + bc) - bd$
$= (ac - bd) + i(ad + bc)$

4. Division $\dfrac{z_1}{z_2} = \dfrac{(a + ib)}{(c + id)} \cdot \dfrac{(c - id)}{(c - id)}$

[multiplying numerator and denominator by $c - id$ where atleast one of c and d is non-zero]

$$= \frac{ac - iad + ibc - i^2 bd}{(c)^2 - (id)^2} = \frac{ac + i(bc - ad) + bd}{c^2 - i^2 d^2}$$

$$= \frac{(ac + bd) + i(bc - ad)}{c^2 + d^2} = \frac{(ac + bd)}{(c^2 + d^2)} + i\frac{(bc - ad)}{(c^2 + d^2)}$$

Remark

$\dfrac{1 + i}{1 - i} = i$ and $\dfrac{1 - i}{1 + i} = -i$, where $i = \sqrt{-1}$.

Properties of Algebraic Operations on Complex Numbers

Let z_1, z_2 and z_3 be any three complex numbers. Then, their algebraic operations satisfy the following properties :

Properties of Addition of Complex Numbers

(i) **Closure law** $z_1 + z_2$ is a complex number.

(ii) **Commutative law** $z_1 + z_2 = z_2 + z_1$

(iii) **Associative law** $(z_1 + z_2) + z_3 = z_1 + (z_2 + z_3)$

(iv) **Additive identity** $z+0=z=0+z$, then 0 is called the additive identity.

(v) **Additive inverse** $-z$ is called the additive inverse of z, i.e. $z+(-z)=0$.

Properties of Multiplication of Complex Numbers

(i) **Closure law** $z_1 \cdot z_2$ is a complex number.

(ii) **Commutative law** $z_1 \cdot z_2 = z_2 \cdot z_1$

(iii) **Associative law** $(z_1 \cdot z_2) z_3 = z_1 (z_2 \cdot z_3)$

(iv) **Multiplicative identity** $z \cdot 1 = z = 1 \cdot z$, then 1 is called the multiplicative identity.

(v) **Multiplicative inverse** If z is a non-zero complex number, then $\frac{1}{z}$ is called the multiplicative inverse of z i.e. $z. \ \frac{1}{z}=1=\frac{1}{z}\cdot z$

(vi) **Multiplication is distributive with respect to addition** $z_1 (z_2+z_3) = z_1 z_2 + z_1 z_3$

Conjugate Complex Numbers

The complex numbers $z=(a,b)=a+ib$ and $\bar{z}=(a,-b)=a-ib$, where a and b are real numbers, $i=\sqrt{-1}$ and $b\neq 0$, are said to be complex conjugate of each other (here, the complex conjugate is obtained by just changing the sign of i).

Note that, sum $=(a+ib)+(a-ib)=2a$, which is real.

And product $=(a+ib)(a-ib)=a^2-(ib)^2$

$$=a^2-i^2b^2=a^2-(-1)b^2$$

$$=a^2+b^2, \text{ which is real.}$$

Geometrically, $\bar{z}$ is the mirror image of z along real axis on argand plane.

Remark

Let $z=-a-ib, a>0, b>0=(-a,-b)$ (III quadrant)

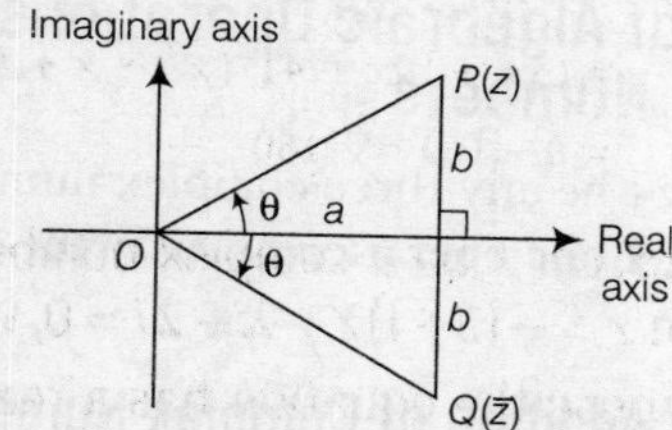

Then, $\bar{z}=-a+ib=(-a,b)$ (II quadrant). Now,

(i) If z lies in I quadrant, then $\bar{z}$ lies in IV quadrant and *vice-versa*.

(ii) If z lies in II quadrant, then $\bar{z}$ lies in III quadrant and *vice-versa*.

Properties of Conjugate Complex Numbers

Let z, z_1 and z_2 be complex numbers. Then,

(i) $\overline{(\bar{z})}=z$

(ii) $z+\bar{z}=2\,\text{Re}(z)$

(iii) $z-\bar{z}=2\,\text{Im}(z)$

(iv) $z+\bar{z}=0 \Rightarrow z=-\bar{z} \Rightarrow z$ is purely imaginary.

(v) $z-\bar{z}=0 \Rightarrow z=\bar{z} \Rightarrow z$ is purely real.

(vi) $\overline{z_1 \pm z_2}=\bar{z}_1 \pm \bar{z}_2$ Ingeneral,

$$\overline{z_1 \pm z_2 \pm z_3 \pm \ldots \pm z_n}=\bar{z}_1 \pm \bar{z}_2 \pm \bar{z}_3 \pm \ldots \pm \bar{z}_n$$

(vii) $\overline{z_1 \cdot z_2}=\bar{z}_1 \cdot \bar{z}_2$

In general, $\overline{z_1 \cdot z_2 \cdot z_3 \ldots z_n}=\bar{z}_1 \cdot \bar{z}_2 \cdot \bar{z}_3 \ldots \bar{z}_n$

(viii) $\overline{\left(\frac{z_1}{z_2}\right)}=\frac{\bar{z}_1}{\bar{z}_2}, z_2 \neq 0$

(ix) $\overline{z^n}=(\bar{z})^n$

(x) $z_1\bar{z}_2+\bar{z}_1 z_2=2\,\text{Re}(z_1\bar{z}_2)=2\,\text{Re}(\bar{z}_1 z_2)$

(xi) If $z=f(z_1,z_2)$, then $\bar{z}=f(\bar{z}_1,\bar{z}_2)$

Example 18. If $\frac{x-3}{3+i}+\frac{y-3}{3-i}=i$, where $x, y \in R$ and $i=\sqrt{-1}$, find the values of x and y.

Sol. $\because \frac{x-3}{3+i}+\frac{y-3}{3-i}=i$

$$\Rightarrow (x-3)(3-i)+(y-3)(3+i)=i(3+i)(3-i)$$

$$\Rightarrow (3x-xi-9+3i)+(3y+yi-9-3i)=10i$$

$$\Rightarrow (3x+3y-18)+i(y-x)=10i$$

On comparing real and imaginary parts, we get

$$3x+3y-18=0$$

$$\Rightarrow x+y=6 \quad \ldots\text{(i)}$$

and $$y-x=10 \quad \ldots\text{(ii)}$$

On solving Eqs. (i) and (ii), we get

$$x=-2, y=8$$

Example 19. If $(a+ib)^5=p+iq$, where $i=\sqrt{-1}$, prove that $(b+ia)^5=q+ip$.

Sol. $\because (a+ib)^5=p+iq$

$$\therefore \overline{(a+ib)^5}=\overline{p+iq} \Rightarrow (a-ib)^5=(p-iq)$$

$$\Rightarrow (-i^2a-ib)^5=(-i^2p-iq) \quad [\because i^2=-1]$$

$$\Rightarrow (-i)^5(b+ia)^5=(-i)(q+ip)$$

$$\Rightarrow (-i)(b+ia)^5=(-i)(q+ip)$$

$$\therefore (b+ia)^5=(q+ip)$$

Example 20. Find the least positive integral value of n, for which $\left(\frac{1-i}{1+i}\right)^n$, where $i=\sqrt{-1}$, is purely imaginary with positive imaginary part.

Sol. $\left(\frac{1-i}{1+i}\right)^n = \left(\frac{1-i}{1+i}\times\frac{1-i}{1-i}\right)^n = \left(\frac{1+i^2-2i}{2}\right)^n = \left(\frac{1-1-2i}{2}\right)^n$

$= (-i)^n = \text{Imaginary}$

$\Rightarrow \quad n = 1, 3, 5, \ldots$ for positive imaginary part $n = 3$.

Example 21. If the multiplicative inverse of a complex number is $(\sqrt{3}+4i)/19$, where $i=\sqrt{-1}$, find complex number.

Sol. Let z be the complex number.

Then, $z\cdot\left(\frac{\sqrt{3}+4i}{19}\right) = 1$

or $\quad z = \frac{19}{(\sqrt{3}+4i)} \times \frac{(\sqrt{3}-4i)}{(\sqrt{3}-4i)}$

$= \frac{19(\sqrt{3}-4i)}{19} = (\sqrt{3}-4i)$

Example 22. Find real θ, such that $\frac{3+2i\sin\theta}{1-2i\sin\theta}$, where $i=\sqrt{-1}$, is

(i) purely real. (ii) purely imaginary.

Sol. Let $z = \frac{3+2i\sin\theta}{1-2i\sin\theta}$

On multiplying numerator and denominator by conjugate of denominator,

$$z = \frac{(3+2i\sin\theta)(1+2i\sin\theta)}{(1-2i\sin\theta)(1+2i\sin\theta)} = \frac{(3-4\sin^2\theta)+8i\sin\theta}{(1+4\sin^2\theta)}$$

$$= \frac{(3-4\sin^2\theta)}{(1+4\sin^2\theta)} + i\frac{(8\sin\theta)}{(1+4\sin^2\theta)}$$

(i) For purely real, $\text{Im}(z) = 0$

$\Rightarrow \quad \frac{8\sin\theta}{1+4\sin^2\theta} = 0$ or $\sin\theta = 0$

$\therefore \quad \theta = n\pi, n\in I$

(ii) For purely imaginary, $\text{Re}(z) = 0$

$\Rightarrow \quad \frac{(3-4\sin^2\theta)}{(1+4\sin^2\theta)} = 0$ or $3-4\sin^2\theta = 0$

or $\quad \sin^2\theta = \frac{3}{4} = \left(\frac{\sqrt{3}}{2}\right)^2 = \left(\sin\frac{\pi}{3}\right)^2$

$\therefore \quad \theta = n\pi \pm \frac{\pi}{3}, n\in I$

Example 23. Find real values of x and y for which the complex numbers $-3+ix^2y$ and x^2+y+4i, where $i=\sqrt{-1}$, are conjugate to each other.

Sol. Given, $\quad -3+ix^2y = \overline{x^2+y+4i}$

$\Rightarrow \quad -3-ix^2y = x^2+y+4i$

On comparing real and imaginary parts, we get

$x^2+y = -3 \quad$ ...(i)

and $\quad -x^2y = 4 \quad$ ...(ii)

From Eq. (ii), we get $x^2 = -\frac{4}{y}$

Then, $\quad -\frac{4}{y}+y = -3 \quad \left[\text{putting } x^2 = -\frac{4}{y} \text{ in Eq. (i)}\right]$

$y^2+3y-4 = 0 \Rightarrow (y+4)(y-1) = 0$

$\therefore \quad y = -4, 1$

For $\quad y = -4, x^2 = 1 \Rightarrow x = \pm 1$

For $\quad y = 1, x^2 = -4 \quad$ [impossible]

$\therefore \quad x = \pm 1, y = -4$

Example 24. If $x = -5+2\sqrt{-4}$, find the value of $x^4+9x^3+35x^2-x+4$.

Sol. Since, $\quad x = -5+2\sqrt{-4} \Rightarrow x+5 = 4i$

$\Rightarrow \quad (x+5)^2 = (4i)^2 \Rightarrow x^2+10x+25 = -16$

$\therefore \quad x^2+10x+41 = 0 \quad$ ...(i)

Now,

$x^2+10x+41 \,\big)\, x^4+9x^3+35x^2-x+4 \,\big(\, x^2-x+4$

$\quad x^4+10x^3+41x^2$
$\quad - \quad - \quad -$
$\quad -x^3-6x^2-x+4$
$\quad -x^3-10x^2-41x$
$\quad + \quad + \quad +$
$\quad 4x^2+40x+4$
$\quad 4x^2+40x+164$
$\quad - \quad - \quad -$
$\quad -160$

$\therefore \quad x^4+9x^3+35x^2-x+4$

$= (x^2+10x+41)(x^2-x+4)-160$

$= 0-160 = -160 \quad$ [from Eq. (i)]

Example 25. Let z be a complex number satisfying the equation $z^2-(3+i)z+\lambda+2i = 0$, where $\lambda\in R$ and $i=\sqrt{-1}$. Suppose the equation has a real root, find the non-real root.

Sol. Let α be the real root. Then,

$\alpha^2-(3+i)\alpha+\lambda+2i = 0$

$\Rightarrow \quad (\alpha^2 - 3\alpha + \lambda) + i(2 - \alpha) = 0$

On comparing real and imaginary parts, we get

$$\alpha^2 - 3\alpha + \lambda = 0 \quad \text{...(i)}$$

$$\Rightarrow \quad 2 - \alpha = 0 \quad \text{...(ii)}$$

From Eq. (ii), $\alpha = 2$

Let other root be β.

Then, $\alpha + \beta = 3 + i \Rightarrow 2 + \beta = 3 + i$

$\therefore \quad \beta = 1 + i$

Hence, the non-real root is $1 + i$.

Representation of a Complex Number in Various Forms

Cartesian Form

(Geometrical Representation)

Every complex number $z = x + iy$, where $x, y \in R$ and $i = \sqrt{-1}$, can be represented by a point in the cartesian plane known as complex plane (Argand plane) by the ordered pair (x, y).

Modulus and Argument of a Complex Number

Let $\quad z = x + iy = (x, y)$ for all $x, y \in R$ and $i = \sqrt{-1}$.

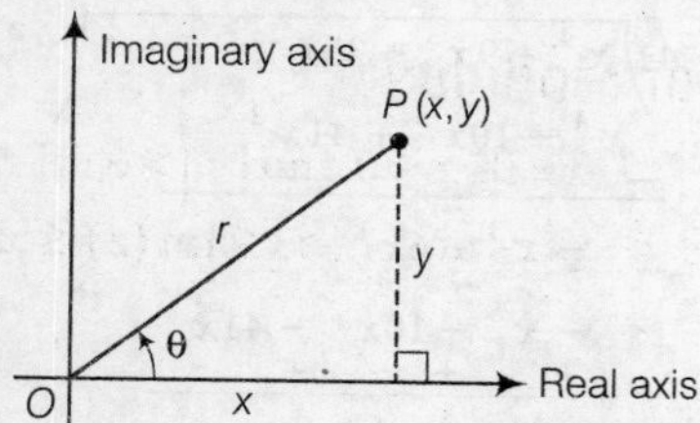

The length OP is called modulus of the complex number z denoted by $|z|$,

i.e. $\quad OP = r = |z| = \sqrt{(x^2 + y^2)}$

and if $(x, y) \neq (0, 0)$, then θ is called the argument or amplitude of z,

i.e. $\theta = \tan^{-1}\left(\dfrac{y}{x}\right)$ [angle made by OP with positive X-axis]

or $\arg(z) = \tan^{-1}(y/x)$

Also, argument of a complex number is not unique, since if θ is a value of the argument, so also is $2n\pi + \theta$, where $n \in I$. But usually, we take only that value for which $0 \le \theta < 2\pi$. Any two arguments of a complex number differ by $2n\pi$.

Argument of z will be $\theta, \pi - \theta, \pi + \theta$ and $2\pi - \theta$ according as the point z lies in I, II, III and IV quadrants respectively, where $\theta = \tan^{-1}\left|\dfrac{y}{x}\right|$.

Example 26. Find the arguments of $z_1 = 5 + 5i$, $z_2 = -4 + 4i$, $z_3 = -3 - 3i$ and $z_4 = 2 - 2i$, where $i = \sqrt{-1}$.

Sol. Since, z_1, z_2, z_3 and z_4 lies in I, II, III and IV quadrants respectively. The arguments are given by

$$\arg(z_1) = \tan^{-1}\left|\frac{5}{5}\right| = \tan^{-1} 1 = \pi/4$$

$$\arg(z_2) = \pi - \tan^{-1}\left|\frac{4}{-4}\right| = \pi - \tan^{-1} 1 = \pi - \frac{\pi}{4} = \frac{3\pi}{4}$$

$$\arg(z_3) = \pi + \tan^{-1}\left|\frac{-3}{-3}\right| = \pi + \tan^{-1} 1 = \pi + \frac{\pi}{4} = \frac{5\pi}{4}$$

and $$\arg(z_4) = 2\pi - \tan^{-1}\left|\frac{-2}{2}\right|$$

$$= 2\pi - \tan^{-1} 1 = 2\pi - \frac{\pi}{4} = \frac{7\pi}{4}$$

Principal Value of the Argument

The value θ of the argument which satisfies the inequality $-\pi < \theta \le \pi$ is called the **principal value** of the argument.

If $z = x + iy = (x, y), \forall\, x, y \in R$ and $i = \sqrt{-1}$, then

$\arg(z) = \tan^{-1}\left(\dfrac{y}{x}\right)$ always gives the principal value. It depends on the quadrant in which the point (x, y) lies.

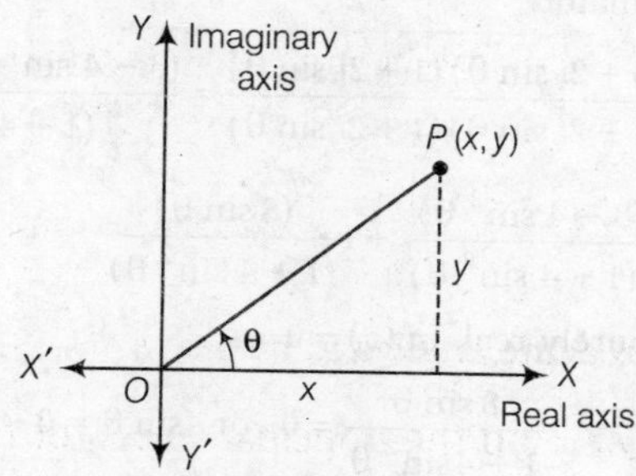

(i) $(x, y) \in$ first quadrant $x > 0, y > 0$.

The principal value of $\arg(z) = \theta = \tan^{-1}\left(\dfrac{y}{x}\right)$

It is an acute angle and positive.

(ii) $(x, y) \in$ second quadrant $x < 0, y > 0$.

The principal value of $\arg(z) = \theta$

$$= \pi - \tan^{-1}\left(\frac{y}{|x|}\right)$$

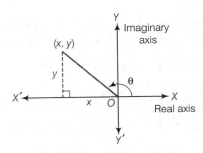

It is an obtuse angle and positive.

(iii) $(x, y) \in$ third quadrant $x < 0, y < 0$.

The principal value of $\arg(z) = \theta = -\pi + \tan^{-1}\left(\frac{y}{x}\right)$

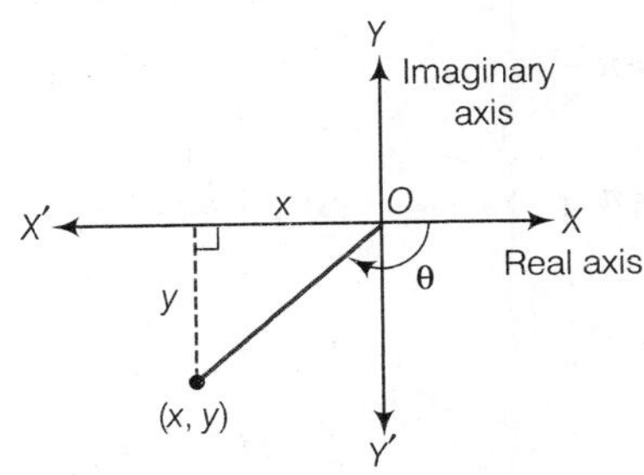

It is an obtuse angle and negative.

(iv) $(x, y) \in$ fourth quadrant $x > 0, y < 0$.

The principal value of $\arg(z) = \theta$

$$= -\tan^{-1}\left(\frac{|y|}{x}\right)$$

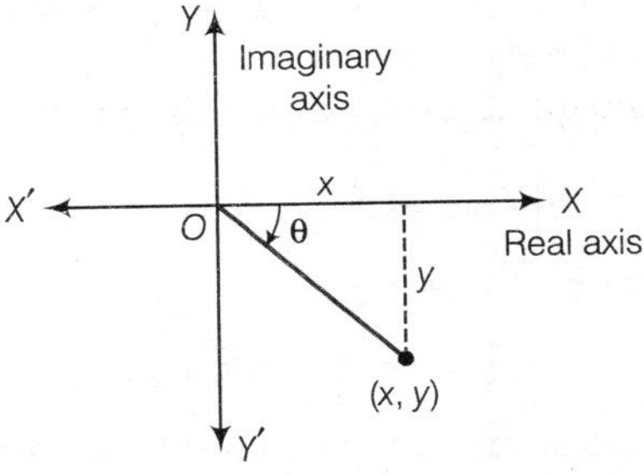

It is an acute angle and negative.

Example 27. Find the principal values of the arguments of $z_1 = 2 + 2i$, $z_2 = -3 + 3i$, $z_3 = -4 - 4i$ and $z_4 = 5 - 5i$, where $i = \sqrt{-1}$.

Sol. Since, z_1, z_2, z_3 and z_4 lies in I, II, III and IV quadrants respectively. The principal values of the arguments are given by

$$\tan^{-1}\left(\frac{2}{2}\right),\ \pi - \tan^{-1}\left(\frac{3}{|-3|}\right),\ -\pi + \tan^{-1}\left(\frac{-4}{-4}\right),\ -\tan^{-1}\left(\frac{|-5|}{5}\right)$$

or $\tan^{-1} 1, \pi - \tan^{-1} 1, -\pi + \tan^{-1} 1, -\tan^{-1} 1$

or $\frac{\pi}{4}, \pi - \frac{\pi}{4}, -\pi + \frac{\pi}{4}, -\frac{\pi}{4}$ or $\frac{\pi}{4}, \frac{3\pi}{4}, -\frac{3\pi}{4}, -\frac{\pi}{4}$

Hence, the principal values of the arguments of z_1, z_2, z_3 and z_4 are $\frac{\pi}{4}, \frac{3\pi}{4}, -\frac{3\pi}{4}, -\frac{\pi}{4}$, respectively.

Remark

1. Unless otherwise stated, amp z implies principal value of the argument.
2. Argument of the complex number 0 is not defined.
3. If $z_1 = z_2 \Leftrightarrow |z_1| = |z_2|$ and $\arg(z_1) = \arg(z_2)$.
4. If $\arg(z) = \pi/2$ or $-\pi/2$, z is purely imaginary.
5. If $\arg(z) = 0$ or π, z is purely real.

Example 28. Find the argument and the principal value of the argument of the complex number $z = \frac{2+i}{4i + (1+i)^2}$, where $i = \sqrt{-1}$.

Sol. Since, $z = \frac{2+i}{4i + (1+i)^2} = \frac{2+i}{4i + 1 + i^2 + 2i} = \frac{2+i}{6i} = \frac{1}{6} - \frac{1}{3} i$

$\therefore$ z lies in IV quadrant.

Here, $\theta = \tan^{-1}\left|\frac{-\frac{1}{3}}{\frac{1}{6}}\right| = \tan^{-1} 2$

$\therefore$ $\arg(z) = 2\pi - \theta = 2\pi - \tan^{-1} 2$

Hence, principal value of $\arg(z) = -\theta = -\tan^{-1} 2$.

Properties of Modulus

(i) $|z| \ge 0 \Rightarrow |z| = 0$, iff $z = 0$ and $|z| > 0$, iff $z \ne 0$

(ii) $-|z| \le \text{Re}(z) \le |z|$ and $-|z| \le \text{Im}(z) \le |z|$

(iii) $|z| = |\bar{z}| = |-z| = |-\bar{z}|$

(iv) $z\bar{z} = |z|^2$

(v) $|z_1 z_2| = |z_1||z_2|$

In general, $|z_1 z_2 z_3 \ldots z_n| = |z_1||z_2||z_3| \ldots |z_n|$

(vi) $\left|\frac{z_1}{z_2}\right| = \frac{|z_1|}{|z_2|}$ $(z_2 \ne 0)$

(vii) $|z_1 \pm z_2| \le |z_1| + |z_2|$

In general, $|z_1 \pm z_2 \pm z_3 \pm \ldots \pm z_n| \le |z_1| + |z_2| + |z_3| + \ldots + |z_n|$

(viii) $|z_1 \pm z_2| \ge ||z_1| - |z_2||$

(ix) $|z^n| = |z|^n$

(x) $||z_1| - |z_2|| \le |z_1 + z_2| \le |z_1| + |z_2|$

Thus, $|z_1|+|z_2|$ is the greatest possible value of $|z_1+z_2|$ and $||z_1|-|z_2||$ is the least possible value of $|z_1+z_2|$.

(xi) $|z_1 \pm z_2|^2 = (z_1 \pm z_2)(\bar{z}_1 \pm \bar{z}_2) = |z_1|^2 + |z_2|^2 \pm (z_1\bar{z}_2 + \bar{z}_1 z_2)$

or $|z_1|^2 + |z_2|^2 \pm 2\,\text{Re}\,(z_1\bar{z}_2)$

(xii) $z_1\bar{z}_2 + \bar{z}_1 z_2 = 2|z_1||z_2|\cos(\theta_1 - \theta_2)$, where $\theta_1 = \arg(z_1)$ and $\theta_2 = \arg(z_2)$

(xiii) $|z_1 + z_2|^2 = |z_1|^2 + |z_2|^2 \Leftrightarrow \dfrac{z_1}{z_2}$ is purely imaginary.

(xiv) $|z_1+z_2|^2 + |z_1 - z_2|^2 = 2\{|z_1|^2 + |z_2|^2\}$

(xv) $|az_1 - bz_2|^2 + |bz_1 + az_2|^2 = (a^2+b^2)(|z_1|^2 + |z_2|^2)$, where $a, b \in R$

(xvi) Unimodular i.e., unit modulus

If z is unimodular, then $|z| = 1$. In case of unimodular, let $z = \cos\theta + i\sin\theta, \theta \in R$ and $i = \sqrt{-1}$.

Remark

1. If $f(z)$ is unimodular, then $|f(z)| = 1$ and let $f(z) = \cos\theta + i\sin\theta, \theta \in R$ and $i = \sqrt{-1}$.
2. $\dfrac{z}{|z|}$ is always a unimodular complex number, if $z \neq 0$.

(xvii) The multiplicative inverse of a non-zero complex number z is same as its reciprocal and is given by $\dfrac{1}{z} = \dfrac{\bar{z}}{z\bar{z}} = \dfrac{\bar{z}}{|z|^2}$.

Example 29. If $\theta_i \in [0, \pi/6], i = 1, 2, 3, 4, 5$ and $\sin\theta_1 z^4 + \sin\theta_2 z^3 + \sin\theta_3 z^2 + \sin\theta_4 z + \sin\theta_5 = 2$, show that $\dfrac{3}{4} < |z| < 1$.

Sol. Given that,

$$\sin\theta_1 z^4 + \sin\theta_2 z^3 + \sin\theta_3 z^2 + \sin\theta_4 z + \sin\theta_5 = 2$$

or $2 = |\sin\theta_1 z^4 + \sin\theta_2 z^3 + \sin\theta_3 z^2 + \sin\theta_4 z + \sin\theta_5|$

$2 \le |\sin\theta_1 z^4| + |\sin\theta_2 z^3| + |\sin\theta_3 z^2| + |\sin\theta_4 z| + |\sin\theta_5|$ [by property (vii)]

$\Rightarrow 2 \le |\sin\theta_1||z^4| + |\sin\theta_2||z^3| + |\sin\theta_3||z^2| + |\sin\theta_4||z| + |\sin\theta_5|$ [by property (v)]

$\Rightarrow 2 \le |\sin\theta_1||z|^4 + |\sin\theta_2||z|^3 + |\sin\theta_3||z|^2 + |\sin\theta_4||z| + |\sin\theta_5|$ [by property (ix)] ...(i)

But given, $\theta_i \in [0, \pi/6]$

$\therefore \quad \sin\theta_i \in \left[0, \dfrac{1}{2}\right]$,

i.e. $\quad 0 \le \sin\theta_i \le \dfrac{1}{2}$

$\therefore$ Inequality Eq. (i) becomes,

$$2 \le \frac{1}{2}|z|^4 + \frac{1}{2}|z|^3 + \frac{1}{2}|z|^2 + \frac{1}{2}|z| + \frac{1}{2}$$

$\Rightarrow \quad 3 \le |z|^4 + |z|^3 + |z|^2 + |z|$

$\Rightarrow \quad 3 \le |z| + |z|^2 + |z|^3 + |z|^4 < |z| + |z|^2 + |z|^3 + |z|^4 + \ldots + \infty$

$\Rightarrow \quad 3 < |z| + |z|^2 + |z|^3 + |z|^4 + \ldots + \infty$

$\Rightarrow \quad 3 < \dfrac{|z|}{1-|z|}$ [here, $|z| < 1$]

$\Rightarrow \quad 3 - 3|z| < |z| \Rightarrow 3 < 4|z|$

$\therefore \quad |z| > \dfrac{3}{4}$

Hence, $\quad \dfrac{3}{4} < |z| < 1$ [$\because |z| < 1$]

Example 30. If $|z - 2 + i| \le 2$, find the greatest and least values of $|z|$, where $i = \sqrt{-1}$.

Sol. Given that, $|z - 2 + i| \le 2$ ...(i)

$\because \quad |z - 2 + i| \ge ||z| - |2 - i||$ [by property (x)]

$\therefore \quad |z - 2 + i| \ge ||z| - \sqrt{5}|$ ...(ii)

From Eqs. (i) and (ii), we get

$$||z| - \sqrt{5}| \le |z - 2 + i| \le 2$$

$\therefore \quad ||z| - \sqrt{5}| \le 2$

$\Rightarrow \quad -2 \le |z| - \sqrt{5} \le 2$

$\Rightarrow \quad \sqrt{5} - 2 \le |z| \le \sqrt{5} + 2$

Hence, greatest value of $|z|$ is $\sqrt{5} + 2$ and least value of $|z|$ is $\sqrt{5} - 2$.

Example 31. If z is any complex number such that $|z + 4| \le 3$, find the greatest value of $|z + 1|$.

Sol. $\because |z+1| = |(z+4) - 3|$

$= |(z+4) + (-3)| \le |z+4| + |-3|$

$= |z+4| + 3$

$\le 3 + 3 = 6$ [$\because |z+4| \le 3$]

$\therefore \quad |z+1| \le 6$

Hence, the greatest value of $|z+1|$ is 6.

Example 32. If $|z_1|=1, |z_2|=2, |z_3|=3$ and $|9z_1z_2+4z_3z_1+z_2z_3|=6$, find the value of $|z_1+z_2+z_3|$.

Sol. $\because \quad |z_1|=1 \Rightarrow |z_1|^2=1$

$\Rightarrow \quad z_1\bar{z}_1=1 \Rightarrow \frac{1}{z_1}=\bar{z}_1$

$|z_2|=2 \Rightarrow |z_2|^2=4 \Rightarrow z_2\bar{z}_2=4$

$\Rightarrow \quad \frac{4}{z_2}=\bar{z}_2$ and $|z_3|=3 \Rightarrow |z_3|^2=9$

$\Rightarrow \quad z_3\bar{z}_3=9 \Rightarrow \frac{9}{z_3}=\bar{z}_3$

and given $|9z_1z_2+4z_3z_1+z_2z_3|=6$

$\Rightarrow \quad |z_1z_2z_3|\left|\frac{9}{z_3}+\frac{4}{z_2}+\frac{1}{z_1}\right|=6$

$\Rightarrow \quad |z_1||z_2||z_3||\bar{z}_3+\bar{z}_2+\bar{z}_1|=6$

$\left[\because \frac{1}{z_1}=\bar{z}_1, \frac{4}{z_2}=\bar{z}_2 \text{ and } \frac{9}{z_3}=\bar{z}_3\right]$

$\Rightarrow \quad 1\cdot2\cdot3\,|\overline{z_1+z_2+z_3}|=6$

$\therefore \quad |z_1+z_2+z_3|=1 \quad [\because |\bar{z}|=|z|]$

Example 33. Prove that

$$|z_1|+|z_2|=\left|\frac{1}{2}(z_1+z_2)+\sqrt{z_1z_2}\right|+\left|\frac{1}{2}(z_1+z_2)-\sqrt{z_1z_2}\right|.$$

Sol. RHS $=\left|\frac{1}{2}(z_1+z_2)+\sqrt{z_1z_2}\right|+\left|\frac{1}{2}(z_1+z_2)-\sqrt{z_1z_2}\right|$

$=\left|\frac{z_1+z_2+2\sqrt{z_1z_2}}{2}\right|+\left|\frac{z_1+z_2-2\sqrt{z_1z_2}}{2}\right|$

$=\frac{1}{2}\{|\sqrt{z_1}+\sqrt{z_2}|^2+|\sqrt{z_1}-\sqrt{z_2}|^2\}$

$=\frac{1}{2}\cdot2\{|\sqrt{z_1}|^2+|\sqrt{z_2}|^2\}$ [by property (xiv)]

$=|z_1|+|z_2|=$ LHS

Example 34. z_1 and z_2 are two complex numbers, such that $\frac{z_1-2z_2}{2-z_1\cdot\bar{z}_2}$ is unimodular, while z_2 is not unimodular. Find $|z_1|$.

Sol. Here, $\left|\frac{z_1-2z_2}{2-z_1\bar{z}_2}\right|=1$

$\Rightarrow \quad \frac{|z_1-2z_2|}{|2-z_1\bar{z}_2|}=1$ [by property (vi)]

$\Rightarrow \quad |z_1-2z_2|=|2-z_1\bar{z}_2|$

$\Rightarrow \quad |z_1-2z_2|^2=|2-z_1\bar{z}_2|^2$

$\Rightarrow \quad (z_1-2z_2)\overline{(z_1-2z_2)}=(2-z_1\bar{z}_2)\overline{(2-z_1\bar{z}_2)}$

[by property (iv)]

$\Rightarrow \quad (z_1-2z_2)(\bar{z}_1-2\bar{z}_2)=(2-z_1\bar{z}_2)(2-\bar{z}_1z_2)$

$\Rightarrow \quad z_1\bar{z}_1-2z_1\bar{z}_2-2z_2\bar{z}_1+4z_2\bar{z}_2$

$=4-2z_1\bar{z}_2-2\bar{z}_1z_2+z_1\bar{z}_1z_2\bar{z}_2$

$\Rightarrow \quad |z_1|^2+4|z_2|^2=4+|z_1|^2|z_2|^2$

$\Rightarrow \quad |z_1|^2-|z_1|^2\cdot|z_2|^2+4|z_2|^2-4=0$

$\Rightarrow \quad (|z_1|^2-4)(1-|z_2|^2)=0$

But $\quad |z_2|\neq1$ [given]

$\therefore \quad |z_1|^2=4$

Hence, $\quad |z_1|=2$

Properties of Arguments

(i) $\arg(z_1z_2)=\arg(z_1)+\arg(z_2)+2k\pi, k\in I$

In general, $\arg(z_1z_2z_3\ldots z_n)$

$=\arg(z_1)+\arg(z_2)+\arg(z_3)+\ldots+\arg(z_n)+2k\pi$, $k\in I$.

(ii) $\arg\left(\frac{z_1}{z_2}\right)=\arg(z_1)-\arg(z_2)+2k\pi, k\in I$

(iii) $\arg\left(\frac{z}{\bar{z}}\right)=2\arg(z)+2k\pi, k\in I$

(iv) $\arg(z^n)=n.\arg(z)+2k\pi, k\in I$, where proper value of k must be chosen, so that RHS lies in $(-\pi,\pi]$.

(v) If $\arg\left(\frac{z_2}{z_1}\right)=\theta$, then $\arg\left(\frac{z_1}{z_2}\right)=2n\pi-\theta$, where $n\in I$.

(vi) $\arg(\bar{z})=-\arg(z)$

Example 35. If $\arg(z_1)=\frac{17\pi}{18}$ and $\arg(z_2)=\frac{7\pi}{18}$, find the principal argument of z_1z_2 and (z_1/z_2).

Sol. $\arg(z_1z_2)=\arg(z_1)+\arg(z_2)+2k\pi$

$=\frac{17\pi}{18}+\frac{7\pi}{18}+2k\pi$

$=\frac{4\pi}{3}+2k\pi$

$=\frac{4\pi}{3}-2\pi=-\frac{2\pi}{3}$ [for $k=-1$]

and $\arg\left(\frac{z_1}{z_2}\right)=\arg(z_1)-\arg(z_2)+2k\pi$

$=\frac{17\pi}{18}-\frac{7\pi}{18}+2k\pi=\frac{10\pi}{18}+2k\pi$

$=\frac{5\pi}{9}+0=\frac{5\pi}{9}$ [for $k=0$]

Example 36. If z_1 and z_2 are conjugate to each other, find the principal argument of $(-z_1z_2)$.

Sol. $\because z_1$ and z_2 are conjugate to each other i.e., $z_2 = \overline{z_1}$, therefore, $z_1z_2 = z_1\overline{z_1} = |z_1|^2$

$$\therefore \arg(-z_1z_2) = \arg(-|z_1|^2) = \arg \quad [\text{negative real number}]$$
$$= \pi$$

Example 37. Let z be any non-zero complex number, then find the value of $\arg(z) + \arg(\bar{z})$.

Sol. $\arg(z) + \arg(\bar{z}) = \arg(z\bar{z})$

$$= \arg(|z|^2) = \arg \quad [\text{positive real number}]$$
$$= 0$$

(a) Mixed Properties of Modulus and Arguments

(i) $|z_1 + z_2| = |z_1| + |z_2| \Leftrightarrow \arg(z_1) = \arg(z_2)$

(ii) $|z_1 + z_2| = |z_1| - |z_2| \Leftrightarrow \arg(z_1) - \arg(z_2) = \pi$

Proof (i) Let $\arg(z_1) = \theta$ and $\arg(z_2) = \phi$

$$\therefore \quad |z_1 + z_2| = |z_1| + |z_2|$$

On squaring both sides, we get

$$|z_1 + z_2|^2 = |z_1|^2 + |z_2|^2 + 2|z_1||z_2|$$

$$\Rightarrow \quad |z_1|^2 + |z_2|^2 + 2|z_1||z_2| \cos(\theta - \phi)$$
$$= |z_1|^2 + |z_2|^2 + 2|z_1||z_2|$$

$$\Rightarrow \quad \cos(\theta - \phi) = 1$$

$$\therefore \quad \theta - \phi = 0 \text{ or } \theta = \phi$$

$$\therefore \quad \arg(z_1) = \arg(z_2)$$

(ii) $\because |z_1 + z_2| = |z_1| - |z_2|$

On squaring both sides, we get

$$|z_1 + z_2|^2 = |z_1|^2 + |z_2|^2 - 2|z_1||z_2|$$

$$\Rightarrow \quad |z_1|^2 + |z_2|^2 + 2|z_1||z_2|\cos(\theta - \phi)$$
$$= |z_1|^2 + |z_2|^2 - 2|z_1||z_2|$$

$$\Rightarrow \quad \cos(\theta - \phi) = -1$$

$$\therefore \quad \theta - \phi = \pi \text{ or } \arg(z_1) - \arg(z_2) = \pi$$

Remark

1. $|z_1 - z_2| = |z_1| + |z_2| \Leftrightarrow \arg(z_1) = \arg(z_2)$
2. $|z_1 - z_2| = |z_1| - |z_2| \Leftrightarrow \arg(z_1) - \arg(z_2) = \pi$
3. $|z_1 - z_2| = |z_1 + z_2| \Leftrightarrow \arg(z_1) - \arg(z_2) = \pm\frac{\pi}{2}$, $\bar{z}_1 z_2$ and $\frac{z_1}{z_2}$ are purely imaginary.

(b) Trigonometric or Polar or Modulus Argument Form of a Complex Number

Let $z = x + iy$, where $x, y \in R$ and $i = \sqrt{-1}$, z is represented by $P(x, y)$ in the argand plane.

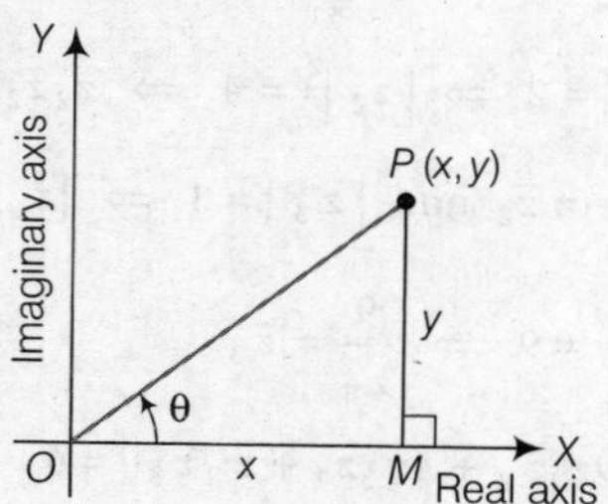

By geometrical representation,

$$OP = \sqrt{(x^2 + y^2)} = |z|$$

$$\angle POM = \theta = \arg(z)$$

In ΔOPM, $x = OP\cos(\angle POM) = |z|\cos(\arg z)$

and $y = OP\sin(\angle POM) = |z|\sin(\arg z)$

$\because$ $z = x + iy$

$\therefore$ $z = |z|(\cos(\arg z) + i\sin(\arg z))$

or $z = r(\cos\theta + i\sin\theta)$

$\bar{z} = r(\cos\theta - i\sin\theta)$

where, $r = |z|$ and θ = principal value of $\arg(z)$.

Remark

1. $\cos\theta + i\sin\theta$ is also written as $CiS\ \theta$.
2. **Remember**

$1 = \cos 0 + i\sin 0 \quad \Rightarrow \quad -1 = \cos\pi + i\sin\pi$

$i = \cos\frac{\pi}{2} + i\sin\frac{\pi}{2} \quad \Rightarrow \quad -i = \cos\frac{\pi}{2} - i\sin\frac{\pi}{2}$

Example 38. Write the polar form of $-\frac{1}{2} - \frac{i\sqrt{3}}{2}$ (where, $i = \sqrt{-1}$).

Sol. Let $z = -\frac{1}{2} - \frac{i\sqrt{3}}{2}$. Since, $\left(-\frac{1}{2}, -\frac{\sqrt{3}}{2}\right)$ lies in III quadrant.

$\therefore$ Principal value of $\arg(z) = -\pi + \tan^{-1}\left|\frac{-\sqrt{3}/2}{-1/2}\right|$

$$= -\pi + \tan^{-1}\sqrt{3} = -\pi + \frac{\pi}{3} = -\frac{2\pi}{3}$$

and $|z| = \sqrt{\left(-\frac{1}{2}\right)^2 + \left(-\frac{\sqrt{3}}{2}\right)^2} = \sqrt{\left(\frac{1}{4} + \frac{3}{4}\right)} = \sqrt{1} = 1$

$\therefore$ Polar form of $z = |z|[\cos(\arg z) + i\sin(\arg z)]$

i.e. $-\frac{1}{2} - \frac{i\sqrt{3}}{2} = \left[\cos\left(-\frac{2\pi}{3}\right) + i\sin\left(-\frac{2\pi}{3}\right)\right]$

(c) Euler's Form

If $\theta \in R$ and $i = \sqrt{-1}$, then $e^{i\theta} = \cos\theta + i\sin\theta$ is known as Euler's identity.

Now, $e^{-i\theta} = \cos\theta - i\sin\theta$

Let $z = e^{i\theta}$

$\therefore$ $|z| = 1$ and $\arg(z) = \theta$

Also, $e^{i\theta} + e^{-i\theta} = 2\cos\theta$ and $e^{i\theta} - e^{-i\theta}$ $2i\sin\theta$

and if $\theta, \phi \in R$ and $i = \sqrt{-1}$, then

(i) $e^{i\theta} + e^{i\phi} = e^{i\left(\frac{\theta+\phi}{2}\right)} \cdot 2\cos\left(\frac{\theta-\phi}{2}\right)$

$\therefore$ $\left|e^{i\theta} + e^{i\phi}\right| = 2\left|\cos\left(\frac{\theta-\phi}{2}\right)\right|$

and $\arg(e^{i\theta} + e^{i\phi}) = \left(\frac{\theta+\phi}{2}\right)$

(ii) $e^{i\theta} - e^{i\phi} = e^{i\left(\frac{\theta+\phi}{2}\right)} \cdot 2i\sin\left(\frac{\theta-\phi}{2}\right)$

$\therefore$ $\left|e^{i\theta} - e^{i\phi}\right| = 2\left|\sin\left(\frac{\theta-\phi}{2}\right)\right|$

and $\arg(e^{i\theta} - e^{i\phi}) = \frac{\theta+\phi}{2} + \frac{\pi}{2}$ $[\because i = e^{i\pi/2}]$

Remark

1. $e^{i\theta} + 1 = e^{i\theta/2} \cdot 2\cos(\theta/2)$ (Remember)
2. $e^{i\theta} - 1 = e^{i\theta/2} \cdot 2i\sin(\theta/2)$ (Remember)
3. $\frac{e^{i\theta} - 1}{e^{i\theta} + 1} = i\tan(\theta/2)$ (Remember)
4. If $z = re^{i\theta}$; $|z| = r$, then $\arg(z) = \theta$, $\bar{z} = re^{-i\theta}$
5. If $|z - z_0| = 1$, then $z - z_0 = e^{i\theta}$

Example 39. Given that $|z - 1| = 1$, where z is a point on the argand plane, show that $\frac{z-2}{z} = i\tan(\arg z)$, where $i = \sqrt{-1}$.

Sol. Given, $|z - 1| = 1$

$\therefore$ $z - 1 = e^{i\theta} \Rightarrow z = e^{i\theta} + 1 = e^{i\theta/2} \cdot 2\cos(\theta/2)$

$\therefore$ $\arg(z) = \theta/2$ ...(i)

$$\text{LHS} = \frac{z-2}{z} = \frac{1 + e^{i\theta} - 2}{1 + e^{i\theta}} = \frac{e^{i\theta} - 1}{e^{i\theta} + 1} = i\tan(\theta/2)$$

$= i\tan(\arg z) = \text{RHS}$ [from Eq. (i)]

Example 40. Let z be a non-real complex number lying on $|z| = 1$, prove that $z = \frac{1 + i\tan\left(\frac{\arg(z)}{2}\right)}{1 - i\tan\left(\frac{\arg(z)}{2}\right)}$ (where, $i = \sqrt{-1}$).

Sol. Given, $|z| = 1$

$\therefore$ $z = e^{i\theta}$ ...(i)

$\Rightarrow$ $\arg(z) = \theta$ ...(ii)

$$\text{RHS} = \frac{1 + i\tan\left(\frac{\arg(z)}{2}\right)}{1 - i\tan\left(\frac{\arg(z)}{2}\right)} = \frac{1 + i\tan(\theta/2)}{1 - i\tan(\theta/2)} \quad \text{[from Eq. (ii)]}$$

$$= \frac{\cos\theta/2 + i\sin\theta/2}{\cos\theta/2 - i\sin\theta/2} = \frac{e^{i\theta/2}}{e^{-i\theta/2}}$$

$= e^{i\theta} = z = \text{LHS}$ [from Eq. (i)]

Example 41. Prove that $\tan\left(i\ln\left(\frac{a-ib}{a+ib}\right)\right) = \frac{2ab}{a^2 - b^2}$ (where $a, b \in R^+$ and $i = \sqrt{-1}$).

Sol. $\because$ $\left|\frac{a-ib}{a+ib}\right| = \frac{|a-ib|}{|a+ib|} = 1$ $[\because |\bar{z}| = |z|]$

Let $\frac{a-ib}{a+ib} = e^{i\theta}$ ...(i)

By componendo and dividendo, we get

$$\frac{(a-ib)-(a+ib)}{(a-ib)+(a+ib)} = \frac{e^{i\theta} - 1}{e^{i\theta} + 1} - \frac{b}{a}i = i\tan(\theta/2)$$

or $\tan\left(\frac{\theta}{2}\right) = -\frac{b}{a}$ ...(ii)

$\therefore$ $\text{LHS} = \tan\left(i\ln\left(\frac{a-ib}{a+ib}\right)\right)$

$= \tan(i\ln(e^{i\theta}))$ [from Eq. (i)]

$= \tan(i \cdot i\theta) = -\tan\theta$

$$= -\frac{2\tan\theta/2}{1 - \tan^2\theta/2}$$

$$= -\frac{2(-b/a)}{1 - (-b/a)^2} \quad \text{[from Eq. (ii)]}$$

$$= \frac{2ab}{a^2 - b^2} = \text{RHS}$$

Applications of Euler's Form

If $x, y, \theta \in R$ and $i = \sqrt{-1}$, then

let $z = x + iy$ [cartesian form]

$= |z|(\cos\theta + i\sin\theta)$ [polar form]

$= |z|e^{i\theta}$ [Euler's form]

(i) Product of Two Complex Numbers

Let two complex numbers be

$$z_1 = |z_1|e^{i\theta_1} \text{ and } z_2 = |z_2|e^{i\theta_2},$$

where $\theta_1, \theta_2 \in R$ and $i = \sqrt{-1}$

$$\therefore \quad z_1 \cdot z_2 = |z_1| e^{i\theta_1} \cdot |z_2| e^{i\theta_2} = |z_1||z_2| e^{i(\theta_1 + \theta_2)}$$
$$= |z_1||z_2|(\cos(\theta_1 + \theta_2) + i\sin(\theta_1 + \theta_2))$$

Thus, $|z_1 z_2| = |z_1||z_2|$

and $\arg(z_1 z_2) = \theta_1 + \theta_2 = \arg(z_1) + \arg(z_2)$

(ii) Division of Two Complex Numbers

Let two complex numbers be

$$z_1 = |z_1| e^{i\theta_1} \text{ and } z_2 = |z_2| e^{i\theta_2},$$

where $\theta_1, \theta_2 \in R$ and $i = \sqrt{-1}$

$$\therefore \quad \frac{z_1}{z_2} = \frac{|z_1| e^{i\theta_1}}{|z_2| e^{i\theta_2}} = \frac{|z_1|}{|z_2|} e^{i(\theta_1 - \theta_2)}$$
$$= \frac{|z_1|}{|z_2|}(\cos(\theta_1 - \theta_2) + i\sin(\theta_1 - \theta_2))$$

Thus, $\left|\dfrac{z_1}{z_2}\right| = \dfrac{|z_1|}{|z_2|}, (z_2 \neq 0)$

and $\arg\left(\dfrac{z_1}{z_2}\right) = \theta_1 - \theta_2 = \arg(z_1) - \arg(z_2)$

(iii) Logarithm of a Complex Number

$$\log_e(z) = \log_e(|z| e^{i\theta}) = \log_e |z| + \log_e(e^{i\theta})$$
$$= \log_e |z| + i\theta = \log_e |z| + i\arg(z)$$

So, the general value of $\log_e(z)$

$$= \log_e(z) + 2n\pi i (-\pi < \arg z < \pi).$$

Example 42. If m and x are two real numbers and $i = \sqrt{-1}$, prove that $e^{2mi\cot^{-1}x}\left(\dfrac{xi+1}{xi-1}\right)^m = 1.$

Sol. Let $\cot^{-1} x = \theta$, then $\cot\theta = x$

$$\therefore \text{LHS} = e^{2mi\cot^{-1}x}\left(\frac{xi+1}{xi-1}\right)^m = e^{2mi\theta}\left(\frac{i\cot\theta + 1}{i\cot\theta - 1}\right)^m$$
$$= e^{2mi\theta}\left(\frac{i(\cot\theta - i)}{i(\cot\theta + i)}\right)^m = e^{2mi\theta}\left(\frac{\cos\theta - i\sin\theta}{\cos\theta + i\sin\theta}\right)^m$$
$$= e^{2mi\theta} \cdot \left(\frac{e^{-i\theta}}{e^{i\theta}}\right)^m = e^{2mi\theta} \cdot (e^{-2i\theta})^m$$
$$= e^{2mi\theta} \cdot e^{-2mi\theta} = e^0 = 1 = \text{RHS}$$

Example 43. If z and w are two non-zero complex numbers such that $|z| = |w|$ and $\arg(z) + \arg(w) = \pi$, prove that $z = -\overline{w}$.

Sol. Let $\arg(w) = \theta$, then $\arg(z) = \pi - \theta$

$$\therefore \quad z = |z|(\cos(\arg z) + i\sin(\arg z))$$
$$= |z|(\cos(\pi - \theta) + i\sin(\pi - \theta))$$
$$= |z|(-\cos\theta + i\sin\theta) = -|z|(\cos\theta - i\sin\theta)$$
$$= -|w|(\cos(\arg w) - i\sin(\arg w))$$
$$= -|w|(\cos(-\arg w) + i\sin(-\arg w))$$
$$= -|\overline{w}|(\cos(\arg\overline{w}) + i\sin(\arg\overline{w})) = -\overline{w}$$

Example 44. Express $(1+i)^{-i}$, (where, $i = \sqrt{-1}$) in the form $A + iB$.

Sol. Let $A + iB = (1+i)^{-i}$

On taking logarithm both sides, we get

$$\log_e(A + iB) = -i\log_e(1+i)$$
$$= -i\log_e\left(\sqrt{2}\left(\frac{1}{\sqrt{2}} + \frac{i}{\sqrt{2}}\right)\right)$$
$$= -i\log_e\left(\sqrt{2}\left(\cos\frac{\pi}{4} + i\sin\frac{\pi}{4}\right)\right)$$
$$= -i\log_e(\sqrt{2}\, e^{i\pi/4}) = -i(\log_e\sqrt{2} + \log_e e^{i\pi/4})$$
$$= -i\left(\frac{1}{2}\log_e 2 + \frac{i\pi}{4}\right) = -\frac{i}{2}\log_e 2 + \frac{\pi}{4}$$
$$\therefore A + iB = e^{-\frac{i}{2}\log_e 2 + \frac{\pi}{4}} = e^{\pi/4} \cdot e^{i\log_e 2^{-1/2}}$$
$$= e^{\pi/4} \cdot (\cos(\log_e 2^{-1/2}) + i\sin(\log_e 2^{-1/2}))$$
$$= e^{\pi/4} \cdot \cos\left(\log_e\left(\frac{1}{\sqrt{2}}\right)\right) + i\, e^{\pi/4}\sin\left(\log_e\left(\frac{1}{\sqrt{2}}\right)\right)$$

Example 45. If $\sin(\log_e i^i) = a + ib$, where $i = \sqrt{-1}$, find a and b, hence and find $\cos(\log_e i^i)$.

Sol. $a + ib = \sin(\log_e i^i) = \sin(i\log_e i)$

$$= \sin(i(\log_e |i| + i\arg i))$$
$$= \sin(i(\log_e 1 + (i\pi/2)))$$
$$= \sin(i(0 + (i\pi/2))) = \sin(-\pi/2) = -1$$

$\therefore \quad a = -1, b = 0$

Now, $\cos(\log_e i^i) = \sqrt{1 - \sin^2(\log_e i^i)}$

$$= \sqrt{1 - (-1)^2} = \sqrt{(1-1)} = 0$$

Aliter

$$\because \quad i^i = (e^{i\pi/2})^i = e^{-\pi/2}$$
$$\therefore \sin(\log_e i^i) = \sin(\log_e e^{-\pi/2}) = \sin\left(-\frac{\pi}{2}\log_e e\right)$$
$$= \sin(-\pi/2) = -1 = a + ib \quad \text{[given]}$$
$$\therefore \quad a = -1, b = 0$$

and $\cos(\log_e i^i) = \cos(\log_e e^{-\pi/2})$

$$= \cos\left(-\frac{\pi}{2}\log_e e\right) = \cos\left(-\frac{\pi}{2}\right) = 0$$

Example 46. Find the general value of $\log_2(5i)$, where $i = \sqrt{-1}$.

Sol. $\log_2 5i = \dfrac{\log_e 5i}{\log_e 2} = \dfrac{1}{\log_e 2}\{\log_e |5i| + i\arg(5i) + 2n\pi i\}$

$$= \frac{1}{\log_e 2}\left\{\log_e 5 + \frac{i\pi}{2} + 2n\pi i\right\}, n \in I$$

Exercise for Session 2

1 If $\dfrac{1-ix}{1+ix} = a - ib$ and $a^2 + b^2 = 1$, where $a, b \in R$ and $i = \sqrt{-1}$, then x is equal to

(a) $\dfrac{2a}{(1+a)^2 + b^2}$ (b) $\dfrac{2b}{(1+a)^2 + b^2}$ (c) $\dfrac{2a}{(1+b)^2 + a^2}$ (d) $\dfrac{2b}{(1+b)^2 + a^2}$

2 The least positive integer n for which $\left(\dfrac{1+i}{1-i}\right)^n = \dfrac{2}{\pi}\left(\sec^{-1}\dfrac{1}{x} + \sin^{-1} x\right)$ (where, $x \neq 0, -1 \leq x \leq 1$ and $i = \sqrt{-1}$), is

(a) 2 (b) 4 (c) 6 (d) 8

3 If $z = (3+4i)^6 + (3-4i)^6$, where $i = \sqrt{-1}$, then $\mathrm{Im}(z)$ equals to

(a) -6 (b) 0 (c) 6 (d) None of these

4 If $(x+iy)^{1/3} = a + ib$, where $i = \sqrt{-1}$, then $\left(\dfrac{x}{a} + \dfrac{y}{b}\right)$ is equal to

(a) $4a^2b^2$ (b) $4(a^2 - b^2)$ (c) $4a^2 - b^2$ (d) $a^2 + b^2$

5 If $\dfrac{3}{2 + \cos\theta + i\sin\theta} = a + ib$, where $i = \sqrt{-1}$ and $a^2 + b^2 = \lambda a - 3$, the value of λ is

(a) 3 (b) 4 (c) 5 (d) 6

6 If $\dfrac{z-1}{z+1}$ is purely imaginary, then $|z|$ is equal to

(a) $\dfrac{1}{2}$ (b) 1 (c) $\sqrt{2}$ (d) 2

7 The complex numbers $\sin x + i\cos 2x$ and $\cos x - i\sin 2x$, where $i = \sqrt{-1}$, are conjugate to each other, for

(a) $x = n\pi, n \in I$ (b) $x = 0$ (c) $x = \left(n + \dfrac{1}{2}\right), n \in I$ (d) no value of x

8 If α and β are two different complex numbers with $|\beta| = 1$, then $\left|\dfrac{\beta - \alpha}{1 - \bar{\alpha}\beta}\right|$ is equal to

(a) 0 (b) $\dfrac{1}{2}$ (c) 1 (d) 2

9 If $x = 3 + 4i$ (where, $i = \sqrt{-1}$), the value of $x^4 - 12x^3 + 70x^2 - 204x + 225$, is

(a) -45 (b) 0 (c) 35 (d) 15

10 If $|z_1 - 1| \leq 1, |z_2 - 2| \leq 2, |z_3 - 3| \leq 3$, the greatest value of $|z_1 + z_2 + z_3|$ is

(a) 6 (b) 12 (c) 17 (d) 23

11 The principal value of arg (z), where $z = \left(1 + \cos\dfrac{8\pi}{5}\right) + i\sin\dfrac{8\pi}{5}$ (where, $i = \sqrt{-1}$) is given by

(a) $-\dfrac{\pi}{5}$ (b) $-\dfrac{4\pi}{5}$ (c) $\dfrac{\pi}{5}$ (d) $\dfrac{4\pi}{5}$

12 If $|z_1| = 2$, $|z_2| = 3$, $|z_3| = 4$ and $|z_1 + z_2 + z_3| = 5$, then $|4z_2z_3 + 9z_3z_1 + 16z_1z_2|$ is

(a) 24 (b) 60 (c) 120 (d) 240

13 If $|z - i| \leq 5$ and $z_1 = 5 + 3i$ (where, $i = \sqrt{-1}$), the greatest and least values of $|iz + z_1|$ are

(a) 7 and 3 (b) 9 and 1 (c) 10 and 0 (d) None of these

14 If z_1, z_2 and z_3, z_4 are two pairs of conjugate complex numbers, then $\arg\left(\dfrac{z_1}{z_4}\right) + \arg\left(\dfrac{z_2}{z_3}\right)$ equals to

(a) 0 (b) $\dfrac{\pi}{2}$ (c) π (d) $\dfrac{3\pi}{2}$

Session 3

amp(z) − amp (−z) = ± π; According as amp (z) is Positive or Negative, Square Root of a Complex Number, Solution of Complex Equations, De-Moivre's Theorem, Cube Roots of Unity

amp (z) − amp (− z) = ± π, According as amp (z) is Positive or Negative

Case I **amp (*z*) is positive.**

If amp $(z) = \theta$, we have

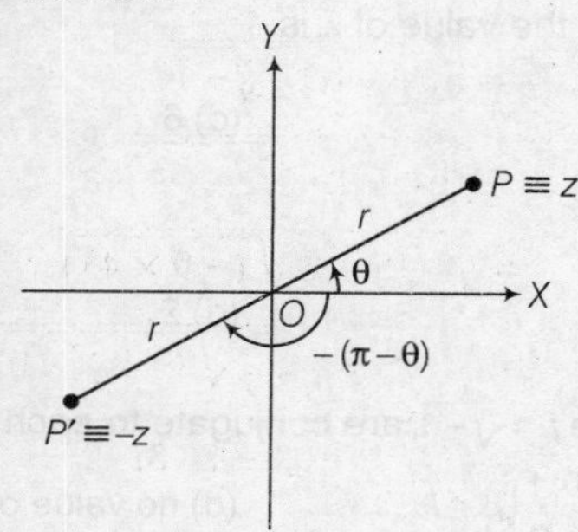

$$\text{amp}(-z) = -(\angle P'OX) = -(\pi - \theta)$$

$\therefore$ $\quad$ **amp (*z*) − amp (−*z*) = π** $\quad$ [here, $OP = OP'$]

Case II **amp (*z*) is negative.**

If $\quad \text{amp}(z) = -\theta$

We have, $\quad \text{amp}(-z) = \angle P'OX = \pi - \theta$

$\therefore$ **amp (*z*) − amp (−*z*) = − π** $\quad$ [here, $OP = OP'$]

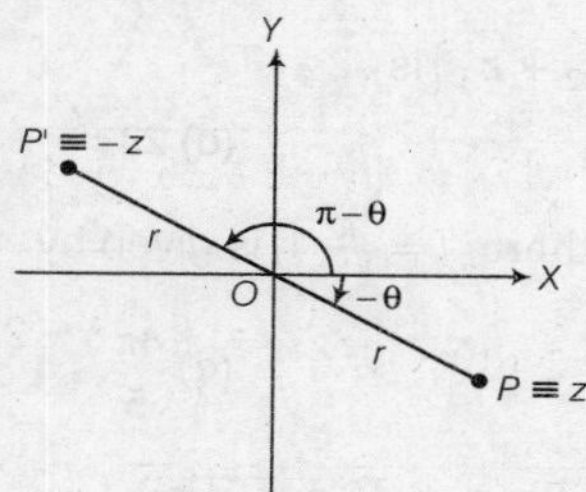

Example 47. If $|z_1| = |z_2|$ and $\arg(z_1/z_2) = \pi$, then find the value of $z_1 + z_2$.

Sol. $\because \arg\left(\dfrac{z_1}{z_2}\right) = \pi$

$\Rightarrow \quad \arg(z_1) - \arg(z_2) = \pi \quad$ ...(i)

$\because \quad z_1 = |z_1|(\cos(\arg z_1) + i\sin(\arg z_1)) \quad$ ...(ii)

and $\quad z_2 = |z_2|(\cos(\arg z_2) + i\sin(\arg z_2)) \quad$ ...(iii)

From Eq. (ii), we get

$$z_1 = |z_2|(\cos(\pi + \arg(z_2)) + i\sin(\pi + \arg(z_2)))$$

[from Eq. (i) and $|z_1| = |z_2|$]

$$= |z_2|(-\cos(\arg z_2) - i\sin(\arg z_2)) = -z_2$$

[from Eq. (iii)]

$\therefore z_1 + z_2 = 0$

Example 48. Let z and w be two non-zero complex numbers, such that $|z| = |w|$ and $\text{amp}(z) + \text{amp}(w) = \pi$, then find the relation between z and w.

Sol. Given, $\text{amp}(z) + \text{amp}(w) = \pi$

$\Rightarrow \quad \text{amp}(z) - \text{amp}(\overline{w}) = \pi$

Here, $\quad |z| = |\overline{w}| = |w| \quad$ [given $|z| = |w|$]

and $\quad \text{amp}(z) > 0$

Then, $\quad z + \overline{w} = 0$

Square Root of a Complex Number

Let $\quad z = x + iy$,

where $x, y \in R$ and $i = \sqrt{-1}$.

Suppose $\sqrt{(x + iy)} = a + ib \quad$ ...(i)

On squaring both sides, we get

$$(x + iy) = (a^2 - b^2) + 2iab$$

On comparing the real and imaginary parts, we get

$$a^2 - b^2 = x \quad \text{...(ii)}$$

and $\quad 2ab = y \quad$ ...(iii)

$$\therefore \quad a^2 + b^2 = \sqrt{(a^2 - b^2)^2 + 4a^2b^2} = \sqrt{(x^2 + y^2)}$$

$$a^2 + b^2 = |z| \quad \text{...(iv)}$$

From Eqs. (ii) and (iv), we get

$$a = \pm\sqrt{\left(\frac{|z| + x}{2}\right)}, \; b = \pm\sqrt{\left(\frac{|z| - x}{2}\right)}$$

or $\quad a = \pm\sqrt{\left(\dfrac{|z| + \text{Re}(z)}{2}\right)}, \; b = \pm\sqrt{\left(\dfrac{|z| - \text{Re}(z)}{2}\right)}$

Now, from Eq. (i), the required square roots,

i.e. $\sqrt{z}=\begin{cases}\pm\left(\sqrt{\dfrac{|z|+\text{Re}(z)}{2}}+i\sqrt{\dfrac{|z|-\text{Re}(z)}{2}}\right), \text{ if Im}(z)>0\\ \pm\left(\sqrt{\dfrac{|z|+\text{Re}(z)}{2}}-i\sqrt{\dfrac{|z|-\text{Re}(z)}{2}}\right), \text{ if Im}(z)<0\end{cases}$

Aliter

If $\sqrt{(x+iy)}$, where $x, y\in R$ and $i=\sqrt{-1}$, then

(i) If y is not even, then multiply and divide in y by 2, then $\sqrt{(x+iy)}$ convert in

$$\sqrt{x+y\sqrt{-1}}=\sqrt{\left(x+2\sqrt{-\frac{y^2}{4}}\right)}.$$

(ii) Factorise: $-\dfrac{y^2}{4}$ say $\alpha, \beta\ (\alpha<\beta)$.

Take that possible factor which satisfy

$$x=(\alpha i)^2+\beta^2, \text{if } x>0 \text{ or } x=\alpha^2+(i\beta)^2, \text{if } x<0$$

(iii) Finally, write $x+iy=(\alpha i)^2+\beta^2+2i\alpha\beta$

or $\alpha^2+(i\beta)^2+2i\alpha\beta$

and take their square root.

(iv) $\sqrt{(x+iy)}=\begin{cases}\pm(\alpha i+\beta)\\ \text{or} \pm(\alpha+i\beta)\end{cases}$ and $\sqrt{(x-iy)}=\begin{cases}\pm(\beta-i\alpha)\\ \text{or}\pm(\alpha-i\beta)\end{cases}$

Remark

1. The square root of i is $\pm\left(\dfrac{1+i}{\sqrt{2}}\right)$, where $i=\sqrt{-1}$.
2. The square root of $(-i)$ is $\left(\dfrac{1-i}{\sqrt{2}}\right)$.

| Example 49. Find the square roots of the following

(i) $4+3i$ (ii) $-5+12i$

(iii) $-8-15i$ (iv) $7-24i$ (where, $i=\sqrt{-1}$)

Sol. (i) Let $z=4+3i$

$\therefore\quad |z|=5, \text{Re}(z)=4, \text{Im}(z)=3>0$

$\because\quad \sqrt{z}=\pm\left(\sqrt{\dfrac{|z|+\text{Re}(z)}{2}}+i\sqrt{\dfrac{|z|-\text{Re}(z)}{2}}\right)$

$\therefore\ \sqrt{(4+3i)}=\pm\left(\sqrt{\left(\dfrac{5+4}{2}\right)}+i\sqrt{\left(\dfrac{5-4}{2}\right)}\right)=\pm\left(\dfrac{3+i}{\sqrt{2}}\right)$

Aliter

$$\sqrt{(4+3i)}=\sqrt{4+3\sqrt{-1}}=\sqrt{4+2\sqrt{\left(-\frac{9}{4}\right)}}$$

$$=\sqrt{\frac{9}{2}-\frac{1}{2}+2\sqrt{\left(-\frac{9}{4}\right)}}$$

$$=\sqrt{\left\{\left(\frac{3}{\sqrt{2}}\right)^2+\left(\frac{i}{\sqrt{2}}\right)^2+2\cdot\frac{3}{\sqrt{2}}\cdot\frac{i}{\sqrt{2}}\right\}}$$

$$=\sqrt{\left(\frac{3+i}{\sqrt{2}}\right)^2}=\pm\left(\frac{3+i}{\sqrt{2}}\right)$$

(ii) Let $z=-5+12i$

$\therefore\quad |z|=13, \text{Re}(z)=-5, \text{Im}(z)=12>0$

$\because\quad \sqrt{z}=\pm\left(\sqrt{\dfrac{|z|+\text{Re}(z)}{2}}+i\sqrt{\dfrac{|z|-\text{Re}(z)}{2}}\right)$

$\therefore\ \sqrt{(-5+12i)}=\pm\left(\sqrt{\left(\dfrac{13-5}{2}\right)}+i\sqrt{\left(\dfrac{13+5}{2}\right)}\right)$

$=\pm(2+3i)$

Aliter

$$\sqrt{(-5+12i)}=\sqrt{(-5+12\sqrt{-1})}$$

$$=\sqrt{(-5+2\sqrt{(-36)}}$$

$$=\sqrt{(-5+2\sqrt{(-9\times4)})}$$

$$=\sqrt{(-9+4+2\sqrt{(-9\times4)})}$$

$$=\sqrt{(3i)^2+2^2+2\cdot3i\cdot2}$$

$$=\sqrt{(2+3i)^2}=\pm(2+3i)$$

(iii) Let $z=-8-15i$

$\therefore\quad |z|=17, \text{Re}(z)=-8, \text{Im}(z)=-15<0$

$\therefore\ \sqrt{(-8-15i)}=\pm\left(\sqrt{\left(\dfrac{17-8}{2}\right)}-i\sqrt{\left(\dfrac{17+8}{2}\right)}\right)$

$=\pm\left(\dfrac{3-5i}{\sqrt{2}}\right)$

Aliter $\sqrt{(-8-15i)}=\sqrt{(-8-15\sqrt{-1})}$

$$=\sqrt{\left(-8-2\sqrt{\left(-\frac{225}{4}\right)}\right)}=\sqrt{\left(-8-2\sqrt{\left(-\frac{25}{2}\times\frac{9}{2}\right)}\right)}$$

$$=\sqrt{\left(\frac{9}{2}-\frac{25}{2}-2\sqrt{\left(-\frac{25}{2}\times\frac{9}{2}\right)}\right)}$$

$$=\sqrt{\left(\frac{3}{\sqrt{2}}\right)^2+\left(\frac{5i}{\sqrt{2}}\right)^2-2\cdot\frac{3}{\sqrt{2}}\cdot\frac{5i}{\sqrt{2}}}$$

$$=\sqrt{\left(\frac{3-5i}{\sqrt{2}}\right)^2}=\pm\left(\frac{3-5i}{\sqrt{2}}\right)$$

(iv) Let $z = 7 - 24i$

$\therefore |z| = 25, \text{Re}(z) = 7, \text{Im}(z) = -24 < 0$

$$\because \sqrt{z} = \pm\left(\sqrt{\frac{|z| + \text{Re}(z)}{2}} - i\sqrt{\frac{|z| - \text{Re}(z)}{2}}\right)$$

$$\therefore \sqrt{(7-24i)} = \pm\left(\sqrt{\left(\frac{25+7}{2}\right)} - i\sqrt{\left(\frac{25-7}{2}\right)}\right)$$

$$= \pm(4-3i)$$

Aliter

$$\sqrt{(7-24i)} = \sqrt{(7-24\sqrt{-1})} = \sqrt{7-2\sqrt{(-144)}}$$

$$= \sqrt{7-2\sqrt{(16\times -9)}}$$

$$= \sqrt{16-9-2\sqrt{(16\times -9)}}$$

$$= \sqrt{(4)^2+(3i)^2-2\cdot 4\cdot 3i}$$

$$= \sqrt{(4-3i)^2} = \pm(4-3i)$$

Example 50. Find the square root of $x + \sqrt{(-x^4 - x^2 - 1)}$.

Sol. Let $z = x + \sqrt{(-x^4 - x^2 - 1)}$

$$= x + i\sqrt{(x^4 + x^2 + 1)} \qquad [\because \sqrt{-1} = i]$$

$$\therefore \quad |z| = \sqrt{x^2 + (x^4 + x^2 + 1)}$$

$$= \sqrt{(x^4 + 2x^2 + 1)} = \sqrt{(x^2+1)^2}$$

$$\therefore \quad |z| = (x^2 + 1)$$

$\text{Re}(z) = x$

$\text{Im}(z) = \sqrt{(x^4 + x^2 + 1)} > 0$

$$\because \quad \sqrt{z} = \pm\left(\sqrt{\frac{|z| + \text{Re}(z)}{2}} + i\sqrt{\frac{|z| - \text{Re}(z)}{2}}\right)$$

$$\therefore \quad \sqrt{x + \sqrt{(-x^4 - x^2 - 1)}}$$

$$= \pm\left(\sqrt{\left(\frac{x^2+1+x}{2}\right)} + i\sqrt{\left(\frac{x^2+1-x}{2}\right)}\right)$$

Aliter

$$\sqrt{x + \sqrt{(-x^4 - x^2 - 1)}} = \sqrt{x + 2\sqrt{\left(\frac{-x^4 - x^2 - 1}{4}\right)}}$$

$$= \sqrt{x + 2\sqrt{\left(\frac{-(x^2+x+1)(x^2-x+1)}{4}\right)}}$$

$$= \sqrt{x + 2\sqrt{\left[\left(\frac{x^2+x+1}{2}\right) \times -\left(\frac{x^2-x+1}{2}\right)\right]}}$$

$$= \sqrt{\left(\frac{x^2+x+1}{2}\right) - \left(\frac{x^2-x+1}{2}\right) + 2\sqrt{\left[\left(\frac{x^2+x+1}{2}\right) \times -\left(\frac{x^2-x+1}{2}\right)\right]}}$$

$$= \sqrt{\left(\sqrt{\left(\frac{x^2+x+1}{2}\right)}\right)^2 + \left(i\sqrt{\left(\frac{x^2-x+1}{2}\right)}\right)^2 + 2\sqrt{\left(\frac{x^2+x+1}{2}\right)} \cdot i\sqrt{\left(\frac{x^2-x+1}{2}\right)}}$$

$$= \sqrt{\left(\sqrt{\left(\frac{x^2+x+1}{2}\right)} + i\sqrt{\left(\frac{x^2-x+1}{2}\right)}\right)^2}$$

$$= \pm\left(\sqrt{\left(\frac{x^2+x+1}{2}\right)} + i\sqrt{\left(\frac{x^2-x+1}{2}\right)}\right)$$

Solution of Complex Equations

Putting $z = x + iy$, where $x, y \in R$ and $i = \sqrt{-1}$ in the given equation and equating the real and imaginary parts, we get x and y, then required solution is $z = x + iy$.

Example 51. Solve the equation $z^2 + |z| = 0$.

Sol. Let $z = x + iy$, where $x, y \in R$ and $i = \sqrt{-1}$ ...(i)

$\Rightarrow \quad z^2 = (x+iy)^2 = x^2 - y^2 + 2ixy$

and $|z| = \sqrt{(x^2 + y^2)}$

Then, given equation reduces to

$$x^2 - y^2 + 2ixy + \sqrt{(x^2+y^2)} = 0$$

On comparing the real and imaginary parts, we get

$$x^2 - y^2 + \sqrt{(x^2+y^2)} = 0 \qquad \text{...(ii)}$$

and $$2xy = 0 \qquad \text{...(iii)}$$

From Eq. (iii), let $x = 0$ and from Eq. (ii),

$$-y^2 + \sqrt{y^2} = 0$$

$$\Rightarrow \quad -|y|^2 + |y| = 0$$

$$\therefore \quad |y| = 0, 1$$

$$\Rightarrow \quad y = 0, \pm 1$$

From Eq. (iii), let $y = 0$ and from Eq. (ii),

$$x^2 + \sqrt{x^2} = 0$$

$$\Rightarrow \quad x^2 + |x| = 0$$

$$\Rightarrow \quad |x|^2 + |x| = 0 \Rightarrow x = 0$$

$\therefore$ $x + iy$ are $0 + 0\cdot i$, $0 + i$, $0 - i$

i.e. $z = 0, i, -i$ are the solutions of the given equation.

Example 52. Find the number of solutions of the equation $z^2 + |z|^2 = 0$.

Sol. $\because$ $z^2 + |z|^2 = 0$ or $z^2 + z\bar{z} = 0$

$\Rightarrow$ $z(z + \bar{z}) = 0$

$\therefore$ $z = 0$ ...(i)

and $z + \bar{z} = 0 \Rightarrow 2\text{Re}(z) = 0$

$\therefore$ $\text{Re}(z) = 0$

If $z = x + iy$ $[\because x = \text{Re}(z)]$

$= 0 + iy, y \in R$

and $i = \sqrt{-1}$ ...(ii)

On combining Eqs. (i) and (ii), then we can say that the given equation has infinite solutions.

Example 53. Find all complex numbers satisfying the equation $2|z|^2 + z^2 - 5 + i\sqrt{3} = 0$, where $i = \sqrt{-1}$.

Sol. Let $z = x + iy$, where $x, y \in R$ and $i = \sqrt{-1}$

$\Rightarrow$ $z^2 = (x + iy)^2 = x^2 - y^2 + 2ixy$

and $|z| = \sqrt{(x^2 + y^2)}$

Then, given equation reduces to

$2(x^2 + y^2) + x^2 - y^2 + 2ixy - 5 + i\sqrt{3} = 0$

$\Rightarrow$ $(3x^2 + y^2 - 5) + i(2xy + \sqrt{3}) = 0 = 0 + i \cdot 0$

On comparing the real and imaginary parts, we get

$3x^2 + y^2 - 5 = 0$ ...(i)

and $2xy + \sqrt{3} = 0$ ...(ii)

On substituting the value of x from Eq. (ii) in Eq. (i), we get

$$3\left(-\frac{\sqrt{3}}{2y}\right)^2 + y^2 - 5 = 0$$

$\Rightarrow$ $\dfrac{9}{4y^2} + y^2 = 5$

or $4y^4 - 20y^2 + 9 = 0$

$\Rightarrow$ $(2y^2 - 9)(2y^2 - 1) = 0$

$\therefore$ $y^2 = \dfrac{9}{2}, y^2 = \dfrac{1}{2}$ or $y = \pm\dfrac{3}{\sqrt{2}}, y = \pm\dfrac{1}{\sqrt{2}}$

or $y = -\dfrac{3}{\sqrt{2}}, \dfrac{3}{\sqrt{2}}, -\dfrac{1}{\sqrt{2}}, \dfrac{1}{\sqrt{2}}$

From Eq. (ii), we get

$$x = \frac{1}{\sqrt{6}}, -\frac{1}{\sqrt{6}}, \sqrt{\frac{3}{2}}, -\sqrt{\frac{3}{2}}$$

$\therefore$ $z = x + iy$

$$= \frac{1}{\sqrt{6}} - \frac{3i}{\sqrt{2}}, -\frac{1}{\sqrt{6}} + \frac{3i}{\sqrt{2}}, \sqrt{\frac{3}{2}} - \frac{i}{\sqrt{2}}, -\sqrt{\frac{3}{2}} + \frac{i}{\sqrt{2}}$$

are the solutions of the given equation.

De-Moivre's Theorem

Statements

(i) If $\theta_1, \theta_2, \theta_3, \ldots, \theta_n \in R$ and $i = \sqrt{-1}$, then

$$(\cos\theta_1 + i\sin\theta_1)(\cos\theta_2 + i\sin\theta_2)(\cos\theta_3 + i\sin\theta_3)\ldots(\cos\theta_n + i\sin\theta_n)$$
$$= \cos(\theta_1 + \theta_2 + \theta_3 + \ldots + \theta_n) + i\sin(\theta_1 + \theta_2 + \theta_3 + \ldots + \theta_n)$$

(ii) If $\theta \in R, n \in I$ (set of integers) and $i = \sqrt{-1}$, then

$$(\cos\theta + i\sin\theta)^n = \cos n\theta + i\sin n\theta$$

(iii) If $\theta \in R$, $n \in Q$ (set of rational numbers) and $i = \sqrt{-1}$, then $\cos n\theta + i\sin n\theta$ is one of the values of $(\cos\theta + i\sin\theta)^n$.

Proof

(i) By Euler's formula, $e^{i\theta} = \cos\theta + i\sin\theta$

$$\text{LHS} = (\cos\theta_1 + i\sin\theta_1)(\cos\theta_2 + i\sin\theta_2)(\cos\theta_3 + i\sin\theta_3)\ldots(\cos\theta_n + i\sin\theta_n)$$
$$= e^{i\theta_1} \cdot e^{i\theta_2} \cdot e^{i\theta_3} \ldots e^{i\theta_n} = e^{i(\theta_1 + \theta_2 + \theta_3 + \ldots + \theta_n)}$$
$$= \cos(\theta_1 + \theta_2 + \theta_3 + \ldots + \theta_n) + i\sin(\theta_1 + \theta_2 + \theta_3 + \ldots + \theta_n) = \text{RHS}$$

(ii) If $\theta_1 = \theta_2 = \theta_3 = \ldots = \theta_n = \theta$, then from the above result (i), $(\cos\theta + i\sin\theta)(\cos\theta + i\sin\theta)(\cos\theta + i\sin\theta)\ldots$ upto n factors

$$= \cos(\theta + \theta + \theta + \ldots \text{ upto } n \text{ times}) + i\sin(\theta + \theta + \theta + \ldots \text{ upto } n \text{ times})$$

i.e., $(\cos\theta + i\sin\theta)^n = \cos n\theta + i\sin n\theta$

(iii) Let $n = \dfrac{p}{q}$, where $p, q \in I$ and $q \neq 0$, from above result (ii),

we have $\left(\cos\left(\dfrac{p}{q}\theta\right) + i\sin\left(\dfrac{p}{q}\theta\right)\right)^q$

$$= \cos\left(\left(\frac{p}{q}\theta\right)q\right) + i\sin\left(\left(\frac{p}{q}\theta\right)q\right) = \cos p\theta + i\sin p\theta$$

$\Rightarrow \cos\left(\dfrac{p\theta}{q}\right) + i\sin\left(\dfrac{p\theta}{q}\right)$ is one of the values of $(\cos p\theta + i\sin p\theta)^{1/q}$

$\Rightarrow \cos\left(\dfrac{p\theta}{q}\right) + i\sin\left(\dfrac{p\theta}{q}\right)$ is one of the values of $[(\cos\theta + i\sin\theta)^p]^{1/q}$

$\Rightarrow \cos\left(\frac{p\theta}{q}\right) + i\sin\left(\frac{p\theta}{q}\right)$ is one of the values of $(\cos\theta + i\sin\theta)^{p/q}$

Other Forms of De-Moivre's Theorem

1. $(\cos\theta - i\sin\theta)^n = \cos n\theta - i\sin n\theta, \forall n \in I$

   Proof $(\cos\theta - i\sin\theta)^n = (\cos(-\theta) + i\sin(-\theta))^n$
   $= \cos(-n\theta) + i\sin(-n\theta) = \cos n\theta - i\sin n\theta$

2. $(\sin\theta + i\cos\theta)^n = (i)^n (\cos n\theta - i\sin n\theta), \forall n \in I$

   Proof $(\sin\theta + i\cos\theta)^n = (i(\cos\theta - i\sin\theta))^n$
   $= i^n(\cos\theta - i\sin\theta)^n = (i)^n(\cos n\theta - i\sin n\theta)$ [from remark (1)]

3. $(\sin\theta - i\cos\theta)^n = (-i)^n(\cos n\theta + i\sin n\theta), \forall n \in I$

   Proof $(\sin\theta - i\cos\theta)^n = (-i(\cos\theta + i\sin\theta))^n$
   $= (-i)^n(\cos\theta + i\sin\theta)^n$
   $= (-i)^n(\cos n\theta + i\sin n\theta)$

4. $(\cos\theta + i\sin\phi)^n \neq \cos n\theta + i\sin n\phi, \forall n \in I$

   [here, $\theta \neq \phi \therefore$ De-Moivre's theorem is not applicable]

5. $\frac{1}{\cos\theta + i\sin\theta} = (\cos\theta + i\sin\theta)^{-1}$
   $= \cos(-\theta) + i\sin(-\theta) = \cos\theta - i\sin\theta$

Example 54. If $z_r = \cos\left(\frac{\pi}{3^r}\right) + i\sin\left(\frac{\pi}{3^r}\right)$, where $i = \sqrt{-1}$, prove that $z_1 z_2 z_3 \ldots$ upto infinity $= i$.

Sol. We have, $z_r = \cos\left(\frac{\pi}{3^r}\right) + i\sin\left(\frac{\pi}{3^r}\right)$

$$\therefore z_1 z_2 z_3 \ldots \infty = \cos\left(\frac{\pi}{3} + \frac{\pi}{3^2} + \frac{\pi}{3^3} + \ldots + \infty\right) + i\sin\left(\frac{\pi}{3} + \frac{\pi}{3^2} + \frac{\pi}{3^3} + \ldots + \infty\right)$$

$$= \cos\left(\frac{\frac{\pi}{3}}{1 - \frac{1}{3}}\right) + i\sin\left(\frac{\frac{\pi}{3}}{1 - \frac{1}{3}}\right) = \cos\left(\frac{\pi}{2}\right) + i\sin\left(\frac{\pi}{2}\right)$$

$$= 0 + i \cdot 1 = i$$

Example 55. Express $\frac{(\cos\theta + i\sin\theta)^4}{(\sin\theta + i\cos\theta)^5}$ in $a + ib$ form, where $i = \sqrt{-1}$.

Sol. $\because (\sin\theta + i\cos\theta)^5 = (i)^5(\cos\theta - i\sin\theta)^5$
$= i(\cos\theta + i\sin\theta)^{-5}$

$$\therefore \frac{(\cos\theta + i\sin\theta)^4}{(\sin\theta + i\cos\theta)^5} = \frac{(\cos\theta + i\sin\theta)^4}{i(\cos\theta + i\sin\theta)^{-5}}$$

$$= \frac{(\cos\theta + i\sin\theta)^9}{i}$$

$$= \frac{\cos 9\theta + i\sin 9\theta}{i} = -i\cos 9\theta + \sin 9\theta$$

$$= \sin 9\theta - i\cos 9\theta$$

To Find the Roots of $(a + ib)^{p/q}$, where $a, b \in R$; $p, q \in I, q \neq 0$ and $i = \sqrt{-1}$

Let $a + ib = r(\cos\theta + i\sin\theta)$ [polar form]

$$\therefore (a + ib)^{p/q} = \{r(\cos(2n\pi + \theta) + i\sin(2n\pi + \theta))\}^{p/q}, n \in I$$

$$= r^{p/q}(\cos(2n\pi + \theta) + i\sin(2n\pi + \theta))^{p/q}$$

$$= r^{p/q}\left(\cos\left(\frac{p}{q}(2n\pi + \theta)\right) + i\sin\left(\frac{p}{q}(2n\pi + \theta)\right)\right),$$

where, $n = 0, 1, 2, 3, \ldots, q - 1$

Example 56. Find all roots of $x^5 - 1 = 0$.

Sol. $\because x^5 - 1 = 0 \Rightarrow x^5 = 1$

$$\therefore x = (1)^{1/5} = (\cos 0 + i\sin 0)^{1/5},$$

where $i = \sqrt{-1}$

$$= [\cos(2n\pi + 0) + i\sin(2n\pi + 0)]^{1/5}$$

$$= \cos\left(\frac{2n\pi}{5}\right) + i\sin\left(\frac{2n\pi}{5}\right),$$

where, $n = 0, 1, 2, 3, 4$

$\therefore$ Roots are

$$1, \cos\left(\frac{2\pi}{5}\right) + i\sin\left(\frac{2\pi}{5}\right), \cos\left(\frac{4\pi}{5}\right) + i\sin\left(\frac{4\pi}{5}\right),$$

$$\cos\left(\frac{6\pi}{5}\right) + i\sin\left(\frac{6\pi}{5}\right), \cos\left(\frac{8\pi}{5}\right) + i\sin\left(\frac{8\pi}{5}\right)$$

Now, $\cos\left(\frac{6\pi}{5}\right) + i\sin\left(\frac{6\pi}{5}\right)$

$$= \cos\left(2\pi - \frac{4\pi}{5}\right) + i\sin\left(2\pi - \frac{4\pi}{5}\right)$$

$$= \cos\left(\frac{4\pi}{5}\right) - i\sin\left(\frac{4\pi}{5}\right)$$

and $\cos\left(\frac{8\pi}{5}\right) + i\sin\left(\frac{8\pi}{5}\right)$

$$= \cos\left(2\pi - \frac{2\pi}{5}\right) + i\sin\left(2\pi - \frac{2\pi}{5}\right)$$

$$= \cos\left(\frac{2\pi}{5}\right) - i\sin\left(\frac{2\pi}{5}\right)$$

Hence, roots are 1, $\cos\left(\frac{2\pi}{5}\right) \pm i\sin\left(\frac{2\pi}{5}\right)$

and $\cos\left(\frac{4\pi}{5}\right) \pm i\sin\left(\frac{4\pi}{5}\right)$.

Remark

Five roots are 1, $z_1, z_2, \bar{z}_1, \bar{z}_2$ (one real, two complex and two conjugate of complex roots).

Example 57. Find all roots of the equation $x^6 - x^5 + x^4 - x^3 + x^2 - x + 1 = 0$.

Sol. $\because \quad 1 - x + x^2 - x^3 + x^4 - x^5 + x^6 = 0$

$$\Rightarrow \quad 1 \cdot \frac{[1-(-x)^7]}{1-(-x)} = 0, 1 + x \neq 0$$

or $\quad 1 + x^7 = 0, \ x \neq -1$ or $x^7 = -1$

$$\therefore \quad x = (-1)^{1/7} = (\cos \pi + i \sin \pi)^{1/7}, i = \sqrt{-1}$$

$$= [\cos (2n+1)\pi + i \sin (2n+1)\pi]^{1/7}$$

$$= \cos \left(\frac{(2n+1)\pi}{7}\right) + i \sin \left(\frac{(2n+1)\pi}{7}\right)$$

for $n = 0, 1, 2, 4, 5, 6$.

Remark

$\because$ For $n = 3, x = -1$ but here $x \neq -1$

$\therefore \quad n \neq 3$

Cube Roots of Unity

Let $z = (1)^{1/3} \Rightarrow z^3 = 1 \Rightarrow z^3 - 1 = 0$

$\Rightarrow (z-1)(z^2 + z + 1) = 0 \Rightarrow z - 1 = 0$ or $z^2 + z + 1 = 0$

$$\therefore \quad z = 1 \text{ or } z = \frac{-1 \pm \sqrt{(1-4)}}{2} = \frac{-1 \pm i\sqrt{3}}{2}$$

Therefore, $\mathbf{z = 1, \dfrac{-1 + i\sqrt{3}}{2}, \dfrac{-1 - i\sqrt{3}}{2}}$, where $i = \sqrt{-1}$.

If second root is represented by ω (omega), third root will be ω^2.

$\therefore$ Cube roots of unity are $1, \omega, \omega^2$ and ω, ω^2 are called non-real complex cube roots of unity.

Remark

1. $\overline{\omega} = \omega^2, (\overline{\omega})^2 = \omega$
2. $\sqrt{\omega} = \pm \omega^2, \sqrt{\omega^2} = \pm \omega$.
3. $|\omega| = |\omega^2| = 1$

Aliter

Let $\quad z = (1)^{1/3} = (\cos 0 + i \sin 0)^{1/3}, i = \sqrt{-1}$

$$= [\cos (2n\pi + 0) + i \sin (2n\pi + 0)]^{1/3}$$

$$= \cos \left(\frac{2n\pi}{3}\right) + i \sin \left(\frac{2n\pi}{3}\right), \text{ where, } n = 0, 1, 2$$

Therefore, roots are

$$1, \cos\left(\frac{2\pi}{3}\right) + i \sin\left(\frac{2\pi}{3}\right), \cos\left(\frac{4\pi}{3}\right) + i \sin\left(\frac{4\pi}{3}\right)$$

or $\quad 1, e^{2\pi i/3}, e^{4\pi i/3}$

If second root is represented by ω, then third root will be ω^2 or if third root is represented by ω, then second root will be ω^2.

Properties of Cube Roots of Unity

(i) $1 + \omega + \omega^2 = 0$ and $\omega^3 = 1$

(ii) **To find the value of $\omega^n (n > 3)$.**

First divide n by 3. Let q be the quotient and r be the remainder.

$$3)\, n\,(q \\ \underline{-3q} \\ r$$

i.e. $\quad n = 3q + r$, where $0 \leq r \leq 2$

$$\therefore \quad \omega^n = \omega^{3q+r} = (\omega^3)^q \cdot \omega^r = \omega^r$$

In general, $\boldsymbol{\omega^{3n} = 1, \omega^{3n+1} = \omega, \omega^{3n+2} = \omega^2}$

(iii) $1 + \omega^r + \omega^{2r} = \begin{cases} 3, \text{ when } n \text{ is a multiple of } 3 \\ 0, \text{ when } n \text{ is not a multiple of } 3 \end{cases}$

(iv) Cube roots of -1 are $-1, -\omega$ and $-\omega^2$.

(v) $a + b\omega + c\omega^2 = 0 \Rightarrow a = b = c$, if $a, b, c \in R$.

(vi) If a, b, c are non-zero numbers such that $a + b + c = 0 = a^2 + b^2 + c^2$, then $a : b : c = 1 : \omega : \omega^2$.

(vii) A complex number $a + ib$ (where $i = \sqrt{-1}$), for which $|a : b| = 1 : \sqrt{3}$ or $\sqrt{3} : 1$ can always be expressed in terms of ω or ω^2.

For example,

(a) $1 + i\sqrt{3} = -(-1 - i\sqrt{3}) \quad [\because |1 : \sqrt{3}| = 1 : \sqrt{3}]$

$$= -2\left(\frac{-1 - i\sqrt{3}}{2}\right) = -2\omega^2$$

(b) $\sqrt{3} + i = \dfrac{i(\sqrt{3} + i)}{i} = \dfrac{(-1 + i\sqrt{3})}{i}$

$$= \left(\frac{-1 + i\sqrt{3}}{2}\right)\left(\frac{2}{i}\right) \quad [\because |\sqrt{3} : 1| = \sqrt{3} : 1]$$

$$= \frac{2\omega}{i} = -2i\omega$$

(viii) The cube roots of unity when represented on complex plane lie on vertices of an equilateral triangle inscribed in a unit circle, having centre at origin. One vertex being on positive real axis.

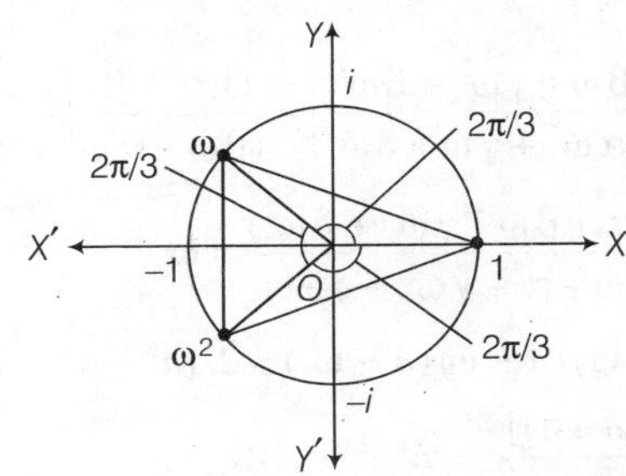

Important Relations in Terms of Cube Root of Unity

(i) $a^2 + ab + b^2 = (a - b\omega)(a - b\omega^2)$

(ii) $a^2 - ab + b^2 = (a + b\omega)(a + b\omega^2)$

(iii) $a^3 + b^3 = (a + b)(a + b\omega)(a + b\omega^2)$

(iv) $a^3 - b^3 = (a - b)(a - b\omega)(a - b\omega^2)$

(v) $a^2 + b^2 + c^2 - ab - bc - ca$

$$= (a + b\omega + c\omega^2)(a + b\omega^2 + c\omega)$$

(vi) $a^3 + b^3 + c^3 - 3abc$

$$= (a + b + c)(a + b\omega + c\omega^2)(a + b\omega^2 + c\omega)$$

Example 58. If ω is a non-real complex cube root of unity, find the values of the following.

(i) ω^{1999}

(ii) ω^{-998}

(iii) $\left(\dfrac{-1 + i\sqrt{3}}{2}\right)^{3n+2}$, $n \in N$ and $i = \sqrt{-1}$

(iv) $(1+\omega)(1+\omega^2)(1+\omega^4)(1+\omega^8)\ldots$ upto $2n$ factors

(v) $\left(\dfrac{\alpha + \beta\omega + \gamma\omega^2 + \delta\omega^2}{\beta + \alpha\omega^2 + \gamma\omega + \delta\omega}\right)$, where $\alpha, \beta, \gamma, \delta \in R$

(vi) $1\cdot(2-\omega)(2-\omega^2) + 2\cdot(3-\omega)(3-\omega^2) + 3\cdot(4-\omega)(4-\omega^2) + \ldots + \ldots + (n-1)\cdot(n-\omega)(n-\omega^2)$

Sol. (i) $\omega^{1999} = \omega^{3 \times 666 + 1} = \omega$

(ii) $\omega^{-998} = \dfrac{1}{\omega^{998}} = \dfrac{\omega}{\omega^{999}} = \omega$

(iii) $\left(\dfrac{-1 + i\sqrt{3}}{2}\right)^{3n+2} = \omega^{3n+2} = \omega^{3n}\cdot\omega^2 = (\omega^3)^n \cdot \omega^2$

$$= (1)^n \cdot \omega^2 = \omega^2$$

(iv) $(1+\omega)(1+\omega^2)(1+\omega^4)(1+\omega^8)\ldots$ upto $2n$ factors

$= (1+\omega)(1+\omega^2)(1+\omega)(1+\omega^2)\ldots$ upto $2n$ factors

$= (-\omega^2)(-\omega)(-\omega^2)(-\omega)\ldots$ upto $2n$ factors

$= (\omega^3)(\omega^3)\ldots$ upto n factors $= 1\cdot 1\cdot 1\cdot\ldots$ upto n factors

$= (1)^n = 1$

(v) $\left(\dfrac{\alpha + \beta\omega + \gamma\omega^2 + \delta\omega^2}{\beta + \alpha\omega^2 + \gamma\omega + \delta\omega}\right) = \dfrac{\omega(\alpha + \beta\omega + \gamma\omega^2 + \delta\omega^2)}{(\beta\omega + \alpha\omega^3 + \gamma\omega^2 + \delta\omega^2)}$

$$= \frac{\omega(\alpha + \beta\omega + \gamma\omega^2 + \delta\omega^2)}{(\beta\omega + \alpha + \gamma\omega^2 + \delta\omega^2)} = \omega$$

(vi) $\Sigma(n-1)(n-\omega)(n-\omega^2) = \Sigma(n^3 - 1) = \Sigma n^3 - \Sigma 1$

$$= \left\{\frac{n(n+1)}{2}\right\}^2 - n$$

Example 59. If α, β and γ are the roots of $x^3 - 3x^2 + 3x + 7 = 0$, find the value of $\dfrac{\alpha - 1}{\beta - 1} + \dfrac{\beta - 1}{\gamma - 1} + \dfrac{\gamma - 1}{\alpha - 1}$.

Sol. We have, $x^3 - 3x^2 + 3x + 7 = 0$

$\Rightarrow (x-1)^3 + 8 = 0$

$\Rightarrow (x-1)^3 + 2^3 = 0$

$\Rightarrow (x - 1 + 2)(x - 1 + 2\omega)(x - 1 + 2\omega^2) = 0$

$\Rightarrow (x+1)(x - 1 + 2\omega)(x - 1 + 2\omega^2) = 0$

$\therefore x = -1, 1 - 2\omega, 1 - 2\omega^2$

$\Rightarrow \alpha = -1, \beta = 1 - 2\omega, \gamma = 1 - 2\omega^2$

Then, $\dfrac{\alpha - 1}{\beta - 1} + \dfrac{\beta - 1}{\gamma - 1} + \dfrac{\gamma - 1}{\alpha - 1} = \dfrac{-2}{-2\omega} + \dfrac{-2\omega}{-2\omega^2} + \dfrac{-2\omega^2}{-2}$

$$= \frac{1}{\omega} + \frac{1}{\omega} + \omega^2 = \omega^2 + \omega^2 + \omega^2 = 3\omega^2$$

Example 60. If $z = \dfrac{\sqrt{3} + i}{2}$, where $i = \sqrt{-1}$, find the value of $(z^{101} + i^{103})^{105}$.

Sol. $\because z = \dfrac{\sqrt{3} + i}{2} = \dfrac{1}{i}\left(\dfrac{i\sqrt{3} + i^2}{2}\right)$ $[\because i^2 = -1]$

$$= -i\left(\frac{-1 + i\sqrt{3}}{2}\right) = -i\omega$$

$\therefore z^{101} = (-i\omega)^{101} = -i^{101}\cdot\omega^{101} = -i\omega^2$ and $i^{103} = i^3 = -i$

Then, $z^{101} + i^{103} = -i\omega^2 - i = -i(\omega^2 + 1)$

$$= -i(-\omega) = i\omega$$

Hence, $(z^{101} + i^{103})^{105} = (i\omega)^{105} = i^{105}\cdot\omega^{105} = i\cdot 1 = i$

Example 61. If $\left(\dfrac{3}{2} + \dfrac{i\sqrt{3}}{2}\right)^{50} = 3^{25}(x - iy)$, where $x, y \in R$ and $i = \sqrt{-1}$, find the ordered pair of (x, y).

Sol. $\because \dfrac{3}{2} + \dfrac{i\sqrt{3}}{2} = \sqrt{3}\left(\dfrac{\sqrt{3} + i}{2}\right) = \dfrac{\sqrt{3}}{i}\left(\dfrac{i\sqrt{3} + i^2}{2}\right)$

$$= -i\sqrt{3}\left(\frac{-1 + i\sqrt{3}}{2}\right) = -i\sqrt{3}\,\omega$$

$\therefore \left(\dfrac{3}{2} + \dfrac{i\sqrt{3}}{2}\right)^{50} = (-i\sqrt{3}\,\omega)^{50} = i^{50}\cdot 3^{25}\cdot\omega^{50}$

$$= -1\cdot 3^{25}\cdot\omega^2 = -3^{25}\cdot\left(\frac{-1 - i\sqrt{3}}{2}\right)$$

$$= 3^{25}\left(\frac{1}{2} + \frac{i\sqrt{3}}{2}\right) = 3^{25}(x - iy) \qquad \text{[given]}$$

$\therefore \quad x = \frac{1}{2}, y = -\frac{\sqrt{3}}{2}$

$\Rightarrow$ Ordered pair is $\left(\frac{1}{2}, -\frac{\sqrt{3}}{2}\right)$.

Example 62. If the polynomial $7x^3 + ax + b$ is divisible by $x^2 - x + 1$, find the value of $2a + b$.

Sol. Let $\quad f(x) = 7x^3 + ax + b$

and $x^2 - x + 1 = (x + \omega)(x + \omega^2)$

$\because f(x)$ is divisible by $x^2 - x + 1$

Then, $\quad f(-\omega) = 0$ and $f(-\omega^2) = 0$

$\Rightarrow \quad -7\omega^3 - a\omega + b = 0$ and $-7\omega^6 - a\omega^2 + b = 0$

or $\quad -7 - a\omega + b = 0$

and $\quad -7 - a\omega^2 + b = 0$

On adding, we get

$$-14 - a(\omega + \omega^2) + 2b = 0$$

or $\quad -14 + a + 2b = 0$ or $a + 2b = 14 \qquad$ ...(i)

and on subtracting, we get

$$-a(\omega - \omega^2) = 0$$

$\Rightarrow \quad a = 0 \qquad [\because \omega - \omega^2 \neq 0]$

From Eq. (i), we get $b = 7$

$\therefore \quad 2a + b = 7$

Exercise for Session 3

1 The real part of $(1 - i)^{-i}$, where $i = \sqrt{-1}$ is

(a) $e^{-\pi/4} \cos\left(\frac{1}{2}\log_e 2\right)$ (b) $-e^{-\pi/4} \sin\left(\frac{1}{2}\log_e 2\right)$

(c) $e^{\pi/4} \cos\left(\frac{1}{2}\log_e 2\right)$ (d) $e^{-\pi/4} \sin\left(\frac{1}{2}\log_e 2\right)$

2 The amplitude of $e^{e^{-i\theta}}$, where $\theta \in R$ and $i = \sqrt{-1}$ is

(a) $\sin\theta$ (b) $-\sin\theta$

(c) $e^{\cos\theta}$ (d) $e^{\sin\theta}$

3 If $z = i\log_e(2 - \sqrt{3})$, where $i = \sqrt{-1}$, then the $\cos z$ is equal to

(a) i (b) $2i$ (c) 1 (d) 2

4 If $z = i^{i^i}$, where $i = \sqrt{-1}$, then $|z|$ is equal to

(a) 1 (b) $e^{-\pi/2}$ (c) $e^{-\pi}$ (d) e^{π}

5 $\sqrt{(-8 - 6i)}$ is equal to (where, $i = \sqrt{-1}$)

(a) $1 \pm 3i$ (b) $\pm(1 - 3i)$ (c) $\pm(1 + 3i)$ (d) $\pm(3 - i)$

6 $\dfrac{\sqrt{(5 + 12i)} + \sqrt{(5 - 12i)}}{\sqrt{(5 + 12i)} - \sqrt{(5 - 12i)}}$ is equal to (where, $i = \sqrt{-1}$)

(a) $-\frac{3}{2}i$ (b) $\frac{3}{4}i$ (c) $-\frac{3}{4}i$ (d) $-\frac{3}{2}$

7 If $0 < \text{amp}(z) < \pi$, then $\text{amp}(z) - \text{amp}(-z)$ is equal to

(a) 0 (b) $2\,\text{amp}(z)$ (c) π (d) $-\pi$

8 If $|z_1| = |z_2|$ and $\text{amp}(z_1) + \text{amp}(z_2) = 0$, then

(a) $z_1 = z_2$ (b) $\bar{z}_1 = z_2$ (c) $z_1 + z_2 = 0$ (d) $\bar{z}_1 = \bar{z}_2$

9 The solution of the equation $|z| - z = 1 + 2i$, where $i = \sqrt{-1}$, is

(a) $2 - \frac{3}{2}i$ (b) $\frac{3}{2} + 2i$ (c) $\frac{3}{2} - 2i$ (d) $-2 + \frac{3}{2}i$

10 The number of solutions of the equation $z^2 + \bar{z} = 0$, is

(a) 1 (b) 2
(c) 3 (d) 4

11 If $z_r = \cos\left(\frac{r\alpha}{n^2}\right) + i\sin\left(\frac{r\alpha}{n^2}\right)$, where $r = 1, 2, 3, \ldots, n$ and $i = \sqrt{-1}$, then $\lim_{n\to\infty} z_1 z_2 z_3 \ldots z_n$ is equal to

(a) $e^{i\alpha}$ (b) $e^{-i\alpha/2}$
(c) $e^{i\alpha/2}$ (d) $\sqrt[3]{e^{i\alpha}}$

12 If $\theta \in R$ and $i = \sqrt{-1}$, then $\left(\frac{1+\sin\theta + i\cos\theta}{1+\sin\theta - i\cos\theta}\right)^n$ is equal to

(a) $\cos\left(\frac{n\pi}{2} - n\theta\right) + i\sin\left(\frac{n\pi}{2} - n\theta\right)$ (b) $\cos\left(\frac{n\pi}{2} + n\theta\right) + i\sin\left(\frac{n\pi}{2} + n\theta\right)$
(c) $\sin\left(\frac{n\pi}{2} - n\theta\right) + i\cos\left(\frac{n\pi}{2} - n\theta\right)$ (d) $\cos\left(n\left(\frac{\pi}{2} + 2\theta\right)\right) + i\sin\left(n\left(\frac{\pi}{2} + 2\theta\right)\right)$

13 If $iz^4 + 1 = 0$, where $i = \sqrt{-1}$, then z can take the value

(a) $\frac{1+i}{\sqrt{2}}$ (b) $\cos\left(\frac{\pi}{8}\right) + i\sin\left(\frac{\pi}{8}\right)$
(c) $\frac{1}{4i}$ (d) i

14 If $\omega (\neq 1)$ is a cube root of unity, then $(1 - \omega + \omega^2)(1 - \omega^2 + \omega^4)(1 - \omega^4 + \omega^8) \ldots$ upto $2n$ factors, is

(a) 2^n (b) 2^{2n}
(c) 0 (d) 1

15 If α, β and γ are the cube roots of p $(p < 0)$, then for any x, y and z, $\frac{x\alpha + y\beta + z\gamma}{x\beta + y\gamma + z\alpha}$ is equal to

(a) $\frac{1}{2}(-1 - i\sqrt{3}), i = \sqrt{-1}$ (b) $\frac{1}{2}(1 + i\sqrt{3}), i = \sqrt{-1}$
(c) $\frac{1}{2}(1 - i\sqrt{3}), i = \sqrt{-1}$ (d) None of these

Session 4

*n*th Root of Unity, Vector Representation of Complex Numbers, Geometrical Representation of Algebraic Operation on Complex Numbers, Rotation Theorem (Coni Method), Shifting the Origin in Case of Complex Numbers, Inverse Points, Dot and Cross Product, Use of Complex Numbers in Coordinate Geometry

*n*th Root of Unity

Let x be the nth root of unity, then

$$x = (1)^{1/n} = (\cos 0 + i \sin 0)^{1/n}$$

$$= (\cos (2k\pi + 0) + i \sin (2k\pi + 0))^{1/n}$$

[where k is an integer]

$$= (\cos 2k\pi + i \sin 2k\pi)^{1/n}$$

$$\therefore \quad x = \cos\left(\frac{2k\pi}{n}\right) + i \sin\left(\frac{2k\pi}{n}\right)$$

where, $k = 0, 1, 2, 3, \ldots, n-1$

Let $\alpha = \cos \frac{2\pi}{n} + i \sin \frac{2\pi}{n}$, the n, nth roots of unity are α^k $(k = 0, 1, 2, 3, \ldots, n-1)$ i.e, the n, nth roots of unity are $1, \alpha, \alpha^2, \alpha^3, \ldots, \alpha^{n-1}$ which are in GP with common ratio $= e^{2\pi i/n}$.

(a) **Sum of n, nth roots of unity**

$$1 + \alpha + \alpha^2 + \alpha^3 + \ldots + \alpha^{n-1} = \frac{1 \cdot (1 - \alpha^n)}{(1 - \alpha)}$$

$$= \frac{1 - (\cos 2\pi + i \sin 2\pi)}{1 - \alpha}$$

$$= \frac{1 - (1 + 0)}{1 - \alpha} = 0$$

Remark

$1 + \alpha + \alpha^2 + \alpha^3 + \ldots + \alpha^{n-1} = 0$ is the basic concept to be understood.

(b) **Product of n, nth roots of unity**

$$1 \times \alpha \times \alpha^2 \times \alpha^3 \times \ldots \times \alpha^{n-1} = \alpha^{1 + 2 + 3 + \ldots + (n-1)}$$

$$= \alpha^{\frac{(n-1)n}{2}} = \left(\cos \frac{2\pi}{n} + i \sin \frac{2\pi}{n}\right)^{\frac{(n-1)n}{2}}$$

$$= \cos (n-1)\pi + i \sin (n-1)\pi$$

$$= (\cos \pi + i \sin \pi)^{n-1} = (-1)^{n-1}$$

Remark

$1 \cdot \alpha \cdot \alpha^2 \cdot \alpha^3 \ldots \alpha^{n-1} = (-1)^{n-1}$ is the basic concept to be understood.

(c) If α is an imaginary nth root of unity, then other roots are given by $\alpha^2, \alpha^3, \alpha^4, \ldots, \alpha^n$.

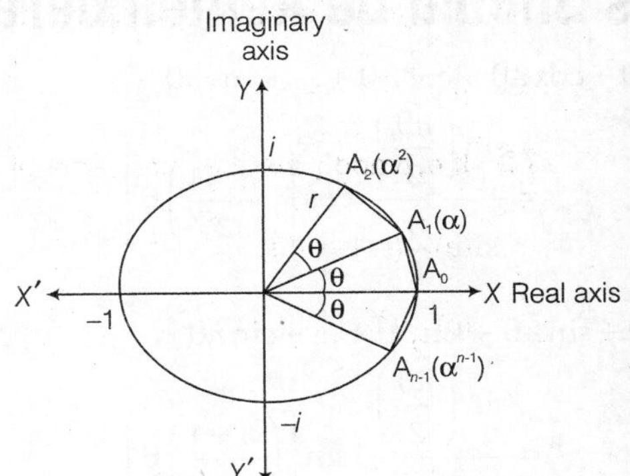

(d) $\because \; 1 + \alpha + \alpha^2 + \ldots + \alpha^{n-1} = 0$

$$\Rightarrow \quad \sum_{k=0}^{n-1} \alpha^k = 0$$

$$\text{or} \quad \sum_{k=0}^{n-1} \cos\left(\frac{2\pi k}{n}\right) + i \sum_{k=0}^{n-1} \sin\left(\frac{2\pi k}{n}\right) = 0$$

$$\Rightarrow \quad \sum_{k=0}^{n-1} \cos\left(\frac{2\pi k}{n}\right) = 0$$

$$\text{and} \quad \sum_{k=0}^{n-1} \sin\left(\frac{2\pi k}{n}\right) = 0$$

These roots are located at the vertices of a regular plane polygon of n sides inscribed in a unit circle having centre at origin, one vertex being on positive real axis.

(e) $x^n - 1 = (x - 1)(x - \alpha)(x - \alpha^2) \ldots (x - \alpha^{n-1})$.

Important Benefits

1. If $1, \alpha_1, \alpha_2, \alpha_3, \ldots, \alpha_{n-1}$ are the n, nth root of unity, then
$(1)^p + (\alpha_1)^p + (\alpha_2)^p + \ldots + (\alpha_{n-1})^p$
$= \begin{cases} 0, \text{ if } p \text{ is not an integral multiple of } n \\ n, \text{ if } p \text{ is an integral multiple of } n \end{cases}$
2. $(1+\alpha_1)(1+\alpha_2)\ldots(1+\alpha_{n-1}) = \begin{cases} 0, \text{ if } n \text{ is even} \\ 1, \text{ if } n \text{ is odd} \end{cases}$
3. $(1-\alpha_1)(1-\alpha_2)\ldots(1-\alpha_{n-1}) = n$
4. $z^n - 1 = (z-1)(z+1)\prod_{r=1}^{(n-2)/2}\left(z^2 - 2z\cos\frac{2r\pi}{n} + 1\right)$, if '$n$' is even.
5. $z^n + 1 = \prod_{r=0}^{(n-2)/2}\left(z^2 - 2z\cos\left(\frac{(2r+1)\pi}{n}\right) + 1\right)$, if n is even.
6. $z^n + 1 = (z+1)\prod_{r=0}^{(n-3)/2}\left(z^2 - 2z\cos\left(\frac{(2r+1)\pi}{n}\right) + 1\right)$, if '$n$' is odd.

The Sum of the Following Series Should be Remembered

(i) $\cos\theta + \cos 2\theta + \cos 3\theta + \ldots + \cos n\theta$

$$= \frac{\sin\left(\frac{n\theta}{2}\right)}{\sin\left(\frac{\theta}{2}\right)} \cdot \cos\left[\left(\frac{n+1}{2}\right)\theta\right]$$

(ii) $\sin\theta + \sin 2\theta + \sin 3\theta + \ldots + \sin n\theta$

$$= \frac{\sin\left(\frac{n\theta}{2}\right)}{\sin\left(\frac{\theta}{2}\right)} \cdot \sin\left[\left(\frac{n+1}{2}\right)\theta\right]$$

Proof

(i) $\cos\theta + \cos 2\theta + \cos 3\theta + \ldots + \cos n\theta$

$$= \text{Re}\{e^{i\theta} + e^{2i\theta} + e^{3i\theta} + \ldots + e^{ni\theta}\}, \text{ where } i = \sqrt{-1}$$

$$= \text{Re}\left\{\frac{e^{i\theta}\{(e^{i\theta})^n - 1\}}{e^{i\theta} - 1}\right\} = \text{Re}\left\{\frac{e^{i\theta} \cdot e^{ni\theta/2} \cdot 2i\sin\left(\frac{n\theta}{2}\right)}{e^{i\theta/2} \cdot 2i\sin(\theta/2)}\right\}$$

$$= \text{Re}\left\{\frac{\sin\left(\frac{n\theta}{2}\right)}{\sin\left(\frac{\theta}{2}\right)} \cdot e^{\left(\frac{n+1}{2}\right)i\theta}\right\} = \frac{\sin\left(\frac{n\theta}{2}\right)}{\sin\left(\frac{\theta}{2}\right)} \cdot \cos\left[\left(\frac{n+1}{2}\right)\theta\right]$$

(ii) $\sin\theta + \sin 2\theta + \sin 3\theta + \ldots + \sin n\theta$

$$= \text{Im}\{e^{i\theta} + e^{2i\theta} + e^{3i\theta} + \ldots + e^{ni\theta}\}, \text{ where } i = \sqrt{-1}$$

$$= \text{Im}\left\{\frac{e^{i\theta}\{(e^{i\theta})^n - 1\}}{e^{i\theta} - 1}\right\} = \text{Im}\left\{\frac{e^{i\theta} \cdot e^{\frac{ni\theta}{2}} \cdot 2i\sin\left(\frac{n\theta}{2}\right)}{e^{i\theta/2} \cdot 2i\sin\left(\frac{\theta}{2}\right)}\right\}$$

$$= \text{Im}\left\{\frac{\sin\left(\frac{n\theta}{2}\right)}{\sin\left(\frac{\theta}{2}\right)} \cdot e^{\left(\frac{n+1}{2}\right)i\theta}\right\} = \frac{\sin\left(\frac{n\theta}{2}\right)}{\sin\left(\frac{\theta}{2}\right)} \cdot \sin\left[\left(\frac{n+1}{2}\right)\theta\right]$$

Remark

For $\theta = \frac{2\pi}{n}$, we get

1. $1 + \cos\left(\frac{2\pi}{n}\right) + \cos\left(\frac{4\pi}{n}\right) + \cos\left(\frac{6\pi}{n}\right) + \ldots + \cos\left(\frac{(2n-2)\pi}{n}\right) = 0$

2. $\sin\left(\frac{2\pi}{n}\right) + \sin\left(\frac{4\pi}{n}\right) + \sin\left(\frac{6\pi}{n}\right) + \ldots + \sin\left(\frac{(2n-2)\pi}{n}\right) = 0$

| Example 63. If $1, \omega, \omega^2, \ldots, \omega^{n-1}$ are n, nth roots of unity, find the value of $(9-\omega)(9-\omega^2)\ldots(9-\omega^{n-1})$.

Sol. Let $x = (1)^{1/n} \Rightarrow x^n - 1 = 0$

has n roots $1, \omega, \omega^2, \ldots, \omega^{n-1}$

$$\therefore \quad x^n - 1 = (x-1)(x-\omega)(x-\omega^2)\ldots(x-\omega^{n-1})$$

On putting $x = 9$ in both sides, we get

$$\frac{9^n - 1}{9 - 1} = (9-\omega)(9-\omega^2)(9-\omega^3)\ldots(9-\omega^{n-1})$$

or $$(9-\omega)(9-\omega^2)\ldots(9-\omega^{n-1}) = \frac{9^n - 1}{8}$$

Remark

$$\frac{x^n - 1}{x - 1} = (x-\omega)(x-\omega^2)\ldots(x-\omega^{n-1})$$

$$\therefore \lim_{x\to 1}\frac{x^n - 1}{x - 1} = \lim_{x\to 1}(x-\omega)(x-\omega^2)\ldots(x-\omega^{n-1})$$

$$\Rightarrow \quad n = (1-\omega)(1-\omega^2)\ldots(1-\omega^{n-1})$$

| Example 64. If $a = \cos\left(\frac{2\pi}{7}\right) + i\sin\left(\frac{2\pi}{7}\right)$, where $i = \sqrt{-1}$, find the quadratic equation whose roots are $\alpha = a + a^2 + a^4$ and $\beta = a^3 + a^5 + a^6$.

Sol. $\because \quad a = \cos\left(\frac{2\pi}{7}\right) + i\sin\left(\frac{2\pi}{7}\right)$

$$\therefore \quad a^7 = \cos 2\pi + i\sin 2\pi = 1 + 0 = 1$$

or $a = (1)^{1/7}$

$\therefore$ $1, a, a^2, a^3, a^4, a^5, a^6$ are 7, 7 th roots of unity.

$$\therefore \quad 1 + a + a^2 + a^3 + a^4 + a^5 + a^6 = 0 \quad \ldots(i)$$

$$\Rightarrow \quad (a + a^2 + a^4) + (a^3 + a^5 + a^6) = -1 \text{ or } \alpha + \beta = -1$$

and $\alpha\beta = (a + a^2 + a^4)(a^3 + a^5 + a^6)$

$$= a^4 + a^6 + a^7 + a^5 + a^7 + a^8 + a^7 + a^9 + a^{10}$$

$$= a^4 + a^6 + 1 + a^5 + 1 + a + 1 + a^2 + a^3 \quad [\because a^7 = 1]$$

$$= (1 + a + a^2 + a^3 + a^4 + a^5 + a^6) + 2$$

$$= 0 + 2 \quad \text{[from Eq. (i)]}$$

$$= 2$$

Therefore, the required equation is

$$x^2 - (\alpha + \beta)x + \alpha\beta = 0 \text{ or } x^2 + x + 2 = 0$$

| Example 65. Find the value of $\sum_{k=1}^{10}\left[\sin\left(\frac{2\pi k}{11}\right) - i\cos\left(\frac{2\pi k}{11}\right)\right]$, where $i = \sqrt{-1}$.

Sol. $\sum_{k=1}^{10}\left[\sin\left(\frac{2\pi k}{11}\right) - i\cos\left(\frac{2\pi k}{11}\right)\right]$

$$= -i\sum_{k=1}^{10}\left[\cos\left(\frac{2\pi k}{11}\right) + i\sin\left(\frac{2\pi k}{11}\right)\right]$$

$$= -i\left\{\sum_{k=0}^{10}\left[\cos\left(\frac{2\pi k}{11}\right) + i\sin\left(\frac{2\pi k}{11}\right)\right] - 1\right\}$$

$$= -i(0 - 1) \quad \text{[sum of 11, 11th roots of unity]}$$

$$= i$$

| Example 66. If $\alpha_0, \alpha_1, \alpha_2, \ldots, \alpha_{n-1}$ are the n, nth roots of the unity, then find the value of $\sum_{i=0}^{n-1}\frac{\alpha_i}{2-\alpha_i}$.

Sol. Let $x = (1)^{1/n} \Rightarrow x^n = 1 \quad \therefore \quad x^n - 1 = 0$

or $\quad x^n - 1 = (x - \alpha_0)(x - \alpha_1)(x - \alpha_2)\ldots(x - \alpha_{n-1})$

$$= \prod_{i=0}^{n-1}(x - \alpha_i)$$

On taking logarithm both sides, we get

$$\log_e(x^n - 1) = \sum_{i=0}^{n-1}\log_e(x - \alpha_i)$$

On differentiating both sides w.r.t. x, we get

$$\frac{nx^{n-1}}{x^n - 1} = \sum_{i=0}^{n-1}\left(\frac{1}{x - \alpha_i}\right)$$

On putting $x = 2$, we get

$$\frac{n(2)^{n-1}}{2^n - 1} = \sum_{i=0}^{n-1}\frac{1}{(2 - \alpha_i)} \quad \ldots\text{(i)}$$

Now, $\sum_{i=0}^{n-1}\frac{\alpha_i}{(2-\alpha_i)} = \sum_{i=0}^{n-1}\left(-1 + \frac{2}{2-\alpha_i}\right)$

$$= -\sum_{i=0}^{n-1}1 + 2\sum_{i=0}^{n-1}\frac{1}{(2-\alpha_i)} = -(n) + \frac{2\cdot n\cdot 2^{n-1}}{2^n - 1} \quad \text{[from Eq. (i)]}$$

$$= -n + \frac{n\cdot 2^n}{2^n - 1} = \frac{n}{2^n - 1}$$

| Example 67. If $n \geq 3$ and $1, \alpha_1, \alpha_2, \alpha_3, \ldots, \alpha_{n-1}$ are the n, nth roots of unity, then find the value of $\sum\sum_{1 \leq i < j \leq n-1}\alpha_i\alpha_j$.

Sol. Let $\quad x = (1)^{1/n}$

$\therefore \quad x^n = 1$ or $x^n - 1 = 0$

$\therefore \quad 1 + \alpha_1 + \alpha_2 + \alpha_3 + \ldots + \alpha_{n-1} = 0$

or $\quad \alpha_1 + \alpha_2 + \alpha_3 + \ldots + \alpha_{n-1} = -1$

On squaring both sides, we get

$$\alpha_1^2 + \alpha_2^2 + \alpha_3^2 + \ldots + \alpha_{n-1}^2 + 2(\alpha_1\alpha_2 + \alpha_1\alpha_3 + \ldots + \alpha_1\alpha_{n-1} + \alpha_2\alpha_3 + \ldots + \alpha_2\alpha_{n-1} + \ldots + \alpha_{n-2}\alpha_{n-1}) = 1$$

or $1^2 + (\alpha_1)^2 + (\alpha_2)^2 + (\alpha_3)^2 + \ldots + (\alpha_{n-1})^2 + 2\sum\sum_{1 \leq i < j \leq n-1}\alpha_i\alpha_j = 1 + 1^2$

$$0 + 2\sum\sum_{1 \leq i < j \leq n-1}\alpha_i\alpha_j = 2$$

[here, p is not a multiple of n]

$$\therefore \quad \sum\sum_{1 \leq i < j \leq n-1}\alpha_i\alpha_j = 1$$

Aliter

$\because \quad x^n - 1 = (x - 1)(x - \alpha_1)(x - \alpha_2)\ldots(x - \alpha_{n-1})$

On comparing the coefficient of x^{n-2} both sides, we get

$$0 = \sum\sum_{0 \leq i < j \leq n-1}\alpha_i\alpha_j + \alpha_1 + \alpha_2 + \ldots + \alpha_{n-1}$$

$$0 = \sum\sum_{1 \leq i < j \leq n-1}\alpha_i\alpha_j - 1$$

$$[\because 1 + \alpha_1 + \alpha_2 + \ldots + \alpha_{n-1} = 0]$$

$$\therefore \quad \sum\sum_{1 \leq i < j \leq n-1}\alpha_i\alpha_j = 1$$

Vector Representation of Complex Numbers

If P is the point (x, y) on the argand plane corresponding to the complex number $z = x + iy$, where $x, y \in R$ and $i = \sqrt{-1}$.

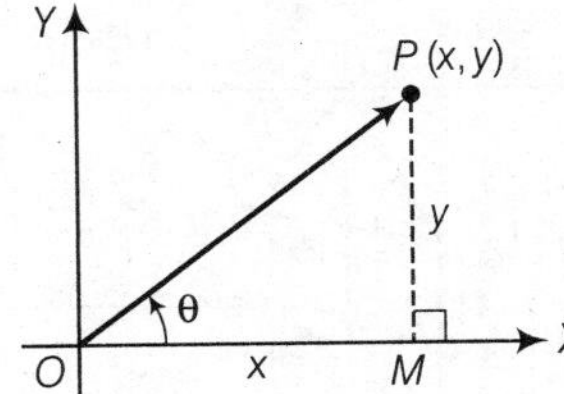

Then, $\quad \overrightarrow{OP} = x\hat{i} + y\hat{j} \Rightarrow \left|\overrightarrow{OP}\right| = \sqrt{(x^2 + y^2)} = |z|$

and $\arg(z) =$ direction of the vector $\overrightarrow{OP} = \tan^{-1}(y/x) = \theta$

Therefore, complex number z can also be represented by $\overrightarrow{OP}$.

Geometrical Representation of Algebraic Operation on Complex Numbers

(a) Sum

Let the complex numbers $z_1 = x_1 + iy_1 = (x_1, y_1)$ and $z_2 = x_2 + iy_2 = (x_2, y_2)$ be represented by the points P and Q on the argand plane.

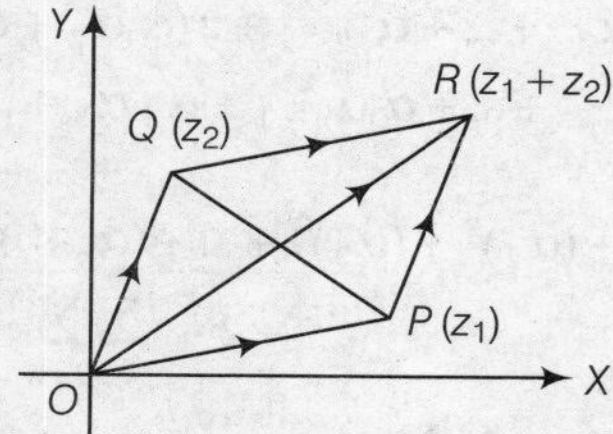

Complete the parallelogram $OPRQ$. Then, the mid-points of PQ and OR are the same. The mid-point of $PQ = \left(\frac{x_1 + x_2}{2}, \frac{y_1 + y_2}{2}\right)$.

Hence, $R = (x_1 + x_2, y_1 + y_2)$

Therefore, complex number z can also be represented by

$\overrightarrow{\mathbf{OR}} = (x_1 + x_2) + i(y_1 + y_2) = (x_1 + iy_1) + (x_2 + iy_2)$
$= z_1 + z_2 = (x_1, y_1) + (x_2, y_2)$

In vector notation, we have

$$z_1 + z_2 = \overrightarrow{\mathbf{OP}} + \overrightarrow{\mathbf{OQ}} = \overrightarrow{\mathbf{OP}} + \overrightarrow{\mathbf{PR}} = \overrightarrow{\mathbf{OR}}$$

(b) Difference

We first represent $-z_2$ by Q', so that QQ' is bisected at O. Complete the parallelogram $OPRQ'$. Then, the point R represents the difference $z_1 - z_2$.

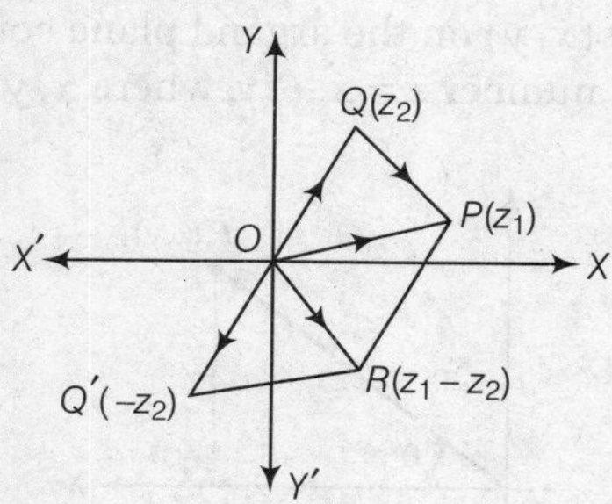

We see that $ORPQ$ is a parallelogram, so that $\overrightarrow{\mathbf{OR}} = \overrightarrow{\mathbf{QP}}$

We have in vectorial notation,

$$z_1 - z_2 = \overrightarrow{\mathbf{OP}} - \overrightarrow{\mathbf{OQ}} = \overrightarrow{\mathbf{OP}} + \overrightarrow{\mathbf{QO}}$$
$$= \overrightarrow{\mathbf{OP}} + \overrightarrow{\mathbf{PR}} = \overrightarrow{\mathbf{OR}} = \overrightarrow{\mathbf{QP}}$$

(c) Product

Let $\quad z_1 = r_1 (\cos\theta_1 + i\sin\theta_1) = r_1 e^{i\theta_1}$

$\therefore \quad |z_1| = r_1$ and $\arg(z_1) = \theta_1$

and $\quad z_2 = r_2(\cos\theta_2 + i\sin\theta_2) = r_2 e^{i\theta_2}$

$\therefore \quad |z_2| = r_2$ and $\arg(z_2) = \theta_2$

Then, $z_1 z_2 = r_1 r_2 (\cos\theta_1 + i\sin\theta_1)(\cos\theta_2 + i\sin\theta_2)$
$= r_1 r_2 \{\cos(\theta_1 + \theta_2) + i\sin(\theta_1 + \theta_2)\}$

$\therefore \quad |z_1 z_2| = r_1 r_2$ and $\arg(z_1 z_2) = \theta_1 + \theta_2$

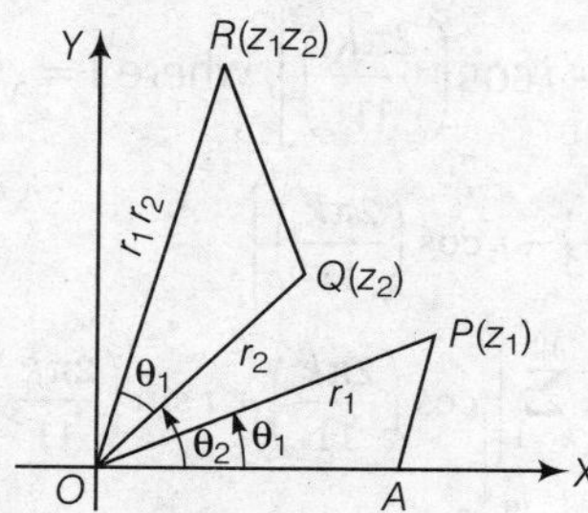

Let P and Q represent the complex numbers z_1 and z_2, respectively.

$\therefore \quad OP = r_1, OQ = r_2$

$\angle POX = \theta_1$ and $\angle QOX = \theta_2$

Take a point A on the real axis OX, such that $OA = 1$ unit. Complete the $\angle OPA$

Now, taking OQ as the base, construct a ΔOQR similar to ΔOPA, so that $\frac{OR}{OQ} = \frac{OP}{OA}$

i.e. $\quad OR = OP \cdot OQ = r_1 r_2 \quad$ [since, $OA = 1$ unit]

and $\quad \angle ROX = \angle ROQ + \angle QOX = \theta_1 + \theta_2$

Hence, R is the point representing product of complex numbers z_1 and z_2.

Remark

1. Multiplication by i
   Since, $z = r(\cos\theta + i\sin\theta)$ and $i = \left(\cos\frac{\pi}{2} + i\sin\frac{\pi}{2}\right)$
   $\therefore \quad iz = r\left[\cos\left(\frac{\pi}{2} + \theta\right) + i\sin\left(\frac{\pi}{2} + \theta\right)\right]$
   Hence, multiplication of z with i, then vector for z rotates a right angle in the positive sense.
2. Thus, to multiply a vector by (-1) is to turn it through two right angles.
3. Thus, to multiply a vector by $(\cos\theta + i\sin\theta)$ is to turn it through the angle θ in the positive sense.

(d) Division

Let $\quad z_1 = r_1(\cos\theta_1 + i\sin\theta_1) = r_1 e^{i\theta_1}$

$\therefore \quad |z_1| = r_1$ and $\arg(z_1) = \theta_1$

and $\quad z_2 = r_2(\cos\theta_2 + i\sin\theta_2) = r_2 e^{i\theta_2}$

$\therefore \quad |z_2| = r_2$ and $\arg(z_2) = \theta_2$

Then, $\dfrac{z_1}{z_2} = \dfrac{r_1}{r_2} \cdot \dfrac{(\cos\theta_1 + i\sin\theta_1)}{(\cos\theta_2 + i\sin\theta_2)}$ $\quad [z_2 \neq 0, r_2 \neq 0]$

$$\frac{z_1}{z_2} = \frac{r_1}{r_2}[\cos(\theta_1 - \theta_2) + i\sin(\theta_1 - \theta_2)]$$

$$\therefore \quad \left|\frac{z_1}{z_2}\right| = \frac{r_1}{r_2}, \arg\left(\frac{z_1}{z_2}\right) = \theta_1 - \theta_2$$

Let P and Q represent the complex numbers z_1 and z_2, respectively.

$\therefore \quad OP = r_1, OQ = r_2, \angle POX = \theta_1$ and $\angle QOX = \theta_2$

Let OS be new position of OP, take a point A on the real axis OX, such that $OA = 1$ unit and through A draw a line making with OA an angle equal to the $\angle OQP$ and meeting OS in R.

Then, R represented by (z_1/z_2).

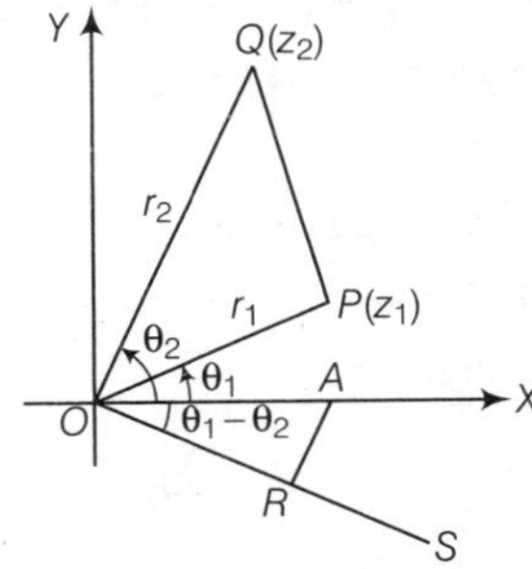

Now, in similar ΔOPQ and ΔOAR.

$$\frac{OR}{OA} = \frac{OP}{OQ} \Rightarrow OR = \frac{r_1}{r_2}$$

since $OA = 1$ and $\angle AOR = \angle POR - \angle POX = \theta_2 - \theta_1$

Hence, the vectorial angle of R is $-(\theta_2 - \theta_1)$ i.e., $\theta_1 - \theta_2$.

Remark

If θ_1 and θ_2 are the principal values of z_1 and z_2, then $\theta_1 + \theta_2$ and $\theta_1 - \theta_2$ are not necessarily the principal value of $\arg(z_1z_2)$ and $\arg(z_1/z_2)$.

Rotation Theorem (Coni Method)

Let z_1, z_2 and z_3 be the affixes of three points A, B and C respectively taken on argand plane.

Then, we have $\overrightarrow{\mathbf{AC}} = z_3 - z_1$ and $\overrightarrow{\mathbf{AB}} = z_2 - z_1$

and let $\quad \arg \overrightarrow{\mathbf{AC}} = \arg(z_3 - z_1) = \theta$

and $\quad \arg \overrightarrow{\mathbf{AB}} = \arg(z_2 - z_1) = \phi$

Let $\quad \angle CAB = \alpha$

$$\angle CAB = \alpha = \theta - \phi = \arg \overrightarrow{\mathbf{AC}} - \arg \overrightarrow{\mathbf{AB}}$$
$$= \arg(z_3 - z_1) - \arg(z_2 - z_1)$$
$$= \arg\left(\frac{z_3 - z_1}{z_2 - z_1}\right)$$

or angle between AC and AB

$$= \arg\left(\frac{\text{affix of } C - \text{affix of } A}{\text{affix of } B - \text{affix of } A}\right)$$

For any complex number z, we have

$$z = |z| e^{i(\arg z)}$$

Similarly, $\left(\dfrac{z_3 - z_1}{z_2 - z_1}\right) = \left|\dfrac{z_3 - z_1}{z_2 - z_1}\right| e^{i\left[\arg\left(\frac{z_3 - z_1}{z_2 - z_1}\right)\right]}$

or $\quad \dfrac{z_3 - z_1}{z_2 - z_1} = \dfrac{|z_3 - z_1|}{|z_2 - z_1|} e^{i(\angle CAB)} = \dfrac{AC}{AB} e^{i\alpha}$

Remark

1. Here, only principal values of the arguments are considered.
2. $\arg\left(\dfrac{z_1 - z_2}{z_3 - z_4}\right) = \theta$, if AB coincides with CD, then $\arg\left(\dfrac{z_1 - z_2}{z_3 - z_4}\right) = 0$ or π, so that $\dfrac{z_1 - z_2}{z_3 - z_4}$ is real. It follows that if $\dfrac{z_1 - z_2}{z_3 - z_4}$ is real, then the points A, B, C, D are collinear.
3. If AB is perpendicular to CD, then $\arg\left(\dfrac{z_1 - z_2}{z_3 - z_4}\right) = \pm\dfrac{\pi}{2}$, so $\dfrac{z_1 - z_2}{z_3 - z_4}$ is purely imaginary.
4. It follows that, if $z_1 - z_2 = \pm k(z_3 - z_4)$, where k is purely imaginary number, then AB and CD are perpendicular to each other.

Example 68. Complex numbers z_1, z_2 and z_3 are the vertices A, B, C respectively of an isosceles right angled triangle with right angle at C. Show that $(z_1 - z_2)^2 = 2(z_1 - z_3)(z_3 - z_2)$.

Sol. Since, $\angle ACB = 90°$ and $AC = BC$, then by Coni method

$$\frac{z_1 - z_3}{z_2 - z_3} = \frac{AC}{BC} e^{i\pi/2} = i$$

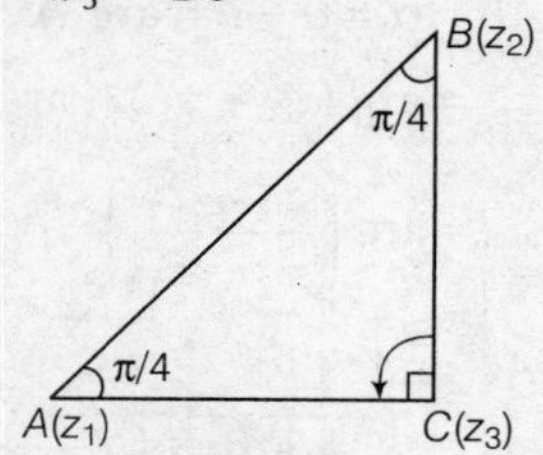

$$\Rightarrow \quad z_1 - z_3 = i(z_2 - z_3)$$

On squaring both sides, we get

$$(z_1 - z_3)^2 = -(z_2 - z_3)^2$$

$$\Rightarrow \quad z_1^2 + z_3^2 - 2z_1z_3 = -(z_2^2 + z_3^2 - 2z_2z_3)$$

$$\Rightarrow \quad z_1^2 + z_2^2 - 2z_1z_2 = 2(z_1z_3 - z_1z_2 - z_3^2 + z_2z_3)$$

Therefore, $(z_1 - z_2)^2 = 2(z_1 - z_3)(z_3 - z_2)$

Aliter $\quad CA = CB = \frac{1}{\sqrt{2}} BA$

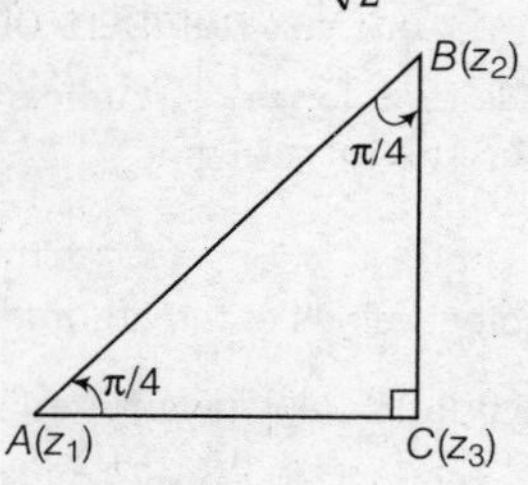

$\because \quad \angle BAC = (\pi/4)$

$$\therefore \quad \frac{z_2 - z_1}{z_3 - z_1} = \frac{BA}{CA} e^{(i\pi/4)}$$

or

$$\frac{z_1 - z_2}{z_1 - z_3} = \sqrt{2}\, e^{(i\pi/4)} \quad \text{...(i)}$$

and $\quad \angle CBA = (\pi/4)$

$$\therefore \quad \frac{z_3 - z_2}{z_1 - z_2} = \frac{CB}{AB} e^{(i\pi/4)} \text{ or } \frac{z_3 - z_2}{z_1 - z_2} = \frac{1}{\sqrt{2}} e^{(i\pi/4)} \quad \text{...(ii)}$$

On dividing Eq. (i) by Eq. (ii), we get

$$(z_1 - z_2)^2 = 2(z_1 - z_3)(z_3 - z_2)$$

Example 69. Complex numbers z_1, z_2, z_3 are the vertices of A, B, C respectively of an equilateral triangle. Show that

$$z_1^2 + z_2^2 + z_3^2 = z_1z_2 + z_2z_3 + z_3z_1.$$

Sol. Let $\quad AB = BC = CA = a$

$$\because \quad \angle ABC = \frac{\pi}{3}$$

From Coni method, $\quad \frac{z_1 - z_2}{z_3 - z_2} = \frac{a}{a} e^{i\pi/3} \quad \text{...(i)}$

and $\quad \angle BAC = \frac{\pi}{3}$

From Coni method, $\quad \frac{z_3 - z_1}{z_2 - z_1} = \frac{a}{a} e^{i\pi/3} \quad \text{...(ii)}$

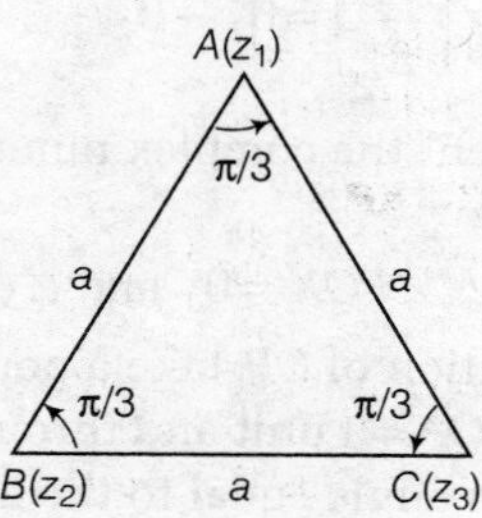

From Eqs. (i) and (ii), we get $\frac{z_1 - z_2}{z_3 - z_2} = \frac{z_3 - z_1}{z_2 - z_1}$

$$\Rightarrow \quad (z_1 - z_2)(z_2 - z_1) = (z_3 - z_1)(z_3 - z_2)$$

$$\Rightarrow \quad z_1^2 + z_2^2 + z_3^2 = z_1z_2 + z_2z_3 + z_3z_1$$

Remark

Triangle with vertices z_1, z_2, z_3, then

(i) $(z_1 - z_2)^2 + (z_2 - z_3)^2 + (z_3 - z_1)^2 = 0$

(ii) $(z_1 - z_2)^2 = (z_2 - z_3)(z_3 - z_1)$

(iii) $\sum (z_1 - z_2)(z_2 - z_3) = 0$ $\quad$ (iv) $\sum \frac{1}{(z_1 - z_2)} = 0$

Complex Number as a Rotating Arrow in the Argand Plane

Let $\quad z = r(\cos\theta + i\sin\theta) = re^{i\theta} \quad \text{...(i)}$

be a complex number representing a point P in the argand plane.

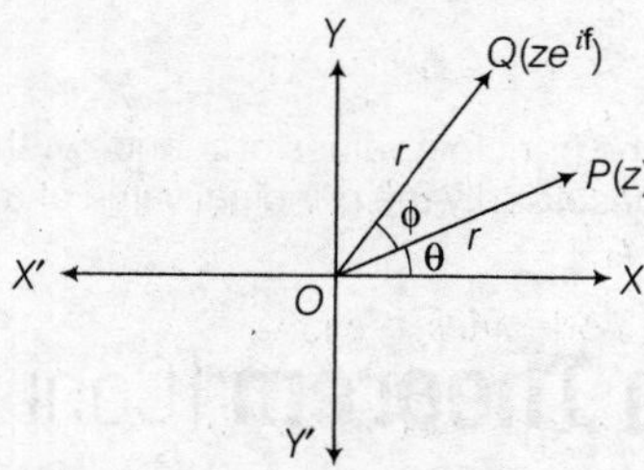

Then, $OP = |z| = r$ and $\angle POX = \theta$

Now, consider complex number $z_1 = ze^{i\phi}$

or $\quad z_1 = re^{i\theta} \cdot e^{i\phi} = re^{i(\theta + \phi)}$ $\quad$ [from Eq. (i)]

Clearly, the complex number z_1 represents a point Q in the argand plane, when $OQ = r$ and $\angle QOX = \theta + \phi$

Clearly, multiplication of z with $e^{i\phi}$ rotates the vector $\overrightarrow{\mathbf{OP}}$ through angle ϕ in anti-clockwise sense. Similarly, multiplication of z with $e^{-i\phi}$ will rotate the vector $\overrightarrow{\mathbf{OP}}$ in clockwise sense.

Remark

1. If z_1, z_2 and z_3 are the affixes of the three points A, B and C, such that $AC = AB$ and $\angle CAB = \theta$. Therefore,

$$\overrightarrow{\mathbf{AB}} = z_2 - z_1, \ \overrightarrow{\mathbf{AC}} = z_3 - z_1.$$

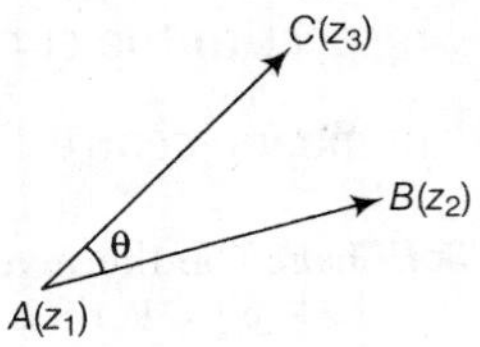

Then, $\overrightarrow{\mathbf{AC}}$ will be obtained by rotating $\overrightarrow{\mathbf{AB}}$ through an angle θ in anti-clockwise sense and therefore,

$$\overrightarrow{\mathbf{AC}} = \overrightarrow{\mathbf{AB}}\, e^{i\theta}$$

or $(z_3 - z_1) = (z_2 - z_1)\, e^{i\theta}$ or $\dfrac{z_3 - z_1}{z_2 - z_1} = e^{i\theta}$

2. If A, B and C are three points in argand plane, such that $AC = AB$ and $\angle CAB = \theta$, then use the rotation about A to find $e^{i\theta}$, but if $AC \neq AB$, then use Coni method.

Example 70. Let z_1 and z_2 be roots of the equation $z^2 + pz + q = 0$, where the coefficients p and q may be complex numbers. Let A and B represent z_1 and z_2 in the complex plane. If $\angle AOB = \alpha \neq 0$ and $OA = OB$, where O is the origin, prove that $p^2 = 4q\cos^2(\alpha/2)$.

Sol. Clearly, $\overrightarrow{\mathbf{OB}}$ is obtained by rotating $\overrightarrow{\mathbf{OA}}$ through angle α.

$\therefore$ $\overrightarrow{\mathbf{OB}} = \overrightarrow{\mathbf{OA}}\, e^{i\alpha}$

$\Rightarrow$ $z_2 = z_1 e^{i\alpha}$

$\Rightarrow$ $\dfrac{z_2}{z_1} = e^{i\alpha}$ ...(i)

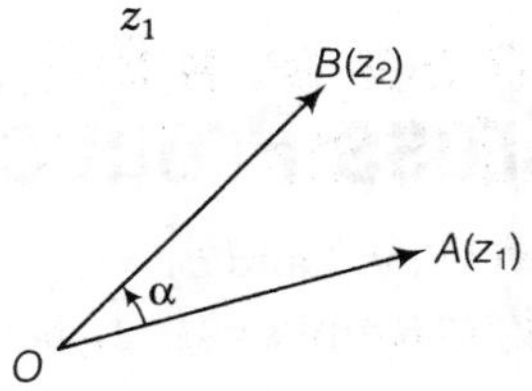

or $\dfrac{z_2}{z_1} + 1 = (e^{i\alpha} + 1)$

$\Rightarrow$ $\dfrac{(z_1 + z_2)}{z_1} = e^{i\alpha/2} \cdot 2\cos(\alpha/2)$

On squaring both sides, we get

$$\frac{(z_1 + z_2)^2}{z_1^2} = e^{i\alpha} \cdot (4\cos^2 \alpha/2)$$

$\Rightarrow$ $\dfrac{(z_1 + z_2)^2}{z_1^2} = \dfrac{z_2}{z_1} \cdot (4\cos^2 \alpha/2)$ [from Eq. (i)]

$$(z_1 + z_2)^2 = 4 z_1 z_2 \cos^2(\alpha/2)$$

$$(-p)^2 = 4q\cos^2(\alpha/2)$$

$\left[\because z_1 \text{ and } z_2 \text{ are the roots of } z^2 + pz + q = 0 \;\; \therefore z_1 + z_2 = -p \text{ and } z_1 z_2 = q\right]$

or $p^2 = 4q\cos^2(\alpha/2)$

Shifting the Origin in Case of Complex Numbers

Let O be the origin and P be a point with affix z_0. Let a point Q has affix z with respect to the coordinate system passing through O. When origin is shifted to the point P (z_0), then the new affix Z of the point Q with respect to new origin P is given by $Z = z - z_0$.

i.e., to shift the origin at z_0, we should replace z by $Z + z_0$.

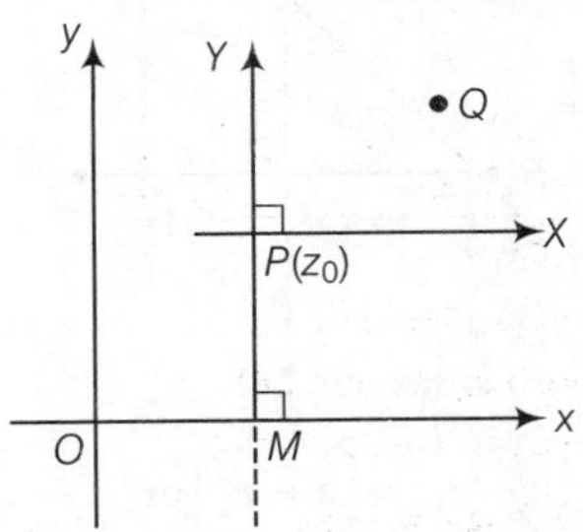

Example 71. If z_1, z_2 and z_3 are the vertices of an equilateral triangle with z_0 as its circumcentre, then changing origin to z_0, show that $Z_1^2 + Z_2^2 + Z_3^2 = 0$, where Z_1, Z_2, Z_3 are new complex numbers of the vertices.

Sol. In an equilateral triangle, the circumcentre and the centroid are the same point.

So, $z_0 = \dfrac{z_1 + z_2 + z_3}{3}$

$\therefore$ $z_1 + z_2 + z_3 = 3z_0$ ...(i)

To shift the origin at z_0, we have to replace z_1, z_2, z_3 and z_0 by $Z_1 + z_0, Z_2 + z_0, Z_3 + z_0$ and $0 + z_0$.

Then, Eq. (i) becomes

$$(Z_1 + z_0) + (Z_2 + z_0) + (Z_3 + z_0) = 3(0 + z_0)$$

$\Rightarrow$ $Z_1 + Z_2 + Z_3 = 0$

On squaring, we get

$Z_1^2 + Z_2^2 + Z_3^2 + 2(Z_1Z_2 + Z_2Z_3 + Z_3Z_1) = 0$ ...(ii)

But triangle with vertices Z_1, Z_2 and Z_3 is equilateral, then

$Z_1^2 + Z_2^2 + Z_3^2 = Z_1Z_2 + Z_2Z_3 + Z_3Z_1$ ...(iii)

From Eqs. (ii) and (iii), we get

$$3(Z_1^2 + Z_2^2 + Z_3^2) = 0$$

Therefore, $Z_1^2 + Z_2^2 + Z_3^2 = 0$

Inverse Points

(a) **Inverse points with respect to a line** Two points P and Q are said to be the inverse points with respect to the line RS. If Q is the image of P in RS, i.e., if the line RS is the right bisector of PQ.

Example 72. Show that z_1, z_2 are the inverse points with respect to the line $z\bar{a}+a\bar{z}=b$, if $z_1\bar{a}+a\bar{z}_2=b$.

Sol. Let RS be the line represented by the equation,

$$z\,\bar{a}+a\,\bar{z}=b \quad \text{...(i)}$$

Let P and Q are the inverse points with respect to the line RS. The point Q is the reflection (inverse) of the point P in the line RS, if the line RS is the right bisector of PQ. Take any point z in the line RS, then lines joining z to P and z to Q are equal.

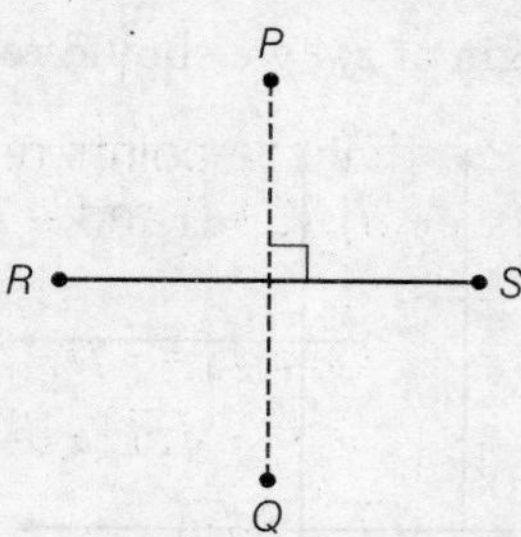

i.e., $\quad |z-z_1|=|z-z_2|$ or $|z-z_1|^2=|z-z_2|^2$

i.e., $(z-z_1)(\bar{z}-\bar{z}_1)=(z-z_2)(\bar{z}-\bar{z}_2)$

$$\Rightarrow z(\bar{z}_2-\bar{z}_1)+\bar{z}(z_2-z_1)+(z_1\bar{z}_1-z_2\bar{z}_2)=0 \quad \text{...(ii)}$$

Hence, Eqs. (i) and (ii) are identical, therefore, comparing coefficients, we get

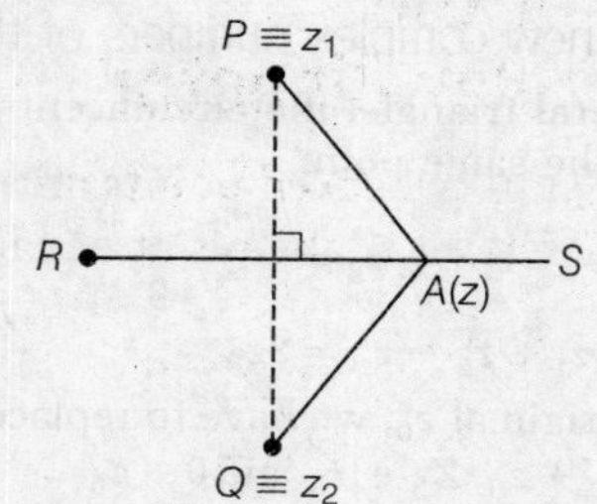

$$\frac{\bar{a}}{\bar{z}_2-\bar{z}_1}=\frac{a}{z_2-z_1}=\frac{-b}{z_1\bar{z}_1-z_2\bar{z}_2}$$

So that, $\quad \dfrac{z_1\bar{a}}{z_1(\bar{z}_2-\bar{z}_1)}=\dfrac{a\bar{z}_2}{\bar{z}_2(z_2-z_1)}$

$$=\frac{-b}{z_1\bar{z}_1-z_2\bar{z}_2}=\frac{z_1\bar{a}+a\bar{z}_2-b}{0}$$

[by ratio and proportion rule]

$$z_1\bar{a}+a\bar{z}_2-b=0 \text{ or } z_1\bar{a}+a\bar{z}_2=b$$

(b) **Inverse points with respect to a circle** If C is the centre of the circle and P, Q are the inverse points with respect to the circle, then three points C, P, Q are collinear and also $CP\cdot CQ=r^2$, where r is the radius of the circle.

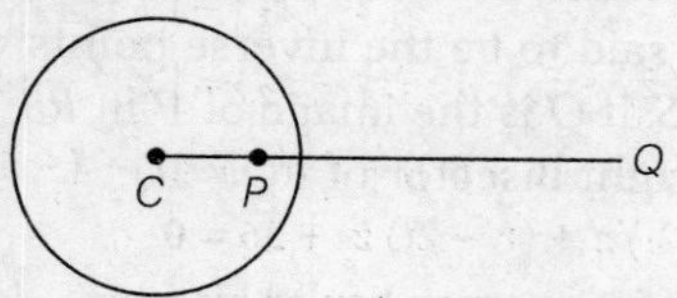

Example 73. Show that inverse of a point a with respect to the circle $|z-c|=R$ (a and c are complex numbers, centre c and radius R) is the point $c+\dfrac{R^2}{\bar{a}-\bar{c}}$.

Sol. Let a' be the inverse point of a with respect to the circle $|z-c|=R$, then by definition,

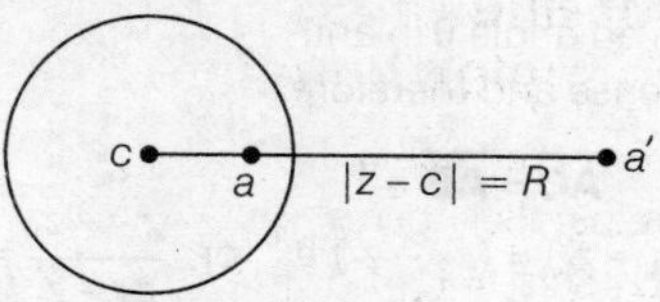

The points c, a, a' are collinear.

We have, $\arg(a'-c)=\arg(a-c)$

$$=-\arg(\bar{a}-\bar{c}) \quad [\because \arg\bar{z}=-\arg z]$$

$$\Rightarrow \arg(a'-c)+\arg(\bar{a}-\bar{c})=0$$

$$\Rightarrow \arg\{(a'-c)(\bar{a}-\bar{c})\}=0$$

$\therefore (a'-c)(\bar{a}-\bar{c})$ is purely real and positive.

By definition, $|a'-c||a-c|=R^2 \quad [\because CP\cdot CQ=r^2]$

$$\Rightarrow |a'-c||\bar{a}-\bar{c}|=R^2 \quad [\because |z|=|\bar{z}|]$$

$$\Rightarrow |(a'-c)(\bar{a}-\bar{c})|=R^2$$

$$\Rightarrow (a'-c)(\bar{a}-\bar{c})=R^2$$

[$\because (a'-c)(\bar{a}-\bar{c})$ is purely real and positive]

$$\Rightarrow a'-c=\frac{R^2}{\bar{a}-\bar{c}} \Rightarrow a'=c+\frac{R^2}{\bar{a}-\bar{c}}$$

Dot and Cross Product

Let $z_1=x_1+iy_1\equiv(x_1,y_1)$ and $z_2=x_2+iy_2\equiv(x_2,y_2)$, where $x_1,y_1,x_2,y_2\in R$ and $i=\sqrt{-1}$, be two complex numbers.

If $\angle POQ=\theta$, then from Coni method,

$$\frac{z_2-0}{z_1-0}=\frac{|z_2|}{|z_1|}e^{i\theta}$$

$$\Rightarrow \frac{z_2\bar{z}_1}{z_1\bar{z}_1}=\frac{|z_2|}{|z_1|}e^{i\theta}$$

$$\Rightarrow \frac{z_2\bar{z}_1}{|z_1|^2}=\frac{|z_2|}{|z_1|}e^{i\theta}$$

$$z_2\bar{z}_1=|z_1||z_2|e^{i\theta}$$

$$z_2\bar{z}_1=|z_1||z_2|(\cos\theta+i\sin\theta)$$

$$\Rightarrow \operatorname{Re}(z_2\bar{z}_1)=|z_1||z_2|\cos\theta \quad \text{...(i)}$$

and $\quad \operatorname{Im}(z_2\bar{z}_1)=|z_1||z_2|\sin\theta \quad$ ...(ii)

The dot product z_1 and z_2 is defined by,

$$z_1\cdot z_2=|z_1||z_2|\cos\theta$$

$$=\operatorname{Re}(\bar{z}_1 z_2)=x_1x_2+y_1y_2 \quad \text{[from Eq. (i)]}$$

and cross product of z_1 and z_2 is defined by

$$z_1 \times z_2 = |z_1||z_2|\sin\theta$$
$$= \text{Im}(\bar{z}_1 z_2) = x_1 y_2 - x_2 y_1 \quad \text{[from Eq. (ii)]}$$

Hence, $z_1 \cdot z_2 = x_1 x_2 + y_1 y_2 = \text{Re}(\bar{z}_1 z_2)$

and $z_1 \times z_2 = x_1 y_2 - x_2 y_1 = \text{Im}(\bar{z}_1 z_2)$

Results for Dot and Cross Products of Complex Number

1. If z_1 and z_2 are perpendicular, then $z_1 \cdot z_2 = 0$
2. If z_1 and z_2 are parallel, then $z_1 \times z_2 = 0$
3. Projection of z_1 on $z_2 = (z_1 \cdot z_2)/|z_2|$
4. Projection of z_2 on $z_1 = (z_1 \cdot z_2)/|z_1|$
5. Area of triangle, if two sides represented by z_1 and z_2 is $\frac{1}{2}|z_1 \times z_2|$.
6. Area of a parallelogram having sides z_1 and z_2 is $|z_1 \times z_2|$.
7. Area of parallelogram, if diagonals represented by z_1 and z_2 is $\frac{1}{2}|z_1 \times z_2|$.

Example 74. If $z_1 = 2 + 5i, z_2 = 3 - i$, where $i = \sqrt{-1}$, find

(i) $z_1 \cdot z_2$ (ii) $z_1 \times z_2$

(iii) $z_2 \cdot z_1$ (iv) $z_2 \times z_1$

(v) acute angle between z_1 and z_2.

(vi) projection of z_1 on z_2.

Sol. (i) $z_1 \cdot z_2 = x_1 x_2 + y_1 y_2 = (2)(3) + (5)(-1) = 1$

(ii) $z_1 \times z_2 = x_1 y_2 - x_2 y_1 = (2)(-1) - (3)(5) = -17$

(iii) $z_2 \cdot z_1 = x_1 x_2 + y_1 y_2 = (2)(3) + (5)(-1) = 1$

(iv) $z_2 \times z_1 = x_2 y_1 - x_1 y_2 = (3)(5) - (2)(-1) = 17$

(v) Let angle between z_1 and z_2 be θ, then

$$z_1 \cdot z_2 = |z_1||z_2|\cos\theta$$

$$\Rightarrow \quad 1 = \sqrt{(4+25)}\sqrt{(9+1)}\cos\theta$$

$$\therefore \quad \cos\theta = \frac{1}{\sqrt{290}} \quad \therefore \quad \theta = \cos^{-1}\left(\frac{1}{\sqrt{290}}\right)$$

(vi) Projection of z_1 on $z_2 = \dfrac{z_1 \cdot z_2}{|z_2|} = \dfrac{1}{\sqrt{(9+1)}} = \dfrac{1}{\sqrt{10}}$

Use of Complex Numbers in Coordinate Geometry

(a) Distance Formula

The distance between two points $P(z_1)$ and $Q(z_2)$ is given by

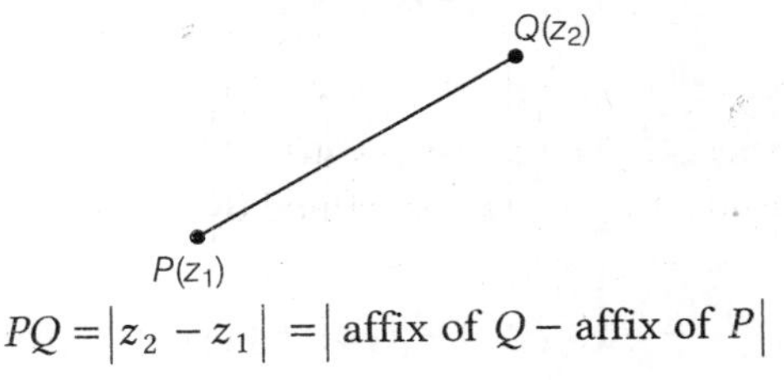

$$PQ = |z_2 - z_1| = |\text{affix of } Q - \text{affix of } P|$$

Remark

1. The distance of a point z from origin, $|z - 0| = |z|$
2. Three points $A(z_1)$, $B(z_2)$ and $C(z_3)$ are collinear, then $AB + BC = AC$

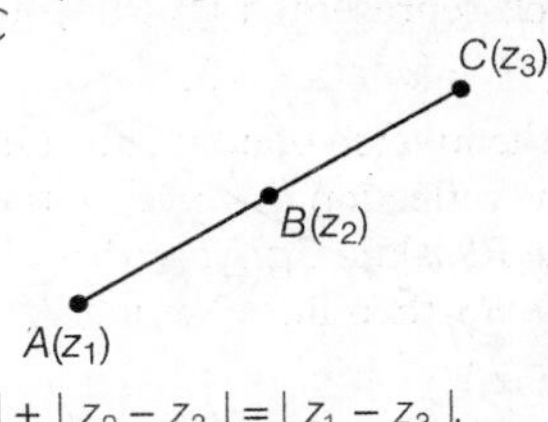

i.e. $|z_1 - z_2| + |z_2 - z_3| = |z_1 - z_3|$.

Example 75. Show that the points representing the complex numbers $(3 + 2i), (2 - i)$ and $-7i$, where $i = \sqrt{-1}$, are collinear.

Sol. Let $z_1 = 3 + 2i, z_2 = 2 - i$ and $z_3 = -7i$.

Then, $|z_1 - z_2| = |1 + 3i| = \sqrt{10}, |z_2 - z_3| = |2 + 6i|$
$= \sqrt{40} = 2\sqrt{10}$

and $|z_1 - z_3| = |3 + 9i| = \sqrt{90} = 3\sqrt{10}$

$\therefore \quad |z_1 - z_2| + |z_2 - z_3| = |z_1 - z_3|$

Hence, the points $(3 + 2i), (2 - i)$ and $-7i$ are collinear.

(b) Equation of the Perpendicular Bisector

If $P(z_1)$ and $Q(z_2)$ are two fixed points and $R(z)$ is moving point, such that it is always at equal distance from $P(z_1)$ and $Q(z_2)$.

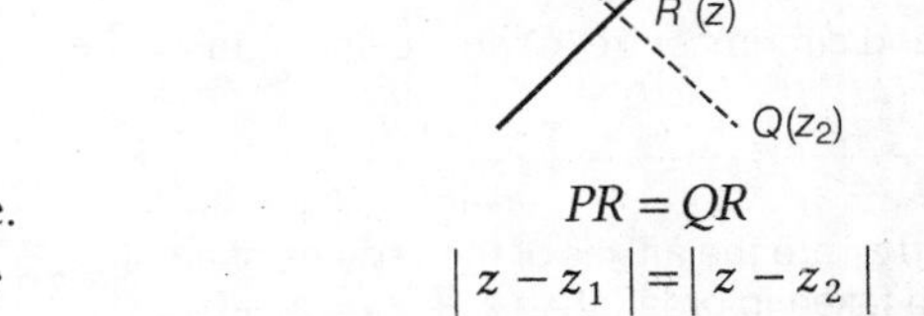

i.e. $PR = QR$

or $|z - z_1| = |z - z_2|$

or $z(\bar{z}_1 - \bar{z}_2) + \bar{z}(z_1 - z_2) = z_1\bar{z}_1 - z_2\bar{z}_2$

or $z(\bar{z}_1 - \bar{z}_2) + \bar{z}(z_1 - z_2) = |z_1|^2 - |z_2|^2$

Hence, z lies on the perpendicular bisectors of z_1 and z_2.

Example 76. Find the perpendicular bisector of $3 + 4i$ and $-5 + 6i$, where $i = \sqrt{-1}$.

Sol. Let $z_1 = 3 + 4i$ and $z_2 = -5 + 6i$

If z is moving point, such that it is always equal distance from z_1 and z_2.

i.e. $|z - z_1| = |z - z_2|$

or $z(\bar{z}_1 - \bar{z}_2) + \bar{z}(z_1 - z_2) = |z_1|^2 - |z_2|^2$

$\Rightarrow z((3 - 4i) - (-5 - 6i)) + \bar{z}((3 + 4i) - (-5 + 6i)) = 25 - 61$

Hence, $(8 + 2i)z + (8 - 2i)\bar{z} + 36 = 0$

which is required perpendicular bisector.

(c) Section Formula

If $R(z)$ divides the joining of $P(z_1)$ and $Q(z_2)$ in the ratio $m_1 : m_2$ $(m_1, m_2 > 0)$.

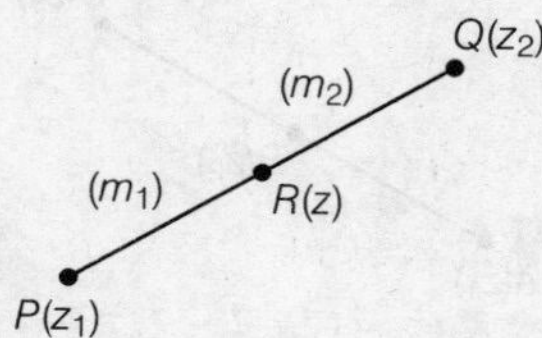

(i) If $R(z)$ divides the segment PQ internally in the ratio of $m_1 : m_2$, then $z = \dfrac{m_1 z_2 + m_2 z_1}{m_1 + m_2}$

(ii) If $R(z)$ divides the segment PQ externally in the ratio of $m_1 : m_2$, then $z = \dfrac{m_1 z_2 - m_2 z_1}{m_1 - m_2}$

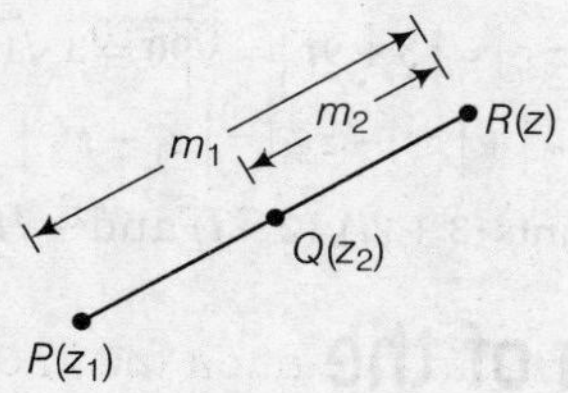

Remark

1. If $R(z)$ is the mid-point of PQ, then affix of R is $\dfrac{z_1 + z_2}{2}$.
2. If z_1, z_2 and z_3 are affixes of the vertices of a triangle, then affix of its centroid is $\dfrac{z_1 + z_2 + z_3}{3}$.
3. In acute angle triangle, orthocentre (O), nine point centre (N), centroid (G) and circumcentre (C) are collinear and $\dfrac{OG}{GC} = \dfrac{2}{1}$, $\dfrac{ON}{NG} = \dfrac{1}{1}$.
4. If z_1, z_2, z_3 and z_4 are the affixes of the vertices of a parallelogram taken in order, then $z_1 + z_3 = z_2 + z_4$.

Example 77. If z_1, z_2 and z_3 are the affixes of the vertices of a triangle having its circumcentre at the origin. If z is the affix of its orthocentre, prove that $z_1 + z_2 + z_3 - z = 0$.

Sol. We know that orthocentre O, centroid G and circumcentre C of a triangle are collinear, such that G divides OC in the ratio $2:1$. Since, affix of G is $\dfrac{z_1 + z_2 + z_3}{3}$ and C is the origin. Therefore, by section formula, we get

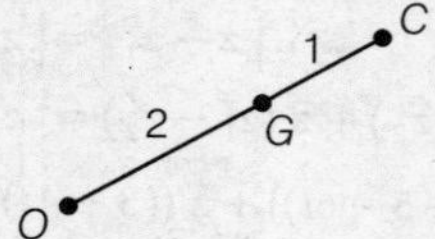

$$\Rightarrow \quad \frac{z_1 + z_2 + z_3}{3} = \frac{2 \cdot 0 + 1 \cdot z}{2 + 1}$$

$$\Rightarrow \quad z_1 + z_2 + z_3 = z$$

Therefore, $z_1 + z_2 + z_3 - z = 0$

Example 78. Let z_1, z_2 and z_3 be three complex numbers and $a, b, c \in R$, such that $a + b + c = 0$ and $az_1 + bz_2 + cz_3 = 0$, then show that z_1, z_2 and z_3 are collinear.

Sol. Given, $\quad a + b + c = 0 \quad$ ...(i)

and $\quad az_1 + bz_2 + cz_3 = 0 \quad$ ...(ii)

$\Rightarrow \quad az_1 + bz_2 - (a + b) z_3 = 0 \quad$ [from Eq. (i)]

or $\quad z_3 = \dfrac{az_1 + bz_2}{a + b}$

It follows that z_3 divides the line segment joining z_1 and z_2 internally in the ratio $b : a$. (If a, b are of same sign and opposite sign, then externally.)

Hence, z_1, z_2 and z_3 are collinear.

(d) Area of Triangle

If z_1, z_2 and z_3 are the affixes of the vertices of a triangle,

then its area $= \dfrac{1}{4} \left| \begin{vmatrix} z_1 & \bar{z}_1 & 1 \\ z_2 & \bar{z}_2 & 1 \\ z_3 & \bar{z}_3 & 1 \end{vmatrix} \right|$

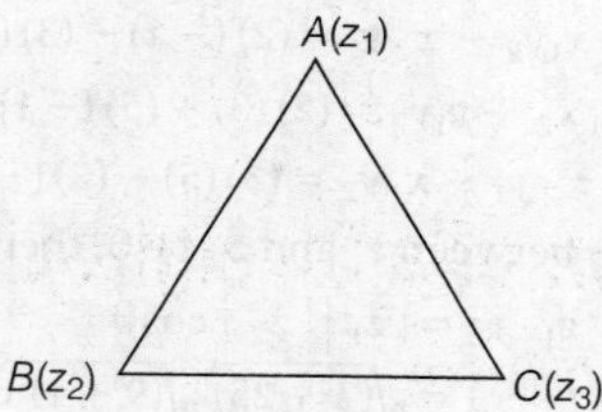

Remark

The area of the triangle with vertices z, ωz and $z + \omega z$ is $\dfrac{\sqrt{3}}{4}|z|^2$, where ω is the cube root of unity.

Example 79. Show that the area of the triangle on the argand plane formed by the complex numbers z, iz and $z + iz$ is $\dfrac{1}{2}|z|^2$, where $i = \sqrt{-1}$.

Sol. Required area $= \dfrac{1}{4} \left| \begin{vmatrix} z & \bar{z} & 1 \\ iz & \overline{iz} & 1 \\ z + iz & \overline{z + iz} & 1 \end{vmatrix} \right|$

$$= \frac{1}{4} \left| \begin{vmatrix} z & \bar{z} & 1 \\ iz & \overline{iz} & 1 \\ z + iz & \overline{z + iz} & 1 \end{vmatrix} \right|$$

$$= \frac{1}{4}\left|\begin{vmatrix} z & \bar{z} & 1 \\ iz & -i\bar{z} & 1 \\ z+iz & \bar{z}-i\bar{z} & 1 \end{vmatrix}\right|$$

On applying $R_3 \to R_3 - (R_1 + R_2)$, we get

$$\text{Area} = \frac{1}{4}\left|\begin{vmatrix} z & \bar{z} & 1 \\ iz & -i\bar{z} & 1 \\ 0 & 0 & -1 \end{vmatrix}\right| = \frac{1}{4}\left|(-1)(-iz\bar{z} - iz\bar{z})\right|$$

$$= \frac{1}{4}\left|2iz\bar{z}\right| = \frac{1}{2}|i||z\bar{z}| = \frac{1}{2}|z|^2$$

Aliter

We have, $iz = z(\cos(\pi/2) + i\sin(\pi/2)) = ze^{(i\pi/2)}$ iz is the vector obtained by rotating vector z in anti-clockwise direction through $(\pi/2)$. Therefore, $OA \perp AB$,

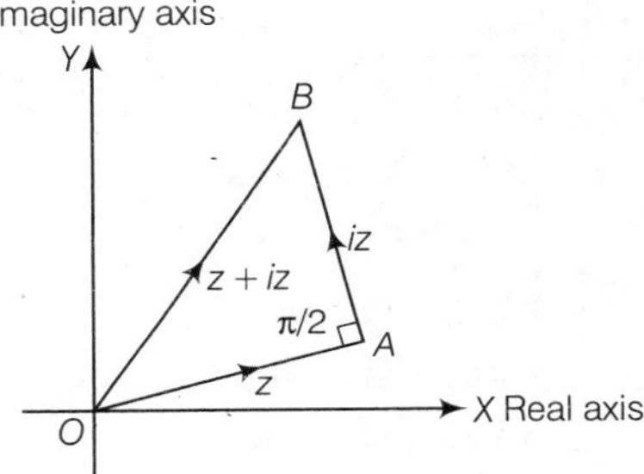

Now, area of $\Delta OAB = \frac{1}{2} OA \times AB = \frac{1}{2}|z||iz|$

$$= \frac{1}{2}|z||i||z| = \frac{1}{2}|z|^2$$

(e) Equation of a Straight Line

(i) Parametric form

Equation of the straight line joining the points having affixes z_1 and z_2 is

$$z = tz_1 + (1-t)z_2, \text{ where } t \in R \sim \{0\}$$

Proof

$$\because \quad z = tz_1 + (1-t)z_2 = \frac{tz_1 + (1-t)z_2}{t + (1-t)}$$

Hence, z divides the line joining z_1 and z_2 in the ratio $1-t:t$. Thus, the points z_1, z_2, z are collinear.

(ii) Non-parametric form

Equation of the straight line joining the points having affixes z_1 and z_2 is

$$\begin{vmatrix} z & \bar{z} & 1 \\ z_1 & \bar{z}_1 & 1 \\ z_2 & \bar{z}_2 & 1 \end{vmatrix} = 0$$

or $z(\bar{z}_1 - \bar{z}_2) - \bar{z}(z_1 - z_2) + z_1\bar{z}_2 - \bar{z}_1 z_2 = 0$

Proof Equation of the straight line joining points having affixes z_1 and z_2 is

$$z = tz_1 + (1-t)z_2, \text{ where } t \in R \sim \{0\}$$

$\Rightarrow \quad z - z_2 = t(z_1 - z_2)$ ...(i)

and $\quad \overline{z - z_2} = t\overline{(z_1 - z_2)}$

or $\quad \bar{z} - \bar{z}_2 = t(\bar{z}_1 - \bar{z}_2)$ ...(ii)

From Eqs. (i) and (ii), we get

$$\frac{z - z_2}{\bar{z} - \bar{z}_2} = \frac{z_1 - z_2}{\bar{z}_1 - \bar{z}_2} \Rightarrow \frac{z - z_2}{z_1 - z_2} = \frac{\bar{z} - \bar{z}_2}{\bar{z}_1 - \bar{z}_2}$$

$$\Rightarrow \begin{vmatrix} z - z_2 & \bar{z} - \bar{z}_2 & 0 \\ z_1 - z_2 & \bar{z}_1 - \bar{z}_2 & 0 \\ z_2 & \bar{z}_2 & 1 \end{vmatrix} = 0$$

Now, applying $R_1 \to R_1 + R_3$ and $R_2 \to R_2 + R_3$, we get

$$\begin{vmatrix} z & \bar{z} & 1 \\ z_1 & \bar{z}_1 & 1 \\ z_2 & \bar{z}_2 & 1 \end{vmatrix} = 0$$

or $z(\bar{z}_1 - \bar{z}_2) - \bar{z}(z_1 - z_2) + z_1\bar{z}_2 - \bar{z}_1 z_2 = 0$

Aliter

Let $P(z)$ be an arbitrary point on the line, which pass through $A(z_1)$ and $B(z_2)$.

$\therefore \quad \angle BAP = 0$ or π

$\therefore \quad \arg\left(\frac{z - z_1}{z_2 - z_1}\right) = 0$ or π [by rotation theorem]

$\Rightarrow \quad \frac{z - z_1}{z_2 - z_1}$ is purely real.

$$\therefore \quad \left(\frac{z - z_1}{z_2 - z_1}\right) = \left(\overline{\frac{z - z_1}{z_2 - z_1}}\right) \Rightarrow \frac{z - z_1}{z_2 - z_1} = \frac{\bar{z} - \bar{z}_1}{\bar{z}_2 - \bar{z}_1}$$

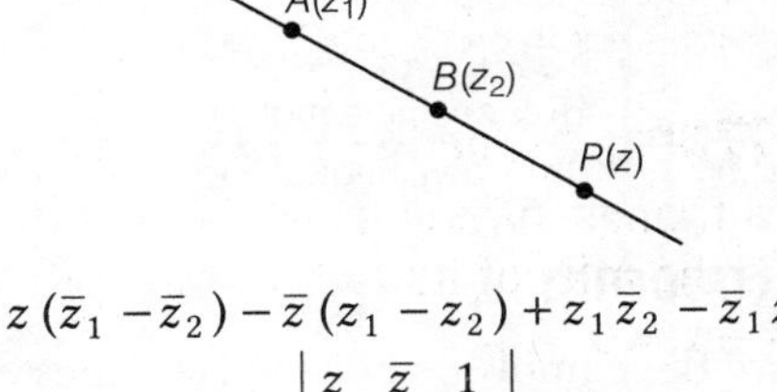

$$z(\bar{z}_1 - \bar{z}_2) - \bar{z}(z_1 - z_2) + z_1\bar{z}_2 - \bar{z}_1 z_2 = 0$$

or $$\begin{vmatrix} z & \bar{z} & 1 \\ z_1 & \bar{z}_1 & 1 \\ z_2 & \bar{z}_2 & 1 \end{vmatrix} = 0$$

Remark

If z_1, z_2 and z_3 are collinear, $\begin{vmatrix} z_1 & \bar{z}_1 & 1 \\ z_2 & \bar{z}_2 & 1 \\ z_3 & \bar{z}_3 & 1 \end{vmatrix} = 0$

or $\sum \bar{z}_1(z_2 - z_3) = 0.$

(iii) General form The general equation of a straight line is of the form $\bar{a}\,z + a\,\bar{z} + b = 0$, where a is a complex number and b is a real number.

Sol. The equation of a straight line passing through points having affixes z_1 and z_2 is given by

$$z(\bar{z}_1 - \bar{z}_2) - \bar{z}(z_1 - z_2) + z_1\bar{z}_2 - \bar{z}_1 z_2 = 0 \quad \text{...(i)}$$

On multiplying Eq. (i) by i (where, $i = \sqrt{-1}$), we get

$$zi(\bar{z}_1 - \bar{z}_2) - \bar{z}\,i(z_1 - z_2) + i(z_1\bar{z}_2 - \bar{z}_1 z_2) = 0$$

$$\Rightarrow \bar{z}\{-i(z_1 - z_2)\} + z\{i(\bar{z}_1 - \bar{z}_2)\} + i(z_1\bar{z}_2 - \bar{z}_1 z_2) = 0$$

$$\Rightarrow \bar{z}\{-i(z_1 - z_2)\} + z\{\overline{-i(z_1 - z_2)}\} + \{i(2i\,\text{Im}(z_1\bar{z}_2))\} = 0$$

$$\Rightarrow \bar{z}\{-i(z_1 - z_2)\} + z\{\overline{-i(z_1 - z_2)}\} + \{(-2\,\text{Im}(z_1\bar{z}_2)\} = 0$$

$$\Rightarrow \bar{z}\,a + z\,\bar{a} + b = 0,$$

where, $a = -i(z_1 - z_2)$, $b = -2\,\text{Im}(z_1\bar{z}_2)$

Hence, the general equation of a straight line is of the form $\bar{a}\,z + a\,\bar{z} + b = 0$,

where a is complex number and b is a real number.

(iv) Slope of the line $\bar{a}\,z + a\,\bar{z} + b = 0$

Let $A(z_1)$ and $B(z_2)$ be two points on the line $\bar{a}\,z + a\,\bar{z} + b = 0$, then

$$\bar{a}\,z_1 + a\,\bar{z}_1 + b = 0$$

and $$\bar{a}\,z_2 + a\,\bar{z}_2 + b = 0$$

$$\therefore \quad \bar{a}(z_1 - z_2) + a(\bar{z}_1 - \bar{z}_2) = 0$$

$$\Rightarrow \quad \frac{z_1 - z_2}{\bar{z}_1 - \bar{z}_2} = -\frac{a}{\bar{a}} \quad \text{[Remember]}$$

$$\text{Complex slope of } AB = -\frac{a}{\bar{a}} = -\frac{\text{coefficient of } \bar{z}}{\text{coefficient of } z}$$

Thus, the complex slope of the line $\bar{a}\,z + a\,\bar{z} + b = 0$ is $-\dfrac{a}{\bar{a}}$.

Remark

The real slope of the line $\bar{a}z + a\bar{z} + b = 0$ is $-\dfrac{\text{Re}(a)}{\text{Im}(a)}$, i.e. $-\dfrac{\text{Re (coefficient of } \bar{z})}{\text{Im (coefficient of } \bar{z})}$.

Important Theorem

If α_1 and α_2 are the complex slopes of two lines on the argand plane, then prove that the lines are

(i) perpendicular, if $\alpha_1 + \alpha_2 = 0$.

(ii) parallel, if $\alpha_1 = \alpha_2$.

Proof Let z_1 and z_2 be the affixes of two points on one line with complex slope α_1 and z_3 and z_4 be the affixes of two points another line with complex slope α_2. Then,

$$\alpha_1 = \frac{z_1 - z_2}{\bar{z}_1 - \bar{z}_2} \quad \text{and} \quad \alpha_2 = \frac{z_3 - z_4}{\bar{z}_3 - \bar{z}_4} \quad \text{...(i)}$$

(i) If the lines are perpendicular, then

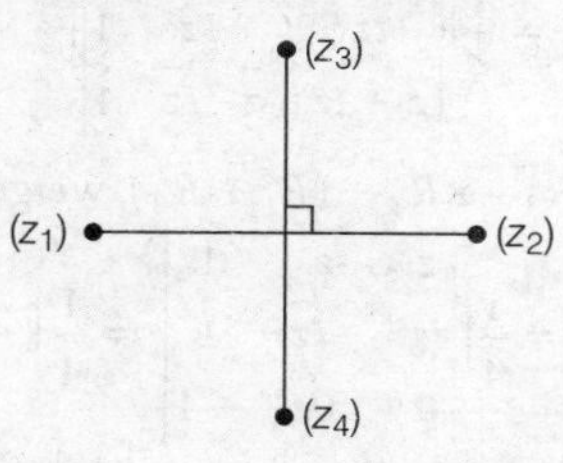

$$\frac{(z_1 - z_2)}{|z_1 - z_2|} = \frac{(z_3 - z_4)}{|z_3 - z_4|}e^{i\pi/2}$$

$$\Rightarrow \frac{(z_1 - z_2)^2}{|z_1 - z_2|^2} = \frac{(z_3 - z_4)^2}{|z_3 - z_4|^2}e^{i\pi}$$

$$\Rightarrow \frac{(z_1 - z_2)^2}{(z_1 - z_2)(\bar{z}_1 - \bar{z}_2)} = \frac{(z_3 - z_4)^2}{(z_3 - z_4)(\bar{z}_3 - \bar{z}_4)}e^{i\pi}$$

$$\Rightarrow \frac{(z_1 - z_2)}{(\bar{z}_1 - \bar{z}_2)} = \frac{(z_3 - z_4)}{(\bar{z}_3 - \bar{z}_4)}(-1)$$

$$\Rightarrow \alpha_1 = -\alpha_2 \quad \text{[from Eq. (i)]}$$

$$\therefore \alpha_1 + \alpha_2 = 0$$

(ii) If the lines are parallel, then

$$\frac{z_1 - z_2}{|z_1 - z_2|} = \frac{z_3 - z_4}{|z_3 - z_4|}e^0$$

$$\Rightarrow \frac{(z_1 - z_2)^2}{|z_1 - z_2|^2} = \frac{(z_3 - z_4)^2}{|z_3 - z_4|^2}$$

$$\Rightarrow \frac{(z_1 - z_2)^2}{(z_1 - z_2)(\bar{z}_1 - \bar{z}_2)} = \frac{(z_3 - z_4)^2}{(z_3 - z_4)(\bar{z}_3 - \bar{z}_4)}$$

$$\Rightarrow \frac{(z_1 - z_2)}{(\bar{z}_1 - \bar{z}_2)} = \frac{(z_3 - z_4)}{(\bar{z}_3 - \bar{z}_4)}$$

$$\Rightarrow \alpha_1 = \alpha_2$$

Remark

1. The equation of a line parallel to the line $\bar{a}z + a\bar{z} + b = 0$ is $\bar{a}z + a\bar{z} + \lambda = 0$, where $\lambda \in R$.
2. The equation of a line perpendicular to the line $\bar{a}\,z + a\bar{z} + b = 0$ is $\bar{a}\,z - a\,\bar{z} + i\,\lambda = 0$ where, $\lambda \in R$ and $i = \sqrt{-1}$

(v) Length of perpendicular from a given point on a given line

The length of perpendicular from a point $P(z_1)$ to the line

$\bar{a}\,z + a\,\bar{z} + b = 0$ is given by $\dfrac{|\bar{a}z_1 + a\bar{z}_1 + b|}{2|a|}$.

Proof Let PM be perpendicular from P on the line $\bar{a}z + a\bar{z} + b = 0$ and let the affix of M be z_2, then

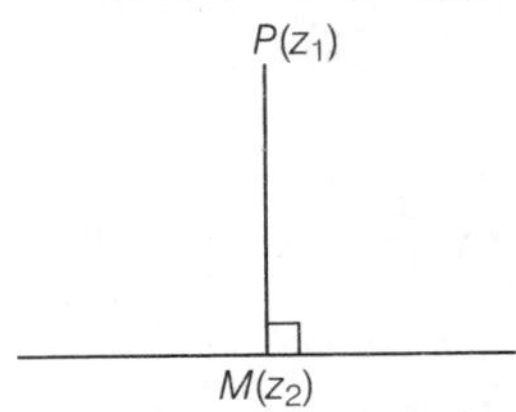

$$PM = |z_1 - z_2|$$
$$\bar{a}z + a\bar{z} + b = 0$$

and $M(z_2)$ lies on $\bar{a}z + a\bar{z} + b = 0$, then

$$\bar{a}z_2 + a\bar{z}_2 + b = 0 \quad \text{...(i)}$$

Since, PM perpendicular to the line $(\bar{a}z + a\bar{z} + b = 0)$.

Therefore, $\frac{z_1 - z_2}{\bar{z}_1 - \bar{z}_2} + \left(-\frac{a}{\bar{a}}\right) = 0$

$\Rightarrow \quad \bar{a}z_1 - \bar{a}z_2 - a\bar{z}_1 + a\bar{z}_2 = 0$

$\Rightarrow \quad \bar{a}z_1 + a\bar{z}_1 + b = 2a\bar{z}_1 + \bar{a}z_2 - a\bar{z}_2 + b$

$= 2a\bar{z}_1 - a\bar{z}_2 + (\bar{a}z_2 + b)$

$= 2a\bar{z}_1 - a\bar{z}_2 - a\bar{z}_2 \quad [\because \bar{a}z_2 + b = -a\bar{z}_2]$

$= 2a(\bar{z}_1 - \bar{z}_2)$

or $\quad |\bar{a}z_1 + a\bar{z}_1 + b| = 2|a||\bar{z}_1 - \bar{z}_2|$

$= 2|a||z_1 - z_2| \quad [\because |\bar{z}| = |z|]$

$= 2|a|PM$

$\therefore \quad PM = \frac{|\bar{a}z_1 + a\bar{z}_1 + b|}{2|a|}$

Example 80. Show that the point a' is the reflection of the point a in the line $z\bar{b} + \bar{z}b + c = 0$, if $a'\bar{b} + \bar{a}b + c = 0$.

Sol. Since, a' is the reflection of point a through the line.
So, the mid-point of PQ

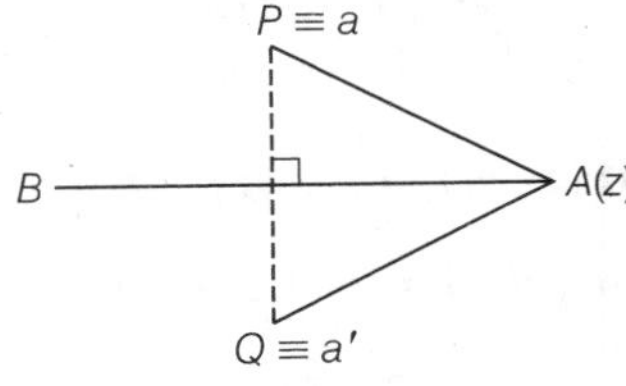

i.e., $\frac{a + a'}{2}$ lies on $z\bar{b} + \bar{z}b + c = 0$

or $\quad \bar{b}\left(\frac{a + a'}{2}\right) + b\left(\frac{\bar{a} + \bar{a}'}{2}\right) + c = 0$

$\Rightarrow \quad \bar{b}(a + a') + b(\bar{a} + \bar{a}') + 2c = 0 \quad \text{...(i)}$

Since, $PQ \perp AB$. Therefore,
Complex slope of PQ + Complex slope of $AB = 0$

$\Rightarrow \quad \frac{a - a'}{\bar{a} - \bar{a}'} + \left(-\frac{b}{\bar{b}}\right) = 0$

$\Rightarrow \quad \bar{b}(a - a') - b(\bar{a} - \bar{a}') = 0 \quad \text{...(ii)}$

On subtracting Eq. (ii) from Eq. (i), we get

$$a'\bar{b} + \bar{a}b + c = 0$$

Aliter

Equation of perpendicular bisector of PQ is

$z(\bar{a}' - \bar{a}) + \bar{z}(a' - a) - a'\bar{a}' + a\bar{a} = 0 \quad \text{...(i)}$

and given line $\quad z\bar{b} + \bar{z}b + c = 0 \quad \text{...(ii)}$

Since, Eqs. (i) and (ii) are identical, we have

$$\frac{\bar{a}' - \bar{a}}{\bar{b}} = \frac{a' - a}{b} = \frac{a\bar{a} - a'\bar{a}'}{c} = k \quad \text{[say]}$$

$\therefore \quad \bar{a}' - \bar{a} = \bar{b}k,\ a' - a = bk$

and $\quad a\bar{a} - a'\bar{a}' = ck$

Now, $\quad a'\bar{b} + \bar{a}b = \left\{a'\left(\frac{\bar{a}' - \bar{a}}{k}\right) + \bar{a}\left(\frac{a' - a}{k}\right)\right\}$

$= \frac{1}{k}\{a'\bar{a}' - a\bar{a}\} = \frac{1}{k}(-ck) = -c$

Hence, $a'\bar{b} + \bar{a}b + c = 0$

(f) Circle

The equation of a circle whose centre is at point affix z_0 and radius r, is $|z - z_0| = r$.

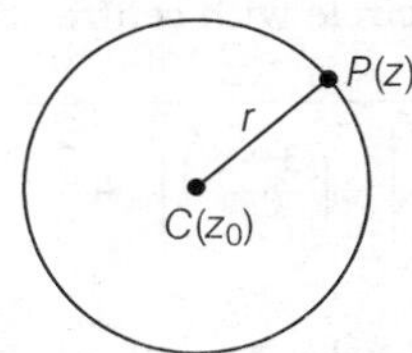

Remark

1. If the centre of the circle is at origin and radius r, then its equation is $|z| = r$.
2. $|z - z_0| < r$ represents interior of a circle $|z - z_0| = r$ and $|z - z_0| > r$ represent exterior of the circle $|z - z_0| = r$.
3. $r < |z - z_0| < R$, this region is known as **annulus**.

(i) General Equation of a Circle

The general equation of the circle is

$$z\bar{z} + \bar{a}z + a\bar{z} + b = 0,$$

where a is a complex number and $b \in R$, having centre at $(-a)$ and radius $= \sqrt{|a|^2 - b}$.

Proof The equation of circle having centre at z_0 and radius r is

$$|z - z_0| = r$$

$$\Rightarrow \quad |z - z_0|^2 = r^2$$

$$\Rightarrow \quad (z - z_0)(\bar{z} - \bar{z}_0) = r^2$$

$$\Rightarrow \quad z\bar{z} - z\bar{z}_0 - z_0\bar{z} + z_0\bar{z}_0 = r^2$$

$$\Rightarrow \quad z\bar{z} + (-\bar{z}_0)z + (-z_0)\bar{z} + |z_0|^2 - r^2 = 0$$

$$\Rightarrow \quad z\bar{z} + \bar{a}z + a\bar{z} + b = 0$$

where, $a = -z_0$ and $b = |z_0|^2 - r^2$

$$\Rightarrow \quad z\bar{z} + \bar{a}z + a\bar{z} + b = 0$$

where, $b \in R$ represents a circle having centre at $(-a)$ and radius $= \sqrt{|z_0|^2 - b} = \sqrt{|a|^2 - b}$.

Remark

Rule to find the centre and radius of a circle whose equation is given

1. Make the coefficient of $z\bar{z}$ equal to 1 and right hand side equal to zero.
2. The centre of circle will be $= (-a) = (-$ coefficient of $\bar{z})$.
3. Radius $= \sqrt{(|a|^2 - \text{constant term})}$

Example 81. Find the centre and radius of the circle $2z\bar{z} + (3 - i)z + (3 + i)\bar{z} - 7 = 0$, where $i = \sqrt{-1}$.

Sol. The given equation can be written as

$$z\bar{z} + \left(\frac{3+i}{2}\right)z + \left(\frac{3+i}{2}\right)\bar{z} - \frac{7}{2} = 0$$

So, it represent a circle with centre at $-\left(\frac{3+i}{2}\right)$ and radius

$$= \sqrt{\left|-\left(\frac{3+i}{2}\right)\right|^2 + \frac{7}{2}} = \sqrt{\left(\frac{9}{4} + \frac{1}{4} + \frac{7}{2}\right)} = \sqrt{6}$$

(ii) Equation of Circle Through Three Non-Collinear Points

Let $A(z_1), B(z_2), C(z_3)$ be three points on the circle and $P(z)$ be any point on the circle, then

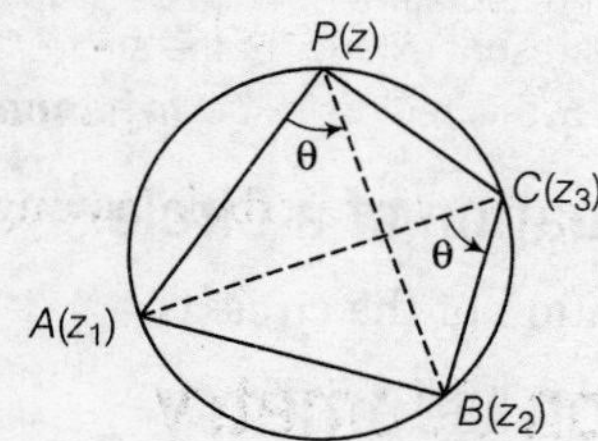

$$\angle ACB = \angle APB$$

Using Coni method,

in ΔACB, $$\frac{z_2 - z_3}{z_1 - z_3} = \frac{BC}{CA} e^{i\theta} \quad \text{...(i)}$$

in ΔAPB, $$\frac{z_2 - z}{z_1 - z} = \frac{BP}{AP} e^{i\theta} \quad \text{...(ii)}$$

From Eqs. (i) and (ii), we get

$$\frac{(z - z_1)(z_2 - z_3)}{(z - z_2)(z_1 - z_3)} = \text{Real} \quad \text{...(iii)}$$

Remark

If four points z_1, z_2, z_3, z_4 are concyclic, then $\frac{(z_4 - z_1)(z_2 - z_3)}{(z_4 - z_2)(z_1 - z_3)} =$ real [replacing z by z_4 in Eq. (iii)]

or $$\arg\left[\frac{(z_2 - z_3)(z_4 - z_1)}{(z_1 - z_3)(z_4 - z_2)}\right] = \pi, 0.$$

(iii) Equation of Circle in Diametric Form

If end points of diameter represented by $A(z_1)$ and $B(z_2)$ and $P(z)$ is any point on circle.

$$\therefore \quad \angle APB = 90°$$

$\therefore$ Complex slope of PA + Complex slope of $PB = 0$

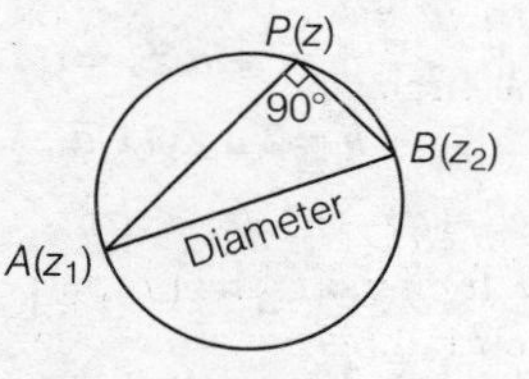

$$\Rightarrow \quad \left(\frac{z - z_1}{\bar{z} - \bar{z}_1}\right) + \left(\frac{z - z_2}{\bar{z} - \bar{z}_2}\right) = 0$$

Hence, $(z - z_1)(\bar{z} - \bar{z}_2) + (z - z_2)(\bar{z} - \bar{z}_1) = 0$ which is required equation of circle in diametric form.

(iv) Other Forms of Circle

(a) Equation of all circles which are orthogonal to $|z - z_1| = r_1$ and $|z - z_2| = r_2$.

Let the circle be $|z - \alpha| = r$ cut given circles orthogonally.

$$\therefore \quad r^2 + r_1^2 = |\alpha - z_1|^2 \quad \text{...(i)}$$

and $$r^2 + r_2^2 = |\alpha - z_2|^2 \quad \text{...(ii)}$$

On solving,

$$r_2^2 - r_1^2 = \alpha(\bar{z}_1 - \bar{z}_2) + \bar{\alpha}(z_1 - z_2) + |z_2|^2 - |z_1|^2$$

and let $\alpha = a + ib$, $i = \sqrt{-1}$, $a, b \in R$

(b) **Apollonius circle** $\left|\frac{z - z_1}{z - z_2}\right| = k \neq 1$

It is the circle with join of z_3 and z_4 as a diameter, where $z_3 = \frac{z_1 + kz_2}{1 + k}$, $z_4 = \frac{z_1 - kz_2}{1 - k}$

for $k = 1$, the circle reduces to the straight line which is perpendicular bisector of the line segment from z_1 to z_2.

(c) **Circular arc** $\arg\left(\dfrac{z-z_1}{z-z_2}\right)=\alpha$

This is an arc of a circle in which the chord joining z_1 and z_2 subtends angle α at any point on the arc.

If $\alpha=\pm\dfrac{\pi}{2}$, then locus of z is a circle with the join of z_1 and z_2 as diameter. If $\alpha=0$ or π, then locus is a straight line through the points z_1 and z_2.

(d) The equation $|z-z_1|^2+|z-z_2|^2=k$, will represent a circle, if $k\geq\dfrac{1}{2}|z_1-z_2|^2$.

Example 82. Find all circles which are orthogonal to $|z|=1$ and $|z-1|=4$.

Sol. Let $\quad |z-\alpha|=k \quad$ ...(i)

(where, $\alpha=a+ib$ and $a, b, k\in R$ and $i=\sqrt{-1}$) be a circle which cuts the circles

$$|z|=1 \quad \text{...(ii)}$$

and $\quad |z-1|=4 \quad$ ...(iii)

Orthogonally, then using the property that the sum of squares of their radii is equal to square of distance between centres. Thus, the circle (i) will cut the circles (ii) and (iii) orthogonally, if

$$k^2+1=|\alpha-0|^2=\alpha\overline{\alpha}$$

and $\quad k^2+16=|\alpha-1|^2=(\alpha-1)(\overline{\alpha}-1)$

$$=\alpha\overline{\alpha}-(\alpha+\overline{\alpha})+1$$

$\therefore\ 1-(\alpha+\overline{\alpha})-15=0\Rightarrow\alpha+\overline{\alpha}=-14$

$\therefore\quad 2a=-14\Rightarrow a=-7$

$\Rightarrow\quad \alpha=a+ib=-7+ib$

Also, $\quad k^2=|\alpha|^2-1=(-7)^2+b^2-1=b^2+48$

$\Rightarrow\quad k=\sqrt{(b^2+48)}$

Therefore, required family of circles is given by

$$|z+7-ib|=\sqrt{(48+b^2)}.$$

(g) Equation of Parabola

Now, for parabola

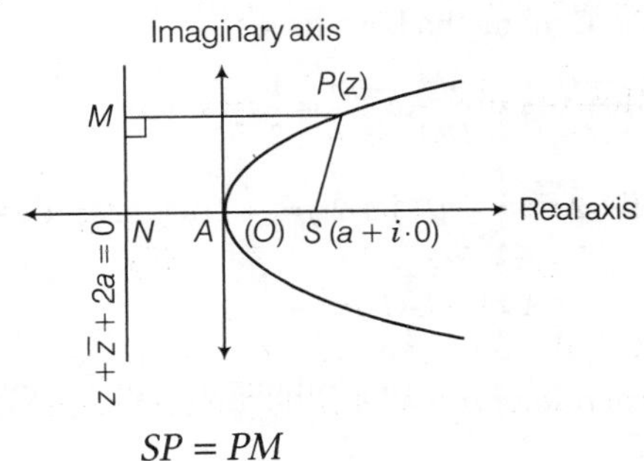

$$SP=PM$$

$$|z-a|=\frac{|z+\overline{z}+2a|}{2}$$

or $\quad z\overline{z}-4a(z+\overline{z})=\dfrac{1}{2}\{z^2+(\overline{z})^2\}$

where, $a\in R$ (focus), directrix is $z+\overline{z}+2a=0$.

(h) Equation of Ellipse

For ellipse

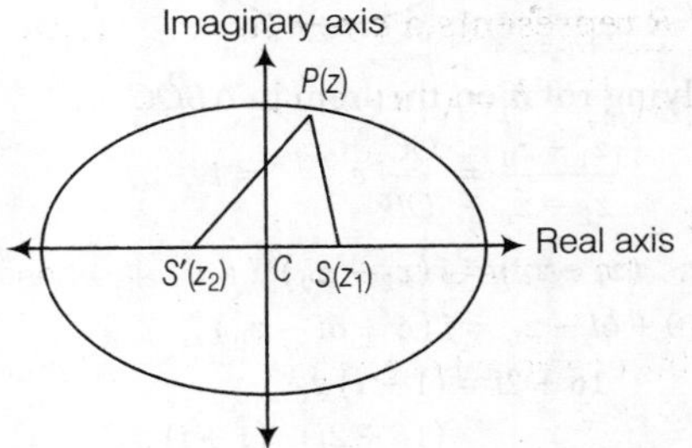

$$SP+S'P=2a$$

$\Rightarrow\quad |z-z_1|+|z-z_2|=2a$

where, $2a>|z_1-z_2|$ [since, eccentricity <1]

Then, point z describes an ellipse having foci at z_1 and z_2 and $a\in R^+$.

(i) Equation of Hyperbola

For hyperbola

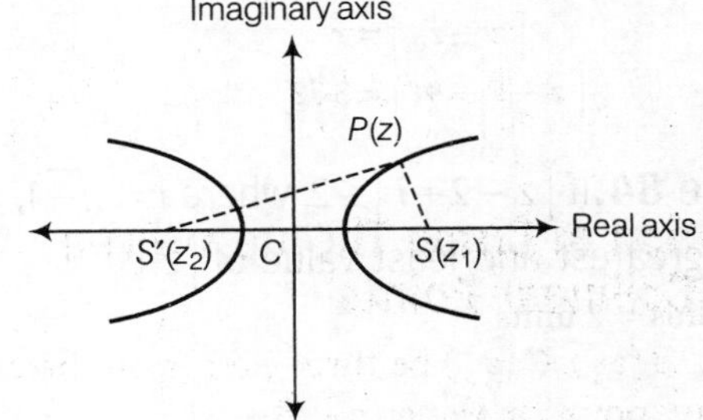

$$SP-S'P=2a\Rightarrow|z-z_1|-|z-z_2|=2a$$

where, $\quad 2a<|z_1-z_2|$ [since, eccentricity >1]

Then, point z describes a hyperbola having foci at z_1 and z_2 and $a\in R^+$.

Examples on Geometry

Example 83. Let $z_1=10+6i$, $z_2=4+6i$, where $i=\sqrt{-1}$. If z is a complex number, such that the argument of $(z-z_1)/(z-z_2)$ is $\pi/4$, then prove that $|z-7-9i|=3\sqrt{2}$.

Sol. $\because\quad \arg\left(\dfrac{z-z_1}{z-z_2}\right)=\dfrac{\pi}{4}$

It is clear that z, z_1, z_2 are non-collinear points. Always a circle passes through z, z_1 and z_2. Let z_0 be the centre of the circle.

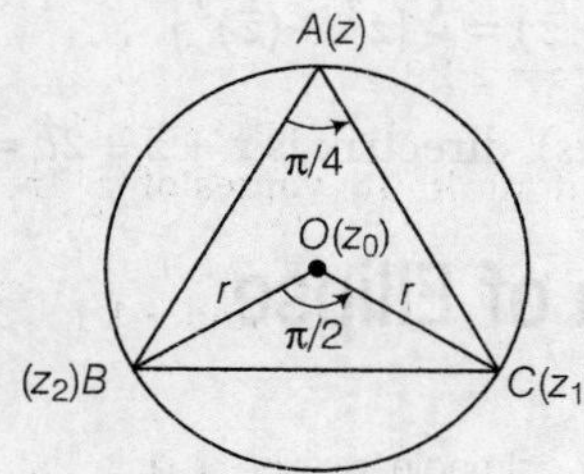

On applying rotation theorem in ΔBOC,

$$\frac{z_1 - z_0}{z_2 - z_0} = \frac{OC}{OB} e^{(i\pi/2)} = i \qquad [\because OC = OB]$$

$$\Rightarrow \quad (z_1 - z_0) = i(z_2 - z_0)$$

$$\Rightarrow \quad 10 + 6i - z_0 = i(4 + 6i - z_0)$$

$$\Rightarrow \quad 16 + 2i = (1 - i) z_0$$

or
$$z_0 = \frac{(16 + 2i)}{(1 - i)} \cdot \frac{(1 + i)}{(1 + i)}$$

$$= \frac{16 + 16i + 2i + 2i^2}{2}$$

$$= \frac{14 + 18i}{2} = 7 + 9i$$

and radius, $r = OC = | z_0 - z_1 | = | 7 + 9i - 10 - 6i |$

$$= | -3 + 3i |$$

$$= \sqrt{(9 + 9)} = 3\sqrt{2}$$

Hence, required equation is

$$| z - z_0 | = r$$

$$\Rightarrow \quad | z - 7 - 9i | = 3\sqrt{2}$$

Example 84. If $| z - 2 + i | \le 2$, where $i = \sqrt{-1}$, then find the greatest and least value of $| z |$.

Sol. $\because$ Radius = 2 units

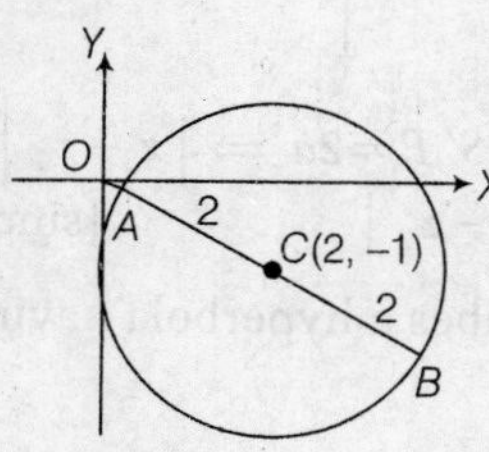

i.e., $AC = CB = 2$ units

$\therefore$ Least value of $| z | = OA = OC - AC = \sqrt{5} - 2$

and greatest value of $| z | = OB = OC + CB = \sqrt{5} + 2$

Hence, greatest value of $| z |$ is $\sqrt{5} + 2$ and least value of $| z |$ is $\sqrt{5} - 2$.

Example 85. In the argand plane, the vector $z = 4 - 3i$, where $i = \sqrt{-1}$, is turned in the clockwise sense through $180°$ and stretched three times. Then, find the complex number represented by the new vector.

Sol. $\because \quad z = 4 - 3i \Rightarrow | z | = \sqrt{(4)^2 + (-3)^2} = 5$

Let z_1 be the new vector obtained by rotating z in the clockwise sense through 180°, therefore

$$z_1 = z e^{-i\pi} = -z = -(4 - 3i) = -4 + 3i.$$

The unit vector in the direction of z_1 is $-\frac{4}{5} + \frac{3}{5} i$.

Therefore, required vector $= 3 | z | \left(-\frac{4}{5} + \frac{3}{5} i \right)$

$$= 15 \left(-\frac{4}{5} + \frac{3}{5} i \right) = -12 + 9i$$

Aliter

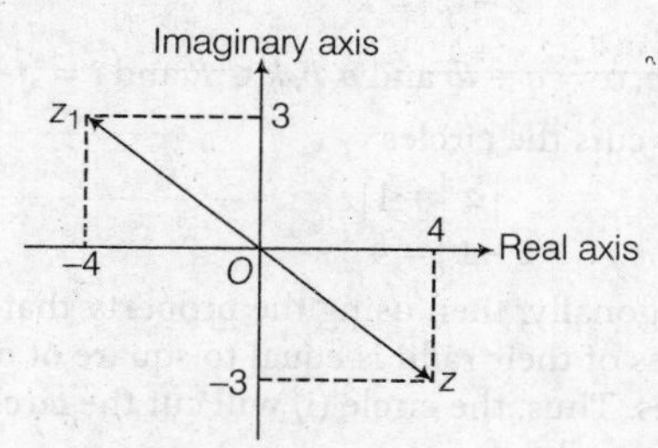

Here, $z_1 = -4 + 3i$

Hence, $3 z_1 = -12 + 9i$

Example 86. $ABCD$ is a rhombus. Its diagonals AC and BD intersect at the point M and satisfy $BD = 2AC$. If the points D and M represents the complex numbers $1 + i$ and $2 - i$, where $i = \sqrt{-1}$, respectively, find A.

Sol. Let $\quad A \equiv z$

$\because \quad BD = 2AC$ or $DM = 2AM$

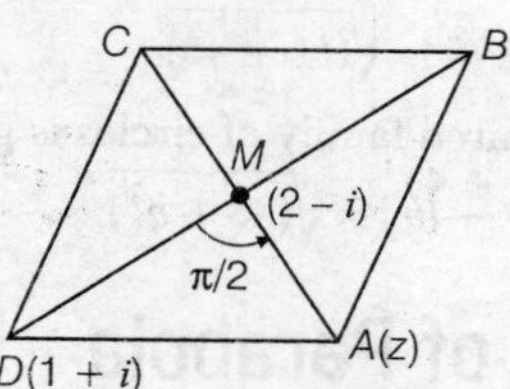

Now, in ΔDMA,

Applying Coni method, we have

$$\frac{z - (2 - i)}{(1 + i) - (2 - i)} = \frac{AM}{DM} e^{i\pi/2} = \frac{1}{2} i$$

$$\Rightarrow \quad z - 2 + i = \frac{i}{2}(-1 + 2i) = -\frac{i}{2} - 1 \text{ or } z = 1 - \frac{3}{2} i$$

$$\therefore \quad A \equiv 1 - \frac{3}{2} i \text{ or } 3 - \frac{i}{2}$$

[if positions of A and C interchange]

If $\left| z \pm \frac{b}{z} \right| = a$, then the greatest and least values of $|z|$ are $\frac{a + \sqrt{(a^2 + 4|b|)}}{2}$ and $\frac{-a + \sqrt{(a^2 + 4|b|)}}{2}$, respectively.

Proof $\quad \left| z \pm \frac{b}{z} \right| \ge \left| |z| - \left| \frac{b}{z} \right| \right|$

$\Rightarrow \quad a \ge \left| |z| - \frac{|b|}{|z|} \right|$

or $\quad -a \le |z| - \frac{|b|}{|z|} \le a$

Now, $\quad |z| - \frac{|b|}{|z|} \le a$

$\Rightarrow \quad |z|^2 - a|z| - |b| \le 0$

$\therefore \quad \frac{a - \sqrt{(a^2 + 4|b|)}}{2} \le |z| \le \frac{a + \sqrt{(a^2 + 4|b|)}}{2}$

or $\quad 0 \le |z| \le \frac{a + \sqrt{(a^2 + 4|b|)}}{2} \quad$ ...(i)

and $\quad |z| - \frac{|b|}{|z|} \ge -a \Rightarrow |z|^2 + a|z| - |b| \ge 0$

$\therefore \quad |z| \ge \frac{-a + \sqrt{(a^2 + 4|b|)}}{2} \quad$ ...(ii)

From Eqs. (i) and (ii), we get

$$\frac{-a + \sqrt{(a^2 + 4|b|)}}{2} \le |z| \le \frac{a + \sqrt{(a^2 + 4|b|)}}{2}$$

Hence, the greatest value of $|z|$ is $\frac{a + \sqrt{(a^2 + 4|b|)}}{2}$

and the least value of $|z|$ is $\frac{-a + \sqrt{(a^2 + 4|b|)}}{2}$.

Corollary For $b = 1$, $\left| z \pm \frac{1}{z} \right| = a$

Then, $\frac{-a + \sqrt{(a^2 + 4)}}{2} \le |z| \le \frac{a + \sqrt{(a^2 + 4)}}{2}$

Example 87. Find the maximum and minimum values of $|z|$ satisfying $\left| z + \frac{1}{z} \right| = 2$.

Sol. Here, $b = 1$ and $a = 2$

$\therefore$ Maximum and minimum values of $|z|$ are $\frac{2 + \sqrt{(4 + 4)}}{2}$ and $\frac{-2 + \sqrt{(4 + 4)}}{2}$ i.e., $1 + \sqrt{2}$ and $-1 + \sqrt{2}$, respectively.

Example 88. If $\left| z + \frac{4}{z} \right| = 2$, find the maximum and minimum values of $|z|$.

Sol. Here, $b = 4$ and $a = 2$.

$\therefore$ Maximum and minimum values of $|z|$ are $\frac{2 + \sqrt{(4 + 16)}}{2}$ and $\frac{-2 + \sqrt{(4 + 16)}}{2}$

i.e. $1 + \sqrt{5}$ and $-1 + \sqrt{5}$, respectively.

Example 89. If $|z| \ge 3$, then determine the least value of $\left| z + \frac{1}{z} \right|$.

Sol. $\because \quad \left| z + \frac{1}{z} \right| \ge \left| |z| - \left| \frac{1}{z} \right| \right| = \left| |z| - \frac{1}{|z|} \right| \quad$ ...(i)

$\because \quad |z| \ge 3 \Rightarrow \frac{1}{|z|} \le \frac{1}{3}$ or $-\frac{1}{|z|} \ge -\frac{1}{3}$

$\therefore \quad |z| - \frac{1}{|z|} \ge 3 - \frac{1}{3} = \frac{8}{3} \Rightarrow |z| - \frac{1}{|z|} \ge \frac{8}{3}$

or $\quad \left| |z| - \frac{1}{|z|} \right| \ge \frac{8}{3} \quad$ ...(ii)

From Eqs. (i) and (ii), we get

$$\left| z + \frac{1}{z} \right| \ge \frac{8}{3}$$

$\therefore$ Least value of $\left| z + \frac{1}{z} \right|$ is $\frac{8}{3}$.

Exercise for Session 4

1 If z_1, z_2, z_3 and z_4 are the roots of the equation $z^4 = 1$, the value of $\sum_{i=1}^{4} z_i^3$ is

(a) 0 (b) 1 (c) $i, i = \sqrt{-1}$ (d) $1 + i, i = \sqrt{-1}$

2 If $z_1, z_2, z_3, \ldots, z_n$ are n, nth roots of unity, then for $k = 1, 2, 3, \ldots, n$

(a) $|z_k| = k|z_{k+1}|$ (b) $|z_{k+1}| = k|z_k|$

(c) $|z_{k+1}| = |z_k| + |z_{k-1}|$ (d) $|z_k| = |z_{k+1}|$

3 If $1, \alpha_1, \alpha_2, \alpha_3, \ldots, \alpha_{n-1}$ are n, nth roots of unity, then $(1-\alpha_1)(1-\alpha_2)(1-\alpha_3)\ldots(1-\alpha_{n-1})$ equals to

(a) 0 (b) 1 (c) n (d) n^2

4 The value of $\sum_{k=1}^{6}\left(\sin\left(\frac{2\pi k}{7}\right) - i\cos\left(\frac{2\pi k}{7}\right)\right)$, where $i = \sqrt{-1}$, is

(a) -1 (b) 0 (c) $-i$ (d) i

5 If $\alpha \neq 1$ is any nth root of unity, then $S = 1 + 3\alpha + 5\alpha^2 + \ldots$ upto n terms is equal to

(a) $\frac{2n}{1-\alpha}$ (b) $\frac{2n}{1-\alpha}$ (c) $\frac{n}{1-\alpha}$ (d) $-\frac{n}{1-\alpha}$

6 If a and b are real numbers between 0 and 1, such that the points $z_1 = a + i, z_2 = 1 + bi$ and $z_3 = 0$ form an equilateral triangle, then

(a) $a = b = 2 + \sqrt{3}$ (b) $a = b = 2 - \sqrt{3}$

(c) $a = 2 - \sqrt{3}, b = 2 + \sqrt{3}$ (d) None of these

7 If $|z| = 2$, the points representing the complex numbers $-1 + 5z$ will lie on

(a) a circle (b) a straight line (c) a parabola (d) an ellipse

8 If $|z-2|/|z-3| = 2$ represents a circle, then its radius is equal to

(a) 1 (b) $\frac{1}{3}$ (c) $\frac{3}{4}$ (d) $\frac{2}{3}$

9 If centre of a regular hexagon is at origin and one of the vertex on argand diagram is $1 + 2i$, where $i = \sqrt{-1}$, its perimeter is

(a) $2\sqrt{5}$ (b) $6\sqrt{2}$ (c) $4\sqrt{5}$ (d) $6\sqrt{5}$

10 If z is a complex number in the argand plane, the equation $|z-2| + |z+2| = 8$ represents

(a) a parabola (b) an ellipse (c) a hyperbola (d) a circle

11 If $|z - 2 - 3i| + |z + 2 - 6i| = 4$, where $i = \sqrt{-1}$, then locus of $P(z)$ is

(a) an ellipse (b) ϕ

(c) line segment of points $2 + 3i$ and $-2 + 6i$ (d) None of these

12 Locus of the point z satisfying the equation $|iz - 1| + |z - 1| = 2$, is (where, $i = \sqrt{-1}$)

(a) a straight line (b) a circle (c) an ellipse (d) a pair of straight lines

13 If z, iz and $z + iz$ are the vertices of a triangle whose area is 2 units, the value of $|z|$ is

(a) 1 (b) 2 (c) 4 (d) 8

14 If $\left|z - \frac{4}{z}\right| = 2$, the greatest value of $|z|$ is

(a) $\sqrt{5} - 1$ (b) $\sqrt{3} + 1$ (c) $\sqrt{5} + 1$ (d) $\sqrt{3} - 1$

Shortcuts and Important Results to Remember

1 $||z_1|-|z_2|| \le |z_1+z_2| \le |z_1|+|z_2|$

Thus, $|z_1|+|z_2|$ is the greatest possible value of $|z_1+z_2|$ and $||z_1|-|z_2||$ is the least possible value of $|z_1+z_2|$.

2 If $\left|z \pm \frac{b}{z}\right| = a$, then the greatest and least values of $|z|$ are $\frac{a+\sqrt{(a^2+4|b|)}}{2}$ and $\frac{-a+\sqrt{(a^2+4|b|)}}{2}$, respectively.

3 $\left|z_1+\sqrt{(z_1^2-z_2^2)}\right| + \left|z_2-\sqrt{(z_1^2-z_2^2)}\right|$

$= |z_1+z_2| + |z_1-z_2|$

4 $|z_1+z_2| = |z_1|+|z_2| \Leftrightarrow \arg(z_1) = \arg(z_2)$

i.e. z_1 and z_2 are parallel.

5 $|z_1+z_2| = |z_1|-|z_2| \Leftrightarrow \arg(z_1)-\arg(z_2) = \pi$

6 $|z_1+z_2| = |z_1-z_2| \Leftrightarrow \arg(z_1)-\arg(z_2) = \pm\pi/2$

7 If $|z_1| = |z_2|$ and $\arg(z_1)+\arg(z_2) = 0$, then z_1 and z_2 are conjugate complex numbers of each other.

8 The equation $|z-z_1|^2 + |z-z_2|^2 = k, k \in R$ will represent a circle with centre at $\frac{1}{2}(z_1+z_2)$ and radius is $\frac{1}{2}\sqrt{2k-|z_1-z_2|^2}$ provided $k \ge \frac{1}{2}|z_1-z_2|^2$.

9 Area of triangle whose vertices are z, iz and $z+iz$, where $i=\sqrt{-1}$, is $\frac{1}{2}|z|^2$.

10 Area of triangle whose vertices are z, ωz and $z+\omega z$ is $\frac{\sqrt{3}}{4}|z|^2$, where ω is cube root of unity.

11 $\arg(z)-\arg(-z) = \pi$ or $-\pi$ according as $\arg(z)$ is positive or negative.

12 If $\arg\left(\frac{z-z_1}{z-z_2}\right) = \alpha$ (fixed), then the locus of z is a segment of circle.

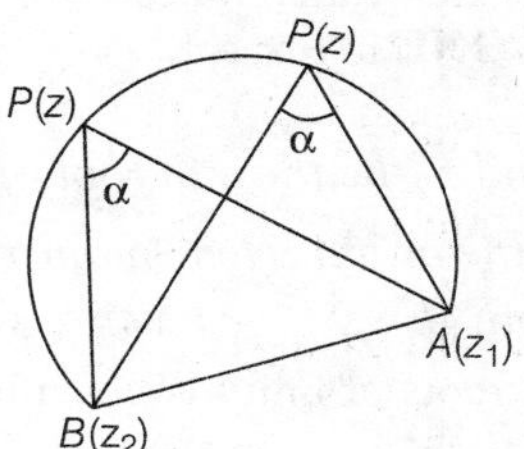

13 If $\arg\left(\frac{z-z_1}{z-z_2}\right) = \pm\pi/2$, the locus of z is a circle with z_1 and z_2 as the vertices of diameter.

14 If $\arg\left(\frac{z-z_1}{z-z_2}\right) = 0$ or π, the locus of z is a straight line passing through z_1 and z_2.

15 If three complex numbers are in AP, they lie on a straight line in the complex plane.

16 If three points z_1, z_2, z_3 connected by relation $az_1+bz_2+cz_3=0$, where $a+b+c=0$, the three points are collinear.

17 If z_1, z_2, z_3 are vertices of a triangle, its centroid

$z_0 = \frac{z_1+z_2+z_3}{3}$, circumcentre $z_1 = \frac{\sum |z_1|^2(z_2-z_3)}{\sum \bar{z}_1(z_2-z_3)}$,

orthocentre $z = \frac{\sum \bar{z}_1(\bar{z}_2-\bar{z}_3) + \sum |z_1|^2(z_2-z_3)}{\sum (z_1\bar{z}_2-\bar{z}_1z_2)}$

and its area $= \frac{1}{4}\left|\begin{vmatrix} z_1 & \bar{z}_1 & 1 \\ z_2 & \bar{z}_2 & 1 \\ z_3 & \bar{z}_3 & 1 \end{vmatrix}\right|$.

18 If $|z_1| = n_1, |z_2| = n_2, |z_3| = n_3, \ldots, |z_m| = n_m$,

then $\left|\frac{n_1^2}{z_1}+\frac{n_2^2}{z_2}+\frac{n_3^2}{z_3}+\ldots+\frac{n_m^2}{z_m}\right| = |z_1+z_2+z_3+\ldots+z_m|$.

JEE Type Solved Examples :
Single Option Correct Type Questions

- This section contains **10 multiple choice examples.** Each example has four choices (a), (b), (c) and (d) out of which **ONLY ONE** is correct.

Ex. 1 *If z_1 and z_2 be the n th root of unity which subtend right angled at the origin. Then, n must be of the form*

(a) $4k+1$ (b) $4k+2$ (c) $4k+3$ (d) $4k$

Sol. (*d*) The *n*th roots of unity is given by

$$\cos\left(\frac{2r\pi}{n}\right)+i\sin\left(\frac{2r\pi}{n}\right)=e^{2r\pi i/n},$$

where $r=0,1,2,\ldots,(n-1)$

So, let $z_1=e^{2\pi r_1 i/n}$ and $z_2=e^{2\pi r_2 i/n}$, where $0\le r_1, r_2<n$, $r_1\ne r_2$.

It is given that the line segment joining the points having affixes z_1 and z_2, subtends a right angled at the origin. Therefore,

$$\arg\left(\frac{z_1}{z_2}\right)=\pm\frac{\pi}{2}$$

$$\Rightarrow \quad \frac{2\pi r_1}{n}-\frac{2\pi r_2}{n}=\pm\frac{\pi}{2}$$

$$\Rightarrow \quad n=\pm 4(r_1-r_2)$$

$$\therefore \quad n=4k, \text{ where } k=\pm(r_1-r_2)$$

Ex. 2 *If $|z|=1$ and $\omega=\dfrac{z-1}{z+1}$ (where $z\ne-1$), then $\text{Re}(\omega)$ is*

(a) 0 (b) $-\dfrac{1}{|z+1|^2}$

(c) $\left|\dfrac{z}{z+1}\right|\cdot\dfrac{1}{|z+1|^2}$ (d) $\dfrac{\sqrt{2}}{|z+1|^2}$

Sol. (*a*) We have, $|z|=1$.

Let $z=e^{i\theta}$, where $\theta\in R$ and $i=\sqrt{-1}$.

Then, $\omega=\dfrac{z-1}{z+1}=\dfrac{e^{i\theta}-1}{e^{i\theta}+1}=i\tan\left(\dfrac{\theta}{2}\right)$

$\therefore \quad \text{Re}(\omega)=0$

Ex. 3 *If a, b, c, a_1, b_1 and c_1 are non-zero complex numbers satisfying $\dfrac{a}{a_1}+\dfrac{b}{b_1}+\dfrac{c}{c_1}=1+i$ and $\dfrac{a_1}{a}+\dfrac{b_1}{b}+\dfrac{c_1}{c}=0$, where $i=\sqrt{-1}$, the value of $\dfrac{a^2}{a_1^2}+\dfrac{b^2}{b_1^2}+\dfrac{c^2}{c_1^2}$ is*

(a) $2i$ (b) $2+2i$ (c) 2 (d) None of these

Sol. (*a*) We have, $\dfrac{a}{a_1}+\dfrac{b}{b_1}+\dfrac{c}{c_1}=1+i$

On squaring both sides, we get

$$\frac{a^2}{a_1^2}+\frac{b^2}{b_1^2}+\frac{c^2}{c_1^2}+2\left(\frac{ab}{a_1b_1}+\frac{bc}{b_1c_1}+\frac{ca}{c_1a_1}\right)=1+i^2+2i$$

$$\Rightarrow \quad \frac{a^2}{a_1^2}+\frac{b^2}{b_1^2}+\frac{c^2}{c_1^2}+2\frac{abc}{a_1b_1c_1}\left(\frac{c_1}{c}+\frac{a_1}{a}+\frac{b_1}{b}\right)=1-1+2i$$

$$\Rightarrow \quad \frac{a^2}{a_1^2}+\frac{b^2}{b_1^2}+\frac{c^2}{c_1^2}+0=2i$$

$$\therefore \quad \frac{a^2}{a_1^2}+\frac{b^2}{b_1^2}+\frac{c^2}{c_1^2}=2i$$

Ex. 4 *Let z and ω be complex numbers. If $\text{Re}(z)=|z-2|$, $\text{Re}(\omega)=|\omega-2|$ and $\arg(z-\omega)=\dfrac{\pi}{3}$, the value of $\text{Im}(z+\omega)$ is*

(a) $\dfrac{1}{\sqrt{3}}$ (b) $\dfrac{2}{\sqrt{3}}$ (c) $\sqrt{3}$ (d) $\dfrac{4}{\sqrt{3}}$

Sol. (*d*) Let $z=x+iy$, $x, y\in R$ and $i=\sqrt{-1}$

$$\because \quad \text{Re}(z)=|z-2|$$

$$\Rightarrow \quad x=\sqrt{(x-2)^2+y^2}$$

$$\Rightarrow \quad y^2=4(x-1)$$

$\therefore z=1+t^2+2ti$, parametric form and let $\omega=p+iq$

Similarly, $\omega=1+s^2+2si$

$$\therefore \quad z-\omega=(t^2-s^2)+2i(t-s)$$

$$\Rightarrow \quad \arg(z-\omega)=\frac{\pi}{3} \quad \text{[given]}$$

$$\therefore \quad \tan^{-1}\left(\frac{2}{t+s}\right)=\frac{\pi}{3} \Rightarrow \frac{2}{t+s}=\sqrt{3}$$

$$\Rightarrow \quad (t+s)=\frac{2}{\sqrt{3}}$$

Now, $z+\omega=2+t^2+s^2+2i(t+s)$

$$\therefore \quad \text{Im}(z+\omega)=2(t+s)=\frac{4}{\sqrt{3}}$$

Ex. 5 *The mirror image of the curve $\arg\left(\dfrac{z-3}{z-i}\right)=\dfrac{\pi}{6}$, $i=\sqrt{-1}$ in the real axis, is*

(a) $\arg\left(\frac{z+3}{z+i}\right)=\frac{\pi}{6}$ (b) $\arg\left(\frac{z-3}{z+i}\right)=\frac{\pi}{6}$

(c) $\arg\left(\frac{z+i}{z+3}\right)=\frac{\pi}{6}$ (d) $\arg\left(\frac{z+i}{z-3}\right)=\frac{\pi}{6}$

Sol. (*d*) $\because$ The image of z in the real axis is $\bar{z}$.

The image is given by

$$\arg\left(\frac{\bar{z}-3}{\bar{z}-i}\right)=\frac{\pi}{6}$$

$$\Rightarrow \quad -\arg\left(\frac{z-3}{z+i}\right)=\frac{\pi}{6} \quad [\because \arg(\bar{z})=-\arg(z)]$$

$$\Rightarrow \quad \arg\left(\frac{z+i}{z-3}\right)=\frac{\pi}{6} \quad \left[\because \arg\left(\frac{z_1}{z_2}\right)=-\arg\left(\frac{z_2}{z_1}\right)\right]$$

Ex. 6 *The mirror image of the curve* $\arg\left(\frac{z+i}{z-1}\right)=\frac{\pi}{4}$, $i=\sqrt{-1}$ *in the line* $x-y=0$, *is*

(a) $\arg\left(\frac{z+i}{z+1}\right)=\frac{\pi}{4}$ (b) $\arg\left(\frac{z+1}{z-i}\right)=\frac{\pi}{4}$

(c) $\arg\left(\frac{z-i}{z+1}\right)=\frac{\pi}{4}$ (d) $\arg\left(\frac{z+i}{z-1}\right)=\frac{\pi}{4}$

Sol. (c) $\because$ The image of z in the line $y=x$ is $i\bar{z}$.

$\therefore$ The image of the given curve is

$$\arg\left(\frac{i\bar{z}+i}{i\bar{z}-1}\right)=\frac{\pi}{4}$$

$$\Rightarrow \quad \arg\left(\frac{\bar{z}+1}{\bar{z}+i}\right)=\frac{\pi}{4}$$

$$\Rightarrow \quad -\arg\left(\frac{z+1}{z-i}\right)=\frac{\pi}{4} \quad [\because \arg(\bar{z})=-\arg(z)]$$

$$\Rightarrow \quad \arg\left(\frac{z-i}{z+1}\right)=\frac{\pi}{4} \quad \left[\because \arg\left(\frac{z_1}{z_2}\right)=-\arg\left(\frac{z_2}{z_1}\right)\right]$$

Ex. 7 *If* $z+\frac{1}{z}=1$ *and* $a=z^{2017}+\frac{1}{z^{2017}}$ *and b is the last digit of the number* $2^{2^n}-1$, *when the integer* $n>1$, *the value of* a^2+b^2 *is*

(a) 23 (b) 24 (c) 26 (d) 27

Sol. (c) $\because z+\frac{1}{z}=1 \Rightarrow z^2-z+1=0$

$$\therefore \quad z=\frac{-(-1)\pm\sqrt{(1-4)}}{2}=-\omega,-\omega^2$$

[ω is cube root of unity]

and $z^{2017}=(-\omega)^{2017}=-\omega$,

$z^{2017}=(-\omega^2)^{2017}=-\omega^2$

$$\therefore \quad a=z^{2017}+\frac{1}{z^{2017}}=-\left(\omega+\frac{1}{\omega}\right)=-(\omega+\omega^2)=1$$

and $2^{2^n}=2^{4\cdot2^{n-4}}=16^{2^{n-4}}$ has last digit 6.

$\therefore \quad b=6-1=5$

Hence, $a^2+b^2=1^2+5^2=26$

Ex. 8 *If* ω *is complex cube root of unity and a, b, c are such that* $\frac{1}{a+\omega}+\frac{1}{b+\omega}+\frac{1}{c+\omega}=2\omega^2$ *and* $\frac{1}{a+\omega^2}+\frac{1}{b+\omega^2}+\frac{1}{c+\omega^2}=2\,\omega$, *then the value of* $\frac{1}{a+1}+\frac{1}{b+1}+\frac{1}{c+1}$ *is equal to*

(a) −2 (b) −1 (c) 1 (d) 2

Sol. (*d*) $\because \frac{1}{a+\omega}+\frac{1}{b+\omega}+\frac{1}{c+\omega}=2\omega^2=\frac{2}{\omega}$

and $\frac{1}{a+\omega^2}+\frac{1}{b+\omega^2}+\frac{1}{c+\omega^2}=2\omega=\frac{2}{\omega^2}$

It is clear that, ω and ω^2 are the roots of the equation

$$\frac{1}{a+x}+\frac{1}{b+x}+\frac{1}{c+x}=\frac{2}{x} \quad \text{...(i)}$$

$\Rightarrow \quad x\sum(b+x)(c+x)=2(a+x)(b+x)(c+x)$

$\Rightarrow \quad x^3-(ab+bc+ca)x-2abc=0$

$\because$ Coefficient of $x^2=0$, the sum of roots $=0$

$\Rightarrow \quad \alpha+\omega+\omega^2=0 \Rightarrow \alpha-1=0$

$\therefore \quad \alpha=1$

$\therefore$ Third root is 1.

From Eq. (i), we get

$$\frac{1}{a+1}+\frac{1}{b+1}+\frac{1}{c+1}=2$$

Ex. 9 *If a, b and c are distinct integers and* $\omega(\neq1)$ *is a cube root of unity, then the minimum value of* $|a+b\omega+c\omega^2|+|a+b\omega^2+c\,\omega|$, *is*

(a) $2\sqrt{3}$ (b) 3 (c) $4\sqrt{2}$ (d) 2

Sol. (*a*) Let $z=a+b\omega+c\,\omega^2$. Then,

$$\begin{aligned}|z|^2&=z\bar{z}=(a+b\omega+c\omega^2)(a+b\bar{\omega}+c\,\overline{\omega^2})\\&=(a+b\omega+c\omega^2)(a+b\omega^2+c\omega)\\&=a^2+b^2+c^2-ab-bc-ca\\&=\frac{1}{2}[(a-b)^2+(b-c)^2+(c-a)^2]\end{aligned}$$

$$\Rightarrow |z|^2\geq\frac{1}{2}\times6=3 \quad \left[\begin{array}{l}\because a\neq b\neq c\\ \therefore |a-b|\geq1, |b-c|\geq1\\ \text{and } |a-c|\geq2\end{array}\right]$$

$\therefore \quad |z| \geq \sqrt{3}$

$\therefore \quad |a + b\omega + c\omega^2| + |a + b\omega^2 + c\omega|$

$= |a + b\omega + c\omega^2| + |\overline{a + b\omega^2 + c\overline{\omega}}|$

$= |a + b\omega + c\omega^2| + |a + b\omega + c\omega^2|$

$= 2|a + b\omega + c\omega^2| = 2|z| \geq 2\sqrt{3}$

Hence, the minimum value of $|a + b\omega + c\omega^2| + |a + b\omega^2 + c\omega|$ is $2\sqrt{3}$.

• **Ex. 10** *If $|z - 2i| \leq \sqrt{2}$, where $i = \sqrt{-1}$, then the maximum value of $|3 - i(z - 1)|$, is*

(a) $\sqrt{2}$ (b) $2\sqrt{2}$ (c) $2 + \sqrt{2}$ (d) $3 + 2\sqrt{2}$

Sol. (b) $\because \ |3 - i(z - 1)| = |-i(z - 1 - 3i)| = |-i||z - 1 - 3i|$
$= |z - 1 - 3i|$ ...(i)

and $|z - 1 - 3i| = |(z - 2i) + (-1 - i)| \leq |z - 2i| + |-1 - i|$ $[\because |z_1 + z_2| \leq |z_1| + |z_2|]$

$\therefore \quad |z - 1 - 3i| \leq |z - 2i| + \sqrt{2}$

$\Rightarrow \quad |z - 1 - 3i| \leq \sqrt{2} + \sqrt{2}$ $[\because |z - 2i| \leq \sqrt{2}]$

$\Rightarrow \quad |z - 1 - 3i| \leq 2\sqrt{2}$

From Eq. (i), we get

$$|3 - i(z - 1)| \leq 2\sqrt{2}$$

Hence, the maximum value of $|3 - i(z - 1)|$ is $2\sqrt{2}$.

JEE Type Solved Examples : More than One Correct Option Type Questions

- This section contains **5 multiple choice examples.** Each example has four choices (a), (b), (c) and (d) out of **which more than one** may be correct.

• **Ex. 11** *If $z_1 = a + ib$ and $z_2 = c + id$ are complex numbers such that $|z_1| = |z_2| = 1$ and $\text{Re}(z_1\bar{z}_2) = 0$, where $i = \sqrt{-1}$, then the complex numbers $\omega_1 = a + ic$ and $\omega_2 = b + id$ satisfy*

(a) $|\omega_1| = 1$ (b) $|\omega_2| = 1$
(c) $\text{Re}(\omega_1\bar{\omega}_2) = 0$ (d) None of these

Sol. (a, b, c)

$\because \quad |z_1| = 1, |z_2| = 1 \Rightarrow z_1 = CiS\,\theta, z_2 = CiS\,\phi$

$\text{Re}(z_1\bar{z}_2) = \text{Re}(CiS(\theta - \phi)) = 0$ [given]

$\Rightarrow \quad \cos(\theta - \phi) = 0 \Rightarrow \theta - \phi = \frac{\pi}{2} \Rightarrow \phi = \theta - \frac{\pi}{2}$

and $a = \cos\theta, b = \sin\theta, c = \cos\phi, d = \sin\phi$

$\therefore \quad \omega_1 = a + ic = \cos\theta + i\cos\phi = \cos\theta + i\sin\theta$ $\left[\because \phi = \theta - \frac{\pi}{2}\right]$

and $\omega_2 = b + id = \sin\theta + i\sin\phi = \sin\theta - i\cos\theta$ $\left[\because \phi = \theta - \frac{\pi}{2}\right]$

$\therefore \quad |\omega_1| = 1, |\omega_2| = 1$

and $\text{Re}(\omega_1\bar{\omega}_2) = \text{Re}(\cos\theta + i\sin\theta)(\sin\theta + i\cos\theta) = 0$

• **Ex. 12** *The complex numbers z_1, z_2, z_3 satisfying $(z_2 - z_3) = (1 + i)(z_1 - z_3)$, where $i = \sqrt{-1}$, are vertices of a triangle which is*

(a) equilateral (b) isosceles
(c) right angled (d) scalene

Sol. (b,c)

$\because \quad (z_2 - z_3) = (1 + i)(z_1 - z_3)$

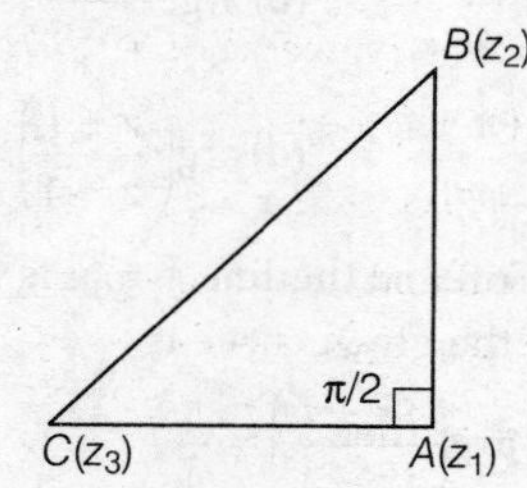

$\Rightarrow \quad (z_2 - z_1) = i(z_1 - z_3)$

$\Rightarrow \quad (z_2 - z_1) = -i(z_3 - z_1)$

or $\quad (z_3 - z_1) = i(z_2 - z_1)$

$\Rightarrow \quad \frac{z_3 - z_1}{z_2 - z_1} = e^{i\pi/2}$

AC is obtained by rotating AB about A through $\frac{\pi}{2}$ anti-clockwise.

$\therefore \quad AB = AC, \angle CAB = \frac{\pi}{2}$

Hence, z_1, z_2, z_3 form isosceles right angled triangle.

• **Ex. 13** *If z satisfies the inequality $|z - 1| < |z + 1|$, then one has*

(a) $|z - 2 - i| < |z + 2 - i|, i = \sqrt{-1}$

(b) $|\arg(z + i)| < \frac{\pi}{2}, i = \sqrt{-1}$

(c) $\text{Re}(z) < 0$

(d) $\text{Im}(i\bar{z}) > 0, i = \sqrt{-1}$

Sol. (a, b, d)

On putting $z = x + iy$ in the given relation, we have

$$(x - 1)^2 + y^2 < (x + 1)^2 + y^2$$

$\Rightarrow \quad x > 0$

i.e. $\quad \text{Re}(z) > 0 \quad$ ...(i)

and on putting $z = x + iy$ in alternate (a), then

$$(x-2)^2 + (y-1)^2 < (x+2)^2 + (y-1)^2$$

$\Rightarrow \quad x > 0 \quad$ [from Eq. (i)]

which is true.

$\therefore$ Real part of $(z + i) = x > 0$,

then $\arg(z + i)$ lies between $-\frac{\pi}{2}$ and $\frac{\pi}{2}$

and hence $|\arg(z+i)| < \frac{\pi}{2}$

and $\quad \text{Im}(i\bar{z}) = \text{Im}(i(x - iy)) = \text{Im}(y + ix)$

$= x > 0 \quad$ [from Eq. (i)]

which is true.

Ex. 14 *The equation $z^2 - i|z-1|^2 = 0$, where $i = \sqrt{-1}$, has*

(a) no real root

(b) no purely imaginary root

(c) all roots inside $|z| = 1$

(d) atleast two roots

Sol. (a, b, c)

On putting $z = x + iy$, we have

$$(x+iy)^2 - i|x+iy-1|^2 = 0$$

$$\Rightarrow \quad x^2 - y^2 + 2ixy - i((x-1)^2 + y^2) = 0$$

On comparing real and imaginary parts, we get

$$x^2 - y^2 = 0 \text{ and } 2xy = (x-1)^2 + y^2$$

***Case* I** When $y = x$, then $2xy = (x-1)^2 + y^2$ reduces to

$$2x^2 = (x-1)^2 + x^2$$

$$\Rightarrow \quad 0 = -2x + 1$$

$$\therefore \quad x = \frac{1}{2} = y$$

$$\Rightarrow \quad z = x + iy = \frac{1+i}{2} \quad \text{...(i)}$$

***Case* II** When $y = -x$, then $2xy = (x-1)^2 + y^2$ reduces to

$$-2x^2 = (x-1)^2 + x^2$$

$\Rightarrow (x-1)^2 + 3x^2 = 0$ which is not possible. ...(ii)

From Eqs. (i) and (ii), we get $z = \frac{1+i}{2}$

i.e., no real and no purely imaginary roots

and $\quad |z| = \frac{1}{\sqrt{2}} < 1$

Ex. 15 *Let z_1 and z_2 be two complex numbers represented by points on circles $|z| = 1$ and $|z| = 2$ respectively, then*

(a) $\max.|2z_1 + z_2| = 4$ (b) $\min.|z_1 - z_2| = 1$

(c) $\left|z_2 + \frac{1}{z_1}\right| \le 3$ (d) $\left|z_1 + \frac{2}{z_2}\right| \le 2$

Sol. (a, b, c, d)

$\because \quad |z_1| = 1$ and $|z_2| = 2$

$\therefore \quad |2z_1 + z_2| \le |2z_1| + |z_2| = 2|z_1| + |z_2|$

$\Rightarrow \quad |2z_1 + z_2| \le 2|z_1| + |z_2| = 2 + 2 = 4$

$\therefore \quad |2z_1 + z_2| \le 4$

$\Rightarrow \quad \max.|2z_1 + z_2| = 4 \quad$ [alternate (a)]

and $\quad |z_1 - z_2| \ge ||z_1| - |z_2|| = |1 - 2| = 1$

$\Rightarrow \quad |z_1 - z_2| \ge 1$

$\therefore \quad \min.|z_1 - z_2| = 1 \quad$ [alternate (b)]

$$\left|z_2 + \frac{1}{z_1}\right| \le |z_2| + \left|\frac{1}{z_1}\right| = |z_2| + \frac{1}{|z_1|} = 2 + \frac{1}{1} = 3$$

$\therefore \quad \left|z_2 + \frac{1}{z_1}\right| \le 3 \quad$ [alternate (c)]

and $\quad \left|z_1 + \frac{2}{z_2}\right| \le |z_1| + \left|\frac{2}{z_2}\right| = |z_1| + \frac{2}{|z_2|} = 1 + \frac{2}{2} = 2$

$\therefore \quad \left|z_1 + \frac{2}{z_2}\right| \le 2 \quad$ [alternate (d)]

JEE Type Solved Examples : Passage Based Questions

- This section contains **2 solved passages** based upon each of the passage **3 multiple choice** examples have to be answered. Each of these examples has four choices (a), (b), (c) and (d) out of which **ONLY ONE** is correct.

Passage I (Ex. Nos. 16 to 18)

Consider a quadratic equation $az^2 + bz + c = 0$, where a, b and c are complex numbers.

16. The condition that the equation has one purely imaginary root, is

(a) $(a\bar{b} - \bar{a}b)(b\bar{c} + \bar{b}c) + (c\bar{a} - \bar{c}a)^2 = 0$

(b) $(a\bar{b} + \bar{a}b)(b\bar{c} + \bar{b}c) + (c\bar{a} - \bar{c}a)^2 = 0$

(c) $(a\bar{b} - \bar{a}b)(b\bar{c} - \bar{b}c) + (c\bar{a} + \bar{c}a)^2 = 0$

(d) $(a\bar{b} + \bar{a}b)(b\bar{c} - \bar{b}c) + (c\bar{a} - \bar{c}a)^2 = 0$

Sol. (b) $\because \quad az^2 + bz + c = 0 \quad$ ...(i)

$\therefore \quad \overline{az^2 + bz + c} = \bar{0}$

$\Rightarrow \quad \bar{a}(\bar{z})^2 + \bar{b}\bar{z} + \bar{c} = 0$

For purely imaginary root,

$$\bar{z} = -z$$

Then, $\quad \bar{a}z^2 - \bar{b}z + \bar{c} = 0 \quad$ ...(ii)

From Eqs. (i) and (ii), we get

$$\frac{z^2}{b\bar{c}+\bar{b}c}=\frac{z}{c\bar{a}-\bar{c}a}=\frac{1}{-a\bar{b}-\bar{a}b}$$

$$\Rightarrow \quad z=\frac{b\bar{c}+\bar{b}c}{c\bar{a}-\bar{c}a}=\frac{c\bar{a}-\bar{c}a}{-a\bar{b}-\bar{a}b}$$

$$\therefore \quad (a\bar{b}+\bar{a}b)(b\bar{c}+\bar{b}c)+(c\bar{a}-\bar{c}a)^2=0$$

17. The condition that the equation has one purely real root, is

(a) $(a\bar{b}+\bar{a}b)(b\bar{c}-\bar{b}c)=(c\bar{a}+\bar{c}a)^2$

(b) $(a\bar{b}-\bar{a}b)(b\bar{c}+\bar{b}c)=(c\bar{a}+\bar{c}a)^2$

(c) $(a\bar{b}-\bar{a}b)(b\bar{c}-\bar{b}c)=(c\bar{a}-\bar{c}a)^2$

(d) $(a\bar{b}-\bar{a}b)(b\bar{c}-\bar{b}c)=(c\bar{a}+\bar{c}a)^2$

Sol. (c) $\because \; az^2+bz+c=0$ ...(i)

$$\Rightarrow \quad \overline{az^2+bz+c}=\bar{0}$$

$$\Rightarrow \quad \bar{a}(\bar{z})^2+\bar{b}\bar{z}+\bar{c}=0$$

For purely real root, $\bar{z}=z$

Then, $\quad \bar{a}z^2+\bar{b}z+\bar{c}=0$ ...(ii)

From Eqs. (i) and (ii), we get

$$\frac{z^2}{b\bar{c}-\bar{b}c}=\frac{z}{c\bar{a}-\bar{c}a}=\frac{1}{a\bar{b}-\bar{a}b}$$

$$\Rightarrow \quad z=\frac{b\bar{c}-\bar{b}c}{c\bar{a}-\bar{c}a}=\frac{c\bar{a}-\bar{c}a}{a\bar{b}-\bar{a}b}$$

$$\Rightarrow \quad (a\bar{b}-\bar{a}b)(b\bar{c}-\bar{b}c)=(c\bar{a}-\bar{c}a)^2$$

18. The condition that the equation has two purely imaginary roots, is

(a) $\frac{a}{\bar{a}}=\frac{b}{\bar{b}}=\frac{c}{\bar{c}}$ (b) $-\frac{a}{\bar{a}}=\frac{b}{\bar{b}}=\frac{c}{\bar{c}}$

(c) $\frac{a}{\bar{a}}=\frac{b}{\bar{b}}=-\frac{c}{\bar{c}}$ (d) $\frac{a}{\bar{a}}=-\frac{b}{\bar{b}}=\frac{c}{\bar{c}}$

Sol. (d) $\because \quad az^2+bz+c=0$ ...(i)

$$\therefore \quad \overline{az^2+bz+c}=\bar{0}$$

$$\Rightarrow \bar{a}(\bar{z})^2+\bar{b}\bar{z}+\bar{c}=0$$

Since, both roots are purely imaginary.

$$\therefore \quad \bar{z}=-z$$

Then, $\quad \bar{a}z^2-\bar{b}z+\bar{c}=0$ ...(ii)

Hence, Eqs. (i) and (ii) are identical.

$$\therefore \quad \frac{a}{\bar{a}}=-\frac{b}{\bar{b}}=\frac{c}{\bar{c}}$$

Passage II (Ex. Nos. 19 to 21)

Let P be a point denoting a complex number z on the complex plane.

i.e. $\quad z=\operatorname{Re}(z)+i\operatorname{Im}(z)$, where $i=\sqrt{-1}$

If $\quad \operatorname{Re}(z)=x$ and $\operatorname{Im}(z)=y$, then $z=x+iy$

19. If P moves such that

$$|\operatorname{Re}(z)|+|\operatorname{Im}(z)|=a\ (a\in R^+)$$

The locus of P is

(a) a parallelogram which is not a rhombus

(b) a rhombus which is not a square

(c) a rectangle which is not a square

(d) a square

Sol. (d) $\because \quad |\operatorname{Re}(z)|+|\operatorname{Im}(z)|=a$

$$\Rightarrow \quad |x|+|y|=a$$

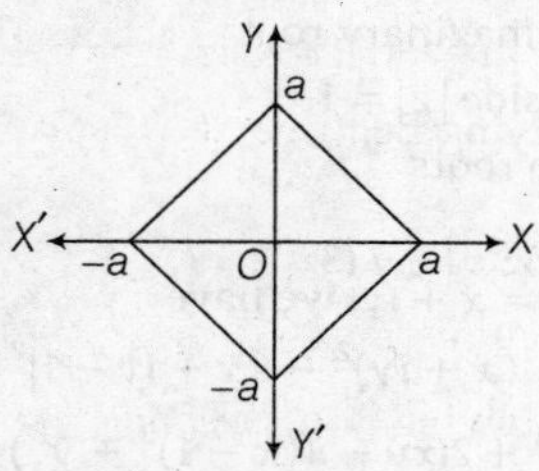

$\therefore$ Locus of P is a square.

20. The area of the circle inscribed in the region denoted by $|\operatorname{Re}(z)|+|\operatorname{Im}(z)|=10$ equals to

(a) $50\,\pi$ sq units (b) $100\,\pi$ sq units

(c) 55 sq units (d) 110 sq units

Sol. (a) From above, $a=10$

Diameter of circle = Distance between sides of square

= Length of side of square $=a\sqrt{2}=10\sqrt{2}$

or $\quad 2r=10\sqrt{2}$

$$\Rightarrow \quad r=5\sqrt{2}$$

$\therefore$ Area of a circle $=\pi r^2=50\pi$ sq units

21. Number of integral solutions satisfying the inequality $|\operatorname{Re}(z)|+|\operatorname{Im}(z)|<21$, is

(a) 841 (b) 839

(c) 840 (d) 842

Sol. (c) $\because \quad |x|+|y|<21 \;\Rightarrow\; 0\le |x|+|y|\le 20$

If $\quad x>0,\ y>0,\ 0\le x+y\le 20$

Number of solutions $={}^{21}C_2=\frac{21\cdot 20}{2}=210$

$\therefore$ Total integral solutions $=4\times 210=840$

JEE Type Solved Examples : Single Integer Answer Type Questions

- This section contains **2 examples.** The answer to each example is a **single digit integer** ranging from **0** to **9** (both inclusive).

Ex. 22 *If $z_1, z_2 \in C$, $z_1^2 + z_2^2 \in R$, $z_1(z_1^2 - 3z_2^2) = 2$ and $z_2(3z_1^2 - z_2^2) = 11$, the value of $z_1^2 + z_2^2$ is*

Sol. (5) We have, $\quad z_1(z_1^2 - 3z_2^2) = 2 \quad$ ...(i)

and $\quad z_2(3z_1^2 - z_2^2) = 11 \quad$ ...(ii)

multiplying Eq. (ii) by $i\ (\sqrt{-1})$ and then adding in Eq. (i), we get

$$z_1^3 - 3z_1z_2^2 + i(3z_1^2z_2 - z_2^3) = 2 + 11i$$

$$\Rightarrow \quad (z_1 + iz_2)^3 = 2 + 11i \quad \text{...(iii)}$$

Again, multiplying Eq. (ii) by $(-i)$ and then adding in Eq. (i), we get

$$z_1^3 - 3z_1z_2^2 - i(3z_1^2z_2 - z_2^3) = 2 - 11i$$

$$\Rightarrow \quad (z_1 - iz_2)^3 = 2 - 11i \quad \text{...(iv)}$$

Now, on multiplying Eqs. (iii) and (iv), we get

$$(z_1^2 + z_2^2)^3 = 4 + 121 = 125 = 5^3$$

$$\therefore \quad z_1^2 + z_2^2 = 5$$

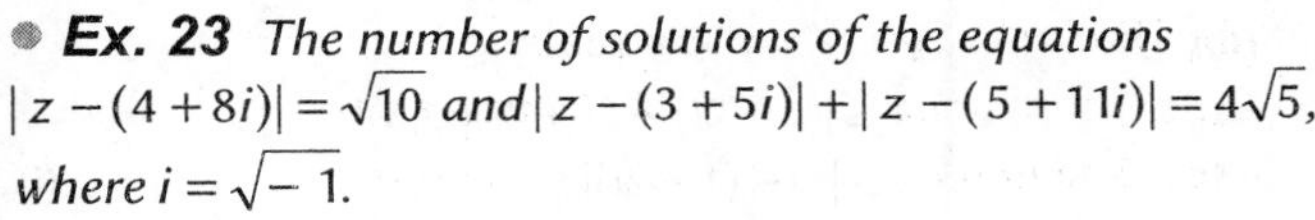

Ex. 23 *The number of solutions of the equations $|z - (4 + 8i)| = \sqrt{10}$ and $|z - (3 + 5i)| + |z - (5 + 11i)| = 4\sqrt{5}$, where $i = \sqrt{-1}$.*

Sol. (2) Here, $|z - (4 + 8i)| = \sqrt{10}$

represents a circle with centre (4, 8) and radius $\sqrt{10}$.

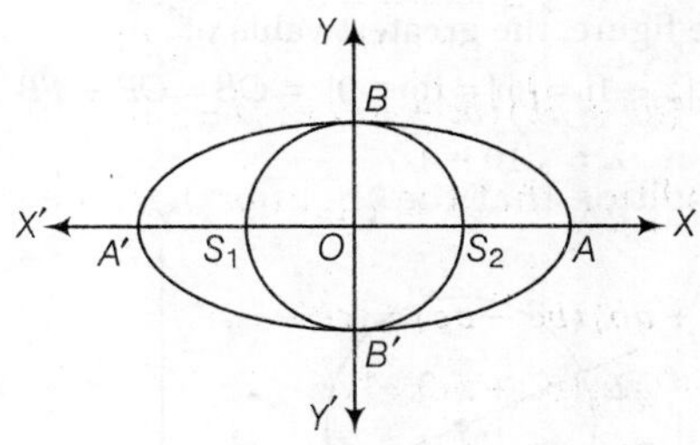

Also, $\quad |z - (3 + 5i)| + |z - (5 + 11i)| = 4\sqrt{5}$

represents an ellipse.

$\therefore \quad |(3 + 5i) - (5 + 11i)| = \sqrt{4 + 36} = \sqrt{40} < 4\sqrt{5}$

with foci $S_1(3, 5)$ and $S_2(5, 11)$.

Distance between foci $= S_1S_2 = \sqrt{40} = 2\sqrt{10}$ = Diameter of circle

i.e., $\quad 2ae = 2\sqrt{10}$

$\Rightarrow \quad ae = \sqrt{10}$ and $2a = 4\sqrt{5} \Rightarrow a = 2\sqrt{5}$

$\therefore \quad e = \dfrac{ae}{a} = \dfrac{1}{\sqrt{2}}$

Now, $b = a\sqrt{(1 - e^2)} = 2\sqrt{5}\sqrt{\left(1 - \dfrac{1}{2}\right)} = \sqrt{10}$ = Radius of circle

$\therefore$ Centre of the ellipse = Mid-point of S_1 and S_2

$$= \frac{3 + 5i + 5 + 11i}{2} = 4 + 8i \text{ i.e., } (4, 8)$$

which coincides with the centre of the circle and length of minor-axis is equal to the radius of the circle. Hence, there are only (2) two solutions of the given equations.

JEE Type Solved Examples : Matching Type Questions

- This section contains **2 examples.** Examples 24 and 25 have three statements (A, B and C) given in Column I and four statements (p, q, r and s) in **Column II.** Any given statement in **Column I** can have correct matching with one or more statement(s) given in **Column II.**

Ex. 24

	Column I		Column II
(A)	If λ and μ are the greatest and least values of $|z - 1|$, if $|z + 2 + i| \le 1$, where $i = \sqrt{-1}$, then	(p)	$\lambda + \mu$ = rational
(B)	If λ and μ are the greatest and least values of $|z - 2|$, if $|z + i| \le 1$, where $i = \sqrt{-1}$, then	(q)	$\lambda + \mu$ = irrational
(C)	If λ and μ are the greatest and least values of $|z + 2i|$, if $1 \le |z - 1| \le 3$, where $i = \sqrt{-1}$, then	(r)	$\lambda - \mu$ = rational
		(s)	$\lambda - \mu$ = irrational

Sol. (A) → (q, r); (B) → (q, r); (C) → (p, s)

(A) $\because$ $|z+2+i| \le 1$

$\Rightarrow$ $|(z-1)+(3+i)| \le 1$

$\Rightarrow$ $|\omega+(3+i)| \le 1$ where, $\omega = z-1$

From the figure, the greatest value of

$$|z-1| = |\omega| = |\omega - 0| = OB = OP + PB = \sqrt{10}+1$$

$\therefore$ $\lambda = \sqrt{10}+1$

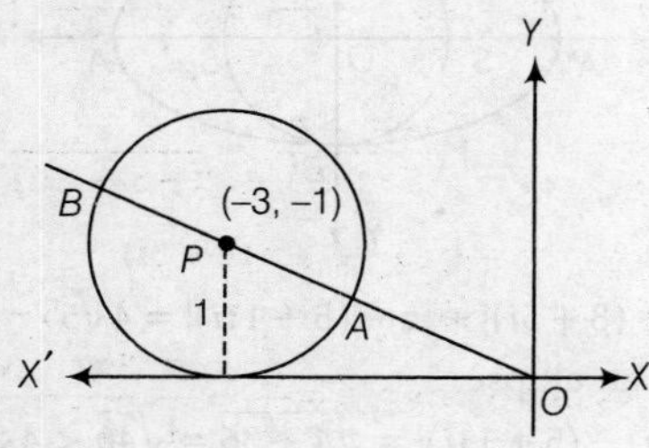

and the least value of $|z-1| = |\omega|$

$$= |\omega - 0| = OP - AP = \sqrt{10}-1$$

$\therefore$ $\mu = \sqrt{10}-1$

$\Rightarrow$ $\lambda + \mu = (\sqrt{10}+1)+(\sqrt{10}-1) = 2\sqrt{10} =$ irrational

and $\lambda - \mu = (\sqrt{10}+1)-(\sqrt{10}-1) = 2 =$ rational

Aliter

$\because$ $|z+2+i| \le 1$

$\Rightarrow$ $|(z-1)+(3+i)| \le 1$

$\Rightarrow$ $|\omega+(3+i)| \le 1$ ...(i)

where, $\omega = z-1$

$\therefore$ $|\omega+(3+i)| \ge ||\omega| - |3+i||$

or $|\omega+(3+i)| \ge ||\omega| - \sqrt{10}|$ ...(ii)

From Eqs. (i) and (ii), we get

$$||\omega| - \sqrt{10}| \le |\omega+3+i| \le 1$$

$\Rightarrow$ $||\omega| - \sqrt{10}| \le 1$

or $-1 \le |\omega| - \sqrt{10} \le 1$

or $\sqrt{10}-1 \le |\omega| \le \sqrt{10}+1$

$\therefore$ $\lambda = \sqrt{10}+1$ and $\mu = \sqrt{10}-1$

$\Rightarrow$ $\lambda+\mu = 2\sqrt{10} =$ irrational

and $\lambda - \mu = 2 =$ rational

(B) $\because$ $|z+i| \le 1$

$\Rightarrow$ $|(z-2)+(2+i)| \le 1$

$\Rightarrow$ $|\omega+(2+i)| \le 1$

where, $\omega = z-2$

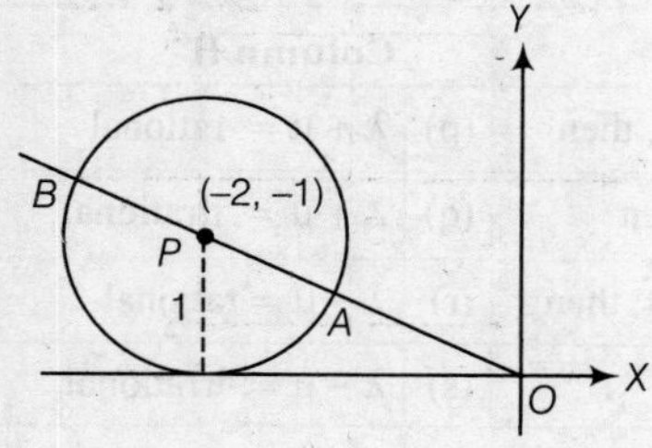

From the figure, the greatest value of $|z-2| = |\omega|$

$$= |\omega - 0| = OB$$

$$= OP + PB = \sqrt{5}+1$$

$\therefore$ $\lambda = \sqrt{5}+1$

and the least value of $|z-2| = |\omega|$

$$= |\omega - 0| = OA = OP - AP = \sqrt{5}-1$$

$\therefore$ $\mu = \sqrt{5}-1$

$\Rightarrow$ $\lambda+\mu = (\sqrt{5}+1)+(\sqrt{5}-1) = 2\sqrt{5} =$ irrational

and $\lambda-\mu = (\sqrt{5}+1)-(\sqrt{5}-1) = 2 =$ rational

Aliter

$\because$ $|z+i| \le 1$

$\Rightarrow$ $|(z-2)+(2+i)| \le 1$

$\Rightarrow$ $|\omega+(2+i)| \le 1$

where, $\omega = z-2$ ...(i)

$\because$ $|\omega+(2+i)| \ge ||\omega| - |2+i||$

or $|\omega+(2+i)| \ge ||\omega| - \sqrt{5}|$ ...(ii)

From Eqs. (i) and (ii), we get

$$||\omega| - \sqrt{5}| \le |\omega+2+i| \le 1$$

$\Rightarrow$ $||\omega| - \sqrt{5}| \le 1$

or $-1 \le |\omega| - \sqrt{5} \le 1$ or $\sqrt{5}-1 \le |\omega| \le \sqrt{5}+1$

$\therefore$ $\lambda = \sqrt{5}+1$ and $\mu = \sqrt{5}-1$

$\Rightarrow$ $\lambda+\mu = 2\sqrt{5} =$ irrational

and $\lambda-\mu = 2 =$ rational

(C) $\because$ $1 \le |z-1| \le 3$

$\Rightarrow$ $1 \le |(z+2i)-(1+2i)| \le 3$

$\Rightarrow$ $1 \le |\omega-(1+2i)| \le 3$ ...(i)

where, $\omega = z+2i$

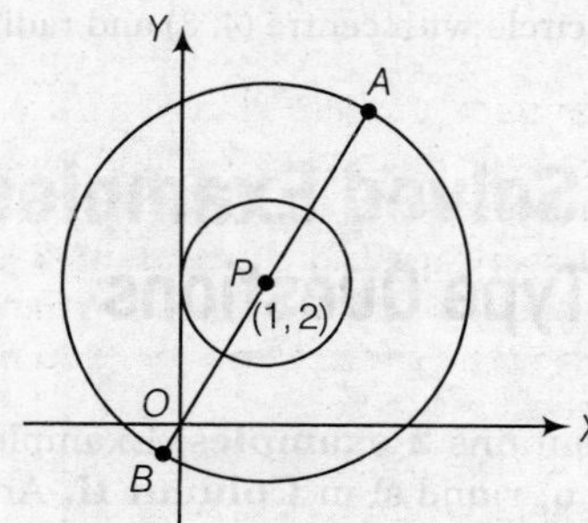

From the figure, the greatest value of $|z+2i| = |\omega|$

$$= |\omega - 0| = OA = OP + PA = \sqrt{5}+3$$

$\therefore$ $\lambda = 3+\sqrt{5}$

and the least value of $|z+2i| = |\omega|$

$$= |\omega - 0| = OB = PB - OP = 3-\sqrt{5}$$

$\therefore$ $\mu = 3-\sqrt{5}$

$\Rightarrow$ $\lambda+\mu = (3+\sqrt{5})+(3-\sqrt{5}) = 6 =$ rational

and $\lambda-\mu = (3+\sqrt{5})-(3-\sqrt{5}) = 2\sqrt{5} =$ irrational

• Ex. 25

Column I	Column II	
(A) If $\sqrt{(3-4i)}+\sqrt{(-3-4i)}=z$, the principal value of arg (z) can be (where $i=\sqrt{-1}$)	(p)	0
(B) If $\sqrt{(5+12i)}+\sqrt{(-5+12i)}=z$, the principal value of arg (z) can be (where $i=\sqrt{-1}$)	(q)	$\pm\frac{\pi}{4}$
(C) If $\sqrt{(-15+8i)}+\sqrt{(-15-8i)}=z$, the principal value of arg (z) can be (where $i=\sqrt{-1}$)	(r)	$\pm\frac{\pi}{2}$
	(s)	$\pm\frac{3\pi}{4}$

Sol. (A) → (q, s); (B) → (q, s); (C) → (p, r)

$$\because\ \sqrt{z}=\pm\left(\sqrt{\frac{|z|+\text{Re}(z)}{2}}+i\sqrt{\frac{|z|-\text{Re}(z)}{2}}\right),\ \text{Im}(z)>0$$

$$=\pm\left(\sqrt{\frac{|z|+\text{Re}(z)}{2}}-i\sqrt{\frac{|z|-\text{Re}(z)}{2}}\right),\ \text{Im}(z)<0$$

(A) $\sqrt{(3-4i)}=\pm\left(\sqrt{\frac{5+3}{2}}-i\sqrt{\frac{5-3}{2}}\right)=\pm(2-i)$

$$\sqrt{(-3-4i)}=\pm\left(\sqrt{\frac{5-3}{2}}-i\sqrt{\frac{5+3}{2}}\right)=\pm(1-2i)$$

$$\because\quad z=\sqrt{(3-4i)}+\sqrt{(-3-4i)}$$

$$\therefore\quad z=\pm(2-i)\pm(1-2i)$$

$$=3-3i,1+i,-1-i,-3+3i$$

$\therefore$ Principal values of arg $(z)=-\frac{\pi}{4},\frac{\pi}{4},-\frac{3\pi}{4},\frac{3\pi}{4}$

(B) $\sqrt{(5+12i)}=\pm\left(\sqrt{\frac{13+5}{2}}+i\sqrt{\frac{13-5}{2}}\right)$

$$=\pm(3+2i)$$

$$\sqrt{(-5+12i)}=\pm\left(\sqrt{\frac{13-5}{2}}+i\sqrt{\frac{13+5}{2}}\right)$$

$$=\pm(2+3i)$$

$$\because\quad z=\sqrt{(5+12i)}+\sqrt{(-5+12i)}$$

$$=\pm(3+2i)\pm(2+3i)$$

$$=5+5i,1-i,-1+i,-5-5i$$

$\therefore$ Principal values of arg $(z)=\frac{\pi}{4},-\frac{\pi}{4},\frac{3\pi}{4},-\frac{3\pi}{4}$

(C) $\sqrt{-15+8i}=\pm\left(\sqrt{\frac{17-15}{2}}+i\sqrt{\frac{17+15}{2}}\right)$

$$=\pm(1+4i)$$

and $\sqrt{-15-8i}=\overline{\sqrt{-15+8i}}=\pm\overline{(1+4i)}$

$$=\pm(1-4i)$$

$$\because\quad z=\sqrt{(-15+8i)}+\sqrt{(-15-8i)}$$

$$=\pm(1+4i)\pm(1-4i)=2,8i,-8i,-2$$

$\therefore$ Principal values of arg $(z)=0,\frac{\pi}{2},-\frac{\pi}{2},\pi.$

JEE Type Solved Examples : Statement I and II Type Questions

- **Directions** Example numbers 26 and 27 are Assertion-Reason type examples. Each of these examples contains two statements:
  Statement-1 (Assertion) and **Statement-2** (Reason)
  Each of these examples also has four alternative choices, only one of which is the correct answer. You have to select the correct choice as given below.
  (a) Statement-1 is true, Statement-2 is true; Statement-2 is a correct explanation for Statement-1
  (b) Statement-1 is true, Statement-2 is true; Statement-2 is not a correct explanation for Statement-1
  (c) Statement-1 is true, Statement-2 is false
  (d) Statement-1 is false, Statement-2 is true

• Ex. 26 *Consider four complex numbers $z_1=2+2i$, $z_2=2-2i$, $z_3=-2-2i$ and $z_4=-2+2i$, where $i=\sqrt{-1}$.*

Statement-1 *z_1,z_2,z_3 and z_4 constitute the vertices of a square on the complex plane because*

Statement-2 *The non-zero complex numbers $z,\bar{z},-z,-\bar{z}$ always constitute the vertices of a square.*

Sol. (*c*) **Statement-1**

$$AB=|z_1-z_2|=|4i|=4,$$
$$BC=|z_2-z_3|=|4|=4,$$
$$CD=|z_3-z_4|=|-4i|=4$$
$$DA=|z_4-z_1|=|-4|=4$$
$$AC=|z_1-z_3|=|4+4i|=4\sqrt{2}$$
and $$BD=|z_2-z_4|=|4-4i|=4\sqrt{2}$$

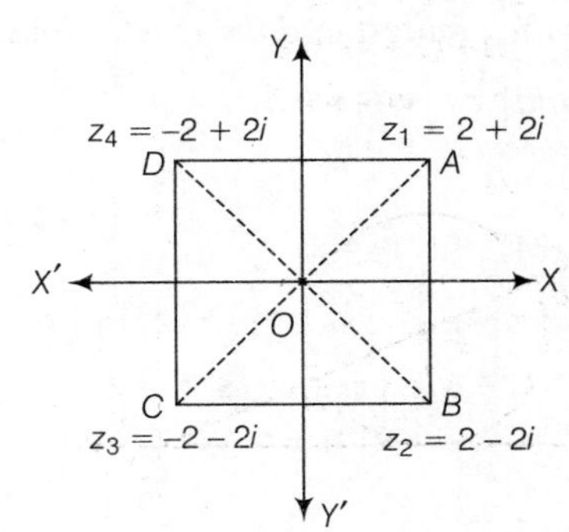

It is clear that, $AB = BC = CD = DA$ and $AC = BD$

Hence, z_1, z_2, z_3 and z_4 are the vertices of a square.

$\therefore$ Statement-1 is true.

Statement-2 If $z = a + ib$

If $a \neq b$

Then, $AB = |z - \bar{z}| = |(a + ib) - (a - ib)| = 2|b|$

$BC = |\bar{z} - (-z)| = |\bar{z} + z| = |a - ib + a + ib| = 2|a|$

$\therefore \quad AB \neq BC$

Statement-2 is false.

● ***Ex. 27*** *Consider z_1 and z_2 are two complex numbers such that $|z_1 + z_2| = |z_1| + |z_2|$*

Statement-1 *$amp(z_1) - amp(z_2) = 0$*

Statement-2 *The complex numbers z_1 and z_2 are collinear with origin.*

Sol. (b) **Statement-1**

$\because \quad |z_1 + z_2| = |z_1| + |z_2| \quad \ldots(i)$

If $amp(z_1) = \theta_1$ and $amp(z_2) = \theta_2$, then

$$|z_1 + z_2|^2 = |z_1|^2 + |z_2|^2 + 2|z_1||z_2|\cos(\theta_1 - \theta_2)$$

$\Rightarrow \quad (|z_1| + |z_2|)^2 = |z_1|^2 + |z_2|^2 + 2|z_1||z_2|\cos(\theta_1 - \theta_2)$ [from Eq. (i)]

$\Rightarrow \quad |z_1|^2 + |z_2|^2 + 2|z_1||z_2| = |z_1|^2 + |z_2|^2 + 2|z_1||z_2|\cos(\theta_1 - \theta_2)$

$\therefore \quad \cos(\theta_1 - \theta_2) = 1$

$z_1 \qquad z_2 \qquad O$

$\Rightarrow \quad \theta_1 - \theta_2 = 0$

or $\quad amp(z_1) - amp(z_2) = 0$

$\therefore$ Statement-1 is true.

Statement-2 Since, z_1, z_2 and O (origin) are collinear, then

$$amp\left(\frac{O - z_1}{O - z_2}\right) = 0$$

$\Rightarrow \quad amp\left(\frac{z_1}{z_2}\right) = 0$

$\Rightarrow \quad amp(z_1) - amp(z_2) = 0$

$\therefore$ Statement-2 is true, which is not a correct explanation of Statement-1.

Subjective Type Examples

- In this section, there are **24 subjective** solved examples.

● ***Ex. 28*** *If $|z - i\,\text{Re}(z)| = |z - \text{Im}(z)|$, then prove that z lies on the bisectors of the quadrants, where $i = \sqrt{-1}$.*

Sol. Let $z = x + iy$, where $x, y \in R$ and $i = \sqrt{-1}$

$\therefore \quad \text{Re}(z) = x$ and $\text{Im}(z) = y$

Then, $|z - i\,\text{Re}(z)| = |z - \text{Im}(z)|$

$\Rightarrow \quad |x + iy - ix| = |x + iy - y|$

$\Rightarrow \quad |x - i(x - y)| = |(x - y) + iy|$

$\Rightarrow \quad \sqrt{x^2 + (x - y)^2} = \sqrt{(x - y)^2 + y^2}$

$\Rightarrow \quad x^2 + (x - y)^2 = (x - y)^2 + y^2$

$\Rightarrow \quad x^2 = y^2$ or $y = \pm x$

Hence, z lies on the bisectors of the quadrants.

● ***Ex. 29*** *Find the greatest and the least values of $|z_1 + z_2|$, if $z_1 = 24 + 7i$ and $|z_2| = 6$, where $i = \sqrt{-1}$.*

Sol. $\because \quad z_1 = 24 + 7i$

$\therefore \quad |z_1| = \sqrt{(24)^2 + (7)^2} = 25$

$$||z_1| - |z_2|| \leq |z_1 + z_2| \leq |z_1| + |z_2|$$

$\Rightarrow \quad |25 - 6| \leq |z_1 + z_2| \leq 25 + 6$

or $\quad 19 \leq |z_1 + z_2| \leq 31$

Hence, the least value of $|z_1 + z_2|$ is 19 and the greatest value of $|z_1 + z_2|$ is 31.

● ***Ex. 30*** *Let S denotes the real part of the complex number $z = \frac{5 + 2i}{2 - 5i} + \frac{20 + 5i}{7 + 6i} + 3i$, where $i = \sqrt{-1}$, K denotes the sum of the imaginary parts of the roots of the equation $z^2 - 8(1 - i)z + 63 - 16i = 0$ and G denotes the value of $\sum_{r=4}^{2012} i^r$, where $i = \sqrt{-1}$, find the value of $S - K + G$.*

Sol. For S,

$$z = \frac{(5 + 2i)}{(2 - 5i)} + \frac{(20 + 5i)}{(7 + 6i)} + 3i$$

$$= \frac{(5 + 2i)(2 + 5i)}{29} + \frac{(20 + 5i)(7 - 6i)}{85} + 3i$$

$$= \frac{0 + 29i}{29} + \frac{170 - 85i}{85} + 3i$$

$$= i + 2 - i + 3i = 2 + 3i$$

$\therefore \quad \text{Re}(z) = 2 \qquad \therefore \quad S = 2$

For K,

Put $z = x + iy$ in the given equation, then

$$(x + iy)^2 - 8(1 - i)(x + iy) + 63 - 16i = 0$$

On comparing the real and imaginary parts, we get

$$x^2 - y^2 - 8(x+y) + 63 = 0 \quad \text{...(i)}$$

and $$xy + 4(x - y) = 8 \quad \text{...(ii)}$$

On substituting the value of x from Eq. (ii) in Eq. (i), we get

$$y^4 + 16y^3 + \ldots = 0$$

$$\therefore \quad K = -16$$

For G, $$G = \sum_{r=4}^{2012} i^r = \sum_{r=1}^{2009} i^{r+3} = i^{1+3} + 0 = 1$$

$$\therefore \quad S - K + G = 2 - (-16) + 1 = 19$$

Ex. 31 *If $|z-1| = 1$, where z is a point on the argand plane, show that $\frac{z-2}{z} = i \tan(\arg z)$, where $i = \sqrt{-1}$.*

Sol. Given, $|z-1| = 1 \Rightarrow |z-1|^2 = 1$

$$\Rightarrow (z-1)(\bar{z}-1) = 1 \Rightarrow z\bar{z} - z - \bar{z} = 0$$

$$\Rightarrow (z+\bar{z}) = z\bar{z} \Rightarrow \frac{z}{\bar{z}} + 1 = z$$

$$\Rightarrow \frac{z}{\bar{z}} = z - 1 \quad \text{...(i)}$$

Now, RHS $= i \tan(\arg z) = i\left(\frac{\operatorname{Im}(z)}{\operatorname{Re}(z)}\right)$

$$= i\left\{\frac{\frac{z-\bar{z}}{2i}}{\frac{z+\bar{z}}{2}}\right\} = i\left(\frac{z-\bar{z}}{i(z+\bar{z})}\right)$$

$$= \frac{z-\bar{z}}{z+\bar{z}} = \frac{\frac{z}{\bar{z}} - 1}{\frac{z}{\bar{z}} + 1} = \frac{(z-1)-1}{(z-1)+1} = \frac{z-2}{z} \quad \text{[from Eq. (i)]}$$

$= \text{LHS}$

Aliter

We have, $|z-1| = 1$ i.e. $(z-1)$ is unimodular, so we can take

$$z - 1 = \cos\theta + i\sin\theta$$

$$\therefore \quad z - 2 = -1 + \cos\theta + i\sin\theta$$

$$= -2\sin^2\frac{\theta}{2} + 2i\sin\frac{\theta}{2}\cos\frac{\theta}{2}$$

$$= 2i^2\sin^2\frac{\theta}{2} + 2i\sin\frac{\theta}{2}\cos\frac{\theta}{2}$$

or $$z - 2 = 2i\sin\frac{\theta}{2}\left(\cos\frac{\theta}{2} + i\sin\frac{\theta}{2}\right) \quad \text{...(i)}$$

and $$z = 1 + \cos\theta + i\sin\theta$$

$$= 2\cos^2\frac{\theta}{2} + 2i\sin\frac{\theta}{2}\cos\frac{\theta}{2}$$

$$z = 2\cos\frac{\theta}{2}\left(\cos\frac{\theta}{2} + i\sin\frac{\theta}{2}\right) \quad \text{...(ii)}$$

From Eqs. (i) and (ii), we get

$$\frac{z-2}{z} = i\tan\frac{\theta}{2}$$

Therefore, $\frac{z-2}{z} = i\tan(\arg z)$ [$\because \arg(z) = \theta/2$ from Eq. (ii)]

Ex. 32 *If $\arg(z^{1/3}) = \frac{1}{2}\arg(z^2 + \bar{z}z^{1/3})$, find the value of $|z|$.*

Sol. We have, $\arg(z^{1/3}) = \frac{1}{2}\arg(z^2 + \bar{z}z^{1/3})$

$$\Rightarrow 2\arg(z^{1/3}) = \arg(z^2 + \bar{z}z^{1/3})$$

$$\Rightarrow \arg(z^{2/3}) = \arg(z^2 + \bar{z}z^{1/3}) \quad \text{[by property]}$$

$$\Rightarrow \arg(z^2 + \bar{z}z^{1/3}) - \arg(z^{2/3}) = 0$$

$$\Rightarrow \arg\left(\frac{z^2 + \bar{z}z^{1/3}}{z^{2/3}}\right) = 0 \quad \text{[by property]}$$

$$\Rightarrow \arg\left(z^{4/3} + \frac{\bar{z}}{z^{1/3}}\right) = 0$$

$$\Rightarrow z^{4/3} + \frac{\bar{z}}{z^{1/3}} \text{ is purely real.}$$

$$\Rightarrow \operatorname{Im}\left(z^{4/3} + \frac{\bar{z}}{z^{1/3}}\right) = 0$$

$$\Rightarrow \frac{\left(z^{4/3} + \frac{\bar{z}}{z^{1/3}}\right) - \overline{\left(z^{4/3} + \frac{\bar{z}}{z^{1/3}}\right)}}{2i} = 0$$

$$\Rightarrow z^{4/3} + \frac{\bar{z}}{z^{1/3}} = (\bar{z})^{4/3} + \frac{(z)}{(\bar{z})^{1/3}}$$

$$\Rightarrow z^{4/3} + \frac{(\bar{z})(\bar{z})^{1/3}}{|z|^{2/3}} = (\bar{z})^{4/3} + \frac{z(z)^{1/3}}{|z|^{2/3}}$$

$$[\because z^{1/3}(\bar{z})^{1/3} = (z\bar{z})^{1/3} = |z|^{2/3}]$$

$$\Rightarrow z^{4/3} - (\bar{z})^{4/3} - \frac{1}{|z|^{2/3}}((z)^{4/3} - (\bar{z})^{4/3}) = 0$$

$$\Rightarrow \{z^{4/3} - (\bar{z})^{4/3}\}\left[1 - \frac{1}{|z|^{2/3}}\right] = 0$$

$$\therefore \quad |z|^{2/3} = 1 \quad [\because z \neq \bar{z}]$$

Therefore, $$|z| = 1$$

Ex. 33 *C is the complex numbers $f : C \to R$ is defined by $f(z) = |z^3 - z + 2|$. Find the maximum value of $f(z)$, if $|z| = 1$.*

Sol. $\because \quad |z| = 1$

$$\therefore \quad z = e^{i\theta}$$

$$\therefore f(e^{i\theta}) = |e^{3i\theta} - e^{i\theta} + 2| = |e^{2i\theta}(e^{i\theta} - e^{-i\theta}) + 2|$$

$$= |e^{2i\theta} \cdot 2i\sin\theta + 2|$$

$$= |(\cos 2\theta + i\sin 2\theta) \cdot 2i\sin\theta + 2|$$

$$= |(2 - 2\sin 2\theta\sin\theta) + 2i\sin\theta\cos 2\theta|$$

$$= 2|(1 - \sin 2\theta\sin\theta) + i\sin\theta\cos 2\theta|$$

$$= 2\sqrt{(1 - \sin 2\theta\sin\theta)^2 + (\sin\theta\cos 2\theta)^2}$$

$$= 2\sqrt{(1+\sin^2\theta - 2\sin\theta\sin 2\theta)}$$
$$= 2\sqrt{1+\sin^2\theta(1-4\cos\theta)}$$
$$= 2\sqrt{1+(1-\cos\theta)(1+\cos\theta)(1-4\cos\theta)}$$

For maximum value, $\cos\theta = -\frac{1}{2}$ $\left[\because \cos\theta \neq -1, 1, \frac{1}{4}\right]$

$\therefore$ Maximum value of $f(z) = 2\cdot\sqrt{1+\left(\frac{3}{2}\right)\left(\frac{1}{2}\right)(3)} = \sqrt{13}$

• ***Ex. 34*** *Prove that the complex numbers z_1 and z_2 and the origin form an isosceles triangle with vertical angle $\frac{2\pi}{3}$, if $z_1^2 + z_2^2 + z_1z_2 = 0$.*

Sol. Given, $z_1^2 + z_2^2 + z_1z_2 = 0$

$\Rightarrow (z_1 - \omega z_2)(z_1 - \omega^2 z_2) = 0$

$\Rightarrow z_1 = \omega z_2$ or $z_1 = \omega^2 z_2$

In the first case, $|z_1| = |\omega z_2| \Rightarrow |z_1| = |\omega||z_2| \Rightarrow |z_1| = |z_2|$

Hence, two sides equal

$\text{amp}(z_1) = \text{amp}(\omega)z_2 = \text{amp}(\omega) + \text{amp}(z_2)$

$\Rightarrow \text{amp}(z_1) = \frac{2\pi}{3} + \text{amp}(z_2)$

$\Rightarrow \text{amp}(z_1) - \text{amp}(z_2) = \frac{2\pi}{3}$

So, the angle between two sides is $\frac{2\pi}{3}$.

Similarly, the other case

I. Aliter

Given, $z_1^2 + z_2^2 + z_1z_2 = 0$

$\Rightarrow (z_1 - \omega z_2)(z_1 - \omega^2 z_2) = 0$

$\Rightarrow z_1 = \omega z_2$ or $z_1 = \omega^2 z_2$

In the first case, $z_1 = \omega z_2$

$\Rightarrow (z_1 - 0) = (z_2 - 0)e^{2\pi i/3}$ $\left[\because \omega = e^{\frac{2\pi i}{3}}\right]$

$\Rightarrow \overrightarrow{\mathbf{OA}} = \overrightarrow{\mathbf{OB}}e^{2\pi i/3}$

i.e., $\overrightarrow{\mathbf{OA}}$ is obtained by rotating $\mathbf{OB}$ through angle of $\frac{2\pi}{3}$.

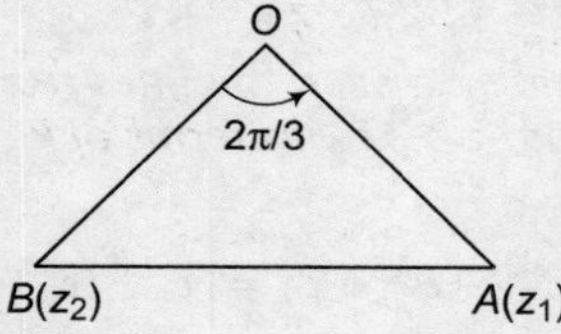

$\Rightarrow OA = OB$ and $\angle AOB = \frac{2\pi}{3}$

Thus, triangle formed by z_1, z_2 and origin is isosceles with vertical angle $\frac{2\pi}{3}$.

II. Aliter

Here, $OA = OB$ ...(i)

From Rotation theorem,

$$\frac{z_1 - 0}{z_2 - 0} = \frac{OA}{OB}e^{2\pi i/3}$$

$\Rightarrow \frac{z_1}{z_2} = \left(\cos\frac{2\pi}{3} + i\sin\frac{2\pi}{3}\right)$ [from Eq. (i)]

$\Rightarrow \frac{z_1}{z_2} = -\frac{1}{2} + \frac{i\sqrt{3}}{2}$

$\Rightarrow \left(\frac{z_1}{z_2} + \frac{1}{2}\right) = \frac{i\sqrt{3}}{2}$ ...(ii)

On squaring both sides in Eq. (ii), we get

$\Rightarrow \frac{z_1^2}{z_2^2} + \frac{1}{4} + \frac{z_1}{z_2} = -\frac{3}{4}$

$\Rightarrow \frac{z_1^2}{z_2^2} + \frac{z_1}{z_2} + 1 = 0$

$\Rightarrow z_1^2 + z_1z_2 + z_2^2 = 0$

$\therefore z_1^2 + z_2^2 + z_1z_2 = 0$

• ***Ex. 35*** *If $\alpha = e^{2\pi i/7}$, where $i = \sqrt{-1}$ and $f(x) = A_0 + \sum_{k=1}^{20} A_k x^k$, then find the value of $f(x) + f(\alpha x) + f(\alpha^2 x) + \ldots + f(\alpha^6 x)$ independent of α.*

Sol. $\because \alpha = e^{2\pi i/7}$

$\therefore \alpha^7 = e^{2\pi i} = \cos 2\pi + i\sin 2\pi = 1 + 0 = 1$ or $\alpha = (1)^{1/7}$

$\therefore 1, \alpha, \alpha^2, \alpha^3, \alpha^4, \alpha^5, \alpha^6$ are the seven, 7th roots of unity.

$\because f(x) = A_0 + \sum_{k=1}^{20} A_k x^k = \sum_{k=0}^{20} A_k x^k$

Now, $f(x) + f(\alpha x) + f(\alpha^2 x) + \ldots + f(\alpha^6 x)$

$$= \sum_{k=0}^{20} A_k x^k [((1)^k + (\alpha)^k + (\alpha^2)^k + \ldots + (\alpha^6)^k]$$

$$= A_0 x^0(7) + A_7 x^7(7) + A_{14}x^{14}(7)$$

$$= 7(A_0 + A_7 x^7 + A_{14}x^{14})$$

$$\left[\because (1)^k + (\alpha)^k + (\alpha^2)^k + \ldots + (\alpha^6)^k = \begin{cases} 7, k \text{ is multiple of } 7 \\ 0, k \text{ is not multiple of } 7 \end{cases}\right]$$

• ***Ex. 36*** *Show that all the roots of the equation $a_1z^3 + a_2z^2 + a_3z + a_4 = 3$, (where $|a_i| \leq 1, i = 1, 2, 3, 4$) lie outside the circle with centre at origin and radius $2/3$.*

Sol. Given that, $a_1z^3 + a_2z^2 + a_3z + a_4 = 3$

We have, $|3| = |a_1z^3 + a_2z^2 + a_3z + a_4|$

$$3 \le |a_1z^3| + |a_2z^2| + |a_3z| + |a_4|$$

$$\Rightarrow \quad 3 \le |a_1||z^3| + |a_2||z^2| + |a_3||z| + |a_4|$$

$$\Rightarrow \quad 3 \le |a_1||z|^3 + |a_2||z|^2 + |a_3||z| + |a_4|$$

$$\Rightarrow \quad 3 \le |z|^3 + |z|^2 + |z| + 1 \quad [\because |a_i| \le 1]$$

$$\Rightarrow \quad 3 \le 1 + |z| + |z|^2 + |z|^3 < 1 + |z| + |z|^2 + |z|^3 + \ldots$$

$$\Rightarrow \quad 3 < 1 + |z| + |z|^2 + |z|^3 + \ldots$$

$$= \frac{1}{1-|z|} \Rightarrow 3 < \frac{1}{1-|z|}$$

$$\Rightarrow \quad 1 - |z| < \frac{1}{3} \Rightarrow \frac{2}{3} - |z| < 0$$

$$\Rightarrow \quad |z| > 2/3 \text{ or } |z - 0| > 2/3$$

Hence, all the roots lie in the exterior of circle, $|z - 0| = 2/3$.

Ex. 37 *If A, B and C represent the complex numbers z_1, z_2 and z_3 respectively on the complex plane and the angles at B and C are each equal to $\frac{1}{2}(\pi - \alpha)$, then prove that $(z_2 - z_3)^2 = 4(z_3 - z_1)(z_1 - z_2)\sin^2\left(\frac{\alpha}{2}\right)$.*

Sol. It is given that,

$$\angle ABC = \angle ACB = \frac{\pi}{2} - \frac{\alpha}{2}$$

$$\Rightarrow \quad \angle A = \alpha$$

$$\therefore \quad AC = AB \quad \ldots(i)$$

So, ΔABC is an isosceles triangle.

Considering rotation of AB about A through angle α, we get

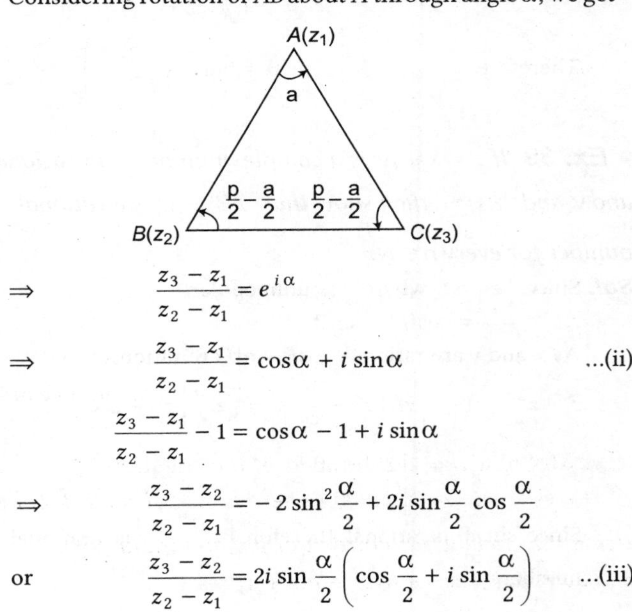

$$\Rightarrow \quad \frac{z_3 - z_1}{z_2 - z_1} = e^{i\alpha}$$

$$\Rightarrow \quad \frac{z_3 - z_1}{z_2 - z_1} = \cos\alpha + i\sin\alpha \quad \ldots(ii)$$

$$\frac{z_3 - z_1}{z_2 - z_1} - 1 = \cos\alpha - 1 + i\sin\alpha$$

$$\Rightarrow \quad \frac{z_3 - z_2}{z_2 - z_1} = -2\sin^2\frac{\alpha}{2} + 2i\sin\frac{\alpha}{2}\cos\frac{\alpha}{2}$$

$$\text{or} \quad \frac{z_3 - z_2}{z_2 - z_1} = 2i\sin\frac{\alpha}{2}\left(\cos\frac{\alpha}{2} + i\sin\frac{\alpha}{2}\right) \quad \ldots(iii)$$

On squaring both sides, we get

$$\frac{(z_3 - z_2)^2}{(z_2 - z_1)^2} = -4\sin^2\frac{\alpha}{2}\left(\cos\frac{\alpha}{2} + i\sin\frac{\alpha}{2}\right)^2$$

$$= -4\sin^2\frac{\alpha}{2}(\cos\alpha + i\sin\alpha)$$

[from De-Moivre's theorem]

$$\frac{(z_3 - z_2)^2}{(z_2 - z_1)^2} = -4\sin^2\frac{\alpha}{2}\left(\frac{z_3 - z_1}{z_2 - z_1}\right) \quad \text{[from Eq. (ii)]}$$

Therefore, $(z_2 - z_3)^2 = 4\sin^2(\alpha/2)(z_3 - z_1)(z_1 - z_2)$

Aliter

$$\because \quad \angle ABC = \left(\frac{\pi}{2} - \frac{\alpha}{2}\right)$$

From Coni method, we have

$$\frac{z_1 - z_2}{z_3 - z_2} = \frac{AB}{BC} e^{i\left(\frac{\pi}{2} - \frac{\alpha}{2}\right)} \quad \ldots(i)$$

$$\text{and} \quad \angle ACB = \left(\frac{\pi}{2} - \frac{\alpha}{2}\right)$$

From Coni method, we have

$$\frac{z_2 - z_3}{z_1 - z_3} = \frac{BC}{AC} e^{i\left(\frac{\pi}{2} - \frac{\alpha}{2}\right)} \quad \ldots(ii)$$

On dividing Eq. (ii) by Eq. (i), we get

$$\frac{(z_2 - z_3)^2}{(z_3 - z_1)(z_1 - z_2)} = \frac{(BC)^2}{AB \cdot AC} = \left(\frac{BC}{AB}\right)^2 \quad [\because AB = AC]$$

$$= \left(\frac{\sin\alpha}{\sin\left(\frac{\pi}{2} - \frac{\alpha}{2}\right)}\right)^2 \quad \text{[using sine rule]}$$

$$= \left(\frac{2\sin\left(\frac{\alpha}{2}\right)\cos\left(\frac{\alpha}{2}\right)}{\cos\left(\frac{\alpha}{2}\right)}\right)^2 = 4\sin^2\left(\frac{\alpha}{2}\right)$$

Therefore, $(z_2 - z_3)^2 = 4(z_3 - z_1)(z_1 - z_2)\sin^2\alpha/2$

Ex. 38 *If z_1 and z_2 are two complex numbers such that $\left|\frac{z_1 - z_2}{z_1 + z_2}\right| = 1$, then prove that $\frac{iz_1}{z_2} = k$, where k is a real number. Find the angle between the lines from the origin to the points $z_1 + z_2$ and $z_1 - z_2$ in terms of k.*

Sol. (i) Given, $\left|\frac{z_1 - z_2}{z_1 + z_2}\right| = 1$

$$\Rightarrow \quad \left|\frac{\frac{z_1}{z_2} - 1}{\frac{z_1}{z_2} + 1}\right| = 1$$

$$\Rightarrow \quad \left|\frac{z_1}{z_2} - 1\right| = \left|\frac{z_1}{z_2} + 1\right| \quad \ldots(i)$$

On squaring Eq. (i) both sides, we have

$$\left|\frac{z_1}{z_2}\right|^2 + 1 - 2\,\text{Re}\left(\frac{z_1}{z_2}\right) = \left|\frac{z_1}{z_2}\right|^2 + 1 + 2\,\text{Re}\left(\frac{z_1}{z_2}\right)$$

$$\Rightarrow \quad 4\,\text{Re}\left(\frac{z_1}{z_2}\right) = 0$$

$\Rightarrow \frac{z_1}{z_2}$ is purely imaginary number

$\Rightarrow \frac{z_1}{z_2}$ can be written as $i\frac{z_1}{z_2} = k$, where k is a real number.

(ii) Let θ be the angle between $z_1 - z_2$ and $z_1 + z_2$, then

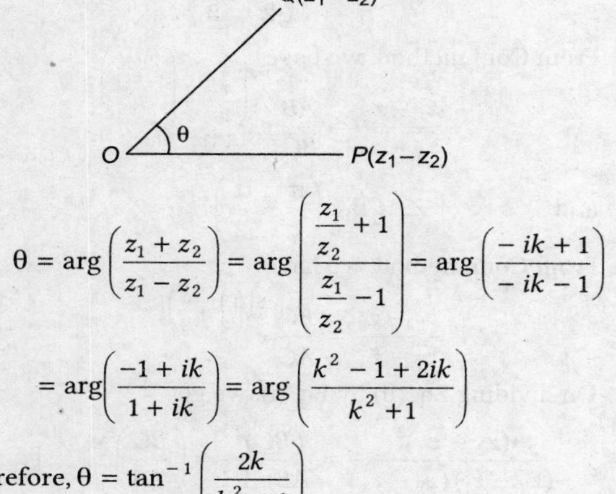

$$\theta = \arg\left(\frac{z_1 + z_2}{z_1 - z_2}\right) = \arg\left(\frac{\frac{z_1}{z_2} + 1}{\frac{z_1}{z_2} - 1}\right) = \arg\left(\frac{-ik + 1}{-ik - 1}\right)$$

$$= \arg\left(\frac{-1 + ik}{1 + ik}\right) = \arg\left(\frac{k^2 - 1 + 2ik}{k^2 + 1}\right)$$

Therefore, $\theta = \tan^{-1}\left(\frac{2k}{k^2 - 1}\right)$

Aliter (i) Given, $\left|\frac{z_1 - z_2}{z_1 + z_2}\right| = 1$ ...(i)

Let $\frac{z_1 - z_2}{z_1 + z_2} = \frac{\cos\alpha + i\sin\alpha}{1}$

$\Rightarrow \frac{(z_1 - z_2) + (z_1 + z_2)}{(z_1 + z_2) - (z_1 - z_2)} = \frac{1 + \cos\alpha + i\sin\alpha}{1 - \cos\alpha - i\sin\alpha}$ [by componendo and dividendo]

$$\Rightarrow \frac{z_1}{z_2} = \frac{2\cos^2\left(\frac{\alpha}{2}\right) + 2i\sin\left(\frac{\alpha}{2}\right)\cos\left(\frac{\alpha}{2}\right)}{2\sin^2\left(\frac{\alpha}{2}\right) - 2i\sin\left(\frac{\alpha}{2}\right)\cos\left(\frac{\alpha}{2}\right)}$$

$$\Rightarrow = \frac{2\cos\left(\frac{\alpha}{2}\right)\left(\cos\left(\frac{\alpha}{2}\right) + i\sin\left(\frac{\alpha}{2}\right)\right)}{-2i\sin\left(\frac{\alpha}{2}\right)\left(\cos\left(\frac{\alpha}{2}\right) + i\sin\left(\frac{\alpha}{2}\right)\right)}$$

$$\Rightarrow \frac{z_1}{z_2} = -\frac{\cot\left(\frac{\alpha}{2}\right)}{i}$$

$$\Rightarrow \frac{iz_1}{z_2} = -\cot\left(\frac{\alpha}{2}\right) = k\text{ (say)} = \text{real}$$

Hence, $\frac{iz_1}{z_2} = k$ ...(ii)

(ii) Now, let the angle between OB and OA be θ, then from Coni method,

$$\frac{z_1 + z_2 - 0}{z_1 - z_2 - 0} = \frac{OB}{OA}e^{i\theta}$$

$$= \left|\frac{z_1 + z_2}{z_1 - z_2}\right| e^{i\theta}$$

$$\Rightarrow \left(\frac{z_1 + z_2}{z_1 - z_2}\right) = e^{i\theta} \quad \text{[from Eq. (i)]}$$

$$\Rightarrow \left(\frac{\frac{z_1}{z_2} + 1}{\frac{z_1}{z_2} - 1}\right) = e^{i\theta} \Rightarrow \frac{-ki + 1}{-ki - 1} = e^{i\theta} \quad \text{[from Eq. (ii)]}$$

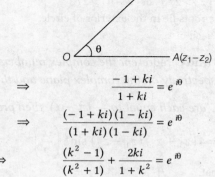

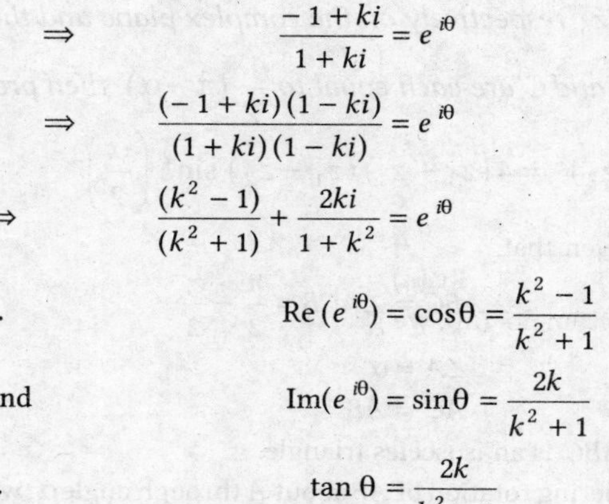

$$\Rightarrow \frac{-1 + ki}{1 + ki} = e^{i\theta}$$

$$\Rightarrow \frac{(-1 + ki)(1 - ki)}{(1 + ki)(1 - ki)} = e^{i\theta}$$

$$\Rightarrow \frac{(k^2 - 1)}{(k^2 + 1)} + \frac{2ki}{1 + k^2} = e^{i\theta}$$

$$\therefore \quad \text{Re}(e^{i\theta}) = \cos\theta = \frac{k^2 - 1}{k^2 + 1}$$

and $\quad \text{Im}(e^{i\theta}) = \sin\theta = \frac{2k}{k^2 + 1}$

$$\therefore \quad \tan\theta = \frac{2k}{k^2 - 1}$$

Therefore, $\quad \theta = \tan^{-1}\left(\frac{2k}{k^2 - 1}\right)$

• Ex. 39 *If $z = x + iy$ is a complex number with rationals x and y and $|z| = 1$, then show that $|z^{2n} - 1|$ is a rational number for every $n \in N$.*

Sol. Since, $|z| = 1$, where z is unimodular

$$\therefore \quad z = \cos\theta + i\sin\theta$$

As x and y are rational, $\cos\theta, \sin\theta$ are rationals

$$\therefore \quad |z^{2n} - 1| = \left|z^n\left(z^n - \frac{1}{z^n}\right)\right| = |z|^n\,|z^n - z^{-n}|$$

$$= 1\,|2i\sin n\theta|$$

$$= 2\,|\sin n\theta|$$

Since, $\sin n\theta$ is rational, therefore $|z^{2n} - 1|$ is a rational number.

Ex. 40 *If a is a complex number such that $|a| = 1$, then find the value of a, so that equation $az^2 + z + 1 = 0$ has one purely imaginary root.*

Sol. We have, $az^2 + z + 1 = 0$ ...(i)

On taking conjugate both sides, we get

$$\overline{az^2 + z + 1} = \overline{0}$$

$$\Rightarrow \quad \bar{a}(\bar{z})^2 + \bar{z} + 1 = 0$$

$$\Rightarrow \quad \bar{a}(-z)^2 + (-z) + 1 = 0$$

[since, z is purely imaginary, $\bar{z} = -z$]

or $\quad \bar{a}z^2 - z + 1 = 0$ ...(ii)

Eliminating z from Eqs. (i) and (ii) by cross-multiplication rule, we get

$$(\bar{a} - a)^2 + 2(a + \bar{a}) = 0$$

On dividing each by 4, we get

$$\left(\frac{\bar{a} - a}{2}\right)^2 + \left(\frac{a + \bar{a}}{2}\right) = 0$$

$$\Rightarrow \quad -\left(\frac{a - \bar{a}}{2i}\right)^2 + \left(\frac{a + \bar{a}}{2}\right) = 0$$

or $\quad -(\text{Im}(a))^2 + \text{Re}(a) = 0$ ...(iii)

Given, $\quad |a| = 1$

Let $\quad a = \cos\alpha + i\sin\alpha$

$\therefore \quad \text{Re}(a) = \cos\alpha, \text{Im}(a) = \sin\alpha$

Then, from Eq. (iii), we get

$$-\sin^2\alpha + \cos\alpha = 0 \text{ or } \cos^2\alpha + \cos\alpha - 1 = 0$$

$$\therefore \quad \cos\alpha = \frac{-1 \pm \sqrt{1 + 4}}{2}$$

Only feasible value of $\cos\alpha = \dfrac{\sqrt{5} - 1}{2}$

Hence, $\quad a = \cos\alpha + i\sin\alpha$

where, $\quad \alpha = \cos^{-1}\left(\dfrac{\sqrt{5} - 1}{2}\right)$

Ex. 41 *If $n \in N > 1$, find the sum of real parts of the roots of the equation $z^n = (z + 1)^n$.*

Sol. The equation $z^n = (z + 1)^n$ will have exactly $n - 1$ roots.

We have,

$$\left(\frac{z + 1}{z}\right)^n = 1 \Rightarrow \left|\left(\frac{z + 1}{z}\right)^n\right| = |1|$$

$$\Rightarrow \quad \frac{|z + 1|}{|z|} = 1$$

$$\Rightarrow \quad |z + 1| = |z|$$

$$\Rightarrow \quad |z - (-1)| = |z - 0|$$

Therefore, z lies on the right bisector of the segment connecting the points $0 + i \cdot 0$ and $-1 + 0 \cdot i$. Thus, $\text{Re}(z) = -1/2$. Hence, roots are collinear and will have their real parts equal to $-1/2$. Hence, sum of the real parts of roots is $\left(-\dfrac{1}{2}(n - 1)\right)$.

Aliter

$$\because \quad z^n = (z + 1)^n$$

$$\Rightarrow \quad \left(\frac{z + 1}{z}\right)^n = 1 \text{ or } \frac{z + 1}{z} = (1)^{1/n}$$

$$= (\cos 0 + i\sin 0)^{1/n}$$

$$= (\cos 2r\pi + i\sin 2r\pi)^{1/n}$$

$$\Rightarrow \quad 1 + \frac{1}{z} = \cos\left(\frac{2r\pi}{n}\right) + i\sin\left(\frac{2r\pi}{n}\right) = e^{2r\pi i/n}$$

or $\quad \dfrac{1}{z} = (e^{2r\pi i/n} - 1) = e^{\frac{r\pi i}{n}} \cdot 2i\sin\left(\dfrac{\pi r}{n}\right)$

or $\quad z = -\left(\dfrac{1}{2}\right)i \cdot \dfrac{1}{\sin\left(\dfrac{\pi r}{n}\right)} \cdot e^{-\frac{\pi r i}{n}}$

$$= -\left(\frac{i}{2}\right) \cdot \frac{\left(\cos\dfrac{\pi r}{n} - i\sin\dfrac{\pi r}{n}\right)}{\sin\dfrac{\pi r}{n}}$$

$\therefore \quad \text{Re}(z) = -\dfrac{1}{2}$ [here $r \neq 0$]

where, $r = 1, 2, 3, \ldots, n - 1$

Sum of real parts of $z = -\dfrac{1}{2} - \dfrac{1}{2} - \dfrac{1}{2} - \ldots - (n - 1)$ times

$$= -\frac{1}{2}(n - 1).$$

Ex. 42 *Prove that the angle between the line $\bar{a}z + a\bar{z} = 0$ and its reflection in the real axis is*

$$\theta = \tan^{-1}\left\{\frac{2\,\text{Re}(a)\,\text{Im}(a)}{\{\text{Im}(a)\}^2 - \{\text{Re}(a)\}^2}\right\}.$$

Sol. Let $z = x + iy$, then equation $\bar{a}z + a\bar{z} = 0$ can be written as

$$(\bar{a} + a)x + i(\bar{a} - a)y = 0$$

$$\Rightarrow \quad \left(\frac{a + \bar{a}}{2}\right)x + \left(\frac{a - \bar{a}}{2i}\right)y = 0$$

$$\Rightarrow \quad \{\text{Re}(a)\}x + \{\text{Im}(a)\}y = 0$$

$\therefore$ Slope of the given line $(m) = -\dfrac{\{\text{Re}(a)\}}{\{\text{Im}(a)\}}$

Then, $\quad \tan(180° - \phi) = -\dfrac{\{\text{Re}(a)\}}{\{\text{Im}(a)\}} \Rightarrow \tan\phi = \dfrac{\{\text{Re}(a)\}}{\{\text{Im}(a)\}}$

Hence, angle between the given line and its reflection in real axis

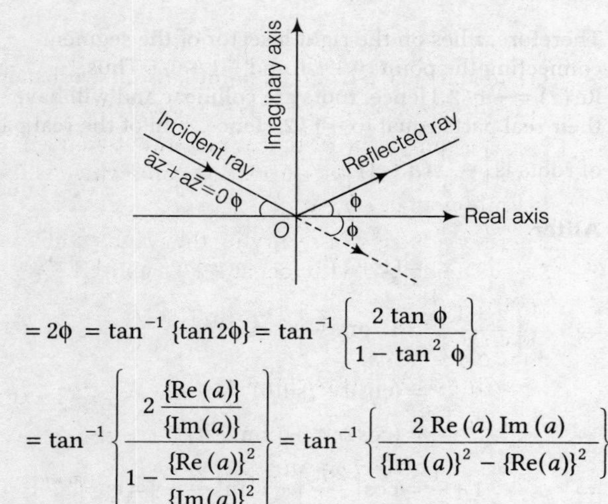

$$= 2\phi = \tan^{-1}\{\tan 2\phi\} = \tan^{-1}\left\{\frac{2\tan\phi}{1-\tan^2\phi}\right\}$$

$$= \tan^{-1}\left\{\frac{2\dfrac{\{\text{Re}(a)\}}{\{\text{Im}(a)\}}}{1-\dfrac{\{\text{Re}(a)\}^2}{\{\text{Im}(a)\}^2}}\right\} = \tan^{-1}\left\{\frac{2\,\text{Re}(a)\,\text{Im}(a)}{\{\text{Im}(a)\}^2-\{\text{Re}(a)\}^2}\right\}$$

● **Ex. 43** *Among the complex numbers z which satisfies $|z-25i| \le 15$, find the complex numbers z having*

(i) least positive argument.

(ii) maximum positive argument.

(iii) least modulus.

(iv) maximum modulus.

Sol. The complex numbers z satisfying the condition

$$|z-25i| \le 15 \qquad \text{...(i)}$$

are represented by the points inside and on the circle of radius 15 and centre at the point C (0, 25).

The complex numbers having least positive argument and maximum positive arguments in this region are the points of contact of tangents drawn from origin to the circle.

Here, θ = Least positive argument

and ϕ = Maximum positive argument

$\therefore$ In ΔOCP, $OP = \sqrt{(OC)^2-(CP)^2} = \sqrt{(25)^2-(15)^2} = 20$

and $\sin\theta = \dfrac{OP}{OC} = \dfrac{20}{25} = \dfrac{4}{5}$

$\therefore \quad \tan\theta = \dfrac{4}{3} \Rightarrow \theta = \tan^{-1}\left(\dfrac{4}{3}\right)$

Thus, complex number at P has modulus 20 and argument $\theta = \tan^{-1}\left(\dfrac{4}{3}\right)$

$\therefore \quad z_P = 20(\cos\theta + i\sin\theta) = 20\left(\dfrac{3}{5}+i\dfrac{4}{5}\right)$

$\therefore \quad z_P = 12+16i$

Similarly, $\quad z_Q = -12+16i$

From the figure, E is the point with least modulus and D is the point with maximum modulus.

Hence, $\quad z_E = \overrightarrow{\mathbf{OE}} = \overrightarrow{\mathbf{OC}} - \overrightarrow{\mathbf{EC}} = 25i-15i = 10i$

and $\quad z_D = \overrightarrow{\mathbf{OD}} = \overrightarrow{\mathbf{OC}} + \overrightarrow{\mathbf{CD}} = 25i+15i = 40i$

● **Ex. 44** *Two different non-parallel lines meet the circle $|z| = r$ in the points a, b and c, d, respectively. Prove that these lines meet in the point z given by $z = \dfrac{a^{-1}+b^{-1}-c^{-1}-d^{-1}}{a^{-1}b^{-1}-c^{-1}d^{-1}}$, where a, b, c, d are complex constants.*

Sol. Let two non-parallel straight lines PQ, RS meet the circle $|z| = r$ in the points a, b and c, d, then $|a| = r, |b| = r, |c| = r$ and $|d| = r$

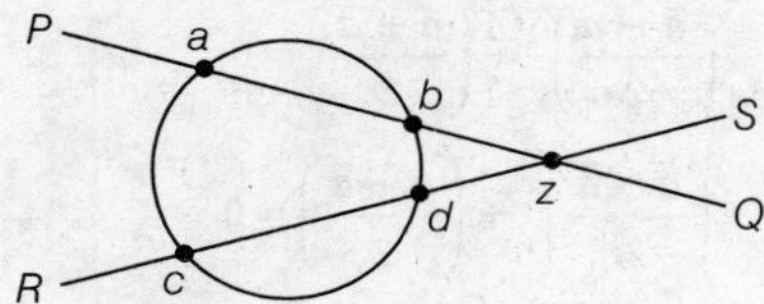

or $\quad |a|^2 = |b|^2 = |c|^2 = |d|^2 = r^2$

$\Rightarrow \quad a\bar{a} = b\bar{b} = c\bar{c} = d\bar{d} = r^2$

$\therefore \quad \bar{a} = \dfrac{r^2}{a}, \bar{b} = \dfrac{r^2}{b}, \bar{c} = \dfrac{r^2}{c}$ and $\bar{d} = \dfrac{r^2}{d}$

For line PQ, points a, b and z are collinear, then

$$\begin{vmatrix} z & \bar{z} & 1 \\ a & \bar{a} & 1 \\ b & \bar{b} & 1 \end{vmatrix} = 0$$

$$\Rightarrow \quad z(\bar{a}-\bar{b}) - \bar{z}(a-b) + (a\bar{b}-\bar{a}b) = 0$$

$$\Rightarrow \quad z\left(\frac{r^2}{a}-\frac{r^2}{b}\right) - \bar{z}(a-b) + \left(\frac{ar^2}{b}-\frac{br^2}{a}\right) = 0$$

On dividing both sides by $(b-a)$, we get

$$\frac{r^2}{ab}z + \bar{z} - \frac{r^2}{ab}(a+b) = 0$$

$$\Rightarrow \quad \frac{z}{ab} + \frac{\bar{z}}{r^2} - \frac{(a+b)}{ab} = 0 \qquad \text{...(i)}$$

Similarly, for line RS, we get

$$\frac{z}{cd} + \frac{\bar{z}}{r^2} - \frac{(c+d)}{cd} = 0 \qquad \text{...(ii)}$$

On subtracting Eq. (ii) from Eq. (i), we get

$$z\left(\frac{1}{ab}-\frac{1}{cd}\right) - \frac{(a+b)}{ab} + \frac{(c+d)}{cd} = 0$$

$$\Rightarrow \quad z(a^{-1}b^{-1}-c^{-1}d^{-1}) = a^{-1}+b^{-1}-c^{-1}-d^{-1}$$

Therefore, $\quad z = \dfrac{a^{-1}+b^{-1}-c^{-1}-d^{-1}}{a^{-1}b^{-1}-c^{-1}d^{-1}}$

• Ex. 45 *If n is an odd integer but not a multiple of 3, then prove that $xy(x+y)(x^2+y^2+xy)$ is a factor of $(x+y)^n - x^n - y^n$.*

Sol. We have, $xy(x+y)(x^2+y^2+xy) = xy(x+y)(x-\omega y)(x-\omega^2 y)$

and let $f(x, y) = (x+y)^n - x^n - y^n$ ...(i)

On putting $x = 0$ in Eq. (i), we get

$$f(0, y) = y^n - 0 - y^n = 0$$

$\therefore$ $x - 0$ is a factor of Eq. (i).

On putting $y = 0$ in Eq. (i), we get

$$f(x, 0) = x^n - x^n = 0$$

$\therefore$ $y - 0$ is a factor of Eq. (i).

On putting $x = -y$ in Eq. (i), we get

$$f(-y, y) = (-y+y)^n - (-y)^n - y^n$$
$$= 0 - (-y)^n - y^n = y^n - y^n = 0 \quad \text{[because } n \text{ is odd]}$$

$\therefore$ $x + y$ is a factor of Eq. (i).

On putting $x = \omega y$ in Eq. (i), we get

$$f(\omega y, y) = (\omega y + y)^n - (\omega y)^n - y^n$$
$$= y^n[(\omega+1)^n - \omega^n - 1]$$
$$= y^n[(-\omega^2)^n - \omega^n - 1)] \quad [\because 1 + \omega + \omega^2 = 0]$$
$$= -y^n\{\omega^{2n} + \omega^n + 1\} \quad \text{[because } n \text{ is odd]}$$

Since, n is odd but not a multiple of 3, then $n = 3k + 1$ or $n = 3k + 2$, where k is an integer.

$\therefore$ $\omega^{2n} + \omega^n + 1 = 0$ [in both cases] ...(ii)

$\therefore$ $f(\omega y, y) = 0$

$\therefore$ $x - \omega y$ is a factor of Eq. (i).

On putting $x = \omega^2 y$ in Eq. (i), we get

$$f(\omega^2 y, y) = (\omega^2 y + y)^n - (\omega^2 y)^n - y^n$$
$$= y^n\{(\omega^2+1)^n - \omega^{2n} - 1\}$$
$$= y^n\{(-\omega)^n - \omega^{2n} - 1\}$$
$$= -y^n\{\omega^n + \omega^{2n} + 1\} \quad \text{[because, } n \text{ is odd]}$$
$$= 0 \quad \text{[from Eq. (ii)]}$$

$\therefore$ $x - \omega^2 y$ is a factor of Eq. (i).

Combining all the factors, we get

$$(x-0)(y-0)(x+y)(x-\omega y)(x-\omega^2 y)$$

Therefore, $xy(x+y)(x^2+xy+y^2)$ is a factor of $f(x, y) = (x+y)^n - x^n - y^n$.

• Ex. 46 *Interpret the following equations geometrically on the Argand plane.*

(i) $|z-1| + |z+1| = 4$ *(ii)* $\arg(z+i) - \arg(z-i) = \frac{\pi}{2}$

(iii) $1 < |z-2-3i| < 4$ *(iv)* $\frac{\pi}{4} < \arg(z) < \frac{\pi}{3}$

(v) $\log_{\cos \pi/3}\left\{\frac{|z-1|+4}{3|z-1|-2}\right\} > 1$

Sol. (i) Since, $|z-1| + |z+1| = 4$

i.e., (distance of z from the point $1 + 0 \cdot i$) + (distance of z from the point $-1 + 0 \cdot i$) = 4 (constant)

i.e., The sum of the distances of z from two fixed points $1 + 0 \cdot i$ and $-1 + 0 \cdot i$ is constant, which is the definition of an ellipse.

Therefore, locus of z satisfying the given condition will be an ellipse with foci at $1 + 0 \cdot i$ and $-1 + 0 \cdot i$ and centre at origin.

(ii) Given that,

$$\arg(z+i) - \arg(z-i) = \frac{\pi}{2}$$

or $$\arg\left(\frac{z+i}{z-i}\right) = \frac{\pi}{2} \quad \text{...(i)}$$

Let the points A and B have affixes i and $-i$ and the point P has affix z. Then, Eq. (i) can be written as

$$\angle BPA = \frac{\pi}{2} \quad \left[\because \angle BPA = \arg\left(\frac{z+i}{z-i}\right)\right]$$

Thus, locus of $P(z)$ is such that the angle subtended at P by the line joining points A and B is $\frac{\pi}{2}$. This is the definition of a circle with diameter AB.

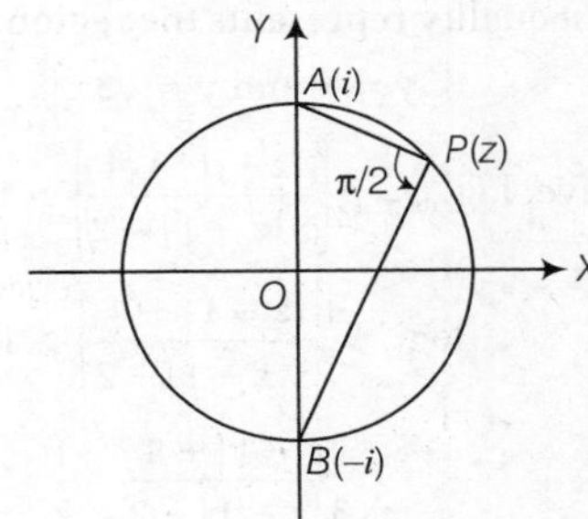

Therefore, locus of point z is a circle with diameter AB and centre at origin with radius 1.

(iii) We have, $1 < |z-2-3i| < 4$ represents a circle with centre at $(2, 3)$ and radius $r \in (1, 4)$.

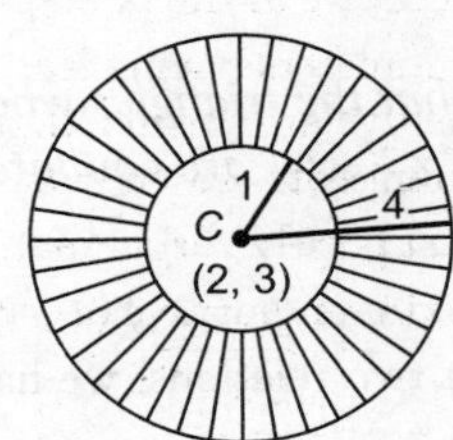

Since, $|z-2-3i| > 1$ represents the region in the plane outside the circle.

$\therefore$ $|z-2-3i| = 1$ ...(i)

and $|z-2-3i| < 4$ represents the region inside circle.

$\therefore$ $|z-2-3i| = 4$ ...(ii)

Hence, $1 < |z-2-3i| < 4$ represent the angular space between the two circles (i) and (ii).

(iv) We have, $\frac{\pi}{4} < \arg(z) < \frac{\pi}{3}$

Let $z = x + iy \Rightarrow \arg(z) = \tan^{-1}\left(\frac{y}{x}\right)$

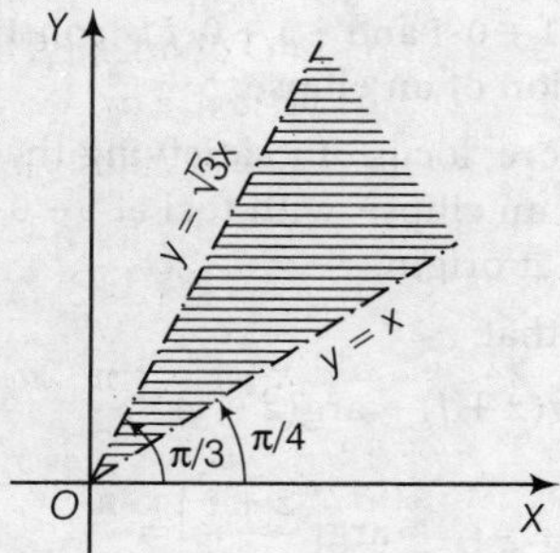

The given inequality can be written as

$$\frac{\pi}{4} < \tan^{-1}\left(\frac{y}{x}\right) < \frac{\pi}{3}$$

$$\Rightarrow \quad \tan\frac{\pi}{4} < \frac{y}{x} < \tan\frac{\pi}{3}$$

$$\Rightarrow \quad 1 < \frac{y}{x} < \sqrt{3}$$

$$\Rightarrow \quad x < y < \sqrt{3}\,x$$

This inequality represents the region between the lines

$$y = x \text{ and } y = \sqrt{3}x$$

(v) We have, $\log_{\cos \pi/3}\left\{\frac{|z-1|+4}{3|z-1|-2}\right\} > 1$

$$\text{or} \quad \log_{1/2}\left\{\frac{|z-1|+4}{3|z-1|-2}\right\} > 1$$

$$\Rightarrow \quad \frac{|z-1|+4}{3|z-1|-2} < \frac{1}{2}$$

$$\text{or} \quad 2|z-1| + 8 < 3|z-1| - 2$$

$$\Rightarrow \quad |z-1| > 10$$

Hence, the inequality represents exterior of a circle of radius 10 with centre at (1, 0).

• ***Ex. 47*** *Show that the triangles whose vertices are z_1, z_2, z_3 and z_1', z_2', z_3' are equilateral, if*

$$(z_1 - z_2)(z_1' - z_2') = (z_2 - z_3)(z_2' - z_3') = (z_3 - z_1)(z_3' - z_1')$$

Sol. From the first two relations, we have

$$\frac{z_1 - z_2}{z_2' - z_3'} = \frac{z_2 - z_3}{z_1' - z_2'}$$

$$= \frac{(z_1 - z_2) + (z_2 - z_3)}{(z_2' - z_3') + (z_1' - z_2')} = \frac{z_1 - z_3}{z_1' - z_3'}$$

$$\therefore \quad \frac{z_1 - z_2}{z_2' - z_3'} = \frac{z_1 - z_3}{z_1' - z_3'} \quad \text{...(i)}$$

Also, from the last two relations

$$(z_2 - z_3)(z_2' - z_3') = (z_3 - z_1)(z_3' - z_1') \quad \text{...(ii)}$$

On multiplying Eqs. (i) and (ii), we get

$$(z_1 - z_2)(z_2 - z_3) = (z_1 - z_3)^2$$

$$\text{or} \quad z_1^2 + z_2^2 + z_3^2 = z_1 z_2 + z_2 z_3 + z_3 z_1$$

Hence, the triangle whose vertices are z_1, z_2 and z_3 is equilateral.

Similarly, it can be shown that the triangle whose vertices are z_1', z_2' and z_3' is also equilateral.

• ***Ex. 48*** *Show that the triangle whose vertices are z_1, z_2, z_3 and z_1', z_2', z_3' are directly similar, if*

$$\begin{vmatrix} z_1 & z_1' & 1 \\ z_2 & z_2' & 1 \\ z_3 & z_3' & 1 \end{vmatrix} = 0.$$

Sol. Let A, B, C be the points of affix z_1, z_2, z_3 and A', B', C' be the points of affix z_1', z_2', z_3'.

Since, the triangles ABC and $A'B'C'$ are similar, if

$$\overrightarrow{\mathbf{BC}} = \lambda\,\overrightarrow{\mathbf{B'C'}}$$

$$\text{i.e.,} \quad (z_3 - z_2) = \lambda(z_3' - z_2') \quad \text{...(i)}$$

$$\text{and} \quad \overrightarrow{\mathbf{CA}} = \lambda\,\overrightarrow{\mathbf{C'A'}}$$

$$\text{i.e.,} \quad (z_1 - z_3) = \lambda(z_1' - z_3') \quad \text{...(ii)}$$

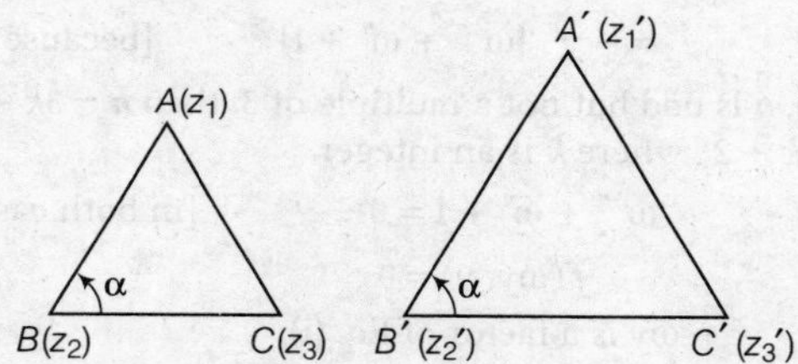

On dividing Eq. (i) by Eq. (ii), we get

$$\frac{z_3 - z_2}{z_1 - z_3} = \frac{z_3' - z_2'}{z_1' - z_3'}$$

$$\Rightarrow \quad z_3(z_1' - z_3') - z_2(z_1' - z_3') = z_1(z_3' - z_2') - z_3(z_3' - z_2')$$

$$\Rightarrow z_1(z_2' - z_3') - z_2(z_1' - z_3') + z_3(z_1' - z_2') = 0$$

$$\text{Hence,} \quad \begin{vmatrix} z_1 & z_1' & 1 \\ z_2 & z_2' & 1 \\ z_3 & z_3' & 1 \end{vmatrix} = 0$$

Aliter

Since, ΔABC and $\Delta A'B'C'$ are similar.

If $\frac{AB}{A'B'} = \frac{BC}{B'C'}$ and $\angle ABC = \angle A'B'C' = \alpha$ [say]

Then, from Coni method in ΔABC and $\Delta A'B'C'$, we have

$$\frac{z_1 - z_2}{z_3 - z_2} = \frac{AB}{BC} e^{i\alpha} \quad \text{...(i)}$$

$$\text{and} \quad \frac{z_1' - z_2'}{z_3' - z_2'} = \frac{A'B'}{B'C'} e^{i\alpha} \quad \text{...(ii)}$$

Since, $\dfrac{AB}{A'B'} = \dfrac{BC}{B'C'} \therefore \dfrac{AB}{BC} = \dfrac{A'B'}{B'C'}$

From Eqs. (i) and (ii), we get $\dfrac{z_1 - z_2}{z_3 - z_2} = \dfrac{z_1' - z_2'}{z_3' - z_2'}$,

On simplifying as in Ist method, we get $\begin{vmatrix} z_1 & z_1' & 1 \\ z_2 & z_2' & 1 \\ z_3 & z_3' & 1 \end{vmatrix} = 0$

Ex. 49 *If ω is the nth root of unity and z_1, z_2 are any two complex numbers, then prove that*

$$\sum_{k=0}^{n-1} \left| z_1 + \omega^k z_2 \right|^2 = n\{|z_1|^2 + |z_2|^2\}, \text{ where } n \in N.$$

Sol. If $1, \omega, \omega^2, \omega^3, \ldots, \omega^{n-1}$ are the n, nth roots of unity, then

$$\sum_{k=0}^{n-1} \omega^k = 0 \text{ and } \sum_{k=0}^{n-1} (\overline{\omega})^k = 0 \quad \ldots(i)$$

$$\text{LHS} = \sum_{k=0}^{n-1} \left| z_1 + \omega^k z_2 \right|^2$$

$$= \sum_{k=0}^{n-1} (z_1 + \omega^k z_2)(\overline{z}_1 + (\overline{\omega})^k \overline{z}_2)$$

$$= \sum_{k=0}^{n-1} \{z_1\overline{z}_1 + z_1\overline{z}_2 (\overline{\omega})^k + \overline{z}_1 z_2 \omega^k + z_2\overline{z}_2 (\omega^k)(\overline{\omega})^k\}$$

$$= \sum_{k=0}^{n-1} |z_1|^2 + \sum_{k=0}^{n-1} z_1\overline{z}_2 (\overline{\omega})^k + \sum_{k=0}^{n-1} \overline{z}_1 z_2 \omega^k + \sum_{k=0}^{n-1} |z_2|^2$$

$$= |z_1|^2 \sum_{k=0}^{n-1} 1 + z_1\overline{z}_2 \sum_{k=0}^{n-1} (\overline{\omega})^k + \overline{z}_1 z_2 \sum_{k=0}^{n-1} (\omega)^k + |z_2|^2 \sum_{k=0}^{n-1} 1$$

$$= n|z_1|^2 + 0 + 0 + n|z|^2 \quad \text{[from Eq. (i)]}$$

$$= n\{|z_1|^2 + |z_2|^2\} = \text{RHS}$$

Ex. 50 *Let $\sum_{i=1}^{4} a_i = 0$ and $\sum_{j=1}^{4} a_j z_j = 0$, then prove that z_1, z_2, z_3 and z_4 are concyclic, if $a_1a_2|z_1 - z_2|^2 = a_3a_4|z_3 - z_4|^2$.*

Sol. $\because \sum_{i=1}^{4} a_i = 0$

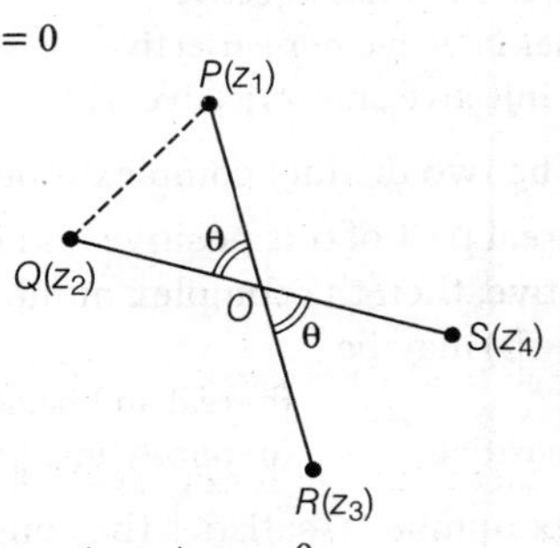

$$\therefore \quad a_1 + a_2 + a_3 + a_4 = 0$$

$$\Rightarrow \quad (a_1 + a_3) = -(a_2 + a_4) \quad \ldots(i)$$

and $\sum_{j=1}^{4} a_j z_j = 0$

$$\therefore \quad a_1z_1 + a_2z_2 + a_3z_3 + a_4z_4 = 0$$

$$\Rightarrow \quad (a_1z_1 + a_3z_3) = -(a_2z_2 + a_4z_4) \quad \ldots(ii)$$

On dividing Eq. (ii) by Eq. (i), we get

$$\frac{a_1z_1 + a_3z_3}{a_1 + a_3} = \frac{a_2z_2 + a_4z_4}{a_2 + a_4} \quad \ldots(iii)$$

Eq. (iii) implies that point O divides PR in the ratio $a_3 : a_1$ and O divides QS in the ratio $a_4 : a_2$.

Let $OR = a_1k$, $OP = a_3k$, $OQ = a_4l$, $OS = a_2l$

Now, in ΔOPQ,

$$(PQ)^2 = (OP)^2 + (OQ)^2 - 2(OP)(OQ)\cos\theta$$

$$\Rightarrow \quad |z_1 - z_2|^2 = a_3^2k^2 + a_4^2l^2 - 2a_3a_4lk\cos\theta$$

$$\therefore \quad a_1a_2|z_1 - z_2|^2 = a_1a_2a_3^2k^2 + a_1a_2a_4^2l^2 - 2a_1a_2a_3a_4lk\cos\theta$$

Similarly, $a_3a_4|z_3 - z_4|^2 = a_3a_4a_1^2k^2 + a_3a_4a_2^2l^2 - 2a_1a_2a_3a_4lk\cos\theta$

From given condition, $a_1a_2|z_1 - z_2|^2 = a_3a_4|z_3 - z_4|^2$

$$\therefore a_1a_2a_3^2k^2 + a_1a_2a_4^2l^2 = a_3a_4a_1^2k^2 + a_3a_4a_2^2l^2$$

$$\Rightarrow \quad k^2a_3a_1(a_2a_3 - a_1a_4) = l^2a_2a_4(a_2a_3 - a_1a_4)$$

$$\Rightarrow \quad (a_1k)(a_3k) = (a_2l)(a_4l)$$

$$\Rightarrow \quad OP \cdot OR = OQ \cdot OS$$

So, P, Q, R and S are concyclic.

Ex. 51 *If α and β are the roots of $z + \frac{1}{z} = 2(\cos\theta + i\sin\theta)$, where $0 < \theta < \pi$ and $i = \sqrt{-1}$, show that $|\alpha - i| = |\beta - i|$.*

Sol. Since, $z + \frac{1}{z} = 2(\cos\theta + i\sin\theta)$

$$\therefore \quad z + \frac{1}{z} = 2e^{i\theta} \Rightarrow z^2 - 2e^{i\theta}z + 1 = 0$$

$$\Rightarrow \quad z = \frac{2e^{i\theta} \pm \sqrt{(4e^{2i\theta} - 4)}}{2}$$

$$\Rightarrow \quad z = e^{i\theta} \pm \sqrt{(e^{2i\theta} - 1)} \Rightarrow z = e^{i\theta} \pm \sqrt{e^{i\theta} \cdot 2i\sin\theta}$$

$$\Rightarrow \quad z - i = e^{i\theta} - i \pm \sqrt{e^{i\theta} \cdot 2i\sin\theta}$$

$$= (e^{i\theta} - e^{i\pi/2}) \pm \sqrt{e^{i(\theta+\pi/2)} \cdot 2\sin\theta}$$

$$= e^{i\left(\frac{\theta}{2}+\frac{\pi}{4}\right)} \cdot 2i\sin\left(\frac{\theta}{2}-\frac{\pi}{4}\right) \pm e^{i(\theta/2+\pi/4)} \cdot \sqrt{2\sin\theta}$$

$$= e^{i(\theta/2+\pi/4)}\left\{2i\sin\left(\frac{\theta}{2}-\frac{\pi}{4}\right) \pm \sqrt{2\sin\theta}\right\}$$

$$\therefore \quad |z - i| = 1 \cdot \sqrt{4\sin^2\left(\frac{\theta}{2}-\frac{\pi}{4}\right) + 2\sin\theta}$$

$$= \sqrt{2\left(1 - \cos\left(\theta - \frac{\pi}{2}\right)\right) + 2\sin\theta}$$

$$= \sqrt{2 - 2\sin\theta + 2\sin\theta} = \sqrt{2}$$

$$\Rightarrow \quad |\alpha - i| = |\beta - i| = \sqrt{2} \quad \text{[here, } \alpha, \beta \text{ are two values of } z - i\text{]}$$

Complex Numbers Exercise 1 :
Single Option Correct Type Questions

- This section contains **30 multiple choice questions.** Each question has four choices (a), (b), (c) and (d) out of which **ONLY ONE** is correct

1. If $\cos(1-i) = a + ib$, where $a, b \in R$ and $i = \sqrt{-1}$, then

(a) $a = \frac{1}{2}\left(e - \frac{1}{e}\right)\cos 1,\ b = \frac{1}{2}\left(e + \frac{1}{e}\right)\sin 1$

(b) $a = \frac{1}{2}\left(e + \frac{1}{e}\right)\cos 1,\ b = \frac{1}{2}\left(e - \frac{1}{e}\right)\sin 1$

(c) $a = \frac{1}{2}\left(e + \frac{1}{e}\right)\cos 1,\ b = \frac{1}{2}\left(e + \frac{1}{e}\right)\sin 1$

(d) $a = \frac{1}{2}\left(e - \frac{1}{e}\right)\cos 1,\ b = \frac{1}{2}\left(e - \frac{1}{e}\right)\sin 1$

2. Number of roots of the equation $z^{10} - z^5 - 992 = 0$, where real parts are negative, is

(a) 3 (b) 4 (c) 5 (d) 6

3. If z and $\bar{z}$ represent adjacent vertices of a regular polygon of n sides with centre at origin and if $\frac{\text{Im}(z)}{\text{Re}(z)} = \sqrt{2} - 1$, the value of n is equal to

(a) 2 (b) 4 (c) 6 (d) 8

4. If $\prod_{p=1}^{r} e^{ip\theta} = 1$, where $\prod$ denotes the continued product and $i = \sqrt{-1}$, the most general value of θ is

(a) $\frac{2n\pi}{r(r-1)}, n \in I$ (b) $\frac{2n\pi}{r(r+1)}, n \in I$

(c) $\frac{4n\pi}{r(r-1)}, n \in I$ (d) $\frac{4n\pi}{r(r+1)}, n \in I$

(where, n is an integer)

5. If $(3+i)(z+\bar{z}) - (2+i)(z-\bar{z}) + 14i = 0$, where $i = \sqrt{-1}$, then $z\bar{z}$ is equal to

(a) 10 (b) 8

(c) -9 (d) -10

6. The centre of a square $ABCD$ is at $z = 0$, A is z_1. Then, the centroid of ΔABC is

(a) $z_1(\cos\pi \pm i\sin\pi)$ (b) $\frac{z_1}{3}(\cos\pi \pm i\sin\pi)$

(c) $z_1\left(\cos\frac{\pi}{2} \pm i\sin\frac{\pi}{2}\right)$ (d) $\frac{z_1}{3}\left(\cos\frac{\pi}{2} \pm i\sin\frac{\pi}{2}\right)$

(where, $i = \sqrt{-1}$)

7. If $z = \frac{\sqrt{3} - i}{2}$, where $i = \sqrt{-1}$, then $(i^{101} + z^{101})^{103}$ equals to

(a) iz (b) z

(c) $\bar{z}$ (d) None of these

8. Let a and b be two fixed non-zero complex numbers and z is a variable complex number. If the lines $a\bar{z} + \bar{a}z + 1 = 0$ and $b\bar{z} + \bar{b}z - 1 = 0$ are mutually perpendicular, then

(a) $ab + \bar{a}\bar{b} = 0$ (b) $ab - \bar{a}\bar{b} = 0$

(c) $\bar{a}b - a\bar{b} = 0$ (d) $a\bar{b} + \bar{a}b = 0$

9. If $\alpha = \cos\left(\frac{8\pi}{11}\right) + i\sin\left(\frac{8\pi}{11}\right)$, where $i = \sqrt{-1}$, then $\text{Re}(\alpha + \alpha^2 + \alpha^3 + \alpha^4 + \alpha^5)$ is

(a) $\frac{1}{2}$ (b) $-\frac{1}{2}$ (c) 0 (d) None of these

10. The set of points in an Argand diagram which satisfy both $|z| \le 4$ and $0 \le \arg(z) \le \frac{\pi}{3}$, is

(a) a circle and a line (b) a radius of a circle

(c) a sector of a circle (d) an infinite part line

11. If $f(x) = g(x^3) + xh(x^3)$ is divisible by $x^2 + x + 1$, then

(a) $g(x)$ is divisible by $(x-1)$ but not $h(x)$

(b) $h(x)$ is divisible by $(x-1)$ but not $g(x)$

(c) both $g(x)$ and $h(x)$ are divisible by $(x-1)$

(d) None of the above

12. If the points represented by complex numbers $z_1 = a + ib$, $z_2 = c + id$ and $z_1 - z_2$ are collinear, where $i = \sqrt{-1}$, then

(a) $ad + bc = 0$ (b) $ad - bc = 0$

(c) $ab + cd = 0$ (d) $ab - cd = 0$

13. Let C denotes the set of complex numbers and R is the set of real numbers. If the function $f : C \to R$ is defined by $f(z) = |z|$, then

(a) f is injective but not surjective

(b) f is surjective but not injective

(c) f is neither injective nor surjective

(d) f is both injective and surjective

14. Let α and β be two distinct complex numbers, such that $|\alpha| = |\beta|$. If real part of α is positive and imaginary part of β is negative, then the complex number $(\alpha + \beta)/(\alpha - \beta)$ may be

(a) zero (b) real and negative

(c) real and positive (d) purely imaginary

15. The complex number z, satisfies the condition $\left|z - \frac{25}{z}\right| = 24$. The maximum distance from the origin of coordinates to the point z, is

(a) 25 (b) 30

(c) 32 (d) None of these

16. The points A, B and C represent the complex numbers $z_1, z_2, (1-i)z_1 + iz_2$ respectively, on the complex plane (where, $i = \sqrt{-1}$). The ΔABC, is

(a) isosceles but not right angled
(b) right angled but not isosceles
(c) isosceles and right angled
(d) None of the above

17. The system of equations $|z+1-i| = \sqrt{2}$ and $|z| = 3$ has (where, $i = \sqrt{-1}$)

(a) no solution (b) one solution
(c) two solutions (d) None of these

18. Dividing $f(z)$ by $z - i$, we obtain the remainder $1 - i$ and dividing it by $z + i$, we get the remainder $1 + i$. Then, the remainder upon the division of $f(z)$ by $z^2 + 1$, is

(a) $i + z$ (b) $1 + z$
(c) $1 - z$ (d) None of these

19. The centre of the circle represented by $|z+1| = 2|z-1|$ on the complex plane, is

(a) 0 (b) $\frac{5}{3}$
(c) $\frac{1}{3}$ (d) None of these

20. If $x = 9^{1/3} \cdot 9^{1/9} \cdot 9^{1/27} \dots \infty$, $y = 4^{1/3} \cdot 4^{-1/9} \cdot 4^{1/27} \dots \infty$ and $z = \sum_{r=1}^{\infty} (1+i)^{-r}$, where $i = \sqrt{-1}$, then $\arg(x + yz)$ is equal to

(a) 0 (b) $-\tan^{-1}\left(\frac{\sqrt{2}}{3}\right)$
(c) $-\tan^{-1}\left(\frac{2}{\sqrt{3}}\right)$ (d) $\pi - \tan^{-1}\left(\frac{\sqrt{2}}{3}\right)$

21. If centre of a regular hexagon is at origin and one of the vertices on Argand diagram is $1 + 2i$, where $i = \sqrt{-1}$, then its perimeter is

(a) $2\sqrt{5}$ (b) $4\sqrt{5}$
(c) $6\sqrt{5}$ (d) $8\sqrt{5}$

22. Let $|z_r - r| \le r, \forall\ r = 1, 2, 3, \dots, n$, then $\left|\sum_{r=1}^{n} z_r\right|$ is less than

(a) n (b) $2n$
(c) $n(n+1)$ (d) $\frac{n(n+1)}{2}$

23. If $\arg\left(\frac{z_1 - \frac{z}{|z|}}{\frac{z}{|z|}}\right) = \frac{\pi}{2}$ and $\left|\frac{z}{|z|} - z_1\right| = 3$, then $|z_1|$ equals to

(a) $\sqrt{3}$ (b) $2\sqrt{2}$ (c) $\sqrt{10}$ (d) $\sqrt{26}$

24. If $|z - 2 - i| = |z| \left|\sin\left(\frac{\pi}{4} - \arg z\right)\right|$, where $i = \sqrt{-1}$, then locus of z, is

(a) a pair of straight lines (b) circle
(c) parabola (d) ellipse

25. If $1, z_1, z_2, z_3, \dots, z_{n-1}$ are the n, nth roots of unity, then the value of $\sum_{r=1}^{n-1} \frac{1}{(3 - z_r)}$, is

(a) $\frac{n \cdot 3^{n-1}}{3^n - 1} + \frac{1}{2}$ (b) $\frac{n \cdot 3^{n-1}}{3^n - 1} - 1$
(c) $\frac{n \cdot 3^{n-1}}{3^n - 1} + 1$ (d) None of these

26. If $z = (3 + 7i)(\lambda + i\mu)$, when $\lambda, \mu \in I \sim \{0\}$ and $i = \sqrt{-1}$, is purely imaginary then minimum value of $|z|^2$ is

(a) 0 (b) 58
(c) $\frac{3364}{3}$ (d) 3364

27. Given, $z = f(x) + ig(x)$, where $i = \sqrt{-1}$ and $f, g : (0, 1) \to (0, 1)$ are real-valued functions, which of the following hold good?

(a) $z = \frac{1}{1 - ix} + i\left(\frac{1}{1 + ix}\right)$ (b) $z = \frac{1}{1 + ix} + i\left(\frac{1}{1 - ix}\right)$
(c) $z = \frac{1}{1 + ix} + i\left(\frac{1}{1 + ix}\right)$ (d) $z = \frac{1}{1 - ix} + i\left(\frac{1}{1 - ix}\right)$

28. If $z^3 + (3 + 2i)z + (-1 + ia) = 0$, where $i = \sqrt{-1}$, has one real root, the value of a lies in the interval ($a \in R$)

(a) $(-2, -1)$ (b) $(-1, 0)$
(c) $(0, 1)$ (d) $(1, 2)$

29. If m and n are the smallest positive integers satisfying the relation $\left(2\, CiS\, \frac{\pi}{6}\right)^m = \left(4\, CiS\, \frac{\pi}{4}\right)^n$, where $i = \sqrt{-1}$, $(m + n)$ equals to

(a) 60 (b) 72 (c) 96 (d) 120

30. Number of imaginary complex numbers satisfying the equation, $z^2 = \bar{z} \cdot 2^{1-|z|}$ is

(a) 0 (b) 1 (c) 2 (d) 3

Complex Numbers Exercise 2 :
More than One Option Correct Type Questions

- This section contains **15 multiple choice questions.** Each question has four choices (a), (b), (c) and (d) out of which **MORE THAN ONE** may be correct.

31. If $\dfrac{z+1}{z+i}$ is a purely imaginary number (where $i=\sqrt{-1}$), then z lies on a
(a) straight line
(b) circle
(c) circle with radius $=\dfrac{1}{\sqrt{2}}$
(d) circle passing through the origin

32. If z satisfies $|z-1|<|z+3|$, then $\omega=2z+3-i$ (where, $i=\sqrt{-1}$) satisfies
(a) $|\omega-5-i|<|\omega+3+i|$ (b) $|\omega-5|<|\omega+3|$
(c) $\text{Im}\,(i\omega)>1$ (d) $|\arg(\omega-1)|<\dfrac{\pi}{2}$

33. If the complex number is $(1+ri)^3=\lambda\,(1+i)$, when $i=\sqrt{-1}$, for some real λ, the value of r can be
(a) $\cos\dfrac{\pi}{5}$ (b) $\text{cosec}\,\dfrac{3\pi}{2}$
(c) $\cot\dfrac{\pi}{12}$ (d) $\tan\dfrac{\pi}{12}$

34. If $z\in C$, which of the following relation(s) represents a circle on an Argand diagram?
(a) $|z-1|+|z+1|=3$ (b) $|z-3|=2$
(c) $|z-2+i|=\dfrac{7}{3}$ (d) $(z-3+i)(\bar{z}-3-i)=5$
(where, $i=\sqrt{-1}$)

35. If $1, z_1, z_2, z_3, \dots, z_{n-1}$ be the n, nth roots of unity and ω be a non-real complex cube root of unity, then $\prod_{r=1}^{n-1}(\omega-z_r)$ can be equal to
(a) $1+\omega$ (b) -1
(c) 0 (d) 1

36. If z is a complex number which simultaneously satisfies the equations
$3|z-12|=5|z-8i|$ and $|z-4|=|z-8|$, where $i=\sqrt{-1}$, then $\text{Im}\,(z)$ can be
(a) 8 (b) 17
(c) 7 (d) 15

37. If $P(z_1)$, $Q(z_2)$, $R(z_3)$ and $S(z_4)$ are four complex numbers representing the vertices of a rhombus taken in order on the complex plane, which one of the following is hold good?
(a) $\dfrac{z_1-z_4}{z_2-z_3}$ is purely real
(b) $\dfrac{z_1-z_3}{z_2-z_4}$ is purely imaginary
(c) $|z_1-z_3|\neq|z_2-z_4|$
(d) $\text{amp}\left(\dfrac{z_1-z_4}{z_2-z_4}\right)\neq\text{amp}\left(\dfrac{z_2-z_4}{z_3-z_4}\right)$

38. If $|z-3|=\min\{|z-1|, |z-5|\}$, then $\text{Re}(z)$ is equal to
(a) 2 (b) 2.5 (c) 3.5 (d) 4

39. If $\arg(z+a)=\dfrac{\pi}{6}$ and $\arg(z-a)=\dfrac{2\pi}{3}$ $(a\in R^+)$, then
(a) $|z|=a$ (b) $|z|=2a$
(c) $\arg(z)=\dfrac{\pi}{3}$ (d) $\arg(z)=\dfrac{\pi}{2}$

40. If $z=x+iy$, where $i=\sqrt{-1}$, then the equation $\left|\dfrac{(2z-i)}{(z+i)}\right|=m$ represents a circle, then m can be
(a) $\dfrac{1}{2}$ (b) 1 (c) 2 (d) $\in(3, 2\sqrt{3})$

41. Equation of tangent drawn to circle $|z|=r$ at the point $A(z_0)$, is
(a) $\text{Re}\left(\dfrac{z}{z_0}\right)=1$ (b) $\text{Im}\left(\dfrac{z}{z_0}\right)=1$
(c) $\text{Im}\left(\dfrac{z_0}{z}\right)=1$ (d) $z\,\bar{z}_0+z_0\,\bar{z}=2r^2$

42. z_1 and z_2 are the roots of the equation $z^2-az+b=0$, where $|z_1|=|z_2|=1$ and a, b are non-zero complex numbers, then
(a) $|a|\le 1$ (b) $|a|\le 2$
(c) $\arg(a)=\arg(b^2)$ (d) $\arg(a^2)=\arg(b)$

43. If α is a complex constant, such that $\alpha z^2+z+\bar{\alpha}=0$ has a real root, then
(a) $\alpha+\bar{\alpha}=1$
(b) $\alpha+\bar{\alpha}=0$
(c) $\alpha+\bar{\alpha}=-1$
(d) the absolute value of real root is 1

44. If the equation $z^3+(3+i)z^2-3z-(m+i)=0$, where $i=\sqrt{-1}$ and $m\in R$, has atleast one real root, value of m is
(a) 1 (b) 2 (c) 3 (d) 5

45. If $z^3+(3+2i)z+(-1+ia)=0$, where $i=\sqrt{-1}$, has one real root, the value of a lies in the interval $(a\in R)$
(a) $(-2, 1)$ (b) $(-1, 0)$ (c) $(0, 1)$ (d) $(-2, 3)$

Complex Numbers Exercise 3 : Passage Based Questions

- This section contains **4 passages**. Based upon each of the passage **3 multiple choice questions** have to be answered. Each of these questions has four choices (a), (b), (c) and (d) out of which **ONLY ONE** is correct.

Passage I

(Q. Nos. 46 to 48)

$\arg(\bar{z}) + \arg(-z) = \begin{cases} \pi, & \text{if } \arg(z) < 0 \\ -\pi, & \text{if } \arg(z) > 0 \end{cases}$, where $-\pi < \arg(z) \le \pi$.

46. If $\arg(z) > 0$, then $\arg(-z) - \arg(z)$ is equal to

(a) $-\pi$ (b) $-\dfrac{\pi}{2}$

(c) $\dfrac{\pi}{2}$ (d) π

47. Let z_1 and z_2 be two non-zero complex numbers, such that $|z_1| = |z_2|$ and $\arg(z_1 z_2) = \pi$, then z_1 is equal to

(a) z_2 (b) $\bar{z}_2$

(c) $-z_2$ (d) $-\bar{z}_2$

48. If $\arg(4z_1) - \arg(5z_2) = \pi$, then $\left|\dfrac{z_1}{z_2}\right|$ is equal to

(a) 1 (b) 1.25

(c) 1.50 (d) 2.50

Passage II

(Q. Nos. 49 to 51)

Sum of four consecutive powers of i (iota) is zero.

i.e., $i^n + i^{n+1} + i^{n+2} + i^{n+3} = 0, \forall n \in I$.

49. If $\sum_{n=1}^{25} i^{n!} = a + ib$, where $i = \sqrt{-1}$, then $a - b$, is

(a) prime number

(b) even number

(c) composite number

(d) perfect number

50. If $\sum_{r=-2}^{95} i^r + \sum_{r=0}^{50} i^{r!} = a + ib$, where $i = \sqrt{-1}$, the unit place digit of $a^{2011} + b^{2012}$, is

(a) 2 (b) 3

(c) 5 (d) 6

51. If $\sum_{r=4}^{100} i^{r!} + \prod_{r=1}^{101} i^r = a + ib$, where $i = \sqrt{-1}$, then $a + 75b$, is

(a) 11 (b) 22

(c) 33 (d) 44

Passage III

(Q. Nos. 52 to 54)

For any two complex numbers z_1 and z_2,

$|z_1 - z_2| \ge \begin{cases} |z_1| - |z_2| \\ |z_2| - |z_1| \end{cases}$

and equality holds iff origin z_1 and z_2 are collinear and z_1, z_2 lie on the same side of the origin.

52. If $\left| z - \dfrac{1}{z} \right| = 2$ and sum of greatest and least values of $|z|$ is λ, then λ^2, is

(a) 2 (b) 4 (c) 6 (d) 8

53. If $\left| z + \dfrac{2}{z} \right| = 4$ and sum of greatest and least values of $|z|$ is λ, then λ^2, is

(a) 12 (b) 18 (c) 24 (d) 30

54. If $\left| z - \dfrac{3}{z} \right| = 6$ and sum of greatest and least values of $|z|$ is 2λ, then λ^2, is

(a) 12 (b) 18 (c) 24 (d) 30

Passage IV

(Q. Nos. 55 to 57)

Consider the two complex numbers z and w, such that $w = \dfrac{z-1}{z+2} = a + ib$, where $a, b \in R$ and $i = \sqrt{-1}$.

55. If $z = C\,iS\,\theta$, which of the following does hold good?

(a) $\sin\theta = \dfrac{9b}{1-4a}$

(b) $\cos\theta = \dfrac{1-5a}{1+4a}$

(c) $(1+5a)^2 + (3b)^2 = (1-4a)^2$

(d) All of these

56. Which of the following is the value of $-\dfrac{b}{a}$, whenever it exists?

(a) $3\tan\left(\dfrac{\theta}{2}\right)$ (b) $\dfrac{1}{3}\tan\left(\dfrac{\theta}{2}\right)$

(c) $-\dfrac{1}{3}\cot\theta$ (d) $3\cot\dfrac{\theta}{2}$

57. Which of the following equals to $|z|$?

(a) $|w|$ (b) $(a+1)^2 + b^2$

(c) $a^2 + (b+2)^2$ (d) $(a+1)^2 + (b+1)^2$

Complex Numbers Exercise 4 : Single Integer Answer Type Questions

- This section contains **10 questions**. The answer to each question is a **single digit integer**, ranging from 0 to 9 (both inclusive).

58. The number of values of z (real or complex) simultaneously satisfying the system of equations

$$1 + z + z^2 + z^3 + \ldots + z^{17} = 0$$
and $$1 + z + z^2 + z^3 + \ldots + z^{13} = 0 \text{ is}$$

59. Number of complex numbers z satisfying $z^3 = \bar{z}$ is

60. Let $z = 9 + ai$, where $i = \sqrt{-1}$ and a be non-zero real.

If $\text{Im}(z^2) = \text{Im}(z^3)$, sum of the digits of a^2 is

61. Number of complex numbers z, such that $|z| = 1$ and $\left|\frac{z}{\bar{z}} + \frac{\bar{z}}{z}\right| = 1$ is

62. If $x = a + ib$, where $a, b \in R$ and $i = \sqrt{-1}$ and $x^2 = 3 + 4i$, $x^3 = 2 + 11i$, the value of $(a + b)$ is

63. If $z = \frac{\pi}{4}(1 + i)^4 \left(\frac{1 - \sqrt{\pi}\, i}{\sqrt{\pi} + i} + \frac{\sqrt{\pi} - i}{1 + \sqrt{\pi}\, i}\right)$, where $i = \sqrt{-1}$, then $\left(\frac{|z|}{\text{amp}(z)}\right)$ equals to

64. Suppose A is a complex number and $n \in N$, such that $A^n = (A + 1)^n = 1$, then the least value of n is

65. Let z_r; $r = 1, 2, 3, \ldots, 50$ be the roots of the equation $\sum_{r=0}^{50} (z)^r = 0$. If $\sum_{r=1}^{50} \frac{1}{(z_r - 1)} = -5\lambda$, then λ equals to

66. If $P = \sum_{p=1}^{32} (3p + 2)\left(\sum_{q=1}^{10}\left(\sin\frac{2q\pi}{11} - i\cos\frac{2q\pi}{11}\right)\right)^p$, where $i = \sqrt{-1}$ and if $(1 + i)P = n(n!)$, $n \in N$, then the value of n is

67. The least positive integer n for which $\left(\frac{1 + i}{1 - i}\right)^n = \frac{2}{\pi}\sin^{-1}\left(\frac{1 + x^2}{2x}\right)$, where $x > 0$ and $i = \sqrt{-1}$ is

Complex Numbers Exercise 5 : Matching Type Questions

- This section contains **4 questions**. Questions 68 and 69 have three statements (A, B and C) given in **Column I** and four statements (p, q, r and s) in **Column II** and questions 70 and 71 have four statements (A, B, C and D) given in **Column I** and five statements (p, q, r, s and t) in **Column II**. Any given statement in **Column I** can have correct matching with one or more statement(s) given in **Column II**.

68.

	Column I		Column II
(A)	If $\left|z - \frac{1}{z}\right| = 2$ and if greatest and least values of $|z|$ are G and L respectively, then $G - L$, is	(p)	natural number
(B)	If $\left|z + \frac{2}{z}\right| = 4$ and if greatest and least values of $|z|$ are G and L respectively, then $G - L$, is	(q)	prime number
(C)	If $\left|z - \frac{3}{z}\right| = 6$ and if greatest and least values of $|z|$ are G and L respectively, then $G - L$, is	(r)	composite number
		(s)	perfect number

69.

	Column I		Column II
(A)	If $\sqrt{(6 + 8i)} + \sqrt{(-6 + 8i)} = z_1, z_2, z_3, z_4$ (where $i = \sqrt{-1}$), then $|z_1|^2 + |z_2|^2 + |z_3|^2 + |z_4|^2$ is divisible by	(p)	7
(B)	If $\sqrt{(5 - 12i)} + \sqrt{(-5 - 12i)} = z_1, z_2, z_3, z_4$ (where $i = \sqrt{-1}$), then $|z_1|^2 + |z_2|^2 + |z_3|^2 + |z_4|^2$ is divisible by	(q)	8
(C)	If $\sqrt{(8 + 15i)} + \sqrt{(-8 - 15i)} = z_1, z_2, z_3, z_4$ (where $i = \sqrt{-1}$), then $|z_1|^2 + |z_2|^2 + |z_3|^2 + |z_4|^2$ is divisible by	(r)	13
		(s)	17

70.

	Column I		Column II
(A)	If λ and μ are the unit's place digits of $(143)^{861}$ and $(5273)^{1358}$ respectively, then $\lambda + \mu$ is divisible by	(p)	2
(B)	If λ and μ are the unit's place digits of $(212)^{7820}$ and $(1322)^{1594}$ respectively, then $\lambda + \mu$ is divisible by	(q)	3
(C)	If λ and μ are the unit's place digits of $(136)^{786}$ and $(7138)^{13491}$ respectively, then $\lambda + \mu$ is divisible by	(r)	4
		(s)	5
		(t)	6

71.

	Column I		Column II
(A)	If $\left\| z - \frac{6}{z} \right\| = 5$ and maximum and minimum values of $\|z\|$ are λ and μ respectively, then	(p)	$\lambda^{\mu} + \mu^{\lambda} = 8$
(B)	If $\left\| z - \frac{7}{z} \right\| = 6$ and maximum and minimum values of $\|z\|$ are λ and μ respectively, then	(q)	$\lambda^{\mu} - \mu^{\lambda} = 7$
(C)	If $\left\| z - \frac{8}{z} \right\| = 7$ and maximum and minimum values of $\|z\|$ are λ and μ respectively, then	(r)	$\lambda^{\mu} + \mu^{\lambda} = 7$
		(s)	$\lambda^{\mu} - \mu^{\lambda} = 6$
		(t)	$\lambda^{\mu} + \mu^{\lambda} = 9$

Complex Numbers Exercise 6 :
Statement I and II Type Questions

- **Directions** (Q. Nos. 72 to 78) are Assertion-Reason type questions. Each of these questions contains two statements:
Statement-1 (Assertion) and **Statement-2** (Reason) Each of these questions also has four alternative choices, only one of which is the correct answer. You have to select the correct choice as given below.
  (a) Statement-1 is true, Statement-2 is true; Statement-2 is a correct explanation for Statement-1
  (b) Statement-1 is true, Statement-2 is true; Statement-2 is not a correct explanation for Statement-1
  (c) Statement1 is true, Statement-2 is false
  (d) Statement-1 is false, Statement-2 is true

72. **Statement-1** $3 + 7i > 2 + 4i$, where $i = \sqrt{-1}$.

Statement-2 $3 > 2$ and $7 > 4$

73. **Statement-1** $(\cos\theta + i\sin\phi)^3 = \cos 3\theta + i \sin 3\phi$, $i = \sqrt{-1}$

Statement-2 $\left(\cos\frac{\pi}{4} + i\sin\frac{\pi}{4}\right)^2 = i$

74. **Statement-1** Let z_1, z_2 and z_3 be three complex numbers, such that $|3z_1 + 1| = |3z_2 + 1| = |3z_3 + 1|$ and $1 + z_1 + z_2 + z_3 = 0$, then z_1, z_2, z_3 will represent vertices of an equilateral triangle on the complex plane.

Statement-2 z_1, z_2 and z_3 represent vertices of an equilateral triangle, if $z_1^2 + z_2^2 + z_3^2 + z_1z_2 + z_2z_3 + z_3z_1 = 0$.

75. **Statement-1** Locus of z satisfying the equation $|z-1| + |z-8| = 5$ is an ellipse.

Statement-2 Sum of focal distances of any point on ellipse is constant for an ellipse.

76. Let z_1, z_2 and z_3 be three complex numbers in AP.

Statement-1 Points representing z_1, z_2 and z_3 are collinear.

Statement-2 Three numbers a, b and c are in AP, if $b - a = c - b$.

77. **Statement-1** If the principal argument of a complex number z is θ, the principal argument of z^2 is 2θ.

Statement-2 $\arg(z^2) = 2\arg(z)$

78. Consider the curves on the Argand plane as

$$C_1 : \arg(z) = \frac{\pi}{4},$$
$$C_2 : \arg(z) = \frac{3\pi}{4}$$

and $C_3 : \arg(z - 5 - 5i) = \pi$, where $i = \sqrt{-1}$.

Statement-1 Area of the region bounded by the curves C_1, C_2 and C_3 is $\frac{25}{2}$.

Statement–2 The boundaries of C_1, C_2 and C_3 constitute a right isosceles triangle.

Complex Numbers Exercise 7 : Subjective Type Questions

- In this section, there are **24 subjective** questions.

79. If z_1, z_2 and z_3 are three complex numbers, then prove that $z_1 \operatorname{Im}(\bar{z}_2 z_3) + z_2 \operatorname{Im}(\bar{z}_3 z_1) + z_3 \operatorname{Im}(\bar{z}_1 z_2) = 0$.

80. The roots z_1, z_2 and z_3 of the equation $x^3 + 3ax^2 + 3bx + c = 0$ in which a, b and c are complex numbers, correspond to the points A, B, C on the Gaussian plane. Find the centroid of the ΔABC and show that it will be equilateral, if $a^2 = b$.

81. If $1, \alpha_1, \alpha_2, \alpha_3$ and α_4 are the roots of $x^5 - 1 = 0$, then prove that

$$\frac{\omega - \alpha_1}{\omega^2 - \alpha_1} \cdot \frac{\omega - \alpha_2}{\omega^2 - \alpha_2} \cdot \frac{\omega - \alpha_3}{\omega^2 - \alpha_3} \cdot \frac{\omega - \alpha_4}{\omega^2 - \alpha_4} = \omega,$$ where ω is a non-real complex root of unity.

82. If z_1 and z_2 both satisfy the relation $z + \bar{z} = 2|z - 1|$ and $\arg(z_1 - z_2) = \frac{\pi}{4}$, find the imaginary part of $(z_1 + z_2)$.

83. If $ax + cy + bz = X, cx + by + az = Y, bx + ay + cz = Z$, show that

(i) $(a^2 + b^2 + c^2 - bc - ca - ab)(x^2 + y^2 + z^2 - yz - zx - xy) = X^2 + Y^2 + Z^2 - YZ - ZX - XY$

(ii) $(a^3 + b^3 + c^3 - 3abc)(x^3 + y^3 + z^3 - 3xyz) = X^3 + Y^3 + Z^3 - 3XYZ$.

84. For every real number $c \ge 0$, find all complex numbers z which satisfy the equation $|z|^2 - 2iz + 2c(1 + i) = 0$, where $i = \sqrt{-1}$.

85. Find the equations of two lines making an angle of 45° with the line $(2 - i)z + (2 + i)\bar{z} + 3 = 0$, where $i = \sqrt{-1}$ and passing through $(-1, 4)$.

86. For $n \ge 2$, show that

$$\left[1+\left(\frac{1+i}{2}\right)\right]\left[1+\left(\frac{1+i}{2}\right)^2\right]\left[1+\left(\frac{1+i}{2}\right)^{2^2}\right]\ldots\left[1+\left(\frac{1+i}{2}\right)^{2^n}\right] = (1+i)\left(1-\frac{1}{2^{2^n}}\right),$$ where $i = \sqrt{-1}$.

87. Find the point of intersection of the curves $\arg(z - 3i) = 3\pi/4$ and $\arg(2z + 1 - 2i) = \frac{\pi}{4}$, where $i = \sqrt{-1}$.

88. Show that if a and b are real, then the principal value of $\arg(a)$ is 0 or π, according as a is positive or negative and that of b is $\frac{\pi}{2}$ or $-\frac{\pi}{2}$, according as b is positive or negative.

89. Two different non-parallel lines meet the circle $|z| = r$. One of them at points a and b and the other which is tangent to the circle at c. Show that the point of intersection of two lines is $\frac{2c^{-1} - a^{-1} - b^{-1}}{c^{-2} - a^{-1}b^{-1}}$.

90. A, B and C are the points representing the complex numbers z_1, z_2 and z_3 respectively, on the complex plane and the circumcentre of ΔABC lies at the origin. If the altitude of the triangle through the vertex A meets the circumcircle again at P, prove that P represents the complex number $\left(-\frac{z_2 z_3}{z_1}\right)$.

91. If $|z| \le 1$ and $|\omega| \le 1$, show that $|z - \omega|^2 \le (|z| - |\omega|)^2 + \{\arg(z) - \arg(\omega)\}^2$.

92. Let z, z_0 be two complex numbers. It is given that $|z| = 1$ and the numbers $z, z_0, z\bar{z}_0, 1$ and 0 are represented in an Argand diagram by the points P, P_0, Q, A and the origin, respectively. Show that ΔPOP_0 and ΔAOQ are congruent. Hence, or otherwise, prove that $|z - z_0| = |z\bar{z}_0 - 1|$.

93. Suppose the points $z_1, z_2, \ldots, z_n$ $(z_i \ne 0)$ all lie on one side of a line drawn through the origin of the complex planes. Prove that the same is true of the points $\frac{1}{z_1}, \frac{1}{z_2}, \ldots, \frac{1}{z_n}$. Moreover, show that

$$z_1 + z_2 + \ldots + z_n \ne 0 \text{ and } \frac{1}{z_1} + \frac{1}{z_2} + \ldots + \frac{1}{z_n} \ne 0.$$

94. If a, b and c are complex numbers and z satisfies $az^2 + bz + c = 0$, prove that $|a||b| = \sqrt{a(\bar{b})^2 c}$ and $|a| = |c| \Leftrightarrow |z| = 1$.

95. Let z_1, z_2 and z_3 be three non-zero complex numbers and $z_1 \ne z_2$. If $\begin{vmatrix} |z_1| & |z_2| & |z_3| \\ |z_2| & |z_3| & |z_1| \\ |z_3| & |z_1| & |z_2| \end{vmatrix} = 0$, prove that

(i) z_1, z_2, z_3 lie on a circle with the centre at origin.

(ii) $\arg\left(\frac{z_3}{z_2}\right) = \arg\left(\frac{z_3 - z_1}{z_2 - z_1}\right)^2$.

96. Prove that, if z_1 and z_2 are two complex numbers and $c > 0$, then $|z_1 + z_2|^2 \le (1+c)|z_1|^2 + \left(1 + \frac{1}{c}\right)|z_2|^2$.

97. Find the circumcentre of the triangle whose vertices are given by the complex numbers z_1, z_2 and z_3.

98. Find the orthocentre of the triangle whose vertices are given by the complex numbers z_1, z_2 and z_3.

99. Prove that the roots of the equation $8x^3 - 4x^2 - 4x + 1 = 0$ are $\cos\frac{\pi}{7}$, $\cos\frac{3\pi}{7}$ and $\cos\frac{5\pi}{7}$.

Hence, obtain the equations whose roots are

(i) $\sec^2\frac{\pi}{7}, \sec^2\frac{3\pi}{7}, \sec^2\frac{5\pi}{7}$

(ii) $\tan^2\frac{\pi}{7}, \tan^2\frac{3\pi}{7}, \tan^2\frac{5\pi}{7}$

(iii) Evaluate $\sec\frac{\pi}{7} + \sec\frac{3\pi}{7} + \sec\frac{5\pi}{7}$

100. Solve the equation $z^7 + 1 = 0$ and deduce that

(i) $\cos\frac{\pi}{7}\cos\frac{3\pi}{7}\cos\frac{5\pi}{7} = -\frac{1}{8}$

(ii) $\cos\frac{\pi}{14}\cos\frac{3\pi}{14}\cos\frac{5\pi}{14} = \frac{\sqrt{7}}{8}$

(iii) $\sin\frac{\pi}{14}\sin\frac{3\pi}{14}\sin\frac{5\pi}{14} = \frac{1}{8}$

(iv) $\tan\frac{\pi}{14}\tan\frac{3\pi}{14}\tan\frac{5\pi}{14} = \frac{1}{\sqrt{7}}$

Also, show that

$$(1+y)^7 + (1-y)^7 = 14\left(y^2 + \tan^2\frac{\pi}{14}\right)\left(y^2 + \tan^2\frac{3\pi}{14}\right)\left(y^2 + \tan^2\frac{5\pi}{14}\right)$$

and then deduce that

$$\tan^2\left(\frac{\pi}{14}\right) + \tan^2\left(\frac{3\pi}{14}\right) + \tan^2\left(\frac{5\pi}{14}\right) = 5$$

101. If the complex number z is to satisfy $|z| = 3, |z - \{a(1+i) - i\}| \le 3$ and $|z + 2a - (a+1)i| > 3$, where $i = \sqrt{-1}$ simultaneously for atleast one z, then find all $a \in R$.

102. Write equations whose roots are equal to numbers

(i) $\sin^2\frac{\pi}{2n+1}, \sin^2\frac{2\pi}{2n+1}, \sin^2\frac{3\pi}{2n+1}, \ldots, \sin^2\frac{n\pi}{2n+1}$.

(ii) $\cot^2\frac{\pi}{2n+1}, \cot^2\frac{2\pi}{2n+1}, \cot^2\frac{3\pi}{2n+1}, \ldots, \cot^2\frac{n\pi}{2n+1}$.

Complex Numbers Exercise 8 : Questions Asked in Previous 13 Years' Exams

- This section contains questions asked in **IIT-JEE, AIEEE, JEE Main & JEE Advanced** from year **2005** to year **2017**.

103. If ω is a cube root of unity but not equal to 1, then minimum value of $|a + b\omega + c\omega^2|$, (where a, b and c are integers but not all equal), is **[IIT-JEE 2005, 3M]**

(a) 0 (b) $\frac{\sqrt{3}}{2}$ (c) 1 (d) 2

104. PQ and PR are two infinite rays. QAR is an arc. Point lying in the shaded region excluding the boundary satisfies **[IIT-JEE 2005, 3M]**

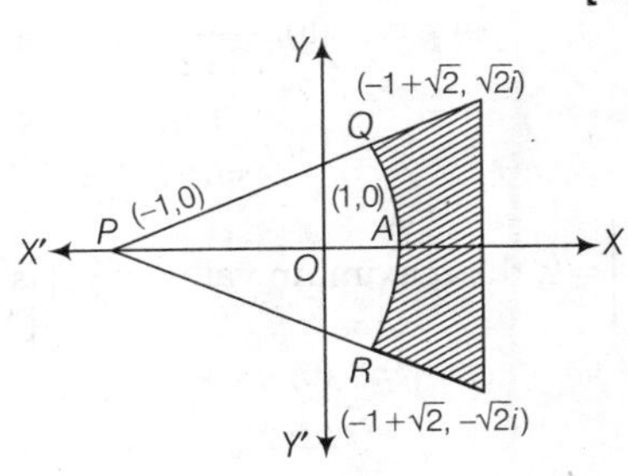

(a) $|z-1| > 2; |\arg(z-1)| < \frac{\pi}{4}$

(b) $|z-1| > 2; |\arg(z-1)| < \frac{\pi}{2}$

(c) $|z+1| > 2; |\arg(z+1)| < \frac{\pi}{4}$

(d) $|z+1| > 2; |\arg(z+1)| < \frac{\pi}{3}$

105. If one of the vertices of the square circumscribing the circle $|z-1| = \sqrt{2}$ is $2 + \sqrt{3}i$, where $i = \sqrt{-1}$. Find the other vertices of the square. **[IIT-JEE 2005, 4M]**

106. If z_1 and z_2 are two non-zero complex numbers, such that $|z_1 + z_2| = |z_1| + |z_2|$, then $\arg(z_1) - \arg(z_2)$ is equal to **[AIEEE 2005, 3M]**

(a) $-\pi$ (b) $-\pi/2$
(c) $\pi/2$ (d) 0

107. If $1, \omega, \omega^2$ are the cube roots of unity, then the roots of the equation $(x-1)^3 + 8 = 0$ are **[AIEEE 2005, 3M]**

(a) $-1, 1+2\omega, 1+2\omega^2$ (b) $-1, 1-2\omega, 1-2\omega^2$
(c) $-1, -1, -1$ (d) None of these

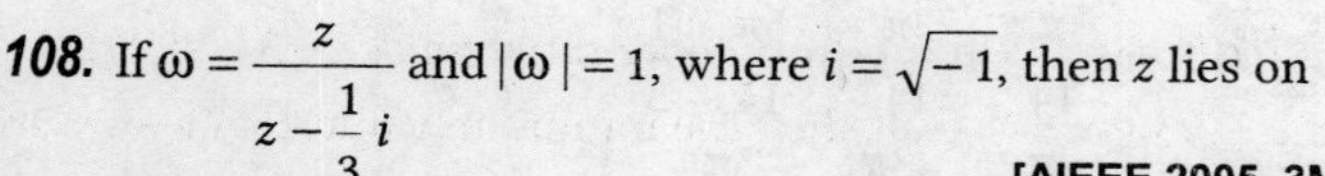

108. If $\omega = \dfrac{z}{z - \frac{1}{3}i}$ and $|\omega| = 1$, where $i = \sqrt{-1}$, then z lies on **[AIEEE 2005, 3M]**

(a) a straight line (b) a parabola
(c) an ellipse (d) a circle

109. If $\omega = \alpha + i\beta$, where $\beta \neq 0$, $i = \sqrt{-1}$ and $z \neq 1$, satisfies the condition that $\left(\dfrac{\omega - \bar{\omega} z}{1 - z}\right)$ is purely real, the set of values of z is **[IIT-JEE 2006, 3M]**

(a) $\{z : |z| = 1\}$ (b) $\{z : z = \bar{z}\}$
(c) $\{z : z \neq 1\}$ (d) $\{z : |z| = 1, z \neq 1\}$

110. The value of $\sum_{k=1}^{10}\left(\sin\dfrac{2k\pi}{11} + i\cos\dfrac{2k\pi}{11}\right)$ (where $i = \sqrt{-1}$) is **[AIEEE 2006, 3M]**

(a) i (b) 1
(c) -1 (d) $-i$

111. If $z^2 + z + 1 = 0$, where z is a complex number, the value of $\left(z + \dfrac{1}{z}\right)^2 + \left(z^2 + \dfrac{1}{z^2}\right)^2 + \left(z^3 + \dfrac{1}{z^3}\right)^2 + \ldots + \left(z^6 + \dfrac{1}{z^6}\right)^2$ is **[AIEEE 2006, 6M]**

(a) 18 (b) 54
(c) 6 (d) 12

112. A man walks a distance of 3 units from the origin towards the North-East (N 45° E) direction. From there, he walks a distance of 4 units towards the North-West (N 45° W) direction to reach a point P. Then, the position of P in the Argand plane, is **[IIT-JEE 2007, 3M]**

(a) $3e^{i\pi/4} + 4i$ (b) $(3 - 4i)e^{i\pi/4}$
(c) $(4 + 3i)e^{i\pi/4}$ (d) $(3 + 4i)e^{i\pi/4}$
(where $i = \sqrt{-1}$)

113. If $|z| = 1$ and $z \neq \pm 1$, then all the values of $\dfrac{z}{1 - z^2}$ lie on **[IIT-JEE 2007, 3M]**

(a) a line not passing through the origin
(b) $|z| = \sqrt{2}$
(c) the X-axis
(d) the Y-axis

114. If $|z + 4| \leq 3$, the maximum value of $|z + 1|$ is **[AIEEE 2007, 3M]**

(a) 4 (b) 10
(c) 6 (d) 0

Passage (Q. Nos. 115 to 117)

Let A, B and C be three sets of complex numbers as defined below:
$A = \{z : \text{Im}(z) \geq 1\}$
$B = \{z : |z - 2 - i| = 3\}$
$C = \{z : \text{Re}((1 - i)z) = \sqrt{2}\}$, where $i = \sqrt{-1}$
[IIT-JEE 2008, 4+4+4M]

115. The number of elements in the set $A \cap B \cap C$, is

(a) 0 (b) 1
(c) 2 (d) ∞

116. Let z be any point in $A \cap B \cap C$. Then, $|z + 1 - i|^2 + |z - 5 - i|^2$ lies between

(a) 25 and 29 (b) 30 and 34
(c) 35 and 39 (d) 40 and 44

117. Let z be any point in $A \cap B \cap C$ and ω be any point satisfying $|\omega - 2 - i| < 3$. Then, $|z| - |\omega| + 3$ lies between

(a) -6 and 3 (b) -3 and 6
(c) -6 and 6 (d) -3 and 9

118. A particle P starts from the point $z_0 = 1 + 2i$, $i = \sqrt{-1}$. It moves first horizontally away from origin by 5 units and then vertically away from origin by 3 units to reach a point z_1. From z_1, the particle moves $\sqrt{2}$ units in the direction of the vector $\hat{\mathbf{i}} + \hat{\mathbf{j}}$ and then it moves through an angle $\dfrac{\pi}{2}$ in anti-clockwise direction on a circle with centre at origin, to reach a point z_2, then the point z_2 is given by **[IIT-JEE 2008, 3M]**

(a) $6 + 7i$ (b) $-7 + 6i$
(c) $7 + 6i$ (d) $-6 + 7i$

119. If the conjugate of a complex numbers is $\dfrac{1}{i - 1}$, where $i = \sqrt{-1}$. Then, the complex number is **[AIEEE 2008, 3M]**

(a) $\dfrac{-1}{i - 1}$ (b) $\dfrac{1}{i + 1}$
(c) $\dfrac{-1}{i + 1}$ (d) $\dfrac{1}{i - 1}$

120. Let $z = x + iy$ be a complex number, where x and y are integers and $i = \sqrt{-1}$. Then, the area of the rectangle whose vertices are the roots of the equation $z\bar{z}^3 + \bar{z}z^3 = 350$, is **[IIT-JEE 2009, 3M]**

(a) 48 (b) 32
(c) 40 (d) 80

121. Let $z = \cos\theta + i\sin\theta$, where $i = \sqrt{-1}$. Then the value of $\sum_{m=1}^{15} \text{Im}(z^{2m-1})$ at $\theta = 2°$ is **[IIT-JEE 2009, 3M]**

(a) $\dfrac{1}{\sin 2°}$ (b) $\dfrac{1}{3\sin 2°}$
(c) $\dfrac{1}{2\sin 2°}$ (d) $\dfrac{1}{4\sin 2°}$

122. If $\left|z - \dfrac{4}{z}\right| = 2$, the maximum value of $|z|$ is equal to **[AIEEE 2009, 4M]**

(a) $2 + \sqrt{2}$ (b) $\sqrt{3} + 1$
(c) $\sqrt{5} + 1$ (d) 2

123. Let z_1 and z_2 be two distinct complex numbers and $z = (1-t) z_1 + iz_2$, for some real number t with $0 < t < 1$ and $i = \sqrt{-1}$. If arg (w) denotes the principal argument of a non-zero complex number w, then **[IIT-JEE 2010, 3M]**

(a) $|z - z_1| + |z - z_2| = |z_1 - z_2|$
(b) $\arg(z - z_1) = \arg(z - z_2)$
(c) $\begin{vmatrix} z - z_1 & \bar{z} - \bar{z}_1 \\ z_2 - z_1 & \bar{z}_2 - \bar{z}_1 \end{vmatrix} = 0$
(d) $\arg(z - z_1) = \arg(z_2 - z_1)$

124. Let ω be the complex number $\cos\frac{2\pi}{3} + i\sin\frac{2\pi}{3}$, where $i = \sqrt{-1}$, then the number of distinct complex numbers z satisfying $\begin{vmatrix} z+1 & \omega & \omega^2 \\ \omega & z+\omega^2 & 1 \\ \omega^2 & 1 & z+\omega \end{vmatrix} = 0$, is equal to **[IIT-JEE 2010, 3M]**

(a) 0
(b) 1
(c) 2
(d) 3

125. Match the statements in **Column I** with those in **Column II**.

[**Note** Here, z takes values in the complex plane and Im (z) and Re (z) denote respectively, the imaginary part and the real part of z.] **[IIT- JEE 2010, 8M]**

	Column I		Column II
(A)	The set of points z satisfying $\lvert z - i\lvert z\rvert\rvert = \lvert z + i\lvert z\rvert\rvert$, where $i = \sqrt{-1}$, is contained in or equal to	(p)	an ellipse with eccentricity 4/5
(B)	The set of points z satisfying $\lvert z+4\rvert + \lvert z-4\rvert = 10$ is contained in or equal to	(q)	the set of points z satisfying Im $(z) = 0$
(C)	If $\lvert w\rvert = 2$, the set of points $z = w - \frac{1}{w}$ is contained in or equal to	(r)	the set of points z satisfying $\lvert\text{Im}(z)\rvert \le 1$
(D)	If $\lvert w\rvert = 1$, the set of points $z = w + \frac{1}{w}$ is contained in or equal to	(s)	the set of points satisfying $\lvert\text{Re}(z)\rvert \le 2$
		(t)	the set of points z satisfying $\lvert z\rvert \le 3$

126. If α and β are the roots of the equation $x^2 - x + 1 = 0$, $\alpha^{2009} + \beta^{2009}$ is equal to **[AIEEE 2010, 4M]**

(a) -1
(b) 1
(c) 2
(d) -2

127. The number of complex numbers z, such that $|z-1| = |z+1| = |z-i|$, where $i = \sqrt{-1}$, equals to **[AIEEE 2010, 4M]**

(a) 1
(b) 2
(c) ∞
(d) 0

128. If z is any complex number satisfying $|z - 3 - 2i| \le 2$, where $i = \sqrt{-1}$, then the minimum value of $|2z - 6 + 5i|$, is **[IIT-JEE 2011, 4M]**

129. The set $\left\{\text{Re}\left(\frac{2iz}{1-z^2}\right) : z \text{ is a complex number } |z| = 1, z \ne \pm 1\right\}$ is **[IIT-JEE 2011, 2M]**

(a) $(-\infty, -1] \cap [1, \infty)$
(b) $(-\infty, 0) \cup (0, \infty)$
(c) $(-\infty, -1) \cup (1, \infty)$
(d) $[2, \infty)$

130. The maximum value of $\left|\arg\left(\frac{1}{1-z}\right)\right|$ for $|z| = 1, z \ne 1$, is given by **[IIT-JEE 2011, 2M]**

(a) $\frac{\pi}{6}$
(b) $\frac{\pi}{3}$
(c) $\frac{\pi}{2}$
(d) $\frac{2\pi}{3}$

131. Let $w = e^{i\pi/3}$, where $i = \sqrt{-1}$ and a, b, c, x, y and z be non-zero complex numbers such that

$$a + b + c = x$$
$$a + bw + cw^2 = y$$
$$a + bw^2 + cw = z.$$

The value of $\frac{|x|^2 + |y|^2 + |z|^2}{|a|^2 + |b|^2 + |c|^2}$, is **[IIT-JEE 2011, 4M]**

132. Let α and β be real and z be a complex number. If $z^2 + \alpha z + \beta = 0$ has two distinct roots on the line Re $(z) = 1$, then it is necessary that **[AIEEE 2011, 4M]**

(a) $\beta \in (-1, 0)$
(b) $|\beta| = 1$
(c) $\beta \in (1, \infty)$
(d) $\beta \in (0, 1)$

133. If $\omega (\ne 1)$ is a cube root of unity and $(1+\omega)^7 = A + B\omega$, then (A, B) equals to **[AIEEE 2011, 4M]**

(a) (1, 1)
(b) (1, 0)
(c) (−1, 1)
(d) (0, 1)

134. Let z be a complex number such that the imaginary part of z is non-zero and $a = z^2 + z + 1$ is real. Then, a **cannot** take the value **[IIT-JEE 2012, 3M]**

(a) -1
(b) $\frac{1}{3}$
(c) $\frac{1}{2}$
(d) $\frac{3}{4}$

135. If $z \ne 1$ and $\frac{z^2}{z-1}$ is real, the point represented by the complex number z lies **[AIEEE 2012, 4M]**

(a) on a circle with centre at the origin
(b) either on the real axis or on a circle not passing through the origin
(c) on the imaginary axis
(d) either on the real axis or on a circle passing through the origin

136. If z is a complex number of unit modulus and argument θ, then $\arg\left(\frac{1+z}{1+\bar{z}}\right)$ equals to **[JEE Main 2013, 4M]**

(a) $\frac{\pi}{2}-\theta$ (b) θ

(c) $\pi-\theta$ (d) $-\theta$

137. Let complex numbers α and $\frac{1}{\bar{\alpha}}$ lie on circles $(x-x_0)^2+(y-y_0)^2=r^2$ and $(x-x_0)^2+(y-y_0)^2=4r^2$, respectively. If $z_0=x_0+iy_0$ satisfies the equation $2|z_0|^2=r^2+2$, then $|\alpha|$ equals to **[JEE Advanced 2013, 2M]**

(a) $\frac{1}{\sqrt{2}}$ (b) $\frac{1}{2}$ (c) $\frac{1}{\sqrt{7}}$ (d) $\frac{1}{3}$

138. Let $w=\frac{\sqrt{3}+i}{2}$ and $P=\{w^n: n=1,2,3,\ldots\}$. Further,
$H_1=\left\{z\in C:\text{Re}(z)>\frac{1}{2}\right\}$ and $H_2=\left\{z\in C:\text{Re}(z)<\left(-\frac{1}{2}\right)\right\}$,
where C is the set of all complex numbers. If $z_1\in P\cap H_1$, $z_2\in P\cap H_2$ and O represents the origin, then $\angle z_1Oz_2$ equals to **[JEE Advanced 2013, 3M]**

(a) $\frac{\pi}{2}$ (b) $\frac{\pi}{6}$

(c) $\frac{2\pi}{3}$ (d) $\frac{5\pi}{6}$

Passage (Q. Nos. 139 to 140)

Let $S=S_1\cap S_2\cap S_3$, where

$S_1=\{z\in C:|z|<4\}$,

$S_2=\left\{z\in C:\text{Im}\left[\frac{z-1+\sqrt{3}i}{1-\sqrt{3}i}\right]>0\right\}$

and $S_3=\{z\in C:\text{Re }z>0\}$. **[JEE Advanced 2013, 3+3M]**

139. $\min_{z\in S}|1-3i-z|$ equals to

(a) $\frac{2-\sqrt{3}}{2}$ (b) $\frac{2+\sqrt{3}}{2}$

(c) $\frac{3-\sqrt{3}}{2}$ (d) $\frac{3+\sqrt{3}}{2}$

140. Area of S equals to

(a) $\frac{10\pi}{3}$ (b) $\frac{20\pi}{3}$

(c) $\frac{16\pi}{3}$ (d) $\frac{32\pi}{3}$

141. If z is a complex number such that $|z|\geq 2$, then the minimum value of $\left|z+\left(\frac{1}{2}\right)\right|$, is **[JEE Main 2014, 4M]**

(a) is strictly greater than $\frac{5}{2}$

(b) is equal to $\frac{5}{2}$

(c) is strictly greater than $\frac{3}{2}$ but less than $\frac{5}{2}$

(d) lies in the interval (1, 2)

142. Let $z_k=\cos\left(\frac{2k\pi}{10}\right)+i\sin\left(\frac{2k\pi}{10}\right)$; $k=1,2,\ldots,9$. Then, match the column.

	Column I		Column II
(A)	For each z_k there exists a z_j such that $z_k\cdot z_j=1$	(1)	True
(B)	There exists a $k\in\{1,2,\ldots,9\}$ such that $z_1\cdot z=z_k$ has no solution z in the set of complex numbers	(2)	False
(C)	$\frac{|1-z_1||1-z_2|\ldots|1-z_9|}{10}$ equals to	(3)	1
(D)	$1-\sum_{k=1}^{9}\cos\left(\frac{2k\pi}{10}\right)$ equals to	(4)	2

[JEE Advanced 2014, 3M]

Codes

	A	B	C	D		A	B	C	D
(a)	1	2	4	3	(b)	2	1	3	4
(c)	1	2	3	4	(d)	2	1	4	3

143. A complex number z is said to be unimodular if $|z|=1$. Suppose z_1 and z_2 are complex numbers such that $\frac{z_1-2z_2}{2-z_1\bar{z}_2}$ is unimodular and z_2 is not unimodular. Then the point z_1 lies on a **[JEE Main 2015, 4M]**

(a) circle of radius z

(b) circle of radius $\sqrt{2}$

(c) straight line parallel to X-axis

(d) straight line parallel to Y-axis

144. Let $\omega\neq 1$ be a complex cube root of unity. If $(3-3\omega+2\omega^2)^{4n+3}+(2+3\omega-3\omega^2)^{4n+3}+(-3+2\omega+3\omega^2)^{4n+3}=0$, then possible value(s) of n is (are) **[JEE Advanced 2015, 2M]**

(a) 1 (b) 2

(c) 3 (d) 4

145. For any integer k, let $\alpha_k=\cos\left(\frac{k\pi}{7}\right)+i\sin\left(\frac{k\pi}{7}\right)$, where $i=\sqrt{-1}$. The value of the expression $\frac{\sum_{k=1}^{12}|\alpha_{k+1}-\alpha_k|}{\sum_{k=1}^{3}|\alpha_{4k-1}-\alpha_{4k-2}|}$ is **[JEE Advanced 2015, 4M]**

146. A value of θ for which $\dfrac{2+3i\sin\theta}{1-2i\sin\theta}$ is purely imaginary, is **[JEE Main 2016, 4M]**

(a) $\dfrac{\pi}{6}$ (b) $\sin^{-1}\left(\dfrac{\sqrt{3}}{4}\right)$

(c) $\sin^{-1}\left(\dfrac{1}{\sqrt{3}}\right)$ (d) $\dfrac{\pi}{3}$

147. Let $a, b \in R$ and $a^2 + b^2 \neq 0$.

Suppose $S = \left\{z \in C : z = \dfrac{1}{a+ibt}, t \in R, t \neq 0\right\}$, where $i = \sqrt{-1}$. If $z = x + iy$ and $z \in S$, then (x, y) lies on **[JEE Advanced 2016 4M]**

(a) the circle with radius $\dfrac{1}{2a}$ and centre $\left(\dfrac{1}{2a}, 0\right)$ for $a > 0, b \neq 0$

(b) the circle with radius $-\dfrac{1}{2a}$ and centre $\left(-\dfrac{1}{2a}, 0\right)$ for $a < 0, b \neq 0$

(c) the X-axis for $a \neq 0, b = 0$

(d) the Y-axis for $a = 0, b \neq 0$

148. Let ω be a complex number such that $2\omega + 1 = z$, when $z = \sqrt{-3}$ if $\begin{vmatrix} 1 & 1 & 1 \\ 1 & -\omega^2 - 1 & \omega^2 \\ 1 & \omega^2 & \omega^7 \end{vmatrix} = 3k$, then k is equal to **[JEE Main 2017, 4M]**

(a) 1 (b) $-z$ (c) z (d) -1

Answers

Exercise for Session 1

1. (d) 2. (c) 3. (b) 4. (b) 5. (c) 6. (b) 7. (d) 8. (a)

Exercise for Session 2

1. (b) 2. (b) 3. (b) 4. (b) 5. (b) 6. (b) 7. (d) 8. (c) 9. (b) 10. (b) 11. (a) 12. (c) 13. (c) 14. (a)

Exercise for Session 3

1. (a) 2. (b) 3. (d) 4. (a) 5. (b) 6. (a) 7. (c) 8. (b) 9. (c) 10. (d) 11. (c) 12. (a) 13. (b) 14. (b) 15. (a)

Exercise for Session 4

1. (a) 2. (d) 3. (c) 4. (d) 5. (b) 6. (b) 7. (a) 8. (d) 9. (d) 10. (b) 11. (b) 12. (a) 13. (b) 14. (c)

Chapter Exercises

1. (b) 2. (c) 3. (d) 4. (d) 5. (a) 6. (d) 7. (b) 8. (d) 9. (b) 10. (c) 11. (c) 12. (b) 13. (c) 14. (d) 15. (a) 16. (c) 17. (a) 18. (c) 19. (b) 20. (b) 21. (c) 22. (c) 23. (c) 24. (c) 25. (d) 26. (d) 27. (b) 28. (b) 29. (b) 30. (c)

31. (b,c,d) 32. (b,c,d) 33. (b,c,d) 34. (b,c,d) 35. (a,c,d) 36. (a,b) 37. (a,b,c) 38. (a,d) 39. (a,c) 40. (a,b,d) 41. (a,d) 42. (b,d) 43. (a,c,d) 44. (a,d) 45. (a,b,d)

46. (a) 47. (d) 48. (b) 49. (a) 50. (c) 51. (b) 52. (d) 53. (c) 54. (a) 55. (c) 56. (d) 57. (b) 58. (1) 59. (5) 60. (9) 61. (8) 62. (3) 63. (4) 64. (6) 65. (5) 66. (4) 67. (4)

68. A $\to$ (p, q); B $\to$ (p, r); C $\to$ (p, r, s)

69. A $\to$ (q); B $\to$ (q, r); C $\to$ (q, s)

70. A $\to$ (p, q, r, t); B $\to$ (p, s); C $\to$ (p, r)

71. A $\to$ (r); B $\to$ (p, s); C $\to$ (q, t)

72. (d) 73. (d) 74. (c) 75. (d) 76. (a) 77. (d) 78. (d)

82. 2

84. $z = c + i(-1 \pm \sqrt{(1 - c^2 - 2c)})$ for $0 \leq c \leq \sqrt{2} - 1$ and no solution for $c > \sqrt{2} - 1$

85. $(1-3i)z + (1+3i)\bar{z} - 22 = 0$ and $(3+i)z + (3-i)\bar{z} + 14 = 0$

87. No solution 97. $\dfrac{\sum |z_1|^2 (z_2 - z_3)}{\sum \overline{z_1}(z_2 - z_3)}$

98. $\dfrac{\sum z_1^2(\bar{z}_2 - \bar{z}_3) + \sum |z_1|^2 (z_2 - z_3)}{\sum (z_1 \overline{z_2} - z_2 \overline{z_1})}$

99. (i) $x^3 - 24x^2 + 80x - 64 = 0$

(ii) $x^3 - 21x^2 + 35x - 7 = 0$

(iii) 4

100. Roots of $z^7 + 1 = 0$ are $-1, \alpha, \alpha^3, \alpha^5, \bar{\alpha}, \bar{\alpha}^3, \bar{\alpha}^5$, where $\alpha = \cos\dfrac{\pi}{7} + i\sin\dfrac{\pi}{7}$

101. $a \in \left(\dfrac{1-\sqrt{71}}{2}, \dfrac{-1-4\sqrt{11}}{5}\right) \cup \left(\dfrac{-1+4\sqrt{11}}{5}, \dfrac{1+\sqrt{71}}{2}\right)$

102. (i) ${}^{2n+1}C_1(1-x)^n - {}^{2n+1}C_3(1-x)^{n-1}x + \ldots + (-1)^n x^n = 0$

(ii) ${}^{2n+1}C_1 x^n - {}^{2n+1}C_3 x^{n-1} + {}^{2n+1}C_5 x^{n-2} - \ldots = 0$

103. (c) 104. (c) 105. $(1-\sqrt{3}) + i, -i\sqrt{3}, (\sqrt{3}+1) - i$ 106. (d)

107. (b) 108. (a) 109. (d) 110. (d) 111. (d) 112. (d) 113. (d) 114. (c) 115. (b) 116. (c) 117. (d) 118. (d) 119. (c) 120. (a) 121. (d) 122. (c) 123. (a, c, d) 124. (b)

125. A $\to$ (q, r); B $\to$ (p); C $\to$ (p, s); D $\to$ (q, r, s, t) 126. (b) 127. (a)

128. (5) 129. (a) 130. (c) 131. (3) 132. (c) 133. (a) 134. (d) 135. (d) 136. (b) 137. (c) 138. (c) 139. (c) 140. (b) 141. (d) 142. (c) 143. (a) 144. (a, b, d) 145. (4) 146. (c) 147. (a,c,d) 148. (b)

Solutions

1. We have,

$$a + ib = \cos(1 - i) = \cos 1 \cos i + \sin 1 \sin i$$
$$= \cos 1 \cosh 1 + \sin 1\, i \sinh 1$$
$$[\because \cos i = \cosh 1, \sin i \cdot 1 = i \sinh 1]$$
$$= \cos 1 \left(\frac{e + e^{-1}}{2}\right) + i \sin 1 \left(\frac{e - e^{-1}}{2}\right)$$
$$= \frac{1}{2}\left(e + \frac{1}{e}\right) \cos 1 + i \cdot \frac{1}{2}\left(e - \frac{1}{e}\right) \sin 1$$

$$\therefore \quad a = \frac{1}{2}\left(e + \frac{1}{e}\right) \cos 1$$

and $$b = \frac{1}{2}\left(e - \frac{1}{e}\right) \sin 1$$

2. Given that, $z^{10} - z^5 - 992 = 0$

Let $$t = z^5$$

$$\Rightarrow \quad t^2 - t - 992 = 0$$

$$\Rightarrow \quad t = \frac{1 \pm \sqrt{1 + 3968}}{2} = \frac{1 \pm 63}{2} = 32, -31$$

$$\therefore \quad z^5 = 32$$

and $$z^5 = -31$$

But the real part is negative, therefore $z^5 = 32$ does not hold.

$\therefore$ Number of solutions is 5.

3. From Coni method,

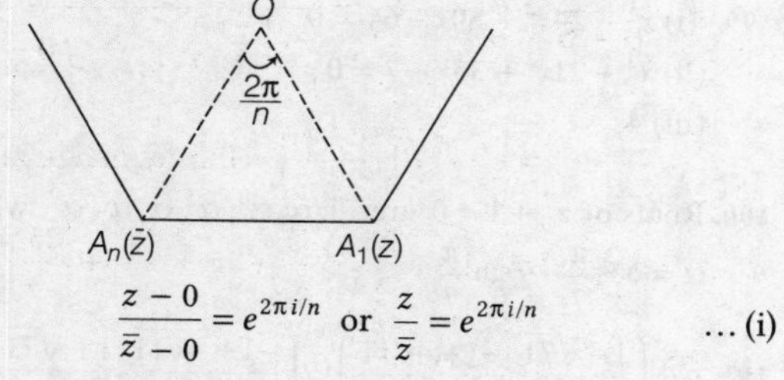

$$\frac{z - 0}{\bar{z} - 0} = e^{2\pi i/n} \text{ or } \frac{z}{\bar{z}} = e^{2\pi i/n} \quad \dots \text{(i)}$$

But given $$\frac{\text{Im}(z)}{\text{Re}(z)} = \sqrt{2} - 1$$

$$\Rightarrow \quad \frac{\frac{z - \bar{z}}{2i}}{\frac{z + \bar{z}}{2}} = \sqrt{2} - 1 \Rightarrow \frac{1}{i}\left(\frac{\frac{z}{\bar{z}} - 1}{\frac{z}{\bar{z}} + 1}\right) = \sqrt{2} - 1$$

$$\Rightarrow \quad \left(\frac{e^{2\pi i/n} - 1}{e^{2\pi i/n} + 1}\right) = i(\sqrt{2} - 1) \quad \text{[from Eq. (i)]}$$

$$\Rightarrow \quad i \tan\left(\frac{\pi}{n}\right) = i(\sqrt{2} - 1)$$

$$\Rightarrow \quad \tan\left(\frac{\pi}{n}\right) = \tan\left(\frac{\pi}{8}\right)$$

$$\therefore \quad n = 8$$

4. We have, $\prod_{p=1}^{r} e^{ip\theta} = 1$

$$\Rightarrow \quad e^{i\theta} \cdot e^{2i\theta} \cdot e^{3i\theta} \dots e^{ri\theta} = 1$$

$$\Rightarrow \quad e^{i\theta(1 + 2 + 3 + \dots + r)} = 1 \Rightarrow e^{i\theta\left(\frac{r(r+1)}{2}\right)} = 1$$

$$\text{or } \cos\left\{\frac{r(r+1)}{2}\theta\right\} + i \sin\left\{\frac{r(r+1)}{2}\theta\right\} = 1 + i \cdot 0$$

On comparing, we get

$$\cos\left\{\frac{r(r+1)}{2}\theta\right\} = 1 \text{ and } \sin\left\{\frac{r(r+1)}{2}\theta\right\} = 0$$

$$\Rightarrow \quad \frac{r(r+1)}{2}\theta = 2m\pi \text{ and } \frac{r(r+1)}{2}\theta = m_1\pi$$

$$\Rightarrow \quad \theta = \frac{4m\pi}{r(r+1)} \text{ and } \theta = \frac{2m_1\pi}{r(r+1)}$$

where, $m, m_1 \in I$

Hence, $\theta = \dfrac{4n\pi}{r(r+1)}, n \in I.$

5. Let $z = x + iy$, then

$(3 + i)(z + \bar{z}) - (2 + i)(z - \bar{z}) + 14i = 0$ reduces to

$$(3 + i)\, 2x - (2 + i)(2iy) + 14i = 0$$

$$\Rightarrow \quad 6x + 2y + i(2x - 4y + 14) = 0$$

On comparing real and imaginary parts, we get

$$6x + 2y = 0$$

$$\Rightarrow \quad 3x + y = 0 \quad \dots\text{(i)}$$

and $$2x - 4y + 14 = 0$$

$$\Rightarrow \quad x - 2y + 7 = 0 \quad \dots\text{(ii)}$$

On solving Eqs. (i) and (ii), we get

$$x = -1 \text{ and } y = 3$$

$$\therefore \quad z = -1 + 3i$$

$$\therefore \quad z\bar{z} = |z|^2 = |-1 + 3i|^2 = (-1)^2 + (3)^2 = 10$$

6. Since, affix of A is z_1.

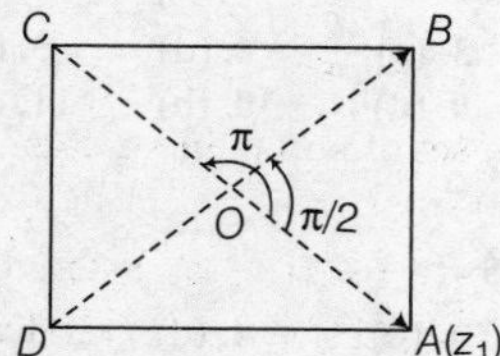

$\therefore \overrightarrow{\mathbf{OA}} = z_1$ and $\overrightarrow{\mathbf{OB}}$ and $\overrightarrow{\mathbf{OC}}$ are obtained by rotating $\overrightarrow{\mathbf{OA}}$ through $\frac{\pi}{2}$ and π. Therefore, $\overrightarrow{\mathbf{OB}} = iz_1$ and $\overrightarrow{\mathbf{OC}} = -z_1$.

Hence, centroid of $\Delta ABC = \dfrac{z_1 + iz_1 + (-z_1)}{3}$

$$= \frac{i}{3} z_1 = \frac{z_1}{3}\left(\cos\frac{\pi}{2} + i \sin\frac{\pi}{2}\right)$$

If A, B and C are taken in clockwise, then centroid of ΔABC

$$= \frac{1}{3} z_1 \left(\cos\frac{\pi}{2} - i \sin\frac{\pi}{2}\right)$$

$$\therefore \quad \text{Centroid of } \Delta ABC = \frac{z_1}{3}\left(\cos\frac{\pi}{2} \pm i \sin\frac{\pi}{2}\right)$$

7. Given that, $z = \frac{\sqrt{3} - i}{2} = i\left(\frac{-1 - i\sqrt{3}}{2}\right) = i\omega^2$

$\therefore \quad z^{101} = (i\omega^2)^{101} = i^{101}\,\omega^{202} = i\omega$

Now, $i^{101} + z^{101} = i + i\omega = i(-\omega^2)$

$\therefore \quad (i^{101} + z^{101})^{103} = -\,i^{103}\,\omega^{206} = -\,i^3\,\omega^2 = i\omega^2 = z$

8. The complex slope of the line $a\bar{z} + \bar{a}z + 1 = 0$ is $\alpha = -\frac{a}{\bar{a}}$

and the complex slope of the line $b\bar{z} + \bar{b}z - 1 = 0$ is $\beta = -\frac{b}{\bar{b}}$

Since, both lines are mutually perpendicular, then

$$\therefore \quad \alpha + \beta = 0$$

$$\Rightarrow \quad -\frac{a}{\bar{a}} - \frac{b}{\bar{b}} = 0$$

$$\Rightarrow \quad a\bar{b} + \bar{a}b = 0$$

9. We have, $\alpha = \cos\left(\frac{8\pi}{11}\right) + i\sin\left(\frac{8\pi}{11}\right)$

Now, Re $(\alpha + \alpha^2 + \alpha^3 + \alpha^4 + \alpha^5)$

$$= \frac{\alpha + \alpha^2 + \alpha^3 + \alpha^4 + \alpha^5 + \bar{\alpha} + \bar{\alpha}^2 + \bar{\alpha}^3 + \bar{\alpha}^4 + \bar{\alpha}^5}{2}$$

$$= \frac{-1 + (1 + \alpha + \alpha^2 + \alpha^3 + \alpha^4 + \alpha^5 + \bar{\alpha} + \bar{\alpha}^2 + \bar{\alpha}^3 + \bar{\alpha}^4 + \bar{\alpha}^5}{2}$$

$$= \frac{-1 + 0}{2} \quad \text{[sum of 11, 11th roots of unity]}$$

$$= -\frac{1}{2}$$

10. $$|z| \le 4 \quad \ldots(\text{i})$$

and $$0 \le \arg(z) \le \frac{\pi}{3} \quad \ldots(\text{ii})$$

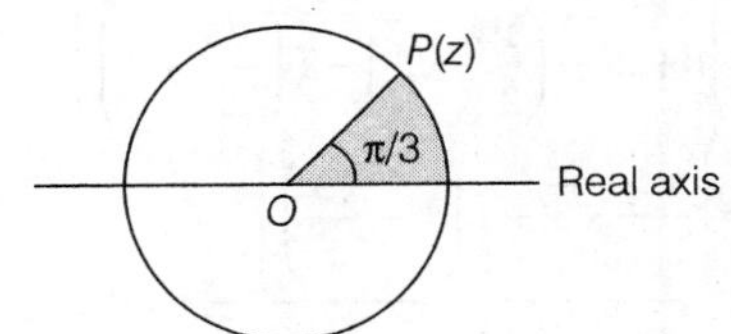

which implies the set of points in an argand plane, is a sector of a circle.

11. Since, $x^2 + x + 1 = (x - \omega)(x - \omega^2)$, where ω is the cube root of unity and $f(x) = g(x^3) + x\,h(x^3)$ is divisible by $x^2 + x + 1$. Therefore, ω and ω^2 are the roots of $f(x) = 0$.

$$\Rightarrow \quad f(\omega) = 0 \text{ and } f(\omega^2) = 0$$

$$\Rightarrow \quad g(\omega^3) + \omega\,h(\omega^3) = 0$$

$$\text{and} \quad g((\omega^2)^3) + \omega^2 h(\omega^2)^3 = 0$$

$$\Rightarrow \quad g(1) + \omega\,h(1) = 0$$

$$\text{and} \quad g(1) + \omega^2 h(1) = 0$$

$$\Rightarrow \quad g(1) = h(1) = 0$$

Hence, $g(x)$ and $h(x)$ both are divisible by $(x - 1)$.

12. Since, z_1, z_2 and $z_1 - z_2$ are collinear.

$$\therefore \quad \begin{vmatrix} z_1 & \bar{z}_1 & 1 \\ z_2 & \bar{z}_2 & 1 \\ z_1 - z_2 & \overline{z_1 - z_2} & 1 \end{vmatrix} = 0$$

$$\Rightarrow \quad \begin{vmatrix} z_1 & \bar{z}_1 & 1 \\ z_2 & \bar{z}_2 & 1 \\ z_1 - z_2 & \bar{z}_1 - \bar{z}_2 & 1 \end{vmatrix} = 0$$

Applying $R_3 \to R_3 - R_1 + R_2$, then $\begin{vmatrix} z_1 & \bar{z}_1 & 1 \\ & & \vdots \\ z_2 & \bar{z}_2 & 1 \\ & & \vdots \\ 0\ldots & 0 & \ldots 1 \end{vmatrix} = 0$

Expand w.r.t. R_3, then

$$z_1\bar{z}_2 - \bar{z}_1 z_2 = 0$$

$$\Rightarrow \quad z_1\bar{z}_2 - (\overline{z_1\bar{z}_2}) = 0$$

$$\Rightarrow \quad \text{Im}\,(z_1\bar{z}_2) = 0$$

$$\Rightarrow \quad \text{Im}\,((a + ib)\,\overline{(c + id)}) = 0$$

$$\Rightarrow \quad \text{Im}\,((a + ib)(c - id)) = 0$$

$$\Rightarrow \quad bc - ad = 0 \Rightarrow ad - bc = 0$$

13. Let $z = a + ib$

$\therefore f(a + ib) = \sqrt{(a^2 + b^2)}$

$$\Rightarrow \quad f(z) = f(\bar{z}) = f(-z) = f(-\bar{z}) = \sqrt{(a^2 + b^2)}$$

$\therefore$ f is not injective (i.e., it is many-one).

but $|z| > 0$ i.e. $f(z) > 0 \Rightarrow f(z) \in R^+$ (Range)

$\Rightarrow R^+ \subset R$

$\therefore$ f is not surjective (i.e., into).

Hence, f is neither injective nor surjective.

14. Let $\alpha = re^{i\theta}, \beta = re^{i\phi}$ $\quad [\because |\alpha| = |\beta|, \text{given}]$

where, $\theta \in \left(-\frac{\pi}{2}, \frac{\pi}{2}\right)$ and $\phi \in (-\pi, 0)$

$$\therefore \quad \frac{\alpha + \beta}{\alpha - \beta} = \frac{re^{i\theta} + re^{i\phi}}{re^{i\theta} - re^{i\phi}} = \frac{e^{i\left(\frac{\theta + \phi}{2}\right)} \cdot 2\cos\left(\frac{\theta - \phi}{2}\right)}{e^{i\left(\frac{\theta + \phi}{2}\right)} \cdot 2i\sin\left(\frac{\theta - \phi}{2}\right)}$$

$$= -i\cot\left(\frac{\theta - \phi}{2}\right) = \text{Purely imaginary}$$

15. We have, $|z| = \left|z + \frac{25}{z} - \frac{25}{z}\right| \le \left|z + \frac{25}{z}\right| + \left|\frac{25}{-z}\right|$

$$\Rightarrow \quad |z| \le 24 + \frac{25}{|z|}$$

$$\Rightarrow |z|^2 - 24|z| - 25 \le 0 \Rightarrow (|z| - 25)(|z| + 1) \le 0$$

$$\therefore \quad |z| - 25 \le 0 \quad [\because |z| + 1 > 0]$$

$$\Rightarrow \quad |z| \le 25 \text{ or } |z - 0| \le 25$$

Hence, the maximum distance from the origin of coordinates to the point z is 25.

16. $\because \quad A \equiv z_1, B \equiv z_2, C \equiv (1 - i)\,z_1 + iz_2$

$$\therefore \quad AB = |z_1 - z_2|$$

$$BC = |z_2 - (1 - i)\,z_1 - iz_2| = |(1 - i)(z_2 - z_1)|$$

$$= \sqrt{2}\,|z_1 - z_2|$$

and $$CA = |(1 - i)\,z_1 + iz_2 - z_1| = |-i\,(z_1 - z_2)|$$

$$= |-i||z_1 - z_2| = |z_1 - z_2|$$

It is clear that, $AB = CA$ and $(AB)^2 + (CA)^2 = (BC)^2$

$\therefore$ $\Delta\, ABC$ is isosceles and right angled.

17. Centre and radius of circle $|z| = 3$ ...(i)

are $C_1 \equiv 0,\ r_1 = 3$

and centre and radius of circle

$|z + 1 - i| = \sqrt{2}$ ...(ii)

and $C_2 = -1 + i,\ r_2 = \sqrt{2}$

$\because$ $|C_1C_2| = |-1 + i| = \sqrt{2}$

and $|C_1C_2| < r_1 - r_2$

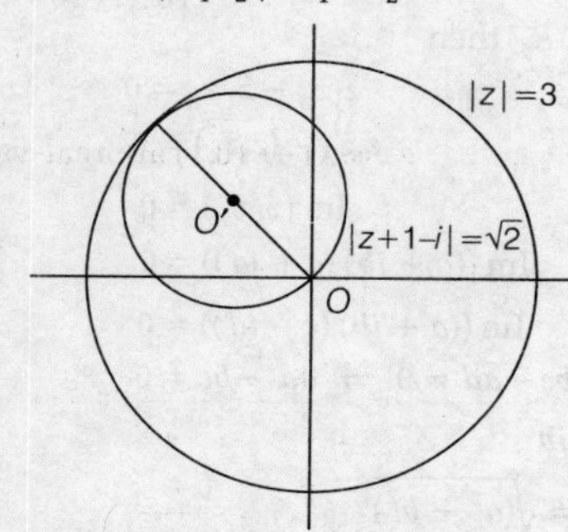

Hence, circle (ii) completely inside circle (i)

$\therefore$ Number of solutions = 0

18. We have, $f(z) = g(z)(z^2 + 1) + h(z)$

where, degree of $h(z) <$ degree of $(z^2 + 1)$

$\Rightarrow$ $h(z) = az + b;\ a, b \in C$

$\therefore$ $f(z) = g(z)(z^2 + 1) + az + b;\ a, b \in C$

$\Rightarrow$ $f(z) = g(z)(z - i)(z + i) + az + b;\ a, b \in C$ ...(i)

Now, $f(i) = 1 - i$ [given]

$\Rightarrow$ $ai + b = 1 - i$ [from Eq. (i)] ...(ii)

and $f(-i) = 1 + i$ [given]

$\Rightarrow$ $a(-i) + b = 1 + i$ [from Eq. (i)] ...(iii)

On solving Eqs. (ii) and (iii) for a and b, we get

$a = -1$ and $b = 1$

$\therefore$ Required remainder, $h(z) = az + b = -z + 1 = 1 - z$

19. We have, $|z + 1| = 2|z - 1|$

Put $z = x + iy$, we get

$$(x + 1)^2 + y^2 = 4[(x - 1)^2 + y^2]$$

$$\Rightarrow \quad 3x^2 + 3y^2 - 10x + 3 = 0$$

$$\Rightarrow \quad x^2 + y^2 - \frac{10}{3}x + 1 = 0 \quad ...(i)$$

On comparing Eq. (i) with the standard equation

$$x^2 + y^2 + 2gx + 2fy + c = 0$$

$$\Rightarrow \quad g = -\frac{10}{6} = -\frac{5}{3} \text{ and } f = 0$$

$\therefore$ Required centre of circle $\equiv (-g, -f) \equiv \left(\frac{5}{3}, 0\right)$

i.e. $\frac{5}{3} + 0 \cdot i = \frac{5}{3}$

20. $\because$ $x = 9^{1/3} \cdot 9^{1/9} \cdot 9^{1/27} \dots \infty$

$$= 9^{1/3 + 1/9 + 1/27 + \dots \infty} = 9^{\frac{1/3}{1 - 1/3}} = 9^{1/2} = 3$$

$$y = 4^{1/3} \cdot 4^{-1/9} \cdot 4^{1/27} \dots \infty = 4^{1/3 - 1/9 + 1/27 \dots \infty}$$

$$= 4^{\frac{1/3}{1 + 1/3}} = 4^{1/4} = \sqrt{2}$$

and $z = \sum_{r=1}^{\infty} (1 + i)^{-r} = \frac{1}{(1 + i)} + \frac{1}{(1 + i)^2} + \frac{1}{(1 + i)^3} + \dots \infty$

$$= \frac{\frac{1}{(1 + i)}}{1 - \frac{1}{(1 + i)}} = \frac{1}{i} = i$$

Now, $x + yz = 3 - i\sqrt{2}$

$\therefore$ $\arg(x + yz) = \arg(3 - i\sqrt{2}) = -\tan^{-1}\left(\frac{\sqrt{2}}{3}\right)$

21. $\because$ $A_1 \equiv 1 + 2i$

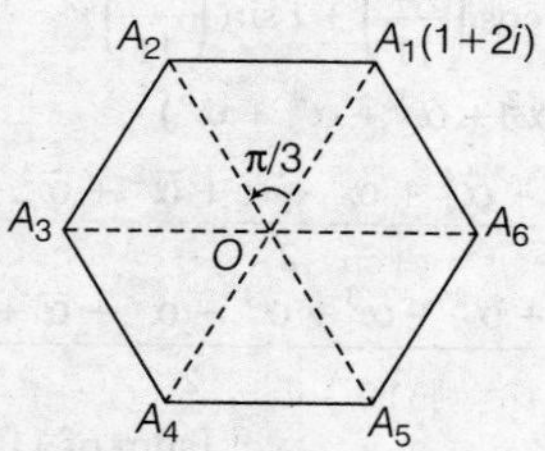

$\therefore$ $A_2 = (1 + 2i)e^{i\pi/3}$

$$= (1 + 2i)\left(\frac{1}{2} + \frac{i\sqrt{3}}{2}\right) = \frac{1}{2} + \frac{i\sqrt{3}}{2} + i - \sqrt{3}$$

$$= \left(\frac{1}{2} - \sqrt{3}\right) + i\left(\frac{\sqrt{3}}{2} + 1\right)$$

$$\therefore |A_1A_2| = \left|1 + 2i - \left(\frac{1}{2} - \sqrt{3}\right) - i\left(\frac{\sqrt{3}}{2} + 1\right)\right|$$

$$= \left|\frac{1}{2} + \sqrt{3} + i\left(1 - \frac{\sqrt{3}}{2}\right)\right|$$

$$= \sqrt{\left(\frac{1}{2} + \sqrt{3}\right)^2 + \left(1 - \frac{\sqrt{3}}{2}\right)^2} = \sqrt{5}$$

$\therefore$ Perimeter $= 6|A_1A_2| = 6\sqrt{5}$

22. We have,

$$\left|\sum_{r=1}^{n} z_r\right| = \left|\sum_{r=1}^{n} (z_r - r) + r\right| \le \sum_{r=1}^{n} (|z_r - r| + |r|)$$

$$= \sum_{r=1}^{n} |z_r - r| + \sum_{r=1}^{n} |r| \le \sum_{r=1}^{n} r + \sum_{r=1}^{n} |r|$$

$$= \frac{n(n + 1)}{2} + \frac{n(n + 1)}{2} = n(n + 1)$$

$$\therefore \quad \left|\sum_{r=1}^{n} z_r\right| \le n(n + 1)$$

23. We have, $\arg\left(\frac{z_1 - \frac{z}{|z|}}{\frac{z}{|z|}}\right) = \frac{\pi}{2}$ and $\left|\frac{z}{|z|} - z_1\right| = 3$

which implies the following diagram

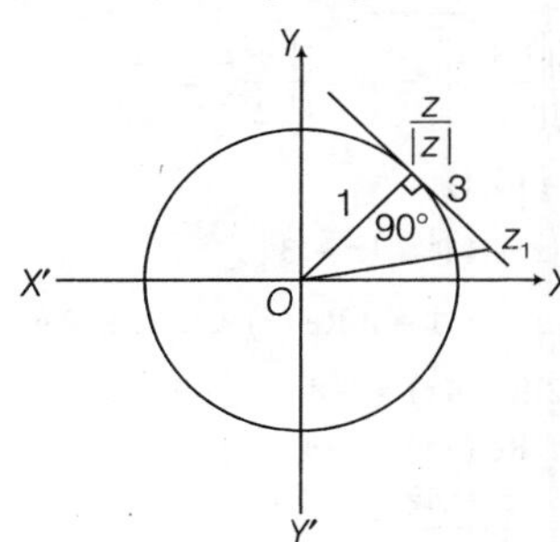

$$\Rightarrow \left|\frac{z}{|z|} - z_1\right| = 3 \Rightarrow |z_1| = \sqrt{9+1} = \sqrt{10}$$

24. Let $z = x + iy = r(\cos\theta + i\sin\theta)$

$\therefore$ $|z| = r, \arg(z) = \theta$

Given, $|z - 2 - i| = |z|\left|\sin\left(\frac{\pi}{4} - \arg(z)\right)\right|$

$$\Rightarrow |x + iy - 2 - i| = r\left|\sin\left(\frac{\pi}{4} - \theta\right)\right|$$

$$\Rightarrow |(x-2) + i(y-1)| = r\left|\frac{1}{\sqrt{2}}(\cos\theta - \sin\theta)\right|$$

$$\Rightarrow \sqrt{(x-2)^2 + (y-1)^2} = \frac{1}{\sqrt{2}}|x - y|$$

On squaring both sides, we get

$$2(x^2 + y^2 - 4x - 2y + 5) = x^2 + y^2 - 2xy$$

$$\Rightarrow \quad (x+y)^2 = 2(4x + 2y - 5)$$

which is a parabola.

25. Since, $1, z_1, z_2, z_3, \ldots, z_{n-1}$ are the n, nth roots of unity.

$$\therefore \quad (z^n - 1) = (z-1)(z-z_1)(z-z_2)(z-z_3)\ldots(z-z_{n-1})$$

$$= (z-1)\prod_{r=1}^{n-1}(z - z_r)$$

Taking log on both sides, we get

$$\log_e(z^n - 1) = \log_e(z-1) + \sum_{r=1}^{n-1}\log_e(z - z_r)$$

On differentiating both sides w.r.t.z, we get

$$\frac{nz^{n-1}}{(z^n - 1)} - \frac{1}{(z-1)} = \sum_{r=1}^{n-1}\frac{1}{(z - z_r)}$$

Putting $z = 3$, we get

$$\sum_{r=1}^{n-1}\frac{1}{(3 - z_r)} = \frac{n\cdot 3^{n-1}}{(3^n - 1)} - \frac{1}{2}$$

26. We have,

$$z = (3 + 7i)(\lambda + i\mu)$$
$$= (3\lambda - 7\mu) + i(7\lambda + 3\mu)$$

Since, z is purely imaginary.

$$\therefore \quad 3\lambda - 7\mu = 0$$

$$\Rightarrow \quad \frac{\lambda}{\mu} = \frac{7}{3}$$

$\because$ $\lambda, \mu \in I - \{0\}$

For minimum value $\lambda = 7, \mu = 3$

$$\therefore \quad |z|^2 = |(3 + 7i)(\lambda + i\mu)|^2$$
$$= |3 + 7i|^2|\lambda + i\mu|^2 = 58(\lambda^2 + \mu^2)$$
$$= 58(7^2 + 3^2) = (58)^2 = 3364$$

27. We have,

$$z = f(x) + ig(x)$$

where, $i = \sqrt{-1}$ and $f, g : (0,1) \to (0,1)$ are real-valued functions.

(a) $z = \frac{1}{1 - ix} + i\left(\frac{1}{1 + ix}\right)$

$$= \frac{1 + ix}{1 + x^2} + \frac{x + i}{1 + x^2} = \frac{1 + x}{1 + x^2} + i\frac{(1 + x)}{1 + x^2}$$

$$\Rightarrow f(x) = \frac{1 + x}{1 + x^2} \text{ and } g(x) = \frac{1 + x}{1 + x^2}$$

But for $x = 0.5$, $f(0.5) > 1$ and $g(0.5) > 1$, which is out of range.

Hence, (a) is not a correct option.

(b) $z = \frac{1}{1 + ix} + i\left(\frac{1}{1 - ix}\right)$

$$= \frac{1 - ix}{1 + x^2} + \frac{(i - x)}{1 + x^2} = \left(\frac{1 - x}{1 + x^2}\right) + i\left(\frac{1 - x}{1 + x^2}\right)$$

$$\Rightarrow f(x) = \frac{1 - x}{1 + x^2} \text{ and } g(x) = \frac{1 - x}{1 + x^2}$$

Clearly, $f(x), g(x) \in (0,1)$, if $x \in (0,1)$

Hence, (b) is the correct option.

(c) $z = \frac{1 - ix}{1 + x^2} + \frac{i(1 - ix)}{1 + x^2} = \frac{(1 + x)}{(1 + x^2)} + \frac{i(1 - x)}{(1 + x^2)}$

Hence, (c) is not a correct option.

(d) $z = \frac{1}{1 - ix} + i\left(\frac{1}{1 - ix}\right) = \frac{1 + ix}{1 + x^2} + \frac{i(1 + ix)}{(1 + x^2)}$

$$= \frac{(1 - x)}{(1 + x^2)} + \frac{i(1 + x)}{(1 + x^2)}$$

Hence, (d) is not a correct option.

28. Let $z = \alpha$ be a real roots of equation.

$$z^3 + (3 + 2i)z + (-1 + ia) = 0$$

$$\Rightarrow \quad \alpha^3 + (3 + 2i)\alpha + (-1 + ia) = 0$$

$$\Rightarrow \quad (\alpha^3 + 3\alpha - 1) + i(a + 2\alpha) = 0$$

On comparing the real and imaginary parts, we get

$$\alpha^3 + 3\alpha - 1 = 0 \text{ and } a + 2\alpha = 0$$

$$\Rightarrow \quad \alpha = -\frac{a}{2}$$

$$\Rightarrow \quad -\frac{a^3}{8} - \frac{3a}{2} - 1 = 0$$

$$\Rightarrow \quad a^3 + 12a + 8 = 0$$

Let $\quad f(a) = a^3 + 12a + 8$

$\Rightarrow \quad f(-1) < 0$ and $f(0) > 0$

$\therefore \quad a \in (-1, 0)$

29. $CiS\,\frac{\pi}{6} = \cos\frac{\pi}{6} + i\sin\frac{\pi}{6}$

$$= \left(\frac{\sqrt{3}+i}{2}\right) = \frac{1}{i}\left(\frac{-1+i\sqrt{3}}{2}\right) = \frac{\omega}{i} = -i\omega$$

$$\therefore \left(2\,CiS\,\frac{\pi}{6}\right)^m = (-2i\omega)^m = ((-2i\omega)^3)^{m/3} = (8i)^{m/3}$$

and $\left(4\,CiS\frac{\pi}{4}\right)^n = \left(4\left(\cos\frac{\pi}{4} + i\sin\frac{\pi}{4}\right)\right)^n = (2\sqrt{2}\,(1+i)^n$

$$= (8(1+i)^2)^{n/2} = (16i)^{n/2}$$

Thus, $(8i)^{m/3} = (16i)^{n/2}$

which is satisfy only when $m = 48$ and $n = 24$

$\therefore \quad m + n = 72$

30. We have, $\quad z^2 = \bar{z} \cdot 2^{1-|z|}$

Taking modulus on both sides, we get

$$|z|^2 = |z| \cdot 2^{1-|z|}$$

$\Rightarrow \quad |z|(|z| - 2^{1-|z|}) = 0 \quad$ ...(i)

and $\quad \arg(z^2) = \arg(\bar{z} \cdot 2^{1-|z|})$

$\Rightarrow \quad 2\arg(z) = \arg(\bar{z}) = -\arg(z)$

$\Rightarrow \quad 3\arg(z) = 0$

$\therefore \quad \arg(z) = 0$

Then, $\quad y = 0 \quad [\because z = x + iy]$

From Eq. (i), $|z| = 0 \Rightarrow x = 0 \quad [\because y = 0]$

One solution is $z = 0 + i \cdot 0 = 0$.

Also, from Eq. (i),

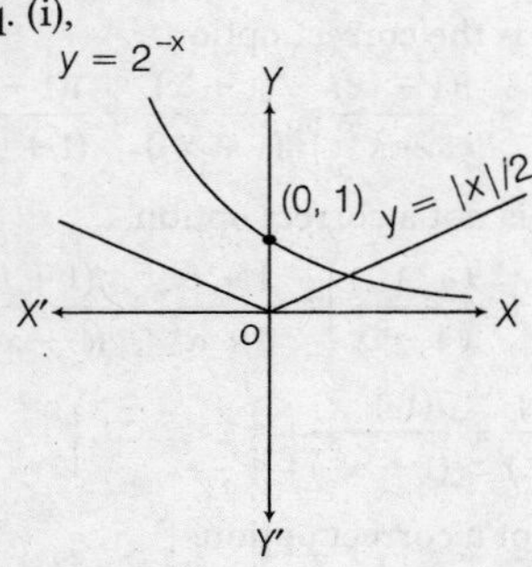

$\quad |z| = 2^{1-|z|} \Rightarrow |x| = 2^{1-x}$

$\Rightarrow \quad \frac{|x|}{2} = 2^{-x} = y$ (say)

Hence, total number of solutions = 2

31. $\because \frac{z+1}{z+i}$ is a purely imaginary number.

$$\therefore \quad \overline{\left(\frac{z+1}{z+i}\right)} = -\left(\frac{z+1}{z+i}\right) \Rightarrow \frac{\bar{z}+1}{\bar{z}-i} = -\left(\frac{z+1}{z+i}\right)$$

$\Rightarrow \quad (\bar{z}+1)(z+i) + (\bar{z}-i)(z+1) = 0$

$\Rightarrow \quad 2z\bar{z} + \bar{z}(1+i) + z(1-i) = 0$

$\Rightarrow \quad z\bar{z} + \left(\frac{1+i}{2}\right)\bar{z} + \left(\frac{1-i}{2}\right)z = 0$

which is a circle and passing through the origin

and radius $= \sqrt{\left|\frac{1+i}{2}\right|^2 - 0} = \left|\frac{1+i}{2}\right| = \frac{1}{\sqrt{2}}$

32. Given, $\quad |z-1| < |z+3|$

$\Rightarrow \quad |z-1|^2 < |z+3|^2$

$\Rightarrow \quad |z|^2 + 1 - 2\,\text{Re}(z) < |z|^2 + 9 + 2\,\text{Re}(3z)$

$\Rightarrow \quad 2\,\text{Re}(4z) > -8$

$\Rightarrow \quad \text{Re}(4z) > -4$

$\Rightarrow \quad \frac{4z + 4\bar{z}}{2} > -4$

$\therefore \quad z + \bar{z} > -2$

and $\quad \omega = 2z + 3 - i$

$\therefore \quad \omega + \bar{\omega} = 2z + 3 - i + 2\bar{z} + 3 + i$

$$= 2(z + \bar{z}) + 6 > -4 + 6$$

$\Rightarrow \quad \omega + \bar{\omega} > 2$

Option (a) $|\omega - 5 - i| < |\omega + 3 + i|$

$\Rightarrow |2z + 3 - i - 5 - i| < |2z + 3 - i + 3 + i|$

$\Rightarrow \quad |2z - 2 - 2i| < |2z + 6|$

$\Rightarrow \quad |z - 1 - i| < |z + 3|$

which is false.

Option (b) $|\omega - 5| < |\omega + 3|$

$\Rightarrow |2z + 3 - i - 5| < |2z + 3 - i + 3|$

$\Rightarrow \quad |2z - 2 - i| < |2z + 6 - i|$

$\Rightarrow \quad \left|z - 1 - \frac{i}{2}\right| < \left|z + 3 - \frac{i}{2}\right|$

$\Rightarrow \quad |z - 1| < |z + 3|$

which is true.

Option (c) $\quad \text{Im}(i\omega) > 1$

$\Rightarrow \quad \frac{i\omega - \overline{i\omega}}{2i} > 1$

$\Rightarrow \quad \frac{i\omega + i\bar{\omega}}{2i} > 1$

$\Rightarrow \quad \omega + \bar{\omega} > 2$

which is true.

Option (d) $\quad |\arg(\omega - 1)| < \frac{\pi}{2}$

$\Rightarrow \quad |\arg(2z + 3 - i - 1)| < \frac{\pi}{2}$

$\Rightarrow \quad |\arg(2z + 2 - i)| < \frac{\pi}{2}$

$\Rightarrow \quad \left|\tan^{-1}\left(\frac{\text{Im}(2z + 2 - i)}{\text{Re}(2z + 2 - i)}\right)\right| < \frac{\pi}{2}$

$\therefore \quad \text{Re}(2z + 2 - i) > 0$

$\Rightarrow \quad \frac{(2z + 2 - i) + (2\bar{z} + 2 + i)}{2} > 0$

$\Rightarrow \quad z + \bar{z} + 2 > 0$

$\Rightarrow \quad z + \bar{z} > -2$

which is true.

33. $\therefore (1 + ri)^3 = \lambda(1 + i)$

$\Rightarrow \quad 1 + (ri)^3 + 3(1)^2 ri + 3(1)(ri)^2 = \lambda(1 + i)$

$\Rightarrow \quad 1 - r^3 i + 3ri - 3r^2 = \lambda + i\lambda$

On comparing real and imaginary parts, we get

$$1 - 3r^2 = \lambda$$

and $\quad -r^3 + 3r = \lambda$

Then, $\quad -r^3 + 3r = 1 - 3r^2$

$\Rightarrow \quad r^3 - 3r^2 - 3r + 1 = 0$

$\Rightarrow \quad (r^3 + 1) - 3r(r+1) = 0$

$\Rightarrow \quad (r+1)(r^2 - r + 1 - 3r) = 0$

$\Rightarrow \quad (r+1)(r^2 - 4r + 1) = 0$

$\therefore \quad r = -1, 2 \pm \sqrt{3}$

$\Rightarrow \quad r = \operatorname{cosec}\frac{3\pi}{2}, \tan\frac{\pi}{12}, \cot\frac{\pi}{12}$

34. **Option** (a) $|z-1| + |z+1| = 3$

Here, $|1-(-1)| < 3$

i.e. $2 < 3$, which is an ellipse.

Option (b) $|z-3| = 2$

It is a circle with centre 3 and radius 2.

Option (c) $|z - 2 + i| = \frac{7}{3}$

It is a circle with centre $(2-i)$ and radius $\frac{7}{3}$.

Option (d) $\quad (z - 3 + i)(\bar{z} - 3 - i) = 5$

$\Rightarrow \quad (z-3+i)\overline{(z-3+i)} = 5$

$\Rightarrow \quad |z-3+i|^2 = 5$

$\Rightarrow \quad |z-3+i| = \sqrt{5}$

It is a circle with centre at $(3-i)$ and radius $\sqrt{5}$.

35. Since, $1, z_1, z_2, z_3, \ldots, z_{n-1}$ are the n, nth roots of unity.

Therefore,

$$z^n - 1 = (z-1)(z-z_1)(z-z_2)\ldots(z-z_{n-1})$$

$$\Rightarrow \quad \frac{z^n - 1}{z-1} = (z-z_1)(z-z_2)\ldots(z-z_{n-1})$$

$$= \prod_{r=1}^{n-1}(z - z_r)$$

Now, putting $z = \omega$, we get

$$\prod_{r=1}^{n-1}(\omega - z_r) = \frac{\omega^n - 1}{\omega - 1}$$

$$= \begin{cases} 0, & \text{if } n = 3r, r \in Z \\ 1, & \text{if } n = 3r+1, r \in Z \\ 1+\omega, & \text{if } n = 3r+2, r \in Z \end{cases}$$

36. $\because \quad 3|z-12| = 5|z-8i|$

$\therefore \; 9|z-12|^2 = 25|z-8i|^2$

$\Rightarrow \quad 9(z-12)(\bar{z}-12) = 25(z-8i)(\bar{z}+8i)$

$\Rightarrow \quad 9(z\bar{z} - 12(z+\bar{z}) + 144) = 25(z\bar{z} + 8i(z-\bar{z}) + 64)$

$\Rightarrow \quad 16z\bar{z} + 108(z+\bar{z}) + 200(z-\bar{z})i + 304 = 0$

$\Rightarrow \quad 16(x^2+y^2) + 216x - 400y + 304 = 0$

$\Rightarrow \quad 2(x^2+y^2) + 27x - 50y + 38 = 0 \quad \ldots(i)$

and $\quad |z-4| = |z-8| \Rightarrow |z-4|^2 = |z-8|^2$

$\Rightarrow \quad |z|^2 + 16 - 2\operatorname{Re}(4z) = |z|^2 + 64 - 2\operatorname{Re}(8z)$

$\Rightarrow \quad 8\operatorname{Re}(z) = 48$

$\therefore \quad \operatorname{Re}(z) = 6$

$\Rightarrow \quad x = 6 \quad \ldots(ii)$

From Eqs. (i) and (ii), we get

$$2(36 + y^2) + 162 - 50y + 38 = 0$$

$\Rightarrow \quad y^2 - 25y + 136 = 0$

$\Rightarrow \quad (y-17)(y-8) = 0$

$\Rightarrow \quad y = 17, 8$

$\therefore \quad \operatorname{Im}(z) = 17, 8$

37.

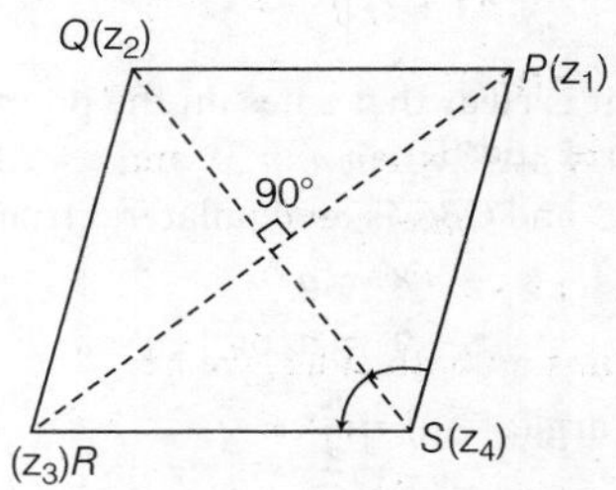

Option (a) $\because \; PS \| QR$

$\therefore \quad \arg\left(\frac{z_1 - z_4}{z_2 - z_3}\right) = 0$

$\Rightarrow \quad \frac{z_1 - z_4}{z_2 - z_3}$ is purely real.

Option (b) $\because$ Diagonals of rhombus are perpendicular.

Then, $\arg\left(\frac{z_1 - z_3}{z_2 - z_4}\right) = \frac{\pi}{2}$

$\Rightarrow \quad \frac{z_1 - z_3}{z_2 - z_4}$ is purely imaginary.

Option (c) $\because \quad PR \neq QS$

$\therefore \quad |z_1 - z_3| \neq |z_2 - z_4|$

Option (d) $\because \quad \angle QSP = \angle RSQ$

$\therefore \quad \operatorname{amp}\left(\frac{z_2 - z_4}{z_1 - z_4}\right) = \operatorname{amp}\left(\frac{z_3 - z_4}{z_2 - z_4}\right)$

$\Rightarrow \quad -\operatorname{amp}\left(\frac{z_1 - z_4}{z_2 - z_4}\right) = -\operatorname{amp}\left(\frac{z_2 - z_4}{z_3 - z_4}\right)$

$\Rightarrow \quad \operatorname{amp}\left(\frac{z_1 - z_4}{z_2 - z_4}\right) = \operatorname{amp}\left(\frac{z_2 - z_4}{z_3 - z_4}\right)$

38. $\because \; |z-3| = \min\{|z-1|, |z-5|\}$

Case I If $|z-3| = |z-1|$

On squaring both sides, we get

$$|z-3|^2 = |z-1|^2$$

$\Rightarrow \quad |z|^2 + 9 - 2\operatorname{Re}(3z) = |z|^2 + 1 - 2\operatorname{Re}(z)$

$\Rightarrow \quad 4\operatorname{Re}(z) = 8$

$\Rightarrow \quad \operatorname{Re}(z) = 2$

***Case* II** If $|z-3| = |z-5|$

On squaring both sides, we get

$$|z-3|^2 = |z-5|^2$$

$\Rightarrow$ $|z|^2 + 9 - 2\,\text{Re}(3z) = |z|^2 + 25 - 2\,\text{Re}(5z)$

$\Rightarrow$ $4\,\text{Re}(z) = 16 \Rightarrow \text{Re}(z) = 4$

39.

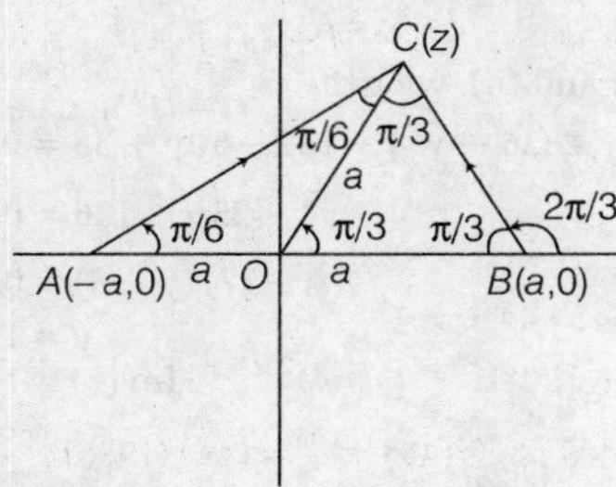

From figure, it is clear that z lies on the point of intersection of the rays from A and B.

$\because \angle ACB = 90^\circ$ and OBC is an equilateral triangle.

Hence, $OC = a$

$\Rightarrow$ $|z - 0| = a$ or $|z| = a$

and $\arg(z) = \arg(z-0) = \dfrac{\pi}{3}$

40. $\because$ $\left|\dfrac{2z-i}{z+i}\right| = m$

$\Rightarrow$ $\left|\dfrac{z-i/2}{z+i}\right| = \dfrac{m}{2}$

For circle, $\dfrac{m}{2} \neq 1$

$\Rightarrow$ $m \neq 2$ and $m > 0$

41. $\therefore$ $A(z_0)$ lie on $|z| = r$

$\Rightarrow$ $|z_0| = r \Rightarrow |z_0|^2 = r^2 \Rightarrow z_0\bar{z}_0 = r^2$

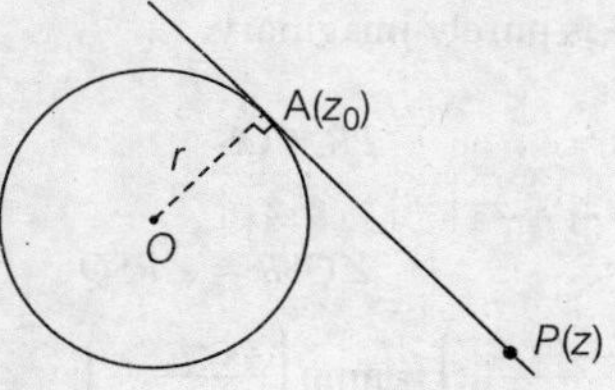

Let $P(z)$ be any point on tangent, then

$\therefore$ $\angle PAO = \dfrac{\pi}{2}$

Complex slope of AP + Complex slope of $OA = 0$

$\Rightarrow$ $\dfrac{z-z_0}{\bar{z}-\bar{z}_0} + \dfrac{z_0-0}{\bar{z}_0-0} = 0$

$\Rightarrow$ $z\bar{z}_0 + z_0\bar{z} = 2z_0\bar{z}_0$

$\Rightarrow$ $z\bar{z}_0 + z_0\bar{z} = 2r^2$

$\Rightarrow$ $z\bar{z}_0 = \bar{z}z_0$

Also, $\dfrac{z\bar{z}_0}{r^2} + \dfrac{z_0\bar{z}}{r^2} = 2$

$\Rightarrow$ $\dfrac{z\bar{z}_0}{z_0\bar{z}_0} + \dfrac{z_0\bar{z}}{z_0\bar{z}_0} = 2$

$\Rightarrow$ $\dfrac{\dfrac{z}{z_0} + \left(\dfrac{\bar{z}}{\bar{z}_0}\right)}{2} = 1$

$\therefore$ $\text{Re}\left(\dfrac{z}{z_0}\right) = 1$

42. $\because$ $z_1 + z_2 = a,\ z_1z_2 = b$

and given $|z_1| = |z_2| = 1$

Let $z_1 = e^{i\theta}$ and $z_2 = e^{i\phi}$

$\because$ $|a| = |z_1 + z_2| \le |z_1| + |z_2| = 1 + 1 = 2$

$\therefore$ $|a| \le 2$

Also, $\arg(a) = \arg(z_1 + z_2) = \arg(e^{i\theta} + e^{i\phi}) = \dfrac{\theta+\phi}{2}$,

and $\arg(b) = \arg(z_1z_2) = \arg(e^{i(\theta+\phi)}) = \theta + \phi$

$\therefore$ $2\arg(a) = \arg(b) \Rightarrow \arg(a^2) = \arg(b)$

43. $\because$ $\alpha z^2 + z + \bar{\alpha} = 0$ ...(i)

Then, $\overline{\alpha z^2 + z + \bar{\alpha}} = \bar{0}$

$\Rightarrow$ $\bar{\alpha}(\bar{z})^2 + \bar{z} + \alpha = 0$

$\Rightarrow$ $\bar{\alpha}z^2 + z + \alpha = 0$ $[\because \bar{z} = z]$ ...(ii)

On subtracting Eq. (ii) from Eq. (i), we get

$$(\alpha - \bar{\alpha})z^2 - (\alpha - \bar{\alpha}) = 0$$

$\Rightarrow$ $\alpha - \bar{\alpha} = 0$ and $z^2 = 1$

$\therefore$ $\alpha = \bar{\alpha}$ and $z = \pm 1$

Put $z = \pm 1$ in Eq. (i), we get

$$\alpha + \bar{\alpha} = \pm 1$$

and absolute value of real root = 1

i.e., $|z| = |\pm 1| = 1$

44. Let $z = \alpha$ be a real root of equation

$$z^3 + (3+i)z^2 - 3z - (m+i) = 0$$

$\Rightarrow$ $\alpha^3 + (3+i)\alpha^2 - 3\alpha - (m+i) = 0$

$\Rightarrow$ $(\alpha^3 + 3\alpha^2 - 3\alpha - m) + i(\alpha^2 - 1) = 0$

On comparing real and imaginary parts, we get

$$\alpha^3 + 3\alpha^2 - 3\alpha - m = 0$$

and $\alpha^2 - 1 = 0 \Rightarrow \alpha = \pm 1$

For $\alpha = 1$, we get

$$1 + 3 - 3 - m = 0 \Rightarrow m = 1$$

For $\alpha = -1$, we get

$$-1 + 3 + 3 - m = 0 \Rightarrow m = 5$$

45. Let $z = \alpha$ be a real root of equation

$$z^3 + (3+2i)z + (-1+ia) = 0$$

$\Rightarrow$ $\alpha^3 + (3+2i)\alpha + (-1+ia) = 0$

$\Rightarrow$ $(\alpha^3 + 3\alpha - 1) + i(a + 2\alpha) = 0$

On comparing real and imaginary parts, we get

$$\alpha^3 + 3\alpha - 1 = 0$$

and $a + 2\alpha = 0$

$\Rightarrow \quad \alpha = -\dfrac{a}{2}$

$\Rightarrow \quad -\dfrac{a^3}{8} - \dfrac{3a}{2} - 1 = 0 \Rightarrow a^3 + 12a + 8 = 0$

Let $\quad f(a) = a^3 + 12a + 8$

$\therefore \quad f(-1) < 0, f(0) > 0, f(-2) < 0$

$f(1) > 0$ and $f(3) > 0$

$\Rightarrow \quad a \in (-2,1)$ or $a \in (-1,0)$ or $a \in (-2,3)$

Sol. (Q. Nos. 46 to 48)

46. $\because$ arg $(z) > 0$

$\therefore \quad \arg(\bar{z}) + \arg(-z) = -\pi$

$\Rightarrow \quad -\arg(z) + \arg(-z) = -\pi$

$\Rightarrow \quad \arg(-z) - \arg(z) = -\pi$

47. $\because$ $\arg(z_1 z_2) = \pi$

$\Rightarrow \quad \arg(z_1) + \arg(z_2) = \pi$

$\Rightarrow \quad \arg(z_1) - \arg(\bar{z}_2) = \pi$

Given, $\quad |z_1| = |z_2|$

$\therefore \quad |z_1| = |\bar{z}_2| = |z_2|$

Then, $\quad z_1 + \bar{z}_2 = 0$

$\Rightarrow \quad z_1 = -\bar{z}_2$

48. $\arg(4z_1) - \arg(5z_2) = \pi$

is possible only when $|4z_1| = |5z_2|$

$\Rightarrow \quad \left|\dfrac{z_1}{z_2}\right| = \dfrac{5}{4} = 1.25$

and also $\quad 4z_1 + 5z_2 = 0$

$\Rightarrow \quad \dfrac{z_1}{z_2} = -\dfrac{5}{4}$

$\therefore \quad \left|\dfrac{z_1}{z_2}\right| = \dfrac{5}{4} = 1.25$

Sol. (Q. Nos. 49 to 51)

49. $\because$ $n\,!$ is divisible by 4, $\forall\, n \geq 4$.

$\therefore \quad \sum_{n=4}^{25} i^{n!} = \sum_{n=1}^{22} i^{(n+3)!}$

$= i^0 + i^0 + i^0 + \ldots (22 \text{ times}) = 22 \quad \ldots(\text{i})$

$\therefore \quad \sum_{n=1}^{25} i^{n!} = i^{1!} + i^{2!} + i^{3!} + \sum_{n=4}^{25} i^{n!}$

$= i + i^2 + i^6 + 22 \quad$ [from Eq. (i)]

$= i - 1 - 1 + 22 = 20 + i$

$\therefore \quad a = 20, b = 1$

$\therefore \quad a - b = 20 - 1 = 19$

which is a prime number.

50. $\therefore \sum_{r=-2}^{95} i^r + \sum_{r=0}^{50} i^{r!}$

$= \sum_{r=1}^{98} i^{r-3} + \left(i^{0!} + i^{1!} + i^{2!} + i^{3!} + \sum_{r=4}^{50} i^{r!}\right)$

$= (i^{-2} + i^{-1} + 0) + \left(i^1 + i^1 + i^2 + i^6 + \sum_{r=1}^{47} i^{(r+3)!}\right)$

$= (-1 - i) + (i + i - 1 - 1$

$+ (i^0 + i^0 + i^0 + \ldots 47 \text{ times}))$

$= (-1 - i) + (2i - 2 + 47)$

$= 44 + i = a + ib \quad$ [given]

$\therefore \quad a = 44, b = 1$

Unit place digit of $a^{2011} = (44)^{2011}$

$= (44)\,((44)^2)^{1005} = (44)\,(1936)^{1005}$

$=$ (Unit place of 44)

$\times$ (Unit place digit of $(1936)^{1005}$)

$=$ Unit place of $(4 \times 6) = 4$

and unit place digit of $b^{2012} = (1)^{2012} = 1$

Hence, the unit place digit of $a^{2011} + b^{2012} = 4 + 1 = 5$.

51. $\because \sum_{r=4}^{100} i^{r!} + \prod_{r=1}^{101} i^r$

$= \sum_{r=1}^{97} i^{(r+3)!} + i^1 \cdot i^2 \cdot i^3 \ldots i^{101}$

$= (i^0 + i^0 + i^0 + \ldots 97 \text{ times}) + i^{1+2+3+\ldots+101}$

$= 97 + i^{5151} = 97 + i^3 = 97 - i$

$\therefore \quad a = 97$ and $b = -1$

Hence, $a + 75b = 97 - 75 = 22$

Sol. (Q. Nos. 52 to 54)

If $\left|z \pm \dfrac{a}{z}\right| = b$, where $a, b > 0$

$\therefore \quad \left|z \pm \dfrac{a}{z}\right| \leq |z| + \dfrac{a}{|z|}$

$\Rightarrow \quad b \leq |z| + \dfrac{a}{|z|}$

$\Rightarrow \quad |z|^2 - b|z| + a \geq 0$

$\therefore \quad |z| \leq \dfrac{b - \sqrt{b^2 - 4a}}{2}$

and $\quad |z| \geq \dfrac{b + \sqrt{b^2 - 4a}}{2} \quad \ldots(\text{i})$

Also, $\quad \left|z \pm \dfrac{a}{z}\right| \geq \left||z| - \dfrac{a}{|z|}\right|$

$\Rightarrow \quad b \geq \left||z| - \dfrac{a}{|z|}\right|$

$\Rightarrow \quad -b \leq |z| - \dfrac{a}{|z|} \leq b$

$\Rightarrow \quad -b|z| \leq |z|^2 - a \leq b|z|$

Case I $-b|z| \le |z|^2 - a$

$\Rightarrow |z|^2 + b|z| - a \ge 0$

$\therefore \quad |z| \le \dfrac{-b-\sqrt{b^2+4a}}{2}$

and $\quad |z| \ge \dfrac{-b+\sqrt{b^2-4a}}{2}$

Case II $|z|^2 - a \le b|z|$

$\Rightarrow |z|^2 - b|z| - a \le 0$

$\therefore \quad \dfrac{b-\sqrt{b^2+4a}}{2} \le |z| \le \dfrac{b+\sqrt{b^2+4a}}{2}$

From Case I and Case II, we get

$$\frac{-b+\sqrt{b^2+4a}}{2} \le |z| \le \frac{b+\sqrt{b^2+4a}}{2} \quad \text{...(ii)}$$

From Eqs. (i) and (ii), we get

$$\frac{-b+\sqrt{b^2+4a}}{2} \le |z| \le \frac{b+\sqrt{(b^2+4a)}}{2}$$

$\therefore$ The greatest value of $|z|$ is $\dfrac{b+\sqrt{b^2+4a}}{2}$

and the least value of $|z|$ is $\dfrac{-b+\sqrt{b^2+4a}}{2}$.

52. Here, $a = 1$ and $b = 2$

$\lambda =$ Sum of the greatest and least values of $|z|$

$= \sqrt{b^2+4a} = \sqrt{4+4} = \sqrt{8}$

$\therefore \quad \lambda^2 = 8$

53. Here, $a = 2$ and $b = 4$

$\lambda =$ Sum of the greatest and least value of $|z|$.

$= \sqrt{b^2+4a} = \sqrt{16+8} = \sqrt{24}$

$\therefore \quad \lambda^2 = 24$

54. Here, $a = 3$ and $b = 6$

$\lambda =$ Sum of the greatest and least value of $|z|$

$= \sqrt{b^2+4a} = \sqrt{36+12} = \sqrt{48} = 4\sqrt{3}$

$\Rightarrow \quad \lambda = 2\sqrt{3}$

$\therefore \quad \lambda^2 = 12$

Sol. (Q. Nos. 55 to 57)

$\because \quad W = \dfrac{z-1}{z+2} = a + ib$

55. $\because \quad z = CiS\,\theta = e^{i\theta}$

$\therefore \quad \dfrac{e^{i\theta}-1}{e^{i\theta}+2} = a + ib$

$\Rightarrow (\cos\theta + i\sin\theta - 1) = (a+ib)(\cos\theta + i\sin\theta + 2)$

On comparing real and imaginary parts, we get

$$\cos\theta - 1 = a\cos\theta + 2a - b\sin\theta$$

$\Rightarrow \quad (1-a)\cos\theta + b\sin\theta = 2a + 1 \quad \text{...(i)}$

and $\sin\theta = a\sin\theta + b\cos\theta + 2b$

$(1-a)\sin\theta - b\cos\theta = 2b \quad \text{...(ii)}$

On squaring and adding Eqs. (i) and (ii), we get

$$(1-a)^2 + b^2 = (2a+1)^2 + (2b)^2$$

$\Rightarrow \quad 3a^2 + 3b^2 + 6a = 0$

$\Rightarrow \quad a^2 + b^2 + 2a = 0$

From option (c),

$$(1+5a)^2 + (3b)^2 = (1-4a)^2$$

$\Rightarrow \quad 9a^2 + 9b^2 + 18a = 0$

$\therefore \quad a^2 + b^2 + 2a = 0$

56. From Eq. (i), we get

$$(1-a)\left(\frac{1-\tan^2\theta/2}{1+\tan^2\theta/2}\right) + b\left(\frac{2\tan\theta/2}{1+\tan^2\theta/2}\right) = 2a+1$$

$\Rightarrow \quad (1-a) - (1-a)\tan^2\dfrac{\theta}{2} + 2b\tan\dfrac{\theta}{2}$

$$= (2a+1) + (2a+1)\tan^2\frac{\theta}{2}$$

$\Rightarrow \quad (2+a)\tan^2\dfrac{\theta}{2} - 2b\tan\dfrac{\theta}{2} + 3a = 0$

$\therefore \quad \tan\dfrac{\theta}{2} = \dfrac{2b \pm \sqrt{4b^2 - 12a(2+a)}}{2(2+a)}$

$= \dfrac{2b \pm \sqrt{4b^2 - 12(-b^2)}}{-2b^2/a} \quad [\because a^2 + b^2 + 2a = 0]$

$= \dfrac{(2b \pm 4b)\,a}{-2b^2} = \dfrac{6ba}{-2b^2}$ or $\dfrac{-2ab}{-2b^2} = -\dfrac{3a}{b}$ or $\dfrac{a}{b}$

$\therefore \quad \cot\dfrac{\theta}{2} = -\dfrac{b}{3a}$ or $\dfrac{b}{a}$ or $-\dfrac{b}{a} = 3\cot\dfrac{\theta}{2}$ or $-\cot\dfrac{\theta}{2}$

57. $\therefore \quad a^2 + b^2 + 2a = 0 \Rightarrow (a+1)^2 + b^2 = 1$

Now, $|z| = 1 = (a+1)^2 + b^2$

58. $\because \quad 1 + z + z^2 + z^3 + \ldots + z^{17} = 0$

$\therefore \quad \dfrac{1\cdot(1-z^{18})}{(1-z)} = 0$

$\Rightarrow \quad 1 - z^{18} = 0, 1 - z \ne 0$

$\therefore \quad z^{18} = 1, z \ne 1 \quad \text{...(i)}$

and $\quad 1 + z + z^2 + z^3 + \ldots + z^{13} = 0$

$\therefore \quad \dfrac{1\cdot(1-z^{14})}{(1-z)} = 0$

$\Rightarrow \quad 1 - z^{14} = 0, 1 - z \ne 0$

$\therefore \quad z^{14} = 1, z \ne 1 \quad \text{...(ii)}$

From Eqs. (i) and (ii), we get

$$z^{14}\cdot z^4 = 1 \Rightarrow 1\cdot z^4 = 1$$

$\therefore \quad z^4 = 1$

Then, $\quad z = 1, -1, i, -i$

$\because \quad z \ne 1$

$\because \quad z = -1, i, -i$

Hence, only $z = -1$ satisfy both Eqs. (i) and (ii).

$\therefore$ Number of values of z is 1.

59. We have, $z^3 = \bar{z}$ ...(i)

$\Rightarrow \quad |z|^3 = |\bar{z}| = |z|$

$\Rightarrow \quad |z|(|z|^2 - 1) = 0$

$\Rightarrow \quad |z| = 0 \text{ and } |z|^2 = 1$

Now, $|z|^2 = 1$

$\Rightarrow \quad z\bar{z} = 1 \Rightarrow \bar{z} = \frac{1}{z}$

On putting this value in Eq. (i), we get

$$z^3 = \frac{1}{z}$$

$\Rightarrow \quad z^4 = 1$ ...(ii)

Clearly, Eq. (ii) has 4 solutions.

Therefore, the required number of solutions is 5.

60. We have, $z = 9 + ai$

$\Rightarrow \quad z^2 = (81 - a^2) + 18ai$

$z^3 = (729 - 27a^2) + (243a - a^3)\, i$

According to the question, we have

$$\text{Im}(z^2) = \text{Im}(z^3)$$

$\Rightarrow \quad 18a = 243a - a^3 \Rightarrow a(a^2 - 225) = 0$

$\Rightarrow \quad a = 0 \text{ or } a^2 = 225$

But $\quad a \neq 0$

$\therefore \quad a^2 = 225$

$\therefore$ The sum of digits of $a^2 = 2 + 2 + 5 = 9$

61. Let $z = x + iy$

$\because \quad |z| = 1$ ...(i)

$\therefore \quad x^2 + y^2 = 1$

and $\quad \left|\frac{z}{\bar{z}} + \frac{\bar{z}}{z}\right| = 1$

$\Rightarrow \quad \left|\frac{x+iy}{x-iy} + \frac{x-iy}{x+iy}\right| = 1$

$\Rightarrow \quad \left|\frac{(x+iy)^2 + (x-iy)^2}{x^2+y^2}\right| = 1$

$\Rightarrow \quad \left|\frac{2(x^2-y^2)}{1}\right| = 1$ [from Eq. (i)]

$\Rightarrow \quad x^2 - y^2 = \pm \frac{1}{2}$ ...(ii)

From Eqs. (i) and (ii), we get

$$2x^2 = 1 \pm \frac{1}{2} = \frac{1}{2}, \frac{3}{2}$$

$\Rightarrow \quad x^2 = \frac{1}{4}, \frac{3}{4} \Rightarrow x = \pm\frac{1}{2}, \pm\frac{\sqrt{3}}{2}$

For $x = \frac{1}{2}, y = \pm\frac{\sqrt{3}}{2}$ [from Eq. (i)]

For $x = -\frac{1}{2}, y = \pm\frac{\sqrt{3}}{2}$ [from Eq. (i)]

For $x = \frac{\sqrt{3}}{2}, y = \pm\frac{1}{2}$ [from Eq. (i)]

For $x = -\frac{\sqrt{3}}{2}, y = \pm\frac{1}{2}$ [from Eq. (i)]

$\therefore$ Solutions are $\frac{1}{2} \pm \frac{i\sqrt{3}}{2}, -\frac{1}{2} \pm \frac{i\sqrt{3}}{2}, \frac{\sqrt{3}}{2} \pm \frac{i}{2}, -\frac{\sqrt{3}}{2} \pm \frac{i}{2}$

Hence, number of solutions is 8.

62. We have, $x = a + ib$

$\Rightarrow \quad x^2 = (a^2 - b^2) + 2iab = 3 + 4i$ [given]

$\therefore \quad a^2 - b^2 = 3 \text{ and } ab = 2$ ...(i)

and $x^3 = x \cdot x^2 = (a + ib)\,[(a^2 - b^2) + 2iab]$

$= (a^3 - ab^2 - 2ab^2) + i[2a^2b + b(a^2 - b^2)]$

$= (a^3 - 3ab^2) + i(3a^2b - b^3) = 2 + 11i$ [given]

$\therefore \quad a^3 - 3ab^2 = 2$

and $3a^2b - b^3 = 11$ ...(ii)

From Eq. (i), we get

$$a^2 + b^2 = \sqrt{(a^2 - b^2)^2 + 4a^2b^2} = 5$$

Then, $\quad 2a^2 = 8, 2b^2 = 2$

$\therefore \quad a^2 = 4, b^2 = 1$

$\Rightarrow \quad a = 2, b = 1$

and $\quad a = -2, b = -1$ [$\because ab = 2$]

Finally, $a = 2, b = 1$ satisfies Eq. (ii).

Hence, $\quad a + b = 2 + 1 = 3$

63. $\because \quad (1+i)^4 = [(1+i)^2]^2$

$= (1 + i^2 + 2i)^2 = (1 - 1 + 2i)^2$

$= 4i^2 = -4$ ...(i)

and $\frac{1 - \sqrt{\pi}\, i}{\sqrt{\pi} + i} + \frac{\sqrt{\pi} - i}{1 + \sqrt{\pi}\, i}$

$= \frac{(1 - \sqrt{\pi}\, i)(\sqrt{\pi} - i)}{\pi + 1} + \frac{(\sqrt{\pi} - i)(1 - \sqrt{\pi}\, i)}{1 + \pi}$

$= \frac{\sqrt{\pi} - i - \pi i - \sqrt{\pi} + \sqrt{\pi} - \pi i - i - \sqrt{\pi}}{\pi + 1}$

$= \frac{-2\pi i - 2i}{\pi + 1} = -2i$ ...(ii)

Given, $z = \frac{\pi}{4}(1+i)^4 \left(\frac{1 - \sqrt{\pi}\, i}{\sqrt{\pi} + i} + \frac{\sqrt{\pi} - i}{1 + \sqrt{\pi}\, i}\right)$

$= \frac{\pi}{4}(-4)(-2i) = 2\pi i$ [from Eqs. (i) and (ii)]

Now, $\left(\frac{|z|}{\text{amp}(z)}\right) = \frac{2\pi}{\pi/2} = 4$

64. $\because \quad A^n = 1$

$\Rightarrow \quad A = (1)^{1/n} = e^{2\pi r i/n}, r = 0, 1, 2, \ldots, n-1$

$\therefore \quad A = 1, e^{2\pi i/n}, e^{4\pi i/n}, e^{6\pi i/n}, \ldots, e^{2\pi(n-1)i/n}$

and $\quad (A+1)^n = 1 \Rightarrow A + 1 = (1)^{1/n} = e^{2\pi p i/n}$

$$\Rightarrow \quad A = e^{2\pi pi/n} - 1 = e^{p\pi i/n} \cdot 2i \sin\left(\frac{\pi p}{n}\right),$$

$$p = 0, 1, 2, \ldots, n-1$$

$$\therefore \quad A = 0, e^{\pi i/n} \cdot 2i \sin\left(\frac{\pi}{n}\right), e^{2\pi i/n}\, 2i \sin\left(\frac{2\pi}{n}\right), \ldots, e^{\pi i(n-1)/n} \cdot 2i \sin\left(\frac{\pi(n-1)}{n}\right)$$

For $n = 6$,

$$e^{4\pi i/n} = e^{4\pi i/6} = e^{2\pi i/3}$$

$$= \cos\frac{2\pi}{3} + i \sin\frac{2\pi}{3} = -\frac{1}{2} + \frac{i\sqrt{3}}{2}$$

and $$e^{\pi i/n} \cdot 2i \sin\left(\frac{\pi}{n}\right) = e^{\pi i/6} \cdot 2i \sin\left(\frac{\pi}{6}\right)$$

$$= \left(\cos\frac{\pi}{6} + i \sin\frac{\pi}{6}\right) \cdot i$$

$$= \left(\frac{\sqrt{3}}{2} + \frac{i}{2}\right) i = -\frac{1}{2} + \frac{i\sqrt{3}}{2}$$

Hence, the least value of n is 6.

65. Given, $z_1, z_2, z_3, \ldots, z_{50}$ are the roots of the equation

$\sum_{r=0}^{50} (z)^r = 0$, then

$$\sum_{r=0}^{50} (z)^r = (z - z_1)(z - z_2)(z - z_3) \ldots (z - z_{50}) = \prod_{r=1}^{50} (z - z_r)$$

Taking log on both sides on base e, we get

$$\log_e\left(\sum_{r=0}^{50} (z)^r\right) = \sum_{r=1}^{50} \log_e (z - z_r)$$

On differentiating both sides w.r.t. z, we get

$$\frac{\sum_{r=0}^{50} r(z)^{r-1}}{\sum_{r=0}^{50} (z)^r} = \sum_{r=1}^{50} \frac{1}{(z - z_r)}$$

On putting $z = 1$ in both sides, we get

$$\frac{\sum_{r=0}^{50} r}{\sum_{r=0}^{50} 1} = \sum_{r=1}^{50} \frac{1}{(1 - z_r)}$$

$$\Rightarrow \quad \frac{(1 + 2 + 3 + \ldots + 50)}{51} = -\sum_{r=1}^{50} \frac{1}{(z_r - 1)}$$

$$= -(-5\lambda) \qquad \text{[given]}$$

$$\Rightarrow \quad \frac{\frac{50}{2} \times 51}{51} = 5\lambda$$

$$\Rightarrow \quad \lambda = 5$$

66. $\because \sum_{q=1}^{10}\left(\sin\frac{2q\pi}{11} - i \cos\frac{2q\pi}{11}\right)$

$$= -i \sum_{q=1}^{10}\left(\cos\frac{2q\pi}{11} + i \sin\frac{2q\pi}{11}\right)$$

$$= -i \left\{\sum_{q=0}^{10}\left(\cos\frac{2q\pi}{11} + i \sin\frac{2q\pi}{11}\right) - 1\right\}$$

$= -i$ {(sum of 11, 11th roots of unity) $-$ 1}

$$= -i(0 - 1) = i$$

$$\because \quad P = \sum_{p=1}^{32} (3p + 2)\left(\sum_{q=1}^{10}\left(\sin\frac{2q\pi}{11} - i \cos\frac{2q\pi}{11}\right)\right)^p$$

$$= \sum_{p=1}^{32} (3p + 2)(i)^p$$

$$= 3\sum_{p=1}^{32} p(i)^p + 2\sum_{p=1}^{32} (i)^p$$

$$= 3\sum_{p=1}^{32} p(i)^p + 0 = 3S \text{ (say)}$$

where, $S = \sum_{p=1}^{32} p(i)^p$

$$S = 1 \cdot i + 2 \cdot i^2 + 3 \cdot i^3 + \ldots + 31 \cdot i^{31} + 32 \cdot i^{32}$$

$$iS = 1 \cdot i^2 + 2 \cdot i^3 + \ldots + 31 \cdot i^{32} + 32 i^{33}$$

$$(1 - i) S = (i + i^2 + i^3 + \ldots + i^{32}) - 32 i^{33}$$

$$= (0) - 32i$$

$$\therefore \quad S = -\frac{32i \cdot (1 + i)}{(1 - i) \cdot (1 + i)}$$

$$= -16(i - 1) = 16(1 - i)$$

$$\therefore \quad P = 3S = 48(1 - i)$$

Given, $(1 + i) P = n(n!) \Rightarrow (1 + i) \cdot 48(1 - i) = n(n!)$

$$\Rightarrow \quad 96 = n(n!) \Rightarrow 4(4!) = n(n!)$$

$$\therefore \quad n = 4$$

67. $$\because \quad \frac{1 + i}{1 - i} = \frac{(1 + i)^2}{(1 - i)(1 + i)} = \frac{1 + i^2 + 2i}{2} = i$$

Given, $$\left(\frac{1 + i}{1 - i}\right)^n = \frac{2}{\pi} \sin^{-1}\left(\frac{1 + x^2}{2x}\right)$$

$$\Rightarrow \quad i^n = \frac{2}{\pi} \sin^{-1}\left(\frac{1 + x^2}{2x}\right)$$

$$\Rightarrow \quad \sin^{-1}\left(\frac{1 + x^2}{2x}\right) = \frac{\pi}{2}(i)^n$$

$$\Rightarrow \quad \frac{1 + x^2}{2x} = \sin\left(\frac{\pi}{2}(i)^n\right) \qquad \ldots(i)$$

Now, AM $\geq$ GM

$$\frac{x + \frac{1}{x}}{2} \geq 1 \Rightarrow \frac{x^2 + 1}{2x} \geq 1$$

$$\Rightarrow \quad \sin\left(\frac{\pi}{2}(i)^n\right) \geq 1 \qquad [\because -1 \leq \sin\theta \leq 1]$$

$$\therefore \quad \sin\left(\frac{\pi}{2}(i)^n\right) = 1$$

$$\Rightarrow \quad n = 4, 8, 12, 16, \ldots$$

$\therefore$ Least positive integer, $n = 4$

68. (A) $\to$ (p,q), (B) $\to$ (p,r),(C) $\to$ (p,r,s)

If $\left|z \pm \frac{a}{z}\right| = b$, where $a > 0$ and $b > 0$, then

$$\frac{-b+\sqrt{b^2+4a}}{2} \le |z| \le \frac{b+\sqrt{b^2+4a}}{2}$$

(A) Here, $a = 1$ and $b = 2$

Then, $-1+\sqrt{2} \le |z| \le 1+\sqrt{2}$

$\therefore \quad G = 1+\sqrt{2}$

and $\quad L = -1+\sqrt{2}$

$\Rightarrow \quad G - L = 2$ [natural number and prime number]

(B) Here, $a = 2$ and $b = 4$

Then, $-2+\sqrt{6} \le |z| \le 2+\sqrt{6}$

$\therefore \quad G = 2+\sqrt{6}$

and $\quad L = -2+\sqrt{6}$

$\Rightarrow \quad G - L = 4$ [natural number and composite number]

(C) Here, $a = 3$ and $b = 6$

Then, $-3+2\sqrt{3} \le |z| \le 3+2\sqrt{3}$

$\therefore \quad G = 3+2\sqrt{3}$

and $\quad L = -3+2\sqrt{3}$

$\Rightarrow \quad G - L = 6$

[natural number, composite number and perfect number]

69. (A) $\to$ (q), B $\to$ (q, r), C $\to$ (q, s)

We know that,

$$\sqrt{z} = \pm\left(\sqrt{\frac{|z| - \text{Re}(z)}{2}} + i\sqrt{\frac{|z| - \text{Re}(z)}{2}}\right)$$

If $\text{Im}(z) > 0 = \pm\left(\sqrt{\frac{|z| + \text{Re}(z)}{2}} - i\sqrt{\frac{|z| - \text{Re}(z)}{2}}\right)$

If $\text{Im}(z) < 0$

(A) $\sqrt{6+8i} = \pm\left(\sqrt{\frac{10+6}{2}} + i\sqrt{\frac{10-6}{2}}\right)$

$= \pm(2\sqrt{2} + i\sqrt{2})$

$= \pm\sqrt{2}(2+i)$

and $\sqrt{-6+8i} = \pm\left(\sqrt{\frac{10-6}{2}} + i\sqrt{\frac{10+6}{2}}\right)$

$= \pm(\sqrt{2} + i2\sqrt{2}) = \pm\sqrt{2}(1+2i)$

$\therefore \quad z = \sqrt{6+8i} + \sqrt{-6+8i}$

$= \pm\sqrt{2}(2+i) \pm \sqrt{2}(1+2i)$

$= 3\sqrt{2}(1+i), \sqrt{2}(1-i), -3\sqrt{2}(1+i), \sqrt{2}(-1+i)$

$\therefore \quad z_1 = 3\sqrt{2}(1+i), z_2 = \sqrt{2}(1-i),$

$z_3 = -3\sqrt{2}(1+i)$

and $\quad z_4 = \sqrt{2}(-1+i)$

$\therefore |z_1|^2 + |z_2|^2 + |z_3|^2 + |z_4|^2$

$= 36 + 4 + 36 + 4 = 80$ which is divisible by 8.

(B) $\sqrt{5-12i} = \pm\left(\sqrt{\frac{13+5}{2}} - i\sqrt{\frac{13-5}{2}}\right) = \pm(3-2i)$

and $\sqrt{-5-12i} = \pm\left(\sqrt{\frac{13-5}{2}} - i\sqrt{\frac{13+5}{2}}\right) = \pm(2-3i)$

$\therefore \quad z = \sqrt{5-12i} + \sqrt{-5-12i} = \pm(3-2i) \pm (2-3i)$

$= 5-5i, -1-i, -5+5i, 1+i$

$\therefore \quad z_1 = 5-5i, \; z_2 = -1-i,$

$z_3 = -5+5i$ and $z_4 = 1+i$

$\therefore \; |z_1|^2 + |z_2|^2 + |z_3|^2 + |z_4|^2 = 50 + 2 + 50 + 2$

$= 104 = 8 \times 13$

(C) $\sqrt{8+15i} = \pm\left(\sqrt{\frac{17+8}{2}} + i\sqrt{\frac{17-8}{2}}\right)$

$= \pm\left(\frac{5}{\sqrt{2}} + \frac{3i}{\sqrt{2}}\right) = \pm\frac{1}{\sqrt{2}}(5+3i)$

and $\sqrt{-8-15i} = \pm\left(\sqrt{\frac{17-8}{2}} - i\sqrt{\frac{17+8}{2}}\right)$

$= \pm\left(\frac{3}{\sqrt{2}} - \frac{5}{\sqrt{2}}i\right) = \pm\frac{1}{\sqrt{2}}(3-5i)$

$\therefore \quad z = \sqrt{8+15i} + \sqrt{-8-15i}$

$= \pm\frac{1}{\sqrt{2}}(5+3i) \pm \frac{1}{\sqrt{2}}(3-5i)$

$z = \frac{1}{\sqrt{2}}(8-2i), \frac{1}{\sqrt{2}}(-2-8i),$

$\frac{1}{\sqrt{2}}(-8+2i), \frac{1}{\sqrt{2}}(2+8i)$

$\therefore \quad z_1 = \sqrt{2}(4-i), \; z_2 = \sqrt{2}(-1-4i)$

$z_3 = \sqrt{2}(-4+i)$ and $z_4 = \sqrt{2}(1+4i)$

$\therefore \; |z_1|^2 + |z_2|^2 + |z_3|^2 + |z_4|^2 = 34 + 34 + 34 + 34$

$= 136 = 17 \times 8$

70. (A) $\to$ (p, q, r, t);(B) $\to$ (p,s);(C) $\to$ (p,r)

(A) Here, the last digit of 143 is 3. The remainder when 861 is divided by 4 is 1. Then, press switch number 1 and we get 3. Hence, the digit in the units place of $(143)^{861}$ is 3.

$\therefore \quad \lambda = 3$

Next, the last digit of 5273 is 3. The remainder when 1358 is divided by 4 is 2. Then, press switch number 2 and we get 9. Hence, the digit in the units place of $(5273)^{1358}$ is 9.

$\therefore \quad \mu = 9$

Hence, $\quad \lambda + \mu = 3 + 9 = 12$

which is divisible by 2, 3, 4 and 6.

(B) Here, the last digit of 212 is 2. The remainder when 7820 is divided by 4 is 0. Then, press switch number 0 and we get 6. Hence, the digit in the unit's place of $(212)^{7820}$ is 6.

$\therefore \quad \lambda = 6$

Next, the last digit of 1322 is 2. The remainder when 1594 is divided by 4 is 2. Then, press switch number 2 and we get 4.

Hence, the digit in the unit's place of $(1322)^{1594}$ is 4.

$\therefore \quad \mu = 4$

Hence, $\lambda + \mu = 6 + 4 = 10$, which is divisible by 2 and 5.

(C) Here, the last digit of 136 is 6. Therefore, the unit's place of $(136)^{786}$ is 6.

$\therefore \quad \lambda = 6$

Next, the last digit of 7138 is 8. The remainder when 13491 is divided by 4 is 3. Then, press switch number 3 and we get 2. Hence, unit's place of $(7138)^{13491}$ is 2.

$\therefore \quad \mu = 2$

Hence, $\quad \lambda + \mu = 6 + 2 = 8$

which is divisible by 2 and 4.

71. (A) → (r); (B) → (p,s); (C) → (q,t)

If $\left|z - \frac{a}{z}\right| = b$, where $a > 0$ and $b > 0$, then

$$\frac{-b + \sqrt{b^2 + 4a}}{2} \le |z| \le \frac{b + \sqrt{b^2 + 4a}}{2}$$

$$\therefore \quad \lambda = \frac{b + \sqrt{b^2 + 4a}}{2} \text{ and } \mu = \frac{-b + \sqrt{b^2 + 4a}}{2}$$

(A) Here, $a = 6$ and $b = 5$

$\therefore \quad \lambda = 6$ and $\mu = 1$

$\Rightarrow \quad \lambda^\mu + \mu^\lambda = 6^1 + 1^6 = 7$

and $\quad \lambda^\mu - \mu^\lambda = 6^1 - 1^6 = 5$

(B) Here, $a = 7$ and $b = 6$

$\therefore \quad \lambda = 7$ and $\mu = 1$

$\therefore \quad \lambda^\mu + \mu^\lambda = 7^1 + 1^7 = 8$

and $\quad \lambda^\mu - \mu^\lambda = 7^1 - 1^7 = 6$

(C) Here, $a = 8$ and $b = 7$

$\therefore \quad \lambda = 8$ and $\mu = 1$

$\Rightarrow \quad \lambda^\mu + \mu^\lambda = 8^1 + 1^8 = 9$

and $\quad \lambda^\mu - \mu^\lambda = 8^1 - 1^8 = 7$

72. Statement-1 is false because $3 + 7i > 2 + 4i$ is meaningless in the set of complex number as set of complex number does not hold ordering. But Statement-2 is true.

73. Statement-1 is false as

$$(\cos\theta + i\sin\phi)^n \ne \cos n\theta + i\sin n\phi$$

Now, $\left(\cos\frac{\pi}{4} + i\sin\frac{\pi}{4}\right)^2 = \cos\frac{\pi}{2} + i\sin\frac{\pi}{2}$

$= i$ [by De-Moivre's theorem]

$\therefore$ Statement-2 is true.

74. We have,

$$|3z_1 + 1| = |3z_2 + 1| = |3z_3 + 1|$$

$\therefore z_1, z_2$ and z_3 are equidistant from $\left(-\frac{1}{3}, 0\right)$ and circumcentre of triangle is $\left(-\frac{1}{3}, 0\right)$.

Also, $\quad 1 + z_1 + z_2 + z_3 = 0$

$$\Rightarrow \quad \frac{1 + z_1 + z_2 + z_3}{3} = 0$$

$$\Rightarrow \quad \frac{z_1 + z_2 + z_3}{3} = -\frac{1}{3}$$

$\therefore$ Centroid of the triangle is $\left(-\frac{1}{3}, 0\right)$.

So, the circumcentre and centroid of the triangle coincide. Hence, required triangle is an equilateral triangle.

Therefore, Statement-1 is true. Also, z_1, z_2 and z_3 represent vertices of an equilateral triangle, if $z_1^2 + z_2^2 + z_3^2 - (z_1z_2 + z_2z_3 + z_3z_1) = 0$.

Therefore, Statement-2 is false.

75. We have,

$$|z - 1| + |z - 8| = 5 \quad \text{...(i)}$$

Here, $\quad z_1 = 1, z_2 = 8$ and $2a = 5$

Now, $\quad |z_1 - z_2| = |1 - 8| = |-7| = 7$

$\therefore \quad 2a = 5 < 7$

Therefore, locus of Eq. (i) does not represent an ellipse. Hence, Statement-1 is false. Statement-2 is true by the property of ellipse.

76. Since, z_1, z_2 and z_3 are in AP.

$\therefore \quad 2z_2 = z_1 + z_3$

$\Rightarrow \quad z_2 = \frac{z_1 + z_3}{2}$

It is clear that, z_2 is the mid-point of z_1 and z_3.

$\therefore z_1, z_2$ and z_3 are collinear.

Statement-1 is true, Statement-2 is true; Statement-2 is a correct explanation of Statement-1.

77. Principal argument of a complex number depend upon quadrant and principal argument lies in $(-\pi, \pi]$.

Hence, Statement-1 is always not true and Statement-2 is obviously true.

78. We have, $\quad C_1 : \arg(z) = \frac{\pi}{4}$

$\Rightarrow \quad \tan^{-1}\left(\frac{y}{x}\right) = \frac{\pi}{4}$ [let $z = x + iy$]

$\Rightarrow \quad \frac{y}{x} = \tan\frac{\pi}{4} = 1$

$\Rightarrow \quad y = x$

$\therefore \quad C_1 : y = x \quad$ ...(i)

$C_2 : \arg(z) = \frac{3\pi}{4}$

$\Rightarrow \quad \tan^{-1}\left(\frac{y}{x}\right) = \frac{3\pi}{4}$ [let $z = x + iy$]

$\Rightarrow \quad \frac{y}{x} = \tan\frac{3\pi}{4} = -1$

$\Rightarrow \quad y = -x$

$\therefore \quad C_2 : y = -x \quad$ ...(ii)

and $C_3 : \arg(z - 5 - 5i) = \pi$

$\Rightarrow \quad \tan^{-1}\left(\frac{y - 5}{x - 5}\right) = \pi$ [let $z = x + iy$]

$$\Rightarrow \quad \frac{y-5}{x-5} = \tan\pi = 0 \Rightarrow y = 5$$

$$\therefore \quad C_3 : y = 5 \qquad \text{...(iii)}$$

We get the following figure.

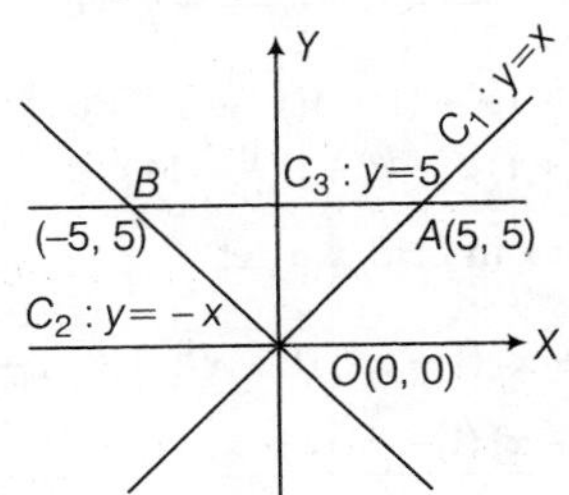

$\therefore$ Area of the region bounded by C_1, C_2 and C_3

$$= \frac{1}{2}\left\|\begin{matrix} 5-0 & 5-0 \\ -5-0 & 5-0 \end{matrix}\right\| = 25$$

$\therefore$ Statement-1 is false.

Now, $\quad OA = 5\sqrt{2}, OB = 5\sqrt{2}$ and $AB = 10$

$\because \quad (OA)^2 + (OB)^2 = (AB)^2$ and $OA = OB$

Therefore, the boundary of C_1, C_2 and C_3 constitutes right isosceles triangle.

Hence, Statement-2 is true.

79. Since, $\text{Im}(\bar{z}_2 z_3) = \dfrac{\bar{z}_2 z_3 - (\overline{\bar{z}_2 z_3})}{2i} = \dfrac{1}{2i}\{\bar{z}_2 z_3 - z_2 \bar{z}_3\}$

$$z_1 \,\text{Im}(\bar{z}_2 z_3) = \frac{1}{2i}\{z_1 \bar{z}_2 z_3 - z_1 z_2 \bar{z}_3\} \qquad \text{...(i)}$$

Similarly, $z_2 \,\text{Im}(\bar{z}_3 z_1) = \dfrac{1}{2i}\{z_2 \bar{z}_3 z_1 - z_2 \bar{z}_1 z_3\}$ $\qquad$ ...(ii)

and $\quad z_3 \,\text{Im}(\bar{z}_1 z_2) = \dfrac{1}{2i}\{z_3 \bar{z}_1 z_2 - z_3 z_1 \bar{z}_2\}$ $\qquad$ ...(iii)

On adding Eqs. (i), (ii) and (iii), we get

$$z_1 \,\text{Im}(\bar{z}_2 z_3) + z_2 \,\text{Im}(\bar{z}_3 z_1) + z_3 \,\text{Im}(\bar{z}_1 z_2) = 0$$

Therefore, this is proved.

80. Since, z_1, z_2 and z_3 are the roots of

$$x^3 + 3ax^2 + 3bx + c = 0,$$

we get $\quad z_1 + z_2 + z_3 = -3a$

$$\Rightarrow \quad \frac{z_1 + z_2 + z_3}{3} = -a$$

and $\quad z_1 z_2 + z_2 z_3 + z_3 z_1 = 3b$

Hence, the centroid of the ΔABC is the point of affix $(-a)$.

Now, the triangle will be equilateral, if

$$z_1^2 + z_2^2 + z_3^2 = z_1 z_2 + z_2 z_3 + z_3 z_1$$

$$\Rightarrow \quad (z_1 + z_2 + z_3)^2 = 3(z_1 z_2 + z_2 z_3 + z_3 z_1)$$

$$\Rightarrow \quad (-3a)^2 = 3(3b)$$

Therefore, the condition is $a^2 = b$.

81. $\because \quad x^5 - 1 = 0$ has roots $1, \alpha_1, \alpha_2, \alpha_3, \alpha_4$.

$\therefore (x^5 - 1) = (x-1)(x-\alpha_1)(x-\alpha_2)(x-\alpha_3)(x-\alpha_4)$

$$\Rightarrow \frac{x^5 - 1}{x-1} = (x-\alpha_1)(x-\alpha_2)(x-\alpha_3)(x-\alpha_4) \qquad \text{...(i)}$$

On putting $x = \omega$ in Eq. (i), we get

$$\frac{\omega^5 - 1}{\omega - 1} = (\omega - \alpha_1)(\omega - \alpha_2)(\omega - \alpha_3)(\omega - \alpha_4)$$

$$\Rightarrow \quad \frac{\omega^2 - 1}{\omega - 1} = (\omega - \alpha_1)(\omega - \alpha_2)(\omega - \alpha_3)(\omega - \alpha_4) \qquad \text{...(ii)}$$

and putting $x = \omega^2$ in Eq. (i), we get

$$\frac{\omega^{10} - 1}{\omega^2 - 1} = (\omega^2 - \alpha_1)(\omega^2 - \alpha_2)(\omega^2 - \alpha_3)(\omega^2 - \alpha_4)$$

$$\Rightarrow \quad \frac{\omega - 1}{\omega^2 - 1} = (\omega^2 - \alpha_1)(\omega^2 - \alpha_2)(\omega^2 - \alpha_3)(\omega^2 - \alpha_4) \qquad \text{...(iii)}$$

On dividing Eq. (ii) by Eq. (iii), we get

$$\frac{\omega - \alpha_1}{\omega^2 - \alpha_1} \cdot \frac{\omega - \alpha_2}{\omega^2 - \alpha_2} \cdot \frac{\omega - \alpha_3}{\omega^2 - \alpha_3} \cdot \frac{\omega - \alpha_4}{\omega^2 - \alpha_4} = \frac{(\omega^2 - 1)^2}{(\omega - 1)^2}$$

$$= \frac{\omega^4 + 1 - 2\omega^2}{\omega^2 + 1 - 2\omega} = \frac{\omega + 1 - 2\omega^2}{\omega^2 + 1 - 2\omega}$$

$$= \frac{-\omega^2 - 2\omega^2}{-\omega - 2\omega} = \frac{-3\omega^2}{-3\omega} = \omega$$

82. Let $z = x + iy$, then $\dfrac{z + \bar{z}}{2} = x$

$\therefore$ From given relation, we get

$$\Rightarrow \quad x = |x + iy - 1|$$

$$\Rightarrow \quad x = |(x-1) + iy|$$

$$\Rightarrow \quad x^2 = (x-1)^2 + y^2 \Rightarrow 2x = 1 + y^2$$

If $z_1 = x_1 + iy_1$ and $z_2 = x_2 + iy_2$

Then, $\quad 2x_1 = 1 + y_1^2$ $\qquad$ ...(i)

and $\quad 2x_2 = 1 + y_2^2$ $\qquad$ ...(ii)

On subtracting Eq. (ii) from Eq. (i), we get

$$2(x_1 - x_2) = y_1^2 - y_2^2$$

$$2(x_1 - x_2) = (y_1 + y_2)(y_1 - y_2) \qquad \text{...(iii)}$$

But, given that $\arg(z_1 - z_2) = \pi/4$

Then, $\quad \tan^{-1}\left(\dfrac{y_1 - y_2}{x_1 - x_2}\right) = \dfrac{\pi}{4} \Rightarrow \dfrac{y_1 - y_2}{x_1 - x_2} = 1$

$$\therefore \quad y_1 - y_2 = x_1 - x_2 \qquad \text{...(iv)}$$

From Eqs. (iii) and (iv), we get

$$y_1 + y_2 = 2 \qquad [\because y_1 - y_2 \neq 0]$$

$$\therefore \quad \text{Im}(z_1 + z_2) = 2$$

Hence, the imaginary part $(z_1 + z_2)$ is 2.

83. (i) LHS $= (a^2 + b^2 + c^2 - bc - ca - ab)$

$$(x^2 + y^2 + z^2 - yz - zx - xy)$$

$$= (a + b\omega + c\omega^2)(a + b\omega^2 + c\omega)$$
$$(x + y\omega + z\omega^2)(x + y\omega^2 + z\omega)$$

$$= \{(a + b\omega + c\omega^2)(x + y\omega + z\omega^2)\}$$
$$\{(a + b\omega^2 + c\omega)(x + y\omega^2 + z\omega)\}$$

$$= \{ax + cy + bz + \omega(bx + ay + cz) + \omega^2(cx + by + az)\} \times \{ax + cy + bz + \omega^2(bx + ay + cz) + \omega(cx + by + az)\}$$

$$= (X + \omega Z + \omega^2 Y)(X + \omega^2 Z + \omega Y)$$

$$= \text{RHS}$$

(ii) $\text{LHS} = (a^3 + b^3 + c^3 - 3abc)(x^3 + y^3 + z^3 - 3xyz)$

$$= (a + b + c)(a^2 + b^2 + c^2 - ab - bc - ca) \times (x + y + z)(x^2 + y^2 + z^2 - xy - yz - zx)$$

$$= (a + b + c)(x + y + z)(a^2 + b^2 + c^2 - ab - bc - ca) \times (x^2 + y^2 + z^2 - xy - yz - zx) \text{ [using (i) part]}$$

$$= (ax + ay + az + bx + by + bz + cx + cy + cz)(X^2 + Y^2 + Z^2 - YZ - ZX - XY)$$

$$= \{(ax + cy + bz) + (cx + by + az) + (bx + ay + cz)\}(X^2 + Y^2 + Z^2 - YZ - ZX - XY)$$

$$= (X + Y + Z)(X^2 + Y^2 + Z^2 - YZ - ZX - XY)$$

$$= X^3 + Y^3 + Z^3 - 3XYZ = \text{RHS}$$

84. Let $z = x + iy$

$\therefore \quad |z|^2 = x^2 + y^2$

$\therefore \quad x^2 + y^2 - 2i(x + iy) + 2c(1 + i) = 0$

$(x^2 + y^2 + 2y + 2c) + i(-2x + 2c) = 0$

On comparing the real and imaginary parts, we get

$$x^2 + y^2 + 2y + 2c = 0 \quad \text{...(i)}$$

and $$-2x + 2c = 0 \quad \text{...(ii)}$$

From Eqs. (i) and (ii), we get

$$y^2 + 2y + c^2 + 2c = 0$$

$$\Rightarrow \quad y = \frac{-2 \pm \sqrt{4 - 4(c^2 + 2c)}}{2} = -1 \pm \sqrt{(1 - c^2 - 2c)}$$

$\because$ x and y are real.

$\therefore \quad 1 - c^2 - 2c \geq 0$ or $c^2 + 2c + 1 \leq 2$

$(c + 1)^2 \leq (\sqrt{2})^2 \Rightarrow -\sqrt{2} - 1 \leq c \leq \sqrt{2} - 1$

$\therefore \quad 0 \leq c \leq \sqrt{2} - 1 \quad$ [$\because$ given $c \geq 0$]

Hence, the solution is $z = x + iy = c + i(-1 \pm \sqrt{1 - c^2 - 2c})$ for $0 \leq c \leq \sqrt{2} - 1$

and $z = x + iy \equiv$ no solution for $c > \sqrt{2} - 1$

85. Let $z = x + iy$

$$\therefore \quad \text{Re}(z) = x = \frac{z + \bar{z}}{2} \quad \text{...(i)}$$

and $$\text{Im}(z) = y = \frac{z - \bar{z}}{2i} \quad \text{...(ii)}$$

The equation $(2 - i)z + (2 + i)\bar{z} + 3 = 0$ can be written as

$$2(z + \bar{z}) - i(z - \bar{z}) + 3 = 0$$

or $$4x + 2y + 3 = 0$$

$\therefore$ Slope of the given line, $m = -2$

Let slope of the required line be m_1, then

$$\tan 45^\circ = \left|\frac{m_1 - m}{1 + m_1 m}\right| \Rightarrow 1 = \left|\frac{m_1 + 2}{1 - 2m_1}\right| \Rightarrow \pm 1 = \frac{m_1 + 2}{1 - 2m_1}$$

$$\therefore \quad m_1 = -\frac{1}{3}, 3$$

$\therefore$ Equation of straight lines through $(-1, 4)$ and having slopes $-\frac{1}{3}$ and 3 are $y - 4 = -\frac{1}{3}(x + 1)$ and $y - 4 = 3(x + 1)$

$\Rightarrow \quad x + 3y - 11 = 0$ and $3x - y + 7 = 0$

Using Eqs. (i) and (ii), then equations of lines are

$$\frac{z + \bar{z}}{2} + \frac{3(z - \bar{z})}{2i} - 11 = 0$$

and $$\frac{3(z + \bar{z})}{2} - \frac{(z - \bar{z})}{2i} + 7 = 0$$

i.e., $$(1 - 3i)z + (1 + 3i)\bar{z} - 22 = 0$$

and $$(3 + i)z + (3 - i)\bar{z} + 14 = 0$$

86. Putting $\frac{1 + i}{2} = x$ in LHS, we get

$$\text{LHS} = (1 + x)(1 + x^2)(1 + x^{2^2}) \dots (1 + x^{2^n})$$

$$= \frac{(1 - x)(1 + x)(1 + x^2)(1 + x^{2^2}) \dots (1 + x^{2^n})}{(1 - x)}$$

$$= \frac{(1 - x^2)(1 + x^2)(1 + x^{2^2}) \dots (1 + x^{2^n})}{(1 - x)}$$

$$= \frac{(1 - x^{2^2})(1 + x^{2^2}) \dots (1 + x^{2^n})}{(1 - x)}$$

$$= \frac{(1 - x^{2^n})(1 + x^{2^n})}{(1 - x)} = \frac{1 - (x^2)^{2^n}}{(1 - x)}$$

$$= \frac{1 - \left(\frac{i}{2}\right)^{2^n}}{1 - \left(\frac{1 + i}{2}\right)} \quad \left[\because x = \frac{1 + i}{2}\right]$$

$$= \frac{1 - \frac{1}{2^{2^n}}(1)}{\left(\frac{1 - i}{2}\right)} \frac{(1 + i)}{(1 + i)} = (1 + i)\left(1 - \frac{1}{2^{2^n}}\right) = \text{RHS}$$

87. Since, $\arg(z - 3i) = 3\pi/4$ is a ray which is start from $3i$ and makes an angle $3\pi/4$ with positive real axis as shown in the figure.

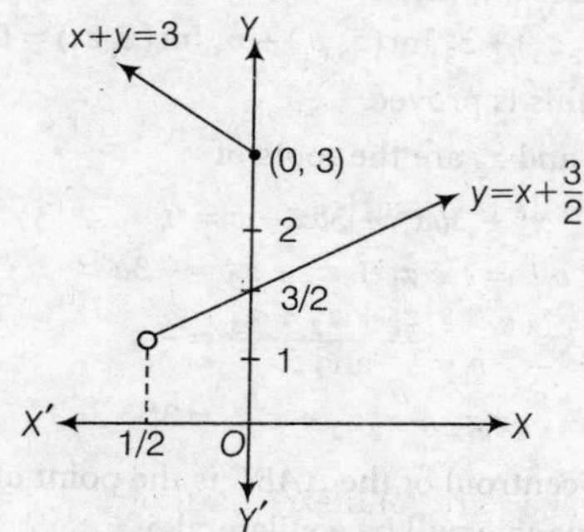

$\therefore$ Equation of ray in cartesian form is

$$y - 3 = \tan(3\pi/4)(x - 0)$$

or $$y - 3 = -x \text{ or } x + y = 3$$

and $$\arg(2z + 1 - 2i) = \pi/4$$

$$\Rightarrow \quad \arg\left(2\left(z + \frac{1}{2} - i\right)\right) = \pi/4$$

or $$\arg(2) + \arg\left(z + \frac{1}{2} - i\right) = \pi/4$$

or $$0 + \arg\left(z + \frac{1}{2} - i\right) = \pi/4$$

or $\quad \arg\left(z - \left(-\frac{1}{2} + i\right)\right) = \pi/4$

which is a ray that start from point $-\frac{1}{2} + i$ and makes an angle $\pi/4$ with positive real axis as shown in the figure.

$\therefore$ Equation of ray in cartesian form is

$$y - 1 = 1[x - (-1/2)] \Rightarrow y = x + 3/2$$

From the figure, it is clear that the system of equations has no solution.

88. Let $\quad a = r\cos\alpha$ and $0 = r\sin\alpha$ ...(i)

So that, $\quad a^2 + 0^2 = r^2$

$\therefore \quad r = |a|$

Then, $\quad a = |a|\cos\alpha$ [from Eq. (i)]

$\therefore \quad \cos\alpha = \pm 1$

Then, $\cos\alpha = 1$ or -1 according as a is + ve or − ve and $\sin\alpha = 0$.

Hence, $\alpha = 0$ or π according as a is + ve and − ve.

Again, let $0 = r_1\cos\beta$ or $b = r_1\sin\beta$ ...(ii)

So that, $\quad 0^2 + b^2 = r_1^2$

$\therefore \quad r_1 = |b|$

From Eq. (ii), we get $b = |b|\sin\beta$

$\therefore \quad \sin\beta = \pm 1$

Then, $\sin\beta = 1$ or -1 according as b is + ve or − ve and $\cos\beta = 0$.

Hence, $\beta = \frac{\pi}{2}$ or $-\frac{\pi}{2}$ according as b is +ve or −ve.

89. Let two non-parallel straight lines PQ, RS meet the circle $|z| = r$ in the points a, b and c.

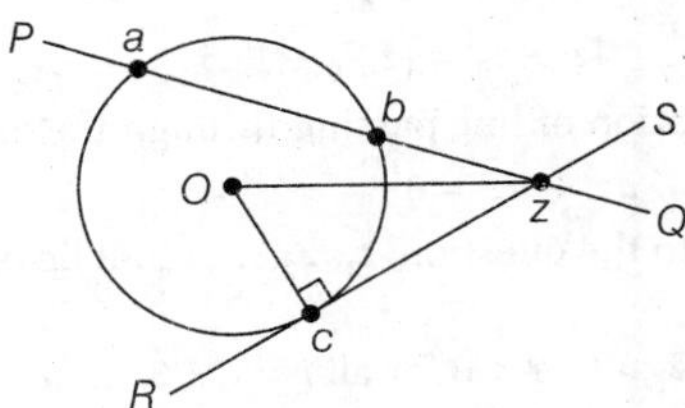

Then, $|a| = r, |b| = r$ and $|c| = r$ or $|a|^2 = |b|^2 = |c|^2 = r^2$

$\therefore \quad a\bar{a} = b\bar{b} = c\bar{c} = r^2,$

then $\quad \bar{a} = \frac{r^2}{a}, \ \bar{b} = \frac{r^2}{b}$ and $\bar{c} = \frac{r^2}{c}$

Points a, b and z are collinear, then $\begin{vmatrix} z & \bar{z} & 1 \\ a & \bar{a} & 1 \\ b & \bar{b} & 1 \end{vmatrix} = 0$

$$\therefore \quad z(\bar{a} - \bar{b}) - \bar{z}(a - b) + a\bar{b} - \bar{a}b = 0$$

$$\Rightarrow \quad z\left(\frac{r^2}{a} - \frac{r^2}{b}\right) - \bar{z}(a - b) + \frac{r^2 a}{b} - \frac{r^2 b}{a} = 0$$

On dividing both sides by $r^2(b - a)$, we get

$$\frac{z}{ab} + \frac{\bar{z}}{r^2} = a^{-1} + b^{-1} \quad \text{...(i)}$$

For RS, replace $a = b = c$ in Eq. (i), then

$$\frac{z}{c^2} + \frac{\bar{z}}{r^2} = 2c^{-1} \quad \text{...(ii)}$$

On subtracting Eq. (i) from Eq. (ii), we get

$$z(c^{-2} - a^{-1}b^{-1}) = 2c^{-1} - a^{-1} - b^{-1}$$

Hence, $\quad z = \frac{2c^{-1} - a^{-1} - b^{-1}}{c^{-2} - a^{-1}b^{-1}}$

which is a required point.

90. $\because AD \perp BC$

$\therefore AP$ is also perpendicular to BC.

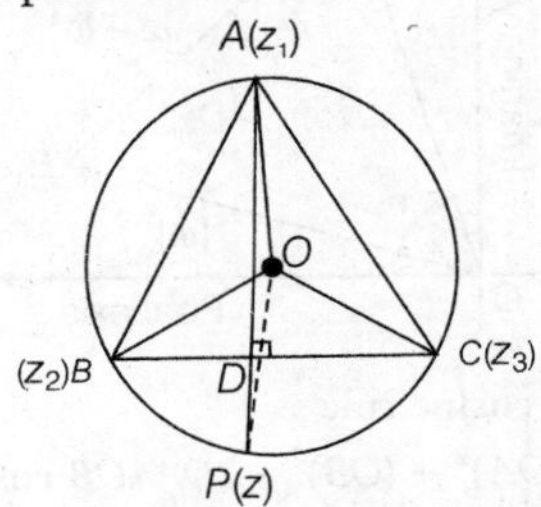

Then, $\quad \arg\left(\frac{z_1 - z}{z_3 - z_2}\right) = \frac{\pi}{2}$

$\therefore \quad \text{Re}\left(\frac{z_1 - z}{z_3 - z_2}\right) = 0$

$$\Rightarrow \quad \frac{\frac{z_1 - z}{z_3 - z_2} + \frac{\bar{z}_1 - \bar{z}}{\bar{z}_3 - \bar{z}_2}}{2} = 0$$

$$\Rightarrow \quad \frac{z_1 - z}{z_3 - z_2} + \frac{\bar{z}_1 - \bar{z}}{\bar{z}_3 - \bar{z}_2} = 0 \quad \text{...(i)}$$

But O is the circumcentre of ΔABC, then

$$OP = OA = OB = OC$$

$$|z| = |z_1| = |z_2| = |z_3|$$

On squaring the above relation, we get

$$|z|^2 = |z_1|^2 = |z_2|^2 = |z_3|^2$$

$$\Rightarrow \quad z\bar{z} = z_1\bar{z}_1 = z_2\bar{z}_2 = z_3\bar{z}_3$$

From first two relations $\frac{\bar{z}_1}{\bar{z}} = \frac{z}{z_1}$ ...(ii)

From first and third relation $\frac{\bar{z}_2}{\bar{z}} = \frac{z}{z_2}$ ...(iii)

and from first and fourth relation $\frac{\bar{z}_3}{\bar{z}} = \frac{z}{z_3}$ ...(iv)

From Eq. (i), we get $\frac{z_1 - z}{z_3 - z_2} + \frac{\frac{\bar{z}_1}{\bar{z}} - 1}{\frac{\bar{z}_3}{\bar{z}} - \frac{\bar{z}_2}{\bar{z}}} = 0$ ...(v)

From Eqs. (ii), (iii), (iv) and (v), we get

$$\frac{z_1 - z}{z_3 - z_2} + \frac{\frac{z}{z_1} - 1}{\frac{z}{z_3} - \frac{z}{z_2}} = 0$$

$$\Rightarrow \quad \left(\frac{z_1 - z}{z_3 - z_2}\right)\left\{1 + \frac{z_2 z_3}{z z_1}\right\} = 0 \quad \left[\because \frac{z_1 - z}{z_3 - z_2} \neq 0\right]$$

$$\Rightarrow \quad 1 + \frac{z_2 z_3}{z z_1} = 0 \Rightarrow z = -\frac{z_2 z_3}{z_1}$$

91. From the figure,

$$\alpha = (\arg(z) - \arg(\omega)) \quad \text{...(i)}$$

and for every α, $\sin^2 \frac{\alpha}{2} \le \left(\frac{\alpha}{2}\right)^2$ ...(ii)

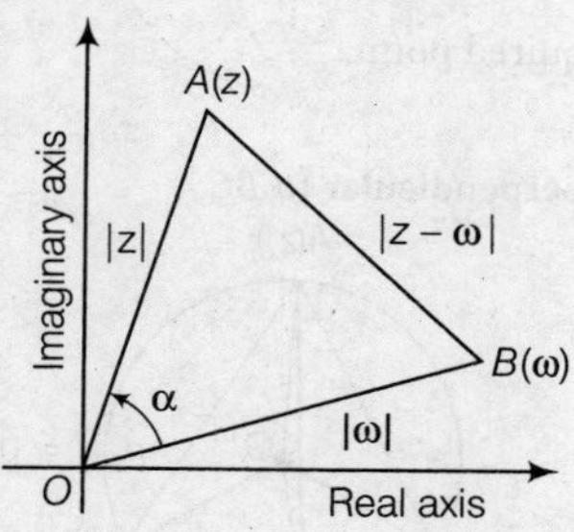

In ΔOAB, from cosine rule

$$(AB)^2 = (OA)^2 + (OB)^2 - 2OA \cdot OB \cos\alpha$$

$\Rightarrow |z - \omega|^2 = |z|^2 + |\omega|^2 - 2|z||\omega|\cos\alpha$

$\Rightarrow |z - \omega|^2 = (|z| - |\omega|)^2 + 2|z||\omega|(1 - \cos\alpha)$

$\Rightarrow |z - \omega|^2 = (|z| - |\omega|)^2 + 4|z||\omega|\sin^2\frac{\alpha}{2}$

$\Rightarrow |z - \omega|^2 \le (|z| - |\omega|)^2 + 4|z||\omega|\left(\frac{\alpha}{2}\right)^2$ [from Eq. (ii)]

$\Rightarrow |z - \omega|^2 \le (|z| - |\omega|)^2 + \alpha^2$ [$\because |z| \le 1, |\omega| \le 1$]

$|z - \omega|^2 \le (|z| - |\omega|)^2 + (\arg(z) - \arg(\omega))^2$ [from Eq. (i)]

I. Aliter

Let $z = r(\cos\theta + i\sin\theta)$ and $\omega = r_1(\cos\theta_1 + i\sin\theta_1)$,
then $|z| = r$ and $|\omega| = r_1$

Also, $\arg(z) = \theta$ and $\arg(\omega) = \theta_1$

and $r \le 1$ and $r_1 \le 1$ [$\because$ given $|z| \le 1, |\omega| \le 1$]

We have, $z - \omega = (r\cos\theta - r_1\cos\theta_1) + i(r\sin\theta - r_1\sin\theta_1)$

$\therefore |z - \omega|^2 = (r\cos\theta - r_1\cos\theta_1)^2 + (r\sin\theta - r_1\sin\theta_1)^2$

$\Rightarrow |z - \omega|^2 = r^2 + r_1^2 - 2rr_1\cos(\theta - \theta_1)$

$= (r - r_1)^2 + 2rr_1 - 2rr_1\cos(\theta - \theta_1)$

$= (r - r_1)^2 + 2rr_1(1 - \cos(\theta - \theta_1))$

$= (r - r_1)^2 + 4rr_1\sin^2\left(\frac{\theta - \theta_1}{2}\right)$

$\le (r - r_1)^2 + 4rr_1\left(\frac{\theta - \theta_1}{2}\right)^2$ [$\because |\sin\theta| \le |\theta|$]

$= (r - r_1)^2 + rr_1(\theta - \theta_1)^2$

$\le (r - r_1)^2 + (\theta - \theta_1)^2$ [$\because r, r_1 \le 1$]

$\Rightarrow |z - \omega|^2 \le (|z| - |\omega|)^2 + (\arg z - \arg\omega)^2$

II. Aliter

Let $z = r\cos\theta$

and $\omega = r_1\cos\theta_1$

$\therefore r^2 + r_1^2 - 2rr_1\cos(\theta - \theta_1) \le r^2 + r_1^2 - 2rr_1 + (\theta - \theta_1)^2$

$\Rightarrow rr_1\sin^2\left(\frac{\theta - \theta_1}{2}\right) \le \left(\frac{\theta - \theta_1}{2}\right)^2$ $\left[\because r, r_1 \le 1 \text{ and } \sin^2 x \le x^2\right]$

92. Given, $OA = 1$ and $|z| = 1$

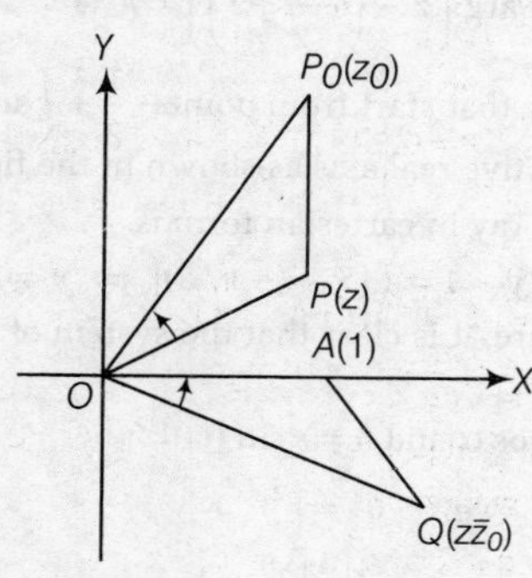

$\therefore OP = |z - 0| = |z| = 1$

$\therefore OP = OA$

$OP_0 = |z_0 - 0| = |z_0|$

and $OQ = |z\bar{z}_0 - 0| = |z\bar{z}_0| = |z||\bar{z}_0| = 1|\bar{z}_0| = |z_0|$

$\therefore OP_0 = OQ$

Also, $\angle P_0OP = \arg\left(\frac{z_0 - 0}{z - 0}\right) = \arg\left(\frac{z_0}{z}\right) = \arg\left(\frac{\bar{z}z_0}{z\bar{z}}\right)$

$= \arg\left(\frac{\bar{z}z_0}{|z|^2}\right) = \arg\left(\frac{\bar{z}z_0}{1}\right) = -\arg(\overline{\bar{z}z_0})$

$= -\arg(z\bar{z}_0) = \arg\left(\frac{1}{z\bar{z}_0}\right)$

$= \arg\left(\frac{1 - 0}{z\bar{z}_0 - 0}\right) = \angle AOQ$

Thus, the triangles POP_0 and AOQ are congruent.

$\therefore PP_0 = AQ$

$|z - z_0| = |z\bar{z}_0 - 1|$

93. Let the equation of line passing through the origin be

$$\bar{a}z + a\bar{z} = 0 \quad \text{...(i)}$$

According to the question, $z_1, z_2, \ldots, z_n$ all lie on one side of line (i)

$\therefore \bar{a}z_i + a\bar{z}_i > 0$ or < 0 for all $i = 1, 2, 3, \ldots, n$ ...(ii)

$\Rightarrow \bar{a}\sum_{i=1}^{n} z_i + a\sum_{i=1}^{n}\bar{z}_i > 0$ or < 0 ...(iii)

$\Rightarrow \sum_{i=1}^{n} z_i \ne 0$ $\left\{\text{If } \sum_{i=1}^{n} z_i = 0, \text{ then } \sum_{i=1}^{n}\bar{z}_i = 0, \text{ hence } \bar{a}\sum_{i=1}^{n} z_i + a\sum_{i=1}^{n}\bar{z}_i = 0\right\}$

From Eq. (ii), we get

$\bar{a}z_i + a\bar{z}_i > 0$ or < 0 for all $i = 1, 2, 3, \ldots, n$

$\Rightarrow \frac{\bar{a}z_i\bar{z}_i}{\bar{z}_i} + \frac{a\bar{z}_iz_i}{z_i} > 0$ or < 0

$\Rightarrow |z_i|^2\left\{\frac{\bar{a}}{\bar{z}_i} + \frac{a}{z_i}\right\} > 0$ or < 0

$\Rightarrow \frac{\bar{a}}{\bar{z}_i} + \frac{a}{z_i} > 0$ or < 0 for all $i = 1, 2, 3, \ldots, n$

$\Rightarrow \frac{1}{z_1}, \frac{1}{z_2}, \ldots, \frac{1}{z_n}$ lie on one side of the line $\bar{a}z + a\bar{z} = 0$

or $\quad \bar{a} \sum_{i=1}^{n} \frac{1}{\bar{z}_i} + a \sum_{i=1}^{n} \frac{1}{z_i} > 0$ or < 0

Therefore, $\sum_{i=1}^{n} \frac{1}{z_i} \neq 0 \left\{ \text{If } \sum_{i=1}^{n} \frac{1}{z_i} = 0, \text{ then } \sum_{i=1}^{n} \frac{1}{\bar{z}_i} = 0 \right.$

$\left. \Rightarrow \quad \bar{a} \sum_{i=1}^{n} \frac{1}{\bar{z}_i} + a \sum_{i=1}^{n} \frac{1}{z_i} = 0 \right\}$

94. Given, $|a||b| = \sqrt{a\bar{b}^2 c}$; $|a| = |c|$; $az^2 + bz + c = 0$, then we have to prove that $|z| = 1$

On squaring, we get

$|a|^2 |b|^2 = a\,\bar{b}^2 c$ and $|a|^2 = |c|^2$

$\Rightarrow a\,\bar{a}\,b\,\bar{b} = a\,\bar{b}^2 c \quad$ and $\quad a\,\bar{a} = c\,\bar{c}$

$\Rightarrow \quad \bar{a}\,b = \bar{b}\,c \quad$ and $\quad a\,\bar{a} = c\,\bar{c}$ ...(i)

If z_1 and z_2 are the roots of $az^2 + bz + c = 0$

Then, $\bar{z}_1$ and $\bar{z}_2$ are the roots of $\bar{a}\,(\bar{z})^2 + \bar{b}\bar{z} + \bar{c} = 0$ ...(A)

$$\left.\begin{aligned} \therefore \quad & z_1 + z_2 = -\frac{b}{a}, z_1 z_2 = \frac{c}{a} \\ \text{and} \quad & \bar{z}_1 + \bar{z}_2 = -\frac{\bar{b}}{\bar{a}}, \bar{z}_1\bar{z}_2 = \frac{\bar{c}}{\bar{a}} \end{aligned}\right\} \quad ...(ii)$$

$\because \quad \frac{1}{z_1} + \frac{1}{z_2} = \frac{z_1 + z_2}{z_1 z_2} = \frac{-b/a}{c/a} = -\frac{b}{c} = -\frac{\bar{b}}{\bar{a}} = \bar{z}_1 + \bar{z}_2$

[from Eqs. (i) and (ii)]

and $\quad \frac{1}{\bar{z}_1} + \frac{1}{\bar{z}_2} = \frac{\bar{z}_1 + \bar{z}_2}{\bar{z}_1\,\bar{z}_2} = \frac{-\bar{b}/\bar{a}}{\bar{c}/\bar{a}}$

$= -\frac{\bar{b}}{\bar{c}} = -\frac{\bar{a}\,bc}{ca\,\bar{a}} = -\frac{b}{a} = z_1 + z_2$

[from Eqs. (i) and (ii)]

Now, it is clear that $z_1 = \frac{1}{\bar{z}_1}$ and $z_2 = \frac{1}{\bar{z}_2}$

Then, $|z_1|^2 = 1$ and $|z_2|^2 = 1$

Hence, $\quad |z| = 1$

Conversely For $az^2 + bz + c = 0$, we have to prove

$|z| = 1 \Rightarrow |a||b| = \sqrt{a\,\bar{b}^2 c}$

and $\quad |a| = |c|$

$|z| = 1 \Rightarrow |z|^2 = 1 \Rightarrow z\,\bar{z} = 1 \Rightarrow z = \frac{1}{\bar{z}}$

From Eq. (A), we get

$$\bar{a}\left(\frac{1}{z}\right)^2 + \bar{b}\left(\frac{1}{z}\right) + \bar{c} = 0 \text{ or } \bar{c}z^2 + \bar{b}z + \bar{a} = 0$$

Also, $az^2 + bz + c = 0$, on comparing

$$\frac{\bar{c}}{a} = \frac{\bar{b}}{b} = \frac{\bar{a}}{c}$$

$\therefore \quad a\,\bar{a} = c\,\bar{c}$ and $\bar{a}\,b = \bar{b}$ cs

$\Rightarrow |a| = |c|$ and $|a||b| = \sqrt{a\,\bar{b}^2 c}$

95. (i) Let $z_1 = r_1(\cos\alpha + i\sin\alpha)$,

$z_2 = r_2(\cos\beta + i\sin\beta)$ and $z_3 = r_3(\cos\gamma + i\sin\gamma)$

$\therefore \; |z_1| = r_1, |z_2| = r_2, |z_3| = r_3$

and $\arg(z_1) = \alpha, \arg(z_2) = \beta, \arg(z_3) = \gamma$

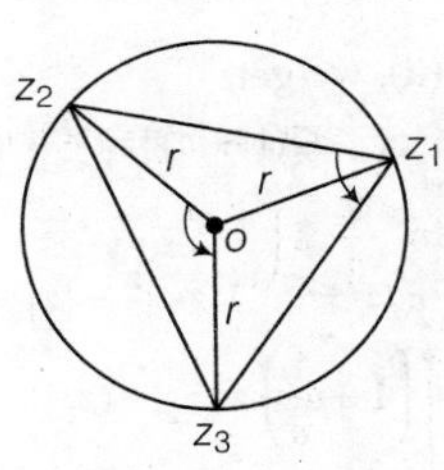

From the given condition,

$$\begin{vmatrix} r_1 & r_2 & r_3 \\ r_2 & r_3 & r_1 \\ r_3 & r_1 & r_2 \end{vmatrix} = 0$$

$\Rightarrow \quad r_1^3 + r_2^3 + r_3^3 - 3r_1r_2r_3 = 0$

$\Rightarrow \frac{1}{2}(r_1 + r_2 + r_3)\{(r_1 - r_2)^2 + (r_2 - r_3)^2 + (r_3 - r_1)^2\} = 0$

Since, $\quad r_1 + r_2 + r_3 \neq 0$,

then $\quad (r_1 - r_2)^2 + (r_2 - r_3)^2 + (r_3 - r_1)^2 = 0$

It is possible only when

$r_1 - r_2 = r_2 - r_3 = r_3 - r_1 = 0$

$\therefore \quad r_1 = r_2 = r_3$

and $\quad |z_1| = |z_2| = |z_3| = r \quad$ [say]

Hence, z_1, z_2, z_3 lie on a circle with the centre at the origin.

(ii) Again, in $\Delta\, oz_2z_3$ by Coni method

$\arg\left(\frac{z_3 - 0}{z_2 - 0}\right) = \angle z_2oz_3 \Rightarrow \arg\left(\frac{z_3}{z_2}\right) = \angle z_2oz_3$ ...(i)

In $\Delta\, z_2z_1z_3$ by Coni method

$\arg\left(\frac{z_3 - z_1}{z_2 - z_1}\right) = \angle z_2\,z_1\,z_3 = \frac{1}{2}\angle z_2oz_3$ [property of circle]

$= \frac{1}{2}\arg\left(\frac{z_3}{z_1}\right)$ [from Eq. (i)]

$\therefore \quad \arg\left(\frac{z_3}{z_1}\right) = 2\arg\left(\frac{z_3 - z_1}{z_2 - z_1}\right)$

Hence, $\arg\left(\frac{z_3}{z_1}\right) = \arg\left(\frac{z_3 - z_1}{z_2 - z_1}\right)^2$

96. We know that,

$\text{Re}(z_1\bar{z}_2) \leq |z_1\bar{z}_2|$

$\therefore \; |z_1|^2 + |z_2|^2 + 2\,\text{Re}(z_1\bar{z}_2) \leq |z_1|^2 + |z_2|^2 + 2|z_1\bar{z}_2|$

$\Rightarrow \quad |z_1 + z_2|^2 \leq |z_1|^2 + |z_2|^2 + 2|z_1||z_2|$ ...(i)

Also, AM $\geq$ GM

$$\therefore \quad \frac{(\sqrt{c}\,|z_1|)^2 + \left(\frac{1}{\sqrt{c}}|z_2|\right)^2}{2} \geq \left\{\sqrt{c}\cdot|z_1|^2\cdot\frac{1}{\sqrt{c}}|z_2|^2\right\}^{1/2} \quad [\because c > 0]$$

$\Rightarrow c|z_1|^2 + \frac{1}{c}|z_2|^2 \geq 2|z_1||z_2|$

$\therefore \; |z_1|^2 + |z_2|^2 + 2|z_1||z_2| \leq |z_1|^2 + |z_2|^2 + c|z_1|^2 + \frac{1}{c}|z_2|^2$

$\Rightarrow |z_1|^2 + |z_2|^2 + 2|z_1||z_2| \leq (1 + c)|z_1|^2 + (1 + c^{-1})(|z_2|^2)$

...(ii)

From Eqs. (i) and (ii), we get

$$|z_1 + z_2|^2 \le (1+c)|z_1|^2 + (1+c^{-1})|z_2|^2$$

Aliter

Here, $(1+c)|z_1|^2 + (1+c^{-1})|z_2|^2 - |z_1+z_2|^2$

$$= (1+c)z_1\bar{z}_1 + \left(1+\frac{1}{c}\right)z_2\bar{z}_2 - (z_1+z_2)(\bar{z}_1+\bar{z}_2)$$

$$= (1+c)z_1\bar{z}_1 + \left(1+\frac{1}{c}\right)z_2\bar{z}_2 - z_1\bar{z}_1 - z_1\bar{z}_2 - z_2\bar{z}_1 - z_2\bar{z}_2$$

$$= cz_1\bar{z}_1 + \frac{1}{c}z_2\bar{z}_2 - z_1\bar{z}_2 - z_2\bar{z}_1$$

$$= \frac{1}{c}\{c^2z_1\bar{z}_1 + z_2\bar{z}_2 - cz_1\bar{z}_2 - cz_2\bar{z}_1\}$$

$$= \frac{1}{c}\{cz_1(c\bar{z}_1 - \bar{z}_2) - z_2(c\bar{z}_1 - \bar{z}_2)\}$$

$$= \frac{1}{c}(cz_1 - z_2)(c\bar{z}_1 - \bar{z}_2) = \frac{1}{c}(cz_1 - z_2)\overline{(cz_1 - z_2)}$$

$$= \frac{1}{c}|cz_1 - z_2|^2 \ge 0 \text{ as } c > 0$$

$$\therefore \quad (1+c)|z_1|^2 + \left(1+\frac{1}{c}\right)|z_2|^2 - |z_1+z_2|^2 \ge 0$$

Hence, $|z_1+z_2|^2 \le (1+c)|z_1|^2 + \left(1+\frac{1}{c}\right)|z_2|^2$

97. If z be the complex number corresponding to the circumcentre O, then we have

$$OA = OB = OC$$

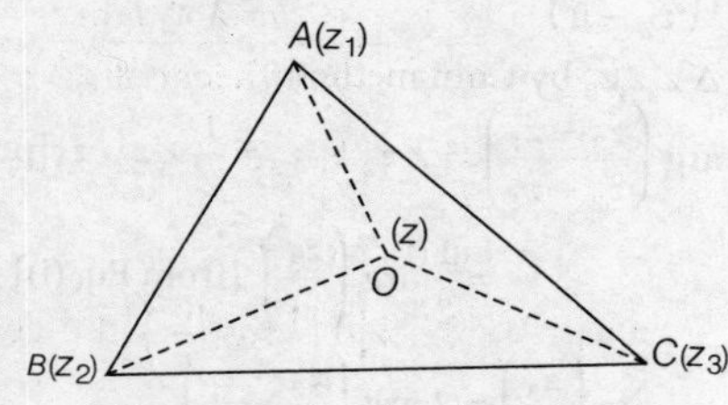

$$\Rightarrow \quad |z - z_1| = |z - z_2| = |z - z_3|$$

$$\Rightarrow \quad |z - z_1|^2 = |z - z_2|^2 = |z - z_3|^2$$

$$\Rightarrow \quad (z - z_1)(\bar{z} - \bar{z}_1) = (z - z_2)(\bar{z} - \bar{z}_2)$$

$$= (z - z_3)(\bar{z} - \bar{z}_3) \quad \text{...(i)}$$

From first two members of Eq. (i), we get

$$\bar{z}(z_2 - z_1) = \bar{z}_1(z - z_1) - \bar{z}_2(z - z_2) \quad \text{...(ii)}$$

and from last two members of Eq. (i), we get

$$\bar{z}(z_3 - z_2) = \bar{z}_2(z - z_2) - \bar{z}_3(z - z_3) \quad \text{...(iii)}$$

Eliminating $\bar{z}$ from Eqs. (ii) and (iii), we get

$$(z_2 - z_1)[\bar{z}_2(z - z_2) - \bar{z}_3(z - z_3)] = (z_3 - z_2)[\bar{z}_1(z - z_1) - \bar{z}_2(z - z_2)]$$

or $z[z_2(z_2 - z_1) - \bar{z}_3(z_2 - z_1) - \bar{z}_1(z_3 - z_2) + \bar{z}_2(z_3 - z_2)]$

$$= z_2\bar{z}_2(z_2 - z_1) - z_3\bar{z}_3(z_2 - z_1) - z_1\bar{z}_1(z_3 - z_2) + z_2\bar{z}_2(z_3 - z_2)$$

or $z\sum \bar{z}_1(z_2 - z_3) = \sum z_1\bar{z}_1(z_2 - z_3)$

or $$z = \frac{\sum |z_1|^2(z_2 - z_3)}{\sum \bar{z}_1(z_2 - z_3)}$$

98. Let z be the complex number corresponding to the orthocentre O, since $AD \perp BC$, we get

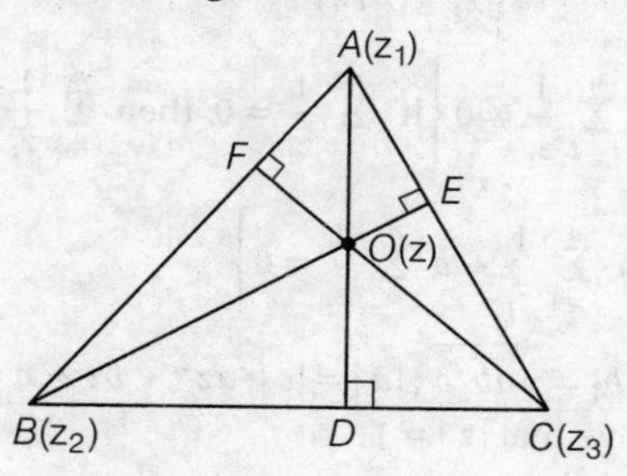

$$\arg\left(\frac{z - z_1}{z_2 - z_3}\right) = \frac{\pi}{2}$$

i.e. $\dfrac{z - z_1}{z_2 - z_3}$ is purely imaginary.

i.e. $\text{Re}\left(\dfrac{z - z_1}{z_2 - z_3}\right) = 0$ or $\dfrac{z - z_1}{z_2 - z_3} + \dfrac{\bar{z} - \bar{z}_1}{\bar{z}_2 - \bar{z}_3} = 0$ ...(i)

Similarly, $\dfrac{z - z_2}{z_3 - z_1} + \dfrac{\bar{z} - \bar{z}_2}{\bar{z}_3 - \bar{z}_1} = 0$ $[\because BE \perp CA]$ ...(ii)

From Eq. (i), we get

$$\bar{z} = \bar{z}_1 - \frac{(z - z_2)(\bar{z}_2 - \bar{z}_3)}{(z_2 - z_3)} \quad \text{...(iii)}$$

From Eq. (ii), we get

$$\bar{z} = \bar{z}_2 - \frac{(z - z_2)(\bar{z}_3 - \bar{z}_1)}{(z_3 - z_1)} \quad \text{...(iv)}$$

Eliminating $\bar{z}$ from Eqs. (iii) and (iv), we get

$$\bar{z}_1 - \bar{z}_2 = \frac{(z - z_1)}{(z_2 - z_3)}(\bar{z}_2 - \bar{z}_3) - \frac{(z - z_2)(\bar{z}_3 - \bar{z}_1)}{(z_3 - z_1)}$$

or $(z - z_1)(\bar{z}_2 - \bar{z}_3)(z_3 - z_1) - (z - z_2)(\bar{z}_3 - \bar{z}_1)(z_2 - z_3)$

$$= (\bar{z}_1 - \bar{z}_2)(z_2 - z_3)(z_3 - z_1)$$

or $z\{(\bar{z}_2 - \bar{z}_3)(z_3 - z_1) - (\bar{z}_3 - \bar{z}_1)(z_2 - z_3)\}$

$$= (\bar{z}_1 - \bar{z}_2)(z_2 - z_3)(z_3 - z_1) + z_1(\bar{z}_2 - \bar{z}_3)(z_3 - z_1) - z_2(\bar{z}_3 - \bar{z}_1)(z_2 - z_3)$$

$$\Rightarrow z[\bar{z}_2 z_3 - \bar{z}_2 z_1 - z_3\bar{z}_3 + \bar{z}_3 z_1 - \bar{z}_3 z_2 + z_3\bar{z}_3 + \bar{z}_1 z_2 - \bar{z}_1 z_3]$$

$$= (\bar{z}_1 - \bar{z}_2)\{z_2 z_3 - z_2 z_1 - z_3^2 + z_3 z_1\} + (\bar{z}_2 - \bar{z}_3)(z_3 z_1 - z_1^2) + (\bar{z}_3 - \bar{z}_1)(z_2 z_3 - z_2^2)$$

$$= -\{z_1^2(\bar{z}_2 - \bar{z}_3) + z_2^2(\bar{z}_3 - \bar{z}_1) + z_3^2(\bar{z}_1 - \bar{z}_2)\}$$

$$+ \{\bar{z}_1 z_2 z_3 - z_2 z_1\bar{z}_1 + z_3 z_1\bar{z}_1 + \bar{z}_2 z_1 z_3 - z_1 z_3\bar{z}_3 + z_2 z_3\bar{z}_3 - \bar{z}_1 z_2 z_3\} - z\sum(z_1\bar{z}_2 - z_2\bar{z}_1)$$

$$= -\sum z_1^2(\bar{z}_2 - \bar{z}_3) - \sum z_1\bar{z}_1(z_2 - z_3)$$

Hence, $$z = \frac{\sum z_1^2(\bar{z}_2 - \bar{z}_3) + \sum |z_1|^2(z_2 - z_3)}{\sum(z_1\bar{z}_2 - z_2\bar{z}_1)}$$

99. Let $\theta = \frac{1}{7}(2n+1)\pi$, where $n = 0, 1, 2, 3, \ldots, 6$

$\therefore\ 7\theta = (2n+1)\pi$ or $4\theta = (2n+1)\pi - 3\theta$

or $\cos 4\theta = -\cos 3\theta$

or $2\cos^2 2\theta - 1 = -(4\cos^3\theta - 3\cos\theta)$

or $2(2\cos^2\theta - 1)^2 - 1 = -(4\cos^3\theta - 3\cos\theta)$

or $8\cos^4\theta + 4\cos^3\theta - 8\cos^2\theta - 3\cos\theta + 1 = 0$

Now, if $\cos\theta = x$, then we have

$8x^4 + 4x^3 - 8x^2 - 3x + 1 = 0$

or $(x+1)(8x^3 - 4x^2 - 4x + 1) = 0$

$$x + 1 \neq 0 \quad [\because \theta \neq \pi]$$

$$\therefore \quad 8x^3 - 4x^2 - 4x + 1 = 0 \quad \text{...(i)}$$

Hence, the roots of this equation are

$$\cos\frac{\pi}{7}, \cos\frac{3\pi}{7}, \cos\frac{5\pi}{7}.$$

$$\left[\text{since } \cos\frac{9\pi}{7} = \cos\frac{5\pi}{7}, \cos\frac{11\pi}{7} = \cos\frac{3\pi}{7}, \cos\frac{13\pi}{7} = \cos\frac{\pi}{7} \text{ and Eq. (i) is cubic}\right]$$

(i) On putting $\frac{1}{x^2} = y$ or $x = \frac{1}{\sqrt{y}}$ in Eq. (i), then Eq. (i) becomes

$$\Rightarrow \quad \frac{8}{y\sqrt{y}} - \frac{4}{y} - \frac{4}{\sqrt{y}} + 1 = 0$$

$$\Rightarrow \quad \left(1 - \frac{4}{y}\right)^2 = \left[\frac{4}{\sqrt{y}}\left(1 - \frac{2}{y}\right)\right]^2$$

$$\text{or} \quad 1 + \frac{16}{y^2} - \frac{8}{y} = \frac{16}{y}\left(1 + \frac{4}{y^2} - \frac{4}{y}\right)$$

$$\text{or} \quad y^3 - 24y^2 + 80y - 64 = 0 \quad \text{...(ii)}$$

$$\text{where} \quad y = \frac{1}{x^2} = \frac{1}{\cos^2\theta} = \sec^2\theta$$

Thus, the roots of $x^3 - 24x^2 + 80x - 61 = 0$

are $\sec^2\frac{\pi}{7}, \sec^2\frac{3\pi}{7}, \sec^2\frac{5\pi}{7}$

(ii) Again, putting $y = 1 + z$ i.e. $z = y - 1$
$= \sec^2\theta - 1 = \tan^2\theta$, Eq. (ii) reduces to

$$(1+z)^3 - 24(1+z)^2 + 80(1+z) - 64 = 0$$

$$\text{or} \quad z^3 - 21z^2 + 35z - 7 = 0 \quad \text{...(iii)}$$

Hence, $\tan^2\frac{\pi}{7}, \tan^2\frac{3\pi}{7}, \tan^2\frac{5\pi}{7}$ are the roots of

$$x^3 - 21x^2 + 35x - 7 = 0$$

(iii) Putting $x = \frac{1}{u}$ in Eq. (i), then Eq. (i) reduces to

$u^3 - 4u^2 - 4u + 8 = 0$ whose roots are

$$\sec\frac{\pi}{7}, \sec\frac{3\pi}{7}, \sec\frac{5\pi}{7}.$$

Therefore, sum of the roots is

$$\sec\frac{\pi}{7} + \sec\frac{3\pi}{7} + \sec\frac{5\pi}{7} = 4$$

100. Let roots of $z^7 + 1 = 0$ are $-1, \alpha, \alpha^3, \alpha^5, \bar{\alpha}, \bar{\alpha}^3, \bar{\alpha}^5$,

where $\alpha = \cos\frac{\pi}{7} + i\sin\frac{\pi}{7}$

$$\therefore \quad (z^7 + 1) = (z+1)(z-\alpha)(z-\bar{\alpha})(z-\alpha^3)(z-\bar{\alpha}^3)(z-\alpha^5)(z-\bar{\alpha}^5)$$

$$\Rightarrow \frac{(z^7+1)}{(z+1)} = (z-\alpha)(z-\bar{\alpha})(z-\alpha^3)(z-\bar{\alpha}^3)(z-\alpha^5)(z-\bar{\alpha}^5)$$

$$\Rightarrow z^6 - z^5 + z^4 - z^3 + z^2 - z + 1 = \left(z^2 + 1 - 2z\cos\frac{\pi}{7}\right)\left(z^2 + 1 - 2z\cos\frac{3\pi}{7}\right)\left(z^2 + 1 - 2z\cos\frac{5\pi}{7}\right) \quad \text{...(A)}$$

Dividing by z^3 on both sides, we get

$$\left(z^3 + \frac{1}{z^3}\right) - \left(z^2 + \frac{1}{z^2}\right) + \left(z + \frac{1}{z}\right) - 1 = \left(z + \frac{1}{z} - 2\cos\frac{\pi}{7}\right)\left(z + \frac{1}{z} - 2\cos\frac{3\pi}{7}\right)\left(z + \frac{1}{z} - 2\cos\frac{5\pi}{7}\right)$$

On putting $z + \frac{1}{z} = 2x$, we get

$$(8x^3 - 6x) - (4x^2 - 2) + 2x - 1 = 8\left(x - \cos\frac{\pi}{7}\right)\left(x - \cos\frac{3\pi}{7}\right)\left(x - \cos\frac{5\pi}{7}\right)$$

$$\text{or} \quad 8x^3 - 4x^2 - 4x + 1 = 8\left(x - \cos\frac{\pi}{7}\right)\left(x - \cos\frac{3\pi}{7}\right)\left(x - \cos\frac{5\pi}{7}\right) \quad \text{...(i)}$$

So, $8x^3 - 4x^2 - 4x + 1 = 0$ and this equation has roots $\cos\frac{\pi}{7}, \cos\frac{3\pi}{7}, \cos\frac{5\pi}{7}$

$$\therefore \quad \cos\frac{\pi}{7}\cos\frac{3\pi}{7}\cos\frac{5\pi}{7} = -\frac{\text{Constant term}}{\text{Coefficient of } x^3}$$

$$\cos\frac{\pi}{7}\cos\frac{3\pi}{7}\cos\frac{5\pi}{7} = -\frac{1}{8} \quad \text{[proved (i) part]}$$

On putting $x = 1$ in Eq. (i), we get

$$1 = 8\left(1 - \cos\frac{\pi}{7}\right)\left(1 - \cos\frac{3\pi}{7}\right)\left(1 - \cos\frac{5\pi}{7}\right)$$

$$\text{or} \quad 1 = 8\left(8\sin^2\frac{\pi}{14}\sin^2\frac{3\pi}{14}\sin^2\frac{5\pi}{14}\right)$$

Since, $\sin\theta > 0$ for $0 < \theta < \pi/2$, we get

$$\therefore \quad \sin\frac{\pi}{14}\sin\frac{3\pi}{14}\sin\frac{5\pi}{14} = \frac{1}{8} \quad \text{...(ii) [proved (iii) part]}$$

Again, putting $x = -1$ in Eq. (i), we get

$$-7 = -8\left(1 + \cos\frac{\pi}{7}\right)\left(1 + \cos\frac{3\pi}{7}\right)\left(1 + \cos\frac{5\pi}{7}\right)$$

$$7 = 8\left(8\cos^2\frac{\pi}{14}\cos^2\frac{3\pi}{14}\cos^2\frac{5\pi}{14}\right)$$

Since, $\cos\theta > 0$ for $0 < \theta < \pi/2$, we get

$$\cos\frac{\pi}{14}\cos\frac{3\pi}{14}\cos\frac{5\pi}{14} = \frac{\sqrt{7}}{8} \quad \text{...(iii) [proved (ii) part]}$$

On dividing Eq. (ii) by Eq. (iii), we get

$$\tan\frac{\pi}{14}\tan\frac{3\pi}{14}\tan\frac{5\pi}{14} = \frac{1}{\sqrt{7}} \quad \text{[proved (iv) part]}$$

On putting $z = \dfrac{(1+y)}{(1-y)}$ in Eq. (A), we get

$$\frac{(1+y)^7+(1-y)^7}{2(1-y)^6} = \frac{2^6\cos^2\frac{\pi}{14}\cos^2\frac{3\pi}{14}\cos^2\frac{5\pi}{14}}{(1-y)^6}\left(y^2+\tan^2\frac{\pi}{14}\right)\left(y^2+\tan^2\frac{3\pi}{14}\right)\left(y^2+\tan^2\frac{5\pi}{14}\right)$$

$$\therefore\quad (1+y)^7+(1-y)^7 = 2^7\cdot\frac{7}{64}\left(y^2+\tan^2\frac{\pi}{14}\right)\left(y^2+\tan^2\frac{3\pi}{14}\right)\left(y^2+\tan^2\frac{5\pi}{14}\right)$$

Using result (ii), we get

$$(1+y)^7+(1-y)^7 = 14\left(y^2+\tan^2\frac{\pi}{14}\right)\left(y^2+\tan^2\frac{3\pi}{14}\right)\left(y^2+\tan^2\frac{5\pi}{14}\right)$$

Equating the coefficient of y^4 on both sides, we get

$${}^7C_4 + {}^7C_4 = 14\left[\tan^2\frac{\pi}{14}+\tan^2\frac{3\pi}{14}+\tan^2\frac{5\pi}{14}\right]$$

Therefore, $\tan^2\dfrac{\pi}{14}+\tan^2\dfrac{3\pi}{14}+\tan^2\dfrac{5\pi}{14} = 5$

101. Equation $|z| = 3$ represents boundary of a circle and equation $|z - \{a(1+i) - i\}| \le 3$ represents the interior and the boundary of a circle and equation $|z + 2a - (a+1)i| > 3$ represents the exterior of a circle. Then, any point which satisfies all the three conditions will lie on first circle, on or inside the second circle and outside the third circle.

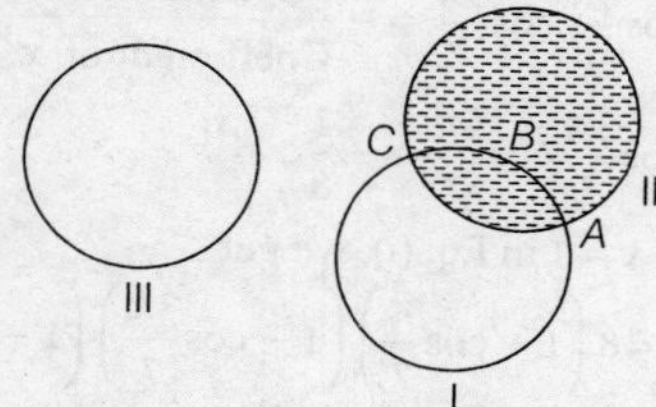

For the existence of such a point first two circles must cut or atleast touch each other and first and third circles must not intersect each other. The arcABC of first circle lying inside the second but outside the third circle, represents all such possible points.

Let $z = x + iy$, then equation of circles are

$$x^2 + y^2 = 9 \quad \text{...(i)}$$

$$(x-a)^2 + (y-a+1)^2 = 9 \quad \text{...(ii)}$$

and $(x+2a)^2 + (y-a-1)^2 = 9$ ...(iii)

Circles (i) and (ii) should cut or touch, then distance between their centres $\le$ sum of their radii

$$\Rightarrow \quad \sqrt{(a-0)^2 + (a-1-0)^2} \le 3+3$$

$$\Rightarrow \quad a^2 + (a-1)^2 \le 36$$

$$\Rightarrow \quad 2a^2 - 2a - 35 \le 0$$

$$\Rightarrow \quad a^2 - a - \frac{35}{2} \le 0 \text{ or } \left(a - \frac{1+\sqrt{71}}{2}\right)\left(a - \frac{1-\sqrt{71}}{2}\right) \le 0$$

$$\therefore \quad \frac{1-\sqrt{71}}{2} \le a \le \frac{1+\sqrt{71}}{2} \quad \text{...(iv)}$$

Again, circles (i) and (iii) should not cut or touch, then distance between their centres > sum of their radii

$$\sqrt{(-2a-0)^2 + (a+1-0)^2} > 3+3$$

or $\sqrt{5a^2+2a+1} > 6$

$\Rightarrow \quad 5a^2 + 2a + 1 > 36$

or $5a^2 + 2a - 35 > 0$

$\Rightarrow \quad a^2 + \dfrac{2a}{5} - 7 > 0$

or $\left(a - \dfrac{-1-4\sqrt{11}}{5}\right)\left(a - \dfrac{-1+4\sqrt{11}}{5}\right) > 0$

$$\therefore \quad a \in \left(-\infty, \frac{-1-4\sqrt{11}}{5}\right) \cup \left(\frac{-1+4\sqrt{11}}{5}, \infty\right) \quad \text{...(v)}$$

Hence, the common values of a satisfying Eqs. (iv) and (v) are

$$a \in \left(\frac{1-\sqrt{71}}{2}, \frac{-1-4\sqrt{11}}{5}\right) \cup \left(\frac{-1+4\sqrt{11}}{5}, \frac{1+\sqrt{71}}{2}\right)$$

102. (i) From De-moivre's theorem, we know that

$$\sin(2n+1)\alpha = {}^{2n+1}C_1(1-\sin^2\alpha)^n \sin\alpha - {}^{2n+1}C_3(1-\sin^2\alpha)^{n-1}\sin^3\alpha + \dots + (-1)^n\sin^{2n+1}\alpha$$

It follows that the numbers

$$\sin\frac{\pi}{2n+1}, \sin\frac{2\pi}{2n+1}, \dots, \sin\frac{n\pi}{2n+1}$$

are the roots of the equation.

$${}^{2n+1}C_1(1-x^2)^n x - {}^{2n+1}C_3(1-x^2)^{n-1}x^3 + \dots + (-1)^n x^{2n+1} = 0 \text{ of the } (2n+1)\text{ th degree}$$

Consequently, the numbers

$\sin^2\dfrac{\pi}{2n+1}, \sin^2\dfrac{2\pi}{2n+1}, \dots, \sin^2\dfrac{n\pi}{2n+1}$ are the roots of the equation

${}^{2n+1}C_1(1-x)^n - {}^{2n+1}C_3(1-x)^{n-1}x + \dots + (-1)^n x^n = 0$ of the nth degree

(ii) From De-moivre's theorem, we know that

$$\sin(2n+1)\alpha = {}^{2n+1}C_1(\cos\alpha)^{2n}\sin\alpha - {}^{2n+1}C_3(\cos\alpha)^{2n-2}\sin^3\alpha + \dots + (-1)^n\sin^{2n+1}\alpha$$

or $\sin(2n+1)\alpha = \sin^{2n+1}\alpha$

$$\{{}^{2n+1}C_1\cot^{2n}\alpha - {}^{2n+1}C_3\cot^{2n-2}\alpha + {}^{2n+1}C_5\cot^{2n-4}\alpha - \dots\}$$

It follows that $\alpha = \dfrac{\pi}{2n+1}, \dfrac{2\pi}{2n+1}, \dfrac{3\pi}{2n+1}, \dots, \dfrac{n\pi}{2n+1}$

Therefore, equality holds

$${}^{2n+1}C_1\cot^{2n}\alpha - {}^{2n+1}C_3\cot^{2n-2}\alpha + {}^{2n+1}C_5\cot^{2n-4}\alpha - \dots = 0$$

It follows that the numbers

$\cot^2\dfrac{\pi}{2n+1}, \cot^2\dfrac{2\pi}{2n+1}, \dots, \cot^2\dfrac{n\pi}{2n+1}$ are the roots of the equation

$${}^{2n+1}C_1x^n - {}^{2n+1}C_3x^{n-1} + {}^{2n+1}C_5x^{n-2} - \dots = 0$$

of the nth degree.

103. Let $y = |a + b\omega + c\omega^2|$. For y to be minimum, y^2 must be minimum.

$\therefore \quad y^2 = |a + b\omega + c\omega^2|^2 = (a + b\omega + c\omega^2)\overline{(a + b\omega + c\omega^2)}$

$= (a + b\omega + c\omega^2)(a + b\bar{\omega} + c\bar{\omega}^2)$

$y^2 = (a + b\omega + c\omega^2)(a + b\omega^2 + c\omega)3$

$= (a^2 + b^2 + c^2 - ab - bc - ca)$

$= \frac{1}{2}[(a-b)^2 + (b-c)^2 + (c-a)^2]$

Since, a, b and c are not equal at a time, so minimum value of y^2 occurs when any two are same and third is differ by 1.

$\Rightarrow$ Minimum of $y = 1$ (as a, b, c are integers)

104. Equation of ray PQ is $\arg(z + 1) = \frac{\pi}{4}$

Equation of ray PR is $\arg(z + 1) = -\frac{\pi}{4}$

Shaded region is $-\frac{\pi}{4} < \arg(z + 1) < \frac{\pi}{4} \Rightarrow |\arg(z + 1)| < \frac{\pi}{4}$

$\therefore \quad |PQ| = \sqrt{(\sqrt{2})^2 + (\sqrt{2})^2} = 2$

So, arc QAR is of a circle of radius 2 units with centre at $P(-1, 0)$. All the points in the shaded region are exterior to this circle $|z + 1| = 2$.

i.e. $|z + 1| > 2$ and $|\arg(z + 1)| < \frac{\pi}{4}$.

105. In ΔAOB from Coni method, $\frac{z_B - 1}{z_A - 1} = e^{i\pi/2} = i$

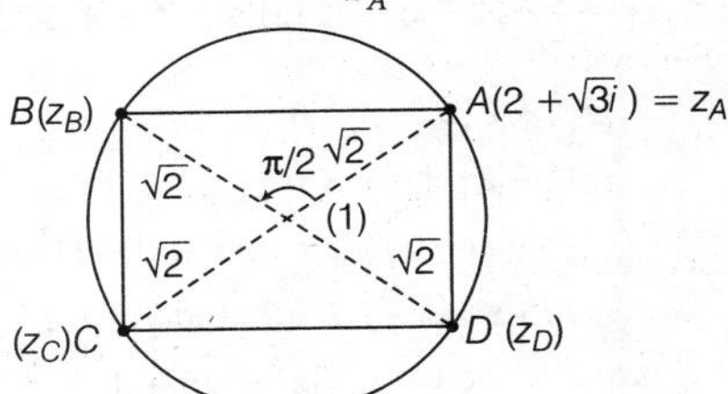

$z_B - 1 = (z_A - 1)i$

$\therefore \quad z_B = 1 + (2 + \sqrt{3}i - 1)i = 1 + (1 + i\sqrt{3})i$

$= 1 + i - \sqrt{3} = 1 - \sqrt{3} + i$

$z_C = 2 - z_A = 2 - (2 + \sqrt{3}i) = -\sqrt{3}\,i$

and $\quad z_D = 2 - z_B = 2 - (1 - \sqrt{3} + i) = 1 + \sqrt{3} - i$

Hence, other vertices are $(1 - \sqrt{3}) + i, -\sqrt{3}i, (1 + \sqrt{3}) - i$.

106. Let $z_1 = r_1(\cos\theta_1 + i\sin\theta_1)$ and $z_2 = r_2(\cos\theta_2 + i\sin\theta_2)$

$\therefore |z_1 + z_2| = [(r_1\cos\theta_1 + r_2\cos\theta_2)^2 + (r_1\sin\theta_1 + r_2\sin\theta_2)^2]^{1/2}$

$= [|r_1^2 + r_2^2 + 2r_1r_2\cos(\theta_1 - \theta_2)]^{1/2} = [(r_1 + r_2)^2]^{1/2}$

$\therefore |z_1 + z_2| = |z_1| + |z_2|$

Therefore, $\cos(\theta_1 - \theta_2) = 1$

$\Rightarrow \quad \theta_1 - \theta_2 = 0$

$\Rightarrow \quad \theta_1 = \theta_2$

Thus, $\arg(z_1) - \arg(z_2) = 0$

107. $(x-1)^3 = -8 \Rightarrow x - 1 = (-8)^{1/3}$

$\Rightarrow \quad x - 1 = -2, -2\omega, -2\omega^2$

$\Rightarrow \quad x = -1, 1 - 2\omega, 1 - 2\omega^2$

108. $\left|\frac{z}{z - \frac{i}{3}}\right| = 1 \Rightarrow |z| = \left|z - \frac{i}{3}\right|$

Clearly, locus of z is perpendicular bisector of line joining points having complex number $0 + i\,0$ and $0 + \frac{i}{3}$.

Hence, z lies on a straight line.

109. Given, $\left(\frac{\omega - \bar{\omega}z}{1 - z}\right)$ is purely real $\Rightarrow z \neq 1$

$\therefore \quad \left(\frac{\omega - \bar{\omega}z}{1 - z}\right) = \overline{\left(\frac{\omega - \bar{\omega}z}{1 - z}\right)} = \frac{\bar{\omega} - \omega\bar{z}}{1 - \bar{z}}$

$\Rightarrow \quad (\bar{\omega} - \bar{\omega}z)(1 - \bar{z}) = (1 - z)(\bar{\omega} - \omega\bar{z})$

$\Rightarrow \quad (z\bar{z} - 1)(\omega - \bar{\omega}) = 0$

$\Rightarrow \quad (|z|^2 - 1)(2i\beta) = 0 \qquad [\because \omega = \alpha + i\beta]$

$\therefore \quad |z|^2 - 1 = 0$

$\Rightarrow \quad |z| = 1$ and $z \neq 1 \qquad [\because \beta \neq 0]$

110. $\sum_{k=1}^{10} \sin\left(\frac{2k\pi}{11}\right) + i\cos\left(\frac{2k\pi}{11}\right)$

$= i\sum_{k=1}^{10}\left\{\cos\left(\frac{2k\pi}{11}\right) - i\sin\left(\frac{2k\pi}{11}\right)\right\} = i\sum_{k=1}^{10} e^{\frac{-2k\pi i}{11}}$

$= i\left(\sum_{k=0}^{10} e^{\frac{-2k\pi i}{11}} - 1\right) = i(0 - 1)$ [$\because$ sum of 11, 11th roots of unity = 0]

$= -i$

111. $\because \quad z^2 + z + 1 = 0$

$\therefore \quad z = \omega, \omega^2$

$\because \quad z + \frac{1}{z} = \omega + \frac{1}{\omega} = \omega + \omega^2 = -1$

$\Rightarrow \quad z^2 + \frac{1}{z^2} = \omega^2 + \frac{1}{\omega^2} = \omega^2 + \omega = -1$

$\therefore \quad z^3 + \frac{1}{z^3} = \omega^3 + \frac{1}{\omega^3} = 1 + 1 = 2$

$z^4 + \frac{1}{z^4} = \omega^4 + \frac{1}{\omega^4} = \omega + \frac{1}{\omega} = -1$

$z^5 + \frac{1}{z^5} = \omega^5 + \frac{1}{\omega^5} = \omega^2 + \omega = -1$

and $\quad z^6 + \frac{1}{z^6} = \omega^6 + \frac{1}{\omega^6} = 2$

$\therefore$ Required sum $= (-1)^2 + (-1)^2 + (2)^2 + (-1)^2 + (-1)^2 + (2)^2 = 12$

112. Let $OA = 3$, so that the complex number associated with A is $3e^{i\pi/4}$. If z is the complex number associated with P, then

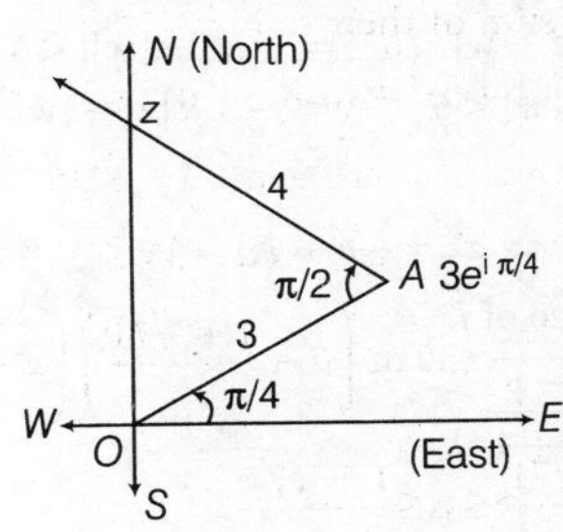

$$\frac{z-3e^{i\pi/4}}{0-3e^{i\pi/4}}=\frac{4}{3}e^{-\pi/2}=-\frac{4i}{3}$$

$$\Rightarrow \quad 3z-9e^{i\pi/4}=12ie^{i\pi/4} \Rightarrow z=(3+4i)e^{i\pi/4}$$

113. Let $z=\cos\theta+i\sin\theta$

$$\Rightarrow \frac{z}{1-z^2}=\frac{\cos\theta+i\sin\theta}{1-(\cos 2\theta+i\sin 2\theta)}$$

$$=\frac{\cos\theta+i\sin\theta}{2\sin^2\theta-2i\sin\theta\cos\theta}$$

$$=\frac{\cos\theta+i\sin\theta}{-2i\sin\theta(\cos\theta+i\sin\theta)}=\frac{i}{2\sin\theta}$$

Hence, $\frac{z}{1-z^2}$ lies on the imaginary axis i.e. $x=0$ or on Y-axis.

Aliter

Let $E=\frac{z}{1-z^2}=\frac{z}{z\bar{z}-z^2}=\frac{1}{\bar{z}-z}=-\frac{1}{z-\bar{z}}=-\frac{1}{\left(\frac{z-\bar{z}}{2i}\right)2i}$

$=\frac{i}{2\,\text{Im}\,|z|}$ which is imaginary.

114. $|z+4|\le 3$

$\Rightarrow z$ lies inside or on the circle of radius 3 and centre at $(-4, 0)$.

$\therefore$ Maximum value of $|z+1|$ is 6.

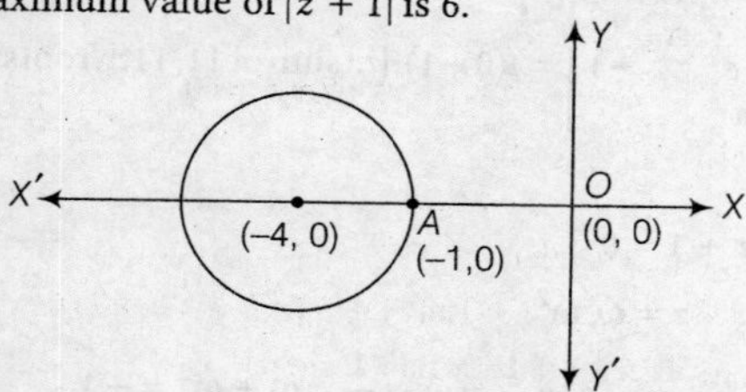

115. Let A = set of points on and above the line $y=1$ in the argand plane.

B = set of points on the circle $(x-2)^2+(y-1)^2=3^2$

$C=\text{Re}\,(1-i)\,z=\text{Re}\,[(1-i)(x+iy)]=x+y$

$\Rightarrow \quad x+y=\sqrt{2}$

Hence, $(A\cap B\cap C)$ has only one point of intersection.

116. The points $(-1+i)$ and $(5+i)$ are the extremities of diameter of the given circle.

Hence, $|z+1-i|^2+|z-5-i|^2=36$

117. $\because |z-w|\le\big||z|-|w|\big|$

and $|z-w|$ = distance between z and w

z is fixed, hence distance between z and w would be maximum for diametrically opposite points.

$\Rightarrow \quad |z-w|<6 \quad\Rightarrow\quad \big||z|-|w|\big|<6$

$\Rightarrow -6<|z|-|w|<6 \quad\Rightarrow -3<|z|-|w|+3<9$

118. $\because \quad z_0=1+2i$

$\therefore \; z_1=6+5i \quad\Rightarrow z_2=-6+7i$

119. Put $(-i)$ in place of i.

Hence, $\quad \frac{-1}{i+1}$

120. $\because z\bar{z}(\bar{z}^2+z^2)=350$

Put $\quad z=x+iy$

$\Rightarrow \quad (x^2+y^2)\cdot 2(x^2-y^2)=350$

$\Rightarrow \quad (x^2+y^2)(x^2-y^2)=175=25\times 7$

$\Rightarrow \quad x^2+y^2=25,\ x^2-y^2=7$

$\Rightarrow \quad x^2=16,\ y^2=9$

$\therefore \quad x=\pm 4,\ y=\pm 3;\ x, y\in I$

Area of rectangle $=8\times 6=48$ sq units

121. $\sum_{m=1}^{15}\text{Im}\,(z^{2m-1})=\sum_{m=1}^{15}\text{Im}\,[e^{(2m-1)i\theta}]=\sum_{m=1}^{15}\sin(2m-1)\theta$

$$=\sum_{m=1}^{15}\frac{2\sin(2m-1)\theta\sin\theta}{2\sin\theta}$$

$$=\sum_{m=1}^{15}\frac{\cos(2m-2)\theta-\cos 2m\theta}{2\sin\theta}$$

$$=\frac{\cos 0^\circ-\cos 30\theta}{2\sin\theta}=\frac{1-\cos 60^\circ}{2\sin 2^\circ} \qquad (\because \theta=2^\circ)$$

$$=\frac{1-\frac{1}{2}}{2\sin 2^\circ}=\frac{1}{4\sin 2^\circ}$$

122. $\left|z-\frac{4}{z}\right|\ge\left||z|-\frac{4}{|z|}\right| \quad\Rightarrow 2\ge\left||z|-\frac{4}{|z|}\right|$

$\Rightarrow \quad -2\le|z|-\frac{4}{|z|}\le 2 \quad\Rightarrow -2|z|\le|z|^2-4\le 2|z|$

$\Rightarrow \quad |z|^2+2|z|-4\ge 0$

and $\quad 1^2-2|z|-4\le 0$

$\Rightarrow \quad (|z|+1)^2\ge 5$ and $(|z|-1)^2\le 5$

$-\sqrt{5}\le|z|-1\le\sqrt{5}$ and $|z|+1\ge\sqrt{5}$

$\Rightarrow \quad \sqrt{5}-1\le|z|\le\sqrt{5}+1$

123. As $z=(1-t)z_1+tz_2$

$z_1 \quad t \quad z \quad 1-t \quad z_2$

$\Rightarrow z_1, z$ and z_2 are collinear.

Thus, options (a) and (d) are correct.

Also, $\frac{z-z_1}{z_2-z_1}=\frac{\bar{z}-\bar{z}_1}{\bar{z}_2-\bar{z}_1}$

Hence, option (c) is correct.

124. $\omega=\cos\frac{2\pi}{3}+i\sin\frac{2\pi}{3}=-\frac{1}{2}+i\frac{\sqrt{3}}{2}$

ω is one of the cube root of unity.

$$\therefore \quad \begin{vmatrix} z+1 & \omega & \omega^2 \\ \omega & z+\omega^2 & 1 \\ \omega^2 & 1 & z+\omega \end{vmatrix}=0$$

Applying $R_1\to R_1+R_2+R_3$, we get

$$\begin{vmatrix} z & z & z \\ \omega & z+\omega^2 & 1 \\ \omega^2 & 1 & z+\omega \end{vmatrix}=0 \qquad [\because 1+\omega+\omega^2=0]$$

Now, applying $C_2 \to C_2 - C_1, C_3 \to C_3 - C_1$, we get

$$\begin{vmatrix} z & 0 & 0 \\ \omega & z+\omega^2-\omega & 1-\omega \\ \omega^2 & 1-w^2 & z+\omega-\omega^2 \end{vmatrix} = 0$$

$\Rightarrow z[(z+\omega^2-\omega)(z+\omega-\omega^2)-(1-\omega)(1-\omega^2)] = 0$

$\Rightarrow \quad z[z^2-(\omega^2-\omega)^2-(1-\omega^2-\omega+\omega^3)] = 0$

$\Rightarrow \quad z[z^2-(\omega^4+\omega^2-2\omega^3)-1+\omega^2+\omega-\omega^3] = 0$

$\Rightarrow \quad z^3 = 0$

$\therefore \quad z = 0$

125. $|z-i|z||=|z+i|z||$

(A) Putting $z = x+iy$, we get $y\sqrt{x^2+y^2} = 0$

i.e. $\text{Im}(z) = 0$

(B) $2ae = 8, 2a = 10 \Rightarrow 10e = 8 \Rightarrow e = \frac{4}{5}$

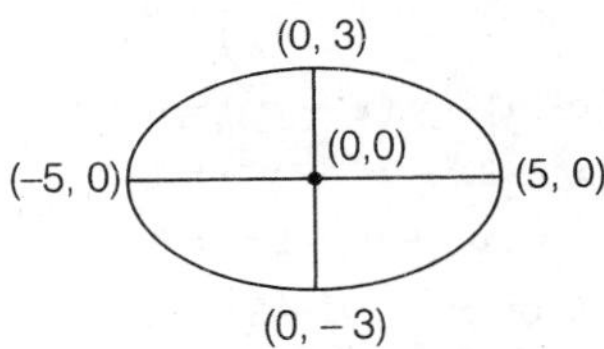

$\therefore \quad b^2 = 25\left(1-\frac{16}{25}\right) = 9$

$\Rightarrow \quad \frac{x^2}{25}+\frac{y^2}{9} = 1$

(C) $z = 2(\cos\theta + i\sin\theta) - \frac{1}{2(\cos\theta+i\sin\theta)}$

$= 2(\cos\theta+i\sin\theta) - \frac{1}{2}(\cos\theta - i\sin\theta)$

$z = \frac{3}{2}\cos\theta + \frac{5}{2}i\sin\theta$

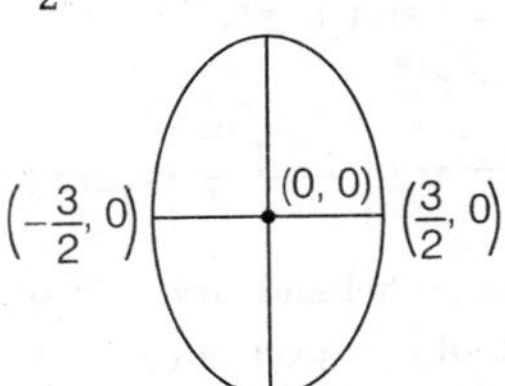

Let $z = x+iy$, then

$x = \frac{3}{2}\cos\theta$ and $y = \frac{5}{2}\sin\theta$

$\Rightarrow \quad \left(\frac{2x}{3}\right)^2 + \left(\frac{2y}{5}\right)^2 = 1$

$\Rightarrow \quad \frac{4x^2}{9}+\frac{4y^2}{25} = 1$

$\Rightarrow \quad \frac{x^2}{9/4}+\frac{y^2}{25/4} = 1$

$\Rightarrow \quad \frac{9}{4} = \frac{25}{4}(1-e^2)$

$\therefore \quad e^2 = 1-\frac{9}{25} = \frac{16}{25} \Rightarrow e = \frac{4}{5}$

(D) Let $w = \cos\theta + i\sin\theta$, then

$z = x+iy = w+\frac{1}{w}$

$\Rightarrow \quad x+iy = 2\cos\theta$

$\therefore \quad x = 2\cos\theta$ and $y = 0$

126. $\because \quad x^2-x+1 = 0$

$\therefore \quad x = \frac{1\pm\sqrt{(1-4)}}{2} = \frac{1\pm i\sqrt{3}}{2}$

$= \frac{1+i\sqrt{3}}{2}$ and $\frac{1-i\sqrt{3}}{2}$

$\therefore \quad x = -\omega^2, -\omega$

$\therefore \quad \alpha = -\omega^2, \beta = -\omega$

$\Rightarrow \quad \alpha^{2009}+\beta^{2009} = -\omega^{4018}-\omega^{2009}$

$= -\omega-\omega^2 = -(\omega+\omega^2)$

$= -(-1) = 1$

127. $|z-1| = |z+1| = |z-i|$

$\Rightarrow \quad |z-1|^2 = |z+1|^2 = |z-i|^2$

$\Rightarrow (z-1)(\bar{z}-1) = (z+1)(\bar{z}+1) = (z-i)(\bar{z}+i)$

$\Rightarrow z\bar{z}-z-\bar{z}+1 = z\bar{z}+z+\bar{z}+1 = z\bar{z}+iz-i\bar{z}+1$

$\Rightarrow \quad -z-\bar{z} = z+\bar{z} = i(z-\bar{z})$

From first two relations,

$2(z+\bar{z}) = 0 \Rightarrow \text{Re}(z) = 0$ ...(i)

From last two relations,

$z+\bar{z} = i(z-\bar{z}) \Rightarrow 2\,\text{Re}(z) = -2\,\text{Im}(z)$

From Eq. (i), $\quad \text{Im}(z) = 0$

$\therefore \quad z = \text{Re}(z)+i\,\text{Im}(z) = 0+i\cdot 0 = 0$

Hence, number of solutions is one.

128. We have, $\quad |z-3-2i| \le 2$

$\Rightarrow \quad |2z-6-4i| \le 4$ ...(i)

Now, $\quad |2z-6-4i| = |(2z-6+5i)-9i|$

$\ge ||2z-6+5i|-9|$ ...(ii)

From Eqs. (i) and (ii), we get

$||2z-6+5i|-9| \le 4$

$\Rightarrow -4 \le |2z-6+5i|-9 \le 4$

$\Rightarrow \quad 5 \le |2z-6+5i| \le 13$

Hence, the minimum value of $|2z-6+5i|$ is 5.

129. $\because |z| = 1 \quad \therefore z = e^{i\theta}$

$\therefore \quad \text{Re}\left(\frac{2iz}{1-z^2}\right) = \text{Re}\left(\frac{2ie^{i\theta}}{1-e^{2i\theta}}\right) = \text{Re}\left(\frac{2i}{e^{-i\theta}-e^{i\theta}}\right)$

$= \text{Re}\left(\frac{2i}{-2i\sin\theta}\right) = \text{Re}\left(-\frac{1}{\sin\theta}\right)$

$= -\frac{1}{\sin\theta} = -\text{cosec}\,\theta$

$\because \quad \text{cosec}\,\theta \le -1 \Rightarrow \text{cosec}\,\theta \ge 1$

$\Rightarrow -\text{cosec}\,\theta \ge 1 \Rightarrow -\text{cosec}\,\theta \le -1$

$\Rightarrow -\text{cosec}\,\theta \in (-\infty, -1] \cap [1, \infty)$

$\therefore \quad \text{Re}\left(\frac{2iz}{1-z^2}\right) \in (-\infty, -1] \cap [1, \infty)$

130. $\because$ $|z| = 1$. Let $z = e^{i\theta}$

$\therefore \quad z - 1 = e^{i\theta} - 1 = e^{i\theta/2} \cdot 2i \sin(\theta/2)$

$$\Rightarrow \quad \frac{1}{z-1} = \frac{1}{2ie^{i\theta/2} \cdot \sin(\theta/2)} = -\frac{ie^{-i\theta/2}}{2\sin(\theta/2)}$$

$$\Rightarrow \quad \frac{1}{1-z} = \frac{i \cdot e^{-i\theta/2}}{2\sin(\theta/2)} \quad \therefore \arg\left(\frac{1}{1-z}\right) = \left(\frac{\pi}{2} - \frac{\theta}{2}\right)$$

$$\Rightarrow \quad \left|\arg\left(\frac{1}{1-z}\right)\right| = \left|\frac{\pi}{2} - \frac{\theta}{2}\right|$$

$\therefore$ Maximum value of $\left|\arg\left(\frac{1}{1-z}\right)\right| = \frac{\pi}{2}$

131. $\because$ $|x|^2 = x\bar{x} = (a + b + c)(\overline{a} + \overline{b} + \overline{c})$

$= (a + b + c)(\bar{a} + \bar{b} + \bar{c})$

$= |a|^2 + |b|^2 + |c|^2 + a\bar{b} + \bar{a}b + b\bar{c} + \bar{b}c + c\bar{a} + \bar{c}a \quad$ ...(i)

$|y|^2 = y\bar{y} = (a + b\omega + c\omega^2)(\bar{a} + \bar{b}\omega + \bar{c}\omega^2)$

$= (a + b\omega + c\omega^2)(\bar{a} + \bar{b}\bar{\omega} + \bar{c}\bar{\omega}^2)$

$= (a + b\omega + c\omega^2)(\bar{a} + \bar{b}\omega^2 + \bar{c}\omega)$

$= |a|^2 + |b|^2 + |c|^2 + a\bar{b}\omega^2 + \bar{a}b\omega$

$+ b\bar{c}\omega^2 + \bar{b}c\omega + c\bar{a}\omega^2 + \bar{c}a\omega \quad$ ...(ii)

and $|z|^2 = z\bar{z} = (a + b\omega^2 + c\omega)(a + b\omega^2 + c\omega)$

$= (a + b\omega^2 + c\omega)(\bar{a} + \bar{b}\bar{\omega}^2 + \bar{c}\bar{\omega})$

$= (a + b\omega^2 + c\omega)(\bar{a} + \bar{b}\omega + \bar{c}\omega^2)$

$= |a|^2 + |b|^2 + |c|^2 + a\bar{b}\omega + \bar{a}b\omega^2$

$+ b\bar{c}w + \bar{b}c\omega^2 + c\bar{a}\omega + \bar{c}a\omega^2 \quad$ ...(iii)

On adding Eqs. (i), (ii) and (iii), we get

$|x|^2 + |y|^2 + |z|^2 = 3(|a|^2 + |b|^2 + |c|^2)$

$+ 0 + 0 + 0 + 0 + 0 + 0 + 0 \quad (\because 1 + \omega + \omega^2 = 0)$

$$\therefore \quad \frac{|x|^2 + |y|^2 + |z|^2}{|a|^2 + |b|^2 + |c|^2} = 3$$

132. $\because$ $\text{Re}(z) = 1 \quad \therefore \frac{z + \bar{z}}{2} = 1 \Rightarrow z + \bar{z} = 2$

Since, $\alpha, \beta \in R$

$\therefore$ The complex roots are conjugate to each other, if z_1, z_2 are two distinct roots, then $z_1 = \bar{z}_2$ or $\bar{z}_1 = z_2$

$\therefore$ Product of the roots $= z_1 z_2 = \beta$

$\Rightarrow \quad z_1\bar{z}_1 = \beta$

$\therefore \quad \beta = |z_1|^2 = [\text{Re}(z_1)]^2 + \text{Im}|z_1|^2$

$= 1 + \text{Im}|z_1|^2 > 1$

$[\because$ roots are distinct $\therefore \text{Im}(z_1) \neq 0]$

$\therefore \quad \beta > 1$ or $\beta \in (1, \infty)$

133. $\because$ $(1 + \omega)^7 = (-\omega^2)^7 = -\omega^{14} = -\omega^2 = 1 + \omega$

Given, $(1 + \omega)^7 = A + B\omega \Rightarrow 1 + \omega = A + B\omega$

On comparing, we get $A = 1, B = 1$

$\therefore \quad (A, B) = (1, 1)$

134. Given, $z^2 + z + 1 = a \Rightarrow z^2 + z + 1 - a = 0$

$$\therefore \quad z = \frac{-1 \pm \sqrt{(4a-3)}}{2}$$

Hence, $\quad a \neq \frac{3}{4}$ [for $a = 3/4$, z will be purely real]

135. Let $z = x + iy$, then

$$\frac{z^2}{z-1} = \frac{(x+iy)^2}{(x+iy-1)} = \frac{(x^2 - y^2 + 2ix)}{(x - 1 + iy)}$$

$$= \frac{(x^2 - y^2 + 2ixy)(x - 1 - iy)}{(x - 1 + iy)(x - 1 - iy)}$$

$$= \frac{(x-1)(x^2 - y^2) + 2xy^2 + i[2xy(x-1) - y(x^2 - y^2)]}{(x-1)^2 + y^2}$$

Now, $\quad \text{Im}\left(\frac{z^2}{z-1}\right) = 0$

$\Rightarrow \quad 2xy(x-1) - y(x^2 - y^2) = 0$

$\Rightarrow \quad y(2x^2 - 2x - x^2 + y^2) = 0$

$\Rightarrow \quad y(x^2 + y^2 - 2x) = 0$

$\Rightarrow \quad y = 0$ or $x^2 + y^2 - 2x = 0$

Hence, z lies on the real axis or on a circle passing through the origin.

136. Given, $|z| = 1$ and $\arg(z) = \theta \quad$ ...(i)

$\Rightarrow \quad |z|^2 = 1 \Rightarrow z\bar{z} = 1$

$\Rightarrow \quad \bar{z} = \frac{1}{z} \quad$ ...(ii)

$\therefore \quad \arg\left(\frac{1+z}{1+\bar{z}}\right) = \arg\left(\frac{1+z}{1+1/z}\right) \quad$ [from Eq. (ii)]

$= \arg(z) = \theta \quad$ [from Eq. (i)]

Aliter I

Given, $\quad |z| = 1$ and $\arg(z) = \theta$

$\Rightarrow \quad z = e^{i\theta}$

$$\therefore \quad \arg\left(\frac{1+z}{1+\bar{z}}\right) = \arg\left(\frac{1+e^{i\theta}}{1+e^{-i\theta}}\right) = \arg(e^{i\theta}) = \arg(z) = \theta$$

Aliter II Given, $|z| = 1$ and $\arg(z) = \theta$

Let $z = \omega$ (cube root of unity)

$$\therefore \quad \arg\left(\frac{1+z}{1+\bar{z}}\right) = \arg\left(\frac{1+\omega}{1+\bar{\omega}}\right) = \arg\left(\frac{1+\omega}{1+\omega^2}\right) \quad (\because \bar{\omega} = \omega^2)$$

$$= \arg\left(\frac{-\omega^2}{-\omega}\right) \quad (\because 1 + \omega + \omega^2 = 0)$$

$= \arg(\omega) = \arg(z) = \theta$

137. $\quad z_0 = 2\alpha - \frac{1}{\bar{\alpha}}$

$\because \quad 2|z_0|^2 = r^2 + 2$

$$\therefore \quad 2\left|2\alpha - \frac{1}{\bar{\alpha}}\right|^2 = r^2 + 2 \Rightarrow 2\left|2\alpha - \frac{1}{\bar{\alpha}}\right|^2 = \left|\alpha - \frac{1}{\bar{\alpha}}\right|^2 + 2$$

$$\Rightarrow 7|\alpha|^2 + \frac{1}{|\alpha|^2} - 8 = 0 \Rightarrow |\alpha|^2 = 1 \text{ or } \frac{1}{7} \Rightarrow |\alpha| = 1 \text{ or } \frac{1}{\sqrt{7}}$$

138.

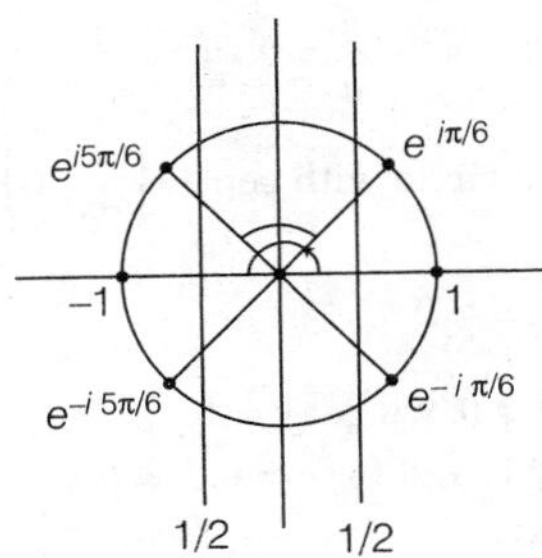

$$\omega = \frac{\sqrt{3}+i}{2} = e^{i\pi/6}, \quad P = e^{in\pi/6}$$

As $z_1 \in P \cap H_1 \Rightarrow z_1 = 1, e^{i\pi/6}, e^{-i\pi/6}$

As $z_2 \in P \cap H_2 \Rightarrow z_2 = -1, e^{i5\pi/6}, e^{-i5\pi/6}$

$\angle z_1Oz_2 = 2\pi/3$, where $z_1 = e^{i\pi/6}$, $z_2 = e^{i5\pi/6}$

Sol. (Q. Nos. 139-140)

Let $z = x + iy, S_1 : x^2 + y^2 < 16$

Now, $\text{Im}\left[\frac{(x-1)+i(y+\sqrt{3})}{1-\sqrt{3}i}\right] > 0$

$\Rightarrow \quad S_2 : \sqrt{3}x + y > 0 \Rightarrow S_3 : x > 0$

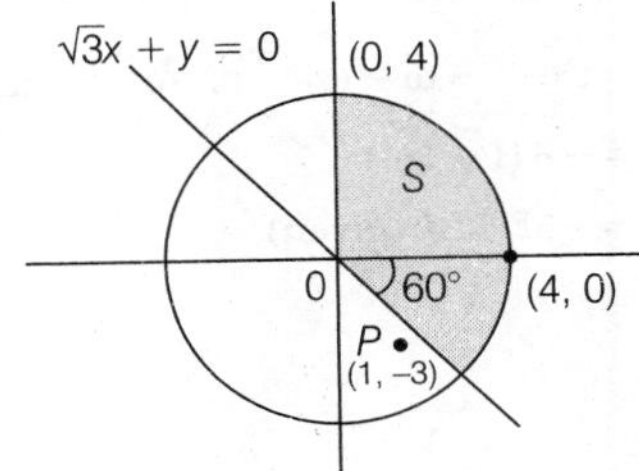

139. $\min|1-3i-z| = \min|z-1+3i|$

= perpendicular distance of the point $(1, -3)$ from the straight line $\sqrt{3}x + y = 0 = \left|\frac{\sqrt{3}-3}{2}\right| = \frac{3-\sqrt{3}}{2}$

140. Area of $S = \left(\frac{1}{4}\right)\pi \times 4^2 + \left(\frac{1}{6}\right)\pi \times 4^2 = \frac{20\pi}{3}$

141. Since, $|z| \geq 2$ is the region lying on or outside circle centered at $(0, 0)$ and radius 2. Therefore, $|z + (1/2)|$ is the distance of z from $(-1/2, 0)$, which lies inside the circle.

Hence, minimum value of $|z + (1/2)|$

$= \text{distance of } (-1/2, 0) \text{ from } (-2, 0)$

$$= \sqrt{\left(-\frac{1}{2}+2\right)^2 + |0-0|^2} = 3/2$$

Aliter

$\because \quad |z + (1/2)| \geq \left||z| - \frac{1}{2}\right| \geq \left|2 - \frac{1}{2}\right| \quad [\because |z| \geq 2]$

$\therefore \quad |z + (1/2)| \geq 3/2$

142. Clearly, $z_k^{10} = 1, \forall k$, where $z_k \neq 1$

(A) $z_k \cdot z_j = e^{i(2\pi/10)(k+j)} = 1$, if $(k+j)$ is multiple of 10

i.e. possible for each k.

(B) $z_1 \cdot z = z_k$ is clearly incorrect.

(C) Expression $= \frac{\left|\lim\limits_{z\to 1} \frac{z^{10}-1}{z-1}\right|}{10} = 1$

(D) $1 + \Sigma z_k = 0 \Rightarrow 1 + \sum\limits_{k=1}^{9} \cos\left(\frac{2k\pi}{10}\right) = 0$

$\therefore$ Expression = 2

143. $\because \quad \left|\frac{z_1 - 2z_2}{2 - z_1\bar{z}_2}\right| = 1$

$\Rightarrow |z_1 - 2z_2|^2 = |2 - z_1\bar{z}_2|^2$

$\Rightarrow (z_1 - 2z_2)\overline{(z_1 - 2z_2)} = (2 - z_1\bar{z}_2)\overline{(2 - z_1\bar{z}_2)}$

$\Rightarrow (z_1 - 2z_2)(\bar{z}_1 - 2\bar{z}_2) = (2 - z_1\bar{z}_2)(2 - \bar{z}_1 z_2)$

$\Rightarrow z_1\bar{z}_1 - 2z_1\bar{z}_2 - 2\bar{z}_1z_2 + 4z_2\bar{z}_2 = 4 - 2\bar{z}_1z_2 - 2z_1\bar{z}_2 + z_1\bar{z}_1z_2\bar{z}_2$

$\Rightarrow |z_1|^2 + 4|z_2|^2 + 4 + |z_1|^2|z_2|^2$

$\Rightarrow \quad (|z_1|^2 - 4)(1 - |z_2|^2) = 0$

$\because \quad |z_2| \neq 1$

$\therefore \quad |z_1|^2 = 4$ or $|z_1| = 2$

$\Rightarrow$ Point z_1 lies on circle of radius 2.

144. Let $a = 3, b = -3, c = 2$, then

$(a + b\omega + c\omega^2)^{4n+3} + (c + a\omega + b\omega^2)^{4n+3} + (b + c\omega + a\omega^2)^{4n+3} = 0$

$\Rightarrow (a + b\omega + c\omega^2)^{4n+3}$

$$\left\{1 + \left(\frac{(c + a\omega + b\omega^2)^{4n+3}}{a + b\omega + c\omega^2}\right)^{4n+3} + \left(\frac{b + c\omega + a\omega^2)}{a + b\omega + c\omega^2}\right)^{4n+3}\right\} = 0$$

$\Rightarrow \quad (a + b\omega + c\omega^2)^{4n+3}(1 + \omega^{4n+3} + (\omega^2)^{4n+3}) = 0$

$\Rightarrow \quad 4n + 3$ should be an integer other than multiple of 3.

$\therefore \quad n = 1, 2, 4, 5$

145. $\because \quad \alpha_k = \cos\left(\frac{k\pi}{7}\right) + i\sin\left(\frac{k\pi}{7}\right) = e^{i\pi k/7}$

$\therefore \alpha_{k+1} - \alpha k = e^{i\pi(k+1)/7} - e^{i\pi k/7} = e^{i\pi k/7}(e^{i\pi/7} - 1)$

$= e^{i\pi k/7} \cdot e^{i\pi/14} \cdot 2i\sin\left(\frac{\pi}{14}\right)$

$\Rightarrow \quad |\alpha_{k+1} - \alpha_k| = 2\sin\left(\frac{\pi}{14}\right)$

$$\sum_{k=1}^{12} |\alpha_{k+1} - \alpha_k| = 12 \times 2\sin\left(\frac{\pi}{14}\right) = 24\sin\left(\frac{\pi}{14}\right)$$

and $\alpha_{4k-1} - \alpha_{4k-2} = e^{i\pi(4k-1)/7} - e^{i\pi(4k-2)/7} = e^{i\pi(4k-2)/7}(e^{i\pi/7} - 1)$

$= e^{i\pi(4k-2)/7} \cdot e^{i\pi/14} \cdot 2i\sin\left(\frac{\pi}{14}\right)$

$\Rightarrow \quad |\alpha_{4k-1} - \alpha_{4k-2}| = 2\sin\left(\frac{\pi}{14}\right)$

$$\therefore \quad \sum_{k=1}^{3} |\alpha_{4k-1} - \alpha_{4k-2}| = 3 \times 2\sin\left(\frac{\pi}{14}\right) = 6\sin\left(\frac{\pi}{14}\right)$$

Hence, $$\frac{\sum_{k=1}^{12}|\alpha_{k+1}-\alpha_k|}{\sum_{k=1}^{3}|\alpha_{4k-1}-\alpha_{4k-2}|}=4$$

146. Let $z=\dfrac{2+3i\sin\theta}{1-2i\sin\theta}$

$\because$ z is purely imaginary

$\therefore$ $\bar{z}=-z$

$$\Rightarrow \overline{\left(\frac{2+3i\sin\theta}{1-2i\sin\theta}\right)}=-\left(\frac{2+3i\sin\theta}{1-2i\sin\theta}\right)$$

$$\Rightarrow \left(\frac{2-3i\sin\theta}{1+2i\sin\theta}\right)=-\left(\frac{2+3i\sin\theta}{1-2i\sin\theta}\right)$$

$\Rightarrow (2-3i\sin\theta)(1-2i\sin\theta)+(1+2i\sin\theta)(2+3i\sin\theta)=0$

$\Rightarrow 4-12\sin^2\theta=0$ or $\sin^2\theta=\dfrac{1}{3}$

$\therefore$ $\theta=\sin^{-1}\left(\dfrac{1}{\sqrt{3}}\right)$

147. $\because$ $$x+iy=\frac{1}{a+ibt}$$

$$\Rightarrow x+iy=\frac{a-ibt}{a^2+b^2t^2}$$

$$\Rightarrow x=\frac{a}{(a^2+b^2t^2)},\ y=-\frac{bt}{(a^2+b^2t^2)}$$

or $$x^2+y^2=\frac{1}{a^2+b^2t^2}=\frac{x}{a}$$

or $$x^2+y^2-\frac{x}{a}=0$$

$\therefore$ Locus of z is a circle with centre $\left(\dfrac{1}{2a},0\right)$

and radius $=\dfrac{1}{2a}$, $a>0$.

Also for $b=0$, $a\neq0$, we get $y=0$.

$\therefore$ locus is X-axis and for $a=0$, $b\neq0$, we get $x=0$

$\therefore$ locus is Y-axis.

148. Let $\Delta=\begin{vmatrix}1&1&1\\1&-\omega^2-1&\omega^2\\1&\omega^2&\omega^7\end{vmatrix}=\begin{vmatrix}1&1&1\\1&\omega&\omega^2\\1&\omega^2&\omega\end{vmatrix}$

$(\because 1+\omega+\omega^2=0$ and $\omega^3=1)$

Applying $C_1\to C_1+C_2+C_3$, then we get

$$\Delta=\begin{vmatrix}3&1&1\\0&\omega&\omega^2\\0&\omega^2&\omega\end{vmatrix}\quad(\because 1+\omega+\omega^2=0)$$

$=3(\omega^2-\omega^4)$

$=3(-1-\omega-\omega)$ $\quad(\because \omega^3=1$ and $1+\omega+\omega^2=0)$

$=-3(1+2\omega)$

$=-3z=3k$ (given) $\quad(\because 1+2\omega=z)$

$\therefore$ $k=-z$

CHAPTER

02

Theory of Equations

Learning Part

Session 1

- Polynomial in One Variable
- Linear Equation
- Standard Quadratic Equation
- Identity
- Quadratic Equations

Session 2

- Transformation of Quadratic Equations
- Condition for Common Roots

Session 3

- Quadratic Expression
- Wavy Curve Method
- Condition for Resolution into Linear Factors
- Location of Roots (Interval in which Roots Lie)

Session 4

- Equations of Higher Degree
- Rational Algebraic Inequalities
- Roots of Equation with the Help of Graphs

Session 5

- Irrational Equations
- Irrational Inequations
- Exponential Equations
- Exponential Inequations
- Logarithmic Equations
- Logarithmic Inequations

Practice Part

- JEE Type Examples
- Chapter Exercises

Arihant on Your Mobile !

Exercises with the symbol can be practised on your mobile. See inside cover page to activate for free.

Session 1

Polynomial in One Variable, Identity, Linear Equation, Quadratic Equations, Standard Quadratic Equation

Polynomial in One Variable

An algebraic expression containing many terms of the form cx^n, n being a non-negative integer is called a polynomial,

i.e., $$f(x) = a_0 \cdot x^n + a_1 \cdot x^{n-1} + a_2 \cdot x^{n-2} + \dots + a_{n-1} \cdot x + a_n,$$

where x is a variable, $a_0, a_1, a_2, \dots, a_n$ are constants and $a_0 \neq 0$.

1. Real Polynomial

Let $a_0, a_1, a_2, \dots, a_n$ be real numbers and x is a real variable.

Then,

$f(x) = a_0 \cdot x^n + a_1 \cdot x^{n-1} + a_2 \cdot x^{n-2} + \dots + a_{n-1} \cdot x + a_n$

is called a real polynomial of real variable (x) with real coefficients.

For example, $5x^3 - 3x^2 + 7x - 4$, $x^2 - 3x + 1$, etc., are real polynomials.

2. Complex Polynomial

Let $a_0, a_1, a_2, \dots, a_n$ are complex numbers and x is a varying complex number.

Then $f(x) = a_0 \cdot x^n + a_1 \cdot x^{n-1} + a_2 \cdot x^{n-2} + \dots + a_{n-1} \cdot x + a_n$ is called a complex polynomial or a polynomial of complex variable with complex coefficients.

For example, $x^3 - 7ix^2 + (3-2i)x + 13$, $3x^2 - (2+3i)x + 5i$, etc. (where $i = \sqrt{-1}$) are complex polynomials.

3. Rational Expression or Rational Function

An expression of the form $\frac{P(x)}{Q(x)}$, where $P(x)$ and $Q(x)$ are polynomials in x, is called a rational expression. As a particular case when $Q(x)$ is a non-zero constant, $\frac{P(x)}{Q(x)}$ reduces to a polynomial.

Thus, every polynomial is a rational expression but a rational expression may or may not be a polynomial.

For example,

(i) $x^2 - 7x + 8$ (ii) $\frac{2}{x-3}$

(iii) $\frac{x^3 - 6x^2 + 11x - 6}{(x-4)}$ (iv) $x + \frac{3}{x}$ or $\frac{x^2 + 3}{x}$

4. Degree of Polynomial

The highest power of variable (x) present in the polynomial is called the degree of the polynomial.

For example, $f(x) = a_0 \cdot x^n + a_1 \cdot x^{n-1} + a_2 \cdot x^{n-2} + \dots + a_{n-1} \cdot x + a_n$ is a polynomial in x of degree n.

Remark

A polynomial of degree one is generally called a linear polynomial. Polynomials of degree 2, 3, 4 and 5 are known as quadratic, cubic, biquadratic and pentic polynomials, respectively.

5. Polynomial Equation

If $f(x)$ is a polynomial, real or complex, then $f(x) = 0$ is called a polynomial equation.

(i) A polynomial equation has atleast one root.

(ii) A polynomial equation of degree n has n roots.

Remarks

1. A polynomial equation of degree one is called a **linear equation** i.e. $ax + b = 0$, where $a, b \in C$, set of all complex numbers and $a \neq 0$.
2. A polynomial equation of degree two is called a **quadratic equation** i.e., $ax^2 + bx + c$, where $a, b, c \in C$ and $a \neq 0$.
3. A polynomial equation of degree three is called a **cubic equation** i.e., $ax^3 + bx^2 + cx + d = 0$, where $a, b, c, d \in C$ and $a \neq 0$.
4. A polynomial equation of degree four is called a **biquadratic equation** i.e., $ax^4 + bx^3 + cx^2 + dx + e = 0$, where $a, b, c, d, e \in C$ and $a \neq 0$.
5. A polynomial equation of degree five is called a **pentic equation** i.e., $ax^5 + bx^4 + cx^3 + dx^2 + ex + f = 0$, where $a, b, c, d, e, f \in C$ and $a \neq 0$.

6. Roots of an Equation

The values of the variable for which an equation is satisfied are called the roots of the equation.

If $x=\alpha$ is a root of the equation $f(x)=0$, then $f(\alpha)=0$.

Remark

The real roots of an equation $f(x)=0$ are the values of x, where the curve $y=f(x)$ crosses X-axis.

7. Solution Set

The set of all roots of an equation in a given domain is called the solution set of the equation.

For example, The roots of the equation $x^3-2x^2-5x+6=0$ are $1, -2, 3$, the solution set is $\{1, -2, 3\}$.

Remark

Solve or solving an equation means finding its solution set or obtaining all its roots.

Identity

If two expressions are equal for all values of x, then the statement of equality between the two expressions is called an identity.

For example, $(x+1)^2=x^2+2x+1$ is an identity in x.

or

If $f(x)=0$ is satisfied by every value of x in the domain of $f(x)$, then it is called an identity.

For example, $f(x)=(x+1)^2-(x^2+2x+1)=0$ is an identity in the domain C, as it is satisfied by every complex number.

or

If $f(x)=a_0\cdot x^n+a_1\cdot x^{n-1}+a_2\cdot x^{n-2}+\ldots+a_{n-1}\cdot x+a_n=0$ have more than n distinct roots, it is an identity, then

$$a_0=a_1=a_2=\ldots=a_{n-1}=a_n=0$$

For example, If $ax^2+bx+c=0$ is satisfied by more than two values of x, then $a=b=c=0$.

or

In an identity in x coefficients of similar powers of x on the two sides are equal.

For example, If $ax^4+bx^3+cx^2+dx+e=5x^4-3x^3+4x^2-7x-9$ be an identity in x, then

$$a=5, b=-3, c=4, d=-7, e=-9.$$

Thus, an identity in x satisfied by all values of x, where as an equation in x is satisfied by some particular values of x.

| Example 1. If equation $(\lambda^2-5\lambda+6)x^2+(\lambda^2-3\lambda+2)x+(\lambda^2-4)=0$ is satisfied by more than two values of x, find the parameter λ.

Sol. If an equation of degree two is satisfied by more than two values of unknown, then it must be an identity. Then, we must have

$$\lambda^2-5\lambda+6=0, \lambda^2-3\lambda+2=0, \lambda^2-4=0$$

$\Rightarrow$ $\lambda=2, 3$ and $\lambda=2, 1$ and $\lambda=2, -2$

Common value of λ which satisfies each condition is $\lambda=2$.

| Example 2. Show that $\frac{(x+b)(x+c)}{(b-a)(c-a)}+\frac{(x+c)(x+a)}{(c-b)(a-b)}+\frac{(x+a)(x+b)}{(a-c)(b-c)}=1$ *is an identity.*

Sol. Given relation is

$$\frac{(x+b)(x+c)}{(b-a)(c-a)}+\frac{(x+c)(x+a)}{(c-b)(a-b)}+\frac{(x+a)(x+b)}{(a-c)(b-c)}=1 \quad \ldots\text{(i)}$$

When $x=-a$, then LHS of Eq. (i) $=\frac{(b-a)(c-a)}{(b-a)(c-a)}=1$

= RHS of Eq. (i)

When $x=-b$, then LHS of Eq. (i)

$=\frac{(c-b)(a-b)}{(c-b)(a-b)}=1=$ RHS of Eq. (i)

and when $x=-c$, then LHS of Eq. (i) $=\frac{(a-c)(b-c)}{(a-c)(b-c)}=1$

= RHS of Eq. (i).

Thus, highest power of x occurring in relation of Eq. (i) is 2 and this relation is satisfied by three distinct values of $x\ (=-a, -b, -c)$. Therefore, it cannot be an equation and hence it is an identity.

| Example 3. Show that $x^2-3|x|+2=0$ is an equation.

Sol. Put $x=0$ in $x^2-3|x|+2=0$

$\Rightarrow$ $0^2-3|0|+2=2\neq 0$

Since, the relation $x^2-3|x|+2=0$ is not satisfied by $x=0$. Hence, it is an equation.

Linear Equation

An equation of the form

$$ax+b=0 \quad \ldots\text{(i)}$$

where $a, b\in R$ and $a\neq 0$, is a linear equation.

Eq. (i) has an unique root equal to $-\frac{b}{a}$.

Example 4. Solve the equation $\frac{x}{2}+\frac{(3x-1)}{6}=1-\frac{x}{2}$

Sol. We have, $\frac{x}{2}+\frac{(3x-1)}{6}=1-\frac{x}{2}$

or $\frac{x}{2}+\frac{x}{2}+\frac{x}{2}=1+\frac{1}{6}$

or $\frac{3x}{2}=\frac{7}{6}$

or $x=\frac{7}{9}$

Example 5. Solve the equation $(a-3)x+5=a+2$.

Sol. ***Case* I** For $a \neq 3$, this equation is linear, then

$(a-3)\,x=(a-3)$

$\therefore \quad x=\frac{(a-3)}{(a-3)}=1$

***Case* II** For $a=3$,

$0 \cdot x+5=3+2$

$\Rightarrow \quad 5=5$

Therefore, any real number is its solution.

Quadratic Equations

An equation in which the highest power of the unknown quantity is 2, is called a quadratic equation. Quadratic equations are of two types :

1. Purely Quadratic Equation

A quadratic equation in which the term containing the first degree of the unknown quantity is absent, is called a purely quadratic equation.

i.e., $ax^2+c=0$,

where $a, c \in C$ and $a \neq 0$.

2. Adfected Quadratic Equation

A quadratic equation in which it contains the terms of first as well as second degrees of the unknown quantity, is called an adfected (or complete) quadratic equation.

i.e., $ax^2+bx+c=0$,

where $a, b, c \in C$ and $a \neq 0, b \neq 0$.

Standard Quadratic Equation

An equation of the form

$$ax^2+bx+c=0 \quad \text{...(i)}$$

where $a, b, c \in C$ and $a \neq 0$, is called a standard quadratic equation.

The numbers a, b, c are called the coefficients of this equation.

A root of the quadratic Eq. (i) is a complex number α, such that $a\alpha^2+b\alpha+c=0$. Recall that $D=b^2-4ac$ is the discriminant of the Eq. (i) and its roots are given by the following formula.

$$x=\frac{-b \pm \sqrt{D}}{2a} \quad \text{[Shridharacharya method]}$$

Nature of Roots

1. If $a, b, c \in R$ and $a \neq 0$, then

(i) If $D<0$, then Eq. (i) has non-real complex roots.

(ii) If $D>0$, then Eq. (i) has real and distinct roots, namely

$$x_1=\frac{-b+\sqrt{D}}{2a},\ x_2=\frac{-b-\sqrt{D}}{2a} \text{ and then}$$

$$ax^2+bx+c=a(x-x_1)(x-x_2). \quad \text{...(ii)}$$

(iii) If $D=0$, then Eq. (i) has real and equal roots, then

$$x_1=x_2=-\frac{b}{2a} \text{ and then}$$

$$ax^2+bx+c=a(x-x_1)^2. \quad \text{...(iii)}$$

To represent the quadratic ax^2+bx+c in form Eqs. (ii) or (iii), is to expand it into linear factors.

(iv) If $D \geq 0$, then Eq. (i) has real roots.

(v) If D_1 and D_2 be the discriminants of two quadratic equations, then

(a) If $D_1+D_2 \geq 0$, then

- atleast one of D_1 and $D_2 \geq 0$.
- if $D_1<0$, then $D_2>0$ and if $D_1>0$, then $D_2<0$.

(b) If $D_1+D_2<0$, then

- atleast one of D_1 and $D_2<0$.
- If $D_1<0$, then $D_2>0$ and if $D_1>0$, then $D_2<0$.

2. If $a, b, c \in Q$ and D is a perfect square of a rational number, the roots are rational and in case it is not a perfect square, the roots are irrational.

3. If $a, b, c \in R$ and $p+iq$ is one root of Eq. (i) $(q \neq 0)$, then the other must be the conjugate $(p-iq)$ and *vice-versa* (where, $p, q \in R$ and $i=\sqrt{-1}$).

4. If $a, b, c \in Q$ and $p+\sqrt{q}$ is one root of Eq. (i), then the other must be the conjugate $p-\sqrt{q}$ and *vice-versa* (where, p is a rational and $\sqrt{q}$ is a surd).

5. If $a=1$ and $b, c \in I$ and the roots of Eq. (i) are rational numbers, these roots must be integers.

6. If $a+b+c=0$ and a, b, c are rational, 1 is a root of the Eq. (i) and roots of the Eq. (i) are rational.

7. $a^2+b^2+c^2-ab-bc-ca=\frac{1}{2}$

$$\{(a-b)^2+(b-c)^2+(c-a)^2\}$$
$$=-\{(a-b)(b-c)+(b-c)(c-a)+(c-a)(a-b)\}$$

| Example 6. Find all values of the parameter a for which the quadratic equation

$$(a+1)x^2+2(a+1)x+a-2=0$$

(i) has two distinct roots.
(ii) has no roots.
(iii) has two equal roots.

Sol. By the hypothesis, this equation is quadratic and therefore $a \neq -1$ and the discriminant of this equation,

$$D = 4(a+1)^2 - 4(a+1)(a-2)$$
$$= 4(a+1)(a+1-a+2)$$
$$= 12(a+1)$$

(i) For $a > (-1)$, then $D > 0$, this equation has two distinct roots.

(ii) For $a < (-1)$, then $D < 0$, this equation has no roots.

(iii) This equation cannot have two equal roots. Since, $D = 0$ only for $a = -1$ and this contradicts the hypothesis.

| Example 7. Solve for x, $(5+2\sqrt{6})^{x^2-3}+(5-2\sqrt{6})^{x^2-3}=10$.

Sol. $\because \quad (5+2\sqrt{6})(5-2\sqrt{6})=1$

$\therefore \quad (5-2\sqrt{6})=\dfrac{1}{(5+2\sqrt{6})}$

$\therefore \quad (5+2\sqrt{6})^{x^2-3}+(5-2\sqrt{6})^{x^2-3}=10$

reduces to $(5+2\sqrt{6})^{x^2-3}+\left(\dfrac{1}{5+2\sqrt{6}}\right)^{x^2-3}=10$

Put $(5+2\sqrt{6})^{x^2-3}=t$, then $t+\dfrac{1}{t}=10$

$\Rightarrow \quad t^2-10t+1=0$

or $\quad t=\dfrac{10\pm\sqrt{(100-4)}}{2}=(5\pm2\sqrt{6})$

$\Rightarrow \quad (5+2\sqrt{6})^{x^2-3}=(5\pm2\sqrt{6})=(5+2\sqrt{6})^{\pm1}$

$\therefore \quad x^2-3=\pm1$

$\Rightarrow \quad x^2-3=1$ or $x^2-3=-1$

$\Rightarrow \quad x^2=4$ or $x^2=2$

Hence, $\quad x=\pm2, \pm\sqrt{2}$

| Example 8. Show that if p, q, r and s are real numbers and $pr=2(q+s)$, then atleast one of the equations $x^2+px+q=0$ and $x^2+rx+s=0$ has real roots.

Sol. Let D_1 and D_2 be the discriminants of the given equations $x^2+px+q=0$ and $x^2+rx+s=0$, respectively.

Now, $D_1+D_2=p^2-4q+r^2-4s=p^2+r^2-4(q+s)$

$=p^2+r^2-2pr$ [given, $pr=2(q+s)$]

$=(p-r)^2\geq0$ [$\because$ p and q are real]

or $\quad D_1+D_2\geq0$

Hence, atleast one of the equations $x^2+px+q=0$ and $x^2+rx+s=0$ has real roots.

| Example 9. If α, β are the roots of the equation $(x-a)(x-b)=c, c\neq0$. Find the roots of the equation $(x-\alpha)(x-\beta)+c=0$.

Sol. Since, α, β are the roots of

$$(x-a)(x-b)=c$$

or $\quad (x-a)(x-b)-c=0,$

Then $\quad (x-a)(x-b)-c=(x-\alpha)(x-\beta)$

$\Rightarrow \quad (x-\alpha)(x-\beta)+c=(x-a)(x-b)$

Hence, roots of $(x-\alpha)(x-\beta)+c=0$ are a, b.

| Example 10. Find all roots of the equation $x^4+2x^3-16x^2-22x+7=0$, if one root is $2+\sqrt{3}$.

Sol. All coefficients are real, irrational roots will occur in conjugate pairs.

Hence, another root is $2-\sqrt{3}$.

$\therefore$ Product of these roots $=(x-2-\sqrt{3})(x-2+\sqrt{3})$

$=(x-2)^2-3=x^2-4x+1.$

On dividing $x^4+2x^3-16x^2-22x+7$ by x^2-4x+1, then the other quadratic factor is x^2+6x+7.

Then, the given equation reduce in the form

$$(x^2-4x+1)(x^2+6x+7)=0$$

$\therefore \quad x^2+6x+7=0$

Then, $\quad x=\dfrac{-6\pm\sqrt{36-28}}{2}=-3\pm\sqrt{2}$

Hence, the other roots are $2-\sqrt{3}, -3\pm\sqrt{2}$.

Relation between Roots and Coefficients

1. **Relation between roots and coefficients of quadratic equation** If roots of the equation $ax^2+bx+c=0\ (a\neq0)$ be real and distinct and $\alpha<\beta$, then $\alpha=\dfrac{-b+\sqrt{D}}{2a}, \beta=\dfrac{-b-\sqrt{D}}{2a}$.

(i) Sum of roots

$= S = \alpha + \beta = -\frac{b}{a} = -\frac{\text{Coefficient of } x}{\text{Coefficient of } x^2}$.

(ii) Product of roots

$= P = \alpha\beta = \frac{c}{a} = \frac{\text{Constant term}}{\text{Coefficient of } x^2}$.

(iii) Difference of roots

$= D' = \alpha - \beta = \frac{\sqrt{D}}{a} = \frac{\sqrt{\text{Discriminant}}}{\text{Coefficient of } x^2}$.

2. **Formation of an equation with given roots** A quadratic equation whose roots are α and β, is given by $(x-\alpha)(x-\beta)=0$ or $x^2-(\alpha+\beta)x+\alpha\beta=0$ i.e. x^2 − (Sum of roots) x + Product of roots = 0

$\therefore \quad x^2 - Sx + P = 0.$

3. **Symmetric function of roots** A function of α and β is said to be symmetric function, if it remains unchanged, when α and β are interchanged.

For example, $\alpha^3+3\alpha^2\beta+3\alpha\beta^2+\beta^3$ is a symmetric function of α and β, whereas $\alpha^3-\beta^3+5\alpha\beta$ is not a symmetric function of α and β. In order to find the value of a symmetric function in terms of $\alpha+\beta, \alpha\beta$ and $\alpha-\beta$ and also in terms of a, b and c.

(i) $\alpha^2+\beta^2 = (\alpha+\beta)^2 - 2\alpha\beta$

$$= \left(-\frac{b}{a}\right)^2 - 2\left(\frac{c}{a}\right) = \frac{b^2-2ac}{a^2}$$

(ii) $\alpha^2-\beta^2 = (\alpha+\beta)(\alpha-\beta)$

$$= \left(-\frac{b}{a}\right)\left(\frac{\sqrt{D}}{a}\right) = -\frac{b\sqrt{D}}{a^2}.$$

(iii) $\alpha^3+\beta^3 = (\alpha+\beta)^3 - 3\alpha\beta(\alpha+\beta)$

$$= \left(-\frac{b}{a}\right)^3 - 3\left(\frac{c}{a}\right)\left(-\frac{b}{a}\right) = -\left(\frac{b^3-3abc}{a^3}\right).$$

(iv) $\alpha^3-\beta^3 = (\alpha-\beta)^3 + 3\alpha\beta(\alpha-\beta)$

$$= \left(\frac{\sqrt{D}}{a}\right)^3 + 3\left(\frac{c}{a}\right)\left(\frac{\sqrt{D}}{a}\right) = \frac{\sqrt{D}(D+3ac)}{a^3}.$$

(v) $\alpha^4+\beta^4 = (\alpha^2+\beta^2)^2 - 2\alpha^2\beta^2$

$$= \left(\frac{b^2-2ac}{a^2}\right)^2 - 2\left(\frac{c}{a}\right)^2 = \frac{b^4+2a^2c^2-4acb^2}{a^4}.$$

(vi) $\alpha^4-\beta^4 = (\alpha^2+\beta^2)(\alpha^2-\beta^2)$

$$= -\frac{b\sqrt{D}(b^2-2ac)}{a^4}.$$

(vii) $\alpha^5+\beta^5 = (\alpha^2+\beta^2)(\alpha^3+\beta^3) - \alpha^2\beta^2(\alpha+\beta)$

$$= \left(\frac{b^2-2ac}{a^2}\right)\left(-\frac{(b^3-3abc)}{a^3}\right) - \frac{c^2}{a^2}\left(-\frac{b}{a}\right)$$

$$= \frac{-(b^5-5ab^3c+5a^2bc^2)}{a^5}.$$

(viii) $\alpha^5-\beta^5 = (\alpha^2+\beta^2)(\alpha^3-\beta^3) + \alpha^2\beta^2(\alpha-\beta)$

$$= \left(\frac{b^2-2ac}{a^2}\right)\left(\frac{\sqrt{D}(D+3ac)}{a^3}\right) + \left(\frac{c}{a}\right)^2\left(\frac{\sqrt{D}}{a}\right)$$

$$= \frac{\sqrt{D}(b^4-3acb^2+3a^2c^2)}{a^5}.$$

Example 11. If one root of the equation $x^2 - ix - (1+i) = 0, (i=\sqrt{-1})$ is $1+i$, find the other root.

Sol. All coefficients of the given equation are not real, then other root $\neq 1-i$.

Let other root be α, then sum of roots $= i$

i.e. $\quad 1+i+\alpha = i \Rightarrow \alpha = (-1)$

Hence, the other root is (-1).

Example 12. If one root of the equation $x^2 - \sqrt{5}x - 19 = 0$ is $\frac{9+\sqrt{5}}{2}$, then find the other root.

Sol. All coefficients of the given equation are not rational, then other root $\neq \frac{9-\sqrt{5}}{2}$.

Let other root be α, sum of roots $= \sqrt{5}$

$$\Rightarrow \quad \frac{9+\sqrt{5}}{2} + \alpha = \sqrt{5} \Rightarrow \alpha = \frac{-9+\sqrt{5}}{2}$$

Hence, other root is $\frac{-9+\sqrt{5}}{2}$.

Example 13. If the difference between the corresponding roots of the equations $x^2+ax+b=0$ and $x^2+bx+a=0 \, (a \neq b)$ is the same, find the value of $a+b$.

Sol. Let α, β be the roots of $x^2+ax+b=0$ and γ, δ be the roots of $x^2+bx+a=0$, then given

$$\alpha - \beta = \gamma - \delta$$

$$\Rightarrow \quad \frac{\sqrt{a^2-4b}}{1} = \frac{\sqrt{b^2-4a}}{1} \quad \left[\because \alpha - \beta = \frac{\sqrt{D}}{a}\right]$$

$$\Rightarrow \quad a^2 - 4b = b^2 - 4a$$

$$\Rightarrow \quad (a^2-b^2) + 4(a-b) = 0 \Rightarrow (a-b)(a+b+4) = 0$$

$$\because \quad a - b \neq 0$$

$$\therefore \quad a+b+4 = 0 \text{ or } a+b = -4.$$

Example 14. If $a+b+c=0$ and a,b,c are rational. Prove that the roots of the equation

$$(b+c-a)x^2+(c+a-b)x+(a+b-c)=0$$

are rational.

Sol. Given equation is

$$(b+c-a)x^2+(c+a-b)x+(a+b-c)=0 \quad \text{...(i)}$$

$\because (b+c-a)+(c+a-b)+(a+b-c)=a+b+c=0$

$\therefore x=1$ is a root of Eq. (i), let other root of Eq. (i) is α, then

Product of roots $=\dfrac{a+b-c}{b+c-a}$

$$\Rightarrow \quad 1\times\alpha=\frac{-c-c}{-a-a} \quad [\because a+b+c=0]$$

$$\therefore \quad \alpha=\frac{c}{a} \quad \text{[rational]}$$

Hence, both roots of Eq. (i) are rational.

Aliter

Let $b+c-a=A, c+a-b=B, a+b-c=C$

Then, $A+B+C=0 \quad [\because a+b+c=0]$ ...(ii)

Now, Eq. (i) becomes

$$Ax^2+Bx+C=0 \quad \text{...(iii)}$$

Discriminant of Eq. (iii),

$$D=B^2-4AC$$
$$=(-C-A)^2-4AC \quad [\because A+B+C=0]$$
$$=(C+A)^2-4AC$$
$$=(C-A)^2=(2a-2c)^2$$
$$=4(a-c)^2=\text{A perfect square}$$

Hence, roots of Eq. (i) are rational.

Example 15. If the roots of equation $a(b-c)x^2+b(c-a)x+c(a-b)=0$ be equal, prove that a,b,c are in HP.

Sol. Given equation is

$$a(b-c)x^2+b(c-a)x+c(a-b)=0 \quad \text{...(i)}$$

Here, coefficient of x^2 + coefficient of x + constant term = 0

i.e., $a(b-c)+b(c-a)+c(a-b)=0$

Then, 1 is a root of Eq. (i).

Since, its roots are equal.

Therefore, its other root will be also equal to 1.

Then, product of roots $=1\times1=\dfrac{c(a-b)}{a(b-c)}$

$$\Rightarrow \quad ab-ac=ca-bc$$

$$\therefore \quad b=\frac{2ac}{a+c}$$

Hence, a, b and c are in HP.

Example 16. If α is a root of $4x^2+2x-1=0$. Prove that $4\alpha^3-3\alpha$ is the other root.

Sol. Let other root is β,

then $\alpha+\beta=-\dfrac{2}{4}=-\dfrac{1}{2}$ or $\beta=-\dfrac{1}{2}-\alpha$ ...(i)

and so $4\alpha^2+2\alpha-1=0$, because α is a root of $4x^2+2x-1=0$.

Now, $\beta=4\alpha^3-3\alpha=\alpha(4\alpha^2-3)$

$$=\alpha(1-2\alpha-3) \quad [\because 4\alpha^2+2\alpha-1=0]$$
$$=-2\alpha^2-2\alpha$$
$$=-\frac{1}{2}(4\alpha^2)-2\alpha$$
$$=-\frac{1}{2}(1-2\alpha)-2\alpha \quad [\because 4\alpha^2+2\alpha-1=0]$$
$$=-\frac{1}{2}-\alpha=\beta \quad \text{[from Eq. (i)]}$$

Hence, $4\alpha^3-3\alpha$ is the other root.

Example 17. If α,β are the roots of the equation $\lambda(x^2-x)+x+5=0$. If λ_1 and λ_2 are two values of λ for which the roots α,β are related by $\dfrac{\alpha}{\beta}+\dfrac{\beta}{\alpha}=\dfrac{4}{5}$, find the value of $\dfrac{\lambda_1}{\lambda_2}+\dfrac{\lambda_2}{\lambda_1}$.

Sol. The given equation can be written as

$$\lambda x^2-(\lambda-1)x+5=0$$

$\because \alpha,\beta$ are the roots of this equation.

$$\therefore \quad \alpha+\beta=\frac{\lambda-1}{\lambda} \text{ and } \alpha\beta=\frac{5}{\lambda}$$

But, given $\dfrac{\alpha}{\beta}+\dfrac{\beta}{\alpha}=\dfrac{4}{5}$

$$\Rightarrow \quad \frac{\alpha^2+\beta^2}{\alpha\beta}=\frac{4}{5}$$

$$\Rightarrow \quad \frac{(\alpha+\beta)^2-2\alpha\beta}{\alpha\beta}=\frac{4}{5} \Rightarrow \frac{\frac{(\lambda-1)^2}{\lambda^2}-\frac{10}{\lambda}}{\frac{5}{\lambda}}=\frac{4}{5}$$

$$\Rightarrow \quad \frac{(\lambda-1)^2-10\lambda}{5\lambda}=\frac{4}{5} \Rightarrow \lambda^2-12\lambda+1=4\lambda$$

$$\Rightarrow \quad \lambda^2-16\lambda+1=0$$

It is a quadratic in λ, let roots be λ_1 and λ_2, then

$$\lambda_1+\lambda_2=16 \text{ and } \lambda_1\lambda_2=1$$

$$\therefore \quad \frac{\lambda_1}{\lambda_2}+\frac{\lambda_2}{\lambda_1}=\frac{\lambda_1^2+\lambda_2^2}{\lambda_1\lambda_2}=\frac{(\lambda_1+\lambda_2)^2-2\lambda_1\lambda_2}{\lambda_1\lambda_2}$$

$$=\frac{(16)^2-2(1)}{1}=254$$

Example 18. If α, β are the roots of the equation $x^2 - px + q = 0$, find the quadratic equation the roots of which are $(\alpha^2 - \beta^2)(\alpha^3 - \beta^3)$ and $\alpha^3\beta^2 + \alpha^2\beta^3$.

Sol. Since, α, β are the roots of $x^2 - px + q = 0$.

$\therefore \quad \alpha + \beta = p, \alpha\beta = q$

$\Rightarrow \quad \alpha - \beta = \sqrt{(p^2 - 4q)}$

Now, $(\alpha^2 - \beta^2)(\alpha^3 - \beta^3)$

$= (\alpha + \beta)(\alpha - \beta)(\alpha - \beta)(\alpha^2 + \alpha\beta + \beta^2)$

$= (\alpha + \beta)(\alpha - \beta)^2 \{(\alpha + \beta)^2 - \alpha\beta\}$

$= p(p^2 - 4q)(p^2 - q)$

and $\alpha^3\beta^2 + \alpha^2\beta^3 = \alpha^2\beta^2(\alpha + \beta) = pq^2$

$S = $ Sum of roots $= p(p^2 - 4q)(p^2 - q) + pq^2$

$= p(p^4 - 5p^2q + 5q^2)$

$P = $ Product of roots $= p^2q^2(p^2 - 4q)(p^2 - q)$

$\therefore$ Required equation is $x^2 - Sx + P = 0$

i.e. $x^2 - p(p^4 - 5p^2q + 5q^2)x + p^2q^2(p^2 - 4q)(p^2 - q) = 0$

Exercise for Session 1

1. If $(a^2 - 1)x^2 + (a - 1)x + a^2 - 4a + 3 = 0$ be an identity in x, then the value of a is/are

(a) -1 (b) 1 (c) 3 (d) $-1, 1, 3$

2. The roots of the equation $x^2 + 2\sqrt{3}x + 3 = 0$ are

(a) real and unequal (b) rational and equal
(c) irrational and equal (d) irrational and unequal

3. If $a, b, c \in Q$, then roots of the equation $(b + c - 2a)x^2 + (c + a - 2b)x + (a + b - 2c) = 0$ are

(a) rational (b) non-real (c) irrational (d) equal

4. If $P(x) = ax^2 + bx + c$ and $Q(x) = -ax^2 + dx + c$, where $ac \neq 0$, then $P(x)Q(x) = 0$ has atleast

(a) four real roots (b) two real roots
(c) four imaginary roots (d) None of these

5. If roots of the equation $(q - r)x^2 + (r - p)x + (p - q) = 0$ are equal, then p, q, r are in

(a) AP (b) GP (c) HP (d) AGP

6. If one root of the quadratic equation $ix^2 - 2(i + 1)x + (2 - i) = 0, i = \sqrt{-1}$ is $2 - i$, the other root is

(a) $-i$ (b) i (c) $2 + i$ (d $2 - i$

7. If the difference of the roots of $x^2 - \lambda x + 8 = 0$ be 2, the value of λ is

(a) ± 2 (b) ± 4 (c) ± 6 (d) ± 8

8. If $3p^2 = 5p + 2$ and $3q^2 = 5q + 2$ where $p \neq q$, pq is equal to

(a) $\frac{2}{3}$ (b) $-\frac{2}{3}$ (c) $\frac{3}{2}$ (d) $-\frac{3}{2}$

9. If α, β are the roots of the quadratic equation $x^2 + bx - c = 0$, the equation whose roots are b and c, is

(a) $x^2 + \alpha x - \beta = 0$ (b) $x^2 - [(\alpha + \beta) + \alpha\beta]x - \alpha\beta(\alpha + \beta) = 0$
(c) $x^2 + [(\alpha + \beta) + \alpha\beta]x + \alpha\beta(\alpha + \beta) = 0$ (d) $x^2 + [(\alpha + \beta) + \alpha\beta]x - \alpha\beta(\alpha + \beta) = 0$

10. Let $p, q \in \{1, 2, 3, 4\}$. The number of equations of the form $px^2 + qx + 1 = 0$ having real roots, is

(a) 15 (b) 9 (c) 8 (d) 7

11. If α and β are the roots of the equation $ax^2 + bx + c = 0$ ($a \neq 0$, a, b, c being different), then $(1 + \alpha + \alpha^2)(1 + \beta + \beta^2)$ is equal to

(a) zero (b) positive (c) negative (d) None of these

Session 2

Transformation of Quadratic Equations, Condition for Common Roots

Transformation of Quadratic Equations

Let α, β be the roots of the equation $ax^2 + bx + c = 0$, then the equation

(i) whose roots are $\alpha + k, \beta + k$, is

$a(x-k)^2 + b(x-k) + c = 0$ [replace x by $(x-k)$]

(ii) whose roots are $\alpha - k, \beta - k$, is

$a(x+k)^2 + b(x+k) + c = 0$ [replace x by $(x+k)$]

(iii) whose roots are $\alpha k, \beta k$, is

$ax^2 + kbx + k^2 c = 0$ $\left[\text{replace } x \text{ by} \left(\frac{x}{k}\right)\right]$

(iv) whose roots are $\frac{\alpha}{k}, \frac{\beta}{k}$, is

$ak^2x^2 + bkx + c = 0$ [replace x by xk]

(v) whose roots are $-\alpha, -\beta$, is

$ax^2 - bx + c = 0$ [replace x by $(-x)$]

(vi) whose roots are $\frac{1}{\alpha}, \frac{1}{\beta}$, is

$cx^2 + bx + a = 0$ $\left[\text{replace } x \text{ by} \left(\frac{1}{x}\right)\right]$

(vii) whose roots are $-\frac{1}{\alpha}, -\frac{1}{\beta}$, is

$cx^2 - bx + a = 0$ $\left[\text{replace } x \text{ by} \left(-\frac{1}{x}\right)\right]$

(viii) whose roots are $\frac{k}{\alpha}, \frac{k}{\beta}$, is

$cx^2 + kbx + k^2 a = 0$ $\left[\text{replace } x \text{ by} \left(\frac{k}{x}\right)\right]$

(ix) whose roots are $p\alpha + q, p\beta + q$, is

$a\left(\frac{x-q}{p}\right)^2 + b\left(\frac{x-q}{p}\right) + c = 0$ $\left[\text{replace } x \text{ by} \left(\frac{x-q}{p}\right)\right]$

(x) whose roots are $\alpha^n, \beta^n, n \in N$, is

$a(x^{1/n})^2 + b(x^{1/n}) + c = 0$ [replace x by $(x^{1/n})$]

(xi) whose roots are $\alpha^{1/n}, \beta^{1/n}, n \in N$ is

$a(x^n)^2 + b(x^n) + c = 0$ [replace x by (x^n)]

| Example 19. If α, β be the roots of the equation $x^2 - px + q = 0$, then find the equation whose roots are $\frac{q}{p-\alpha}$ and $\frac{q}{p-\beta}$.

Sol. Let $\frac{q}{p-\alpha} = x \Rightarrow \alpha = p - \frac{q}{x}$

So, we replacing x by $p - \frac{q}{x}$ in the given equation, we get

$$\left(p - \frac{q}{x}\right)^2 - p\left(p - \frac{q}{x}\right) + q = 0$$

$$\Rightarrow \quad p^2 + \frac{q^2}{x^2} - \frac{2pq}{x} - p^2 + \frac{pq}{x} + q = 0$$

$$\Rightarrow \quad q - \frac{pq}{x} + \frac{q^2}{x^2} = 0$$

or $\quad qx^2 - pqx + q^2 = 0$ or $x^2 - px + q = 0$

is the required equation whose roots are $\frac{q}{p-\alpha}$ and $\frac{q}{p-\beta}$.

| Example 20. If α and β are the roots of $ax^2 + bx + c = 0$, then find the roots of the equation $ax^2 - bx(x-1) + c(x-1)^2 = 0$.

Sol. $\because ax^2 - bx(x-1) + c(x-1)^2 = 0$ ...(i)

$$\Rightarrow \quad a\left(\frac{x}{x-1}\right)^2 - b\left(\frac{x}{x-1}\right) + c = 0$$

or $\quad a\left(\frac{x}{1-x}\right)^2 + b\left(\frac{x}{1-x}\right) + c = 0$

Now, α, β are the roots of $ax^2 + bx + c = 0$.

Then, $\quad \alpha = \frac{x}{1-x}$ and $\beta = \frac{x}{1-x}$

$$\Rightarrow \quad x = \frac{\alpha}{\alpha+1} \text{ and } x = \frac{\beta}{\beta+1}$$

Hence, $\frac{\alpha}{\alpha+1}, \frac{\beta}{\beta+1}$ are the roots of the Eq. (i).

| Example 21. If α, β be the roots of the equation $3x^2 + 2x + 1 = 0$, then find value of $\left(\frac{1-\alpha}{1+\alpha}\right)^3 + \left(\frac{1-\beta}{1+\beta}\right)^3$.

Sol. Let $\frac{1-\alpha}{1+\alpha} = x \Rightarrow \alpha = \frac{1-x}{1+x}$

So, replacing x by $\frac{1-x}{1+x}$ in the given equation, we get

$$3\left(\frac{1-x}{1+x}\right)^2+2\left(\frac{1-x}{1+x}\right)+1=0 \Rightarrow x^2-2x+3=0 \quad \text{...(i)}$$

It is clear that $\frac{1-\alpha}{1+\alpha}$ and $\frac{1-\beta}{1+\beta}$ are the roots of Eq. (i).

$$\therefore \quad \left(\frac{1-\alpha}{1+\alpha}\right)+\left(\frac{1-\beta}{1+\beta}\right)=2 \quad \text{...(ii)}$$

and
$$\left(\frac{1-\alpha}{1+\alpha}\right)\left(\frac{1-\beta}{1+\beta}\right)=3 \quad \text{...(iii)}$$

$$\therefore \quad \left(\frac{1-\alpha}{1+\alpha}\right)^3+\left(\frac{1-\beta}{1+\beta}\right)^3=\left(\frac{1-\alpha}{1+\alpha}+\frac{1-\beta}{1+\beta}\right)^3-3$$

$$\left(\frac{1-\alpha}{1+\alpha}\right)\left(\frac{1-\beta}{1+\beta}\right)\left(\frac{1-\alpha}{1+\alpha}+\frac{1-\beta}{1+\beta}\right)=2^3-3\cdot3\cdot2=8-18=-10$$

Roots Under Special Cases

Consider the quadratic equation $ax^2+bx+c=0$ ...(i)

where $a, b, c \in R$ and $a \neq 0$. Then, the following hold good :

(i) If roots of Eq. (i) are equal in magnitude but opposite in sign, then sum of roots is zero as well as $D>0$, i.e. $b=0$ and $D>0$.

(ii) If roots of Eq. (i) are reciprocal to each other, then product of roots is 1 as well as $D \geq 0$ i.e., $a=c$ and $D \geq 0$.

(iii) If roots of Eq. (i) are of opposite signs, then product of roots <0 as well as $D>0$ i.e., $a>0, c<0$ and $D>0$ or $a<0, c>0$ and $D>0$.

(iv) If both roots of Eq. (i) are positive, then sum and product of roots >0 as well as $D \geq 0$ i.e., $a>0, b<0, c>0$ and $D \geq 0$ or $a<0, b>0, c<0$ and $D \geq 0$.

(v) If both roots of Eq. (i) are negative, then sum of roots <0, product of roots >0 as well as $D \geq 0$ i.e., $a>0, b>0, c>0$ and $D \geq 0$ or $a<0, b<0, c<0$ and $D \geq 0$.

(vi) If atleast one root of Eq. (i) is positive, then either one root is positive or both roots are positive i.e., point (iii) $\cup$ (iv).

(vii) If atleast one root of Eq. (i) is negative, then either one root is negative or both roots are negative i.e., point (iii) $\cup$ (v).

(viii) If greater root in magnitude of Eq. (i) is positive, then sign of $b=$ sign of $c \neq$ sign of a.

(ix) If greater root in magnitude of Eq. (i) is negative, then sign of $a=$ sign of $b \neq$ sign of c.

(x) If both roots of Eq. (i) are zero, then $b=c=0$.

(xi) If roots of Eq. (i) are 0 and $\left(-\frac{b}{a}\right)$, then $c=0$.

(xii) If roots of Eq. (i) are 1 and $\frac{c}{a}$, then $a+b+c=0$.

Example 22. For what values of m, the equation $x^2+2(m-1)x+m+5=0$ has $(m \in R)$

(i) roots are equal in magnitude but opposite in sign?

(ii) roots are reciprocals to each other?

(iii) roots are opposite in sign?

(iv) both roots are positive?

(v) both roots are negative?

(vi) atleast one root is positive?

(vii) atleast one root is negative?

Sol. Here, $a=1, b=2(m-1)$ and $c=m+5$

$\therefore \quad D=b^2-4ac=4(m-1)^2-4(m+5)$
$=4(m^2-3m-4)$

$\therefore \quad D=4(m-4)(m+1)$ and here $a=1>0$

(i) $b=0$ and $D>0$

$\Rightarrow 2(m-1)=0$ and $4(m-4)(m+1)>0$

$\Rightarrow \quad m=1$ and $m \in (-\infty,-1) \cup (4,\infty)$

$\therefore \quad m \in \phi$ [null set]

(ii) $a=c$ and $D \geq 0$

$\Rightarrow \quad 1=m+5$ and $4(m-4)(m+1) \geq 0$

$\Rightarrow \quad m=-4$ and $m \in (-\infty,-1] \cup [4,\infty)$

$\therefore \quad m=-4$

(iii) $a>0, c<0$ and $D>0$

$\Rightarrow \quad 1>0, m+5<0$ and $4(m-4)(m+1)>0$

$\Rightarrow \quad m<-5$ and $m \in (-\infty,-1) \cup (4,\infty)$

$\therefore \quad m \in (-\infty,-5)$

(iv) $a>0, b<0, c>0$ and $D \geq 0$

$\Rightarrow \quad 1>0, 2(m-1)<0, m+5>0$

and $\quad 4(m-4)(m+1) \geq 0$

$\Rightarrow \quad m<1, m>-5$ and $m \in (-\infty,-1] \cup [4,\infty)$

$\Rightarrow \quad m \in (-5,-1]$

(v) $a>0, b>0, c>0$ and $D \geq 0$

$\Rightarrow \quad 1>0, 2(m-1)>0, m+5>0$

and $\quad 4(m-4)(m+1) \geq 0$

$\Rightarrow \quad m>1, m>-5$ and $m \in (-\infty,-1] \cup [4,\infty)$

$\therefore \quad m \in [4,\infty)$

(vi) Either one root is positive or both roots are positive

i.e., (c) $\cup$ (d)

$\Rightarrow \quad m \in (-\infty,-5) \cup (-5,-1]$

(vii) Either one root is negative or both roots are negative

i.e., (c) $\cup$ (e)

$\Rightarrow \quad m \in (-\infty,-5) \cup [4,\infty)$

Condition for Common Roots

1. Only One Root is Common

Consider two quadratic equations

$$ax^2 + bx + c = 0 \text{ and } a'x^2 + b'x + c' = 0$$

[where $a, a' \neq 0$ and $ab' - a'b \neq 0$]

Let α be a common root, then

$$a\alpha^2 + b\alpha + c = 0 \text{ and } a'\alpha^2 + b'\alpha + c' = 0.$$

On solving these two equations by cross-multiplication, we have

$$\frac{\alpha^2}{bc' - b'c} = \frac{\alpha}{ca' - c'a} = \frac{1}{ab' - a'b}$$

From first two relations, we get

$$\alpha = \frac{bc' - b'c}{ca' - c'a} \quad \text{...(i)}$$

and from last two relations, we get

$$\alpha = \frac{ca' - c'a}{ab' - a'b} \quad \text{...(ii)}$$

From Eqs. (i) and (ii), we get

$$\frac{bc' - b'c}{ca' - c'a} = \frac{ca' - c'a}{ab' - a'b}$$

$$\Rightarrow \quad (ab' - a'b)(bc' - b'c) = (ca' - c'a)^2$$

or

$$\begin{vmatrix} a & b \\ a' & b' \end{vmatrix} \times \begin{vmatrix} b & c \\ b' & c' \end{vmatrix} = \begin{vmatrix} c & a \\ c' & a' \end{vmatrix}^2 \quad \text{[remember]}$$

This is the required condition for one root of two quadratic equations to be common.

2. Both Roots are Common

Let α, β be the common roots of the equations $ax^2 + bx + c = 0$ and $a'x^2 + b'x + c' = 0$, then

$$\alpha + \beta = -\frac{b}{a} = -\frac{b'}{a'} \Rightarrow \frac{a}{a'} = \frac{b}{b'} \quad \text{...(iii)}$$

and

$$\alpha\beta = \frac{c}{a} = \frac{c'}{a'} \Rightarrow \frac{a}{a'} = \frac{c}{c'} \quad \text{...(iv)}$$

From Eqs. (iii) and (iv), we get $\dfrac{a}{a'} = \dfrac{b}{b'} = \dfrac{c}{c'}$

This is the required condition for both roots of two quadratic equations to be identical.

Remark

To find the common root between the two equations, make the same coefficient of x^2 in both equations and then subtract of the two equations.

Example 23. Find the value of λ, so that the equations $x^2 - x - 12 = 0$ and $\lambda x^2 + 10x + 3 = 0$ may have one root in common. Also, find the common root.

Sol. $\because$ $x^2 - x - 12 = 0$

$\Rightarrow$ $(x-4)(x+3) = 0$

$\therefore$ $x = 4, -3$

If $x = 4$ is a common root, then

$$\lambda(4)^2 + 10(4) + 3 = 0$$

$\therefore$ $\lambda = -\dfrac{43}{16}$

and if $x = -3$ is a common root, then

$$\lambda(-3)^2 + 10(-3) + 3 = 0$$

$\therefore$ $\lambda = 3$

Hence, for $\lambda = -\dfrac{43}{16}$, common root is $x = 4$

and for $\lambda = 3$, common root is $x = -3$.

Example 24. If equations $ax^2 + bx + c = 0$, (where $a, b, c \in R$ and $a \neq 0$) and $x^2 + 2x + 3 = 0$ have a common root, then show that $a : b : c = 1 : 2 : 3$.

Sol. Given equations are

$$ax^2 + bx + c = 0 \quad \text{...(i)}$$

and

$$x^2 + 2x + 3 = 0 \quad \text{...(ii)}$$

Clearly, roots of Eq. (ii) are imaginary, since Eqs. (i) and (ii) have a common root. Therefore, common root must be imaginary and hence both roots will be common.

Therefore, Eqs. (i) and (ii) are identical.

$\therefore$ $\dfrac{a}{1} = \dfrac{b}{2} = \dfrac{c}{3}$ or $a : b : c = 1 : 2 : 3$

Example 25. If a, b, c are in GP, show that the equations $ax^2 + 2bx + c = 0$ and $dx^2 + 2ex + f = 0$ have a common root, if $\dfrac{a}{d}, \dfrac{b}{e}, \dfrac{c}{f}$ are in HP.

Sol. Given equations are

$$ax^2 + 2bx + c = 0 \quad \text{...(i)}$$

and

$$dx^2 + 2ex + f = 0 \quad \text{...(ii)}$$

Since, a, b, c are in GP.

$\therefore$ $b^2 = ac$ or $b = \sqrt{ac}$

From Eq. (i), $ax^2 + 2\sqrt{ac}\,x + c = 0$

or $(\sqrt{a}\,x + \sqrt{c})^2 = 0$ or $x = -\dfrac{\sqrt{c}}{\sqrt{a}}$

$\because$ Given Eqs. (i) and (ii) have a common root.

Hence, $x = -\dfrac{\sqrt{c}}{\sqrt{a}}$ also satisfied Eq. (ii), then

$$d\left(\frac{c}{a}\right) - 2e\frac{\sqrt{c}}{\sqrt{a}} + f = 0$$

$$\Rightarrow \quad \frac{d}{a} - \frac{2e}{\sqrt{ac}} + \frac{f}{c} = 0$$

or $$\frac{d}{a} - \frac{2e}{b} + \frac{f}{c} = 0 \qquad [\because b = \sqrt{ac}]$$

or $$\frac{d}{a} + \frac{f}{c} = \frac{2e}{b}$$

$\therefore \frac{d}{a}, \frac{e}{b}, \frac{f}{c}$ are in AP.

Hence, $\frac{a}{d}, \frac{b}{e}, \frac{c}{f}$ are in HP.

Exercise for Session 2

1. If α and β are the roots of the equation $2x^2 - 3x + 4 = 0$, then the equation whose roots are α^2 and β^2, is

(a) $4x^2 + 7x + 16 = 0$ (b) $4x^2 + 7x + 6 = 0$ (c) $4x^2 + 7x + 1 = 0$ (d) $4x^2 - 7x + 16 = 0$

2. If α, β are the roots of $x^2 - 3x + 1 = 0$, then the equation whose roots are $\left(\frac{1}{\alpha - 2}, \frac{1}{\beta - 2}\right)$, is

(a) $x^2 + x - 1 = 0$ (b) $x^2 + x + 1 = 0$ (c) $x^2 - x - 1 = 0$ (d) None of these

3. The equation formed by decreasing each root of $ax^2 + bx + c = 0$ by 1 is $2x^2 + 8x + 2 = 0$, then

(a) $a = -b$ (b) $b = -c$ (c) $c = -a$ (d) $b = a + c$

4. If the roots of equation $\frac{x^2 - bx}{ax - c} = \frac{m - 1}{m + 1}$ are equal but opposite in sign, then the value of m will be

(a) $\frac{a - b}{a + b}$ (b) $\frac{b - a}{a + b}$ (c) $\frac{a + b}{a - b}$ (d) $\frac{b + a}{b - a}$

5. If $x^2 + px + q = 0$ is the quadratic equation whose roots are $a - 2$ and $b - 2$, where a and b are the roots of $x^2 - 3x + 1 = 0$, then

(a) $p = 1, q = 5$ (b) $p = 1, q = -5$ (c) $p = -1, q = 1$ (d) None of these

6. If both roots of the equation $x^2 - (m - 3)x + m = 0 \ (m \in R)$ are positive, then

(a) $m \in (3, \infty)$ (b) $m \in (-\infty, 1]$ (c) $m \in [9, \infty)$ (d) $m \in (1, 3)$

7. If the equation $(1 + m)x^2 - 2(1 + 3m)x + (1 + 8m) = 0$, where $m \in R \sim \{-1\}$, has atleast one root is negative, then

(a) $m \in (-\infty, -1)$ (b) $m \in \left(-\frac{1}{8}, \infty\right)$ (c) $m \in \left(-1, -\frac{1}{8}\right)$ (d) $m \in R$

8. If both the roots of $\lambda(6x^2 + 3) + rx + 2x^2 - 1 = 0$ and $6\lambda(2x^2 + 1) + px + 4x^2 - 2 = 0$ are common, then $2r - p$ is equal to

(a) -1 (b) 0 (c) 1 (d) 2

9. If $ax^2 + bx + c = 0$ and $bx^2 + cx + a = 0$ have a common root $a \neq 0$, then $\frac{a^3 + b^3 + c^3}{abc}$ is equal to

(a) 1 (b) 2 (c) 3 (d) None of these

10. If $a(p + q)^2 + 2bpq + c = 0$ and $a(p + r)^2 + 2bpr + c = 0$, then qr is equal to

(a) $p^2 + \frac{c}{a}$ (b) $p^2 + \frac{a}{c}$ (c) $p^2 + \frac{a}{b}$ (d) $p^2 + \frac{b}{a}$

Session 3

Quadratic Expression, Wavy Curve Method, Condition for Resolution into Linear Factors, Location of Roots

Quadratic Expression

An expression of the form $ax^2 + bx + c$, where $a, b, c \in R$ and $a \neq 0$ is called a quadratic expression in x. So, in general quadratic expression is represented by

$$f(x) = ax^2 + bx + c \text{ or } y = ax^2 + bx + c.$$

Graph of a Quadratic Expression

We have, $y = ax^2 + bx + c = f(x)$, $[a \neq 0]$

$$\Rightarrow \quad y = a\left[\left(x + \frac{b}{2a}\right)^2 - \frac{D}{4a^2}\right]$$

or $$\left(y + \frac{D}{4a}\right) = a\left(x + \frac{b}{2a}\right)^2$$

Now, let $y + \frac{D}{4a} = Y$ and $x + \frac{b}{2a} = X$

$$\therefore \quad Y = aX^2$$

$$\Rightarrow \quad X^2 = \frac{Y}{a}$$

1. The shape of the curve $y = f(x)$ is parabolic.
2. The axis of parabola is $X = 0$ or $x + \frac{b}{2a} = 0$

   or $x = -\frac{b}{2a}$ i.e. parallel to Y-axis.
3. (i) If $\frac{1}{a} > 0 \Rightarrow a > 0$, the parabola open upwards.

   (ii) If $\frac{1}{a} < 0 \Rightarrow a < 0$, the parabola open downwards.

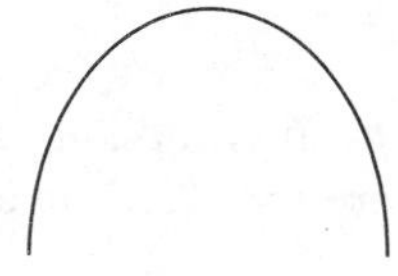

4. **Intersection with axes**

   (i) **Intersection with X-axis**

   For X-axis, $y = 0$.

$$\therefore \quad ax^2 + bx + c = 0 \Rightarrow x = \frac{-b \pm \sqrt{D}}{2a}$$

For $D > 0$, parabola cuts X-axis in two real and distinct points

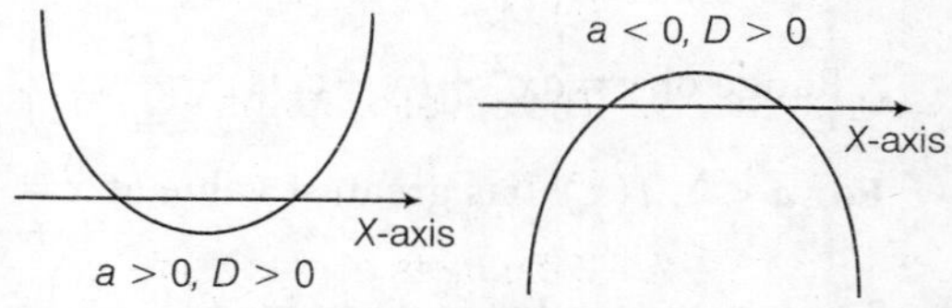

For $D = 0$, parabola touches X-axis in one point i.e., $x = -\frac{b}{2a}$.

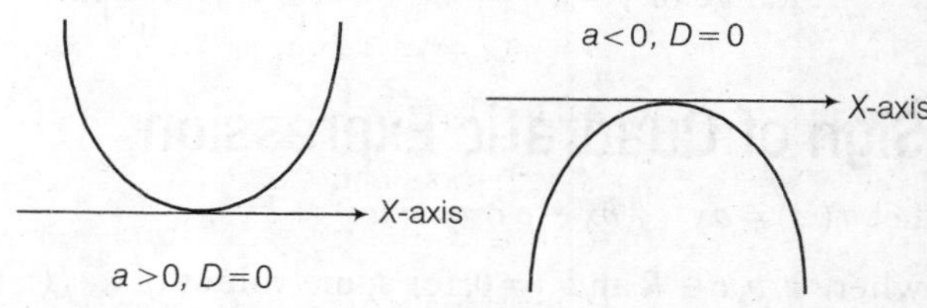

For $D < 0$, parabola does not cut X-axis i.e., imaginary values of x.

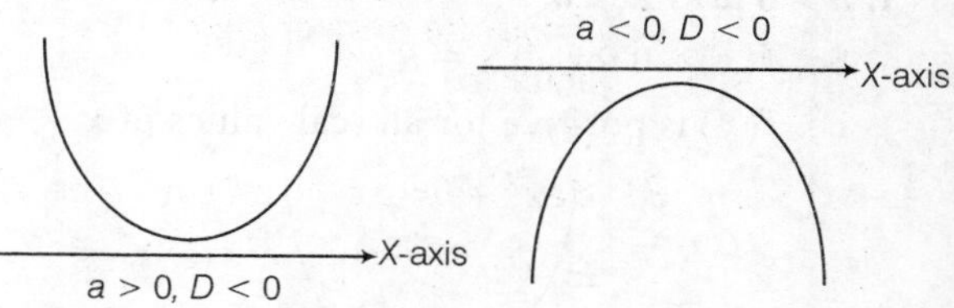

   (ii) **Intersection with Y-axis**

   For Y-axis, $x = 0$.

$$\therefore \quad y = c$$

5. **Greatest and least values of $f(x)$**

   Vertex of the parabola $X^2 = \frac{1}{a}Y$ is

$$X = 0, Y = 0$$

$$\Rightarrow \quad x + \frac{b}{2a} = 0, y + \frac{D}{4a} = 0$$

or $$x = -\frac{b}{2a}, y = -\frac{D}{4a}$$

Hence, vertex of $y = ax^2 + bx + c$ is $\left(-\frac{b}{2a}, -\frac{D}{4a}\right)$.

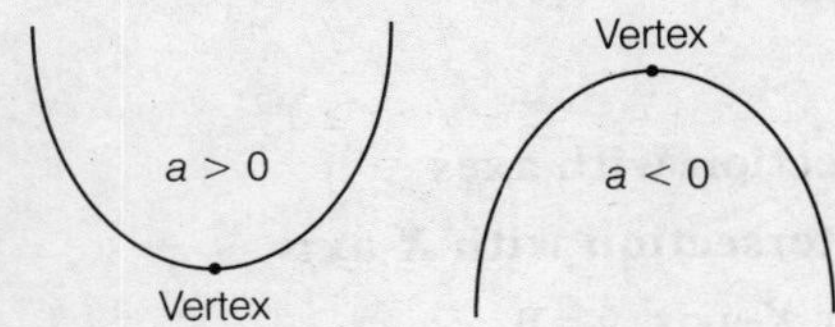

For $a > 0$, $f(x)$ has least value at $x = -\frac{b}{2a}$.

This least value is given by $f\left(-\frac{b}{2a}\right) = -\frac{D}{4a}$

or $y_{\text{least}} = -\frac{D}{4a}$.

$\therefore$ Range of $y = ax^2 + bx + c$ is $\left[-\frac{D}{4a}, \infty\right)$.

For $a < 0$, $f(x)$ has greatest value at $x = -\frac{b}{2a}$.

This greatest value is given by $f\left(-\frac{b}{2a}\right) = -\frac{D}{4a}$

or $y_{\text{greatest}} = -\frac{D}{4a}$

$\therefore$ Range of $y = ax^2 + bx + c$ is $\left(-\infty, -\frac{D}{4a}\right]$.

Sign of Quadratic Expression

Let $f(x) = ax^2 + bx + c$ or $y = ax^2 + bx + c$, where $a, b, c \in R$ and $a \neq 0$, for some values of x, $f(x)$ may be positive, negative or zero. This gives the following cases :

1. $a > 0$ and $D < 0$.

So, $f(x) > 0$ for all $x \in R$,

i.e. $f(x)$ is positive for all real values of x.

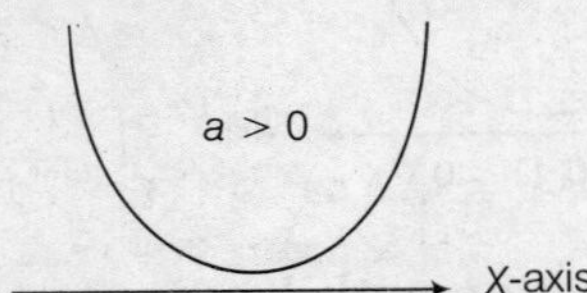

2. $a < 0$ and $D < 0$. So, $f(x) < 0$ for all $x \in R$,

i.e. $f(x)$ is negative for all real values of x.

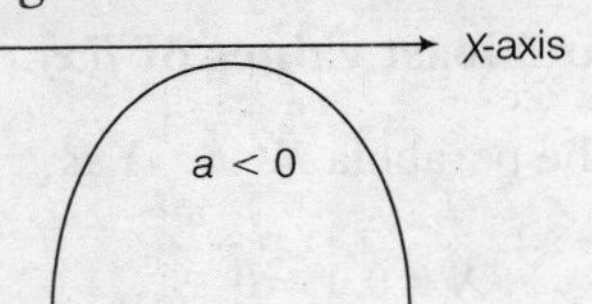

3. $a > 0$ and $D = 0$. So, $f(x) \geq 0$ for all $x \in R$,

i.e. $f(x)$ is positive for all real values of x except at vertex, where $f(x) = 0$.

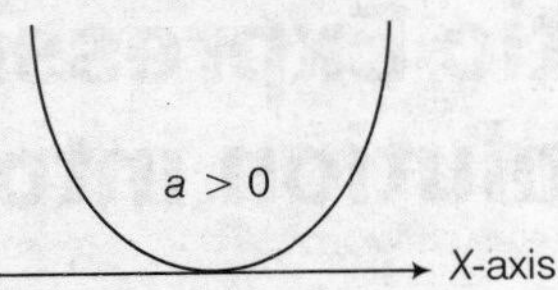

4. $a < 0$ and $D = 0$. So, $f(x) \leq 0$ for all $x \in R$,

i.e. $f(x)$ is negative for all real values of x except at vertex, where $f(x) = 0$.

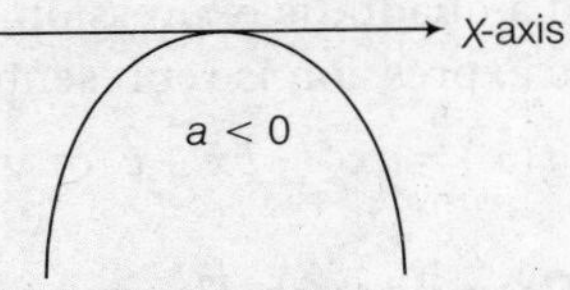

5. $a > 0$ and $D > 0$.

Let $f(x) = 0$ have two real roots α and β $(\alpha < \beta)$, then $f(x) > 0$ for all $x \in (-\infty, \alpha) \cup (\beta, \infty)$ and $f(x) < 0$ for all $x \in (\alpha, \beta)$.

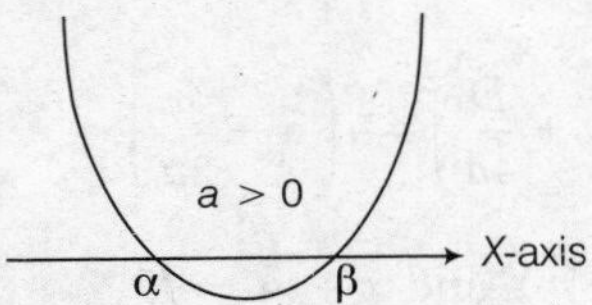

6. $a < 0$ and $D > 0$

Let $f(x) = 0$ have two real roots α and β $(\alpha < \beta)$, then $f(x) < 0$ for all $x \in (-\infty, \alpha) \cup (\beta, \infty)$ and $f(x) > 0$ for all $x \in (\alpha, \beta)$.

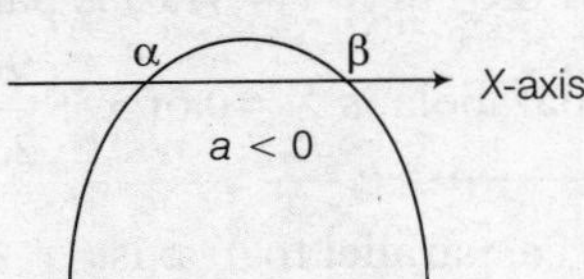

Wavy Curve Method

(Generalised Method of Intervals)

Wave Curve Method is used for solving inequalities of the form

$$f(x) = \frac{(x - a_1)^{k_1}(x - a_2)^{k_2}\ldots(x - a_m)^{k_m}}{(x - b_1)^{p_1}(x - b_2)^{p_2}\ldots(x - b_n)^{p_n}} > 0$$

$$(< 0, \geq 0 \text{ or } \leq 0),$$

where, $k_1, k_2, \ldots, k_m, p_1, p_2, \ldots, p_n$ are natural numbers and such that $a_i \neq b_j$, where $i = 1, 2, \ldots, m$ and $j = 1, 2, \ldots, n$.

We use the following methods:

1. Solve $(x-a_1)^{k_1}(x-a_2)^{k_2}\ldots(x-a_m)^{k_m}=0$ and $(x-b_1)^{p_1}(x-a_2)^{p_2}\ldots(x-b_n)^{p_n}=0$, then we get $x=a_1,a_2,\ldots,a_m,b_1,b_2,\ldots,b_n$ [critical points]
2. Assume $a_1<a_2<\ldots<a_m<b_1<b_2<\ldots<b_n$ Plot them on the real line. Arrange inked (black) circles (●) and un-inked (white) circles (○), such that

	$a_1\ a_2\ \ldots\ a_m$	$b_1\ b_2\ \ldots\ b_n$
If $f(x)>0$	○ ○ ... ○	○ ○ ... ○
$f(x)<0$	○ ○ ... ○	○ ○ ... ○
$f(x)\geq 0$	● ● ... ●	○ ○ ... ○
$f(x)\leq 0$	● ● ... ●	○ ○ ... ○

3. Obviously, b_n is the greatest root. If in all brackets before x positive sign and expression has also positive sign, then wave start from right to left, beginning above the number line, i.e.

$$+\frac{(x-a_1)^{k_1}(x-a_2)^{k_2}\ldots(x-a_m)^{k_m}}{(x-b_1)^{p_1}(x-b_2)^{p_2}\ldots(x-b_n)^{p_n}},\text{ then}$$

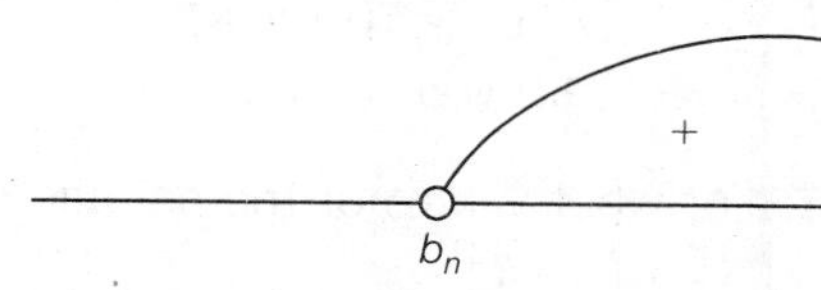

and if in all brackets before x positive sign and expression has negative sign, then wave start from right to left, beginning below the number line, i.e.

$$-\frac{(x-a_1)^{k_1}(x-a_2)^{k_2}\ldots(x-a_m)^{k_m}}{(x-b_1)^{p_1}(x-b_2)^{p_2}\ldots(x-b_n)^{p_n}},\text{ then}$$

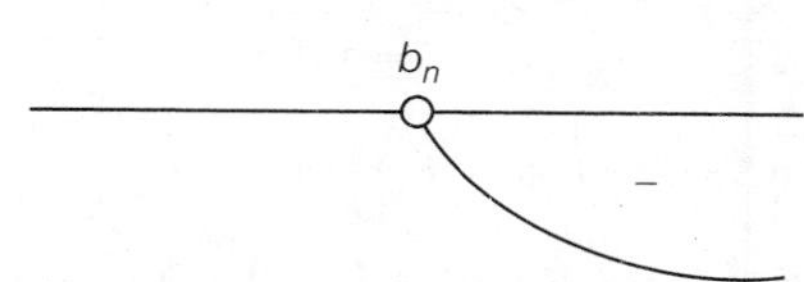

4. If roots occur even times, then sign remain same from right to left side of the roots and if roots occur odd times, then sign will change from right to left through the roots of $x=a_1,a_2,\ldots,a_m,b_1,b_2,\ldots,b_n$.
5. The solution of $f(x)>0$ or $f(x)\geq 0$ is the union of all intervals in which we have put the plus sign and the solution of $f(x)<0$ or $f(x)\leq 0$ is the union of all intervals in which we have put the minus sign.

Important Results

1. The point where denominator is zero or function approaches infinity, will never be included in the answer.
2. For $x^2<a^2$ or $|x|<a \Leftrightarrow -a<x<a$
   i.e., $x\in(-a,a)$
3. For $0<x^2<a^2$ or $0<|x|<a$
   $\Leftrightarrow -a<x<a\sim\{0\}$
   i.e., $x\in(-a,a)\sim\{0\}$
4. For $x^2\geq a^2$ or $|x|\geq a \Leftrightarrow x\leq -a$ or $x\geq a$
   i.e., $x\in(-\infty,-a]\cup[a,\infty)$
5. For $x^2>a^2$ or $|x|>a \Leftrightarrow x<-a$ or $x>a$
   i.e., $x\in(-\infty,-a)\cup(a,\infty)$
6. For $a^2\leq x^2\leq b^2$ or $a\leq|x|\leq b$
   $\Leftrightarrow a\leq x\leq b$ or $-b\leq x\leq -a$
   i.e., $x\in[-b,-a]\cup[a,b]$
7. For $a^2<x^2\leq b^2$ or $a<|x|\leq b$
   $\Leftrightarrow a<x\leq b$ or $-b\leq x<-a$
   i.e., $x\in[-b,-a)\cup(a,b]$
8. For $a^2\leq x^2<b^2$ or $a\leq|x|<b$
   $\Leftrightarrow a\leq x<b$ or $-b<x\leq -a$
   i.e., $x\in(-b,-a]\cup[a,b)$
9. For $a^2<x^2<b^2$ or $a<|x|<b$
   $\Leftrightarrow a<x<b$ or $-b<x<-a$
   i.e., $x\in(-b,-a)\cup(a,b)$
10. For $(x-a)(x-b)<0$ and $a<b$, then $a<x<b$
    i.e., $x\in(a,b)$
11. If $(x-a)(x-b)\leq 0$ and $a<b$,
    then $a\leq x\leq b, x\in[a,b]$
12. If $(x-a)(x-b)>0$ and $a<b$, then $x<a$ or $x>b$
    i.e., $x\in(-\infty,a)\cup(b,\infty)$
13. If $(x-a)(x-b)\geq 0$ and $a<b$,
    then $x\leq a$ or $x\geq b$
    i.e., $x\in(-\infty,a]\cup[b,\infty)$

Example 26. Solve the inequality $(x+3)(3x-2)^5(7-x)^3(5x+8)^2\geq 0$.

Sol. We have, $(x+3)(3x-2)^5(7-x)^3(5x+8)^2\geq 0$

$\Rightarrow\quad -(x+3)(3x-2)^5(x-7)^3(5x+8)^2\geq 0$

$\Rightarrow\quad (x+3)(3x-2)^5(x-7)^3(5x+8)^2\leq 0$

[take before x, + ve sign in all brackets]

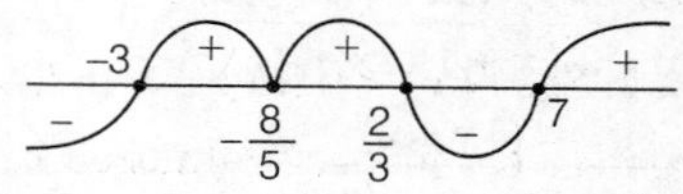

The critical points are $(-3),\left(-\frac{8}{5}\right),\frac{2}{3},7$.

Hence, $x\in(-\infty,-3]\cup\left[\frac{2}{3},7\right]\cup\left\{-\frac{8}{5}\right\}$.

Example 27. Solve the inequality
$$\frac{(x-2)^{10000}(x+1)^{253}\left(x-\frac{1}{2}\right)^{971}(x+8)^4}{x^{500}(x-3)^{75}(x+2)^{93}} \geq 0$$

Sol. We have, $\frac{(x-2)^{10000}(x+1)^{253}\left(x-\frac{1}{2}\right)^{971}(x+8)^4}{x^{500}(x-3)^{75}(x+2)^{93}} \geq 0$

The critical points are $(-8), (-2), (-1), 0, \frac{1}{2}, 2, 3.$

$[\because x \neq -2, 0, 3]$

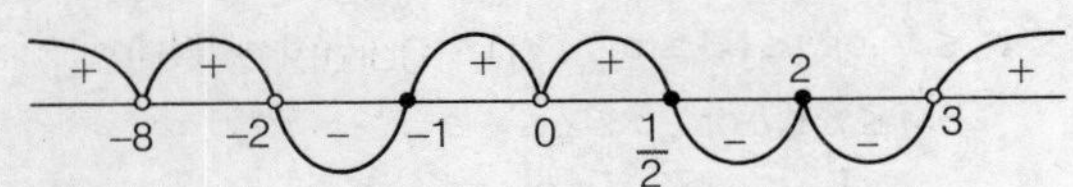

Hence, $x \in (-\infty, -8] \cup [-8, -2) \cup [-1, 0) \cup \left(0, \frac{1}{2}\right] \cup (3, \infty)$

or $x \in (-\infty, -2) \cup [-1, 0) \cup \left(0, \frac{1}{2}\right] \cup (3, \infty)$

Example 28. Let $f(x) = \frac{(x-3)(x+2)(x+6)}{(x+1)(x-5)}$.

Find intervals, where $f(x)$ is positive or negative.

Sol. We have, $f(x) = \frac{(x-3)(x+2)(x+6)}{(x+1)(x-5)}$

The critical points are $(-6), (-2), (-1), 3, 5$

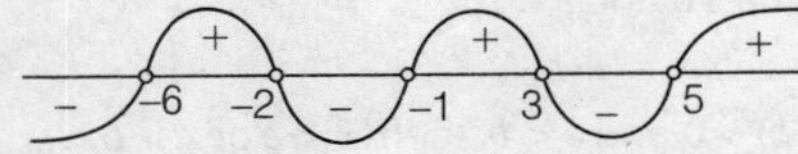

For $f(x) > 0, \forall x \in (-6, -2) \cup (-1, 3) \cup (5, \infty)$

For $f(x) < 0, \forall x \in (-\infty, -6) \cup (-2, -1) \cup (3, 5)$

Example 29. Find the set of all x for which
$$\frac{2x}{(2x^2+5x+2)} > \frac{1}{(x+1)}.$$

Sol. We have, $\frac{2x}{(2x^2+5x+2)} > \frac{1}{(x+1)}$

$\Rightarrow \quad \frac{2x}{(x+2)(2x+1)} - \frac{1}{(x+1)} > 0$

$\Rightarrow \quad \frac{(2x^2+2x)-(2x^2+5x+2)}{(x+2)(x+1)(2x+1)} > 0$

$\Rightarrow \quad -\frac{(3x+2)}{(x+2)(x+1)(2x+1)} > 0$

or $\quad \frac{(3x+2)}{(x+2)(x+1)(2x+1)} < 0$

The critical points are $(-2), (-1), \left(-\frac{2}{3}\right), \left(-\frac{1}{2}\right)$.

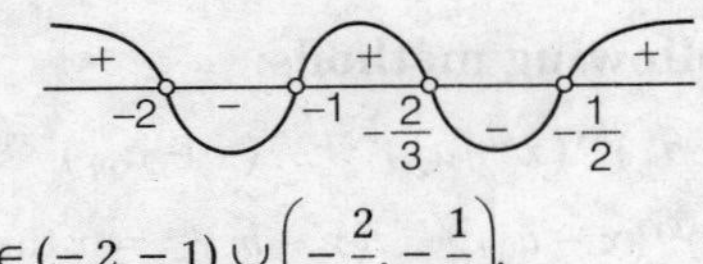

Hence, $x \in (-2, -1) \cup \left(-\frac{2}{3}, -\frac{1}{2}\right)$.

Example 30. For $x \in R$, prove that the given expression $\frac{x^2+34x-71}{x^2+2x-7}$ cannot lie between 5 and 9.

Sol. Let $\frac{x^2+34x-71}{x^2+2x-7} = y$

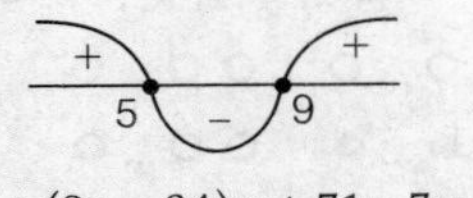

$\Rightarrow \quad x^2(y-1) + (2y-34)x + 71 - 7y = 0$

For real values of x, discriminant ≥ 0

$\therefore \quad (2y-34)^2 - 4(y-1)(71-7y) \geq 0$

$\Rightarrow \quad 8y^2 - 112y + 360 \geq 0$

$\Rightarrow \quad y^2 - 14y + 45 \geq 0$

$\Rightarrow \quad (y-9)(y-5) \geq 0$

$\Rightarrow \quad y \in (-\infty, 5] \cup [9, \infty)$

Hence, y can never lie between 5 and 9.

Example 31. For what values of the parameter k in the inequality $\left|\frac{x^2+kx+1}{x^2+x+1}\right| < 3$, satisfied for all real values of x?

Sol. We have, $\left|\frac{x^2+kx+1}{x^2+x+1}\right| < 3$

$\Rightarrow \quad -3 < \frac{x^2+kx+1}{x^2+x+1} < 3$

Since, $\quad x^2+x+1 = \left(x+\frac{1}{2}\right)^2 + \frac{3}{4} > 0$

$\therefore \quad -3(x^2+x+1) < x^2+kx+1 < 3(x^2+x+1)$

$\therefore \quad 4x^2 + (k+3)x + 4 > 0 \quad$ ...(i)

and $\quad 2x^2 - (k-3)x + 2 > 0 \quad$ ...(ii)

$\because \quad 4 > 0$ and $2 > 0$

The inequality (i) will be valid, if

$(k+3)^2 - 4 \cdot 4 \cdot 4 < 0 \Rightarrow (k+3)^2 < 64$

or $\quad -8 < k+3 < 8$

or $\quad -11 < k < 5 \quad$ ...(iii)

and the inequality (ii) will be valid, if

$(k-3)^2 - 4 \cdot 2 \cdot 2 < 0$ or $(k-3)^2 < 16$

or $\quad -4 < k-3 < 4$

or $\quad -1 < k < 7 \quad$ ...(iv)

The conditions (iii) and (iv) will hold simultaneously, if

$-1 < k < 5$

Condition for Resolution into Linear Factors

The quadratic function

$$f(x, y) = ax^2 + 2hxy + by^2 + 2gx + 2fy + c$$

may be resolved into two linear factors, iff

$$\Delta = abc + 2fgh - af^2 - bg^2 - ch^2 = 0$$

i.e.,
$$\begin{vmatrix} a & h & g \\ h & b & f \\ g & f & c \end{vmatrix} = 0$$

| Example 32. Find the value of m for which the expression $12x^2 - 10xy + 2y^2 + 11x - 5y + m$ can be resolved into two rational linear factors.

Sol. Comparing the given expression with $ax^2 + 2hxy + by^2 + 2gx + 2fy + c$, we have

$$a = 12, h = -5, b = 2, g = \frac{11}{2}, f = \left(-\frac{5}{2}\right), c = m$$

The given expression will have two linear factors, if and only if

$$abc + 2fgh - af^2 - bg^2 - ch^2 = 0$$

or $$(12)(2)(m) + 2\left(-\frac{5}{2}\right)\left(\frac{11}{2}\right)(-5) - (12)\left(-\frac{5}{2}\right)^2 - (2)\left(\frac{11}{2}\right)^2 - (m)(-5)^2 = 0$$

$$\Rightarrow \quad 24m + \frac{275}{2} - 75 - \frac{121}{2} - 25m = 0 \text{ or } m = 2$$

| Example 33. If the expression $ax^2 + by^2 + cz^2 + 2ayz + 2bzx + 2cxy$ can be resolved into two rational factors, prove that

$$a^3 + b^3 + c^3 = 3abc.$$

Sol. Given expression is

$$ax^2 + by^2 + cz^2 + 2ayz + 2bzx + 2cxy \quad \text{...(i)}$$

$$= z^2\left[a\left(\frac{x}{z}\right)^2 + b\left(\frac{y}{z}\right)^2 + c + 2a\left(\frac{y}{z}\right) + 2b\left(\frac{x}{z}\right) + 2c\left(\frac{x}{z}\right)\left(\frac{y}{z}\right)\right]$$

$$= z^2[aX^2 + bY^2 + c + 2aY + 2bX + 2cXY]$$

where, $\frac{x}{z} = X$ and $\frac{y}{z} = Y$

Expression (i) will have two rational linear factors in x, y and z, if expression

$aX^2 + bY^2 + 2cXY + 2bX + 2aY + c$ will have two linear factors, if

$$abc + 2abc - aa^2 - bb^2 - cc^2 = 0$$

or $$a^3 + b^3 + c^3 = 3abc$$

| Example 34. Find the linear factors of $x^2 - 5xy + 4y^2 + x + 2y - 2$.

Sol. Given expression is

$$x^2 - 5xy + 4y^2 + x + 2y - 2 \quad \text{...(i)}$$

Its corresponding equation is

$$x^2 - 5xy + 4y^2 + x + 2y - 2 = 0$$

or $$x^2 - x(5y - 1) + 4y^2 + 2y - 2 = 0$$

$$\therefore \quad x = \frac{(5y-1) \pm \sqrt{(5y-1)^2 - 4\cdot 1\cdot(4y^2 + 2y - 2)}}{2}$$

$$= \frac{(5y-1) \pm \sqrt{(9y^2 - 18y + 9)}}{2}$$

$$= \frac{(5y-1) \pm \sqrt{(3y-3)^2}}{2}$$

$$= \frac{(5y-1) \pm (3y-3)}{2} = 4y - 2, y + 1$$

$\therefore$ The required linear factors are $(x - 4y + 2)$ and $(x - y - 1)$.

Location of Roots

(Interval in which Roots Lie)

Let $f(x) = ax^2 + bx + c$, $a, b, c \in R$, $a \neq 0$ and α, β be the roots of $f(x) = 0$. Suppose $k, k_1, k_2 \in R$ and $k_1 < k_2$. Then, the following hold good :

1. Conditions for Number *k*

(If both the roots of $f(x) = 0$ are less than k)

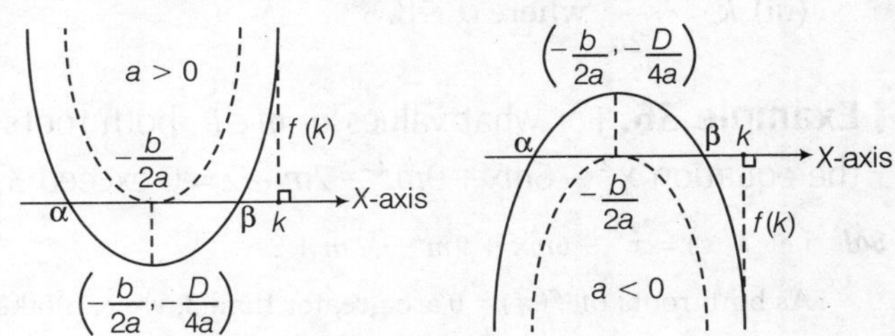

(i) $D \geq 0$ (roots may be equal)

(ii) $af(k) > 0$

(iii) $k > -\frac{b}{2a}$, where $\alpha \leq \beta$.

| Example 35. Find the values of m, for which both roots of equation $x^2 - mx + 1 = 0$ are less than unity.

Sol. Let $f(x) = x^2 - mx + 1$, as both roots of $f(x) = 0$ are less than 1, we can take $D \geq 0$, $af(1) > 0$ and $-\frac{b}{2a} < 1$.

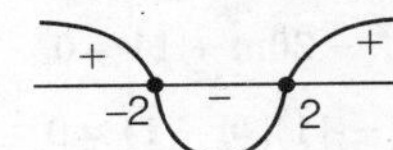

(i) **Consider $D \geq 0$** $(-m)^2 - 4 \cdot 1 \cdot 1 \geq 0$

$\Rightarrow \quad (m+2)(m-2) \geq 0$

$\Rightarrow \quad m \in (-\infty, -2] \cup [2, \infty)$ ...(i)

(ii) **Consider $af(1) > 0$** $1(1 - m + 1) > 0$

$\Rightarrow \quad m - 2 < 0 \Rightarrow m < 2$

$\Rightarrow \quad m \in (-\infty, 2)$ ...(ii)

(iii) **Consider $\left(-\dfrac{b}{2a} < 1\right)$**

$\dfrac{m}{2} < 1 \Rightarrow m < 2$

$\Rightarrow \quad m \in (-\infty, 2)$ ...(iii)

Hence, the values of m satisfying Eqs. (i), (ii) and (iii) at the same time are $m \in (-\infty, -2]$.

2. Conditions for a Number *k*

If both the roots of $f(x) = 0$ are greater than k

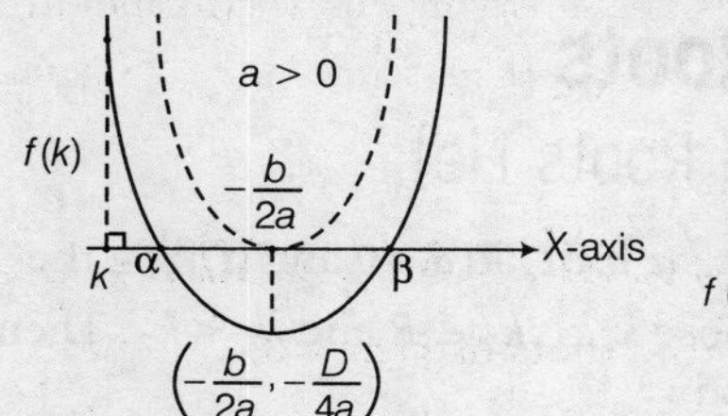

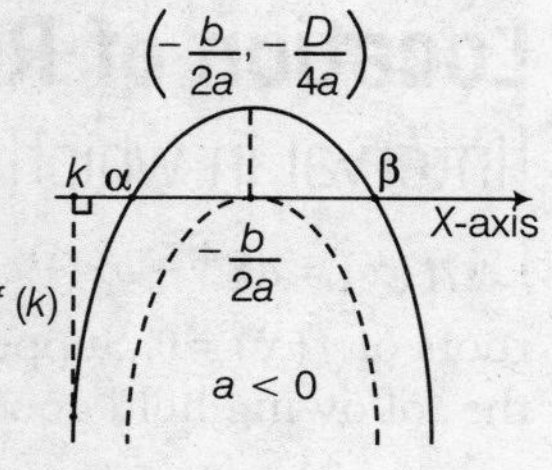

(i) $D \geq 0$ (roots may be equal)

(ii) $af(k) > 0$

(iii) $k < -\dfrac{b}{2a}$, where $\alpha \leq \beta$.

Example 36. For what values of $m \in R$, both roots of the equation $x^2 - 6mx + 9m^2 - 2m - 2 = 0$ exceed 3?

Sol. Let $f(x) = x^2 - 6mx + 9m^2 - 2m + 2$

As both roots of $f(x) = 0$ are greater than 3, we can take $D \geq 0$, $af(3) > 0$ and $-\dfrac{b}{2a} > 3$.

(i) **Consider $D \geq 0$**

$(-6m)^2 - 4 \cdot 1(9m^2 - 2m + 2) \geq 0 \Rightarrow 8m - 8 \geq 0$

$\therefore \quad m \geq 1$ or $m \in [1, \infty)$ ...(i)

(ii) **Consider $af(3) \geq 0$**

$1 \cdot (9 - 18m + 9m^2 - 2m + 2) > 0$

$\Rightarrow \quad 9m^2 - 20m + 11 > 0$

$\Rightarrow \quad (9m - 11)(m - 1) > 0$

$\Rightarrow \quad \left(m - \dfrac{11}{9}\right)(m - 1) > 0$

$\Rightarrow \quad m \in (-\infty, 1) \cup \left(\dfrac{11}{9}, \infty\right)$ ...(ii)

(iii) **Consider $\left(-\dfrac{b}{2a} > 3\right)$**

$\dfrac{6m}{2} > 3$

$\Rightarrow \quad m > 1$

$\Rightarrow \quad m \in (1, \infty)$ ...(iii)

Hence, the values of m satisfying Eqs. (i), (ii) and (iii) at the same time are $m \in \left(\dfrac{11}{9}, \infty\right)$.

3. Conditions for a Number *k*

If k lies between the roots of $f(x) = 0$

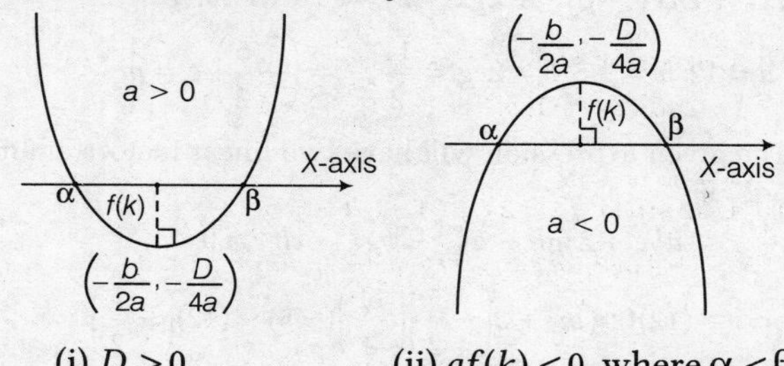

(i) $D > 0$ (ii) $af(k) < 0$, where $\alpha < \beta$

Example 37. Find all values of p, so that 6 lies between roots of the equation $x^2 + 2(p-3)x + 9 = 0$.

Sol. Let $f(x) = x^2 + 2(p-3)x + 9$, as 6 lies between the roots of $f(x) = 0$, we can take $D > 0$ and $af(6) < 0$

(i) **Consider $D > 0$**

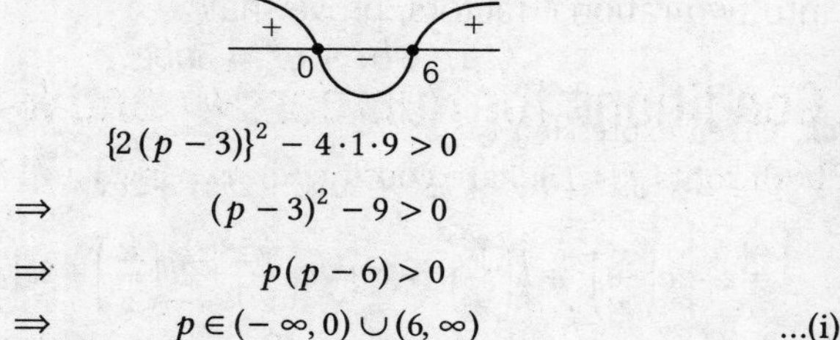

$\{2(p-3)\}^2 - 4 \cdot 1 \cdot 9 > 0$

$\Rightarrow \quad (p-3)^2 - 9 > 0$

$\Rightarrow \quad p(p-6) > 0$

$\Rightarrow \quad p \in (-\infty, 0) \cup (6, \infty)$ ...(i)

(ii) **Consider $af(6) < 0$**

$1 \cdot \{36 + 12(p-3) + 9\} < 0$

$\Rightarrow \quad 12p + 9 < 0 \Rightarrow p + \dfrac{3}{4} < 0$

$\Rightarrow \quad p \in \left(-\infty, -\dfrac{3}{4}\right)$ ...(ii)

Hence, the values of p satisfying Eqs. (i) and (ii) at the same time are $p \in \left(-\infty, -\dfrac{3}{4}\right)$.

4. Conditions for Numbers k_1 and k_2

If exactly one root of $f(x) = 0$ lies in the interval (k_1, k_2)

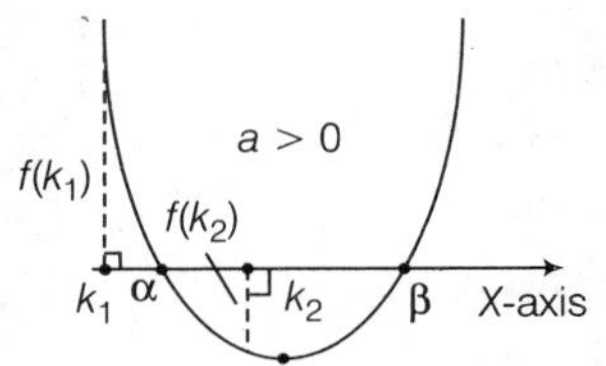

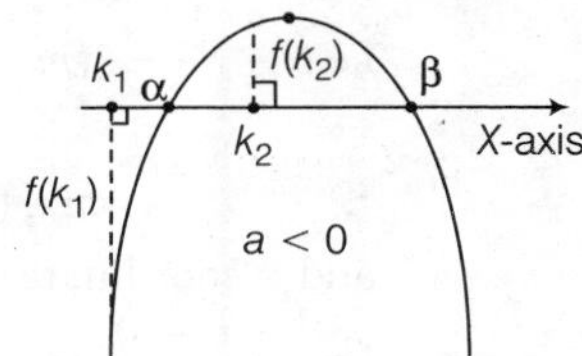

(i) $D > 0$

(ii) $f(k_1)\, f(k_2) < 0$, where $\alpha < \beta$.

Example 38. Find the values of m, for which exactly one root of the equation $x^2 - 2mx + m^2 - 1 = 0$ lies in the interval $(-2, 4)$.

Sol. Let $f(x) = x^2 - 2mx + m^2 - 1$, as exactly one root of $f(x) = 0$ lies in the interval $(-2, 4)$, we can take $D > 0$ and $f(-2)\, f(4) < 0$.

(i) **Consider $D > 0$**

$(-2m)^2 - 4 \cdot 1 (m^2 - 1) > 0 \Rightarrow 4 > 0$

$\therefore \quad m \in R \quad$ ...(i)

(ii) **Consider $f(-2)\, f(4) < 0$**

$(4 + 4m + m^2 - 1)(16 - 8m + m^2 - 1) < 0$

$\Rightarrow \quad (m^2 + 4m + 3)(m^2 - 8m + 15) < 0$

$\Rightarrow \quad (m + 1)(m + 3)(m - 3)(m - 5) < 0$

$\Rightarrow \quad (m + 3)(m + 1)(m - 3)(m - 5) < 0$

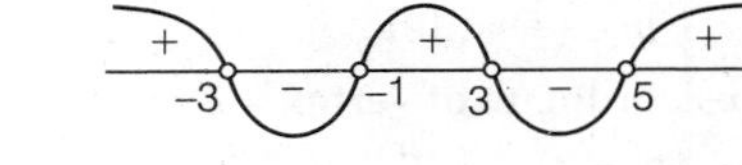

$\therefore \quad m \in (-3, -1) \cup (3, 5) \quad$ ...(ii)

Hence, the values of m satisfying Eqs. (i) and (ii) at the same time are $m \in (-3, -1) \cup (3, 5)$.

5. Conditions for Numbers k_1 and k_2

(If both roots $f(x) = 0$ are confined between k_1 and k_2)

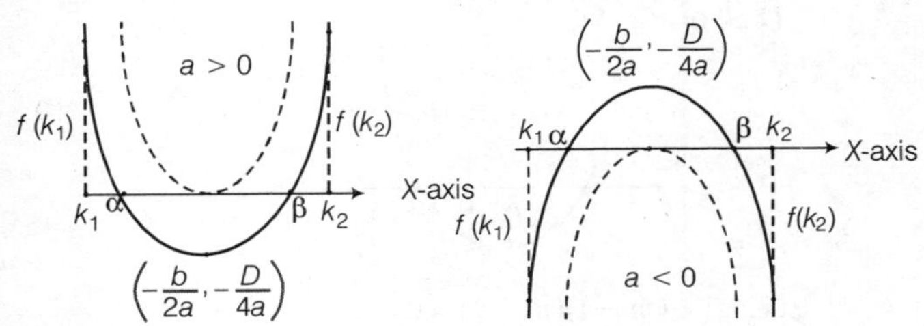

(i) $D \geq 0$ (roots may be equal)

(ii) $af(k_1) > 0$

(iii) $af(k_2) > 0$

(iv) $k_1 < -\dfrac{b}{2a} < k_2$, where $\alpha \leq \beta$ and $k_1 < k_2$.

Example 39. Find all values of a for which the equation $4x^2 - 2x + a = 0$ has two roots lie in the interval $(-1, 1)$.

Sol. Let $f(x) = 4x^2 - 2x + a$ as both roots of the equation, $f(x) = 0$ are lie between $(-1, 1)$, we can take $D \geq 0$, $af(-1) > 0$, $af(1) > 0$ and $-1 < \dfrac{1}{4} < 1$.

(i) **Consider $D \geq 0$**

$(-2)^2 - 4 \cdot 4 \cdot a \geq 0 \Rightarrow a \leq \dfrac{1}{4} \quad$ ...(i)

(ii) **Consider $a\, f(-1) > 0$**

$4(4 + 2 + a) > 0$

$\Rightarrow \quad a > -6 \Rightarrow a \in (-6, \infty) \quad$ ...(ii)

(iii) **Consider $a\, f(1) > 0$**

$4(4 - 2 + a) > 0 \Rightarrow a > -2$

$\Rightarrow \quad a \in (-2, \infty) \quad$ ...(iii)

Hence, the values of a satisfying Eqs. (i), (ii) and (iii) at the same time are $a \in \left(-2, \dfrac{1}{4}\right]$.

6. Conditions for Numbers k_1 and k_2

(If k_1 and k_2 lie between the roots of $f(x) = 0$)

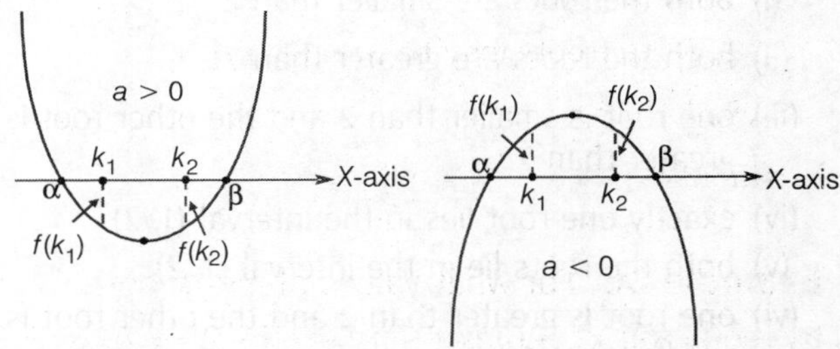

(i) $D > 0$

(ii) $af(k_1) < 0$

(iii) $af(k_2) < 0$, where $\alpha < \beta$.

Example 40. Find the values of a for which one root of equation $(a - 5)x^2 - 2ax + a - 4 = 0$ is smaller than 1 and the other greater than 2.

Sol. The given equation can be written as

$$x^2 - \left(\frac{2a}{a-5}\right)x + \left(\frac{a-4}{a-5}\right) = 0,\ a \neq 5.$$

Now, let $f(x) = x^2 - \left(\dfrac{2a}{a-5}\right)x + \left(\dfrac{a-4}{a-5}\right)$

As 1 and 2 lie between the roots of $f(x) = 0$, we can take $D > 0$, $1 \cdot f(1) < 0$ and $1 \cdot f(2) < 0$.

(i) **Consider $D > 0$**

$$\left(-\left(\frac{2a}{a-5}\right)\right)^2 - 4\cdot 1\cdot\left(\frac{a-4}{a-5}\right) > 0$$

$$\Rightarrow \quad \frac{36\left(a-\frac{20}{9}\right)}{(a-5)^2} > 0 \quad [\because a \neq 5]$$

or $\quad a > \frac{20}{9}$ ...(i)

(ii) **Consider $1\cdot f(1) < 0$**

$$1^2 - \left(\frac{2a}{a-5}\right) + \left(\frac{a-4}{a-5}\right) < 0 \Rightarrow \frac{9}{(a-5)} > 0 \text{ or } a > 5 \text{ ...(ii)}$$

(iii) **Consider $1\cdot f(2) < 0$**

$$4 - \frac{4a}{(a-5)} + \left(\frac{a-4}{a-5}\right) < 0$$

$$\Rightarrow \quad \frac{(4a-20-4a+a-4)}{(a-5)} < 0 \Rightarrow \frac{(a-24)}{(a-5)} < 0$$

or $\quad 5 < a < 24$ ...(iii)

Hence, the values of a satisfying Eqs. (i), (ii) and (iii) at the same time are $a \in (5, 24)$.

Example 41. Let $x^2 - (m-3)x + m = 0 \ (m \in R)$ be a quadratic equation. Find the value of m for which

(i) both the roots are smaller than 2.
(ii) both the roots are greater than 2.
(iii) one root is smaller than 2 and the other root is greater than 2.
(iv) exactly one root lies in the interval (1, 2).
(v) both the roots lie in the interval (1, 2).
(vi) one root is greater than 2 and the other root is smaller than 1.
(vii) atleast one root lie in the interval (1, 2).
(viii) atleast one root is greater than 2.

Sol. Let $\quad f(x) = x^2 - (m-3)x + m$

Here, $\quad a = 1, b = -(m-3), c = m$

and $\quad D = b^2 - 4ac = (m-3)^2 - 4m$
$= m^2 - 10m + 9 = (m-1)(m-9)$

and x-coordinate of vertex $= -\frac{b}{2a} = \frac{(m-3)}{2}$

(i) **Both the roots are smaller than 2**

$D \geq 0$

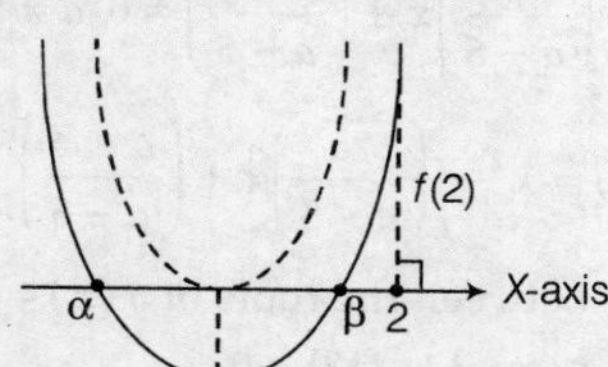

i.e., $(m-1)(m-9) \geq 0$

$\therefore \quad m \in (-\infty, 1] \cup [9, \infty)$ ...(i)

$f(2) > 0$

i.e., $\quad 4 - 2(m-3) + m > 0$

$\Rightarrow \quad m < 10$

$\therefore \quad m \in (-\infty, 10)$ ...(ii)

and x-coordinate of vertex < 2

i.e., $\quad \frac{(m-3)}{2} < 2 \Rightarrow m < 7$

$\therefore \quad m \in (-\infty, 7)$ ...(iii)

On combining Eqs. (i), (ii) and (iii), we get

$m \in (-\infty, 1]$

(ii) **Both the roots are greater than 2**

$D \geq 0$

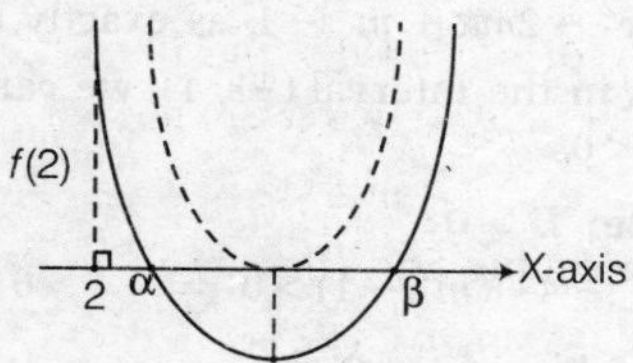

i.e. $\quad (m-1)(m-9) \geq 0$

$\therefore \quad m \in (-\infty, 1] \in [9, \infty)$ ...(i)

$f(2) > 0$

i.e. $\quad 4 - 2(m-3) + m > 0$

$\Rightarrow \quad m < 10$

$\therefore \quad m \in (-\infty, 10)$ ...(ii)

and x-coordinate of vertex > 2

i.e., $\quad \frac{(m-3)}{2} > 2 \Rightarrow m > 7$

$\therefore \quad m \in (7, \infty)$ ...(iii)

On combining Eqs. (i), (ii) and (iii), we get

$m \in [9, 10)$

(iii) **One root is smaller than 2 and the other root is greater than 2**

$D > 0$

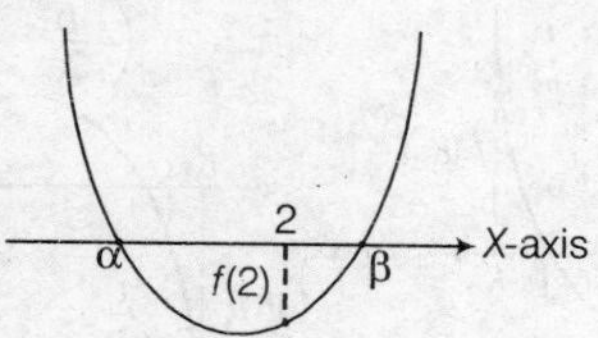

i.e., $\quad (m-1)(m-9) > 0$

$\therefore \quad m \in (-\infty, 1) \cup (9, \infty)$ ...(i)

$f(2) < 0$

i.e. $4 - 2(m-3) + m < 0$

$\therefore \quad m > 10$

$\therefore \quad m \in (10, \infty)$ ...(ii)

On combining Eqs. (i) and (ii), we get

$$m \in (10, \infty).$$

(iv) **Exactly one root lies in the interval (1, 2)**

$D > 0$

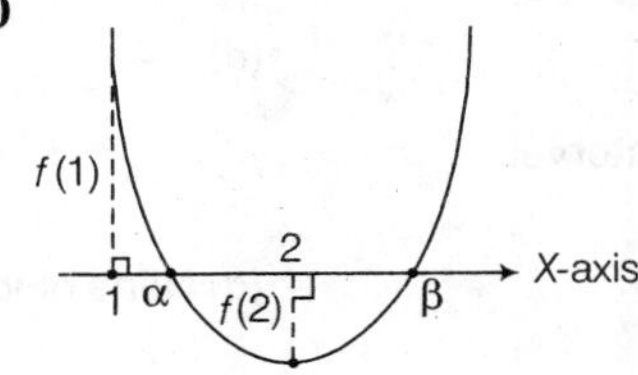

i.e., $(m-1)(m-9) > 0$

$\therefore \quad m \in (-\infty, 1) \cup (9, \infty)$ ...(i)

$f(1) f(2) < 0$

$$(1-(m-3)+m)(4-2(m-3)+m) < 0$$

$\Rightarrow \quad 4(-m+10) < 0$

$\Rightarrow \quad m - 10 > 0 \Rightarrow m > 10$

$\therefore \quad m \in (10, \infty)$ ...(ii)

On combining Eqs. (i) and (ii), we get

$$m \in (10, \infty)$$

(v) **Both the roots lie in the interval (1, 2)**

$D \geq 0$

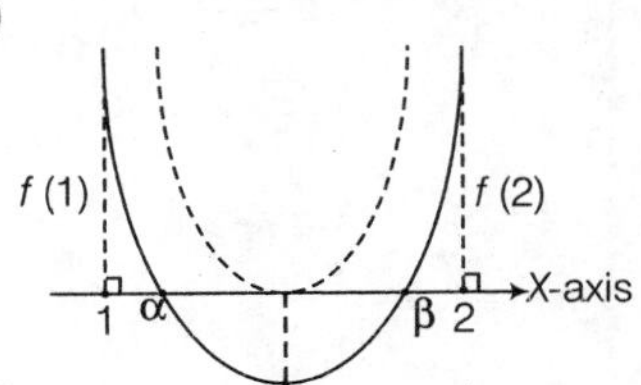

i.e., $(m-1)(m-9) \geq 0$

$\therefore \quad m \in (-\infty, 1] \cup [9, \infty)$ ...(i)

$f(1) > 0$

i.e., $(1-(m-3)+m) > 0 \Rightarrow 4 > 0$

$\therefore \quad m \in R$ ...(ii)

$f(2) > 0$

i.e., $4 - 2(m-3) + m > 0 \Rightarrow m < 10$

$\therefore \quad m \in (-\infty, 10)$ ...(iii)

$1 <$ *x*-coordinate of vertex < 2

i.e., $1 < \dfrac{(m-3)}{2} < 2$

$\Rightarrow \quad 2 < m - 3 < 4$ or $5 < m < 7$

$\therefore \quad m \in (5, 7)$ ...(iv)

On combining Eqs. (i), (ii), (iii) and (iv), we get

$$m \in \phi$$

(vi) **One root is greater than 2 and the other root is smaller than 1 $D > 0$**

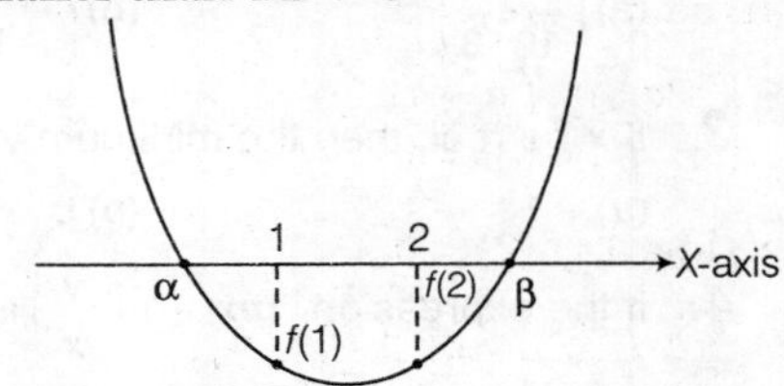

i.e., $(m-1)(m-9) > 0$

$\therefore \quad m \in (-\infty, 1) \cup (9, \infty)$ ...(i)

$f(1) < 0$

i.e., $4 < 0$, which is not possible.

Thus, no such 'm' exists.

(vii) **At least one root lie in the interval (1, 2)**

***Case* I** Exactly one root lies in (1, 2)

$m \in (10, \infty)$ [from (iv) part]

***Case* II** Both roots lie in the interval (1, 2).

$m \in \phi$ [from (v) part]

Hence, at least one root lie in the interval (1, 2)

$$m \in (10, \infty) \cup \phi \text{ or } m \in (10, \infty)$$

(viii) **Atleast one root is greater than 2**

***Case* I** One root is smaller than 2 and the other root is greater than 2.

Then, $m \in (10, \infty)$ [from (iii) part]

***Case* II** Both the roots are greater than 2, then $m \in [9, 10)$.

Hence, atleast one root is greater than 2.

$\therefore \quad m \in (10, \infty) \cup [9, 10)$ or $m \in [9, 10) \cup (10, \infty)$

Exercise for Session 3

1. If x is real, the maximum and minimum values of expression $\frac{x^2 + 14x + 9}{x^2 + 2x + 3}$ will be

(a) 4, −5 (b) 5, −4 (c) −4, 5 (d) −4, −5

2. If x is real, the expression $\frac{x+2}{(2x^2 + 3x + 6)}$ takes all values in the interval

(a) $\left(\frac{1}{13}, \frac{1}{3}\right)$ (b) $\left[-\frac{1}{13}, \frac{1}{3}\right]$ (c) $\left(-\frac{1}{3}, \frac{1}{13}\right)$ (d) None of these

3. If x be real, then the minimum value of $x^2 - 8x + 17$, is

(a) −1 (b) 0 (c) 1 (d) 2

4. If the expression $\left(mx - 1 + \frac{1}{x}\right)$ is non-negative for all positive real x, the minimum value of m must be

(a) $-\frac{1}{2}$ (b) 0

(c) $\frac{1}{4}$ (d) $\frac{1}{2}$

5. If the inequality $\frac{mx^2 + 3x + 4}{x^2 + 2x + 2} < 5$ is satisfied for all $x \in R$ then

(a) $1 < m < 5$ (b) $-1 < m < 5$

(c) $1 < m < 6$ (d) $m < \frac{71}{24}$

6. The largest negative integer which satisfies $\frac{(x^2 - 1)}{(x-2)(x-3)} > 0$, is

(a) −4 (b) −3

(c) −2 (d) −1

7. If the expression $2x^2 + mxy + 3y^2 - 5y - 2$ can be resolved into two rational factors, the value of $|m|$ is

(a) 3 (b) 5

(c) 7 (d) 9

8. If $c > 0$ and $4a + c < 2b$, then $ax^2 - bx + c = 0$ has a root in the interval

(a) (0, 2) (b) (2, 4)

(c) (0, 1) (d) (−2, 0)

9. If the roots of the equation $x^2 - 2ax + a^2 + a - 3 = 0$ are less than 3 then

(a) $a < 2$ (b) $2 \le a \le 3$

(c) $3 < a \le 4$ (d) $a > 4$

10. The set of values of a for which the inequation $x^2 + ax + a^2 + 6a < 0$ is satisfied for all $x \in (1, 2)$ lies in the interval

(a) (1, 2) (b) [1, 2]

(c) [−7, 4] (d) None of these

Session 4

Equations of Higher Degree, Rational Algebraic Inequalities, Roots of Equation with the Help of Graphs,

Equations of Higher Degree

The equation $a_0 x^n + a_1 x^{n-1} + a_2 x^{n-2} + \ldots + a_{n-1} x + a_n = 0$, where $a_0, a_1, a_2, \ldots, a_{n-1}, a_n$ are constants but $a_0 \neq 0$, is a polynomial equation of degree n. It has n and only n roots.

Let $\alpha_1, \alpha_2, \alpha_3, \ldots, \alpha_{n-1}, \alpha_n$ be n roots, then

- $\Sigma \alpha_1 = \alpha_1 + \alpha_2 + \alpha_3 + \ldots + \alpha_{n-1} + \alpha_n = (-1)^1 \dfrac{a_1}{a_0}$ **[sum of all roots]**
- $\Sigma \alpha_1 \alpha_2 = \alpha_1\alpha_2 + \alpha_1\alpha_3 + \ldots + \alpha_1\alpha_n + \alpha_2\alpha_3 + \ldots + \alpha_2\alpha_n + \ldots + \alpha_{n-1}\alpha_n$
  $= (-1)^2 \dfrac{a_2}{a_0}$ [sum of products taken two at a time]
- $\Sigma \alpha_1 \alpha_2 \alpha_3 = (-1)^3 \dfrac{a_3}{a_0}$ **[sum of products taken three at a time]**
- $\alpha_1 \alpha_2 \alpha_3 \ldots \alpha_n = (-1)^n \dfrac{a_n}{a_0}$ **[product of all roots]**

In general, $\Sigma \alpha_1 \alpha_2 \alpha_3 \ldots \alpha_p = (-1)^p \dfrac{a_p}{a_0}$

Remark

1. A polynomial equation of degree n has n roots (real or imaginary).
2. If all the coefficients, i.e., $a_0, a_1, a_2, \ldots, a_n$ are real, then the imaginary roots occur in pairs, i.e. number of imaginary roots is always even.
3. If the degree of a polynomial equation is odd, then atleast one of the roots will be real.
4. $(x-\alpha_1)(x-\alpha_2)(x-\alpha_3)\ldots(x-\alpha_n)$
   $= x^n + (-1)^1 \Sigma\alpha_1 \cdot x^{n-1} + (-1)^2 \Sigma\alpha_1\alpha_2 \cdot x^{n-2} + \ldots + (-1)^n \alpha_1\alpha_2\alpha_3\ldots\alpha_n$

In Particular

(i) For $n = 3$, if α, β, γ are the roots of the equation $ax^3 + bx^2 + cx + d = 0$, where a, b, c, d are constants and $a \neq 0$, then $\Sigma\alpha = \alpha + \beta + \gamma = (-1)^1 \dfrac{b}{a} = -\dfrac{b}{a}$,

$$\Sigma\alpha\beta = \alpha\beta + \beta\gamma + \gamma\alpha = (-1)^2 \frac{c}{a} = \frac{c}{a}$$

and $\alpha\beta\gamma = (-1)^3 \dfrac{d}{a} = -\dfrac{d}{a}$

or $ax^3 + bx^2 + cx + d = a(x-\alpha)(x-\beta)(x-\gamma)$
$= a(x^3 - \Sigma\alpha \cdot x^2 + \Sigma\alpha\beta \cdot x - \alpha\beta\gamma)]$

(ii) For $n = 4$, if $\alpha, \beta, \gamma, \delta$ are the roots of the equation $ax^4 + bx^3 + cx^2 + dx + e = 0$, where a, b, c, d, e are constants and $a \neq 0$, then

$$\Sigma\alpha = \alpha + \beta + \gamma + \delta = (-1)^1 \frac{b}{a} = -\frac{b}{a},$$

$$\Sigma\alpha\beta = (\alpha+\beta)(\gamma+\delta) + \alpha\beta + \gamma\delta = (-1)^2 \frac{c}{a} = \frac{c}{a},$$

$$\Sigma\alpha\beta\gamma = \alpha\beta(\gamma+\delta) + \gamma\delta(\alpha+\beta) = (-1)^3 \frac{d}{a} = -\frac{d}{a}$$

and $\alpha\beta\gamma\delta = (-1)^4 \dfrac{e}{a} = \dfrac{e}{a}$

or $ax^4 + bx^3 + cx^2 + dx + e = a(x-\alpha)(x-\beta)(x-\gamma)(x-\delta)$
$= a(x^4 - \Sigma\alpha \cdot x^3 + \Sigma\alpha\beta \cdot x^2 - \Sigma\alpha\beta\gamma \cdot x + \alpha\beta\gamma\delta)$

| Example 42. Find the conditions, if roots of the equation $x^3 - px^2 + qx - r = 0$ are in

(i) AP (ii) GP (iii) HP

Sol. (i) Let roots of the given equation are $A - D, A, A + D$, then

$$A - D + A + A + D = p \Rightarrow A = \frac{p}{3}$$

Now, A is the roots of the given equation, then it must be satisfy

$$A^3 - pA^2 + qA - r = 0$$

$$\Rightarrow \left(\frac{p}{3}\right)^3 - p\left(\frac{p}{3}\right)^2 + q\left(\frac{p}{3}\right) - r = 0$$

$$\Rightarrow p^3 - 3p^3 + 9qp - 27r = 0$$

or $2p^3 - 9pq + 27r = 0,$

which is the required condition.

(ii) Let roots of the given equation are $\frac{A}{R}, A, AR$, then

$$\frac{A}{R}\cdot A\cdot AR=(-1)^3\cdot\left(-\frac{r}{1}\right)=r$$

$$\Rightarrow \quad A^3=r$$

$$\Rightarrow \quad A=r^{\frac{1}{3}}$$

Now, A is the roots of the given equation, then

$$A^3-pA^2+qA-r=0$$

$$\Rightarrow \quad r-p(r)^{2/3}=q(r)^{1/3}-r=0$$

or $$p(r)^{2/3}=q(r)^{1/3}$$

or $$p^3r^2=q^3r$$

or $$p^3r=q^3$$

which is the required condition.

(iii) Given equation is

$$x^3-px^2+qx-r=0 \quad \text{...(i)}$$

On replacing x by $\frac{1}{x}$ in Eq. (i), then

$$\left(\frac{1}{x}\right)^3-p\left(\frac{1}{x}\right)^2+q\left(\frac{1}{x}\right)-r=0$$

$$\Rightarrow \quad rx^3-qx^2+px-1=0 \quad \text{...(ii)}$$

Now, roots of Eq. (ii) are in AP.

Let roots of Eq. (ii) are $A-P, A, A+P$, then

$$A-P+A+A+P=\frac{q}{r} \quad \text{or} \quad A=\frac{q}{3r}$$

$\because A$ is a root of Eq. (ii), then

$$rA^3-qA^2+pA-1=0$$

$$\Rightarrow \quad r\left(\frac{q}{3r}\right)^3-q\left(\frac{q}{3r}\right)^2+p\left(\frac{q}{3r}\right)-1=0$$

$$\Rightarrow \quad q^3-3q^3+9pqr-27r^2=0$$

$$\Rightarrow \quad 2q^3-9pqr+27r^2=0,$$

which is the required condition.

Example 43. Solve $6x^3-11x^2+6x-1=0$, if roots of the equation are in HP.

Sol. Put $x=\frac{1}{y}$ in the given equation, then

$$\frac{6}{y^3}-\frac{11}{y^2}+\frac{6}{y}-1=0$$

$$\Rightarrow \quad y^3-6y^2+11y-6=0 \quad \text{...(i)}$$

Now, roots of Eq. (i) are in AP.

Let the roots be $\alpha-\beta, \alpha, \alpha+\beta$.

Then, sum of roots $=\alpha-\beta+\alpha+\alpha+\beta=6$

$$\Rightarrow \quad 3\alpha=6$$

$$\therefore \quad \alpha=2$$

Product of roots $=(\alpha-\beta)\cdot\alpha\cdot(\alpha+\beta)=6$

$$\Rightarrow \quad (2-\beta)2(2+\beta)=6 \Rightarrow 4-\beta^2=3$$

$$\therefore \quad \beta=\pm 1$$

$\therefore$ Roots of Eqs. (i) are 1, 2, 3 or 3, 2, 1.

Hence, roots of the given equation are $1, \frac{1}{2}, \frac{1}{3}$ or $\frac{1}{3}, \frac{1}{2}, 1$.

Example 44. If α, β, γ are the roots of the equation $x^3-px^2+qx-r=0$, find

(i) $\Sigma\alpha^2$. (ii) $\Sigma\alpha^2\beta$. (iii) $\Sigma\alpha^3$.

Sol. Since, α, β, γ are the roots of $x^3-px^2+qx-r=0$.

$$\therefore \quad \Sigma\alpha=p, \Sigma\alpha\beta=q \text{ and } \alpha\beta\gamma=r$$

(i) $\because \Sigma\alpha\cdot\Sigma\alpha=p\cdot p$

$$\Rightarrow \quad (\alpha+\beta+\gamma)(\alpha+\beta+\gamma)=p^2$$

$$\Rightarrow \alpha^2+\beta^2+\gamma^2+2(\alpha\beta+\beta\gamma+\gamma\alpha)=p^2$$

or $$\Sigma\alpha^2+2\Sigma\alpha\beta=p^2$$

or $$\Sigma\alpha^2=p^2-2q$$

(ii) $\because \Sigma\alpha\cdot\Sigma\alpha\beta=p\cdot q$

$$\Rightarrow \quad (\alpha+\beta+\gamma)\cdot(\alpha\beta+\beta\gamma+\gamma\alpha)=pq$$

$$\Rightarrow \alpha^2\beta+\alpha\beta\gamma+\alpha^2\gamma+\beta^2\alpha+\beta^2\gamma+\alpha\beta\gamma$$
$$+\gamma^2\beta+\gamma^2\alpha=pq$$

$$\Rightarrow \quad (\alpha^2\beta+\alpha^2\alpha+\beta^2\gamma+\beta^2\gamma+\gamma^2\alpha+\gamma^2\beta)$$
$$+3\alpha\beta\gamma=pq$$

or $$\Sigma\alpha^2\beta+3r=pq$$

or $$\Sigma\alpha^2\beta=pq-3r$$

(iii) $\because \Sigma\alpha^2\cdot\Sigma\alpha=(p^2-2q)\cdot p$ [from result (i)]

$$\Rightarrow \quad (\alpha^2+\beta^2+\gamma^2)(\alpha+\beta+\gamma)=p^3-2pq$$

$$\Rightarrow \quad \alpha^3+\beta^3+\gamma^3+(\alpha^2\beta+\alpha^2\gamma+\beta^2\alpha+\beta^2\gamma$$
$$+\gamma^2\alpha+\gamma^2\beta)=p^3-2pq$$

$$\Rightarrow \quad \Sigma\alpha^3+\Sigma\alpha^2\beta=p^3-2pq$$

$$\Rightarrow \quad \Sigma\alpha^3+pq-3r=p^3-2pq \quad \text{[from result (ii)]}$$

or $$\Sigma\alpha^3=p^3-3pq+3r$$

Example 45. If α, β, γ are the roots of the cubic equation $x^3+qx+r=0$, then find the equation whose roots are $(\alpha-\beta)^2, (\beta-\gamma)^2, (\gamma-\alpha)^2$.

Sol. $\because \alpha, \beta, \gamma$ are the roots of the cubic equation

$$x^3+qx+r=0 \quad \text{...(i)}$$

Then, $$\Sigma\alpha=0, \Sigma\alpha\beta=q, \alpha\beta\gamma=-r \quad \text{...(ii)}$$

If y is a root of the required equation, then

$$y=(\alpha-\beta)^2=(\alpha+\beta)^2-4\alpha\beta$$

$$=(\alpha+\beta+\gamma-\gamma)^2-\frac{4\alpha\beta\gamma}{\gamma}$$

$$= (0 - \gamma)^2 + \frac{4r}{\gamma} \quad \text{[from Eq. (ii)]}$$

$$\Rightarrow \quad y = \gamma^2 + \frac{4r}{\gamma}$$

[replacing γ by x which is a root of Eq. (i)]

$$\therefore \quad y = x^2 + \frac{4r}{x}$$

or $\quad x^3 - yx + 4r = 0 \quad$ ...(iii)

The required equation is obtained by eliminating x between Eqs. (i) and (iii).

Now, subtracting Eq. (iii) from Eq. (i), we get

$$(q + y)\,x - 3r = 0$$

or $\quad x = \dfrac{3r}{q + y}$

On substituting the value of x in Eq. (i), we get

$$\left(\frac{3r}{q + y}\right)^3 + q\left(\frac{3r}{q + y}\right) + r = 0$$

Thus, $\quad y^3 + 6qy^2 + 9q^2y + (4q^3 + 27r^2) = 0$

which is the required equation.

Remark

$\Sigma(\alpha - \beta)^2 = -6q, \quad \Pi(\alpha - \beta)^2 = -(4q^3 + 27r^2)$

Some Results on Roots of a Polynomial Equation

1. **Remainder Theorem** If a polynomial $f(x)$ is divided by a linear function $x - \lambda$, then the remainder is $f(\lambda)$,

   i.e. Dividend = Divisor × Quotient + Remainder

   Let $Q(x)$ be the quotient and R be the remainder, thus

   $$f(x) = (x - \lambda)\,Q(x) + R$$

   $$\Rightarrow \quad f(\lambda) = (\lambda - \lambda)\,Q(\lambda) + R = 0 + R = R$$

| Example 46. If the expression $2x^3 + 3px^2 - 4x + p$ has a remainder of 5 when divided by $x + 2$, find the value of p.

Sol. Let $\quad f(x) = 2x^3 + 3px^2 - 4x + p$

$\because \quad f(x) = (x + 2)Q(x) + 5$

$\Rightarrow \quad f(-2) = 5$

$\Rightarrow \quad 2(-2)^3 + 3p(-2)^2 - 4(-2) + p = 5$ or $13p = 13$

$\therefore \quad p = 1$

2. **Factor Theorem** Factor theorem is a special case of Remainder theorem.

   Let $f(x) = (x - \lambda)\,Q(x) + R = (x - \lambda)\,Q(x) + f(\lambda)$

   If $f(\lambda) = 0$, $f(x) = (x - \lambda)\,Q(x)$, therefore $f(x)$ is exactly divisible by $x - \lambda$.

   or

   If λ is a root of the equation $f(x) = 0$, then $f(x)$ is exactly divisible by $(x - \lambda)$ and conversely, if $f(x)$ is exactly divisible by $(x - \lambda)$, then λ is a root of the equation $f(x) = 0$ and the remainder obtained is $f(\lambda)$.

| Example 47. If $x^2 + ax + 1$ is a factor of $ax^3 + bx + c$, find the conditions.

Sol. $\because ax^3 + bx + c = (x^2 + ax + 1)Q(x)$

Let $\quad Q(x) = Ax + B,$

then $\quad ax^3 + bx + c = (x^2 + ax + 1)(Ax + B)$

On comparing coefficients of x^3, x^2, x and constant on both sides, we get

$a = A, \quad$ ...(i)

$0 = B + aA, \quad$ ...(ii)

$b = aB + A, \quad$ ...(iii)

and $\quad c = B \quad$ ...(iv)

From Eqs. (i) and (iv), we get

$$A = a \text{ and } B = c$$

From Eqs. (ii) and (iii), $a^2 + c = 0$ and $b = ac + a$ are the required conditions.

| Example 48. A certain polynomial $f(x), x \in R$, when divided by $x - a, x - b$ and $x - c$ leaves remainders a, b and c, respectively. Then, find the remainder when $f(x)$ is divided by $(x - a)(x - b)(x - c)$, where a, b, c are distinct.

Sol. By Remainder theorem $f(a) = a$, $f(b) = b$ and $f(c) = c$

Let the quotient be $Q(x)$ and remainder is $R(x)$.

$\therefore \quad f(x) = (x - a)(x - b)(x - c)Q(x) + R(x)$

$\therefore \quad f(a) = 0 + R(a) \Rightarrow R(a) = a$

$f(b) = 0 + R(b) \Rightarrow R(b) = b$ and $f(c) = 0 + R(c)$

$\Rightarrow \quad R(c) = c$

So, the equation $R(x) - x = 0$ has three roots a, b and c. But its degree is atmost two. So, $R(x) - x$ must be zero polynomial (or identity).

Hence, $R(x) = x$.

3. Every equation of an odd degree has atleast one real root, whose sign is opposite to that of its last term, provided that the coefficient of the first term is positive.
4. Every equation of an even degree has atleast two real roots, one positive and one negative, whose last term is negative, provided that the coefficient of the first term is positive.
5. If an equation has no odd powers of x, then all roots of the equation are complex provided all the coefficients of the equation have positive sign.

6. If $x = \alpha$ is root repeated m times in $f(x) = 0$ ($f(x) = 0$ is an nth degree equation in x), then $f(x) = (x - \alpha)^m g(x)$ where, $g(x)$ is a polynomial of degree $(n - m)$ and the root $x = \alpha$ is repeated $(m - 1)$ time in $f'(x) = 0$, $(m - 2)$ times in $f''(x) = 0, \ldots, (m - (m - 1))$ times in $f^{m-1}(x) = 0$.

7. Let $f(x) = 0$ be a polynomial equation and λ, μ are two real numbers.

Then, $f(x) = 0$ will have atleast one real root or an odd number of roots between λ and μ, if $f(\lambda)$ and $f(\mu)$ are of opposite signs.

But if $f(\lambda)$ and $f(\mu)$ are of same signs, then either $f(x) = 0$ has no real roots or an even number of roots between λ and μ.

Illustration by Graphs

Since, $f(x)$ be a polynomial in x, then graph of $y = f(x)$ will be continuous in every interval.

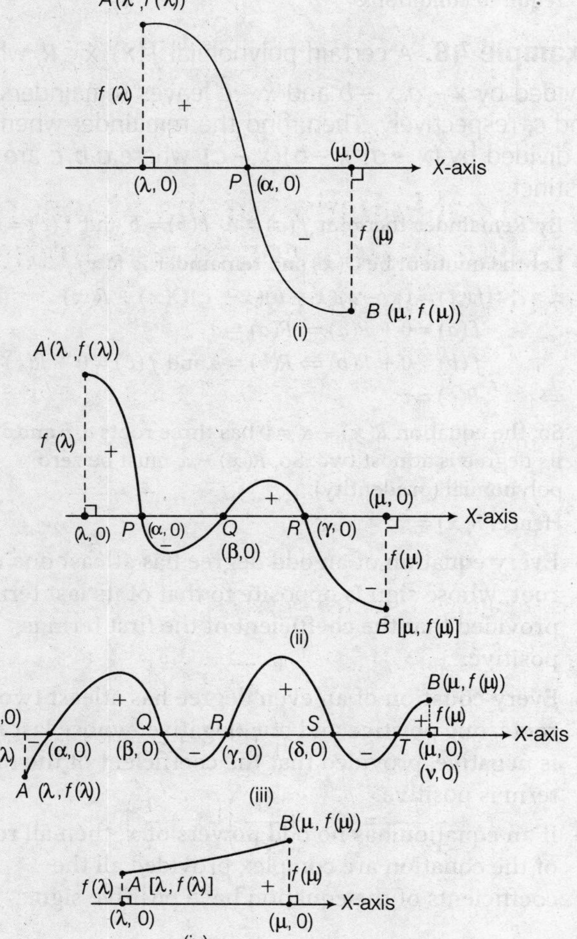

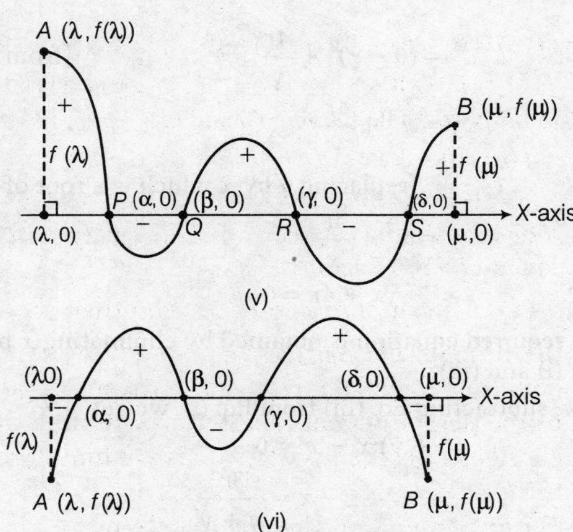

(a) In figure (i), (ii) and (iii), $f(\lambda)$ and $f(\mu)$ have opposite signs and equation $f(x) = 0$, has one, three, five roots between λ and μ, respectively.

(b) In figure (iv), (v) and (vi), $f(\lambda)$ and $f(\mu)$ have same signs and equation $f(x) = 0$, has no, four and four roots between λ and μ, respectively.

Example 49. If a, b, c are real numbers, $a \neq 0$. If α is root of $a^2x^2 + bx + c = 0$, β is a root of $a^2x^2 - bx - c = 0$ and $0 < \alpha < \beta$, show that the equation $a^2x^2 + 2bx + 2c = 0$ has a root γ that always satisfies $\alpha < \gamma < \beta$.

Sol. Since, α is a root of $a^2x^2 + bx + c = 0$.

Then, $$a^2\alpha^2 + b\alpha + c = 0 \quad \ldots \text{(i)}$$

and β is a root of $a^2x^2 - bx - c = 0$,

then $$a^2\beta^2 - b\beta - c = 0 \quad \ldots \text{(ii)}$$

Let $$f(x) = a^2x^2 + 2bx + 2c$$

$$\therefore \quad f(\alpha) = a^2\alpha^2 + 2b\alpha + 2c = a^2\alpha^2 - 2a^2\alpha^2 \quad \text{[from Eq. (i)]}$$

$$= -a^2\alpha^2$$

$$\Rightarrow \quad f(\alpha) < 0 \text{ and } f(\beta) = a^2\beta^2 + 2b\beta + 2c$$

$$= a^2\beta^2 + 2a^2\beta^2 \quad \text{[from Eq. (ii)]}$$

$$= 3a^2\beta^2$$

$$\Rightarrow \quad f(\beta) > 0$$

Since, $f(\alpha)$ and $f(\beta)$ are of opposite signs, then it is clear that a root γ of the equation $f(x) = 0$ lies between α and β.

Hence, $$\alpha < \gamma < \beta \quad [\because \alpha < \beta]$$

Example 50. If $a < b < c < d$, then show that $(x - a)(x - c) + 3(x - b)(x - d) = 0$ has real and distinct roots.

Sol. Let $f(x) = (x - a)(x - c) + 3(x - b)(x - d)$

Then, $f(a) = 0 + 3(a-b)(a-d) > 0$ $[\because a-b<0, a-d<0]$
and $f(b) = (b-a)(b-c) + 0 < 0$ $[\because b-a>0, b-c<0]$
Thus, one root will lie between a and b.
and $f(c) = 0 + 3(c-b)(c-d) < 0$ $[\because c-b>0, c-d<0]$
and $f(d) = (d-a)(d-c) + 0 > 0$ $[\because d-a>0, d-c>0]$
Thus, one root will lie between c and d. Hence, roots of equation are real and distinct.

8. Let $f(x)=0$ be a polynomial equation then

(a) the number of positive roots of a polynomial equation $f(x)=0$ (arranged in decreasing order of the degree) cannot exceed the number of changes of signs in $f(x)=0$ as we move from left to right.

For example, Consider the equation
$$2x^3 - x^2 - x + 1 = 0.$$
The number of changes of signs from left to right is 2 (+ to –, then – to +). Then, number of positive roots cannot exceed 2.

(b) The number of negative roots of a polynomial equation $f(x)=0$ cannot exceed the number of changes of signs in $f(-x)$.

For example, Consider the equation
$$5x^4 + 3x^3 - 2x^2 + 5x - 8 = 0$$
Let $f(x) = 4x^4 + 3x^3 - 2x^2 + 5x - 8$
$\therefore$ $f(-x) = 5x^4 - 3x^3 - 2x^2 - 5x - 8$
The number of changes of signs from left to right is (+ to –). Then number of negative roots cannot exceed 1.

(c) If equation $f(x)=0$ have atmost r positive roots and atmost t negative roots, then equation $f(x)=0$ will have atmost $(r+t)$ real roots, i.e. it will have atleast $n-(r+t)$ imaginary roots, where n is the degree of polynomial.

For example, Consider the equation
$$5x^6 - 8x^3 + 3x^5 + 5x^2 + 8 = 0$$
The given equation can be written as
$$5x^6 + 3x^5 - 8x^3 + 5x^2 + 8 = 0$$
Let $f(x) = 5x^6 + 3x^5 - 8x^3 + 5x^2 + 8$
Here, $f(x)$ has two changes in signs.
So, $f(x)$ has atmost two positive real roots
and $f(-x) = 5x^6 - 3x^5 + 8x^3 + 5x^2 + 8$
Here, $f(-x)$ has two changes in signs.
So, $f(x)$ has atmost two negative real roots.
and $x=0$ cannot be root of $f(x)=0$.
Hence, $f(x)=0$ has atmost four real roots, therefore atleast two imaginary roots.

9. **Rolle's Theorem** If $f(x)$ is continuous function in the interval $[a, b]$ and differentiable in interval (a, b) and $f(a) = f(b)$, then equation $f'(x)=0$ will have atleast one root between a and b. Since, every polynomial $f(x)$ is always continuous and differentiable in every interval. Therefore, Rolle's theorem is always applicable to polynomial function in every interval $[a, b]$ if $f(a) = f(b)$.

Example 51. If $2a + 3b + 6c = 0$; $a, b, c \in R$, then show that the equation $ax^2 + bx + c = 0$ has atleast one root between 0 and 1.

Sol. Given, $2a + 3b + 6c = 0$
$$\Rightarrow \quad \frac{a}{3} + \frac{b}{2} + c = 0 \quad \text{...(i)}$$
Let $f'(x) = ax^2 + bx + c$,
Then, $f(x) = \dfrac{ax^3}{3} + \dfrac{bx^2}{2} + cx + d$
Now, $f(0) = d$ and $f(1) = \dfrac{a}{3} + \dfrac{b}{2} + c + d$
$= 0 + d$ [from Eq. (i)]
Since, $f(x)$ is a polynomial of three degree, then $f(x)$ is continuous and differentiable everywhere and $f(0) = f(1)$, then by Rolle's theorem $f'(x) = 0$ i.e., $ax^2 + bx + c = 0$ has atleast one real root between 0 and 1.

Reciprocal Equation of the Standard Form can be Reduced to an Equation of Half Its Dimensions

Let the equation be
$$ax^{2m} + bx^{2m-1} + cx^{2m-2} + \ldots + kx^m + \ldots + cx^2 + bx + a = 0$$
On dividing by x^m, then
$$ax^m + bx^{m-1} + cx^{m-2} + \ldots + k + \ldots + \frac{c}{x^{m-2}} + \frac{b}{x^{m-1}} + \frac{a}{x^m} = 0$$
On rearranging the terms, we have
$$a\left(x^m + \frac{1}{x^m}\right) + b\left(x^{m-1} + \frac{1}{x^{m-1}}\right) + c\left(x^{m-2} + \frac{1}{x^{m-2}}\right) + \ldots + k = 0$$
Now, $$x^{p+1} + \frac{1}{x^{p+1}} = \left(x^p + \frac{1}{x^p}\right)\left(x + \frac{1}{x}\right) - \left(x^{p-1} + \frac{1}{x^{p-1}}\right)$$

Hence, writing z for $x+\frac{1}{x}$ and given to p succession the values 1, 2, 3, ..., we obtain

$$x^2+\frac{1}{x^2}=z^2-2$$

$$x^3+\frac{1}{x^3}=z(z^2-2)-z=z^3-3z$$

$$x^4+\frac{1}{x^4}=z(z^3-3z)-(z^2-2)=z^4-4z^2+2$$

and so on and **generally $x^m+\frac{1}{x^m}$ is of m dimensions in z and therefore the equation in z is of m dimensions.**

Example 52. Solve the equation $2x^4+x^3-11x^2+x+2=0$.

Sol. Since, $x=0$ is not a solution of the given equation.

On dividing by x^2 in both sides of the given equation, we get

$$2\left(x^2+\frac{1}{x^2}\right)+\left(x+\frac{1}{x}\right)-11=0 \quad \text{...(i)}$$

Put $x+\frac{1}{x}=y$ in Eq. (i), then Eq. (i) reduce in the form

$$2(y^2-2)+y-11=0$$

$$\Rightarrow \quad 2y^2+y-15=0$$

$$\therefore \quad y_1=-3 \text{ and } y_2=\frac{5}{2}$$

Consequently, the original equation is equivalent to the collection of equations

$$\left[\begin{array}{l} x+\frac{1}{x}=-3, \\ x+\frac{1}{x}=\frac{5}{2} \end{array}\right.$$

we find that, $x_1=\frac{-3-\sqrt{5}}{2}$, $x_2=\frac{-3+\sqrt{5}}{2}$, $x_3=\frac{1}{2}$, $x_4=2$

Equations which can be Reduced to Linear, Quadratic and Biquadratic Equations

***Type* I An equation of the form**

$$(x-a)(x-b)(x-c)(x-d)=A$$

where, $a<b<c<d$, $b-a=d-c$, can be solved by a change of variable.

i.e.
$$y=\frac{(x-a)+(x-b)+(x-c)+(x-d)}{4}$$

$$y=x-\frac{(a+b+c+d)}{4}$$

Example 53. Solve the equation $(12x-1)(6x-1)(4x-1)(3x-1)=5$.

Sol. The given equation can be written as

$$\left(x-\frac{1}{12}\right)\left(x-\frac{1}{6}\right)\left(x-\frac{1}{4}\right)\left(x-\frac{1}{3}\right)=\frac{5}{12\cdot 6\cdot 4\cdot 3} \quad \text{...(i)}$$

Since, $\frac{1}{12}<\frac{1}{6}<\frac{1}{4}<\frac{1}{3}$ and $\frac{1}{6}-\frac{1}{12}=\frac{1}{3}-\frac{1}{4}$

We can introduced a new variable,

$$y=\frac{1}{4}\left[\left(x-\frac{1}{12}\right)+\left(x-\frac{1}{6}\right)+\left(x-\frac{1}{4}\right)+\left(x-\frac{1}{3}\right)\right]$$

$$y=x-\frac{5}{24}$$

On substituting $x=y+\frac{5}{24}$ in Eq. (i), we get

$$\left(y+\frac{3}{24}\right)\left(y+\frac{1}{24}\right)\left(y-\frac{1}{24}\right)\left(y-\frac{3}{24}\right)=\frac{5}{12\cdot 6\cdot 4\cdot 3}$$

$$\Rightarrow \quad \left[y^2-\left(\frac{1}{24}\right)^2\right]\left[y^2-\left(\frac{3}{24}\right)^2\right]=\frac{5}{12\cdot 6\cdot 4\cdot 3}$$

Hence, we find that

$$y^2=\frac{49}{24^2}$$

i.e. $\quad y_1=\frac{7}{24}$ and $y_2=-\frac{7}{24}$

Hence, the corresponding roots of the original equation are $\frac{1}{12}$ and $\frac{1}{2}$.

***Type* II** An equation of the form

$$(x-a)(x-b)(x-c)(x-d)=Ax^2$$

where, $ab=cd$ can be reduced to a collection of two quadratic equations by a change of variable $y=x+\frac{ab}{x}$.

Example 54. Solve the equation $(x+2)(x+3)(x+8)(x+12)=4x^2$.

Sol. Since, $(-2)(-12)=(-3)(-8)$, so we can write given equation as

$$(x+2)(x+12)(x+3)(x+8)=4x^2$$

$$\Rightarrow \quad (x^2+14x+24)(x^2+11x+24)=4x^2 \quad \text{...(i)}$$

Now, $x=0$ is not a root of given equation.

On dividing by x^2 in both sides of Eq. (i), we get

$$\left(x+\frac{24}{x}+14\right)\left(x+\frac{24}{x}+11\right)=4 \quad \text{...(ii)}$$

Put $x+\frac{24}{x}=y$, then Eq. (ii) can be reduced in the form

$$(y+14)(y+11)=4 \text{ or } y^2+25y+150=0$$

$$\therefore \quad y_1=-15 \text{ and } y_2=-10$$

Thus, the original equation is equivalent to the collection of equations

$$\left[\begin{array}{l} x+\dfrac{24}{x}=-15, \\ x+\dfrac{24}{x}=-10, \end{array}\right.$$

i.e. $$\left[\begin{array}{l} x^2+15x+24=0 \\ x^2+10x+24=0 \end{array}\right.$$

On solving these collection, we get

$$x_1=\frac{-15-\sqrt{129}}{2},\ x_2=\frac{-15+\sqrt{129}}{2},\ x_3=-6,\ x_4=-4$$

***Type* III An equation of the form $(x-a)^4+(x-b)^4=A$** can also be solved by a change of variable, i.e. making a substitution $y=\dfrac{(x-a)+(x-b)}{2}$.

Example 55. Solve the equation $(6-x)^4+(8-x)^4=16$.

Sol. After a change of variable,

$$y=\frac{(6-x)+(8-x)}{2}$$

$\therefore$ $y=7-x$ or $x=7-y$

Now, put $x=7-y$ in given equation, we get

$$(y-1)^4+(y+1)^4=16$$

$\Rightarrow$ $y^4+6y^2-7=0$

$\Rightarrow$ $(y^2+7)(y^2-1)=0$

$y^2+7\neq 0$

[y gives imaginary values]

$\therefore$ $y^2-1=0$

Then, $y_1=-1$ and $y_2=1$

Thus, $x_1=8$ and $x_2=6$ are the roots of the given equation.

Rational Algebraic Inequalities

Consider the following types of rational algebraic inequalities

$$\frac{P(x)}{Q(x)}>0,\ \frac{P(x)}{Q(x)}<0,$$

$$\frac{P(x)}{Q(x)}\geq 0,\ \frac{P(x)}{Q(x)}\leq 0$$

If $P(x)$ and $Q(x)$ can be resolved in linear factors, then use *Wavy curve method*, otherwise we use the following statements for solving inequalities of this kind.

(1) $\dfrac{P(x)}{Q(x)}>0\Rightarrow\{P(x)Q(x)>0\Rightarrow\left\{\begin{array}{l} P(x)>0, Q(x)>0 \\ \text{or} \\ P(x)<0, Q(x)<0 \end{array}\right.$

(2) $\dfrac{P(x)}{Q(x)}<0\Rightarrow\{P(x)Q(x)<0\Rightarrow\left\{\begin{array}{l} P(x)>0, Q(x)<0 \\ \text{or} \\ P(x)<0, Q(x)>0 \end{array}\right.$

(3) $\dfrac{P(x)}{Q(x)}\geq 0\Rightarrow\left\{\begin{array}{l} P(x)Q(x)\geq 0 \\ Q(x)\neq 0 \end{array}\right.\Rightarrow\left\{\begin{array}{l} P(x)\geq 0, Q(x)>0 \\ \text{or} \\ P(x)\leq 0, Q(x)<0 \end{array}\right.$

(4) $\dfrac{P(x)}{Q(x)}\leq 0\Rightarrow\left\{\begin{array}{l} P(x)Q(x)\leq 0 \\ Q(x)\neq 0 \end{array}\right.\Rightarrow\left\{\begin{array}{l} P(x)\geq 0, Q(x)<0 \\ \text{or} \\ P(x)\leq 0, Q(x)>0 \end{array}\right.$

Example 56. Find all values of a for which the set of all solutions of the system

$$\left\{\begin{array}{l} \dfrac{x^2+ax-2}{x^2-x+1}<2 \\ \dfrac{x^2+ax-2}{x^2-x+1}>-3 \end{array}\right.$$

is the entire number line.

Sol. The system is equivalent to

$$\left\{\begin{array}{l} \dfrac{x^2-(a+2)x+4}{x^2-x+1}>0 \\ \dfrac{4x^2+(a-3)x+1}{x^2-x+1}>0 \end{array}\right.$$

Since, $x^2-x+1=\left(x-\dfrac{1}{2}\right)^2+\dfrac{3}{4}>0$, this system is equivalent to $\left\{\begin{array}{l} x^2-(a+2)x+4>0 \\ 4x^2+(a-3)x+1>0 \end{array}\right.$

Hence, the discriminants of the both equations of this system are negative.

i.e., $\left\{\begin{array}{l} (a+2)^2-16<0 \\ (a-3)^2-16<0 \end{array}\right.\Rightarrow (a+6)(a-2)<0$

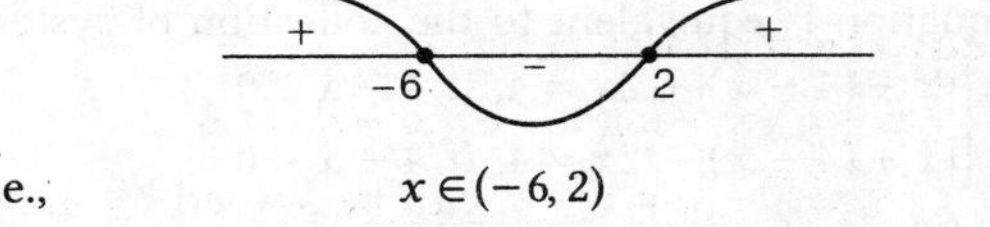

i.e., $x\in(-6,2)$ ...(i)

$\Rightarrow$ $(a+1)(a-7)<0$

+ − +
−1 7

i.e. $x\in(-1,7)$ ...(ii)

Hence, from Eqs. (i) and (ii), we get

$$x\in(-1,2)$$

Equations Containing Absolute Values

By definition, $|x| = x$, if $x \geq 0$ $|x| = -x$, if $x < 0$

Example 57. Solve the equation $x^2 - 5|x| + 6 = 0$.

Sol. The given equation is equivalent to the collection of systems

$$\begin{cases} x^2 - 5x + 6 = 0, \text{ if } x \geq 0 \\ x^2 + 5x + 6 = 0, \text{ if } x < 0 \end{cases} \Rightarrow \begin{cases} (x-2)(x-3) = 0, \text{ if } x \geq 0 \\ (x+2)(x+3) = 0, \text{ if } x < 0 \end{cases}$$

Hence, the solutions of the given equation are

$$x_1 = 2, x_2 = 3, x_3 = -2, x_4 = -3$$

Example 58. Solve the equation

$$\left|\frac{x^2 - 8x + 12}{x^2 - 10x + 21}\right| = -\frac{x^2 - 8x + 12}{x^2 - 10x + 21}.$$

Sol. This equation has the form $|f(x)| = -f(x)$

when, $f(x) = \dfrac{x^2 - 8x + 12}{x^2 - 10x + 21}$

such an equation is equivalent to the collection of systems

$$\begin{cases} f(x) = -f(x), \text{ if } f(x) \geq 0 \\ f(x) = f(x), \text{ if } f(x) < 0 \end{cases}$$

The first system is equivalent to $f(x) = 0$ and the second system is equivalent to $f(x) < 0$ the combining both systems, we get

$$f(x) \leq 0$$

$$\therefore \quad \frac{x^2 - 8x + 12}{x^2 - 10x + 21} \leq 0$$

$$\Rightarrow \quad \frac{(x-2)(x-6)}{(x-3)(x-7)} \leq 0$$

+ 2 − 3 + 6 − 7 +

Hence, by *Wavy curve method,*

$$x \in [2, 3) \cup [6, 7)$$

Example 59. Solve the equation $|x - |4 - x|| - 2x = 4$.

Sol. This equation is equivalent to the collection of systems

$$\begin{cases} |x - (4 - x)| - 2x = 4, \text{ if } 4 - x \geq 0 \\ |x + (4 - x)| - 2x = 4, \text{ if } 4 - x < 0 \end{cases}$$

$$\Rightarrow \begin{cases} |2x - 4| - 2x = 4, & \text{if } x \leq 4 \\ 4 - 2x = 4, & \text{if } x > 4 \end{cases} \quad \text{...(i)}$$

The second system of this collection

gives $x = 0$

but $x > 4$

Hence, second system has no solution.

The first system of collection Eq. (i) is equivalent to the system of collection

$$\begin{cases} 2x - 4 - 2x = 4, \text{ if } 2x \geq 4 \\ -2x + 4 - 2x = 4, \text{ if } 2x < 4 \end{cases}$$

$$\Rightarrow \begin{cases} -4 = 4, \text{ if } x \geq 2 \\ -4x = 0, \text{ if } x < 2 \end{cases}$$

The first system is failed and second system gives $x = 0$. Hence, $x = 0$ is unique solution of the given equation.

Important Forms Containing Absolute Values

***Form* 1 The equation of the form**

$$|f(x) + g(x)| = |f(x)| + |g(x)|$$

is equivalent of the system

$$f(x)\, g(x) \geq 0.$$

Example 60. Solve the equation

$$\left|\frac{x}{x-1}\right| + |x| = \frac{x^2}{|x-1|}.$$

Sol. Let $f(x) = \dfrac{x}{x-1}$ and $g(x) = x$,

Then, $f(x) + g(x) = \dfrac{x}{x-1} + x = \dfrac{x^2}{x-1}$

$\therefore$ The given equation can be reduced in the form

$$|f(x)| + |g(x)| = |f(x) + g(x)|$$

Hence, $f(x) \cdot g(x) \geq 0$

$$\Rightarrow \quad \frac{x^2}{x-1} \geq 0$$

− 0 − 1 +

From *Wavy curve method,* $x \in (1, \infty) \cup \{0\}$.

***Form* 2 The equation of the form**

$$|f_1(x)| + |f_2(x)| + \ldots + |f_n(x)| = g(x) \quad \text{...(i)}$$

where, $f_1(x), f_2(x), \ldots, f_n(x), g(x)$ are functions of x and $g(x)$ may be constant.

Equations of this form solved by the **method of intervals**. We first find all critical points of $f_1(x), f_2(x), \ldots, f_n(x)$, if coefficient of x is positive, then graph start with positive sign (+) and if coefficient of x is negative, then graph start with negative sign (−). Then, using the definition of the absolute value, we pass from Eq. (i) to a collection of systems which do not contain the absolute value symbols.

Example 61. Solve the equation $|x-1|+|7-x|+2|x-2|=4$.

Sol. Here, critical points are 1, 2, 7 using the method of intervals, we find intervals when the expressions $x-1, 7-x$ and $x-2$ are of constant signs.

i.e. $x<1, 1<x<2, 2<x<7, x>7$

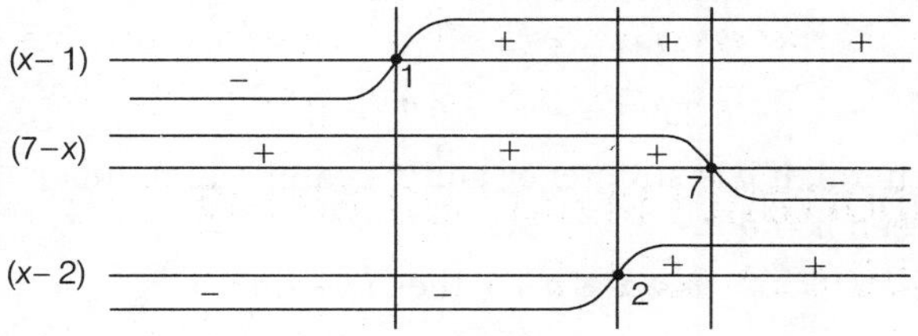

Thus, the given equation is equivalent to the collection of four systems,

$$\left[\begin{array}{l}\begin{cases}x<1\\-(x-1)+(7-x)-2(x-2)=4\end{cases}\\\begin{cases}1\le x<2\\(x-1)+(7-x)-2(x-2)=4\end{cases}\\\begin{cases}2\le x<7\\(x-1)+(7-x)+2(x-2)=4\end{cases}\\\begin{cases}x\ge 7\\(x-1)-(7-x)+2(x-2)=4\end{cases}\end{array}\right. \Rightarrow \left[\begin{array}{l}\begin{cases}x<1\\x=2\end{cases}\\\begin{cases}1\le x<2\\x=3\end{cases}\\\begin{cases}2\le x<7\\x=1\end{cases}\\\begin{cases}x\ge 7\\x=4\end{cases}\end{array}\right.$$

From the collection of four systems, the given equation has no solution.

Inequations Containing Absolute Values

By definition, $|x|<a \Rightarrow -a<x<a\,(a>0)$

$|x|\le a \Rightarrow -a\le x\le a$

$|x|>a \Rightarrow x<-a$ and $x>a$

and $|x|\ge a \Rightarrow x\le -a$ and $x\ge a$.

Example 62. Solve the inequation $\left|1-\dfrac{|x|}{1+|x|}\right|\ge\dfrac{1}{2}$.

Sol. The given inequation is equivalent to the collection of systems

$$\left[\begin{array}{l}\left|1-\dfrac{x}{1+x}\right|\ge\dfrac{1}{2}, \text{ if } x\ge 0\\\left|1+\dfrac{x}{1-x}\right|\ge\dfrac{1}{2}, \text{ if } x<0\end{array}\right. \Rightarrow \left[\begin{array}{l}\dfrac{1}{|1+x|}\ge\dfrac{1}{2}, \text{ if } x\ge 0\\\dfrac{1}{|1-x|}\ge\dfrac{1}{2}, \text{ if } x<0\end{array}\right.$$

$$\Rightarrow \left[\begin{array}{l}\dfrac{1}{1+x}\ge\dfrac{1}{2}, \text{ if } x\ge 0\\\dfrac{1}{1-x}\ge\dfrac{1}{2}, \text{ if } x<0\end{array}\right. \Rightarrow \left[\begin{array}{l}\dfrac{1-x}{1+x}\ge 0, \text{ if } x\ge 0\\\dfrac{1+x}{1-x}\ge 0, \text{ if } x<0\end{array}\right.$$

$$\Rightarrow \left[\begin{array}{l}\dfrac{x-1}{x+1}\le 0, \text{ if } x\ge 0\\\dfrac{x+1}{x-1}\le 0, \text{ if } x<0\end{array}\right.$$

For $\dfrac{x-1}{x+1}\le 0$, if $x\ge 0$

$\therefore \quad 0\le x\le 1 \quad$ ...(i)

For $\dfrac{x+1}{x-1}\le 0$, if $x<0$

$\therefore \quad -1\le x<0 \quad$ ...(ii)

Hence, from Eqs. (i) and (ii), the solution of the given equation is $x\in[-1, 1]$.

Aliter

$$\left|1-\frac{|x|}{1+|x|}\right|\ge\frac{1}{2} \Rightarrow \left|\frac{1}{1+|x|}\right|\ge\frac{1}{2}$$

$$\Rightarrow \frac{1}{1+|x|}\ge\frac{1}{2} \Rightarrow 1+|x|\le 2 \text{ or } |x|\le 1$$

$$\therefore \quad -1\le x\le 1 \text{ or } x\Rightarrow[-1, 1]$$

Equations Involving Greatest Integer, Least Integer and Fractional Part

1. Greatest Integer

$[x]$ denotes the greatest integer less than or equal to x i.e., $[x]\le x$. It is also known as **floor** of x.

Thus, $[3.5779]=3, [0.89]=0, [3]=3$

$[-8.7285]=-9$

$[-0.6]=-1$

$[-7]=-7$

In general, if n is an integer and x is any real number between n and $n+1$.

i.e. $n\le x<n+1$, then $[x]=n$

Properties of Greatest Integer

(i) $[x\pm n]=[x]\pm n, n\in I$

(ii) $[-x]=-[x], x\in I$

(iii) $[-x]=-1-[x], x\notin I$

(iv) $[x]-[-x]=2n$, if $x=n, n\in I$

(v) $[x]-[-x]=2n+1$, if $x=n+\{x\}, n\in I$ and $0<\{x\}<1$

(vi) $[x]\ge n \Rightarrow x\ge n, n\in I$

(vii) $[x]>n \Rightarrow x\ge n+1, n\in I$

(viii) $[x]\le n \Rightarrow x<n+1, n\in I$

(ix) $[x]<n \Rightarrow x<n, n\in I$

(x) $n_2\le[x]\le n_1 \Rightarrow n_2\le x<n_1+1, n_1, n_2\in I$

(xi) $[x+y]\ge[x]+[y]$

(xii) $\left[\frac{[x]}{n}\right]=\left[\frac{x}{n}\right], n\in N$

(xiii) $\left[\frac{n+1}{2}\right]+\left[\frac{n+2}{4}\right]+\left[\frac{n+4}{8}\right]+\left[\frac{n+8}{16}\right]+\ldots=n, n\in N$

(xiv) $[x]+\left[x+\frac{1}{n}\right]+\left[x+\frac{2}{n}\right]+\ldots+\left[x+\frac{n-1}{n}\right]=[nx],$

$n\in N$

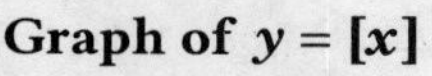

Graph of $y = [x]$

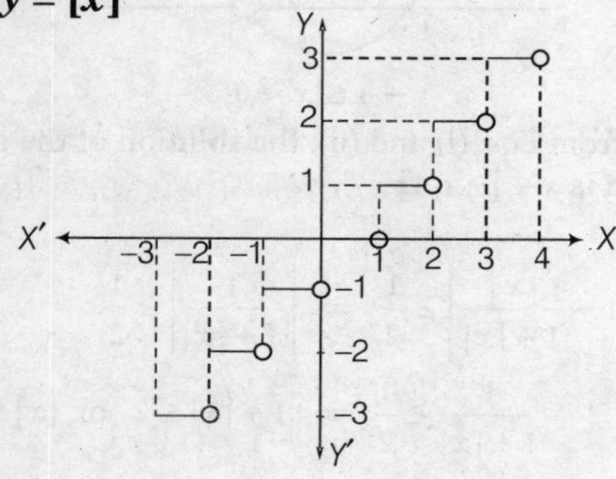

Remark

Domain and Range of $[x]$ are R and I, respectively.

| Example 63. If $[x]$ denotes the integral part of x for real x, then find the value of

$$\left[\frac{1}{4}\right]+\left[\frac{1}{4}+\frac{1}{200}\right]+\left[\frac{1}{4}+\frac{1}{100}\right]+\left[\frac{1}{4}+\frac{3}{200}\right]+\ldots+\left[\frac{1}{4}+\frac{199}{200}\right].$$

Sol. The given expression can be written as

$$\left[\frac{1}{4}\right]+\left[\frac{1}{4}+\frac{1}{200}\right]+\left[\frac{1}{4}+\frac{2}{200}\right]+\left[\frac{1}{4}+\frac{3}{200}\right]+\ldots+\left[\frac{1}{4}+\frac{199}{200}\right]$$

$$=\left[200\cdot\frac{1}{4}\right]=[50]=50 \quad \text{[from property (xiv)]}$$

| Example 64. Let $[a]$ denotes the larger integer not exceeding the real number a. If x and y satisfy the equations $y=2[x]+3$ and $y=3[x-2]$ simulaneously, determine $[x+y]$.

Sol. We have, $\quad y=2[x]+3=3[x-2] \quad$ ...(i)

$\Rightarrow \quad 2[x]+3=3([x]-2) \quad$ [from property (i)]

$\Rightarrow \quad 2[x]+3=3[x]-6$

$\Rightarrow \quad [x]=9$

From Eq. (i), $y=2\times 9+3=21$

$\therefore \quad [x+y]=[x+21]=[x]+21=9+21=30$

Hence, the value of $[x+y]$ is 30.

2. Least Integer

(x) or $\lceil x \rceil$ denotes the least integer greater than or equal to x i.e., $(x)\geq x$ or $\lceil x \rceil \geq x$. It is also known as **ceilling** of x.

Thus, $\quad (3.578)=4, (0.87)=1,$

$(4)=4$

$\lceil -8.239 \rceil=-8, \lceil -0.7 \rceil=0$

In general, if n is an integer and x is any real number between n and $n+1$

i.e., $\quad n<x\leq n+1$, then $(x)=n+1$

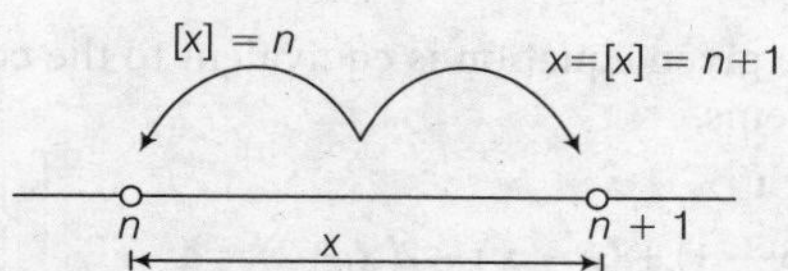

Relation between Greatest Integer and Least Integer

$$(x)=\begin{cases}[x], & x\in I\\ [x]+1, & x\notin I\end{cases}$$

i.e. If $x\in I$, then $x=[x]=(x)$. [remember]

Remark

If $(x)=n$, then $(n-1)<x\leq n$

Graph of $y=(x)=\lceil x \rceil$

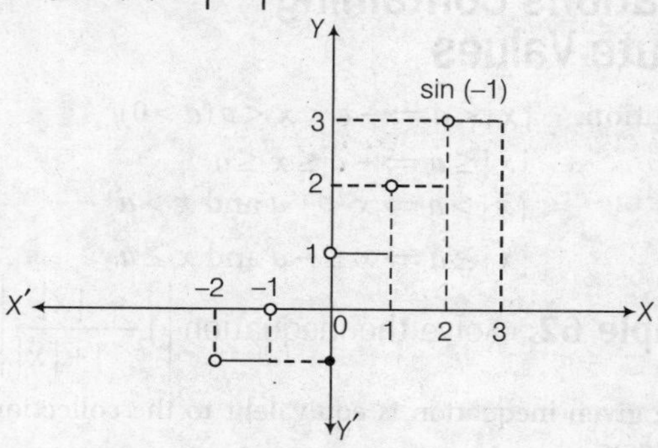

Remark

Domain and Range of (x) are R and $[x]+1$, respectively.

| Example 65. If $[x]$ and (x) are the integral part of x and nearest integer to x, then solve $(x)[x]=1$.

Sol. ***Case* I** If $x\in I$, then $x=[x]=(x)$

$\therefore$ Given equation convert in $x^2=1$.

$\therefore \quad x=(\pm 1)$

***Case* II** If $x\notin I$, then $(x)=[x]+1$

$\therefore$ Given equation convert in

$$([x]+1)[x]=1 \Rightarrow [x]^2+[x]-1=0$$

or $$[x]=\frac{-1\pm\sqrt{5}}{2} \quad \text{[impossible]}$$

Then, final answer is $x=\pm 1$.

Example 66. Find the solution set of $(x)^2+(x+1)^2=25$, where (x) is the least integer greater than or equal to x.

Sol. ***Case* I** If $x \in I$, then $x=(x)=[x]$

Then, $(x)^2+(x+1)^2=25$ reduces to

$$x^2+\overline{x+1}^2=25 \Rightarrow 2x^2+2x-24=0$$

$$\Rightarrow x^2+x-12=0 \Rightarrow (x+4)(x-3)=0$$

$$\therefore x=-4, 3 \quad \text{...(i)}$$

***Case* II** If $x \notin I$, then $(x)=[x]+1$

Then, $(x)^2+(x+1)^2=25$ reduces to

$$\{[x]+1\}^2+\{[x+1]+1\}^2=25$$

$$\Rightarrow \{[x]+1\}^2+\{[x]+2\}^2=25$$

$$\Rightarrow 2[x]^2+6[x]-20=0$$

$$\Rightarrow [x]^2+3[x]-10=0$$

$$\Rightarrow \{[x]+5\}\{[x]-2\}=0$$

$$\therefore [x]=-5 \text{ and } [x]=2$$

$$\Rightarrow x\in[-5,-4)\cup[2,3)$$

$$\because x \notin I,$$

$$\therefore x\in(-5,-4)\cup(2,3) \quad \text{...(ii)}$$

On combining Eqs. (i) and (ii), we get

$$x\in(-5,-4]\cup(2,3]$$

3. Fractional Part

$\{x\}$ denotes the fractional part of x, i.e. $0\le\{x\}<1$.

Thus, $\{2\cdot 7\}=0.7$, $\{5\}=0$, $\{-3.72\}=0.28$

If x is a real number, then $x=[x]+\{x\}$

i.e., $x=n+f$, where $n\in I$ and $0\le f<1$

Properties of Fractional Part of x

(i) $\{x\pm n\}=\{x\}, n\in I$ (ii) If $0\le x<1$, then $\{x\}=x$

Graph of $y=\{x\}$

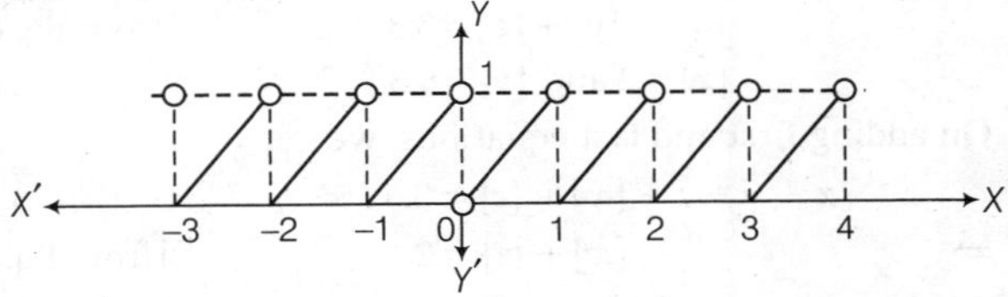

Remark

1. For proper fraction $0<\{x\}<1$.
2. Domain and range of $\{x\}$ are R and $[0, 1)$, respectively.
3. $\{-5.238\}=\{-5-0.238\}=\{-5-1+1-0.238\}$
$=\{-6+0.762\}=\{\bar{6}.762\}=0.762$

Example 67. If $\{x\}$ and $[x]$ represent fractional and integral part of x respectively, find the value of $[x]+\sum_{r=1}^{2000}\frac{\{x+r\}}{2000}$.

Sol. $$[x]+\sum_{r=1}^{2000}\frac{\{x+r\}}{2000}=[x]+\sum_{r=1}^{2000}\frac{\{x\}}{2000} \quad \text{[from property (i)]}$$

$$=[x]+\frac{\{x\}}{2000}\sum_{r=1}^{2000}1=[x]+\frac{\{x\}}{2000}\times 2000=[x]+\{x\}=x$$

Example 68. If $\{x\}$ and $[x]$ represent fractional and integral part of x respectively, then solve the equation $x-1=(x-[x])(x-\{x\})$.

Sol. $$\because x=[x]+\{x\}, 0\le\{x\}<1$$

Thus, given equation reduces to

$$[x]+\{x\}-1=\{x\}[x]$$

$$\Rightarrow \{x\}[x]-[x]-\{x\}+1=0$$

$$\Rightarrow ([x]-1)(\{x\}-1)=0$$

Now, $$\{x\}-1\neq 0 \quad [\because 0\le\{x\}<1]$$

$$\therefore [x]-1=0$$

$$\Rightarrow [x]=1$$

$$\therefore x\in[1,2)$$

Problem Solving Cycle

If a problem has $x, |x|, [x], (x), \{x\}$, then first solve $|x|$, then problem convert in $x, [x], (x), \{x\}$.

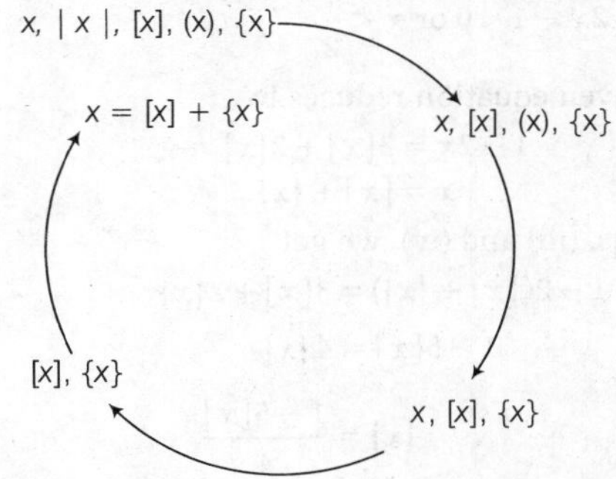

Secondly, solve $(x)=\begin{cases}[x], & x\in I\\ [x]+1, & x\notin I\end{cases}$

Then, problem convert in $x, [x], \{x\}$.

Now, put $x=[x]+\{x\}$

Then, problem convert in $[x]$ and $\{x\}$. ...(i)

Since, $0\le\{x\}<1$, then we get $[x]$

From Eq. (i), we get $\{x\}$

Hence, final solution is $x=[x]+\{x\}$.

Example 69. Let $\{x\}$ and $[x]$ denotes the fractional and integral parts of a real number x, respectively. Solve $4\{x\}=x+[x]$.

Sol. $\because \quad x=[x]+\{x\}$ ...(i)

Then, given equation reduces to

$$4\{x\}=[x]+\{x\}+[x]$$

$\Rightarrow \quad \{x\}=\frac{2}{3}[x]$ ...(ii)

$\because \quad 0\le\{x\}<1 \Rightarrow 0\le\frac{2}{3}[x]<1$ or $0\le[x]<\frac{3}{2}$

$\therefore \quad [x]=0,1$

From Eq. (ii), $\{x\}=0,\frac{2}{3}$

From Eq. (i), $x=0,1+\frac{2}{3}$ i.e., $x=0,\frac{5}{3}$

Example 70. Let $\{x\}$ and $[x]$ denotes the fractional and integral part of a real number (x), respectively. Solve $|2x-1|=3[x]+2\{x\}$.

Sol. ***Case* I** $2x-1\ge0$ or $x\ge\frac{1}{2}$

Then, given equation convert to

$$2x-1=3[x]+2\{x\} \quad ...(i)$$

$\because \quad x=[x]+\{x\}$ ...(ii)

From Eqs. (i) and (ii), we get

$$2([x]+\{x\})-1=3[x]+2\{x\}$$

$\therefore \quad [x]=-1$

$\therefore \quad -1\le x<0$

No solution $\left[\because x\ge\frac{1}{2}\right]$

***Case* II** $2x-1<0$ or $x<\frac{1}{2}$

Then, given equation reduces to

$$1-2x=3[x]+2\{x\} \quad ...(iii)$$

$\because \quad x=[x]+\{x\}$ ...(iv)

From Eqs. (iii) and (iv), we get

$$1-2([x]+\{x\})=3[x]+2\{x\}$$

$\Rightarrow \quad 1-5[x]=4\{x\}$

$\therefore \quad \{x\}=\frac{1-5[x]}{4}$ ...(v)

Now, $\quad 0\le\{x\}<1$

$\Rightarrow \quad 0\le\frac{1-5[x]}{4}<1$

$\Rightarrow \quad 0\le1-5[x]<4$

$\Rightarrow \quad 0\ge-1+5[x]>-4$

$\Rightarrow \quad 1\ge5[x]>-3$ or $-\frac{3}{5}<[x]\le\frac{1}{5}$

$\therefore \quad [x]=0$

From Eq. (v), $\{x\}=\frac{1}{4}$

$\therefore \quad x=0+\frac{1}{4}=\frac{1}{4}$

Example 71. Solve the equation

$$(x)^2=[x]^2+2x$$

where, $[x]$ and (x) are integers just less than or equal to x and just greater than or equal to x, respectively.

Sol. ***Case* I** If $x\in I$ then

$$x=[x]=(x)$$

The given equation reduces to

$$x^2=x^2+2x$$

$\Rightarrow \quad 2x=0$ or $x=0$ ...(i)

***Case* II** If $x\notin I$, then $(x)=[x]+1$

The given equation reduces to

$$([x]+1)^2=[x]^2+2x$$

$\Rightarrow \quad 1=2(x-[x])$ or $\{x\}=\frac{1}{2}$

$\therefore \quad x=[x]+\frac{1}{2}=n+\frac{1}{2}, n\in I$ ...(ii)

Hence, the solution of the original equation is $x=0, n+\frac{1}{2}$, $n\in I$.

Example 72. Solve the system of equations in x, y and z satisfying the following equations:

$$x+[y]+\{z\}=3\cdot1$$
$$\{x\}+y+[z]=4\cdot3$$
$$[x]+\{y\}+z=5\cdot4$$

where, $[\cdot]$ and $\{\cdot\}$ denotes the greatest integer and fractional parts, respectively.

Sol. $\because [x]+\{x\}=x,\ [y]+\{y\}=y$ and $[z]+\{z\}=z$,

On adding all the three equations, we get

$$2(x+y+z)=12.8$$

$\Rightarrow \quad x+y+z=6.4$ ...(i)

Now, adding first two equations, we get

$$x+y+z+[y]+\{x\}=7.4$$

$\Rightarrow \quad 6.4+[y]+\{x\}=7.4$ [from Eq. (i)]

$\Rightarrow \quad [y]+\{x\}=1$

$\therefore \quad [y]=1$ and $\{x\}=0$ ...(ii)

On adding last two equations, we get

$$x+y+z+\{y\}+[z]=9.7$$

$\{y\}+[z]=3.3$ [from Eq. (ii)]

$\therefore \quad [z]=3$ and $\{y\}=0.3$ ...(iii)

On adding first and last equations, we get

$$x+y+z+[x]+\{z\}=8.5$$

$\Rightarrow \quad [x]+\{z\}=2.1$ [from Eq. (i)]

$\therefore \quad [x]=2, \{z\}=0.1$ ...(iv)

From Eqs. (i), (ii) and (iii), we get

$$x=[x]+\{x\}=2+0=2$$
$$y=[y]+\{y\}=1+0.3=1.3$$

and $\quad z=[z]+\{z\}=3+0.1=3.1$

Roots of Equation with the Help of Graphs

Here, we will discuss some examples to find the roots of equations with the help of graphs.

Important Graphs

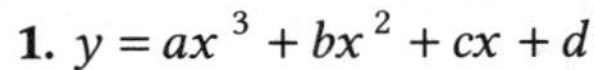

1. $y = ax^3 + bx^2 + cx + d$

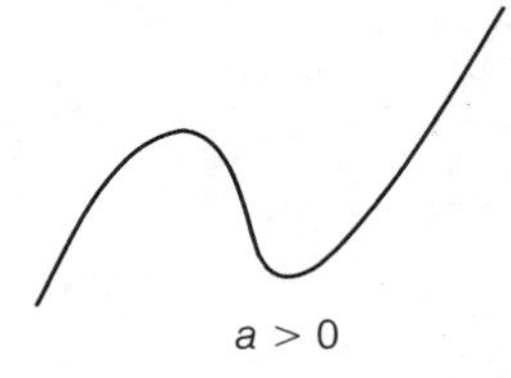

$a > 0$

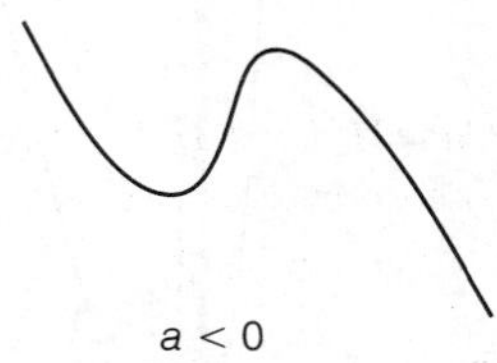

$a < 0$

2. $x = ay^3 + by^2 + cy + d$

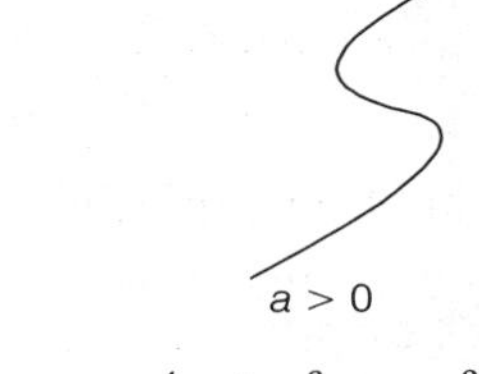

$a > 0$

$a < 0$

3. $y = ax^4 + bx^3 + cx^2 + dx + e$

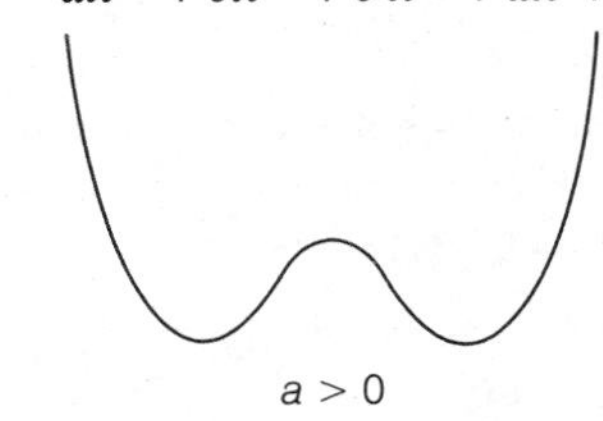

$a > 0$

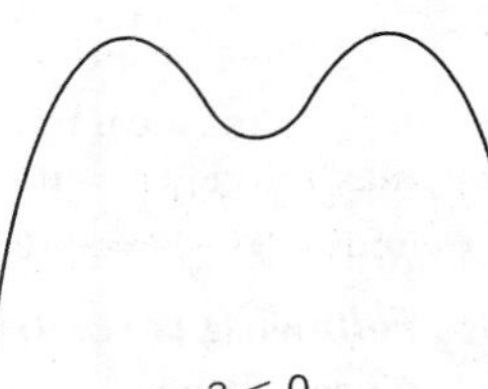

$a < 0$

| Example 73. Solve the equation $x^3 - [x] = 3$, where $[x]$ denotes the greatest integer less than or equal to x.

Sol. We have, $x^3 - [x] = 3$

$\Rightarrow \quad x^3 - 3 = [x]$

Let $\quad f(x) = x^3 - 3$ and $g(x) = [x]$.

It is clear from the graphs, the point of intersection of two curves $y = f(x)$ and $y = g(x)$ lies between $(1, 0)$ and $(2, 0)$.

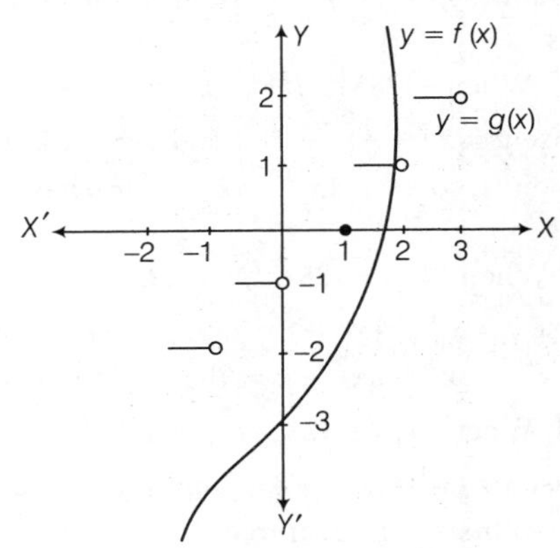

$\therefore \quad 1 < x < 2$

We have, $f(x) = x^3 - 3$ and $g(x) = 1$

or $\quad x^3 - 3 = 1 \Rightarrow x^3 = 4$

$\therefore \quad x = (4)^{1/3}$

Hence, $x = 4^{1/3}$ is the solution of the equation $x^3 - [x] = 3$.

Aliter

$\because \quad x = [x] + f, 0 \le f < 1,$

Then, given equation reduces to

$$x^3 - (x - f) = 3 \Rightarrow x^3 - x = 3 - f$$

Hence, it follows that

$$2 < x^3 - x \le 3$$

$$\Rightarrow \quad 2 < x(x+1)(x-1) \le 3$$

Further for $x \ge 2$, we have $x(x+1)(x-1) \ge 6 > 3$

For $x < -1$, we have $x(x+1)(x-1) < 0 < 2$

For $x = -1$, we have $x(x+1)(x-1) = 0 < 2$

For $-1 < x \le 0$, we have $x(x+1)(x-1) \le -x < 1$

and for $0 < x \le 1$, we have $x(x+1)(x-1) < x < x^3 \le 1$

Therefore, x must be $1 < x < 2$

$\therefore \quad [x] = 1$

Now, the original equation can be written as

$$x^3 - 1 = 3 \Rightarrow x^3 = 4$$

Hence, $x = 4^{1/3}$ is the solution of the given equation.

| Example 74. Solve the equation $x^3 - 3x - a = 0$ for different values of a.

Sol. We have, $x^3 - 3x - a = 0 \Rightarrow x^3 - 3x = a$

Let $f(x) = x^3 - 3x$ and $g(x) = a$

$\because \quad f'(x) = 0$

$\Rightarrow \quad 3x^2 - 3 = 0$

$\Rightarrow \quad x = -1, 1$

$$f''(x) = 6x$$

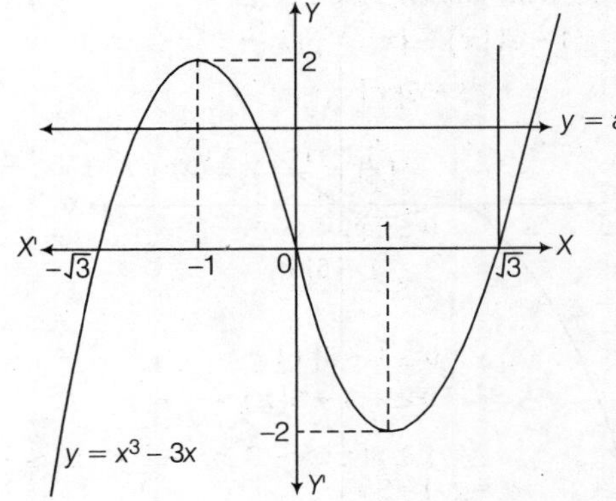

$\therefore \quad f''(-1) = -6 < 0$ and $f''(1) = 6 > 0$

$\therefore f(x)$ local maximum at $x = (-1)$ and local minimum at $x = 1$ and $f(-1) = 2$ and $f(1) = -2$ and $y = g(x) = a$ is a straight line parallel to X-axis.

Following cases arise

***Case* I** When $a > 2$,

In this case $y = f(x)$ and $y = g(x)$ intersects at only one point, so $x^3 - 3x - a = 0$ has only one real root.

***Case* II** When $a = 2$,

In this case $y = f(x)$ and $y = g(x)$ intersects at two points, so $x^3 - 3x - a = 0$ has three real roots, two are equal and one different.

***Case* III** When $-2 < a < 2$,

In this case $y = f(x)$ and $y = g(x)$ intersects at three points, so $x^3 - 3x - a = 0$ has three distinct real roots.

***Case* IV** When $a = -2$,

In this case $y = f(x)$ and $y = g(x)$ touch at one point and intersect at other point, so $x^3 - 3x - a = 0$ has three real roots, two are equal and one different.

***Case* V** When $a < -2$,

In this case $y = f(x)$ and $y = g(x)$ intersects at only one point, so $x^3 - 3x - a = 0$ has only one real root.

| Example 75. Show that the equation $x^3 + 2x^2 + x + 5 = 0$ has only one real root, such that $[\alpha] = -3$, where $[x]$ denotes the integral point of x.

Sol. We have, $x^3 + 2x^2 + x + 5 = 0$

$\Rightarrow \quad x^3 + 2x^2 + x = -5$

Let $\quad f(x) = x^3 + 2x^2 + x$ and $g(x) = -5$

$\because \quad f'(x) = 0 \Rightarrow 3x^2 + 4x + 1 = 0$

$\Rightarrow \quad x = -1, -\frac{1}{3}$ and $f''(x) = 6x + 4$

$\therefore \quad f''(-1) = -2 < 0$ and $f''\left(-\frac{1}{3}\right) = -2 + 4 = 2 > 0$

$\therefore f(x)$ local maximum at $x = -1$ and local minimum at $x = -\frac{1}{3}$

and $\quad f(-1) = 0, f\left(-\frac{1}{3}\right) = -\frac{4}{27}$

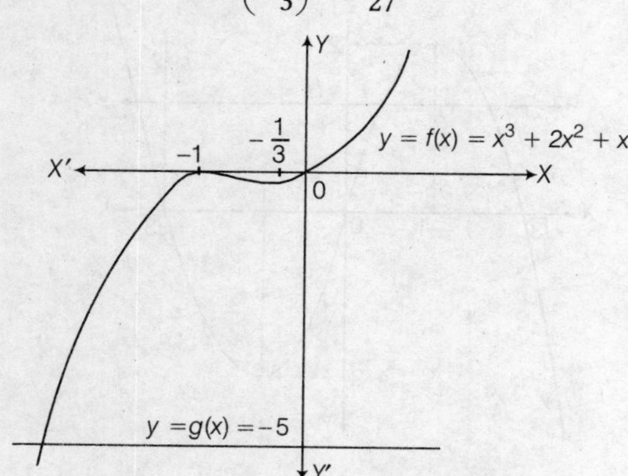

and $\quad f(-2) = -2$ and $f(-3) = -12$

Therefore, x must lie between (-3) and (-2).

i.e. $\quad -3 < \alpha < -2 \Rightarrow [\alpha] = -3$

| Example 76. Find all values of the parameter k for which all the roots of the equation $x^4 + 4x^3 - 8x^2 + k = 0$ are real.

Sol. We have, $x^4 + 4x^3 - 8x^2 + k = 0$

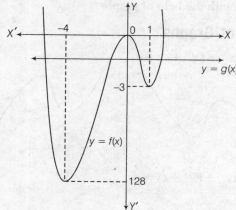

$\Rightarrow \quad x^4 + 4x^3 - 8x^2 = -k$

Let $\quad f(x) = x^4 + 4x^3 - 8x^2$ and $g(x) = -k$

$\because \quad f'(x) = 0$

$\Rightarrow \quad 4x^3 + 12x^2 - 16x = 0 \Rightarrow x = -4, 0, 1$

and $\quad f''(x) = 12x^2 + 24x - 16$

$\therefore f''(-4) = 80, \ f''(0) = -16, \ f''(1) = 20$

$\therefore f(x)$ has local minimum at $x = -4$ and $x = 1$ and local maximum at $x = 0$

and $\quad f(-4) = -128, f(0) = 0, f(1) = -3.$

Following cases arise

***Case* I** When $-k > 0$ i.e., $k < 0$

In this case $y = x^4 + 4x^3 - 8x^2$ and $y = (-k)$ intersect at two points, so $x^4 + 4x^3 - 8x^2 + k = 0$ has two real roots.

***Case* II** When $-k = 0$ and $-k = -3$, i.e. $k = 0, 3$

In this case $y = x^4 + 4x^3 - 8x^2$ and $y = -k$ intersect at four points, so $x^4 + 4x^3 - 8x^2 + k = 0$ has two distinct real roots and two equal roots.

***Case* III** When $-3 < -k < 0$, i.e. $0 < k < 3$

In this case $y = x^4 + 4x^3 - 8x^2$ and $y = -k$ intersect at four distinct points, so $x^4 + 4x^3 - 8x^2 + k = 0$ has four distinct real roots.

***Case* IV** When $-128 < -k < -3$, i.e. $3 < k < 128$

In this case $y = x^4 + 4x^3 - 8x^2$ and $y = -k$ intersect at two distinct points, so $x^4 + 4x^3 - 8x^2 + k = 0$ has two distinct real roots.

***Case* V** When $-k = -128$ i.e., $k = 128$

In this case $y = x^4 + 4x^3 - 8x^2$ and $y = -k$ touch at one point, so $x^4 + 4x^3 - 8x^2 + k = 0$ has two real and equal roots.

***Case* VI** When $-k < -128$, i.e. $k > 128$

In this case $y = x^4 + 4x^3 - 8x^2$ and $y = -k$ do not intersect, so there is no real root.

Example 77. Let $-1 \le p \le 1$, show that the equation $4x^3 - 3x - p = 0$ has a unique root in the interval $\left[\frac{1}{2}, 1\right]$ and identify it.

Sol. We have, $4x^3 - 3x - p = 0$

$$\Rightarrow \quad 4x^3 - 3x = p$$

Let $f(x) = 4x^3 - 3x$ and $g(x) = p$

$$\therefore \quad f'(x) = 0$$

$$\Rightarrow \quad 12x^2 - 3 = 0$$

$$\Rightarrow \quad x = -\frac{1}{2}, -\frac{1}{2} \text{ and } f''(x) = 24x$$

$$\therefore \quad f''\left(-\frac{1}{2}\right) = -12 < 0 \text{ and } f''\left(\frac{1}{2}\right) = 12 > 0$$

$\therefore f(x)$ has local maximum at $\left(x = -\frac{1}{2}\right)$ and local minimum at $\left(x = \frac{1}{2}\right)$.

Also, $f\left(-\frac{1}{2}\right) = -\frac{4}{8} + \frac{3}{2} = 1$ and $f\left(\frac{1}{2}\right) = \frac{4}{8} - \frac{3}{2} = -1$

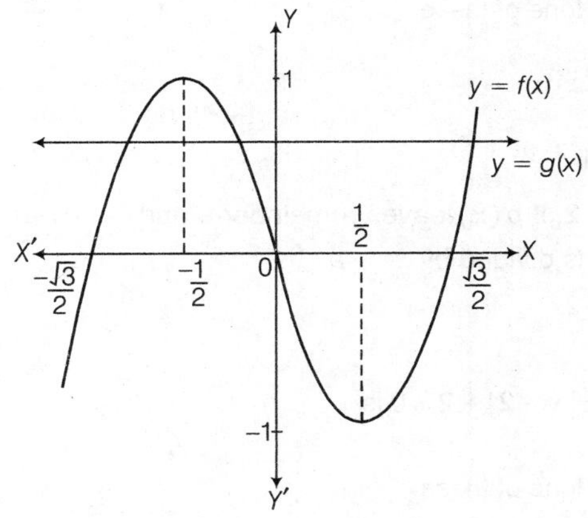

We observe that, the line $y = g(x) = p$, where $-1 \le p \le 1$ intersect the curve $y = f(x)$ exactly at point $\alpha \in \left[\frac{1}{2}, 1\right]$.

Hence, $4x^3 - 3x - p = 0$ has exactly one root in the interval $\left[\frac{1}{2}, 1\right]$.

Now, we have to find the value of root α.

Let $\alpha = \cos\theta$, then $4\cos^3\theta - 3\cos\theta - p = 0$

$$\Rightarrow \quad \cos 3\theta = p \Rightarrow 3\theta = \cos^{-1}(p) \text{ or } \theta = \frac{1}{3}\cos^{-1}(p)$$

$$\therefore \quad \alpha = \cos\theta = \cos\left\{\frac{1}{3}\cos^{-1}(p)\right\}$$

Aliter

Let $\quad \phi(x) = 4x^3 - 3x - p$

$$\therefore \quad \phi'(x) = 12x^2 - 3 = 12\left(x + \frac{1}{2}\right)\left(x - \frac{1}{2}\right)$$

Clearly, $\phi'(x) > 0$ for $x \in \left[\frac{1}{2}, 1\right]$.

Hence, $\phi(x)$ can have atmost one root in $\left[\frac{1}{2}, 1\right]$.

Also, $\phi\left(\frac{1}{2}\right) = -1 - p$ and $\phi(1) = 1 - p$

$$\therefore \quad \phi\left(\frac{1}{2}\right)\phi(1) = -(1 - p^2) = (p^2 - 1) \le 0 \qquad [\because -1 \le p \le 1]$$

Since, $\phi(x)$ being a polynomial, continuous on $\left[\frac{1}{2}, 1\right]$ and $\phi\left(\frac{1}{2}\right)\phi(1) \le 0$. Therefore, by intermediate value theorem $\phi(x)$ has atleast one root in $\left[\frac{1}{2}, 1\right]$.

Hence, $\phi(x)$ has exactly one root in $\left[\frac{1}{2}, 1\right]$.

Exercise for Session 4

1. If α, β, γ are the roots of $x^3 - x^2 - 1 = 0$, the value of $\sum\left(\frac{1+\alpha}{1-\alpha}\right)$, is equal to

(a) -7
(b) -6
(c) -5
(d) -4

2. If r, s, t are the roots of the equation $8x^3 + 1001x + 2008 = 0$. The value of $(r+s)^3 + (s+t)^3 + (t+r)^3$ is

(a) 751
(b) 752
(c) 753
(d) 754

3. If $\alpha, \beta, \gamma, \delta$ are the roots of equation $x^4 + 4x^3 - 6x^2 + 7x - 9 = 0$, the value of $\prod(1+\alpha^2)$ is

(a) 9
(b) 11
(c) 13
(d) 15

4. If a, b, c, d are four consecutive terms of an increasing AP, the roots of the equation $(x-a)(x-c) + 2(x-b)(x-d) = 0$ are

(a) non-real complex
(b) real and equal
(c) integers
(d) real and distinct

5. If $x^2 + px + 1$ is a factor of the expression $ax^3 + bx + c$ then

(a) $a^2 - c^2 = ab$
(b) $a^2 + c^2 = -ab$
(c) $a^2 - c^2 = -ab$
(d) None of these

6. The number of real roots of the equation $x^2 - 3|x| + 2 = 0$ is

(a) 1
(b) 2
(c) 3
(d) 4

7. Let $a \neq 0$ and $p(x)$ be a polynomial of degree greater than 2, if $p(x)$ leaves remainder a and $(-a)$ when divided respectively by $x + a$ and $x - a$, the remainder when $p(x)$ is divided by $x^2 - a^2$, is

(a) $2x$
(b) $-2x$
(c) x
(d) $-x$

8. The product of all the solutions of the equation $(x-2)^2 - 3|x-2| + 2 = 0$ is

(a) 2
(b) -4
(c) 0
(d) None of these

9. If $0 < x < 1000$ and $\left[\frac{x}{2}\right] + \left[\frac{x}{3}\right] + \left[\frac{x}{5}\right] = \frac{31}{30}x$, where $[x]$ is the greatest integer less than or equal to x, the number of possible values of x is

(a) 32
(b) 33
(c) 34
(d) None of these

10. If $[x]$ is the greatest integer less than or equal to x and (x) be the least integer greater than or equal to x and $[x]^2 + (x)^2 > 25$ then x belongs to

(a) $[3, 4]$
(b) $(-\infty, -4]$
(c) $[4, \infty)$
(d) $(-\infty, -4] \cup [4, \infty)$

Session 5

Irrational Equations, Irrational Inequations, Exponential Equations, Exponential Inequations, Logarithmic Equations, Logarithmic Inequations

Irrational Equations

Here, we consider equations of the type which contain the unknown under the radical sign and the value under the radical sign is known as radicand.

- If roots are all even (i.e. $\sqrt{x}$, $\sqrt[4]{x}$, $\sqrt[6]{x}$,..., etc) of an equation are arithmetic. In other words, if the radicand is negative (i.e. $x<0$), then the root is imaginary, if the radicand is zero, then the root is also zero and if the radicand is positive, then the value of the root is also positive.
- If roots are all odd (i.e. $\sqrt[3]{x}, \sqrt[5]{x}, \sqrt[7]{x}$,... etc) of an equation, then it is defined for all real values of the radicand. If the radicand is negative, then the root is negative, if the radicand is zero, then the root is zero and if the radicand is positive, then the root is positive.

Some Standard Formulae to Solve Irrational Equations

If f and g be functions of $x, k \in N$. Then,

1. $\sqrt[2k]{f}\,\sqrt[2k]{g} = \sqrt[2k]{fg}, f \geq 0, g \geq 0$

2. $\sqrt[2k]{f} \,/\, \sqrt[2k]{g} = \sqrt[2k]{(f/g)}, f \geq 0, g > 0$

3. $|f|\sqrt[2k]{g} = \sqrt[2k]{(f^{2k} g)}, g \geq 0$

4. $\sqrt[2k]{(f/g)} = \sqrt[2k]{|f|} \,/\, \sqrt[2k]{|g|}, fg \geq 0, g \neq 0$

5. $\sqrt[2k]{fg} = \sqrt[2k]{|f|}\,\sqrt[2k]{g}, fg \geq 0$

| Example 78. Prove that the following equations has no solutions.

(i) $\sqrt{(2x+7)} + \sqrt{(x+4)} = 0$ (ii) $\sqrt{(x-4)} = -5$

(iii) $\sqrt{(6-x)} - \sqrt{(x-8)} = 2$ (iv) $\sqrt{-2-x} = \sqrt[5]{(x-7)}$

(v) $\sqrt{x} + \sqrt{(x+16)} = 3$ (vi) $7\sqrt{x} + 8\sqrt{-x} + \dfrac{15}{x^3} = 98$

(vii) $\sqrt{(x-3)} - \sqrt{x+9} = \sqrt{(x-1)}$

Sol. (i) We have, $\sqrt{(2x+7)} + \sqrt{(x+4)} = 0$

This equation is defined for $2x+7 \geq 0$

and $x+4 \geq 0 \Rightarrow \begin{cases} x \geq -\dfrac{7}{2} \\ x \geq -4 \end{cases}$

$\therefore \quad x \geq -\dfrac{7}{2}$

For $x \geq -\dfrac{7}{2}$, the left hand side of the original equation is positive, but right hand side is zero. Therefore, the equation has no roots.

(ii) We have, $\sqrt{(x-4)} = -5$

The equation is defined for $x-4 \geq 0$

$\therefore \quad x \geq 4$

For $x \geq 4$, the left hand side of the original equation is positive, but right hand side is negative.

Therefore, the equation has no roots.

(iii) We have, $\sqrt{(6-x)} - \sqrt{x-8} = 2$

The equation is defined for

$6-x \geq 0$ and $x-8 \geq 0$

$\therefore \quad \begin{cases} x \leq 6 \\ x \geq 8 \end{cases}$

Consequently, there is no x for which both expressions would have sense. Therefore, the equation has no roots.

(iv) We have, $\sqrt{(-2-x)} = \sqrt[5]{(x-7)}$

This equation is defined for

$-2-x \geq 0 \quad \Rightarrow \quad x \leq -2$

For $x \leq -2$ the left hand side is positive, but right hand side is negative.

Therefore, the equation has no roots.

(v) We have, $\sqrt{x} + \sqrt{(x+16)} = 3$

The equation is defined for

$x \geq 0$ and $x+16 \geq 0 \Rightarrow \begin{cases} x \geq 0 \\ x \geq -16 \end{cases}$

Hence, $\quad x \geq 0$

For $x \geq 0$ the left hand side ≥ 4, but right hand side is 3. Therefore, the equation has no roots.

(vi) We have, $7\sqrt{x} + 8\sqrt{-x} + \dfrac{15}{x^3} = 98$

For $x < 0$, the expression $7\sqrt{x}$ is meaningless,
For $x > 0$, the expression $8\sqrt{-x}$ is meaningless

and for $x = 0$, the expression $\frac{15}{x^3}$ is meaningless.

Consequently, the left hand side of the original equation is meaningless for any $x \in R$. Therefore, the equation has no roots.

(vii) We have, $\sqrt{(x-3)} - \sqrt{(x+9)} = \sqrt{x-1}$

This equation is defined for

$$\begin{cases} x-3 \geq 0 \\ x+9 \geq 0 \\ x-1 \geq 0 \end{cases} \Rightarrow \begin{cases} x \geq 3 \\ x \geq -9 \\ x \geq 1 \end{cases}$$

Hence, $x \geq 3$

For $x \geq 3$, $\sqrt{x-3} < \sqrt{x+9}$ i.e. $\sqrt{(x-3)} - \sqrt{(x+9)} < 0$

Hence, for $x \geq 3$, the left hand side of the original equation is negative and right hand side is positive. Therefore, the equation has no roots.

Some Standard Forms to Solve Irrational Equations

***Form* 1 An equation of the form $f^{2n}(x) = g^{2n}(x), n \in N$ is equivalent to $f(x) = g(x)$.**

Then, find the roots of this equation. If root of this equation satisfies the original equation, then its root of the original equation, otherwise, we say that this root is its **extraneous root.**

Remark

Squaring an Equation May Give Extraneous Roots

Squaring should be avoided as for as possible. If squaring is necessary, then the roots found after squaring must be checked whether they satisfy the original equation or not. If some values of x which do not satisfy the original equation. These values of x are called extraneous roots and are rejected.

| Example 79. Solve the equation $\sqrt{x} = x - 2$.

Sol. We have, $\sqrt{x} = x - 2$

On squaring both sides, we obtain

$$x = (x-2)^2$$

$$\Rightarrow \quad x^2 - 5x + 4 = 0 \Rightarrow (x-1)(x-4) = 0$$

$$\therefore \quad x_1 = 1 \text{ and } x_2 = 4$$

Hence, $x_1 = 4$ satisfies the original equation, but $x_2 = 1$ does not satisfy the original equation.

$\therefore$ $x_2 = 1$ is the extraneous root.

| Example 80. Solve the equation

$$3\sqrt{(x+3)} - \sqrt{(x-2)} = 7.$$

Sol. We have, $3\sqrt{(x+3)} - \sqrt{x-2} = 7$

$$\Rightarrow \quad 3\sqrt{(x+3)} = 7 + \sqrt{(x-2)}$$

On squaring both sides of the equation, we obtain

$$9x + 27 = 49 + x - 2 + 14\sqrt{x-2}$$

$$\Rightarrow \quad 8x \;\; 20 = 14\sqrt{(x-2)}$$

$$(4x - 10) = 7\sqrt{x-2}$$

Again, squaring both sides, we obtain

$$16x^2 + 100 - 80x = 49x - 98$$

$$\Rightarrow \quad 16x^2 - 129x + 198 = 0$$

$$\Rightarrow \quad (x-6)\left(x - \frac{33}{16}\right) = 0$$

$$x_1 = 6 \text{ and } x_2 = \frac{33}{16}$$

Hence, $x_1 = 6$ satisfies the original equation, but $x_2 = \frac{33}{16}$ does not satisfy the original equation.

$\therefore$ $x_2 = \frac{33}{16}$ is the extraneous root.

***Form* 2 An equation in the form $\sqrt[2n]{f(x)} = g(x), n \in N$ is equivalent to the system $\begin{cases} g(x) \geq 0 \\ f(x) = g^{2n}(x) \end{cases}$**

| Example 81. Solve the equation

$$\sqrt{(6 - 4x - x^2)} = x + 4.$$

Sol. We have, $\sqrt{(6 - 4x - x^2)} = x + 4$

This equation is equivalent to the system

$$\begin{cases} x + 4 \geq 0 \\ 6 - 4x - x^2 = (x+4)^2 \end{cases}$$

$$\Rightarrow \quad \begin{cases} x \geq -4 \\ x^2 + 6x + 5 = 0 \end{cases}$$

On solving the equation $x^2 + 6x + 5 = 0$

We find that, $x_1 = (-1)$ and $x_2 = (-5)$ only $x_1 = (-1)$ satisfies the condition $x \geq -4$.

Consequently, the number -1 is the only solution of the given equation.

***Form* 3 An equation in the form**

$$\sqrt[3]{f(x)} + \sqrt[3]{g(x)} = h(x) \quad \text{...(i)}$$

where $f(x)$, $g(x)$ are the functions of x, but $h(x)$ is a function of x or constant, can be solved as follows cubing both sides of the equation, we obtain

$$f(x) + g(x) + 3\sqrt[3]{f(x)\,g(x)}\,(\sqrt[3]{f(x)} + \sqrt[3]{g(x)}) = h^3(x)$$

$$\Rightarrow \quad f(x) + g(x) + 3\sqrt[3]{f(x)\,g(x)}\,(h(x)) = h^3(x)$$

[from Eq. (i)]

We find its roots and then substituting, then into the original equation, we choose those which are the roots of the original equation.

| Example 82. Solve the equation

$$\sqrt[3]{(2x-1)}+\sqrt[3]{(x-1)}=1.$$

Sol. We have, $\sqrt[3]{(2x-1)}+\sqrt[3]{(x-1)}=1$ ...(i)

Cubing both sides of Eq. (i), we obtain

$$2x-1+x-1+3\cdot\sqrt[3]{(2x-1)(x-1)}$$
$$(\sqrt[3]{(2x-1)}+\sqrt[3]{(x-1)})=1$$

$\Rightarrow$ $3x-2+3\cdot\sqrt[3]{(2x^2-3x+1)}\,(1)=1$ [from Eq. (i)]

$\Rightarrow$ $3\cdot\sqrt[3]{(2x^2-3x+1)}=3-3x$

$\Rightarrow$ $\sqrt[3]{(2x^2-3x+1)}=(1-x)$

Again cubing both sides, we obtain

$$2x^2-3x+1=(1-x)^3$$

$\Rightarrow$ $(2x-1)(x-1)=(1-x)^3$

$\Rightarrow$ $(2x-1)(x-1)=-(x-1)^3$

$\Rightarrow$ $(x-1)\{2x-1+(x-1)^2\}=0$

$\Rightarrow$ $(x-1)(x^2)=0$

$\therefore$ $x_1=0$ and $x_2=1$

$\because x_1=0$ is not satisfies the Eq. (i), then $x_1=0$ is an extraneous root of the Eq. (i), thus $x_2=1$ is the only root of the original equation.

***Form* 4 An equation of the form**

$$\sqrt[n]{a-f(x)}+\sqrt[n]{b+f(x)}=g(x).$$

Let $u=\sqrt[n]{a-f(x)},\ v=\sqrt[n]{b+f(x)}$

Then, the given equation reduces to the solution of the system of algebraic equations.

$$\begin{cases} u+v=g(x)\\ u^n+v^n=a+b\end{cases}$$

| Example 83. Solve the equation

$$\sqrt{(2x^2+5x-2)}-\sqrt{2x^2+5x-9}=1.$$

Sol. Let $u=\sqrt{(2x^2+5x-2)}$

and $v=\sqrt{(2x^2+5x-9)}$

$\therefore$ $u^2=2x^2+5x-2$

and $v^2=2x^2+5x-9$

Then, the given equation reduces to the solution of the system of algebraic equations.

$$u-v=1$$
$$u^2-v^2=7$$

$\Rightarrow$ $(u+v)(u-v)=7$

$\Rightarrow$ $u+v=7$ $[\because u-v=1]$

We get, $u=4, v=3$

$\therefore$ $\sqrt{2x^2+5x-2}=4$

$\therefore$ $2x^2+5x-18=0$

$\therefore$ $x_1=2$ and $x_2=-9/2$

Both roots satisfies the original equation.

Hence, $x_1=2$ and $x_2=-9/2$ are the roots of the original equation.

Irrational Inequations

We consider, here inequations which contain the unknown under the radical sign.

Some Standard Forms to Solve Irrational Inequations

***Form* 1** An inequation of the form

$$\sqrt[2n]{f(x)}<\sqrt[2n]{g(x)}, n\in N$$

is equivalent to the system $\begin{cases} f(x)\geq 0\\ g(x)>f(x)\end{cases}$

and inequation of the form $\sqrt[2n+1]{f(x)}<\sqrt[2n+1]{g(x)}, n\in N$

is equivalent to the inequation $f(x)<g(x)$.

| Example 84. Solve the inequation

$$\sqrt[5]{\left[\frac{3}{x+1}+\frac{7}{x+2}\right]}<\sqrt[5]{\frac{6}{x-1}}.$$

Sol. The given inequation is equivalent to

$$\frac{3}{x+1}+\frac{7}{x+2}<\frac{6}{x-1}$$

$\Rightarrow$ $\dfrac{4x^2-15x-25}{(x+1)(x+2)(x-1)}<0$

$\Rightarrow$ $\dfrac{(x+5/4)(x-5)}{(x+1)(x+2)(x-1)}<0$

From Wavy Curve Method :

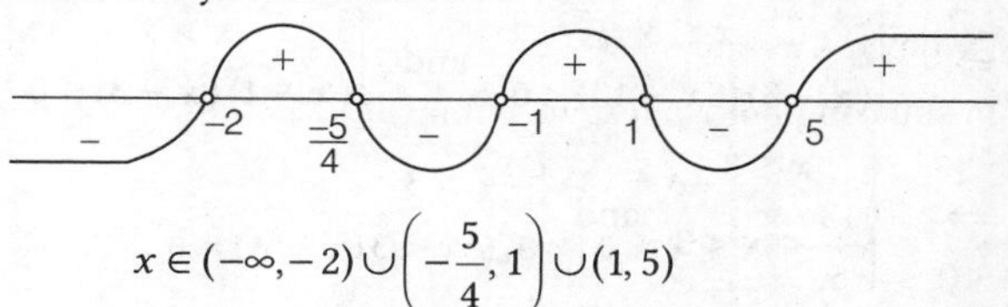

$$x\in(-\infty,-2)\cup\left(-\frac{5}{4},1\right)\cup(1,5)$$

***Form* 2 An inequation of the form**

$$\sqrt[2n]{f(x)}<g(x), n\in N.$$

is equivalent to the system $\begin{cases} f(x)\geq 0\\ g(x)>0\\ f(x)<g^{2n}(x),\end{cases}$

and inequation of the form $\sqrt[2n+1]{f(x)} < g(x), n \in N$ is equivalent to the inequation $f(x) < g^{2n+1}(x)$.

| Example 85. Solve the inequation $\sqrt{(x+14)} < (x+2)$.

Sol. We have, $\sqrt{(x+14)} < (x+2)$

This inequation is equivalent to the system

$$\begin{cases} x+14 \ge 0 \\ x+2>0 \\ x+14<(x+2)^2 \end{cases} \Rightarrow \begin{cases} x \ge -14 \\ x>-2 \\ x^2+3x-10>0 \end{cases}$$

$$\Rightarrow \begin{cases} x \ge -14 \\ x>-2 \\ (x+5)(x-2)>0 \end{cases} \Rightarrow \begin{cases} x \ge -14 \\ x>-2 \\ x<-5 \text{ and } x>2 \end{cases}$$

On combining all three inequation of the system, we get

$$x>2, \text{ i.e. } x \in (2, \infty)$$

***Form* 3** An inequation of the form

$$\sqrt[2n]{f(x)} > g(x), n \in N$$

is equivalent to the collection of two systems of inequations

i.e. $$\begin{cases} g(x) \ge 0 \\ f(x) > g^{2n}(x) \end{cases} \text{ and } \begin{cases} g(x)<0 \\ f(x) \ge 0 \end{cases}$$

and inequation of the form $\sqrt[2n+1]{f(x)} > g(x), n \in N$ is equivalent to the inequation $f(x) > g^{2n+1}(x)$.

| Example 86. Solve the inequation $\sqrt{(-x^2+4x-3)} > 6-2x$.

Sol. We have, $\sqrt{(-x^2+4x-3)} > 6-2x$

This inequation is equivalent to the collection of two systems, of inequations

i.e. $$\begin{cases} 6-2x \ge 0 \\ -x^2+4x-3>(6-2x)^2 \end{cases} \text{ and } \begin{cases} 6-2x<0 \\ -x^2+4x-3 \ge 0 \end{cases}$$

$$\Rightarrow \begin{cases} x \le 3 \\ (x-3)(5x-13)<0 \end{cases} \text{ and } \begin{cases} x>3 \\ (x-1)(x-3) \le 0 \end{cases}$$

$$\Rightarrow \begin{cases} x \le 3 \\ \frac{13}{5}<x<3 \end{cases} \text{ and } \begin{cases} x>3 \\ 1 \le x<3 \end{cases}$$

The second system has no solution and the first system has solution in the interval $\left(\frac{13}{5}<x<3\right)$.

Hence, $x \in \left(\frac{13}{5}, 3\right)$ is the set of solution of the original inequation.

Exponential Equations

If we have an equation of the form $a^x = b (a>0)$, then

(i) $x \in \phi$, if $b \le 0$

(ii) $x = \log_a b$, if $b>0, a \ne 1$

(iii) $x \in \phi$, if $a=1, b \ne 1$

(iv) $x \in R$, if $a=1, b=1$ (since, $1^x = 1 \Rightarrow 1=1, x \in R$)

| Example 87. Solve the equation $\sqrt{(6-x)}\,(3^{x^2-7.2x+3.9} - 9\sqrt{3}) = 0$.

Sol. We have,

$$\sqrt{(6-x)}\,(3^{x^2-7.2x+3.9} - 9\sqrt{3}) = 0$$

This equation is defined for

$$6-x \ge 0 \text{ i.e., } x \le 6 \quad \text{...(i)}$$

This equation is equivalent to the collection of equations

$$\sqrt{6-x} = 0 \text{ and } 3^{x^2-7.2x+3.9} - 9\sqrt{3} = 0$$

$$\therefore \quad x_1 = 6 \text{ and } 3^{x^2-7.2x+3.9} = 3^{2.5}$$

then $$x^2-7.2x+3.9 = 2.5$$

$$x^2-7.2x+1.4 = 0$$

We find that, $$x_2 = \frac{1}{5} \text{ and } x_3 = 7$$

Hence, solution of the original equation are [which satisfies Eq. (i)]

$$x_1 = 6, x_2 = \frac{1}{5}.$$

Some Standard Forms to Solve Exponential Equations

***Form* 1 An equation in the form $a^{f(x)} = 1, a>0, a \ne 1$** is equivalent to the equation $f(x) = 0$

| Example 88. Solve the equation $5^{x^2+3x+2} = 1$.

Sol. This equation is equivalent to

$$x^2+3x+2=0$$

$$\Rightarrow \quad (x+1)(x+2)=0$$

$\therefore x_1 = -1, x_2 = -2$ consequently, this equation has two roots $x_1 = -1$ and $x_2 = -2$.

***Form* 2** An equation in the form

$$f(a^x) = 0$$

is equivalent to the equation $f(t) = 0$, where $t = a^x$.

If $t_1, t_2, t_3, \ldots, t_k$ are the roots of $f(t) = 0$, then

$$a^x = t_1, a^x = t_2, a^x = t_3, \ldots, a^x = t_k$$

Example 89. Solve the equation $5^{2x} - 24 \cdot 5^x - 25 = 0$.

Sol. Let $5^x = t$, then the given equation can reduce in the form

$$t^2 - 24t - 25 = 0$$

$$\Rightarrow \quad (t-25)(t+1) = 0 \Rightarrow t \neq -1,$$

$$\therefore \quad t = 25,$$

then $\quad 5^x = 25 = 5^2$, then $x = 2$

Hence, $x_1 = 2$ is only one root of the original equation.

***Form* 3** An equation of the form

$$\alpha a^{f(x)} + \beta b^{f(x)} + \gamma c^{f(x)} = 0,$$

where $\alpha, \beta, \gamma \in R$ and $\alpha, \beta, \gamma \neq 0$ and the bases satisfy the condition $b^2 = ac$ is equivalent to the equation

$$\alpha t^2 + \beta t + \gamma = 0, \text{ where } t = (a/b)^{f(x)}$$

If roots of this equation are t_1 and t_2, then

$$(a/b)^{f(x)} = t_1 \text{ and } (a/b)^{f(x)} = t_2$$

Example 90. Solve the equation $64 \cdot 9^x - 84 \cdot 12^x + 27 \cdot 16^x = 0$.

Sol. Here, $9 \times 16 = (12)^2$.

Then, we divide its both sides by 12^x and obtain

$$\Rightarrow \quad 64 \cdot \left(\frac{3}{4}\right)^x - 84 + 27 \cdot \left(\frac{4}{3}\right)^x = 0 \quad \text{...(i)}$$

Let $\left(\frac{3}{4}\right)^x = t$, then Eq. (i) reduce in the form

$$64t^2 - 84t + 27 = 0$$

$$\therefore \quad t_1 = \frac{3}{4} \text{ and } t_2 = \frac{9}{16}$$

then, $\left(\frac{3}{4}\right)^x = \left(\frac{3}{4}\right)^1$ and $\left(\frac{3}{4}\right)^x = \left(\frac{3}{4}\right)^2$

$$\therefore \quad x_1 = 1 \text{ and } x_2 = 2$$

Hence, roots of the original equation are $x_1 = 1$ and $x_2 = 2$.

***Form* 4 An equation in the form**

$$\alpha \cdot a^{f(x)} + \beta \cdot b^{f(x)} + c = 0,$$

where $\alpha, \beta, c \in R$ and $\alpha, \beta, c \neq 0$ and $ab = 1$ (a and b are inverse positive numbers) is equivalent to the equation

$$\alpha t^2 + ct + \beta = 0, \text{ where } t = a^{f(x)}.$$

If roots of this equation are t_1 and t_2, then $a^{f(x)} = t_1$ and $a^{f(x)} = t_2$.

Example 91. Solve the equation $15 \cdot 2^{x+1} + 15 \cdot 2^{2-x} = 135$.

Sol. This equation rewrite in the form

$$30.2^x + \frac{60}{2^x} = 135$$

Let $\quad t = 2^x$

Then, $\quad 30t^2 - 135t + 60 = 0$

$$\Rightarrow \quad 6t^2 - 27t + 12 = 0$$

$$\Rightarrow \quad 6t^2 - 24t - 3t + 12 = 0$$

$$\Rightarrow \quad (t-4)(6t-3) = 0$$

Then, $\quad t_1 = 4$ and $t_2 = \frac{1}{2}$

Thus, given equation is equivalent to

$$2^x = 4 \text{ and } 2^x = \frac{1}{2}$$

Then, $\quad x_1 = 2$ and $x_2 = -1$

Hence, roots of the original equation are $x_1 = 2$ and $x_2 = -1$.

***Form* 5 An equation of the form $a^{f(x)} + b^{f(x)} = c$,** where $a, b, c \in R$ and a, b, c satisfies the condition $a^2 + b^2 = c$, then solution of this equation is $f(x) = 2$ and no other solution of this equation.

Example 92. Solve the equation $3^{x-4} + 5^{x-4} = 34$.

Sol. Here, $3^2 + 5^2 = 34$, then given equation has a solution $x - 4 = 2$.

$\therefore$ $x_1 = 6$ is a root of the original equation.

***Form* 6 An equation of the form $\{f(x)\}^{g(x)}$ is equivalent to the equation**

$$\{f(x)\}^{g(x)} = 10^{g(x) \log f(x)},$$

where $f(x) > 0$.

Example 93. Solve the equation $5^x \sqrt[x]{8^{x-1}} = 500$.

Sol. We have, $\quad 5^x \sqrt[x]{8^{x-1}} = 5^3 \cdot 2^2$

$$\Rightarrow \quad 5^x \cdot 8^{\left(\frac{x-1}{x}\right)} = 5^3 \cdot 2^2$$

$$\Rightarrow \quad 5^x \cdot 2^{\frac{3x-3}{x}} = 5^3 \cdot 2^2$$

$$\Rightarrow \quad 5^{x-3} \cdot 2^{\left(\frac{x-3}{x}\right)} = 1$$

$$\Rightarrow \quad (5.2^{1/x})^{(x-3)} = 1$$

is equivalent to the equation

$$10^{(x-3)\log(5 \cdot 2^{1/x})} = 1$$

$$\Rightarrow \quad (x-3)\log(5 \cdot 2^{1/x}) = 0$$

Thus, original equation is equivalent to the collection of equations

$$x - 3 = 0, \ \log(5 \cdot 2^{1/x}) = 0$$

$$\therefore \quad x_1 = 3, 5 \cdot 2^{1/x} = 1 \Rightarrow 2^{1/x} = \left(\frac{1}{5}\right)$$

$$\therefore \quad x_2 = -\log_5 2$$

Hence, roots of the original equation are $x_1 = 3$ and $x_2 = -\log_5 2$.

Exponential Inequations

When we solve exponential inequation $a^{f(x)} > b\ (a > 0)$, we have

(i) $x \in D_f$, if $b \le 0$

(ii) If $b > 0$, then we have $f(x) > \log_a b$, if $a > 1$ and $f(x) < \log_a b$, if $0 < a < 1$ for $a = 1$, then $b < 1$.

Remark

The inequation $a^{f(x)} \le b$ has no solution for $b \le 0$, $a > 0$, $a \ne 1$.

Example 94. Solve the inequation $3^{x+2} > \left(\frac{1}{9}\right)^{1/x}$.

Sol. We have, $3^{x+2} > (3^{-2})^{1/x} \Rightarrow 3^{x+2} > 3^{-2/x}$

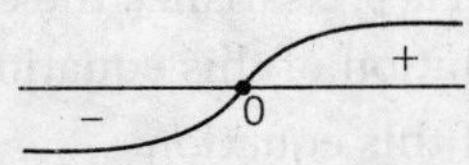

Here, base $3 > 1$

$$\Rightarrow \quad x + 2 > -\frac{2}{x} \Rightarrow \frac{x^2 + 2x + 2}{x} > 0$$

$$\Rightarrow \quad \frac{(x+1)^2 + 1}{x} > 0 \Rightarrow x > 0$$

$$\therefore \quad x \in (0, \infty)$$

Some Standard Forms to Solve Exponential Inequations

Form 1 An inequation of the form

$$f(a^x) \ge 0 \quad \text{or } f(a^x) \le 0$$

is equivalent to the system of collection

$$\begin{cases} t > 0, & \text{where } t = a^x \\ f(t) \ge 0 \ \text{ or } & f(t) \le 0 \end{cases}$$

Example 95. Solve the inequation $4^{x+1} - 16^x < 2\log_4 8$.

Sol. Let $4^x = t$, then given inequation reduce in the form

$$4t - t^2 > 2 \cdot \frac{3}{2}$$

$$\Rightarrow \quad t^2 - 4t + 3 < 0 \Rightarrow (t-1)(t-3) < 0$$

$$\Rightarrow \quad 1 < t < 3 \qquad [\because t > 0]$$

$$\Rightarrow \quad 1 < 4^x < 3$$

$$\Rightarrow \quad 0 < x < \log_4 3$$

$$\therefore \quad x \in (0, \log_4 3)$$

Form 2 An inequation of the form

$$\alpha a^{f(x)} + \beta b^{f(x)} + \gamma c^{f(x)} \ge 0$$

or

$$\alpha a^{f(x)} + \beta b^{f(x)} + \gamma c^{f(x)} \le 0$$

where $\alpha, \beta, \gamma \in R$ and $\alpha, \beta, \gamma \ne 0$ and the bases satisfy the condition $b^2 = ac$ is equivalent to the inequation

$$\alpha t^2 + \beta t + \gamma \ge 0 \quad \text{or} \quad \alpha t^2 + \beta t + \gamma \le 0,$$

where $t = (a/b)^{f(x)}$.

Form 3 An inequation of the form

$$\alpha a^{f(x)} + \beta b^{f(x)} + \gamma \ge 0$$

or

$$\alpha a^{f(x)} + \beta b^{f(x)} + \gamma \le 0$$

where $\alpha, \beta, \gamma \in R$ and $\alpha, \beta, \gamma \ne 0$ and $ab = 1$(a and b are inverse (+ve) numbers) is equivalent to the inequation

$$\alpha t^2 + \beta t + \gamma \ge 0 \quad \text{or} \quad \alpha t^2 + \beta t + \gamma \le 0$$

where $t = a^{f(x)}$

Form 4 If an inequation of the exponential form reduces to the solution of homogeneous algebraic inequation, i.e.

$$a_0 f^n(x) + a_1 f^{n-1}(x)\, g(x) + a_2 f^{n-2}(x) g^2(x) + \dots + a_{n-1} f(x)\, g^{n-1}(x) + a_n\, g^n(x) \ge 0,$$

where $a_0, a_1, a_2, \dots, a_n$ are constants ($a_0 \ne 0$) and $f(x)$ and $g(x)$ are functions of x.

Example 96. Solve the inequation $2^{2x^2 - 10x + 3} + 6^{x^2 - 5x + 1} \ge 3^{2x^2 - 10x + 3}$.

Sol. The given inequation is equivalent to

$$8 \cdot 2^{2(x^2 - 5x)} + 6 \cdot 2^{x^2 - 5x} \cdot 3^{x^2 - 5x} - 27 \cdot 3^{2(x^2 - 5x)} \ge 0$$

Let $2^{x^2 - 5x} = f(x)$ and $3^{x^2 - 5x} = g(x)$,

then $8 \cdot f^2(x) + 6 f(x) \cdot g(x) - 27 g^2(x) \ge 0$

On dividing in each by $g^2(x)$ $\qquad [\because g(x) > 0]$

Then, $8\left(\frac{f(x)}{g(x)}\right)^2 + 6\left(\frac{f(x)}{g(x)}\right) - 27 \ge 0$

and let $\frac{f(x)}{g(x)} = t \qquad [\because t > 0]$

then $8t^2 + 6t - 27 \ge 0$

$$\Rightarrow \quad \left(t - \frac{3}{2}\right)(t + 9/4) \ge 0$$

$$\Rightarrow \quad t \ge 3/2 \text{ and } t \le -9/4$$

The second inequation has no root. $\qquad [\because t > 0]$

From the first inequation, $t > 3/2$

$$\left(\frac{2}{3}\right)^{x^2 - 5x} \ge \left(\frac{2}{3}\right)^{-1} \qquad \left[\because \frac{2}{3} < 1\right]$$

$$\Rightarrow \quad x^2 - 5x \le -1 \Rightarrow x^2 - 5x + 1 \le 0$$

$$\therefore \quad \frac{5 - \sqrt{21}}{2} \le x \le \frac{5 + \sqrt{21}}{2}$$

Hence, $x \in \left[\frac{5 - \sqrt{21}}{2}, \frac{5 + \sqrt{21}}{2}\right]$.

Logarithmic Equations

If we have an equation of the form

$$\log_a f(x) = b, (a > 0), a \neq 1$$

is equivalent to the equation

$$f(x) = a^b \quad (f(x) > 0).$$

Example 97. Solve the equation $\log_3(5 + 4\log_3(x-1)) = 2$.

Sol. We have, $\log_3(5 + 4\log_3(x-1)) = 2$

is equivalent to the equation (here, base $\neq 1, > 0$).

$\therefore \quad 5 + 4\log_3(x-1) = 3^2$

$\Rightarrow \quad \log_3(x-1) = 1 \Rightarrow x - 1 = 3^1$

$\therefore \quad x = 4$

Hence, $x_1 = 4$ is the solution of the original equation.

Some Standard Formulae to Solve Logarithmic Equations

f and g are some functions and $a > 0, a \neq 1$, then, if $f > 0, g > 0$, we have

(i) $\log_a(fg) = \log_a f + \log_a g$

(ii) $\log_a(f/g) = \log_a f - \log_a g$

(iii) $\log_a f^{2\alpha} = 2\alpha \log_a |f|$ (iv) $\log_{a^\beta} f^\alpha = \dfrac{\alpha}{\beta}\log_a f$

(v) $f^{\log_a g} = g^{\log_a f}$ (vi) $a^{\log_a f} = f$

Example 98. Solve the equation $2x^{\log_4 3} + 3^{\log_4 x} = 27$.

Sol. The domain of the admissible values of the equation is $x > 0$. The given equation is equivalent to

$2.3^{\log_4 x} + 3^{\log_4 x} = 27$ [from above result (v)]

$\Rightarrow \quad 3.3^{\log_4 x} = 27$

$\Rightarrow \quad 3^{\log_4 x} = 9$

$\Rightarrow \quad 3^{\log_4 x} = 3^2$

$\Rightarrow \quad \log_4 x = 2$

$\Rightarrow \quad x_1 = 4^2 = 16$ is its only root.

Some Standard Forms to Solve Logarithmic Equations

***Form* 1** An equation of the form $\log_x a = b, a > 0$ has

(i) Only root $x = a^{1/b}$, if $a \neq 1$ and $b = 0$.

(ii) Any positive root different from unity, if $a = 1$ and $b = 0$.

(iii) No roots, if $a = 1, b \neq 0$.

(iv) No roots, if $a \neq 1, b = 0$.

Example 99. Solve the equation $\log_{(\log_5 x)} 5 = 2$.

Sol. We have, $\log_{(\log_5 x)} 5 = 2$

Base of logarithm > 0 and $\neq 1$.

$\therefore \quad \log_5 x > 0$ and $\log_5 x \neq 1$

$\Rightarrow \quad x > 1$ and $x \neq 5$

$\therefore$ The original equation is equivalent to

$$\log_5 x = 5^{1/2} = \sqrt{5}$$

$\therefore \quad x_1 = 5^{\sqrt{5}}$

Hence, $5^{\sqrt{5}}$ is the only root of the original equation.

***Form* 2** Equations of the form

(i) $f(\log_a x) = 0, a > 0, a \neq 1$ and

(ii) $g(\log_x A) = 0, A > 0$

Then, Eq. (i) is equivalent to

$f(t) = 0$, where $t = \log_a x$

If $t_1, t_2, t_3, \ldots, t_k$ are the roots of $f(t) = 0$, then

$\log_a x = t_1, \log_a x = t_2, \ldots, \log_a x = t_k$

and Eq. (ii) is equivalent to $f(y) = 0$, where $y = \log_x A$.

If $y_1, y_2, y_3, \ldots, y_k$ are the roots of $f(y) = 0$, then

$\log_x A = y_1, \log_x A = y_2, \ldots, \log_x A = y_k$

Example 100. Solve the equation $\dfrac{1 - 2(\log x^2)^2}{\log x - 2(\log x)^2} = 1$.

Sol. The given equation can rewrite in the form

$$\frac{1 - 2(2\log x)^2}{\log x - 2(\log x)^2} = 1$$

$$\Rightarrow \quad \frac{1 - 8(\log x)^2}{\log x - 2(\log x)^2} - 1 = 0$$

Let $\quad \log x = t,$

then $\dfrac{1 - 8t^2}{t - 2t^2} - 1 = 0 \Rightarrow \dfrac{1 - 8t^2 - t + 2t^2}{t - 2t^2} = 0$

$$\Rightarrow \quad \frac{1 - t - 6t^2}{(t - 2t^2)} = 0 \Rightarrow \frac{(1 + 2t)(1 - 3t)}{t(1 - 2t)} = 0$$

$$\Rightarrow \quad \begin{cases} t = -\dfrac{1}{2} \\ t = \dfrac{1}{3} \end{cases} \Rightarrow \begin{cases} \log x = -\dfrac{1}{2} \\ \log x = \dfrac{1}{3} \end{cases} \Rightarrow \begin{cases} x_1 = 10^{-1/2} \\ x_2 = 10^{1/3} \end{cases}$$

Hence, $x_1 = \dfrac{1}{\sqrt{10}}$ and $x_2 = \sqrt[3]{10}$ are the roots of the original equation.

Example 101. Solve the equation
$\log_x^3 10 - 6\log_x^2 10 + 11\log_x 10 - 6 = 0.$

Sol. Put $\log_x 10 = t$ in the given equation, we get

$$t^3 - 6t^2 + 11t - 6 = 0 \Rightarrow (t-1)(t-2)(t-3) = 0,$$

then $\begin{cases} t = 1 \\ t = 2 \\ t = 3 \end{cases}$

It follows that

$$\begin{cases} \log_x 10 = 1 \\ \log_x 10 = 2 \\ \log_x 10 = 3 \end{cases} \Rightarrow \begin{cases} x = 10 \\ x^2 = 10 \\ x^3 = 10 \end{cases} \Rightarrow \begin{cases} x = 10 \\ x = \sqrt{10} \\ x = \sqrt[3]{10} \end{cases} \quad [\because x > 0 \text{ and} \neq 1]$$

$[\because x > 0 \text{ and} \neq 1]$

$\therefore x_1 = 10, x_2 = \sqrt{10}$ and $x_3 = \sqrt[3]{10}$ are the roots of the original equation.

***Form* 3** Equations of the form

(i) $\log_a f(x) = \log_a g(x), a > 0, a \neq 1$ **is equivalent to** two ways.

Method I $\begin{cases} g(x) > 0 \\ f(x) = g(x) \end{cases}$

Method II $\begin{cases} f(x) > 0 \\ f(x) = g(x) \end{cases}$

(ii) $\log_{f(x)} A = \log_{g(x)} A, A > 0$ **is equivalent to two** ways.

Method I $\begin{cases} g(x) > 0 \\ g(x) \neq 1 \\ f(x) = g(x) \end{cases}$

Method II $\begin{cases} f(x) > 0 \\ f(x) \neq 1 \\ f(x) = g(x) \end{cases}$

Example 102. Solve the equation
$\log_{1/3}\left[2\left(\frac{1}{2}\right)^x - 1\right] = \log_{1/3}\left[\left(\frac{1}{4}\right)^x - 4\right].$

Sol. The given equation is equivalent to

$$\begin{cases} 2\left(\frac{1}{2}\right)^x - 1 > 0 \\ 2\left(\frac{1}{2}\right)^x - 1 = \left(\frac{1}{4}\right)^x - 4 \end{cases}$$

$$\Rightarrow \begin{cases} \left(\frac{1}{2}\right)^x > \frac{1}{2} \\ \left(\frac{1}{2}\right)^{2x} - 2\left(\frac{1}{2}\right)^x - 3 = 0 \end{cases}$$

$$\Rightarrow \begin{cases} x < 1 \\ \left[\left(\frac{1}{2}\right)^x - 3\right]\left[\left(\frac{1}{2}\right)^x + 1\right] = 0 \end{cases}$$

$$\Rightarrow \begin{cases} x < 1 \\ \left(\frac{1}{2}\right)^x = 3, \left(\frac{1}{2}\right)^x + 1 \neq 0 \end{cases} \Rightarrow \begin{cases} x < 1 \\ x = (-\log_2 3) \end{cases}$$

Hence, $x_1 = -\log_2 3$ is the root of the original equation.

Example 103. Solve the equation $\log_{\left(\frac{2+x}{10}\right)} 7 = \log_{\left(\frac{2}{x+1}\right)} 7.$

Sol. The given equation is equivalent to

$$\begin{cases} \frac{2}{x+1} > 0 \\ \frac{2}{x+1} \neq 1 \\ \frac{2+x}{10} = \frac{2}{x+1} \end{cases} \Rightarrow \begin{cases} x + 1 > 0 \\ x \neq 1 \\ x = -6, 3 \end{cases}$$

$\therefore x_1 = 3$ is root of the original equation.

***Form* 4** Equations of the form

(i) $\log_{f(x)} g(x) = \log_{f(x)} h(x)$ **is equivalent to two** ways.

Method I $\begin{cases} g(x) > 0 \\ f(x) > 0 \\ f(x) \neq 1 \\ g(x) = h(x) \end{cases}$ Method II $\begin{cases} h(x) > 0 \\ f(x) > 0 \\ f(x) \neq 1 \\ g(x) = h(x) \end{cases}$

(ii) $\log_{g(x)} f(x) = \log_{h(x)} f(x)$ **is equivalent to two** ways.

Method I $\begin{cases} f(x) > 0 \\ g(x) > 0 \\ g(x) \neq 1 \\ g(x) = h(x) \end{cases}$

Method II $\begin{cases} f(x) > 0 \\ h(x) > 0 \\ h(x) \neq 1 \\ g(x) = h(x) \end{cases}$

Example 104. Solve the equation
$\log_{(x^2-1)}(x^3 + 6) = \log_{(x^2-1)}(2x^2 + 5x).$

Sol. This equation is equivalent to the system

$$\begin{cases} 2x^2 + 5x > 0 \\ x^2 - 1 > 0 \\ x^2 - 1 \neq 1 \\ x^3 + 6 = 2x^2 + 5x \end{cases} \Rightarrow \begin{cases} x < -\frac{5}{2} \text{ and } x > 0 \\ x < -1 \text{ and } x > 1 \\ x \neq \pm\sqrt{2} \\ x = -2, 1, 3 \end{cases}$$

Hence, $x_1 = 3$ is only root of the original equation.

Example 105. Solve the equation
$\log_{(x^3+6)}(x^2-1)=\log_{(2x^2+5x)}(x^2-1)$.

Sol. This equation is equivalent to

$$\begin{cases} x^2-1>0 \\ 2x^2+5x>0 \\ 2x^2+5x\neq 1 \\ x^3+6=2x^2+5x \end{cases}$$

$$\Rightarrow \begin{cases} x<-1 \text{ and } x>1 \\ x<-\frac{5}{2} \text{ and } x>0 \\ x\neq \frac{-5\pm\sqrt{33}}{4} \\ x=-2,1,3 \end{cases}$$

Hence, $x_1=3$ is only root of the original equation.

***Form* 5 An equation of the form**
$\log_{h(x)}(\log_{g(x)} f(x))=0$ **is equivalent to the system**

$$\begin{cases} h(x)>0 \\ h(x)\neq 1 \\ g(x)>0 \\ g(x)\neq 1 \\ f(x)=g(x) \end{cases}$$

Example 106. Solve the equation
$\log_{x^2-6x+8}[\log_{2x^2-2x+8}(x^2+5x)]=0$.

Sol. This equation is equivalent to the system

$$\begin{cases} x^2-6x+8>0 \\ x^2-6x+8\neq 1 \\ 2x^2-2x-8>0 \\ 2x^2-2x-8\neq 1 \\ x^2+5x=2x^2-2x-8 \end{cases}$$

Solve the equations of this system

$$\Rightarrow \begin{cases} x<2 \text{ and } x>4 \\ x\neq 3\pm\sqrt{2} \\ x<\frac{1-\sqrt{17}}{2} \text{ and } x>\frac{1+\sqrt{17}}{2} \\ x\neq \frac{1\pm\sqrt{19}}{2} \\ x=-1,8 \end{cases}$$

$x=-1$, does not satisfy the third relation of this system.
Hence, $x_1=8$ is only root of the original equation.

***Form* 6 An equation of the form**
$2m\log_a f(x)=\log_a g(x), a>0, a\neq 1, m\in N$ **is** equivalent to the system

$$\begin{cases} f(x)>0 \\ f^{2m}(x)=g(x) \end{cases}$$

Example 107. Solve the equation
$2\log 2x=\log(7x-2-2x^2)$.

Sol. This equation is equivalent to the system

$$\begin{cases} 2x>0 \\ (2x)^2=7x-2-2x^2 \end{cases}$$

$$\Rightarrow \begin{cases} x>0 \\ 6x^2-7x+2=0 \end{cases}$$

$$\Rightarrow \begin{cases} x>0 \\ (x-1/2)(x-2/3)=0 \end{cases}$$

$$\Rightarrow \begin{cases} x=1/2 \\ x=2/3 \end{cases}$$

Hence, $x_1=1/2$ and $x_2=2/3$ are the roots of the original equation.

***Form* 7 An equation of the form**

$$(2m+1)\log_a f(x)=\log_a g(x), a>0, a\neq 1, m\in N$$

is equivalent to the system $\begin{cases} g(x)>0 \\ f^{2m+1}(x)=g(x) \end{cases}$.

Example 108. Solve the equation
$\log(3x^2+x-2)=3\log(3x-2)$.

Sol. This equation is equivalent to the system

$$\begin{cases} 3x^2+x-2>0 \\ 3x^2+x-2=(3x-2)^3 \end{cases}$$

$$\Rightarrow \begin{cases} (x-2/3)(x-2)>0 \\ (x-2/3)(9x^2-13x+3)=0 \end{cases}$$

$$\Rightarrow \begin{cases} x<2/3 \text{ and } x>2 \\ x=\frac{2}{3}, x=\frac{13\pm\sqrt{61}}{18} \end{cases}$$

Original equation has the only root $x_1=\frac{13-\sqrt{61}}{18}$.

***Form* 8 An equation of the form**

$$\log_a f(x)+\log_a g(x)=\log_a m(x), a>0, a\neq 1$$

is equivalent to the system

$$\begin{cases} f(x)>0 \\ g(x)>0 \\ f(x)\,g(x)=m(x) \end{cases}$$

Example 109. Solve the equation
$2\log_3 x+\log_3(x^2-3)=\log_3 0.5+5^{\log_5(\log_3 8)}$

Sol. This equation can be written as

$$\log_3 x^2+\log_3(x^2-3)=\log_3 0.5+\log_3 8$$

$$\log_3 x^2+\log_3(x^2-3)=\log_3(4)$$

This is equivalent to the system

$$\begin{cases} x^2 > 0 \\ x^2 - 3 > 0 \\ x^2(x^2-3) = 4 \end{cases} \Rightarrow \begin{cases} x < 0 \text{ and } x > 0 \\ x < -\sqrt{3} \text{ and } x > \sqrt{3} \\ (x^2-4)(x^2+1) = 0 \end{cases}$$

$$\Rightarrow \quad x^2 - 4 = 0 \quad \therefore \quad x = \pm 2, \text{ but } x > 0$$

Consequently, $x_1 = 2$ is only root of the original equation.

***Form* 9 An equation of the form**

$\mathbf{\log_a f(x) - \log_a g(x) = \log_a h(x) - \log_a t(x), a > 0, a \neq 1}$

is equivalent to the equation

$\log_a f(x) + \log_a t(x) = \log_a g(x) + \log_a h(x)$,

which is equivalent to the system

$$\begin{cases} f(x) > 0 \\ t(x) > 0 \\ g(x) > 0 \\ h(x) > 0 \\ f(x) \cdot t(x) = g(x) \cdot h(x) \end{cases}$$

Example 110. Solve the equation

$$\log_2(3-x) - \log_2\left(\frac{\sin\frac{3\pi}{4}}{5-x}\right) = \frac{1}{2} + \log_2(x+7).$$

Sol. This equation is equivalent to

$$\log_2(3-x) = \log_2\left(\frac{\sin\frac{3\pi}{4}}{5-x}\right) + \frac{1}{2}\log_2 2 + \log_2(x+7)$$

$$\Rightarrow \log_2(3-x) = \log_2\left(\frac{1}{\sqrt{2}(5-x)}\right) + \log_2\sqrt{2} + \log_2(x+7)$$

which is equivalent to the system

$$\begin{cases} 3-x > 0 \\ \dfrac{1}{\sqrt{2}(5-x)} > 0 \\ x+7 > 0 \\ (3-x) = \dfrac{\sqrt{2}(x+7)}{\sqrt{2}\,(5-x)} \end{cases}$$

$$\Rightarrow \begin{cases} x < 3 \\ x < 5 \\ x > -7 \\ (x-1)(x-8) = 0 \end{cases}$$

Hence, $x_1 = 1$ is only root of the original equation.

Logarithmic Inequations

When we solve logarithmic inequations

(i) $\begin{cases} \log_a f(x) > \log_a g(x) \\ a > 1 \end{cases}$

$$\Rightarrow \begin{cases} g(x) > 0 \\ a > 1 \\ f(x) > g(x) \end{cases}$$

(ii) $\begin{cases} \log_a f(x) > \log_a g(x) \\ 0 < a < 1 \end{cases}$

$$\Rightarrow \begin{cases} f(x) > 0 \\ 0 < a < 1 \\ f(x) < g(x) \end{cases}$$

Example 111. Solve the inequation

$$\log_{2x+3} x^2 < \log_{2x+3}(2x+3).$$

Sol. This inequation is equivalent to the collection of the systems

$$\left[\begin{array}{l} \begin{cases} 2x+3 > 1 \\ x^2 < 2x+3 \end{cases} \\ \begin{cases} 0 < 2x+3 < 1 \\ x^2 > 2x+3 \end{cases} \end{array}\right. \Rightarrow \left[\begin{array}{l} \begin{cases} x > -1 \\ (x-3)(x+1) < 0 \end{cases} \\ \begin{cases} -\frac{3}{2} < x < -1 \\ (x-3)(x+1) > 0 \end{cases} \end{array}\right.$$

$$\Rightarrow \left[\begin{array}{l} \begin{cases} x > -1 \\ -1 < x < 3 \end{cases} \Rightarrow -1 < x < 3 \\ \begin{cases} -\frac{3}{2} < x < -1 \\ x < -1 \text{ and } x > 3 \end{cases} \Rightarrow -\frac{3}{2} < x < -1 \end{array}\right.$$

Hence, the solution of the original inequation is

$$x \in \left(-\frac{3}{2}, -1\right) \cup (-1, 3).$$

Canonical Logarithmic Inequalities

1. $\begin{cases} \log_a x > 0 \\ a > 1 \end{cases} \Rightarrow \begin{cases} x > 1 \\ a > 1 \end{cases}$

2. $\begin{cases} \log_a x > 0 \\ 0 < a < 1 \end{cases} \Rightarrow \begin{cases} 0 < x < 1 \\ 0 < a < 1 \end{cases}$

3. $\begin{cases} \log_a x < 0 \\ a > 1 \end{cases} \Rightarrow \begin{cases} 0 < x < 1 \\ a > 1 \end{cases}$

4. $\begin{cases} \log_a x < 0 \\ 0 < a < 1 \end{cases} \Rightarrow \begin{cases} x > 1 \\ 0 < a < 1 \end{cases}$

Some Standard Forms to Solve Logarithmic Inequations

Form **1 Inequations of the form**

Forms		Collection of systems
(a) $\log_{g(x)} f(x) > 0$	$\Leftrightarrow$	$\begin{cases} f(x) > 1, \\ g(x) > 1, \end{cases} \begin{cases} 0 < f(x) < 1 \\ 0 < g(x) < 1 \end{cases}$
(b) $\log_{g(x)} f(x) \ge 0$	$\Leftrightarrow$	$\begin{cases} f(x) \ge 1, \\ g(x) > 1, \end{cases} \begin{cases} 0 < f(x) \le 1 \\ 0 < g(x) < 1 \end{cases}$
(c) $\log_{g(x)} f(x) < 0$	$\Leftrightarrow$	$\begin{cases} f(x) > 1, \\ 0 < g(x) < 1, \end{cases} \begin{cases} 0 < f(x) < 1 \\ g(x) > 1 \end{cases}$
(d) $\log_{g(x)} f(x) \le 0$	$\Leftrightarrow$	$\begin{cases} f(x) \ge 1, \\ 0 < g(x) < 1, \end{cases} \begin{cases} 0 < f(x) \le 1 \\ g(x) > 1 \end{cases}$

Example 112. Solve the inequation

$$\log_{\left(\frac{x^2-12x+30}{10}\right)}\left(\log_2 \frac{2x}{5}\right) > 0.$$

Sol. This inequation is equivalent to the collection of two systems

$$\begin{cases} \dfrac{x^2 - 12x + 30}{10} > 1, \\ \log_2\left(\dfrac{2x}{5}\right) > 1, \end{cases}$$

$$\begin{cases} 0 < \dfrac{x^2 - 12x + 30}{10} < 1 \\ 0 < \log_2\left(\dfrac{2x}{5}\right) < 1 \end{cases}$$

On solving the first system, we have

$$\Rightarrow \begin{cases} x^2 - 12x + 20 > 0 \\ \dfrac{2x}{5} > 2 \end{cases}$$

$$\Leftrightarrow \begin{cases} (x - 10)(x - 2) > 0 \\ x > 5 \end{cases}$$

$$\Leftrightarrow \begin{cases} x < 2 \text{ and } x > 10 \\ x > 5 \end{cases}$$

Therefore, the system has solution $x > 10$.

On solving the second system, we have

$$\Rightarrow \begin{cases} 0 < x^2 - 12x + 30 < 10 \\ 1 < \dfrac{2x}{5} < 2 \end{cases}$$

$$\Leftrightarrow \begin{cases} x^2 - 12x + 30 > 0 \text{ and } x^2 - 12x + 20 < 0 \\ 5/2 < x < 5 \end{cases}$$

$$\Leftrightarrow \begin{cases} x < 6 - \sqrt{6} \text{ and } x > 6 + \sqrt{6} \text{ and } 2 < x < 10 \\ 0 < x < 5 \end{cases}$$

Therefore, the system has solution $2 < x < 6 - \sqrt{6}$ combining both systems, then solution of the original inequations is
$x \in (2, 6 - \sqrt{6}) \cup (10, \infty)$.

Form 2 Inequations of the form

Forms		Collection of systems
(a) $\log_{\phi(x)} f(x) > \log_{\phi(x)} g(x)$	$\Leftrightarrow$	$\begin{cases} f(x) > g(x), \\ g(x) > 0, \\ \phi(x) > 1, \end{cases}$ $\begin{cases} f(x) < g(x) \\ f(x) > 0 \\ 0 < \phi(x) < 1 \end{cases}$
(b) $\log_{\phi(x)} f(x) \ge \log_{\phi(x)} g(x)$	$\Leftrightarrow$	$\begin{cases} f(x) \ge g(x), \\ g(x) > 0, \\ \phi(x) > 1, \end{cases}$ $\begin{cases} f(x) \le g(x) \\ f(x) > 0 \\ 0 < \phi(x) < 1 \end{cases}$
(c) $\log_{\phi(x)} f(x) < \log_{\phi(x)} g(x)$	$\Leftrightarrow$	$\begin{cases} f(x) < g(x), \\ f(x) > 0, \\ \phi(x) > 1, \end{cases}$ $\begin{cases} f(x) > g(x) \\ g(x) > 0 \\ 0 < \phi(x) < 1 \end{cases}$
(d) $\log_{\phi(x)} f(x) \le \log_{\phi(x)} g(x)$	$\Leftrightarrow$	$\begin{cases} f(x) \le g(x), \\ f(x) > 0, \\ \phi(x) > 1, \end{cases}$ $\begin{cases} f(x) \ge g(x) \\ g(x) > 0 \\ 0 < \phi(x) < 1 \end{cases}$

Example 113. Solve the inequation
$\log_{(x-3)}(2(x^2 - 10x + 24)) \ge \log_{(x-3)}(x^2 - 9)$.

Sol. This inequation is equivalent to the collection of systems

$$\begin{cases} 2(x^2 - 10x + 24) \ge x^2 - 9, \\ x^2 - 9 > 0, \\ x - 3 > 1, \end{cases}$$

$$\begin{cases} 2(x^2 - 10x + 24) \le x^2 - 9 \\ 2(x^2 - 10x + 24) > 0 \\ 0 < x - 3 < 1 \end{cases}$$

On solving the first system, we have

$$\begin{cases} x^2 - 20x + 57 \ge 0, \\ (x+3)(x-3) > 0, \\ x > 4, \end{cases}$$

$$\Leftrightarrow \begin{cases} x \in (-\infty, 10 - \sqrt{43}] \cup [10 + \sqrt{43}, \infty) \\ x \in (-\infty, -3) \cup (3, \infty) \\ x \in (4, \infty) \end{cases}$$

Therefore, the system has solution

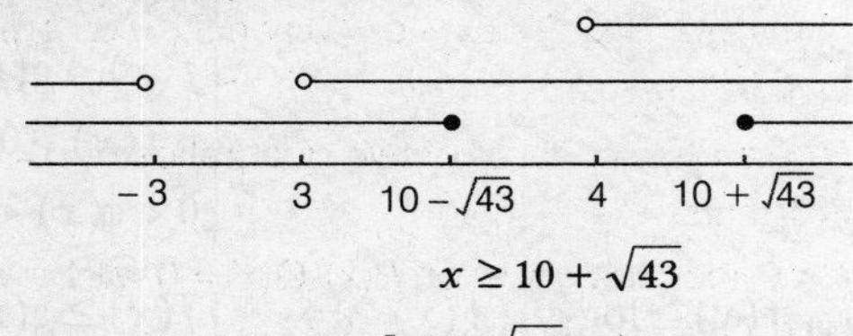

$$x \ge 10 + \sqrt{43}$$

i.e. $\quad x \in [10 + \sqrt{43}, \infty)$

On solving the second system, we have

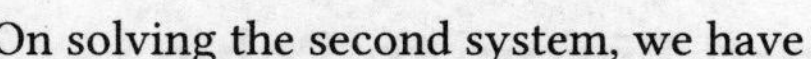

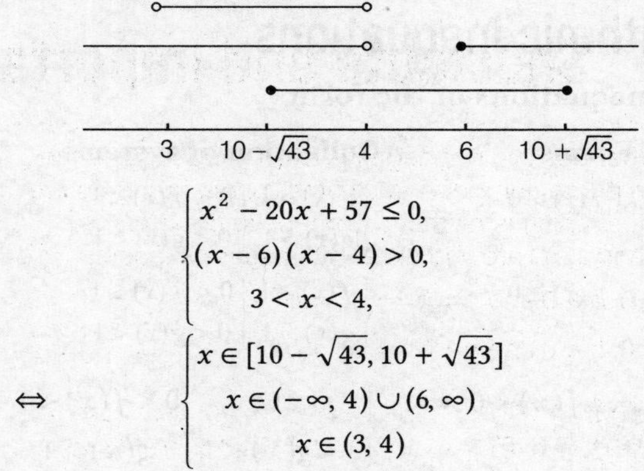

$$\begin{cases} x^2 - 20x + 57 \le 0, \\ (x-6)(x-4) > 0, \\ 3 < x < 4, \end{cases}$$

$$\Leftrightarrow \begin{cases} x \in [10 - \sqrt{43}, 10 + \sqrt{43}] \\ x \in (-\infty, 4) \cup (6, \infty) \\ x \in (3, 4) \end{cases}$$

Therefore, the system has solution

$$10 - \sqrt{43} \le x < 4,$$

i.e., $\quad x \in [10 - \sqrt{43}, 4)$

On combining the both systems, the solution of the original inequation is

$$x \in [10 - \sqrt{43}, 4) \cup [10 + \sqrt{43}, \infty).$$

Exercise for Session 5

1. The equation $\sqrt{(x+1)} - \sqrt{(x-1)} = \sqrt{(4x-1)}$ has

(a) no solution (b) one solution (c) two solutions (d) more than two solutions

2. The number of real solutions of $\sqrt{(x^2 - 4x + 3)} + \sqrt{(x^2 - 9)} = \sqrt{(4x^2 - 14x + 6)}$ is

(a) one (b) two (c) three (d) None of these

3. The number of real solutions of $\sqrt{(3x^2 - 7x - 30)} - \sqrt{(2x^2 - 7x - 5)} = x - 5$ is

(a) one (b) two (c) three (d) None of these

4. The number of integral values of x satisfying $\sqrt{(-x^2 + 10x - 16)} < x - 2$ is

(a) 0 (b) 1 (c) 2 (d) 3

5. The number of real solutions of the equation $\left(\frac{9}{10}\right)^x = -3 + x - x^2$ is

(a) 2 (b) 1 (c) 0 (d) None of these

6. The set of all x satisfying $3^{2x} - 3^x - 6 > 0$ is given by

(a) $0 < x < 1$ (b) $x > 1$ (c) $x > 3^{-2}$ (d) None of these

7. The number of real solutions of the equation $2^{x/2} + (\sqrt{2} + 1)^x = (3 + 2\sqrt{2})^{x/2}$ is

(a) one (b) two (c) four (d) infinite

8. The sum of the values of x satisfying the equation $(31 + 8\sqrt{15})^{x^2 - 3} + 1 = (32 + 8\sqrt{15})^{x^2 - 3}$ is

(a) 3 (b) 0 (c) 2 (d) None of these

9. The number of real solutions of the equation $\log_{0.5} x = |x|$ is

(a) 0 (b) 1 (c) 2 (d) None of these

10. The inequality $(x - 1)\ln(2 - x) < 0$ holds, if x satisfies

(a) $1 < x < 2$ (b) $x > 0$ (c) $0 < x < 1$ (d) None of these

Shortcuts and Important Results to Remember

1 '0' is neither positive nor negative even integer, '2' is the only even prime number and all other prime numbers are odd, '1' (i.e. unity) is neither a composite nor a prime number and 1, −1 are two units in the set of integers.

2 (i) If $a > 0, b > 0$ and $a < b \Rightarrow a^2 < b^2$

(ii) If $a < 0, b < 0$ and $a < b \Rightarrow a^2 > b^2$

(iii) If $a_1, a_2, a_3, \ldots, a_n \in R$ and $a_1^2 + a_2^2 + a_3^2 + \ldots + a_n^2 = 0$

$\Rightarrow a_1 = a_2 = a_3 = \ldots = a_n = 0$

3 (i) Max $(a, b) = \frac{1}{2}(|a+b| + |a-b|)$

(ii) Min $(a, b) = \frac{1}{2}(|a+b| - |a-b|)$

4 If the equation $f(x) = 0$ has two real roots α and β, then $f'(x) = 0$ will have a real root lying between α and β.

5 If two quadratic equations $P(x) = 0$ and $Q(x) = 0$ have an irrational common root, both roots will be common.

6 In the equation $ax^2 + bx + c = 0$ $[a, b, c \in R]$, if $a + b + c = 0$, the roots are $1, \frac{c}{a}$ and if $a - b + c = 0$, the roots are -1 and $\frac{c}{a}$.

7 The condition that the roots of $ax^2 + bx + c = 0$ may be in the ratio $p : q$, is

$pq\, b^2 = ac\,(p+q)^2$ (here, $\alpha : \beta = p : q$)

i.e., $$\sqrt{\frac{p}{q}} + \sqrt{\frac{q}{p}} = \pm\sqrt{\frac{b^2}{ac}}$$

(i) If one root of $ax^2 + bx + c = 0$ is n times that of the other, then $nb^2 = ac\,(n+1)^2$, here $\alpha : \beta = n : 1$.

(ii) If one root of $ax^2 + bx + c = 0$ is double of the other here $n = 2$, then $2b^2 = 9ac$.

8 If one root of $ax^2 + bx + c = 0$ is nth power of the other, then $(a^n c)^{\frac{1}{n+1}} + (ac^n)^{\frac{1}{n+1}} = -b$.

9 If one root of $ax^2 + bx + c = 0$ is square of the other, then $a^2c + ac^2 + b^3 = 3abc$.

10 If the ratio of the roots of the equation $ax^2 + bx + c = 0$ is equal to the ratio of the roots of $Ax^2 + Bx + C = 0$ and $a \neq 0, A \neq 0$, then $\frac{b^2}{ac} = \frac{B^2}{AC}$.

11 If sum of the roots is equal to sum of their squares then $2ac = ab + b^2$.

12 If sum of roots of $ax^2 + bx + c = 0$ is equal to the sum of their reciprocals, then

$2a^2c = ab^2 + bc^2$, i.e. ab^2, bc^2, ca^2 are in AP

or $\frac{2a}{b} = \frac{b}{c} + \frac{c}{a}$ i.e. $\frac{c}{a}, \frac{a}{b}, \frac{b}{c}$ are in AP.

13 Given, $y = ax^2 + bx + c$

(i) If $a > 0$, $y_{\min} = \frac{4ac - b^2}{4a}$

(ii) If $a < 0$, $y_{\max} = \frac{4ac - b^2}{4a}$

14 If α, β are the roots of $ax^2 + bx + c = 0$ and $S_n = \alpha^n + \beta^n$, then $aS_{n+1} + bS_n + cS_{n-1} = 0$.

15 If D_1 and D_2 are discriminants of two quadratics $P(x) = 0$ and $Q(x) = 0$, then

(i) If $D_1D_2 < 0$, then the equation $P(x)\cdot Q(x) = 0$ will have two real roots.

(ii) If $D_1D_2 > 0$, then the equation $P(x)\cdot Q(x) = 0$ has either four real roots or no real root.

(iii) If $D_1D_2 = 0$, then the equation $P(x)\cdot Q(x) = 0$ will have

(a) two equal roots and two distinct roots such that $D_1 > 0$ and $D_2 = 0$ or $D_1 = 0$ and $D_2 > 0$.

(b) only one real solution such that $D_1 < 0$ and $D_2 = 0$ or $D_1 = 0$ and $D_2 < 0$.

16 If $a > 0$ and $x = \sqrt{a + \sqrt{a + \sqrt{a + \ldots + \infty}}}$, then $x = \frac{1 + \sqrt{(4a+1)}}{2}$.

17 If $a_1, a_2, a_3, \ldots, a_n$ are positive real numbers, then least value of $(a_1 + a_2 + a_3 + \ldots + a_n)\left(\frac{1}{a_1} + \frac{1}{a_2} + \frac{1}{a_3} + \ldots + \frac{1}{a_n}\right)$ is n^2.

(i) Least value of $(a+b+c)\left(\frac{1}{a} + \frac{1}{b} + \frac{1}{c}\right) = 3^2 = 9$

(ii) Least value of

$$(a+b+c+d)\left(\frac{1}{a} + \frac{1}{b} + \frac{1}{c} + \frac{1}{d}\right) = 4^2 = 16$$

18 **Law of Proportions** If $\frac{a}{b} = \frac{c}{d} = \frac{e}{f} = \ldots$, then each of these ratios is also equal to

(i) $\frac{a + c + e + \ldots}{b + d + f + \ldots}$

(ii) $\left(\frac{pa^n + qc^n + re^n + \ldots}{pb^n + qd^n + rf^n + \ldots}\right)^{1/n}$ (where, $p, q, r, \ldots, n \in R$)

(iii) $\frac{\sqrt{ac}}{\sqrt{bd}} = \frac{\sqrt[n]{(ace\ldots)}}{\sqrt[n]{(bdf\ldots)}}$

19 **Lagrange's Mean Value Theorem** Let $f(x)$ be a function defined on $[a, b]$ such that

contd...

(i) $f(x)$ is continuous on $[a, b]$ and

(ii) $f(x)$ is derivable on (a, b), then $c \in (a, b)$ such that

$$f'(c) = \frac{f(b) - f(a)}{b - a}$$

20 Lagrange's Identity If $a_1, a_2, a_3, b_1, b_2, b_3 \in R$, then

$$(a_1^2 + a_2^2 + a_3^2)(b_1^2 + b_2^2 + b_3^2) - (a_1b_1 + a_2b_2 + a_3b_3)^2$$
$$= (a_1b_2 - a_2b_1)^2 + (a_2b_3 - a_3b_2)^2 + (a_3b_1 - a_1b_3)^2$$

or $(a_1^2 + a_2^2 + a_3^2)(b_1^2 + b_2^2 + b_3^2) - (a_1b_1 + a_2b_2 + a_3b_3)^2$

$$= \begin{vmatrix} a_1 & a_2 \\ b_1 & b_2 \end{vmatrix}^2 + \begin{vmatrix} a_2 & a_3 \\ b_2 & b_3 \end{vmatrix}^2 + \begin{vmatrix} a_3 & a_1 \\ b_3 & b_1 \end{vmatrix}^2$$

Remark

If $(a_1^2 + a_2^2 + a_3^2)(b_1^2 + b_2^2 + b_3^2) \le (a_1b_1 + a_2b_2 + a_3b_3)^2$,

then $\dfrac{a_1}{b_1} = \dfrac{a_2}{b_2} = \dfrac{a_3}{b_3}$.

21 Horner's Method of Synthetic, Division When, we divide a polynomial of degree ≥ 1 by a linear monic polynomial, the quotient and remainder can be found by this method. Consider

$f(x) = a_0 x^n + a_1 x^{n-1} + a_2 x^{n-2} + \ldots + a_n$

where $a_0 \ne 0$ and $a_0, a_1, a_2, \ldots, a_n \in R$.

Let $g(x) = (x - \alpha)$ be a linear monic polynomial $\alpha \in R$.

When $g(x) \mid f(x)$; we can find quotient and remainder as follows :

α	a_0	a_1	a_2	$\ldots$	a_n
	0	αa_0	$b_1\alpha$		αb_{n-1}
	$a_0 = b_0$	$a_1 + \alpha a_0 = b_1$	$a_2 + b_1\alpha = b_2$		$a_n + \alpha b_{n-1} = 0$

$\therefore \; f(x) = (x - \alpha)(b_0 x^{n-1} + b_1 x^{n-2} + b_2 x^{n-3} + \ldots + b_{n-1})$

e.g. Find all roots of $x^3 - 6x^2 + 11x - 6 = 0$.

$\because (x - 1)$ is a factor of $x^3 - 6x^2 + 11x - 6$, then

$x = 1$	1	–6	11	–6
	0	1	–5	6
	1	–5	6	0

$$\therefore \; x^3 - 6x^2 + 11x - 6 = (x - 1)(x^2 - 5x + 6)$$
$$= (x - 1)(x - 2)(x - 3)$$

Hence, roots of $x^3 - 6x^2 + 11x - 6 = 0$ are 1, 2 and 3.

JEE Type Solved Examples : Single Option Correct Type Questions

- This section contains **10 multiple choice examples.** Each example has four choices (a), (b), (c) and (d) out of which **ONLY ONE** is correct.

• Ex. 1 *If α and $\beta (\alpha < \beta)$, are the roots of the equation $x^2 + bx + c = 0$, where $c < 0 < b$, then*

(a) $0 < \alpha < \beta$ (b) $\alpha < 0 < \beta < |\alpha|$
(c) $\alpha < \beta < 0$ (d) $\alpha < 0 < |\alpha| < \beta$

Sol. (b) $\because \quad \alpha + \beta = -b, \; \alpha\beta = c \quad \ldots(i)$

$\because \quad c < 0 \Rightarrow \alpha\beta < 0$

Let $\quad \alpha < 0, \beta > 0$

$\therefore \quad |\alpha| = -\alpha$ and $\alpha < 0 < \beta \quad [\because \alpha < \beta] \ldots(ii)$

From Eq. (i), we get $-|\alpha| + \beta < 0$

$\Rightarrow \quad \beta < |\alpha| \quad \ldots(iii)$

From Eqs. (ii) and (iii), we get

$$\alpha < 0 < \beta < |\alpha|$$

• Ex. 2 *Let α, β be the roots of the equation $x^2 - x + p = 0$ and γ, δ be the roots of the equation $x^2 - 4x + q = 0$. If α, β, γ and δ are in GP, the integral values of p and q respectively, are*

(a) $-2, -32$ (b) $-2, 3$
(c) $-6, 3$ (d) $-6, -32$

Sol. (a) Let r be the common ratio of the GP, then

$$\beta = \alpha r, \gamma = \alpha r^2 \text{ and } \delta = \alpha r^3$$

$\therefore \quad \alpha + \beta = 1 \Rightarrow \alpha + \alpha r = 1$

or $\quad \alpha(1 + r) = 1 \quad \ldots(i)$

and $\quad \alpha\beta = p \Rightarrow \alpha(\alpha r) = p$

or $\quad \alpha^2 r = p \quad \ldots(ii)$

and $\quad \gamma + \delta = 4 \Rightarrow \alpha r^2 + \alpha r^3 = 4$

or $\quad \alpha r^2(1 + r) = 4 \quad \ldots(iii)$

and $\quad \gamma\delta = q$

$\Rightarrow \quad (\alpha r^2)(\alpha r^3) = q$

or $\quad \alpha^2 r^5 = q \quad \ldots(iv)$

On dividing Eq. (iii) by Eq. (i), we get

$$r^2 = 4 \Rightarrow r = -2, 2$$

If we take $r = 2$, then α is not integer, so we take $r = -2$.
On substituting $r = -2$ in Eq. (i), we get $\alpha = -1$

Now, from Eqs. (ii) and (iv), we get

$$p = \alpha^2 r = (-1)^2(-2) = -2$$

and $\quad q = \alpha^2 r^5 = (-1)^2(-2)^5 = -32$

Hence, $\quad (p, q) = (-2, -32)$

• Ex. 3 *Let $f(x) = \int_1^x \sqrt{(2 - t^2)}\, dt$, the real roots of the equation $x^2 - f'(x) = 0$ are*

(a) ± 1 (b) $\pm \frac{1}{\sqrt{2}}$
(c) $\pm \frac{1}{2}$ (d) 0 and 1

Sol. (a) We have, $f(x) = \int_1^x \sqrt{(2 - t^2)}\, dt$

$\Rightarrow \quad f'(x) = \sqrt{(2 - x^2)}$

$\therefore \quad x^2 - f'(x) = 0$

$\Rightarrow \quad x^2 - \sqrt{(2 - x^2)} = 0 \Rightarrow x^4 + x^2 - 2 = 0$

$\Rightarrow \quad x^2 = 1, -2$

$\Rightarrow \quad x = \pm 1 \quad$ [only for real value of x]

• Ex. 4 *If $x^2 + 3x + 5 = 0$ and $ax^2 + bx + c = 0$ have a common root and $a, b, c \in N$, the minimum value of $a + b + c$ is*

(a) 3 (b) 9
(c) 6 (d) 12

Sol. (b) $\because$ Roots of the equation $x^2 + 3x + 5 = 0$ are non-real. Thus, given equations will have two common roots.

$\Rightarrow \quad \frac{a}{1} = \frac{b}{3} = \frac{c}{5} = \lambda \quad$ [say]

$\therefore \quad a + b + c = 9\lambda$

Thus, minimum value of $a + b + c = 9 \quad [\because a, b, c \in N]$

• Ex. 5 *If $x_1, x_2, x_3, \ldots, x_n$ are the roots of the equation $x^n + ax + b = 0$, the value of $(x_1 - x_2)(x_1 - x_3)(x_1 - x_4) \ldots (x_1 - x_n)$ is*

(a) $nx_1 + b$
(b) $n(x_1)^{n-1}$
(c) $n(x_1)^{n-1} + a$
(d) $n(x_1)^{n-1} + b$

Sol. (c) $\because x^n + ax + b = (x - x_1)(x - x_2)(x - x_3)\ldots(x - x_n)$

$$\Rightarrow (x - x_2)(x - x_3)\ldots(x - x_n) = \frac{x^n + ax + b}{x - x_1}$$

On taking $\lim_{x \to x_1}$ both sides, we get

$$(x_1 - x_2)(x_1 - x_3)\ldots(x_1 - x_n) = \lim_{x \to x_1} \frac{x^n + ax + b}{x - x_1} \left[\frac{0}{0} \text{form}\right]$$

$$= \lim_{x \to x_1} \frac{nx^{n-1} + a}{1} = n(x_1)^{n-1} + a$$

• Ex. 6 *If α, β are the roots of the equation $ax^2 + bx + c = 0$ and $A_n = \alpha^n + \beta^n$, then $aA_{n+2} + bA_{n+1} + cA_n$ is equal to*

(a) 0 (b) 1 (c) $a + b + c$ (d) abc

Sol. (a) $\because \alpha + \beta = -\dfrac{b}{a}$ and $\alpha\beta = \dfrac{c}{a}$

$$\therefore \quad A_{n+2} = \alpha^{n+2} + \beta^{n+2}$$
$$= (\alpha + \beta)(\alpha^{n+1} + \beta^{n+1}) - \alpha\beta^{n+1} - \beta\alpha^{n+1}$$
$$= (\alpha + \beta)(\alpha^{n+1} + \beta^{n+1}) - \alpha\beta(\alpha^n + \beta^n)$$
$$= -\frac{b}{a}A_{n+1} - \frac{c}{a}A_n$$
$$\Rightarrow \quad aA_{n+2} + bA_{n+1} + cA_n = 0$$

• Ex. 7 *If x and y are positive integers such that $xy + x + y = 71$, $x^2y + xy^2 = 880$, then $x^2 + y^2$ is equal to*

(a) 125 (b) 137 (c) 146 (d) 152

Sol. (c) $\because$ $xy + x + y = 71 \Rightarrow xy + (x + y) = 71$

and $x^2y + xy^2 = 880 \Rightarrow xy(x + y) = 880$

$\Rightarrow xy$ and $(x + y)$ are the roots of the quadratic equation.

$$t^2 - 71t + 880 = 0$$
$$\Rightarrow \quad (t - 55)(t - 16) = 0$$
$$\Rightarrow \quad t = 55, 16$$
$$\therefore \quad x + y = 16 \text{ and } xy = 55$$

So, $x^2 + y^2 = (x + y)^2 - 2xy = (16)^2 - 110 = 146$

• Ex. 8 *If α, β are the roots of the equation $x^2 - 3x + 5 = 0$ and γ, δ are the roots of the equation $x^2 + 5x - 3 = 0$, then the equation whose roots are $\alpha\gamma + \beta\delta$ and $\alpha\delta + \beta\gamma$, is*

(a) $x^2 - 15x - 158 = 0$ (b) $x^2 + 15x - 158 = 0$

(c) $x^2 - 15x + 158 = 0$ (d) $x^2 + 15x + 158 = 0$

Sol. (d) $\because$ $\alpha + \beta = 3, \alpha\beta = 5, \gamma + \delta = (-5), \gamma\delta = (-3)$

Sum of roots $= (\alpha\gamma + \beta\delta) + (\alpha\delta + \beta\gamma)$
$$= (\alpha + \beta)(\gamma + \delta) = 3 \times (-5) = (-15)$$

Product of roots $= (\alpha\gamma + \beta\delta)(\alpha\delta + \beta\gamma)$
$$= \alpha^2\gamma\delta + \alpha\beta\gamma^2 + \beta\alpha\delta^2 + \beta^2\gamma\delta$$
$$= \gamma\delta(\alpha^2 + \beta^2) + \alpha\beta(\gamma^2 + \delta^2)$$
$$= -3(\alpha^2 + \beta^2) + 5(\gamma^2 + \delta^2)$$
$$= -3[(\alpha + \beta)^2 - 2\alpha\beta] + 5[(\gamma + \delta)^2 - 2\gamma\delta]$$
$$= -3[9 - 10] + 5[25 + 6] = 158$$

$\therefore$ Required equation is $x^2 + 15x + 158 = 0$.

• Ex. 9 *The number of roots of the equation $\dfrac{1}{x} + \dfrac{1}{\sqrt{(1 - x^2)}} = \dfrac{35}{12}$ is*

(a) 0 (b) 1

(c) 2 (d) 3

Sol. (d) Let $\dfrac{1}{x} = u$ and $\dfrac{1}{\sqrt{(1 - x^2)}} = v$, then

$$u + v = \frac{35}{12} \text{ and } u^2 + v^2 = u^2v^2$$
$$\Rightarrow \quad (u + v)^2 = \left(\frac{35}{12}\right)^2$$
$$\Rightarrow \quad u^2 + v^2 + 2uv = \left(\frac{35}{12}\right)^2$$
$$\Rightarrow \quad u^2v^2 + 2uv = \left(\frac{35}{12}\right)^2 \quad [\because u^2 + v^2 = u^2v^2]$$
$$\Rightarrow \quad u^2v^2 + 2uv - \left(\frac{35}{12}\right)^2 = 0$$
$$\Rightarrow \quad \left(uv + \frac{49}{12}\right)\left(uv - \frac{25}{12}\right) = 0$$
$$\Rightarrow \quad uv = -\frac{49}{12}, uv = \frac{25}{12}$$

***Case* I** If $uv = -\dfrac{49}{12}$, then

$$\frac{1}{x} \cdot \frac{1}{\sqrt{(1 - x^2)}} = -\frac{49}{12} \quad [\text{here } x < 0]$$
$$\Rightarrow \quad x^4 - x^2 + \frac{(12)^2}{(49)^2} = 0$$
$$\Rightarrow \quad x = -\frac{(5 + \sqrt{73})}{14}$$

***Case* II** If $uv = \dfrac{25}{12}$, then

$$\frac{1}{x} \cdot \frac{1}{\sqrt{(1 - x^2)}} = \frac{25}{12} \quad [\text{here } x > 0]$$
$$\Rightarrow \quad x^4 - x^2 + \frac{(12)^2}{(25)^2} = 0$$
$$\Rightarrow \quad \left(x^2 - \frac{9}{25}\right)\left(x^2 - \frac{16}{25}\right) = 0 \Rightarrow x = \frac{3}{5}, \frac{4}{5}$$

On combining both cases,

$$x = -\frac{(5 + \sqrt{73})}{14}, \frac{3}{5}, \frac{4}{5}$$

Hence, number of roots = 3

• Ex. 10 *The sum of the roots of the equation $2^{33x - 2} + 2^{11x + 2} = 2^{22x + 1} + 1$ is*

(a) $\dfrac{1}{11}$ (b) $\dfrac{2}{11}$ (c) $\dfrac{3}{11}$ (d) $\dfrac{4}{11}$

Sol. (b) Let $2^{11x} = t$, given equation reduces to

$$\frac{t^3}{4} + 4t = 2t^2 + 1$$
$$\Rightarrow \quad t^3 - 8t^2 + 16t - 4 = 0 \Rightarrow t_1 \cdot t_2 \cdot t_3 = 4$$
$$\Rightarrow \quad 2^{11x_1} \cdot 2^{11x_2} \cdot 2^{11x_3} = 4 \Rightarrow 2^{11(x_1 + x_2 + x_3)} = 2^2$$
$$\Rightarrow \quad 11(x_1 + x_2 + x_3) = 2$$
$$\therefore \quad x_1 + x_2 + x_3 = \frac{2}{11}$$

JEE Type Solved Examples : More than One Correct Option Type Questions

- This section contains **5 multiple choice examples.** Each example has four choices (a), (b), (c) and (d) out of **which more than one** may be correct.

Ex. 11 *For the equation* $2x^2 - 6\sqrt{2}x - 1 = 0$

(a) roots are rational
(b) roots are irrational
(c) if one root is $(p + \sqrt{q})$, the other is $(-p + \sqrt{q})$
(d) if one root is $(p + \sqrt{q})$, the other is $(p - \sqrt{q})$

Sol. (b,c) As the coefficients are not rational, irrational roots need not appear in conjugate pair.

Here, $\alpha + \beta = 3\sqrt{2}$ and $\alpha\beta = -\dfrac{1}{2}$

Let $\alpha = p + \sqrt{q}$, then prove that other root $\beta = -p + \sqrt{q}$.

Ex. 12 *Given that* α, γ *are roots of the equation* $Ax^2 - 4x + 1 = 0$ *and* β, δ *the roots of the equation* $Bx^2 - 6x + 1 = 0$, *such that* α, β, γ *and* δ *are in HP then*

(a) $A = 3$ (b) $A = 4$ (c) $B = 2$ (d) $B = 8$

Sol. (a,d) Since, α, β, γ and δ are in HP, hence $\dfrac{1}{\alpha}, \dfrac{1}{\beta}, \dfrac{1}{\gamma}$ and $\dfrac{1}{\delta}$ are in AP and they may be taken as $a - 3d$, $a - d$, $a + d$ and $a + 3d$. Replacing x by $\dfrac{1}{x}$, we get the equation whose roots are $a - 3d$, $a + d$ is $x^2 - 4x + A = 0$ and equation whose roots are $a - d$, $a + 3d$ is $x^2 - 6x + B = 0$, then

$$(a - 3d) + (a + d) = 4 \Rightarrow 2(a - d) = 4$$

and $$(a - d) + (a + 3d) = 6 \Rightarrow 2(a + d) = 6$$

$\therefore$ $$a = \frac{5}{2} \text{ and } d = \frac{1}{2}$$

Now, $A = (a - 3d)(a + d) = \left(\dfrac{5}{2} - \dfrac{3}{2}\right)\left(\dfrac{5}{2} + \dfrac{1}{2}\right) = 3$

and $B = (a - d)(a + 3d) = \left(\dfrac{5}{2} - \dfrac{1}{2}\right)\left(\dfrac{5}{2} + \dfrac{3}{2}\right) = 8$

Ex. 13 *If* $|ax^2 + bx + c| \le 1$ *for all* x *in [0, 1], then*

(a) $|a| \le 8$ (b) $|b| > 8$
(c) $|c| \le 1$ (d) $|a| + |b| + |c| \le 17$

Sol. (a,c,d) On putting $x = 0, 1$ and $\dfrac{1}{2}$, we get

$$|c| \le 1 \quad \text{...(i)}$$

$$|a + b + c| \le 1 \quad \text{...(ii)}$$

and $$|a + 2b + 4c| \le 4 \quad \text{...(iii)}$$

From Eqs. (i), (ii) and (iii), we get

$$|b| \le 8 \text{ and } |a| \le 8$$

$\Rightarrow$ $$|a| + |b| + |c| \le 17$$

Ex. 14 *If* $\cos^4\theta + p$, $\sin^4\theta + p$ *are the roots of the equation* $x^2 + a(2x + 1) = 0$ *and* $\cos^2\theta + q$, $\sin^2\theta + q$ *are the roots of the equation* $x^2 + 4x + 2 = 0$ *then* a *is equal to*

(a) −2 (b) −1 (c) 1 (d) 2

Sol. (b,d)

$\because$ $$\cos^4\theta - \sin^4\theta = \cos 2\theta$$

$\Rightarrow$ $$\cos^4\theta - \sin^4\theta = \cos^2\theta - \sin^2\theta$$

$\Rightarrow$ $$(\cos^4\theta + p) - (\sin^4\theta + p) = (\cos^2\theta + q) - (\sin^2\theta + q)$$

$\Rightarrow$ $$\frac{\sqrt{4a^2 - 4a}}{1} = \frac{\sqrt{16 - 8}}{1} \quad \left[\because \alpha - \beta = \frac{\sqrt{D}}{a}\right]$$

$\Rightarrow$ $$4a^2 - 4a = 8 \text{ or } a^2 - a - 2 = 0$$

or $$(a - 2)(a + 1) = 0 \text{ or } a = 2, -1$$

Ex. 15 *If* α, β, γ *are the roots of* $x^3 - x^2 + ax + b = 0$ *and* β, γ, δ *are the roots of* $x^3 - 4x^2 + mx + n = 0$. *If* α, β, γ *and* δ *are in AP with common difference* d *then*

(a) $a = m$ (b) $a = m - 5$
(c) $n = b - a - 2$ (d) $b = m + n - 3$

Sol. (b,c,d)

$\because$ a, β, γ, δ are in AP with common difference d, then

$$\beta = \alpha + d,\ \gamma = \alpha + 2d \text{ and } \delta = \alpha + 3d \quad \text{...(i)}$$

Given, a, β, γ are the roots of $x^3 - x^2 + ax + b = 0$, then

$$\alpha + \beta + \gamma = 1 \quad \text{...(ii)}$$

$$\alpha\beta + \beta\gamma + \gamma\alpha = a \quad \text{...(iii)}$$

$$\alpha\beta\gamma = -b \quad \text{...(iv)}$$

Also, β, γ, δ are the roots of $x^3 - 4x^2 + mx + n = 0$, then

$$\beta + \gamma + \delta = 4 \quad \text{...(v)}$$

$$\beta\gamma + \gamma\delta + \delta\beta = m \quad \text{...(vi)}$$

$$\beta\gamma\delta = -n \quad \text{...(vii)}$$

From Eqs. (i) and (ii), we get

$$3\alpha + 3d = 1 \quad \text{...(viii)}$$

and from Eqs. (i) and (v), we get

$$3\alpha + 6d = 4 \quad \text{...(ix)}$$

From Eqs. (viii) and (ix), we get

$$d = 1, \alpha = -\frac{2}{3}$$

Now, from Eq. (i), we get

$$\beta = \frac{1}{3}, \gamma = \frac{4}{3} \text{ and } \delta = \frac{7}{3}$$

From Eqs. (iii), (iv), (vi) and (vii), we get

$$a = -\frac{2}{3}, b = \frac{8}{27}, m = \frac{13}{3}, n = -\frac{28}{27}$$

$\therefore$ $$a = m - 5, n = b - a - 2 \text{ and } b = m + n - 3$$

JEE Type Solved Examples : Passage Based Questions

- This section contains **2 solved passages** based upon each of the passage **3 multiple choice** examples have to be answered. Each of these examples has four choices (a), (b), (c) and (d) out of which **ONLY ONE** is correct.

Passage I

(Ex. Nos. 16 to 18)

If G and L are the greatest and least values of the expression $\dfrac{x^2-x+1}{x^2+x+1}, x \in R$ *respectively, then*

16. The least value of G^5+L^5 is

(a) 0 (b) 2 (c) 16 (d) 32

Sol. (*b*) Let $y=\dfrac{x^2-x+1}{x^2+x+1}$

$$\Rightarrow x^2y+xy+y=x^2-x+1$$

$$\Rightarrow (y-1)x^2+(y+1)x+y-1=0 \quad [\because x \in R]$$

$$\therefore (y+1)^2-4\cdot(y-1)(y-1)\ge 0 \quad [\because b^2-4ac\ge 0]$$

$$\Rightarrow (y+1)^2-(2y-2)^2\ge 0$$

$$\Rightarrow (3y-1)(y-3)\le 0$$

$$\therefore \frac{1}{3}\le y\le 3 \Rightarrow G=3 \text{ and } L=\frac{1}{3} \quad \therefore GL=1$$

$$\frac{G^5+L^5}{2}\ge (GL)^{1/5}=(1)^{1/5}=1$$

$$\Rightarrow \frac{G^5+L^5}{2}\ge 1 \text{ or } G^5+L^5\ge 2$$

$\therefore$ Minimum value of G^5+L^5 is 2.

17. G and L are the roots of the equation

(a) $3x^2-10x+3=0$ (b) $4x^2-17x+4=0$
(c) $x^2-7x+10=0$ (d) $x^2-5x+6=0$

Sol. (*a*) Equation whose roots are G and L, is

$$x^2-(G+L)x+GL=0$$

$$\Rightarrow x^2-\frac{10}{3}x+1=0 \text{ or } 3x^2-10x+3=0$$

18. If $L<\lambda<G$ and $\lambda \in N$, the sum of all values of λ is

(a) 2 (b) 3 (c) 4 (d) 5

Sol. (*b*) $\because L<\lambda<G \Rightarrow \frac{1}{3}<\lambda<3 \quad \therefore \lambda=1,2$

Sum of values of $\lambda=1+2=3$

Passage II

(Ex. Nos. 19 to 21)

Let a, b, c *and* d *are real numbers in GP. Suppose* u, v, w *satisfy the system of equations* $u+2v+3w=6, 4u+5v+6w=12$ *and* $6u+9v=4$. *Further, consider the expressions*

$$f(x)=\left(\frac{1}{u}+\frac{1}{v}+\frac{1}{w}\right)x^2+[(b-c)^2+(c-a)^2+(d-b)^2]$$

$x+u+v+w=0$ *and* $g(x)=20x^2+10(a-d)^2x-9=0$

19. $(b-c)^2+(c-a)^2+(d-b)^2$ is equal to

(a) $a-d$ (b) $(a-d)^2$ (c) a^2-d^2 (d) $(a+d)^2$

Sol. (*b*) Let $b=ar, c=ar^2$ and $d=ar^3$

Now, $(b-c)^2+(c-a)^2+(d-b)^2$

$$=(ar-ar^2)^2+(ar^2-a)^2+(ar^3-ar)^2$$

$$=a^2r^2(1-r)^2+a^2(r^2-1)^2+a^2r^2(r^2-1)^2$$

$$=a^2(1-r)^2\{r^2+(r+1)^2+r^2(r+1)^2\}$$

$$=a^2(1-r)^2(r^4+2r^3+3r^2+2r+1)$$

$$=a^2(1-r)^2(1+r+r^2)^2=a^2(1-r^3)^2$$

$$=(a-ar^3)^2=(a-d)^2$$

20. $(u+v+w)$ is equal to

(a) 2 (b) $\frac{1}{2}$ (c) 20 (d) $\frac{1}{20}$

Sol. (*a*) Now, $u+2v+3w=6$ ...(i)

$4u+5v+6w=12$ ...(ii)

and $6u+9v=4$ ...(iii)

From Eqs. (i) and (ii), we get

$2u+v=0$ ...(iv)

Solving Eqs. (iii) and (iv), we get

$$u=-\frac{1}{3}, v=\frac{2}{3}$$

Now, from Eq. (i), we get $w=\frac{5}{3}$

$$\therefore v+u+w=-\frac{1}{3}+\frac{2}{3}+\frac{5}{3}=2$$

21. If roots of $f(x)=0$ be α, β, the roots of $g(x)=0$ will be

(a) α, β (b) $-\alpha, -\beta$ (c) $\frac{1}{\alpha}, \frac{1}{\beta}$ (d) $-\frac{1}{\alpha}, -\frac{1}{\beta}$

Sol. (*c*) Now, $f(x)=\left(\frac{1}{u}+\frac{1}{v}+\frac{1}{w}\right)x^2+[(b-c)^2$

$$+(c-a)^2+(d-b)^2]x+u+v+w=0$$

$$\Rightarrow f(x)=-\frac{9}{10}x^2+(a-d)^2x+2=0$$

$$\Rightarrow f(x)=-9x^2+10(a-d)^2x+20=0 \quad \text{...(v)}$$

Given, roots of $f(x)=0$ are α and β.

Now, replace x by $\frac{1}{x}$ in Eq. (v), then

$$\frac{-9}{x^2}+\frac{10(a-d)^2}{x}+20=0$$

$$\Rightarrow 20x^2+10(a-d)^2x-9=0$$

$$g(x)=0$$

$\therefore$ Roots of $g(x)=0$ are $\frac{1}{\alpha}, \frac{1}{\beta}$.

JEE Type Solved Examples : Single Integer Answer Type Questions

- This section contains **2 examples.** The answer to each example is a **single digit integer** ranging from **0** to **9** (both inclusive).

● ***Ex. 22*** *If the roots of the equation* $10x^3 - cx^2 - 54x - 27 = 0$ *are in harmonic progression, the value of c is*

Sol. (9) Given, roots of the equation

$$10x^3 - cx^2 - 54x - 27 = 0 \text{ are in HP.} \quad \text{...(i)}$$

Now, replacing x by $\frac{1}{x}$ in Eq. (i), we get

$$27x^3 + 54x^2 + cx - 10 = 0 \quad \text{...(ii)}$$

Hence, the roots of Eq. (ii) are in AP.

Let $a-d$, a and $a+d$ are the roots of Eq. (ii).

Then, $$a - d + a + a + d = -\frac{54}{27}$$

$$\Rightarrow \quad a = -\frac{2}{3} \quad \text{...(iii)}$$

Since, a is a root of Eq. (ii), then

$$27a^3 + 54a^2 + ca - 10 = 0$$

$$\Rightarrow 27\left(-\frac{8}{27}\right) + 54\left(\frac{4}{9}\right) + c\left(-\frac{2}{3}\right) - 10 = 0 \quad \text{[from Eq. (iii)]}$$

$$\Rightarrow \quad 6 - \frac{2c}{3} = 0 \text{ or } c = 9$$

● ***Ex. 23*** *If a root of the equation* $n^2 \sin^2 x - 2\sin x - (2n+1) = 0$ *lies in* $[0, \pi/2]$, *the minimum positive integer value of n is*

Sol. (3) $\because \; n^2 \sin^2 x - 2\sin x - (2n+1) = 0$

$$\Rightarrow \quad \sin x = \frac{2 \pm \sqrt{4 + 4n^2(2n+1)}}{2n^2}$$

[by Shridharacharya method]

$$= \frac{1 \pm \sqrt{(2n^3 + n^2 + 1)}}{n^2}$$

$\because \quad 0 \le \sin x \le 1 \quad [\because x \in [0, \pi/2]]$

$$\Rightarrow \quad 0 \le \frac{1 + \sqrt{(2n^3 + n^2 + 1)}}{n^2} \le 1$$

$$\Rightarrow \quad 0 \le 1 + \sqrt{(2n^3 + n^2 + 1)} \le n^2$$

$$\Rightarrow \sqrt{(2n^3 + n^2 + 1)} \le (n^2 - 1) \quad [\because n > 1]$$

On squaring both sides, we get

$$2n^3 + n^2 + 1 \le n^4 - 2n^2 + 1$$

$$\Rightarrow \quad n^4 - 2n^3 - 3n^2 \ge 0$$

$$\Rightarrow \quad n^2 - 2n - 3 \ge 0 \Rightarrow (n-3)(n+1) \ge 0$$

$$\Rightarrow \quad n \ge 3$$

$$\therefore \quad n = 3, 4, 5, \dots$$

Hence, the minimum positive integer value of n is 3.

JEE Type Solved Examples : Matching Type Questions

- This section contains **2 examples.** Examples 24 and 25 have three statements (A, B and C) given in Column I and four statements (p, q, r and s) in **Column II.** Any given statement in **Column I** can have correct matching with one or more statement(s) given in **Column II.**

● ***Ex. 24*** *Column I contains rational algebraic expressions and Column II contains possible integers which lie in their range. Match the entries of Column I with one or more entries of the elements of Column II.*

	Column I		Column II
(A)	$y = \dfrac{x^2 - 2x + 9}{x^2 + 2x + 9}, x \in R$	(p)	1
(B)	$y = \dfrac{x^2 - 3x - 2}{2x - 3}, x \in R$	(q)	3
(C)	$y = \dfrac{2x^2 - 2x + 4}{x^2 - 4x + 3}, x \in R$	(r)	−4
		(s)	−9

Sol. (A) → (p); (B) → (p, q, r, s); (C) → (p, q, s)

(A) $y = \dfrac{x^2 - 2x + 9}{x^2 + 2x + 9} \Rightarrow x^2 y + 2xy + 9y = x^2 - 2x + 9$

$$\Rightarrow \quad (y-1)x^2 + 2x(y+1) + 9(y-1) = 0$$

$$\because \quad x \in R$$

$$\therefore \quad 4(y+1)^2 - 4 \cdot 9 \cdot (y-1)^2 \ge 0$$

$$\Rightarrow \quad (y+1)^2 - (3y-3)^2 \ge 0$$

$$\Rightarrow \quad (4y-2)(-2y+4) \ge 0$$

$$\Rightarrow \quad (2y-1)(y-2) \le 0$$

$$\therefore \quad \frac{1}{2} \le y \le 2 \Rightarrow y = 1, 2 \text{ (p)}$$

(B) $\because \quad y = \dfrac{x^2 - 3x - 2}{2x - 3} \Rightarrow 2xy - 3y = x^2 - 3x - 2$

$$\Rightarrow \quad x^2 - x(3 + 2y) + 3y - 2 = 0 \quad \because x \in R$$

$$\therefore \quad (3 + 2y)^2 - 4 \cdot 1 \cdot (3y - 2) \ge 0$$

$$\Rightarrow \quad 4y^2 + 17 \ge 0$$

$$\therefore \quad y \in R \text{ (p, q, r, s)}$$

(C) ∵ $y = \dfrac{2x^2 - 2x + 4}{x^2 - 4x + 3}$

$\Rightarrow \quad x^2y - 4xy + 3y = 2x^2 - 2x + 4$

$\Rightarrow \quad x^2(y-2) + 2x(1-2y) + 3y - 4 = 0$

$\because \quad x \in R$

$\therefore \quad 4(1-2y)^2 - 4(y-2)(3y-4) \geq 0$

$\Rightarrow \quad (4y^2 - 4y + 1) - (3y^2 - 10y + 8) \geq 0$

$\Rightarrow \quad y^2 + 6y - 7 \geq 0$

$\Rightarrow \quad (y+7)(y-1) \geq 0$

$\therefore \quad y \leq -7$ or $y \geq 1$(p,q,s)

• ***Ex. 25*** *Entries of Column I are to be matched with one or more entries of Column II.*

	Column I		Column II
(A)	If $a + b + 2c = 0$ but $c \neq 0$, then $ax^2 + bx + c = 0$ has	(p)	atleast one root in $(-2, 0)$
(B)	If $a, b, c \in R$ such that $2a - 3b + 6c = 0$, then equation has	(q)	atleast one root in $(-1, 0)$
(C)	Let a, b, c be non-zero real numbers such that $\int_0^1 (1+\cos^8 x)(ax^2+bx+c)dx = \int_0^2 (1+\cos^8 x)(ax^2+bx+c)dx$, the equation $ax^2 + bx + c = 0$ has	(r)	atleast one root in $(-1, 1)$
		(s)	atleast one root in $(0, 1)$
		(t)	atleast one root in $(0, 2)$

Sol. (A) → (r, s, t); (B) → (p, q, r); (C) → (r, s, t)

(A) Let $f(x) = ax^2 + bx + c$

Then, $f(1) = a + b + c = -c \quad [\because a + b + 2c = 0]$

and $f(0) = c$

$\therefore \quad f(0)f(1) = -c^2 < 0 \quad [\because c \neq 0]$

∴ Equation $f(x) = 0$ has a root in (0, 1).

∴ $f(x)$ has a root in (0, 2) as well as in (−1, 1) (r)

(B) Let $f'(x) = ax^2 + bx + c$

$\therefore \quad f(x) = \dfrac{ax^3}{3} + \dfrac{bx^2}{2} + cx + d$

$\therefore \quad f(0) = d$

and $f(-1) = -\dfrac{a}{3} + \dfrac{b}{2} + c + d = -\left(\dfrac{2a - 3b + 6c}{6}\right) + d$

$= 0 + d = d \quad [\because 2a - 3b + 6c = 0]$

Hence, $f(0) = f(-1)$

Hence, $f'(x) = 0$ has atleast one root in (−1,0) (q)

∴ $f(x) = 0$ has a root in (−2,0) (p) as well as (−1,1) (r)

(C) Let $f(x) = \int (1 + \cos^8 x)(ax^2 + bx + c)dx$

Given, $f(1) - f(0) = f(2) - f(0)$

$\Rightarrow \quad f(1) = f(2)$

$\Rightarrow \quad f'(x) = 0$ has atleast one root in (0,1).

$\Rightarrow (1 + \cos^8 x)(ax^2 + bx + c) = 0$ has atleast one root in (0,1).

$\Rightarrow ax^2 + bx + c = 0$ has atleast one root in (0, 1) (s)

∴ $ax^2 + bx + c = 0$ has a root in (0, 2) (t) as well as in (−1, 1)(r)

JEE Type Solved Examples : Statement I and II Type Questions

■ **Directions** Example numbers 26 and 27 are Assertion-Reason type examples. Each of these examples contains two statements:

Statement-1 (Assertion) and **Statement-2** (Reason)

Each of these examples also has four alternative choices, only one of which is the correct answer. You have to select the correct choice as given below.

(a) Statement-1 is true, Statement-2 is true; Statement-2 is a correct explanation for Statement-1

(b) Statement-1 is true, Statement-2 is true; Statement-2 is not a correct explanation for Statement-1

(c) Statement-1 is true, Statement-2 is false

(d) Statement-1 is false, Statement-2 is true

• ***Ex. 26*** **Statement 1** *Roots of* $x^2 - 2\sqrt{3}x - 46 = 0$ *are rational.*

Statement 2 *Discriminant of* $x^2 - 2\sqrt{3}x - 46 = 0$ *is a perfect square.*

Sol. (*d*) In $ax^2 + bx + c = 0$, $a, b, c \in Q$

[here Q is the set of rational number]

If $D > 0$ and is a perfect square, then roots are real, distinct and rational.

But, here $2\sqrt{3} \notin Q$

∴ Roots are not rational.

Here, roots are $\dfrac{2\sqrt{3} \pm \sqrt{(12 + 184)}}{2}$

i.e. $\sqrt{3} \pm 7$. [irrational]

But $D = 12 + 184 = 196 = (14)^2$

∴ Statement-1 is false and Statement-2 is true.

• ***Ex. 27*** **Statement 1** *The equation* $a^x + b^x + c^x - d^x = 0$ *has only one real root, if* $a > b > c > d$.

Statement 2 *If* $f(x)$ *is either strictly increasing or decreasing function, then* $f(x) = 0$ *has only one real root.*

Sol. (*c*) $\because \quad a^x + b^x + c^x - d^x = 0$

$\Rightarrow \quad a^x + b^x + c^x = d^x$

Let $f(x)=\left(\frac{a}{d}\right)^x+\left(\frac{b}{d}\right)^x+\left(\frac{c}{d}\right)^x-1$

$\therefore\quad f'(x)=\left(\frac{a}{d}\right)^x\ln\left(\frac{a}{d}\right)+\left(\frac{b}{d}\right)^x\ln\left(\frac{b}{d}\right)+\left(\frac{c}{d}\right)^x\ln\left(\frac{c}{d}\right)>0$

and $f(0)=2$

$\therefore$ $f(x)$ is increasing function and $\lim_{x\to-\infty} f(x)=-1$

$\Rightarrow$ $f(x)$ has only one real root.

But Statement-2 is false.

For example, $f(x)=e^x$ is increasing but $f(x)=0$ has no solution.

Subjective Type Examples

- In this section, there are **24 subjective** solved examples.

• Ex. 28 *If* α,β *are roots of the equation* $x^2-p(x+1)-c=0$, *show that* $(\alpha+1)(\beta+1)=1-c$. *Hence, prove that* $\frac{\alpha^2+2\alpha+1}{\alpha^2+2\alpha+c}+\frac{\beta^2+2\beta+1}{\beta^2+2\beta+c}=1.$

Sol. Since, α and β are the roots of the equation,

$$x^2-px-p-c=0$$

$\therefore\quad \alpha+\beta=p$

and $\quad \alpha\beta=-p-c$

Now, $(\alpha+1)(\beta+1)=\alpha\beta+\alpha+\beta+1$

$$=-p-c+p+1=1-c$$

Hence, $\quad (\alpha+1)(\beta+1)=1-c \quad$ ...(i)

Second Part LHS $=\frac{\alpha^2+2\alpha+1}{\alpha^2+2\alpha+c}+\frac{\beta^2+2\beta+1}{\beta^2+2\beta+c}$

$$=\frac{(\alpha+1)^2}{(\alpha+1)^2-(1-c)}+\frac{(\beta+1)^2}{(\beta+1)^2-(1-c)}$$

$$=\frac{(\alpha+1)^2}{(\alpha+1)^2-(\alpha+1)(\beta+1)}+\frac{(\beta+1)^2}{(\beta+1)^2-(\alpha+1)(\beta+1)}\quad\text{[from Eq. (i)]}$$

$$=\frac{\alpha+1}{\alpha-\beta}+\frac{\beta+1}{\beta-\alpha}=\frac{\alpha-\beta}{\alpha-\beta}=1=\text{RHS}$$

Hence, RHS = LHS

• Ex. 29 *Solve the equation* $x^2+px+45=0$. *It is given that the squared difference of its roots is equal to 144.*

Sol. Let α,β be the roots of the equation $x^2+px+45=0$ and given that

$$(\alpha-\beta)^2=144$$

$\Rightarrow\quad p^2-4\cdot1\cdot45=144\quad\left[\because \alpha-\beta=\frac{\sqrt{D}}{a}\right]$

$\Rightarrow\quad p^2=324$

$\therefore\quad p=(\pm 18)$

On substituting $p=18$ in the given equation, we obtain

$$x^2+18x+45=0$$

$\Rightarrow\quad (x+3)(x+15)=0$

$\Rightarrow\quad x=-3,5$

and substituting $p=-18$ in the given equation, we obtain

$$x^2-18x+45=0$$

$$(x-3)(x-15)=0$$

$\Rightarrow\quad x=3,15$

Hence, the roots of the given equation are $(-3),(-15),3$ and 15.

• Ex. 30 *If the roots of the equation* $ax^2+bx+c=0\ (a\neq0)$ *be* α *and* β *and those of the equation* $Ax^2+Bx+C=0$ $(A\neq0)$ *be* $\alpha+k$ *and* $\beta+k$. *Prove that*

$$\frac{b^2-4ac}{B^2-4AC}=\left(\frac{a}{A}\right)^2.$$

Sol. $\because \alpha-\beta=(\alpha+k)-(\beta+k)$

$\Rightarrow\quad \frac{\sqrt{b^2-4ac}}{a}=\frac{\sqrt{(B^2-4AC)}}{A}\quad\left[\because \alpha-\beta=\frac{\sqrt{D}}{a}\right]$

$\Rightarrow\quad \sqrt{\left(\frac{b^2-4ac}{B^2-4AC}\right)}=\left(\frac{a}{A}\right)$

On squaring both sides, then we get

$$\frac{b^2-4ac}{B^2-4AC}=\left(\frac{a}{A}\right)^2$$

• Ex. 31 *Let a, b and c be real numbers such that* $a+2b+c=4$. *Find the maximum value of* $(ab+bc+ca)$.

Sol. Given, $\quad a+2b+c=4$

$\Rightarrow\quad a=4-2b-c$

Let $\quad y=ab+bc+ca=a(b+c)+bc$

$$=(4-2b-c)(b+c)+bc$$

$$=-2b^2+4b-2bc+4c-c^2$$

$\Rightarrow\quad 2b^2+2(c-2)b-4c+c^2+y=0$

Since, $b\in R$, so

$$4(c-2)^2-4\times2\times(-4c+c^2+y)\geq0$$

$$\Rightarrow \quad (c-2)^2 + 8c - 2c^2 - 2y \geq 0$$
$$\Rightarrow \quad c^2 - 4c + 2y - 4 \leq 0$$

Since, $c \in R$, so $16 - 4(2y-4) \geq 0 \Rightarrow y \leq 4$

Hence, maximum value of $ab + bc + ca$ is 4.

Aliter

$$\because \quad AM \geq GM$$
$$\Rightarrow \quad \frac{(a+b)+(b+c)}{2} \geq \sqrt{(a+b)(b+c)}$$
$$\Rightarrow \quad 2 \geq \sqrt{(ab+bc+ca+b^2)} \quad [\because a + 2b + c = 4]$$
$$\Rightarrow \quad ab + bc + ca \leq 4 - b^2$$

$\therefore$ Maximum value of $(ab + bc + ca)$ is 4.

- **Ex. 32** *Find a quadratic equation whose roots x_1 and x_2 satisfy the condition $x_1^2 + x_2^2 = 5, 3(x_1^5 + x_2^5) = 11(x_1^3 + x_2^3)$ (assume that x_1, x_2 are real).*

Sol. We have, $3(x_1^5 + x_2^5) = 11(x_1^3 + x_2^3)$

$$\Rightarrow \quad \frac{x_1^5 + x_2^5}{x_1^3 + x_2^3} = \frac{11}{3}$$
$$\Rightarrow \quad \frac{(x_1^2 + x_2^2)(x_1^3 + x_2^3) - x_1^2 x_2^2 (x_1 + x_2)}{(x_1^3 + x_2^3)} = \frac{11}{3}$$
$$\Rightarrow \quad (x_1^2 + x_2^2) - \frac{x_1^2 x_2^2 (x_1 + x_2)}{(x_1 + x_2)(x_1^2 + x_2^2 - x_1 x_2)} = \frac{11}{3}$$
$$[\because x_1^2 + x_2^2 = 5]$$
$$\Rightarrow \quad 5 - \frac{x_1^2 x_2^2}{5 - x_1 x_2} = \frac{11}{3}$$
$$\Rightarrow \quad \frac{4}{3} = \frac{x_1^2 x_2^2}{5 - x_1 x_2}$$
$$\Rightarrow \quad 3x_1^2 x_2^2 + 4x_1 x_2 - 20 = 0$$
$$\Rightarrow 3x_1^2 x_2^2 + 10x_1 x_2 - 6x_1 x_2 - 20 = 0$$
$$\Rightarrow \quad (x_1 x_2 - 2)(3x_1 x_2 + 10) = 0$$
$$\therefore \quad x_1 x_2 = 2, \left(-\frac{10}{3}\right)$$

We have, $(x_1 + x_2)^2 = x_1^2 + x_2^2 + 2x_1 x_2 = 5 + 2x_1 x_2$

$$\therefore \quad (x_1 + x_2)^2 = 5 + 4 = 9 \quad [\text{if } x_1 x_2 = 2]$$
$$\therefore \quad x_1 + x_2 = \pm 3$$

and $(x_1 + x_2)^2 = 5 + 2\left(-\frac{10}{3}\right) = -\frac{5}{3}\left[\text{if } x_1 x_2 = -\frac{10}{3}\right]$

which is not possible, since x_1, x_2 are real.

Thus, required quadratic equations are $x^2 \pm 3x + 2 = 0$.

- **Ex. 33** *If each pair of the three equations $x^2 + ax + b = 0, x^2 + cx + d = 0$ and $x^2 + ex + f = 0$ has exactly one root in common, then show that $(a + c + e)^2 = 4(ac + ce + ea - b - d - f)$.*

Sol. Given equations are

$$x^2 + ax + b = 0 \quad \text{...(i)}$$
$$x^2 + cx + d = 0 \quad \text{...(ii)}$$
$$x^2 + ex + f = 0 \quad \text{...(iii)}$$

Let α, β be the roots of Eq. (i), β, γ be the roots of Eq. (ii) and γ, δ be the roots of Eq. (iii), then

$$\alpha + \beta = -a, \alpha\beta = b \quad \text{...(iv)}$$
$$\beta + \gamma = -c, \beta\gamma = d \quad \text{...(v)}$$
$$\gamma + \alpha = -e, \gamma\alpha = f \quad \text{...(vi)}$$
$$\therefore \text{LHS} = (a + c + e)^2 = (-\alpha - \beta - \beta - \gamma - \gamma - \alpha)^2$$
[from Eqs. (iv), (v) and (vi)]
$$= 4(\alpha + \beta + \gamma)^2 \quad \text{...(vii)}$$
$$\text{RHS} = 4(ac + ce + ea - b - d - f)$$
$$= 4\{(\alpha + \beta)(\beta + \gamma) + (\beta + \gamma)(\gamma + \alpha) + (\gamma + \alpha)(\alpha + \beta) - \alpha\beta - \beta\gamma - \gamma\alpha\}$$
[from Eqs. (iv), (v) and (vi)]
$$= 4(\alpha^2 + \beta^2 + \gamma^2 + 2\alpha\beta + 2\beta\gamma + 2\gamma\alpha)$$
$$= 4(\alpha + \beta + \gamma)^2 \quad \text{...(viii)}$$

From Eqs. (vii) and (viii), then we get

$$(a + c + e)^2 = 4(ac + ce + ea - b - d - f)$$

- **Ex. 34** *If α, β are the roots of the equation $x^2 + px + q = 0$ and γ, δ are the roots of the equation $x^2 + rx + s = 0$, evaluate $(\alpha - \gamma)(\alpha - \delta)(\beta - \gamma)(\beta - \delta)$ in terms of p, q, r and s. Deduce the condition that the equations have a common root.*

Sol. $\because \alpha, \beta$ are the roots of the equation

$$x^2 + px + q = 0$$
$$\therefore \quad \alpha + \beta = -p, \alpha\beta = q \quad \text{...(i)}$$

and γ, δ are the roots of the equation $x^2 + rx + s = 0$

$$\therefore \quad \gamma + \delta = -r, \gamma\delta = s \quad \text{...(ii)}$$

Now, $(\alpha - \gamma)(\alpha - \delta)(\beta - \gamma)(\beta - \delta)$

$$= [\alpha^2 - \alpha(\gamma + \delta) + \gamma\delta][\beta^2 - \beta(\gamma + \delta) + \gamma\delta]$$
$$= (\alpha^2 + r\alpha + s)(\beta^2 + r\beta + s) \quad [\text{from Eq. (ii)}]$$
$$= \alpha^2\beta^2 + r\alpha\beta(\alpha + \beta) + r^2\alpha\beta + s(\alpha^2 + \beta^2) + sr(\alpha + \beta) + s^2$$
$$= \alpha^2\beta^2 + r\alpha\beta(\alpha + \beta) + r^2\alpha\beta + s[(\alpha + \beta)^2 - 2\alpha\beta] + sr(\alpha + \beta) + s^2$$
$$= q^2 - pqr + r^2 q + s(p^2 - 2q) + sr(-p) + s^2$$
$$= (q - s)^2 - rpq + r^2 q + sp^2 - prs$$
$$= (q - s)^2 - rq(p - r) + sp(p - r)$$
$$= (q - s)^2 + (p - r)(sp - rq) \quad \text{...(iii)}$$

For a common root (let $\alpha = \gamma$ or $\beta = \delta$), then $(\alpha - \gamma)(\alpha - \delta)(\beta - \gamma)(\beta - \delta) = 0$ ...(iv)

From Eqs. (iii) and (iv), we get

$$(q-s)^2+(p-r)(sp-rq)=0$$

$\Rightarrow (q-s)^2=(p-r)(rq-sp)$, which is the required condition .

Ex. 35 *Find all integral values of a for which the quadratic Expresion $(x-a)(x-10)+1$ can be factored as a product $(x+\alpha)(x+\beta)$ of two factors and $\alpha, \beta \in I$.*

Sol. We have, $(x-a)(x-10)+1=(x+\alpha)(x+\beta)$

On putting $x=-\alpha$ in both sides, we get

$$(-\alpha-a)(-\alpha-10)+1=0$$

$\therefore \quad (\alpha+a)(\alpha+10)=-1$

$\alpha+a$ and $\alpha+10$ are integers. $\quad [\because a, \alpha \in I]$

$\therefore \quad \alpha+a=-1$ and $\alpha+10=1$

or $\quad \alpha+a=1$ and $\alpha+10=-1$

(i) If $\alpha+10=1$

$\therefore \quad \alpha=-9$, then $a=8$

Similarly, $\beta=-9$

Here, $(x-8)(x-10)+1=(x-9)^2$

(ii) If $\alpha+10=-1$

$\therefore \quad \alpha=-11$, then $a=12$

Similarly, $\beta=12$

Here, $(x-12)(x-10)+1=(x-11)^2$

Hence, $a=8, 12$

Ex. 36 *Solve the equation*

$$\sqrt{x+3-4\sqrt{(x-1)}}+\sqrt{x+8-6\sqrt{(x-1)}}=1.$$

Sol. Let $\sqrt{(x-1)}=t$

We have, $\quad x=t^2+1, t\geq 0$

The given equation reduce in the form

$$\sqrt{(t^2+4-4t)}+\sqrt{(t^2+9-6t)}=1$$

$$\Rightarrow \quad |t-2|+|t-3|=1$$

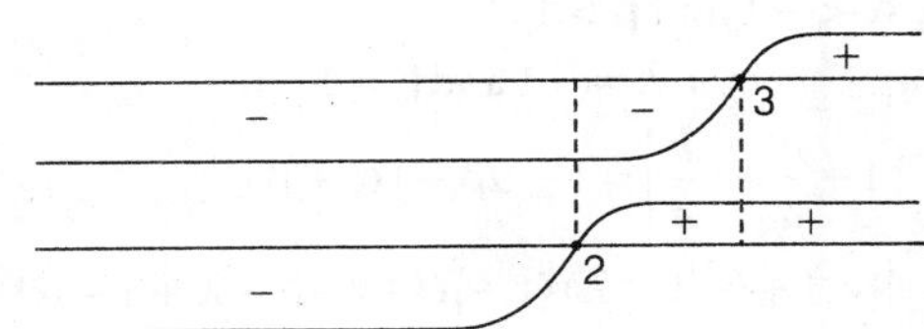

$\therefore \quad 2\leq t\leq 3$

$\Rightarrow \quad 4\leq t^2\leq 9$

$\Rightarrow \quad 4\leq x-1\leq 9$

$\Rightarrow \quad 5\leq x\leq 10$

$\therefore$ Solution of the original equation is $x\in[5,10]$.

Ex. 37 *Solve for 'x'*

$1!+2!+3!+\ldots+(x-1)!+x!=k^2$ and $k\in I$.

Sol. For $x<4$, the given equation has the only solutions $x=1, k=\pm 1$ and $x=3, k=\pm 3$. Now, let us prove that there are no solutions for $x\geq 4$. The expressions

$$\left.\begin{aligned} 1!+2!+3!+4! &= 33 \\ 1!+2!+3!+4!+5! &= 153 \\ 1!+2!+3!+4!+5!+6! &= 873 \\ 1!+2!+3!+4!+5!+6!+7! &= 5913 \end{aligned}\right\} \text{ends with the digit}$$

3.

Now, for $x\geq 4$ the last digit of the sum $1!+2!+\ldots+x!$ is equal to 3 and therefore, this sum cannot be equal to a square of a whole number k (because a square of a whole number cannot end with 3).

Ex. 38 *Find the real roots of the equation*

$$\underbrace{\sqrt{x+2\sqrt{x+2\sqrt{x+\ldots+2\sqrt{x+2\sqrt{3x}}}}}}_{n \text{ radical signs}}=x$$

Sol. Rewrite the given equation

$$\sqrt{x+2\sqrt{x+2\sqrt{x+\ldots+2\sqrt{x+2\sqrt{x+2x}}}}}=x \quad \ldots(\text{i})$$

On replacing the last letter x on the LHS of Eq. (i) by the value of x expressed by Eq. (i), we get

$$x=\underbrace{\sqrt{x+2\sqrt{x+2\sqrt{x+\ldots+\sqrt{x+2x}}}}}_{2n \text{ radical signs}}$$

Further, let us replace the last letter x by the same expression again and again yields.

$$\therefore \quad x=\underbrace{\sqrt{x+2\sqrt{x+2\sqrt{x+\ldots+2\sqrt{x+2x}}}}}_{3n \text{ radical signs}}$$

$$=\underbrace{\sqrt{x+2\sqrt{x+2\sqrt{x+\ldots+2\sqrt{x+2x}}}}}_{4n \text{ radical signs}}=\ldots$$

We can write,

$$x=\sqrt{x+2\sqrt{x+2\sqrt{x+\ldots}}}$$

$$=\lim_{N\to\infty}\underbrace{\sqrt{x+2\sqrt{x+2\sqrt{x+\ldots+2\sqrt{x+2x}}}}}_{N \text{ radical signs}}$$

If follows that

$$x=\sqrt{x+2\sqrt{x+2\sqrt{x+\ldots}}}$$

$$=\sqrt{x+2(\sqrt{x+2\sqrt{x+\ldots}})}=\sqrt{(x+2x)}$$

Hence, $\quad x^2=x+2x$

$\Rightarrow \quad x^2-3x=0$

$\therefore \quad x=0, 3$

Ex. 39 *Solve the inequation,* $(x^2 + x + 1)^x < 1$.

Sol. Taking logarithm both sides on base 10,

then $x \log(x^2 + x + 1) < 0$

which is equivalent to the collection of systems

$$\left[\begin{cases} x > 0, \\ \log(x^2 + x + 1) < 0, \end{cases} \atop \begin{cases} x < 0, \\ \log(x^2 + x + 1) > 0, \end{cases}\right. \Rightarrow \left[\begin{cases} x > 0, \\ x^2 + x + 1 < 1, \end{cases} \atop \begin{cases} x < 0, \\ x^2 + x + 1 > 1, \end{cases}\right.$$

$$\Rightarrow \left[\begin{cases} x > 0, \\ x(x+1) < 0, \end{cases} \atop \begin{cases} x < 0, \\ x(x+1) > 0 \end{cases}\right. \Rightarrow \left[\begin{cases} x > 0, \\ -1 < x < 0 \end{cases} \atop \begin{cases} x < 0, \\ x > 0 \text{ and } x < (-1) \end{cases}\right.$$

$$\Rightarrow \left[\begin{array}{l} x \in \phi, \\ x < (-1) \end{array}\right.$$

Consequently, the interval $x \in (-\infty, -1)$ is the set of all solutions of the original inequation.

Remark

When the inequation is in power, then it is better to take log.

Ex. 40 *Solve the equation*

$$1 + \cfrac{1}{1 + \cfrac{1}{1 + \cfrac{1}{1 + \ddots \cfrac{}{1 + \cfrac{1}{x}}}}} = x$$

When in expression on left hand side the sign of a fraction is repeated n times.

Sol. Given equation is

$$1 + \cfrac{1}{1 + \cfrac{1}{1 + \cfrac{1}{1 + \ddots \cfrac{}{1 + \cfrac{1}{x}}}}} = x$$

Let us replace x on the LHS of the given equation by the expression of x. This result in an equation of the same form, which however involves $2n$ fraction lines. Continuing this process on the basis of this transformation, we can write

$$x = 1 + \lim_{n \to \infty} 1 + \cfrac{1}{1 + \cfrac{1}{1 + \cfrac{1}{1 + \ddots \cfrac{}{1 + \cfrac{1}{x}}}}} \quad [n \text{ fractions}]$$

$$\Rightarrow \quad x = 1 + \frac{1}{x} \Rightarrow x^2 - x - 1 = 0$$

$$\therefore \quad x = \frac{1 \pm \sqrt{5}}{2}$$

$$\therefore \quad x_1 = \frac{1 + \sqrt{5}}{2}, x_2 = \frac{1 - \sqrt{5}}{2}$$

satisfy the given equation and this equation has no other roots.

Ex. 41 *Solve the system of equations*

$$\begin{cases} |x - 1| + |y - 2| = 1 \\ y = 2 - |x - 1| \end{cases}.$$

Sol. On substituting $|x - 1| = 2 - y$ from second equation in first equation of this system, we get

$$2 - y + |y - 2| = 1$$

Now, consider the following cases

If $\quad y \geq 2,$

then $\quad 2 - y + y - 2 = 1 \Rightarrow 0 = 1$

No value of y for $y \geq 2$.

If $\quad y < 2,$

then $\quad 2 - y + 2 - y = 1 \Leftrightarrow y = \frac{3}{2}$, which is true.

From the second equation of this system,

$$\frac{3}{2} = 2 - |x - 1|$$

$$\Rightarrow \quad |x - 1| = \frac{1}{2} \Rightarrow x - 1 = \pm \frac{1}{2}$$

$$\Rightarrow \quad x = 1 \pm \frac{1}{2} \Rightarrow x = \frac{1}{2}, \frac{3}{2}$$

Consequently, the set of all solutions of the original system is the set of pairs (x, y), where $x = \frac{1}{2}, \frac{3}{2}$ and $y = \frac{3}{2}$.

Ex. 42 *Let a, b, c be real and* $ax^2 + bx + c = 0$ *has two real roots* α *and* β, *where* $\alpha < -1$ *and* $\beta > 1$, *then show that* $1 + \frac{c}{a} + \left|\frac{b}{a}\right| < 0$.

Sol. Since, $\alpha < -1$ and $\beta > 1$

$$\alpha + \lambda = -1 \text{ and } \beta = 1 + \mu \quad [\lambda, \mu > 0]$$

Now, $\quad 1 + \frac{c}{a} + \left|\frac{b}{a}\right| = 1 + \alpha\beta + |\alpha + \beta|$

$$= 1 + (-1 - \lambda)(1 + \mu) + |-1 - \lambda + 1 + \mu|$$

$$= 1 - 1 - \mu - \lambda - \lambda\mu + |\mu - \lambda|$$

$$= -\mu - \lambda - \lambda\mu + \mu - \lambda \quad [\text{if } \mu > \lambda]$$

and $\quad = -\mu - \lambda - \lambda\mu + \lambda - \mu \quad [\text{if } \lambda > \mu]$

$$\therefore \quad 1 + \frac{c}{a} + \left|\frac{b}{a}\right| = -2\lambda - \lambda\mu \text{ or } -2\mu - \lambda\mu$$

On both cases, $\quad 1 + \frac{c}{a} + \left|\frac{b}{a}\right| < 0 \quad [\because \lambda, \mu > 0]$

Aliter

$\because \quad ax^2 + bx + c = 0, a \neq 0$

$$x^2 + \frac{b}{a}x + \frac{c}{a} = 0$$

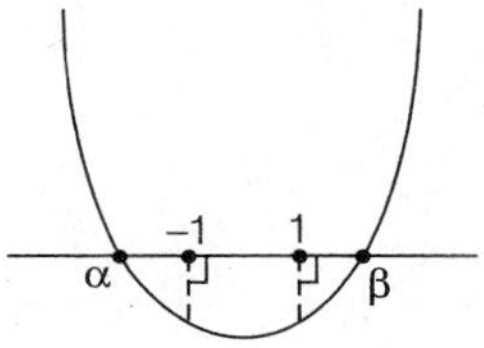

Let $\quad f(x) = x^2 + \frac{b}{a}x + \frac{c}{a}$

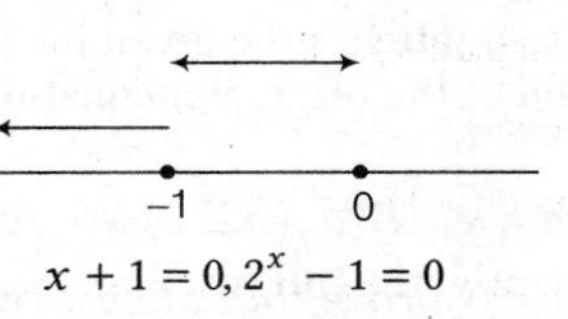

$f(-1) < 0$ and $f(1) < 0$

$\Rightarrow \quad 1 - \frac{b}{a} + \frac{c}{a} < 0$ and $1 + \frac{b}{a} + \frac{c}{a} < 0$

Then, $1 + \left|\frac{b}{a}\right| + \frac{c}{a} < 0$

- **Ex. 43** *Solve the equation* $x\left(\frac{3-x}{x+1}\right)\left(x + \frac{3-x}{x+1}\right) = 2.$

Sol. Hence, $x + 1 \neq 0$

and let $\quad x\left(\frac{3-x}{x+1}\right) = u$ and $x + \frac{3-x}{x+1} = v$

$\therefore \quad uv = 2 \quad$ ...(i)

and $\quad u + v = x\left(\frac{3-x}{x+1}\right) + x + \left(\frac{3-x}{x+1}\right)$

$$= (x+1)\left(\frac{3-x}{x+1}\right) + x = 3 - x + x = 3$$

$\therefore \quad u + v = 3 \quad$ and $\quad uv = 2$

Then, $\quad u = 2, v = 1$ or $u = 1, v = 2$

Given equation is equivalent to the collection

$$\therefore \quad \begin{cases} x\left(\frac{3-x}{x+1}\right) = 2 \\ x + \frac{3-x}{x+1} = 1 \end{cases} \text{or} \begin{cases} x\left(\frac{3-x}{x+1}\right) = 1 \\ x + \frac{3-x}{x+1} = 2 \end{cases}$$

$$\Rightarrow \quad \begin{cases} x^2 - x + 2 = 0 \\ x^2 - x + 2 = 0 \end{cases} \text{or} \begin{cases} x^2 - 2x + 1 = 0 \\ x^2 - 2x + 1 = 0 \end{cases}$$

$$\Rightarrow \quad \begin{cases} x^2 - x + 2 = 0 \\ x^2 - 2x + 1 = 0 \end{cases} \Rightarrow \begin{cases} \left(x - \frac{1}{2}\right)^2 + \frac{7}{4} \neq 0 \\ (x-1)^2 = 0 \end{cases}$$

$$\therefore \quad (x-1)^2 = 0$$

$\Rightarrow x = 1$ is a unique solution of the original equation.

- **Ex. 44** *Show that for any real numbers* $a_3, a_4, a_5, \ldots, a_{85}$, *the roots of the equation* $a_{85}x^{85} + a_{84}x^{84} + \ldots + a_3x^3 + 3x^2 + 2x + 1 = 0$ *are not real.*

Sol. Let $\quad P(x) = a_{85}x^{85} + a_{84}x^{84}$

$$+ \ldots + a_3x^3 + 3x^2 + 2x + 1 = 0 \quad \text{...(i)}$$

Since, $P(0) = 1$, then 0 is not a root of Eq. (i).

Let $\alpha_1, \alpha_2, \alpha_3, \ldots, \alpha_{85}$ be the complex roots of Eq. (i).

Then, the $\beta_i \left(\text{let} \frac{1}{\alpha_i}\right)$ the complex roots of the polynomial

$$Q(y) = y^{85} + 2y^{84} + 3y^{83} + a_3y^{82} + \ldots + a_{85}$$

It follows that

$$\sum_{i=1}^{85} \beta_i = -2 \text{ and } \sum_{1 \le i < j \le 85} \sum \beta_i\beta_j = 3$$

Then, $\quad \sum_{i=1}^{85} \beta_i^2 = \left(\sum_{i=1}^{85} \beta_i\right)^2 - 2 \sum_{1 \le i < j \le 85} \sum \beta_i\beta_j$

$$= 4 - 6 = -2 < 0$$

Thus, the β_i's is not all real and then α_i's are not all real.

- **Ex. 45** *Solve the equation*

$$2^{|x+1|} - 2^x = |2^x - 1| + 1.$$

Sol. Find the critical points :

(number line with critical points −1 and 0)

$$x + 1 = 0, 2^x - 1 = 0$$

$\therefore \quad x = -1, x = 0$

Now, consider the following cases :

$\boldsymbol{x < -1}$

$$2^{-(x+1)} - 2^x = -(2^x - 1) + 1$$

$\Rightarrow \quad 2^{-(x+1)} = 2$

$\therefore \quad -(x+1) = 1$

$\therefore \quad x = -2 \quad$ ...(i)

$\boldsymbol{-1 \le x < 0}$

$$2^{x+1} - 2^x = -(2^x - 1) + 1$$

$\Rightarrow \quad 2^{x+1} = 2$

$\therefore \quad x + 1 = 1$

$\therefore \quad x = 0$

$\quad x \neq 0 \quad [\because -1 \le x < 0]$

$\boldsymbol{x \ge 0}$

$$2^{x+1} - 2^x = 2^x - 1 + 1$$

$\Rightarrow \quad 2^{x+1} = 2 \cdot 2^x$

$\Rightarrow \quad 2^{x+1} = 2^{x+1}$

which is true for $\quad x \ge 0. \quad$ ...(ii)

Now, combining all cases, we have the final solution as

$$x \in [0, \infty) \cup \{-2\}$$

- **Ex. 46** *Solve the inequation*

$$-|y| + x - \sqrt{(x^2 + y^2 - 1)} \ge 1.$$

Sol. We have, $-|y| + x - \sqrt{(x^2 + y^2 - 1)} \ge 1$

$\Rightarrow \quad x - |y| \ge 1 + \sqrt{(x^2 + y^2 - 1)}$

if $\quad x \ge |y|,$

then squaring both sides,

$$x^2 + y^2 - 2x|y| \ge 1 + x^2 + y^2 - 1 + 2\sqrt{(x^2 + y^2 - 1)}$$

$\Rightarrow \quad -x|y| \ge \sqrt{(x^2 + y^2 - 1)} \quad$ ...(i)

Since, $\quad x \ge |y| \ge 0 \quad$ ...(ii)

Then, LHS of Eq. (i) is non-positive and RHS of Eq. (ii) is non-negative. Therefore, the system is satisfied only, when both sides are zero.

$\therefore$ The inequality Eq. (i) is equivalent to the system.

$$\begin{cases} x|y| = 0 \\ x^2 + y^2 - 1 = 0 \end{cases}$$

The Eq.(i) gives $x = 0$ or $y = 0$. If $x = 0$, then we find $y = \pm 1$ from Eq. (ii) but $x \geq |y|$ which is impossible.

If $y = 0$, then from Eq. (ii), we find

$$x^2 = 1$$

$$\therefore \quad x = 1, -1$$

Taking $\quad x = 1 \quad [\because x \geq |y|]$

$\therefore$ The pair (1, 0) satisfies the given inequation. Hence, (1, 0) is the solution of the original inequation.

Ex. 47 *If $a_1, a_2, a_3, \ldots, a_n (n \geq 2)$ are real and $(n-1)a_1^2 - 2na_2 < 0$, prove that atleast two roots of the equation $x^n + a_1 x^{n-1} + a_2 x^{n-2} + \ldots + a_n = 0$ are imaginary.*

Sol. Let $\alpha_1, \alpha_2, \alpha_3, \ldots, \alpha_n$ are the roots of the given equation.

Then, $\quad \Sigma\alpha_1 = \alpha_1 + \alpha_2 + \alpha_3 + \ldots + \alpha_n = -a_1$

and $\quad \Sigma\alpha_1\alpha_2 = \alpha_1\alpha_2 + \alpha_1\alpha_3 + \ldots + \alpha_{n-1}\alpha_n = a_2$

Now, $(n-1)a_1^2 - 2na_2 = (n-1)(\Sigma\alpha_1)^2 - 2n\Sigma\alpha_1\alpha_2$

$$= n\{(\Sigma\alpha_1)^2 - 2\Sigma\alpha_1\alpha_2\} - (\Sigma\alpha_1)^2$$

$$= n\Sigma\alpha_1^2 - (\Sigma a_1)^2$$

$$= \sum_{1 \leq i < j \leq n} \Sigma(\alpha_i - \alpha_j)^2$$

But given that $(n-1)a_1^2 - 2na_2 < 0$

$$\Rightarrow \quad \sum_{1 \leq i < j \leq n} \Sigma(\alpha_i - \alpha_j)^2 < 0$$

which is true only, when atleast two roots are imaginary.

Ex. 48 *Solve the inequation $|a^{2x} + a^{x+2} - 1| \geq 1$ for all values of $a (a > 0, a \neq 1)$.*

Sol. Using $a^x = t$,

the given inequation can be written in the form

$$|t^2 + a^2 t - 1| \geq 1 \quad \ldots \text{(i)}$$

$\because \quad a > 0$ and $a \neq 1$, then $a^x > 0$

$$\therefore \quad t > 0 \quad \ldots \text{(ii)}$$

Inequation (i) write in the forms,

$$t^2 + a^2 t - 1 \geq 1 \text{ and } t^2 + a^2 t - 1 \leq -1$$

$$\therefore \quad t \leq \frac{-a^2 - \sqrt{a^4 + 8}}{2}, t \geq \frac{-a^2 + \sqrt{(a^4 + 8)}}{2}$$

and $\quad -a^2 \leq t \leq 0$

But $\quad t > 0 \quad$ [from Eq. (ii)]

$$\therefore \quad t \geq \frac{-a^2 + \sqrt{(a^4 + 8)}}{2}$$

$$\therefore \quad a^x \geq \frac{-a^2 + \sqrt{(a^4 + 8)}}{2}$$

For $\quad 0 < a < 1$,

$$x \leq \log_a \left(\frac{-a^2 + \sqrt{(a^4 + 8)}}{2} \right)$$

$$\therefore \quad x \in \left[-\infty, \log_a \left(\frac{-a^2 + \sqrt{(a^4 + 8)}}{2} \right) \right]$$

and for $a > 1$, $x \geq \log_a \left(\frac{-a^2 + \sqrt{(a^4 + 8)}}{2} \right)$

$$\therefore \quad x \in \left(\log_a \left(\frac{-a^2 + \sqrt{(a^4 + 8)}}{2} \right), \infty \right)$$

Ex. 49 *Solve the inequation*

$$\log_{|x|}(\sqrt{(9 - x^2)} - x - 1) \geq 1.$$

Sol. We rewrite the given inequation in the form,

$$\log_{|x|}(\sqrt{(9 - x^2)} - x - 1) \geq \log_{|x|}(|x|)$$

This inequation is equivalent to the collection of systems.

$$\left[\begin{array}{l} \sqrt{(9 - x^2)} - x - 1 \geq |x|, \text{ if } |x| > 1 \\ \sqrt{(9 - x^2)} - x - 1 \leq |x| \text{ if } \; 0 < |x| < 1 \end{array} \right.$$

$$\left[\begin{array}{l} \left\{ \begin{array}{c} \text{For } x > 1 \\ \sqrt{(9 - x^2)} - x - 1 \geq x \\ \text{For } x < -1 \\ \sqrt{(9 - x^2)} - x - 1 \geq -x \end{array} \right. \\ \text{and} \\ \left\{ \begin{array}{c} \text{For } 0 < x < 1 \\ \sqrt{(9 - x^2)} - x - 1 \leq x \\ \text{For } -1 < x < 0 \\ \sqrt{(9 - x^2)} - x - 1 \leq -x \end{array} \right. \end{array} \right. \Rightarrow \left[\begin{array}{l} \left\{ \begin{array}{c} \text{For } x > 1 \\ \sqrt{(9 - x^2)} \geq 2x + 1 \\ \text{For } x < -1 \\ \sqrt{(9 - x^2)} \geq 1 \end{array} \right. \\ \left\{ \begin{array}{c} \text{For } 0 < x < 1 \\ \sqrt{(9 - x^2)} \leq 2x + 1 \\ \text{For } -1 < x < 0 \\ \sqrt{(9 - x^2)} \leq 1 \end{array} \right. \end{array} \right.$$

$$\Rightarrow \left[\begin{array}{l} \left\{ \begin{array}{c} \text{For } x > 1 \\ -\frac{2}{5}(\sqrt{11} + 1) \leq x \leq \frac{2}{5}(\sqrt{11} - 1) \\ \text{For } x < -1 \\ -2\sqrt{2} \leq x \leq 2\sqrt{2} \end{array} \right. \\ \left\{ \begin{array}{c} \text{For } 0 < x < 1 \\ x \leq -\frac{2}{5}(\sqrt{11} + 1) \text{ and } x \geq \frac{2}{5}(\sqrt{11} - 1) \\ \text{For } -1 < x < 0 \\ x \leq -2\sqrt{2} \text{ and } x \geq 2\sqrt{2} \end{array} \right. \end{array} \right.$$

$$\Rightarrow \left[\begin{array}{l} \begin{cases} x \in \phi \\ -2\sqrt{2} \le x < -1 \end{cases} \\ \begin{cases} \frac{2}{5}(\sqrt{11}-1) \le x < 1 \\ x \in \phi \end{cases} \end{array}\right.$$

Hence, the original inequation consists of the intervals

$$-2\sqrt{2} \le x < -1 \text{ and } \frac{2}{5}(\sqrt{11}-1) \le x < 1.$$

Hence, $x \in [-2\sqrt{2}, -1) \cup \left[\frac{2}{5}(\sqrt{11}-1), 1\right)$

• Ex. 50 *Find all values of 'a' for which the equation* $4^x - a2^x - a + 3 = 0$ has atleast one solution.

Sol. Putting $2^x = t > 0$, then the original equation reduced in the form

$$t^2 - at - a + 3 = 0 \quad \text{...(i)}$$

that the quadratic Eq. (i) should have atleast one positive root $(t > 0)$, then

Discriminant, $D = (-a)^2 - 4 \cdot 1 \cdot (-a + 3) \ge 0$

$$\Rightarrow \quad a^2 + 4a - 12 \ge 0$$

$$\Rightarrow \quad (a + 6)(a - 2) \ge 0$$

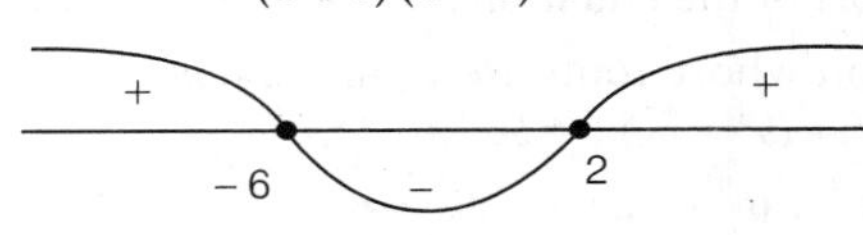

$$\therefore \quad a \in (-\infty, -6] \cup [2, \infty)$$

If roots of Eq. (i) are t_1 and t_2, then

$$\begin{cases} t_1 + t_2 = a \\ t_1 t_2 = 3 - a \end{cases}$$

For $a \in (-\infty, -6]$

$t_1 + t_2 < 0$ and $t_1 t_2 > 0$. Therefore, both roots are negative and consequently, the original equation has no solutions.

For $a \in [2, \infty)$

$t_1 + t_2 > 0$ and $t_1 t_2 \gtreqless 0$, consequently, atleast one of the roots t_1 or t_2, is greater than zero.

Thus, for $a \in [2, \infty)$, the given equation has atleast one solution.

• Ex. 51 *Find all the values of the parameter a for which the inequality* $a9^x + 4(a-1)3^x + a > 1$, *is satisfied for all real values of x.*

Sol. Putting $t = 3^x$ in the original equation, then we obtain

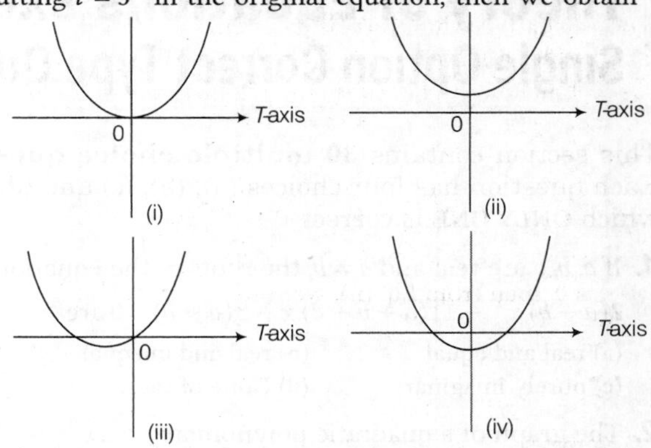

$$at^2 + 4(a-1)t + a > 1$$

$$\Rightarrow \quad at^2 + 4(a-1)t + (a-1) > 0 \quad [t > 0, \because 3^x > 0]$$

This is possible in two cases. First the parabola $f(t) = at^2 + 4(a-1)t + (a-1)$ opens upwards, with its vertex (turning point) lying in the non-positive part of the T-axis, as shown in the following four figures.

$\therefore \quad a > 0$ and sum of roots ≤ 0

$$\Rightarrow \quad -\frac{4(a-1)}{2a} \le 0 \text{ and } f(0) \ge 0$$

$$\therefore \quad a > 0, a - 1 \ge 0 \text{ and } a - 1 \ge 0$$

Hence, $\quad a \ge 1$

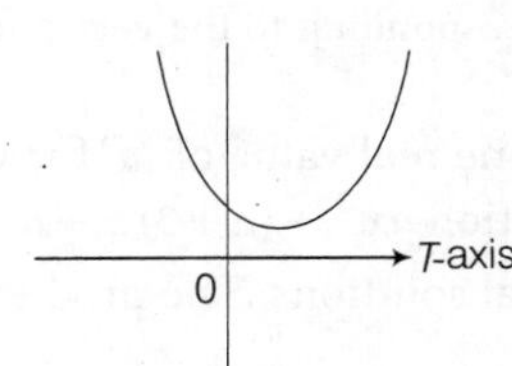

Second the parabola $f(t)$ opens upward, with its vertex lying in positive direction of t, then

$$a > 0, -\frac{4(a-1)}{2a} > 0 \text{ and } D \le 0$$

$$\Rightarrow \quad a > 0, (a-1) < 0$$

and $\quad 16(a-1)^2 - 4(a-1)a \le 0$

$$\Rightarrow \quad a > 0, a < 1$$

and $\quad 4(a-1)(3a-4) \le 0$

$$\Rightarrow \quad a > 0, a < 1 \text{ and } 1 \le a \le \frac{4}{3}$$

These inequalities cannot have simultaneously.
Hence, $a \ge 1$ from Eq. (i).

Theory of Equations Exercise 1 :
Single Option Correct Type Questions

- This section contains **30 multiple choice questions.** Each question has four choices (a), (b), (c) and (d) out of which **ONLY ONE** is correct

1. If a, b, c are real and $a \neq b$, the roots of the equation $2(a-b)x^2 - 11(a+b+c)x - 3(a-b) = 0$ are
(a) real and equal (b) real and unequal
(c) purely imaginary (d) None of these

2. The graph of a quadratic polynomial $y = ax^2 + bx + c$; $a, b, c \in R$ is as shown.

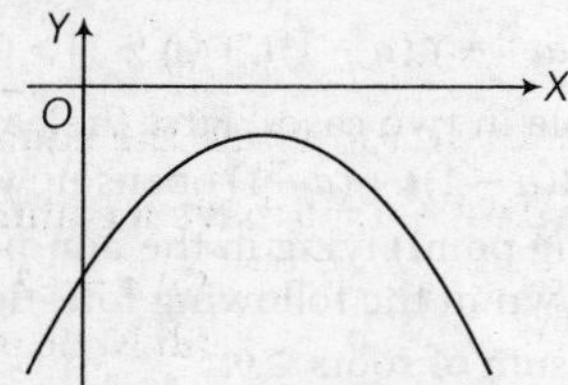

Which one of the following is not correct?
(a) $b^2 - 4ac < 0$ (b) $\frac{c}{a} < 0$
(c) c is negative
(d) Abscissa corresponding to the vertex is $\left(-\frac{b}{2a}\right)$

3. There is only one real value of 'a' for which the quadratic equation $ax^2 + (a+3)x + a - 3 = 0$ has two positive integral solutions. The product of these two solutions is
(a) 9 (b) 8 (c) 6 (d) 12

4. If for all real values of a one root of the equation $x^2 - 3ax + f(a) = 0$ is double of the other, $f(x)$ is equal to
(a) $2x$ (b) x^2 (c) $2x^2$ (d) $2\sqrt{x}$

5. A quadratic equation the product of whose roots x_1 and x_2 is equal to 4 and satisfying the relation $\frac{x_1}{x_1 - 1} + \frac{x_2}{x_2 - 1} = 2$, is
(a) $x^2 - 2x + 4 = 0$ (b) $x^2 - 4x + 4 = 0$
(c) $x^2 + 2x + 4 = 0$ (d) $x^2 + 4x + 4 = 0$

6. If both roots of the quadratic equation $x^2 - 2ax + a^2 - 1 = 0$ lie in $(-2, 2)$, which one of the following can be $[a]$? (where $[\cdot]$ denotes the greatest integer function)
(a) -1 (b) 1 (c) 2 (d) 3

7. If $(-2, 7)$ is the highest point on the graph of $y = -2x^2 - 4ax + \lambda$, then λ equals
(a) 31 (b) 11 (c) -1 (d) $-\frac{1}{3}$

8. If the roots of the quadratic equation $(4p - p^2 - 5)x^2 - (2p - 1)x + 3p = 0$ lie on either side of unity, the number of integral values of p is
(a) 1 (b) 2 (c) 3 (d) 4

9. Solution set of the equation $3^{2x^2} - 2 \cdot 3^{x^2 + x + 6} + 3^{2(x+6)} = 0$ is
(a) $\{-3, 2\}$ (b) $\{6, -1\}$ (c) $\{-2, 3\}$ (d) $\{1, -6\}$

10. Consider two quadratic expressions $f(x) = ax^2 + bx + c$ and $g(x) = ax^2 + px + q$ $(a, b, c, p, q \in R, b \neq p)$ such that their discriminants are equal. If $f(x) = g(x)$ has a root $x = \alpha$, then
(a) α will be AM of the roots of $f(x) = 0$ and $g(x) = 0$
(b) α will be AM of the roots of $f(x) = 0$
(c) α will be AM of the roots of $f(x) = 0$ or $g(x) = 0$
(d) α will be AM of the roots of $g(x) = 0$.

11. If x_1 and x_2 are the arithmetic and harmonic means of the roots of the equation $ax^2 + bx + c = 0$, the quadratic equation whose roots are x_1 and x_2, is
(a) $abx^2 + (b^2 + ac)x + bc = 0$
(b) $2abx^2 + (b^2 + 4ac)x + 2bc = 0$
(c) $2abx^2 + (b^2 + ac)x + bc = 0$
(d) None of the above

12. $f(x)$ is a cubic polynomial $x^3 + ax^2 + bx + c$ such that $f(x) = 0$ has three distinct integral roots and $f(g(x)) = 0$ does not have real roots, where $g(x) = x^2 + 2x - 5$, the minimum value of $a + b + c$ is
(a) 504 (b) 532 (c) 719 (d) 764

13. The value of the positive integer n for which the quadratic equation $\sum_{k=1}^{n} (x + k - 1)(x + k) = 10n$ has solutions α and $\alpha + 1$ for some α, is
(a) 7 (b) 11 (c) 17 (d) 25

14. If one root of the equation $x^2 - \lambda x + 12 = 0$ is even prime, while $x^2 + \lambda x + \mu = 0$ has equal roots, then μ is
(a) 8 (b) 16 (c) 24 (d) 32

15. Number of real roots of the equation $\sqrt{x} + \sqrt{x - \sqrt{(1-x)}} = 1$ is
(a) 0 (b) 1 (c) 2 (d) 3

16. The value of $\sqrt{7 + \sqrt{7 - \sqrt{7 + \sqrt{7 - \dots}}}}$ upto ∞ is
(a) 5 (b) 4
(c) 3 (d) 2

17. For any real x, the expression $2(k-x)[x+\sqrt{x^2+k^2}]$ cannot exceed

(a) k^2 (b) $2k^2$
(c) $3k^2$ (d) None of these

18. Given that, for all $x \in R$, the expression $\frac{x^2-2x+4}{x^2+2x+4}$ lies between $\frac{1}{3}$ and 3, the values between which the expression $\frac{9\cdot 3^{2x}+6\cdot 3^x+4}{9\cdot 3^{2x}-6\cdot 3^x+4}$ lies, are

(a) -3 and 1 (b) $\frac{3}{2}$ and 2
(c) -1 and 1 (d) 0 and 2

19. Let α, β, γ be the roots of the equation $(x-a)(x-b)(x-c)=d, d \neq 0$, the roots of the equation $(x-\alpha)(x-\beta)(x-\gamma)+d=0$ are

(a) a, b, d (b) b, c, d
(c) a, b, c (d) $a+d, b+d, c+d$

20. If one root of the equation $ix^2-2(1+i)x+2-i=0$ is $(3-i)$, where $i=\sqrt{-1}$, the other root is

(a) $3+i$ (b) $3+\sqrt{-1}$
(c) $-1+i$ (d) $-1-i$

21. The number of solutions of $|[x]-2x|=4$, where $[x]$ denotes the greatest integer $\leq x$ is

(a) infinite (b) 4 (c) 3 (d) 2

22. If x^2+x+1 is a factor of ax^3+bx^2+cx+d, the real root of $ax^3+bx^2+cx+d=0$ is

(a) $-\frac{d}{a}$ (b) $\frac{d}{a}$ (c) $\frac{a}{d}$ (d) None of these

23. The value of x which satisfy the equation $\sqrt{(5x^2-8x+3)}-\sqrt{(5x^2-9x+4)}=\sqrt{(2x^2-2x)}-\sqrt{(2x^2-3x+1)}$, is

(a) 3 (b) 2
(c) 1 (d) 0

24. The roots of the equation

$$(a+\sqrt{b})^{x^2-15}+(a-\sqrt{b})^{x^2-15}=2a,$$

where $a^2-b=1$, are

(a) $\pm 2, \pm\sqrt{3}$ (b) $\pm 4, \pm\sqrt{14}$
(c) $\pm 3, \pm\sqrt{5}$ (d) $\pm 6, \pm\sqrt{20}$

25. The number of pairs (x, y) which will satisfy the equation $x^2-xy+y^2=4(x+y-4)$, is

(a) 1 (b) 2
(c) 4 (d) None of these

26. The number of positive integral solutions of $x^4-y^4=3789108$ is

(a) 0 (b) 1 (c) 2 (d) 4

27. The value of 'a' for which the equation $x^3+ax+1=0$ and $x^4+ax^2+1=0$, have a common root, is

(a) $a=2$ (b) $a=-2$
(c) $a=0$ (d) None of these

28. The necessary and sufficient condition for the equation $(1-a^2)x^2+2ax-1=0$ to have roots lying in the interval $(0, 1)$, is

(a) $a>0$ (b) $a<0$
(c) $a>2$ (d) None of these

29. Solution set of $x-\sqrt{1-|x|}<0$, is

(a) $\left[-1, \frac{-1+\sqrt{5}}{2}\right)$ (b) $[-1, 1]$
(c) $\left[-1, \frac{-1+\sqrt{5}}{2}\right]$ (d) $\left(-1, \frac{-1+\sqrt{5}}{2}\right)$

30. If the quadratic equations $ax^2+2cx+b=0$ and $ax^2+2bx+c=0\,(b \neq c)$ have a common root, $a+4b+4c$, is equal to

(a) -2 (b) -1
(c) 0 (d) 1

Theory of Equations Exercise 2 :
More than One Correct Option Type Questions

- This section contains **15 multiple choice questions**. Each question has four choices (a), (b), (c) and (d) out of which **MORE THAN ONE** may be correct.

31. If $0<a<b<c$ and the roots α, β of the equation $ax^2+bx+c=0$ are non-real complex numbers, then

(a) $|\alpha|=|\beta|$ (b) $|\alpha|>1$
(c) $|\beta|<1$ (d) None of these

32. If A, G and H are the arithmetic mean, geometric mean and harmonic mean between unequal positive integers. Then, the equation $Ax^2-|G|x-H=0$ has

(a) both roots are fractions
(b) atleast one root which is negative fraction
(c) exactly one positive root
(d) atleast one root which is an integer

33. The adjoining graph of $y = ax^2 + bx + c$ shows that

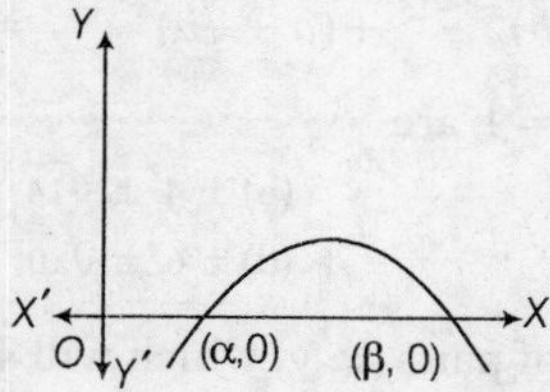

(a) $a < 0$
(b) $b^2 < 4ac$
(c) $c > 0$
(d) a and b are of opposite signs

34. If the equation $ax^2 + bx + c = 0\ (a > 0)$ has two roots α and β such that $\alpha < -2$ and $\beta > 2$, then

(a) $b^2 - 4ac > 0$ (b) $c < 0$
(c) $a + |b| + c < 0$ (d) $4a + 2|b| + c < 0$

35. If $b^2 \geq 4ac$ for the equation $ax^4 + bx^2 + c = 0$, then all the roots of the equation will be real, if

(a) $b > 0, a < 0, c > 0$ (b) $b < 0, a > 0, c > 0$
(c) $b > 0, a > 0, c > 0$ (d) $b > 0, a < 0, c < 0$

36. If roots of the equation $x^3 + bx^2 + cx - 1 = 0$ from an increasing GP, then

(a) $b + c = 0$
(b) $b \in (-\infty, -3)$
(c) one of the roots is 1
(d) one root is smaller than one and one root is more than one

37. Let $f(x) = ax^2 + bx + c$, where $a, b, c \in R, a \neq 0$. Suppose $|f(x)| \leq 1, \forall x \in [0, 1]$, then

(a) $|a| \leq 8$ (b) $|b| \leq 8$
(c) $|c| \leq 1$ (d) $|a| + |b| + |c| \leq 17$

38. $\cos \alpha$ is a root of the equation $25x^2 + 5x - 12 = 0$, $-1 < x < 0$, the value of $\sin 2\alpha$ is

(a) $\frac{24}{25}$ (b) $-\frac{12}{25}$
(c) $-\frac{24}{25}$ (d) $\frac{20}{25}$

39. If $a, b, c \in R\,(a \neq 0)$ and $a + 2b + 4c = 0$, then equation $ax^2 + bx + c = 0$ has

(a) atleast one positive root
(b) atleast one non-integral root
(c) both integral roots
(d) no irrational root

40. For which of the following graphs of the quadratic expression $f(x) = ax^2 + bx + c$, the product of abc is negative

(a)
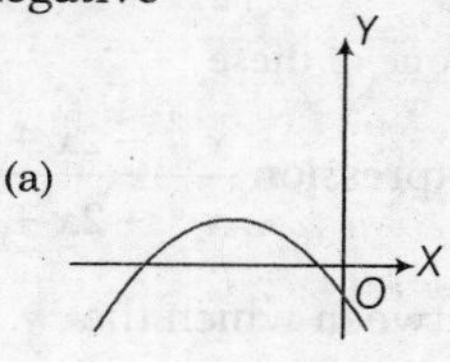

(b)
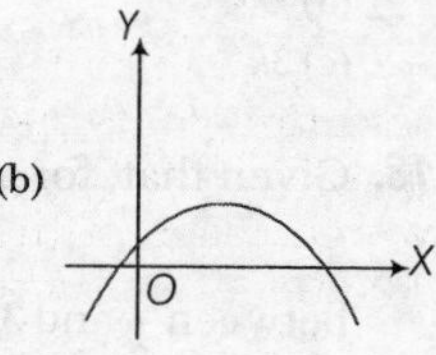

(c)
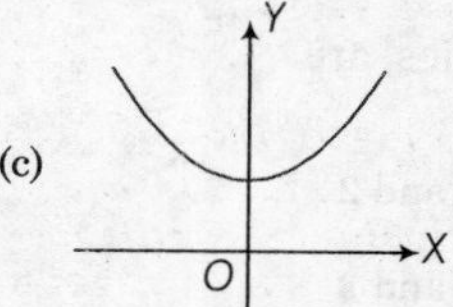

(d)
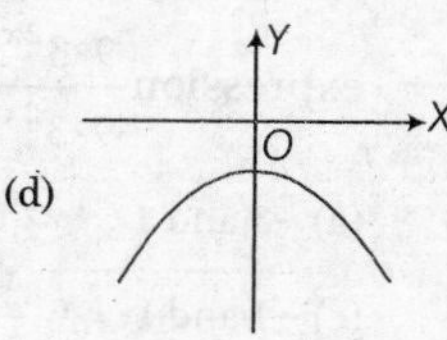

41. If $a, b \in R$ and $ax^2 + bx + 6 = 0, a \neq 0$ does not have two distinct real roots, the

(a) minimum possible value of $3a + b$ is -2
(b) minimum possible value of $3a + b$ is 2
(c) minimum possible value of $6a + b$ is -1
(d) minimum possible value of $6a + b$ is 1

42. If $x^3 + 3x^2 - 9x + \lambda$ is of the form $(x - \alpha)^2 (x - \beta)$, then λ is equal to

(a) 27 (b) -27
(c) 5 (d) -5

43. If $ax^2 + (b - c)x + a - b - c = 0$ has unequal real roots for all $c \in R$, then

(a) $b < 0 < a$ (b) $a < 0 < b$
(c) $b < a < 0$ (d) $b > a > 0$

44. If the equation whose roots are the squares of the roots of the cubic $x^3 - ax^2 + bx - 1 = 0$ is identical with the given cubic equation, then

(a) $a = b = 0$
(b) $a = 0, b = 3$
(c) $a = b = 3$
(d) a, b are roots of $x^2 + x + 2 = 0$

45. If the equation $ax^2 + bx + c = 0\ (a > 0)$ has two real roots α and β such that $\alpha < -2$ and $\beta > 2$, which of the following statements is/are true?

(a) $4a - 2|b| + c < 0$
(b) $9a - 3|b| + c < 0$
(c) $a - |b| + c < 0$
(d) $c < 0, b^2 - 4ac > 0$

Theory of Equations Exercise 3 : Passage Based Questions

- This section contains **6 passages**. Based upon each of the passage **3 multiple choice questions** have to be answered. Each of these questions has four choices (a), (b), (c) and (d) out of which **ONLY ONE** is correct.

Passage I
(Q. Nos. 46 to 48)

If G and L are the greatest and least values of the expression $\dfrac{2x^2-3x+2}{2x^2+3x+2}$, $x \in R$ *respectively.*

46. The least value of $G^{100}+L^{100}$ is

(a) 2^{100} (b) 3^{100} (c) 7^{100} (d) None of these

47. G and L are the roots of the equation

(a) $5x^2-26x+5=0$ (b) $7x^2-50x+7=0$

(c) $9x^2-82x+9=0$ (d) $11x^2-122x+11=0$

48. If $L^2<\lambda<G^2, \lambda \in N$, the sum of all values of λ is

(a) 1035 (b) 1081 (c) 1225 (d) 1176

Passage II
(Q. Nos. 49 to 51)

If roots of the equation $x^4-12x^3+cx^2+dx+81=0$ *are positive.*

49. The value of c is

(a) -27 (b) 27 (c) -54 (d) 54

50. The value of d is

(a) -27 (b) -54 (c) -81 (d) -108

51. Root of the equation $2cx+d=0$, is

(a) -1 (b) $-\frac{1}{2}$ (c) 1 (d) $\frac{1}{2}$

Passage II
(Q. Nos. 52 to 54)

In the given figure vertices of ΔABC *lie on* $y=f(x)=ax^2+bx+c$. *The* ΔABC *is right angled isosceles triangle whose hypotenuse* $AC=4\sqrt{2}$ *units.*

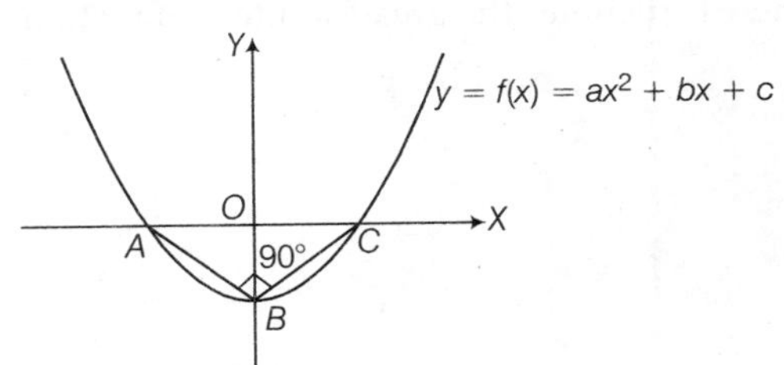

52. $y=f(x)$ is given by

(a) $y=x^2-8$ (b) $y=\dfrac{x^2}{2\sqrt{2}}-2\sqrt{2}$

(c) $y=x^2-4$ (d) $y=\dfrac{x^2}{2}-\sqrt{2}$

53. Minimum value of $y=f(x)$ is

(a) $-4\sqrt{2}$ (b) $-2\sqrt{2}$

(c) 0 (d) $2\sqrt{2}$

54. Number of integral value of λ for which $\frac{\lambda}{2}$ lies between the roots of $f(x)=0$, is

(a) 9 (b) 10 (c) 11 (d) 12

Passage III
(Q. Nos. 55 to 57)

Let $f(x)=x^2+bx+c$ *and* $g(x)=x^2+b_1x+c_1$.

Let the real roots of $f(x)=0$ *be* α, β *and real roots of* $g(x)=0$ *be* $\alpha+k, \beta+k$ *for same constant k. The least value of* $f(x)$ *is* $-\frac{1}{4}$ *and least value of* $g(x)$ *occurs at* $x=\frac{7}{2}$.

55. The value of b_1 is

(a) -8 (b) -7 (c) -6 (d) 5

56. The least value of $g(x)$ is

(a) -1 (b) $-\frac{1}{2}$ (c) $-\frac{1}{3}$ (d) $-\frac{1}{4}$

57. The roots of $f(x)=0$ are

(a) 3, 4 (b) -3, 4

(c) -3, -4 (d) 3, -4

Passage IV
(Q. Nos. 58 to 60)

If $ax^2-bx+c=0$ *have two distinct roots lying in the interval* $(0,1)$; $a, b, c \in N$.

58. The least value of a is

(a) 3 (b) 4

(c) 5 (d) 6

59. The least value of b is

(a) 5 (b) 6

(c) 7 (d) 8

60. The least value of $\log_5 abc$ is

(a) 1 (b) 2

(c) 3 (d) 4

Passage V

(Q. Nos. 61 to 63)

If $2x^3 + ax^2 + bx + 4 = 0$ (a and b are positive real numbers) has three real roots.

61. The minimum value of a^3 is

(a) 108 (b) 216
(c) 432 (d) 864

62. The minimum value of b^3 is

(a) 432 (b) 864
(c) 1728 (d) None of these

63. The minimum value of $(a+b)^3$ is

(a) 1728 (b) 3456
(c) 6912 (d) 864

Passage VI

(Q. Nos. 64 to 66)

If $\alpha, \beta, \gamma, \delta$ are the roots of the equation $x^4 + Ax^3 + Bx^2 + Cx + D = 0$ such that $\alpha\beta = \gamma\delta = k$ and A, B, C, D are the roots of $x^4 - 2x^3 + 4x^2 + 6x - 21 = 0$ such that $A + B = 0$.

64. The value of $\frac{C}{A}$ is

(a) $-\frac{k}{2}$ (b) $-k$ (c) $\frac{k}{2}$ (d) k

65. The value of $(\alpha+\beta)(\gamma+\delta)$ in terms of B and k is

(a) $B - 2k$ (b) $B - k$ (c) $B + k$ (d) $B + 2k$

66. The correct statement is

(a) $C^2 = AD$ (b) $C^2 = A^2D$ (c) $C^2 = AD^2$ (d) $C^2 = (AD)^2$

Theory of Equations Exercise 4 :
Single Integer Answer Type Questions

- This section contains **10 questions**. The answer to each question is a **single digit integer**, ranging from 0 to 9 (both inclusive).

67. The sum of all the real roots of the equation $|x-2|^2 + |x-2| - 2 = 0$ is

68. The harmonic mean of the roots of the equation $(5+\sqrt{2})x^2 - (4+\sqrt{5})x + 8 + 2\sqrt{5} = 0$ is

69. If product of the real roots of the equation, $x^2 - ax + 30 = 2\sqrt{(x^2 - ax + 45)}, a > 0,$ is λ and minimum value of sum of roots of the equation is μ. The value of (μ) (where $(\cdot)$ denotes the least integer function) is

70. The minimum value of $\dfrac{\left(x+\frac{1}{x}\right)^6 - \left(x^6 + \frac{1}{x^6}\right) - 2}{\left(x+\frac{1}{x}\right)^3 + x^3 + \frac{1}{x^3}}$ is (for $x > 0$)

71. Let a, b, c, d are distinct real numbers and a, b are the roots of the quadratic equation $x^2 - 2cx - 5d = 0$. If c and d are the roots of the quadratic equation $x^2 - 2ax - 5b = 0$, the sum of the digits of numerical values of $a + b + c + d$ is

72. If the maximum and minimum values of $y = \dfrac{x^2 - 3x + c}{x^2 + 3x + c}$ are 7 and $\frac{1}{7}$ respectively, the value of c is

73. Number of solutions of the equation $\sqrt{x^2} - \sqrt{(x-1)^2} + \sqrt{(x-2)^2} = \sqrt{5}$ is

74. If α and β are the complex roots of the equation $(1+i)x^2 + (1-i)x - 2i = 0$, where $i = \sqrt{-1}$, the value of $|\alpha - \beta|^2$ is

75. If α, β be the roots of the equation $4x^2 - 16x + c = 0, c \in R$ such that $1 < \alpha < 2$ and $2 < \beta < 3$, then the number of integral values of c, are

76. Let r, s and t be the roots of the equation $8x^3 + 1001x + 2008 = 0$ and if $99\lambda = (r+s)^3 + (s+t)^3 + (t+r)^3$, the value of $[\lambda]$ is (where $[\cdot]$ denotes the greatest integer function)

Theory of Equations Exercise 5 : Matching Type Questions

- This section contains **4 questions**. Questions 78 and 80 have three statements (A, B and C) given in **Column I** and four statements (p, q, r and s) in **Column II** and questions 77 and 79 have three statements (A, B and C) given in **Column I** and five statements (p, q, r, s and t) in **Column II**. Any given statement in **Column I** can have correct matching with one or more statement(s) given in **Column II**.

77. Column I contains rational algebraic expressions and Column II contains possible integers which lie in their range. Match the entries of Column I with one or more entries of the elements of Column II.

	Column I		Column II
(A)	$y=\dfrac{x^2-2x+4}{x^2+2x+4}, x \in R$	(p)	-2
(B)	$y=\dfrac{2x^2+4x+1}{x^2+4x+2}, x \in R$	(q)	-1
(C)	$y=\dfrac{x^2-3x+4}{x-3}, x \in R$	(r)	2
		(s)	3
		(t)	8

78.

	Column I		Column II
(A)	If a, b, c, d are four non-zero real numbers such that $(d+a-b)^2+(d+b-c)^2=0$ and the roots of the equation $a(b-c)x^2+b(c-a)x+c(a-b)=0$ are real and equal, then	(p)	$a+b+c=0$
(B)	If the equation $ax^2+bx+c=0$ and $x^3-3x^2+3x-1=0$ have a common real root, then	(q)	a, b, c are in AP
(C)	Let a, b, c be positive real numbers such that the expression $bx^2+(\sqrt{(a+c)^2+4b^2})x+(a+c)$ is non-negative, $\forall x \in R$, then	(r)	a, b, c are in GP
		(s)	a, b, c are in HP

79. Column I contains rational algebraic expressions and Column II contains possible integers of a.

	Column I		Column II
(A)	$y=\dfrac{ax^2+3x-4}{3x-4x^2+a}, x \in R$ and $y \in R$	(p)	0
(B)	$y=\dfrac{ax^2+x-2}{a+x-2x^2}, x \in R$ and $y \in R$	(q)	1
(C)	$y=\dfrac{x^2+2x+a}{x^2+4x+3a}, x \in R$ and $y \in R$	(r)	3
		(s)	5
		(t)	7

80.

	Column I		Column II
(A)	The equation $x^3-6x^2+9x+\lambda=0$ have exactly one root is (1, 3), then $\|[\lambda+1]\|$ is (where $[\cdot]$ denotes the greatest integer function)	(p)	0
(B)	If $-3<\dfrac{x^2-\lambda x-2}{x^2+x+1}<2, \forall x \in R$, then $\|[\lambda]\|$ is (where $[\cdot]$ denotes the greatest integer function)	(q)	1
(C)	If $x^2+\lambda x+1=0$ and $(b-c)x^2+(c-a)x+(a-b)=0$ have both the roots common, then $\|[\lambda-1]\|$, (where $[\cdot]$ denotes the greatest integer function)	(r)	2
		(s)	3

Theory of Equations Exercise 6 : Statement I and II Type Questions

- Directions (Q. Nos. 81 to 87) are Assertion-Reason type questions. Each of these questions contains two statements:
Statement-1 (Assertion) and **Statement-2** (Reason)
Each of these questions also has four alternative choices, only one of which is the correct answer. You have to select the correct choice as given below.
  (a) Statement-1 is true, Statement-2 is true; Statement-2 is a correct explanation for Statement-1
  (b) Statement-1 is true, Statement-2 is true; Statement-2 is not a correct explanation for Statement-1
  (c) Statement1 is true, Statement-2 is false
  (d) Statement-1 is false, Statement-2 is true

81. Statement-1 If the equation $(4p-3)x^2 + (4q-3)x + r = 0$ is satisfied by $x = a$, $x = b$ and $x = c$ (where a, b, c are distinct), then $p = q = \frac{3}{4}$ and $r = 0$.

Statement-2 If the quadratic equation $ax^2 + bx + c = 0$ has three distinct roots, then a, b and c are must be zero.

82. Statement-1 The equation $x^2 + (2m+1)x + (2n+1) = 0$, where $m, n \in I$, cannot have any rational roots.

Statement-2 The quantity $(2m+1)^2 - 4(2n+1)$, where $m, n \in I$, can never be perfect square.

83. Statement-1 In the equation $ax^2 + 3x + 5 = 0$, if one root is reciprocal of the other, then a is equal to 5.

Statement-2 Product of the roots is 1.

84. Statement-1 If one root of $Ax^3 + Bx^2 + Cx + D = 0$, $A \neq 0$, is the arithmetic mean of the other two roots, then the relation $2B^3 + k_1 ABC + k_2 A^2 D = 0$ holds good and then $(k_2 - k_1)$ is a perfect square.

Statement-2 If a, b, c are in AP, then b is the arithmetic mean of a and c.

85. Statement-1 If x, y, z be real variables satisfying $x + y + z = 6$ and $xy + yz + zx = 8$, the range of variables x, y and z are identical.

Statement-2 $x + y + z = 6$ and $xy + yz + zx = 8$ remains same, if x, y, z interchange their positions.

86. Statement-1 $ax^3 + bx + c = 0$, where $a, b, c \in R$ cannot have 3 non-negative real roots.

Statement-2 Sum of roots is equal to zero.

87. Statement-1 The quadratic polynomial $y = ax^2 + bx + c$ $(a \neq 0$ and $a, b, c \in R)$ is symmetric about the line $2ax + b = 0$.

Statement-2 Parabola is symmetric about its axis of symmetry.

Theory of Equations Exercise 7 : Subjective Type Questions

- In this section, there are **24 subjective** questions.

88. For what values of m, the equation $(1+m)x^2 - 2(1+3m)x + (1+8m) = 0$ has $(m \in R)$
  (i) both roots are imaginary?
  (ii) both roots are equal?
  (iii) both roots are real and distinct?
  (iv) both roots are positive?
  (v) both roots are negative?
  (vi) roots are opposite in sign?
  (vii) roots are equal in magnitude but opposite in sign?
  (viii) atleast one root is positive?
  (ix) atleast one root is negative?
  (x) roots are in the ratio 2 : 3?

89. For what values of m, then equation $2x^2 - 2(2m+1)x + m(m+1) = 0$ has $(m \in R)$
  (i) both roots are smaller tha 2?
  (ii) both roots are greater than 2?
  (iii) both roots lie in the interval (2, 3)?
  (iv) exactly one root lie in the interval (2, 3)?
  (v) one root is smaller than 1 and the other root is greater than 1?
  (vi) one root is greater than 3 and the other root is smaller than 2?
  (vii) atleast one root lies in the interval (2, 3)?
  (viii) atleast one root is greater than 2?
  (ix) atleast one root is smaller than 2?
  (x) roots α and β, such that both 2 and 3 lie between α and β?

90. If r is the ratio of the roots of the equation $ax^2 + bx + c = 0$, show that $\frac{(r+1)^2}{r} = \frac{b^2}{ac}$.

91. If the roots of the equation $\frac{1}{x+p} + \frac{1}{x+q} = \frac{1}{r}$ are equal in magnitude but opposite in sign, show that $p + q = 2r$ and that the product of the roots is equal to $\left(-\frac{p^2+q^2}{2}\right)$.

92. If one root of the quadratic equation $ax^2 + bx + c = 0$ is equal to the nth power of the other, then show that $(ac^n)^{\frac{1}{n+1}} + (a^n c)^{\frac{1}{n+1}} + b = 0$.

93. If α, β are the roots of the equation $ax^2 + bx + c = 0$ and γ, δ those of equation $lx^2 + mx + n = 0$, then find the equation whose roots are $\alpha\gamma + \beta\delta$ and $\alpha\delta + \beta\gamma$.

94. Show that the roots of the equation

$$(a^2 - bc)x^2 + 2(b^2 - ac)x + c^2 - ab = 0$$

are equal, if either $b = 0$ or $a^3 + b^3 + c^3 - 3abc = 0$.

95. If the equation $x^2 - px + q = 0$ and $x^2 - ax + b = 0$ have a common root and the other root of the second equation is the reciprocal of the other root of the first, then prove that $(q - b)^2 = bq(p - a)^2$.

96. If the equation $x^2 - 2px + q = 0$ has two equal roots, then the equation $(1 + y)x^2 - 2(p + y)x + (q + y) = 0$ will have its roots real and distinct only, when y is negative and p is not unity.

97. Solve the equation $x^{\log_x (x+3)^2} = 16$.

98. Solve the equation

$$(2+\sqrt{3})^{x^2-2x+1} + (2-\sqrt{3})^{x^2-2x-1} = \frac{101}{10(2-\sqrt{3})}.$$

99. Solve the equation $x^2 + \left(\frac{x}{x-1}\right)^2 = 8$.

100. Solve the equation

$$\sqrt{(x+8) + 2\sqrt{(x+7)}} + \sqrt{(x+1) - \sqrt{(x+7)}} = 4.$$

101. Find all values of a for which the inequation $4^{x^2} + 2(2a+1)2^{x^2} + 4a^2 - 3 > 0$ is satisfied for any x.

102. Solve the inequation $\log_{x^2+2x-3}\left(\frac{|x+4| - |x|}{x-1}\right) > 0$.

103. Solve the system $|x^2 - 2x| + y = 1, x^2 + |y| = 1$.

104. If α, β, γ are the roots of the cubic $x^3 - px^2 + qx - r = 0$. Find the equations whose roots are

(i) $\beta\gamma + \frac{1}{\alpha}, \gamma\alpha + \frac{1}{\beta}, \alpha\beta + \frac{1}{\gamma}$

(ii) $(\beta + \gamma - \alpha), (\gamma + \alpha - \beta), (\alpha + \beta - \gamma)$

Also, find the value of $(\beta + \gamma - \alpha)(\gamma + \alpha - \beta)(\alpha + \beta - \gamma)$.

105. If $A_1, A_2, A_3, \ldots, A_n, a_1, a_2, a_3, \ldots, a_n, a, b, c \in R$, show that the roots of the equation

$$\frac{A_1^2}{x-a_1} + \frac{A_2^2}{x-a_2} + \frac{A_3^2}{x-a_3} + \ldots + \frac{A_n^2}{x-a_n} = ab^2 + c^2x + ac$$ are real.

106. For what values of the parameter a the equation $x^4 + 2ax^3 + x^2 + 2ax + 1 = 0$ has atleast two distinct negative roots?

107. If $[x]$ is the integral part of a real number x. Then solve $[2x] - [x+1] = 2x$.

108. Prove that for any value of a, the inequation $(a^2 + 3)x^2 + (a+2)x - 6 < 0$ is true for atleast one negative x.

109. How many real solutions of the equation $6x^2 - 77[x] + 147 = 0$, where $[x]$ is the integral part of x?

110. If α, β are the roots of the equation $x^2 - 2x - a^2 + 1 = 0$ and γ, δ are the roots of the equation $x^2 - 2(a+1)x + a(a-1) = 0$, such that $\alpha, \beta \in (\gamma, \delta)$, find the value of '$a$'.

111. If the equation $x^4 + px^3 + qx^2 + rx + 5 = 0$ has four positive real roots, find the minimum value of pr.

Theory of Equations Exercise 8 : Questions Asked in Previous 13 Years' Exam

- This section contains questions asked in **IIT-JEE, AIEEE, JEE Main & JEE Advanced** from year **2005** to year **2017**.

112. If α, β are the roots of $ax^2 + bx + c = 0$ and $\alpha + \beta$, $\alpha^2 + \beta^2, \alpha^3 + \beta^3$ are in GP, where $\Delta = b^2 - 4ac$, then **[IIT-JEE 2005, 3M]**

(a) $\Delta \neq 0$ (b) $b\Delta = 0$ (c) $cb \neq 0$ (d) $c\Delta = 0$

113. If S is a set of $P(x)$ is polynomial of degree ≤ 2 such that $P(0) = 0, P(1) = 1, P'(x) > 0, \forall x \in (0,1)$, then **[IIT-JEE 2005, 3M]**

(a) $S = 0$

(b) $S = ax + (1-a)x^2, \forall a \in (0, \infty)$

(c) $S = ax + (1-a)x^2, \forall a \in R$

(d) $S = ax + (1-a)x^2, \forall a \in (0, 2)$

114. If the roots of $x^2 - bx + c = 0$ are two consecutive integers, then $b^2 - 4c$ is **[AIEEE 2005, 3M]**

(a) 1 (b) 2
(c) 3 (d) 4

115. If the equation $a_n x^n + a_{n-1} x^{n-1} + \ldots + a_1 x = 0, a_1 \neq 0$, $n \geq 2$, has a positive root $x = \alpha$, then the equation $na_n x^{n-1} + (n-1) a_{n-1} x^{n-2} + \ldots + a_1 = 0$ has a positive root, which is **[AIEEE 2005, 3M]**

(a) greater than or equal to α
(b) equal to α
(c) greater than α
(d) smaller than α

116. If both the roots of the quadratic equation

$$x^2 - 2kx + k^2 + k - 5 = 0$$

are less than 5, k lies in the interval **[AIEEE 2005, 3M]**

(a) $(-\infty, 4)$ (b) $[4, 5]$
(c) $(5, 6)$ (d) $(6, \infty)$

117. Let a and b be the roots of equation $x^2 - 10cx - 11d = 0$ and those of $x^2 - 10ax - 11b = 0$ are c and d, the value of $a + b + c + d$, when $a \neq b \neq c \neq d$, is **IIT-JEE 2006, 6M]**

118. Let a, b, c be the sides of a triangle. No two of them are equal and $\lambda \in R$. If the roots of the equation $x^2 + 2(a+b+c)x + 3\lambda(ab+bc+ca) = 0$ are real, then **[IIT-JEE 2006, 3M]**

(a) $\lambda < \frac{4}{3}$ (b) $\lambda < \frac{5}{3}$
(c) $\lambda \in \left(\frac{1}{3}, \frac{5}{3}\right)$ (d) $\lambda \in \left(\frac{4}{3}, \frac{5}{3}\right)$

119. All the values of m for which both roots of the equation $x^2 - 2mx + m^2 - 1 = 0$ are greater than -2 but less than 4, lie in the interval **[AIEEE 2006, 3M]**

(a) $-2 < m < 0$ (b) $m > 3$
(c) $-1 < m < 3$ (d) $1 < m < 4$

120. If the roots of the quadratic equation $x^2 + px + q = 0$ are $\tan 30°$ and $\tan 15°$, respectively, the value of $2 + q - p$ is **[AIEEE 2006, 3M]**

(a) 2 (b) 3
(c) 0 (d) 1

121. Let α, β be the roots of the equation $x^2 - px + r = 0$ and $\frac{\alpha}{2}, 2\beta$ be the roots of the equation $x^2 - qx + r = 0$. The value of r is **[IIT-JEE 2007, 3M]**

(a) $\frac{2}{9}(p-q)(2q-p)$ (b) $\frac{2}{9}(q-p)(2p-q)$
(c) $\frac{2}{9}(q-2p)(2q-p)$ (d) $\frac{2}{9}(2p-q)(2q-p)$

122. If the difference between the roots of the equation $x^2 + ax + 1 = 0$ is less than $\sqrt{5}$, the set of possible values of a, is **[AIEEE 2007, 3M]**

(a) $(-3, 3)$ (b) $(-3, \infty)$
(c) $(3, \infty)$ (d) $(-\infty, -3)$

123. Let a, b, c, p, q be real numbers. Suppose α, β are roots of the equation $x^2 + 2px + q = 0$ and $\alpha, \frac{1}{\beta}$ are the roots of the equation $ax^2 + 2bx + c = 0$, where $\beta^2 \notin \{-1, 0, 1\}$.

Statement-1 $(p^2 - q)(b^2 - ac) \geq 0$ and

Statement-2 $b \neq pa$ or $c \neq qa$ **[IIT-JEE 2008, 3M]**

(a) Statement-1 is true, Statement-2, is true; Statement-2 is a correct explanation for Statement-1
(b) Statement-1 is true, Statement-2 is true; Statement-2 is not a correct explanation for Statement-1
(c) Statement-1 is true, Statement-2 is false
(d) Statement-1 is false, Statement-2 is true

124. The quadratic equation $x^2 - 6x + a = 0$ and $x^2 - cx + 6 = 0$ have one root in common. The other roots of the first and second equations are integers in the ratio 4 : 3. The common root is **[AIEEE 2008, 3M]**

(a) 4 (b) 3 (c) 2 (d) 1

125. How many real solutions does the equation $x^7 + 14x^5 + 16x^3 + 30x - 560 = 0$ have? **[AIEEE 2008, 3M]**

(a) 1 (b) 3 (c) 5 (d) 7

126. Suppose the cubic $x^3 - px + q = 0$ has three distinct real roots, where $p > 0$ and $q < 0$. Which one of the following holds? **[AIEEE 2008, 3M]**

(a) The cubic has minima at $\left(-\sqrt{\frac{p}{3}}\right)$ and maxima at $\sqrt{\frac{p}{3}}$
(b) The cubic has minima at both $\sqrt{\frac{p}{3}}$ and $\left(-\sqrt{\frac{p}{3}}\right)$
(c) The cubic has maxima at both $\sqrt{\frac{p}{3}}$ and $\left(-\sqrt{\frac{p}{3}}\right)$
(d) The cubic has minima at $\sqrt{\frac{p}{3}}$ and maxima at $\left(-\sqrt{\frac{p}{3}}\right)$

127. The smallest value of k, for which both roots of the equation $x^2 - 8kx + 16(k^2 - k + 1) = 0$ are real, distinct and have value at least 4, is **[IIT-JEE 2009, 4M]**

(a) 6 (b) 4 (c) 2 (d) 0

128. If the roots of the equation $bx^2 + cx + a = 0$ be imaginary, then for all real values of x, the expression $3b^2x^2 + 6bcx + 2c^2$, is **[AIEEE 2009, 4M]**

(a) less than $(-4ab)$ (b) greater than $4ab$
(c) less than $4ab$ (d) greater than $(-4ab)$

129. Let p and q be real numbers such that $p \neq 0, p^3 \neq -q$. If α and β are non-zero complex numbers satisfying $\alpha + \beta = -p$ and $\alpha^3 + \beta^3 = q$, a quadratic equation having $\frac{\alpha}{\beta}$ and $\frac{\beta}{\alpha}$ as its roots, is **[IIT-JEE 2010, 3M]**

(a) $(p^3 + q)x^2 - (p^3 + 2q)x + (p^3 + q) = 0$

(b) $(p^3 + q)x^2 - (p^3 - 2q)x + (p^3 + q) = 0$

(c) $(p^3 - q)x^2 - (5p^3 - 2q)x + (p^3 - q) = 0$

(d) $(p^3 - q)x^2 - (5p^3 + 2q)x + (p^3 - q) = 0$

130. Consider the polynomial $f(x) = 1 + 2x + 3x^2 + 4x^3$. Let s be the sum of all distinct real roots of $f(x)$ and let $t = |s|$, real number s lies in the interval **[IIT-JEE 2010, 3M]**

(a) $\left(-\frac{1}{4}, 0\right)$ (b) $\left(-11, \frac{3}{4}\right)$ (c) $\left(-\frac{3}{4}, -\frac{1}{2}\right)$ (d) $\left(0, \frac{1}{4}\right)$

131. Let α and β be the roots of $x^2 - 6x - 2 = 0$, with $\alpha > \beta$. If $a_n = \alpha^n - \beta^n$ for $n \geq 1$, the value of $\frac{a_{10} - 2a_8}{2a_9}$ is

[IIT-JEE 2011, 3 and JEE Main 2015,4M]

(a) 1 (b) 2 (c) 3 (d) 4

132. A value of b for which the equations

$$x^2 + bx - 1 = 0 \quad x^2 + x + b = 0$$

have one root in common, is **[IIT-JEE 2011, 3M]**

(a) $-\sqrt{2}$ (b) $-i\sqrt{3}, i = \sqrt{-1}$

(c) $i\sqrt{5}, i = \sqrt{-1}$ (d) $\sqrt{2}$

133. The number of distinct real roots of $x^4 - 4x^3 + 12x^2 + x - 1 = 0$ is **[IIT-JEE 2011, 4M]**

134. Let for $a \neq a_1 \neq 0$, $f(x) = ax^2 + bx + c$, $g(x) = a_1x^2 + b_1x + c_1$ and $p(x) = f(x) - g(x)$. If $p(x) = 0$ only for $x = (-1)$ and $p(-2) = 2$, the value of $p(2)$ is **[AIEEE 2011, 4M]**

(a) 18 (b) 3 (c) 9 (d) 6

135. Sachin and Rahul attempted to solve a quadratic equation. Sachin made a mistake in writing down the constant term and ended up in roots (4, 3). Rahul made a mistake in writing down coefficient of x to get roots (3, 2). The correct roots of equation are **[AIEEE 2011, 4M]**

(a) $-4, -3$ (b) 6, 1 (c) 4, 3 (d) $-6, -1$

136. Let $\alpha(a)$ and $\beta(a)$ be the roots of the equation

$$(\sqrt[3]{(1+a)} - 1)x^2 + (\sqrt{(1+a)} - 1)x + (\sqrt[6]{(1+a)} - 1) = 0,$$

where $a > -1$, then $\lim_{a \to 0^+} \alpha(a)$ and $\lim_{a \to 0^+} \beta(a)$, are

[IIT-JEE 2012, 3M]

(a) $\left(-\frac{5}{2}\right)$ and 1 (b) $\left(-\frac{1}{2}\right)$ and (-1)

(c) $\left(-\frac{7}{2}\right)$ and 2 (d) $\left(-\frac{9}{2}\right)$ and 3

137. The equation $e^{\sin x} - e^{-\sin x} - 4 = 0$ has **[AIEEE 2012, 4M]**

(a) exactly one real root

(b) exactly four real roots

(c) infinite number of real roots

(d) no real roots

138. If the equations $x^2 + 2x + 3 = 0$ and $ax^2 + bx + c = 0$, $a, b, c \in R$ have a common root, then $a : b : c$ is

[JEE Main 2013, 4M]

(a) 3 : 2 : 1 (b) 1 : 3 : 2 (c) 3 : 1 : 2 (d) 1 : 2 : 3

139. If $a \in R$ and the equation $-3(x - [x])^2 + 2(x - [x]) + a^2 = 0$ (where $[\cdot]$ denotes the greatest integer function) has no integral solution, then all possible values of a lie in the interval

[JEE Main 2014, 4M]

(a) $(-2, -1)$

(b) $(-\infty, -2) \cup (2, \infty)$

(c) $(-1, 0) \cup (0, 1)$

(d) (1,2)

140. Let α, β be the roots of the equation $px^2 + qx + r = 0$, $p \neq 0$. If p, q, r are in AP and $\frac{1}{\alpha} + \frac{1}{\beta} = 4$, the value of $|\alpha - \beta|$, is **[JEE Main 2014, 4M]**

(a) $\frac{\sqrt{34}}{9}$ (b) $\frac{2\sqrt{13}}{9}$

(c) $\frac{\sqrt{61}}{9}$ (d) $\frac{2\sqrt{17}}{9}$

141. Let $a \in R$ and let $f : R \to R$ be given by $f(x) = x^5 - 5x + a$. Then, **[JEE Advanced 2014, 3M]**

(a) $f(x)$ has three real roots, if $a > 4$

(b) $f(x)$ has only one real root, if $a > 4$

(c) $f(x)$ has three real roots, if $a < -4$

(d) $f(x)$ has three real roots, if $-4 < a < 4$

142. The quadratic equation $p(x) = 0$ with real coefficients has purely imaginary roots. Then, $p(p(x)) = 0$ has

[JEE Advanced 2014, 3M]

(a) only purely imaginary roots

(b) all real roots

(c) two real and two purely imaginary roots

(d) neither real nor purely imaginary roots

143. Let S be the set of all non-zero real numbers α such that the quadratic equation $\alpha x^2 - x + \alpha = 0$ has two distinct real roots x_1 and x_2 satisfying the inequality $|x_1 - x_2| < 1$.

Which of the following intervals is (are) a subset(s) of S?

[JEE Advanced 2015, 4M]

(a) $\left(-\frac{1}{2}, -\frac{1}{\sqrt{5}}\right)$ (b) $\left(-\frac{1}{\sqrt{5}}, 0\right)$

(c) $\left(0, \frac{1}{\sqrt{5}}\right)$ (d) $\left(\frac{1}{\sqrt{5}}, \frac{1}{2}\right)$

144. The sum of all real values of x satisfying the equation

$(x^2 - 5x + 5)^{x^2 + 4x - 60} = 1$ is **[JEE Main 2016, 4M]**

(a) 6 (b) 5 (c) 3 (d) −4

145. Let $-\frac{\pi}{6} < \theta < -\frac{\pi}{12}$. Suppose α_1 and β_1 are the roots of equation $x^2 - 2x \sec\theta + 1 = 0$ and α_2 and β_2 are the roots of the equation $x^2 + 2x \tan\theta - 1 = 0$. If $\alpha_1 > \beta_1$ and $\alpha_2 > \beta_2$, then $\alpha_1 + \beta_2$ equals **[JEE Advanced 2016, 3M]**

(a) $2(\sec\theta - \tan\theta)$ (b) $2\sec\theta$
(c) $-2\tan\theta$ (d) 0

146. If for a positive integer n, the quadratic equation $x(x+1) + (x+1)(x+2) \ldots + (x+n-1)(x+n) = 10n$ has two consecutive integral solutions, then n is equal to **[JEE Main 2017, 4M]**

(a) 11 (b) 12
(c) 9 (d) 10

Answers

Exercise for Session 1

1.(b) 2. (c) 3. (a) 4. (b) 5. (a) 6. (a)
7.(c) 8. (b) 9. (c) 10. (d) 11. (b)

Exercise for Session 2

1.(a) 2. (c) 3. (b) 4. (a) 5.(d) 6. (c)
7. (c) 8. (b) 9. (c) 10. (a)

Exercise for Session 3

1.(a) 2. (b) 3. (c) 4. (c) 5.(d) 6. (c)
7.(c) 8. (a) 9. (a) 10. (d)

Exercise for Session 4

1.(c) 2. (c) 3. (c) 4. (d) 5.(a) 6. (d)
7.(d) 8. (c) 9. (b) 10. (d)

Exercise for Session 5

1.(a) 2. (a) 3. (b) 4. (c) 5.(c) 6. (b)
7.(a) 8. (b) 9. (b) 10. (d)

Chapter Exercises

1.(b) 2. (b) 3. (b) 4. (c) 5. (a) 6. (a)
7.(c) 8. (b) 9. (c) 10. (a) 11. (b) 12. (c)
13.(b) 14. (b) 15. (b) 16. (c) 17. (b) 18. (b)
19.(c) 20. (d) 21. (b) 22. (a) 23. (c) 24. (b)
25.(a) 26. (a) 27. (b) 28. (c) 29. (a) 30. (c)
31.(a,b) 32.(b,c) 33.(a,d) 34.(a,b,c,d) 35. (b,d) 36. (a,b,c,d)
37.(a, b,c,d) 38. (a,c) 39. (a,b) 40. (a,b,c,d) 41. (a,c) 42. (b,c)
43.(c,d) 44.(a,c,d) 45.(a,c,d)
46.(d) 47. (b) 48. (d) 49.(d) 50.(d) 51. (c)
52.(b) 53. (b) 54. (c) 55. (b) 56. (d) 57. (a)
58.(c) 59. (a) 60. (b) 61. (c) 62. (b) 63. (c)
64.(d) 65. (a) 66. (b) 67. (4) 68. (4) 69. (9)
70. (6) 71. (3) 72. (4) 73. (2) 74. (5) 75.(3)
76.(7) 77. (A) → (r,s), (B) → (p,q,r,s,t), (C) → (p,q,t)
78. (A) → (q,r,s), (B) → (p), (C) → (q)
79. (A) → (q,r,s,t), (B) → (q,r), (C) → (p,q)
80.(A) → (p,q,r,s), (B) → (p,q), (C) → (s) 81.(d) 82. (a)
83. (a) 84. (a) 85. (a) 86. (d) 87.(a)

88. (i) $m \in (0, 3)$ (ii) $m = 0, 3$
(iii) $m \in (-\infty, 0) \cup (3, \infty)$ (iv) $m \in (-\infty, -1) \cup [3, \infty)$
(v) $m \in \phi$ (vi) $m \in (-1, -1/8)$
(vii) $m = -1/3$ (viii) $m \in (-\infty, -1) \cup (-1, -1/8) \cup [3, \infty)$
(ix) $m \in (-1, -1/8)$ (x) $m = \frac{81 \pm \sqrt{6625}}{32}$

89. (i) $m \in \left(-\infty, \frac{7-\sqrt{33}}{2}\right)$ (ii) $m \in \left(\frac{7+\sqrt{33}}{2}, \infty\right)$ (iii) $m \in \phi$
(iv) $m \in \left(\frac{7-\sqrt{33}}{2}, \frac{11-\sqrt{73}}{2}\right) \cup \left(\frac{7+\sqrt{33}}{2}, \frac{11+\sqrt{73}}{2}\right)$
(v) $m \in (0, 3)$ (vi) $m \in \left(\frac{7-\sqrt{33}}{2}, \frac{7+\sqrt{33}}{2}\right)$
(vii) $m \in \left(\frac{7-\sqrt{33}}{2}, \frac{11-\sqrt{73}}{2}\right) \cup \left(\frac{7+\sqrt{33}}{2}, \frac{11+\sqrt{73}}{2}\right)$
(viii) $m \in \left(\frac{7-\sqrt{33}}{2}, \frac{7+\sqrt{33}}{2}\right) \cup \left(\frac{7+\sqrt{33}}{2}, \infty\right)$
(ix) $m \in \left(-\infty, \frac{7-\sqrt{33}}{2}\right) \cup \left(\frac{7-\sqrt{33}}{2}, \frac{7+\sqrt{33}}{2}\right)$
(x) $m \in \left(\frac{11-\sqrt{73}}{2}, \frac{7+\sqrt{33}}{2}\right)$

93. $a^2 l^2 x^2 - ablmx + (b^2 - 2ac)ln + (m^2 - 2ln)ac = 0$
97. $x \in \phi$
98. $x_1 = 1 + \sqrt{1 + \log_{2+\sqrt{3}} 10}$, $x_2 = 1 - \sqrt{1 + \log_{2+\sqrt{3}} 10}$
99. $x_1 = 2$, $x_2 = -1 + \sqrt{3}$ and $x_3 = -1 - \sqrt{3}$
100. $x_1 = 2$
101. $a \in (-\infty, -1) \cup \left(\frac{\sqrt{3}}{2}, \infty\right)$
102. $x \in (-1 - \sqrt{5}, -3) \cup (\sqrt{5} - 1, 5)$
103. The pairs (0, 1), (1, 0), $\left(\frac{1-\sqrt{5}}{2}, \frac{1-\sqrt{5}}{2}\right)$ are solutions of the original system of equations.
104. (i) $ry^3 - q(r+1)y^2 + p(r+1)^2 y - (r+1)^3 = 0$
(ii) $y^3 - py^2 + (4q - p^2)y + (8r - 4pq + p^3) = 0$ and $4pq - p^3 - 8r$
106. $a \in \left(\frac{3}{4}, \infty\right)$ 107. $x_1 = -1, x_2 = -1/2$ 109. Four
110. $a \in \left(-\frac{1}{4}, 1\right)$ 111. 80 112. (d) 113. (d) 114. (a)
115. (d) 116. (a) 117. 1210 118.(a) 119. (c) 120. (b)
121. (d) 122. (a) 123. (b) 124. (c) 125. (a) 126. (d)
127. (c) 128. (d) 129. (b) 130. (c) 131. (c) 132. (b)
133.(2) 134. (a) 135. (b) 136. (b) 137. (d) 138. (d)
139. (c) 140. (b) 141.(b,d) 142. (d) 143. (a, d)
144. (c) 145. (c) 146. (a)

Solutions

1. We have,

$$2(a-b)x^2 - 11(a+b+c)x - 3(a-b) = 0$$

$\therefore \quad D = \{-11(a+b+c)\}^2 - 4\cdot 2(a-b)\cdot(-3)(a-b)$

$= 121(a+b+c)^2 + 24(a-b)^2 > 0$

Therefore, the roots are real and unequal.

2. Here, $a < 0$

Cut-off Y-axis, $x = 0$

$\Rightarrow \quad y = c < 0$ [from graph]

$\therefore \quad c < 0$

x-coordinate of vertex > 0

$\Rightarrow \quad -\frac{b}{2a} > 0$

$\Rightarrow \quad \frac{b}{a} < 0$

But $\quad a < 0$

$\therefore \quad b > 0$

and y-coordinate of vertex < 0

$\Rightarrow \quad -\frac{D}{4a} < 0 \Rightarrow \frac{D}{4a} > 0$

$\therefore \quad D < 0$ $[\because a < 0]$

i.e. $\quad b^2 - 4ac < 0$

$\therefore \quad \frac{c}{a} > 0$ $[\because c < 0, a < 0]$

3. Sum of the roots $= -\frac{(a+3)}{a} = I^+$ [let]

$\therefore \quad a = \left(-\frac{3}{I^+ + 1}\right)$ ...(i)

Product of the roots $= \alpha\beta = \frac{a-3}{a} = I^+ + 2$ ...(ii)

and $\quad D = (a+3)^2 - 4a(a+3)$

$= \frac{9}{(I^+ + 1)^2}\{(I^+ - 2)^2 - 12\}$ [from Eq. (i)]

D must be perfect square, then $I^+ = 6$

From Eq. (ii),

Product of the roots $= I^+ + 2 = 6 + 2 = 8$

4. Let α be one root of

$$x^2 - 3ax + f(a) = 0$$

$\Rightarrow \quad \alpha + 2\alpha = 3a \Rightarrow 3\alpha = 3a$

$\Rightarrow \quad \alpha = a$ ...(i)

and $\quad \alpha\cdot 2\alpha = f(a)$

$\Rightarrow \quad f(a) = 2\alpha^2 = 2a^2$ [using Eq. (i)]

$\Rightarrow \quad f(x) = 2x^2$

5. $\because \quad x_1x_2 = 4$ ...(i)

and $\quad \frac{x_1}{x_1 - 1} + \frac{x_2}{x_2 - 1} = 2$

$\Rightarrow \quad 2x_1x_2 - x_1 - x_2 = 2(x_1x_2 - x_1 - x_2 + 1)$

$\Rightarrow \quad 8 - x_1 - x_2 = 2(4 - x_1 - x_2 + 1)$ [from Eq. (i)]

or $\quad x_1 + x_2 = 2$ ...(ii)

From Eqs. (i) and (ii), required equation is

$$x^2 - (x_1 + x_2)x + x_1x_2 = 0$$

or $\quad x^2 - 2x + 4 = 0$

6. Let $f(x) = x^2 - 2ax + a^2 - 1$

Now, four cases arise:

***Case* I** $D \geq 0$

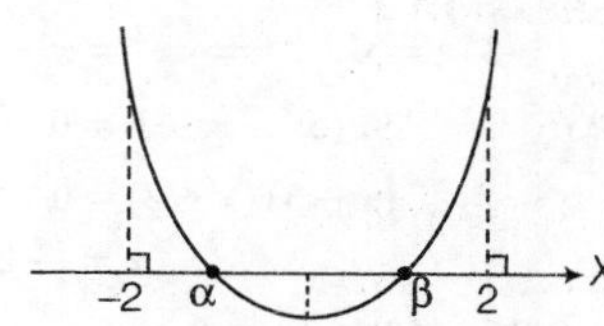

$\Rightarrow \quad (-2a)^2 - 4\cdot 1(a^2 - 1) \geq 0$

$\Rightarrow \quad 4 \geq 0$

$\therefore \quad a \in R$

***Case* II** $f(-2) > 0$

$\Rightarrow \quad 4 + 4a + a^2 - 1 > 0$

$\Rightarrow \quad a^2 + 4a + 3 > 0$

$\Rightarrow \quad (a+1)(a+3) > 0$

$\therefore \quad a \in (-\infty, -3) \cup (-1, \infty)$

***Case* III** $f(2) > 0$

$\Rightarrow \quad 4 - 4a + a^2 - 1 > 0$

$\Rightarrow \quad a^2 - 4a + 3 > 0$

$\Rightarrow \quad (a-1)(a-3) > 0$

$\therefore \quad a \in (-\infty, 1) \cup (3, \infty)$

***Case* IV** $-2 <$ x-coordinate of vertex < 2

$\Rightarrow \quad -2 < 2a < 2$

$\therefore \quad a \in (-1, 1)$

Combining all cases, we get $a \in (-1, 1)$

Hence, $\quad [a] = -1, 0$

7. We have, $-\left(\frac{-4a}{2(-2)}\right) = -2$

$\Rightarrow \quad a = 2$

$\therefore \quad y = -2x^2 - 8x + \lambda$ ...(i)

Since, Eq. (i) passes through points $(-2, 7)$

$\therefore \quad 7 = -2(-2)^2 - 8(-2) + \lambda$

$\Rightarrow \quad 7 = -8 + 16 + \lambda$

$\therefore \quad \lambda = -1$

8. Since, the coefficient of $n^2 = (4p - p^2 - 5) < 0$

Therefore, the graph is open downward.

According to the question, 1 must lie between the roots.

Hence, $f(1) > 0$

$\Rightarrow \quad 4p - p^2 - 5 - 2p + 1 + 3p > 0$

$\Rightarrow \quad -p^2 + 5p - 4 > 0$

$\Rightarrow \quad p^2 - 5p + 4 < 0$

$\Rightarrow \quad (p-4)(p-1) < 0$

$\Rightarrow \quad 1 < p < 4$

$\therefore \quad p = 2, 3$

Hence, number of integral values of p is 2.

9. We have, $3^{2x^2} - 2 \cdot 3^{x^2 + x + 6} + 3^{2(x+6)} = 0$

$\Rightarrow \quad (3^{x^2} - 3^{x+6})^2 = 0$

$\Rightarrow \quad 3^{x^2} - 3^{x+6} = 0$

$\Rightarrow \quad 3^{x^2} = 3^{x+6} \Rightarrow x^2 = x + 6$

$\Rightarrow \quad x^2 - x - 6 = 0$

$\Rightarrow \quad (x-3)(x+2) = 0$

$\therefore \quad x = \{-2, 3\}$

10. Given, $b^2 - 4ac = p^2 - 4aq$ ...(i)

and $f(x) = g(x)$

$\Rightarrow \quad ax^2 + bx + c = ax^2 + px + q$

$\Rightarrow \quad (b-p)x = q - c$

$\therefore \quad x = \dfrac{q-c}{b-p} = \alpha$ [given] ...(ii)

From Eq. (i), we get

$(b+p)(b-p) + 4a(q-c) = 0$

$\Rightarrow \quad (b+p)(b-p) + 4a\alpha(b-p) = 0$ [from Eq. (ii)]

or $\alpha = -\dfrac{(b+p)}{4a}$ [$\because b \neq p$]

$= \dfrac{\left(-\dfrac{b}{a}\right) + \left(-\dfrac{p}{a}\right)}{4}$

$= \dfrac{\left[\begin{array}{l}\text{Sum of the roots of } (f(x)=0) \\ + \text{ Sum of the roots of } (g(x)=0)\end{array}\right]}{4}$

$=$ AM of the roots of $f(x) = 0$

and $g(x) = 0$

11. Let α and β be the roots of $ax^2 + bx + c = 0$.

$\therefore \quad x_1 = \dfrac{\alpha + \beta}{2} = -\dfrac{b}{2a}$

and $x_2 = \dfrac{2\alpha\beta}{\alpha + \beta} = \dfrac{2 \cdot \dfrac{c}{a}}{-\dfrac{b}{a}} = -\dfrac{2c}{b}$

$\therefore$ The required equation is

$$x^2 - \left[\left(-\frac{b}{2a}\right) + \left(-\frac{2c}{b}\right)\right] x + \frac{2bc}{2ab} = 0$$

i.e. $2abx^2 + (b^2 + 4ac)x + 2bc = 0$

12. Let α_1, α_2 and α_3 be the roots of $f(x) = 0$, such that

$\alpha_1 < \alpha_2 < \alpha_3$

and $g(x)$ can take all values from $[-6, \infty)$.

$\because \quad g(x) = (x+1)^2 - 6 \geq -6$

$\therefore \quad \alpha_3 \leq -7, \alpha_2 \leq -8, \alpha_1 \leq -9$

$\therefore \quad a + b + c \geq 719$

$\therefore$ Minimum value of $a + b + c$ is 719.

$\because \quad \alpha_1 + \alpha_2 + \alpha_3 = -a$

$\Rightarrow \quad -a \leq -24$

$\Rightarrow \quad a \geq 24$

$\alpha_1\alpha_2 + \alpha_2\alpha_3 + \alpha_3\alpha_1 = b$

$\Rightarrow \quad b \geq 191$

and $\alpha_1\alpha_2\alpha_3 = -c$

$\Rightarrow \quad -c \leq -504$

$\Rightarrow \quad c \geq 504$

$\therefore \quad a + b + c \geq 719$

Hence, minimum value of $a + b + c$ is 719.

13. $\because \displaystyle\sum_{k=1}^{n} (x + k - 1)(x + k) = 10n$

$\Rightarrow \quad \displaystyle\sum_{k=1}^{n} x^2 + x(2k-1) + (k-1)k = 10n$

$\Rightarrow \quad nx^2 + x(1 + 3 + 5 + \ldots + (2n-1))$

$+ (0 + 1 \cdot 2 + 2 \cdot 3 + 3 \cdot 4 + \ldots + (n-1)n) = 10n$

$\Rightarrow \quad nx^2 + x \cdot \dfrac{n}{2}(1 + 2n - 1)$

$+ \left(\dfrac{n(n+1)(2n+1)}{6} - \dfrac{n(n+1)}{2}\right) = 10n$

$\Rightarrow \quad nx^2 + n^2x + \dfrac{n(n^2-1)}{3} = 10n$

$\Rightarrow \quad x^2 + nx + \dfrac{(n^2-31)}{3} = 0$ [dividing by n]

$\because \quad (\alpha + 1) - \alpha = \dfrac{\sqrt{D}}{1}$

$1 = \sqrt{D}$

$\Rightarrow \quad D = 1$

$\Rightarrow \quad n^2 - 4 \cdot 1 \cdot \dfrac{(n^2 - 31)}{3} = 1$

$\Rightarrow \quad 3n^2 - 4n^2 + 124 = 3$

$\Rightarrow \quad n^2 = 121$

$\therefore \quad n = 11$

14. Since, 2 is only even prime.

Therefore, we have

$2^2 + \lambda \cdot 2 + 12 = 0$

$\Rightarrow \quad \lambda = 8$

$\therefore \quad x^2 + \lambda x + \mu = 0$

$\Rightarrow \quad x^2 + 8x + \mu = 0$ ...(i)

But Eq. (i) has equal roots.

$\therefore \quad D = 0$

$\Rightarrow \quad 8^2 - 4 \cdot 1 \cdot \mu = 0$

$\Rightarrow \quad \mu = 16$

15. We have, $\sqrt{x} + \sqrt{x - \sqrt{(1-x)}} = 1$

$\Rightarrow \quad \sqrt{x - \sqrt{1-x}} = 1 - \sqrt{x}$

On squaring both sides, we get

$$x - \sqrt{1-x} = 1 + x - 2\sqrt{x}$$

$\Rightarrow \quad -\sqrt{1-x} = 1 - 2\sqrt{x}$

Again, squaring on both sides, we get

$$1 - x = 1 + 4x - 4\sqrt{x}$$

$$4\sqrt{x} = 5x$$

$\Rightarrow \quad \sqrt{x} = \frac{4}{5}$ [on squaring both sides]

$\Rightarrow \quad x = \frac{16}{25}$

Hence, the number of real solutions is 1.

16. Let $x = \sqrt{7 + \sqrt{7 - \sqrt{7 + \sqrt{7 - \ldots \infty}}}}$

$\Rightarrow \quad x = \sqrt{7 + \sqrt{7 - x}}$ [on squaring both sides]

$\Rightarrow \quad x^2 - 7 = \sqrt{7 - x}$

$\Rightarrow \quad (x^2 - 7)^2 = 7 - x$ [again, squaring on both sides]

$\Rightarrow \quad x^4 - 14x^2 + x + 42 = 0$

$\Rightarrow \quad (x - 3)(x^3 + 3x^2 - 5x - 14) = 0$

$\Rightarrow \quad (x - 3)(x + 2)(x^2 + x - 7) = 0$

$\Rightarrow \quad x = 3, -2, \frac{-1 \pm \sqrt{29}}{2}$

$\therefore \quad x = 3$ $[\because x > \sqrt{7}]$

17. Let $y = 2(k - x)(x + \sqrt{(x^2 + k^2)})$

$\Rightarrow \quad y - 2(k - x)x = 2(k - x)\sqrt{(x^2 + k^2)}$

On squaring both sides, we get

$\Rightarrow \quad y^2 + 4(k - x)^2 x^2 - 4xy(k - x) = 4(k - x)^2 (x^2 + k^2)$

$\Rightarrow \quad y^2 - 4xy(k - x) = 4(k - x)^2 k^2$

$\Rightarrow \quad 4(k^2 - y)x^2 - 4(2k^3 - ky)x - y^2 + 4k^4 = 0$

Since, x is real.

$\therefore \quad D \ge 0$

$\Rightarrow \quad 16(2k^3 - ky)^2 - 4 \cdot 4(k^2 - y)(4k^4 - y^2) \ge 0$

[using, $b^2 - 4ac \ge 0$]

$\Rightarrow \quad 4k^6 + k^2y^2 - 4k^4y - (-k^2y^2 + 4k^6 + y^3 - 4yk^4) \ge 0$

$\Rightarrow \quad 2k^2y^2 - y^3 \ge 0$

$\Rightarrow \quad y^2(y - 2k^2) \le 0$

$\therefore \quad y \le 2k^2$

18. We have, $\frac{1}{3} < \frac{x^2 - 2x + 4}{x^2 + 2x + 4} < 3, \forall x \in R$

$$\frac{1}{3} < \frac{x^2 + 2x + 4}{x^2 - 2x + 4} < 3, \forall x \in R$$

Let $y = \frac{9 \cdot 3^{2x} + 6 \cdot 3^x + 4}{9 \cdot 3^{2x} - 6 \cdot 3^x + 4} = \frac{(3^{x+1})^2 + 2 \cdot 3^{x+1} + 4}{(3^{x+1})^2 - 2 \cdot 3^{x+1} + 4}$

$= \frac{t^2 + 2t + 4}{t^2 - 2t + 4}$, where $t = 3^{x+1}$

$\Rightarrow \quad (y - 1)t^2 - 2(y + 1)t + 4(y - 1) = 0$

By the given condition, for every $t \in R$,

$$\frac{1}{3} < y < 3 \quad \ldots(i)$$

But $\quad t = 3^{x+1} > 0$

We have, product of the roots = 4 > 0, which is true.

And sum of the roots $= \frac{2(y + 1)}{(y - 1)} > 0$

$\Rightarrow \quad \frac{y + 1}{y - 1} > 0$

$\therefore \quad y \in (-\infty, -1) \cup (1, \infty) \quad \ldots(ii)$

From Eqs. (i) and (ii), we get

$$1 < y < 3$$

19. Since α, β and γ are the roots of

$$(x - a)(x - b)(x - c) = d$$

$\Rightarrow \quad (x - a)(x - b)(x - c) - d = (x - \alpha)(x - \beta)(x - \gamma)$

$\Rightarrow \quad (x - \alpha)(x - \beta)(x - \gamma) + d = (x - a)(x - b)(x - c)$

$\Rightarrow$ a, b and c are the roots of

$$(x - \alpha)(x - \beta)(x - \gamma) + d = 0$$

20. Since, all the coefficients of given equation are not real.

Therefore, other root $\ne 3 + i$.

Let other root be α.

Then, sum of the roots $= \frac{2(1 + i)}{i}$

$\Rightarrow \quad \alpha + 3 - i = \frac{2(1 + i)}{i}$

$\Rightarrow \quad \alpha + 3 - i = 2 - 2i$

$\therefore \quad \alpha = -1 - i$

21. We have, $|[x] - 2x| = 4$

$\Rightarrow \quad |[x] - 2([x] + \{x\})| = 4$

$\Rightarrow \quad |[x] + 2\{x\}| = 4$

which is possible only when

$$2\{x\} = 0, 1$$

If $\{x\} = 0$, then $[x] = \pm 4$ and then $x = -4, 4$ and if $\{x\} = \frac{1}{2}$, then

$$[x] + 1 = \pm 4$$

$\Rightarrow \quad [x] = 3, -5$

$\therefore \quad x = 3 + \frac{1}{2}$ and $-5 + \frac{1}{2}$

$\Rightarrow \quad x = \frac{7}{2}, -\frac{9}{2} \Rightarrow x = -4, -\frac{9}{2}, \frac{7}{2}, 4$

22. We know that, $x^2 + x + 1$ is a factor of $ax^3 + bx^2 + cx + d$.

Hence, roots of $x^2 + x + 1 = 0$ are also roots of $ax^3 + bx^2 + cx + d = 0$. Since, ω and ω^2

$\left(\text{where } \omega = -\frac{1}{2} + \frac{3i}{2}\right)$ are two complex roots of $x^2 + x + 1 = 0$.

Therefore, ω and ω^2 are two complex roots of $ax^3 + bx^2 + cx + d = 0$.

We know that, a cubic equation has atleast one real root. Let real root be α. Then,

$$\alpha \cdot \omega \cdot \omega^2 = -\frac{d}{a} \Rightarrow \alpha = -\frac{d}{a}$$

23. We have, $\sqrt{(5x^2 - 8x + 3)} - \sqrt{(5x^2 - 9x + 4)}$

$$= \sqrt{(2x^2 - 2x)} - \sqrt{(2x^2 - 3x + 1)}$$

$$\Rightarrow \sqrt{(5x-3)(x-1)} - \sqrt{(5x-4)(x-1)} = \sqrt{2x(x-1)} - \sqrt{(2x-1)(x-1)}$$

$$\Rightarrow \sqrt{x-1}\,(\sqrt{5x-3} - \sqrt{5x-4}) = \sqrt{x-1}\,(\sqrt{2x} - \sqrt{2x-1})$$

$$\Rightarrow \sqrt{x-1} = 0$$

$$\Rightarrow x = 1$$

24. We have, $(a + \sqrt{b})(a - \sqrt{b}) = a^2 - b = 1$ [given]

$$\therefore (a + \sqrt{b})^{x^2 - 15} + (a - \sqrt{b})^{x^2 - 15} = 2a$$

$$\Rightarrow (a + \sqrt{b})^{x^2 - 15} + \frac{1}{(a + \sqrt{b})^{x^2 - 15}} = 2a$$

Let $y = (a + \sqrt{b})^{x^2 - 15}$

$$\Rightarrow y + \frac{1}{y} = 2a \Rightarrow y^2 - 2ay + 1 = 0$$

$$\Rightarrow y = \frac{2a \pm \sqrt{4a^2 - 4}}{2} = a \pm \sqrt{a^2 - 1}$$

$$\therefore y = a \pm \sqrt{b} = (a + \sqrt{b})^{\pm 1} \quad [\because a^2 - b = 1]$$

$$\Rightarrow (a + \sqrt{b})^{x^2 - 15} = (a + \sqrt{b})^{\pm 1}$$

$$\therefore x^2 - 15 = \pm 1$$

$$\Rightarrow x^2 = 15 \pm 1 \Rightarrow x^2 = 16, 14$$

$$\Rightarrow x = \pm 4, \pm \sqrt{14}$$

25. We have, $x^2 - xy + y^2 = 4(x + y - 4)$

$$\Rightarrow x^2 - x(y + 4) + y^2 - 4y + 16 = 0$$

$$\because x \in R$$

$$\therefore (-(y + 4))^2 - 4 \cdot 1 \cdot (y^2 - 4y + 16) \geq 0$$

[using, $b^2 - 4ac \geq 0$]

$$\Rightarrow y^2 + 8y + 16 - 4y^2 + 16y - 64 \geq 0$$

$$\Rightarrow 3y^2 - 24y + 48 \leq 0$$

$$\Rightarrow y^2 - 8y + 16 \leq 0 \Rightarrow (y - 4)^2 \leq 0$$

$$\therefore (y - 4)^2 = 0$$

$$\therefore y = 4$$

Then, $x^2 - 4x + 16 = 4(x + 4 - 4)$

$$x^2 - 8x + 16 = 0$$

$$(x - 4)^2 = 0$$

$$x = 4$$

Number of pairs is 1 i.e., (4, 4).

26. Since, 3789108 is an even integer. Therefore, $x^4 - y^4$ is also an even integer. So, either both x and y are even integers or both of them are odd integers.

Now, $x^4 - y^4 = (x - y)(x + y)(x^2 + y^2)$

$\Rightarrow x - y, x + y, x^2 + y^2$ must be even integers.

Therefore, $(x - y)(x + y)(x^2 + y^2)$ must be divisible by 8. But 3789108 is not divisible by 8. Hence, the given equation has no solution.

$\therefore$ Number of solutions = 0

27. We have, $x^3 + ax + 1 = 0$

or $x^4 + ax^2 + x = 0$ ...(i)

and $x^4 + ax^2 + 1 = 0$ ...(ii)

From Eqs. (i) and (ii), we get

$$x - 1 = 0$$

$$\Rightarrow x = 1$$

which is a common root.

$$\therefore 1 + a + 1 = 0$$

$$\Rightarrow a = -2$$

28. $\because (1 - a^2)x^2 + 2ax - 1 = 0$

$$1 - a^2 \neq 0$$

$$x^2 + \left(\frac{2a}{1 - a^2}\right)x - \left(\frac{1}{1 - a^2}\right) = 0$$

Let $f(x) = x^2 + \left(\frac{2a}{1 - a^2}\right)x - \left(\frac{1}{(1 - a^2)}\right)$

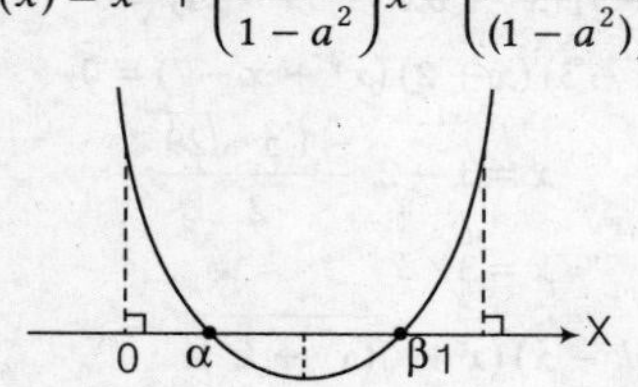

The following cases arise:

***Case* I** $D \geq 0$

$$\left(\frac{2a}{1 - a^2}\right)^2 - 4 \cdot 1 \cdot \left(\frac{-1}{1 - a^2}\right) \geq 0$$

$$\Rightarrow \frac{4a^2}{(1 - a^2)^2} + \frac{4}{(1 - a^2)} \geq 0$$

$$\Rightarrow \frac{4a^2 + 4 - 4a^2}{(1 - a^2)^2} \geq 0$$

$$\Rightarrow \frac{4}{(1 - a^2)^2} \geq 0 \quad \text{[always true]}$$

***Case* II** $f(0) > 0$

$$\Rightarrow \frac{-1}{(1 - a^2)} > 0 \Rightarrow \frac{1}{1 - a^2} < 0$$

$$\Rightarrow 1 - a^2 < 0$$

$$\therefore a \in (-\infty, -1) \cup (1, \infty)$$

***Case* III** $f(1) > 0$

$$\Rightarrow 1 + \frac{2a}{(1 - a^2)} - \frac{1}{(1 - a^2)} > 0$$

$$\Rightarrow \quad \frac{1 - a^2 + 2a - 1}{(1 - a^2)} > 0 \Rightarrow \frac{a^2 - 2a}{1 - a^2} < 0$$

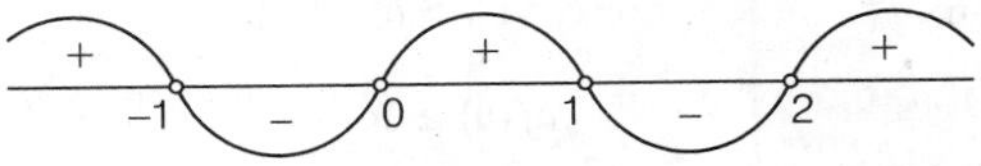

$$\Rightarrow \quad \frac{a(a - 2)}{(a + 1)(a - 1)} > 0$$

$$\therefore \quad a \in (-\infty, -1) \cup (0, 1) \cup (2, \infty)$$

***Case* IV** $0 <$ x-coordinate of vertex < 1

$$\Rightarrow \quad 0 < -\frac{2a}{2(1 - a^2)} < 1 \Rightarrow 0 < \frac{a}{a^2 - 1} < 1$$

$$\Rightarrow \quad 0 < \frac{a}{(a + 1)(a - 1)} \text{ and } 1 - \frac{a}{a^2 - 1} > 0$$

$$\Rightarrow \quad \frac{a}{(a + 1)(a - 1)} > 0$$

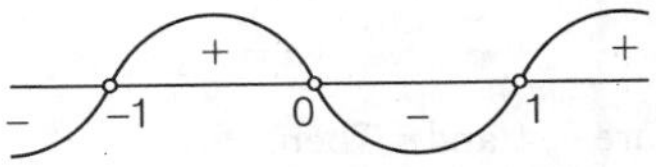

$$\Rightarrow \quad a \in (-1, 0) \cup (1, \infty)$$

and
$$\frac{\left(a - \frac{1 + \sqrt{5}}{2}\right)\left(a - \frac{1 - \sqrt{5}}{2}\right)}{(a + 1)(a - 1)} > 0$$

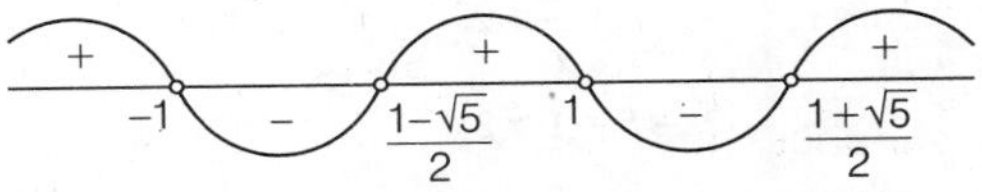

and $\quad a \in (-\infty, -1) \cup \left(\frac{1 - \sqrt{5}}{2}, 1\right) \cup \left(\frac{1 + \sqrt{5}}{2}, \infty\right)$

$$\therefore \quad a \in \left(\frac{1 - \sqrt{5}}{2}, 0\right) \cup \left(\frac{1 + \sqrt{5}}{2}, \infty\right)$$

Combining all cases, we get

$$a > 2$$

29. We have, $\quad x - \sqrt{1 - |x|} < 0 \quad$ ...(i)

which is defined only when

$$1 - |x| \geq 0$$

$$\Rightarrow \quad |x| \leq 1$$

$$\Rightarrow \quad x \in [-1, 1]$$

Now, from Eq. (i), we get

$$x < \sqrt{1 - |x|}$$

***Case* I** If $x \geq 0$, i.e., $0 \leq x \leq 1$

$$x - \sqrt{(1 - |x|)} < 0$$

$$\Rightarrow \quad x < \sqrt{(1 - x)}$$

On squaring both sides, we get

$$x^2 + x - 1 < 0$$

$$\Rightarrow \quad \frac{-1 - \sqrt{5}}{2} < x < \frac{-1 + \sqrt{5}}{2}$$

But $\quad x \geq 0$

$$\therefore \quad x \in \left[0, \frac{-1 + \sqrt{5}}{2}\right)$$

***Case* II** If $x < 0$, i.e., $-1 \leq x < 0$

$$x - \sqrt{(1 + x)} < 0$$

$$\Rightarrow \quad x < \sqrt{1 + x} \quad \text{[always true]}$$

$$x \in [-1, 0)$$

Combining both cases, we get

$$x \in \left[-1, \frac{-1 + \sqrt{5}}{2}\right)$$

30. We have, $(a \cdot 2b - 2c \cdot a)(2c \cdot c - b \cdot 2b) = (ba - ca)^2$

$$\Rightarrow \quad 2a(b - c) \cdot 2(c^2 - b^2) = a^2(b - c)^2$$

$$\Rightarrow \quad 4a(c - b)(c + b) = a^2(b - c) \quad [\because b \neq c]$$

$$\Rightarrow \quad 4a(c + b) = -a^2$$

$$\Rightarrow \quad a + 4b + 4c = 0$$

31. $0 < a < b < c, \alpha + \beta = \left(-\frac{b}{a}\right)$ and $\alpha\beta = \frac{c}{a}$

For non-real complex roots,

$$b^2 - 4ac < 0$$

$$\Rightarrow \quad \frac{b^2}{a^2} - \frac{4c}{a} < 0$$

$$\Rightarrow \quad (\alpha + \beta)^2 - 4\alpha\beta < 0$$

$$\Rightarrow \quad (\alpha - \beta)^2 < 0$$

$$\because \quad 0 < a < b < c$$

$\therefore$ Roots are conjugate, then $|\alpha| = |\beta|$

But $\quad \alpha\beta = \frac{c}{a}$

$$|\alpha\beta| = \left|\frac{c}{a}\right| > 1 \quad \left[\because a < c, \therefore \frac{c}{a} > 1\right]$$

$$\Rightarrow \quad |\alpha||\beta| > 1$$

$$\Rightarrow \quad |\alpha|^2 > 1 \text{ or } |\alpha| > 1$$

32. Given equation is

$$Ax^2 - |G|x - H = 0 \quad \text{...(i)}$$

$$\therefore \quad \text{Discriminant} = (-|G|)^2 - 4A(-H)$$

$$= G^2 + 4AH$$

$$= G^2 + 4G^2 \quad [\because G^2 = AH]$$

$$= 5G^2 > 0$$

$\therefore$ Roots of Eq. (i) are real and distinct.

$$\because \quad A = \frac{a + b}{2} > 0, G = \sqrt{ab} > 0, H = \frac{2ab}{a + b} > 0$$

[$\because$ a and b are two unequal positive integers]

Let α and β be the roots of Eq. (i). Then,

$$\alpha + \beta = \frac{|G|}{A} > 0$$

and
$$\alpha\beta = -\frac{H}{A} < 0$$

and
$$\alpha - \beta = \frac{\sqrt{D}}{A} = \frac{G\sqrt{5}}{A} > 0$$

$\therefore \quad \alpha = \dfrac{|G| + G\sqrt{5}}{2A} > 0$

and $\quad \beta = \dfrac{|G| - G\sqrt{5}}{2A} < 0$

Exactly one positive root and atleast one root which is negative fraction.

33. It is clear from graph that the equation $y = ax^2 + bx + c = 0$ has two real and distinct roots. Therefore,

$$b^2 - 4ac > 0 \quad \text{...(i)}$$

$\because$ Parabola open downwards.

$\therefore \quad a < 0$

and $y = ax^2 + bx + c$ cuts-off Y-axis at, $x = 0$.

$\therefore \quad y = c < 0$

$\Rightarrow \quad c < 0$

and x-coordinate of vertex > 0

$\Rightarrow \quad -\dfrac{b}{2a} > 0 \Rightarrow \dfrac{b}{a} < 0$

$\Rightarrow \quad b > 0 \quad [\because a < 0]$

It is clear that a and b are of opposite signs.

34. Let $y = ax^2 + bx + c$

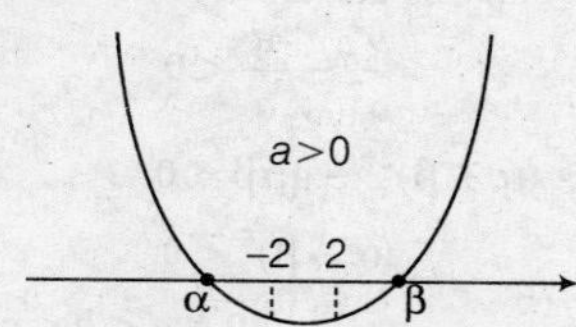

Consider the following cases:

***Case* I** $D > 0$

$\Rightarrow \quad b^2 - 4ac > 0$

***Case* II** $af(-2) < 0$

$\Rightarrow \quad a(4a - 2b + c) < 0$

$\Rightarrow \quad 4a - 2b + c < 0$

***Case* III** $af(2) > 0$

$\Rightarrow \quad a(4a + 2b + c) > 0$

$\Rightarrow \quad 4a + 2b + c > 0$

Combining *Case* II and *Case* III, we get

$$4a + 2|b| + c < 0$$

Also, at $x = 0$, $\quad y < 0 \Rightarrow c < 0$

Also, since for $-2 < x < 2$,

$$y < 0$$

$\Rightarrow \quad ax^2 + bx + c < 0$

For $x = 1$, $\quad a + b + c < 0 \quad$ ...(i)

and for $x = -1$, $\quad a - b + c < 0 \quad$ ...(ii)

Combining Eqs. (i) and (ii), we get

$$a + |b| + c < 0$$

35. Put $x^2 = y$.

Then, the given equation can be written as

$$f(y) = ay^2 + by + c = 0 \quad \text{...(i)}$$

The given equation will have four real roots, i.e. Eq. (i) has two non-negative roots.

Then, $\quad -\dfrac{b}{a} \geq 0$

$$af(0) \geq 0$$

and $\quad b^2 - 4ac \geq 0 \quad$ [given]

$\Rightarrow \quad \dfrac{b}{a} \leq 0$

$$ac \geq 0$$

$\Rightarrow \quad a > 0, b < 0, c > 0$

or $\quad a < 0, b > 0, c < 0$

36. Let the roots be $\dfrac{a}{r}$, a and ar, where $a > 0$, $r > 1$

$\therefore$ Product of the roots $= 1$

$\Rightarrow \quad \dfrac{a}{r} \cdot a \cdot ar = 1$

$\Rightarrow \quad a^3 = 1$

$\therefore \quad a = 1 \quad$ [one root is 1]

Now, roots are $\dfrac{1}{r}$, 1 and r. Then,

$$\frac{1}{r} + 1 + r = -b$$

$\Rightarrow \quad \dfrac{1}{r} + r = -b - 1 \quad$ ...(i)

$\because \quad r + \dfrac{1}{r} > 2$

$\Rightarrow \quad -b - 1 > 2$

$\Rightarrow \quad b < -3 \quad$ [from Eq. (i)]

or $\quad b \in (-\infty, -3)$

Also, $\quad \dfrac{1}{r} \cdot 1 + 1 \cdot r + r \cdot \dfrac{1}{r} = c$

$\Rightarrow \quad \dfrac{1}{r} + r + 1 = c = -b \quad$ [from Eq. (i)]

$\therefore \quad b + c = 0$

Now, first root $= \dfrac{1}{r} < 1 \quad$ [$\because$ one root is smaller than one]

Second root $= 1$

Third root $= r > 1 \quad$ [$\because$ one root is greater than one]

37. We have, $\quad f(x) = ax^2 + bx + c$

$a, b, c \in R \quad [\because a \neq 0]$

On putting $x = 0, 1, \dfrac{1}{2}$, we get

$$|c| \leq 1$$

$$|a + b + c| \leq 1$$

and $\quad \left|\dfrac{1}{4}a + \dfrac{1}{2}b + c\right| \leq 1$

$\Rightarrow \quad -1 \leq c \leq 1,$

$$-1 \leq a + b + c \leq 1$$

and $\quad -4 \leq a + 2b + 4c \leq 4$

$\Rightarrow \quad -4 \leq 4a + 4b + 4c \leq 4$

and $\quad -4 \leq -a - 2b - 4c \leq 4$

On adding, we get

$$-8 \le 3a + 2b \le 8$$

Also, $\quad -8 \le a + 2b \le 8$

$\therefore \quad -16 \le 2a \le 16$

$\Rightarrow \quad |a| \le 8$

$\because \quad -1 \le -c \le 1, -8 \le -a \le 8$

We get, $\quad -16 \le 2b \le 16$

$\Rightarrow \quad |b| \le 8$

$\therefore \quad |a| + |b| + |c| \le 17$

38. $\because \quad x = \dfrac{-5 \pm \sqrt{25 + 1200}}{50} = \dfrac{-5 \pm 35}{50} = \dfrac{30}{50}, \dfrac{-40}{50}$

or $\quad \cos\alpha = \dfrac{3}{5}, \dfrac{-4}{5}$

But $\quad -1 < x < 0$

$\therefore \quad \cos\alpha = -\dfrac{4}{5}$ [lies in II and III quadrants]

$\therefore \quad \sin\alpha = \dfrac{3}{5}$ [lies in II quadrant]

$\therefore \quad \sin\alpha = -\dfrac{3}{5}$ [lies in III quadrant]

$\therefore \quad \sin 2\alpha = 2 \cdot \sin\alpha \cdot \cos\alpha = -\dfrac{24}{25}$

[lies in II quadrant]

$\therefore \quad \sin 2\alpha = 2 \cdot \sin\alpha \cdot \cos\alpha = \dfrac{24}{25}$ [lies in III quadrant]

39. $\because a + 2b + 4c = 0$

$\therefore \quad a\left(\dfrac{1}{2}\right)^2 + b\left(\dfrac{1}{2}\right) + c = 0$

It is clear that one root is $\dfrac{1}{2}$.

Let other root be α. Then, $\alpha + \dfrac{1}{2} = -\dfrac{b}{a}$

$\Rightarrow \quad \alpha = -\dfrac{1}{2} - \dfrac{b}{a}$

which depends upon a and b.

40. $\because$ Cut-off Y-axis, put $x = 0$, i.e. $f(0) = c$

Option (a) $a < 0, c < 0, -\dfrac{b}{2a} < 0$

or $\quad a < 0, c < 0, b < 0$

$\therefore \quad abc < 0$

Option (b) $\quad a < 0, c > 0, -\dfrac{b}{2a} > 0$

or $\quad a < 0, c > 0, b > 0$

$\therefore \quad abc < 0$

Option (c) $a > 0, c > 0, -\dfrac{b}{2a} > 0$

or $\quad a > 0, c > 0, b < 0$

$\therefore \quad abc < 0$

Option (d) $a < 0, c < 0, -\dfrac{b}{2a} < 0$

or $\quad a < 0, c < 0, b < 0$

$\therefore \quad abc < 0$

41. Here, $D \le 0$

and $\quad f(x) \ge 0, \forall x \in R$

$\therefore \quad f(3) \ge 0$

$\Rightarrow \quad 9a + 3b + 6 \ge 0$

or $\quad 3a + b \ge -2$

$\Rightarrow$ Minimum value of $3a + b$ is -2.

and $\quad f(6) \ge 0$

$\Rightarrow \quad 36a + 6b + 6 \ge 0$

$\Rightarrow \quad 6a + b \ge -1$

$\Rightarrow$ Minimum value of $6a + b$ is -1.

42. Since, $f(x) = x^3 + 3x^2 - 9x + \lambda = (x - \alpha)^2(x - \beta)$

$\therefore \alpha$ is a double root.

$\therefore f'(x) = 0$ has also one root α.

i.e. $3x^2 + 6x - 9 = 0$ has one root α.

$\therefore \quad x^2 + 2x - 3 = 0$ or $(x + 3)(x - 1) = 0$

has the root α which can either -3 or 1.

If $\alpha = 1$, then $f(1) = 0$ gives $\lambda - 5 = 0 \Rightarrow \lambda = 5$.

If $\alpha = -3$, then $f(-3) = 0$ gives

$$-27 + 27 + 27 + \lambda = 0$$

$\Rightarrow \quad \lambda = -27$

43. We have, $\quad D = (b - c)^2 - 4a(a - b - c) > 0$

$\Rightarrow \quad b^2 + c^2 - 2bc - 4a^2 + 4ab + 4ac > 0$

$\Rightarrow \quad c^2 + (4a - 2b)c - 4a^2 + 4ab + b^2 > 0, \forall c \in R$

Since, $c \in R$, so we have

$$(4a - 2b)^2 - 4(-4a^2 + 4ab + b^2) < 0$$

$\Rightarrow \quad 4a^2 - 4ab + b^2 + 4a^2 - 4ab - b^2 < 0$

$\Rightarrow \quad a(a - b) < 0$

If $a > 0$, then $a - b < 0$

i.e. $\quad 0 < a < b$

or $\quad b > a > 0$

If $a < 0$, then $a - b > 0$

i.e. $\quad 0 > a > b$

or $\quad b < a < 0$

44. We have, $\quad x^3 - ax^2 + bx - 1 = 0 \quad$ ...(i)

Then, $\quad \alpha^2 + \beta^2 + \gamma^2 = (\alpha + \beta + \gamma)^2 - 2(\alpha\beta + \beta\gamma + \gamma\alpha)$

$$= a^2 - 2b$$

$$\alpha^2\beta^2 + \beta^2\gamma^2 + \gamma^2\alpha^2 = (\alpha\beta + \beta\gamma + \gamma\alpha)^2$$

$$-2\alpha\beta\gamma(\alpha + \beta + \gamma) = b^2 - 2a$$

and $\quad \alpha^2\beta^2\gamma^2 = 1$

Therefore, the equation whose roots are α^2, β^2 and γ^2, is

$$x^3 - (a^2 - 2b)x^2 + (b^2 - 2a)x - 1 = 0 \quad \text{...(ii)}$$

Since, Eqs. (i) and (ii) are indentical, therefore

$$a^2 - 2b = a \text{ and } b^2 - 2a = b$$

Eliminating b, we have

$$\frac{(a^2-a)^2}{4} - 2a = \frac{a^2-a}{2}$$

$\Rightarrow$ $a\{a(a-1)^2 - 8 - 2(a-1)\} = 0$

$\Rightarrow$ $a(a^3 - 2a^2 - a - 6) = 0$

$\Rightarrow$ $a(a-3)(a^2+a+2) = 0$

$\Rightarrow$ $a = 0$ or $a = 3$ or $a^2 + a + 2 = 0$

$\Rightarrow$ $b = 0$ or $b = 3$

or $b^2 + b + 2 = 0$

$\therefore$ $a = b = 0$

or $a = b = 3$

or a and b are roots of $x^2 + x + 2 = 0$.

45. Here, $D > 0$

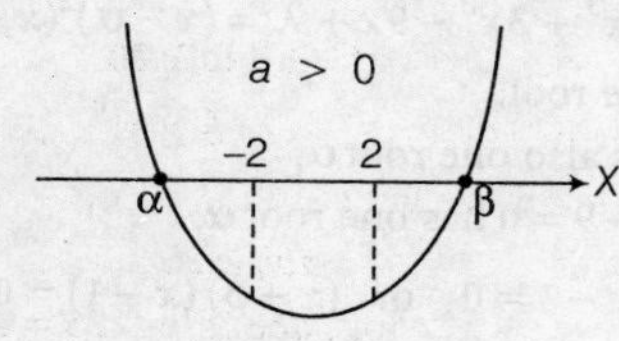

$b^2 - 4ac > 0$

or $b^2 > 4ac$ ...(i)

and $f(0) < 0$

$\Rightarrow$ $c < 0$ ...(ii)

$f(1) < 0$

$\Rightarrow$ $a + b + c < 0$ ...(iii)

$f(-1) < 0$

$\Rightarrow$ $a - b + c < 0$ ...(iv)

$f(2) < 0$

$\Rightarrow$ $4a + 2b + c < 0$ ...(v)

$f(-2) < 0$

$\Rightarrow$ $4a - 2b + c < 0$ ...(vi)

From Eqs. (i) and (ii), we get

$$c < 0,\ b^2 - 4ac > 0$$

From Eqs. (iii) and (iv), we get

$$a - |b| + c < 0$$

and from Eqs. (v) and (vi), we get

$$4a - 2|b| + c < 0$$

Solutions (Q. Nos. 46 to 48)

Let $y = \dfrac{2x^2 - 3x + 2}{2x^2 + 3x + 2}$

$\Rightarrow$ $2x^2y + 3xy + 2y = 2x^2 - 3x + 2$

$\Rightarrow$ $2(y-1)x^2 + 3(y+1)x + 2(y-1) = 0$

As $x \in R$

$\therefore$ $D \geq 0$

$\Rightarrow$ $9(y+1)^2 - 4 \cdot 2(y-1) \cdot 2(y-1) \geq 0$

$\Rightarrow$ $9(y+1)^2 - 16(y-1)^2 \geq 0$

$\Rightarrow$ $(3y+3)^2 - (4y-4)^2 \geq 0$

$\Rightarrow$ $(7y-1)(7-y) \geq 0$

$\Rightarrow$ $(7y-1)(y-7) \leq 0$

$\therefore$ $\frac{1}{7} \leq y \leq 7$

$\therefore$ $G = 7$ and $L = \frac{1}{7}$

$\therefore$ $GL = 1$

Now, $\dfrac{G^{100} + L^{100}}{2} \geq (GL)^{100} \Rightarrow \dfrac{G^{100} + L^{100}}{2} \geq 1$

$\Rightarrow$ $G^{100} + L^{100} \geq 2$

46. Least value of $G^{100} + L^{100}$ is 2.

47. The quadratic equation having roots G and L, is

$$x^2 - (G+L)x + GL = 0$$

$\Rightarrow$ $x^2 - \frac{50}{7}x + 1 = 0$

$\Rightarrow$ $7x^2 - 50x + 7 = 0$

48. We have, $L^2 < \lambda < G^2$

$\Rightarrow$ $\left(\frac{1}{7}\right)^2 < \lambda < 7^2$

$\Rightarrow$ $\frac{1}{49} < \lambda < 49$

$\Rightarrow$ $\lambda = 1, 2, 3, \ldots, 48$ as $\lambda \in N$

$\therefore$ Sum of all values of $\lambda = 1 + 2 + 3 + \ldots + 48 = \dfrac{48 \times 49}{2} = 1176$

Solutions (Q. Nos. 49 to 51)

Let roots be $\alpha, \beta, \gamma, \delta > 0$.

$\therefore$ $\alpha + \beta + \gamma + \delta = 12$

$(\alpha+\beta)(\gamma+\delta) + \alpha\beta + \gamma\delta = c$

$\alpha\beta(\gamma+\delta) + \gamma\delta(\alpha+\beta) = -d$

$\alpha\beta\gamma\delta = 81$

$\because$ $AM = \dfrac{\alpha+\beta+\gamma+\delta}{4} = 3$

and $GM = (\alpha\beta\gamma\delta)^{1/4} = (81)^{1/4} = 3$

$\therefore$ $AM = GM$

$\Rightarrow$ $\alpha = \beta = \gamma = \delta = 3$

49. $c = (\alpha+\beta)(\gamma+\delta) + \alpha\beta + \gamma\delta$

$= (3+3)(3+3) + 3 \cdot 3 + 3 \cdot 3 = 36 + 18 = 54$

50. $\because \alpha\beta(\gamma+\delta) + \gamma\delta(\alpha+\beta) = -d$

$\therefore$ $d = -\{3 \cdot 3 \cdot (3+3) + 3 \cdot 3 \cdot (3+3)\} = -108$

51. Required root $= -\dfrac{d}{2c} = -\dfrac{(-108)}{2 \times 54} = 1$

Solutions (Q. Nos. 52 to 54)

Given that, $AC = 4\sqrt{2}$ units

$\therefore$ $AB = BC = \dfrac{AC}{\sqrt{2}} = 4$ units

and $OB = \sqrt{(BC)^2 - (OC)^2}$

$= \sqrt{(4)^2 - (2\sqrt{2})^2}$ $\left[\because OC = \dfrac{AC}{2}\right]$

$= 2\sqrt{2}$ units

$\therefore$ Vertices are $A \equiv (-2\sqrt{2}, 0)$,

$$B \equiv (0, -2\sqrt{2})$$

and $C \equiv (2\sqrt{2}, 0)$

52. Since, $y = f(x) = ax^2 + bx + c$ passes through A, B and C, then

$$0 = 8a - 2\sqrt{2}b + c - 2\sqrt{2} = c$$

and $0 = 8a + 2\sqrt{2}b + c$

We get, $b = 0, a = \dfrac{1}{2\sqrt{2}}$ and $c = -2\sqrt{2}$

$$\therefore \quad y = f(x) = \frac{x^2}{2\sqrt{2}} - 2\sqrt{2}$$

53. Minimum value of $y = \dfrac{x^2}{2\sqrt{2}} - 2\sqrt{2}$ is at $x = 0$.

$$\therefore \quad (y)_{\min} = -2\sqrt{2}$$

54. $f(x) = 0$

$$\Rightarrow \quad \frac{x^2}{2\sqrt{2}} - 2\sqrt{2} = 0 \Rightarrow x = \pm 2\sqrt{2}$$

Given, $-2\sqrt{2} < \dfrac{\lambda}{2} < 2\sqrt{2}$

or $-4\sqrt{2} < \lambda < 4\sqrt{2}$

$\therefore$ Initial values of λ are

$$-5, -4, -3, -2, -1, 0, 1, 2, 3, 4, 5.$$

$\therefore$ Number of integral values is 11.

Solutions. (Q. Nos. 55 to 57)

We have, $(\alpha - \beta) = (\alpha + k) - (\beta + k)$

$$\Rightarrow \quad \frac{\sqrt{b^2 - 4c}}{1} = \frac{\sqrt{b_1^2 - 4c_1}}{1}$$

$$\Rightarrow \quad b^2 - 4c = b_1^2 - 4c_1 \quad \text{...(i)}$$

Given, least value of $f(x) = -\dfrac{1}{4} - \dfrac{(b^2 - 4c)}{4 \times 1} = -\dfrac{1}{4}$

$$\Rightarrow \quad b^2 - 4c = 1$$

$$\therefore \quad b^2 - 4c = 1 = b_1^2 - 4c_1 \quad \text{[from Eq. (i)] ...(ii)}$$

Also, given least value of $g(x)$ occurs at $x = \dfrac{7}{2}$.

$$\therefore \quad -\frac{b_1}{2 \times 1} = \frac{7}{2}$$

$$\therefore \quad b_1 = -7$$

55. $b_1 = -7$

56. Least value of $g(x) = -\dfrac{b_1^2 - 4c_1}{4 \times 1} = -\dfrac{1}{4}$ [from Eq. (ii)]

57. $\because g(x) = 0$

$$\therefore \quad x^2 + b_1 x + c_1 = 0$$

$$\Rightarrow \quad x = \frac{-b_1 \pm \sqrt{b_1^2 - 4c_1}}{2}$$

$$= \frac{7 \pm 1}{2} = 3, 4$$

$\therefore$ Roots of $g(x) = 0$ are 3, 4.

Solutions (Q. Nos. 58 to 60)

Let $f(x) = ax^2 - bx + c$ has two distinct roots α and β. Then, $f(x) = a(x - \alpha)(x - \beta)$. Since, $f(0)$ and $f(1)$ are of same sign.

Therefore, $c(a - b + c) > 0$

$$\Rightarrow \quad c(a - b + c) \ge 1$$

$$\therefore \quad a^2 \alpha\beta (1 - \alpha)(1 - \beta) \ge 1$$

But $\alpha(1 - \alpha) = \dfrac{1}{4} - \left(\dfrac{1}{2} - \alpha\right)^2 \le \dfrac{1}{4}$

$$\therefore \quad a^2 \alpha\beta (1 - \alpha)(1 - \beta) < \frac{a^2}{16}$$

$$\Rightarrow \quad \frac{a^2}{16} > 1 \Rightarrow a > 4 \quad [\because \alpha \ne \beta]$$

$$\Rightarrow \quad a \ge 5 \text{ as } a \in I$$

Also, $b^2 - 4ac \ge 0$

$$\Rightarrow \quad b^2 \ge 4ac \ge 20$$

$$\Rightarrow \quad b \ge 5$$

Next, $a \ge 5, b \ge 5$, we get $c \ge 1$

$$\therefore \quad abc \ge 25$$

$$\therefore \quad \log_5 abc \ge \log_5 25 = 2$$

58. Least value of a is 5.

59. Least value of b is 5.

60. Least value of $\log_b abc$ is 2.

Solutions. (Q. Nos. 61 to 63)

Let α, β and γ be the roots of $2x^3 + ax^2 + bx + 4 = 0$.

$$\therefore \quad \alpha + \beta + \gamma = -\frac{a}{2}$$

$$\alpha\beta + \beta\gamma + \gamma\alpha = \frac{b}{2} \text{ and } \alpha\beta\gamma = -2$$

61. $\because$ AM $\ge$ GM

$$\therefore \quad \frac{(-\alpha) + (-\beta) + (-\gamma)}{3} \ge \{(-\alpha)(-\beta)(-\gamma)\}^{1/3}$$

$$\Rightarrow \quad \frac{\frac{a}{2}}{3} \ge (2)^{1/3}$$

$$\therefore \quad a \ge 6(2)^{1/3} \quad \text{...(i)}$$

or $a^3 \ge 432$

Hence, minimum value of a^3 is 432.

62. $\because$ AM $\ge$ GM

$$\therefore \quad \frac{(-\alpha)(-\beta) + (-\beta)(-\gamma) + (-\gamma)(-\alpha)}{3} \ge \{(-\alpha)(-\beta)(-\beta)(-\gamma)(-\gamma)(-\alpha)\}^{1/3}$$

$$\Rightarrow \quad \frac{b/2}{3} \ge (4)^{1/3}$$

$$\Rightarrow \quad b \ge 6(4)^{1/3} \quad \text{...(ii)}$$

or $b^3 \ge 864$

Hence, minimum value of b^3 is 864.

63. From Eqs. (i) and (ii), we get

$$ab \ge 6(2)^{1/3} \cdot 6(4)^{1/3}$$

$\Rightarrow \quad ab \geq 36 \times 2$

$\because \quad \frac{a+b}{2} \geq \sqrt{ab} \geq 6\sqrt{2} \Rightarrow \frac{a+b}{2} \geq 6\sqrt{2}$

$\therefore \quad a + b \geq 12\sqrt{2}$

or $\quad (a+b)^3 \geq 3456\sqrt{2}$

Hence, minimum value of $(a+b)^3$ is $3456\sqrt{2}$.

Solutions (Q. Nos. 64 to 66)

$\therefore \quad \alpha + \beta + \gamma + \delta = -A \quad$ ...(i)

$(\alpha+\beta)(\gamma+\delta) + \alpha\beta + \gamma\delta = B \quad$ ...(ii)

$\alpha\beta(\gamma+\delta) + \gamma\delta(\alpha+\beta) = -C \quad$ ...(iii)

and $\quad \alpha\beta\gamma\delta = D \quad$ ...(iv)

64. $\because \quad \frac{C}{A} = \frac{\alpha\beta(\gamma+\delta) + \gamma\delta(\alpha+\beta)}{\alpha+\beta+\gamma+\delta}$

$= \frac{k(\gamma+\delta) + k(\alpha+\beta)}{\alpha+\beta+\gamma+\delta} \quad [\because \alpha\beta = \gamma\delta = k]$

$= k \quad$ ...(v)

65. From Eq. (ii), we get

$(\alpha+\beta)(\gamma+\delta) = B - (\alpha\beta + \gamma\delta) = B - 2k \quad [\because \alpha\beta = \gamma\delta = k]$

66. From Eq. (iv), we get

$\alpha\beta\gamma\delta = D$

$\Rightarrow \quad k \cdot k = D \quad [\because \alpha\beta = \gamma\delta = k]$

$\Rightarrow \quad \left(\frac{C}{A}\right)^2 = D \quad$ [from Eq. (v)]

$\therefore \quad C^2 = A^2 D$

67. The given equation is $|x-2|^2 + |x-2| - 2 = 0$.

There are two cases:

***Case* I** If $x \geq 2$, then $(x-2)^2 + x - 2 - 2 = 0$

$\Rightarrow \quad x^2 - 3x = 0$

$\Rightarrow \quad x(x-3) = 0$

$\Rightarrow \quad x = 0, 3$

Here, 0 is not possible.

$\therefore \quad x = 3$

***Case* II** If $x < 2$, then

$(x-2)^2 - x + 2 - 2 = 0$

$\Rightarrow \quad x^2 - 5x + 4 = 0$

$\Rightarrow \quad (x-1)(x-4) = 0$

$\Rightarrow \quad x = 1, 4$

Here, 4 is not possible.

$\therefore \quad x = 1$

$\therefore$ The sum of roots $= 1 + 3 = 4$

Aliter

Let $|x-2| = y$.

Then, we get $\quad y^2 + y - 2 = 0$

$\Rightarrow \quad (y-1)(y+2) = 0 \Rightarrow y = 1, -2$

But -2 is not possible.

Hence, $\quad |x-2| = 1 \Rightarrow x = 1, 3$

$\therefore$ Sum of the roots $= 1 + 3 = 4$

68. We have,

$(5+\sqrt{2})x^2 - (4+\sqrt{5})x + 8 + 2\sqrt{5} = 0$

$\therefore$ Sum of the roots $= \frac{4+\sqrt{5}}{5+\sqrt{2}}$

and product of the roots $= \frac{8+2\sqrt{5}}{5+\sqrt{2}}$

$\therefore$ The harmonic mean of the roots

$= \frac{2 \times \text{Product of the roots}}{\text{Sum of the roots}} = \frac{2 \times (8 + 2\sqrt{5})}{(4+\sqrt{5})} = 4$

69. Let $x^2 - ax + 30 = y$

$\therefore \quad y = 2\sqrt{y + 15} \quad$ ...(i)

$\Rightarrow \quad y^2 - 4y - 60 = 0$

$\Rightarrow \quad (y-10)(y+6) = 0$

$\therefore \quad y = 10, -6$

$\Rightarrow \quad y = 10, y \neq -6 \quad [\because y > 0]$

Now, $\quad x^2 - ax + 30 = 10$

$\Rightarrow \quad x^2 - ax + 20 = 0$

Given, $\quad \alpha\beta = \lambda = 20$

$\therefore \quad \frac{\alpha+\beta}{2} \geq \sqrt{\alpha\beta} = \sqrt{20}$

$\Rightarrow \quad \alpha + \beta \geq 2\sqrt{20}$

or $\quad \mu = 4\sqrt{5}$

$\therefore$ Minimum value of μ is $4\sqrt{5}$.

i.e., $\quad \mu = 4\sqrt{5} = 8.9 \Rightarrow (\mu) = 9$

70. $\because N^r = \left(x + \frac{1}{x}\right)^6 - \left(x^6 + \frac{1}{x^6}\right) - 2$

$= \left(x + \frac{1}{x}\right)^6 - \left(x^3 + \frac{1}{x^3}\right)^2 = \left(\left(x + \frac{1}{x}\right)^3 + \left(x^3 + \frac{1}{x^3}\right)\right) \left(\left(x + \frac{1}{x}\right)^3 - \left(x^3 + \frac{1}{x^3}\right)\right)$

$= D^r \cdot \left(3\left(x + \frac{1}{x}\right)\right)$

$\therefore \quad \frac{N^r}{D^r} = 3\left(x + \frac{1}{x}\right) \geq 6$

Hence, minimum value of $\frac{N^r}{D^r}$ is 6.

71. $\quad a + b = 2c \quad$ ...(i)

$ab = -5d \quad$ ...(ii)

$c + d = 2a \quad$ ...(iii)

$cd = -5b$...(iv)

From Eqs. (i) and (iii), we get

$a + b + c + d = 2(a + c)$

$\therefore \quad a + c = b + d \quad$ ...(v)

From Eqs. (i) and (iii), we get

$$b - d = 3(c - a) \quad \text{...(vi)}$$

Also, a is a root of $x^2 - 2cx - 5d = 0$

$\therefore \quad a^2 - 2ac - 5d = 0 \quad$ ...(vii)

And c is a root of

$$c^2 - 2ac - 5b = 0 \quad \text{...(viii)}$$

From Eqs. (vii) and (viii), we get

$$a^2 - c^2 - 5(d - b) = 0$$

$\Rightarrow \quad (a + c)(a - c) + 5(b - d) = 0$

$\Rightarrow \quad (a + c)(a - c) + 15(c - a) = 0 \quad$ [from Eq. (vi)]

$\Rightarrow \quad (a - c)(a + c - 15) = 0$

$\therefore \quad a + c = 15, a - c \neq 0$

From Eq. (v), we get $b + d = 15$

$\therefore \quad a + b + c + d = a + c + b + d = 15 + 15 = 30$

$\Rightarrow$ Sum of digits of $a + b + c + d = 3 + 0 = 3$

72. $\because \quad y = \dfrac{x^2 - 3x + c}{x^2 + 3x + c}$

$\Rightarrow \quad x^2(y - 1) + 3x(y + 1) + c(y - 1) = 0$

$\because \quad x \in R$

$\therefore \quad 9(y + 1)^2 - 4c(y - 1)^2 \geq 0$

$$(2\sqrt{c}y - 2\sqrt{c})^2 - (3y + 3)^2 \leq 0$$

$\Rightarrow \quad \{(2\sqrt{c} + 3)y - (2\sqrt{c} - 3)\}\{(2\sqrt{c} - 3)y - (2\sqrt{c} + 3)\} \leq 0$

or $\quad \dfrac{2\sqrt{c} - 3}{2\sqrt{c} + 3} \leq y \leq \dfrac{2\sqrt{c} + 3}{2\sqrt{c} - 3}$

But given, $\quad \dfrac{2\sqrt{c} + 3}{2\sqrt{c} - 3} = 7$

$\Rightarrow \quad 2\sqrt{c} + 3 = 14\sqrt{c} - 21$

or $\quad 12\sqrt{c} = 24$ or $\sqrt{c} = 2$

$\therefore \quad c = 4$

73. We have, $\sqrt{x^2} - \sqrt{(x - 1)^2} + \sqrt{(x - 2)^2} = \sqrt{5}$

$\Rightarrow \quad |x| - |x - 1| + |x - 2| = \sqrt{5}$

***Case* I** If $x < 0$, then

$$-x + (x - 1) - (x - 2) = \sqrt{5}$$

$$x = 1 - \sqrt{5}$$

***Case* II** If $0 \leq x < 1$, then

$$x + (x - 1) - (x - 2) = \sqrt{5}$$

$\Rightarrow \quad x = \sqrt{5} - 1$, which is not possible.

***Case* III** If $1 \leq x < 2$, then

$$x - (x - 1) - (x - 2) = \sqrt{5}$$

$\Rightarrow \quad x = 3 - \sqrt{5}$, which is not possible.

***Case* IV** If $x > 2$, then

$$x - (x - 1) + (x - 2) = \sqrt{5}$$

$\Rightarrow \quad x = 1 + \sqrt{5}$

Hence, number of solutions is 2.

74. $\because \quad (1 + i)x^2 + (1 - i)x - 2i = 0$

$\Rightarrow \quad x^2 + \dfrac{(1 - i)}{(1 + i)}x - \dfrac{2i}{(1 + i)} = 0$

$\Rightarrow \quad x^2 - ix - (1 + i) = 0$

$\therefore \quad \alpha + \beta = i$, and $\alpha\beta = -(1 + i)$

$\therefore \quad \alpha - \beta = \sqrt{(\alpha + \beta)^2 - 4\alpha\beta} = \sqrt{i^2 + 4(1 + i)} = \sqrt{(3 + 4i)}$

$$|\alpha - \beta| = \sqrt{\sqrt{9 + 16}} = \sqrt{5}$$

$\therefore \quad |\alpha - \beta|^2 = 5$

75. $\because 4x^2 - 16x + c = 0$

$\Rightarrow \quad x^2 - 4x + \dfrac{c}{4} = 0$

Let $\quad f(x) = x^2 - 4x + \dfrac{c}{4}$

Then, the following cases arises:

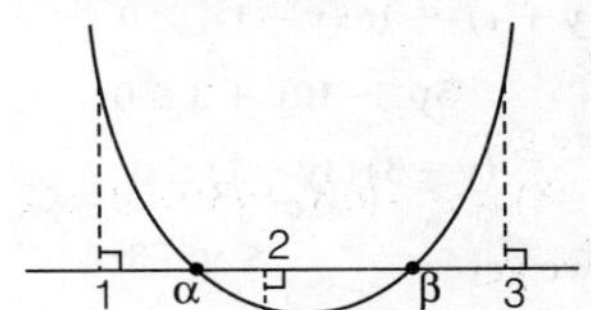

***Case* I** $\quad D > 0$

$\Rightarrow \quad 16 - c > 0$

$\therefore \quad c < 16$

***Case* II** $\quad f(1) > 0$

$\Rightarrow \quad 1 - 4 + \dfrac{c}{4} > 0$

$\Rightarrow \quad \dfrac{c}{4} > 3$

$\therefore \quad c > 12$

***Case* III** $\quad f(2) < 0$

$\Rightarrow \quad 4 - 8 + \dfrac{c}{4} < 0$

$\Rightarrow \quad \dfrac{c}{4} < 4$

$\therefore \quad c < 16$

***Case* IV** $\quad f(3) > 0$

$\Rightarrow \quad 9 - 12 + \dfrac{c}{4} > 0$

$\Rightarrow \quad \dfrac{c}{4} > 3$

$\Rightarrow \quad c > 12$

Combining all cases, we get

$$12 < c < 16$$

Thus, integral values of c are 13, 14 and 15.

Hence, number of integral values of c is 3.

76. We have, $\quad r + s + t = 0 \quad$ ...(i)

$$rs + st + tr = \frac{1001}{8} \quad \text{...(ii)}$$

and $\quad rst = -\dfrac{2008}{8} = -251 \quad$ ...(iii)

Now, $(r+s)^3+(s+t)^3+(t+r)^3=(-t)^3+(-r)^3+(-s)^3$ $[\because r+s+t=0]$

$=-(t^3+r^3+s^3)=-3\,rst$ $[\because r+s+t=0]$

$=-3(-251)=753$

Now, $99\lambda=(r+s)^3+(s+t)^3+(t+r)^3=753$

$\therefore \quad \lambda=\frac{753}{99}=7.6$

$\therefore \quad [\lambda]=7$

77. A → (r,s); B → (p,q,r,s,t); C → (p,q,t)

(A) We have, $y=\frac{x^2-2x+4}{x^2+2x+4}$

$\Rightarrow x^2(y-1)+2(y+1)x+4(y-1)=0$

As $x\in R$, we get

$$D\ge 0$$
$$\Rightarrow 4(y+1)^2-16(y-1)^2\ge 0$$
$$\Rightarrow 3y^2-10y+3\le 0$$
$$\Rightarrow (y-3)(3y-1)\le 0$$
$$\Rightarrow \frac{1}{3}\le y\le 3$$

(B) We have, $y=\frac{2x^2+4x+1}{x^2+4x+2}$

$\Rightarrow x^2(y-2)+4(y-1)x+2y-1=0$

As $x\in R$, we get

$$D\ge 0$$
$$\Rightarrow 16(y-1)^2-4(y-2)(2y-1)\ge 0$$
$$\Rightarrow 4(y-1)^2-(y-2)(2y-1)\ge 0$$
$$\Rightarrow 2y^2-3y+2\ge 0$$
$$\Rightarrow y^2-\frac{3}{2}y+1\ge 0$$
$$\Rightarrow \left(y-\frac{3}{4}\right)^2+\frac{7}{16}\ge 0$$
$$\therefore y\in R$$

(C) We have, $y=\frac{x^2-3x+4}{x-3}$

$$\Rightarrow x^2-(3+y)x+3y+4=0$$

As $x\in R$, we get

$D\ge 0\Rightarrow (3+y)^2-4(3y+4)\ge 0$

$\Rightarrow y^2-6y-7\ge 0\Rightarrow (y+1)(y-7)\ge 0$

$\Rightarrow y\in(-\infty,-1]\cup[7,\infty)$

78. A → (q,r,s); B → (p); C → (q)

(A) $\because (d+a-b)^2+(d+b-c)^2=0$

which is possible only when

$$d+a-b=0,\ d+b-c=0$$
$$\Rightarrow b-a=c-b$$
$$\Rightarrow 2b=a+c$$

$\therefore$ *a*, *b* and *c* are in AP. ...(i)

$\because \quad a(b-c)+b(c-a)+c(a-b)=0$

$\therefore$ $x=1$ is a root of

$a(b-c)x^2+b(c-a)x+c(a-b)=0$ ...(ii)

Given, roots [Eq. (ii)] are equal.

$$\therefore 1\times 1=\frac{c(a-b)}{a(b-c)}$$
$$\Rightarrow a(b-c)=c(a-b)$$

or $b=\frac{2ac}{a+c}$

$\therefore$ *a*, *b* and *c* are in HP. ...(iii)

From Eqs. (i) and (ii), we get

$$a=b=c$$

$\therefore$ *a*, *b* and *c* are in AP, GP and HP.

(B) $\because \quad x^3-3x^2+3x-1=0$

$$\Rightarrow (x-1)^3=0$$
$$\therefore x=1,1,1$$

$\Rightarrow$ Common root, $x=1$

$$\therefore a(1)^2+b(1)+c=0$$
$$\Rightarrow a+b+c=0$$

(C) Given, $bx^2+(\sqrt{(a+c)^2+4b^2})\,x+(a+c)\ge 0$

$$\therefore D\le 0$$
$$\Rightarrow (a+c)^2+4b^2-4b(a+c)\le 0$$
$$\Rightarrow (a+c-2b)^2\le 0$$

or $(a+c-2b)^2=0$

$$\therefore a+c=2b$$

Hence *a*, *b* and *c* are in AP.

79. A → (q,r,s,t); B → (q,r); C → (p,q)

(A) We have, $y=\frac{ax^2+3x-4}{3x-4x^2+a}$

$\Rightarrow x^2(a+4y)+3(1-y)x-(ay+4)=0$

As $x\in R$, we get

$$D\ge 0$$
$$\Rightarrow 9(1-y)^2+4(a+4y)(ay+4)\ge 0$$

$\Rightarrow (9+16a)y^2+(4a^2+46)y+(9+16a)\ge 0,\ \forall\ y\in R$

$\Rightarrow$ If $9+16a>0$, then $D\le 0$

Now, $D\le 0$

$$\Rightarrow (4a^2+46)^2-4(9+16a)^2\le 0$$
$$\Rightarrow 4[(2a^2+23)^2-(9+16a)^2]\le 0$$
$$\Rightarrow [(2a^2+23)+(9+16a)][(2a^2+23)-(9+16a)]\le 0$$
$$\Rightarrow (2a^2+16a+32)(2a^2-16a+14)\le 0$$
$$\Rightarrow 4(a+4)^2(a^2-8a+7)\le 0$$
$$\Rightarrow a^2-8a+7\le 0$$
$$\Rightarrow (a-1)(a-7)\le 0$$
$$\Rightarrow 1\le a\le 7$$
$$\therefore 9+16a>0 \text{ and } 1\le a\le 7$$
$$\Rightarrow 1\le a\le 7$$

(B) We have, $y = \dfrac{ax^2 + x - 2}{a + x - 2x^2}$

$\Rightarrow \quad x^2(a + 2y) + x(1 - y) - (2 + ay) = 0$

As $x \in R$, we get

$$D \geq 0$$

$$\Rightarrow \quad (1 - y)^2 + 4(2 + ay)(a + 2y) \geq 0$$

$$\Rightarrow \quad (1 + 8a)y^2 + (4a^2 + 14)y + (1 + 8a) \geq 0$$

$\Rightarrow$ If $1 + 8a > 0$, then $D \leq 0$

$$\Rightarrow \quad (4a^2 + 14)^2 - 4(1 + 8a)^2 \leq 0$$

$$\Rightarrow \quad 4[(2a^2 + 7)^2 - (1 + 8a)^2] \leq 0$$

$$\Rightarrow \quad [(2a^2 + 7) + (1 + 8a)][(2a^2 + 7) - (1 + 8a)] \leq 0$$

$$\Rightarrow \quad (2a^2 + 8a + 8)(2a^2 - 8a + 6) \leq 0$$

$$\Rightarrow \quad 4(a + 2)^2(a^2 - 4a + 3) \leq 0$$

$$\Rightarrow \quad a^2 - 4a + 3 \leq 0$$

$$\Rightarrow \quad (a - 1)(a - 3) \leq 0$$

$$\Rightarrow \quad 1 \leq a \leq 3$$

Thus, $1 + 8a > 0$ and $1 \leq a \leq 3$

$$\Rightarrow \quad 1 \leq a \leq 3$$

(C) We have, $y = \dfrac{x^2 + 2x + a}{x^2 + 4x + 3a}$

$$\Rightarrow \quad x^2(y - 1) + 2(2y - 1)x + a(3y - 1) = 0$$

As $x \in R$, we get

$$D \geq 0$$

$$\Rightarrow \quad 4(2y - 1)^2 - 4(y - 1)a(3y - 1) \geq 0$$

$$\Rightarrow \quad (4 - 3a)y^2 - (4 - 4a)y + (1 - a) \geq 0$$

$\Rightarrow$ If $4 - 3a > 0$, then $D \leq 0$

$$\Rightarrow \quad (4 - 4a)^2 - 4(4 - 3a)(1 - a) \leq 0$$

$$\Rightarrow \quad 4(2 - 2a)^2 - 4(4 - 3a)(1 - a) \leq 0$$

$$\Rightarrow \quad 4 + 4a^2 - 8a - (4 - 7a + 3a^2) \leq 0$$

$$\Rightarrow \quad a^2 - a \leq 0$$

$$\Rightarrow \quad a(a - 1) \leq 0$$

$$\Rightarrow \quad 0 \leq a \leq 1$$

80. A $\rightarrow$ (p,q,r,s); B $\rightarrow$ (p,q); C $\rightarrow$ (s)

(A) Let $y = f(x) = x^3 - 6x^2 + 9x + \lambda$

$$f'(x) = 3x^2 - 12x + 9 = 0$$

$$\therefore \quad x = 1, 3$$

$$f''(x) = 6x - 12$$

$$f''(1) < 0 \quad \text{and} \quad f''(3) > 0$$

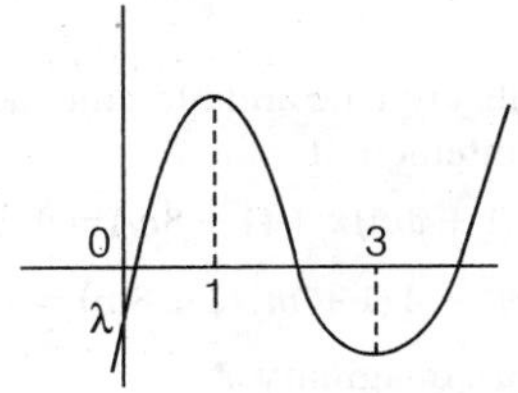

Also, $f(0) < 0 \Rightarrow \lambda < 0$ ...(i)

$$f(1) > 0$$

$$\Rightarrow \quad 1 - 6 + 9 + \lambda > 0$$

$$\Rightarrow \quad \lambda > -4 \qquad \text{...(ii)}$$

and $f(3) < 0$

$$\Rightarrow \quad 27 - 54 + 27 + \lambda < 0$$

$$\Rightarrow \quad \lambda < 0 \qquad \text{...(iii)}$$

From Eqs. (i), (ii) and (iii), we get

$$-4 < \lambda < 0$$

$$\Rightarrow \quad -3 < \lambda + 1 < 1$$

$$\therefore \quad [\lambda + 1] = -3, -2, -1, 0$$

$$\therefore \quad |[\lambda + 1]| = 3, 2, 1, 0$$

(B) $\because \quad x^2 + x + 1 > 0, \forall x \in R$

Given, $-3 < \dfrac{x^2 - \lambda x - 2}{x^2 + x + 1} < 2$

$$\Rightarrow \quad -3x^2 - 3x - 3 < x^2 - \lambda x - 2 < 2x^2 + 2x + 2$$

$$\Rightarrow \quad 4x^2 - (\lambda - 3)x + 1 > 0$$

and $x^2 + (\lambda + 2)x + 4 > 0$

$$\therefore \quad (\lambda - 3)^2 - 4 \cdot 4 \cdot 1 < 0$$

and $(\lambda + 2)^2 - 4 \cdot 1 \cdot 4 < 0$

$$\Rightarrow \quad (\lambda - 3)^2 - 4^2 < 0$$

and $(\lambda + 2)^2 - 4^2 < 0$

$$\Rightarrow \quad -4 < \lambda - 3 < 4$$

and $-4 < \lambda + 2 < 4$

or $-1 < \lambda < 7$

and $-6 < \lambda < 2$

We get, $-1 < \lambda < 2$

$$\therefore \quad [\lambda] = -1, 0, 1$$

$$\Rightarrow \quad |[\lambda]| = 0, 1$$

(C) $\because \quad (b - c) + (c - a) + (a - b) = 0$

$\therefore x = 1$ is a root of

$$(b - c)x^2 + (c - a)x + (a - b) = 0$$

Also, $x = 1$ satisfies

$$x^2 + \lambda x + 1 = 0$$

$$\Rightarrow \quad 1 + \lambda + 1 = 0$$

$$\therefore \quad \lambda = -2$$

Now, $\lambda - 1 = -3$

$$[\lambda - 1] = -3$$

$$\Rightarrow \quad |[\lambda - 1]| = 3$$

81. If quadratic equation $ax^2 + bx + c = 0$ is satisfied by more than two values of x, then it must be an identity.

Therefore, $a = b = c = 0$

$\therefore$ Statement-2 is true.

But in Statement-1,

$$4p - 3 = 4q - 3 = r = 0$$

Then, $p = q = \dfrac{3}{4}, r = 0$

which is false.

Since, at one value of p or q or r, all coefficients at a time $\neq 0$.

$\therefore$ Statement-1 is false.

82. We have, $x^2 + (2m+1)x + (2n+1) = 0$ ...(i)

$m, n \in I$

$\therefore \quad D = b^2 - 4ac$

$= (2m+1)^2 - 4(2n+1)$

is never be a perfect square.

Therefore, the roots of Eq. (i) can never be integers. Hence, the roots of Eq. (i) cannot have any rational root as $a = 1, b, c \in I$.

Hence, both statements are true and Statements −2 is a correct explanation of Statement-1.

83. Let α be one root of equation $ax^2 + 3x + 5 = 0$. Therefore,

$$\alpha \cdot \frac{1}{\alpha} = \frac{5}{a}$$

$$\Rightarrow \quad 1 = \frac{5}{a}$$

$$\Rightarrow \quad a = 5$$

Hence, both the statements are true and Statement-2 is the correct explanation of Statement-1.

84. Let roots of $Ax^3 + Bx^2 + Cx + D = 0$ ...(i)

are $\alpha - \beta, \alpha, \alpha + \beta$ (in AP).

Then, $(\alpha - \beta) + \alpha + (\alpha + \beta) = -\dfrac{B}{A}$

$\Rightarrow \quad \alpha = -\dfrac{B}{3A}$, which is a root of Eq. (i).

Then, $A\alpha^3 + B\alpha^2 + C\alpha + D = 0$

$$\Rightarrow \quad A\left(-\frac{B}{3A}\right)^3 + B\left(-\frac{B}{3A}\right)^2 + C\left(-\frac{B}{3A}\right) + D = 0$$

$$\Rightarrow \quad -\frac{B^3}{27A^2} + \frac{B^3}{9A^2} - \frac{BC}{3A} + D = 0$$

$$\Rightarrow \quad 2B^3 - 9ABC + 27A^2D = 0$$

Now, comparing with $2B^3 + k_1ABC + k_2A^2D = 0$, we get

$$k_1 = -9, k_2 = 27$$

$$\therefore \quad k_2 - k_1 = 27 - (-9) = 36 = 6^2$$

Hence, both statements are true and Statement-2 is a correct explanation of Statement-1.

85. $\because x, y, z \in R$

$x + y + z = 6$ ...(i)

and $xy + yz + zx = 8$ ...(ii)

$\Rightarrow \quad xy + (x+y)\{6 - (x+y)\} = 8$ [from Eq. (i)]

$\Rightarrow \quad xy + 6x + 6y - (x^2 + 2xy + y^2) = 8$

or $\quad y^2 + (x-6)y + x^2 - 6x + 8 = 0$

$\therefore \quad (x-6)^2 - 4 \cdot 1 \cdot (x^2 - 6x + 8) \ge 0, \forall y \in R$

$\Rightarrow \quad -3x^2 + 12x + 4 \ge 0$ or $3x^2 - 12x - 4 \le 0$

or $\quad 2 - \dfrac{4}{\sqrt{3}} \le x \le 2 + \dfrac{4}{\sqrt{3}}$

or $\quad x \in \left[2 - \dfrac{4}{\sqrt{3}}, 2 + \dfrac{4}{\sqrt{3}}\right]$

Similarly, $\quad y \in \left[2 - \dfrac{4}{\sqrt{3}}, 2 + \dfrac{4}{\sqrt{3}}\right]$

and $\quad z \in \left[2 - \dfrac{4}{\sqrt{3}}, 2 + \dfrac{4}{\sqrt{3}}\right]$

Since, Eqs. (i) and (ii) remains same, if x, y, z interchange their positions.

Hence, both statements are true and Statement-2 is a correct explanation of Statement-1.

86. Let $y = ax^3 + bx + c$

$$\therefore \quad \frac{dy}{dx} = 3ax^2 + b$$

For maximum or minimum $\dfrac{dy}{dx} = 0$, we get

$$x = \pm\sqrt{-\frac{b}{3a}}$$

Case **I** If $a > 0, b > 0$, then $\dfrac{dy}{dx} > 0$

In this case, function is increasing, so it has exactly one root

Case **II** If $a < 0, b < 0$, then $\dfrac{dy}{dx} < 0$

In this case, function is decreasing, so it has exactly one root.

Case **III** $a > 0, b < 0$ or $a < 0, b > 0$, then $y = ax^3 + bx + c$ is maximum at one point and minimum at other point.

Hence, all roots can never be non-negative.

$\therefore$ Statement-1 is false. But

$$\text{Sum of roots} = -\frac{\text{Coefficient of } x^2}{\text{Coefficient of } x^3} = 0$$

i.e., Statement-2 is true.

87. Statement-2 is obviously true.

But $\quad y = ax^2 + bx + c$

$$y = a\left(x^2 + \frac{b}{a}x + \frac{c}{a}\right)$$

$$= a\left\{\left(x + \frac{b}{2a}\right)^2 - \frac{D}{4a^2}\right\} \quad [\text{where, } D = b^2 - 4ac]$$

$$\Rightarrow \quad \left(x + \frac{b}{2a}\right)^2 = \frac{1}{a}\left(y + \frac{D}{4a}\right)$$

Let $\quad x + \dfrac{b}{2a} = X$ and $y + \dfrac{D}{4a} = Y$.

$$\therefore \quad X^2 = \frac{1}{a}Y$$

Equation of axis, $X = 0$ i.e. $x + \dfrac{b}{2a} = 0$

or $\quad 2ax + b = 0$

Hence, $y = ax^2 + bx + c$ is symmetric about the line $2ax + b = 0$.

$\therefore$ Both statements are true and Statement-2 is a correct explanation of Statement-1.

88. $\because (1+m)x^2 - 2(1+3m)x + (1+8m) = 0$

$\therefore \quad D = 4(1+3m)^2 - 4(1+m)(1+8m) = 4m(m-3)$

(i) Both roots are imaginary.

$\therefore \quad D < 0$

$\Rightarrow \quad 4m(m-3) < 0$

$\Rightarrow \quad 0 < m < 3$

or $\quad m \in (0, 3)$

(ii) Both roots are equal.

$\therefore \quad D = 0$

$\Rightarrow \quad 4m(m-3) = 0$

$\Rightarrow \quad m = 0, 3$

(iii) Both roots are real and distinct.

$\therefore \quad D > 0$

$\Rightarrow \quad 4m(m-3) > 0$

$\Rightarrow \quad m < 0$ or $m > 3$

$\therefore \quad m \in (-\infty, 0) \cup (3, \infty)$

(iv) Both roots are positive.

***Case* I** Sum of the roots > 0

$$\Rightarrow \quad \frac{2(1+3m)}{(1+m)} > 0$$

$$\Rightarrow \quad m \in (-\infty, -1) \cup \left(-\frac{1}{3}, \infty\right)$$

***Case* II** Product of the roots > 0

$$\Rightarrow \quad \frac{(1+8m)}{(1+m)} > 0$$

$$m \in (-\infty, -1) \cup \left(-\frac{1}{8}, \infty\right)$$

***Case* III** $\quad D \geq 0$

$\Rightarrow \quad 4m(m-3) \geq 0$

$m \in (-\infty, 0] \cup [3, \infty)$

Combining all Cases, we get

$m \in (-\infty, -1) \cup [3, \infty)$

(v) Both roots are negative.

Consider the following cases:

***Case* I** Sum of the roots $< 0 \Rightarrow \dfrac{2(1+3m)}{(1+m)} < 0$

$$\Rightarrow \quad m \in \left(-1, -\frac{1}{3}\right)$$

***Case* II** Product of the roots $> 0 \Rightarrow \dfrac{(1+8m)}{(1+m)} > 0$

$$\Rightarrow \quad m \in (-\infty, 1) \cup \left(-\frac{1}{8}, \infty\right)$$

***Case* III** $D \geq 0$

$4m(m-3) \geq 0 \Rightarrow m \in (-\infty, 0] \cup [3, \infty)$

Combining all cases, we get

$m \in \phi$

(vi) Roots are opposite in sign, then

***Case* I** Consider the following cases:

Product of the roots < 0

$$\Rightarrow \quad \frac{(1+8m)}{(1+m)} < 0$$

$$m \in \left(-1, -\frac{1}{8}\right)$$

***Case* II** $\quad D > 0 \Rightarrow 4m(m-3) > 0$

$\Rightarrow \quad m \in (-\infty, 0) \cup (3, \infty)$

Combining all cases, we get

$$m \in \left(-1, -\frac{1}{8}\right)$$

(vii) Roots are equal in magnitude but opposite in sign, then

Consider the following cases:

***Case* I** Sum of the roots $= 0$

$$\Rightarrow \quad \frac{2(1+3m)}{(1+m)} = 0$$

$$\Rightarrow \quad m = -\frac{1}{3}, m \neq 1$$

***Case* II** $\quad D > 0 \Rightarrow 4m(m-3) > 0$

$\Rightarrow \quad m \in (-\infty, 0) \cup (3, \infty)$

Combining all cases, we get

$$m = -\frac{1}{3}$$

(viii) Atleast one root is positive, then either one root is positive or both roots are positive.

i.e. $\quad (d) \cup (f)$

or $\quad m \in (-\infty, -1) \cup \left(-1, -\dfrac{1}{8}\right) \cup [3, \infty)$

(ix) Atleast one root is negative, then either one root is negative or both roots are negative.

i.e. $\quad (e) \cup (f)$ or $m \in \left(-1, -\dfrac{1}{8}\right)$

(x) Let roots are 2α are 3α. Then,

Consider the following cases:

***Case* I** Sum of the roots $= 2\alpha + 3\alpha = \dfrac{2(1+3m)}{(1+m)}$

$$\Rightarrow \quad \alpha = \frac{2(1+3m)}{5(1+m)}$$

***Case* II** Product of the roots $= 2\alpha \cdot 3\alpha = \dfrac{(1+8m)}{(1+m)}$

$$\Rightarrow \quad 6\alpha^2 = \frac{(1+8m)}{(1+m)}$$

From Eqs. (i) and (ii), we get

$$6\left\{\frac{2(1+3m)}{5(1+m)}\right\}^2 = \frac{(1+8m)}{(1+m)}$$

$\Rightarrow \quad 24(1+3m)^2 = 25(1+8m)(1+m)$

$\Rightarrow \quad 24(9m^2 + 6m + 1) = 25(8m^2 + 9m + 1)$

$16m^2 - 81m - 1 = 0$

or $\quad m = \dfrac{81 \pm \sqrt{(-81)^2 + 64}}{32}$

$\Rightarrow \quad m = \dfrac{81 \pm \sqrt{6625}}{32}$

89. $\because 2x^2 - 2(2m+1)x + m(m+1) = 0 \quad [\because m \in R]$

$\therefore \quad D = [-2(2m+1)]^2 - 8m(m+1) \quad [D = b^2 - 4ac]$

$= 4\{(2m+1)^2 - 2m(m+1)\}$

$= 4(2m^2 + 2m + 1)$

$$= 8\left(m^2 + m + \frac{1}{2}\right) = 8\left\{\left(m + \frac{1}{2}\right)^2 + \frac{1}{4}\right\} > 0$$

or $\quad D > 0, \forall\, m \in R \quad$ ...(i)

x-coordinate of vertex $= -\dfrac{b}{2a} = \dfrac{2(2m+1)}{4} = \left(m + \dfrac{1}{2}\right) \quad$ ...(ii)

and let

$$f(x) = x^2 - (2m+1)x + \frac{1}{2}m(m+1) \quad \text{...(iii)}$$

(i) Both roots are smaller than 2.

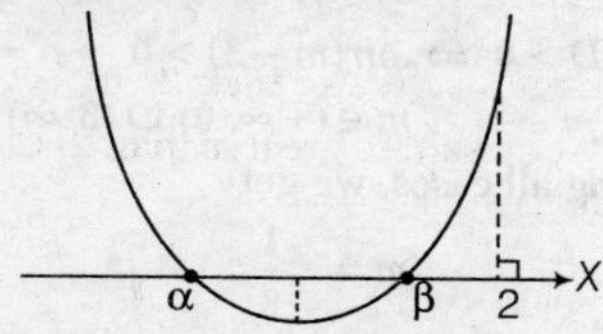

Consider the following cases:

***Case* I** $D \geq 0$

$\therefore \quad m \in R \quad$ [from Eq. (i)]

***Case* II** x-coordinate of vertex < 2.

$\Rightarrow \quad m + \dfrac{1}{2} < 2 \quad$ [from Eq. (ii)]

or $\quad m < \dfrac{3}{2}$

***Case* III** $f(2) > 0$

$\Rightarrow \quad 4 - (2m+1)2 + \dfrac{1}{2}m(m+1) > 0$

$\Rightarrow \quad m^2 - 7m + 4 > 0$

$\therefore \quad m \in \left(-\infty, \dfrac{7-\sqrt{33}}{2}\right) \cup \left(\dfrac{7+\sqrt{33}}{2}, \infty\right)$

Combining all cases, we get

$$m \in \left(-\infty, \frac{7-\sqrt{33}}{2}\right)$$

(ii) Both roots are greater than 2.

Consider the following cases:

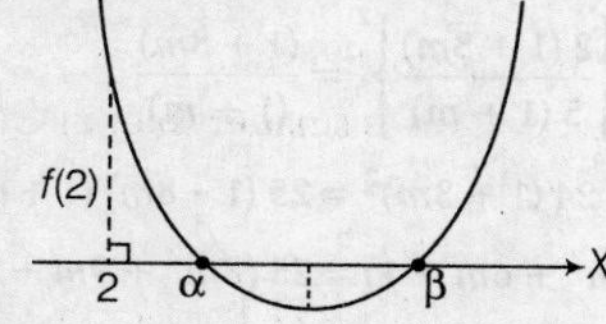

***Case* I** $D \geq 0$

$\therefore \quad m \in R \quad$ [from Eq. (i)]

***Case* II** x-coordinate of vertex > 2

$\Rightarrow \quad m + \dfrac{1}{2} > 2 \quad$ [from Eq. (ii)]

$\therefore \quad m > \dfrac{3}{2}$

***Case* III** $f(2) > 0$

$m \in \left(-\infty, \dfrac{7-\sqrt{33}}{2}\right) \cup \left(7 + \dfrac{\sqrt{33}}{2}, \infty\right) \quad$ [from part (a)]

Combining all cases, we get

$$m \in \left(\frac{7+\sqrt{33}}{2}, \infty\right)$$

(iii) Both roots lie in the interval (2, 3).

Consider the following cases:

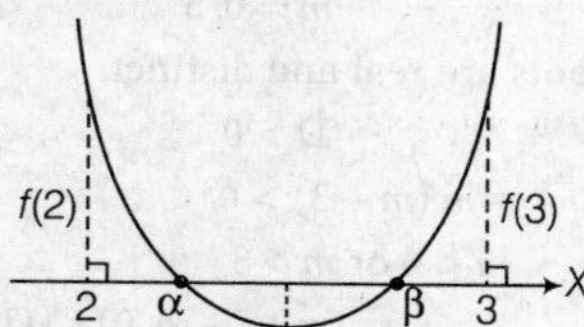

***Case* I** $D \geq 0$

$\therefore \quad m \in R \quad$ [from Eq. (i)]

***Case* II** $f(2) > 0$

$\therefore \quad m \in \left(-\infty, \dfrac{7-\sqrt{33}}{2}\right) \cup \left(\dfrac{7+\sqrt{33}}{2}, \infty\right) \quad$ [from part (a)]

***Case* III** $f(3) > 0$

$\Rightarrow \quad 9 - 3(2m+1) + \dfrac{1}{2}m(m+1) > 0$

or $\quad m^2 - 11m + 12 > 0$

$\therefore \quad m \in \left(-\infty, \dfrac{11-\sqrt{73}}{2}\right) \cup \left(\dfrac{11+\sqrt{73}}{2}, \infty\right)$

***Case* IV** $2 <$ x-coordinate of vertex < 3

$\Rightarrow \quad 2 < m + \dfrac{1}{2} < 3$

or $\quad \dfrac{3}{2} < m < \dfrac{5}{2}$ or $m \in \left(\dfrac{3}{2}, \dfrac{5}{2}\right)$

Combining all cases, we get

$$m \in \phi$$

(iv) Exactly one root lie in the interval (2,3).

Consider the following cases:

***Case* I** $D > 0$

$\therefore \quad m \in R \quad$ [from Eq. (i)]

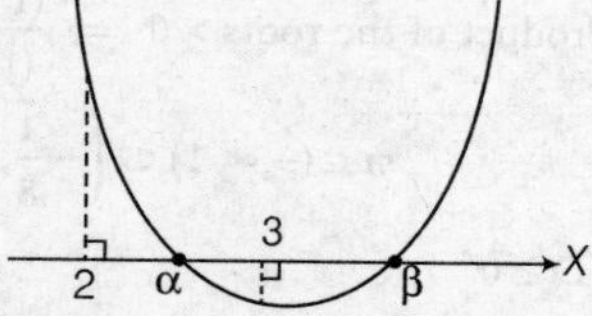

***Case* II** $f(2)\, f(3) < 0$

$$\left(4 - 2(2m+1) + \frac{1}{2}m(m+1)\right)\left(9 - 3(2m+1) + \frac{1}{2}m(m+1)\right) < 0$$

$\Rightarrow \quad (m^2 - 7m + 4)(m^2 - 11m + 12) < 0$

$\Rightarrow \quad \left(m - \dfrac{7-\sqrt{33}}{2}\right)\left(m - \dfrac{7+\sqrt{33}}{2}\right)\left(m - \dfrac{11-\sqrt{73}}{2}\right)\left(m - \dfrac{11+\sqrt{73}}{2}\right) < 0$

$$\frac{7-\sqrt{33}}{2} \quad \frac{7-\sqrt{73}}{2} \quad \frac{7+\sqrt{33}}{2} \quad \frac{11+\sqrt{73}}{2}$$

$$\therefore \; m \in \left(\frac{7-\sqrt{33}}{2}, \frac{11-\sqrt{73}}{2}\right) \cup \left(\frac{7+\sqrt{33}}{2}, \frac{11+\sqrt{73}}{2}\right)$$

Combining all cases, we get

$$m \in \left(\frac{7-\sqrt{33}}{2}, \frac{11-\sqrt{73}}{2}\right) \cup \left(\frac{7+\sqrt{33}}{2}, \frac{11+\sqrt{73}}{2}\right)$$

(v) One root is smaller than 1 and the other root is greater than 1.

Consider the following cases:

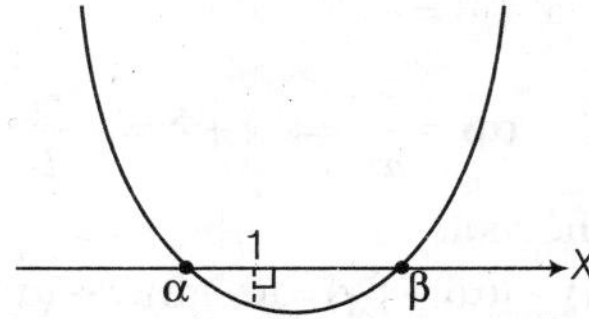

***Case* I** $D > 0$

$\therefore \quad m \in R$ [from Eq. (i)]

***Case* II** $f(1) < 0$

$\Rightarrow \quad 1-(2m+1)+\frac{1}{2}m(m+1) < 0$ [from Eq. (iii)]

$\Rightarrow \quad m^2 - 3m < 0$

$\Rightarrow \quad m(m-3) < 0$

$\therefore \quad m \in (0, 3)$

Combining both cases, we get

$$m \in (0, 3)$$

(vi) One root is greater than 3 and the other root is smaller than 2.

Consider the following cases:

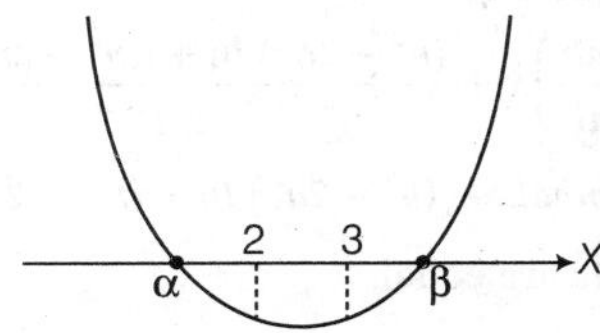

***Case* I** $D > 0$

$\therefore \quad m \in R$ [from Eq. (i)]

***Case* II** $f(2) < 0$

$\Rightarrow \quad m^2 - 7m + 4 < 0$

$$\therefore \quad \frac{7-\sqrt{33}}{2} < m < \frac{7+\sqrt{33}}{2}$$

$$\therefore \quad m \in \left(\frac{7-\sqrt{33}}{2}, \frac{7+\sqrt{33}}{2}\right)$$

***Case* III** $f(3) < 0$

$\Rightarrow \quad m^2 - 11m + 12 < 0$

$$\therefore \quad \frac{11-\sqrt{73}}{2} < m < \frac{11+\sqrt{73}}{2}$$

$$\therefore \quad m \in \left(\frac{11-\sqrt{73}}{2}, \frac{11+\sqrt{73}}{2}\right)$$

Combining all cases, we get

$$m \in \left(\frac{7-\sqrt{33}}{2}, \frac{7+\sqrt{33}}{2}\right)$$

(vii) Atleast one root lies in the interval (2, 3).

i.e. $(d) \cup (c)$

$$\therefore \; m \in \left(\frac{7-\sqrt{33}}{2}, \frac{11-\sqrt{73}}{2}\right) \cup \left(\frac{7+\sqrt{33}}{2}, \frac{11+\sqrt{73}}{2}\right)$$

(viii) Atleast one root is greater than 2.

i.e. (Exactly one root is greater than 2) ∪ (Both roots are greater than 2)

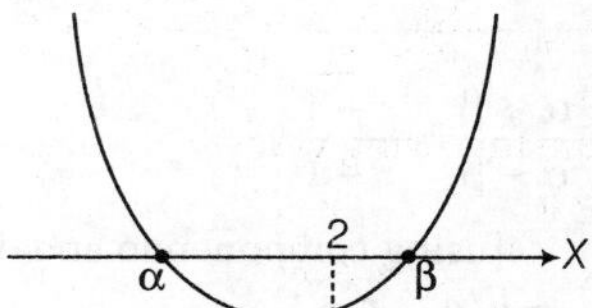

or(Exactly one root is greater than 2) $\cup (b)$ ...(I)

Consider the following cases:

***Case* I** $D > 0$

$\therefore \quad m \in R$ [from Eq. (i)]

***Case* II** $f(2) < 0$

$\Rightarrow \quad m^2 - 7m + 4 < 0$

$$\therefore \quad m \in \left(\frac{7-\sqrt{33}}{2}, \frac{7+\sqrt{33}}{2}\right)$$

Combining both cases, we get

$$m \in \left(\frac{7-\sqrt{33}}{2}, \frac{7+\sqrt{33}}{2}\right) \quad \text{...(II)}$$

Finally from Eqs. (I) and (II), we get

$$m \in \left(\frac{7-\sqrt{33}}{2}, \frac{7+\sqrt{33}}{2}\right) \cup \left(\frac{7+\sqrt{33}}{2}, \infty\right)$$

(ix) Atleast one root is smaller than 2.

i.e. (Exactly one root is smaller than 2) ∪(Both roots are smaller than 2)

or (h) (II) ∪ (a)

$$\text{We get,} \quad m \in \left(-\infty, \frac{7-\sqrt{33}}{2}\right) \cup \left(\frac{7-\sqrt{33}}{2}, \frac{7+\sqrt{33}}{2}\right)$$

(x) Both 2 and 3 lie between α and β.

Consider the following cases:

***Case* I** $D > 0$

$\therefore \quad m \in R$ [from Eq. (i)]

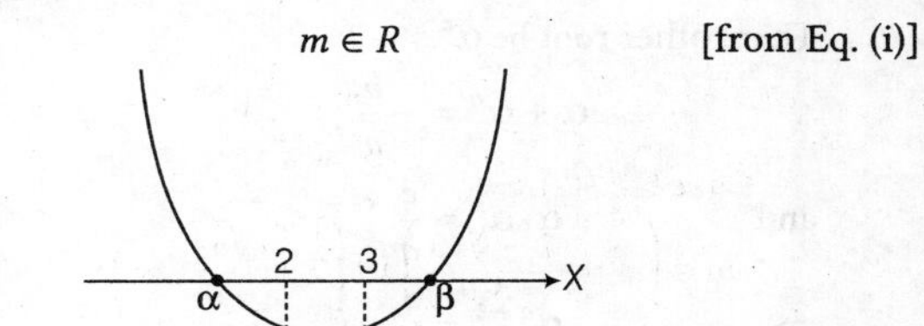

***Case* II** $f(2) < 0$

$$\Rightarrow \quad m^2 - 7m + 4 < 0$$

$$\therefore \quad m \in \left(\frac{7-\sqrt{33}}{2}, \frac{7+\sqrt{33}}{2}\right)$$

***Case* III** $f(3) < 0$

$$\Rightarrow \quad m^2 - 11m + 12 < 0$$

$$\therefore \quad m \in \left(\frac{11-\sqrt{73}}{2}, \frac{11+\sqrt{73}}{2}\right)$$

Combining all cases, we get

$$m \in \left(\frac{11-\sqrt{73}}{2}, \frac{7+\sqrt{33}}{2}\right)$$

90. $\because \quad \dfrac{\alpha}{\beta} = r$

$$\Rightarrow \quad \frac{\alpha+\beta}{\alpha-\beta} = \frac{r+1}{r-1}$$

[using componendo and dividendo method]

$$\Rightarrow \quad \frac{-b/a}{\dfrac{\sqrt{D}}{a}} = \frac{r+1}{r-1} \Rightarrow b(1-r) = (1+r)\sqrt{D}$$

On squaring both sides, we get

$$\Rightarrow \quad b^2(1-r)^2 = (1+r)^2(b^2 - 4ac)$$

or $\quad (1+r)^2 \cdot 4ac = b^2(4r)$ or $\dfrac{(1+r)^2}{r} = \dfrac{b^2}{ac}$

91. We have, $\quad \dfrac{1}{x+p} + \dfrac{1}{x+q} = \dfrac{1}{r}$

$$\Rightarrow \quad \frac{(x+q)+(x+p)}{x^2+(p+q)x+pq} = \frac{1}{r}$$

$$\Rightarrow \quad x^2 + (p+q-2r)x + pq - (p+q)r = 0$$

Now, since the roots are equal in magnitudes, but opposite in sign. Therefore,

Sum of the roots = 0

$$\Rightarrow \quad p + q - 2r = 0$$

$$\Rightarrow \quad p + q = 2r \quad \text{...(i)}$$

and product of the roots $= pq - (p+q)r$

$$= pq - (p+q)\left(\frac{p+q}{2}\right) \quad \text{[from Eq. (i)]}$$

$$= \frac{2pq - p^2 - q^2 - 2pq}{2}$$

$$= -\frac{p^2+q^2}{2}$$

92. Let α be one root of the equation $ax^2 + bx + c = 0$.

Then, other root be α^n.

$$\therefore \quad \alpha + \alpha^n = -\frac{b}{a} \quad \text{...(i)}$$

and $\quad \alpha \cdot \alpha^n = \dfrac{c}{a}$

$$\Rightarrow \quad \alpha^{n+1} = \frac{c}{a}$$

$$\Rightarrow \quad \alpha = \left(\frac{c}{a}\right)^{\frac{1}{n+1}}$$

$\therefore$ From Eq. (i), we get

$$\left(\frac{c}{a}\right)^{\frac{1}{n+1}} + \left(\frac{c}{a}\right)^{\frac{n}{n+1}} = -\frac{b}{a}$$

$$\Rightarrow \quad (c)^{\frac{1}{n+1}} \cdot a^{-\frac{1}{n+1}+1} + (c^n)^{\frac{1}{n+1}} \cdot a^{-\frac{n}{n+1}+1} + b = 0$$

$$\Rightarrow \quad c^{\frac{1}{n+1}} \cdot a^{\frac{n}{n+1}} + (c^n)^{\frac{1}{n+1}} \cdot a^{\frac{1}{n+1}} + b = 0$$

$$\Rightarrow \quad (a^n c)^{\frac{1}{n+1}} + (c^n a)^{\frac{1}{n+1}} + b = 0$$

93. We have, $\quad \alpha + \beta = -\dfrac{b}{a}$

$$\alpha\beta = \frac{c}{a} \quad \Rightarrow \gamma + \delta = -\frac{m}{l} \text{ and } \gamma\delta = \frac{n}{l}$$

Now, sum of the roots

$$= (\alpha\gamma + \beta\delta) + (\alpha\delta + \beta\gamma) = (\alpha + \beta)\gamma + (\alpha + \beta)\delta$$

$$= (\alpha + \beta)(\gamma + \delta)$$

$$= \left(-\frac{b}{a}\right)\left(-\frac{m}{l}\right) = \frac{mb}{al}$$

and product of the roots

$$= (\alpha\gamma + \beta\delta)(\alpha\delta + \beta\gamma)$$

$$= (\alpha^2 + \beta^2)\gamma\delta + \alpha\beta(\gamma^2 + \delta^2)$$

$$= \{(\alpha+\beta)^2 - 2\alpha\beta\}\gamma\delta + \alpha\beta\{(\gamma+\delta)^2 - 2\gamma\delta\}$$

$$= \left\{\left(-\frac{b}{a}\right)^2 - \frac{2c}{a}\right\}\frac{n}{l} + \frac{c}{a}\left\{\left(-\frac{m}{l}\right)^2 - \frac{2n}{l}\right\}$$

$$= \left\{\frac{b^2 - 2ac}{a^2}\right\}\frac{n}{l} + \frac{c}{a}\left\{\frac{m^2 - 2nl}{l^2}\right\} = \frac{(b^2 - 2ac)\,ln + (m^2 - 2nl)\,ac}{a^2l^2}$$

$\therefore$ Required equation is

$$x^2 - \left(\frac{mb}{al}\right)x + \frac{(b^2 - 2ac)\,ln + (m^2 - 2nl)\,ac}{a^2l^2} = 0$$

$$\Rightarrow \quad a^2l^2x^2 - mbalx + (b^2 - 2ac)\,ln + (m^2 - 2nl)\,ac = 0$$

94. Since, the roots are equal.

$$\therefore \quad D = 0$$

$$\Rightarrow \quad 4(b^2 - ac)^2 - 4(a^2 - bc)(c^2 - ab) = 0$$

$$\Rightarrow \quad (b^2 - ac)^2 - (a^2 - bc)(c^2 - ab) = 0$$

$$\Rightarrow \quad b(a^3 + b^3 + c^3 - 3abc) = 0$$

$$\Rightarrow \quad b = 0 \text{ or } a^3 + b^3 + c^3 - 3abc = 0$$

95. Let α and β be the roots of $x^2 - px + q = 0$. Then,

$$\alpha + \beta = p \quad \text{...(i)}$$

$$\alpha\beta = q \quad \text{...(ii)}$$

And α and $\dfrac{1}{\beta}$ be the roots of $x^2 - ax + b = 0$. Then,

$$\alpha + \frac{1}{\beta} = a \quad \text{...(iii)}$$

$$\frac{\alpha}{\beta} = b \quad \text{... (iv)}$$

Now, $\text{LHS} = (q-b)^2$

$$= \left(\alpha\beta - \frac{\alpha}{\beta}\right)^2 \quad \text{[from Eqs. (ii) and (iv)]}$$

$$= \alpha^2\left(\beta - \frac{1}{\beta}\right)^2 = \alpha^2\left[(\alpha+\beta) - \left(\alpha + \frac{1}{\beta}\right)\right]^2$$

$$= \alpha^2 (p-a)^2 \text{ [from Eqs. (i) and (iii)]}$$

$$= \alpha\beta \cdot \frac{\alpha}{\beta}(p-a)^2$$

$$= bq\,(p-a)^2 \quad \text{[from Eqs. (ii) and (iv)]}$$

$$= \text{RHS}$$

96. Since, roots of $x^2 - 2px + q = 0$ are equal.

$\therefore \quad D = 0$

i.e., $\quad (-2p)^2 - 4q = 0$ or $p^2 = q \quad$ ...(i)

Now, $(1+y)\,x^2 - 2\,(p+y)\,x + (q+y) = 0$

$\therefore$ Discriminant $= 4\,(p+y)^2 - 4\,(1+y)\,(q+y)$

$$= 4\,(p^2 + 2py + y^2 - q - y - qy - y^2)$$

$$= 4\,[(2p - q - 1)\,y + p^2 - q]$$

$$= 4\,[(2p - p^2 - 1)\,y + 0] \quad \text{[from Eq. (i)]}$$

$$= -\,4\,(p-1)^2 y$$

$$> 0 \quad [\because y < 0 \text{ and } p \neq 1]$$

Hence, roots of $(1+y)\,x^2 - 2\,(p+y)\,x + (q+y) = 0$ are real and distinct.

97. $x^{\log_x (x+3)^2} = 16 \quad$ ...(i)

Equation is defined, when

$$x > 0,\ x \neq 1,\ x \neq -3,$$

Then, $\quad (x+3)^2 = 4^2 \quad$ [by property]

$\Rightarrow \quad x + 3 = \pm 4$

$\therefore \quad x = 1$ and $x = -7$

But $\quad x \neq 1,\ x \neq -7$

i.e. no solution.

$\therefore \quad x \in \phi$

98. $\because (2+\sqrt{3})^{x^2 - 2x + 1} + (2-\sqrt{3})^{x^2 - 2x - 1} = \dfrac{101}{10\,(2-\sqrt{3})}$

$$\Rightarrow \quad (2+\sqrt{3})^{x^2 - 2x} \cdot (2+\sqrt{3})\,(2-\sqrt{3}) + (2-\sqrt{3})^{x^2 - 2x - 1} \cdot (2-\sqrt{3}) = \frac{101}{10}$$

$$\Rightarrow \quad (2+\sqrt{3})^{x^2 - 2x} + (2-\sqrt{3})^{x^2 - 2x} = \frac{101}{10}$$

or $$(2+\sqrt{3})^{x^2 - 2x} + \frac{1}{(2+\sqrt{3})^{x^2 - 2x}} = \frac{101}{10} \quad \text{...(i)}$$

$$\left[\because 2 - \sqrt{3} = \frac{1}{2+\sqrt{3}}\right]$$

Let $(2+\sqrt{3})^{x^2 - 2x} = \lambda$, then Eq. (i) reduces to

$$\lambda + \frac{1}{\lambda} = \frac{101}{10}$$

$\Rightarrow \quad 10\lambda^2 - 101\lambda + 10 = 0$

or $\quad (\lambda - 10)\,(10\lambda - 1) = 0$

$\therefore \quad \lambda = 10, \dfrac{1}{10}$

$\Rightarrow \quad (2+\sqrt{3})^{x^2 - 2x} = 10, 10^{-1}$

$\Rightarrow \quad x^2 - 2x = \log_{2+\sqrt{3}} 10, -\log_{2+\sqrt{3}} 10$

$\Rightarrow \quad (x-1)^2 = 1 + \log_{2+\sqrt{3}} 10, 1 - \log_{2+\sqrt{3}} 10$

$\therefore \quad (x-1)^2 = 1 + \log_{2+\sqrt{3}} 10$

$$[\because (x-1)^2 \neq 1 - \log_{2+\sqrt{3}} 10]$$

$\Rightarrow \quad x = 1 \pm \sqrt{(1 + \log_{2+\sqrt{3}} 10)}$

$\Rightarrow \quad x_1 = 1 + \sqrt{(1 + \log_{2+\sqrt{3}} 10)}$

$\quad x_2 = 1 - \sqrt{(1 + \log_{2+\sqrt{3}} 10)}$

99. We have, $\quad x^2 + \left(\dfrac{x}{x-1}\right)^2 = 8$

$$\Rightarrow \quad \left(x + \frac{x}{x-1}\right)^2 - 2 \cdot x \cdot \frac{x}{(x-1)} = 8$$

$$\Rightarrow \quad \left(\frac{x^2}{x-1}\right)^2 - 2\left(\frac{x^2}{x-1}\right) - 8 = 0 \quad \text{...(i)}$$

Let $y = \dfrac{x^2}{x-1}$. Then, Eq. (i) reduces to

$$y^2 - 2y - 8 = 0$$

$\Rightarrow \quad (y-4)\,(y+2) = 0$

$\therefore \quad y = 4, -2$

If $y = 4$, then $\quad 4 = \dfrac{x^2}{x-1}$

or $\quad x^2 - 4x + 4 = 0$

or $\quad (x-2)^2 = 0$

or $\quad x = 2$

$\therefore \quad x_1 = 2$

and if $y = -2$, then $\quad -2 = \dfrac{x^2}{x-1}$

or $\quad x^2 + 2x - 2 = 0$

$\therefore \quad x = \dfrac{-2 \pm \sqrt{(4+8)}}{2}$

$\Rightarrow \quad x = -1 \pm \sqrt{3}$

$\therefore \quad x_2 = -1 + \sqrt{3},\ x_3 = -1 - \sqrt{3}$

100. We have, $\sqrt{x + 8 + 2\sqrt{(x+7)}} + \sqrt{(x+1) - \sqrt{(x+7)}} = 4 \quad$ ...(i)

Let $\quad \sqrt{(x+7)} = \lambda \quad$ ...(ii)

or $\quad x = \lambda^2 - 7$

Then, Eq. (i) reduces to

$$\sqrt{(\lambda^2 - 7 + 8 + 2\lambda)} + \sqrt{(\lambda^2 - 7 + 1 - \lambda)} = 4$$

$\Rightarrow \quad (\lambda + 1) + \sqrt{(\lambda^2 - \lambda - 6)} = 4$

or $\quad \sqrt{(\lambda^2 - \lambda - 6)} = 3 - \lambda$

On squaring both sides, we get

$$\lambda^2 - \lambda - 6 = 9 + \lambda^2 - 6\lambda$$

$\Rightarrow \quad 5\lambda = 15$

$\therefore \quad \lambda = 3$

$\Rightarrow \quad \sqrt{(x+7)} = 3$ [from Eq. (ii)]

or $\quad x + 7 = 9$

$\therefore \quad x = 2$

and $x = 2$ satisfies Eq. (i).

Hence, $x_1 = 2$

101. We have, $\quad 4^{x^2} + 2(2a+1)2^{x^2} + 4a^2 - 3 > 0$ ...(i)

Putting $t = 2^{x^2}$ in the Eq. (i), we get

$$t^2 + 2(2a+1)t + 4a^2 - 3 > 0$$

Let $\quad f(t) = t^2 + 2(2a+1)t + 4a^2 - 3$ $\quad [\because t > 0, \therefore 2^{x^2} > 0]$

$\because \quad f(t) > 0$

T-axis

Consider the following cases:

***Case* I** Sum of the roots > 0

$$-2\frac{(2a+1)}{1} > 0$$

$\therefore \quad a \in \left(-\infty, -\frac{1}{2}\right)$

***Case* II** Product of the roots > 0

$\Rightarrow \quad \frac{4a^2-3}{1} > 0$

or $\quad a^2 > \frac{3}{4}$

or $\quad a \in \left(-\infty, -\frac{\sqrt{3}}{2}\right) \cup \left(\frac{\sqrt{3}}{2}, \infty\right)$

***Case* III** $\quad D < 0$

$\Rightarrow \quad 4(2a+1)^2 - 4 \cdot 1 \cdot (4a^2 - 3) < 0$

$\Rightarrow \quad 4a + 4 < 0$

$\therefore \quad a < -1$

or $\quad a \in (-\infty, -1)$

Combining all cases, we get

$$a \in (-\infty, -1) \cup \left(\frac{\sqrt{3}}{2}, \infty\right)$$

102. We have, $\quad \log_{x^2+2x-3}\left(\frac{|x+4|-|x|}{x-1}\right) > 0$

The given inequation is valid for

$$\frac{|x+4|-|x|}{(x-1)} > 0$$

and $\quad x^2 + 2x - 3 > 0, \neq 1$ ...(i)

Now, consider the following cases:

***Case* I** If $0 < x^2 + 2x - 3 < 1$

$\Rightarrow \quad 4 < x^2 + 2x + 1 < 5$

$\Rightarrow \quad 4 < (x+1)^2 < 5$

$\Rightarrow \quad -\sqrt{5} < (x+1) < -2$ or $2 < x + 1 < \sqrt{5}$

$\Rightarrow \quad -\sqrt{5} - 1 < x < -3$ or $1 < x < \sqrt{5} - 1$

$\therefore \quad x \in (-\sqrt{5} - 1, -3) \cup (1, \sqrt{5} - 1)$ ...(ii)

Then, $\quad \frac{|x+4|-|x|}{(x-1)} < 1$

Now, $x < -4$, then $\frac{-(x+4)+x}{(x-1)} < 1$

$\Rightarrow \quad 1 + \frac{4}{x-1} > 0$

$\Rightarrow \quad \frac{(x+3)}{(x-1)} > 0$

$\therefore \quad x \in (-\infty, -3) \cup (1, \infty)$

$\Rightarrow \quad x \in (-\infty, -4)$ $\quad [\because x < -4]$ ...(iii)

$-4 \leq x < 0$, then $\frac{x+4+x}{(x-1)} - 1 < 0$

$\Rightarrow \quad \frac{(x+5)}{(x-1)} < 0$

$\therefore \quad x \in (-5, 1)$

$\Rightarrow \quad x \in [-4, 0)$ $\quad [\because -4 \leq x < 0]$ ...(iv)

and $\quad x \geq 0$, then $\frac{(x+4)-x}{(x-1)} < 1$

$\Rightarrow \quad 1 - \frac{4}{x-1} > 0$

$\Rightarrow \quad \frac{(x-5)}{(x-1)} > 0$

$\therefore \quad x \in (-\infty, 1) \cup (5, \infty)$

$\Rightarrow \quad x \in [0, 1) \cup (5, \infty)$ $\quad [\because x \geq 0]$ ...(v)

From Eqs. (iii), (iv) and (v), we get

$$x \in (-\infty, 1) \cup (5, \infty) \quad \text{...(vi)}$$

Now, common values in Eqs. (ii) and (iv) is

$$x \in (-\sqrt{5} - 1, -3) \quad \text{...(vii)}$$

***Case* II** If $\quad x^2 + 2x - 3 > 1$

$\Rightarrow \quad x^2 + 2x + 1 > 5 \Rightarrow (x+1)^2 > 5$

$\Rightarrow \quad x + 1 < -\sqrt{5}$

or $\quad x + 1 > \sqrt{5}$

$\therefore \quad x \in (-\infty, -1 - \sqrt{5}) \cup (\sqrt{5} - 1, \infty)$ ...(viii)

Then, $\quad \frac{|x+4|-|x|}{(x-1)} > 1$

Now, $\quad x < -4$, then $\frac{-4}{x-1} > 1$

$\Rightarrow \quad 1 + \frac{4}{x-1} < 0$

$\Rightarrow \quad \frac{x+3}{x-1} < 0$

$\therefore \quad x \in (-3, 1)$

which is false. $[\because x < -4]$

$-4 \le x < 0$, then $\dfrac{2x+4}{(x-1)} - 1 > 0$

$$\Rightarrow \quad \frac{(x+5)}{(x-1)} > 0$$

$$\therefore \quad x \in (-\infty, -5) \cup (1, \infty)$$

which is false. $[\because -4 \le x < 0]$

and $x \ge 0$, then $\dfrac{4}{x-1} > 1$

$$\Rightarrow \quad 1 - \frac{4}{x-1} < 0$$

$$\Rightarrow \quad \frac{x-5}{x-1} < 0$$

$$\therefore \quad x \in (1, 5) \quad \text{...(ix)}$$

which is false. $[\because x \ge 0]$

Now, common values in Eq. (viii) and (ix) is

$$\therefore \quad x \in (\sqrt{5} - 1, 5) \quad \text{...(x)}$$

Combining Eqs. (viii) and (x), we get

$$x \in (-\sqrt{5} - 1, -3) \cup (\sqrt{5} - 1, 5)$$

103. Let $y \ge 0$, then $|y| = y$

and then given system reduces to

$$|x^2 - 2x| + y = 1 \quad \text{...(i)}$$

and $$x^2 + y = 1 \quad \text{...(ii)}$$

From Eqs. (i) and (ii), we get

$$x^2 = |x^2 - 2x|$$

$$\Rightarrow \quad x^2 = |x||x-2|$$

Now, $\quad x < 0, \quad 0 \le x < 2, \quad x \ge 2$

$$x^2 = x(x-2), \quad x^2 = -x(x-2)$$

$$x^2 = x(x-2)$$

$$\therefore \quad x = 0$$

$$\Rightarrow \quad x(x + x - 2) = 0$$

$$\therefore \quad x = 0$$

fail $\therefore x = 0, 1$ fail

$$\Rightarrow \quad x = 0, 1, \text{ then } y = 1, 0$$

$\therefore$ Solutions are (0, 1) and (1, 0).

If $y < 0$ then $|y| = -y$ and then given system reduces to

$$|x^2 - 2x| + y = 1 \quad \text{...(iii)}$$

and $$x^2 - y = 1 \quad \text{...(iv)}$$

From Eqs. (iii) and (iv), we get

$$|x^2 - 2x| + x^2 = 2$$

$$\Rightarrow \quad |x||x-2| + x^2 = 2$$

Now, $\quad x < 0, \quad 0 \le x < 2, \quad x \ge 2$

$$x(x-2) + x^2 = 2$$

$$-x(x-2) + x^2 = 2$$

$$x(x-2) + x^2 = 2$$

$$\Rightarrow \quad 2x^2 - 2x - 2 = 0 \quad \Rightarrow 2x = 2$$

$$\Rightarrow \quad x^2 - x - 1 = 0$$

$$\Rightarrow \quad x^2 - x - 1 = 0$$

$$\therefore \quad x = 1$$

$$\therefore \quad x = \frac{1 \pm \sqrt{5}}{2}$$

$$\therefore \quad x = \frac{1 \pm \sqrt{5}}{2} \text{ fail}$$

$$\Rightarrow \quad x = \frac{1 - \sqrt{5}}{2} \quad [\because x < 0]$$

$$\Rightarrow \quad x = \frac{1 - \sqrt{5}}{2}, 1, \text{ then } y = \frac{1 - \sqrt{5}}{2}, 0$$

$\therefore$ Solutions are $\left(\dfrac{1-\sqrt{5}}{2}, \dfrac{1-\sqrt{5}}{2}\right)$ and (1, 0).

Hence, all pairs (0, 1), (1, 0) and $\left(\dfrac{1-\sqrt{5}}{2}, \dfrac{1-\sqrt{5}}{2}\right)$ are solutions of the original system of equations.

104. Given, α, β and γ are the roots of the cubic equation

$$x^3 - px^2 + qx - r = 0 \quad \text{...(i)}$$

$$\therefore \quad \alpha + \beta + \gamma = p, \ \alpha\beta + \beta\gamma + \gamma\alpha = q, \ \alpha\beta\gamma = r$$

(i) Let $\quad y = \beta\gamma + \dfrac{1}{\alpha}$

$$\Rightarrow \quad y = \frac{\alpha\beta\gamma + 1}{\alpha} = \frac{r+1}{\alpha}$$

$$\therefore \quad \alpha = \frac{r+1}{y}$$

From Eq. (i), we get

$$\alpha^3 - p\alpha^2 + q\alpha - r = 0$$

$$\Rightarrow \quad \frac{(r+1)^3}{y^3} - \frac{p(r+1)^2}{y^2} + \frac{q(r+1)}{y} - r = 0$$

or $\quad ry^3 - q(r+1)y^2 + p(r+1)^2 y - (r+1)^3 = 0$

(ii) Let $y = \beta + \gamma - \alpha = (\alpha + \beta + \gamma) - 2\alpha = p - 2\alpha$

$$\therefore \quad \alpha = \frac{p - y}{2}$$

From Eq. (i), we get

$$\alpha^3 - p\alpha^2 + q\alpha - r = 0$$

$$\Rightarrow \quad \frac{(p-y)^3}{8} - \frac{p(p-y)^2}{4} + \frac{q(p-y)}{2} - r = 0$$

or $\quad y^3 - py^2 + (4q - p^2)y + (8r - 4pq + p^3) = 0$

Also product of roots $= -(8r - 4pq + p^3)$

105. Assume $\alpha + i\beta$ is a complex root of the given equation, then conjugate of this root, i.e. $\alpha - i\beta$ is also root of this equation. On putting $x = \alpha + i\beta$ and $x = \alpha - i\beta$ in the given equation, we get

$$\frac{A_1^2}{\alpha + i\beta - a_1} + \frac{A_2^2}{\alpha + i\beta - a_2} + \frac{A_3^2}{\alpha + i\beta - a_3} + \dots + \frac{A_n^2}{\alpha + i\beta - a_n}$$
$$= ab^2 + c^2(\alpha + i\beta) + ac \quad \text{...(i)}$$

and $$\frac{A_1^2}{\alpha - i\beta - a_1} + \frac{A_2^2}{\alpha - i\beta - a_2} + \frac{A_3^2}{\alpha - i\beta - a_3} + \dots + \frac{A_n^2}{\alpha - i\beta - a_n}$$
$$= ab^2 + c^2(\alpha - i\beta) + ac \quad \text{...(ii)}$$

On subtracting Eq. (i) from Eq. (ii), we get

$$2i\beta\left[\frac{A_1^2}{(\alpha-a_1)^2+\beta^2}+\frac{A_2^2}{(\alpha-a_2)^2+\beta^2}+\frac{A_3^2}{(\alpha-a_3)^2+\beta^2}+\ldots+\frac{A_n^2}{(\alpha-a_n)^2+\beta^2}+c^2\right]=0$$

The expression in bracket $\neq 0$

$$\therefore \quad 2i\beta = 0 \Rightarrow \beta = 0$$

Hence, all roots of the given equation are real.

106. Given equation is

$$x^4+2ax^3+x^2+2ax+1=0 \qquad \ldots(\text{i})$$

On dividing by x^2, we get

$$x^2+2ax+1+\frac{2a}{x}+\frac{1}{x^2}=0$$

$$\Rightarrow \left(x^2+\frac{1}{x^2}\right)+2a\left(x+\frac{1}{x}\right)+1=0$$

$$\Rightarrow \left(x+\frac{1}{x}\right)^2-2+2a\left(x+\frac{1}{x}\right)+1=0$$

$$\text{or} \quad \left(x+\frac{1}{x}\right)^2+2a\left(x+\frac{1}{x}\right)-1=0$$

$$\text{or} \quad y^2+2ay-1=0, \text{ where } y=x+\frac{1}{x}$$

$$\therefore \quad y=\frac{-2a\pm\sqrt{(4a^2+4)}}{2}=-a\pm\sqrt{(a^2+1)}$$

Taking '+' sign, we get

$$y=-a+\sqrt{(a^2+1)}$$

$$\Rightarrow x+\frac{1}{x}=-a+\sqrt{(a^2+1)}$$

$$\text{or} \quad x^2+(a-\sqrt{(a^2+1)})\,x+1=0 \qquad \ldots(\text{ii})$$

Taking '–' sign, we get $y=-a-\sqrt{(a^2+1)}$

$$\Rightarrow x+\frac{1}{x}=-a-\sqrt{(a^2+1)}$$

$$\text{or} \quad x^2+(a+\sqrt{(a^2+1)})\,x+1=0 \qquad \ldots(\text{iii})$$

Let α, β be the roots of Eq. (ii) and γ, δ be the roots of Eq. (iii).

Then, $\alpha+\beta=\sqrt{(a^2+1)}-a$

and $\alpha\beta=1$

and $\gamma+\delta=-\sqrt{(a^2+1)}-a$

and $\gamma\delta=1$

Clearly, $\alpha+\beta>0$ and $\alpha\beta>0$

$\therefore$Either α, β will be imaginary or both real and positive according to the Eq. (i) has atleast two distinct negative roots. Therefore, both γ and δ must be negative. Therefore,

(i) $\gamma\delta>0$, which is true as $\gamma\delta=1$.

(ii) $\gamma+\delta<0$

$$\Rightarrow -(a+\sqrt{(a^2+1)})<0$$

$$\Rightarrow a+\sqrt{(a^2+1)}>0, \text{ which is true for all } a.$$

$$\therefore \quad a\in R$$

(iii) $D>0$

$$\therefore \quad (a+\sqrt{(a^2+1)})^2-4>0$$

$$\Rightarrow (a+\sqrt{(a^2+1)}+2)(a+\sqrt{(a^2+1)}-2)>0$$

$$\because \quad a+\sqrt{(a^2+1)}+2>0$$

$$\therefore \quad a+\sqrt{(a^2+1)}-2>0$$

$$\Rightarrow \sqrt{(a^2+1)}>2-a$$

$$\begin{cases} a\geq 2 \\ \text{or } a^2+1>(2-a)^2, \text{ if } a<2 \end{cases}$$

$$\Rightarrow \begin{cases} a\geq 2 \\ \text{or } a>\frac{3}{4}, \text{ if } a<2 \end{cases}$$

$$\Rightarrow \begin{cases} a\geq 2 \\ \text{or } \frac{3}{4}<a<2 \end{cases}$$

Hence, $\frac{3}{4}<a<\infty$ or $a\in\left(\frac{3}{4},\infty\right)$

107. We have, $[2x]-[x+1]=2x$

Since, LHS = Integer

$\therefore$ RHS = $2x$ = Integer

$\Rightarrow$ $[2x]=2x$

Now, $-[x+1]=0$

$\Rightarrow$ $[x+1]=0$

or $0\leq x+1<1$

or $-1\leq x<0$

or $-2\leq 2x<0$

$\therefore$ $2x=-2,-1$

or $x=-1,-\frac{1}{2}$

or $x_1=-1, x_2=-\frac{1}{2}$

108. We have, $(a^2+3)x^2+(a+2)x-6<0$

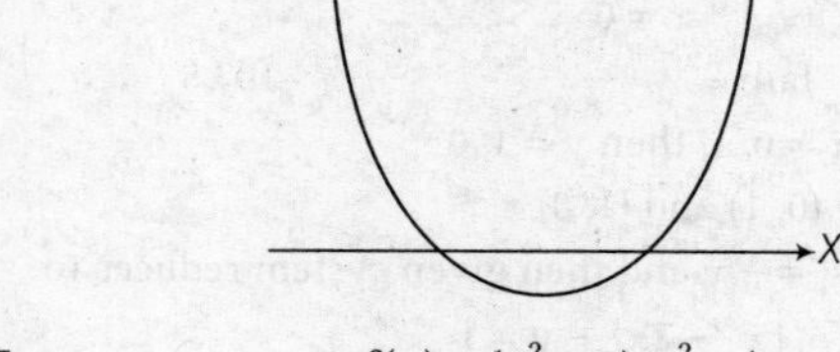

Let $f(x)=(a^2+3)x^2+(a+2)x-6$

$\because$ $(a^2+3)>0$ and $f(x)<0$

$\therefore$ $D>0$

$\Rightarrow (a+2)^2+24(a^2+3)>0$ is true for all $a\in R$.

109. We have, $6x^2-77[x]+147=0$

$$\Rightarrow \frac{6x^2+147}{77}=[x]$$

$$\Rightarrow (0.078)\,x^2=[x]-1.9$$

$$\because \quad (0.078)\,x^2>0 \Rightarrow x^2>0$$

$$\therefore \quad [x]-1.9>0$$

$$\text{or} \quad [x]>1.9$$

$\therefore \quad [x] = 2, 3, 4, 5, \ldots$

If $\quad [x] = 2$, i.e. $2 \le x < 3$

Then, $\quad x^2 = \dfrac{2 - 1.9}{0.078} = 1.28$

$\therefore \quad x = 1.13$ [fail]

If $\quad [x] = 3$, i.e. $3 \le x < 4$

Then, $\quad x^2 = \dfrac{3 - 1.9}{0.078} = 14.1$

$\therefore \quad x = 3.75$ [true]

If $\quad [x] = 4$, i.e. $4 \le x < 5$

Then, $\quad x^2 = \dfrac{4 - 1.9}{0.078} = 26.9$

$\therefore \quad x = 5.18$ [fail]

If $\quad [x] = 5$, i.e. $5 \le x < 6$

Then, $\quad x^2 = \dfrac{5 - 1.9}{0.078} = 39.7$

$\therefore \quad x = 6.3$ [fail]

If $\quad [x] = 6$, i.e. $6 \le x < 7$

Then, $\quad x^2 = \dfrac{6 - 1.9}{0.078} = \dfrac{4.1}{0.078} = 52.56$

$\therefore \quad x = 7.25$ [fail]

If $\quad [x] = 7$, i.e. $7 \le x < 8$

Then, $\quad x^2 = \dfrac{7 - 1.9}{0.078} = \dfrac{5.1}{0.078} = 65.38$

$\therefore \quad x = 8.08$ [fail]

If $\quad [x] = 8$, i.e. $8 \le x < 9$

Then, $\quad x^2 = \dfrac{8 - 1.9}{0.078} = \dfrac{6.1}{0.078} = 78.2$

$\therefore \quad x = 8.8$ [true]

If $\quad [x] = 9$, i.e. $9 \le x < 10$

Then, $\quad x^2 = \dfrac{9 - 1.9}{0.078} = \dfrac{7.1}{0.078} = 91.03$

$\therefore \quad x = 9.5$ [true]

If $\quad [x] = 10$, i.e. $10 \le x < 11$

Then, $\quad x^2 = \dfrac{10 - 1.9}{0.078} = \dfrac{8.1}{0.078} = 103.8$

$\therefore \quad x = 10.2$ [true]

If $\quad [x] = 11$, i.e. $11 \le x < 12$

Then, $\quad x^2 = \dfrac{11 - 1.9}{0.078}$

$= \dfrac{9.1}{0.078} = 116.7$

$\therefore \quad x = 10.8$ [fail]

Other values are fail.

Hence, number of solutions is four.

110. Since, the given equation is

$$x^2 - 2x - a^2 + 1 = 0$$

$\Rightarrow \quad (x - 1)^2 = a^2$

$\therefore \quad x - 1 \ne a$ or $x = 1 \pm a$

$\Rightarrow \quad \alpha = 1 + a$ and $\beta = 1 - a$

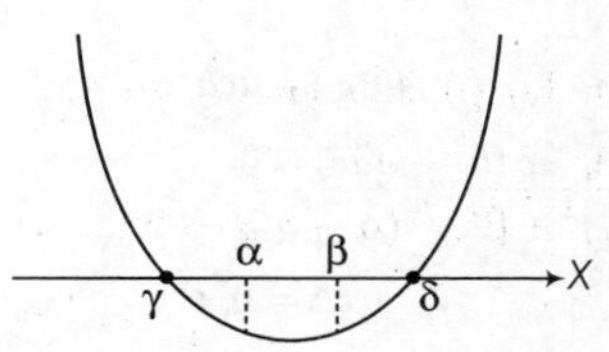

Let $f(x) = x^2 - 2(a + 1)\,x + a\,(a - 1)$, thus the following conditions hold good:

Consider the following cases:

***Case* I** $\quad D > 0$

$\Rightarrow \quad 4\,(a + 1)^2 - 4a\,(a - 1) > 0$

$\Rightarrow \quad 3a + 1 > 0$

$\therefore \quad a > -\dfrac{1}{3}$

***Case* II** $\quad f(\alpha) < 0$

$\Rightarrow \quad f(1 + a) < 0$

$\Rightarrow \quad (1 + a)^2 - 2\,(1 + a)\,(1 + a) + a\,(a - 1) < 0$

$\Rightarrow \quad -(1 + a)^2 + a\,(a - 1) < 0$

$\Rightarrow \quad -3a - 1 < 0$

$\Rightarrow \quad a > -\dfrac{1}{3}$

***Case* III** $\quad f(s) = 0$

$\Rightarrow \quad f(1 - a) < 0$

$\Rightarrow \quad (1 - a)^2 - 2\,(a + 1)\,(1 - a) + a\,(a - 1) < 0$

$\Rightarrow \quad (4a + 1)\,(a - 1) < 0$

$\therefore \quad -\dfrac{1}{4} < a < 1$

Combining all cases we get

$$a \in \left(-\frac{1}{4}, 1\right)$$

111. $pr = (-p)(-r)$

$= (\alpha + \beta + \gamma + \delta)(\alpha\beta\gamma + \alpha\beta\delta + \gamma\delta\alpha + \gamma\delta\beta)$

$= \alpha^2\beta\gamma + \alpha^2\beta\delta + \alpha^2\gamma\delta + \alpha\beta\gamma\delta + \beta^2\gamma\alpha$

$+ \beta^2\alpha\delta + \alpha\beta\gamma\delta + \beta^2\gamma\delta + \gamma^2\alpha\beta + \alpha\beta\gamma\delta$

$+ \gamma^2\delta\alpha + \gamma^2\delta\beta + \alpha\beta\gamma\delta + \alpha\beta\delta^2 + \gamma\alpha\delta^2 + \gamma\beta\delta^2$

$\because \quad$ AM $\ge$ GM

$\Rightarrow \quad \dfrac{pr}{16} \ge (\alpha^{16}\beta^{16}\gamma^{16}\delta^{16})^{1/6} = \alpha\beta\gamma\delta = 5$

$\Rightarrow \quad \dfrac{pr}{16} \ge 5$

or $\quad pr \ge 80$

$\therefore \quad$ Minimum value of pr is 80.

112. $(\alpha^2 + \beta^2)^2 = (\alpha + \beta)\,(\alpha^3 + \beta^3)$

$\Rightarrow \quad \{(\alpha + \beta)^2 - 2\alpha\beta\}^2 = (\alpha + \beta)\,\{(\alpha + \beta)^3 - 3\alpha\beta\,(\alpha + \beta)\}$

$\Rightarrow \quad \left(\dfrac{b^2}{a^2} - \dfrac{2c}{a}\right)^2 = \left(-\dfrac{b}{a}\right)\left(\dfrac{-b^3}{a^3} + \dfrac{3bc}{a^2}\right)$

$\Rightarrow \quad \left(\dfrac{b^2 - 2ac}{a^2}\right)^2 = \left(\dfrac{-b}{a}\right)\left(\dfrac{-b^3 + 3abc}{a^3}\right)$

$\Rightarrow \quad 4a^2c^2 = acb^2$

$\Rightarrow \quad ac\,(b^2 - 4ac) = 0$

As $\quad a \neq 0$

$\Rightarrow \quad c\Delta = 0$

113. Let $P(x) = bx^2 + ax + c$

As $\quad P\,(0) = 0$

$\Rightarrow \quad c = 0$

As $\quad P\,(1) = 1$

$\Rightarrow \quad a + b = 1$

$P\,(x) = ax + (1 - a)\,x^2$

Now, $\quad P'\,(x) = a + 2\,(1 - a)\,x$

As $\quad P'\,(x) > 0$ for $x \in (0, 1)$

Only option (d) satisfies above condition.

114. Let the roots are α and $\alpha + 1$, where $\alpha \in I$.

Then, sum of the roots $= 2\alpha + 1 = b$

Product of the roots $= \alpha(\alpha + 1) = c$

Now, $\quad b^2 - 4c = (2\alpha + 1)^2 - 4\alpha(\alpha + 1)$

$= 4\alpha^2 + 1 + 4\alpha - 4\alpha^2 - 4\alpha = 1$

$\therefore \quad b^2 - 4c = 1$

115. Let $\quad f(x) = a_n\,x^n + a_{n-1}\,x^{n-1} + \ldots + a_1\,x,$

$f(0) = 0; f(\alpha) = 0$

$\Rightarrow \quad f'(x) = 0$ has atleast one root between $(0, \alpha)$.

i.e. Equation

$na_n\,x^{n-1} + (n-1)\,a_{n-1}x^{n-2} + \ldots + a_1 = 0$

has a positive root smaller than α.

116. Let $f(x) = x^2 - 2kx + k^2 + k - 5$

Consider the following cases:

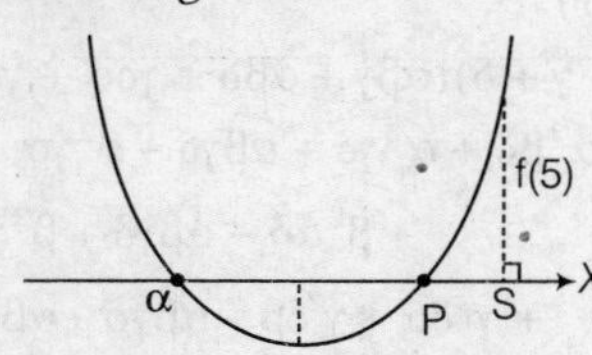

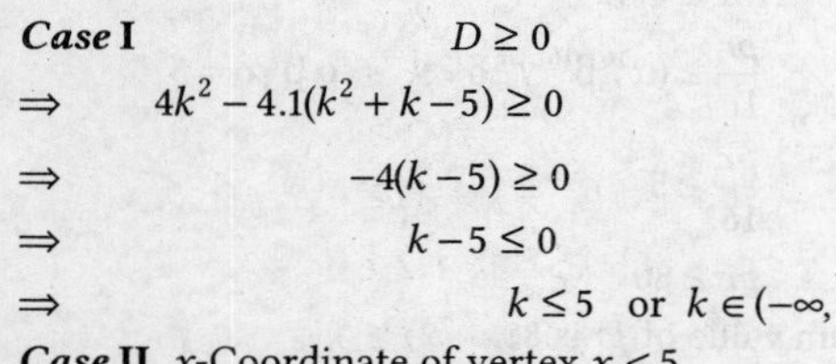

***Case* I** $\quad D \geq 0$

$\Rightarrow \quad 4k^2 - 4.1(k^2 + k - 5) \geq 0$

$\Rightarrow \quad -4(k - 5) \geq 0$

$\Rightarrow \quad k - 5 \leq 0$

$\Rightarrow \quad k \leq 5 \;$ or $\; k \in (-\infty, 5]$

***Case* II** x-Coordinate of vertex $x < 5$

$\Rightarrow \quad \dfrac{2k}{2} < 5$

$\Rightarrow \quad k < 5$ or $k \in (-\infty, 5)$

***Case* III** $\quad f(5) > 0$

$\Rightarrow \quad 25 - 10k + k^2 + k - 5 > 0$

$\Rightarrow \quad k^2 - 9k + 20 > 0$

$\Rightarrow \quad (k-4)(k-5) > 0$ or $k \in (-\infty, 4) \cup (5, \infty)$

Combining all cases, we get

$k \in (-\infty, 4)$

117. We have, $\quad a + b = 10c,\; ab = -11d$

and $\quad c + d = 10a,\; cd = -11b$

$\therefore \quad a + b + c + d = 10\,(a + c)$

and $\quad abcd = 121\,bd$

$\Rightarrow \quad b + d = 9\,(a + c)$

and $\quad ac = 121$

Next, $\quad a^2 - 10ac - 11d = 0$

and $\quad c^2 - 10ac - 11b = 0$

$\Rightarrow \quad a^2 + c^2 - 20\,ac - 11\,(b + d) = 0$

$\Rightarrow \quad (a + c)^2 - 22 \times 121 - 99\,(a + c) = 0$

$\Rightarrow \quad a + c = 121$ or -22

If $a + c = -22 \Rightarrow a = c$, rejecting these values, we have

$a + c = 121$

$\therefore \quad a + b + c + d = 10\,(a + c) = 1210$

118. $\quad D \geq 0$

$4\,(a + b + c)^2 - 12\lambda\,(ab + bc + ca) \geq 0$

$(a^2 + b^2 + c^2) - (3\lambda - 2)\,(ab + bc + ca) \geq 0$

$\therefore \quad (3\lambda - 2) \leq \dfrac{(a^2 + b^2 + c^2)}{(ab + bc + ca)}$

Since, $\quad |a - b| < c$

$\Rightarrow \quad a^2 + b^2 - 2ab < c^2 \quad$ ...(i)

$|b - c| < a$

$\Rightarrow \quad b^2 + c^2 - 2bc < a^2 \quad$ ...(ii)

$|c - a| < b$

$\Rightarrow \quad c^2 + a^2 - 2ca < b^2 \quad$ ...(iii)

From Eqs. (i), (ii) and (iii), we get

$\dfrac{a^2 + b^2 + c^2}{ab + bc + ca} < 2 \quad$ ...(iv)

From Eqs. (i) and (iv), we get

$3\lambda - 2 < 2 \;\Rightarrow\; \lambda < \dfrac{4}{3}$

119. $\because \quad x^2 - 2mx + m^2 - 1 = 0$

$\Rightarrow \quad (x - m)^2 = 1$

$\therefore \quad x - m = \pm 1$ or $x = m - 1, m + 1$

According to the question,

$m - 1 > -2,\; m + 1 > -2$

$\Rightarrow \quad m > -1,\; m > -3$

Then, $\quad m > -1 \quad$ ...(i)

and $\quad m - 1 < 4,\; m + 1 < 4$

$\Rightarrow \quad m < 5,\; m < 3$ and $m < 3 \quad$ ...(ii)

From Eqs. (i) and (ii), we get $-1 < m < 3$

120. $x^2 + px + q = 0$

Sum of the roots $= \tan 30° + \tan 15° = -p$

Product of the roots $= \tan 30° \cdot \tan 15° = q$

$\tan 45° = \tan\,(30° + 15°) = \dfrac{\tan 30° + \tan 15°}{1 - \tan 30° \cdot \tan 15°}$

$\Rightarrow \quad 1 = \dfrac{-p}{1-q} \Rightarrow -p = 1 - q$

$\Rightarrow \quad q - p = 1$

$\therefore \quad 2 + q - p = 3$

121. The equation $x^2 - px + r = 0$ has roots (α, β) and the equation $x^2 - qx + r$ has roots $\left(\dfrac{\alpha}{2}, 2\beta\right)$.

$\Rightarrow \quad r = \alpha\beta$ and $\alpha + \beta = p$ and $\dfrac{\alpha}{2} + 2\beta = q$

$\Rightarrow \quad \beta = \dfrac{2q-p}{3}$ and $\alpha = \dfrac{2(2p-q)}{3}$

$\Rightarrow \quad \alpha\beta = r = \dfrac{2}{9}(2q-p)(2p-q)$

122. $\alpha + \beta = -a$

$|\alpha - \beta| < \sqrt{5} \Rightarrow (\alpha-\beta)^2 < 5$

$\Rightarrow \quad a^2 - 4 < 5 \Rightarrow a \in (-3, 3)$

123. Suppose roots are imaginary, then $\beta = \bar{\alpha}$

and $\quad \dfrac{1}{\beta} = \bar{\alpha}$

$\Rightarrow \quad \beta = -\dfrac{1}{\beta}$ [not possible]

$\Rightarrow$ Roots are real $\Rightarrow (p^2 - q)(b^2 - ac) \geq 0$

$\Rightarrow$ Statement –1 is true.

$-\dfrac{2b}{a} = \alpha + \dfrac{1}{\beta}$

and $\quad \dfrac{\alpha}{\beta} = \dfrac{c}{a}, \alpha + \beta = -2p, \alpha\beta = q$

If $\beta = 1$, then $\alpha = q$

$\Rightarrow \quad c = qa$ [not possible]

Also, $\quad \alpha + 1 = \dfrac{-2b}{a}$

$\Rightarrow \quad -2p = \dfrac{-2b}{a}$

$\Rightarrow \quad b = ap$ [not possible]

$\Rightarrow$ Statement –2 is true but it is not the correct explanation of Statement-1.

124. Let $\alpha, 4\beta$ be roots of $x^2 - 6x + a = 0$ and $\alpha, 3\beta$ be the roots of $x^2 - cx + 6 = 0$.

Then, $\quad \alpha + 4\beta = 6$ and $4\alpha\beta = a$ ...(i)

$\alpha + 3\beta = c$ and $3\alpha\beta = 6$ ...(ii)

From Eqs. (i) and (ii), we get

$a = 8, \alpha\beta = 2$

Now, first equation becomes

$x^2 - 6x + 8 = 0$

$\Rightarrow \quad x = 2, 4$

If $\quad \alpha = 2, 4\beta = 4$, then $3\beta = 3$

If $\quad \alpha = 4, 4\beta = 2$, then $3\beta = \dfrac{3}{2}$ [non-integer]

$\therefore$ Common root is $x = 2$.

125. Let $f(x) = x^7 + 14x^5 + 16x^3 + 30x - 560$

$\therefore \quad f'(x) = 7x^6 + 70x^4 + 48x^2 + 30 > 0, \forall x \in R$

$\Rightarrow f(x)$ is an increasing function, for all $x \in R$

Hence, number of real solutions is 1.

126. Let $f(x) = x^3 - px + q$

$\therefore \quad f'(x) = 3x^2 - p$

$\Rightarrow \quad f''(x) = 6x$

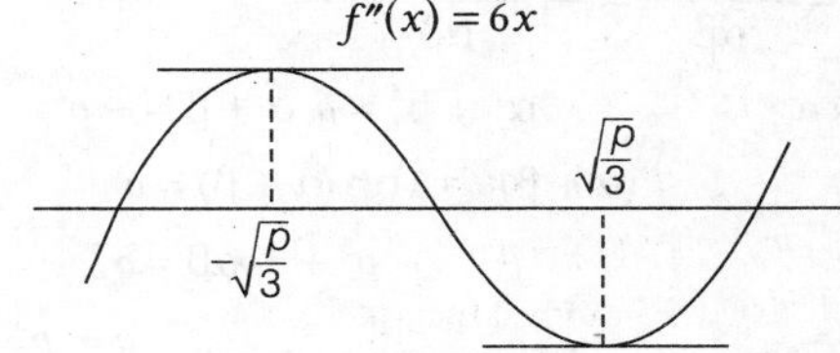

For maxima or minima, $f'(x) = 0$

$\therefore \quad x = \pm\sqrt{\dfrac{p}{3}}$

$\Rightarrow \quad f''\left(\sqrt{\dfrac{p}{3}}\right) = 6\sqrt{\left(\dfrac{p}{3}\right)} > 0$

and $\quad f''\left(-\sqrt{\dfrac{p}{3}}\right) = -6\sqrt{\dfrac{p}{3}} < 0$

Hence, given cubic minima at $x = \sqrt{\dfrac{p}{3}}$ and maxima at $x = -\sqrt{\dfrac{p}{3}}$.

127. Let $f(x) = x^2 - 8kx + 16(k^2 - k + 1)$

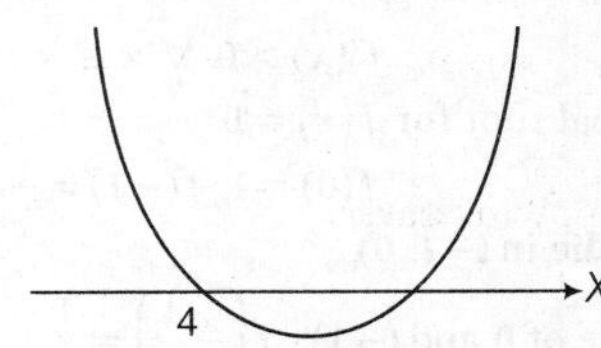

$\therefore \quad D > 0$

$\Rightarrow \quad 64k^2 - 4 \cdot 16(k^2 - k + 1) > 0$

$\Rightarrow \quad k > 1$ ...(i)

$\Rightarrow \quad \dfrac{-b}{2a} > 4 \Rightarrow \dfrac{8k}{2} > 4$

$\Rightarrow \quad k > 1$ ...(ii)

and $\quad f(4) \geq 0$

$\Rightarrow \quad 16 - 32k + 16(k^2 - k + 1) \geq 0$

$\Rightarrow \quad k^2 - 3k + 2 \geq 0$

$\Rightarrow \quad (k-1)(k-2) \geq 0$

$\Rightarrow \quad k \leq 1$ or $k \geq 2$ ...(iii)

From Eqs. (i), (ii) and (iii), we get

$k \geq 2$

$k_{\min} = 2$

128. Since, roots of $bx^2 + cx + a = 0$ are imaginary.

$\therefore \quad c^2 - 4ab < 0$

$\Rightarrow \quad -c^2 > -4ab$ ...(i)

Let $f(x) = 3b^2x^2 + 6bcx + 2c^2$

Since, $3b^2 > 0$

and $D = (6bc)^2 - 4(3b^2)(2c^2) = 12b^2c^2$

$\therefore$ Minimum value of $f(x) = -\dfrac{D}{4a} = -\dfrac{12b^2c^2}{4(3b^2)} = -c^2 > -4ab$

129. $\dfrac{\alpha}{\beta} + \dfrac{\beta}{\alpha} = \dfrac{\alpha^2 + \beta^2}{\alpha\beta} = \dfrac{(\alpha+\beta)^2 - 2\alpha\beta}{\alpha\beta}$ ...(i)

and given, $\alpha^3 + \beta^3 = q, \alpha + \beta = -p$

$\Rightarrow (\alpha+\beta)^3 - 3\alpha\beta(\alpha+\beta) = q$

$\Rightarrow -p^3 + 3p\alpha\beta = q$

or $\alpha\beta = \dfrac{q + p^3}{3p}$

$\therefore$ From Eq. (i), we get

$$\frac{\alpha}{\beta} + \frac{\beta}{\alpha} = \frac{p^2 - \dfrac{2(q+p^3)}{3p}}{\dfrac{(q+p^3)}{3p}} = \frac{p^3 - 2q}{(q+p^3)}$$

and product of the roots $= \dfrac{\alpha}{\beta} \cdot \dfrac{\beta}{\alpha} = 1$

$\therefore$ Required equation is $x^2 - \left(\dfrac{p^3 - 2q}{q + p^3}\right)x + 1 = 0$

or $(q + p^3)x^2 - (p^3 - 2q)x + (q + p^3) = 0$

130. Since, $f'(x) = 12x^2 + 6x + 2$

Here, $D = 6^2 - 4 \cdot 12 \cdot 2 = 36 - 96 = -60 < 0$

$\therefore f'(x) > 0, \forall x \in R$

$\Rightarrow$ Only one real root for $f(x) = 0$

Also, $f(0) = 1, f(-1) = -2$

$\Rightarrow$ Root must lie in $(-1, 0)$.

Taking average of 0 and (-1), $f\left(-\dfrac{1}{2}\right) = \dfrac{1}{4}$

$\Rightarrow$ Root must lie in $\left(-1, -\dfrac{1}{2}\right)$.

Similarly, $f\left(-\dfrac{3}{4}\right) = -\dfrac{1}{2}$

$\Rightarrow$ Root must lie in $\left(-\dfrac{3}{4}, -\dfrac{1}{2}\right)$.

131. $\because \alpha^2 - 6\alpha - 2 = 0 \Rightarrow \alpha^2 - 2 = 6\alpha$ ...(i)

and $\beta^2 - 6\beta - 2 = 0 \Rightarrow \beta^2 - 2 = 6\beta$ ...(ii)

$$\therefore \frac{a_{10} - 2a_8}{2a_9} = \frac{(\alpha^{10} - \beta^{10}) - 2(\alpha^8 - \beta^8)}{2(\alpha^9 - \beta^9)}$$

$$= \frac{\alpha^8(\alpha^2 - 2) - \beta^8(\beta^2 - 2)}{2(\alpha^9 - \beta^9)}$$

$$= \frac{\alpha^8 \cdot 6\alpha - \beta^8 \cdot 6\beta}{2(\alpha^9 - \beta^9)} \quad \text{[from Eqs. (i) and (ii)]}$$

$$= \frac{6(\alpha^9 - \beta^9)}{2(\alpha^9 - \beta^9)} = 3$$

132. Let α be the common root.

Then, $\alpha^2 + b\alpha - 1 = 0$ and $\alpha^2 + \alpha + b = 0$

$$\Rightarrow \begin{vmatrix} 1 & b \\ 1 & 1 \end{vmatrix} \times \begin{vmatrix} b & -1 \\ 1 & b \end{vmatrix} = \begin{vmatrix} -1 & 1 \\ b & 1 \end{vmatrix}^2$$

$\Rightarrow (1 - b)(b^2 + 1) = (-1 - b)^2$

$\Rightarrow b^3 + 3b = 0$

$\therefore b = 0, i\sqrt{3}, -i\sqrt{3}$, where $i = \sqrt{-1}$.

133. Let $f(x) = x^4 - 4x^3 + 12x^2 + x - 1$

$\therefore f'(x) = 4x^3 - 12x^2 + 24x + 1$

$\Rightarrow f''(x) = 12x^2 - 24x + 24$

$= 12(x^2 - 2x + 2)$

$= 12[(x-1)^2 + 1] > 0$

i.e. $f''(x)$ has no real roots.

Hence, $f(x)$ has maximum two distinct real roots, where $f(0) = -1$.

134. Given, $p(x) = f(x) - g(x)$

$\Rightarrow p(x) = (a - a_1)x^2 + (b - b_1)x + (c - c_1)$

It is clear that $p(x) = 0$ has both equal roots -1, then

$-1 - 1 = -\dfrac{(b - b_1)}{(a - a_1)}$

and $-1 \times -1 = \dfrac{c - c_1}{a - a_1}$

$\Rightarrow b - b_1 = 2(a - a_1)$ and $c - c_1 = (a - a_1)$ ...(i)

Also given, $p(-2) = 2$

$\Rightarrow 4(a - a_1) - 2(b - b_1) + (c - c_1) = 2$ ...(ii)

From Eqs. (i) and (ii), we get

$4(a - a_1) - 4(a - a_1) + (a - a_1) = 2$

$\therefore (a - a_1) = 2$ ...(iii)

$\Rightarrow b - b_1 = 4$ and $c - c_1 = 2$ [from Eq. (i)] ...(iv)

Now, $p(2) = 4(a - a_1) + 2(b - b_1) + (c - c_1)$

$= 8 + 8 + 2 = 18$ [from Eqs. (iii) and (iv)]

135. Let the quadratic equation be

$ax^2 + bx + c = 0$

Sachin made a mistake in writing down constant term.

$\therefore$ Sum of the roots is correct.

i.e. $\alpha + \beta = 7$

Rahul made a mistake in writing down coefficient of x.

$\therefore$ Product of the roots is correct.

i.e. $\alpha\beta = 6$

$\Rightarrow$ Correct quadratic equation is

$x^2 - (\alpha + \beta)x + \alpha\beta = 0$

$\Rightarrow x^2 - 7x + 6 = 0$

$\Rightarrow (x - 6)(x - 1) = 0 \Rightarrow x = 6, 1$

Hence, correct roots are 1 and 6.

136. Let $a + 1 = h^6$

$\therefore (h^2 - 1)x^2 + (h^3 - 1)x + (h - 1) = 0$

$$\Rightarrow \quad \left(\frac{h^2-1}{h-1}\right)x^2 + \left(\frac{h^3-1}{h-1}\right)x + 1 = 0$$

As $a \to 0$, then $h \to 1$

$$\lim_{h\to 1}\left(\frac{h^2-1}{h-1}\right)x^2 + \lim_{h\to 1}\left(\frac{h^3-1}{h-1}\right)x + 1 = 0$$

$$\Rightarrow \quad 2x^2 + 3x + 1 = 0$$

$$\Rightarrow \quad 2x^2 + 2x + x + 1 = 0$$

$$\Rightarrow \quad (2x+1)(x+1) = 0$$

$$\therefore \quad x = -1 \text{ and } x = -\frac{1}{2}$$

137. Let $e^{\sin x} = t$ ...(i)

Then, the given equation can be written as

$$t - \frac{1}{t} - 4 = 0 \Rightarrow t^2 - 4t - 1 = 0$$

$$\therefore \quad t = \frac{4 \pm \sqrt{(16+4)}}{2}$$

$$\Rightarrow \quad e^{\sin x} = (2+\sqrt{5}) \quad [\because e^{\sin x} > 0, \therefore \text{taking + ve sign}]$$

$$\Rightarrow \quad \sin x = \log_e(2+\sqrt{5}) \quad \text{...(ii)}$$

$$\because \quad (2+\sqrt{5}) > e \quad [\because e = 2.71828\ldots]$$

$$\Rightarrow \quad \log_e(2+\sqrt{5}) > 1 \quad \text{...(iii)}$$

From Eqs. (ii) and (iii), we get

$$\sin x > 1 \quad [\text{which is impossible}]$$

Hence, no real root exists.

138. Given equations are

$$ax^2 + bx + c = 0 \quad \text{...(i)}$$

and

$$x^2 + 2x + 3 = 0 \quad \text{...(ii)}$$

Clearly, roots of Eq. (ii) are imaginary, since Eqs. (i) and (ii) have a common root, therefore common root must be imaginary and hence both roots will be common. Therefore, Eqs. (i) and (ii) are identical.

$$\therefore \quad \frac{a}{1} = \frac{b}{2} = \frac{c}{3} \text{ or } a:b:c = 1:2:3$$

139. $\because x - [x] = \{x\}$ [fractional part of x]

For no integral solution, $\{x\} \neq 0$

$$\therefore \quad a \neq 0 \quad \text{...(i)}$$

The given equation can be written as

$$3\{x\}^2 - 2\{x\} - a^2 = 0$$

$$\Rightarrow \quad \{x\} = \frac{2 \pm \sqrt{(4+12a^2)}}{6} = \frac{1+\sqrt{(1+3a^2)}}{3} \quad [\because 0 < \{x\} < 1]$$

$$\Rightarrow \quad 0 < \frac{1+\sqrt{(1+3a^2)}}{3} < 1 \Rightarrow \sqrt{(1+3a^2)} < 2$$

$$\Rightarrow \quad a^2 < 1 \Rightarrow -1 < a < 1 \quad \text{...(ii)}$$

From Eqs. (i) and (ii), we get

$$a \in (-1, 0) \cup (0, 1)$$

140. $\because \dfrac{1}{\alpha} + \dfrac{1}{\beta} = 4 \Rightarrow \dfrac{\alpha+\beta}{\alpha\beta} = 4$

$$\Rightarrow \quad \frac{-\frac{q}{p}}{\frac{r}{p}} = 4$$

$$\Rightarrow \quad q = -4r \quad \text{... (i)}$$

Also, given p, q, r are in AP.

$$\therefore \quad 2q = p + r$$

$$\Rightarrow \quad p = -9r \quad [\text{from Eq. (i)}] \text{ ...(ii)}$$

Now, $|\alpha - \beta| = \dfrac{\sqrt{D}}{|a|}$ $\left[\because \text{for } ax^2+bx+c=0, \alpha-\beta = \dfrac{\sqrt{D}}{a}\right]$

$$= \frac{\sqrt{(q^2-4pr)}}{|p|}$$

$$= \frac{\sqrt{(16r^2+36r^2)}}{9|r|} = \frac{\sqrt{52}|r|}{9|r|} \quad [\text{from Eqs. (i) and (ii)}]$$

$$= \frac{2\sqrt{13}}{9}$$

141. $f(x) = x^5 - 5x$ and $g(x) = -a$

$$\therefore \quad f'(x) = 5x^4 - 5$$

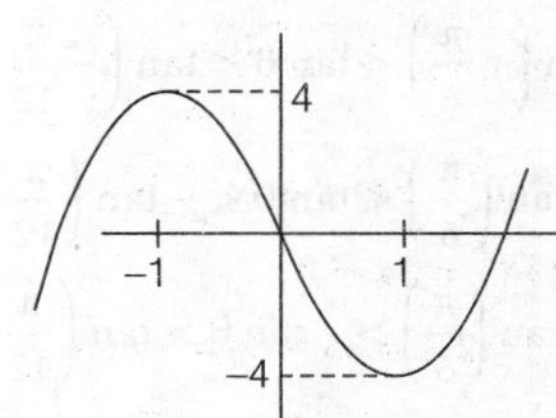

$$= 5(x^2+1)(x-1)(x+1)$$

Clearly, $f(x) = g(x)$ has one real root, if $a > 4$ and three real roots, if $|a| < 4$.

142. Since, $b = 0$ for $p(x) = ax^2 + bx + c$, as roots are pure imaginary.

$\Rightarrow x = \pm\sqrt{\dfrac{(-c \pm i\sqrt{c})}{a}}$, which are clearly neither pure real nor pure imaginary, as $c \neq 0$.

143. $\because \alpha x^2 - x + \alpha = 0$ has distinct real roots.

$$\therefore \quad D > 0$$

$$\Rightarrow \quad 1 - 4\alpha^2 > 0 \Rightarrow \alpha \in \left(-\frac{1}{2}, \frac{1}{2}\right) \quad \text{...(i)}$$

Also, $|x_1 - x_2| < 1 \Rightarrow |x_1 - x_2|^2 < 1$

$$\Rightarrow \quad \frac{D}{a^2} < 1 \Rightarrow \frac{1-4\alpha^2}{\alpha^2} < 1 \Rightarrow \alpha^2 > \frac{1}{5}$$

$$\Rightarrow \quad \alpha \in \left(-\infty, -\frac{1}{\sqrt{5}}\right) \cup \left(\frac{1}{\sqrt{5}}, \infty\right) \quad \text{...(ii)}$$

From Eqs. (i) and (ii), we get

$$S = \left(-\frac{1}{2}, -\frac{1}{\sqrt{5}}\right) \cup \left(\frac{1}{\sqrt{5}}, \frac{1}{2}\right)$$

144. $(x^2 - 5x + 5)^{x^2 + 4x - 60} = 1$

Case I

$x^2 - 5x + 5 = 1$ and $x^2 + 4x - 60$ can be any real number

$\Rightarrow \quad x = 1, 4$

Case II

$x^2 - 5x + 5 = -1$ and $x^2 + 4x - 60$ has to be an even number

$\Rightarrow \quad x = 2, 3$

For $x = 3$, $x^2 + 4x - 60$ is odd, $\therefore x \neq 3$

Hence, $\quad x = 2$

Case III $x^2 - 5x + 5$ can be any real number and

$$x^2 + 4x - 60 = 0$$

$\Rightarrow \quad x = -10, 6$

$\Rightarrow$ Sum of all values of $x = 1 + 4 + 2 - 10 + 6 = 3$

145. $\because x^2 - 2x \sec\theta\, a + 1 = 0 \Rightarrow x = \sec\theta \pm \tan\theta$

and $\quad -\frac{\pi}{6} < \theta < -\frac{\pi}{12}$

$\Rightarrow \quad \sec\left(-\frac{\pi}{6}\right) > \sec\theta > \sec\left(-\frac{\pi}{12}\right)$

or $\quad \sec\left(\frac{\pi}{6}\right) > \sec\theta > \sec\left(\frac{\pi}{12}\right)$

and $\quad \tan\left(-\frac{\pi}{6}\right) < \tan\theta < \tan\left(-\frac{\pi}{12}\right)$

$\Rightarrow \quad -\tan\left(\frac{\pi}{6}\right) < \tan\theta < -\tan\left(\frac{\pi}{12}\right)$

or $\quad \tan\left(\frac{\pi}{6}\right) > -\tan\theta > \tan\left(\frac{\pi}{12}\right)$

$\because \alpha_1, \beta_1$ are roots of $x^2 - 2x\sec\theta + 1 = 0$ and $\alpha_1 > \beta_1$

$\therefore \alpha_1 = \sec\theta - \tan\theta$ and $\beta_1 = \sec\theta + \tan\theta$

$\Rightarrow \alpha_2, \beta_2$ are roots of $x^2 + 2x\tan\theta - 1 = 0$

and $\quad \alpha_2 > \beta_2$

$\therefore \quad \alpha_2 = -\tan\theta + \sec\theta$

and $\quad \beta_2 = -\tan\theta - \sec\theta$

Hence, $\quad \alpha_1 + \beta_2 = -2\tan\theta$

146. $\because x(x+1) + (x+1)(x+2) + \dots + (x + \overline{n-1})(x+n) = 10n$

$\Rightarrow nx^2 + x(1 + 3 + 5 + \dots + (2n-1)) + (1.2 + 2.3 + \dots + (n-1).n) = 10n$

or $nx^2 + n^2x + \frac{1}{3}(n-1)n(n+1) = 10n$

or $\quad 3x^2 + 3nx + (n^2 - 1) = 30 \quad (\because n \neq 0)$

or $\quad 3x^2 + 3nx + (n^2 - 31) = 0$

$\because \quad |\alpha - \beta| = 1$

or $\quad (\alpha - \beta)^2 = 1$

or $\quad \frac{D}{a^2} = 1$

or $\quad D = a^2$

or $\quad 9n^2 - 12.(n^2 - 31) = 9$

or $\quad n^2 = 121$

$\therefore \quad n = 11$

CHAPTER

03

Sequences and Series

Learning Part

Session 1

- Sequence
- Series
- Progression

Session 2

- Arithmetic Progression

Session 3

- Geometric Sequence or Geometric Progression

Session 4

- Harmonic Sequence or Harmonic Progression

Session 5

- Mean

Session 6

- Arithmetico-Geometric Series (AGS)
- Sigma (Σ) Notation
- Natural Numbers

Session 7

- Application to Problems of Maxima and Minima

Practice Part

- JEE Type Examples
- Chapter Exercises

The word "Sequence" in Mathematics has same meaning as in ordinary English. A collection of objects listed in a sequence means it has identified first member, second member, third member and so on. The most common examples are depreciate values of certain commodity like car, machinery and amount deposits in the bank for a number of years.

Session 1

Sequence, Series, Progression

Sequence

A succession of numbers arranged in a definite order or arrangement according to some well-defined law is called a sequence.

Or

A sequence is a function of natural numbers (N) with codomain is the set of real numbers (R) [complex numbers (C)]. If range is subset of real numbers (complex numbers), it is called a real sequence (complex sequence).

Or

A mapping $f: N \to C$, then $f(n) = t_n, n \in N$ is called a sequence to be denoted it by $\{f(1), f(2), f(3), \dots\} = \{t_1, t_2, t_3, \dots\} = \{t_n\}$.

The nth term of a sequence is denoted by $T_n, t_n, a_n, a(n), u_n$, etc.

Remark

The sequence $a_1, a_2, a_3, \dots$ is generally written as $\{a_n\}$.

For example ,

(i) 1, 3, 5, 7, ... is a sequence, because each term (except first) is obtained by adding 2 to the previous term and $T_n = 2n - 1, n \in N$.

Or

If $T_1 = 1, T_{n+1} = T_{n+2}, n \geq 1$

(ii) 1, 2, 3, 5, 8, 13, ... is a sequence, because each term (except first two) is obtained by taking the sum of preceding two terms.

Or

If $T_1 = 1, T_2 = 2, T_{n+2} = T_n + T_{n+1}, n \geq 1$

(iii) 2, 3, 5, 7, 11, 13, 17, 19, ... is a sequence.

Here, we cannot express $T_n, n \in N$ by an algebraic formula.

Recursive Formula

A formula to determine the other terms of the sequence in terms of its preceding terms is known as recursive formula.

For example,

If $T_1 = 1$ and $T_{n+1} = 6T_n, n \in N$.

Then, $T_2 = 6T_1 = 6 \cdot 1 = 6$

$T_3 = 6T_2 = 6 \cdot 6 = 36$

$T_4 = 6T_3 = 6 \cdot 36 = 216 \dots$

Then, sequence is 1, 6, 36, 216,...

Types of Sequences

There are two types of sequences

1. Finite Sequence

A sequence is said to be finite sequence, if it has finite number of terms. A finite sequence is described by $a_1, a_2, a_3, \dots, a_n$ or $T_1, T_2, T_3, \dots, T_n$, where $n \in N$.

For example

(i) 3, 5, 7, 9, ..., 37

(ii) 2, 6, 18, 54, ..., 4374

2. Infinite Sequence

A sequence is said to be an infinite sequence, if it has infinite number of terms. An infinite sequence is described by $a_1, a_2, a_3, \dots$ or $T_1, T_2, T_3, \dots$

For example,

(i) $1, \frac{1}{3}, \frac{1}{9}, \frac{1}{27}, \dots$

(ii) $1, \frac{1}{2}, \frac{1}{4}, \frac{1}{8}, \frac{1}{16}, \dots$

Series

In a sequence, the sum of the directed terms is called a series.

For example, If 1, 4, 7, 10, 13, 16,... is a sequence, then its sum i.e., $1+4+7+10+13+16+\ldots$ is a series.

In general, if $T_1, T_2, T_3, \ldots, T_n, \ldots$ denote a sequence, then the symbolic expression $T_1+T_2+T_3+\ldots+T_n+\ldots$ is called a series associated with the given sequence.

Each member of the series is called its term.

In a series $T_1+T_2+T_3+\ldots+T_r+\ldots$, the sum of first n terms is denoted by S_n. Thus,

$$S_n = T_1+T_2+T_3+\ldots+T_n = \sum_{r=1}^{n} T_r = \sum T_n$$

If S_n denotes the sum of n terms of a sequence.

Then, $S_n - S_{n-1} = (T_1+T_2+T_3+\ldots+T_n) - (T_1+T_2+\ldots+T_{n-1}) = T_n$

Thus, $T_n = S_n - S_{n-1}$

Types of Series

There are two types of series

1. Finite Series

A series having finite number of terms is called a finite series.

For example,

(i) $3+5+7+9+\ldots+21$

(ii) $2+6+18+54+\ldots+4374$

2. Infinite Series

A series having an infinite number of terms is called an infinite series.

For example,

(i) $1+\frac{1}{3}+\frac{1}{9}+\frac{1}{27}+\ldots$

(ii) $1+\frac{1}{2}+\frac{1}{4}+\frac{1}{8}+\ldots$

Progression

If the terms of a sequence can be described by an explicit formula, then the sequence is called a progression.

Or

A sequence is said to be progression, if its terms increases (respectively decreases) numerically.

For example, The following sequences are progression :

(i) $1, 3, 5, 7, \ldots$ (ii) $\frac{1}{2}, \frac{1}{6}, \frac{1}{18}, \frac{1}{54}, \ldots$

(iii) $1, -\frac{1}{3}, \frac{1}{9}, -\frac{1}{27}, \ldots$ (iv) $1, 8, 27, 256, \ldots$

(v) $8, -4, 2, -1, \frac{1}{2}, \ldots$

The sequences (iii) and (v) are progressions, because

$$|1| > \left|-\frac{1}{3}\right| > \left|\frac{1}{9}\right| > \left|-\frac{1}{27}\right| > \ldots$$

i.e. $1 > \frac{1}{3} > \frac{1}{9} > \frac{1}{27} > \ldots$

and $|8| > |-4| > |2| > |-1| > \left|\frac{1}{2}\right| > \ldots$

i.e. $8 > 4 > 2 > 1 > \frac{1}{2} > \ldots$

Remark

All the definitions and formulae are valid for complex numbers in the theory of progressions but it should be assumed (if not otherwise stated) that the terms of the progressions are real numbers.

| Example 1. If $f: N \to R$, where $f(n) = a_n = \frac{n}{(2n+1)^2}$, write the sequence in ordered pair form.

Sol. Here, $a_n = \frac{n}{(2n+1)^2}$

On putting $n = 1, 2, 3, 4, \ldots$ successively, we get

$$a_1 = \frac{1}{(2\cdot1+1)^2} = \frac{1}{9}, \quad a_2 = \frac{2}{(2\cdot2+1)^2} = \frac{2}{25}$$

$$a_3 = \frac{3}{(2\cdot3+1)^2} = \frac{3}{49}, \quad a_4 = \frac{4}{(2\cdot4+1)^2} = \frac{4}{81}$$

$$\vdots \qquad \vdots \qquad \vdots$$

Hence, we obtain the sequence $\frac{1}{9}, \frac{2}{25}, \frac{3}{49}, \frac{4}{81}, \ldots$

Now, the sequence in ordered pair form is

$$\left\{\left(1, \frac{1}{9}\right), \left(2, \frac{2}{25}\right), \left(3, \frac{3}{49}\right), \left(4, \frac{4}{81}\right), \ldots\right\}$$

Example 2. The Fibonacci sequence is defined by $a_1 = 1 = a_2, a_n = a_{n-1} + a_{n-2}, n > 2$. Find $\frac{a_{n+1}}{a_n}$ for $n = 1, 2, 3, 4, 5$.

Sol. $\because \quad a_1 = 1 = a_2$

$\therefore \quad a_3 = a_2 + a_1 = 1 + 1 = 2,$

$a_4 = a_3 + a_2 = 2 + 1 = 3$

$a_5 = a_4 + a_3 = 3 + 2 = 5$

and $\quad a_6 = a_5 + a_4 = 5 + 3 = 8$

$\therefore \quad \frac{a_2}{a_1} = 1, \frac{a_3}{a_2} = \frac{2}{1} = 2, \frac{a_4}{a_3} = \frac{3}{2}, \frac{a_5}{a_4} = \frac{5}{3}$ and $\frac{a_6}{a_5} = \frac{8}{5}$

Example 3. If the sum of n terms of a series is $2n^2 + 5n$ for all values of n, find its 7th term.

Sol. Given, $\quad S_n = 2n^2 + 5n$

$\Rightarrow \quad S_{n-1} = 2(n-1)^2 + 5(n-1) = 2n^2 + n - 3$

$\therefore \quad T_n = S_n - S_{n-1} = (2n^2 + 5n) - (2n^2 + n - 3) = 4n + 3$

Hence, $\quad T_7 = 4 \times 7 + 3 = 31$

Example 4.

(i) Write $\sum_{r=1}^{n} (r^2 + 2)$ in expanded form.

(ii) Write the series $\frac{1}{3} + \frac{2}{4} + \frac{3}{5} + \frac{4}{6} + \ldots + \frac{n}{n+2}$ in sigma form.

Sol. (i) On putting $r = 1, 2, 3, 4, \ldots, n$ in $(r^2 + 2)$, we get $3, 6, 11, 18, \ldots, (n^2 + 2)$

Hence, $\sum_{r=1}^{n} (r^2 + 2) = 3 + 6 + 11 + 18 + \ldots + (n^2 + 2)$

(ii) The rth term of series $= \frac{r}{r+2}$.

Hence, the given series can be written as

$$\frac{1}{3} + \frac{2}{4} + \frac{3}{5} + \frac{4}{6} + \ldots + \frac{n}{n+2} = \sum_{r=1}^{n} \left(\frac{r}{r+2} \right)$$

Exercise for Session 1

1. First term of a sequence is 1 and the $(n + 1)$th term is obtained by adding $(n + 1)$ to the nth term for all natural numbers n, the 6th term of the sequence is
   (a) 7 (b) 13
   (c) 21 (d) 27

2. The first three terms of a sequence are 3, 3, 6 and each term after the second is the sum of two terms preceding it, the 8th term of the sequence is
   (a) 15 (b) 24
   (c) 39 (d) 63

3. If $a_n = \sin\left(\frac{n\pi}{6}\right)$, the value of $\sum_{n=1}^{6} a_n^2$ is
   (a) 2 (b) 3
   (c) 4 (d) 7

4. If for a sequence $\{a_n\}$, $S_n = 2n^2 + 9n$, where S_n is the sum of n terms, the value of a_{20} is
   (a) 65 (b) 75
   (c) 87 (d) 97

5. If $a_1 = 2, a_2 = 3 + a_1$ and $a_n = 2a_{n-1} + 5$ for $n > 1$, the value of $\sum_{r=2}^{5} a_r$ is
   (a) 130 (b) 160
   (c) 190 (d) 220

Session 2

Arithmetic Progression (AP)

Types of Progression

Progressions are various types but in this chapter we will studying only three special types of progressions which are following :

1. Arithmetic Progression (AP)
2. Geometric Progression (GP)
3. Harmonic Progression (HP)

Arithmetic Progression (AP)

An arithmetic progression is a sequence in which the difference between any term and its just preceding term (i.e., term before it) is constant throughout. This constant is called the common difference (abbreviated as CD) and is generally denoted by 'd'.

Or

An arithmetic progression is a sequence whose terms increase or decrease by a fixed number. This fixed number is called the common difference of the AP.

A finite or infinite sequence $\{t_1, t_2, t_3, \ldots, t_n\}$ or $\{t_1, t_2, t_3, \ldots\}$ is said to be an arithmetic progression (AP), if $t_k - t_{k-1} = d$, a constant independent of k, for $k = 2, 3, 4, \ldots, n$ or $k = 2, 3, 4, \ldots$ as the case may be :

The constant d is called the common difference of the AP.

i.e. $$d = t_2 - t_1 = t_3 - t_2 = \ldots = t_n - t_{n-1}$$

Remarks

1. If a be the first term and d be the common difference, then AP can be written as
   $$a, a + d, a + 2d, \ldots, a + (n-1)d, \ldots, \forall\, n \in N.$$
2. If we add the common difference to any term of AP, we get the next following term and if we subtract it from any term, we get the preceding term.
3. The common difference of an AP may be **positive**, **zero**, **negative** or **imaginary.**
4. **Constant AP** common difference of an AP is equal to zero.
5. **Increasing AP** common difference of an AP is greater than zero.
6. **Decreasing AP** common difference of an AP is less than zero.
7. **Imaginary AP** common difference of an AP is imaginary.

Algorithm to determine whether a sequence is an AP or not

***Step* I** Obtain t_n (the nth term of the sequence).

***Step* II** Replace n by $n-1$ in t_n to get t_{n-1}.

***Step* III** Calculate $t_n - t_{n-1}$.

If $t_n - t_{n-1}$ is independent of n, the given sequence is an AP otherwise it is not an AP.

Example 5.

(i) 1, 3, 5, 7, ... (ii) $\pi, \pi + e^{\pi}, \pi + 2e^{\pi}, \ldots$

(iii) $a, a - b, a - 2b, a - 3b, \ldots$

Sol. (i) Here, 2nd term − 1st term = 3rd term − 2nd term = ...

$\Rightarrow$ $3 - 1 = 5 - 3 = \ldots = 2$, which is a common difference.

(ii) Here, 2nd term − 1st term = 3rd term − 2nd term = ...

$\Rightarrow$ $(\pi + e^{\pi}) - \pi = (\pi + 2e^{\pi}) - (\pi + e^{\pi}) = \ldots$

$= e^{\pi}$, which is a common difference.

(iii) Here, 2nd term − 1st term = 3rd term − 2nd term = ...

$\Rightarrow (a - b) - a = (a - 2b) - (a - b) = \ldots$

$= -b$, which is a common difference.

Example 6. Show that the sequence $< t_n >$ defined by $t_n = 5n + 4$ is an AP, also find its common difference.

Sol. We have, $t_n = 5n + 4$

On replacing n by $(n-1)$, we get

$$t_{n-1} = 5(n-1) + 4$$

$$\Rightarrow \quad t_{n-1} = 5n - 1$$

$$\therefore \quad t_n - t_{n-1} = (5n + 4) - (5n - 1) = 5$$

Clearly, $t_n - t_{n-1}$ is independent of n and is equal to 5. So, the given sequence is an AP with common difference 5.

Example 7. Show that the sequence $< t_n >$ defined by $t_n = 3n^2 + 2$ is not an AP.

Sol. We have, $t_n = 3n^2 + 2$

On replacing n by $(n-1)$, we get

$$t_{n-1} = 3(n-1)^2 + 2$$

$$\Rightarrow \quad t_{n-1} = 3n^2 - 6n + 5$$

$$\therefore \quad t_n - t_{n-1} = (3n^2 + 2) - (3n^2 - 6n + 5)$$

$$= 6n - 3$$

Clearly, $t_n - t_{n-1}$ is not independent of n and therefore it is not constant. So, the given sequence is not an AP.

Remark

If the nth term of a sequence is an expression of first degree in n. For example, $t_n = An + B$, where A, B are constants, then that sequence will be in AP for $t_n - t_{n-1} = (An + B) - [A(n-1) + B]$ $= A[n-(n-1)] = A =$ constant = Common difference or coefficient of n in t_n Students are advised to consider the above point as a behaviour of standard result.

General Term of an AP

Let 'a' be the first term, 'd' be the common difference and 'l' be the last term of an AP having 'n' terms, where $n \in N$.

Then, AP can be written as $a, a+d, a+2d, \ldots, l-2d, l-d, l$

(i) nth Term of an AP from Beginning

1st term from beginning $= t_1 = a = a + (1-1)\,d$

2nd term from beginning $= t_2 = a + d = a + (2-1)\,d$

3rd term from beginning $= t_3 = a + 2d = a + (3-1)\,d$

$\vdots \quad \vdots \quad \vdots \quad \vdots$

n th term from beginning $= t_n = a + (n-1)\,d, \forall\, n \in N$

Hence, n th term of an AP from beginning

$$= t_n = a + (n-1)\,d = l \quad \text{[last term]}$$

(ii) nth Term of an AP from End

1st term from end $= t'_1 = l = l - (1-1)\,d$

2nd term from end $= t'_2 = l - d = l - (2-1)\,d$

3rd term from end $= t'_3 = l - 2d = l - (3-1)\,d$

$\vdots \quad \vdots \quad \vdots \quad \vdots$

nth term from end $= t'_n = l - (n-1)\,d, \forall\, n \in N$

Hence, n th term of an AP from end

$t'_n = l - (n-1)\,d = a \quad$ [first term]

Now, it is clear that

$t_n + t'_n = a + (n-1)\,d + l - (n-1)\,d = a + l$

or $\quad t_n + t'_n = a + l$

i.e. In a finite AP, the sum of the terms equidistant from the beginning and end is always same and is equal to the sum of first and last term.

Remark

1. nth term is also called the general term.
2. If last term of AP is t_n and common difference be d, then terms of AP from end are $t_n, t_n - d, t_n - 2d, \ldots$
3. If in a sequence, the terms an alternatively positive and negative, then it cannot be an AP.
4. Common difference of AP $= \dfrac{l-a}{n+1}$, where, a = first term of AP, l = last term of AP and n = number of terms of AP.
5. If t_n, t_{n+1}, t_{n+2} are three consecutive terms of an AP, then $2t_{n+1} = t_n + t_{n+2}$. In particular, if a, b and c are in AP, then $2b = a + c$.

Example 8. Find first negative term of the sequence

$$20, 19\frac{1}{4}, 18\frac{1}{2}, 17\frac{3}{4}, \ldots$$

Sol. The given sequence is an AP in which first term, $a = 20$ and common difference, $d = -\frac{3}{4}$. Let the nth term of the given AP be the first negative term. Then,

$$t_n < 0 \Rightarrow a + (n-1)\,d < 0$$

$$\Rightarrow \quad 20 + (n-1)\left(-\frac{3}{4}\right) < 0$$

$$\Rightarrow \quad 80 - 3n + 3 < 0$$

$$\Rightarrow \quad n > \frac{83}{3} \text{ or } n > 27\frac{2}{3}$$

$$\Rightarrow \quad n = 28$$

Thus, 28th term of the given sequence is the first negative term.

Example 9. If the mth term of an AP is $\frac{1}{n}$ and the nth term is $\frac{1}{m}$, then find mnth term of an AP.

Sol. If A and B are constants, then rth term of AP is

$$t_r = Ar + B$$

Given, $\quad t_m = \frac{1}{n} \Rightarrow Am + B = \frac{1}{n} \quad \ldots\text{(i)}$

and $\quad t_n = \frac{1}{m} \Rightarrow An + B = \frac{1}{m} \quad \ldots\text{(ii)}$

From Eqs. (i) and (ii), we get $A = \frac{1}{mn}$ and $B = 0$

mn th term $= t_{mn} = Amn + B = \frac{1}{mn} \cdot mn + 0 = 1$

Hence, mn th term of the given AP is 1.

Example 10. If $|x-1|$, 3 and $|x-3|$ are first three terms of an increasing AP, then find the 6th term of on AP.

Sol. *Case* I For $x < 1$,

$$|x-1| = -(x-1)$$

and $\quad |x-3| = -(x-3)$

$\therefore 1 - x, 3$ and $3 - x$ are in AP.

$$\Rightarrow \quad 6 = 1 - x + 3 - x$$

$$\Rightarrow \quad x = -1$$

Then, first three terms are 2, 3, 4, which is an increasing AP.

$\therefore$ 6th term is 7. $\quad [\because d = 1]$

Case II For $1 < x < 3$,

$$|x-1| = x - 1$$

and $\quad |x-3| = -(x-3) = 3 - x$

$\therefore x - 1, 3$ and $3 - x$ are in AP.

$$\Rightarrow \quad 6 = x - 1 + 3 - x$$

$$\Rightarrow \quad 6 = 2 \quad \text{[impossible]}$$

***Case* III** For $x > 3$, $|x-1| = x-1$ and $|x-3| = x-3$

$\therefore$ $x-1, 3$ and $x-3$ are in AP.

$\Rightarrow$ $6 = x - 1 + x - 3 \Rightarrow x = 5$

Then, first three terms are 4, 3, 2, which is a decreasing AP.

Example 11. In the sequence 1, 2, 2, 3, 3, 3, 4, 4, 4, 4, ..., where n consecutive terms have the value n, find the 150th term of the sequence.

Sol. Let the 150th term $= n$

Then, $1 + 2 + 3 + \ldots + (n-1) < 150 < 1 + 2 + 3 + \ldots + n$

$\Rightarrow$ $\frac{(n-1)n}{2} < 150 < \frac{n(n+1)}{2}$

$\Rightarrow$ $n(n-1) < 300 < n(n+1)$

Taking first two members

$n(n-1) < 300 \Rightarrow n^2 - n - 300 < 0$

$\Rightarrow$ $\left(n - \frac{1}{2}\right)^2 < 300 + \frac{1}{4}$

$\Rightarrow$ $0 < n < \frac{1}{2} + \frac{\sqrt{1201}}{2}$

$\Rightarrow$ $0 < n < 17.8$ ...(i)

and taking last two members,

$n(n+1) > 300$

$\Rightarrow$ $\left(n + \frac{1}{2}\right)^2 > 300 + \frac{1}{4}$

$\therefore$ $n > -\frac{1}{2} + \frac{\sqrt{1201}}{2}$

$\Rightarrow$ $n > 16.8$ ...(ii)

From Eqs. (i) and (ii), we get

$16.8 < n < 17.8$

$\Rightarrow$ $n = 17$

Example 12. If a_1, a_2, a_3, a_4 and a_5 are in AP with common difference $\neq 0$, find the value of $\sum_{i=1}^{5} a_i$ when $a_3 = 2$.

Sol. $\because$ a_1, a_2, a_3, a_4 and a_5 are in AP, we have

$a_1 + a_5 = a_2 + a_4 = a_3 + a_3$ $[\because t_n + t'_n = a + l]$

$a_1 + a_5 = a_2 + a_4 = 4$ $[\because a_3 = 2]$

$a_1 + a_2 + a_3 + a_4 + a_5 = 4 + 2 + 4 = 10$

$\Rightarrow$ $\sum_{i=1}^{5} a_i = 10$

Sum of a Stated Number of Terms of an Arithmetic Series

More than 200 yr ago, a class of German School Children was asked to find the sum of all integers from 1 to 100 inclusive. One boy in the class, an eight year old named **Carl Fredrick Gauss** (1777-1855) who later established his reputation as one of the greatest Mathematicians announced the answer almost at once. The teacher overawed at this asked Gauss to explain how he got this answer. Gauss explained that he had added these numbers in pairs as follows

$(1+100), (2+99), (3+98), \ldots$

There are $\frac{100}{2} = 50$ pairs. The answer can be obtained by multiplying 101 by 50 to get 5050.

Sum of *n* Terms of an AP

Let 'a' be the first term, 'd' be the common difference, 'l' be the last term of an AP having n terms and S_n be the sum of n terms, then

$S_n = a + (a+d) + (a+2d) + \ldots + (l-2d) + (l-d) + l$ ...(i)

Reversing the right hand terms

$S_n = l + (l-d) + (l-2d) + \ldots + (a+2d) + (a+d) + a$ ...(ii)

On adding Eqs. (i) and (ii), we get

$2S_n = (a+l) + (a+l) + (a+l) + \ldots + (a+l) + (a+l) + (a+l)$

$= (a+l) + (a+l) + \ldots$ upto n terms $= n(a+l)$

$\therefore$ $\boldsymbol{S_n = \frac{n}{2}(a+l)}$ ...(iii)

Now, if we substitute the value of l *viz.*, $l = a + (n-1)d$, in this formula, we get

$S_n = \frac{n}{2}[a + a + (n-1)d] = \frac{n}{2}[2a + (n-1)d]$

$\therefore$ $S_n = \frac{n}{2}[2a + (n-1)d]$

If we substitute the value of a *viz.*,

$l = a + (n-1)d$

or $a = l - (n-1)d$ in Eq. (iii), then

$S_n = \frac{n}{2}[2l - (n-1)d]$

If we substitute the value of $a + l$ *viz.*,

$t_n + t'_n = a + l$ in Eq. (iii), then

$\boldsymbol{S_n = \frac{n}{2}(t_n + t'_n)}$

***Corollary* I** Sum of first n natural numbers

i.e. $1 + 2 + 3 + 4 + \ldots + n$

Here, $a = 1$ and $d = 1$

$\therefore$ $S = \frac{n}{2}[2 \cdot 1 + (n-1) \cdot 1]$

$= \frac{n(n+1)}{2}$

***Corollary* II** Sum of first n odd natural numbers

i.e., $1+3+5+\dots$

Here, $a=1$

and $d=2$

$\therefore \quad S=\frac{n}{2}[2\cdot 1+(n-1)\cdot 2]=n^2$

***Corollary* III** If sum of first n terms is S_n, then sum of next m terms is $S_{m+n}-S_n$.

Important Results with Proof

1. If S_n, t_n and d are sum of n terms, nth term and common difference of an AP respectively, then

$$d=t_n-t_{n-1} \quad [n\ge 2]$$
$$t_n=S_n-S_{n-1} \quad [n\ge 2]$$
$$d=S_n-2S_{n-1}+S_{n-2} \quad [n\ge 3]$$

Proof

$\because \quad S_n=t_1+t_2+t_3+\dots+t_{n-1}+t_n$

$\Rightarrow \quad S_n=S_{n-1}+t_n$

$\therefore \quad t_n=S_n-S_{n-1}$

but $\quad d=t_n-t_{n-1}$

$\quad =(S_n-S_{n-1})-(S_{n-1}-S_{n-2})$

$\therefore \quad d=S_n-2S_{n-1}+S_{n-2}$

2. A sequence is an AP if and only if the sum of its n terms is of the form An^2+Bn, where A and B are constants independent of n.

In this case, the nth term and common difference of the AP are $A(2n-1)+B$ and $2A$, respectively.

Proof As $S_n=An^2+Bn$

$\therefore \quad S_{n-1}=A(n-1)^2+B(n-1)$

$\therefore \quad t_n=S_n-S_{n-1}$

$\quad =(An^2+Bn)-[A(n-1)^2+B(n-1)]$

$\quad =A[n^2-(n-1)^2]+B$

$\quad t_n=A(2n-1)+B$

$\Rightarrow \quad t_{n-1}=A[2(n-1)-1]+B$

$\quad =A(2n-3)+B$

Now, $t_n-t_{n-1}=[A(2n-1)+B]-[A(2n-3)+B]$

$\quad =2A$ [a constant]

Hence, the sequence is an AP.

Conversely, consider an AP with first term a and common difference d.

Sum of first n terms $=\frac{n}{2}[2a+(n-1)d]$

$$=\frac{dn^2}{2}+\left(a-\frac{d}{2}\right)n=An^2+Bn,$$

where, $A=\frac{d}{2}, B=a-\frac{d}{2}$

Hence, $S_n=An^2+Bn$, where A and B are constants independent of n.

Hence, the converse is true.

Corollary $\because \quad S_n=An^2+Bn$

$\therefore \quad t_n=A(2n-1)+B$

$t_n=A$ (replacing n^2 by $2n-1$) + coefficient of n

and $\quad d=2A$

i.e. $\quad d=2$ [coefficient of n^2]

	S_n	t_n	d
1.	$5n^2+3n$	$5(2n-1)+3=10n-2$	10
2.	$-7n^2+2n$	$-7(2n-1)+2$ $=-14n+9$	-14
3.	$-9n^2-4n$	$9(2n-1)-4$ $=-18n+5$	-18
4.	$4n^2-n$	$4(2n-1)-1=8n-5$	8

3. If $S_n=an^2+bn+c$, where S_n denotes the sum of n terms of a series, then whole series is not an AP. It is AP from the second term onwards.

Proof As $S_n=an^2+bn+c$ for $n\ge 1$, we get

$$S_{n-1}=a(n-1)^2+b(n-1)+c \text{ for } n\ge 2$$

Now, $\quad t_n=S_n-S_{n-1}$

$\Rightarrow \quad t_n=a(2n-1)+b, n\ge 2$

$\therefore \quad t_{n-1}=a[2(n-1)-1]+b, n\ge 3$

$\Rightarrow \quad t_{n-1}=a(2n-3)+b, n\ge 3$

$\therefore \quad t_n-t_{n-1}=2a=$ constant, $n\ge 3$

$\therefore \quad t_3-t_2=t_4-t_3=t_5-t_4=\dots$

But $\quad t_2-t_1=(S_2-S_1)-S_1=S_2-2S_1$

$\quad =(4a+2b+c)-2(a+b+c)$

$\quad =(2a-c) \quad [\because S_1=t_1]$

$\therefore \quad t_2-t_1\ne t_3-t_2$

Hence, the whole series is not an AP. It is AP from the second term onwards.

Ratio of Sums is Given

1. If ratio of the sums of m and n terms of an AP is given by

$$\frac{S_m}{S_n} = \frac{Am^2 + Bm}{An^2 + Bn}$$

where A, B are constants and $A \neq 0$.

$$\therefore \quad S_m = (Am^2 + Bm)\,k,$$
$$S_n = (An^2 + Bn)\,k$$
$$\Rightarrow \quad t_m = S_m - S_{m-1} = [A(2m-1) + B]k$$
$$t_n = S_n - S_{n-1} = [A(2n-1) + B]k$$
$$\therefore \quad \frac{t_m}{t_n} = \frac{A(2m-1)+B}{A(2n-1)+B}$$

| Example 13. The ratio of sums of m and n terms of an AP is $m^2 : n^2$. The ratio of the mth and nth terms is

(a) $(2m+1):(2n-1)$ (b) $m:n$
(c) $(2m-1):(2n-1)$ (d) None of these

Sol. (c) Here, $\dfrac{S_m}{S_n} = \dfrac{m^2}{n^2}$ $\quad [\because A = 1, B = 0]$

$$\therefore \quad \frac{t_m}{t_n} = \frac{(2m-1)}{(2n-1)}$$
$$\Rightarrow \quad t_m : t_n = (2m-1):(2n-1)$$

2. If ratio of the sums of n terms of two AP's is given by

$$\frac{S_n}{S'_n} = \frac{An + B}{Cn + D}$$

where, A, B, C, D are constants and $A, C \neq 0$

$$\therefore \quad S_n = n(An + B)\,k,\ S'_n = n(Cn + D)\,k$$
$$\Rightarrow \quad t_n = [A(2n-1) + B]k,\ t'_n = [C(2n-1) + D]k$$
$$\Rightarrow \quad d = t_n - t_{n-1} = 2A,\ d' = t'_n - t'_{n-1} = 2C$$
$$\therefore \quad \frac{t_n}{t'_n} = \frac{A(2n-1)+B}{C(2n-1)+D} \text{ and } \frac{d}{d'} = \frac{A}{C}$$

Note If $A = 0, C = 0$

Then, $\dfrac{S_n}{S'_n} = \dfrac{B}{D} \Rightarrow \dfrac{t_n}{t'_n} = \dfrac{B}{D}$ and $\dfrac{d}{d'} = \dfrac{0}{0} =$ not defined

Remark

If $\dfrac{t_n}{t'_n} = \dfrac{an + b}{cn + d}$

where, a, b, c, d are constants and $a, c \neq 0$, then

$$\frac{S_n}{S'_n} = \frac{a\left(\frac{n+1}{2}\right) + b}{c\left(\frac{n+1}{2}\right) + d}$$

| Example 14. The sums of n terms of two arithmetic progressions are in the ratio $(7n+1):(4n+17)$. Find the ratio of their nth terms and also common differences.

Sol. Given, $S_n : S'_n = (7n + 1):(4n + 17)$

Here, $A = 7, B = 1, C = 4$ and $D = 17$

$$\therefore \quad \frac{t_n}{t'_n} = \frac{7(2n-1)+1}{4(2n-1)+17} = \frac{14n - 6}{8n + 13}$$

and $\dfrac{d}{d'} = \dfrac{A}{C} = \dfrac{7}{4}$

Hence, $t_n : t'_n = (14n - 6):(8n + 13)$ and $d : d' = 7:4$

| Example 15. The sums of n terms of two AP's are in the ratio $(3n-13):(5n+21)$. Find the ratio of their 24th terms.

Sol. Given, $S_n : S'_n = (3n - 13):(5n + 21)$

Here, $A = 3, B = -13, C = 5$ and $D = 21$

$$\therefore \quad \frac{t_{24}}{t'_{24}} = \frac{3(2\times 24 - 1) - 13}{5(2\times 24 - 1) + 21} = \frac{128}{256} = \frac{1}{2}$$
$$\therefore \quad t_{24} : t'_{24} = 1:2$$

| Example 16. How many terms of the series $20 + 19\frac{1}{3} + 18\frac{2}{3} + \dots$ must be taken to make 300? Explain the double answer.

Sol. Here, given series is an AP with first term $a = 20$ and the common difference, $d = -\dfrac{2}{3}$.

Let the sum of n terms of the series be 300.

Then, $S_n = \dfrac{n}{2}\{2a + (n-1)\,d\}$

$$\Rightarrow \quad 300 = \frac{n}{2}\left\{2\times 20 + (n-1)\left(-\frac{2}{3}\right)\right\}$$
$$\Rightarrow \quad 300 = \frac{n}{3}\{60 - n + 1\}$$
$$\Rightarrow \quad n^2 - 61n + 900 = 0$$
$$\Rightarrow \quad (n-25)(n-36) = 0$$
$$\Rightarrow \quad n = 25 \text{ or } n = 36$$

$\therefore$ Sum of 25 terms = Sum of 36 terms = 300

Explanation of double answer

Here, the common difference is negative, therefore terms go on diminishing and $t_{31} = 20 + (31-1)\left(\dfrac{-2}{3}\right) = 0$ i.e., 31st term becomes zero. All terms after 31st term are negative. These negative terms $(t_{32}, t_{33}, t_{34}, t_{35}, t_{36})$ when added to positive terms $(t_{26}, t_{27}, t_{28}, t_{29}, t_{30})$, they cancel out each other i.e., sum of terms from 26th to 36th terms is zero. Hence, the sum of 25 terms as well as that of 36 terms is 300.

Example 17. Find the arithmetic progression consisting of 10 terms, if the sum of the terms occupying the even places is equal to 15 and the sum of those occupying the odd places is equal to $12\frac{1}{2}$.

Sol. Let the successive terms of an AP be $t_1, t_2, t_3, \ldots, t_9, t_{10}$.

By hypothesis,

$$t_2 + t_4 + t_6 + t_8 + t_{10} = 15$$

$$\Rightarrow \frac{5}{2}(t_2 + t_{10}) = 15$$

$$\Rightarrow t_2 + t_{10} = 6$$

$$\Rightarrow (a + d) + (a + 9d) = 6$$

$$\Rightarrow 2a + 10d = 6 \quad \ldots(i)$$

and $$t_1 + t_3 + t_5 + t_7 + t_9 = 12\frac{1}{2}$$

$$\Rightarrow \frac{5}{2}(t_1 + t_9) = \frac{25}{2}$$

$$\Rightarrow t_1 + t_9 = 5$$

$$\Rightarrow a + a + 8d = 5$$

$$\Rightarrow 2a + 8d = 5 \quad \ldots(ii)$$

From Eqs. (i) and (ii), we get $d = \frac{1}{2}$ and $a = \frac{1}{2}$

Hence, the AP is $\frac{1}{2}, 1, 1\frac{1}{2}, 2, 2\frac{1}{2}, \ldots$

Example 18. If N, the set of natural numbers is partitioned into groups $S_1 = \{1\}, S_2 = \{2, 3\}, S_3 = \{4, 5, 6\}, \ldots$, find the sum of the numbers in S_{50}.

Sol. The number of terms in the groups are 1, 2, 3, ...

$\because$ The number of terms in the 50th group = 50

$\therefore$ The last term of 1st group = 1

The last term of 2nd group = 3 = 1 + 2

The last term of 3rd group = 6 = 1 + 2 + 3

$\vdots$

The last term of 49th group = 1 + 2 + 3 + ... + 49

$\therefore$ First term of 50th group = 1 + (1 + 2 + 3 + ... + 49)

$$= 1 + \frac{49}{2}(1 + 49) = 1226$$

$$\therefore S_{50} = \frac{50}{2}\{2 \times 1226 + (50 - 1) \times 1\}$$

$$= 25 \times 2501 = 62525$$

Example 19. Find the sum of first 24 terms of on AP $t_1, t_2, t_3, \ldots$, if it is known that

$$t_1 + t_5 + t_{10} + t_{15} + t_{20} + t_{24} = 225.$$

Sol. We know that, in an AP the sums of the terms equidistant from the beginning and end is always same and is equal to the sum of first and last term.

Then, $t_1 + t_{24} = t_5 + t_{20} = t_{10} + t_{15}$

but given

$$t_1 + t_5 + t_{10} + t_{15} + t_{20} + t_{24} = 225$$

$$\Rightarrow (t_1 + t_{24}) + (t_5 + t_{20}) + (t_{10} + t_{15}) = 225$$

$$\Rightarrow 3(t_1 + t_{24}) = 225$$

$$\Rightarrow t_1 + t_{24} = 75$$

$$\therefore S_{24} = \frac{24}{2}(t_1 + t_{24}) = 12 \times 75 = 900$$

Example 20. If $(1 + 3 + 5 + \ldots + p) + (1 + 3 + 5 + \ldots + q) = (1 + 3 + 5 + \ldots + r)$, where each set of parentheses contains the sum of consecutive odd integers as shown, then find the smallest possible value of $p + q + r$ (where, $p > 6$).

Sol. We know that, $1 + 3 + 5 + \ldots + (2n - 1) = n^2$

Thus, the given equation can be written as

$$\left(\frac{p+1}{2}\right)^2 + \left(\frac{q+1}{2}\right)^2 = \left(\frac{r+1}{2}\right)^2$$

$$\Rightarrow (p + 1)^2 + (q + 1)^2 = (r + 1)^2$$

Therefore, $(p + 1, q + 1, r + 1)$ form a Pythagorean triplet as $p > 6 \Rightarrow p + 1 > 7$

The first Pythagorean triplet containing a number > 7 is (6, 8, 10).

$$\Rightarrow p + 1 = 8, q + 1 = 6, r + 1 = 10$$

$$\Rightarrow p + q + r = 21$$

Properties of Arithmetic Progression

1. If $a_1, a_2, a_3, \ldots$ are in AP with common difference d, then $a_1 \pm k, a_2 \pm k, a_3 \pm k, \ldots$ are also in AP with common difference d.
2. If $a_1, a_2, a_3, \ldots$ are in AP with common difference d, then $a_1k, a_2k, a_3k, \ldots$ and $\frac{a_1}{k}, \frac{a_2}{k}, \frac{a_3}{k}, \ldots$ are also in AP $(k \neq 0)$ with common differences kd and $\frac{d}{k}$, respectively.
3. If $a_1, a_2, a_3, \ldots$ and $b_1, b_2, b_3, \ldots$ are two AP's with common differences d_1 and d_2, respectively. Then, $a_1 \pm b_1, a_2 \pm b_2, a_3 \pm b_3, \ldots$ are also in AP with common difference $(d_1 \pm d_2)$.
4. If $a_1, a_2, a_3, \ldots$ and $b_1, b_2, b_3, \ldots$ are two AP's with common differences d_1 and d_2 respectively, then $a_1b_1, a_2b_2, a_3b_3, \ldots$ and $\frac{a_1}{b_1}, \frac{a_2}{b_2}, \frac{a_3}{b_3}, \ldots$ are not in AP.
5. If $a_1, a_2, a_3, \ldots, a_n$ are in AP, then

$$a_r = \frac{a_{r-k} + a_{r+k}}{2}, \forall k, 0 \leq k \leq n - r$$

6. If three numbers in AP whose sum is given are to be taken as $\alpha-\beta, \alpha, \alpha+\beta$ and if five numbers in AP whose sum is given, are to be taken as $\alpha-2\beta, \alpha-\beta, \alpha, \alpha+\beta, \alpha+2\beta$, etc.

In general, If $(2r+1)$ numbers in AP whose sum is given, are to be taken as $(r \in N)$.
$\alpha-r\beta, \alpha-(r-1)\beta, \ldots, \alpha-\beta, \alpha, \alpha+\beta, \ldots, \alpha+(r-1)\beta, \alpha+r\beta$

Remark

1. Sum of three numbers $= 3\alpha$
   Sum of five numbers $= 5\alpha$
   $\vdots \quad \vdots \quad \vdots \quad \vdots \quad \vdots$
   Sum of $(2r+1)$ numbers $= (2r+1)\,\alpha$
2. From given conditions, find two equations in α and β and then solve them. Now, the numbers in AP can be obtained.

7. If four numbers in AP whose sum is given, are to be taken as
$\alpha-3\beta, \alpha-\beta, \alpha+\beta, \alpha+3\beta$ and if six numbers in AP, whose sum is given are to be taken as $\alpha-5\beta, \alpha-3\beta, \alpha-\beta, \alpha+\beta, \alpha+3\beta, \alpha+5\beta$, etc.

In general If $2r$ numbers in AP whose sum is given, are to be taken as $(r \in N)$.
$\alpha-(2r-1)\beta, \alpha-(2r-3)\beta, \ldots, \alpha-3\beta, \alpha-\beta, \alpha+\beta, \alpha+3\beta, \ldots, \alpha+(2r-3)\beta, \alpha+(2r-1)\beta$

Remark

1. Sum of four numbers $= 4\alpha$
   Sum of six numbers $= 6\alpha$
   $\vdots \quad \vdots \quad \vdots \quad \vdots \quad \vdots$
   Sum of $2r$ numbers $= 2r\alpha$
2. From given conditions, find two conditions in α and β and then solve them. Now, the numbers in AP can be obtained.

Example 21. If $S_1, S_2, S_3, \ldots, S_p$ are the sums of n terms of p AP's whose first terms are $1, 2, 3, \ldots, p$ and common differences are $1, 2, 3, \ldots, (2p-1)$ respectively, show that $\quad S_1+S_2+S_3+\ldots+S_p=\frac{1}{2}np(np+1)$.

Sol. $\because 1, 2, 3, \ldots, p$ are in AP.

Then, $2\cdot1, 2\cdot2, 2\cdot3, \ldots, 2p$ are also in AP. ...(i)
[multiplying 2 to each term]

and $1, 3, 5, \ldots, (2p-1)$ are in AP.

Then, $(n-1)\cdot1, (n-1)\cdot3, (n-1)\cdot5, \ldots, (n-1)(2p-1)$ are also in AP. ...(ii)
[multiplying $(n-1)$ to each term]

From Eqs. (i) and (ii), we get
$2\cdot1+(n-1)\cdot1, 2\cdot2+(n-1)\cdot3, 2\cdot3+(n-1)\cdot5, \ldots, 2p+(n-1)(2p-1)$ are also in AP. ...(iii)
[adding corresponding terms of Eqs. (i) and (ii)]

From Eq. (iii),

$\frac{n}{2}\{2\cdot1+(n-1)\cdot1\}, \frac{n}{2}\{2\cdot2+(n-1)\cdot3\}, \frac{n}{2}\{2\cdot3+(n-1)\cdot5\}, \ldots, \frac{n}{2}\{2p+(n-1)(2p-1)\}$ are also in AP
[multiplying $\frac{n}{2}$ to each term]

i.e. $S_1, S_2, S_3, \ldots, S_p$ are in AP.

$$\therefore \; S_1+S_2+S_3+\ldots+S_p=\frac{p}{2}\{S_1+S_p\}$$
$$=\frac{p}{2}\left\{\frac{n}{2}[2\cdot1+(n-1)\cdot1]+\frac{n}{2}[2\cdot p+(n-1)(2p-1)]\right\}$$
$$=\frac{np}{4}\{2+(n-1)+2p+(n-1)(2p-1)\}$$
$$=\frac{np}{4}(2np+2)=\frac{1}{2}np(np+1)$$

Aliter

Here, $S_1=1+2+3+\ldots$ upto n terms $=\frac{n(n+1)}{2}$

$S_2=2+5+8+\ldots$ upto n terms $=\frac{n}{2}[2\cdot2+(n-1)3]$
$=\frac{n(3n+1)}{2}$

Similarly, $S_3=3+8+13+\ldots$ upto n terms $=\frac{n(5n+1)}{2}$, etc.

Now, $S_1+S_2+S_3+\ldots+S_p$
$$=\frac{n(n+1)}{2}+\frac{n(3n+1)}{2}+\frac{n(5n+1)}{2}+\ldots \text{ upto } p \text{ terms}$$
$$=\frac{n}{2}[(n+3n+5n+\ldots \text{ upto } p \text{ terms})+(1+1+1+\ldots \text{ upto } p \text{ terms})]$$
$$=\frac{n}{2}\left[\frac{p}{2}(2n+(p-1)2n)+p\right]$$
$$=\frac{np}{2}[n+n(p-1)+1]=\frac{1}{2}np(np+1)$$

Example 22. Let α and β be roots of the equation $x^2-2x+A=0$ and let γ and δ be the roots of the equation $x^2-18x+B=0$. If $\alpha<\beta<\gamma<\delta$ are in arithmetic progression, then find the values of A and B.

Sol. $\because \alpha, \beta, \gamma, \delta$ are in AP.

Let $\quad \beta=\alpha+d, \gamma=\alpha+2d, \delta=\alpha+3d, d>0$
[here, sum of $\alpha, \beta, \gamma, \delta$ is not given]

Given, $\quad \alpha+\beta=2, \alpha\beta=A$

$\Rightarrow \quad 2\alpha+d=2, \alpha\beta=A$ ...(i)

and $\quad \gamma+\delta=18, \gamma\delta=B$

$\Rightarrow \quad 2\alpha+5d=18, \gamma\delta=B$ ...(ii)

From Eqs. (i) and (ii), we get

$$d = 4, \alpha = -1$$

$\therefore \quad \beta = 3, \gamma = 7, \delta = 11$

$\Rightarrow \quad A = \alpha\beta = (-1)(3) = -3$

and $\quad B = \gamma\delta = (7)(11) = 77$

Example 23. The digits of a positive integer having three digits are in AP and their sum is 15. The number obtained by reversing the digits is 594 less than the original number. Find the number.

Sol. Let the digit in the unit's place be $a - d$, digit in the ten's place be a and the digit in the hundred's place be $a + d$.

Sum of digits $= a - d + a + a + d = 15$ [given]

$\Rightarrow \quad 3a = 15$

$\therefore \quad a = 5 \quad$ ...(i)

$\therefore$ Original number $= (a - d) + 10a + 100(a + d)$

$= 111a + 99d = 555 + 99d$

and number formed by reversing the digits

$= (a + d) + 10a + 100(a - d)$

$= 111a - 99d = 555 - 99d$

Given, $(555 + 99d) - (555 - 99d) = 594 \Rightarrow 198d = 594$

$\therefore \quad d = 3$

Hence, original number $= 555 + 99 \times 3 = 852$

Example 24. If three positive real numbers are in AP such that $abc = 4$, then find the minimum value of b.

Sol. $\because a, b, c$ are in AP.

Let $\quad a = A - D, b = A, c = A + D$

Then, $\quad a = b - D, c = b + D$

Now, $\quad abc = 4$

$$(b - D)\,b\,(b + D) = 4$$

$\Rightarrow \quad b(b^2 - D^2) = 4$

$\Rightarrow \quad b^2 - D^2 < b^2$

$\Rightarrow \quad b(b^2 - D^2) < b^3 \Rightarrow 4 < b^3$

$\therefore \quad b > (4)^{1/3} \text{ or } b > (2)^{2/3}$

Hence, the minimum value of b is $(2)^{2/3}$

Example 25. If a, b, c, d are distinct integers form an increasing AP such that $d = a^2 + b^2 + c^2$, then find the value of $a + b + c + d$.

Sol. Here, sum of numbers i.e., $a + b + c + d$ is not given.

Let $\quad b = a + D, c = a + 2D, d = a + 3D, \forall D \in N$

According to hypothesis,

$$a + 3D = a^2 + (a + D)^2 + (a + 2D)^2$$

$\Rightarrow \quad 5D^2 + 3(2a - 1)D + 3a^2 - a = 0 \quad$ ...(i)

$\therefore \quad D = \dfrac{-3(2a-1) \pm \sqrt{9(2a-1)^2 - 20(3a^2 - a)}}{10}$

$= \dfrac{-3(2a-1) \pm \sqrt{(-24a^2 - 16a + 9)}}{10}$

Now, $\quad -24a^2 - 16a + 9 \geq 0$

$\Rightarrow \quad 24a^2 + 16a - 9 \leq 0$

$\Rightarrow \quad -\dfrac{1}{3} - \dfrac{\sqrt{70}}{3} \leq a \leq -\dfrac{1}{3} + \dfrac{\sqrt{70}}{12}$

$\Rightarrow \quad a = -1, 0 \quad [\because a \in I]$

When $a = 0$ from Eq. (i), $D = 0, \dfrac{3}{5}$ (not possible $\because D \in N$) and for $a = -1$

From Eq. (i), $\quad D = 1, \dfrac{4}{5}$

$\therefore \quad D = 1 \quad [\because D \in N]$

$\therefore \quad a = -1, b = 0, c = 1, d = 2$

Then, $\quad a + b + c + d = -1 + 0 + 1 + 2 = 2$

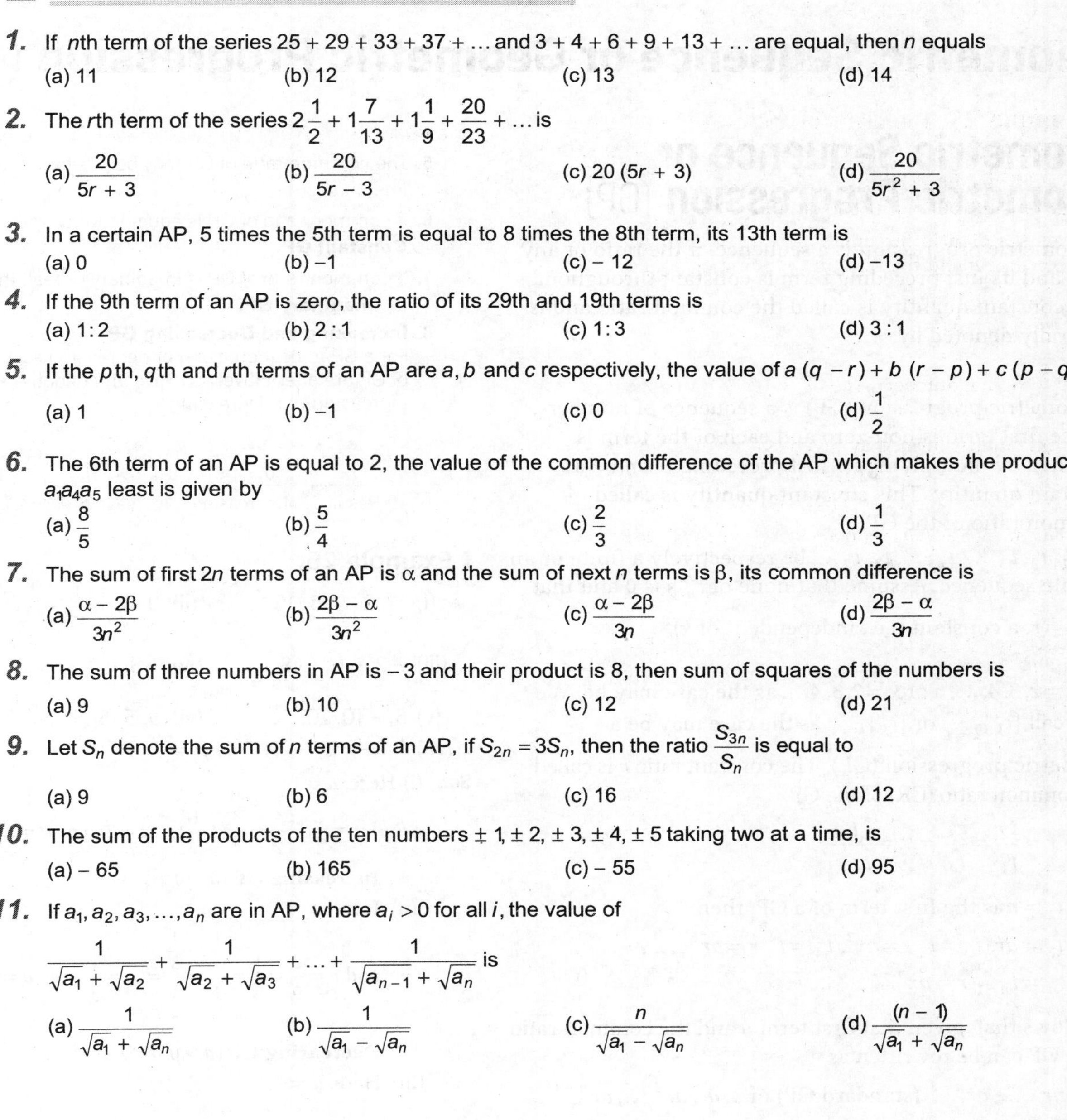

Exercise for Session 2

1. If nth term of the series $25 + 29 + 33 + 37 + \ldots$ and $3 + 4 + 6 + 9 + 13 + \ldots$ are equal, then n equals

(a) 11 (b) 12 (c) 13 (d) 14

2. The rth term of the series $2\frac{1}{2} + 1\frac{7}{13} + 1\frac{1}{9} + \frac{20}{23} + \ldots$ is

(a) $\frac{20}{5r+3}$ (b) $\frac{20}{5r-3}$ (c) $20\,(5r+3)$ (d) $\frac{20}{5r^2+3}$

3. In a certain AP, 5 times the 5th term is equal to 8 times the 8th term, its 13th term is

(a) 0 (b) -1 (c) -12 (d) -13

4. If the 9th term of an AP is zero, the ratio of its 29th and 19th terms is

(a) 1:2 (b) 2:1 (c) 1:3 (d) 3:1

5. If the pth, qth and rth terms of an AP are a, b and c respectively, the value of $a\,(q-r) + b\,(r-p) + c\,(p-q)$ is

(a) 1 (b) -1 (c) 0 (d) $\frac{1}{2}$

6. The 6th term of an AP is equal to 2, the value of the common difference of the AP which makes the product $a_1a_4a_5$ least is given by

(a) $\frac{8}{5}$ (b) $\frac{5}{4}$ (c) $\frac{2}{3}$ (d) $\frac{1}{3}$

7. The sum of first $2n$ terms of an AP is α and the sum of next n terms is β, its common difference is

(a) $\frac{\alpha - 2\beta}{3n^2}$ (b) $\frac{2\beta - \alpha}{3n^2}$ (c) $\frac{\alpha - 2\beta}{3n}$ (d) $\frac{2\beta - \alpha}{3n}$

8. The sum of three numbers in AP is -3 and their product is 8, then sum of squares of the numbers is

(a) 9 (b) 10 (c) 12 (d) 21

9. Let S_n denote the sum of n terms of an AP, if $S_{2n} = 3S_n$, then the ratio $\frac{S_{3n}}{S_n}$ is equal to

(a) 9 (b) 6 (c) 16 (d) 12

10. The sum of the products of the ten numbers $\pm 1, \pm 2, \pm 3, \pm 4, \pm 5$ taking two at a time, is

(a) -65 (b) 165 (c) -55 (d) 95

11. If $a_1, a_2, a_3, \ldots, a_n$ are in AP, where $a_i > 0$ for all i, the value of

$$\frac{1}{\sqrt{a_1} + \sqrt{a_2}} + \frac{1}{\sqrt{a_2} + \sqrt{a_3}} + \ldots + \frac{1}{\sqrt{a_{n-1}} + \sqrt{a_n}}$$ is

(a) $\frac{1}{\sqrt{a_1} + \sqrt{a_n}}$ (b) $\frac{1}{\sqrt{a_1} - \sqrt{a_n}}$ (c) $\frac{n}{\sqrt{a_1} - \sqrt{a_n}}$ (d) $\frac{(n-1)}{\sqrt{a_1} + \sqrt{a_n}}$

Session 3

Geometric Sequence or Geometric Progression (GP)

Geometric Sequence or Geometric Progression (GP)

A geometric progression is a sequence, if the ratio of any term and its just preceding term is constant throughout. This constant quantity is called the common ratio and is generally denoted by 'r'.

Or

A geometric progression (GP) is a sequence of numbers, whose first term is non-zero and each of the term is obtained by multiplying its just preceding term by a constant quantity. This constant quantity is called common ratio of the GP.

Let $t_1, t_2, t_3, \ldots, t_n$; $t_1, t_2, t_3, \ldots$ be respectively a finite or an infinite sequence. Assume that none of t_n''s is 0 and that $\frac{t_k}{t_{k-1}} = r$, a constant (i.e., independent of k).

For $k = 2, 3, 4, \ldots, n$ or $k = 2, 3, 4, \ldots$ as the case may be. We then call $\{t_k\}_{k=1}^{n}$ or $\{t_k\}_{k=1}^{\infty}$ as the case may be a geometric progression (GP). The constant ratio r is called the common ratio (CR) of the GP.

i.e., $r = \frac{t_2}{t_1} = \frac{t_3}{t_2} = \ldots = \frac{t_n}{t_{n-1}}$

If $t_1 = a$ is the first term of a GP, then

$$t_2 = ar,\ t_3 = t_2 r = ar^2,\ t_4 = t_3 r = ar^3, \ldots,$$
$$t_n = t_{n-1} r = ar^{n-1}$$

It follows that, given that first term a and the common ratio r, the GP can be rewritten as

$a, ar, ar^2, \ldots, ar^{n-1}$ (standard GP) or $a, ar, ar^2, \ldots, ar^{n-1}, \ldots$ (standard GP)

according as it is finite or infinite.

Important Results

1. In a GP, neither $a = 0$ nor $r = 0$.
2. In a GP, no term can be equal to '0'.
3. If in a GP, the terms are alternatively positive and negative, then its common ratio is always negative.
4. If we multiply the common ratio with any term of GP, we get the next following term and if we divide any term by the common ratio, we get the preceding term.
5. The common ratio of GP may be positive, negative or imaginary.
6. If common ratio of GP is equal to unity, then GP is known as **Constant GP**.
7. If common ratio of GP is imaginary or real, then GP is known as **Imaginary GP**.
8. **Increasing and Decreasing GP**
For a GP to be increasing or decreasing $r > 0$. If $r < 0$, terms of GP are alternatively positive and negative and so neither increasing nor decreasing.

a	$a > 0$	$a > 0$	$a < 0$	$a < 0$
r	$0 < r < 1$	$r > 1$	$r > 1$	$0 < r < 1$
Result	Decreasing	Increasing	Decreasing	Increasing

Example 26.

(i) 1, 2, 4, 8, 16, ... (ii) $9, 3, 1, \frac{1}{3}, \frac{1}{9}, \ldots$

(iii) $-2, -6, -18, \ldots$ (iv) $-8, -4, -2, -1, -\frac{1}{2}, \ldots$

(v) $5, -10, 20, \ldots$ (vi) 5, 5, 5, 5,...

(vii) $1, 1+i, 2i, -2+2i, \ldots; i = \sqrt{-1}$

Sol. (i) Here, $a = 1$

and $r = \frac{2}{1} = \frac{4}{2} = \frac{8}{4} = \frac{16}{8} = \ldots = 2$ i.e. $a = 1$ and $r = 2$

Increasing GP $(a > 0, r > 1)$

(ii) Here, $a = 9$

and $r = \frac{3}{9} = \frac{1}{3} = \frac{\frac{1}{3}}{1} = \frac{\frac{1}{9}}{\frac{1}{3}} = \ldots = \frac{1}{3}$ i.e. $a = 9, r = \frac{1}{3}$

Decreasing GP $(a > 0, 0 < r < 1)$

(iii) Here, $a = -2$

and $r = \frac{-6}{-2} = \frac{-18}{-6} = \ldots = 3$

i.e. $a = -2, r = 3$

Decreasing GP $(a < 0, r > 1)$

(iv) Here, $a = -8$

and $r = \frac{-4}{-8} = \frac{-2}{-4} = \frac{-1}{-2} = \frac{-\frac{1}{2}}{-1} = \ldots = \frac{1}{2}$

i.e. $a = -8, r = \frac{1}{2}$

Increasing GP $(a < 0, 0 < r < 1)$

(v) Here, $a = 5$

and $r = \frac{-10}{5} = \frac{20}{-10} = \dots = -2$ i.e., $a = 5, r = -2$

Neither increasing nor decreasing $(r < 0)$

(vi) Here, $a = 5$

and $r = \frac{5}{5} = \frac{5}{5} = \frac{5}{5} = \dots = 1$ i.e., $a = 5, r = 1$

Constant GP $(r = 1)$

(vii) Here, $a = 1$

and $r = \frac{1+i}{1} = \frac{2i}{1+i} = \frac{-2+2i}{2i} = \dots$

$$= (1+i) = \frac{2i(1-i)}{(1+i)(1-i)} = \frac{(-1+i)i}{i^2} = \dots$$

$$= (1+i) = (i+1) = (1+i) = \dots$$

i.e., $a = 1, r = 1 + i$

Imaginary GP (r = imaginary)

Example 27. Show that the sequence $< t_n >$ defined by $t_n = \frac{2^{2n-1}}{3}$ for all values of $n \in N$ is a GP. Also, find its common ratio.

Sol. We have, $t_n = \frac{2^{2n-1}}{3}$

On replacing n by $n - 1$, we get

$$t_{n-1} = \frac{2^{2n-3}}{3} \Rightarrow \frac{t_n}{t_{n-1}} = \frac{\frac{2^{2n-1}}{3}}{\frac{2^{2n-3}}{3}} = 2^2 = 4$$

Clearly, $\frac{t_n}{t_{n-1}}$ is independent of n and is equal to 4. So, the given sequence is a GP with common ratio 4.

Example 28. Show that the sequence $< t_n >$ defined by $t_n = 2 \cdot 3^n + 1$ is not a GP.

Sol. We have, $t_n = 2 \cdot 3^n + 1$

On replacing n by $(n-1)$ in t_n, we get

$$t_{n-1} = 2 \cdot 3^{n-1} + 1$$

$$\Rightarrow \quad t_{n-1} = \frac{(2 \cdot 3^n + 3)}{3}$$

$$\therefore \quad \frac{t_n}{t_{n-1}} = \frac{(2 \cdot 3^n + 1)}{\frac{(2 \cdot 3^n + 3)}{3}} = \frac{3(2 \cdot 3^n + 1)}{(2 \cdot 3^n + 3)}$$

Clearly, $\frac{t_n}{t_{n-1}}$ is not independent of n and is therefore not constant. So, the given sequence is not a GP.

General Term of a GP

Let 'a' be the first term, 'r' be the common ratio and 'l' be the last term of a GP having 'n' terms. Then, GP can be written as $a, ar, ar^2, \dots, \frac{l}{r^2}, \frac{l}{r}, l$

(i) nth Term of a GP from Beginning

1st term from beginning $= t_1 = a = ar^{1-1}$

2nd term from beginning $= t_2 = ar = ar^{2-1}$

3rd term from beginning $= t_3 = ar^2 = ar^{3-1}$

$\vdots \quad \vdots \quad \vdots \quad \vdots \quad \vdots$

nth term from beginning $= t_n = ar^{n-1}, \forall n \in N$

Hence, n th term of a GP from beginning

$$t_n = ar^{n-1} = l \quad \text{[last term]}$$

(ii) nth Term of a GP from End

1st term from end $= t'_1 = l = \frac{l}{r^{1-1}}$

2nd term from end $= t'_2 = \frac{l}{r} = \frac{l}{r^{2-1}}$

3rd term from end $= t'_3 = \frac{l}{r^2} = \frac{l}{r^{3-1}}$

$\vdots \quad \vdots \quad \vdots \quad \vdots$

nth term from end $= t'_n = \frac{l}{r^{n-1}}, \forall n \in N$

Hence, nth term of a GP from end

$$= t'_n = \frac{l}{r^{n-1}} = a \quad \text{[first term]}$$

Now, it is clear that $t_k \times t'_k = ar^{k-1} \times \frac{l}{r^{k-1}} = a \times l$

or $\quad t_k \times t'_k = a \times l, \forall 1 \le k \le n$

i.e. in a finite GP of n terms, the product of the k th term from the beginning and the k th term form the end is independent of k and equals the product of the first and last terms.

Remark

1. nth term is also called the general term.
2. If last term of GP be t_n and CR is r, then terms of GP from end are $t_n, \frac{t_n}{r}, \frac{t_n}{r^2}, \dots$
3. If in a GP, the terms are alternatively positive and negative, then its common ratio is always negative.

4. If a and l represent first and last term of a GP respectively, then common ratio of GP $= r = \left(\frac{l}{a}\right)^{\frac{1}{n-1}}$
5. If t_n, t_{n+1}, t_{n+2} are three consecutive terms of a GP, then $\frac{t_{n+1}}{t_n} = \frac{t_{n+2}}{t_{n+1}} \Rightarrow t_{n+1}^2 = t_n\, t_{n+2}$

In particular, if a, b, c are in GP, then $\frac{b}{a} = \frac{c}{b} \Rightarrow b^2 = ac$

On squaring, $\frac{b^2}{a^2} = \frac{c^2}{b^2}$

Hence, a^2, b^2, c^2 are also in GP.

Example 29. If first term of a GP is a, third term is b and $(n+1)$th term is c. The $(2n+1)$th term of a GP is

(a) $c\sqrt{\frac{b}{a}}$ (b) $\frac{bc}{a}$ (c) abc (d) $\frac{c^2}{a}$

Sol. Let common ratio $= r$

$\therefore \quad b = ar^2 \Rightarrow r = \sqrt{\frac{b}{a}}$

Also, $\quad c = ar^n \Rightarrow r^n = \frac{c}{a}$

$\therefore \quad t_{2n+1} = ar^{2n} = a(r^n)^2 = a\left(\frac{c}{a}\right)^2 = \frac{c^2}{a}$

Hence, (d) is the correct answer.

Example 30. The $(m+n)$th and $(m-n)$th terms of a GP are p and q, respectively. Then, the mth term of the GP is

(a) $p\left(\frac{q}{p}\right)^{\frac{m}{2n}}$ (b) $\sqrt{pq}$

(c) $\sqrt{\frac{p}{q}}$ (d) None of these

Sol. Let a be the first term and r be the common ratio, then

$$t_{m+n} = p \Rightarrow ar^{m+n-1} = p \quad \text{...(i)}$$

$$t_{m-n} = q \Rightarrow ar^{m-n-1} = q \quad \text{...(ii)}$$

From Eqs. (i) and (ii), we get

$$ar^{m+n-1} \times ar^{m-n-1} = p \times q$$

$\Rightarrow \quad a^2 r^{2m-2} = pq \Rightarrow ar^{m-1} = \sqrt{pq}$

$\Rightarrow \quad t_m = \sqrt{pq}$

Hence, (b) is the correct answer.

Example 31. If $\sin\theta$, $\sqrt{2}(\sin\theta + 1)$, $6\sin\theta + 6$ are in GP, then the fifth term is

(a) 81 (b) $81\sqrt{2}$ (c) 162 (d) $162\sqrt{2}$

Sol. $[\sqrt{2}(\sin\theta + 1)]^2 = \sin\theta\,(6\sin\theta + 6)$

$\Rightarrow [(\sin\theta + 1)\,2(\sin\theta + 1) - 6\sin\theta] = 0$

We get, $\quad \sin\theta = -1, \frac{1}{2}$

$\therefore \quad \sin\theta = \frac{1}{2} \quad$ [$\sin\theta = -1$ is not possible]

then first term $= a = \sin\theta = \frac{1}{2}$ and common ratio

$$= r = \frac{\sqrt{2}\left(\frac{1}{2} + 1\right)}{\left(\frac{1}{2}\right)} = 3\sqrt{2}$$

$\therefore \quad t_5 = ar^4 = \frac{1}{2}(3\sqrt{2})^4 = 162$

Hence, (c) is the correct answer.

Example 32. The 1025th term in the sequence 1, 22, 4444, 88888888, ... is

(a) 2^9 (b) 2^{10}

(c) 2^{11} (d) 2^{12}

Sol. The number of digits in each term of the sequence are 1, 2, 4, 8, ... which are in GP. Let 1025th term is 2^n. Then,

$$1 + 2 + 4 + 8 + \ldots + 2^{n-1} < 1025 \le 1 + 2 + 4 + 8 + \ldots + 2^n$$

$\Rightarrow \quad \frac{(2-1)(1 + 2 + 2^2 + 2^3 + \ldots + 2^{n-1})}{(2-1)} < 1025$

$\le \frac{(2-1)(1 + 2 + 2^2 + 2^3 + \ldots + 2^n)}{(2-1)}$

$\Rightarrow \quad 2^n - 1 < 1025 \le 2^{n+1} - 1 \Rightarrow 2^n < 1026 \le 2^{n+1} \quad$ ...(i)

or $\quad 2^{n+1} \ge 1026 > 1024$

$\Rightarrow \quad 2^{n+1} > 2^{10} \Rightarrow n + 1 > 10$

$\therefore \quad n > 9 \quad \therefore n = 10$

[which is always satisfy Eq. (i)]

Hence, (b) is the correct answer.

Example 33. If a, b, c are real numbers such that $3(a^2 + b^2 + c^2 + 1) = 2(a + b + c + ab + bc + ca)$, then a, b, c are in

(a) AP only (b) GP only

(c) GP and AP (d) None of these

Sol. Given, $3(a^2 + b^2 + c^2 + 1) = 2(a + b + c + ab + bc + ca)$

$\Rightarrow \quad 2(a^2 + b^2 + c^2 - ab - bc - ca) + (a^2 + b^2 + c^2 - 2a - 2b - 2c + 3)$

$\Rightarrow \quad \{(a-b)^2 + (b-c)^2 + (c-a)^2\} + \{(a-1)^2 + (b-1)^2 + (c-1)^2\} = 0$

$\Rightarrow a - b = b - c = c - a = 0$ and $a - 1 = b - 1 = c - 1 = 0$

$\Rightarrow \quad a = b = c = 1$

$\Rightarrow$ a, b, c are in GP and AP.

Hence, (c) is the correct answer.

Sum of a Stated Number of Terms of a Geometric Series

The game of chess was invented by **Grand Vizier Sissa Ben Dhair** for the Indian king **Shirham.** Pleased with the game, the king asked the **Vizier** what he would like as reward. The **Vizier** asked for one grain of wheat to be placed on the first square of the chess, two grains on the second, four grains on the third and so on (each time doubling the number of grains). The king was surprised of the request and told the **vizier** that he was fool to ask for so little.

The inventor of chess was no fool. He told the king "What I have asked for is more wheat that you have in the entire kingdom, in fact it is more than there is in the whole world" He was right. There are 64 squares on a chess board and on the nth square he was asking for 2^{n-1} grains, if you add the numbers

i.e., $$S = 1 + 2 + 2^2 + 2^3 + \dots + 2^{62} + 2^{63} \quad \dots \text{(i)}$$

On multiplying both sides by 2, then

$$2S = 2 + 2^2 + 2^3 + 2^4 + \dots + 2^{63} + 2^{64} \quad \dots \text{(ii)}$$

On subtracting Eq. (i) from Eq. (ii), we get

$S = 2^{64} - 1 = 18, 446, 744, 073, 709, 551, 615$ grains i.e., represent more wheat that has been produced on the Earth.

Sum of n Terms of a GP

Let a be the first term, r be the common ratio, l be the last term of a GP having n terms and S_n the sum of n terms, then

$$S_n = a + ar + ar^2 + \dots + \frac{l}{r^2} + \frac{l}{r} + l \quad \dots \text{(i)}$$

On multiplying both sides by r (the common ratio)

$$r\,S_n = ar + ar^2 + ar^3 + \dots + \frac{l}{r} + l + lr \quad \dots \text{(ii)}$$

On subtracting Eq. (ii) from Eq. (i), we have

$$S_n - r\,S_n = a - lr \text{ or } S_n(1-r) = a - lr$$

$$\therefore \quad \mathbf{S_n = \frac{a - lr}{1 - r}}, \text{ when } r < 1$$

$$\mathbf{S_n = \frac{lr - a}{r - 1}}, \text{ when } r > 1$$

Now, $$l = t_n = ar^{n-1}$$

Then, above formula can be written as

$$\mathbf{S_n = \frac{a(1-r^n)}{(1-r)}} \text{ when } \mathbf{r < 1}, \mathbf{S_n = \frac{a(r^n - 1)}{(r-1)}},$$

when $\mathbf{r > 1}$

If $r = 1$, the above formulae cannot be used. But, then the GP reduces to $a, a, a, \dots$

$\therefore \quad S_n = a + a + a + \dots n \text{ times} = na$

Sum to Infinity of a GP, when the Numerical Value of the Common Ratio is Less than Unity, i.e. It is a Proper Fraction

If a be the first term, r be the common ratio of a GP, then

$$S_n = \frac{a(1-r^n)}{(1-r)} = \frac{a}{(1-r)} - \frac{ar^n}{(1-r)}$$

Let $-1 < r < 1$ i.e. $|r| < 1$, then $\lim_{n \to \infty} r^n \to 0$

Let S_∞ denote the sum to infinity of the GP, then

$$S_\infty = \frac{a}{(1-r)},$$

where $-1 < r < 1$

Recurring Decimal

Recurring decimal is a very good example of an infinite geometric series and its value can be obtained by means of infinite geometric series as follows

$$0.3\dot{2}\dot{7} = 0.327272727\dots \text{ to infinity}$$

$$= 0.3 + 0.027 + 0.00027 + 0.0000027 + \dots \text{ upto infinity}$$

$$= \frac{3}{10} + \frac{27}{10^3} + \frac{27}{10^5} + \frac{27}{10^7} + \dots \text{ upto infinity}$$

$$= \frac{3}{10} + \frac{27}{10^3}\left(1 + \frac{1}{10^2} + \frac{1}{10^4} + \dots \text{ upto infinity}\right)$$

$$= \frac{3}{10} + \frac{27}{10^3}\left(\frac{1}{1 - \frac{1}{10^2}}\right)$$

$$= \frac{3}{10} + \frac{27}{990} = \frac{297 + 27}{990}$$

$$= \frac{324}{990} \quad \text{[rational number]}$$

Aliter (Best method)

Let P denotes the figure which do not recur and suppose them p in number, Q denotes the recurring period consisting of q figures. Let R denotes the value of the recurring decimal.

Then, $$R = 0 \cdot PQQQ \dots$$

$\therefore$ $$10^p \times R = P \cdot QQQ \dots$$

and $$10^{p+q} \times R = PQ \cdot QQQ \dots$$

$\therefore$ Therefore, by subtraction $R = \dfrac{PQ - P}{(10^{p+q} - 10^p)}$.

***Corollary* I** If $R = 0\cdot QQQ\ldots$

Then, $R = \dfrac{Q}{10^q - 1}$ (when Q denote the recurring period consisting of q figures)

For example, If $R = 0.\dot{3}$, then $R = \dfrac{3}{10^1 - 1} = \dfrac{1}{3}$

***Corollary* II** The value of recurring decimal is always rational number.

| Example 34. Find the value of $0.\dot{3}25\dot{8}$.

Sol. Let $R = 0.32\dot{5}\dot{8}$

$\Rightarrow \quad R = 0.3258585858\ldots \quad \ldots(\text{i})$

Here, number of figures which are not recurring is 2 and number of figures which are recurring is also 2.

Then, $\quad 100R = 32.58585858\ldots \quad \ldots(\text{ii})$

and $\quad 10000R = 3258.58585858\ldots \quad \ldots(\text{iii})$

On subtracting Eq. (ii) from Eq. (iii), we get

$$9900R = 3226$$

$$\therefore \quad R = \frac{3226}{9900}$$

Hence, $\quad R = \dfrac{1613}{4950}$

Shortcut Methods for Recurring Decimals

1. The numerator of the vulgar fraction is obtained by subtracting the non-recurring figure from the given figure.
2. The denominator consists of as many 9's as there are recurring figure and as many zero as there are non-recurring figure.

For example,

(i) $0.36\dot{5}\dot{4} = \dfrac{3654 - 36}{9900} = \dfrac{3618}{9900}$

(ii) $1.3\dot{2}\dot{7} = 1 + 0.3\dot{2}\dot{7} = 1 + \dfrac{327 - 3}{990} = \dfrac{1314}{990}$

(iii) $0.\dot{3} = \dfrac{3 - 0}{9} = \dfrac{1}{3}$

| Example 35. Find the sum upto n terms of the series $a + aa + aaa + aaaa + \ldots,\ \forall\ a \in N$ and $1 \le a \le 9$.

Sol. Let $S = a + aa + aaa + aaaa + \ldots$ upto n terms

$= a\,(1 + 11 + 111 + 1111 + \ldots \text{ upto } n \text{ terms})$

$= \dfrac{a}{9}(9 + 99 + 999 + 9999 + \ldots \text{ upto } n \text{ terms})$

$= \dfrac{a}{9}\{(10^1 - 1) + (10^2 - 1) + (10^3 - 1) + (10^4 - 1) + \ldots \text{ upto } n \text{ terms}\}$

$= \dfrac{a}{9}\{(10 + 10^2 + 10^3 + \ldots \text{ upto } n \text{ terms}) - (1 + 1 + 1 + \ldots n \text{ times})\}$

$= \dfrac{a}{9}\left\{\dfrac{10\,(10^n - 1)}{10 - 1} - n\right\} = \dfrac{a}{9}\left\{\dfrac{10}{9}(10^n - 1) - n\right\}$ [Remember]

In Particular

(i) For $a = 1$, $1 + 11 + 111 + \ldots = \dfrac{1}{9}\left\{\dfrac{10}{9}(10^n - 1) - n\right\}$

(ii) For $a = 2$, $2 + 22 + 222 + \ldots = \dfrac{2}{9}\left\{\dfrac{10}{9}(10^n - 1) - n\right\}$

(iii) For $a = 3$, $3 + 33 + 333 + \ldots = \dfrac{3}{9}\left\{\dfrac{10}{9}(10^n - 1) - n\right\}$

(iv) For $a = 4$, $4 + 44 + 444 + \ldots = \dfrac{4}{9}\left\{\dfrac{10}{9}(10^n - 1) - n\right\}$

(v) For $a = 5$, $5 + 55 + 555 + \ldots = \dfrac{5}{9}\left\{\dfrac{10}{9}(10^n - 1) - n\right\}$

(vi) For $a = 6$, $6 + 66 + 666 + \ldots = \dfrac{6}{9}\left\{\dfrac{10}{9}(10^n - 1) - n\right\}$

(vii) For $a = 7$, $7 + 77 + 777 + \ldots = \dfrac{7}{9}\left\{\dfrac{10}{9}(10^n - 1) - n\right\}$

(viii) For $a = 8$, $8 + 88 + 888 + \ldots = \dfrac{8}{9}\left\{\dfrac{10}{9}(10^n - 1) - n\right\}$

(ix) For $a = 9$, $9 + 99 + 999 + \ldots = \dfrac{9}{9}\left\{\dfrac{10}{9}(10^n - 1) - n\right\}$

| Example 36. Find the sum upto n terms of the series $0.b + 0.bb + 0.bbb + 0.bbbb + \ldots,\ \forall\ b \in N$ and $1 \le b \le 9$.

Sol. Let $S = 0.b + 0.bb + 0.bbb + 0.bbbb + \ldots$ upto n terms

$= b\,(0.1 + 0.11 + 0.111 + 0.1111 + \ldots \text{ upto } n \text{ terms})$

$= \dfrac{b}{9}(0.9 + 0.99 + 0.999 + 0.9999 + \ldots \text{ upto } n \text{ terms})$

$= \dfrac{b}{9}\{(1 - 0.1) + (1 - 0.01) + (1 - 0.001) + (1 - 0.0001) + \ldots \text{ upto } n \text{ terms}\}$

$= \dfrac{b}{9}\{(1 + 1 + 1 + 1 + \ldots \text{ upto } n \text{ times}) - (0.1 + 0.01 + 0.001 + 0.0001 + \ldots \text{ upto } n \text{ terms})\}$

$= \dfrac{b}{9}\left\{n - \left(\dfrac{1}{10} + \dfrac{1}{10^2} + \dfrac{1}{10^3} + \dfrac{1}{10^4} + \ldots \text{ upto } n \text{ terms}\right)\right\}$

$= \dfrac{b}{9}\left\{n - \dfrac{\dfrac{1}{10}\left(1 - \left(\dfrac{1}{10}\right)^n\right)}{1 - \dfrac{1}{10}}\right\} = \dfrac{b}{9}\left\{n - \dfrac{1}{9}\left[1 - \left(\dfrac{1}{10}\right)^n\right]\right\}$

[Remember]

In Particular

(i) For $b=1$,

$$0.1+0.11+0.111+\ldots=\frac{1}{9}\left\{n-\frac{1}{9}\left[1-\left(\frac{1}{10}\right)^n\right]\right\}$$

(ii) For $b=2$,

$$0.2+0.22+0.222+\ldots=\frac{2}{9}\left\{n-\frac{1}{9}\left[1-\left(\frac{1}{10}\right)^n\right]\right\}$$

(iii) For $b=3$,

$$0.3+0.33+0.333+\ldots=\frac{3}{9}\left\{n-\frac{1}{9}\left[1-\left(\frac{1}{10}\right)^n\right]\right\}$$

(iv) For $b=4$,

$$0.4+0.44+0.444+\ldots=\frac{4}{9}\left\{n-\frac{1}{9}\left[1-\left(\frac{1}{10}\right)^n\right]\right\}$$

(v) For $b=5$,

$$0.5+0.55+0.555+\ldots=\frac{5}{9}\left\{n-\frac{1}{9}\left[1-\left(\frac{1}{10}\right)^n\right]\right\}$$

(vi) For $b=6$,

$$0.6+0.66+0.666+\ldots=\frac{6}{9}\left\{n-\frac{1}{9}\left[1-\left(\frac{1}{10}\right)^n\right]\right\}$$

(vii) For $b=7$,

$$0.7+0.77+0.777+\ldots=\frac{7}{9}\left\{n-\frac{1}{9}\left[1-\left(\frac{1}{10}\right)^n\right]\right\}$$

(viii) For $b=8$,

$$0.8+0.88+0.888+\ldots=\frac{8}{9}\left\{n-\frac{1}{9}\left[1-\left(\frac{1}{10}\right)^n\right]\right\}$$

(ix) For $b=9$,

$$0.9+0.99+0.999+\ldots=\frac{9}{9}\left\{n-\frac{1}{9}\left[1-\left(\frac{1}{10}\right)^n\right]\right\}$$

Example 37. If N, the set of natural numbers is partitioned into groups $S_1=\{1\}, S_2=\{2,3\}$, $S_3=\{4,5,6,7\}$, $S_4=\{8,9,10,11,12,13,14,15\},\ldots$, then find the sum of the numbers in S_{50}.

Sol. The number of terms in the groups are $1, 2, 2^2, 2^3, \ldots$

$\therefore$ The number of terms in the 50th group $=2^{50-1}=2^{49}$

$\because$ The first term of 1st group $=1=2^0=2^{1-1}$

The first term of 2nd group $=2=2^1=2^{2-1}$

The first term of 3rd group $=4=2^2=2^{3-1}$

$\vdots \quad \vdots \quad \vdots \quad \vdots \quad \vdots$

The first term of 50th group $=2^{50-1}=2^{49}$

$$\therefore \quad S_{50}=\frac{2^{49}}{2}\{2\times 2^{49}+(2^{49}-1)\times 1\}$$
$$=2^{48}(2^{50}+2^{49}-1)$$
$$=2^{48}[2^{49}(2+1)-1]=2^{48}(3\cdot 2^{49}-1)$$

Example 38. If $S_n=1+\frac{1}{2}+\frac{1}{2^2}+\ldots+\frac{1}{2^{n-1}}$, then calculate the least value of n such that $2-S_n<\frac{1}{100}$.

Sol. Given, $S_n=1+\frac{1}{2}+\frac{1}{2^2}+\ldots+\frac{1}{2^{n-1}}=\dfrac{1\cdot\left[1-\left(\frac{1}{2}\right)^n\right]}{\left(1-\frac{1}{2}\right)}$

$$\Rightarrow \quad S_n=2-\frac{1}{2^{n-1}}$$

$$\Rightarrow \quad 2-S_n=\frac{1}{2^{n-1}}<\frac{1}{100} \qquad \left[\because 2-S_n<\frac{1}{100}\right]$$

$$\Rightarrow \quad 2^{n-1}>100>2^6$$

$$\Rightarrow \quad 2^{n-1}>2^6$$

$$\therefore \quad n-1>6 \Rightarrow n>7$$

Hence, the least value of n is 8.

Example 39. If $x=1+a+a^2+a^3+\ldots+\infty$ and $y=1+b+b^2+b^3+\ldots+\infty$ show that $1+ab+a^2b^2+a^3b^3+\ldots+\infty=\frac{xy}{x+y-1}$, where $0<a<1$ and $0<b<1$.

Sol. Given, $x=1+a+a^2+a^3+\ldots+\infty=\frac{1}{1-a}$

$$\Rightarrow \quad x-ax=1$$

$$\therefore \quad a=\left(\frac{x-1}{x}\right) \qquad \ldots\text{(i)}$$

and $\quad y=1+b+b^2+b^3+\ldots+\infty$

Similarly, $\quad b=\left(\frac{y-1}{y}\right) \qquad \ldots\text{(ii)}$

Since, $\quad 0<a<1, 0<b<1$

$\therefore \quad 0<ab<1$

Now, $1+ab+a^2b^2+a^3b^3+\ldots+\infty=\frac{1}{1-ab}$

$$=\frac{1}{1-\left(\frac{x-1}{x}\right)\left(\frac{y-1}{y}\right)} \qquad \text{[from Eqs. (i) and (ii)]}$$

$$=\frac{xy}{xy-xy+x+y-1}$$

Hence, $1+ab+a^2b^2+a^3b^3+\ldots+\infty=\frac{xy}{x+y-1}$

Properties of Geometric Progression

1. If $a_1, a_2, a_3, \ldots$ are in GP with common ratio r, then $a_1 k, a_2 k, a_3 k, \ldots$ and $\frac{a_1}{k}, \frac{a_2}{k}, \frac{a_3}{k}, \ldots$ are also in GP $(k \neq 0)$ with common ratio r.
2. If $a_1, a_2, a_3, \ldots$ are in GP with common ratio r, then $a_1 \pm k, a_2 \pm k, a_3 \pm k, \ldots$ are not in GP $(k \neq 0)$.
3. If $a_1, a_2, a_3, \ldots$ are in GP with common ratio r, then
   (i) $\frac{1}{a_1}, \frac{1}{a_2}, \frac{1}{a_3}, \ldots$ are also in GP with common ratio $\frac{1}{r}$.
   (ii) $a_1^n, a_2^n, a_3^n, \ldots$ are also in GP with common ratio r^n and $n \in Q$.
   (iii) $\log a_1, \log a_2, \log a_3, \ldots$ are in AP $(a_i > 0, \forall\, i)$
   In this case, the converse also holds good.
4. If $a_1, a_2, a_3, \ldots$ and $b_1, b_2, b_3, \ldots$ are two GP's with common ratios r_1 and r_2, respectively. Then,
   (i) $a_1 b_1, a_2 b_2, a_3 b_3, \ldots$ and $\frac{a_1}{b_1}, \frac{a_2}{b_2}, \frac{a_3}{b_3}, \ldots$ are also in GP with common ratios $r_1 r_2$ and $\frac{r_1}{r_2}$, respectively.
   (ii) $a_1 \pm b_1, a_2 \pm b_2, a_3 \pm b_3, \ldots$ are not in GP.
5. If $a_1, a_2, a_3, \ldots, a_{n-2}, a_{n-1}, a_n$ are in GP. Then,
   (i) $a_1 a_n = a_2 a_{n-1} = a_3 a_{n-2} = \ldots$
   (ii) $a_r = \sqrt{a_{r-k}\, a_{r+k}}, \forall\, k, 0 \le k \le n-r$
   (iii) $\frac{a_2}{a_1} = \frac{a_3}{a_2} = \frac{a_4}{a_3} = \ldots = \frac{a_n}{a_{n-1}}$
   $\Rightarrow \quad a_2^2 = a_3 a_1, a_3^2 = a_2 a_4, \ldots$
   Also, $\quad a_2 = a_1 r, a_3 = a_1 r^2,$
   $a_4 = a_1 r^3, \ldots, a_n = a_1 r^{n-1}$
   where, r is the common ratio of GP.
6. If three numbers in GP whose product is given are to be taken as $\frac{a}{r}$, a, ar and if five numbers in GP whose product is given are to be taken as $\frac{a}{r^2}, \frac{a}{r}, a, ar, ar^2$, etc.

   In general If $(2m+1)$ numbers in GP whose product is given are to be taken as $(m \in N)$
   $$\frac{a}{r^m}, \frac{a}{r^{m-1}}, \ldots, \frac{a}{r}, a, ar, \ldots, ar^{m-1}, ar^m$$

   Remark
   1. Product of three numbers $= a^3$
      Product of five numbers $= a^5$
      ⋮ ⋮ ⋮ ⋮ ⋮
      Product of $(2m+1)$ numbers $= a^{2m+1}$
   2. From given conditions, find two equations in a and r and then solve them. Now, the numbers in GP can be obtained.
7. If four numbers in GP whose product is given are to be taken as $\frac{a}{r^3}, \frac{a}{r}, ar, ar^3$ and if six numbers in GP whose product is given are to be taken as $\frac{a}{r^5}, \frac{a}{r^3}, \frac{a}{r}, ar, ar^3, ar^5$, etc.

   In general If $(2m)$ numbers in GP whose product is given are to be taken as $(m \in N)$
   $$\frac{a}{r^{2m-1}}, \frac{a}{r^{2m-3}}, \ldots, \frac{a}{r^3}, \frac{a}{r}, ar, ar^3, \ldots, ar^{2m-3}, ar^{2m-1}$$

   Remark
   1. Product of four numbers $= a^4$
      Product of six numbers $= a^6$
      ⋮ ⋮ ⋮ ⋮ ⋮
      Product of $(2m)$ numbers $= a^{2m}$
   2. From given conditions, find two equations in a and r and then solve them. Now, the numbers in GP can be obtained.

| Example 40. If $S_1, S_2, S_3, \ldots, S_p$ are the sum of infinite geometric series whose first terms are 1, 2, 3, ..., p and whose common ratios are $\frac{1}{2}, \frac{1}{3}, \frac{1}{4}, \ldots, \frac{1}{p+1}$ respectively, prove that
$$S_1 + S_2 + S_3 + \ldots + S_p = \frac{p(p+3)}{2}.$$

Sol. $\because \quad S_p = \dfrac{p}{1 - \dfrac{1}{p+1}} = (p+1)$

$\therefore \quad S_1 = 2, S_2 = 3, S_3 = 4, \ldots$

$\therefore \quad \text{LHS} = S_1 + S_2 + S_3 + \ldots + S_p$

$= 2 + 3 + 4 + \ldots + (p+1) = \frac{p}{2}(2 + p + 1)$

$= \frac{p(p+3)}{2} = \text{RHS}$

| Example 41. Let x_1 and x_2 be the roots of the equation $x^2 - 3x + A = 0$ and let x_3 and x_4 be the roots of the equation $x^2 - 12x + B = 0$. It is known that the numbers x_1, x_2, x_3, x_4 (in that order) form an increasing GP. Find A and B.

Sol. $\because x_1, x_2, x_3, x_4$ are in GP.

Let $x_2 = x_1 r, x_3 = x_1 r^2, x_4 = x_1 r^3$

[here, product of x_1, x_2, x_3, x_4 are not given]

Given, $x_1 + x_2 = 3, x_1 x_2 = A$

$\Rightarrow x_1(1 + r) = 3, x_1^2 r = A$ ...(i)

and $x_3 + x_4 = 12, x_3 x_4 = B$

$\Rightarrow x_1 r^2 (1 + r) = 12, x_1^2 r^5 = B$ ...(ii)

From Eqs. (i) and (ii),

$r^2 = 4 \Rightarrow r = 2$ [for increasing GP]

From Eq. (i), $x_1 = 1$

Now, $A = x_1^2 r = 1^2 \cdot 2 = 2$ [from Eq. (i)]

and $B = x_1^2 r^5 = 1^2 \cdot 2^5 = 32$ [from Eq. (ii)]

Example 42. Suppose a, b, c are in AP and a^2, b^2, c^2 are in GP, if $a > b > c$ and $a + b + c = \frac{3}{2}$, then find the values of a and c.

Sol. Since, a, b, c are in AP and sum of a, b, c is given.

Let $a = b - D, c = b + D$ $[D < 0][\because a > b > c]$

and given $a + b + c = \frac{3}{2}$

$\Rightarrow b - D + b + b + D = \frac{3}{2}$

$\therefore b = \frac{1}{2}$

Then, $a = \frac{1}{2} - D$ and $c = \frac{1}{2} + D$

Also, given a^2, b^2, c^2 are in GP, then $(b^2)^2 = a^2 c^2$

$\Rightarrow \pm b^2 = ac \Rightarrow \pm \frac{1}{4} = \frac{1}{4} - D^2$

$\Rightarrow D^2 = \frac{1}{4} \pm \frac{1}{4} = \frac{1}{2}$ $[\because D \neq 0]$

$\therefore D = \pm \frac{1}{\sqrt{2}} \Rightarrow D = -\frac{1}{\sqrt{2}}$ $[\because D < 0]$

Hence, $a = \frac{1}{2} + \frac{1}{\sqrt{2}}$ and $c = \frac{1}{2} - \frac{1}{\sqrt{2}}$

Example 43. If the continued product of three numbers in GP is 216 and the sum of their products in pairs is 156, then find the sum of three numbers.

Sol. Here, product of numbers in GP is given.

$\therefore$ Let the three numbers be $\frac{a}{r}, a, ar$.

Then, $\frac{a}{r} \cdot a \cdot ar = 216$

$\Rightarrow a^3 = 216$

$\therefore a = 6$

Sum of the products in pairs = 156

$\Rightarrow \frac{a}{r} \cdot a + a \cdot ar + ar \cdot \frac{a}{r} = 156$

$\Rightarrow a^2 \left(\frac{1}{r} + r + 1 \right) = 156 \Rightarrow 36 \left(\frac{1 + r^2 + r}{r} \right) = 156$

$\Rightarrow 3 \left(\frac{1 + r + r^2}{r} \right) = 13 \Rightarrow 3r^2 - 10r + 3 = 0$

$\Rightarrow (3r - 1)(r - 3) = 0 \Rightarrow r = \frac{1}{3}$ or $r = 3$

Putting the values of a and r, the required numbers are 18, 6, 2 or 2, 6, 18. Hence, the sum of numbers is 26.

Example 44. Find a three-digit number whose consecutive digits form a GP. If we subtract 792 from this number, we get a number consisting of the same digits written in the reverse order. Now, if we increase the second digit of the required number by 2, then the resulting digits will form an AP.

Sol. Let the three digits be a, ar, ar^2, then according to hypothesis

$100a + 10ar + ar^2 - 792 = 100ar^2 + 10ar + a$

$\Rightarrow 99a(1 - r^2) = 792$

$\Rightarrow a(1 + r)(1 - r) = 8$ ...(i)

and $a, ar + 2, ar^2$ are in AP.

Then, $2(ar + 2) = a + ar^2$

$\Rightarrow a(r^2 - 2r + 1) = 4 \Rightarrow a(r - 1)^2 = 4$ ...(ii)

On dividing Eq. (i) by Eq. (ii), we get

$\frac{r + 1}{r - 1} = -2 \Rightarrow r = \frac{1}{3}$

From Eq. (ii), $a = 9$

Thus, digits are 9, 3, 1 and so the required number is 931.

Examples on Application of Progression in Geometrical Figures

Example 45. A square is drawn by joining the mid-points of the sides of a given square. A third square is drawn inside the second square in the same way and this process continues indefinitely. If a side of the first square is 16 cm, then determine the sum of the areas of all the squares.

Sol. Let a be the side length of square, then

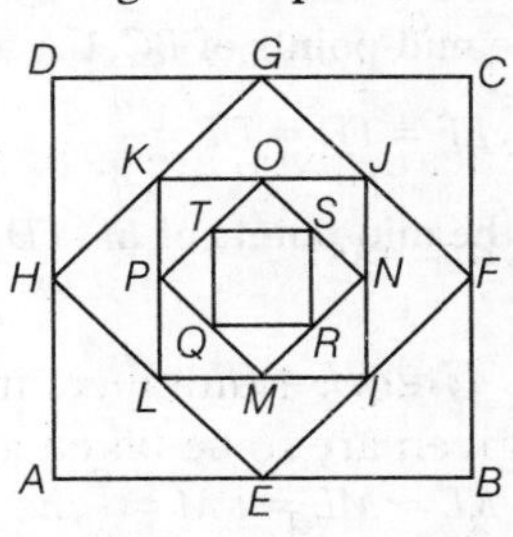

$AB = BC = CD = DA = a$

$\because E, F, G, H$ are the mid-points of AB, BC, CD and DA, respectively.

$$\therefore \quad EF = FG = GH = HE = \frac{a}{\sqrt{2}}$$

and I, J, K, L are the mid-points of EF, FG, GH and HE, respectively.

$$\therefore \quad IJ = JK = KL = LI = \frac{a}{2}$$

Similarly, $\quad MN = NO = OP = PM = \frac{a}{2\sqrt{2}}$ and

$$QR = RS = ST = TQ = \frac{a}{4}, \dots$$

S = Sum of areas

$$= ABCD + EFGH + IJKL + MNOP + QRST + \dots$$

$$= a^2 + \left(\frac{a}{\sqrt{2}}\right)^2 + \left(\frac{a}{2}\right)^2 + \left(\frac{a}{2\sqrt{2}}\right)^2 + \dots$$

$$= a^2\left(1 + \frac{1}{2} + \frac{1}{4} + \frac{1}{8} + \dots\right)$$

$$= a^2\left(\frac{1}{1 - \frac{1}{2}}\right) = 2a^2 = 2(16)^2 \qquad [\because a = 16 \text{ cm}]$$

$$= 512 \text{ sq cm}$$

Example 46. One side of an equilateral triangle is 24 cm. The mid-points of its sides are joined to form another triangle whose mid-points, in turn, are joined to form still another triangle. This process continues, indefinitely. Find the sum of the perimeters of all the triangles.

Sol. Let a be the side length of equilateral triangle, then $AB = BC = CA = a$

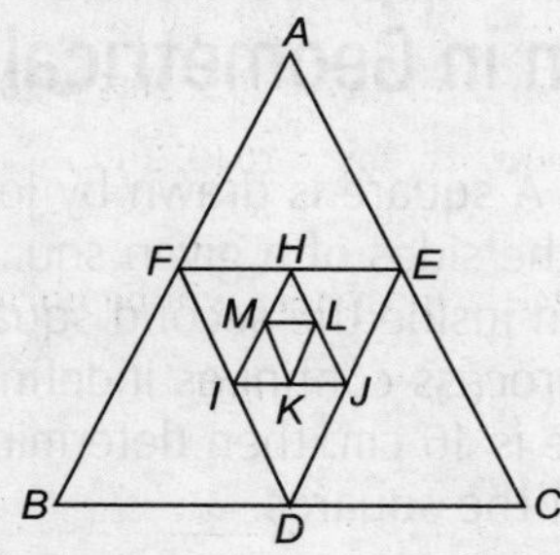

$\because D, E, F$ are the mid-points of BC, CA and AB, respectively.

$$\therefore \quad EF = FD = DE = \frac{a}{2}$$

and H, I, J are the mid-points of EF, FD and DE, respectively.

$$\therefore \quad IJ = JH = HI = \frac{a}{4}$$

Similarly, $\quad KL = ML = KM = \frac{a}{8}, \dots$

$$P = \text{Sum of perimeters} = 3\left(a + \frac{a}{2} + \frac{a}{4} + \frac{a}{8} + \dots\right)$$

$$= 3\left(\frac{a}{1 - \frac{1}{2}}\right) = 6a = 6 \times 24 = 144 \text{ cm} \qquad [\because a = 24 \text{ cm}]$$

Example 47. Let $S_1, S_2, \dots$ be squares such that for each $n \geq 1$, the length of a side of S_n equals the length of a diagonal of S_{n+1}. If the length of a side of S_1 is 10 cm and the area of S_n less than 1 sq cm. Then, find the value of n.

Sol. We have, length of a side of

S_n = length of diagonal of S_{n+1}

$\Rightarrow$ Length of a side of $S_n = \sqrt{2}$ (length of a side of S_{n+1})

$$\Rightarrow \quad \frac{\text{Length of a side of } S_{n+1}}{\text{Length of a side of } S_n} = \frac{1}{\sqrt{2}}, \text{ for all } n \geq 1$$

$\Rightarrow$ Sides of $S_1, S_2, S_3, \dots$ form a GP with common ratio $\frac{1}{\sqrt{2}}$ and first term 10.

$$\therefore \quad \text{Side of } S_n = 10\left(\frac{1}{\sqrt{2}}\right)^{n-1} = \frac{10}{2^{\frac{(n-1)}{2}}}$$

$$\Rightarrow \text{Area of } S_n = (\text{Side})^2 = \frac{100}{2^{n-1}}$$

Now, given area of $S_n < 1$

$$\Rightarrow \quad \frac{100}{2^{n-1}} < 1 \Rightarrow 2^{n-1} > 100 > 2^6$$

$$\Rightarrow \quad 2^{n-1} > 2^6 \Rightarrow n - 1 > 6$$

$$\therefore \quad n > 7 \text{ or } n \geq 8$$

Example 48. The line $x + y = 1$ meets X-axis at A and Y-axis at B, P is the mid-point of AB, P_1 is the foot of perpendicular from P to OA, M_1 is that of P_1 from OP; P_2 is that of M_1 from OA, M_2 is that of P_2 from OP; P_3 is that of M_2 from OA and so on. If P_n denotes the nth foot of the perpendicular on OA, then find OP_n.

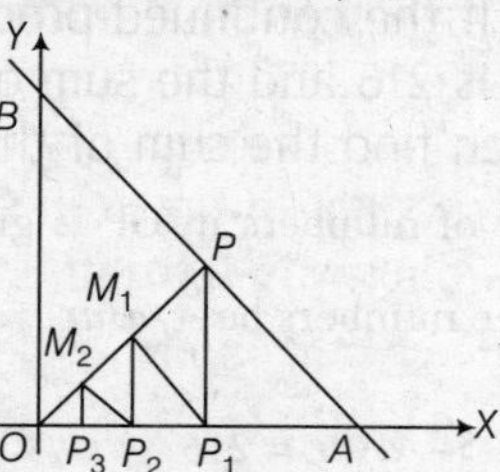

Sol. We have,

$$(OM_{n-1})^2 = (OP_n)^2 + (P_n M_{n-1})^2$$

$$= (OP_n)^2 + (OP_n)^2 = 2(OP_n)^2 = 2\alpha_n^2 \text{ [say]}$$

Also, $(OP_{n-1})^2 = (OM_{n-1})^2 + (P_{n-1}M_{n-1})^2$

$$\Rightarrow \quad \alpha_{n-1}^2 = 2\alpha_n^2 + \frac{1}{2}\alpha_{n-1}^2 \Rightarrow \alpha_n^2 = \frac{1}{4}\alpha_{n-1}^2$$

$$\Rightarrow \quad \alpha_n = \frac{1}{2}\alpha_{n-1}$$

$$\Rightarrow \quad OP_n = \alpha_n = \frac{1}{2}\alpha_{n-1} = \frac{1}{2^2}\alpha_{n-2} = \dots = \frac{1}{2^n}$$

$$\therefore \quad OP_n = \left(\frac{1}{2}\right)^n$$

Use of GP in Solving Practical Problems

In this part, we will see how the formulae relating to GP can be made use of in solving practical problems.

Example 49. Dipesh writes letters to four of his friends. He asks each of them to copy the letter and mail to four different persons with the request that they continue the chain similarly. Assuming that the chain is not broken and that it costs 25 paise to mail one letter, find the total money spent on postage till the 8th set of letters is mailed.

Sol. Number of letters in the 1st set = 4 (These are letters sent by Dipesh)

Number of letters in the 2nd set = 4 + 4 + 4 + 4 = 16

Number of letters in the 3rd set

= 4 + 4 + 4 + ... + 16 terms = 64

⋮ ⋮ ⋮ ⋮

The number of letters sent in the 1st set, 2nd set, 3rd set, ... are respectively 4, 16, 64, ... which is a GP with $a = 4$,

$$r = \frac{16}{4} = \frac{64}{16} = 4$$

∴ Total number of letters in all the first 8 sets

$$= \frac{4(4^8 - 1)}{4 - 1} = 87380$$

∴ Total money spent on letters $= 87380 \times \frac{25}{100} =$ ₹21845

Example 50. An insect starts from a point and travels in a straight path 1 mm in the first second and half of the distance covered in the previous second in the succeeding second. In how much time would it reach a point 3 mm away from its starting point.

Sol. Distance covered by the insect in the 1st second = 1 mm

Distance covered by it in the 2nd second $= 1 \times \frac{1}{2} = \frac{1}{2}$ mm

Distance covered by it in the 3rd second $= \frac{1}{2} \times \frac{1}{2} = \frac{1}{4}$ mm

⋮ ⋮ ⋮ ⋮

The distance covered by the insect in 1st second, 2nd second, 3rd second, ... are respectively $1, \frac{1}{2}, \frac{1}{4}, \dots$, which are in GP with $a = 1$, $r = \frac{1}{2}$. Let time taken by the insect in covering 3 mm be n seconds.

$$\therefore 1 + \frac{1}{2} + \frac{1}{4} + \dots + n \text{ terms} = 3$$

$$\Rightarrow \quad \frac{1 \cdot \left[1 - \left(\frac{1}{2}\right)^n\right]}{1 - \frac{1}{2}} = 3$$

$$\Rightarrow \quad 1 - \left(\frac{1}{2}\right)^n = \frac{3}{2}$$

$$\Rightarrow \quad \left(\frac{1}{2}\right)^n = -\frac{1}{2}$$

$$\Rightarrow \quad 2^n = -2$$

which is impossible because $2^n > 0$

∴ Our supposition is wrong.

∴ There is no $n \in N$, for which the insect could never 3 mm in n seconds.

Hence, it will never to able to cover 3 mm.

Remark

The maximum distance that the insect could cover is 2 mm.

i.e., $$1 + \frac{1}{2} + \frac{1}{4} + \dots = \frac{1}{1 - \frac{1}{2}} = 2$$

Example 51. The pollution in a normal atmosphere is less than 0.01%. Due to leakage of a gas from a factory, the pollution is increased to 20%. If every day 80% of the pollution is neutralised, in how many days the atmosphere will be normal?

Sol. Let the pollution on 1st day = 20

The pollution on 2nd day = 20 × 20% = 20 (0.20)

The pollution on 3rd day = $20(0.20)^2$

⋮ ⋮ ⋮ ⋮

Let in n days the atmosphere will be normal

$$\therefore \quad 20(0.20)^{n-1} < 0.01$$

$$\Rightarrow \quad \left(\frac{2}{10}\right)^{n-1} < \frac{1}{2000}$$

Taking logarithm on base 10, we get

$$(n-1)(\log 2 - \log 10) < \log 1 - \log 2000$$

$$\Rightarrow \quad (n-1)(0.3010 - 1) < 0 - (0.3010 + 3)$$

$$\Rightarrow \quad n - 1 > \frac{3.3010}{0.6990}$$

$$\Rightarrow \quad n > 5.722$$

Hence, the atmosphere will be normal in 6 days.

Exercise for Session 3

1. The fourth, seventh and the last term of a GP are 10, 80 and 2560, respectively. The first term and number of terms in GP are
(a) $\frac{4}{5}$, 12 (b) $\frac{4}{5}$, 10 (c) $\frac{5}{4}$, 12 (d) $\frac{5}{4}$, 10

2. If the first and the nth terms of a GP are a and b respectively and if P is the product of the first n terms, then P^2 is equal to
(a) ab (b) $(ab)^{n/2}$ (c) $(ab)^n$ (d) None of these

3. If $a_1, a_2, a_3, (a_1 > 0)$ are three successive terms of a GP with common ratio r, the value of r for which $a_3 > 4a_2 - 3a_1$ holds is given by
(a) $1 < r < 3$ (b) $-3 < r < -1$ (c) $r < 1$ or $r > 3$ (d) None of these

4. If $x, 2x + 2, 3x + 3$ are in GP, the fourth term is
(a) 27 (b) -27 (c) 13.5 (d) -13.5

5. In a sequence of 21 terms the first 11 terms are in AP with common difference 2 and the last 11 terms are in GP with common ratio 2, if the middle term of the AP is equal to the middle term of GP, the middle term of the entire sequence is
(a) $-\frac{10}{31}$ (b) $\frac{10}{31}$ (c) $-\frac{32}{31}$ (d) $\frac{32}{31}$

6. Three distinct numbers x, y, z form a GP in that order and the numbers $7x + 5y, 7y + 5z, 7z + 5x$ form an AP in that order. The common ratio of GP is
(a) -4 (b) -2 (c) 10 (d) 18

7. The sum to n terms of the series $11 + 103 + 1005 + \dots$ is
(a) $\frac{1}{9}(10^n - 1) + n^2$ (b) $\frac{1}{9}(10^n - 1) + 2n$ (c) $\frac{10}{9}(10^n - 1) + n^2$ (d) $\frac{10}{9}(10^n - 1) + 2n$

8. In an increasing GP, the sum of the first and last term is 66, the product of the second and the last but one is 128 and the sum of the sum of the terms is 126, then the number of terms in the series is
(a) 6 (b) 8 (c) 10 (d) 12

9. If S_1, S_2, S_3 be respectively the sum of $n, 2n$ and $3n$ terms of a GP, then $\frac{S_1(S_3 - S_2)}{(S_2 - S_1)^2}$ is equal to
(a) 1 (b) 2 (c) 3 (d) 4

10. If $|a| < 1$ and $|b| < 1$, then the sum of the series $1 + (1 + a)b + (1 + a + a^2)b^2 + (1 + a + a^2 + a^3)b^3 + \dots$ is
(a) $\frac{1}{(1-a)(1-b)}$ (b) $\frac{1}{(1-a)(1-ab)}$ (c) $\frac{1}{(1-b)(1-ab)}$ (d) $\frac{1}{(1-a)(1-b)(1-ab)}$

11. If the sides of a triangle are in GP and its larger angle is twice the smallest, then the common ratio r satisfies the inequality
(a) $0 < r < \sqrt{2}$ (b) $1 < r < \sqrt{2}$ (c) $1 < r < 2$ (d) $r > \sqrt{2}$

12. If $ax^3 + bx^2 + cx + d$ is divisible by $ax^2 + c$, then a, b, c, d are in
(a) AP (b) GP (c) HP (d) None of these

13. If $(r)_n$ denotes the number $r\,r\,r \dots$ (n digits), where $r = 1, 2, 3, \dots, 9$ and $a = (6)_n, b = (8)_n, c = (4)_{2n}$, then
(a) $a^2 + b + c = 0$ (b) $a^2 + b - c = 0$ (c) $a^2 + b - 2c = 0$ (d) $a^2 + b - 9c = 0$

14. $0.4\dot{2}\dot{7}$ represents the rational number
(a) $\frac{47}{99}$ (b) $\frac{47}{110}$ (c) $\frac{47}{999}$ (d) $\frac{49}{99}$

15. If the product of three numbers in GP be 216 and their sum is 19, then the numbers are
(a) 4, 6, 9 (b) 4, 7, 8 (c) 3, 7, 9 (d) None of these

Session 4

Harmonic Sequence or Harmonic Progression (HP)

Harmonic Sequence or Harmonic Progression (HP)

A Harmonic Progression (HP) is a sequence, if the reciprocals of its terms are in Arithmetic Progression (AP) i.e., $t_1, t_2, t_3, \ldots$ is HP if and only if $\frac{1}{t_1}, \frac{1}{t_2}, \frac{1}{t_3}, \ldots$ is an AP.

For example, The sequence

(i) $\frac{1}{2}, \frac{1}{5}, \frac{1}{8}, \ldots$ (ii) $2, \frac{5}{2}, \frac{10}{3}, \ldots$

(iii) $\frac{1}{a}, \frac{1}{a+d}, \frac{1}{a+2d}, \ldots$ are HP's.

Remark

1. No term of HP can be zero.
2. The most general or standard HP is $\frac{1}{a}, \frac{1}{a+d}, \frac{1}{a+2d}, \frac{1}{a+3d}, \ldots$

Example 52. If a, b, c are in HP, then show that $\frac{a-b}{b-c} = \frac{a}{c}$.

Sol. Since, a, b, c are in HP, therefore

$\frac{1}{a}, \frac{1}{b}, \frac{1}{c}$ are in AP

i.e. $$\frac{1}{b} - \frac{1}{a} = \frac{1}{c} - \frac{1}{b}$$

or $$\frac{a-b}{ab} = \frac{b-c}{bc} \text{ or } \frac{a-b}{b-c} = \frac{a}{c}$$

Remark

A HP may also be defined as a series in which every three consecutive terms (say I, II, III) satisfy $\frac{\text{I}-\text{II}}{\text{II}-\text{III}} = \frac{\text{I}}{\text{III}}$ this relation.

Example 53. Find the first term of a HP whose second term is $\frac{5}{4}$ and the third term is $\frac{1}{2}$.

Sol. Let a be the first term. Then, $a, \frac{5}{4}, \frac{1}{2}$ are in HP.

Then, $$\frac{a - \frac{5}{4}}{\frac{5}{4} - \frac{1}{2}} = \frac{a}{\frac{1}{2}} \quad \text{[from above note]}$$

$$\Rightarrow \frac{4a-5}{5-2} = 2a$$

$$\Rightarrow 4a - 5 = 6a \text{ or } 2a = -5$$

$$\therefore a = -\frac{5}{2}$$

(i) *n*th Term of HP from Beginning

Let a be the first term, d be the common difference of an AP. Then, nth term of an AP from beginning $= a + (n-1)d$

Hence, the nth term of HP from beginning

$$= \frac{1}{a + (n-1)d}, \forall n \in N$$

(ii) *n*th Term of HP from End

Let l be the last term, d be the common difference of an AP. Then,

nth term of an AP from end $= l - (n-1)d$

Hence, the nth term of HP from end $= \frac{1}{l-(n-1)d}, \forall n \in N$

Remark

1. $\frac{1}{n\text{th term of HP from beginning}} + \frac{1}{n\text{th term of HP from end}} = a + l = \frac{1}{\text{first term of HP}} + \frac{1}{\text{last term of HP}}$.
2. There is no general formula for the sum of any number of quantities in HP are generally solved by inverting the terms and making use of the corresponding AP.

Example 54. If $\frac{1}{a} + \frac{1}{c} + \frac{1}{a-b} + \frac{1}{c-b} = 0$, then prove that a, b, c are in HP, unless $b = a + c$.

Sol. We have, $\frac{1}{a} + \frac{1}{c} + \frac{1}{a-b} + \frac{1}{c-b} = 0$

$$\Rightarrow \left(\frac{1}{a} + \frac{1}{c-b}\right) + \left(\frac{1}{c} + \frac{1}{a-b}\right) = 0$$

$$\Rightarrow \frac{(c-b+a)}{a(c-b)} + \frac{(a-b+c)}{c(a-b)} = 0$$

$$\Rightarrow (a+c-b)\left[\frac{1}{a(c-b)} + \frac{1}{c(a-b)}\right] = 0$$

$$\Rightarrow (a+c-b)[2ac - b(a+c)] = 0$$

If $\quad a + c - b \neq 0$, then $2ac - b(a + c) = 0$

or $\quad b = \dfrac{2ac}{a + c}$

Therefore, a, b, c are in HP and if $2ac - b(a + c) \neq 0$, then $a + c - b = 0$ i.e., $b = a + c$.

| Example 55. If $a_1, a_2, a_3, \ldots, a_n$ are in HP, then prove that $a_1a_2 + a_2a_3 + a_3a_4 + \ldots + a_{n-1}a_n = (n-1)a_1a_n$

Sol. Given, $a_1, a_2, a_3, \ldots, a_n$ are in HP.

$\therefore \quad \dfrac{1}{a_1}, \dfrac{1}{a_2}, \dfrac{1}{a_3}, \ldots, \dfrac{1}{a_n}$ are in AP.

Let D be the common difference of the AP, then

$$\frac{1}{a_2} - \frac{1}{a_1} = \frac{1}{a_3} - \frac{1}{a_2} = \frac{1}{a_4} - \frac{1}{a_3} = \ldots = \frac{1}{a_n} - \frac{1}{a_{n-1}} = D$$

$$\Rightarrow \frac{a_1 - a_2}{a_1a_2} = \frac{a_2 - a_3}{a_2a_3} = \frac{a_3 - a_4}{a_3a_4} = \ldots = \frac{a_{n-1} - a_n}{a_{n-1}a_n} = D$$

$$\Rightarrow a_1a_2 = \frac{a_1 - a_2}{D}, a_2a_3 = \frac{a_2 - a_3}{D}, a_3a_4 = \frac{a_3 - a_4}{D},$$

$$\ldots, a_{n-1}a_n = \frac{a_{n-1} - a_n}{D}$$

On adding all such expressions, we get

$$a_1a_2 + a_2a_3 + a_3a_4 + \ldots + a_{n-1}a_n = \frac{a_1 - a_n}{D} = \frac{a_1a_n}{D}\left(\frac{1}{a_n} - \frac{1}{a_1}\right)$$

$$= \frac{a_1a_n}{D}\left[\frac{1}{a_1} + (n-1)D - \frac{1}{a_1}\right] = (n-1)a_1a_n$$

Hence, $a_1a_2 + a_2a_3 + a_3a_4 + \ldots + a_{n-1}a_n = (n-1)a_1a_n$

Remark

In particular case,

1. when $n = 4$ $a_1a_2 + a_2a_3 + a_3a_4 = 3a_1a_4$
2. when $n = 6$ $a_1a_2 + a_2a_3 + a_3a_4 + a_4a_5 + a_5a_6 = 5a_1a_6$

| Example 56. The sum of three numbers in HP is 37 and the sum of their reciprocals is $\frac{1}{4}$. Find the numbers.

Sol. Three numbers in HP can be taken as $\dfrac{1}{a-d}, \dfrac{1}{a}, \dfrac{1}{a+d}$.

Then, $\quad \dfrac{1}{a-d} + \dfrac{1}{a} + \dfrac{1}{a+d} = 37 \quad$ ...(i)

and $\quad a - d + a + a + d = \dfrac{1}{4}$

$\therefore \quad a = \dfrac{1}{12}$

From Eq. (i), $\dfrac{12}{1-12d} + 12 + \dfrac{12}{1+12d} = 37$

$$\Rightarrow \frac{12}{1-12d} + \frac{12}{1+12d} = 25 \Rightarrow \frac{24}{1-144d^2} = 25$$

$$\Rightarrow 1 - 144d^2 = \frac{24}{25} \text{ or } d^2 = \frac{1}{25 \times 144}$$

$$\therefore d = \pm\frac{1}{60}$$

$\therefore$ $a - d, a, a + d$ are $\dfrac{1}{15}, \dfrac{1}{12}, \dfrac{1}{10}$ or $\dfrac{1}{10}, \dfrac{1}{12}, \dfrac{1}{15}$.

Hence, three numbers in HP are 15, 12, 10 or 10, 12, 15.

| Example 57. If pth, qth and rth terms of a HP be respectively a, b and c, then prove that $(q-r)bc + (r-p)ca + (p-q)ab = 0$.

Sol. Let A and D be the first term and common difference of the corresponding AP. Now, a, b, c are respectively the p th, q th and r th terms of HP.

$\therefore \dfrac{1}{a}, \dfrac{1}{b}, \dfrac{1}{c}$ will be respectively the p th, q th and r th terms of the corresponding AP.

$\Rightarrow \quad \dfrac{1}{a} = A + (p-1)D \quad$ ...(i)

$\dfrac{1}{b} = A + (q-1)D \quad$ ...(ii)

$\dfrac{1}{c} = A + (r-1)D \quad$ ...(iii)

On subtracting Eq. (iii) from Eq. (ii), we get

$$\frac{1}{b} - \frac{1}{c} = (q-r)D \Rightarrow bc(q-r) = \frac{(c-b)}{D} = -\frac{(b-c)}{D}$$

So, LHS $= (q-r)bc + (r-p)ca + (p-q)ab$

$$= -\frac{1}{D}\{b - c + c - a + a - b\} = 0 = \text{RHS}$$

Theorem Relating to the Three Series

If a, b, c are three consecutive terms of a series, then

if $\dfrac{a-b}{b-c} = \dfrac{a}{a}$, then a, b, c are in AP.

if $\dfrac{a-b}{b-c} = \dfrac{a}{b}$, then a, b, c are in GP and if $\dfrac{a-b}{b-c} = \dfrac{a}{c}$, then a, b, c are in HP.

Mixed Examples on AP, GP and HP

| Example 58. If a, b, c are in AP and a^2, b^2, c^2 be in HP. Then, prove that $-\dfrac{a}{2}, b, c$ are in GP or else $a = b = c$.

Sol. Given, a, b, c are in AP.

$$\therefore \quad b = \frac{a+c}{2} \quad \text{...(i)}$$

and a^2, b^2, c^2 are in HP.

$$\therefore \quad b^2 = \frac{2a^2c^2}{a^2 + c^2} \quad \text{...(ii)}$$

From Eq. (ii) $b^2 \{(a+c)^2 - 2ac\} = 2a^2c^2$

$$\Rightarrow \quad b^2 \{(2b)^2 - 2ac\} = 2a^2c^2 \quad \text{[from Eq. (i)]}$$

$$\Rightarrow \quad 2b^4 - acb^2 - a^2c^2 = 0$$

$$\Rightarrow \quad (2b^2 + ac)(b^2 - ac) = 0$$

$$\Rightarrow \quad 2b^2 + ac = 0 \text{ or } b^2 - ac = 0$$

If $2b^2 + ac = 0$, then $b^2 = -\frac{1}{2}ac$ or $-\frac{a}{2}, b, c$ are in GP

and if $b^2 - ac = 0 \Rightarrow a, b, c$ are in GP.

But given, a, b, c are in AP.

Which is possible only when $a = b = c$

Example 59. If a, b, c are in HP, b, c, d are in GP and c, d, e are in AP, then show that $e = \frac{ab^2}{(2a-b)^2}$.

Sol. Given, a, b, c are in HP.

$$\therefore \quad b = \frac{2ac}{a+c} \text{ or } c = \frac{ab}{2a-b} \quad \text{...(i)}$$

Given, b, c, d are in GP.

$$\therefore \quad c^2 = bd \quad \text{...(ii)}$$

and given, c, d, e are in AP.

$$\therefore \quad d = \frac{c+e}{2}$$

$$\Rightarrow \quad e = 2d - c$$

$$e = \left(\frac{2c^2}{b} - c\right) \quad \text{[from Eq. (ii)] ...(iii)}$$

From Eqs. (i) and (iii), $e = \frac{2}{b}\left(\frac{ab}{2a-b}\right)^2 - \left(\frac{ab}{2a-b}\right)$

$$= \frac{ab}{(2a-b)^2}\{2a - (2a-b)\}$$

$$= \frac{ab^2}{(2a-b)^2}$$

Example 60. If a, b, c, d and e be five real numbers such that a, b, c are in AP; b, c, d are in GP; c, d, e are in HP. If $a = 2$ and $e = 18$, then find all possible values of b, c and d.

Sol. Given, a, b, c are in AP,

$$\therefore \quad b = \frac{a+c}{2} \quad \text{...(i)}$$

b, c, d are in GP,

$$\therefore \quad c^2 = bd \quad \text{...(ii)}$$

and c, d, e are in HP.

$$\therefore \quad d = \frac{2ce}{c+e} \quad \text{...(iii)}$$

Now, substituting the values of b and d in Eq. (ii), then

$$c^2 = \left(\frac{a+c}{2}\right)\left(\frac{2ce}{c+e}\right)$$

$$\Rightarrow \quad c(c+e) = e(a+c)$$

$$\Rightarrow \quad c^2 = ae \quad \text{...(iv)}$$

Given, $a = 2, e = 18$

From Eq. (iv), $c^2 = (2)(18) = 36$

$$\therefore \quad c = \pm 6$$

From Eq. (i), $b = \frac{2 \pm 6}{2} = 4, -2$

and from Eq. (ii), $d = \frac{c^2}{b} = \frac{36}{b} = \frac{36}{4}$ or $\frac{36}{-2}$

$$\therefore \quad d = 9 \text{ or } -18$$

Hence, $c = 6, b = 4, d = 9$ or $c = -6, b = -2, d = -18$

Example 61. If three positive numbers a, b and c are in AP, GP and HP as well, then find their values.

Sol. Since a, b, c are in AP, GP and HP as well

$$\therefore \quad b = \frac{a+c}{2} \quad \text{...(i)}$$

$$b^2 = ac \quad \text{...(ii)}$$

and

$$b = \frac{2ac}{a+c} \quad \text{...(iii)}$$

From Eqs. (i) and (ii), we have

$$\left(\frac{a+c}{2}\right)^2 = ac$$

or $(a+c)^2 = 4ac$

or $(a+c)^2 - 4ac = 0$

or $(a-c)^2 = 0$

$$\therefore \quad a = c \quad \text{...(iv)}$$

On putting $c = a$ in Eq. (i), we get $b = \frac{a+a}{2} = a$ ...(v)

From Eqs. (iv) and (v), $a = b = c$, thus the three numbers will be equal.

Remark

1. If three positive numbers are in any two of AP, GP and HP, then it will be also in third.
2. Thus, if three positive numbers are in any two of AP, GP and HP, then they will be in the third progression and the numbers will be equal.

Exercise for Session 4

1. If a, b, c are in AP and b, c, d be in HP, then

(a) $ab = cd$ (b) $ad = bc$ (c) $ac = bd$ (d) $abcd = 1$

2. If a, b, c are in AP, then $\frac{a}{bc}, \frac{1}{c}, \frac{2}{b}$ are in

(a) AP (b) GP (c) HP (d) None of these

3. If a, b, c are in AP and a, b, d are in GP, then $a, a - b, d - c$ will be in

(a) AP (b) GP (c) HP (d) None of these

4. If $x, 1, z$ are in AP and $x, 2, z$ are in GP, then $x, 4, z$ will be in

(a) AP (b) GP (c) HP (d) None of these

5. If a, b, c are in GP, $a - b, c - a, b - c$ are in HP, then $a + 4b + c$ is equal to

(a) 0 (b) 1 (c) -1 (d) None of these

6. If $(m + 1)$th, $(n + 1)$th and $(r + 1)$th terms of an AP are in GP and m, n, r are in HP, then the value of the ratio of the common difference to the first term of the AP is

(a) $-\frac{2}{n}$ (b) $\frac{2}{n}$ (c) $-\frac{n}{2}$ (d) $\frac{n}{2}$

7. If a, b, c are in AP and a^2, b^2, c^2 are in HP, then

(a) $a = b = c$ (b) $2b = 3a + c$ (c) $b^2 = \sqrt{\left(\frac{ac}{8}\right)}$ (d) None of these

8. If a, b, c are in HP, then $\frac{a}{b + c}, \frac{b}{c + a}, \frac{c}{a + b}$ are in

(a) AP (b) GP (c) HP (d) None of these

9. If $\frac{x + y}{2}, y, \frac{y + z}{2}$ are in HP, then x, y, z are in

(a) AP (b) GP (c) HP (d) None of these

10. If $\frac{a + b}{1 - ab}, b, \frac{b + c}{1 - bc}$ are in AP, then $a, \frac{1}{b}, c$ are in

(a) AP (b) GP (c) HP (d) None of these

Session 5

Mean

Mean

Arithmetic Mean

If three terms are in AP, then the middle term is called the **Arithmetic Mean** (or shortly written as AM) between the other two, so if a, b, c are in AP, then b is the AM of a and c.

(i) Single AM of n Positive Numbers

Let n positive numbers be $a_1, a_2, a_3, \ldots, a_n$ and A be the AM of these numbers, then

$$A = \frac{a_1 + a_2 + a_3 + \ldots + a_n}{n}$$

In particular Let a and b be two given numbers and A be the AM between them, then a, A, b are in AP.

$$\therefore \quad A = \frac{a+b}{2}$$

Remark

1. AM of $2a, 3b, 5c$ is $\frac{2a + 3b + 5c}{3}$.
2. AM of $a_1, a_2, a_3, \ldots, a_{n-1}, 2a_n$ is $\frac{a_1 + a_2 + a_3 + \ldots + a_{n-1} + 2a_n}{n}$.

(ii) Insert n-Arithmetic Mean Between Two Numbers

Let a and b be two given numbers and $A_1, A_2, A_3, \ldots, A_n$ are AM's between them.

Then, $a, A_1, A_2, A_3, \ldots, A_n, b$ will be in AP.

Now, $b = (n+2)$ th term $= a + (n + 2 - 1)\, d$

$$\therefore \quad d = \left(\frac{b-a}{n+1}\right)$$

[Remember] [where, d = common difference] ...(i)

$$\therefore \quad A_1 = a + d, A_2 = a + 2d, \ldots, A_n = a + nd$$

$$\Rightarrow \quad A_1 = a + \left(\frac{b-a}{n+1}\right), A_2 = a + 2\left(\frac{b-a}{n+1}\right), \ldots, A_n = a + n\left(\frac{b-a}{n+1}\right)$$

***Corollary* I The sum of n AM's between two given quantities is equal to n times the AM between them.**

Let two numbers be a and b and $A_1, A_2, A_3, \ldots, A_n$ are n AM's between them.

Then, $a, A_1, A_2, A_3, \ldots, A_n, b$ will be in AP.

$\therefore$ Sum of n AM's between a and b

$$= A_1 + A_2 + A_3 + \ldots + A_n$$

$$= \frac{n}{2}(A_1 + A_n) \quad [\because A_1, A_2, A_3, \ldots, A_n \text{ are in AP}]$$

$$= \frac{n}{2}(a + d + a + nd) = \frac{n}{2}[2a + (n+1)\,d]$$

$$= \frac{n}{2}(2a + b - a) \quad [\text{from Eq. (i)}]$$

$$= n\left(\frac{a+b}{2}\right) = n \quad [\text{AM between } a \text{ and } b]$$

[Remember]

Aliter $A_1 + A_2 + A_3 + \ldots + A_n$

$$= (a + A_1 + A_2 + A_3 + \ldots + A_n + b) - (a + b)$$

$$= \frac{(n+2)}{2}(a+b) - (a+b) = n\left(\frac{a+b}{2}\right)$$

$$= n \quad [\text{AM of } a \text{ and } b]$$

Aliter

[This method is applicable only when n is even]

$$A_1 + A_2 + A_3 + \ldots + A_{n-2} + A_{n-1} + A_n$$

$$= (A_1 + A_n) + (A_2 + A_{n-1}) + (A_3 + A_{n-2}) + \ldots \text{ upto } \frac{n}{2} \text{ terms}$$

$$= (a+b) + (a+b) + (a+b) + \ldots \text{ upto } \frac{n}{2} \text{ times}$$

$$[\because T_n + T'_n = a + l]$$

$$= \frac{n}{2}(a+b) = n\left(\frac{a+b}{2}\right) = n \quad [\text{AM of } a \text{ and } b]$$

***Corollary* II The sum of m AM's between any two numbers is to the sum of n AM's between them as $m : n$.**

Let two numbers be a and b.

$\therefore$ Sum of m AM's between a and $b = m$ [AM of a and b] ...(i)

Similarly, sum of n AM's between a and $b = n$ [AM of a and b] ...(ii)

$$\therefore \quad \frac{\text{Sum of } m \text{ AM's}}{\text{Sum of } n \text{ AM's}} = \frac{m(\text{AM of } a \text{ and } b)}{n(\text{AM of } a \text{ and } b)} = \frac{m}{n}$$

Example 62. If a, b, c are in AP and p is the AM between a and b and q is the AM between b and c, then show that b is the AM between p and q.

Sol. $\because$ a, b, c are in AP.

$$\therefore \quad 2b = a + c \quad \text{...(i)}$$

$\because$ p is the AM between a and b.

$$\therefore \quad p = \frac{a+b}{2} \quad \text{...(ii)}$$

$\because$ q is the AM between b and c.

$$\therefore \quad q = \frac{b+c}{2} \quad \text{...(iii)}$$

On adding Eqs. (ii) and (iii), then

$$p + q = \frac{a+b}{2} + \frac{b+c}{2} = \frac{a+c+2b}{2} = \frac{2b+2b}{2} \quad \text{[using Eq. (i)]}$$

$$\therefore \quad p + q = 2b \text{ or } b = \frac{p+q}{2}$$

Hence, b is the AM between p and q.

Example 63. Find n, so that $\dfrac{a^{n+1}+b^{n+1}}{a^n+b^n}$ $(a \neq b)$ be the AM between a and b.

Sol. $\because$

$$\frac{a^{n+1}+b^{n+1}}{a^n+b^n} = \frac{a+b}{2}$$

$$\Rightarrow \quad \frac{b^{n+1}\left[\left(\frac{a}{b}\right)^{n+1}+1\right]}{b^n\left[\left(\frac{a}{b}\right)^n+1\right]} = \frac{b}{2}\left[\left(\frac{a}{b}\right)+1\right]$$

$$\Rightarrow \quad 2\left[\left(\frac{a}{b}\right)^{n+1}+1\right] = \left[\left(\frac{a}{b}\right)^n+1\right]\left(\frac{a}{b}+1\right)$$

Let $\quad \dfrac{a}{b} = \lambda$

$$\therefore \quad 2\lambda^{n+1} + 2 = (\lambda^n + 1)(\lambda + 1)$$

$$\Rightarrow \quad 2\lambda^{n+1} + 2 = \lambda^{n+1} + \lambda^n + \lambda + 1$$

$$\Rightarrow \quad \lambda^{n+1} - \lambda^n - \lambda + 1 = 0 \Rightarrow (\lambda^n - 1)(\lambda - 1) = 0$$

$$\lambda - 1 \neq 0 \quad [\because a \neq b]$$

$$\therefore \quad \lambda^n - 1 = 0 \Rightarrow \lambda^n = 1 = \lambda^0$$

$$\Rightarrow \quad n = 0$$

Example 64. There are n AM's between 3 and 54 such that 8th mean is to $(n-2)$ th mean as 3 to 5. Find n.

Sol. Let $A_1, A_2, A_3, \ldots, A_n$ be n AM's between 3 and 54.

If d be the common difference, then

$$d = \frac{54-3}{n+1} = \frac{51}{n+1} \quad \text{...(i)}$$

According to the example,

$$\frac{A_8}{A_{n-2}} = \frac{3}{5}$$

$$\Rightarrow \quad 5(3+8d) = 3[3+(n-2)d] \Rightarrow 6 = d(3n-46)$$

$$\Rightarrow \quad 6 = (3n-46)\frac{51}{(n+1)} \quad \text{[from Eq. (i)]}$$

$$\Rightarrow \quad 6n + 6 = 153n - 2346 \Rightarrow 147n = 2352$$

$$\therefore \quad n = 16$$

Example 65. If 11 AM's are inserted between 28 and 10, then find the three middle terms in the series.

Sol. Let $A_1, A_2, A_3, \ldots, A_{11}$ be 11 AM's between 28 and 10.

If d be the common difference, then

$$d = \frac{10-28}{12} = -\frac{3}{2}$$

Total means = 11 (odd)

$$\therefore \quad \text{Middle mean} = \left(\frac{11+1}{2}\right)\text{th} = 6\text{th} = A_6$$

Then, three middle terms are A_5, A_6 and A_7.

$$\therefore \quad A_5 = 28 + 5d = 28 - \frac{15}{2} = \frac{41}{2}$$

$$A_6 = 28 + 6d = 28 - 9 = 19$$

and $$A_7 = 28 + 7d = 28 - \frac{21}{2} = \frac{35}{2}$$

Example 66. If a, b, c are in AP, then show that $a^2(b+c) + b^2(c+a) + c^2(a+b) = \frac{2}{9}(a+b+c)^3$.

Sol. $\because$ a, b, c are in AP.

$$\therefore \quad b = \frac{a+c}{2} \text{ i.e., } 2b = a + c \quad \text{...(i)}$$

$$\begin{aligned} \text{LHS} &= a^2(b+c) + b^2(c+a) + c^2(a+b) \\ &= (a^2b + a^2c) + b^2(2b) + (c^2a + c^2b) \\ &= b(a^2+c^2) + ac(a+c) + 2b^3 \\ &= b[(a+c)^2 - 2ac] + ac(2b) + 2b^3 \\ &= b(a+c)^2 + 2b^3 = b(2b)^2 + 2b^3 = 6b^3 \end{aligned}$$

$$\begin{aligned} \text{RHS} &= \frac{2}{9}(a+b+c)^3 = \frac{2}{9}(2b+b)^3 \\ &= \frac{2}{9} \times 27b^3 = 6b^3 \end{aligned}$$

Hence, LHS = RHS

Geometric Mean

If three terms are in GP, then the middle term is called the **Geometric Mean** (or shortly written as GM) between the other two, so if a, b, c are in GP, then b is the GM of a and c.

(i) Single GM of *n* Positive Numbers

Let n positive numbers be $a_1, a_2, a_3, \ldots, a_n$ and G be the GM of these numbers, then $G = (a_1 a_2 a_3 \ldots a_n)^{1/n}$

In particular Let a and b be two numbers and G be the GM between them, then a, G, b are in GP.
Hence, $G = \sqrt{ab}$; $a > 0, b > 0$

Remark

1. If $a < 0, b < 0$, then $G = -\sqrt{ab}$
2. If $a < 0, b > 0$ or $a > 0, b < 0$, then GM between a and b does not exist.

Example

(i) The GM between 4 and 9 is given by

$$G = \sqrt{4 \times 9} = 6$$

(ii) The GM between -4 and -9 is given by

$$G = \sqrt{-4 \times -9} = -6$$

(iii) The GM between -4 and 9 or 4 and -9 does not exist.

i.e. $\sqrt{(-4) \times 9} = \sqrt{-1}\sqrt{36} = 6i$

and $\sqrt{4 \times (-9)} = \sqrt{-1}\sqrt{36} = 6i$

(ii) Insert *n*-Geometric Mean Between Two Numbers

Let a and b be two given numbers and $G_1, G_2, G_3, \ldots, G_n$ are n GM's between them.

Then, $a, G_1, G_2, G_3, \ldots, G_n, b$ will be in GP.

Now, $b = (n+2)$ th term $= ar^{n+2-1}$

$$\therefore \quad r = \left(\frac{b}{a}\right)^{\frac{1}{n+1}} \text{ [where } r = \text{common ratio] [Remember]} \quad \ldots(i)$$

$$\therefore \quad G_1 = ar, G_2 = ar^2, \ldots, G_n = ar^n$$

$$\Rightarrow \quad G_1 = a\left(\frac{b}{a}\right)^{\frac{1}{n+1}}, G_2 = a\left(\frac{b}{a}\right)^{\frac{2}{n+1}}, \ldots, G_n = a\left(\frac{b}{a}\right)^{\frac{n}{n+1}}$$

Corollary **The product of n geometric means between a and b is equal to the nth power of the geometric mean between a and b.**

Let two numbers be a and b and $G_1, G_2, G_3, \ldots, G_n$ are n GM's between them.

Then, $a, G_1, G_2, G_3, \ldots, G_n, b$ will be in GP.

$\therefore$ Product of n GM's between a and b

$$= G_1 G_2 G_3 \ldots G_n = (ar)(ar^2)(ar^3)\ldots(ar^n)$$

$$= a^{1+1+1+\ldots+1} \cdot r^{1+2+3+\ldots+n}$$

$$= a^n \cdot r^{\frac{n(n+1)}{2}} = a^n \cdot \left[\left(\frac{b}{a}\right)^{\frac{1}{n+1}}\right]^{\frac{n(n+1)}{2}} \quad \text{[from Eq. (i)]}$$

$$= a^n \left(\frac{b}{a}\right)^{\frac{n}{2}} = a^{n/2} b^{n/2} = (\sqrt{ab})^n$$

$$= [\text{GM of } a \text{ and } b]^n \quad \text{[Remember]}$$

Aliter [This method is applicable only when n is even]

$$G_1 G_2 G_3 \ldots G_{n-2}\, G_{n-1}\, G_n = (G_1\, G_n)(G_2 G_{n-1})(G_3 G_{n-2})\ldots \frac{n}{2} \text{ factors}$$

$$= (ab)(ab)(ab)\ldots \frac{n}{2} \text{ factors} \quad [\because T_n \times T_n' = a \times l]$$

$$= (ab)^{n/2} = (\sqrt{ab})^n = [\text{GM of } a \text{ and } b]^n$$

| Example 67. If a be one AM and G_1 and G_2 be two geometric means between b and c, then prove that $G_1^3 + G_2^3 = 2abc$.

Sol. Given, $a =$ AM between b and c

$$\Rightarrow \quad a = \frac{b+c}{2} \Rightarrow 2a = b + c \quad \ldots(i)$$

Again, b, G_1, G_2, c are in GP.

$$\therefore \quad \frac{G_1}{b} = \frac{G_2}{G_1} = \frac{c}{G_2} \Rightarrow b = \frac{G_1^2}{G_2}, c = \frac{G_2^2}{G_1}$$

$$\text{and} \quad G_1 G_2 = bc \quad \ldots(ii)$$

From Eqs. (i) and (ii),

$$2a = \frac{G_1^2}{G_2} + \frac{G_2^2}{G_1} = \frac{G_1^3 + G_2^3}{G_1 G_2} = \frac{G_1^3 + G_2^3}{bc} \quad [\because G_1 G_2 = bc]$$

$$\Rightarrow \quad G_1^3 + G_2^3 = 2abc$$

| Example 68. If one geometric mean G and two arithmetic means p and q be inserted between two quantities, then show that $G^2 = (2p - q)(2q - p)$.

Sol. Let the two quantities be a and b, then

$$G^2 = ab \quad \ldots(i)$$

Again, a, p, q, b are in AP.

$$\therefore \quad p - a = q - p = b - q$$

$$\Rightarrow \quad a = 2p - q$$

$$b = 2q - p \quad \ldots(ii)$$

From Eqs. (i) and (ii), we get

$$G^2 = (2p - q)(2q - p)$$

| Example 69. Find n, so that $\dfrac{a^{n+1} + b^{n+1}}{a^n + b^n} (a \neq b)$ be the GM between a and b.

Sol. $\because \quad \dfrac{a^{n+1} + b^{n+1}}{a^n + b^n} = \sqrt{ab}$

$$\Rightarrow \frac{b^{n+1}\left[\left(\frac{a}{b}\right)^{n+1}+1\right]}{b^n\left[\left(\frac{a}{b}\right)^n+1\right]} = b\sqrt{\frac{a}{b}} \Rightarrow \frac{\left(\frac{a}{b}\right)^{n+1}+1}{\left(\frac{a}{b}\right)^n+1} = \left(\frac{a}{b}\right)^{\frac{1}{2}}$$

Let $\frac{a}{b} = \lambda$

$$\Rightarrow \frac{\lambda^{n+1}+1}{\lambda^n+1} = \lambda^{\frac{1}{2}} \Rightarrow \lambda^{n+1}+1 = \lambda^{n+\frac{1}{2}} + \lambda^{\frac{1}{2}}$$

$$\Rightarrow \lambda^{n+\frac{1}{2}}(\lambda^{\frac{1}{2}}-1) - (\lambda^{\frac{1}{2}}-1) = 0$$

$$\Rightarrow (\lambda^{\frac{1}{2}}-1)(\lambda^{n+\frac{1}{2}}-1) = 0$$

$$\Rightarrow \lambda^{\frac{1}{2}}-1 \neq 0 \quad [\because a \neq b]$$

$$\therefore \lambda^{n+\frac{1}{2}}-1 = 0$$

$$\Rightarrow \lambda^{n+\frac{1}{2}} = 1 = \lambda^0$$

$$\Rightarrow n+\frac{1}{2} = 0 \text{ or } n = -\frac{1}{2}$$

| Example 70. Insert five geometric means between $\frac{1}{3}$ and 9 and verify that their product is the fifth power of the geometric mean between $\frac{1}{3}$ and 9.

Sol. Let G_1, G_2, G_3, G_4, G_5 be 5 GM's between $\frac{1}{3}$ and 9.

Then, $\frac{1}{3}, G_1, G_2, G_3, G_4, G_5, 9$ are in GP.

Here, $r = \text{common ratio} = \left(\frac{9}{\frac{1}{3}}\right)^{1/6} = 3^{\frac{1}{2}} = \sqrt{3}$

$$\therefore G_1 = ar = \frac{1}{3}\cdot\sqrt{3} = \frac{1}{\sqrt{3}}$$

$$G_2 = ar^2 = \frac{1}{3}\cdot 3 = 1$$

$$G_3 = ar^3 = \frac{1}{3}\cdot 3\sqrt{3} = \sqrt{3}$$

$$G_4 = ar^4 = \frac{1}{3}\cdot 9 = 3$$

$$G_5 = ar^5 = \frac{1}{3}\cdot 9\sqrt{3} = 3\sqrt{3}$$

Now, $\text{Product} = G_1 \times G_2 \times G_3 \times G_4 \times G_5$

$$= \frac{1}{\sqrt{3}} \times 1 \times \sqrt{3} \times 3 \times 3\sqrt{3} = 9\sqrt{3} = (3)^{\frac{5}{2}} = \left(\sqrt{\frac{1}{3}\times 9}\right)^5$$

$$= \left[\text{GM of } \frac{1}{3} \text{ and } 9\right]^5$$

An Important Theorem

Let a and b be two real, positive and unequal numbers and A, G are arithmetic and geometric means between them, then

(i) a and b are the roots of the equation

$$x^2 - 2Ax + G^2 = 0 \quad \text{[Remember]}$$

(ii) a and b are given by $A \pm \sqrt{(A+G)(A-G)}$ [Remember]

(iii) $A > G$ [Remember]

Proof $\because A$ is the AM between a and b, then

$$A = \frac{a+b}{2} \Rightarrow a+b = 2A \quad \text{...(i)}$$

and G is the GM between a and b, then

$$G = \sqrt{ab} \Rightarrow ab = G^2 \quad \text{...(ii)}$$

$\therefore a$ and b are the roots of the equation, then

$x^2 - (\text{sum of roots})\, x + \text{product of roots} = 0$

$$\Rightarrow x^2 - (a+b)\,x + ab = 0$$

i.e. $x^2 - 2Ax + G^2 = 0$ is the required equation.

$$\Rightarrow x = \frac{2A \pm \sqrt{(-2A)^2 - 4\cdot 1\cdot G^2}}{2\cdot 1} = A \pm \sqrt{(A^2 - G^2)}$$

$$\therefore x = A \pm \sqrt{(A+G)(A-G)}$$

Now, for real, positive and unequal numbers of a and b,

$$(A+G)(A-G) > 0 \Rightarrow (A-G) > 0$$

$$\therefore A > G$$

Remark

1. If a and b are real and positive numbers, then $A \geq G$
2. If $a_1, a_2, a_3, \ldots, a_n$ are n positive numbers, then AM $\geq$ GM i.e., $$\frac{a_1 + a_2 + a_3 + \ldots + a_n}{n} \geq (a_1 a_2 a_3 \ldots a_n)^{1/n}$$
3. (i) If $a > 0, b > 0$ or $a < 0, b < 0$ and $\lambda_1 > 0, \lambda_2 > 0$, then $\lambda_1\frac{a}{b} + \lambda_2\frac{b}{a} \geq 2\sqrt{\lambda_1\lambda_2}$
   if $\frac{a}{b} = x > 0$ and $\lambda_1 = \lambda_2 = 1$, then $x + \frac{1}{x} \geq 2$
   (ii) If $a > 0, b < 0$ or $a < 0, b > 0$ and $\lambda_1 > 0, \lambda_2 > 0$, then $\lambda_1\frac{a}{b} + \lambda_2\frac{b}{a} \leq -2\sqrt{\lambda_1\lambda_2}$
   if $\frac{a}{b} = x < 0$ and $\lambda_1 > 0, \lambda_2 > 0$ then, $x + \frac{1}{x} \leq -2$

| Example 71. AM between two numbers whose sum is 100 is to the GM as 5 : 4, find the numbers.

Sol. Let the numbers be a and b.

Then, $a + b = 100$

or $2A = 100$

$\Rightarrow \quad A = 50 \quad \text{...(i)}$

and given, $\frac{A}{G} = \frac{5}{4} \Rightarrow \frac{50}{G} = \frac{5}{4}$ [from Eq. (i)]

$\therefore \quad G = 40 \quad \text{...(ii)}$

From important theorem $a, b = A \pm \sqrt{(A+G)(A-G)}$

$$= 50 \pm \sqrt{(50+40)(50-40)}$$

$$= 50 \pm 30 = 80, 20$$

$\therefore \quad a = 80, b = 20$

or $\quad a = 20, b = 80$

Example 72. If $a_1, a_2, \dots, a_n$ are positive real numbers whose product is a fixed number c, then find the minimum value of $a_1 + a_2 + \dots + a_{n-1} + 3a_n$.

Sol. $\because$ AM $\geq$ GM

$$\therefore \frac{a_1 + a_2 + \dots + a_{n-1} + 3a_n}{n} \geq (a_1 a_2 \dots a_{n-1} 3a_n)^{1/n} = (3c)^{1/n}$$

$$\Rightarrow a_1 + a_2 + \dots + a_{n-1} + 3a_n \geq n(3c)^{1/n}$$

Hence, the minimum value of $a_1 + a_2 + \dots + a_{n-1} + 3a_n$ is $n(3c)^{1/n}$.

Harmonic Mean

If three terms are in HP, then the middle term is called the **Harmonic Mean** (or shortly written as HM) between the other two, so if a, b, c are in HP, then b is the HM of a and c.

(i) Single HM of n Positive Numbers

Let n positive numbers be $a_1, a_2, a_3, \dots, a_n$ and H be the HM of these numbers, then

$$H = \frac{n}{\left(\frac{1}{a_1} + \frac{1}{a_2} + \frac{1}{a_3} + \dots + \frac{1}{a_n}\right)}$$

In particular Let a and b be two given numbers and H be the HM between them a, H, b are in HP.

Hence, $H = \frac{2}{\frac{1}{a} + \frac{1}{b}}$ i.e., $H = \frac{2ab}{(a+b)}$

Remark

HM of a, b, c is $\frac{3}{\frac{1}{a} + \frac{1}{b} + \frac{1}{c}}$ or $\frac{3abc}{ab + bc + ca}$.

Caution The AM between two numbers a and b is $\frac{a+b}{2}$. It does not follow that HM between the same numbers is $\frac{2}{a+b}$. The HM is the reciprocals of $\frac{\frac{1}{a} + \frac{1}{b}}{2}$ i.e., $\frac{2ab}{(a+b)}$.

(ii) Insert n-Harmonic Mean Between Two Numbers

Let a and b be two given numbers and $H_1, H_2, H_3, \dots, H_n$ are n HM's between them.

Then, $a, H_1, H_2, H_3, \dots, H_n, b$ will be in HP, if D be the common difference of the corresponding AP.

$\therefore b = (n+2)$ th term of HP.

$$= \frac{1}{(n+2)\text{th term of corresponding AP}}$$

$$= \frac{1}{\frac{1}{a} + (n+2-1)D}$$

$$\Rightarrow \quad D = \frac{\frac{1}{b} - \frac{1}{a}}{(n+1)} \quad \text{[Remember]}$$

$$\therefore \quad \frac{1}{H_1} = \frac{1}{a} + D, \ \frac{1}{H_2} = \frac{1}{a} + 2D, \dots, \frac{1}{H_n} = \frac{1}{a} + nD$$

$$\Rightarrow \quad \frac{1}{H_1} = \frac{1}{a} + \frac{(a-b)}{ab(n+1)}, \ \frac{1}{H_2} = \frac{1}{a} + \frac{2(a-b)}{ab(n+1)}, \dots, \frac{1}{H_n} = \frac{1}{a} + \frac{n(a-b)}{ab(n+1)}$$

***Corollary* The sum of reciprocals of n harmonic means between two given numbers is n times the reciprocal of single HM between them.**

Let two numbers be a and b and $H_1, H_2, H_3, \dots, H_n$ are n HM's between them. Then, $a, H_1, H_2, H_3, \dots, H_n, b$ will be in HP.

$$\therefore \quad \frac{1}{H_1} + \frac{1}{H_2} + \frac{1}{H_3} + \dots + \frac{1}{H_n} = \frac{n}{2}\left(\frac{1}{H_1} + \frac{1}{H_n}\right) \quad \left[\because S_n = \frac{n}{2}(a+l)\right]$$

$$= \frac{n}{2}\left(\frac{1}{a} + D + \frac{1}{b} - D\right) = \frac{n}{2}\left(\frac{1}{a} + \frac{1}{b}\right)$$

$$= \frac{n}{\left(\frac{2}{\frac{1}{a} + \frac{1}{b}}\right)} = \frac{n}{[\text{HM of } a \text{ and } b]}$$

Aliter [This method is applicable only when n is even]

$$\frac{1}{H_1} + \frac{1}{H_2} + \frac{1}{H_3} + \dots + \frac{1}{H_{n-2}} + \frac{1}{H_{n-1}} + \frac{1}{H_n}$$

$$= \left(\frac{1}{H_1} + \frac{1}{H_n}\right) + \left(\frac{1}{H_2} + \frac{1}{H_{n-1}}\right) + \left(\frac{1}{H_3} + \frac{1}{H_{n-2}}\right) + \dots \text{ upto } \frac{n}{2} \text{ terms}$$

$$=\left(\frac{1}{a}+D+\frac{1}{b}-D\right)+\left(\frac{1}{a}+2D+\frac{1}{b}-2D\right)$$
$$+\left(\frac{1}{a}+3D+\frac{1}{b}-3D\right)+\ldots\text{upto } \frac{n}{2} \text{ terms}$$
$$=\left(\frac{1}{a}+\frac{1}{b}\right)+\left(\frac{1}{a}+\frac{1}{b}\right)+\left(\frac{1}{a}+\frac{1}{b}\right)+\ldots\text{ upto } \frac{n}{2} \text{ terms}$$
$$=\frac{n}{2}\left(\frac{1}{a}+\frac{1}{b}\right)=\frac{n}{\left(\frac{2}{\frac{1}{a}+\frac{1}{b}}\right)}=\frac{n}{(\text{HM of } a \text{ and } b)}$$

Example 73. If H be the harmonic mean between x and y, then show that $\frac{H+x}{H-x}+\frac{H+y}{H-y}=2$

Sol. We have, $H=\frac{2xy}{x+y}$

$$\therefore \quad \frac{H}{x}=\frac{2y}{x+y} \text{ and } \frac{H}{y}=\frac{2x}{x+y}$$

By componendo and dividendo, we have

$$\frac{H+x}{H-x}=\frac{2y+x+y}{2y-x-y}=\frac{x+3y}{y-x}$$
and
$$\frac{H+y}{H-y}=\frac{2x+x+y}{2x-x-y}=\frac{3x+y}{x-y}$$
$$\therefore \quad \frac{H+x}{H-x}+\frac{H+y}{H-y}=\frac{x+3y}{y-x}+\frac{3x+y}{x-y}$$
$$=\frac{x+3y-3x-y}{y-x}=\frac{2(y-x)}{(y-x)}=2$$

Aliter $\frac{H+x}{H-x}+\frac{H+y}{H-y}=2$

$$\Rightarrow \left(\frac{H+x}{H-x}-1\right)=\left(1-\frac{H+y}{H-y}\right) \Rightarrow \frac{2x}{H-x}=\frac{-2y}{H-y}$$

i.e. $Hx-xy=-Hy+xy \Rightarrow H(x+y)=2xy$

i.e. $H=\frac{2xy}{(x+y)}$

which is true as, x, H, y are in HP. Hence, the required result.

Example 74. If $a_1, a_2, a_3, \ldots, a_{10}$ be in AP and $h_1, h_2, h_3, \ldots, h_{10}$ be in HP. If $a_1=h_1=2$ and $a_{10}=h_{10}=3$, then find the value of $a_4 h_7$.

Sol. $\because$ $a_1, a_2, a_3, \ldots, a_{10}$ are in AP.

If d be the common difference, then

$$d=\frac{a_{10}-a_1}{9}=\frac{3-2}{9}=\frac{1}{9}$$
$$\therefore \quad a_4=a_1+3d=2+\frac{3}{9}=2+\frac{1}{3}=\frac{7}{3} \quad \ldots\text{(i)}$$

and given $h_1, h_2, h_3, \ldots, h_{10}$ are in HP.

If D be common difference of corresponding AP.

Then, $D=\frac{\frac{1}{h_{10}}-\frac{1}{h_1}}{9}=\frac{\frac{1}{3}-\frac{1}{2}}{9}=-\frac{1}{54}$

$$\therefore \quad \frac{1}{h_7}=\frac{1}{h_1}+6D=\frac{1}{2}-\frac{6}{54}=\frac{1}{2}-\frac{1}{9}=\frac{7}{18} \Rightarrow h_7=\frac{18}{7}$$

Hence, $a_4 \cdot h_7=\frac{7}{3}\times\frac{18}{7}=6$

Example 75. Find n, so that $\frac{a^{n+1}+b^{n+1}}{a^n+b^n}$ $(a \neq b)$ be HM between a and b.

Sol. $\because$ $\frac{a^{n+1}+b^{n+1}}{a^n+b^n}=\frac{2ab}{a+b}$

$$\Rightarrow \frac{b^{n+1}\left[\left(\frac{a}{b}\right)^{n+1}+1\right]}{b^n\left[\left(\frac{a}{b}\right)^n+1\right]}=\frac{b^2\left[2\left(\frac{a}{b}\right)\right]}{b\left(\frac{a}{b}+1\right)}$$
$$\Rightarrow \frac{\left(\frac{a}{b}\right)^{n+1}+1}{\left(\frac{a}{b}\right)^n+1}=\frac{2\left(\frac{a}{b}\right)}{\left(\frac{a}{b}\right)+1}$$

Let $\frac{a}{b}=\lambda$

Then, $\frac{\lambda^{n+1}+1}{\lambda^n+1}=\frac{2\lambda}{\lambda+1}$

$$\Rightarrow (\lambda+1)(\lambda^{n+1}+1)=2\lambda(\lambda^n+1)$$
$$\Rightarrow \lambda^{n+2}+\lambda+\lambda^{n+1}+1=2\lambda^{n+1}+2\lambda$$
$$\Rightarrow \lambda^{n+2}-\lambda^{n+1}-\lambda+1=0$$
$$\Rightarrow \lambda^{n+1}(\lambda-1)-1(\lambda-1)=0$$
$$\Rightarrow (\lambda-1)(\lambda^{n+1}-1)=0$$
$$\Rightarrow \lambda-1\neq 0 \quad [\because a\neq b]$$
$$\therefore \lambda^{n+1}-1=0$$
$$\Rightarrow \lambda^{n+1}=1=\lambda^0$$
$$\Rightarrow n+1=0 \text{ or } n=-1$$

Example 76. Insert 6 harmonic means between 3 and $\frac{6}{23}$.

Sol. Let $H_1, H_2, H_3, H_4, H_5, H_6$ be 6 HM's between 3 and $\frac{6}{23}$.

Then, $3, H_1, H_2, H_3, H_4, H_5, H_6, \frac{6}{23}$ are in HP.

$$\Rightarrow \frac{1}{3}, \frac{1}{H_1}, \frac{1}{H_2}, \frac{1}{H_3}, \frac{1}{H_4}, \frac{1}{H_5}, \frac{1}{H_6}, \frac{23}{6} \text{ are in AP.}$$

Let common difference of this AP be D.

$$\therefore \quad D = \frac{\frac{23}{6} - \frac{1}{3}}{7} = \frac{(23-2)}{7 \times 6} = \frac{21}{7 \times 6} = \frac{1}{2}$$

$$\therefore \quad \frac{1}{H_1} = \frac{1}{3} + D = \frac{1}{3} + \frac{1}{2} = \frac{5}{6}$$

$$\Rightarrow \quad H_1 = \frac{6}{5} = 1\frac{1}{5}$$

$$\frac{1}{H_2} = \frac{1}{3} + 2D = \frac{1}{3} + 1 = \frac{4}{3} \Rightarrow H_2 = \frac{3}{4}$$

$$\frac{1}{H_3} = \frac{1}{3} + 3D = \frac{1}{3} + \frac{3}{2} = \frac{11}{6} \Rightarrow H_3 = \frac{6}{11}$$

$$\frac{1}{H_4} = \frac{1}{3} + 4D = \frac{1}{3} + 2 = \frac{7}{3} \Rightarrow H_4 = \frac{3}{7}$$

$$\frac{1}{H_5} = \frac{1}{3} + 5D = \frac{1}{3} + \frac{5}{2} = \frac{17}{6} \Rightarrow H_5 = \frac{6}{17}$$

and
$$\frac{1}{H_6} = \frac{1}{3} + 6D = \frac{1}{3} + 3 = \frac{10}{3} \Rightarrow H_6 = \frac{3}{10}$$

$\therefore$ HM's are $1\frac{1}{5}, \frac{3}{4}, \frac{6}{11}, \frac{3}{7}, \frac{6}{17}, \frac{3}{10}$.

Important Theorem 1

Let a and b be two real, positive and unequal numbers and A, G and H are arithmetic, geometric and harmonic means respectively between them, then

(i) A, G, H form a GP i.e., $G^2 = AH$ [Remember]

(ii) $A > G > H$ [Remember]

Proof

(i) $\because \quad A = \frac{a+b}{2}, G = \sqrt{ab}$ and $H = \frac{2ab}{a+b}$

Now, $$AH = \left(\frac{a+b}{2}\right)\left(\frac{2ab}{a+b}\right) = ab = G^2$$

Therefore, $G^2 = AH$ i.e. A, G, H are in GP.

Remark

The result $AH = G^2$ will be true for n numbers, if they are in GP.

(ii) $\because \quad A > G$ [from important theorem of GM] ...(i)

or $$\frac{A}{G} > 1$$

$$\Rightarrow \quad \frac{G}{H} > 1 \quad \left[\because \frac{A}{G} = \frac{G}{H} \Rightarrow G^2 = AH\right]$$

$$\Rightarrow \quad G > H \quad \text{...(ii)}$$

From Eqs. (i) and (ii), we get

$$A > G > H$$

Remark

If $a_1, a_2, a_3, \ldots, a_n$ are n positive numbers, then AM $\geq$ GM $\geq$ HM i.e.,

$$\frac{a_1 + a_2 + \ldots + a_n}{n} \geq (a_1 a_2 \ldots a_n)^{1/n} \geq \frac{n}{\left(\frac{1}{a_1} + \frac{1}{a_2} + \ldots + \frac{1}{a_n}\right)}$$

Sign of equality (AH = GM = HM) holds when numbers are equal i.e., $a_1 = a_2 = \ldots = a_n$.

Important Theorem 2

If A, G, H are arithmetic, geometric and harmonic means of three given numbers a, b and c, then the equation having a, b, c as its roots is

$$\boldsymbol{x^3 - 3Ax^2 + \frac{3G^3}{H}x - G^3 = 0} \quad \text{[Remember]}$$

Proof $\because A =$ AM of $a, b, c = \frac{a+b+c}{3}$

i.e., $$a + b + c = 3A \quad \text{...(i)}$$

$$G = \text{GM of } a, b, c = (abc)^{1/3}$$

i.e. $$abc = G^3 \quad \text{...(ii)}$$

and $$H = \text{HM of } a, b, c$$

$$= \frac{3}{\frac{1}{a} + \frac{1}{b} + \frac{1}{c}} = \frac{3abc}{ab + bc + ca} = \frac{3G^3}{ab + bc + ca}$$

[from Eq. (ii)]

i.e. $$ab + bc + ca = \frac{3G^3}{H} \quad \text{...(iii)}$$

$\therefore a, b, c$ are the roots of the equation

$$x^3 - (a+b+c)x^2 + (ab + bc + ca)x - abc = 0$$

i.e., $$x^3 - 3Ax^2 + \frac{3G^3}{H}x - G^3 = 0$$

[from Eqs. (i), (ii) and (iii)]

Geometrical Proof of $A > G > H$

Let $OA = a$ unit and $OB = b$ unit and AB be a diameter of semi-circle. Draw tangent OT to the circle and TM perpendicular to AB.

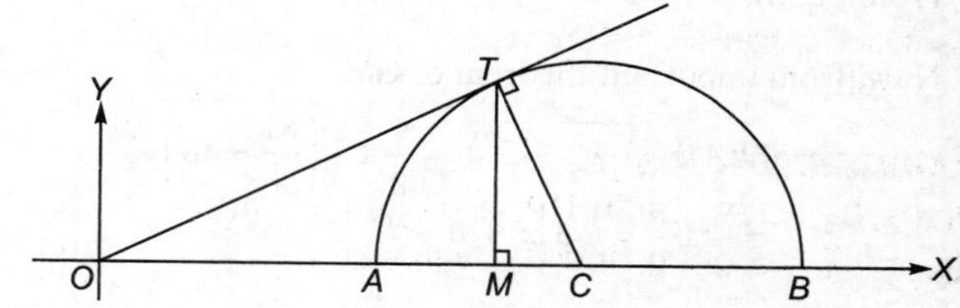

Let C be the centre of the semi-circle.

$$\because \quad \frac{OA + OB}{2} = \frac{(OC - AC) + (OC + CB)}{2}$$

$$= \frac{2\,OC}{2} = OC \quad [\because AC = CB = \text{radius of circle}]$$

$\therefore \quad OC = \dfrac{a+b}{2}$ [i.e. OC = arithmetic mean]

$\Rightarrow \quad A = \dfrac{a+b}{2}$

Now, from geometry

$(OT)^2 = OA \times OB = ab = G^2$

$\therefore \quad OT = G$, the geometric mean

Now, from similar ΔOCT and ΔOMT, we have

$$\frac{OM}{OT} = \frac{OT}{OC} \text{ or } OM = \frac{(OT)^2}{OC} = \frac{ab}{\frac{a+b}{2}} = \frac{2ab}{a+b}$$

$\therefore \quad OM = H$, the harmonic mean

Also, it is clear from the figure, that

$OC > OT > OM$ i.e. $A > G > H$

Example 77. If $A^x = G^y = H^z$, where A, G, H are AM, GM and HM between two given quantities, then prove that x, y, z are in HP.

Sol. Let $A^x = G^y = H^z = k$

Then, $\quad A = k^{1/x}, G = k^{1/y}, H = k^{1/z}$

$\because \quad G^2 = AH \Rightarrow (k^{1/y})^2 = k^{1/x} \cdot k^{1/z}$

$\Rightarrow \quad k^{2/y} = k^{1/x + 1/z} \Rightarrow \dfrac{2}{y} = \dfrac{1}{x} + \dfrac{1}{z} \Rightarrow \dfrac{1}{x}, \dfrac{1}{y}, \dfrac{1}{z}$ are in AP.

Hence, x, y, z are in HP.

Example 78. The harmonic mean of two numbers is 4, their arithmetic mean A and geometric mean G satisfy the relation $2A + G^2 = 27$. Find the numbers.

Sol. Let the numbers be a and b.

Given, $\quad H = 4$

$\because \quad G^2 = AH = 4A$ ...(i)

and given $\quad 2A + G^2 = 27$

$\Rightarrow \quad 2A + 4A = 27$ [from Eq. (i)]

$\therefore \quad A = \dfrac{9}{2}$

From Eq. (i), $G^2 = 4 \times \dfrac{9}{2} = 18$

Now, from important theorem of GM

$$a, b = A \pm \sqrt{(A^2 - G^2)} = \frac{9}{2} \pm \sqrt{\left(\frac{81}{4} - 18\right)}$$

$$= \frac{9}{2} \pm \frac{3}{2} = 6, 3 \text{ or } 3, 6$$

Example 79. If the geometric mean is $\dfrac{1}{n}$ times the harmonic mean between two numbers, then show that the ratio of the two numbers is $1 + \sqrt{(1-n^2)} : 1 - \sqrt{(1-n^2)}$.

Sol. Let the two numbers be a and b.

Given, $\quad G = \dfrac{1}{n} H$ ...(i)

Now, $\quad G^2 = AH$

$\Rightarrow \quad \dfrac{H^2}{n^2} = AH$ [from Eq. (i)]

$\therefore \quad A = \dfrac{H}{n^2}$ ...(ii)

Now, from important theorem of GM

$$a, b = A \pm \sqrt{(A^2 - G^2)} = \frac{H}{n^2} \pm \sqrt{\left(\frac{H^2}{n^4} - \frac{H^2}{n^2}\right)}$$

$$= \frac{H}{n^2}[1 \pm \sqrt{(1-n^2)}]$$

$$\therefore \quad \frac{a}{b} = \frac{\frac{H}{n^2}[1 + \sqrt{(1-n^2)}]}{\frac{H}{n^2}[1 - \sqrt{(1-n^2)}]}$$

$\therefore \quad a : b = 1 + \sqrt{(1-n^2)} : 1 - \sqrt{(1-n^2)}$

Example 80. If three positive unequal quantities a, b, c be in HP, then prove that $a^n + c^n > 2b^n, n \in N$

Sol. $\because \quad G > H$

$\therefore \quad \sqrt{ac} > b$

$\Rightarrow \quad (ac)^{\frac{n}{2}} > b^n$ or $a^{\frac{n}{2}} c^{\frac{n}{2}} > b^n$ ...(i)

Also, $\quad (a^{\frac{n}{2}} - c^{\frac{n}{2}})^2 > 0 \Rightarrow a^n + c^n - 2a^{\frac{n}{2}} c^{\frac{n}{2}} > 0$

$\Rightarrow \quad a^n + c^n > 2 a^{\frac{n}{2}} c^{\frac{n}{2}} > 2b^n$ [from Eq. (i)]

$\therefore \quad a^n + c^n > 2b^n$

Example 81.

(i) If a, b, c, d be four distinct positive quantities in AP, then

(a) $bc > ad$

(b) $c^{-1}d^{-1} + a^{-1}b^{-1} > 2(b^{-1}d^{-1} + a^{-1}c^{-1} - a^{-1}d^{-1})$

(ii) If a, b, c, d be four distinct positive quantities in GP, then

(a) $a + d > b + c$

(b) $c^{-1}d^{-1} + a^{-1}b^{-1} > 2(b^{-1}d^{-1} + a^{-1}c^{-1} - a^{-1}d^{-1})$

(iii) If a, b, c, d be four distinct positive quantities in HP, then

(a) $a + d > b + c$ (b) $ad > bc$

Sol. (i) $\because$ a, b, c, d are in AP.

(a) Applying AM > GM

For first three members, $b > \sqrt{ac}$

$\Rightarrow \quad b^2 > ac$ ...(i)

and for last three members, $c > \sqrt{bd}$

$$\Rightarrow \quad c^2 > bd \quad \text{...(ii)}$$

From Eqs. (i) and (ii), we get

$$b^2c^2 > (ac)(bd)$$

Hence, $\quad bc > ad$

(b) Applying AM > HM

For first three members,

$$b > \frac{2ac}{a+c}$$

$$\Rightarrow \quad ab + bc > 2ac \quad \text{...(iii)}$$

For last three members, $c > \dfrac{2bd}{b+d}$

$$bc + cd > 2bd \quad \text{...(iv)}$$

From Eqs. (iii) and (iv), we get

$$ab + bc + bc + cd > 2ac + 2bd$$

or $\quad ab + cd > 2(ac + bd - bc)$

Dividing in each term by $abcd$, we get

$$c^{-1}d^{-1} + a^{-1}b^{-1} > 2(b^{-1}d^{-1} + a^{-1}c^{-1} - a^{-1}d^{-1})$$

(ii) $\because$ a, b, c, d are in GP.

(a) Applying AM > GM

For first three members,

$$\frac{a+c}{2} > b$$

$$\Rightarrow \quad a + c > 2b \quad \text{...(v)}$$

For last three members, $\dfrac{b+d}{2} > c$

$$\Rightarrow \quad b + d > 2c \quad \text{...(vi)}$$

From Eqs. (v) and (vi), we get

$$a + c + b + d > 2b + 2c \text{ or } a + d > b + c$$

(b) Applying GM > HM

For first three members, $b > \dfrac{2ac}{a+c}$

$$\Rightarrow \quad ab + bc > 2ac \quad \text{...(vii)}$$

For last three members, $c > \dfrac{2bd}{b+d}$

$$\Rightarrow \quad bc + cd > 2bd \quad \text{...(viii)}$$

From Eqs. (vii) and (viii), we get

$$ab + bc + bc + cd > 2ac + 2bd$$

or $\quad ab + cd > 2(ac + bd - bc)$

Dividing in each term by $abcd$, we get

$$c^{-1}d^{-1} + a^{-1}b^{-1} > 2(b^{-1}d^{-1} + a^{-1}c^{-1} - a^{-1}d^{-1})$$

(iii) $\because$ a, b, c, d are in HP.

(a) Applying AM > HM

For first three members,

$$\frac{a+c}{2} > b$$

$$\Rightarrow \quad a + c > 2b \quad \text{...(ix)}$$

For last three members, $\dfrac{b+d}{2} > c$

$$\Rightarrow \quad b + d > 2c \quad \text{...(x)}$$

From Eqs. (ix) and (x), we get

$$a + c + b + d > 2b + 2c$$

or $\quad a + d > b + c$

(b) Applying GM > HM

For first three members, $\sqrt{ac} > b$

$$\Rightarrow \quad ac > b^2 \quad \text{...(xi)}$$

For last three members,

$$\sqrt{bd} > c$$

$$\Rightarrow \quad bd > c^2 \quad \text{...(xii)}$$

From Eqs. (xi) and (xii), we get

$$(ac)(bd) > b^2c^2$$

or $\quad ad > bc$

Exercise for Session 5

1. If the AM of two positive numbers a and b $(a > b)$ is twice of their GM, then $a : b$ is

(a) $2+\sqrt{3} : 2-\sqrt{3}$ (b) $7+4\sqrt{3} : 7-4\sqrt{3}$
(c) $2 : 7+4\sqrt{3}$ (d) $2 : \sqrt{3}$

2. If $A_1, A_2; G_1, G_2$ and H_1, H_2 are two arithmetic, geometric and harmonic means, respectively between two quantities a and b, then which of the following is not the value of ab is?

(a) A_1H_2 (b) A_2H_1
(c) G_1G_2 (d) None of these

3. The GM between -9 and -16, is

(a) 12 (b) -12
(c) -13 (d) None of these

4. Let $n \in N, n > 25$. If A, G and H denote the arithmetic mean, geometric mean and harmonic mean of 25 and n. Then, the least value of n for which $A, G, H \in \{25, 26, \ldots, n\}$, is

(a) 49 (b) 81
(c) 169 (d) 225

5. If 9 harmonic means be inserted between 2 and 3, then the value of $A + \frac{6}{H} + 5$ (where A is any of the AM's and H is the corresponding HM), is

(a) 8 (b) 9
(c) 10 (d) None of these

6. If $H_1, H_2, \ldots, H_n$ be n harmonic means between a and b, then $\frac{H_1+a}{H_1-a} + \frac{H_n+b}{H_n-b}$ is

(a) n (b) $n+1$
(c) $2n$ (d) $2n-2$

7. The AM of two given positive numbers is 2. If the larger number is increased by 1, the GM of the numbers becomes equal to the AM to the given numbers. Then, the HM of the given numbers is

(a) $\frac{3}{2}$ (b) $\frac{2}{3}$
(c) $\frac{1}{2}$ (d) 2

8. If $a, a_1, a_2, a_3, \ldots, a_{2n}, b$ are in AP and $a, b_1, b_2, b_3, \ldots, b_{2n}, b$ are in GP and h is the HM of a and b, then $\frac{a_1+a_{2n}}{b_1b_{2n}} + \frac{a_2+a_{2n-1}}{b_2\, b_{2n-1}} + \ldots + \frac{a_n+a_{n+1}}{b_n\, b_{n+1}}$ is equal to

(a) $\frac{2n}{h}$ (b) $2nh$
(c) nh (d) $\frac{n}{h}$

Session 6

Arithmetico-Geometric Series (AGS), Sigma (Σ) Notation, Natural Numbers

Arithmetico-Geometric Series (AGS)

Definition

A series formed by multiplying the corresponding terms of an AP and a GP is called **Arithmetico - Geometric Series** (or shortly written as AGS)

For example, $1 + 4 + 7 + 10 + \ldots$ is an AP and $1 + x + x^2 + x^3 + \ldots$ is a GP.

Multiplying together the corresponding terms of these series, we get

$1 + 4x + 7x^2 + 10x^3 + \ldots$ which is an Arithmetico-Geometric Series.

Again, $a + (a + d) + (a + 2d) + \ldots + [a + (n-1)d]$ is a typical AP

and $1 + r + r^2 + \ldots + r^{n-1}$ is a typical GP.

Multiplying together the corresponding terms of these series, we get

$$a + (a + d)r + (a + 2d)r^2 + \ldots + [a + (n-1)d]r^{n-1}$$

which is called a standard Arithmetico-Geometric series.

Sum of *n* Terms of an Arithmetico-Geometric Series

Let the series be $a + (a + d)r + (a + 2d)r^2 + \ldots + [a + (n-1)d]r^{n-1}$

Let S_n denotes the sum to n terms, then

$$S_n = a + (a + d)r + (a + 2d)r^2 + \ldots + [a + (n-2)d]r^{n-2} + [a + (n-1)d]r^{n-1} \quad \ldots(\text{i})$$

Multiplying both sides of Eq. (i) by r, we get

$$rS_n = ar + (a + d)r^2 + (a + 2d)r^3 + \ldots + [a + (n-2)d]r^{n-1} + [a + (n-1)d]r^n \quad \ldots(\text{ii})$$

Subtracting Eq. (ii) from Eq. (i), we get

$$(1 - r)S_n = a + (dr + dr^2 + \ldots + dr^{n-1}) - [a + (n-1)d]r^n$$

$$= a + \frac{dr(1 - r^{n-1})}{(1 - r)} - [a + (n-1)d]r^n$$

$$\therefore \quad S_n = \frac{a}{(1 - r)} + \frac{dr(1 - r^{n-1})}{(1 - r)^2} - \frac{[a + (n-1)d]r^n}{(1 - r)} \quad \ldots(\text{iii})$$

Remark

The above result (iii) is not used as standard formula in any examination. You should follow all steps as shown above.

To Deduce the Sum upto Infinity from the Sum upto *n* Terms of an Arithmetico - Geometric Series, when $|r| < 1$

From Eq. (iii), we have

$$S_n = \frac{a}{1 - r} + \frac{dr}{(1 - r)^2} - \frac{dr^n}{(1 - r)^2} - \frac{[a + (n-1)d]r^n}{(1 - r)}$$

If $|r| < 1$, when $n \to \infty, r^n \to 0$

and $\dfrac{dr^n}{(1 - r)^2}$ and $\dfrac{[a + (n-1)d]r^n}{(1 - r)}$ both $\to 0$

$$\therefore \quad S_\infty = \frac{a}{(1 - r)} + \frac{dr}{(1 - r)^2}$$

Independent method Let S_∞ denotes the sum to infinity, then

$$S_\infty = a + (a + d)r + (a + 2d)r^2 + (a + 3d)r^3 + \ldots \text{ upto } \infty \quad \ldots(\text{iv})$$

Multiplying both sides of Eq. (iv) by r, we get

$$rS_\infty = ar + (a + d)r^2 + (a + 2d)r^3 + \ldots \text{ upto } \infty \quad \ldots(\text{v})$$

Subtracting Eq. (v) from Eq. (iv), we get

$$(1 - r)S_\infty = a + (dr + dr^2 + dr^3 + \ldots \text{ upto } \infty)$$

$$= a + \frac{dr}{(1 - r)}$$

$$\therefore \quad S_\infty = \frac{a}{(1 - r)} + \frac{dr}{(1 - r)^2}$$

Example 82. Find the sum of the series $1+\frac{4}{5}+\frac{7}{5^2}+\frac{10}{5^3}+\ldots$

(i) to n terms. (ii) to infinity.

Sol. The given series can be written as

$$1+4\left(\frac{1}{5}\right)+7\left(\frac{1}{5}\right)^2+10\left(\frac{1}{5}\right)^3+\ldots$$

The series is an Arithmetico-Geometric series, since each term is formed by multiplying corresponding terms of the series 1, 4, 7, ... which are in AP and

$1, \frac{1}{5}, \frac{1}{5^2}, \ldots$ which are in GP.

$$\therefore \quad T_n=[n\text{ th term of }1, 4, 7, \ldots]\left[n\text{ th term of }1, \frac{1}{5}, \left(\frac{1}{5}\right)^2, \ldots\right]$$

$$=[1+(n-1)3]\times 1\cdot\left(\frac{1}{5}\right)^{n-1}=(3n-2)\left(\frac{1}{5}\right)^{n-1}$$

$$\therefore T_{n-1}=(3n-5)\left(\frac{1}{5}\right)^{n-2}$$

(i) Let sum of n terms of the series is denoted by S_n.

Then, $S_n=1+4\left(\frac{1}{5}\right)+7\left(\frac{1}{5}\right)^2+\ldots$

$$+(3n-5)\left(\frac{1}{5}\right)^{n-2}+(3n-2)\left(\frac{1}{5}\right)^{n-1} \quad \ldots\text{(i)}$$

Multiplying both the sides of Eq. (i) by $\frac{1}{5}$, we get

$$\therefore \quad \frac{1}{5}S_n=\frac{1}{5}+4\left(\frac{1}{5}\right)^2+7\left(\frac{1}{5}\right)^3+\ldots+(3n-5)\left(\frac{1}{5}\right)^{n-1}$$

$$+(3n-2)\left(\frac{1}{5}\right)^n \quad \ldots\text{(ii)}$$

Subtracting Eq. (ii) from Eq. (i), we get

$$\left(1-\frac{1}{5}\right)S_n=1+3\left[\frac{1}{5}+\left(\frac{1}{5}\right)^2+\left(\frac{1}{5}\right)^3+\ldots+\left(\frac{1}{5}\right)^{n-1}\right]$$

$$-(3n-2)\left(\frac{1}{5}\right)^n$$

$$\text{or}\quad \frac{4}{5}S_n=1+3\left[\left(\frac{1}{5}\right)+\left(\frac{1}{5}\right)^2+\left(\frac{1}{5}\right)^3+\ldots+(n-1)\text{ terms}\right]$$

$$-(3n-2)\left(\frac{1}{5}\right)^n$$

$$=1+3\left\{\frac{\frac{1}{5}\left[1-\left(\frac{1}{5}\right)^{n-1}\right]}{1-\frac{1}{5}}\right\}-(3n-2)\left(\frac{1}{5}\right)^n$$

$$=1+\frac{3}{4}\left\{1-\left(\frac{1}{5}\right)^{n-1}\right\}-(3n-2)\left(\frac{1}{5}\right)^n$$

$$\therefore \quad S_n=\frac{5}{4}+\frac{15}{16}\left[1-\left(\frac{1}{5}\right)^{n-1}\right]-\frac{(3n-2)}{4}\left(\frac{1}{5}\right)^{n-1}$$

$$=\frac{35}{16}-\frac{(12n+7)}{16}\left(\frac{1}{5}\right)^{n-1}$$

(ii) $S_\infty=1+4\left(\frac{1}{5}\right)+7\left(\frac{1}{5}\right)^2+10\left(\frac{1}{5}\right)^3+\ldots$ upto ∞ ...(iii)

Multiplying both sides of Eq. (i) by $\frac{1}{5}$, we get

$$\frac{1}{5}S_\infty=\left(\frac{1}{5}\right)+4\left(\frac{1}{5}\right)^2+7\left(\frac{1}{5}\right)^3+\ldots\text{ upto }\infty \quad \ldots\text{(iv)}$$

Subtracting Eq. (iv) from Eq. (iii), we get

$$\left(1-\frac{1}{5}\right)S_\infty=1+3\left[\left(\frac{1}{5}\right)+\left(\frac{1}{5}\right)^2+\left(\frac{1}{5}\right)^3+\ldots\text{upto }\infty\right]$$

$$=1+3\left(\frac{\frac{1}{5}}{1-\frac{1}{5}}\right)=1+\frac{3}{4}$$

$$\Rightarrow \quad \frac{4}{5}S_\infty=\frac{7}{4}$$

$$\therefore \quad S_\infty=\frac{35}{16}$$

Example 83. If the sum to infinity of the series $1+4x+7x^2+10x^3+\ldots$ is $\frac{35}{16}$, find x.

Sol. Let $S_\infty=1+4x+7x^2+10x^3+\ldots$ upto ∞ ...(i)

Multiplying both sides of Eq. (i) by x we get

$$x\,S_\infty=x+4x^2+7x^3+10x^4+\ldots\text{ upto }\infty \quad \ldots\text{(ii)}$$

Subtracting Eq. (ii) from Eq. (i), we get

$$(1-x)\,S_\infty=1+3x+3x^2+3x^3+\ldots\text{ upto }\infty$$

$$=1+3(x+x^2+x^3+\ldots\text{upto }\infty)=1+3\left(\frac{x}{1-x}\right)=\frac{(1+2x)}{(1-x)}$$

$$\therefore \quad S_\infty=\frac{(1+2x)}{(1-x)^2}=\frac{35}{16} \quad \left[\because S_\infty=\frac{35}{16}\right]$$

$$\Rightarrow \quad 16+32x=35-70x+35x^2$$

$$\Rightarrow \quad 35x^2-102x+19=0$$

$$\Rightarrow \quad (7x-19)(5x-1)=0$$

$$x\neq\frac{19}{7}$$

[$\because$ for infinity series common ratio $-1<x<1$]

Hence, $x=\frac{1}{5}$

Example 84. Find the sum of the series $1+2^2x+3^2x^2+4^2x^3+\ldots$ up to ∞, $|x|<1$.

Sol. Here, the numbers $1^2, 2^2, 3^2, 4^2, \ldots$ i.e. 1, 4, 9, 16, ... are not in AP but 1, $4-1=3$, $9-4=5$, $16-9=7, \ldots$ are in AP.

Let $S_\infty = 1 + 2^2x + 3^2x^2 + 4^2x^3 + \ldots$ upto ∞

$$= 1 + 4x + 9x^2 + 16x^3 + \ldots \text{ upto } \infty \quad \ldots\text{(i)}$$

Multiplying both sides of Eq. (i) by x, we get

$$xS_\infty = x + 4x^2 + 9x^3 + 16x^4 + \ldots \text{ upto } \infty \quad \ldots\text{(ii)}$$

Subtracting Eq. (ii) from Eq. (i), we get

$$(1-x)S_\infty = 1 + 3x + 5x^2 + 7x^3 + \ldots \text{ upto } \infty \quad \ldots\text{(iii)}$$

Again, multiplying both sides of Eq. (iii) by x, we get

$$x(1-x)S_\infty = x + 3x^2 + 5x^3 + 7x^4 + \ldots \text{ upto } \infty \quad \ldots\text{(iv)}$$

Subtracting Eq. (iv) from Eq. (iii), we get

$$(1-x)(1-x)S_\infty = 1 + 2x + 2x^2 + 2x^3 + \ldots \text{ upto } \infty$$

$$= 1 + 2(x + x^2 + x^3 + \ldots \text{ upto } \infty)$$

$$= 1 + 2\left(\frac{x}{1-x}\right) = \frac{(1+x)}{(1-x)}$$

$$\therefore \quad S_\infty = \frac{(1+x)}{(1-x)^3}$$

Sigma (Σ) Notation

Σ is a letter of greek alphabets and it is called 'sigma'. The symbol sigma (Σ) represents the sum of similar terms. Usually sum of n terms of any series is represented by placing Σ the nth term of the series. But if we have to find the sum of k terms of a series whose nth term is u_n, this will be represented by $\sum_{n=1}^{k} u_n$.

For example, $\sum_{n=1}^{n=9} n$, i.e. $\sum_{1}^{9} n$ only means the sum of n similar terms when n varies from 1 to 9.

Thus, $\sum_{1}^{9} n = 1+2+3+4+5+6+7+8+9$

Remark

Shortly Σ is written in place of $\sum_{1}^{n}$.

Properties of Sigma Notation

1. $\sum_{r=1}^{n} T_r = T_1 + T_2 + T_3 + \ldots + T_n$, when T_n is the general term of the series.

2. $\sum_{r=1}^{n} (T_r \pm T_r') = \sum_{r=1}^{n} T_r \pm \sum_{r=1}^{n} T_r'$

[sigma operator is distributive over addition and subtraction]

3. $\sum_{r=1}^{n} T_r T_r' \ne \left(\sum_{r=1}^{n} T_r\right)\left(\sum_{r=1}^{n} T_r'\right)$

[sigma operator is not distributive over multiplication]

4. $\sum_{r=1}^{n} \left(\frac{T_r}{T_r'}\right) \ne \frac{\left(\sum_{r=1}^{n} T_r\right)}{\left(\sum_{r=1}^{n} T_r'\right)}$

[sigma operator is not distributive over division]

5. $\sum_{r=1}^{n} aT_r = a\sum_{r=1}^{n} T_r$ [where a is constant]

6. $\sum_{j=1}^{n} \sum_{i=1}^{n} T_i T_j = \left(\sum_{i=1}^{n} T_i\right)\left(\sum_{j=1}^{n} T_j\right)$

[where i and j are independent]

Examples on Sigma Notation

(i) $\sum_{i=1}^{m} a = a + a + a + \ldots$ upto m times $= am$

(ii) $\sum a = a + a + a + \ldots$ upto n times $= an$

i.e. $\sum 5 = 5n, \sum 3 = 3n$

(iii) $\sum_{i=1}^{5} (i^2 - 3i) = \sum_{i=1}^{5} i^2 - 3\sum_{i=1}^{5} i$

$= (1^2 + 2^2 + 3^2 + 4^2 + 5^2) - 3(1+2+3+4+5)$

$= 55 - 45 = 10$

(iv) $\sum_{r=1}^{3} \left(\frac{r+1}{2r+4}\right) = \left(\frac{1+1}{2\cdot 1+4}\right) + \left(\frac{2+1}{2\cdot 2+4}\right) + \left(\frac{3+1}{2\cdot 3+4}\right)$

$= \frac{2}{6} + \frac{3}{8} + \frac{4}{10} = \frac{40+45+48}{120} = \frac{133}{120} = 1\frac{13}{120}$

Important Theorems on Σ (Sigma) Operator

Theorem 1 $\sum_{r=1}^{n} f(r+1) - f(r) = f(n+1) - f(1)$

Theorem 2

$$\sum_{r=1}^{n} f(r+2) - f(r) = f(n+2) + f(n+1) - f(2) - f(1)$$

Proof (Theorem 1) $\sum_{r=1}^{n} f(r+1) - f(r)$

$= [f(2) - f(1)] + [f(3) - f(2)] + [f(4) - f(3)] + \dots + [f(n+1) - f(n)]$

$= f(n+1) - f(1)$

Proof (Theorem 2)

$$\sum_{r=1}^{n} f(r+2) - f(r) = \sum_{r=1}^{n} [f(r+2) - f(r+1)] + [f(r+1) - f(r)]$$

$$= \sum_{r=1}^{n} f(r+2) - f(r+1) + \sum_{r=1}^{n} f(r+1) - f(r)$$

$= [f(n+2) - f(2)] + [f(n+1) - f(1)]$ [from Theorem 1]

$= f(n+2) + f(n+1) - f(2) - f(1)$

Remark

1. $\sum_{r=1}^{n} f(r+k) - f(r) = \sum_{m=1}^{k} f(n+m) - \sum_{m=1}^{k} f(m), \forall k \in N$
2. $\sum_{r=1}^{n} f(2r+1) - f(2r-1) = f(2n+1) - f(1)$
3. $\sum_{r=1}^{n} f(2r) - f(2r-2) = f(2n) - f(0)$

Natural Numbers

The positive integers 1, 2, 3, ... are called natural numbers. These form an AP with first term and common difference, each equal to unity.

(i) Sum of the First n Natural Numbers

$$1 + 2 + 3 + \dots + n = \frac{n(n+1)}{2} = \Sigma n$$

$\Rightarrow$ $$\Sigma n = \frac{n(n+1)}{2}$$ [Remember]

(ii) Sum of the First n Odd Natural Numbers

$$1 + 3 + 5 + \dots \text{ upto } n \text{ terms} = \frac{n}{2}[2 \cdot 1 + (n-1) \cdot 2] = n^2$$

$\Rightarrow$ $$\sum (2n-1) = n^2$$ [Remember]

(iii) Sum of the Squares of the First n Natural Numbers

$$1^2 + 2^2 + 3^2 + \dots + n^2 = \sum n^2 = \frac{n(n+1)(2n+1)}{6}$$

Proof We know that, $r^3 - (r-1)^3 = 3r^2 - 3r + 1$

Taking $\sum_{r=1}^{n}$ on both sides, we get

$$\sum_{r=1}^{n} r^3 - (r-1)^3 = 3\sum_{r=1}^{n} r^2 - 3\sum_{r=1}^{n} r + \sum_{r=1}^{n} 1$$

$\Rightarrow$ $$n^3 - 0^3 = 3\sum n^2 - 3\sum n + n \quad \text{...(i)}$$

[from important Theorem 1]

Substituting the value of $\sum n$ in Eq. (i), we get

$\Rightarrow$ $$n^3 = 3\sum n^2 - \frac{3 \cdot n(n+1)}{2} + n$$

$\Rightarrow$ $$3\sum n^2 = n^3 + \frac{3n(n+1)}{2} - n = \frac{n}{2}(2n^2 + 3n + 1)$$

$$= \frac{n(n+1)(2n+1)}{2}$$

$\Rightarrow$ $$\sum n^2 = \frac{n(n+1)(2n+1)}{6}$$ [Remember]

Independent Proof We know that,

$$(2r+1)^3 - (2r-1)^3 = 24r^2 + 2$$

Taking $\sum_{r=1}^{n}$ on both sides, we get

$$\sum_{r=1}^{n} (2r+1)^3 - (2r-1)^3 = \sum_{r=1}^{n} (24r^2 + 2)$$

$\Rightarrow$ $$(2n+1)^3 - 1^3 = 24\sum_{r=1}^{n} r^2 + 2\sum_{r=1}^{n} 1$$

[from points to consider-2]

$\Rightarrow$ $$(2n+1)^3 - 1 = 24\sum n^2 + 2n$$

$\Rightarrow$ $$(2n+1)^3 - (2n+1) = 24\sum n^2$$

$\Rightarrow$ $$(2n+1)[(2n+1)^2 - 1] = 24\sum n^2$$

$\Rightarrow$ $$(2n+1)(2n+1+1)(2n+1-1) = 24\sum n^2$$

$\Rightarrow$ $$\Sigma n^2 = \frac{n(n+1)(2n+1)}{6}$$ [Remember]

(iv) Sum of the Cubes of the First n Natural Numbers

$$1^3 + 2^3 + 3^3 + \dots + n^3 = \Sigma n^3 = (\Sigma n)^2 = \left\{\frac{n(n+1)}{2}\right\}^2$$

Proof We know that,

$$r^4 - (r-1)^4 = 4r^3 - 6r^2 + 4r - 1$$

Taking $\sum_{r=1}^{n}$ on both sides, we get

$$\sum_{r=1}^{n} r^4-(r-1)^4 = 4\sum_{r=1}^{n} r^3 - 6\sum_{r=1}^{n} r^2 + 4\sum_{r=1}^{n} r - \sum_{r=1}^{n} 1$$

$$\Rightarrow \quad n^4 - 0^4 = 4\sum n^3 - 6\sum n^2 + 4\sum n - n \quad \text{...(i)}$$

[from important theorem 1]

Substituting the values of $\sum n^2$ and $\sum n$ in Eq. (i), we get

$$\Rightarrow \quad n^4 = 4\sum n^3 - \frac{6\,n(n+1)(2n+1)}{6} + \frac{4n(n+1)}{2} - n$$

$$\Rightarrow 4\sum n^3 = n^4 + n(n+1)(2n+1) - 2n(n+1) + n$$

$$= n[n^3 + (n+1)(2n+1) - 2(n+1) + 1]$$

$$= n(n^3 + 2n^2 + n)$$

$$= n^2(n+1)^2$$

$$\therefore \quad \sum n^3 = \left\{\frac{n(n+1)}{2}\right\}^2 = (\sum n)^2 \quad \text{[Remember]}$$

Independent Proof We know that,

$$r^2(r+1)^2 - r^2(r-1)^2 = 4r^3$$

Taking $\sum_{r=1}^{n}$ on both sides, we get

$$\sum_{r=1}^{n} r^2(r+1)^2 - r^2(r-1)^2 = 4\sum_{r=1}^{n} r^3$$

$$\Rightarrow \quad n^2(n+1)^2 - 1^2 \cdot 0^2 = 4\sum n^3$$

[from important Theorem 1]

$$\Rightarrow \quad \sum n^3 = \left\{\frac{n(n+1)}{2}\right\}^2 = (\sum n)^2 \quad \text{[Remember]}$$

Corollary $1^3 + 2^3 + 3^3 + \ldots + n^3 = (1+2+3+\ldots+n)^2$

(v) Sum of the Powers Four of the First n Natural Numbers

$$1^4 + 2^4 + 3^4 + \ldots + n^4 = \sum n^4$$

$$= \frac{n(n+1)(2n+1)(3n^2+3n-1)}{30}$$

Proof We know that,

$$r^5 - (r-1)^5 = 5r^4 - 10r^3 + 10r^2 - 5r + 1$$

Taking $\sum_{r=1}^{n}$ on both sides, we get

$$\sum_{r=1}^{n} r^5 - (r-1)^5 = 5\sum_{r=1}^{n} r^4 - 10\sum_{r=1}^{n} r^3 + 10\sum_{r=1}^{n} r^2 - 5\sum_{r=1}^{n} r + \sum_{r=1}^{n} 1$$

$$\Rightarrow \quad n^5 - 0^5 = 5\sum n^4 - 10\sum n^3 + 10\sum n^2 - 5\sum n + n \quad \text{...(i)}$$

[from important Theorem 1]

Substituting the values of $\sum n, \sum n^2, \sum n^3$ in Eq. (i), we get

$$\Rightarrow \quad n^5 = 5\sum n^4 - \frac{10\,n^2(n+1)^2}{4} + \frac{10\,n(n+1)(2n+1)}{6} - \frac{5n(n+1)}{2} + n$$

$$\therefore \; 5\sum n^4 = n\left\{n^4 + \frac{5n(n+1)^2}{2} - \frac{5(n+1)(2n+1)}{3} + \frac{5(n+1)}{2} - 1\right\}$$

$$= \frac{n}{6}\{6n^4 + 15n(n^2+2n+1) - 10(2n^2+3n+1) + 15n + 15 - 6\}$$

$$\Rightarrow \; \sum n^4 = \frac{n}{30}(6n^4 + 15n^3 + 10n^2 - 1)$$

$$= \frac{n(n+1)(2n+1)(3n^2+3n-1)}{30}$$

Remark

If nth term of a sequence is given by $T_n = an^3 + bn^2 + cn + d$, where a, b, c, d are constants.

Then, sum of n terms, $S_n = \Sigma T_n = a\Sigma n^3 + b\,\Sigma n^2 + c\,\Sigma n + d\Sigma 1$

This can be evaluated using the above results.

Example 85. Find the sum to n terms of the series $1^2 + 3^2 + 5^2 + \ldots$ upto n terms.

Sol. Let T_n be the nth term of this series, then

$$T_n = [1 + (n-1)2]^2 = (2n-1)^2 = 4n^2 - 4n + 1$$

$\therefore$ Sum of n terms $S_n = \Sigma T_n = 4\Sigma n^2 - 4\Sigma n + \Sigma 1$

$$= \frac{4n(n+1)(2n+1)}{6} - \frac{4n(n+1)}{2} + n$$

$$= \frac{n}{3}(4n^2 + 6n + 2 - 6n - 6 + 3)$$

$$= \frac{n(4n^2-1)}{3}$$

Example 86. Find the sum to n terms of the series $1\cdot 2^2 + 2\cdot 3^2 + 3\cdot 4^2 + \ldots$.

Sol. Let T_n be the nth term of this series, then

$$T_n = (n\text{th term of } 1, 2, 3, \ldots)(n\text{th term of } 2^2, 3^2, 4^2, \ldots)$$

$$= n(n+1)^2 = n^3 + 2n^2 + n$$

$\therefore$ Sum of n terms $S_n = \Sigma T_n$

$$2 = \Sigma n^3 + 2\Sigma n^2 + \Sigma n$$

$$= \left\{\frac{n(n+1)}{2}\right\}^2 + 2\left\{\frac{n(n+1)(2n+1)}{6}\right\} + \frac{n(n+1)}{2}$$

$$= \frac{n(n+1)}{2}\left\{\frac{n(n+1)}{2} + \frac{2(2n+1)}{3} + 1\right\}$$

$$= \frac{n(n+1)}{12}(3n^2 + 3n + 8n + 4 + 6)$$

$$= \frac{n(n+1)(3n^2 + 11n + 10)}{12} = \frac{n(n+1)(n+2)(3n+5)}{12}$$

Example 87. Find the sum of n terms of the series whose nth terms is (i) $n(n-1)(n+1)$ (ii) $n^2 + 3^n$.

Sol. (i) We have, $T_n = n(n-1)(n+1) = n^3 - n$

$\therefore$ Sum of n terms $S_n = \Sigma T_n = \Sigma n^3 - \Sigma n$

$$= \left\{\frac{n(n+1)}{2}\right\}^2 - \left\{\frac{n(n+1)}{2}\right\}$$

$$= \frac{n(n+1)}{2}\left\{\frac{n(n+1)}{2} - 1\right\}$$

$$= \frac{n(n+1)(n-1)(n+2)}{4}$$

(ii) We have, $T_n = n^2 + 3^n$

$\therefore$ Sum of n terms $S_n = \Sigma T_n = \Sigma n^2 + \Sigma 3^n$

$$= \Sigma n^2 + (3^1 + 3^2 + 3^3 + \dots + 3^n)$$

$$= \frac{n(n+1)(2n+1)}{6} + \frac{3(3^n - 1)}{(3-1)}$$

$$= \frac{n(n+1)(2n+1)}{6} + \frac{3}{2}(3^n - 1)$$

Example 88. Find the sum of the series

$$\frac{1^3}{1} + \frac{1^3 + 2^3}{1+3} + \frac{1^3 + 2^3 + 3^3}{1+3+5} + \dots \text{ upto } n \text{ terms.}$$

Sol. Let T_n be the nth term of the given series. Then,

$$T_n = \frac{(1^3 + 2^3 + 3^3 + \dots + n^3)}{(1 + 3 + 5 + \dots + (2n-1))} = \frac{\left\{\frac{n(n+1)}{2}\right\}^2}{\frac{n}{2}(1 + 2n - 1)}$$

$$= \frac{(n+1)^2}{4} = \frac{1}{4}(n^2 + 2n + 1)$$

Let S_n denotes the sum of n terms of the given series. Then,

$$S_n = \Sigma T_n = \frac{1}{4}\Sigma(n^2 + 2n + 1)$$

$$= \frac{1}{4}(\Sigma n^2 + 2\Sigma n + \Sigma 1)$$

$$= \frac{1}{4}\left\{\frac{n(n+1)(2n+1)}{6} + \frac{2n(n+1)}{2} + n\right\}$$

$$= \frac{n}{24}\{2n^2 + 3n + 1 + 6n + 6 + 6\}$$

Hence, $S_n = \dfrac{n(2n^2 + 9n + 13)}{24}$

Example 89. Show that

$$\frac{1\cdot 2^2 + 2\cdot 3^2 + \dots + n\cdot(n+1)^2}{1^2\cdot 2 + 2^2\cdot 3 + \dots + n^2\cdot(n+1)} = \frac{3n+5}{3n+1}.$$

Sol. Let T_n and T_n' be the nth terms of the series in numerator and denominator of LHS. Then,

$\therefore$ $T_n = n(n+1)^2$ and $T_n' = n^2(n+1)$

$$\therefore \quad \text{LHS} = \frac{\Sigma T_n}{\Sigma T_n'} = \frac{\Sigma n(n+1)^2}{\Sigma n^2(n+1)} = \frac{\Sigma(n^3 + 2n^2 + n)}{\Sigma(n^3 + n^2)}$$

$$= \frac{\Sigma n^3 + 2\Sigma n^2 + \Sigma n}{\Sigma n^3 + \Sigma n^2}$$

$$= \frac{\left\{\frac{n(n+1)}{2}\right\}^2 + 2\left\{\frac{n(n+1)(2n+1)}{6}\right\} + \left\{\frac{n(n+1)}{2}\right\}}{\left\{\frac{n(n+1)}{2}\right\}^2 + \left\{\frac{n(n+1)(2n+1)}{6}\right\}}$$

$$= \frac{\frac{n(n+1)}{2}\left\{\frac{n(n+1)}{2} + \frac{2(2n+1)}{3} + 1\right\}}{\frac{n(n+1)}{2}\left\{\frac{n(n+1)}{2} + \frac{(2n+1)}{3}\right\}}$$

$$= \frac{\frac{1}{6}(3n^2 + 3n + 8n + 4 + 6)}{\frac{1}{6}(3n^2 + 3n + 4n + 2)}$$

$$= \frac{(3n^2 + 11n + 10)}{(3n^2 + 7n + 2)} = \frac{(3n+5)(n+2)}{(3n+1)(n+2)} = \frac{(3n+5)}{(3n+1)} = \text{RHS}$$

Example 90. Find the sum of the series $1\cdot 2\cdot 3 + 2\cdot 3\cdot 4 + 3\cdot 4\cdot 5 + \dots$ upto n terms.

Sol. Here, T_n = {nth term of 1, 2, 3, ...}

× {nth term of 2, 3, 4, ...} × {nth term of 3, 4, 5, ...}

$\therefore$ $T_n = n(n+1)(n+2) = n^3 + 3n^2 + 2n$

$\therefore$ S_n = Sum of n terms of the series

$$= \Sigma T_n = \Sigma n^3 + 3\Sigma n^2 + 2\Sigma n$$

$$= \left\{\frac{n(n+1)}{2}\right\}^2 + 3\left\{\frac{n(n+1)(2n+1)}{6}\right\} + 2\left\{\frac{n(n+1)}{2}\right\}$$

$$= \frac{n(n+1)}{2}\left\{\frac{n(n+1)}{2} + (2n+1) + 2\right\}$$

$$= \frac{n(n+1)}{4}(n^2 + n + 4n + 2 + 4)$$

$$= \frac{n(n+1)(n+2)(n+3)}{4}$$

Example 91. Find sum to n terms of the series $1 + (2+3) + (4+5+6) + \dots$.

Sol. Now, number of terms in first bracket is 1, in the second bracket is 2, in the third bracket is 3, etc. Therefore, the number of terms in the nth bracket will be n.

Let the sum of the given series of n terms $= S$

$\therefore$ Number of terms in $S = 1+2+3+\ldots+n = \dfrac{n(n+1)}{2}$

Also, the first term of S is 1 and common difference is also 1.

$$\therefore \quad S = \frac{\left\{\frac{n(n+1)}{2}\right\}}{2}\left[2\cdot 1 + \left(\frac{n(n+1)}{2} - 1\right)\cdot 1\right]$$

$$= \frac{n(n+1)}{8}(4 + n^2 + n - 2)$$

$$= \frac{n(n+1)(n^2+n+2)}{8}$$

Example 92. Find the sum of the series

$1\cdot n + 2\cdot(n-1) + 3\cdot(n-2) + 4\cdot(n-3) + \ldots + (n-1)\cdot 2 + n\cdot 1$ also, find the coefficient of x^{n-1} in the expansion of $(1+2x+3x^2+\ldots+nx^{n-1})^2$.

Sol. The rth term of the given series is

$$T_r = r\cdot(n-r+1) = (n+1)\,r - r^2$$

$\therefore$ Sum of the series

$$S_n = \sum_{r=1}^{n} T_r = (n+1)\sum_{r=1}^{n} r - \sum_{r=1}^{n} r^2 = (n+1)\,\Sigma n - \Sigma n^2$$

$$= (n+1)\frac{n(n+1)}{2} - \frac{n(n+1)(2n+1)}{6}$$

$$= \frac{n(n+1)}{6}(3n+3-2n-1) = \frac{n(n+1)(n+2)}{6}$$

Now,

$$(1+2x+3x^2+\ldots+nx^{n-1})^2 = (1+2x+3x^2+\ldots+nx^{n-1}) \times (1+2x+3x^2+\ldots+nx^{n-1})$$

$\therefore$ Coefficient of x^{n-1} in $(1+2x+3x^2+\ldots+nx^{n-1})^2$

$$= 1\cdot n + 2\cdot(n-1) + 3\cdot(n-2) + \ldots + n\cdot 1$$

$$= S_n = \frac{n(n+1)(n+2)}{6}$$

Method of Differences

If the differences of the successive terms of a series are in AP or GP, we can find the nth term of the series by the following steps.

***Step* I** Denote the nth term and the sum of the series upto n terms of the series by T_n and S_n, respectively.

***Step* II** Rewrite the given series with each term shifted by one place to the right.

***Step* III** Then, subtract the second expression of S_n from the first expression to obtain T_n.

Example 93. Find the nth term and sum of n terms of the series, $1+5+12+22+35+\ldots$.

Sol. The sequence of differences between successive terms is 4, 7, 10, 13,... . Clearly, it is an AP with common difference 3. So, let the nth term of the given series be T_n and sum of n terms be S_n.

Then, $S_n = 1+5+12+22+35+\ldots+T_{n-1}+T_n$ ...(i)

$S_n = 1+5+12+22+\ldots+T_{n-1}+T_n$ ...(ii)

Subtracting Eq. (ii) from Eq. (i), we get

$$0 = 1+4+7+10+13+\ldots+(T_n - T_{n-1}) - T_n$$

$$\Rightarrow \quad T_n = 1+4+7+10+13+\ldots n \text{ terms}$$

$$= \frac{n}{2}\{2\cdot 1 + (n-1)3\} = \frac{1}{2}(3n^2 - n)$$

Hence, $T_n = \dfrac{3}{2}n^2 - \dfrac{1}{2}n$

$\therefore$ Sum of n terms $S_n = \Sigma T_n = \dfrac{3}{2}\Sigma n^2 - \dfrac{1}{2}\Sigma n$

$$= \frac{3}{2}\left(\frac{n(n+1)(2n+1)}{6}\right) - \frac{1}{2}\left(\frac{n(n+1)}{2}\right)$$

$$= \frac{n(n+1)}{4}(2n+1-1)$$

$$= \frac{1}{2}n^2(n+1) = \frac{1}{2}(n^3+n^2)$$

Example 94. Find the nth term and sum of n terms of the series, $1+3+7+15+31+\ldots$.

Sol. The sequence of differences between successive terms is 2, 4, 8, 16, ... Clearly, it is a GP with common ratio 2. So, let the nth term and sum of the series upto n terms of the series be T_n and S_n, respectively. Then,

$S_n = 1+3+7+15+31+\ldots+T_{n-1}+T_n$ ...(i)

$S_n = 1+3+7+15+\ldots+T_{n-1}+T_n$ ...(ii)

Subtracting Eq. (ii) from Eq. (i), we get

$$0 = 1+2+4+8+16+\ldots+(T_n - T_{n-1}) - T_n$$

$$\Rightarrow \quad T_n = 1+2+4+8+16+\ldots \text{ upto } n \text{ terms}$$

$$= \frac{1\cdot(2^n - 1)}{2-1}$$

Hence, $T_n = (2^n - 1)$

$\therefore$ Sum of n terms $S_n = \Sigma T_n = \Sigma(2^n - 1) = \Sigma 2^n - \Sigma 1$

$$= (2+2^2+2^3+\ldots+2^n) - n$$

$$= \frac{2\cdot(2^n-1)}{(2-1)} - n = 2^{n+1} - 2 - n$$

Example 95. Find the nth term of the series $1+4+10+20+35+\ldots$

Sol. The sequence of first consecutive differences is 3, 6, 10, 15, ... and second consecutive differences is 3, 4, 5, ... Clearly, it is an AP with common difference 1. So, let the nth term and sum of the series upto n terms of the series be T_n and S_n, respectively.

Then,

$$S_n = 1 + 4 + 10 + 20 + 35 + \dots + T_{n-1} + T_n \quad \dots(i)$$

$$S_n = \quad 1 + 4 + 10 + 20 + \dots + T_{n-1} + T_n \quad \dots(ii)$$

Subtracting Eq. (ii) from Eq. (i), we get

$$0 = 1 + 3 + 6 + 10 + 15 + \dots + (T_n - T_{n-1}) - T_n$$

$$\Rightarrow \quad T_n = 1 + 3 + 6 + 10 + 15 + \dots \text{ upto } n \text{ terms}$$

or $$T_n = 1 + 3 + 6 + 10 + 15 + \dots + t_{n-1} + t_n \quad \dots(iii)$$

$$T_n = 1 + 3 + 6 + 10 + \dots + t_{n-1} + t_n \quad \dots(iv)$$

Now, subtracting Eq. (iv) from Eq. (iii), we get

$$0 = 1 + 2 + 3 + 4 + 5 + \dots + (t_n - t_{n-1}) - t_n$$

or $$t_n = 1 + 2 + 3 + 4 + 5 + \dots \text{ upto } n \text{ terms}$$

$$= \Sigma n = \frac{n(n+1)}{2}$$

$$\therefore \quad T_n = \Sigma t_n = \frac{1}{2}(\Sigma n^2 + \Sigma n)$$

$$= \frac{1}{2}\left(\frac{n(n+1)(2n+1)}{6} + \frac{n(n+1)}{2}\right)$$

$$= \frac{1}{2} \cdot \frac{n(n+1)}{6}(2n+1+3) = \frac{1}{6}n(n+1)(n+2)$$

| Example 96. Find the nth term of the series $1 + 5 + 18 + 58 + 179 + \dots$

Sol. The sequence of first consecutive differences is 4, 13, 40, 121, ... and second consecutive differences is 9, 27, 81, ... Clearly, it is a GP with common ratio 3. So, let the nth term and sum of the series upto n terms of the series be T_n and S_n, respectively. Then,

$$S_n = 1 + 5 + 18 + 58 + 179 + \dots + T_{n-1} + T_n \quad \dots(i)$$

$$S_n = 1 + 5 + 18 + 58 + \dots + T_{n-1} + T_n \quad \dots(ii)$$

Subtracting Eq. (ii) from Eq. (i), we get

$$0 = 1 + 4 + 13 + 40 + 121 + \dots + (T_n - T_{n-1}) - T_n$$

$$\Rightarrow \quad T_n = 1 + 4 + 13 + 40 + 121 + \dots \text{ upto } n \text{ terms}$$

or $$T_n = 1 + 4 + 13 + 40 + 121 + \dots + t_{n-1} + t_n \quad \dots(iii)$$

$$T_n = \quad 1 + 4 + 13 + 40 + \dots + t_{n-1} + t_n \quad \dots(iv)$$

Now, subtracting Eq. (iv) from Eq. (iii), we get

$$0 = 1 + 3 + 9 + 27 + 81 + \dots + (t_n - t_{n-1}) - t_n$$

or $$t_n = 1 + 3 + 9 + 27 + 81 + \dots \text{ upto } n \text{ terms}$$

$$= \frac{1 \cdot (3^n - 1)}{(3-1)} = \frac{1}{2}(3^n - 1)$$

$$\therefore \quad T_n = \Sigma t_n = \frac{1}{2}(\Sigma 3^n - \Sigma 1)$$

$$= \frac{1}{2}\{(3 + 3^2 + 3^3 + \dots + 3^n) - n\}$$

$$= \frac{1}{2}\left\{\frac{3(3^n - 1)}{(3-1)} - n\right\}$$

$$= \frac{3}{4}(3^n - 1) - \frac{1}{2}n$$

Method of Differences (Shortcut) to find nth term of a Series

The nth term of the series can be written directly on the basis of successively differences, we use the following steps to find the nth term T_n of the given sequence.

***Step* I** If the first consecutive differences of the given sequence are in AP, then take

$T_n = a(n-1)(n-2) + b(n-1) + c$, where a, b, c are constants. Determine a, b, c by putting $n = 1, 2, 3$ and putting the values of T_1, T_2, T_3.

***Step* II** If the first consecutive differences of the given sequence are in GP, then take

$T_n = ar^{n-1} + bn + c$, where a, b, c are constants and r is the common ratio of GP. Determine a, b, c by putting $n = 1, 2, 3$ and putting the values of T_1, T_2, T_3.

***Step* III** If the differences of the differences computed in Step I are in AP, then take

$T_n = a(n-1)(n-2)(n-3) + b(n-1)(n-2) + c(n-1) + d$, where a, b, c, d are constants.Determine by putting $n = 1, 2, 3, 4$ and putting the values of T_1, T_2, T_3, T_4.

***Step* IV** If the differences of the differences computed in Step I are in GP with common ratio r, then take

$T_n = ar^{n-1} + bn^2 + cn + d$, where a, b, c, d are constants. Determine by putting $n = 1, 2, 3, 4$ and putting the values of T_1, T_2, T_3, T_4.

| Example 97. Find the nth term and sum of n terms of the series $2 + 4 + 7 + 11 + 16 + \dots$.

Sol. The sequence of first consecutive differences is 2, 3, 4, 5, ... Clearly, it is an AP.

Then, nth term of the given series be

$$T_n = a(n-1)(n-2) + b(n-1) + c \quad \dots(i)$$

Putting $n = 1, 2, 3$, we get

$$2 = c \Rightarrow 4 = b + c \Rightarrow 7 = 2a + 2b + c$$

After solving, we get $a = \frac{1}{2}, b = 2, c = 2$

Putting the values of a, b, c in Eq. (i), we get

$$T_n = \frac{1}{2}(n-1)(n-2) + 2(n-1) + 2 = \frac{1}{2}(n^2 + n + 2)$$

Hence, sum of series $S_n = \Sigma T_n = \frac{1}{2}(\Sigma n^2 + \Sigma n + 2\Sigma 1)$

$$= \frac{1}{2}\left(\frac{n(n+1)(2n+1)}{6} + \frac{n(n+1)}{2} + 2n\right)$$

$$= \frac{1}{6}n(n^2 + 3n + 8)$$

Example 98. Find the nth term and sum of n terms of the series $5+7+13+31+85+\ldots$.

Sol. The sequence of first consecutive differences is 2, 6, 18, 54, ... Clearly, it is a GP with common ratio 3. Then, nth term of the given series be

$$T_n = a(3)^{n-1} + bn + c \quad \ldots(i)$$

Putting $n = 1, 2, 3$, we get

$$5 = a + b + c \quad \ldots(ii)$$
$$7 = 3a + 2b + c \quad \ldots(iii)$$
$$13 = 9a + 3b + c \quad \ldots(iv)$$

Solving these equations, we get

$$a = 1, b = 0, c = 4$$

Putting the values of a, b, c in Eq. (i), we get

$$T_n = 3^{n-1} + 4$$

Hence, sum of the series

$$S_n = \Sigma T_n = \Sigma(3^{n-1} + 4) = \Sigma(3^{n-1}) + 4\Sigma 1$$
$$= (1 + 3 + 3^2 + \ldots + 3^{n-1}) + 4n$$
$$= 1\cdot\frac{(3^n - 1)}{(3-1)} + 4n = \frac{1}{2}(3^n + 8n - 1)$$

Example 99. Find the nth term of the series $1+2+5+12+25+46+\ldots$.

Sol. The sequence of first consecutive differences is 1, 3, 7, 13, 21, ... The sequence of the second consecutive differences is 2, 4, 6, 8, ... Clearly, it is an AP. Then, nth term of the given series be

$$T_n = a(n-1)(n-2)(n-3) + b(n-1)(n-2) + c(n-1) + d \quad \ldots(i)$$

Putting $n = 1, 2, 3, 4$, we get

$$1 = d \quad \ldots(ii)$$
$$2 = c + d \quad \ldots(iii)$$
$$5 = 2b + 2c + d \quad \ldots(iv)$$
$$12 = 6a + 6b + 3c + d \quad \ldots(v)$$

After, solving these equations, we get

$$a = \frac{1}{3}, b = 1, c = 1, d = 1$$

Putting the values of a, b, c, d in Eq. (i), we get

$$T_n = \frac{1}{3}(n^3 - 6n^2 + 11n - 6) + (n^2 - 3n + 2) + (n-1) + 1$$
$$= \frac{1}{3}(n^3 - 3n^2 + 5n) = \frac{n}{3}(n^2 - 3n + 5)$$

Example 100. Find the nth term of the series $2+5+12+31+86+\ldots$.

Sol. The sequence of first consecutive differences is 3, 7, 19, 55, ... The sequence of the second consecutive differences is 4, 12, 36, ... Clearly, it is a GP with common ratio 3. Then, nth term of the given series be

$$T_n = a(3)^{n-1} + bn^2 + cn + d \quad \ldots(i)$$

Putting $n = 1, 2, 3, 4$, we get

$$2 = a + b + c + d \quad \ldots(ii)$$
$$5 = 3a + 4b + 2c + d \quad \ldots(iii)$$
$$12 = 9a + 9b + 3c + d \quad \ldots(iv)$$
$$31 = 27a + 16b + 4c + d \quad \ldots(v)$$

After, solving these equations, we get

$$a = 1, b = 0, c = 1, d = 0$$

Putting the values of a, b, c, d in Eq. (i), we get

$$T_n = 3^{n-1} + n$$

Method of Differences

(Maha Shortcut)

To find $t_1 + t_2 + t_3 + \ldots + t_{n-1} + t_n$

Let $S_n = t_1 + t_2 + t_3 + \ldots + t_{n-1} + t_n$

Then, $\Delta t_1, \Delta t_2, \Delta t_3, \ldots, \Delta t_{n-1}$ [1st order differences]

$\Delta^2 t_1, \Delta^2 t_2, \Delta^2 t_3, \ldots, \Delta^2 t_{n-1}$ [2nd order differences]

⋮ ⋮ ⋮

$$\therefore t_n = {}^{n-1}C_0\, t_1 + {}^{n-1}C_1\, \Delta t_1 + {}^{n-1}C_2\, \Delta^2 t_1 + \ldots + {}^{n-1}C_{r-1}\, \Delta^{r-1} t_1$$

and $S_n = {}^nC_1\, t_1 + {}^nC_2\, \Delta t_1 + {}^nC_3\, \Delta^2 t_1 + \ldots + {}^nC_r\, \Delta^r t_1$

where, $\Delta t_1 = t_2 - t_1, \Delta t_2 = t_3 - t_2$, etc.

$\Delta^2 t_1 = \Delta t_2 - \Delta t_1, \Delta^3 t_1 = \Delta^2 t_2 - \Delta^2 t_1$, etc.

Example 101. Find the n th term and sum to n terms of the series $12+40+90+168+280+432+\ldots$.

Sol. Let $S_n = 12 + 40 + 90 + 168 + 280 + 432 + \ldots$, then

1st order differences are 28, 50, 78, 112, 152, ... (i.e. $\Delta t_1, \Delta t_2, \Delta t_3, \ldots$)

and 2nd order differences are

22, 28, 34, 40, ... (i.e. $\Delta^2 t_1, \Delta^2 t_2, \Delta^2 t_3, \ldots$)

and 3rd order differences are

6, 6, 6, 6,... (i.e. $\Delta^3 t_1, \Delta^3 t_2, \Delta^3 t_3, \ldots$)

and 4th order differences are

0, 0, 0, 0, ... (i.e. $\Delta^4 t_1, \Delta^4 t_2, \Delta^4 t_3, \ldots$)

$$\therefore \quad t_n = 12\cdot{}^{n-1}C_0 + 28\cdot{}^{n-1}C_1 + 22\cdot{}^{n-1}C_2 + 6\cdot{}^{n-1}C_3$$
$$= 12 + 28(n-1) + \frac{22(n-1)(n-2)}{2} + \frac{6(n-1)(n-2)(n-3)}{1\cdot 2\cdot 3}$$
$$= n^3 + 5n^2 + 6n$$

and $S_n = 12\cdot{}^nC_1 + 28\cdot{}^nC_2 + 22\cdot{}^nC_3 + 6\cdot{}^nC_4$

$$= 12n + \frac{28n(n-1)}{2} + \frac{22n(n-1)(n-2)}{1\cdot 2\cdot 3} + \frac{6\cdot n(n-1)(n-2)(n-3)}{1\cdot 2\cdot 3\cdot 4}$$

$$= \frac{n}{12}(n+1)(3n^2 + 23n + 46)$$

V_n Method

To find the sum of the series of the forms

I. $a_1 a_2 \dots a_r + a_2 a_3 \dots a_{r+1} + \dots + a_n a_{n+1} \dots a_{n+r-1}$

II. $\dfrac{1}{a_1 a_2 \dots a_r} + \dfrac{1}{a_2 a_3 \dots a_{r+1}} + \dots + \dfrac{1}{a_n a_{n+1} \dots a_{n+r-1}}$

where, $a_1, a_2, a_3, \dots, a_n, \dots$ are in AP.

***Solution of form* I** Let S_n be the sum and T_n be the nth term of the series, then

$$S_n = a_1 a_2 \dots a_r + a_2 a_3 \dots a_{r+1} + \dots + a_n a_{n+1} + \dots + a_{n+r-1}$$

$$\therefore \quad T_n = a_n a_{n+1} a_{n+2} \dots a_{n+r-2}\, a_{n+r-1} \quad \dots \text{(i)}$$

Let $V_n = a_n a_{n+1} a_{n+2} \dots a_{n+r-2}\, a_{n+r-1}\, a_{n+r}$

[taking one extra factor in T_n for V_n]

$$\therefore \quad V_{n-1} = a_{n-1} a_n\, a_{n+1} \dots a_{n+r-3}\, a_{n+r-2}\, a_{n+r-1}$$

$$\Rightarrow \quad V_n - V_{n-1} = a_n a_{n+1} a_{n+2} \dots a_{n+r-1}\,(a_{n+r} - a_{n-1})$$

$$= T_n\,(a_{n+r} - a_{n-1}) \quad \text{[from Eq. (i)]} \dots \text{(ii)}$$

Let d be the common difference of AP, then

$$a_n = a_1 + (n-1)\,d$$

Then, from Eq. (ii)

$$V_n - V_{n-1} = T_n\,[\{a_1 + (n+r-1)\,d\} - \{a_1 + (n-2)\,d\}] = (r+1)\,d\,T_n$$

$$\Rightarrow \quad T_n = \frac{1}{(r+1)\,d}(V_n - V_{n-1})$$

$$\therefore \quad S_n = \Sigma T_n = \sum_{n=1}^{n} T_n = \frac{1}{(r+1)\,d}\sum_{n=1}^{n}(V_n - V_{n-1})$$

$$= \frac{1}{(r+1)\,d}(V_n - V_0)$$

[from important Theorem 1 of Σ]

$$= \frac{1}{(r+1)(a_2 - a_1)}(a_n a_{n+1} \dots a_{n+r} - a_0 a_1 \dots a_r)$$

***Corollary* I** If $a_1, a_2, a_3, \dots, a_n, \dots$ are in AP, then

(i) For $r = 2$, $a_1 a_2 + a_2 a_3 + \dots + a_n a_{n+1} = \dfrac{1}{3(a_2 - a_1)}(a_n a_{n+1} a_{n+2} - a_0 a_1 a_2)$

(ii) For $r = 3$,

$$a_1 a_2 a_3 + a_2 a_3 a_4 + \dots + a_n a_{n+1} a_{n+2} = \frac{1}{4(a_2 - a_1)}(a_n a_{n+1} a_{n+2} a_{n+3} - a_0 a_1 a_2 a_3)$$

***Corollary* II**

(i) $1\cdot 2 + 2\cdot 3 + \dots + n(n+1) = \dfrac{1}{3}\{n(n+1)(n+2) - 0\cdot 1\cdot 2\} = \dfrac{n(n+1)(n+2)}{3}$

(ii) $1\cdot 3\cdot 5\cdot 7 + 3\cdot 5\cdot 7\cdot 9 + \dots + (2n-1)\cdot(2n+1)(2n+5)\cdot(2n+3)\cdot$

$$= \frac{1}{11}\{(2n-1)(2n+1)(2n+3)(2n+5)(2n+7) - (-1)\cdot 1\cdot 3\cdot 5\cdot 7\}$$

$$= \frac{1}{11}\{(2n-1)(2n+1)(2n+3)(2n+5)(2n+7) + 105\}$$

***Solution of form* II** Let d be the common difference of AP, then $a_n = a_1 + (n-1)\,d$

Let sum of the series and nth term are denoted by S_n and T_n, respectively. Then,

$$S_n = \frac{1}{a_1 a_2 \dots a_r} + \frac{1}{a_2 a_3 \dots a_{r+1}} + \dots + \frac{1}{a_n a_{n+1} \dots a_{n+r-1}}$$

$$\therefore \quad T_n = \frac{1}{a_n a_{n+1} a_{n+2} \dots a_{n+r-2}\, a_{n+r-1}} \quad \dots \text{(i)}$$

$$\text{Let} \quad V_n = \frac{1}{a_{n+1}\, a_{n+2} \dots a_{n+r-2}\, a_{n+r-1}} \quad \dots \text{(ii)}$$

[leaving first factor from denominator of T_n]

$$\text{So,} \quad V_{n-1} = \frac{1}{a_n a_{n+1} \dots a_{n+r-3}\, a_{n+r-2}}$$

$$\Rightarrow \quad V_n - V_{n-1} = \frac{1}{a_{n+1}\, a_{n+2} \dots a_{n+r-2}\, a_{n+r-1}} - \frac{1}{a_n a_{n+1} \dots a_{n+r-3}\, a_{n+r-2}}$$

$$= \frac{a_n - a_{n+r-1}}{a_n a_{n+1}\, a_{n+2} - a_{n+r-2}\, a_{n+r-1}}$$

$$= T_n\,(a_n - a_{n+r-1}) \quad \text{[from Eq. (i)]}$$

$$= T_n\,[\{a_1 + (n-1)\,d\} - \{a_1 + (n+r-2)\,d\}]$$

$$= d\,(1-r)\,T_n$$

$$\therefore \quad T_n = \frac{(V_n - V_{n-1})}{d\,(1-r)}$$

$$\therefore \quad S_n = \Sigma T_n = \sum_{n=1}^{n}\frac{(V_n - V_{n-1})}{d\,(1-r)} = \frac{1}{d\,(1-r)}(V_n - V_0)$$

[from important Theorem 1 of Σ]

$$= \frac{1}{(a_2 - a_1)(1-r)}\left\{\frac{1}{a_{n+1}\, a_{n+2} \dots a_{n+r-2}\, a_{n+r-1}} - \frac{1}{a_1\, a_2 \dots a_{r-2}\, a_{r-1}}\right\}$$

Hence, the sum of n terms is $S_n = \dfrac{1}{(r-1)(a_2 - a_1)}$

$$\left\{\frac{1}{a_1 a_2 \dots a_{r-1}} - \frac{1}{a_{n+1} a_{n+2} \dots a_{n+r-1}}\right\}$$

***Corollary* I** If $a_1, a_2, a_3, \dots, a_n, \dots$ are in AP, then

(i) For $r = 2$,

$$\frac{1}{a_1 a_2} + \frac{1}{a_2 a_3} + \dots + \frac{1}{a_n a_{n+1}} = \frac{1}{(a_2 - a_1)}$$

$$\left\{\frac{1}{a_1} - \frac{1}{a_{n+1}}\right\} = \frac{1}{d}\left(\frac{a_{n+1} - a_1}{a_1 \, a_{n+1}}\right)$$

$$= \frac{1}{d}\left(\frac{a_1 + nd - a_1}{a_1 a_{n+1}}\right) = \frac{n}{a_1 \, a_{n+1}}$$

(ii) For $r = 3$, $\dfrac{1}{a_1 a_2 a_3} + \dfrac{1}{a_2 a_3 a_4} + \dots + \dfrac{1}{a_n \, a_{n+1} \, a_{n+2}}$

$$= \frac{1}{2(a_2 - a_1)}\left\{\frac{1}{a_1 a_2} - \frac{1}{a_{n+1} \, a_{n+2}}\right\}$$

(iii) For $r = 4$,

$$\frac{1}{a_1 a_2 a_3 a_4} + \frac{1}{a_2 a_3 a_4 a_5} + \dots + \frac{1}{a_n a_{n+1} a_{n+2} a_{n+3}}$$

$$= \frac{1}{3(a_2 - a_1)}\left\{\frac{1}{a_1 a_2 a_3} - \frac{1}{a_{n+1} \, a_{n+2} \, a_{n+3}}\right\}$$

***Corollary* II**

(i) $\dfrac{1}{1 \cdot 2} + \dfrac{1}{2 \cdot 3} + \dfrac{1}{3 \cdot 4} + \dots + \dfrac{1}{n(n+1)} = \dfrac{n}{n+1}$

(ii) $\dfrac{1}{1 \cdot 2 \cdot 3} + \dfrac{1}{2 \cdot 3 \cdot 4} + \dfrac{1}{3 \cdot 4 \cdot 5} + \dots + \dfrac{1}{n(n+1)(n+2)}$

$$= \frac{1}{2}\left\{\frac{1}{1 \cdot 2} - \frac{1}{(n+1)(n+2)}\right\} = \frac{1}{4} - \frac{1}{2(n+1)(n+2)}$$

(iii) $\dfrac{1}{1 \cdot 3 \cdot 5 \cdot 7} + \dfrac{1}{3 \cdot 5 \cdot 7 \cdot 9}$

$$+ \dots + \frac{1}{(2n-1)(2n+1)(2n+3)(2n+5)}$$

$$= \frac{1}{6}\left\{\frac{1}{1 \cdot 3 \cdot 5} - \frac{1}{(2n+1)(2n+3)(2n+5)}\right\}$$

$$= \frac{1}{90} - \frac{1}{6(2n+1)(2n+3)(2n+5)}$$

| Example 102. Find the sum upto n terms of the series $1 \cdot 4 \cdot 7 \cdot 10 + 4 \cdot 7 \cdot 10 \cdot 13 + 7 \cdot 10 \cdot 13 \cdot 16 + \dots$

Sol. Let T_n be the nth term of the given series.

$\therefore T_n =$ (nth term of 1, 4, 7, ...(nth term of 4, 7, 10, ...) (nth term of 7, 10, 13, ...) (nth term of 10, 13, 16, ...)

$$T_n = (3n-2)(3n+1)(3n+4)(3n+7) \quad \dots \text{(i)}$$

$$\therefore V_n = (3n-2)(3n+1)(3n+4)(3n+7)(3n+10)$$

$$V_{n-1} = (3n-5)(3n-2)(3n+1)(3n+4)(3n+7)$$

$$\Rightarrow \quad V_n = (3n+10)\, T_n \quad \text{[from Eq. (i)]}$$

and $\quad V_{n-1} = (3n-5)\, T_n$

$$\therefore \quad V_n - V_{n-1} = 15\, T_n$$

$$\therefore \quad T_n = \frac{1}{15}(V_n - V_{n-1}))$$

$$\therefore \quad S_n = \Sigma T_n = \sum_{n=1}^{n} \frac{1}{15}(V_n - V_{n-1})$$

$$= \frac{1}{15}(V_n - V_0)$$

[from important Theorem 1 of Σ]

$$= \frac{1}{15}\{(3n-2)(3n+1)(3n+4)(3n+7)(3n+10) - (-2)(1)(4)(7)(10)\}$$

$$= \frac{1}{15}\{(3n-2)(3n+1)(3n+4)(3n+7)(3n+10) + 560\}$$

Shortcut Method

$$S_n = \frac{1}{(\text{last factor of III term} - \text{first factor of I term})}$$

(Taking one extra factor in T_n in last – Taking one extra factor in I term in start)

$$= \frac{1}{(16-1)}\{(3n-2)(3n+1)(3n+4)(3n+7)(3n+10) - (-2) \cdot 1 \cdot 4 \cdot 7 \cdot 10\}$$

$$= \frac{1}{15}\{(3n-2)(3n+1)(3n+4)(3n+7)(3n+10) + 560\}$$

| Example 103. Find the sum to n terms of the series $\dfrac{1}{1 \cdot 3 \cdot 5 \cdot 7 \cdot 9} + \dfrac{1}{3 \cdot 5 \cdot 7 \cdot 9 \cdot 11} + \dfrac{1}{5 \cdot 7 \cdot 9 \cdot 11 \cdot 13} + \dots$. Also, find the sum to infinity terms.

Sol. Let T_n be the nth term of the given series.

Then, $\quad T_n = \dfrac{1}{(2n-1)(2n+1)(2n+3)(2n+5)(2n+7)} \quad \dots \text{(i)}$

$$\therefore \quad V_n = \frac{1}{(2n+1)(2n+3)(2n+5)(2n+7)}$$

[leaving first factor from denominator of T_n]

$$V_{n-1} = \frac{1}{(2n-1)(2n+1)(2n+3)(2n+5)}$$

$$\Rightarrow V_n - V_{n-1} = \frac{1}{(2n+1)(2n+3)(2n+5)(2n+7)} - \frac{1}{(2n-1)(2n+1)(2n+3)(2n+5)}$$

$$= \frac{(2n-1) - (2n+7)}{(2n-1)(2n+1)(2n+3)(2n+5)(2n+7)}$$

$$= -8\, T_n \quad \text{[from Eq. (i)]}$$

$$\therefore \quad T_n = -\frac{1}{8}(V_n - V_{n-1})$$

$$\therefore \quad S_n = \Sigma T_n = \sum_{n=1}^{n} T_n = -\frac{1}{8}\sum_{n=1}^{n}(V_n - V_{n-1}) = -\frac{1}{8}(V_n - V_0)$$

[from Important Theorem 1 of Σ]

$$= \frac{1}{8}(V_0 - V_n)$$

$$= \frac{1}{8}\left\{\frac{1}{1\cdot 3\cdot 5\cdot 7} - \frac{1}{(2n+1)(2n+3)(2n+5)(2n+7)}\right\}$$

$$= \frac{1}{840} - \frac{1}{8(2n+1)(2n+3)(2n+5)(2n+7)}$$

and $S_\infty = \frac{1}{840} - \frac{1}{\infty} = \frac{1}{840} - 0 = \frac{1}{840}$

Shortcut Method

$$\frac{1}{1\cdot 3\cdot 5\cdot 7\cdot 9} + \frac{1}{3\cdot 5\cdot 7\cdot 9\cdot 11} + \frac{1}{5\cdot 7\cdot 9\cdot 11\cdot 13} + \dots + \frac{1}{(2n-1)(2n+1)(2n+3)(2n+5)(2n+7)} \quad \dots\text{(i)}$$

Now, in each term in denominator

$$9 - 1 = 11 - 3 = 13 - 5 = \dots = (2n+7) - (2n-1) = 8$$

Then, Eq. (i) can be written as

$$= \frac{1}{8}\left\{\frac{9-1}{1\cdot 3\cdot 5\cdot 7\cdot 9} + \frac{11-3}{3\cdot 5\cdot 7\cdot 9\cdot 11} + \frac{13-5}{5\cdot 7\cdot 9\cdot 11\cdot 13} + \dots + \frac{(2n+7)-(2n-1)}{(2n-1)(2n+1)(2n+3)(2n+5)(2n+7)}\right\}$$

$$= \frac{1}{8}\left\{\frac{1}{1\cdot 3\cdot 5\cdot 7} - \frac{1}{3\cdot 5\cdot 7\cdot 9} + \frac{1}{3\cdot 5\cdot 7\cdot 9} - \frac{1}{5\cdot 7\cdot 9\cdot 11} + \frac{1}{5\cdot 7\cdot 9\cdot 11} - \frac{1}{7\cdot 9\cdot 11\cdot 13} + \dots + \frac{1}{(2n-1)(2n+1)(2n+3)(2n+5)} - \frac{1}{(2n+1)(2n+3)(2n+5)(2n+7)}\right\}$$

$$= \frac{1}{8}\left\{\frac{1}{1\cdot 3\cdot 5\cdot 7} - \frac{1}{(2n+1)(2n+3)(2n+5)(2n+7)}\right\}$$

[middle terms are cancelled out]

$$= \frac{1}{840} - \frac{1}{8(2n+1)(2n+3)(2n+5)(2n+7)} = S_n \quad \text{[say]}$$

$\therefore$ Sum to infinity terms $= S_\infty = \frac{1}{840} - 0 = \frac{1}{840}$

Maha Shortcut Method

Taking $\frac{1}{8}$ outside the bracket $\left(\text{i.e. } \frac{1}{9-1} = \frac{1}{11-3} = \frac{1}{13-5} = \dots\right)$ and in bracket leaving last factor of denominator of first term – leaving first factor of denominator of last term

$$\text{i.e., } S_n = \frac{1}{8}\left(\frac{1}{1\cdot 3\cdot 5\cdot 7} - \frac{1}{(2n+1)(2n+3)(2n+5)(2n+7)}\right)$$

$$\therefore \; S_\infty = \frac{1}{8}\left(\frac{1}{1\cdot 3\cdot 5\cdot 7} - 0\right) = \frac{1}{840}$$

Example 104. If $\sum_{r=1}^{n} T_r = \frac{n(n+1)(n+2)(n+3)}{12}$, where T_r denotes the rth term of the series. Find $\lim_{n\to\infty} \sum_{r=1}^{n} \frac{1}{T_r}$.

Sol. We have, $T_n = \sum_{r=1}^{n} T_r - \sum_{r=1}^{n-1} T_r$

$$= \frac{n(n+1)(n+2)(n+3)}{12} - \frac{(n-1)n(n+1)(n+2)}{12}$$

$$= \frac{n(n+1)(n+2)}{12}[(n+3)-(n-1)]$$

$$= \frac{n(n+1)(n+2)}{3} \quad \frac{1}{T_n} = \frac{3}{n(n+1)(n+2)}$$

$$\therefore \quad \lim_{n\to\infty} \sum_{r=1}^{n} \frac{1}{T_r} = \lim_{n\to\infty} \sum_{r=1}^{n} \frac{3}{r(r+1)(r+2)}$$

$$= 3 \lim_{n\to\infty} \sum_{r=1}^{n} \frac{1}{r(r+1)(r+2)}$$

$$= 3 \lim_{n\to\infty}\left(\frac{1}{1\cdot 2\cdot 3} + \frac{1}{2\cdot 3\cdot 4} + \frac{1}{3\cdot 4\cdot 5} + \dots + \frac{1}{n(n+1)(n+2)}\right)$$

Maha Shortcut Method

$$= 3 \lim_{n\to\infty} \frac{1}{2}\left(\frac{1}{1\cdot 2} - \frac{1}{(n+1)(n+2)}\right)$$

$$= \frac{3}{2}\left(\frac{1}{2} - 0\right) = \frac{3}{4}$$

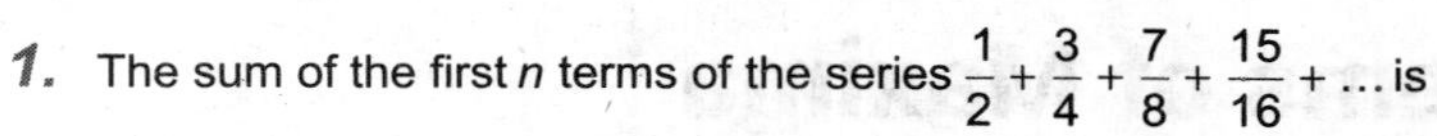

Exercise for Session 6

1. The sum of the first n terms of the series $\frac{1}{2}+\frac{3}{4}+\frac{7}{8}+\frac{15}{16}+\dots$ is

(a) $2^n - n - 1$ (b) $1 - 2^{-n}$ (c) $n + 2^{-n} - 1$ (d) $2^n - 1$

2. $2^{1/4} \cdot 4^{1/8} \cdot 8^{1/16} \cdot 16^{1/32} \dots$ is equal to

(a) 1 (b) $\frac{3}{2}$ (c) 2 (d) $\frac{5}{2}$

3. $1 + 3 + 7 + 15 + 31 + \dots$ upto n terms equals

(a) $2^{n+1} - n$ (b) $2^{n+1} - n - 2$ (c) $2^n - n - 2$ (d) None of these

4. 99th term of the series $2 + 7 + 14 + 23 + 34 + \dots$ is

(a) 9998 (b) 9999 (c) 10000 (d) 100000

5. The sum of the series $1 \cdot 2 \cdot 3 + 2 \cdot 3 \cdot 4 + 3 \cdot 4 \cdot 5 + \dots$ upto n terms is

(a) $n(n+1)(n+2)$ (b) $(n+1)(n+2)(n+3)$

(c) $\frac{1}{4}n(n+1)(n+2)(n+3)$ (d) $\frac{1}{4}(n+1)(n+2)(n+3)$

6. $\frac{1}{1 \cdot 2}+\frac{1}{2 \cdot 3}+\frac{1}{3 \cdot 4}+\dots+\frac{1}{n(n+1)}$ equals

(a) $\frac{1}{n(n+1)}$ (b) $\frac{n}{n+1}$

(c) $\frac{2n}{n+1}$ (d) $\frac{2}{n(n+1)}$

7. Sum of the n terms of the series $\frac{3}{1^2}+\frac{5}{1^2+2^2}+\frac{7}{1^2+2^2+3^3}+\dots$ is

(a) $\frac{2n}{n+1}$ (b) $\frac{4n}{n+1}$

(c) $\frac{6n}{n+1}$ (d) $\frac{9n}{n+1}$

8. If $t_n = \frac{1}{4}(n+2)(n+3)$ for $n = 1, 2, 3, \dots$, then $\frac{1}{t_1}+\frac{1}{t_2}+\frac{1}{t_3}+\dots+\frac{1}{t_{2003}}$ equals

(a) $\frac{4006}{3006}$ (b) $\frac{4003}{3007}$

(c) $\frac{4006}{3008}$ (d) $\frac{4006}{3009}$

9. The value of $\frac{1}{(1+a)(2+a)}+\frac{1}{(2+a)(3+a)}+\frac{1}{(3+a)(4+a)}+\dots$ upto ∞ is

(where, a is constant)

(a) $\frac{1}{1+a}$ (b) $\frac{2}{1+a}$

(c) ∞ (d) None of these

10. If $f(x)$ is a function satisfying $f(x+y) = f(x)f(y)$ for all $x, y \in N$ such that $f(1) = 3$ and $\sum_{x=1}^{n} f(x) = 120$. Then, the value of n is

(a) 4 (b) 5 (c) 6 (d) None of these

Session 7

Application to Problems of Maxima and Minima (Without Calculus)

Application to Problems of Maxima and Minima (Without Calculus)

Suppose that $a_1, a_2, a_3, \ldots, a_n$ are n positive variables and k is constant, then

(i) If $a_1 + a_2 + a_3 + \ldots + a_n = k$ (constant), the value of $a_1 a_2 a_3 \ldots a_n$ is greatest when $a_1 = a_2 = a_3 = \ldots = a_n$, so that the greatest value of $a_1 a_2 a_3 \ldots a_n$ is $\left(\frac{k}{n}\right)^n$.

Proof $\because$ AM $\geq$ GM

$$\therefore \quad \frac{a_1 + a_2 + a_3 + \ldots + a_n}{n} \geq (a_1 a_2 a_3 \ldots a_n)^{1/n}$$

$$\Rightarrow \quad \frac{k}{n} \geq (a_1 a_2 a_3 \ldots a_n)^{1/n}$$

$$\text{or} \quad (a_1 a_2 a_3 \ldots a_n) \leq \left(\frac{k}{n}\right)^n$$

Here, $a_1 = a_2 = a_3 = \ldots = a_n$

$\therefore$ Greatest value of $a_1 a_2 a_3 \ldots a_n$ is $\left(\frac{k}{n}\right)^n$.

| Example 105. Find the greatest value of xyz for positive values of x, y, z subject to the condition $yz + zx + xy = 12$.

Sol. Given, $yz + zx + xy = 12$ (constant), the value of $(yz)(zx)(xy)$ is greatest when $yz = zx = xy$

Here, $n = 3$ and $k = 12$

Hence, greatest value of $(yz)(zx)(xy)$ is $\left(\frac{12}{3}\right)^3$ i.e. 64.

$\therefore$ Greatest value of $x^2y^2z^2$ is 64.

Thus, greatest value of xyz is 8.

Aliter

Given $yz + zx + xy = 12$, the greatest value of $(yz)(zx)(xy)$ is greatest when

$$yz = zx = xy = c \quad \text{[say]}$$

Since, $yz + zx + xy = 12$

$$\therefore \quad c + c + c = 12$$

$$\Rightarrow \quad 3c = 12 \text{ or } c = 4$$

$$\therefore \quad yz = zx = xy = 4$$

Hence, greatest value of $(yz)(zx)(xy)$ is $4 \cdot 4 \cdot 4$

i.e., greatest value of $x^2y^2z^2$ is 64.

Hence, greatest value of xyz is 8.

| Example 106. Find the greatest value of x^3y^4, if $2x + 3y = 7$ and $x \geq 0, y \geq 0$.

Sol. To find the greatest value of x^3y^4 or $(x)(x)(x)(y)(y)(y)(y)$

Here, x repeats 3 times and y repeats 4 times.

Given, $2x + 3y = 7$,

then multiplying and dividing coefficients of x and y by 3 and 4, respectively.

Rewrite $3\left(\frac{2x}{3}\right) + 4\left(\frac{3y}{4}\right) = 7$

$$\text{or} \underset{1}{\left(\frac{2x}{3}\right)} + \underset{2}{\left(\frac{2x}{3}\right)} + \underset{3}{\left(\frac{2x}{3}\right)} + \underset{4}{\left(\frac{3y}{4}\right)} + \underset{5}{\left(\frac{3y}{4}\right)} + \underset{6}{\left(\frac{3y}{4}\right)} + \underset{7}{\left(\frac{3y}{4}\right)} = 7$$

Here, $k = 7$ and $n = 7$

Hence, greatest value of

$$\left(\frac{2x}{3}\right)\left(\frac{2x}{3}\right)\left(\frac{2x}{3}\right)\left(\frac{3y}{4}\right)\left(\frac{3y}{4}\right)\left(\frac{3y}{4}\right)\left(\frac{3y}{4}\right) \text{ is } \left(\frac{7}{7}\right)^7.$$

or greatest value of $\frac{2^3 \cdot 3^4}{3^3 \cdot 4^4} x^3y^4$ is 1.

Thus, greatest value of x^3y^4 is $\frac{32}{3}$.

(ii) If $a_1 a_2 a_3 \ldots a_n = k$ (constant), the value of $a_1 + a_2 + a_3 + \ldots + a_n$ is least when $a_1 = a_2 = a_3 = \ldots = a_n$, so that the least of $a_1 + a_2 + a_3 + \ldots + a_n$ is $n(k)^{1/n}$.

Proof $\because$ AM $\geq$ GM

$$\therefore \frac{a_1 + a_2 + a_3 + \ldots + a_n}{n} \geq (a_1 a_2 a_3 \ldots a_n)^{1/n} = (k)^{1/n}$$

$$\Rightarrow \quad \frac{a_1 + a_2 + a_3 + \ldots + a_n}{n} \geq (k)^{1/n}$$

$$\text{or} \quad a_1 + a_2 + a_3 + \ldots + a_n \geq n(k)^{1/n}$$

Here, $a_1 = a_2 = a_3 = \ldots = a_n$

$\therefore$ Least value of $a_1 + a_2 + a_3 + \ldots + a_n$ is $n(k)^{1/n}$

Example 107. Find the least value of $3x+4y$ for positive values of x and y, subject to the condition $x^2y^3=6$.

Sol. Given, $x^2y^3 = 6$

or $(x)(x)(y)(y)(y) = 6$

Here, x repeats 2 times and y repeats 3 times

$$\therefore \quad 3x+4y = 2\left(\frac{3x}{2}\right)+3\left(\frac{4y}{3}\right)$$

$$= \underset{1}{\left(\frac{3x}{2}\right)}+\underset{2}{\left(\frac{3x}{2}\right)}+\underset{3}{\left(\frac{4y}{3}\right)}+\underset{4}{\left(\frac{4y}{3}\right)}+\underset{5}{\left(\frac{4y}{3}\right)}$$

multiplying and dividing coefficient of x and y by 2 and 3 respectively and write $x^2y^3 = 6$

$$\Rightarrow \left(\frac{3x}{2}\right)\left(\frac{3x}{2}\right)\left(\frac{4y}{3}\right)\left(\frac{4y}{3}\right)\left(\frac{4y}{3}\right) = \frac{3^2}{2^2}\times\frac{4^3}{3^3}\times 6 = 32$$

Here, $n = 5$ and $k = 32$

Hence, least value of $\frac{3x}{2}+\frac{3x}{2}+\frac{4y}{3}+\frac{4y}{3}+\frac{4y}{3}$

$$= 5(32)^{1/5} = 10$$

i.e. least value of $3x+4y = 10$

Example 108. Find the minimum value of $bcx+cay+abz$, when $xyz=abc$.

Sol. To find the minimum value of

$$bcx+cay+abz,$$

write, $xyz = abc$

or $(bcx)(cay)(abz) = a^3b^3c^3 = k$ [constant]

Here, $n = 3$

Hence, minimum value of $bcx+cay+abz = n(k)^{1/n}$

$$= 3(a^3b^3c^3)^{1/3} = 3abc$$

An Important Result

If $a_i > 0,\ i = 1, 2, 3, \ldots, n$ which are not identical, then

(i) $$\frac{a_1^m + a_2^m + \ldots + a_n^m}{n} > \left(\frac{a_1+a_2+\ldots+a_n}{n}\right)^m ;\ \text{If } m<0$$

or $m > 1$

(ii) $$\frac{a_1^m + a_2^m + \ldots + a_n^m}{n} < \left(\frac{a_1+a_2+\ldots+a_n}{n}\right)^m ;$$

If $0 < m < 1$

Remark

If $a_1 = a_2 = \ldots = a_n$, then use equal sign in inequalities.

Example 109. If a, b, c be positive real numbers, prove that $\frac{a}{b+c}+\frac{b}{c+a}+\frac{c}{a+b}\geq\frac{3}{2}$.

Sol. Arithmetic mean of (-1) th powers $\geq (-1)$ th power of arithmetic mean

$$\frac{\left(\frac{b+c}{a+b+c}\right)^{-1}+\left(\frac{c+a}{a+b+c}\right)^{-1}+\left(\frac{a+b}{a+b+c}\right)^{-1}}{3} \geq \left(\frac{\frac{b+c}{a+b+c}+\frac{c+a}{a+b+c}+\frac{a+b}{a+b+c}}{3}\right)^{-1}$$

$$\Rightarrow \frac{\frac{a+b+c}{b+c}+\frac{a+b+c}{c+a}+\frac{a+b+c}{a+b}}{3} \geq \left(\frac{2}{3}\right)^{-1}$$

$$\Rightarrow \frac{a}{b+c}+1+\frac{b}{c+a}+1+\frac{c}{a+b}+1 \geq \frac{9}{2}$$

$$\Rightarrow \frac{a}{b+c}+\frac{b}{c+a}+\frac{c}{a+b} \geq \frac{9}{2}-3$$

or $$\frac{a}{b+c}+\frac{b}{c+a}+\frac{c}{a+b} \geq \frac{3}{2}$$

Example 110. If a and b are positive and $a+b=1$, show that $\left(a+\frac{1}{a}\right)^2+\left(b+\frac{1}{b}\right)^2 > \frac{25}{2}$.

Sol. Since, AM of 2nd powers > 2nd power of AM

$$\therefore \quad \frac{\left(a+\frac{1}{a}\right)^2+\left(b+\frac{1}{b}\right)^2}{2} > \left(\frac{a+\frac{1}{a}+b+\frac{1}{b}}{2}\right)^2$$

$$= \frac{1}{4}(a+b+a^{-1}+b^{-1})^2 = \frac{1}{4}(1+a^{-1}+b^{-1})^2 \quad [\because a+b=1]$$

$$\therefore \quad \left(a+\frac{1}{a}\right)^2+\left(b+\frac{1}{b}\right)^2 > \frac{1}{2}(1+a^{-1}+b^{-1})^2 \quad \ldots\text{(i)}$$

Again, $$\frac{a^{-1}+b^{-1}}{2} > \left(\frac{a+b}{2}\right)^{-1} = \left(\frac{1}{2}\right)^{-1} = 2$$

or $$\frac{a^{-1}+b^{-1}}{2} > 2$$

$$\Rightarrow \quad a^{-1}+b^{-1} > 4$$

$$\therefore \quad (1+a^{-1}+b^{-1}) > 5 \text{ or } (1+a^{-1}+b^{-1})^2 > 25$$

$$\Rightarrow \quad \frac{1}{2}(1+a^{-1}+b^{-1})^2 > \frac{25}{2} \quad \ldots\text{(ii)}$$

From Eqs. (i) and (ii), we get

$$\left(a+\frac{1}{a}\right)^2+\left(b+\frac{1}{b}\right)^2 > \frac{25}{2}$$

Exercise for Session 7

1. The minimum value of $4^x + 4^{2-x}$, $x \in R$ is

(a) 0 (b) 2
(c) 4 (d) 8

2. If $0 < \theta < \pi$, then the minimum value of $\sin^3 \theta + \operatorname{cosec}^3 \theta + 2$, is

(a) 0 (b) 2
(c) 4 (d) 8

3. If a, b, c and d are four real numbers of the same sign, then the value of $\frac{a}{b} + \frac{b}{c} + \frac{c}{d} + \frac{d}{a}$ lies in the interval

(a) $[2, \infty)$ (b) $[3, \infty)$
(c) $(4, \infty)$ (d) $[4, \infty)$

4. If $0 < x < \frac{\pi}{2}$, then the minimum value of $2(\sin x + \cos x + \operatorname{cosec} 2x)^3$ is

(a) 27 (b) 13.5
(c) 6.75 (d) 0

5. If $a + b + c = 3$ and $a > 0, b > 0, c > 0$, then the greatest value of $a^2 b^3 c^2$ is

(a) $\frac{3^4 \cdot 2^{10}}{7^7}$ (b) $\frac{3^{10} \cdot 2^4}{7^7}$
(c) $\frac{3^2 \cdot 2^{12}}{7^7}$ (d) $\frac{3^{12} \cdot 2^2}{7^7}$

6. If $x + y + z = a$ and the minimum value of $\frac{a}{x} + \frac{a}{y} + \frac{a}{z}$ is 81^λ, then the value of λ is

(a) $\frac{1}{2}$ (b) 1
(c) $\frac{1}{4}$ (d) 2

7. a, b, c are three positive numbers and abc^2 has the greatest value $\frac{1}{64}$, then

(a) $a = b = \frac{1}{2}, c = \frac{1}{4}$ (b) $a = b = c = \frac{1}{3}$
(c) $a = b = \frac{1}{4}, c = \frac{1}{2}$ (d) $a = b = c = \frac{1}{4}$

Shortcuts and Important Results to Remember

1 If $T_n = An + B$, i.e. nth term of an AP is a linear expression in n, where A, B are constants, then coefficient of n i.e., A is the common difference.

2 If $S_n = Cn^2 + Dn$ is the sum of n terms of an AP, where C and D are constants, then common difference of AP is $2C$ i.e., 2 times the coefficient of n^2.

3 (i) $d = T_n - T_{n-1}\ [n \ge 2]$ (ii) $T_n = S_n - S_{n-1}\ [n \ge 2]$
(iii) $d = S_n - 2S_{n-1} + S_{n-2}\ [n \ge 3]$

4 If for two different AP's
$$\frac{S_n}{S_n'} = \frac{An^2 + Bn}{Cn^2 + Cn} \text{ or } \frac{An + B}{Cn + D}$$
Then, $\dfrac{T_n}{T_n'} = \dfrac{A(2n-1) + B}{C(2n-1) + D}$

5 If for two different AP's
$$\frac{T_n}{T_n'} = \frac{An + B}{Cn + D}, \text{ then } \frac{S_n}{S_n'} = \frac{A\left(\frac{n+1}{2}\right) + B}{C\left(\frac{n+1}{2}\right) + D}$$

6 If $T_p = q$ and $T_q = p$, then $T_{p+q} = 0, T_r = p + q - r$

7 If $pT_p = qT_q$ of an AP, then $T_{p+q} = 0$

8 If $S_p = S_q$ for an AP, then $S_{p+q} = 0$

9 If $S_p = q$ and $S_q = p$ of an AP, then $S_{p+q} = -(p+q)$

10 If $T_p = P$ and $T_q = Q$ for a GP, then $T_n = \left[\dfrac{P^{n-q}}{Q^{n-p}}\right]^{1/(p-q)}$

11 If $T_{m+n} = p, T_{m-n} = q$ for a GP, then
$$T_m = \sqrt{pq}, \quad T_n = p\left(\frac{q}{p}\right)^{m/2n}$$

12 If $T_m = n, T_n = m$ for a HP, then
$$T_{m+n} = \frac{mn}{(m+n)}, T_{mn} = 1, T_p = \frac{mn}{p}$$

13 If $T_p = qr, T_q = pr$ for a HP, then $T_r = pq$

14 No term of HP can be zero and there is no formula to find S_n for HP.

15 a, b, c are in AP, GP or HP as $\dfrac{a-b}{b-c} = \dfrac{a}{a}$ or $\dfrac{a}{b}$ or $\dfrac{a}{c}$.

16 If A, G, H be AM, GM and HM between a and b, then
$$\frac{a^{n+1} + b^{n+1}}{a^n + b^n} = \begin{cases} A, & \text{when } n = 0 \\ G, & \text{when } n = -\frac{1}{2} \\ H, & \text{when } n = -1 \end{cases}$$

17 If A and G are the AM and GM between two numbers a, b, then a, b are given by $A \pm \sqrt{(A+G)(A-G)}$

18 If a, b, c are in GP, then $a + b, 2b, b + c$ are in HP.

19 If a, b, c are in AP, then $\lambda^a, \lambda^b, \lambda^c$ are in GP, where $\lambda > 0, \lambda \ne 1$.

20 If $-1 < r < 1$, then GP is said to be convergent, if $r < -1$ or $r > 1$, then GP is said to be divergent and if $r = -1$, then series is oscillating.

21 If a, b, c, d are in GP, then
$(a \pm b)^n, (b \pm c)^n, (c \pm d)^n$ are in GP, $\forall\, n \in I$

22 If a, b, c are in AP as well as in GP, then $a = b = c$.

23 The equations $a_1x + a_2y = a_3$, $a_4x + a_5y = a_6$ has a unique solution, if $a_1, a_2, a_3, a_4, a_5, a_6$ are in AP and common difference $\ne 0$.

24 For n positive quantities $a_1, a_2, a_3, \ldots, a_n$
$$\text{AM} \ge \text{GM} \ge \text{HM}$$
sign of equality (AM = GM = HM) holds when quantities are equal
i.e. $a_1 = a_2 = a_3 = \ldots = a_n$.

25 For two positive numbers a and b (AM) (HM) = (GM)^2, the result will be true for n numbers, if they are in GP.

26 If odd numbers of (say $2n + 1$) AM's, GM's and HM's be inserted between two numbers, then their middle means [i.e., $(n+1)$th mean] are in GP.

27 If a^2, b^2, c^2 are in AP.
$$\Rightarrow \quad \frac{1}{b+c}, \frac{1}{c+a}, \frac{1}{a+b} \text{ are in AP.}$$

28 Coefficient of x^{n-1} and x^{n-2} in
$(x - a_1)(x - a_2)(x - a_3)\ldots(x - a_n)$
are $-(a_1 + a_2 + a_3 + \ldots + a_n)$ and Σa_1a_2, respectively
where, $\Sigma a_1a_2 = \dfrac{(\Sigma a_1)^2 - \Sigma a_1^2}{2}$.

29 $1 + 3 + 5 + \ldots$ upto n terms $= n^2$

30 $2 + 6 + 12 + 20 + \ldots$ upto n terms $= \dfrac{n(n+1)(n+2)}{3}$

31 $1 + 3 + 7 + 13 + \ldots$ upto n terms $= \dfrac{n(n^2+2)}{3}$

32 $1 + 5 + 14 + 30 + \ldots$ upto n terms $= \dfrac{n(n+1)^2(n+2)}{12}$

33 If $a_1, a_2, a_3, \ldots, a_n$ are the non-zero terms of a non-constant AP, then
$$\frac{1}{a_1a_2} + \frac{1}{a_2a_3} + \frac{1}{a_3a_4} + \ldots + \frac{1}{a_{n-1}a_n} = \frac{(n-1)}{a_1a_n}$$

JEE Type Solved Examples :
Single Option Correct Type Questions

- This section contains **10 multiple choice examples.** Each example has four choices (a), (b), (c) and (d) out of which **ONLY ONE** is correct.

Ex. 1 *If $b-c$, $2b-\lambda$, $b-a$ are in HP, then $a-\frac{\lambda}{2}$, $b-\frac{\lambda}{2}$, $c-\frac{\lambda}{2}$ are is*

(a) AP (b) GP
(c) HP (d) None of these

Sol. (b) $(2b-\lambda)=\dfrac{2(b-c)(b-a)}{(b-c)+(b-a)}$

$$\Rightarrow \quad (2b-\lambda)=(2b-(a+c))=2[b^2-(a+c)b+ac]$$

$$\Rightarrow \quad 2b^2-2b\lambda+\lambda(a+c)-2ac=0$$

$$\Rightarrow \quad b^2-b\lambda+\frac{\lambda}{2}(a+c)-ac=0$$

$$\Rightarrow \left(b-\frac{\lambda}{2}\right)^2-\frac{\lambda^2}{4}+\frac{\lambda}{2}(a+c)-ac=0$$

$$\Rightarrow \quad \left(b-\frac{\lambda}{2}\right)^2=\frac{\lambda^2}{4}-\frac{\lambda}{2}(a+c)+ac$$

$$\Rightarrow \quad \left(b-\frac{\lambda}{2}\right)^2=\left(a-\frac{\lambda}{2}\right)\left(c-\frac{\lambda}{2}\right)$$

Hence, $a-\frac{\lambda}{2}$, $b-\frac{\lambda}{2}$, $c-\frac{\lambda}{2}$ are in GP.

Ex. 2 *Let $a_1, a_2, a_3, \ldots, a_{10}$ are in GP with $a_{51}=25$ and $\sum_{i=1}^{101} a_i=125$, then the value of $\sum_{i=1}^{101}\left(\frac{1}{a_i}\right)$ equals*

(a) 5 (b) $\frac{1}{5}$ (c) $\frac{1}{25}$ (d) $\frac{1}{125}$

Sol. (b) Let 1st term be a and common ratio be r, then

$$\sum_{i=1}^{101}\frac{1}{a_i}=125$$

$$\Rightarrow \quad (a_1+a_1r+a_1r^2+\ldots+a_1r^{100})=125$$

$$\Rightarrow \quad \frac{a_1(1-r^{101})}{(1-r)}=125 \qquad [\text{let } 0<r<1] \ldots\text{(i)}$$

$$\therefore \quad \sum_{i=1}^{101}\frac{1}{a_i}=\frac{1}{a_i}+\frac{1}{a_ir}+\frac{1}{a_ir^2}+\ldots+\frac{1}{a_ir^{100}}=\frac{\frac{1}{a_i}\left[\left(\frac{1}{r}\right)^{101}-1\right]}{\left(\frac{1}{r}-1\right)}$$

$$\left[\text{here } \frac{1}{r}>1\right]$$

$$=\frac{(1-r^{101})}{a_1r^{100}(1-r)}=\frac{1}{a_1r^{100}}\times\frac{125}{a_1} \qquad [\text{from Eq. (i)}]$$

$$=\frac{125}{(a_1r^{50})^2}=\frac{125}{(a_{51})^2}=\frac{125}{(25)^2}=\frac{1}{5}$$

Ex. 3 *If $x=111\ldots1$ (20 digits), $y=333\ldots3$ (10 digits) and $z=222\ldots2$ (10 digits), then $\frac{x-y^2}{z}$ equals*

(a) $\frac{1}{2}$ (b) 1 (c) 2 (d) 4

Sol. (b) $\because x=\frac{1}{9}(999\ldots9)=\frac{1}{9}(10^{20}-1)$,

$$y=\frac{1}{3}(999\ldots9)=\frac{1}{3}(10^{10}-1)$$

and $$z=\frac{2}{9}(999\ldots9)=\frac{2}{9}(10^{10}-1)]$$

$$\therefore \quad \frac{x-y^2}{z}=\frac{\frac{1}{9}(10^{20}-1)-\frac{1}{9}(10^{10}-1)^2}{\frac{2}{9}(10^{10}-1)}$$

$$=\frac{10^{10}+1-(10^{10}-1)}{2}=1$$

Ex. 4 *Consider the sequence 1, 2, 2, 3, 3, 3, ..., where n occurs n times. The number that occurs as 2011th terms is*

(a) 61 (b) 62
(c) 63 (d) 64

Sol. (c) The last 4 occurs as $1+2+3+4=10$th term. The last n occurs as $\left(\frac{n(n+1)}{2}\right)^{\text{th}}$ term, the last 62 occurs as $\left(\frac{62\times63}{2}\right)^{\text{th}}=1953$rd term and the last 63 occurs as $\left(\frac{63\times64}{2}\right)^{\text{th}}=2016$th term.

$\therefore$ 63 occurs from 1954th term to 2016th term.

Hence, $(2011)^{\text{th}}$ term is 63.

Ex. 5 *Let $S=\sum_{r=1}^{117}\frac{1}{2[\sqrt{r}]+1}$, when $[\cdot]$ denotes the greatest integer function and if $S=\frac{p}{q}$, when p and q are co-primes, the value of $p+q$ is*

(a) 20 (b) 76 (c) 19 (d) 69

Sol. (b) $\because$ $S = \sum_{r=1}^{117} \frac{1}{2[\sqrt{r}]+1}$

$$= \frac{3}{2\cdot1+1} + \frac{5}{2\cdot2+1} + \frac{7}{2\cdot3+1} + \ldots + \frac{19}{2\cdot9+1} + \frac{18}{2\cdot10+1}$$

$$= 9 + \frac{18}{21} = 9 + \frac{6}{7} = \frac{69}{7}$$

$\therefore$ $p = 69$ and $q = 7 \Rightarrow p + q = 69 + 7 = 76$

● ***Ex. 6*** *If a, b, c are non-zero real numbers, then the minimum value of the expression* $\frac{(a^8 + 4a^4 + 1)(b^4 + 3b^2 + 1)(c^2 + 2c + 2)}{a^4b^2}$ *equals*

(a) 12 (b) 24 (c) 30 (d) 60

Sol. (c) Let $P = \frac{(a^8 + 4a^4 + 1)(b^4 + 3b^2 + 1)(c^2 + 2c + 2)}{a^4b^2}$

$$= \left(a^4 + 4 + \frac{1}{a^4}\right)\left(b^2 + 3 + \frac{1}{b^2}\right)\{(c+1)^2 + 1\}$$

$\because$ $= a^4 + 4 + \frac{1}{a^4} \ge 6,\ b^2 + 3 + \frac{1}{b^2} \ge 5$ and $(c+1)^2 + 1 \ge 1$

$\left[\because x + \frac{1}{x} \ge 2 \text{ for } x > 0\right]$

$\therefore$ $P \ge 6\cdot5\cdot1 = 30 \Rightarrow P \ge 30$

Hence, the required minimum value is 30.

● ***Ex. 7*** *If the sum of m consecutive odd integers is* m^4*, then the first integer is*

(a) $m^3 + m + 1$ (b) $m^3 + m - 1$
(c) $m^3 - m - 1$ (d) $m^3 - m + 1$

Sol. (d) Let $2a+1, 2a+3, 2a+5, \ldots$ be the AP, then

$m^4 = (2a+1) + (2a+3) + (2a+5) + \ldots$ upto m terms

$$= \frac{m}{2}\{2(2a+1) + (m-1)\cdot2\} = m(2a+1+m-1)$$

$\Rightarrow$ $m^3 = (2a+1) + m - 1$

$\therefore$ $2a + 1 = m^3 - m + 1$

● ***Ex. 8*** *The value of* $\sum_{r=1}^{\infty} \frac{(4r+5)5^{-r}}{r(5r+5)}$ *is*

(a) $\frac{1}{5}$ (b) $\frac{2}{5}$ (c) $\frac{1}{25}$ (d) $\frac{2}{125}$

Sol. (a) $\sum_{r=1}^{\infty} \frac{(4r+5)5^{-r}}{r(5r+5)} = \lim_{n\to\infty} \sum_{r=1}^{n} \left(\frac{(5r+5)-r}{r(5r+5)}\right)\cdot\frac{1}{5^r}$

$$= \lim_{n\to\infty} \sum_{r=1}^{n} \left(\frac{1}{r} - \frac{1}{5r+5}\right)\frac{1}{5^r}$$

$$= \lim_{n\to\infty} \sum_{r=1}^{n} \left(\frac{1}{r\cdot5^{-r}} - \frac{1}{(r+1)5^{r+1}}\right)$$

$$= \lim_{n\to\infty} \sum_{r=1}^{n} \left(\frac{1}{5} - \frac{1}{(n+1)5^{n+1}}\right) = \frac{1}{5} - 0 = \frac{1}{5}$$

● ***Ex. 9*** *Let* λ *be the greatest integer for which* $5p^2 - 16, 2p\lambda, \lambda^2$ *are distinct consecutive terms of an AP, where* $p \in R$*. If the common difference of the AP is* $\left(\frac{m}{n}\right)$*,* $m, n \in N$ *and m, n are relative prime, the value of* $m + n$ *is*

(a) 133 (b) 138 (c) 143 (d) 148

Sol. (c) $\because 5p^2 - 16, 2p\lambda, \lambda^2$ are in AP, then

$$4p\lambda = 5p^2 - 16 + \lambda^2$$

$\Rightarrow$ $5p^2 - 4p\lambda + \lambda^2 - 16 = 0$ ...(i)

$\therefore$ $B - 4AC \ge 0$ $[\because p \in R]$

$\Rightarrow$ $16\lambda^2 - 4\cdot5\cdot(\lambda^2 - 16) \ge 0$

$\Rightarrow$ $-\lambda^2 + 80 \ge 0$ or $\lambda^2 \ge 80$

$\Rightarrow$ $-\sqrt{80} \le \lambda \le \sqrt{80}$

$\therefore$ $\lambda = 8$ [greatest integer]

From Eq. (i), $5p^2 - 32p + 48 = 0$

$\Rightarrow$ $(p-4)(5p-12) = 0$

$\therefore$ $p = 4, p = \frac{12}{5}$

$\Rightarrow$ $p = \frac{12}{5}, p \ne 4$

[for $p = 4$ all terms are equal]

Now, common difference $= \lambda^2 - 2p\lambda$

$$= 64 - 16\times\frac{12}{5} = 64\left(1 - \frac{3}{5}\right) = \frac{128}{5} = \frac{m}{n} \quad \text{[given]}$$

$\therefore$ $m = 128$ and $n = 5$

Hence, $m + n = 143$

● ***Ex. 10*** *If* $2\lambda, \lambda$ *and* $[\lambda^2 - 14], \lambda \in R - \{0\}$ *and [.] denotes the greatest integer function are the first three terms of a GP in order, then the 51th term of the sequence,* $1, 3\lambda, 6\lambda, 10\lambda, \ldots$ *is*

(a) 5104 (b) 5304
(c) 5504 (d) 5704

Sol. (b) $\because 2\lambda, \lambda, [\lambda^2 - 14]$ are in GP, then

$$\lambda^2 = 2\lambda[\lambda^2 - 14]$$

$\Rightarrow$ $\frac{\lambda}{2} = [\lambda^2 - 14]$

$\therefore$ λ must be an even integer

Hence, $\lambda = 4$

Now, required sequence 1, 12, 24, 40, ...

or 1, $4(1+2), 4(1+2+3), 4(1+2+3+4), \ldots$

$\therefore$ 51th term $= 4(1+2+3+\ldots+51)$

$$= 4\cdot\frac{51}{2}(1+51) = 4\cdot51\cdot26 = 5304$$

JEE Type Solved Examples : More than One Correct Option Type Questions

- This section contains **5 multiple choice examples.** Each example has four choices (a), (b), (c) and (d) out of **which more than one** may be correct.

Ex. 11 *The first three terms of a sequence are* 3, −1, −1. *The next terms are*

(a) 2 (b) 3 (c) $-\frac{5}{27}$ (d) $-\frac{5}{9}$

Sol. (b, d) The given sequence is not an AP or GP or HP. It is an AGP, $3, (3+d)r, (3+2d)r^2, \ldots$

$$\Rightarrow \quad (3+d)r = -1, (3+2d)r^2 = -1$$

Eliminating r, we get $\quad (3+d)^2 = -(3+2d)$

$$\Rightarrow \quad d^2 + 8d + 12 = 0 \Rightarrow d = -2, -6,$$

then $\quad r = -1, \frac{1}{3}$

$\therefore$ Next term is $(3+3d)r^3 = 3, -\frac{5}{9}$

Ex. 12 *There are two numbers a and b whose product is 192 and the quotient of AM by HM of their greatest common divisor and least common multiple is* $\frac{169}{48}$. *The smaller of a and b is*

(a) 2 (b) 4 (c) 6 (d) 12

Sol. (b, d) If G = GED of a and b, L = LCM of a and b, we have $GL = ab = 192$ ...(i)

$$\frac{\text{AM}}{\text{HM}} \text{ of } G \text{ and } L \text{ is } \left(\frac{G+L}{2}\right)\left(\frac{G+L}{2GL}\right) = \frac{169}{48}$$

$$\Rightarrow \quad (G+L)^2 = \frac{169}{12}GL = \frac{169}{12} \times 192 = 13^2 \cdot 4^2$$

$$\Rightarrow \quad G + L = 52 \text{ but } GL = 192$$

$$\Rightarrow \quad G = 4, L = 48 \Rightarrow a = 4, b = 48 \text{ or } a = 12, b = 16$$

Ex. 13 *Consider a series* $\frac{1}{2} + \frac{1}{2^2} + \frac{2}{2^3} + \frac{3}{2^4} + \frac{5}{2^5} + \ldots + \frac{\lambda n}{2^n}$. *If* S_n *denotes its sum to n terms, then* S_n *cannot be*

(a) 2 (b) 3 (c) 4 (d) 5

Sol. (a, b, c, d)

$$\because \quad Sn = \frac{1}{2} + \frac{1}{2^2} + \frac{2}{2^3} + \frac{3}{2^4} + \frac{5}{2^5} + \ldots + \frac{\lambda_n}{2^n}$$

$$= \frac{3}{4} + \frac{1}{4}\left(\frac{1}{2} + \frac{1}{2^2} + \frac{2}{2^3} + \frac{3}{2^4} + \frac{5}{2^5} + \ldots + \frac{\lambda_n}{2^n}\right)$$

$$+ \frac{1}{2}\left(\frac{1}{2} + \frac{1}{2^2} + \frac{2}{2^3} + \ldots + \frac{\lambda_n}{2^n}\right) - \frac{1}{4} - \frac{\lambda_n}{2^{n+2}} - \frac{\lambda_n}{2^{n+1}}$$

$$\Rightarrow \quad S_n = \frac{3}{4} + \frac{1}{4}S_n + \frac{1}{2}S_n - \frac{1}{4} - \frac{\lambda_n}{2^{n+2}} - \frac{\lambda_n}{2^{n+1}}$$

$$\Rightarrow \frac{1}{4}S_n = \frac{1}{2} - \frac{\lambda_n}{2^{n+2}} - \frac{\lambda_n}{2^{n+1}} \Rightarrow S_n = 2 - \frac{\lambda_n}{2^{n+1}} - \frac{\lambda_n}{2^{n-1}} < 2$$

Ex. 14 *If* $S_r = \sqrt{r + \sqrt{r + \sqrt{r + \sqrt{\ldots \infty}}}}$, $r > 0$ *then which the following is/are correct.*

(a) S_r, S_6, S_{12}, S_{20} are in AP

(b) S_4, S_9, S_{16} are irrational

(c) $(2S_{4-1})^2, (2S_{5-1})^2 (2S_{6-1})^2$ are in AP

(d) S_2, S_{12}, S_{56} are in GP

Sol. (a, b, c, d)

$$\because S_r = \sqrt{r + \sqrt{r + \sqrt{+\sqrt{\ldots \infty}}}} = \sqrt{r + S_r}$$

$$\Rightarrow \quad S_r^2 - S_r - r = 0$$

$$\therefore \quad S_r = \frac{1 + \sqrt{(1+4r)}}{2} \quad [\because r > 0]$$

Alternate (a) S_2, S_6, S_{12}, S_{20} i.e., 2, 3, 4, 5 are in AP.

Alternate (b) S_4, S_9, S_{16} i.e., $\frac{1+\sqrt{17}}{2}, \frac{1+\sqrt{37}}{2}, \frac{1+\sqrt{65}}{2}$ are irrationals.

Alternate (c) $(2S_{4-1})^2, (2S_{5-1})^2, (2S_{6-1})^2$ i.e., 17, 21, 25 are in AP

Alternate (d) S_2, S_{12}, S_{56} i.e., 2, 4, 8 are in GP.

Ex. 15 *If* $\frac{1}{a}, \frac{1}{b}, \frac{1}{c}$ *are in AP and a, b, −2c are in GP, where a, b, c are non-zero, then*

(a) $a^3 + b^3 + c^3 = 3abc$ (b) $-2a, b, -2c$ are in AP

(c) $-2a, b, -2c$ are in GP (d) $a^2, b^2, 4c^2$ are in GP

Sol. (a, b, d)

$\because \quad \frac{1}{a}, \frac{1}{b}, \frac{1}{c}$ are in AP $\Rightarrow a, b, c$ are in HP

$$\therefore \quad b = \frac{2ab}{a+c} \quad \ldots(i)$$

and $a, b, -2c$ are in GP, then $b^2 = -2ac$ ...(ii)

From Eqs. (i) and (ii), we get

$$b = \frac{-b^2}{a+c} \Rightarrow a + b + c = 0 \quad [\because b \neq 0]$$

$\therefore \quad a^3 + b^3 + c^3 = 3abc$ and $a, b, -2c$ are in GP

$\Rightarrow \quad a^2, b^2, 4c^2$ are also in GP and $a + b + c = 0$

$$\Rightarrow \quad 2b = -2a - 2c$$

$\therefore \quad -2a, b, -2c$ are in AP.

JEE Type Solved Examples : Passage Based Questions

- This section contains **3 solved passages** based upon each of the passage **3 multiple choice** examples have to be answered. Each of these examples has four choices (a), (b), (c) and (d) out of which **ONLY ONE** is correct.

Passage I

(Ex. Nos. 16 to 18)

Consider a sequence whose sum to n terms is given by the quadratic function $S_n = 3n^2 + 5n$.

16. *The nature of the given series is*

(a) AP (b) GP (c) HP (d) AGP

Sol. (*a*) $\because \quad S_n = 3n^2 + 5n$

$$\therefore \quad T_n = S_n - S_{n-1}$$
$$= (3n^2 + 5n) - [3(n-1)^2 + 5(n-1)]$$
$$= 3(2n-1) + 5 = 6n + 2$$

The nth term is a linear function in n. Hence, sequence must be an AP.

17. *For the given sequence, the number 5456 is the*

(a) 153 th term (b) 932 th term
(c) 707 th term (d) 909 th term

Sol. (*d*) Given, $T_n = 5456$

$$\Rightarrow \quad 6n + 2 = 5456 \Rightarrow 6n = 5454$$
$$\therefore \quad n = 909$$

$\therefore$ The number 5456 is the 909 th term.

18. *Sum of the squares of the first 3 terms of the given series is*

(a) 1100 (b) 660 (c) 799 (d) 1000

Sol. (*b*) $T_1^2 + T_2^2 + T_3^2 = 8^2 + 14^2 + 20^2 = 64 + 196 + 400 = 660$

Passage II

(Ex. Nos. 19 to 21)

Let r be the number of identical terms in the two AP's. Form the sequence of identical terms, it will be an AP, then the rth term of this AP make $t_r \le$ *the smaller of the last term of the two AP's.*

19. *The number of terms common to two AP's* 3, 7, 11, …, 407 *and* 2, 9, 16, …, 709 *is*

(a) 14 (b) 21 (c) 28 (d) 35

Sol. (*a*) Sequence 3, 7, 11, … , 407 has common difference = 4 and sequence 2, 9, 16, … , 709 has common difference = 7.

Hence, the sequence with common terms has common difference LCM of 4 and 7 which is 28.

The first common term is 23.

Hence, the sequence is 23, 51, 79, … , 387 which has 14 terms.

Aliter By inspection, first common term to both the series is 23, second common term is 51, third common term is 79 and so on. These numbers form an AP 23, 51, 79, …

Since, $T_{14} = 23 + 13(28) = 387 < 407$

and $T_{15} = 23 + 14(28) = 415 > 407$

Hence, number of common terms = 14

20. *The 10th common term between the series* $3 + 7 + 11 + \dots$ *and* $1 + 6 + 11 + \dots$ *is*

(a) 189 (b) 191 (c) 211 (d) 213

Sol. (b) Series 3 + 7 + 11 + … has common difference = 4 and series 1 + 6 + 11 + … has common difference = 5

Hence, the series with common terms has common difference LCM of 4 and 5 which is 20.

The first common terms is 11.

Hence, the series is 11 + 31 + 51 + 71 + …

$$\therefore \quad t_{10} = 11 + (10-1)(20) = 191$$

Aliter t_n for $3 + 7 + 11 + \dots = 3 + (n-1)(4) = 4n - 1$

and t_m for $1 + 6 + 11 + \dots = 1 + (m-1)(5) = 5m - 4$

For a common term, $4n - 1 = 5m - 4$ i.e., $4n = 5m - 3$

For $m = 3$, $n = 3$ gives the first common term i.e., 11.

For $m = 7$, $n = 8$ gives the second common term i.e., 31.

For $m = 11$, $n = 13$ gives the third common term i.e., 51.

Hence, the common term series is 11 + 31 + 51 + …

$$\therefore \quad t_{10} = 11 + (10-1)20 = 191$$

21. *The value of largest term common to the sequences* 1, 11, 21, 31, … *upto* 100 *terms and* 31, 36, 41, 46, … *upto* 100 *terms, is*

(a) 281 (b) 381 (c) 471 (d) 521

Sol. (*d*) Sequence 1, 11, 21, 31, … has common difference = 10 and sequence 31, 36, 41, 46, … has common difference = 5. Hence, the sequence with common terms has common difference LCM of 10 and 5 which is 10.

The first common term is 31.

Hence, the sequence is 31, 41, 51, 61, 71, … …(i)

Now, t_{100} of first sequence $= 1 + (100-1)10 = 991$

and t_{100} of second sequence $= 31 + (100-1)5 = 526$

Value of largest common term < 526

$\therefore t_n$ of Eq. (i) is $31 + (n-1)10 = 10n + 21$

$$t_{50} = 10 \times 50 + 21 = 521$$

is the value of largest common term.

Aliter Let mth term of the first sequence be equal to the nth term of the second sequence, then

$$1 + (m-1)10 = 31 + (n-1)5$$

$$\Rightarrow \quad 10m - 9 = 5n + 26 \Rightarrow 10m - 35 = 5n$$
$$\Rightarrow \quad 2m - 7 = n \le 100 \Rightarrow 2m \le 107$$
$$\Rightarrow \quad m \le 53\frac{1}{2}$$

$\therefore$ Largest value of $m = 53$

$\therefore$ Value of largest term $= 1 + (53 - 1)\,10 = 521$

Passage III

(Ex. Nos. 22 to 24)

We are giving the concept of arithmetic mean of mth power. Let $a_1, a_2, a_3, \ldots, a_n$ be n positive real numbers (not all equal) and m be a real number. Then,

$$\frac{a_1^m + a_2^m + a_3^m + \ldots + a_n^m}{n} > \left(\frac{a_1 + a_2 + a_3 + \ldots + a_n}{n}\right)^m,$$

if $m \in R \sim [0, 1]$

However, if $m \in (0, 1)$, then

$$\frac{a_1^m + a_2^m + a_3^m + \ldots + a_n^m}{n} < \left(\frac{a_1 + a_2 + a_3 + \ldots + a_n}{n}\right)^m$$

Obviously, if $m = \{0, 1\}$, then

$$\frac{a_1^m + a_2^m + a_3^m + \ldots + a_n^m}{n} = \left(\frac{a_1 + a_2 + a_3 + \ldots + a_n}{n}\right)^m.$$

22. *If $x > 0, y > 0, z > 0$ and $x + y + z = 1$, the minimum value of $\frac{x}{2-x} + \frac{y}{2-y} + \frac{z}{2-z}$, is*

(a) 0.2 (b) 0.4
(c) 0.6 (d) 0.8

Sol. (c) Since, AM of (-1) th powers $\ge (-1)$ th powers of AM

$$\therefore \frac{(2-x)^{-1} + (2-y)^{-1} + (2-z)^{-1}}{3} \ge \left(\frac{2 - x + 2 - y + 2 - z}{3}\right)^{-1}$$

$$= \left[\frac{6 - (x + y + z)}{3}\right]^{-1} = \left(\frac{6-1}{3}\right)^{-1} = \frac{3}{5} \quad [\because x + y + z = 1]$$

$$\Rightarrow \frac{(2-x)^{-1} + (2-y)^{-1} + (2-z)^{-1}}{3} \ge \frac{3}{5}$$

$$\text{or} \quad \frac{1}{3}\left[\frac{1}{2-x} + \frac{1}{2-y} + \frac{1}{2-z}\right] \ge \frac{3}{5}$$

$$\Rightarrow \frac{1}{2-x} + \frac{1}{2-y} + \frac{1}{2-z} \ge \frac{9}{5}$$

$$\text{or} \quad \frac{2}{2-x} + \frac{2}{2-y} + \frac{2}{2-z} \ge \frac{18}{5}$$

$$\text{or} \quad 1 + \frac{x}{2-x} + 1 + \frac{y}{2-y} + 1 + \frac{z}{2-z} \ge \frac{18}{5}$$

$$\text{or} \quad \frac{x}{2-x} + \frac{y}{2-y} + \frac{z}{2-z} \ge \frac{18}{5} - 3$$

$$\text{Hence,} \quad \frac{x}{2-x} + \frac{y}{2-y} + \frac{z}{2-z} \ge \frac{3}{5} = 0.6$$

$$\Rightarrow \frac{x}{2-x} + \frac{y}{2-y} + \frac{z}{2-z} \ge 0.6$$

Thus, minimum value of $\frac{x}{2-x} + \frac{y}{2-y} + \frac{z}{2-z}$ is 0.6.

23. *If $\sum_{i=1}^{n} a_i^2 = \lambda, \forall a_i \ge 0$ and if greatest and least values of $\left(\sum_{i=1}^{n} a_i\right)^2$ are λ_1 and λ_2 respectively, then $(\lambda_1 - \lambda_2)$ is*

(a) $n\lambda$ (b) $(n-1)\lambda$
(c) $(n+2)\lambda$ (d) $(n+1)\lambda$

Sol. (b) $\because$ AM of 2nd powers $\ge$ 2nd power of AM

$$\therefore \frac{a_1^2 + a_2^2 + a_3^2 + \ldots + a_n^2}{n} \ge \left(\frac{a_1 + a_2 + a_3 + \ldots + a_n}{n}\right)^2$$

$$\Rightarrow \frac{\lambda}{n} \ge \left(\frac{\sum_{i=1}^{n} a_i}{n}\right)^2 \quad \therefore \left(\sum_{i=1}^{n} a_i\right)^2 \le n\lambda \quad \ldots \text{(i)}$$

Also, $(a_1 + a_2 + a_3 + \ldots + a_n)^2 = a_1^2 + a_2^2 + a_3^2 + \ldots + a_n^2 + 2\sum a_1 a_2$

$$= \lambda + 2\sum a_1 a_2 \ge \lambda$$

$$\therefore \left(\sum_{i=1}^{n} a_i\right)^2 \ge \lambda \quad \ldots \text{(ii)}$$

From Eqs. (i) and (ii), we get

$$\lambda \le \left(\sum_{i=1}^{n} a_i\right)^2 \le n\lambda$$

$$\therefore \quad \lambda_1 = n\lambda \text{ and } \lambda_2 = \lambda$$

Then, $\lambda_1 - \lambda_2 = (n-1)\lambda$

24. *If sum of the mth powers of first n odd numbers is λ, $\forall m > 1$, then*

(a) $\lambda < n^m$ (b) $\lambda > n^m$ (c) $\lambda < n^{m+1}$ (d) $\lambda > n^{m+1}$

Sol. (d) $\because m > 1$

$$\therefore \frac{1^m + 3^m + 5^m + \ldots + (2n-1)^m}{n} > \left(\frac{1 + 3 + 5 + \ldots + (2n-1)}{n}\right)^m$$

$$= \left(\frac{\frac{n}{2}(1 + 2n - 1)}{n}\right)^m = n^m$$

$$\therefore 1^m + 3^m + 5^m + \ldots + (2n-1)^m > n^{m+1}$$

Hence, $\lambda > n^{m+1}$

JEE Type Solved Examples : Single Integer Answer Type Questions

- This section contains **2 examples.** The answer to each example is a **single digit integer** ranging from **0** to **9** (both inclusive).

● ***Ex. 25*** *A sequence of positive terms $A_1, A_2, A_3, \ldots, A_n$ satisfies the relation $A_{n+1} = \frac{3(1+A_n)}{(3+A_n)}$. Least integral value of A_1 for which the sequence is decreasing can be*

Sol. (2) $\because \ A_{n+1} = \frac{3(1+A_n)}{(3+A_n)}$. For $n = 1$, $A_2 = \frac{3(1+A_1)}{(3+A_1)}$

For $n = 2$,
$$A_3 = \frac{3(1+A_2)}{(3+A_2)} = \frac{3\left(1+\frac{3(1+A_1)}{(3+A_1)}\right)}{3+\frac{3(1+A_1)}{(3+A_1)}} = \frac{6+4A_1}{4+2A_1} = \frac{3+2A_1}{2+A_1}$$

$\because$ Given, sequence can be written as
$$A_1, \frac{3(1+A_1)}{(3+A_1)}, \frac{(3+2A_1)}{(2+A_1)}, \ldots$$

Given, $A_1 > 0$ and sequence is decreasing, then
$$A_1 > \frac{3(1+A_1)}{(3+A_1)}, \frac{3(1+A_1)}{(3+A_1)} > \frac{(3+2A_1)}{(2+A_1)}$$
$\Rightarrow \quad A_1^2 > 3$ or $A_1 > \sqrt{3}$

$\therefore \quad A_1 = 2$ [least integral value of A_1]

● ***Ex. 26*** *When the ninth term of an AP is divided by its second term we get 5 as the quotient, when the thirteenth term is divided by sixth term the quotient is 2 and the remainder is 5, then the second term is*

Sol. (7) Let a be the first term and d be the common difference, then $T_9 = 5\,T_2$

$\Rightarrow \quad (a+8d) = 5(a+d)$

$\therefore \quad 4a = 3d$ ...(i)

and $\quad T_{13} = T_6 \times 2 + 5$

$\Rightarrow \quad a + 12d = 2(a+5d) + 5$

$\Rightarrow \quad 2d = a + 5$ ...(ii)

From Eqs. (i) and (ii), we get

$a = 3$ and $d = 4$

$\therefore \quad T_2 = a + d = 7$

JEE Type Solved Examples : Matching Type Questions

- This section contains **2 examples.** Examples 27 has three statements (A, B and C) given in **Column I** and four statements (p, q, r and s) in **Column II** example 28 has four statements (A, B, C and D) given in **Column I** and five statements (p, q, r, s and t) in **Column II**. Any given statement in **Column I** can have correct matching with one or more statement(s) given in **Column II.**

● ***Ex. 27***

	Column I		Column II
(A)	If $a_1, a_2, a_3, \ldots$ are in AP and $a_1 + a_6 + a_{10} + a_{21} + a_{25} + a_{30} = 120$, then $\sum_{i=1}^{30} a_i$ is	(p)	400
(B)	If $a_1, a_2, a_3, \ldots$ are in AP and $a_1 + a_5 + a_9 + a_{13} + a_{17} + a_{21} + a_{25} = 112$, then $\sum_{i=1}^{25} a_i$ is	(q)	600
(C)	If $a_1, a_2, a_3, \ldots$ are in AP and $a_1 + a_4 + a_7 + a_{10} + a_{13} + a_{16} = 375$, then $\sum_{i=1}^{16} a_i$ is	(r)	800
		(s)	1000

Sol. (A) → (q); (B) → (p); (C) → (s)

(A) $\because a_1, a_2, a_3, \ldots$ are in AP.

$\therefore \quad a_1 + a_{30} = a_6 + a_{25} = a_{10} + a_{21} = \lambda$ [say]

$\because \quad a_1 + a_6 + a_{10} + a_{21} + a_{25} + a_{30} = 120$

$\therefore \quad 3\lambda = 120$

$\Rightarrow \quad \lambda = 40$

Then, $\quad \sum_{i=1}^{30} a_i = \frac{30}{2}(a_1 + a_{30}) = 15 \times \lambda = 15 \times 40 = 600$

(B) $\because a_1, a_2, a_3, \ldots$ are in AP.

$\therefore \quad a_1 + a_{25} = a_5 + a_{21}$

$= a_9 + a_{17} = a_{13} + a_{13} = \lambda$ [say]

$\because \quad a_1 + a_5 + a_9 + a_{13} + a_{17} + a_{21} + a_{25} = 112$

$\therefore \quad 3\lambda + \frac{\lambda}{2} = 112$

$\Rightarrow \quad \frac{7\lambda}{2} = 112$

$\Rightarrow \quad \lambda = 32$

Then, $\quad \sum_{i=1}^{25} a_i = \frac{25}{2}(a_1 + a_{25}) = \frac{25}{2} \times 32 = 400$

(C) $\because a_1, a_2, a_3, \ldots$ are in AP.

$\therefore \quad a_1 + a_{16} = a_4 + a_{13} = a_7 + a_{10} = \lambda$ [say]

$\because \quad a_1 + a_4 + a_7 + a_{10} + a_{13} + a_{16} = 375$

$\therefore \quad 3\lambda = 375 \;\therefore\; \lambda = 125$

Then, $\displaystyle\sum_{i=1}^{16} a_i = \frac{16}{2}(a_1 + a_{16})$

$= 8 \times \lambda = 8 \times 125 = 1000$

• **Ex. 28**

	Column I		Column II
(A)	If $a > 0, b > 0, c > 0$ and the minimum value of $a(b^2 + c^2) + b(c^2 + a^2) + c(a^2 + b^2)$ is λabc, then λ is	(p)	2
(B)	If a, b, c are positive, $a + b + c = 1$ and the minimum value of $\left(\frac{1}{a} - 1\right)\left(\frac{1}{b} - 1\right)\left(\frac{1}{c} - 1\right)$ is λ, then λ is	(q)	4
(C)	If $a > 0, b > 0, c > 0, s = a + b + c$ and the minimum value of $\frac{2s}{s-a} + \frac{2s}{s-b} + \frac{2s}{s-c}$ is $(\lambda - 1)$, then λ is	(r)	6
(D)	If $a > 0, b > 0, c > 0, a, b, c$ are in GP and the the minimum value of $\left(\frac{a}{b}\right)^{\lambda} + \left(\frac{c}{b}\right)^{\lambda}$ is 2, then λ is	(s)	8
		(t)	10

Sol. (A) → (r); (B) → (s); (C) → (t); (D) → (p, q, r, s, t)

(A) $\because$ AM $\geq$ GM

$$\therefore \frac{ab^2 + ac^2 + bc^2 + ba^2 + ca^2 + cb^2}{6} \geq (ab^2 \cdot ac^2 \cdot bc^2 \cdot ba^2 \cdot ca^2 \cdot cb^2)^{1/6} = abc$$

$\therefore \; a(b^2 + c^2) + b(c^2 + a^2) + c(a^2 + b^2) \geq 6abc$

$\Rightarrow \quad \lambda = 6$

(B) $\because$ AM $\geq$ GM

For b, c, we get $\dfrac{(b+c)}{2} \geq \sqrt{bc}$

$\Rightarrow \quad (b + c) \geq 2\sqrt{bc}$ ...(i)

For c, a, we get $\dfrac{(c+a)}{2} \geq \sqrt{ca}$

$\Rightarrow \quad (c + a) \geq 2\sqrt{ca}$ ...(ii)

and for a, b, we get $\dfrac{(a+b)}{2} \geq \sqrt{ab}$

$\Rightarrow \quad (a + b) \geq 2\sqrt{ab}$ ...(iii)

On multiplying Eqs. (i), (ii) and (iii), we get

$(b + c)(c + a)(a + b) \geq 8abc$

$\Rightarrow \quad (1 - a)(1 - b)(1 - c) \geq 8abc \quad [\because a + b + c = 1]$

$\Rightarrow \quad \left(\frac{1}{a} - 1\right)\left(\frac{1}{b} - 1\right)\left(\frac{1}{c} - 1\right) \geq 8$

$\therefore \quad \lambda = 8$

(C) $\because$ AM $\geq$ HM

$$\frac{(s-a) + (s-b) + (s-c)}{3} \geq \frac{3}{\frac{1}{s-a} + \frac{1}{s-b} + \frac{1}{s-c}}$$

$$\Rightarrow \frac{3s - (a+b+c)}{3} \geq \frac{3}{\frac{1}{s-a} + \frac{1}{s-b} + \frac{1}{s-c}}$$

$$\Rightarrow \frac{3s - s}{3} \geq \frac{3}{\left(\frac{1}{s-a} + \frac{1}{s-b} + \frac{1}{s-c}\right)}$$

$$\Rightarrow \frac{2s}{s-a} + \frac{2s}{s-b} + \frac{2s}{s-c} \geq 9$$

Here, $\lambda - 1 = 9$

$\therefore \quad \lambda = 10$

(D) If a, b, c are in GP.

Then, $a^{\lambda}, b^{\lambda}, c^{\lambda}$ are also in GP.

Then, AM $\geq$ GM

$$\frac{a^{\lambda} + c^{\lambda}}{2} \geq b^{\lambda}$$

$\Rightarrow \quad a^{\lambda} + c^{\lambda} \geq 2b^{\lambda}$

$\Rightarrow \quad \left(\frac{a}{b}\right)^{\lambda} + \left(\frac{c}{b}\right)^{\lambda} \geq 2$

$\therefore \quad \lambda \in R$

Hence, $\lambda = 2, 4, 6, 8, 10$

JEE Type Solved Examples : Statement I and II Type Questions

- **Directions** Example numbers 29 to 32 are Assertion-Reason type examples. Each of these examples contains two statements:
Statement-1 (Assertion) and **Statement-2** (Reason)
Each of these examples also has four alternative choices, only one of which is the correct answer. You have to select the correct choice as given below.
(a) Statement-1 is true, Statement-2 is true; Statement-2 is a correct explanation for Statement-1
(b) Statement-1 is true, Statement-2 is true; Statement-2 is not a correct explanation for Statement-1
(c) Statement-1 is true, Statement-2 is false
(d) Statement-1 is false, Statement-2 is true

- ***Ex. 29.*** **Statement 1** *The sum of first n terms of the series* $1^2 - 2^2 + 3^2 - 4^2 + 5^2 - \dots$ can be $= \pm \frac{n(n+1)}{2}$.
Statement 2 *Sum of first n natural numbers is* $\frac{n(n+1)}{2}$.

Sol. (a) Clearly, nth term of the given series is negative or positive according as n is even or odd, respectively.

***Case* I** When n is even, in this case the given series is

$$1^2 - 2^2 + 3^2 - 4^2 + 5^2 - 6^2 + \dots + (n-1)^2 - n^2$$
$$= (1^2 - 2^2) + (3^2 - 4^2) + (5^2 - 6^2) + \dots + [(n-1)^2 - n^2]$$
$$= (1-2)(1+2) + (3-4)(3+4) + (5-6)(5+6) + \dots + (n-1-n)(n-1+n)$$
$$= -(1+2+3+4+5+6+\dots+(n-1)+n) = -\frac{n(n+1)}{2}$$

***Case* II** When n is odd, in this case the given series is

$$1^2 - 2^2 + 3^2 - 4^2 + 5^2 - 6^2 + \dots + (n-2)^2 - (n-1)^2 + n^2$$
$$= (1^2 - 2^2) + (3^2 - 4^2) + (5^2 - 6^2) + \dots + [(n-2)^2 - (n-1)^2] + n^2$$
$$= (1-2)(1+2) + (3-4)(3+4) + (5-6)(5+6) + \dots + [(n-2)-(n-1)][(n-2)+(n-1)] + n^2$$
$$= -[1+2+3+4+5+6+\dots+(n-2)+(n-1)] + n^2$$
$$= -\frac{(n-1)(n-1+1)}{2} + n^2 = \frac{n(n+1)}{2}$$

It is clear that Statement-1 is true, Statement-2 is true and Statement-2 is correct explanation for Statement-1.

- ***Ex. 30*** **Statement 1** *If a, b, c are three positive numbers in GP, then* $\left(\frac{a+b+c}{3}\right)\left(\frac{3abc}{ab+bc+ca}\right) = (abc)^{2/3}$.

Statement-2 *(AM) (HM)=(GM)^2 is true for positive numbers.*

Sol. (c) If a, b be two real, positive and unequal numbers, then

$$\text{AM} = \frac{a+b}{2}, \text{GM} = \sqrt{ab} \text{ and HM} = \frac{2ab}{a+b}$$

$\therefore$ AM) (HM) = (GM)^2

This result will be true for n numbers, if they are in GP.
Hence, Statement-1 is true and Statement-2 is false.

- ***Ex. 31*** *Consider an AP with a as the first term and d is the common difference such that S_n denotes the sum to n terms and a_n denotes the nth term of the AP. Given that for some $m, n \in N$, $\frac{S_m}{S_n} = \frac{m^2}{n^2}$ $(m \neq n)$.*

Statement 1 *$d = 2a$ because*

Statement 2 $\frac{a_m}{a_n} = \frac{2m+1}{2n+1}$

Sol. (c) $\because$ $\frac{S_m}{S_n} = \frac{m^2}{n^2}$

Let $S_m = m^2k$, $S_n = n^2k$

$\therefore$ $a_m = S_m - S_{m-1} = m^2k - (m-1)^2 k$

$\Rightarrow$ $a_m = (2m-1)k$

Similarly, $a_n = (2n-1)k$ $\therefore$ $\frac{a_m}{a_n} = \frac{2m-1}{2n-1}$

Statement-2 is false.

Also, $\because$ $a_1 = k, a_2 = 3k, a_3 = 5k, \dots$

Given, $a_1 = a = k$

$\therefore$ $a_1 = a, a_2 = 3a, a_3 = 5a, \dots$

$\therefore$ Common difference $d = a_2 - a_1 = a_3 - a_2 = \dots$

$\Rightarrow$ $d = 2a$

$\therefore$ Statement-1 is true.

- ***Ex. 32*** **Statement-1** *1, 2, 4, 8, ... is a GP, 4, 8, 16, 32, ... is a GP and 1 + 4, 2 + 8, 4 + 16, 8 + 32, ... is also a GP.*

Statement-2 *Let general term of a GP with common ratio r be T_{k+1} and general term of another GP with common ratio r be T'_{k+1}, then the series whose general term $T''_{k+1} = T_{k+1} + T'_{k+1}$ is also a GP with common ratio r.*

Sol. (a) 1, 2, 4, 8, ...

Common ratio $r = 2$

$\therefore$ $T_{k+1} = 1 \cdot (2)^{k+1-1} = 2^k$

and 4, 8, 16, 32, ...

Common ratio, $r = 2$

$\therefore$ $T'_{k+1} = 4 \cdot (2)^{k+1-1} = 4 \cdot 2^k$

Then, $T_{k+1} + T'_{k+1} = 5 \cdot 2^k = T''_{k+1}$

Common ratio of $T''_{k+1} = \frac{5 \cdot 2^k}{5 \cdot 2^{k-1}} = 2$, which is true.

Hence, Statement-1 and Statement-2 both are true and Statement-2 is the correct explanation of Statement-1.

Subjective Type Examples

- In this section, there are **24 subjective** solved examples.

● ***Ex. 33*** *In a set of four numbers, the first three are in GP and the last three are in AP with a common difference of 6. If the first number is same as the fourth, then find the four numbers.*

Sol. Let the last three numbers in AP, be $a, a+6, a+12$.

[$\because$ 6 is the common difference]

If first number is b, then four numbers are

$$b, a, a+6, a+12$$

But given, $b = a + 12$

$\therefore$ Four numbers are $a+12, a, a+6, a+12$ ...(i)

Since, first three numbers are in GP.

Then, $a^2 = (a+12)(a+6)$

$\Rightarrow$ $a^2 = a^2 + 18a + 72$

$\Rightarrow$ $18a + 72 = 0$

$\therefore$ $a = -4$ [from Eq. (i)]

Hence, four numbers are 8, − 4, 2, 8.

● ***Ex. 34*** *Find the natural number a for which* $\sum_{k=1}^{n} f(a+k)$ $= 16(2^n - 1)$, *where the function f satisfies* $f(x+y) = f(x)\,f(y)$ *for all natural numbers x, y and further* $f(1) = 2$.

Sol. Given, $f(x+y) = f(x)\,f(y)$ ...(i)

and $f(1) = 2$ ...(ii)

On putting $x = y = 1$ in Eq. (i), we get

$$f(1+1) = f(1)\,f(1) = 2\cdot 2$$

$\therefore$ $f(2) = 2^2$ ...(iii)

Now, on putting $x = 1, y = 2$ in Eq. (i), we get

$f(1+2) = f(1)\,f(2) = 2\cdot 2^2$ [from Eqs. (ii) and (iii)]

$\therefore$ $f(3) = 2^3$

On putting $x = y = 2$ in Eq. (i), we get

$f(2+2) = f(2)\,f(2) = 2^2\cdot 2^2$ [from Eq. (iii)]

$\therefore$ $f(4) = 2^4$

$\vdots \quad \vdots \quad \vdots$

Similarly, $f(\lambda) = 2^{\lambda}, \lambda \in N$

$\therefore$ $f(a+k) = 2^{a+k}, a+k \in N$

$\because$ $\sum_{k=1}^{n} f(a+k) = 16(2^n - 1) \Rightarrow \sum_{k=1}^{n} 2^{a+k} = 16(2^n - 1)$

$\Rightarrow$ $2^a \sum_{k=1}^{n} 2^k = 16(2^n - 1)$

$\Rightarrow$ $2^a(2^1 + 2^2 + 2^3 + \dots + 2^n) = 16(2^n - 1)$

$\Rightarrow$ $2^a \cdot \dfrac{2(2^n - 1)}{(2-1)} = 16(2^n - 1)$

$\Rightarrow$ $2^{a+1} = 16 = 2^4$

$\Rightarrow$ $a + 1 = 4$

$\therefore$ $a = 3$

● ***Ex. 35*** *If n is a root of* $x^2(1-ac) - x(a^2+c^2) - (1+ac) = 0$ *and if n harmonic means are inserted between a and c, find the difference between the first and the last means.*

Sol. Let $H_1, H_2, H_3, \dots, H_n$, are n harmonic means, then $a, H_1, H_2, H_3, \dots, H_n, b$ are in HP.

$\therefore \dfrac{1}{a}, \dfrac{1}{H_1}, \dfrac{1}{H_2}, \dfrac{1}{H_3}, \dots, \dfrac{1}{H_n}, \dfrac{1}{b}$ are in AP.

If d be the common difference, then $\dfrac{1}{c} = \dfrac{1}{a} + (n+2-1)\,d$

$\therefore$ $d = \dfrac{(a-c)}{ac\,(n+1)}$ ...(i)

$\Rightarrow$ $\dfrac{1}{h_1} = \dfrac{1}{a} + d$ and $\dfrac{1}{h_n} = \dfrac{1}{c} - d$

$$\therefore\ h_1 - h_n = \frac{a}{1+ad} - \frac{c}{1-cd} = \frac{a}{1+\dfrac{(a-c)}{c(n+1)}} - \frac{c}{1-\dfrac{(a-c)}{a(n+1)}}$$

$$= \frac{ac\,(n+1)}{cn+a} - \frac{ac\,(n+1)}{an+c} = ac\,(n+1)\left(\frac{1}{cn+a} - \frac{1}{an+c}\right)$$

$$= ac\,(n+1)\left(\frac{an+c-cn-a}{acn^2 + (a^2+c^2)n + ac}\right)$$

$$= \frac{ac\,(a-c)(n^2-1)}{acn^2 + (a^2+c^2)\,n + ac} \quad \text{...(ii)}$$

But given n is a root of

$$x^2(1-ac) - x(a^2+c^2) - (1+ac) = 0.$$

Then, $n^2(1-ac) - n(a^2+c^2) - (1+ac) = 0$

or $acn^2 + (a^2+c^2)n + ac = n^2 - 1$,

then from Eq. (ii), $h_1 - h_n = \dfrac{ac\,(a-c)(n^2-1)}{(n^2-1)} = ac\,(a-c)$

● ***Ex. 36*** *A number consists of three-digits which are in GP the sum of the right hand and left hand digits exceeds twice the middle digit by 1 and the sum of the left hand and middle digits is two third of the sum of the middle and right hand digits. Find the number.*

Sol. Let the three digits be a, ar and ar^2, then number is

$$100a + 10ar + ar^2 \quad \text{...(i)}$$

Given, $a + ar^2 = 2ar + 1$

or $a(r^2 - 2r + 1) = 1$

or $a(r-1)^2 = 1 \quad \text{...(ii)}$

Also, given $a + ar = \frac{2}{3}(ar + ar^2) \Rightarrow 3 + 3r = 2r + 2r^2$

or $2r^2 - r - 3 = 0$ or $(r+1)(2r-3) = 0$

$\therefore \quad r = -1, \frac{3}{2}$

For $r = -1$, $a = \frac{1}{(r-1)^2} = \frac{1}{4} \notin I$

$\therefore \quad r \neq -1$

For $r = \frac{3}{2}$, $a = \frac{1}{\left(\frac{3}{2} - 1\right)^2} = 4$ [from Eq. (ii)]

From Eq. (i), number is $400 + 10 \cdot 4 \cdot \frac{3}{2} + 4 \cdot \frac{9}{4} = 469$

Ex. 37 *Find the value of the expression* $\sum_{i=1}^{n} \sum_{j=1}^{i} \sum_{k=1}^{j} 1.$

Sol. $\sum_{i=1}^{n} \sum_{j=1}^{i} \sum_{k=1}^{j} 1 = \sum_{i=1}^{n} \sum_{j=1}^{i} j = \sum_{i=1}^{n} \frac{i(i+1)}{2}$

$$= \frac{1}{2}\left[\sum_{i=1}^{n} i^2 + \sum_{i=1}^{n} i\right] = \frac{1}{2}\left[\sum n^2 + \sum n\right]$$

$$= \frac{1}{2}\left[\frac{n(n+1)(2n+1)}{6} + \frac{n(n+1)}{2}\right]$$

$$= \frac{n(n+1)}{12}[2n+1+3] = \frac{n(n+1)(n+2)}{6}$$

Ex. 38 *Three numbers are in GP whose sum is 70. If the extremes be each multiplied by 4 and the mean by 5, then they will be in AP. Find the numbers.*

Sol. Let the three numbers in GP be $\frac{a}{r}, a, ar$.

Given, $\frac{a}{r} + a + ar = 70 \quad \text{...(i)}$

and $\frac{4a}{r}, 5a, 4ar$ are in AP.

$\therefore \quad 10a = \frac{4a}{r} + 4ar$ or $\frac{10a}{4} = \frac{a}{r} + ar$

or $\frac{5a}{2} = 70 - a$ [from Eq. (i)]

or $5a = 140 - 2a$ or $7a = 140$

$\therefore \quad a = 20$

From Eq. (i), we get

$$\frac{20}{r} + 20 + 20r = 70$$

or $\frac{20}{r} + 20r = 50$

or $2 + 2r^2 = 5r$ or $2r^2 - 5r + 2 = 0$

or $(r-2)(2r-1) = 0 \quad \therefore \quad r = 2$ or $\frac{1}{2}$

Hence, the three numbers are 10, 20, 40 or 40, 20, 10.

Ex. 39 *If the sum of m terms of an AP is equal to the sum of either the next n terms or the next p terms, then prove that* $(m+n)\left(\frac{1}{m} - \frac{1}{p}\right) = (m+p)\left(\frac{1}{m} - \frac{1}{n}\right)$.

Sol. Let the AP be $a, a+d, a+2d, \ldots$

Given, $T_1 + T_2 + \ldots + T_m = T_{m+1} + T_{m+2} + \ldots + T_{m+n} \quad \text{...(i)}$

On adding $T_1 + T_2 + \ldots + T_m$ both sides in Eq. (i), we get

$2(T_1 + T_2 + \ldots + T_m) = T_1 + T_2 + \ldots + T_m + T_{m+1} + \ldots + T_{m+n}$

$\Rightarrow \quad 2S_m = S_{m+n}$

$\therefore \quad 2 \cdot \frac{m}{2}[2a + (m-1)d] = \frac{m+n}{2}[2a + (m+n-1)d]$

Let $2a + (m-1)d = x$

$\Rightarrow \quad mx = \frac{m+n}{2}\{x + nd\}$

$\Rightarrow \quad (m-n)x = (m+n)nd \quad \text{...(ii)}$

Again, $T_1 + T_2 + \ldots + T_m = T_{m+1} + T_{m+2} + \ldots + T_{m+p}$

Similarly, $(m-p)x = (m+p)pd \quad \text{...(iii)}$

On dividing Eq. (ii) by Eq. (iii), we get

$$\frac{m-n}{m-p} = \frac{(m+n)n}{(m+p)p}$$

$\Rightarrow \quad (m-n)(m+p)p = (m-p)(m+n)n$

On dividing both sides by mnp, we get

$$(m+p)\left(\frac{1}{n} - \frac{1}{m}\right) = (m+n)\left(\frac{1}{p} - \frac{1}{m}\right)$$

Hence, $(m+n)\left(\frac{1}{m} - \frac{1}{p}\right) = (m+p)\left(\frac{1}{m} - \frac{1}{n}\right)$

Ex. 40 *Find the sum of the products of every pair of the first n natural numbers.*

Sol. We find that

$$S = 1 \cdot 2 + 1 \cdot 3 + 1 \cdot 4 + \ldots + 2 \cdot 3 + 2 \cdot 4 + \ldots + 3 \cdot 4 + 3 \cdot 5 + \ldots + (n-1) \cdot n \quad \text{...(i)}$$

$\because \quad [1 + 2 + 3 + \ldots + (n-1) + n]^2 = 1^2 + 2^2 + 3^2 + \ldots + (n-1)^2 + n^2 + 2[1 \cdot 2 + 1 \cdot 3 + 1 \cdot 4 + \ldots + 2 \cdot 3 + 2 \cdot 4 + \ldots + 3 \cdot 4 + 3 \cdot 5 + \ldots + (n-1) \cdot n]$

$(\sum n)^2 = \sum n^2 + 2S$ [from Eq. (i)]

$$\Rightarrow \quad S=\frac{(\Sigma n)^2-\Sigma n^2}{2}$$

$$=\frac{\left\{\frac{n(n+1)}{2}\right\}^2-\frac{n(n+1)(2n+1)}{6}}{2}$$

$$=\frac{\frac{n^2(n+1)^2}{4}-\frac{n(n+1)(2n+1)}{6}}{2}$$

$$=\frac{n(n+1)}{24}[3n(n+1)-2(2n+1)]$$

$$=\frac{n(n+1)(3n^2-n-2)}{24}$$

Hence, $S=\frac{(n-1)n(n+1)(3n+2)}{24}$

● **Ex. 41** *If $I_n=\int_0^{\pi/4}\tan^n x\,dx$, show that $\frac{1}{I_2+I_4},\frac{1}{I_3+I_5},\frac{1}{I_4+I_6},\frac{1}{I_5+I_7},\ldots$ form an AP. Find its common difference.*

Sol. We have,

$$I_n+I_{n+2}=\int_0^{\pi/4}(\tan^n x+\tan^{n+2}x)\,dx$$

$$=\int_0^{\pi/4}\tan^n x(1+\tan^2 x)\,dx$$

$$=\int_0^{\pi/4}\tan^n x\cdot\sec^2 x\,dx=\left[\frac{\tan^{n+1}x}{n+1}\right]_0^{\pi/4}=\frac{1}{n+1}$$

Hence, $\frac{1}{I_n+I_{n+2}}=n+1$

On putting $n=2,3,4,5,\ldots$

$$\therefore \quad \frac{1}{I_2+I_4}=3,\ \frac{1}{I_3+I_5}=4,\ \frac{1}{I_4+I_6}=5,\ \frac{1}{I_5+I_7}=6,\ldots$$

Hence, $\frac{1}{I_2+I_4},\frac{1}{I_3+I_5},\frac{1}{I_4+I_6},\frac{1}{I_5+I_7},\ldots$ are in AP with common difference 1.

● **Ex. 42** *If the sum of the terms of an infinitely decreasing GP is equal to the greatest value of the function $f(x)=x^3+3x-9$ on the interval $[-5,3]$ and the difference between the first and second terms is $f'(0)$, then show that the common ratio of the progression is $\frac{2}{3}$.*

Sol. Given, $f(x)=x^3+3x-9$

$$\therefore \quad f'(x)=3x^2+3$$

Hence, $f'(x)>0$ in $[-5,3]$, then $f(x)$ is an increasing function on $[-5,3]$ and therefore, $f(x)$ will have greatest value at $x=3$.

Thus, greatest value of $f(x)$ is

$$f(x)=3^3+3\cdot3-9=27$$

Let $a, ar, ar^2,\ldots$ be a GP with common ratio $|r|<1$ [∵ given infinitely GP]

and also given $S_\infty=27$

so, $\frac{a}{1-r}=27$ ...(i)

and $a-ar=f'(0)$

$\Rightarrow a(1-r)=f'(0)=3$ [∵ $f'(0)=3$]

$\therefore a(1-r)=3$ ...(ii)

From Eqs. (i) and (ii), we get

$$(1-r)^2=\frac{1}{9}\Rightarrow 1-r=\pm\frac{1}{3}$$

$$\therefore \quad r=1\pm\frac{1}{3}$$

So, $r=\frac{4}{3},\frac{2}{3}\Rightarrow r\neq\frac{4}{3}$ [∵ $|r|<1$]

Hence, $r=\frac{2}{3}$

● **Ex. 43** *Solve the following equations for x and y*

$$\log_{10}x+\frac{1}{2}\log_{10}x+\frac{1}{4}\log_{10}x+\ldots=y$$

and $$\frac{1+3+5+\ldots+(2y-1)}{4+7+10+\ldots+(3y+1)}=\frac{20}{7\log_{10}x}.$$

Sol. From the first equation

$$\log_{10}x\left\{1+\frac{1}{2}+\frac{1}{4}+\ldots+\infty\right\}=y$$

$$\Rightarrow \quad \log_{10}x\left\{\frac{1}{1-\frac{1}{2}}\right\}=y$$

$$\Rightarrow \quad 2\log_{10}x=y \quad \text{...(i)}$$

From the second equation

$$\frac{1+3+5+\ldots+(2y-1)}{4+7+10+\ldots+(3y+1)}=\frac{20}{7\log_{10}x}$$

$$\Rightarrow \quad \frac{\frac{y}{2}(1+2y-1)}{\frac{y}{2}(4+3y+1)}=\frac{20}{7\log_{10}x}$$

$$\Rightarrow \quad \frac{2y}{3y+5}=\frac{20}{7\log_{10}x}$$

$$\Rightarrow \quad 7y(2\log_{10}x)=60y+100$$

$$\Rightarrow \quad 7y(y)=60y+100 \quad \text{[from Eq. (i)]}$$

$$\Rightarrow \quad 7y^2-60y-100=0$$

$$\therefore \quad (y-10)(7y+10)=0$$

$$\therefore \quad y=10,\ y\neq\frac{-10}{7}$$

[because y being the number of terms in series $\Rightarrow y\in N$]

From Eq. (i), we have

$$2\log_{10}x=10\Rightarrow\log_{10}x=5$$

$$\therefore \quad x=10^5$$

Hence, required solution is $x=10^5, y=10$

Ex. 44 *If* $0 < x < \frac{\pi}{2}$, $\exp[(\sin^2 x + \sin^4 x + \sin^6 x + \ldots + \infty)\log_e 2]$ *satisfies the quadratic equation* $x^2 - 9x + 8 = 0$, *find the value of* $\frac{\sin x - \cos x}{\sin x + \cos x}$.

Sol. $0 < x < \frac{\pi}{2}$

$\therefore \quad 0 < \sin^2 x < 1$

Then, $\sin^2 x + \sin^4 x + \sin^6 x + \ldots + \infty$

$$= \frac{\sin^2 x}{1 - \sin^2 x} = \tan^2 x$$

$\therefore \exp[(\sin^2 x + \sin^4 x + \sin^6 x + \ldots + \infty)\log_e 2]$

$$= \exp(\tan^2 x \cdot \log_e 2) = \exp(\log_e 2^{\tan^2 x})$$

$$= e^{\log_e 2^{\tan^2 x}} = 2^{\tan^2 x}$$

Let $y = 2^{\tan^2 x}$

Because y satisfies the quadratic equation.

Then, $y^2 - 9y + 8 = 0$

So, $y = 1, 8$

if $y = 1 = 2^{\tan^2 x}$

$\Rightarrow 2^{\tan^2 x} = 2^0$

$\Rightarrow \tan^2 x = 0$

$\therefore x = 0$ [impossible] [$\because x > 0$]

Now, if $y = 8 = 2^{\tan^2 x}$

$\Rightarrow 2^{\tan^2 x} = 2^3$

$\Rightarrow \tan^2 x = 3$

$\therefore \tan x = \sqrt{3}$

$$\therefore \frac{\sin x - \cos x}{\sin x + \cos x} = \frac{\tan x - 1}{\tan x + 1} = \frac{\sqrt{3} - 1}{\sqrt{3} + 1} \times \frac{\sqrt{3} - 1}{\sqrt{3} - 1}$$

$$= \frac{(\sqrt{3} - 1)^2}{3 - 1} = \frac{3 + 1 - 2\sqrt{3}}{2}$$

Hence, $\frac{\sin x - \cos x}{\sin x + \cos x} = 2 - \sqrt{3}$

Ex. 45 *The natural numbers are arranged in the form given below*

$$\begin{array}{cccccccc} & & & & 1 & & & \\ & & 2 & & & 3 & & \\ & 4 & 5 & & & 6 & 7 & \\ 8 & 9 & 10 & 11 & & 12 & 13 & 14 \quad 15 \end{array}$$

....

....

The rth group containing 2^{r-1} numbers. Prove that sum of the numbers in the nth group is $2^{n-2}[2^n + 2^{n-1} - 1]$.

Sol. Let 1st term of the r th group be T_r and the 1st terms of successive rows are 1, 2, 4, 8, ..., respectively.

$$T_r = 1 \cdot 2^{r-1} = 2^{r-1}$$

Hence, the sum of the numbers in the r th group is

$$= \frac{2^{r-1}}{2}\{2 \cdot 2^{r-1} + (2^{r-1} - 1) \cdot 1\}$$

[$\because$ number of terms in rth group is 2^{r-1}]

$$= 2^{r-2}\{2^r + 2^{r-1} - 1\}$$

Hence, sum of the numbers in the nth group is $2^{n-2}[2^n + 2^{n-1} - 1]$.

Ex. 46 *If a, b, c are in HP, then prove that* $\frac{a+b}{2a-b} + \frac{c+b}{2c-b} > 4$.

Sol. Since, a, b, c are in HP.

$$\therefore \frac{2}{b} = \frac{1}{a} + \frac{1}{c} \quad \text{...(i)}$$

and let $P = \frac{a+b}{2a-b} + \frac{c+b}{2c-b}$

$$= \frac{a + \frac{2ac}{a+c}}{2a - \frac{2ac}{a+c}} + \frac{c + \frac{2ac}{a+c}}{2c - \frac{2ac}{a+c}} \quad \text{[from Eq. (i)]}$$

$$= \frac{a + 3c}{2a} + \frac{3a + c}{2c} = 1 + \frac{3}{2}\left(\frac{c}{a} + \frac{a}{c}\right) \quad \text{...(ii)}$$

$\because$ AM > GM [$\because a \neq c$]

$$\therefore \left(\frac{c}{a} + \frac{a}{c}\right) > 2$$

$$\Rightarrow \frac{3}{2}\left(\frac{c}{a} + \frac{a}{c}\right) > 3$$

or $1 + \frac{3}{2}\left(\frac{c}{a} + \frac{a}{c}\right) > 1 + 3$ or $P > 4$

Hence, $\frac{a+b}{2a-b} + \frac{c+b}{2c-b} > 4$

Ex. 47 *Find the sum of n terms of the series* $\frac{1}{1+1^2+1^4} + \frac{2}{1+2^2+2^4} + \frac{3}{1+3^2+3^4} + \ldots$.

Sol. The n th term of the given series is $T_n = \frac{n}{(1 + n^2 + n^4)}$

$$\therefore \text{Sum of } n \text{ terms} = S_n = \sum T_n = \sum \frac{n}{(1 + n^2 + n^4)}$$

$$= \sum \frac{n}{(1 + n + n^2)(1 - n + n^2)}$$

$$= \frac{1}{2} \sum \left(\frac{1}{1 - n + n^2} - \frac{1}{1 + n + n^2} \right)$$

$$= \frac{1}{2} \left(\frac{1}{1 - 1 + 1} - \frac{1}{1 + n + n^2} \right) \quad \text{[by property]}$$

$$= \frac{(n + n^2)}{2(1 + n + n^2)} = \frac{n(n + 1)}{2(n^2 + n + 1)}$$

● **Ex. 48** *The value of xyz is 55 or $\frac{343}{55}$ according as the series a, x, y, z, b is an AP or HP. Find the values of a and b given that they are positive integers.*

Sol. If a, x, y, z, b are in AP.

Then, $b =$ Fifth term $= a + (5 - 1) d$

where, d is common difference]

$$\therefore \quad d = \frac{b - a}{4}$$

$$\therefore \quad x \cdot y \cdot z = (a + d)(a + 2d)(a + 3d) = 55 \quad \text{[given]}$$

$$\Rightarrow \quad \left(\frac{b + 3a}{4} \right) \left(\frac{2a + 2b}{4} \right) \left(\frac{a + 3b}{4} \right) = 55$$

$$\Rightarrow \quad (a + 3b)(a + b)(3a + b) = 55 \times 32 \quad \text{...(i)}$$

If they are in HP.

The common difference of the associated AP is $\frac{1}{4} \left(\frac{1}{b} - \frac{1}{a} \right)$

i.e. $\quad \frac{(a - b)}{4ab}$

$$\therefore \quad \frac{1}{x} = \frac{1}{a} + \frac{(a - b)}{4ab}$$

$$\Rightarrow \quad x = \frac{4ab}{a + 3b}$$

$$\therefore \quad \frac{1}{y} = \frac{1}{a} + \frac{2(a - b)}{4ab}$$

$$\Rightarrow \quad y = \frac{4ab}{2a + 2b} = \frac{2ab}{a + b}$$

and $\quad \frac{1}{z} = \frac{1}{a} + \frac{3(a - b)}{4ab}$

$$\Rightarrow \quad z = \frac{4ab}{3a + b}$$

$$\therefore \quad xyz = \frac{4ab}{(a + 3b)} \cdot \frac{2ab}{(a + b)} \cdot \frac{4ab}{(3a + b)} = 343 \quad \text{[given]}$$

$$\Rightarrow \quad \frac{32 a^3 b^3}{55 \times 32} = \frac{343}{55} \quad \text{[from Eq. (i)]}$$

or $\quad a^3 b^3 = 343$

$$\Rightarrow \quad ab = 7$$

Hence, $\quad a = 7, b = 1$

or $\quad a = 1, b = 7$

● **Ex. 49** *Find the sum of the first n terms of the series*

$1^3 + 3 \cdot 2^2 + 3^3 + 3 \cdot 4^2 + 5^3 + 3 \cdot 6^2 + \ldots$

If (i) n is even, (ii) n is odd.

Sol. *Case* I If n is even.

Let $\quad n = 2m$

$$\therefore \quad S = 1^3 + 3 \cdot 2^2 + 3^3 + 3 \cdot 4^2 + 5^3 + 3 \cdot 6^2 + \ldots + (2m - 1)^3 + 3(2m)^2$$

$$= \{1^3 + 3^3 + 5^3 + \ldots + (2m - 1)^3\} + 3\{2^2 + 4^2 + 6^2 + \ldots + (2m)^2\}$$

$$= \sum_{r=1}^{m} (2r - 1)^3 + 3 \cdot 4 \sum_{r=1}^{m} r^2$$

$$= \sum_{r=1}^{m} \{8r^3 - 12r^2 + 6r - 1\} + 12 \sum_{r=1}^{m} r^2$$

$$= 8 \sum_{r=1}^{m} r^3 - 12 \sum_{r=1}^{m} r^2 + 6 \sum_{r=1}^{m} r - \sum_{r=1}^{m} 1 + 12 \sum_{r=1}^{m} r^2$$

$$= 8 \sum_{r=1}^{m} r^3 + 6 \sum_{r=1}^{m} r - \sum_{r=1}^{m} 1$$

$$= 8 \cdot \frac{m^2 (m + 1)^2}{4} + 6 \frac{m(m + 1)}{2} - m$$

$$= 2m^2 (m + 1)^2 + 3m(m + 1) - m$$

$$= m[2m^3 + 4m^2 + 5m + 2]$$

$$= \frac{n}{2} \left[2\left(\frac{n}{2}\right)^3 + 4\left(\frac{n}{2}\right)^2 + 5\left(\frac{n}{2}\right) + 2 \right] \quad \left[\because m = \frac{n}{2} \right]$$

Hence, $S = \frac{n}{8}(n^3 + 4n^2 + 10n + 8)$ ...(i)

***Case* II** If n is odd.

Then, $(n + 1)$ is even in the case

Sum of first n terms = Sum of first $(n + 1)$ terms $- (n + 1)$ th term

$$= \frac{(n + 1)}{8} [(n + 1)^3 + 4(n + 1)^2 + 10(n + 1) + 8] - 3(n + 1)^2$$

$$= \frac{1}{8}(n + 1)[n^3 + 3n^2 + 3n + 1 + 4n^2 + 8n + 4 + 10n + 10 + 8 - 24n - 24]$$

Hence, $S = \frac{1}{8}(n + 1)[n^3 + 7n^2 - 3n - 1]$

● **Ex. 50** *Find out the largest term of the sequence*

$\frac{1}{503}, \frac{4}{524}, \frac{9}{581}, \frac{16}{692}, \ldots$

Sol. General term can be written as $T_n = \frac{n^2}{500 + 3n^3}$

Let $$U_n = \frac{1}{T_n} = \frac{500}{n^2} + 3n$$

Then, $$\frac{dU_n}{dn} = -\frac{1000}{n} + 3$$

and $$\frac{d^2U_n}{dn^2} = \frac{3000}{n^4}$$

For maxima or minima of U_n, we have

$$\frac{dU_n}{dn} = 0 \Rightarrow n^3 = \frac{1000}{3}$$

$$\Rightarrow \quad n = \left(\frac{1000}{3}\right)^{1/3} \text{ (not an integer) and } 6 < \left(\frac{1000}{3}\right)^{1/3} < 7$$

But n is an integer, therefore for the maxima or minima of U_n we will take n as the nearest integer to $\left(\frac{1000}{3}\right)^{1/3}$.

Since, $\left(\frac{1000}{3}\right)^{1/3}$ is more close to 7 than to 6. Thus, we take $n = 7$.

Further $\frac{d^2U^n}{dn^2} = +ve$, then U_n will be minimum and therefore, T_n will be maximum for $n = 7$.

Hence, T_7 is largest term. So, largest term in the given sequence is $\frac{49}{1529}$.

• Ex. 51 *If $f(r) = 1 + \frac{1}{2} + \frac{1}{3} + \ldots + \frac{1}{r}$ and $f(0) = 0$, find $\sum_{r=1}^{n}(2r+1)\,f(r)$.*

Sol. Since, $\sum_{r=1}^{n}(2r+1)\,f(r)$

$$= \sum_{r=1}^{n}(r^2 + 2r + 1 - r^2)\,f(r) = \sum_{r=1}^{n}\{(r+1)^2 - r^2\}\,f(r)$$

$$= \sum_{r=1}^{n}\{(r+1)^2 f(r) - (r+1)^2 f(r+1) + (r+1)^2 f(r+1) - r^2 f(r)\}$$

$$= \sum_{r=1}^{n}(r+1)^2\{f(r) - f(r+1)\} + \sum_{r=1}^{n}\{(r+1)^2 f(r+1) - r^2 f(r)\}$$

$$= -\sum_{r=1}^{n}\frac{(r+1)^2}{(r+1)} + \sum_{r=1}^{n-1}(r+1)^2 f(r+1) + (n+1)^2 f(n+1) - \sum_{r=1}^{n} r^2 f(r) \quad \left[\because f(r+1) - f(r) = \frac{1}{r+1}\right]$$

$$= -\sum_{r=1}^{n}(r+1) + \{2^2 f(2) + 3^2 f(3) + \ldots + n^2 f(n)\} + (n+1)^2 f(n+1) - \{1^2 f(1) + 2^2 f(2) + 3^2 f(3) + \ldots + n^2 f(n)\}$$

$$= -\sum_{r=1}^{n} r - \sum_{r=1}^{n} 1 + (n+1)^2 f(n+1) - 1^2 f(1)$$

$$= -\frac{n(n+1)}{2} - n + (n+1)^2 f(n+1) - f(1)$$

$$= (n+1)^2 f(n+1) - \frac{n(n+3)}{2} - 1 \quad [\because f(1) = 1]$$

$$= (n+1)^2 f(n+1) - \frac{(n^2 + 3n + 2)}{2}$$

Hence, this is the required result.

• Ex. 52 *If the equation $x^4 - 4x^3 + ax^2 + bx + 1 = 0$ has four positive roots, find the values of a and b.*

Sol. Let x_1, x_2, x_3, x_4 are the roots of the equation

$$x^4 - 4x^3 + ax^2 + bx + 1 = 0 \quad \ldots(i)$$

$\therefore x_1 + x_2 + x_3 + x_4 = 4$ and $x_1 x_2 x_3 x_4 = 1$

$\because \quad \text{AM} = \frac{x_1 + x_2 + x_3 + x_4}{4} = \frac{4}{4} = 1$

and $\text{GM} = (x_1 x_2 x_3 x_4)^{1/4} = (1)^{1/4} = 1$

i.e., AM = GM

which is true only when $x_1 = x_2 = x_3 = x_4 = 1$

Hence, given equation has all roots identical, equal to 1 i.e., equation have form

$$(x-1)^4 = 0$$

$$\Rightarrow \quad x^4 - 4x^3 + 6x^2 - 4x + 1 = 0 \quad \ldots(ii)$$

On comparing Eqs. (i) and (ii), we get

$$a = 6,\ b = -4$$

• Ex. 53 Evaluate $\sum_{m=1}^{\infty}\sum_{n=1}^{\infty}\frac{m^2 n}{3^m(n\cdot 3^m + m\cdot 3^n)}$.

Sol. Let $$S = \sum_{m=1}^{\infty}\sum_{n=1}^{\infty}\frac{m^2 n}{3^m(n\cdot 3^m + m\cdot 3^n)}$$

$$= \sum_{m=1}^{\infty}\sum_{n=1}^{\infty}\frac{1}{\left(\frac{3^m}{m}\right)\left(\frac{3^m}{m} + \frac{3^n}{n}\right)}$$

Now, let $$a_m = \frac{3^m}{m} \text{ and } a_n = \frac{3^n}{n}$$

Then, $$S = \sum_{m=1}^{\infty}\sum_{n=1}^{\infty}\frac{1}{a_m(a_m + a_n)} \quad \ldots(i)$$

By interchanging m and n, then

$$S = \sum_{m=1}^{\infty}\sum_{n=1}^{\infty}\frac{1}{a_n(a_n + a_m)} \quad \ldots(ii)$$

On adding Eqs. (i) and (ii), we get

$$2S = \sum_{m=1}^{\infty}\sum_{n=1}^{\infty}\frac{1}{a_m a_n} = \sum_{m=1}^{\infty}\sum_{n=1}^{\infty}\frac{mn}{3^m 3^n}$$

$$= \left(\sum_{n=1}^{\infty} \frac{n}{3^n}\right)^2 = \left[1\left(\frac{1}{3}\right) + 2\left(\frac{1}{3}\right)^2 + 3\left(\frac{1}{3}\right)^3 + \dots\right]^2$$

$$= (S')^2 \qquad \dots(\text{iii})$$

where, $S' = 1\left(\frac{1}{3}\right) + 2\left(\frac{1}{3}\right)^2 + 3\left(\frac{1}{3}\right)^3 + \dots + \infty$

$$\frac{1}{3} S' = \quad 1\left(\frac{1}{3}\right)^2 + 2\left(\frac{1}{3}\right)^3 + \dots + \infty$$

$$\frac{2}{3} S' = \frac{1}{3} + \left(\frac{1}{3}\right)^2 + \left(\frac{1}{3}\right)^3 + \dots + \infty$$

$$= \frac{\frac{1}{3}}{1 - \frac{1}{3}} = \frac{1}{2}$$

$$\therefore \quad S' = \frac{3}{4}$$

From Eq. (iii), we get $2S = \left(\frac{3}{4}\right)^2$

$$\therefore \quad S = \frac{9}{32}$$

• *Ex. 54* *Find the value of* $\sum_{i=0}^{\infty} \sum_{j=0}^{\infty} \sum_{k=0}^{\infty} \frac{1}{3^i 3^j 3^k}$ $(i \neq j \neq k)$

Sol. Let $S = \sum_{i=0}^{\infty} \sum_{j=0}^{\infty} \sum_{k=0}^{\infty} \frac{1}{3^i 3^j 3^k}$ $\qquad [i \neq j \neq k]$

We will first of all find the sum without any restriction on i, j, k.

Let $S_1 = \sum_{i=0}^{\infty} \sum_{j=0}^{\infty} \sum_{k=0}^{\infty} \frac{1}{3^i 3^j 3^k} = \left(\sum_{i=0}^{\infty} \frac{1}{3^i}\right)^3$

$$= \left(\frac{3}{2}\right)^3 = \frac{27}{8}$$

***Case* I** If $i = j = k$

Let $S_2 = \sum_{i=0}^{\infty} \sum_{j=0}^{\infty} \sum_{k=0}^{\infty} \frac{1}{3^i 3^j 3^k}$

$$= \sum_{i=0}^{\infty} \frac{1}{3^{3i}} = 1 + \frac{1}{3^3} + \frac{1}{3^6} + \dots = \frac{1}{1 - \frac{1}{3^3}} = \frac{27}{26}$$

***Case* II** If $i = j \neq k$

Let $S_3 = \sum_{i=0}^{\infty} \sum_{j=0}^{\infty} \sum_{k=0}^{\infty} \frac{1}{3^i 3^j 3^k} = \left(\sum_{i=0}^{\infty} \frac{1}{3^{2i}}\right)\left(\sum_{k=0}^{\infty} \frac{1}{3^k}\right)$

$[\because k \neq i]$

$$= \sum_{i=0}^{\infty} \frac{1}{3^{2i}}\left(\frac{3}{2} - \frac{1}{3^i}\right) = \sum_{i=0}^{\infty} \frac{3}{2} \cdot \frac{1}{3^{2i}} - \sum_{i=0}^{\infty} \frac{1}{3^{3i}}$$

$$= \frac{3}{2} \cdot \frac{9}{8} - \frac{27}{26} = \frac{135}{208}$$

Hence required sum, $S = S_1 - S_2 - 3S_3$

$$= \frac{27}{8} - \frac{27}{26} - 3\left(\frac{135}{208}\right) = \frac{27 \times 26 - 27 \times 8 - 3 \times 135}{208} = \frac{81}{208}$$

• *Ex. 55* *Let $S_n, n = 1, 2, 3, \dots$ be the sum of infinite geometric series, whose first term is n and the common ratio is* $\frac{1}{n+1}$*. Evaluate*

$$\lim_{n \to \infty} \frac{S_1 S_n + S_2 S_{n-1} + S_3 S_{n-2} + \dots + S_n S_1}{S_1^2 + S_2^2 + \dots + S_n^2}.$$

Sol. $\because \quad S_n = \frac{n}{1 - \frac{1}{n+1}} \Rightarrow S_n = n + 1$

$$\therefore S_1 S_n + S_2 S_{n-1} + S_3 S_{n-2} + \dots + S_n S_1$$

$$= \sum_{r=1}^{n} S_r S_{n-r+1} = \sum_{r=1}^{n} (r+1)(n-r+2)$$

$$= \sum_{r=1}^{n} [(n+1) r - r^2 + (n+2)]$$

$$= (n+1) \sum_{r=1}^{n} r - \sum_{r=1}^{n} r^2 + (n+2) \sum_{r=1}^{n} 1$$

$$= (n+1) \sum n - \sum n^2 + (n+2) \cdot n$$

$$= \frac{(n+1) n (n+1)}{2} - \frac{n(n+1)(2n+1)}{6} + (n+2) n$$

$$= \frac{n}{6}(n^2 + 9n + 14) \qquad \dots(\text{i})$$

and $S_1^2 + S_2^2 + \dots + S_n^2 = \sum_{r=1}^{n} S_r^2 = \sum_{r=1}^{n} (r+1)^2 = \sum_{r=0}^{n} (r+1)^2 - 1^2$

$$= \frac{(n+1)(n+2)(2n+3)}{6} - 1$$

$$= \frac{n}{6}(2n^2 + 9n + 13) \qquad \dots(\text{ii})$$

From Eqs. (i) and (ii), we get

$$\lim_{n \to \infty} \frac{S_1 S_n + S_2 S_{n-1} + S_3 S_{n-2} + \dots + S_n S_1}{S_1^2 + S_2^2 + \dots + S_n^2}$$

$$= \lim_{n \to \infty} \frac{\frac{n}{6}(n^2 + 9n + 14)}{\frac{n}{6}(2n^2 + 9n + 13)} = \lim_{n \to \infty} \frac{\left(1 + \frac{9}{n} + \frac{14}{n^2}\right)}{\left(2 + \frac{9}{n} + \frac{13}{n^2}\right)}$$

$$= \frac{1 + 0 + 0}{2 + 0 + 0} = \frac{1}{2}$$

● ***Ex. 56*** *The nth term of a series is given by*

$t_n = \dfrac{n^5 + n^3}{n^4 + n^2 + 1}$ *and if sum of its n terms can be expressed as*

$S_n = a_n^2 + a + \dfrac{1}{b_n^2 + b}$, *where a_n and b_n are the nth terms of some arithmetic progressions and a, b are some constants, prove that $\dfrac{b_n}{a_n}$ is a constant.*

Sol. Since, $t_n = \dfrac{n^5 + n^3}{n^4 + n^2 + 1}$

$$= n - \frac{n}{n^4 + n^2 + 1}$$

$$= n + \frac{1}{2(n^2 + n + 1)} - \frac{1}{2(n^2 - n + 1)}$$

Sum of n terms $S_n = \sum t_n$

$$= \sum n + \frac{1}{2}\left\{\sum\left(\frac{1}{n^2 + n + 1} - \frac{1}{n^2 - n + 1}\right)\right\}$$

$$= \frac{n(n+1)}{2} + \frac{1}{2}\left(\frac{1}{n^2 + n + 1} - 1\right) \quad \text{[by property]}$$

$$= \frac{n^2}{2} + \frac{n}{2} - \frac{1}{2} + \frac{1}{2n^2 + 2n + 2}$$

$$= \left(\frac{n}{\sqrt{2}} + \frac{1}{2\sqrt{2}}\right)^2 - \frac{1}{8} - \frac{1}{2} + \frac{1}{\left(n\sqrt{2} + \frac{1}{\sqrt{2}}\right)^2 + \frac{3}{2}}$$

$$= \left(\frac{n}{\sqrt{2}} + \frac{1}{2\sqrt{2}}\right)^2 - \frac{5}{8} + \frac{1}{\left(n\sqrt{2} + \frac{1}{\sqrt{2}}\right)^2 + \frac{3}{2}}$$

but given, $S_n = a_n^2 + a + \dfrac{1}{b_n^2 + b}$

On comparing, we get

$$a_n = \frac{n}{\sqrt{2}} + \frac{1}{2\sqrt{2}},\ a = -\frac{5}{8},\ b_n = \left(n\sqrt{2} + \frac{1}{\sqrt{2}}\right),\ b = \frac{3}{2}$$

$\therefore \quad \dfrac{b_n}{a_n} = 2$, which is constant.

Sequences and Series Exercise 1 : Single Option Correct Type Questions

- This section contains **30 multiple choice questions.** Each question has four choices (a), (b), (c) and (d) out of which **ONLY ONE** is correct

1. If the numbers x, y, z are in HP, then $\frac{\sqrt{yz}}{\sqrt{y}+\sqrt{z}}, \frac{\sqrt{xz}}{\sqrt{x}+\sqrt{z}}, \frac{\sqrt{xy}}{\sqrt{x}+\sqrt{y}}$ are in

(a) AP (b) GP
(c) HP (d) None of these

2. If $a_1, a_2, \ldots$ are in HP and $f_k = \sum_{r=1}^{n} a_r - a_k$, then $2^{\alpha_1}, 2^{\alpha_2}, 2^{\alpha_3}, 2^{\alpha_4}, \ldots$ are in $\left\{\text{where } \alpha_1 = \frac{a_1}{f_1}, \alpha_2 = \frac{a_2}{f_2}, \alpha_3 = \frac{a_3}{f_3}, \ldots\right\}$

(a) AP (b) GP
(c) HP (d) None of these

3. ABC is a right angled triangle in which $\angle B = 90°$ and $BC = a$. If n points $L_1, L_2, \ldots, L_n$ on AB are such that AB is divided in $n+1$ equal parts and $L_1M_1, L_2M_2, \ldots, L_nM_n$ are line segments parallel to BC and $M_1, M_2, \ldots, M_n$ are on AC, the sum of the lengths of $L_1M_1, L_2M_2, \ldots, L_nM_n$ is

(a) $\frac{a(n+1)}{2}$ (b) $\frac{a(n-1)}{2}$
(c) $\frac{an}{2}$
(d) impossible to find from the given data

4. Let S_n $(1 \le n \le 9)$ denotes the sum of n terms of the series $1 + 22 + 333 + \ldots + \underbrace{999\ldots9}_{9 \text{ times}}$, then for $2 \le n \le 9$

(a) $S_n - S_{n-1} = \frac{1}{9}(10^n - n^2 + n)$
(b) $S_n = \frac{1}{9}(10^n - n^2 + 2n - 2)$
(c) $9(S_n - S_{n-1}) = n(10^n - 1)$
(d) None of the above

5. If a, b, c are in GP, then the equations $ax^2 + 2bx + c = 0$ and $dx^2 + 2ex + f = 0$ have a common root, if $\frac{d}{a}, \frac{e}{b}, \frac{f}{c}$ are in

(a) AP (b) GP
(c) HP (d) None of these

6. Sum of the first n terms of the series $\frac{1}{2} + \frac{3}{4} + \frac{7}{8} + \frac{15}{16} + \ldots$ is equal to

(a) $2^n - n - 1$ (b) $1 - 2^{-n}$
(c) $n + 2^{-n} - 1$ (d) $2^n - 1$

7. If in a ΔPQR, $\sin P, \sin Q, \sin R$ are in AP, then

(a) the altitudes are in AP (b) the altitudes are in HP
(c) the medians are in GP (d) the medians are in AP

8. Let $a_1, a_2, \ldots, a_{10}$ be in AP and $h_1, h_2, \ldots, h_{10}$ be in HP. If $a_1 = h_1 = 2$ and $a_{10} = h_{10} = 3$, then a_4h_7 is

(a) 2 (b) 3
(c) 5 (d) 6

9. If $I_n = \int_0^{\pi} \frac{1 - \sin 2nx}{1 - \cos 2x}\, dx$, then $I_1, I_2, I_3, \ldots$ are in

(a) AP (b) GP
(c) HP (d) None of these

10. If $a(b-c)x^2 + b(c-a)xy + c(a-b)y^2$ is a perfect square, the quantities a, b, c are in

(a) AP (b) GP
(c) HP (d) None of these

11. The sum to infinity of the series, $1 + 2\left(1 - \frac{1}{n}\right) + 3\left(1 - \frac{1}{n}\right)^2 + \ldots$ is

(a) n^2 (b) $n(n+1)$
(c) $n\left(1 + \frac{1}{n}\right)^2$ (d) None of these

12. If $\log_3 2, \log_3(2^x - 5)$ and $\log_3\left(2^x - \frac{7}{2}\right)$ are in AP, x is equal to

(a) 2 (b) 3
(c) 4 (d) 2, 3

13. Let a, b, c be three positive prime numbers. The progression in which $\sqrt{a}, \sqrt{b}, \sqrt{c}$ can be three terms (not necessarily consecutive), is

(a) AP (b) GP
(c) HP (d) None of these

14. If n is an odd integer greater than or equal to 1, the value of $n^3 - (n-1)^3 + (n-2)^3 - \ldots + (-1)^{n-1} 1^3$ is

(a) $\frac{(n+1)^2(2n-1)}{4}$ (b) $\frac{(n-1)^2(2n-1)}{4}$
(c) $\frac{(n+1)^2(2n+1)}{4}$ (d) None of these

15. If the sides of a right angled triangle form an AP, the sines of the acute angles are

(a) $\frac{3}{5}, \frac{4}{5}$ (b) $\sqrt{3}, \frac{1}{3}$

(c) $\sqrt{\frac{\sqrt{5}-1}{2}}, \sqrt{\frac{\sqrt{5}+1}{2}}$ (d) $\frac{\sqrt{3}}{2}, \frac{1}{2}$

16. The sixth term of an AP is equal to 2. The value of the common difference of the AP which makes the product $a_1 a_4 a_5$ least, is given by

(a) $\frac{8}{5}$ (b) $\frac{5}{4}$

(c) $\frac{2}{3}$ (d) None of these

17. If the arithmetic progression whose common difference is non-zero, the sum of first $3n$ terms is equal to the sum of the next n terms. The ratio of the sum of the first $2n$ terms to the next $2n$ terms is

(a) $\frac{1}{5}$ (b) $\frac{2}{3}$

(c) $\frac{3}{4}$ (d) None of these

18. The coefficient of x^{n-2} in the polynomial $(x-1)(x-2)(x-3)\ldots(x-n)$, is

(a) $\frac{n(n^2+2)(3n+1)}{24}$

(b) $\frac{n(n^2-1)(3n+2)}{24}$

(c) $\frac{n(n^2+1)(3n+4)}{24}$

(d) None of the above

19. Consider the pattern shown below:

Row 1 1

Row 2 3 5

Row 3 7 9 11

Row 4 13 15 17, 19, etc.

The number at the end of row 60 is

(a) 3659 (b) 3519

(c) 3681 (d) 3731

20. Let a_n be the nth term of an AP. If $\sum_{r=1}^{100} a_{2r} = \alpha$ and $\sum_{r=1}^{100} a_{2r-1} = \beta$, the common difference of the AP is

(a) $\alpha - \beta$ (b) $\beta - \alpha$

(c) $\frac{\alpha-\beta}{2}$ (d) None of these

21. If a_1, a_2, a_3, a_4, a_5 are in HP, then $a_1a_2 + a_2a_3 + a_3a_4 + a_4a_5$ is equal to

(a) $2a_1a_5$ (b) $3a_1a_5$

(c) $4a_1a_5$ (d) $6a_1a_5$

22. If a, b, c and d are four positive real numbers such that $abcd = 1$, the minimum value of $(1+a)(1+b)(1+c)(1+d)$ is

(a) 1 (b) 4

(c) 16 (d) 64

23. If a, b, c are in AP and $(a+2b-c)(2b+c-a)(c+a-b) = \lambda\, abc$, then λ is

(a) 1 (b) 2

(c) 4 (d) None of these

24. If $a_1, a_2, a_3, \ldots$ are in GP with first term a and common ratio r, then

$$\frac{a_1a_2}{a_1^2-a_2^2} + \frac{a_2a_3}{a_2^2-a_3^2} + \frac{a_3a_4}{a_3^2-a_4^2} + \ldots + \frac{a_{n-1}a_n}{a_{n-1}^2-a_n^2}$$ is equal to

(a) $\frac{nr}{1-r^2}$ (b) $\frac{(n-1)r}{1-r^2}$ (c) $\frac{nr}{1-r}$ (d) $\frac{(n-1)r}{1-r}$

25. The sum of the first ten terms of an AP is four times the sum of the first five terms, the ratio of the first term to the common difference is

(a) $\frac{1}{2}$ (b) 2 (c) $\frac{1}{4}$ (d) 4

26. If $\cos(x-y)$, $\cos x$ and $\cos(x+y)$ are in HP, the $\cos x \sec\left(\frac{y}{2}\right)$ is equal to

(a) $\pm\sqrt{2}$ (b) $\frac{1}{\sqrt{2}}$

(c) $-\frac{1}{\sqrt{2}}$ (d) None of these

27. If 11 AM's are inserted between 28 and 10, the number of integral AM's is

(a) 5 (b) 6

(c) 7 (d) 8

28. If x, y, z are in GP $(x, y, z > 1)$, then $\frac{1}{2x+\ln x}, \frac{1}{4x+\ln y}, \frac{1}{6x+\ln z}$ are in

(a) AP (b) GP

(c) HP (d) None of these

29. The minimum value of the quantity $\frac{(a^2+3a+1)(b^2+3b+1)(c^2+3c+1)}{abc}$, where $a, b, c \in R^+$, is

(a) $\frac{11^3}{2^3}$ (b) 125

(c) 25 (d) 27

30. Let $a_1, a_2, \ldots$ be in AP and $q_1, q_2, \ldots$ be in GP. If $a_1 = q_1 = 2$ and $a_{10} = q_{10} = 3$, then

(a) $a_7\, q_{19}$ is not an integer (b) $a_{19}\, q_7$ is an integer

(c) $a_7\, q_{19} = a_{19}\, q_{10}$ (d) None of these

Sequences and Series Exercise 2 :
More than One Correct Option Type Questions

- This section contains **15 multiple choice questions**. Each question has four choices (a), (b), (c) and (d) out of which **MORE THAN ONE** may be correct.

31. If $a(n) = 1 + \frac{1}{2} + \frac{1}{3} + \frac{1}{4} + \ldots + \frac{1}{2^n - 1}$, then

(a) $a(100) < 100$ (b) $a(100) > 100$
(c) $a(200) > 100$ (d) $a(200) < 100$

32. If the first and $(2n-1)$th term of an AP, GP and HP are equal and their nth terms are a, b and c respectively, then

(a) $a = b = c$ (b) $a \geq b \geq c$
(c) $a + c = b$ (d) $ac - b^2 = 0$

33. For $0 < \phi < \frac{\pi}{2}$, if $x = \sum_{n=0}^{\infty} \cos^{2n} \phi$, $y = \sum_{n=0}^{\infty} \sin^{2n} \phi$ and $z = \sum_{n=0}^{\infty} \cos^{2n} \phi \sin^{2n} \phi$, then

(a) $xyz = xz + y$ (b) $xyz = xy + z$
(c) $xyz = x + y + z$ (d) $xyz = yz + x$

34. If a, b, c are in AP and a^2, b^2, c^2 are in HP, then which of the following could hold true?

(a) $-\frac{a}{2}, b, c$ are in GP (b) $a = b = c$
(c) a^3, b^3, c^3 are in GP (d) None of these

35. The next term of the GP $x, x^2 + 2, x^3 + 10$ is

(a) 0 (b) 6 (c) $\frac{729}{16}$ (d) 54

36. If the sum of n consecutive odd numbers is $25^2 - 11^2$, then

(a) $n = 14$ (b) $n = 16$
(c) first odd number is 23 (d) last odd number is 49

37. The GM of two positive numbers is 6. Their AM is A and HM is H satisfy the equation $90A + 5H = 918$, then A may be equal to

(a) $\frac{1}{5}$ (b) 5 (c) $\frac{5}{2}$ (d) 10

38. If the sum to n terms of the series

$$\frac{1}{1\cdot3\cdot5\cdot7} + \frac{1}{3\cdot5\cdot7\cdot9} + \frac{1}{5\cdot7\cdot9\cdot11} + \ldots \text{ is } \frac{1}{90} - \frac{\lambda}{f(n)}, \text{ then}$$

(a) $f(0) = 15$ (b) $f(1) = 105$
(c) $f(\lambda) = \frac{640}{27}$ (d) $\lambda = \frac{1}{3}$

39. For the series,

$$S = 1 + \frac{1}{(1+3)}(1+2)^2 + \frac{1}{(1+3+5)}(1+2+3)^2 + \frac{1}{(1+3+5+7)}(1+2+3+4)^2 + \ldots$$

(a) 7th term is 16 (b) 7th term is 18
(c) sum of first 10 terms is $\frac{505}{4}$ (d) sum of first 10 terms is $\frac{405}{4}$

40. Let $E = \frac{1}{1^2} + \frac{1}{2^2} + \frac{1}{3^2} + \ldots$, then

(a) $E < 3$ (b) $E > \frac{3}{2}$ (c) $E < 2$ (d) $E > 2$

41. Let S_n $(n \geq 1)$ be a sequence of sets defined by

$$S_1 = \{0\}, S_2 = \left\{\frac{3}{2}, \frac{5}{2}\right\}, S_3 = \left\{\frac{8}{3}, \frac{11}{3}, \frac{14}{3}\right\}, S_4 = \left\{\frac{15}{4}, \frac{19}{4}, \frac{23}{4}, \frac{27}{4}\right\}, \ldots, \text{ then}$$

(a) third element in S_{20} is $\frac{439}{20}$
(b) third element in S_{20} is $\frac{431}{20}$
(c) sum of the elements in S_{20} is 589
(d) sum of the elements in S_{20} is 609

42. Which of the following sequences are unbounded?

(a) $\left(1 + \frac{1}{n}\right)^n$ (b) $\left(\frac{2n+1}{n+2}\right)$ (c) $\left(1 + \frac{1}{n}\right)^{n^2}$ (d) $\tan n$

43. Let a sequence $\{a_n\}$ be defined by

$$a_n = \frac{1}{n+1} + \frac{1}{n+2} + \frac{1}{n+3} + \ldots + \frac{1}{3n}, \text{ then}$$

(a) $a_2 = \frac{11}{12}$ (b) $a_2 = \frac{19}{20}$
(c) $a_{n+1} - a_n = \frac{(9n+5)}{(3n+1)(3n+2)(3n+3)}$
(d) $a_{n+1} - a_n = \frac{-2}{3(n+1)}$

44. Let $S_n(x) = \left(x^{n-1} + \frac{1}{x^{n-1}}\right) + 2\left(x^{n-2} + \frac{1}{x^{n-2}}\right) + \ldots + (n-1)\left(x + \frac{1}{x}\right) + n$, then

(a) $S_1(x) = 1$ (b) $S_1(x) = x + \frac{1}{x}$
(c) $S_{100}(x) = \frac{1}{x^{99}}\left(\frac{x^{100}-1}{x-1}\right)^2$ (d) $S_{100}(x) = \frac{1}{x^{100}}\left(\frac{x^{100}-1}{x-1}\right)^2$

45. All the terms of an AP are natural numbers and the sum of the first 20 terms is greater than 1072 and less than 1162. If the sixth term is 32, then

(a) first term is 7 (b) first term is 12
(c) common difference is 4 (d) common difference is 5

Sequences and Series Exercise 3 : Passage Based Questions

- This section contains **8 passages**. Based upon each of the passage **3 multiple choice questions** have to be answered. Each of these questions has four choices (a), (b), (c) and (d) out of which **ONLY ONE** is correct.

Passage I

(Q. Nos. 46 to 48)

S_n be the sum of n terms of the series $\frac{8}{5}+\frac{16}{65}+\frac{24}{325}+\dots$

46. The value of $\lim_{n \to \infty} S_n$ is

(a) 0 (b) $\frac{1}{2}$ (c) 2 (d) 4

47. The seventh term of the series is

(a) $\frac{56}{2505}$ (b) $\frac{56}{6505}$ (c) $\frac{56}{5185}$ (d) $\frac{56}{9605}$

48. The value of S_8, is

(a) $\frac{288}{145}$ (b) $\frac{1088}{545}$ (c) $\frac{81}{41}$ (d) $\frac{107}{245}$

Passage II

(Q. Nos. 49 to 51)

Two consecutive numbers from 1, 2, 3, ..., n are removed. The arithmetic mean of the remaining numbers is $\frac{105}{4}$.

49. The value of n lies in

(a) (41, 51) (b) (52, 62) (c) (63, 73) (d) (74, 84)

50. The removed numbers

(a) are less than 10
(b) lies between 10 to 30
(c) lies between 30 to 70
(d) greater than 70

51. Sum of all numbers is

(a) less than 1000
(b) lies between 1200 to 1500
(c) greater than 1500
(d) None of these

Passage III

(Q. Nos. 52 to 54)

There are two sets A and B each of which consists of three numbers in AP whose sum is 15 and where D and d are the common differences such that $D = 1 + d$, $d > 0$. If $p = 7(q - p)$, where p and q are the product of the numbers respectively in the two series.

52. The value of p is

(a) 105 (b) 140 (c) 175 (d) 210

53. The value of q is

(a) 200 (b) 160 (c) 120 (d) 80

54. The value of $7D + 8d$ is

(a) 37 (b) 22 (c) 67 (d) 52

Passage IV

(Q. Nos. 55 to 57)

There are two sets A and B each of which consists of three numbers in GP whose product is 64 and R and r are the common ratios such that $R = r + 2$. If $\frac{p}{q} = \frac{3}{2}$, where p and q are sum of numbers taken two at a time respectively in the two sets.

55. The value of p is

(a) 66 (b) 72 (c) 78 (d) 84

56. The value of q is

(a) 54 (b) 56 (c) 58 (d) 60

57. The value of $r^R + R^r$ is

(a) 5392 (b) 368 (c) 32 (d) 4

Passage V

(Q. Nos. 58 to 60)

The numbers 1, 3, 6, 10, 15, 21, 28, ... are called triangular numbers. Let t_n denotes the nth triangular number such that $t_n = t_{n-1} + n$, $\forall\, n \geq 2$

58. The value of t_{50} is

(a) 1075 (b) 1175 (c) 1275 (d) 1375

59. The number of positive integers lying between t_{100} and t_{101} are

(a) 99 (b) 100 (c) 101 (d) 102

60. If $(m + 1)$ is the nth triangular number, then $(n - m)$ is

(a) $1 + \sqrt{(m^2 + 2m)}$
(b) $1 + \sqrt{(m^2 + 2)}$
(c) $1 + \sqrt{(m^2 + m)}$
(d) None of these

Passage VI

(Q. Nos. 61 to 63)

Let $A_1, A_2, A_3, \dots, A_m$ be arithmetic means between -3 and 828 and $G_1, G_2, G_3, \dots, G_n$ be geometric means between 1 and 2187. Product of geometric means is 3^{35} and sum of arithmetic means is 14025.

61. The value of n is

(a) 45 (b) 30 (c) 25 (d) 10

62. The value of m is

(a) 17 (b) 34 (c) 51 (d) 68

63. The value of $G_1 + G_2 + G_3 + \dots + G_n$ is

(a) 2044
(b) 1022
(c) 511
(d) None of these

Passage VII

(Q. Nos. 64 to 66)

Suppose α, β are roots of $ax^2 + bx + c = 0$ and γ, δ are roots of $Ax^2 + Bx + C = 0$.

64. If $\alpha, \beta, \gamma, \delta$ are in AP, then common difference of AP is

(a) $\frac{1}{4}\left(\frac{b}{a} - \frac{B}{A}\right)$ (b) $\frac{1}{3}\left(\frac{b}{a} - \frac{B}{A}\right)$

(c) $\frac{1}{2}\left(\frac{c}{a} - \frac{B}{A}\right)$ (d) $\frac{1}{3}\left(\frac{c}{a} - \frac{C}{A}\right)$

65. If a, b, c are in GP as well as $\alpha, \beta, \gamma, \delta$ are in GP, then A, B, C are in

(a) AP only (b) GP only

(c) AP and GP (d) None of these

66. If $\alpha, \beta, \gamma, \delta$ are in GP, then common ratio of GP is

(a) $\sqrt{\left(\frac{bA}{aB}\right)}$ (b) $\sqrt{\left(\frac{aB}{bA}\right)}$

(c) $\sqrt{\left(\frac{bC}{cB}\right)}$ (d) $\sqrt{\left(\frac{cB}{bC}\right)}$

Passage VIII (Q. Nos. 67 to 69)

Suppose p is the first of n $(n > 1)$ arithmetic means between two positive numbers a and b and q the first of n harmonic means between the same two numbers.

67. The value of p is

(a) $\frac{na + b}{n + 1}$ (b) $\frac{nb + a}{n + 1}$ (c) $\frac{na - b}{n + 1}$ (d) $\frac{nb - a}{n + 1}$

68. The value of q is

(a) $\frac{(n - 1)\,ab}{nb + a}$ (b) $\frac{(n + 1)\,ab}{nb + a}$ (c) $\frac{(n + 1)\,ab}{na + b}$ (d) $\frac{(n - 1)\,ab}{na + b}$

69. Final conclusion is

(a) q lies between p and $\left(\frac{n + 1}{n - 1}\right)^2 p$

(b) q lies between p and $\left(\frac{n + 1}{n - 1}\right) p$

(c) q does not lie between p and $\left(\frac{n + 1}{n - 1}\right)^2 p$

(d) q does not lie between p and $\left(\frac{n + 1}{n - 1}\right) p$

Sequences and Series Exercise 4 : Single Integer Answer Type Questions

- This section contains **10 questions**. The answer to each question is a **single digit integer**, ranging from 0 to 9 (both inclusive).

70. Let a, b, c, d be positive real numbers with $a < b < c < d$. Given that a, b, c, d are the first four terms of an AP and a, b, d are in GP. The value of $\frac{ad}{bc}$ is $\frac{p}{q}$, where p and q are prime numbers, then the value of q is

71. If the coefficient of x in the expansion of $\prod_{r=1}^{110} (1 + rx)$ is $\lambda (1 + 10)(1 + 10 + 10^2)$, then the value of λ is

72. A 3-digit palindrome is a 3-digit number (not starting with zero) which reads the same backwards as forwards *For example,* 242. The sum of all even 3-digit palindromes is $2^{n_1} \cdot 3^{n_2} \cdot 5^{n_3} \cdot 7^{n_4} \cdot 11^{n_5}$, alue of $n_1 + n_2 + n_3 + n_4 + n_5$ is

73. If n is a positive integer satisfying the equation
$$2 + (6 \cdot 2^2 - 4 \cdot 2) + (6 \cdot 3^2 - 4 \cdot 3) + \ldots + (6 \cdot n^2 - 4 \cdot n) = 140,$$
then the value of n is

74. Let $S(x) = 1 + x - x^2 - x^3 + x^4 + x^5 - x^6 - x^7 + \ldots + \infty$, where $0 < x < 1$. If $S(x) = \frac{\sqrt{2} + 1}{2}$, then the value of $(x + 1)^2$ is

75. The sequence $a_1, a_2, a_3, \ldots$ is a geometric sequence with common ratio r. The sequence $b_1, b_2, b_3, \ldots$ is also a geometric sequence. If $b_1 = 1$, $b_2 = \sqrt[4]{7} - \sqrt[4]{28} + 1$, $a_1 = \sqrt[4]{28}$ and $\sum_{n=1}^{\infty} \frac{1}{a_n} = \sum_{n=1}^{\infty} b_n$, then the value of $(1 + r^2 + r^4)$ is

76. Let (a_1, b_1) and (a_2, b_2) are the pair of real numbers such that 10, a, b, ab constitute an arithmetic progression. Then, the value of $\left(\frac{2a_1a_2 + b_1b_2}{10}\right)$ is

77. If one root of $Ax^3 + Bx^2 + Cx + D = 0$, $A \neq 0$, is the arithmetic mean of the other two roots, then the relation $2B^3 + \lambda ABC + \mu A^2 D = 0$ holds good. Then, the value of $2\lambda + \mu$ is

78. If $|x| > 1$, then sum of the series $\frac{1}{1 + x} + \frac{2}{1 + x^2} + \frac{2^2}{1 + x^4} + \frac{2^3}{1 + x^8} + \ldots$ upto ∞ is $\frac{1}{x - \lambda}$, then the value of λ is

79. Three non-zero real numbers form an AP and the squares of these numbers taken in same order form a GP. If the possible common ratios are $(3 \pm \sqrt{k})$ where $k \in N$, then the value of $\left[\frac{k}{8} - \frac{8}{k}\right]$ is (where [ ] denotes the greatest integer function).

Sequences and Series Exercise 5 : Matching Type Questions

- This section contains **4 questions**. Questions 80, 81 and 82 have three statements (A, B and C) and question 83 has four statements (A, B, C and D) given in **Column I** and questions 80 and 81 have four statements (p, q, r and s), question 82 has five statements (p, q, r, s and t) and question 83 has three statements (p, q and r) in **Column II**, respectively. Any given statement in **Column I** can have correct matching with one or more statement(s) given in **Column II.**

80.

	Column I		Column II
(A)	a, b, c, d are in AP, then	(p)	$a+d > b+c$
(B)	a, b, c, d are in GP, then	(q)	$ad > bc$
(C)	a, b, c, d are in HP, then	(r)	$\frac{1}{a}+\frac{1}{d} > \frac{1}{b}+\frac{1}{c}$
		(s)	$ad < bc$

81.

	Column I		Column II
(A)	For an AP $a_1, a_2, a_3, \ldots, a_n, \ldots$; $a_1 = \frac{5}{2}$; $a_{10} = 16$. If $a_1 + a_2 + \ldots + a_n = 110$, then '$n$' equals	(p)	9
(B)	The interior angles of a convex non-equiangular polygon of 9 sides are in AP. The least positive integer that limits the upper value of the common difference between the measures of the angles in degrees is	(q)	10
(C)	For an increasing GP, $a_1, a_2, a_3, \ldots, a_n, \ldots$; $a_6 = 4a_4$; $a_9 - a_7 = 192$, if $a_4 + a_5 + a_6 + \ldots + a_n = 1016$, then n equals	(r)	11
		(s)	12

82.

	Column I		Column II
(A)	If $a_1, a_2, a_3, \ldots$ are in AP and $a_1 + a_4 + a_7 + a_{14} + a_{17} + a_{20} = 165$, $\alpha = a_2 + a_6 + a_{15} + a_{19}$ and $\beta = 2(a_9 + a_{12}) - (a_3 + a_{18})$, then	(p)	$\alpha = 2\beta$
(B)	If $a_1, a_2, a_3, \ldots$ are in AP and $a_1 + a_5 + a_{10} + a_{15} + a_{20} + a_{24} = 195$, $\alpha = a_2 + a_7 + a_{18} + a_{23}$ and $\beta = 2(a_3 + a_{22}) - (a_8 + a_{17})$, then	(q)	$\alpha + 2\beta = 260$
(C)	If $a_1, a_2, a_3, \ldots$ are in AP and $a_1 + a_7 + a_{10} + a_{21} + a_{24} + a_{30} = 225$, $\alpha = a_2 + a_7 + a_{24} + a_{29}$ and $\beta = 2(a_{10} + a_{21}) - (a_3 + a_{28})$, then	(r)	$\alpha + 2\beta = 220$
		(s)	$\alpha - \beta = 5\lambda, \lambda \in I$
		(t)	$\alpha + \beta = 15\mu, \mu \in I$

83.

	Column I		Column II
(A)	If $4a^2 + 9b^2 + 16c^2 = 2(3ab + 6bc + 4ca)$, where a, b, c are non-zero numbers, then a, b, c are in	(p)	AP
(B)	If $17a^2 + 13b^2 + 5c^2 = (3ab + 15bc + 5ca)$, where a, b, c are non-zero numbers, then a, b, c are in	(q)	GP
(C)	If $a^2 + 9b^2 + 25c^2 = abc\left(\frac{15}{a} + \frac{5}{b} + \frac{3}{c}\right)$, where a, b, c are non-zero numbers, then a, b, c are in	(r)	HP
(D)	If $(a^2 + b^2 + c^2)p^2 - 2p(ab + bc + ca) + (a^2 + b^2 + c^2) \leq 0$, where a, b, c, p are non-zero numbers, then a, b, c are in		

Sequences and Series Exercise 6 : Statement I and II Type Questions

- **Directions** (Q. Nos. 84 to 90) are Assertion-Reason type questions. Each of these questions contains two statements:
Statement-1 (Assertion) and **Statement-2** (Reason)
Each of these questions also has four alternative choices, only one of which is the correct answer. You have to select the correct choice as given below.
(a) Statement-1 is true, Statement-2 is true; Statement-2 is a correct explanation for Statement-1
(b) Statement-1 is true, Statement-2 is true; Statement-2 is not a correct explanation for Statement-1
(c) Statement1 is true, Statement-2 is false
(d) Statement-1 is false, Statement-2 is true

84. **Statement 1** 4, 8, 16 are in GP and 12, 16, 24 are in HP.
Statement 2 If middle term is added in three consecutive terms of a GP, resultant will be in HP.

85. **Statement 1** If the nth term of a series is $2n^3 + 3n^2 - 4$, then the second order differences must be an AP.
Statement 2 If nth term of a series is a polynomial of degree m, then mth order differences of series are constant.

86. **Statement 1** The sum of the products of numbers $\pm a_1, \pm a_2, \pm a_3, \ldots, \pm a_n$ taken two at a time is $-\sum_{i=1}^{n} a_i^2$.
Statement 2 The sum of products of numbers $a_1, a_2, a_3, \ldots, a_n$ taken two at a time is denoted by $\sum_{1 \le i < j \le n}\sum a_i a_j$.

87. **Statement 1** $a + b + c = 18\,(a, b, c > 0)$, then the maximum value of abc is 216.
Statement 2 Maximum value occurs when $a = b = c$

88. **Statement 1** If $4a^2 + 9b^2 + 16c^2 = 2(3ab + 6bc + 4ca)$, where a, b, c are non-zero real numbers, then a, b, c are in GP.
Statement-2 If $(a_1 - a_2)^2 + (a_2 - a_3)^2 + (a_3 - a_1)^2 = 0$, then $a_1 = a_2 = a_3, \forall\, a_1, a_2, a_3 \in R$.

89. **Statement 1** If a and b be two positive numbers, where $a > b$ and $4 \times \text{GM} = 5 \times \text{HM}$ for the numbers. Then, $a = 4b$.
Statement 2 (AM) (HM) = $(\text{GM})^2$ is true for positive numbers.

90. **Statement1** The difference between the sum of the first 100 even natural numbers and the sum of the first 100 odd natural numbers is 100.
Statement 2 The difference between the sum of the first n even natural numbers and sum of the first n odd natural numbers is n.

Sequences and Series Exercise 7 : Subjective Type Questions

- In this section, there are **24 subjective** questions.

91. The p th, $(2p)$ th and $(4p)$ th terms of an AP, are in GP, then find the common ratio of GP.

92. Find the sum of n terms of the series $(a + b) + (a^2 + ab + b^2) + (a^3 + a^2b + ab^2 + b^3) + \ldots$, where $a \neq 1, b \neq 1$ and $a \neq b$.

93. The sequence of odd natural numbers is divided into groups 1; 3, 5; 7, 9, 11; ... and so on. Show that the sum of the numbers in nth group is n^3.

94. Let a, b, c are respectively the sums of the first n terms, the next n terms and the next n terms of a GP. Show that a, b, c are in GP.

95. If the first four terms of an arithmetic sequence are $a, 2a, b$ and $(a - 6 - b)$ for some numbers a and b, find the sum of the first 100 terms of the sequence.

96. If $\frac{1}{1^2} + \frac{1}{2^2} + \frac{1}{3^2} + \ldots$ upto $\infty = \frac{\pi^2}{6}$, find
(i) $\frac{1}{1^2} + \frac{1}{3^2} + \frac{1}{5^2} + \ldots$ upto ∞
(ii) $1 - \frac{1}{2^2} + \frac{1}{3^2} - \frac{1}{4^2} + \ldots$ upto ∞

97. If the arithmetic mean of $a_1, a_2, a_3, \ldots, a_n$ is a and $b_1, b_2, b_3, \ldots, b_n$ have the arithmetic mean b and $a_i + b_i = 1$ for $i = 1, 2, 3, \ldots, n$, prove that

$$\sum_{i=1}^{n}(a_i - a)^2 + \sum_{i=1}^{n} a_i b_i = nab$$

98. If $a_1, a_2, a_3, \ldots$ is an arithmetic progression with common difference 1 and $a_1 + a_2 + a_3 + \ldots + a_{98} = 137$, then find the value of $a_2 + a_4 + a_6 + \ldots + a_{98}$.

99. If $t_1 = 1, t_r - t_{r-1} = 2^{r-1}, r \ge 2$, find $\sum_{r=1}^{n} t_r$.

100. Prove that $I_1, I_2, I_3, \ldots$ form an AP, if
(i) $I_n = \int_0^{\pi} \frac{\sin 2nx}{\sin x}\,dx$ (ii) $I_n = \int_0^{\pi} \left(\frac{\sin nx}{\sin x}\right)^2 dx$

101. Consider the sequence $S = 7 + 13 + 21 + 31 + \dots + T_n$, find the value of T_{70}.

102. Find value of $\left(x + \frac{1}{x}\right)^3 + \left(x^2 + \frac{1}{x^2}\right)^3 + \dots + \left(x^n + \frac{1}{x^n}\right)^3$.

103. If a_m be the mth term of an AP, show that

$$a_1^2 - a_2^2 + a_3^2 - a_4^2 + \dots + a_{2n-1}^2 - a_{2n}^2 = \frac{n}{(2n-1)}(a_1^2 - a_{2n}^2).$$

104. If three unequal numbers are in HP and their squares are in AP, show that they are in the ratio $1 + \sqrt{3} : -2 : 1 - \sqrt{3}$ or $1 - \sqrt{3} : -2 : 1 + \sqrt{3}$.

105. If $a_1, a_2, a_3, \dots, a_n$ are in AP with $a_1 = 0$, prove that

$$\frac{a_3}{a_2} + \frac{a_4}{a_3} + \dots + \frac{a_n}{a_{n-1}} - a_2\left(\frac{1}{a_2} + \frac{1}{a_3} + \dots + \frac{1}{a_{n-2}}\right) = \frac{a_{n-1}}{a_2} + \frac{a_2}{a_{n-1}}$$

106. Balls are arranged in rows to form an equilateral triangle. The first row consists of one ball, the second row of two balls and so on. If 669 more balls are added, then all the balls can be arranged in the shape of a square and each of the sides, then contains 8 balls less than each side of the triangle. Determine the initial number of balls.

107. If $\theta_1, \theta_2, \theta_3, \dots, \theta_n$ are in AP whose common difference is d, then show that

$$\sin d \{\sec \theta_1 \sec \theta_2 + \sec \theta_2 \sec \theta_3 + \dots + \sec \theta_{n-1} \sec \theta_n\} = \tan \theta_n - \tan \theta_1.$$

108. Show that,

$$(1 + 5^{-1})(1 + 5^{-2})(1 + 5^{-4})(1 + 5^{-8}) \dots (1 + 5^{-2^n}) = \frac{5}{4}(1 - 5^{-2^{n+1}})$$

109. Evaluate $S = \sum_{n=0}^{n} \frac{2^n}{(a^{2^n} + 1)}$ (where $a > 1$).

110. Find the sum to infinite terms of the series

$$\tan^{-1}\left(\frac{1}{3}\right) + \tan^{-1}\left(\frac{2}{9}\right) + \dots + \tan^{-1}\left(\frac{2^{n-1}}{1 + 2^{2n-1}}\right) + \dots$$

111. Find the sum to n terms, whose nth term is $\tan[\alpha + (n-1)\beta]\tan(\alpha + n\beta)$.

112. If $\sum_{r=1}^{n} T_r = \frac{n}{8}(n+1)(n+2)(n+3)$, find $\sum_{r=1}^{n} \frac{1}{T_r}$.

113. If S_1, S_2, S_3 denote the sum of n terms of 3 arithmetic series whose first terms are unity and their common difference are in HP, prove that

$$n = \frac{2S_3S_1 - S_1S_2 - S_2S_3}{S_1 - 2S_2 + S_3}.$$

114. Three friends whose ages form a GP divide a certain sum of money in proportion to their ages. If they do that three years later, when the youngest is half the age of the oldest, then he will receive ₹ 105 more than he gets now and the middle friend will get ₹ 15 more than he gets now. Find the ages of the friends.

Sequences and Series Exercise 8 : Questions Asked in Previous 13 Year's Exam

- This section contains questions asked in **IIT-JEE, AIEEE, JEE Main & JEE Advanced** from year **2005** to year **2017**.

115. If a, b, c are in AP and $|a|, |b|, |c| < 1$ and

$$x = 1 + a + a^2 + \dots + \infty$$
$$y = 1 + b + b^2 + \dots + \infty$$
$$z = 1 + c + c^2 + \dots + \infty$$

Then, x, y, z will be in **[AIEEE 2005, 3M]**

(a) AP (b) GP (c) HP
(d) None of these

116. If $a_n = \frac{3}{4} - \left(\frac{3}{4}\right)^2 + \left(\frac{3}{4}\right)^3 - \dots + (-1)^{n-1}\left(\frac{3}{4}\right)^n$ and $b_n = 1 - a_n$, then find the least natural number n_0 such that $b_n > a_n, \forall n \geq n_0$. **[IIT-JEE 2006, 6M]**

117. Let $a_1, a_2, a_3, \dots$ be terms are in AP, if $\frac{a_1 + a_2 + \dots + a_p}{a_1 + a_2 + \dots + a_q} = \frac{p^2}{q^2}, p \neq q$, then $\frac{a_6}{a_{21}}$ equals **[AIEEE 2006, 4.5M]**

(a) $\frac{41}{11}$ (b) $\frac{7}{2}$
(c) $\frac{2}{7}$ (d) $\frac{11}{41}$

118. If $a_1, a_2, \dots, a_n$ are in HP, then the expression $a_1a_2 + a_2a_3 + \dots + a_{n-1}a_n$ is equal to **[AIEEE 2006, 6M]**

(a) $n(a_1 - a_n)$
(b) $(n-1)(a_1 - a_n)$
(c) na_1a_n
(d) $(n-1)a_1a_n$

119. Let V_r denotes the sum of the first r terms of an arithmetic progression whose first term is r and the common difference is $(2r-1)$. Let $T_r = V_{r+1} - V_r - 2$ and $Q_r = T_{r+1} - T_r$ for $r = 1, 2, \dots$ **[IIT-JEE 2007, 4+4+4M]**

(i) The sum $V_1 + V_2 + \dots + V_n$ is

(a) $\frac{1}{12} n(n+1)(3n^2 - n + 1)$

(b) $\frac{1}{12} n(n+1)(3n^2 + n + 2)$

(c) $\frac{1}{2} n(2n^2 - n + 1)$

(d) $\frac{1}{3}(2n^3 - 2n + 3)$

(ii) T_r is always

(a) an odd number (b) an even number

(c) a prime number (d) a composite number

(iii) Which one of the following is a correct statement?

(a) $Q_1, Q_2, Q_3, \dots$ are in AP with common difference 5

(b) $Q_1, Q_2, Q_3, \dots$ are in AP with common difference 6

(c) $Q_1, Q_2, Q_3, \dots$ are in AP with common difference 11

(d) $Q_1 = Q_2 = Q_3 = \dots$

120. Let A_1, G_1, H_1 denote the arithmetic, geometric and harmonic means respectively, of two distinct positive numbers. For $n \geq 2$, let A_{n-1}, G_{n-1} and H_{n-1} has arithmetic, geometric and harmonic means as A_n, G_n, H_n, respectively. **[IIT-JEE 2007, 4+4+4M]**

(i) Which one of the following statement is correct?

(a) $G_1 > G_2 > G_3 > \dots$ (b) $G_1 < G_2 < G_3 < \dots$

(c) $G_1 = G_2 = G_3 = \dots$

(d) $G_1 < G_3 < G_5 < \dots$ and $G_2 > G_4 > G_6 > \dots$

(ii) Which of the following statement is correct?

(a) $A_1 > A_2 > A_3 > \dots$

(b) $A_1 < A_2 < A_3 < \dots$

(c) $A_1 > A_3 > A_5 > \dots$ and $A_2 < A_4 < A_6 < \dots$

(d) $A_1 < A_3 < A_5 < \dots$ and $A_2 > A_4 > A_6 > \dots$

(iii) Which of the following statement is correct?

(a) $H_1 > H_2 > H_3 > \dots$

(b) $H_1 < H_2 < H_3 < \dots$

(c) $H_1 > H_3 > H_5 > \dots$ and $H_2 < H_4 < H_6 < \dots$

(d) $H_1 < H_3 < H_5 < \dots$ and $H_2 > H_4 > H_6 > \dots$

121. If a geometric progression consisting of positive terms, each term equals the sum of the next two terms, then the common ratio of this progression equals **[AIEEE 2007, 3M]**

(a) $\frac{1}{2}(1 - \sqrt{5})$ (b) $\frac{1}{2}\sqrt{5}$

(c) $\sqrt{5}$ (d) $\frac{1}{2}(\sqrt{5} - 1)$

122. Suppose four distinct positive numbers a_1, a_2, a_3, a_4 are in GP. Let $b_1 = a_1, b_2 = b_1 + a_2, b_3 = b_2 + a_3$ and $b_4 = b_3 + a_4$.

Statement 1 The numbers b_1, b_2, b_3, b_4 are neither in AP nor in GP.

Statement 2 The numbers b_1, b_2, b_3, b_4 are in HP. **[IIT-JEE 2008, 3M]**

(a) Statement-1 is true, Statement-2 is true; Statement-2 is a correct explanation for Statement-1

(b) Statement-1 is true, Statement-2 is true; Statement-2 is not a correct explanation for Statement-1

(c) Statement-1 is true, Statement-2 is false

(d) Statement-1 is false, Statement-2 is true

123. The first two terms of a geometric progression add upto 12 the sum of the third and the fourth terms is 48, if the terms of the geometric progression are alternately positive and negative, then the first term is **[AIEEE 2008, 3M]**

(a) -12 (b) 12 (c) 4 (d) -4

124. If the sum of first n terms of an AP is cn^2, then the sum of squares of these n terms is **[IIT-JEE 2009, 3M]**

(a) $\frac{n(4n^2-1)c^2}{6}$ (b) $\frac{n(4n^2+1)c^2}{3}$

(c) $\frac{n(4n^2-1)c^2}{3}$ (d) $\frac{n(4n^2+1)c^2}{6}$

125. The sum to infinity of the series $1 + \frac{2}{3} + \frac{6}{3^2} + \frac{10}{3^3} + \frac{14}{3^4} + \dots$ is **[AIEEE 2009, 4M]**

(a) 6 (b) 2 (c) 3 (d) 4

126. Let $S_k, k = 1, 2, \dots, 100$, denote the sum of the infinite geometric series whose first term is $\frac{k-1}{k!}$ and common ratio is $\frac{1}{k}$. Then, the value of $\frac{100^2}{100!} + \sum_{k=2}^{100} |(k^2 - 3k + 1) S_k|$ is **[IIT-JEE 2010, 3M]**

127. Let $a_1, a_2, a_3, \dots, a_{11}$ be real numbers satisfying $a_1 = 15, 27 - 2a_2 > 0$ and $a_k = 2a_{k-1} - a_{k-2}$ for $k = 3, 4, \dots, 11$. If $\frac{a_1^2 + a_2^2 + \dots + a_{11}^2}{11} = 90$, then the value of $\frac{a_1 + a_2 + \dots + a_{11}}{11}$ is equal to **[IIT-JEE 2010, 3M]**

128. A person is to count 4500 currency notes. Let a_n denotes the number of notes he counts in the nth minute. If $a_1 = a_2 = \dots = a_{10} = 150$ and $a_{10}, a_{11}, \dots$ are in AP with common difference -2, then the time taken by him to count all notes is **[AIEEE 2010, 8M]**

(a) 34 min (b) 125 min

(c) 135 min (d) 24 min

129. The minimum value of the sum of real numbers $a^{-5}, a^{-4}, 3a^{-3}, 1, a^8$ and a^{10} with $a > 0$ is **[IIT-JEE 2011, 4M]**

130. A man saves ₹ 200 in each of the first three months of his service. In each of the subsequent months his saving increases by ₹ 40 more than the saving of immediately previous month. His total saving from the start of service will be ₹ 11040 after **[AIEEE 2011, 4M (Paper I)]**

(a) 19 months (b) 20 months
(c) 21 months (d) 18 months

131. Let a_n be the nth term of an AP, if $\sum_{r=1}^{100} a_{2r} = \alpha$ and $\sum_{r=1}^{100} a_{2r-1} = \beta$, then the common difference of the AP is **[AIEEE 2011, 4M (Paper II)]**

(a) $\frac{\alpha - \beta}{200}$ (b) $\alpha - \beta$
(c) $\frac{\alpha - \beta}{100}$ (d) $\beta - \alpha$

132. If $a_1, a_2, a_3, \ldots$ be in harmonic progression with $a_1 = 5$ and $a_{20} = 25$. The least positive integer n for which $a_n < 0$ is **[IIT-JEE 2012, 3M]**

(a) 22 (b) 23
(c) 24 (d) 25

133. **Statement 1** The sum of the series $1 + (1 + 2 + 4) + (4 + 6 + 9) + (9 + 12 + 16) + \ldots + (361 + 380 + 400)$ is 8000.

Statement 2 $\sum_{k=1}^{n} (k^3 - (k-1)^3) = n^3$ for any natural number n. **[AIEEE 2012, 4M]**

(a) Statement-1 is true, Statement-2 is true; Statement-2 is a correct explanation for Statement-1
(b) Statement-1 is true, Statement-2 is true; Statement-2 is not a correct explanation for Statement-1
(c) Statement-1 is true, Statement-2 is false
(d) Statement-1 is false, Statement-2 is true

134. If 100 times the 100th term of an AP with non-zero common difference equals the 50 times its 50th term, then the 150th term of this AP is **[AIEEE 2012, 4M]**

(a) 150 times its 50th term (b) 150
(c) zero (d) −150

135. If x, y, z are in AP and $\tan^{-1} x$, $\tan^{-1} y$, $\tan^{-1} z$ are also in AP, then **[JEE Main 2013, 4M]**

(a) $2x = 3y = 6z$ (b) $6x = 3y = 2z$
(c) $6x = 4y = 3z$ (d) $x = y = z$

136. The sum of first 20 terms of the sequence 0.7, 0.77, 0.777, ..., is **[JEE Main 2013, 4M]**

(a) $\frac{7}{9}(99 - 10^{-20})$ (b) $\frac{7}{81}(179 + 10^{-20})$
(c) $\frac{7}{9}(99 + 10^{-20})$ (d) $\frac{7}{81}(179 - 10^{-20})$

137. Let $S_n = \sum_{k=1}^{4n} (-1)^{\frac{k(k+1)}{2}} \cdot k^2$, then S_n can take value(s) **[JEE Advanced 2013, 4M]**

(a) 1056 (b) 1088 (c) 1120 (d) 1332

138. A pack contains n cards numbered from 1 to n. Two consecutive numbered cards are removed from the pack and the sum of the numbers on the remaining cards is 1224. If the smaller of the numbers on the removed cards is k, then $k - 20$ is equal to **[JEE Advanced 2013, 4M]**

139. If $(10)^9 + 2(11)^1(10)^8 + 3(11)^2(10)^7 + \ldots + (10)(11)^9 = k(10)^9$, then k is equal to **[JEE Main 2014, 4M]**

(a) 100 (b) 110 (c) $\frac{121}{10}$ (d) $\frac{441}{100}$

140. Three positive numbers form an increasing GP. If the middle terms in this GP is doubled, the new numbers are in AP. Then, the common ratio of the GP is **[JEE Main 2014, 4M]**

(a) $2 - \sqrt{3}$ (b) $2 + \sqrt{3}$ (c) $\sqrt{2} + \sqrt{3}$ (d) $3 + \sqrt{2}$

141. Let a, b, c be positive integers such that $\frac{b}{a}$ is an integer. If a, b, c are in geometric progression and the arithmetic mean of a, b, c is $b + 2$, the value of $\frac{a^2 + a - 14}{a + 1}$ is **[JEE Advanced 2014, 3M]**

142. The sum of first 9 terms of the series $\frac{1^3}{1} + \frac{1^3 + 2^3}{1 + 3} + \frac{1^3 + 2^3 + 3^3}{1 + 3 + 5} + \ldots$ is **[JEE Main 2015, 4M]**

(a) 192 (b) 71 (c) 96 (d) 142

143. If m is the AM of two distinct real numbers l and n $(l, n > 1)$ and G_1, G_2 and G_3 are three geometric means between l and n, then $G_1^4 + 2G_2^4 + G_3^4$ equals **[JEE Main 2015, 4M]**

(a) $4l^2m^2n^2$ (b) $4l^2mn$
(c) $4lm^2n$ (d) $4lmn^2$

144. Suppose that all the terms of an arithmetic progression (AP) are natural numbers. If the ratio of the sum of the first seven terms to the sum of the first eleven terms is $6 : 11$ and the seventh term lies between 130 and 140, then the common difference of this AP is **[JEE Main 2015, 4M]**

145. If the 2nd, 5th and 9th terms of a non-eustant AP are in GP, then the common ratio of this GP is **[JEE Main 2016, 4M]**

(a) 1 (b) $\frac{7}{4}$ (c) $\frac{8}{5}$ (d) $\frac{4}{3}$

146. If the sum of the first ten terms of the series $\left(1\frac{3}{5}\right)^2 + \left(2\frac{2}{5}\right)^2 + \left(3\frac{1}{5}\right)^2 + 4^2 + \left(4\frac{4}{5}\right)^2 + \ldots$ is $\frac{16}{5}$ m, then m equal to **[JEE Main 2016, 4M]**

(a) 100 (b) 99 (c) 102 (d) 101

147. Let $b_i > 1$ for $i = 1, 2, \ldots, 101$. Suppose $\log_e b_1, \log_e b_2, \log_e b_3, \ldots, \log_e b_{101}$ are in Arithmetic Progression (AP) with the common difference $\log_e 2$. Suppose $a_1, a_2, a_3, \ldots, a_{101}$ are in AP. Such that, $a_1 = b_1$ and $a_{51} = b_{51}$. If $t = b_1 + b_2 + \ldots + b_{51}$ and $s = a_1 + a_2 + \ldots + a_{51}$, then **[JEE Advanced 2016, 3M]**

(a) $s > t$ and $a_{101} > b_{101}$ (b) $s > t$ and $a_{101} < b_{101}$
(c) $s < t$ and $a_{101} > b_{101}$ (d) $s < t$ and $a_{101} < b_{101}$

148. For any three positive real numbers a, b and c, $9(25a^2 + b^2) + 25(c^2 - 3ac) = 15b(3a + c)$. Then **[JEE Main 2017, 4M]**

(a) a, b and c are in GP
(b) b, c and a are in GP
(c) b, c and a are in AP
(d) a, b and c are in AP

Answers

Exercise for Session 1

1. (c) 2. (d) 3. (b) 4. (c) 5. (a)

Exercise for Session 2

1. (b) 2. (a) 3. (a) 4. (b) 5. (c) 6. (c)

Exercise for Session 3

1. (b) 2. (d) 3. (b) 4. (c) 5. (d)

Exercise for Session 4

1. (c) 2. (c) 3. (c) 4. (d) 5. (a) 6. (a)

Exercise for Session 5

1. (c) 2. (a) 3. (a) 4. (c) 5. (b) 6. (b)
7. (b) 8. (b) 9. (a) 10. (b)

Exercise for Session 6

1. (b) 2. (d) 3. (b) 4. (c) 5. (a) 6. (a)
7. (a) 8. (c) 9. (b) 10. (c)

Exercise for Session 7

1. (a) 2. (d) 3. (b) 4. (d) 5. (c) 6. (c)
7. (a) 8. (a)

Exercise for Session 8

1. (c) 2. (c) 3. (b) 4. (a) 5. (c) 6. (b)
7. (c) 8. (d) 9. (a) 10. (a)

Exercise for Session 9

1. (d) 2. (c) 3. (d) 4. (a) 5. (b) 6. (a)
7. (c)

Chapter Exercises

1. (a) 2. (d) 3. (c) 4. (c) 5. (a) 6. (c)
7. (b) 8. (d) 9. (a) 10. (c) 11. (a) 12. (b)
13. (d) 14. (a) 15. (a) 16. (c) 17. (a) 18. (b)
19. (a) 20. (d) 21. (c) 22. (c) 23. (c) 24. (b)
25. (a) 26. (a) 27. (a) 28. (c) 29. (b) 30. (c)
31. (a,c) 32. (b,d) 33. (b,c) 34. (a,b) 35. (c,d) 36. (a,c,d)
37. (a,d) 38. (a,b,c) 39. (a,c) 40. (b,c) 41. (a,c) 42. (c,d)
43. (b,c) 44. (a,c) 45. (a,d)
46. (c) 47. (d) 48. (a) 49. (a) 50. (a) 51. (b)
52. (a) 53. (c) 54. (b) 55. (d) 56. (b) 57. (c)
58. (c) 59. (b) 60. (d) 61. (d) 62. (b) 63. (d)
64. (a) 65. (b) 66. (b) 67. (a) 68. (b) 69. (c)
70. (3) 71. (5) 72. (8) 73. (4) 74. (2) 75. (7)
76. (3) 77. (9) 78. (1) 79. (0)
80. (A) $\rightarrow$ (r, s); (B) $\rightarrow$ (p, r); (C) $\rightarrow$ (p, q)
81. (A) $\rightarrow$ (r); (B) $\rightarrow$ (p); (C) $\rightarrow$ (q)
82. (A) $\rightarrow$ (p,r,s,t); (B) $\rightarrow$ (p,q,s,t); (C) $\rightarrow$ (p,s,t)
83. (A) $\rightarrow$ (r); (B) $\rightarrow$ (p); (C) $\rightarrow$ (r); (D) $\rightarrow$ (q)
84. (a) 85. (a) 86. (b) 87. (a) 88. (d) 89. (c)
90. (a)
91. 2. 92. $\dfrac{1}{(a-b)}\left\{\dfrac{a^2(1-a^n)}{(1-a)} - \dfrac{b^2(1-b^n)}{(1-b)}\right\}$
95. -5050 96. (i) $\dfrac{\pi^2}{8}$ (ii) $\dfrac{\pi^2}{12}$ 98. 93
99. $2^{n+1} - n - 2$ 101. 5113
102. $\dfrac{x^3(1-x^{3n})}{1-x^3} + \dfrac{(1-x^{3n})}{x^{3n}(1-x^3)} + \dfrac{3x(1-x^n)}{(1-x)} + \dfrac{3(1-x^n)}{x^n(1-x)}$
106. 1540 109. $\dfrac{1}{a-1}$
110. $\dfrac{\pi}{4}$ 111. $\dfrac{\dfrac{\sin n\beta}{\cos(\alpha+n\beta)\cos\alpha} - n\tan\beta}{\tan\beta}$
112. $\dfrac{n(n+3)}{2(n+1)(n+2)}$ 114. 12, 18, 27 115. (c)
116. (7) 117. (d) 118. (d) 119. (i) (b), (ii) (d), (iii) (b)
120. (i) (c), (ii) (a), (iii) (b) 121. (d) 122. (c) 123. (a) 124. (c)
125. (c) 126. (3) 127. (0) 128. (a) 129. (8) 130. (c)
131. (c) 132. (d) 133. (a) 134. (c) 135. (d) 136. (b)
137. (a,d) 138. (5) 139. (a) 140. (b) 141. (4) 142. (c)
143. (c) 144. (a) 145. (d) 146. (d) 147. (b) 148. (c)

Solutions

1. $\because x, y, z$ are in HP.

$\therefore \quad \frac{1}{x}, \frac{1}{y}, \frac{1}{z}$ are in AP.

$$\therefore \quad \frac{1}{x} - \frac{1}{y} = \frac{1}{y} - \frac{1}{z} \quad \text{...(i)}$$

$$\frac{\sqrt{yz}}{\sqrt{y} + \sqrt{z}} = \frac{1}{\frac{1}{\sqrt{y}} + \frac{1}{\sqrt{z}}} = a \quad \text{[say]}$$

$$\frac{\sqrt{zx}}{\sqrt{x} + \sqrt{z}} = \frac{1}{\frac{1}{\sqrt{z}} + \frac{1}{\sqrt{x}}} = b \quad \text{[say]}$$

and
$$\frac{\sqrt{xy}}{\sqrt{x} + \sqrt{y}} = \frac{1}{\frac{1}{\sqrt{x}} + \frac{1}{\sqrt{y}}} = c \quad \text{[say]}$$

$$\because \quad \frac{a-b}{b-c} = \frac{\dfrac{1}{\frac{1}{\sqrt{y}} + \frac{1}{\sqrt{z}}} - \dfrac{1}{\frac{1}{\sqrt{z}} + \frac{1}{\sqrt{x}}}}{\dfrac{1}{\frac{1}{\sqrt{z}} + \frac{1}{\sqrt{x}}} - \dfrac{1}{\frac{1}{\sqrt{x}} + \frac{1}{\sqrt{y}}}} = \frac{\frac{1}{x} - \frac{1}{y}}{\frac{1}{y} - \frac{1}{z}} = \frac{a}{a}$$

[from Eq. (i)]

Hence, $\frac{\sqrt{yz}}{\sqrt{y} + \sqrt{z}}, \frac{\sqrt{zx}}{\sqrt{z} + \sqrt{x}}, \frac{\sqrt{xy}}{\sqrt{x} + \sqrt{y}}$ are in AP.

2. $\because a_1, a_2, a_3, \ldots$ are in HP.

$\Rightarrow \frac{1}{a_1}, \frac{1}{a_2}, \frac{1}{a_3}, \ldots$ are in AP. ...(i)

$$\because \quad f_k = \sum_{r=1}^{n} a_r - a_k$$

$$\Rightarrow \quad a_k + f_k = \sum_{r=1}^{n} a_r = \lambda \quad \text{[say]}$$

$$\Rightarrow \quad a_1 + f_1 = a_2 + f_2 = a_3 + f_3 = \ldots = \lambda$$

From Eq. (i), $\frac{\lambda}{a_1}, \frac{\lambda}{a_2}, \frac{\lambda}{a_3}, \ldots$ are also in AP.

$\Rightarrow \frac{a_1 + f_1}{a_1}, \frac{a_2 + f_2}{a_2}, \frac{a_3 + f_3}{a_3}, \ldots$ are also in AP.

Subtracting from each term by 1, we get

$\frac{f_1}{a_1}, \frac{f_2}{a_2}, \frac{f_3}{a_3}, \ldots$ are also in AP.

$\Rightarrow \frac{1}{\alpha_1}, \frac{1}{\alpha_2}, \frac{1}{\alpha_3}, \ldots$ are in AP.

$\therefore \quad \alpha_1, \alpha_2, \alpha_3, \ldots$ are in HP.

$\therefore \quad 2^{\alpha_1}, 2^{\alpha_2}, 2^{\alpha_3}, \ldots$ are not in AP/GP/HP.

3. $\because \quad \frac{AL_1}{AB} = \frac{L_1M_1}{BC} \Rightarrow L_1M_1 = \frac{a}{n+1}$

Similarly, $L_2M_2 = \frac{2a}{n+1}$

$$L_3M_3 = \frac{3a}{n+1}$$

$$\vdots \qquad \vdots \qquad \vdots$$

$$L_nM_n = \frac{na}{n+1}$$

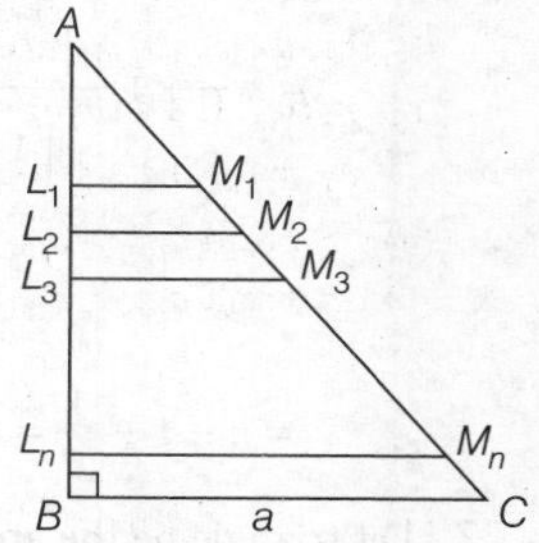

$$L_1M_1 + L_2M_2 + \ldots + L_nM_n$$

$$= \frac{a}{(n+1)}(1 + 2 + 3 + \ldots + n)$$

$$= \frac{a}{(n+1)} \cdot \frac{n(n+1)}{2} = \frac{na}{2}$$

4. $\because \quad S_n = 1 + 22 + 333 + \ldots + \underbrace{nnnn\ldots n}_{n \text{ terms}}$

$$\therefore \quad S_n - S_{n-1} = \underbrace{nnnn\ldots n}_{n \text{ times}} = n\,(\underbrace{111\ldots 1}_{n \text{ times}})$$

$$= n\,(10^{n-1} + 10^{n-2} + \ldots + 10 + 1) = \frac{n\,(10^n - 1)}{10 - 1}$$

$$\therefore \; 9\,(S_n - S_{n-1}) = n\,(10^n - 1)$$

5. Given that a, b, c are in GP.

Then, $\quad b^2 = ac \quad$ ...(i)

and equations $ax^2 + 2bx + c = 0$

and $dx^2 + 2ex + f = 0$ have a common root. ...(A)

Now, $\quad ax^2 + 2bx + c = 0$

$$\Rightarrow \quad ax^2 + 2\sqrt{ac}\,x + c = 0 \quad \text{[by Eq. (i)]}$$

$$\Rightarrow \quad (\sqrt{a}x + \sqrt{c})^2 = 0 \Rightarrow \sqrt{a}x + \sqrt{c} = 0$$

$$\Rightarrow \quad x = -\frac{\sqrt{c}}{\sqrt{a}} \quad \text{[repeated]}$$

By the condition (A), $\left(-\frac{\sqrt{c}}{\sqrt{a}}\right)$ be the root of $dx^2 - 2ex + f = 0$

So, it satisfy the equation

$$d\left(-\sqrt{\frac{c}{a}}\right)^2 + 2e\left(-\sqrt{\frac{c}{a}}\right) + f = 0$$

$$\Rightarrow \quad \frac{dc}{a} - 2e\frac{\sqrt{c}}{\sqrt{a}} + f = 0 \Rightarrow \frac{d}{a} - \frac{2e}{\sqrt{ac}} + \frac{f}{c} = 0$$

$$\Rightarrow \quad \frac{d}{a} - \frac{2e}{b} + \frac{f}{c} = 0 \Rightarrow \frac{d}{a} + \frac{f}{c} = 2\left(\frac{e}{b}\right)$$

So, $\frac{d}{a}, \frac{e}{b}, \frac{f}{c}$ are in AP.

6. $\because \quad S_n = \frac{1}{2} + \frac{3}{4} + \frac{7}{8} + \frac{15}{16} + \ldots n$ up to terms

$$= \left(1 - \frac{1}{2}\right) + \left(1 - \frac{1}{4}\right) + \left(1 - \frac{1}{8}\right) + \ldots n \text{ up to terms}$$

$$= \left(1 - \frac{1}{2}\right) + \left(1 - \frac{1}{2^2}\right) + \left(1 - \frac{1}{2^3}\right) + \ldots + \left(1 - \frac{1}{2^n}\right)$$

$$= n - \frac{1}{2}\left(1 + \frac{1}{2} + \frac{1}{2^2} + \ldots + \frac{1}{2^{n-1}}\right)$$

$$= n - \frac{1}{2} + \frac{1\left[1 - \left(\frac{1}{2}\right)^n\right]}{\left(1 - \frac{1}{2}\right)}$$

$$\left[\text{by sum GP}, S_n = \frac{a(1 - r^n)}{1 - r}, \text{if } 0 < r < 1\right]$$

$$= n - 1 + \frac{1}{2^n} = n - 1 + 2^{-n}$$

7. Let triangle be the area of ΔPQR.

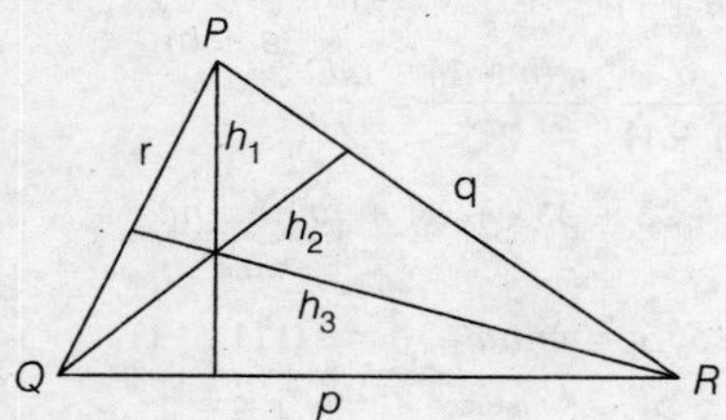

$\therefore \quad \Delta = \frac{1}{2} \times p \times h_1$ [h_1, h_2, h_3 are altitudes]

$\Rightarrow \quad h_1 = \frac{2\Delta}{p}$ ...(i)

Similarly, $h_2 = \frac{2\Delta}{q}$ ...(ii)

and $h_3 = \frac{2\Delta}{r}$ ...(iii)

According to the question, $\sin P, \sin Q, \sin R$ are in AP.

Then, kp, kq, kr are in AP [by sine rule]

$\Rightarrow$ p, q, r are in AP.

$\Rightarrow \frac{2\Delta}{h_1}, \frac{2\Delta}{h_2}, \frac{2\Delta}{h_3}$ are in AP. [by Eqs. (i), (ii) and (iii)]

$\Rightarrow \frac{1}{h_1}, \frac{1}{h_2}, \frac{1}{h_3}$ are in AP.

$\Rightarrow$ h_1, h_2, h_3 are in HP.

$\Rightarrow$ Altitudes are in HP.

8. Given that, $a_1, a_2, \ldots, a_{10}$ be in AP.

Let d be the common difference of AP.

$\therefore \quad d = \frac{a_{10} - a_1}{10 - 1}$

$d = \frac{3 - 2}{9}$ [given that, $a_1 = h_1 = 2$ and $a_{10} = h_{10} = 3$]

$d = \frac{1}{9}$

$\therefore \quad a_4 = a_1 + 3d = 2 + \frac{3}{9} = 2 + \frac{1}{3} = \frac{7}{3}$

Now, $h_1, h_2, \ldots, h_{10}$ be in HP.

So, common difference of respective AP.

$$D = \frac{\frac{1}{h_{10}} - \frac{1}{h_1}}{10 - 1} = \frac{\frac{1}{3} - \frac{1}{2}}{9} = \frac{-1}{9 \times 6} = \frac{-1}{54}$$

So, $\frac{1}{h_7} = \frac{1}{h_1} + 6D \Rightarrow \frac{1}{\lambda_7} = \frac{1}{2} + 6\left(\frac{-1}{54}\right) = \frac{1}{2} - \frac{1}{9}$

$\frac{1}{h_7} = \frac{7}{18} \Rightarrow h_7 = \frac{18}{7}$

So, $a_4 h_7 = \frac{7}{3} \times \frac{18}{7} = 6$

9. $\because \quad I_n = \int_0^\pi \frac{1 - \sin 2nx}{1 - \cos 2x}\,dx \Rightarrow I_n = \int_0^\pi \frac{1 - \sin 2nx}{2\sin^2 x}\,dx$

$\Rightarrow \quad I_{n+1} + I_{n-1} - 2I_n$

$$= \frac{1}{2}\int_0^\pi \frac{[1 - \sin 2(n+1)x + 1 - \sin 2(n-1)x - 2 + 2\sin 2nx]}{\sin^2 x}\,dx$$

$$= \frac{1}{2}\int_0^\pi \frac{[\sin 2nx - \sin 2(n+1)x] + [\sin 2nx - \sin 2(n-1)x]}{\sin^2 x}\,dx$$

$$= \frac{1}{2}\int_0^\pi \frac{-2\cos(2n+1)x\sin(x) + 2\cos(2n-1)x\sin x}{\sin^2 x}\,dx$$

$$= \int_0^\pi \frac{\sin x[\cos(2n-1)x - \cos(2n+1)x]}{\sin^2 x}\,dx$$

$$= \int_0^\pi \frac{2\sin 2nx \sin x}{\sin x}\,dx = 2\int_0^\pi \sin 2nx\,dx = \frac{2}{2n}[-\cos 2nx]_0^\pi$$

$$= -\frac{1}{n}(1 - 1) = 0$$

$\therefore \quad I_{n+1} + I_{n-1} = 2I_n$

$\Rightarrow \quad I_{n-1} + I_n, I_{n+1}$ are in AP.

$\therefore \quad I_1, I_2, I_3, \ldots$ are in AP.

10. Given that,

$a(b - c)x^2 + b(c - a)xy + c(a - b)y^2$ is perfect square.

$\therefore \quad b^2(c - a)^2 = 4a(b - c) \cdot c(a - b)$

$\Rightarrow \quad b^2(c - a)^2 = 4ac(a - b)(b - c)$

$\Rightarrow \quad [a(b - c) + c(a - b)]^2 = 4ac(a - b)(b - c)$

$[\because a(b - c) + b(c - a) + c(a - b) = 0]$

$\Rightarrow \quad [a(b - c) - c(a - b)]^2 = 0$

$\Rightarrow \quad a(b - c) - c(a - b) = 0$

$\Rightarrow \quad ab - ac - ca + bc = 0 \Rightarrow b(a + c) = 2ac$

$\Rightarrow \quad b = \frac{2ac}{a + b}$

$\Rightarrow$ a, b, c are in HP.

11. Let $S = 1 + 2\left(1 - \frac{1}{n}\right) + 3\left(1 - \frac{1}{n}\right)^2 + \ldots + \infty$

$\left(1 - \frac{1}{n}\right)S = \left(1 - \frac{1}{n}\right) + 2\left(1 - \frac{1}{n}\right) + \ldots + \infty$

$S\left(1 - 1 + \frac{1}{n}\right) = 1 + \left(1 - \frac{1}{n}\right) + \left(1 - \frac{1}{n}\right)^2 + \ldots + \infty$

$$\Rightarrow \quad \frac{S}{n} = \frac{1}{1-\left(1-\frac{1}{n}\right)} \qquad \left[S_\infty = \frac{a}{1-r} \text{ by GP}\right]$$

$$\Rightarrow \quad S = \frac{n}{\frac{1}{n}}$$

$$\Rightarrow \quad S = n^2$$

12. $\because \log_3 2, \log_3 (2^x - 5)$ and $\log_3 \left(2^x - \frac{7}{2}\right)$ are in AP. ...(i)

For defined, $2^x - 5 > 0$ and $2^x - \frac{7}{2} > 0$

$$\therefore \quad 2^x > 5 \qquad \text{...(ii)}$$

From Eq. (i), $2, 2^x - 5, 2^x - \frac{7}{2}$ are in GP.

$$\therefore \quad (2^x - 5)^2 = 2 \cdot \left(2^x - \frac{7}{2}\right)$$

$$\Rightarrow \quad 2^{2x} - 12 \cdot 2^x + 32 = 0$$

$$\Rightarrow \quad (2^x - 8)(2^x - 4) = 0$$

$$\therefore \quad 2^x = 8, 4$$

$$\Rightarrow \quad 2^x = 8 = 2^3, 2^x \neq 4 \qquad \text{[fromEq. (ii)]}$$

$$\therefore \quad x = 3$$

13. $\because a, b, c$ are positive prime numbers.

Let $\sqrt{a}, \sqrt{b}, \sqrt{c}$ are 3 terms of AP. [not necessarily consecutive]

Then, $\sqrt{a} = A + (p-1)D$ ...(i)

$\sqrt{b} = A + (q-1)D$ ...(ii)

$\sqrt{c} = A + (r-1)D$ ...(iii)

[A and D be the first term and common difference of AP]

$\sqrt{a} - \sqrt{b} = (p-q)D$ ...(iv)

$\sqrt{b} - \sqrt{c} = (q-r)D$ ...(v)

$\sqrt{c} - \sqrt{a} = (r-p)D$ ...(vi)

On dividing Eq. (iv) by Eq. (v), we get

$$\frac{\sqrt{a} - \sqrt{b}}{\sqrt{b} - \sqrt{c}} = \frac{p-q}{q-r} \qquad \text{...(vii)}$$

Since, p, q, r are natural numbers and a, b, c are positive prime numbers, so

Eq. (vii) does not hold.

So, $\sqrt{a}, \sqrt{b}$ and $\sqrt{c}$ cannot be the 3 terms of AP.

[not necessarily consecutive]

Similarly, we can show that $\sqrt{a}, \sqrt{b}, \sqrt{c}$ cannot be any 3 terms of GP and HP. [not necessarily, consecutive]

14. Given that n is an odd integer greater than or equal to 1.

$$S_n = n^3 - (n-1)^3 + (n-2)^3 - \ldots + (-1)^{n-1} 1^3$$

$$= 1^3 - 2^3 + \ldots + (n-2)^3 - (n-1)^3 + n^3$$

[$\because n$ is odd integer, so $(n-1)$ is even integer]

$$= (1^3 + 2^3 + \ldots + n^3) - 2 \cdot 2^3 \left(1^3 + 2^3 + \ldots + \frac{n-1}{2} \text{terms}\right)$$

$$= \left[\frac{n(n+1)}{2}\right]^2 - 16 \cdot \left[\frac{\frac{n-1}{2}\left(\frac{n-1}{2}+1\right)}{2}\right]^2$$

$$= \frac{n^2(n+1)^2}{4} - \frac{4(n-1)^2(n+1)^2}{16} = \frac{(n+1)^2}{4}[n^2 - (n-1)^2]$$

$$= \frac{(n-1)^2}{4} \cdot (2n-1)(1) = \frac{(2n-1)(n+1)^2}{4}$$

15. Let the sides of right angled triangle be $(a-d), a, (a+d)$ $(a > d)$.

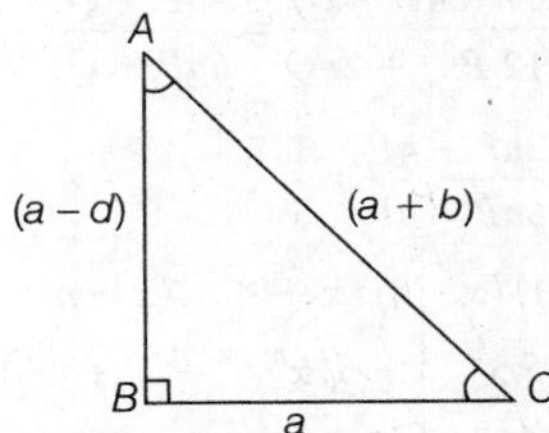

By Pythagoras theorem,

$$(a+d)^2 = a^2 + (a-d)^2$$

$$a^2 + d^2 + 2ad = a^2 + a^2 + d^2 - 2ad$$

$$a^2 = 4ad$$

$$a = 4d \qquad \text{[since } a \neq 0\text{] ...(i)}$$

According to the question, $\sin A = \frac{a}{a+d} = \frac{4d}{5d} = \frac{4}{5}$

$$\sin C = \frac{a-d}{a+d} = \frac{3d}{5d} = \frac{3}{5}$$

16. $T_6 = 2$

Let d be common difference of AP and a be the first term of AP.

$$T_6 = 2$$

$$\Rightarrow \quad a + 5d = 2 \qquad \text{...(i)}$$

Let $A = a_1 a_4 a_5$

$$A = a(a+3d)(a+4d)$$

[using $T_n = a + (n-1)d$ and from Eq. (i) $a = 2 - 5d$]

$$A = (2-5d)(2-2d)(2-d)$$

$$A = 8 - 32d + 34d^2 - 10d^3$$

For max and min values of A, $\frac{dA}{dd} = 0$

$$-30d^2 + 68d - 32 = 0 \Rightarrow 15d^2 - 34d + 16 = 0$$

$$15d^2 - (24d + 10d) + 16 = 0$$

$$15d^2 - 24d - 10d + 16 = 0$$

$$3d(5d-8) - 2(5d-8) = 0$$

$$(5d-8)(3d-2) = 0$$

$$d = \frac{8}{5} \text{ or } d = \frac{2}{3}$$

For $d = \frac{2}{3}$, $\frac{d^2A}{dd^2} > 0$

So, A is least for $d = \frac{2}{3}$.

17. Given, common difference $\neq 0$

$$S_{3n} = S_{4n} - S_{3n}$$

$$\Rightarrow \quad 2 \cdot S_{3n} = S_{4n} \quad [\text{ let } S_n = Pn^2 + Qn]$$

$$\Rightarrow 2 \cdot [P(3n)^2 + Q(3n)] = P(4n)^2 + Q(4n)$$

$$\Rightarrow \quad 2Pn^2 + 2Qn = 0$$

or

$$Q = -nP \quad \text{...(i)}$$

$$\therefore \quad \frac{S_{2n}}{S_{4n} - S_{2n}} = \frac{P(2n)^2 + Q(2n)}{[P(4n)^2 + Q(4n)] - [P(2n)^2 + Q(2n)]}$$

$$= \frac{2n(2nP + Q)}{12Pn^2 + 2nQ} = \frac{2nP + Q}{6nP + Q}$$

$$= \frac{2nP - nP}{6nP - nP} = \frac{1}{5} \quad [\text{from Eq. (i)}]$$

18. Let $f(x) = (x-1)(x-2)(x-3)\dots(x-n)$

$$= x^n - S_1 x^{n-1} + S_2 x^{n-2} - \dots + (-1)^n (1 \cdot 2 \cdot 3 \dots n)$$

So, coefficient of x^{n-2} in $f(x) = S_2 = (1 \cdot 2 + 1 \cdot 3 + \dots)$

= Sum of product of first n natural number taken 2 at time

$$= \frac{1}{2}[(1 + 2 + \dots + n)^2 - (1^2 + 2^2 + \dots + n^2)]$$

$$= \frac{1}{2}\left[\left\{\frac{n(n+1)}{2}\right\}^2 - \frac{n(n+1)(2n+1)}{6}\right]$$

$$= \frac{1}{2} \cdot \frac{n(n+1)}{2}\left[\frac{n(n+1)}{2} - \frac{2n+1}{3}\right]$$

$$= \frac{1}{2} \cdot \frac{n(n+1)}{2}\left[\frac{3n^2 + 3n - 4n - 2}{6}\right]$$

$$= \frac{n(n+1)(3n^2 - n - 2)}{24} = \frac{n(n+1)(3n+2)(n-1)}{24}$$

$$= \frac{n(n^2-1)(3n+2)}{24}$$

19. If last term of nth row is T_n, then

Let $\quad S = 1 + 5 + 11 + 19 + \dots + T_n$

$$S = \quad 1 + 5 + 11 + \dots + T_{n-1} + T_n$$

$$0 = 1 + 4 + 6 + 8 + \dots + n \text{ terms} - T_n$$

$$T_n = 1 + 2(2 + 3 + 4 + \dots + (n-1) \text{ terms})$$

$$= 1 + 2\frac{(n-1)}{2}[2 \cdot 2 + (n-2) \cdot 1]$$

$$= 1 + (n-1)(n+2)$$

$$= 1 + n^2 + n - 2$$

$$\Rightarrow \quad T_n = n^2 + n - 1$$

$$\therefore \quad T_{60} = (60)^2 + 60 - 1 = 3600 + 59 = 3659$$

20. Given that, $\displaystyle\sum_{r=1}^{100} a_{2r} = \alpha$

$$\Rightarrow \quad a_2 + a_4 + \dots + a_{200} = \alpha \quad \text{...(i)}$$

and $\displaystyle\sum_{r=1}^{100} a_{2r-1} = \beta$

$$\Rightarrow \quad a_1 + a_3 + \dots + a_{199} = \beta$$

On subtracting Eq. (ii) from Eq. (i), we get

$$(a_2 - a_1) + (a_4 - a_3) + \dots + (a_{200} - a_{199}) = \alpha - \beta$$

$$d + d + \dots \text{ up to 100 terms} = \alpha - \beta$$

[beacause a_n be the nth term of AP with common difference d]

$$100\,d = \alpha - \beta$$

$$d = \frac{\alpha - \beta}{100}$$

21. Given that, a_1, a_2, a_3, a_4, a_5 are in HP.

$\therefore \quad \dfrac{1}{a_1}, \dfrac{1}{a_2}, \dfrac{1}{a_3}, \dfrac{1}{a_4}, \dfrac{1}{a_5}$ are in AP.

$$\Rightarrow \quad \frac{1}{a_2} - \frac{1}{a_1} = \frac{1}{a_3} - \frac{1}{a_2} = \frac{1}{a_4} - \frac{1}{a_3} = \frac{1}{a_5} - \frac{1}{a_4} = d \quad [\text{say}]$$

$$\therefore \quad a_1 - a_2 = a_1 a_2 d \Rightarrow a_2 - a_3 = a_2 a_3 d$$

$$a_3 - a_4 = a_3 a_4 d \Rightarrow a_4 - a_5 = a_4 a_5 d$$

On adding all, we get

$$a_1a_2 + a_2a_3 + a_3a_4 + a_4a_5 = \frac{a_1 - a_5}{d} = a_1a_5\left(\frac{\frac{1}{a_5} - \frac{1}{a_1}}{d}\right) = 4\,a_1a_5$$

22. $\because (1+a)(1+b)(1+c)(1+d)$

$$= 1 + a + b + c + d + ab + ac + ad + bc + bd + cd + abc + abd + cda + cdb + abcd \quad [16 \text{ terms}]$$

$\therefore$ AM $\geq$ GM

$$\frac{(1+a)(1+b)(1+c)(1+d)}{16} \geq (a^8 b^8 c^8 d^8)^{1/16}$$

$$= (abcd)^{1/2} = (1)^{1/2} = 1 \quad [\because abcd = 1]$$

$$\Rightarrow \quad \frac{(1+a)(1+b)(1+c)(1+d)}{16} \geq 1$$

$$\Rightarrow \quad (1+a)(1+b)(1+c)(1+d) \geq 16$$

$\therefore$ Minimum value of $(1+a)(1+b)(1+c)(1+d)$ is 16.

23. $\because a, b, c$ are in AP.

$$\therefore \quad 2b = a + c \quad \text{...(i)}$$

Now, $\quad (a + 2b - c)(2b + c - a)(c + a - b)$

$$= (a + a + c - c)(a + c + c - a)(2b - b) \quad [\text{from Eq. (i)}]$$

$$= (2a)(2c)(b) = 4abc$$

$$\therefore \quad \lambda = 4$$

24. $a_1, a_2, \dots, a_n$ are in GP with first term a and common ratio r.

$$S_n = \underbrace{\frac{a_1 a_2}{a_1^2 - a_2^2} + \frac{a_2 a_3}{a_2^2 - a_3^2} + \dots + \frac{a_{n-1} a_n}{a_{n-1}^2 - a_n^2}}_{(n-1) \text{ times}} \quad \text{...(i)}$$

$$T_n = \frac{a_{n-1} a_n}{a_{n-1}^2 - a_n^2} = \frac{a_{n-1} a_n}{(a_{n-1} - a_n)(a_{n-1} + a_n)}$$

$$= \frac{1}{\left(1 - \frac{a_n}{a_{n-1}}\right)\left(1 + \frac{a_{n-1}}{a_n}\right)}$$

$$= \frac{1}{(1-r)\left(1 + \frac{1}{r}\right)} = \frac{r}{(r+1)(1-r)} \quad [\text{ by GP}]$$

$$\therefore \quad S_n = \sum_{n=2}^{n} T_n = \sum_{n=2}^{n} \frac{r}{(1-r^2)} = \frac{(n-1)r}{(1-r^2)}$$

25. According to the question, for AP

$$S_{10} = 4\,S_5$$

$$\frac{10}{2}(2a+9d) = 4\cdot\frac{5}{2}(2a+4d) \quad \left[\text{by } S_n = \frac{n}{2}[2a+(n-1)d]\right]$$

$$10a + 45d = 20a + 40d$$

$$\Rightarrow \quad 10a = 5d \Rightarrow \frac{a}{d} = \frac{1}{2}$$

26. $\because \cos(x-y), \cos x, \cos(x+y)$ are in HP.

$$\therefore \quad \cos x = \frac{2\cos(x-y)\cos(x+y)}{\cos(x-y)+\cos(x+y)}$$

$$\Rightarrow \quad \cos x = \frac{2(\cos^2 x - \sin^2 y)}{2\cos x \cos y}$$

$$\Rightarrow \cos^2 x \cos y = \cos^2 x - \sin^2 y$$

$$\Rightarrow \quad \cos^2 x(1-\cos y) = \sin^2 y$$

$$= (1+\cos y)(1-\cos y)$$

$$\Rightarrow \quad \cos^2 x = (1+\cos y) \quad [\because 1-\cos y \neq 0]$$

$$\Rightarrow \quad \cos^2 x = 2\cos^2 \frac{y}{2}$$

$$\Rightarrow \quad \cos^2 x \sec^2\left(\frac{y}{2}\right) = 2$$

$$\therefore \quad \cos x \sec\left(\frac{y}{2}\right) = \pm\sqrt{2}$$

27. Let 11 AM's are $A_1, A_2, A_3, \ldots, A_{11}$.

Given, 28, $A_1, A_2, A_3, \ldots, A_{11}$, 10 are in AP.

$$\therefore \quad d = \frac{10-28}{12} = -\frac{3}{2}$$

$$\therefore \quad A_i = 28 + id = 28 - \frac{3}{2}i$$

It is clear that $A_2, A_4, A_6, A_8, A_{10}$ are integral AM's.

Hence, number of integral AM's are 5.

28. $\because x, y, z$ are in GP $\quad [x, y, z > 1]$

$\therefore \ln x, \ln y, \ln z$ are in AP

and $2x, 4x, 6x$ are also in AP. $\quad [x > 1]$

By property,

$2x + \ln x, 4x + \ln y, 6x + \ln z$ are also in AP.

$\therefore \quad \dfrac{1}{2x+\ln x}, \dfrac{1}{4x+\ln y}, \dfrac{1}{6x+\ln z}$ are in HP.

29. Let $A = \dfrac{(a^2+3a+1)(b^2+3b+1)(c^2+3c+1)}{abc}$

$$= \left(\frac{a^2+3a+1}{a}\right)\left(\frac{b^2+3b+1}{b}\right)\left(\frac{c^2+3c+1}{c}\right)$$

$$= \left(a+3+\frac{1}{a}\right)\left(b+3+\frac{1}{b}\right)\left(c+3+\frac{1}{c}\right),$$

where $a, b, c \in R^+$.

Applying AM $\geq$ GM on a and $\dfrac{1}{a}$,

$$a + \frac{1}{a} \geq 2 \Rightarrow a + \frac{1}{b} + 3 \geq 5$$

Similarly, $\quad b + \dfrac{1}{b} \geq 2 \Rightarrow b + \dfrac{1}{b} + 3 \geq 5$

and $\quad c + \dfrac{1}{c} \geq 2 \Rightarrow c + \dfrac{1}{c} + 3 \geq 5$

$$\therefore \quad \left(a+\frac{1}{a}+3\right)\left(b+\frac{1}{b}+3\right)\left(c+\frac{1}{c}+3\right) \geq 125$$

So, $\quad A \geq 5\cdot5\cdot5 \Rightarrow A \geq 125$

Minimum value of A is 125.

30. $a_1, a_2, \ldots,$ are in AP and $q_1, q_2, \ldots$ are in GP.

$$a_1 = q_1 = 2 \text{ and } a_{10} = q_{10} = 3$$

Let d be the common diference of AP

i.e., $\quad d = \dfrac{3-2}{9} = \dfrac{1}{9}$

Then, $\quad a_7 = a_1 + 6d = 2 + 6d = 2 + 6 \times \dfrac{1}{9} = \dfrac{8}{3}$

$$a_{19} = a_1 + 18d = 2 + 18d$$

$$= 2 + 18 \times \frac{1}{9} = \frac{36}{9} = 4$$

Let r be the common ratio of GP i.e., $r = \left(\dfrac{3}{2}\right)^{1/9}$

Then, $\quad q_7 = q_1 r^6 = 2r^6$

$$= 2\cdot\left(\frac{3}{2}\right)^{6\times\frac{1}{9}} = 2\left(\frac{3}{2}\right)^{2/3}$$

$$q_{10} = q_1 r^9 = 2r^9 = 2\cdot\left(\frac{3}{2}\right)^{9\times\frac{1}{9}} = 3$$

$$q_{19} = q_1 \cdot r^{18} = 2\cdot r^{18}$$

$$= 2\cdot\left(\frac{3}{2}\right)^{18\times\frac{1}{9}} = 2\left(\frac{3}{2}\right)^{18/9} = \frac{9}{2}$$

(a) $a_7 q_{19} = \dfrac{8}{3} \times \dfrac{9}{2} = 12$, which is an integer.

(b) $a_{19} q_7 = 4 \times 2 \times \left(\dfrac{3}{2}\right)^{2/3} = 8\left(\dfrac{3}{2}\right)^{2/3}$,

which is not an integer.

(c) $a_7 q_{19} = \dfrac{8}{3} \times \dfrac{9}{2} = 12$; $a_{19} q_{10} = 4 \times 3 = 12$

31. $\because a(n) = 1 + \dfrac{1}{2} + \dfrac{1}{3} + \ldots + \dfrac{1}{2^n - 1}$

$$= 1 + \left(\frac{1}{2}+\frac{1}{3}\right) + \left(\frac{1}{4}+\frac{1}{5}+\frac{1}{6}+\frac{1}{7}\right) + \left(\frac{1}{8}+\ldots+\frac{1}{15}\right) + \ldots + \frac{1}{2^n-1}$$

$$= 1 + \left(\frac{1}{2}+\frac{1}{2^2-1}\right) + \left(\frac{1}{2^2}+\frac{1}{5}+\frac{1}{6}+\frac{1}{2^3-1}\right) + \ldots + \frac{1}{2^n-1}$$

$$\therefore \quad a(n) < 1 + 1 + \ldots + n \text{ terms}$$

$$\Rightarrow \quad a(n) < n$$

$$\Rightarrow \quad a(100) < 100$$

Also, $a(n) = 1 + \frac{1}{2} + \left(\frac{1}{3} + \frac{1}{4}\right) + \left(\frac{1}{5} + \frac{1}{6} + \frac{1}{7} + \frac{1}{8}\right) + \ldots + \frac{1}{2^n - 1}$

$$= 1 + \frac{1}{2} + \left(\frac{1}{2^1 + 1} + \frac{1}{2^2}\right) + \left(\frac{1}{2^2 + 1} + \frac{1}{6} + \frac{1}{7} + \frac{1}{2^3}\right) + \ldots + \left(\frac{1}{2^{n-1} + 1} + \ldots + \frac{1}{2^n}\right) - \frac{1}{2^n}$$

$$a(n) > 1 + \frac{1}{2} + \frac{2}{4} + \frac{4}{8} + \ldots + \frac{2^{n-1}}{2^n} - \frac{1}{2^n}$$

$$a(n) > \left(1 - \frac{1}{2^n}\right) + \frac{n}{2} \Rightarrow a(n) > \frac{n}{2}$$

$\therefore\ a(200) > 100$

32.

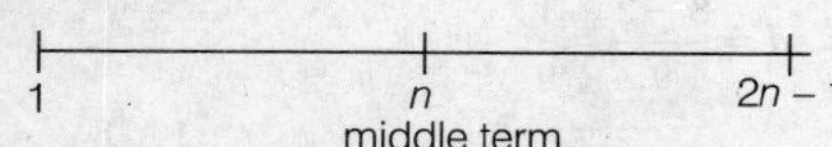

In a AP of $(2n - 1)$ terms, nth term $= a$
In a GP of $(2n - 1)$ terms, nth term $= b$
In a HP of $(2n - 1)$ terms, nth term $= c$
a, b, c will be arithmetic mean, geometric mean, harmonic mean, respectively.
So, $a \geq b \geq c$ and $b^2 = ac$

33. $\because 0 < \phi < \frac{\pi}{2}$

$\therefore$ $0 < \sin \phi < 1$ and $0 < \cos \phi < 1$

$\therefore$ $x = \sum_{n=0}^{\infty} \cos^{2n} \phi = 1 + \cos^2 \phi + \cos^4 \phi + \ldots + \infty$

$$= \frac{1}{1 - \cos^2 \phi} = \frac{1}{\sin^2 \phi}$$

or $\sin^2 \phi = \frac{1}{x}$ ...(i)

and $y = \sum_{n=0}^{\infty} \sin^{2n} \phi = 1 + \sin^2 \phi + \sin^4 \phi + \ldots + \infty$

$$= \frac{1}{1 - \sin^2 \phi} = \frac{1}{\cos^2 \phi}$$

or $\cos^2 \phi = \frac{1}{y}$ ...(ii)

From Eqs. (i) and (ii),

$$\sin^2 \phi + \cos^2 \phi = \frac{1}{x} + \frac{1}{y}$$

$$1 = \frac{1}{x} + \frac{1}{y}$$

$\therefore$ $xy = x + y$ ...(iii)

and $z = \sum_{n=0}^{\infty} \cos^{2n} \phi \sin^{2n} \phi$

$$= 1 + \cos^2 \phi \sin^2 \phi + \cos^4 \phi \sin^4 \phi + \ldots$$

$$= \frac{1}{1 - \sin^2 \phi \cos^2 \phi} = \frac{1}{1 - \frac{1}{xy}}$$ [from Eqs. (i) and (ii)]

$\Rightarrow$ $z = \frac{xy}{xy - 1}$

$\Rightarrow$ $xyz = z + xy$

and $xyz = z + x + y$ [from Eq. (iii)]

34. $\because a, b, c$ are in AP $\Rightarrow b = \frac{a + c}{2}$ ...(i)

and a^2, b^2, c^2 are in HP.

$\Rightarrow$ $b^2 = \frac{2a^2c^2}{a^2 + c^2}$ ...(ii)

$\Rightarrow$ $b^2 \{a^2 + c^2\} = 2a^2c^2$

$\Rightarrow$ $b^2 \{(a + c)^2 - 2ac\} = 2a^2c^2$ [from Eq. (i)]

$\Rightarrow$ $b^2 (4b^2 - 2ac) = 2a^2c^2$

$\Rightarrow$ $2b^4 - ac(b^2) - a^2c^2 = 0$

$\Rightarrow$ $(b^2 - ac)(2b^2 + ac) = 0$

If $b^2 - ac = 0$

a, b, c are in GP.
But given a, b, c are in AP.

$\therefore$ $a = b = c$

and if $2b^2 + ac = 0$

then $\frac{-a}{2}, b, c$ are in GP.

35. According to the question, x, $x^2 + 2$ and $x^3 + 10$ are in GP.

So, $(x^2 + 2)^2 = x(x^3 + 10)$

$\Rightarrow$ $x^4 + 4 + 4x^2 - x^4 - 10x = 0$

$\Rightarrow$ $4x^2 - 10x + 4 = 0$

$\Rightarrow$ $2x^2 - 5x + 2 = 0$

$\Rightarrow$ $2x^2 - 4x - x + 2 = 0$

$\Rightarrow$ $2x(x - 2) - 1(x - 2) = 0$

$\Rightarrow$ $(x - 2)(2x - 1) = 0$

$\Rightarrow$ $x = 2$ or $x = \frac{1}{2}$

For $x = 2$, first 3 terms are 2, 6, 18.
So, 4th term of GP $= 2 \cdot (3)^3 = 54$

For $x = \frac{1}{2}$, first 3 terms are $\frac{1}{2}, \frac{9}{4}, \frac{81}{8}$.

So, $T_4 = \frac{1}{2}\left(\frac{9}{2}\right)^3 = \frac{1}{2} \times \frac{729}{8} = \frac{729}{16}$

36. Let n consecutive odd numbers be

$$2k + 1, 2k + 3, 2k + 5, \ldots, 2k + 2n - 1$$

According to question, sum of these n numbers

$$= \frac{n}{2}[2k + 1 + 2k + 2n - 1] = n(2k + n)$$

$$= n^2 + 2kn = (n + k)^2 - k^2$$

Given that, $(n + k)^2 - k^2 = 25^2 - 11^2$

$\Rightarrow$ $n + k = 25$ and $k = 11$ $\Rightarrow$ $n = 14$ and $k = 11$

So, first term $= 2k + 1 = 23$
Last term $= 2k + 2n - 1 = 22 + 28 - 1 = 22 + 27 = 49$

37. $\because G = 6$ and $G^2 = AH$

$$\Rightarrow \quad H = \frac{36}{A}$$

Given, $90A + 5H = 918$

$$\Rightarrow \quad 90A + 5 \times \frac{36}{A} = 918 \Rightarrow 5A + \frac{10}{A} = 51$$

$$\Rightarrow \quad 5A^2 - 51A + 10 = 0 \Rightarrow (A - 10)(5A - 1) = 0$$

$$\therefore \quad A = 10, \frac{1}{5}$$

38. $\because$

$$T_n = \frac{1}{(2n-1)(2n+1)(2n+3)(2n+5)}$$

$$\therefore \quad S_n = \sum_{n=1}^{n} T_n a$$

$$S_n = \frac{1}{6}\sum_{n=1}^{n} \frac{(2n+5)-(2n-1)}{(2n-1)(2n+1)(2n+3)(2n+5)}$$

$$= \frac{1}{6}\sum_{n=1}^{n}\left(\frac{1}{(2n-1)(2n+1)(2n+3)} - \frac{1}{(2n+1)(2n+3)(2n+5)}\right)$$

$$= \frac{1}{6}\left(\frac{1}{1\cdot 3\cdot 5} - \frac{1}{(2n+1)(2n+3)(2n+5)}\right)$$

$$= \frac{1}{90} - \frac{\frac{1}{6}}{(2n+1)(2n+3)(2n+5)}$$

$$\therefore \quad \lambda = \frac{1}{6}$$

and $f(n) = (2n+1)(2n+3)(2n+5)$

$\therefore$ $f(0) = 15$

$f(1) = 105$

and $f(\lambda) = f\left(\frac{1}{6}\right) = \left(\frac{1}{3}+1\right)\left(\frac{1}{3}+3\right)\left(\frac{1}{3}+5\right) = \frac{640}{27}$

39. $\because S = 1 + \frac{1}{(1+3)}(1+2)^2 + \frac{1}{(1+3+5)}(1+2+3)^2 + \dots$

$$T_n = \frac{1}{(1+3+5+7+\dots n \text{ terms})}\cdot(1+2+3+4+\dots n \text{ terms})^2$$

$$= \frac{1}{\left[\frac{n}{2}[2\cdot 1 + (n-1)\cdot 2]\right]}\cdot\left(\frac{n(n+1)}{2}\right)^2 = \frac{(n+1)^2}{4}$$

(a) $T_7 = \frac{(7+1)^2}{4} = \frac{64}{4} = 16$

(b) $S_{10} = \sum_{n=1}^{10}\left(\frac{n+1}{2}\right)^2 = \frac{1}{4}\sum_{n=1}^{10}(n^2 + 2n + 1)$

$$= \frac{1}{4}\left(\sum_{n=1}^{10} n^2 + 2\sum_{n=1}^{10} n + \sum_{n=1}^{10} 1\right)$$

$$= \frac{1}{4}\left(\frac{10\times 11\times 21}{6} + \frac{2\times 10\times 11}{2} + 10\right)$$

$$= \frac{1}{4}(385 + 110 + 10) = \frac{505}{4}$$

40.

$$E = \frac{1}{1^2} + \frac{1}{2^2} + \frac{1}{3^2} + \dots$$

$$E < 1 + \frac{1}{(1)(2)} + \frac{1}{(2)(3)} + \dots$$

$$E < 1 + \left(1 - \frac{1}{2}\right) + \left(\frac{1}{2} - \frac{1}{3}\right) + \dots$$

$$E < 2 \quad \dots\text{(i)}$$

$$E > 1 + \frac{1}{(2)(3)} + \frac{1}{(3)(4)} + \dots$$

$$E > 1 + \left(\frac{1}{2} - \frac{1}{3}\right) + \left(\frac{1}{3} - \frac{1}{4}\right) + \dots$$

$$E > 1 + \frac{1}{2};\ E > \frac{3}{2}$$

41. $\because S_1 = \{0\}$

$$S_2 = \left\{\frac{3}{2}, \frac{5}{2}\right\}$$

$$S_3 = \left\{\frac{8}{3}, \frac{11}{3}, \frac{14}{3}\right\}$$

$$S_4 = \left\{\frac{15}{4}, \frac{19}{4}, \frac{23}{4}, \frac{27}{4}\right\}$$

$\vdots \quad \vdots \quad \vdots$

Let $S = 3 + 8 + 15 + \dots + T_{19}$

$S = \quad 3 + 8 + \dots + T_{18} + T_{19}$

$0 = 3 + 5 + 7 + \dots + 19 \text{ terms} - T_{19}$

$T_{19} = 3 + 5 + 7 + \dots + 19 \text{ terms}$

$$\therefore \quad T_{19} = \frac{19}{2}(6 + 18\times 2) = \frac{19}{2}\times 42 = 399$$

$$S_{20} = \left\{\frac{399}{20}, \frac{419}{20}, \frac{439}{20}, \dots\right\}$$

$\therefore$ Third element of $S_{20} = \frac{439}{20}$

Sum of elements of $S_{20} = \frac{20}{2}\times\frac{1}{2}[2\times 399 + 19\times 20]$

$= 399 + 190 = 589$

42. (a) $\because S = \left(1 + \frac{1}{n}\right)^n$

$$S = 1 + {}^nC_1\left(\frac{1}{n}\right) + {}^nC_2\left(\frac{1}{n}\right)^2 + {}^nC_3\left(\frac{1}{n}\right)^3 + \dots + {}^nC_n\left(\frac{1}{n}\right)^n$$

$$S = 1 + n\cdot\frac{1}{n} + \frac{n(n-1)}{2!}\left(\frac{1}{n^2}\right) + \frac{n(n-1)(n-2)}{3!}\left(\frac{1}{n^3}\right) + \dots + \frac{n(n-1)\dots 1}{n!}\left(\frac{1}{n^n}\right)$$

$$S = 1 + 1 + \frac{1}{2!}\left(1 - \frac{1}{n}\right) + \frac{1}{3!}\left(1 - \frac{1}{n}\right)\left(1 - \frac{2}{n}\right) + \dots + \frac{1}{n!}\left(1 - \frac{1}{n}\right)\left(1 - \frac{2}{n}\right)\dots\left(1 - \frac{n-1}{n}\right)$$

$$S < 1 + 1 + \frac{1}{2!} + \frac{1}{3!} + \dots + \frac{1}{n!}$$

$$S < 1 + 1 + \frac{1}{1\cdot 2} + \frac{1}{1\cdot 2\cdot 3} + \ldots + \frac{1}{1\cdot 2\cdot 3\ldots n}$$

$$S < 1 + 1 + \frac{1}{2} + \frac{1}{2\cdot 2} + \ldots + \frac{1}{2\cdot 2\ldots 2}$$

$$S < 1 + \frac{1 - \frac{1}{2^n}}{1 - \frac{1}{2}} \Rightarrow S < 1 + 2\left(1 - \frac{1}{2^n}\right)$$

$$S < 3 - \frac{1}{2^{n-1}} \quad \therefore S < 3, \forall\, n$$

Also, $S = 1 + 1 + \frac{1}{2!}\left(1 - \frac{1}{n}\right) + \frac{1}{3!}\left(1 - \frac{1}{n}\right)\left(1 - \frac{2}{n}\right) + \ldots$

$$+ \frac{1}{n!}\left(1 - \frac{1}{n}\right)\left(1 - \frac{2}{n}\right)\ldots\left(1 - \frac{n-1}{n}\right)$$

$S > 1 + 1;\ S > 2$

$\therefore$ S is bounded.

(b) $\because \quad a_n = \frac{2n+1}{n+2}$

For $n_1 = 1$, $a_1 = \frac{3}{3} = 1$,

for $n = 2$, $a_2 = \frac{5}{4} = 1.25$

$\vdots \quad \vdots \quad \vdots$

Now, $a_{n+1} - a_n > 0 \Rightarrow a_{n+1} > a_n$

$\therefore$ a_n represents the increasing sequence

$$\lim_{n\to\infty} a_n = \lim_{n\to\infty} \frac{2n+1}{n+2} = \lim_{n\to\infty} \frac{n\left(2 + \frac{1}{n}\right)}{n\left(1 + \frac{2}{n}\right)} = \frac{2}{1} = 2$$

$\therefore$ $\{a_n\}$ is bounded sequence.

(c) $\because \quad a_n = \left(1 + \frac{1}{n}\right)^{n^2}$

For $n = 1$, $a_1 = 2$,

for $n = 2$, $a_2 = \left(1 + \frac{1}{2}\right)^4 = \left(\frac{3}{2}\right)^4 = \frac{3^4}{2^4} = \frac{81}{16} = 5.06$

[approximate]

$$\lim_{n\to\infty}\left(1 + \frac{1}{n}\right)^{n^2} = e^{\lim_{n\to\infty}\frac{1}{n}\times n^2} = e^{\lim_{n\to\infty} n} = e^{\infty} = \infty$$

$\therefore$ $\{a_n\}$ represents unbounded sequence.

(d) $\because a_n = \tan n$

$$a_n = n + \frac{n^3}{3} + \frac{2}{15}n^5 + \ldots + \infty$$

and we know that $-\infty < \tan n < \infty$

So, $\{a_n\}$ is unbounded sequence.

43. $\because \quad a_n = \frac{1}{n+1} + \frac{1}{n+2} + \frac{1}{n+3} + \ldots + \frac{1}{3n}$

$$a_n = \frac{1}{n+1} + \frac{1}{n+2} + \frac{1}{n+3} + \ldots + \frac{1}{n+2n}$$

$$a_n = \sum_{\alpha=1}^{2n} \frac{1}{n+\alpha}$$

$$a_2 = \sum_{\alpha=1}^{4} \frac{1}{2+\alpha} = \frac{1}{3} + \frac{1}{4} + \frac{1}{5} + \frac{1}{6} = \frac{20+15+12+10}{60}$$

$$= \frac{57}{60} = \frac{19}{20}$$

Now, $a_{n+1} - a_n = \left(\frac{1}{n+2} + \frac{1}{n+3} + \ldots + \frac{1}{3n+3}\right)$

$$- \left(\frac{1}{n+1} + \frac{1}{n+2} + \ldots + \frac{1}{3n}\right)$$

$$= \frac{1}{3n+1} + \frac{1}{3n+2} + \frac{1}{3n+3} - \frac{1}{n+1}$$

$$= \frac{1}{3n+1} + \frac{1}{3n+2} - \frac{2}{3(n+1)}$$

$$= \frac{9n^2 + 15n + 6 + 9n^2 + 12n + 3 - 18n^2 - 18n - 4}{(3n+1)(3n+2)(3n+3)}$$

$$= \frac{9n+5}{(3n+1)(3n+2)(3n+3)}$$

44. $S_n(x) = \left(x^{n-1} + \frac{1}{x^{n-1}}\right) + 2\left(x^{n-2} + \frac{1}{x^{n-2}}\right)$

$$+ \ldots + (n-1)\left(x + \frac{1}{x}\right) + n$$

Let $S' = x^{n-1} + 2x^{n-2} + 3x^{n-3} + \ldots + (n-1)x$

$$\frac{S'}{x} = x^{n-2} + 2x^{n-3} + \ldots + (n-2)x + (n-1)$$

$$-\quad -\quad -\quad -\quad -\quad -$$

$$S'\left(1 - \frac{1}{x}\right) = x^{n-1} + x^{n-2} + x^{n-3} + \ldots + x - (n-1)$$

$$S'\frac{(x-1)}{x} = \frac{x\cdot(x^{n-1} - 1)}{(x-1)} - (n-1)$$

$$\Rightarrow \quad S' = \frac{x^2}{(x-1)^2}(x^{n-1} - 1) - \frac{(n-1)x}{(x-1)}$$

$$S'' = \frac{1}{x^{n-1}} + \frac{2}{x^{n-2}} + \ldots + \frac{(n-1)}{x}$$

$$\Rightarrow \quad S'' = \frac{1}{x^n}[x + 2x^2 + \ldots + (n-1)x^{n-1}]$$

$$= \frac{1}{x^n}\frac{[(n-1)x^n - nx^{n-1} + 1]}{(x-1)^2} \quad \text{[similarly as above]}$$

$\therefore \quad S_n(x) = S' + S'' + n$

$$\Rightarrow \quad S_n(x) = \frac{1}{x^{(n-1)}}\left(\frac{x^n - 1}{x - 1}\right)^2 \quad \ldots\text{(i)}$$

For $\quad n = 1$, $S_1(x) = 1$

$$S_{100}(x) = \frac{1}{x^{99}}\left(\frac{x^{100} - 1}{x - 1}\right)^2$$

45. Let the AP start with n and common difference d, then according to question,

$$n + 5d = 32$$

$$n = 32 - 5d \quad \ldots\text{(i)}$$

and $1072 < n + (n + d) + \ldots + (n + 19d) < 1162$

$$1072 < 20n + \frac{19 \times 20}{2} d < 1162$$

$$1072 < 640 - 100d + 190d < 1162$$

$$432 < 90d < 522$$

$$4.8 < d < 5.8$$

Let d is natural number, so $d = 5$

$\therefore \quad n = 32 - 5 \times 5 = 7$

First term is 7 and common difference is 5.

Sol. (Q. Nos. 46 to 48)

Let $S_n = \frac{8}{5} + \frac{16}{65} + \frac{24}{325} + \dots$

$$T_r = \frac{8r}{4r^4 + 1} = \frac{8r}{(2r^2 + 2r + 1)(2r^2 - 2r + 1)}$$

$$= 2\left[\frac{(2r^2 + 2r + 1) - (2r^2 - 2r + 1)}{(2r^2 + 2r + 1)(2r^2 - 2r + 1)}\right]$$

$$= 2\left[\frac{1}{2r^2 - 2r + 1} - \frac{1}{2r^2 + 2r + 1}\right]$$

46. $\lim_{n \to \infty} S_n = \lim_{n \to \infty} \sum_{r=1}^{n} T_r$

$$= \lim_{n \to \infty} \sum_{r=1}^{n} 2\left(\frac{1}{2r^2 - 2r + 1} - \frac{1}{2r^2 + 2r + 1}\right)$$

$$= 2 \lim_{n \to \infty} \left(1 - \frac{1}{2n^2 + 2n + 1}\right) = 2(1 - 0) = 2$$

47. $T_7 = \frac{8 \times 7}{4 \times 7^4 + 1} = \frac{56}{9605}$

48. $S_8 = \sum_{r=1}^{8} T_r = 2 \sum_{r=1}^{8} \left(\frac{1}{2r^2 - 2r + 1} - \frac{1}{2r^2 + 2r + 1}\right)$

$$= 2\left(1 - \frac{1}{2(8)^2 + 2(8) + 1}\right) = 2\left(1 - \frac{1}{145}\right) = \frac{288}{145}$$

Sol. (Q. Nos. 4-6)

Let p and $(p + 1)$ be removed numbers from 1, 2, 3, ... n, then

Sum of the remaining numbers

$$= \frac{n(n + 1)}{2} - (2p + 1)$$

From given condition,

$$\frac{105}{4} = \frac{\frac{n(n+1)}{2} - (2p + 1)}{(n - 2)}$$

$\Rightarrow \quad 2n^2 - 103n - 8p + 206 = 0$

Since, n and p are integers, so n must be even.

Let $n = 2r$, we get

$$p = \frac{4r^2 + 103(1 - r)}{4}$$

Since, p is an integer, then $(1 - r)$ must be divisible by 4.

Let $r = 1 + 4t$, we get

$$n = 2 + 8t \text{ and } p = 16t^2 - 95t + 1$$

Now, $\quad 1 \le p < n$

$\Rightarrow \quad 1 \le 16t^2 - 95t + 1 < 8t + 2$

$\Rightarrow \quad t = 6 \Rightarrow n = 50$ and $p = 7$

49. Hence, the value of n lies in $(41, 51)$.

50. Hence, removed numbers are 7 and 8.

51. Sum of all numbers $= \frac{50(50 + 1)}{2} = 1275$

Sol. (Q. Nos. 52 to 54)

Let $A = \{A - D, A, A + D\}$; $\quad B = \{a - d, a, a + d\}$

According to the question,

$$A - D + A + A + D = 15$$

$\Rightarrow \quad 3A = 15$

$\Rightarrow \quad A = 5 \quad \text{...(i)}$

and $\quad a - d + a + a + d = 15$

$\Rightarrow \quad a = 5 \quad \text{...(ii)}$

and $\quad D = 1 + d \quad \text{...(iii)}$

$$p = (A - D) A (A + D)$$

$$p = A(A^2 - D^2) \quad \text{...(iv)}$$

$$p = 5(25 - D^2) \quad \text{...(v)}$$

Similarly, $\quad q = 5(25 - d^2)$

Given that, $\quad p = 7(q - p)$

$$8p = 7q$$

From Eqs. (iv) and (v), we get

$$8 \times 5(25 - D^2) = 7 \times 5(25 - d^2)$$

$$200 - 8D^2 = 175 - 7d^2$$

$$25 = 8D^2 - 7d^2$$

$$25 = 8(1 + d)^2 - 7d^2 \quad \text{[from Eq. (iii)]}$$

$$25 = 8 + 8d^2 + 16d - 7d^2$$

$$17 - d^2 - 16d = 0$$

$$d^2 + 16d - 17 = 0$$

$$(d + 17)(d - 1) = 0$$

$$d = -17 \text{ or } d = 1$$

$\Rightarrow \quad d = 1 \quad [\because d > 0]$

$\Rightarrow \quad D = 2$

52. $p = 5(25 - D^2) = 5(25 - 4) = 5(21) = 105$

53. $q = 5(25 - d^2) = 5(25 - 1) = 120$

54. $7D + 8d = 14 + 8 = 22$

Sol. (Q. Nos. 55 to 57)

Let $\quad A = \left\{\frac{A}{R}, A, AR\right\}$

$$B = \left\{\frac{a}{r}, a, ar\right\}$$

According to the question, $\frac{A}{R} \cdot A \cdot AR = 64$

$\Rightarrow \quad A^3 = 64 \Rightarrow A = 4 \quad \text{...(i)}$

$$\frac{a}{r} \cdot a \cdot ar = 64 \Rightarrow a^3 = 64 \Rightarrow a = 4 \quad \text{...(ii)}$$

and $\quad R = r + 2 \quad \text{...(iii)}$

$$p = \frac{A}{R} \cdot A + A \cdot AR + AR \cdot \frac{A}{R}$$

$$= \frac{A^2}{R} + A^2 R + A^2 = \frac{16}{R} + 16R + 16$$

$$q = \frac{a}{r} \cdot a + a \cdot ar + ar \cdot \frac{a}{r}$$

$$= \frac{a^2}{r} + a^2 r + a^2 = \frac{16}{r} + 16r + 16$$

Given that, $\frac{p}{q} = \frac{3}{2}$

So, $\frac{(16 + 16R^2 + 16R)\, r}{(16 + 16r^2 + 16r)\, R} = \frac{3}{2}$

$$\frac{(1 + R^2 + R)\, r}{(1 + r^2 + r)\, R} = \frac{3}{2}$$

From Eq. (iii), $R = r + 2$

$$\Rightarrow \frac{(1 + r^2 + 4 + 4r + r + 2)\, r}{(1 + r + r^2)(r + 2)} = \frac{3}{2}$$

$$\Rightarrow \frac{r^3 + 5r^2 + 7r}{r^3 + 3r^2 + 3r + 2} = \frac{3}{2}$$

$$\Rightarrow r^3 - r^2 - 5r + 6 = 0$$

$$\Rightarrow (r - 2)(r^2 + r - 3) = 0$$

$$\Rightarrow r = 2 \text{ or } r = \frac{-1 \pm \sqrt{13}}{2}$$

So, $R = 4$

55. $p = 16\left(\frac{1}{R} + R + 1\right) = 16\left(\frac{1}{4} + 4 + 1\right) = \frac{16}{4}(21) = 84$

56. $q = 16\left(\frac{1}{r} + r + 1\right) = 16\left(\frac{1}{2} + 2 + 1\right) = \frac{16}{2} \times 7 = 8 \times 7 = 56$

57. $r^R + R^r = (4)^2 + (2)^4 = 16 + 16 = 32$

Sol. (Q. Nos. 58 to 60)

Given sequence, 1, 3, 6, 10, 15, 21, 28, ...

where $t_n = t_{n-1} + n, \forall\, n \ge 2$

So, $t_n = [t_{n-2} + (n - 1)] + n$

$$= t_{n-3} + (n - 2) + (n - 1) + n$$

$$\vdots \qquad \vdots \qquad \vdots$$

$$t_n = t_1 + 2 + 3 + \ldots + (n - 1) + n$$

$$t_n = 1 + 2 + 3 + \ldots + n$$

$$t_n = \frac{n(n+1)}{2} \qquad \ldots(\text{i})$$

58. $t_{50} = \frac{50 \times 51}{2} = 25 \times 51 = 1275$

59. $t_{100} = \frac{100 \times 101}{2} = 5050$

$t_{101} = \frac{101 \times 102}{2} = 101 \times 51 = 5151$

Number of positive integers lying between t_{100} and t_{101}

$$= 5151 - 5050 - 1$$

$$= 101 - 1 = 100$$

60. According to the question, $(m + 1)$ is the nth triangular number, then

$$\frac{n(n+1)}{2} = m + 1$$

$$n^2 + n - 2(m + 1) = 0$$

$$n = \frac{-1 \pm \sqrt{1 + 8(m + 1)}}{2}$$

$$= \frac{-1 + \sqrt{(8m + 9)}}{2}$$

$$\therefore \quad n - m = \frac{-1 + \sqrt{8m + 9} - 2m}{2}$$

Sol. (Q. Nos. 61 to 63)

$A_1, A_2, A_3, \ldots, A_m$ are arithmetic means between -3 and 828.

So, $A_1 + A_2 + \ldots + A_m = m\frac{(a + b)}{2}$

$$\Rightarrow A_1 + A_2 + \ldots + A_m = m\left(\frac{-3 + 288}{2}\right)$$

$$\Rightarrow 14025 = m\left(\frac{825}{2}\right)$$

[given that sum of AM's = 14025]

$$\Rightarrow m = 17 \times 2$$

$$\therefore \quad m = 34 \qquad \ldots(\text{i})$$

Now, $G_1, G_2, \ldots, G_n$ be the GM's between 1 and 2187.

$$\therefore \quad G_1 G_2 G_3 \ldots G_n = (ab)^{n/2}$$

$$\Rightarrow 3^{35} = (1 \times 2187)^{n/2} \Rightarrow 3^{35} = 3^{7n/2}$$

So, $35 = \frac{7n}{2}$

$$\Rightarrow n = 10 \qquad \ldots(\text{ii})$$

61. $n = 10$ [by Eq. (ii)]

62. $m = 34$ [by Eq. (i)]

63. $G_1 + G_2 + \ldots + G_n = r + r^2 + r^3 + \ldots + r^n$

$$= r + r^2 + r^3 + \ldots + r^{10} = r\,\frac{(1 - r^{10})}{1 - r}$$

$$\left[\because r = \left(\frac{l}{a}\right)^{1/n+1} = \left(\frac{2187}{1}\right)^{1/11} = 3^{7/11}\right]$$

$$= 3^{7/11}\,\frac{(1 - 3^{70/11})}{(1 - 3^{7/11})}$$

Solution (Q. Nos. 64 to 66)

$$\because \quad \alpha + \beta = -\frac{b}{a},\ \alpha\beta = \frac{c}{a},\ \alpha - \beta = \frac{\sqrt{b^2 - 4ac}}{a}$$

and $\gamma + \delta = -\frac{B}{A},\ \gamma\delta = \frac{C}{A},\ \gamma - \delta = \frac{\sqrt{B^2 - 4AC}}{A}$

64. Since, α, β, γ are in AP.

Let $\beta = \alpha + D, \gamma = \alpha + 2D$ and $\delta = \alpha + 3D$

$$\because \quad \alpha + \beta = \frac{-b}{a} \Rightarrow \alpha + \alpha + D = -\frac{b}{a}$$

or $2\alpha + D = -\frac{b}{a} \qquad \ldots(\text{i})$

and $\gamma+\delta=-\frac{B}{A}\Rightarrow 2\alpha+5D=-\frac{B}{A}$ ...(ii)

From Eqs. (i) and (ii), we get

$$4D=\left(-\frac{B}{A}+\frac{b}{a}\right) \text{ or } D=\frac{1}{4}\left(\frac{b}{a}-\frac{B}{A}\right)$$

65. Since, $\alpha, \beta, \gamma, \delta, \ldots$ are in GP.

$\therefore \quad \frac{\beta}{\alpha}=\frac{\gamma}{\beta}=\frac{\delta}{\gamma}$

$\Rightarrow \quad \frac{\beta}{\alpha}=\frac{\delta}{\gamma}\Rightarrow\frac{\alpha}{\gamma}=\frac{\beta}{\delta}$

$\Rightarrow \quad \frac{\alpha+\beta}{\gamma+\delta}=\sqrt{\frac{\alpha\beta}{\gamma\delta}}$

$\Rightarrow \quad \frac{-\frac{b}{a}}{-\frac{B}{A}}=\sqrt{\frac{\frac{c}{a}}{\frac{C}{A}}}\Rightarrow\frac{b^2A^2}{a^2B^2}=\frac{cA}{aC}$

$\Rightarrow \quad \frac{ac\,A^2}{aB^2}=\frac{cA}{C}\Rightarrow B^2=AC$

Hence, A, B, C are in GP.

66. Since, $\alpha, \beta, \gamma, \delta, \ldots$ are in GP.

$\therefore \quad r=\frac{\beta}{\alpha}=\frac{\gamma}{\beta}=\frac{\delta}{\gamma}$

$\Rightarrow \quad \alpha+\beta=\alpha+\alpha r=-\frac{b}{a}$

$\Rightarrow \quad \alpha(1+r)=-\frac{b}{a}$ ...(i)

and $\quad \gamma+\delta=\alpha r^2+\alpha r^3=-\frac{B}{A}$

$\Rightarrow \quad \alpha r^2(1+r)=-\frac{B}{A}$ ...(ii)

From Eqs. (i) and (ii), we get

$$r^2=\frac{Ba}{bA}$$

$\therefore \quad r=\sqrt{\frac{aB}{bA}}$

Sol. (Q. Nos. 67 to 69)

For $n>1$, we have $n+1>n-1$

$\Rightarrow \quad \frac{n+1}{n-1}>1\Rightarrow p\left(\frac{n+1}{n-1}\right)^2>p \quad [\because p>0]$ ...(i)

Now, $\quad p=a+d$

Since, a, p, b, are in AP.

And $\quad d=\frac{b-a}{n+1}$

67. $$p=a+\frac{(b-a)}{n+1}=\frac{na+b}{n+1}$$

68. $$\frac{1}{q}=\frac{1}{a}+D=\frac{1}{a}+\frac{\frac{1}{b}-\frac{1}{a}}{n+1}$$

$\Rightarrow \quad q=\frac{ab(n+1)}{a+bn}$

69. Again, $\quad \frac{p}{q}=\left(\frac{an+b}{n+1}\right)\times\left[\frac{a+bn}{ab(n+1)}\right]$

$$=\frac{a^2n+abn^2+b^2n+ab}{ab(n+1)^2}$$

$$=\frac{n\left(\frac{a}{b}+\frac{b}{a}\right)+(n^2+1)}{(n+1)^2}$$

$\Rightarrow \quad \frac{p}{q}-1=\frac{n\left(\frac{a}{b}+\frac{b}{a}-2\right)}{(n+1)^2}=\frac{n\left(\frac{\sqrt{a}}{\sqrt{b}}-\frac{\sqrt{b}}{\sqrt{a}}\right)^2}{(n+1)^2}$

So, $\quad \frac{p}{q}-1>0\Rightarrow\frac{p}{q}>1\Rightarrow p>q$ ...(iii)

From Eqs. (i) and (ii), we get

$$q<p<\left(\frac{n+1}{n-1}\right)^2 p$$

70. a, b, c, d are positive real numbers with

$$a<b<c<d \quad \text{...(A)}$$

According to the question, a, b, c, d are in AP.

$\Rightarrow b=a+\alpha, c=a+2\alpha$ and $d=a+3\alpha$ ...(i)

α be the common difference

and a, b, d are in GP.

$\Rightarrow \quad b^2=ad$ ...(ii)

From Eqs. (i) and (ii), we get

$$(a+\alpha)^2=a(a+3\alpha)$$

$\Rightarrow \quad a^2+\alpha^2+2a\alpha=a^2+3a\alpha$

$\Rightarrow \quad \alpha^2=a\alpha$

$\Rightarrow \quad a(\alpha-a)=0$

$\Rightarrow \quad \alpha=0$ or $\alpha=a$

$a\neq 0$ by (A), so $\alpha=a$

From Eq. (i), $b=2a, c=3a$ and $d=4a$

$$\frac{ad}{bc}=\frac{a\cdot 4a}{2a\cdot 3a}=\frac{2}{3}=\left(\frac{p}{q}\right)$$

where, p and q are prime numbers.

So, $\quad q=3$

71. $\because \sum_{r=1}^{110}(1+rx)=(1+x)(1+2x)(1+3x)\ldots(1+110x)$

$$=1^{110}+(x+2x+3x+\ldots+110x)1^{109}+\ldots$$

So, coefficient of x in

$$\sum_{r=1}^{110}(1+rx)=(1+2+3+\ldots+110)=\frac{110\times 111}{2}=55\times 111$$

$$=6105$$

Now, $\lambda(1+10)(1+10+10^2)=\lambda(11)(111)$

$\Rightarrow \quad \lambda(111)(11)=6105\Rightarrow\lambda=5$

72. Let number of the form palindrome be $\alpha\beta\alpha$.

Now, If $\alpha\beta\alpha$ is even, then α may be 2, 4, 6, 8 and β take values 0, 1, 2, ..., 9 .

So, total number of palindrome (even) $=10\times 4=40$

To find the sum of all even 3 digit plaindrome

So, sum of number start with 2

$= (200 + 2) \times 10 + (0 + 1 + 2 + 3 + \dots + 9) \times 10$

$= 2020 + 450 = 2470$

Sum of number start with 4 $= (404) \times 10 + 450$

Similarly, sum of number start with 6 $= (606) \times 10 + 450$

Similarly, sum of number start with 8 $= (808) \times 10 + 450$

$\therefore$ Total sum $= (202 + 404 + 606 + 808) \times 10 + 450 \times 4$

$= 20200 + 1800 = 22000$

$= 2^4 \times 5^3 \times 11$

On comparing $2^4 \times 5^3 \times 11^1$ with

$$2^{n_1} \times 3^{n_2} \times 5^{n_3} \times 7^{n_4} \times 11^{n_5},$$

$$n_1 = 4, n_2 = 3, n_3 = 0, n_4 = 0, n_5 = 1$$

Now, $n_1 + n_2 + n_3 + n_4 + n_5 = 8$

73. $\because 2 + (6\cdot 2^2 - 4\cdot 2) + (6\cdot 3^2 - 4\cdot 3) + \dots + (6\cdot n^2 - 4\cdot n) = 140$

$\Rightarrow 2 + 6(2^2 + 3^2 + \dots + n^2) - 4\cdot(2 + 3 + \dots + n) = 140$

$\Rightarrow 2 + 6\left(\dfrac{n(n+1)(2n-1)}{6} - 1\right) - 4\left(\dfrac{n(n+1)}{2} - 1\right) = 140$

$\Rightarrow 2 + n(n+1)(2n+1) - 6 - 2n(n+1) + 4 = 140$

$\Rightarrow n(n+1)(2n+1) - 2n(n+1) - 140 = 0$

$\Rightarrow 2n^3 + 3n^2 + n - 2n^2 - 2n - 140 = 0$

$\Rightarrow 2n^3 + n^2 - n - 140 = 0$

$\Rightarrow (n-4)(2n^2 + 9n + 35) = 0$

$\Rightarrow n = 4$ or $2n^2 + 9n + 35 = 0$

$\Rightarrow 2n^2 + 9n + 35 = 0$

$\Rightarrow n = \dfrac{-9 \pm \sqrt{81 - 280}}{4}$

$\therefore n = \dfrac{9 \pm \sqrt{-199}}{4}$ [complex values]

Only positive integer value of n is 4.

74. $S(x) = 1 + x - x^2 - x^3 + x^4 + x^5 - x^6 - x^7 + \dots + \infty$

where $x \in (0, 1)$

$S(x) = (1 + x) - x^2(1 + x) + x^4(1 + x) - x^6(1 + x) + \dots + \infty$

$\Rightarrow S(x) = (1 + x)[1 - x^2 + x^4 - x^6 + \dots + \infty]$

$\Rightarrow S(x) = (1 + x)\left(\dfrac{1}{1 + x^2}\right)$ $\left[\because S_\infty = \dfrac{a}{1 - r} \text{ for GP}\right]$

According to the question, $S(x) = \dfrac{\sqrt{2} + 1}{2}$

So, $\dfrac{1 + x}{1 + x^2} = \dfrac{\sqrt{2} + 1}{2}$

$\Rightarrow 2 + 2x = (\sqrt{2} + 1)x^2 + \sqrt{2} + 1$

$\Rightarrow (\sqrt{2} + 1)x^2 - 2x - 2 + \sqrt{2} + 1 = 0$

$\Rightarrow (\sqrt{2} + 1)x^2 - 2x + \sqrt{2} - 1 = 0$

$\Rightarrow (\sqrt{2} + 1)x^2 - 2x + \dfrac{1}{\sqrt{2} + 1} = 0$

$\Rightarrow [(\sqrt{2} + 1)x]^2 - 2(\sqrt{2} + 1)x + 1 = 0$

$\Rightarrow [(\sqrt{2} + 1)x - 1]^2 = 0$

$\Rightarrow x = \dfrac{1}{\sqrt{2} + 1}$ [repeated]

So, $x = \sqrt{2} - 1$

$\therefore (x + 1)^2 = 2$

75. $a_1, a_2, a_3, \dots$ are in GP with common ratio r

and $b_1, b_2, b_3, \dots$ is also a GP i.e. $b_1 = 1$

$b_2 = \sqrt[4]{7} - \sqrt[4]{28} + 1, a_1 = \sqrt[4]{28}$

and $\displaystyle\sum_{n=1}^{\infty} \frac{1}{a_n} = \sum_{n=1}^{\infty} b_n$

$\dfrac{1}{a_1} + \dfrac{1}{a_2} + \dfrac{1}{a_3} + \dots + \infty = b_1 + b_2 + b_3 + \dots + \infty$

$\Rightarrow \dfrac{1}{\sqrt[4]{28}} + \dfrac{1}{\sqrt[4]{28}\, r} + \dfrac{1}{\sqrt[4]{28}\, r^2} + \dots + \infty$

$= 1 + (\sqrt[4]{7} - \sqrt[4]{28} + 1) + (\sqrt[4]{7} - \sqrt[4]{28} + 1)^2 + \dots + \infty$

$\Rightarrow \dfrac{\frac{1}{\sqrt[4]{28}}}{1 - \frac{1}{r}} = \dfrac{1}{1 - \sqrt[4]{7} + \sqrt[4]{28} - 1}$

$\Rightarrow \dfrac{r}{(r-1)\sqrt[4]{28}} = \dfrac{1}{\sqrt[4]{7}(\sqrt[4]{4} - 1)}$

$\Rightarrow \dfrac{r}{(r-1)} \dfrac{1}{\sqrt[4]{4}} = \dfrac{1}{(\sqrt[4]{4} - 1)}$

Let $\sqrt[4]{4} = \alpha$, we get

$\Rightarrow \dfrac{r}{(r-1)\alpha} = \dfrac{1}{\alpha - 1}$

$\Rightarrow r\alpha - r = r\alpha - \alpha \Rightarrow r = \alpha$

$\Rightarrow r = \sqrt[4]{4}$

Now, $1 + r^2 + r^4 = 1 + (\sqrt[4]{4})^2 + (\sqrt[4]{4})^4$

$= 1 + 4^{1/2} + 4 = 1 + 2 + 4 = 7$

76. Let

$a = 10 + D$ ...(i)

$b = 10 + 2D$ ...(ii)

$ab = 10 + 3D$ ...(iii)

On substituting the values of a and b in Eq. (iii), we get

$(10 + D)(10 + 2D) = (10 + 3D)$

$\Rightarrow 2D^2 + 27D + 90 = 0$

$\therefore D = -6, D = -\dfrac{15}{2}$

$\therefore a_1 = 10 - 6 = 4,$

$a_2 = 10 - \dfrac{15}{2} = \dfrac{5}{2}$

and $b_1 = 10 - 12 = -2, b_2 = 10 - 15 = -5$

Now, $\left(\dfrac{2a_1a_2 + b_1b_2}{10}\right) = \left(\dfrac{2 \times 10 + 10}{10}\right) = 3$

77. Given equation, $Ax^3 + Bx^2 + Cx + D = 0$ ...(i)

where, $A \neq 0$

Let roots are α, β, γ, then $\beta = \dfrac{\alpha + \gamma}{2}$ ...(ii)

Given relation, $2B^3 + \lambda\, ABC + \mu\, A^2D = 0$ ...(iii)

From Eq. (i), $\alpha + \beta + \gamma = -\dfrac{\beta}{A}$

$$\Rightarrow \quad 3\beta = -\frac{B}{A} \quad \text{[from Eq. (ii)]}$$

$$\Rightarrow \quad \beta = -\frac{B}{3A}$$

Now, β satisfy Eq. (i), so

$$A\left(\frac{-B}{3A}\right)^3 + B\left(\frac{-B}{3A}\right)^2 + C\left(\frac{-B}{3A}\right) + D = 0$$

$$\Rightarrow \quad \frac{-B^3}{27A^2} + \frac{B^3}{9A^2} - \frac{BC}{3A} + D = 0$$

$$\Rightarrow \quad \frac{2}{27}\frac{B^3}{A^2} - \frac{BC}{3A} + D = 0$$

$$\Rightarrow \quad 2B^3 - 9\,ABC + 27\,DA^2 = 0$$

Compare with Eq. (iii), we get

$$\lambda = -9, \mu = 27$$

$$2\lambda + \mu = -18 + 27 = 9$$

78. Let $P = \lim_{n \to \infty}\left(\dfrac{1}{1+x} + \dfrac{2}{1+x^2} + \dfrac{2^2}{1+x^4} + \ldots \text{ upto } n \text{ terms}\right)$

$$= \lim_{n \to \infty}\sum_{r=0}^{n}\left(\frac{2^r}{1+x^{2^r}} + \frac{2^r}{1-x^{2^r}} - \frac{2^r}{1-x^{2^r}}\right)$$

$$= \lim_{n \to \infty}\sum_{r=0}^{n}\left(\frac{2^{r+1}}{1-x^{2^{r+1}}} - \frac{2^r}{1-x^{2^r}}\right)$$

$$= \lim_{n \to \infty}\left(\frac{2^{n+1}}{1-x^{2^{n+1}}} - \frac{1}{1-x}\right)$$

$$= \lim_{n \to \infty}\frac{\dfrac{2^{n+1}}{x^{2^{n+1}}}}{\dfrac{1}{x^{2^{n+1}}} - 1} - \frac{1}{1-x} = 0 - \frac{1}{1-x}$$

$$= \frac{1}{x-1} = \frac{1}{x-\lambda} \quad \text{[given]}$$

$$\therefore \quad \lambda = 1$$

79. Let number of AP are $(a-d), a, (a+d)$.

According to the question, $(a-d)^2, a^2, (a+d)^2$ are in GP.

$$\therefore \quad (a^2)^2 = (a-d)^2(a+d)^2$$

$$\Rightarrow \quad a^4 = (a^2 - d^2)^2$$

$$\Rightarrow \quad a^4 = a^4 + d^4 - 2a^2d^2$$

$$\Rightarrow \quad a^2(a^2 - 2d^2) = 0$$

$$\Rightarrow \quad a \neq 0, \text{ so } a^2 = 2d^2$$

$$\Rightarrow \quad a = \pm\sqrt{2}d \quad \text{...(i)}$$

Let common ratio of GP is r.

$$\therefore \quad r^2 = \frac{(a+d)^2}{(a-d)^2}$$

$$\Rightarrow \quad r^2 = \frac{a^2 + d^2 + 2ad}{a^2 + d^2 - 2ad}$$

$$\Rightarrow \quad r^2 = \frac{2d^2 + d^2 + 2\sqrt{2}d^2}{2d^2 + d^2 - 2\sqrt{2}\,d^2}$$

[from Eq. (i) for $a = \sqrt{2}\,d$]

$$\Rightarrow \quad r^2 = \frac{(3 + 2\sqrt{2})\,d^2}{(3 - 2\sqrt{2})\,d^2}$$

$$\Rightarrow \quad r^2 = \frac{(3 + 2\sqrt{2})(3 + 2\sqrt{2})}{9 - 8}$$

$$\Rightarrow \quad r^2 = (3 + 2\sqrt{2})^2$$

$$\Rightarrow \quad r^2 = (3 + \sqrt{8})^2$$

$$\therefore \quad r = \pm(3 + \sqrt{8})$$

$$\Rightarrow \quad r = 3 + \sqrt{8} \quad [\because r \text{ is positive}]$$

Similarly, for $a = -\sqrt{2}\,d$, we get

$$r = \pm(3 - \sqrt{8})$$

$$\Rightarrow \quad r = (3 - \sqrt{8}) \quad [\because r \text{ is positive}]$$

Compare r with $3 \pm \sqrt{k}$, we get

$$k = 8$$

$$\therefore \quad \left[\frac{k}{8} - \frac{8}{k}\right] = \left[\frac{8}{8} - \frac{8}{8}\right]$$

$$= [1 - 1] = [0] = 0$$

80. **(A)** a, b, c, d are in AP [a, b, c, d are positive real numbers]

By AM > GM, for a, b, c

$$b > \sqrt{ac}$$

$$\Rightarrow \quad b^2 > ac \quad \text{...(i)}$$

Now, applying for b, c, d

$$c > \sqrt{bd} \Rightarrow c^2 > bd \quad \text{...(ii)}$$

From Eqs. (i) and (ii), we get

$$b^2c^2 > (ac)(bd) \Rightarrow bc > ad$$

Again, applying AM > HM for a, b, c

$$b > \frac{2}{\dfrac{1}{a} + \dfrac{1}{c}} \Rightarrow \frac{1}{a} + \frac{1}{c} > \frac{2}{b} \quad \text{...(iii)}$$

For last 3 terms b, c, d

$$c > \frac{2}{\dfrac{1}{b} + \dfrac{1}{d}} \Rightarrow \frac{1}{b} + \frac{1}{d} > \frac{2}{c} \quad \text{...(iv)}$$

From Eqs. (iii) and (iv), we get

$$\frac{1}{a} + \frac{1}{c} + \frac{1}{b} + \frac{1}{d} > \frac{2}{b} + \frac{2}{c}$$

$$\Rightarrow \quad \frac{1}{a} + \frac{1}{d} > \frac{1}{b} + \frac{1}{c}$$

(B) a, b, c, d are in GP.

For a, b, c applying AM > GM,

$$\Rightarrow \quad \frac{a+c}{2} > b \Rightarrow a + c > 2b \quad \text{...(i)}$$

Similarly, for b, c, d

$$b + d > 2c \quad \text{...(ii)}$$

From Eqs. (i) and (ii), we get

$$a + b + c + d > 2b + 2c \Rightarrow a + d > b + c$$

Now, applying GM > HM for $a, b\ c$

$$b > \frac{2ac}{a + c}$$

$$\Rightarrow \quad \frac{1}{c} + \frac{1}{a} > \frac{2}{c} \quad \text{...(iii)}$$

Similarly, for b, c, d, we get

$$\frac{1}{d} + \frac{1}{b} > \frac{2}{c} \quad \text{...(iv)}$$

On adding Eqs. (iii) and (iv), we get

$$\frac{1}{a} + \frac{1}{b} + \frac{1}{c} + \frac{1}{d} > 2\left(\frac{1}{b} + \frac{1}{c}\right)$$

$$\Rightarrow \quad \frac{1}{a} + \frac{1}{d} > \frac{1}{b} + \frac{1}{c}$$

(C) a, b, c, d are in HP.

Applying AM > HM for a, b, c

$$\frac{a + c}{2} > b$$

$$\Rightarrow \quad a + c > 2b \quad \text{...(i)}$$

Similarly, for last 3 terms b, c, d

$$\Rightarrow \quad b + d > 2c \quad \text{...(ii)}$$

On adding Eqs. (i) and (ii), we get

$$a + b + c + d > 2b + 2c$$

$$\Rightarrow \quad a + d > b + c$$

Again, applying GM > HM for a, b, c

$$\sqrt{ac} > b$$

$$\Rightarrow \quad ac > b^2 \quad \text{...(iii)}$$

Similarly, for b, c, d

$$\Rightarrow \quad bd > c^2 \quad \text{...(iv)}$$

On multiplying Eqs. (iii) and (iv), we get

$$abcd > b^2c^2$$

$$ad > bc$$

81. **(A)** $a_1, a_2, a_3, \ldots, a_n, \ldots$ are in AP

and $\quad a_1 = \frac{5}{2}, a_{10} = 16$

$$\therefore \quad a_1 + a_2 + \ldots + a_n = 110$$

$$\Rightarrow \quad \frac{n}{2}(a_1 + a_n) = 110$$

$$\Rightarrow \quad \frac{n}{2}\left[\frac{5}{2} + \frac{5}{2} + (n - 1)\,d\right] = 110 \quad \text{...(i)}$$

$$\text{Now, } d = \frac{a_{10} - a_1}{10 - 1} = \frac{16 - \frac{5}{2}}{9} = \frac{27}{9 \times 2} = \frac{3}{2} \quad \text{...(ii)}$$

From Eqs. (i) and (ii), we get

$$\frac{n}{2}\left[5 + (n - 1)\frac{3}{2}\right] = 110$$

$$\Rightarrow \quad 5n + (n^2 - n)\frac{3}{2} = 220$$

$$\Rightarrow \quad 3n^2 + 7n - 440 = 0$$

$$\Rightarrow \quad 3n^2 + 40n - 33n - 440 = 0$$

$$\Rightarrow \quad n(3n + 40) - 11(3n + 40) = 0$$

$$\Rightarrow \quad (3n + 40)(n - 11) = 0$$

So, $\quad n = -\frac{40}{3}$ or $n = 11$

$$\therefore \quad n = 11 \quad [n \in N]$$

(B) Let first angle $= a$ [in degrees]

Common difference $= d$ [in degrees]

Number of sides $n = 9$

$\therefore$ Sum of interior angles $= (n - 2) \times 180°$

$$\Rightarrow \quad \frac{n}{2}[2a + (n - 1)\,d] = (n - 2) \times 180°$$

$$\Rightarrow \quad \frac{9}{2}(2a + 8d) = 7 \times 180°$$

$$\Rightarrow \quad a + 4d = 140°$$

and largest angle $T_9 = a + 8d < 180°$

$$\Rightarrow \quad 4d < 40$$

$$\Rightarrow \quad d < 10$$

$$\therefore \quad d = 9$$

(C) Given increasing GP,

$$a_1, a_2, \ldots, a_n, \ldots$$

where $\quad a_6 = 4a_4$

$$a_1r^5 = 4a_1r^3 \quad [r \text{ is the common ratio}]$$

$$\Rightarrow \quad r^2 = 4$$

$$\Rightarrow \quad r = 2 \quad [\because \text{increasing GP}]$$

and $\quad a_9 - a_7 = 192$

$$a_1(r^8 - r^6) = 192$$

$$a_1(256 - 64) = 192$$

$$a_1 = \frac{192}{192}$$

$$a_1 = 1$$

Then, $a_2 = 2$, $a_3 = 4$ and $a_4 + a_5 + \ldots + a_n = 1016$

$$(a_1 + a_2 + \ldots + a_n) - (a_1 + a_2 + a_3) = 1016$$

$$\frac{1(2^n - 1)}{2 - 1} = 1016 + 7$$

$$2^n = 1023 + 1 = 1024 = 2^{10}$$

$$\therefore \quad n = 10$$

82. **(A)** $a_1, a_2, \ldots$ are in AP.

$a_1 + a_4 + a_7 + a_{14} + a_{17} + a_{20} = 165$ [In an AP, sum of the terms equidistant from the 1st and last is equal to sum of 1st and last terms]

$$\Rightarrow \quad 3(a_1 + a_{20}) = 165$$

$$\Rightarrow \quad a_1 + a_1 + 19d = 55$$

d is the common difference of AP.

$$2a_1 + 19d = 55 \quad \text{...(i)}$$

Now, $\quad \alpha = a_2 + a_6 + a_{15} + a_{19}$

$$\alpha = 2(a_2 + a_{19})$$

$\alpha = 2(a_1 + d + a_1 + 18d)$

$\alpha = 2(2a_1 + 19d)$ ...(ii)

and $\beta = 2(a_9 + a_{12}) - (a_3 + a_{18})$

$\beta = 2(a_1 + 8d + a_1 + 11d) - (a_1 + 2d + a_1 + 17d)$

$\beta = 2(2a_1 + 19d) - (2a_1 + 19d)$

$\beta = 2a_1 + 19d$ ...(iii)

From Eqs. (i) and (iii), we get

$\alpha = 2\beta$

From Eqs. (i), (ii) and (iii), we get

$\alpha + 2\beta = 4(2a_1 + 19d) = 4(55) = 220$ [from Eq.(i)]

$\alpha + \beta = 3(2a_1 + 19d)$

$= 3 \times 55 = 165 = 15 \times 11 = 15\mu$, where $\mu \in I$

$\alpha - \beta = 2a_1 + 19d$

$= 55 = 5 \times 11 = 5\lambda$, where $\lambda \in I$

(B) $a_1, a_2, \ldots$ are in AP.

$a_1 + a_5 + a_{10} + a_{15} + a_{20} + a_{24} = 195$

$3(a_1 + a_{24}) = 195$

$\Rightarrow a_1 + a_{24} = 65$ ...(i)

$\Rightarrow 2a_1 + 23d = 65$

Now, $\alpha = a_2 + a_7 + a_{18} + a_{23}$

$= 2(a_2 + a_{23}) = 2(2a_1 + 23d)$

$\alpha = 130$ [from Eq. (i)]

$\beta = 2(a_2 + a_{22}) - (a_8 + a_{17})$

$= 2(2a_1 + 23d) - (2a_1 + 23d)$

$= 130 - 65 = 65$

Then, $\alpha = 2\beta$

$\alpha + 2\beta = 130 + 130 = 260$

$\alpha + \beta = 195 = 15 \times 13 = 15\mu$, where $\mu = 13$

and $\alpha - \beta = 130 - 65 = 65$

$= 5 \times 13 = 5\lambda$, where $\lambda = 13$

(C) $a_1, a_2, \ldots$ are in AP.

$a_1 + a_7 + a_{10} + a_{21} + a_{24} + a_{30} = 225$

$3(a_1 + a_{30}) = 225$

$2a_1 + 29d = 75$ ...(i)

Now, $\alpha = a_2 + a_7 + a_{24} + a_{29}$

$\alpha = 4a_1 + 58d = 2(2a_1 + 29d)$

$= 2 \times 75 = 150$

$\alpha = 150$ ...(ii)

and $\beta = 2(a_{10} + a_{21}) - (a_3 + a_{28})$

$= 2(2a_1 + 29d) - (2a_1 + 29d) = 150 - 75$

$\beta = 75$ ...(iii)

Then, $\alpha = 2\beta$

$\alpha + 2\beta = 150 + 150 = 300$ and $\alpha - \beta = 150 - 75 = 75$

$= 5 \times 15 = 5\lambda$, where $\lambda = 15$

and $\alpha + \beta = 150 + 75 = 225 = 15 \times 15 = 15\mu$, where $\mu = 15$

83. **(A)** $4a^2 + 9b^2 + 16c^2 = 2(3ab + 6bc + 4ca)$

$(2a)^2 + (3b)^2 + (4c)^2 - (2a)(3b)(4c) - (2a)(4c) = 0$

$\frac{1}{2}\{(2a - 3b)^2 + (3b - 4c)^2 + (4c - 2a)^2\} = 0$

$\Rightarrow 2a - 3b = 0$ and $3b - 4c = 0$

and $4c - 2a = 0 \Rightarrow 2a = 3b$

and $3b = 4c$ and $4c = 2a$

$\Rightarrow a = \frac{3}{2}b$ and $b = \frac{4}{3}c$ and $c = \frac{1}{2}a$

$\Rightarrow a = \frac{3}{2}b$ and $b = \frac{4}{3}c$ and $c = \frac{3}{4}b$

So, a, b, c are $\frac{3}{2}b, b, \frac{3}{4}b$

Reciprocal of the terms $\frac{2}{3b}, \frac{1}{b}, \frac{4}{3b}$,

which is in AP.

So, these a, b, c are in HP.

(B) $17a^2 + 13b^2 + 5c^2 = 3ab + 15bc + 5ca$

$\Rightarrow 34a^2 + 26a^2 + 10c^2 - 6ab - 30bc - 10ca = 0$

$\Rightarrow (3a - b)^2 + (5b - 3c)^2 + (c - 5a)^2 = 0$

$\Rightarrow 3a - b = 0$ and $5b - 3c = 0$ and $c - 5a = 0$

$\Rightarrow \frac{a}{1} = \frac{b}{3} = \frac{c}{5} = \lambda$ [say]

$\therefore a = \lambda, b = 3\lambda, c = 5\lambda$

Hence, a, b, c are in AP.

(C) $a^2 + 9b^2 + 25c^2 = abc\left(\frac{15}{a} + \frac{5}{b} + \frac{3}{c}\right)$

$\Rightarrow (a)^2 + (3b)^2 + (5c)^2 - 15bc - 5ac - 3ab = 0$

$\Rightarrow \frac{1}{2}\{(a - 3b)^2 + (3b - 5c)^2 + (5c - a)^2\} = 0$

$\Rightarrow a - 3b = 0$ and $3b - 5c = 0$ and $5c - a = 0$

$\Rightarrow a = 3b$ and $3b = 5c$ and $5c = a$

$\Rightarrow a = 3b$ and $b = \frac{5}{3}c$ and $c = \frac{a}{5}$

$\Rightarrow a = 3b$ and $b = \frac{5}{3}c$ and $c = \frac{3}{5}b$

So, a, b, c are of the form $3b, b, \frac{3b}{5}$.

Reciprocal of $3b, b, \frac{3b}{5}$ are $\frac{1}{3b}, \frac{1}{b}, \frac{5}{3b}$, which are in AP.

$\left[\because \frac{1}{b} - \frac{1}{3b} = \frac{2}{3b} \text{ and } \frac{5}{3b} - \frac{1}{b} = \frac{2}{3b}\right]$

(D) $(a^2 + b^2 + c^2)p^2 - 2p(ab + bc + ca) + a^2 + b^2 + c^2 \le 0$

$\Rightarrow (a^2p^2 + b^2 - 2abp) + (b^2p^2 + c^2 - 2pbc) + (c^2p^2 + a^2 - 2acp) \le 0$

$\Rightarrow (ap - b)^2 + (bp - c)^2 + (cp - a)^2 \le 0$

$\Rightarrow (ap - b)^2 + (bp - c)^2 + (cp - a)^2 = 0$

$\Rightarrow ap - b = 0$ and $bp - c = 0$ and $cp - a = 0$

$\Rightarrow p = \frac{b}{a}$ and $p = \frac{c}{b}$ and $p = \frac{a}{c}$

$\Rightarrow \frac{b}{a} = \frac{c}{b} = \frac{a}{c}$

$\Rightarrow a, b, c$ are in GP.

84. If a, b, c are in GP.

Then, $b^2 = ac$

If middle term is added, then $a + b, 2b$ and $c + b$ are in GP.

$$\frac{\text{I}-\text{II}}{\text{II}-\text{III}} = \frac{a+b-2b}{2b-(c+b)} \quad [\text{here, I} = a+b, \text{II} = 2b, \text{III} = c+b]$$

$$= \frac{a-b}{b-c} = \frac{ab-b^2}{b^2-bc} = \frac{ab-ac}{ac-bc} \quad [\because b^2 = ac]$$

$$= \frac{a(b-c)(a+b)(b+c)}{c(a-b)(a+b)(b+c)}$$

$$= \frac{a(b^2-c^2)(a+b)}{c(a^2-b^2)(b+c)}$$

$$= \frac{a(ac-c^2)(a+b)}{c(a^2-ac)(b+c)}; \frac{a+b}{b+c} = \frac{\text{I}}{\text{III}}$$

Hence, $a+b$, $2b$, $b+c$ are in HP.

Hence, both statements are true and Statement-2 is correct explanation for Statement-1.

85. $\because T_n = 2n^3 + 3n^2 - 4$

Sequence is 1, 24, 77, 172, 321, ...

First order difference 23, 53, 95, 149, ...

Second order difference 30, 42, 54, ...

which are in AP.

$\therefore$ **Statenemt-1** is true.

$\because T_n$ is of three degree and third order difference will be constant.

Statement-2 is true, which is correct explanation for Statement-1.

86. Statement-1 Let S be the required sum of product of numbers.

$$\left(\sum_{i=1}^{n} x_i\right)^2 = \sum_{i=1}^{n} x_i^2 + 2\sum\sum_{1 \le i < j \le n} x_i x_j$$

$$\therefore \quad (a_1 - a_1 + a_2 - a_2 + \dots + a_n - a_n)^2 = 2\sum_{i=1}^{n} a_i^2 + 2S$$

$$\therefore \quad S = -\sum_{i=1}^{n} a_i^2$$

$\therefore$ **Statement-1** is true.

Statement-2 is true but not correct explanation for Statement-1.

87. Statement-1 $a + b + c = 18$, $a, b, c > 0$

Applying AM $\ge$ GM for a, b, c

$$\frac{a+b+c}{3} \ge \sqrt[3]{abc} \Rightarrow \sqrt[3]{abc} \le 6 \Rightarrow abc \le 216$$

Maximum value of abc is 216 which occurs at $a = b = c$.

Statement-2 is the correct explanation for Statement-1.

88. Statement-1

$$4a^2 + 9b^2 + 16c^2 - 2(3ab + 6bc + 4ca) = 0$$

$$\Rightarrow (2a)^2 + (3b)^2 + (4c)^2 - (2a)(3b) - (3b)(4c) - (2a)(4c) = 0$$

$$\Rightarrow \frac{1}{2}\{(2a-3b)^2 + (3b-4c)^2 + (4c-2a)^2\} = 0$$

$$\Rightarrow 2a - 3b = 0 \text{ and } 3b - 4c = 0 \text{ and } 4c - 2a = 0$$

$$\Rightarrow \text{and } b = \frac{4c}{3} \text{ and } c = \frac{a}{2} \Rightarrow a = \frac{3b}{2} \text{ and } b = \frac{4c}{3} \text{ and } c = \frac{3b}{4}$$

Then, a, b, c are of the form $\frac{3b}{2}, b, \frac{3b}{4}$, which are in HP.

So, Statement-1 is false.

Statement-2 If

$$(a_1 - a_2)^2 + (a_2 - a_3)^2 + (a_3 - a_1)^2 = 0$$

$$\Rightarrow a_1 - a_2 = 0 \text{ and } a_2 - a_3 = 0 \text{ and } a_3 - a_1 = 0$$

$$\Rightarrow a_1 = a_2 = a_3, \forall\, a_1, a_2, a_3 \in R$$

So, Statement-2 is true.

89. $\because A = \frac{a+b}{2}$, $G = \sqrt{ab}$ and $H = \frac{2ab}{a+b}$

Given, $\quad 4G = 5H \quad$ ...(i)

and $\quad G^2 = AH$

$\therefore \quad H = \frac{G^2}{A} \quad$ ...(ii)

From Eqs. (i) and (ii), we get

$$4G = \frac{5G^2}{A} \Rightarrow 4A = 5G$$

$$\Rightarrow 2(a+b) = 5\sqrt{ab}$$

$$\Rightarrow 4(a^2 + b^2 + 2ab) = 25ab$$

$$\Rightarrow 4a^2 - 17ab + 4b^2 = 0$$

$$\Rightarrow (a - 4b)(4a - b) = 0$$

$$a = 4b,\ 4a - b \ne 0 \quad [\because a > b]$$

$\therefore$ Statement-1 is true.

Statement-2 is true only for two numbers, if numbers more than two, then this formula (AM) (HM) = $(\text{GM})^2$ is true, if numbers are in GP.

Statement-2 is false for positive numbers.

90. Statement-1 Sum of first 100 even natural numbers

$$E_1 = 2 + 4 + \dots + 200 = \frac{2(100 \times 101)}{2} = 10100$$

Sum of 100 odd natural numbers = 1 + 3 + ... + 199

$$O = \frac{100}{2}(1 + 199) = 10000$$

$$\therefore \quad E - O = 100$$

So, Statement-1 is true.

Statement-2 Sum of first n natural even numbers

$$E = 2 + 4 + \dots + 2n = \frac{2n(n+1)}{2} = n^2 + n$$

Sum of first n odd natural numbers

$$O = 1 + 3 + \dots + (2n-1)$$

$$= \frac{n}{2}[1 + 2n - 1] = n^2$$

So, $\quad E - O = n^2 + n - n^2 = n$

Statement-2 is true and correct explanation for Statement-1.

91. Let $\quad T_n = An + B$

$$\therefore \quad T_p = Ap + B,$$

$$T_{2p} = 2Ap + B,\ T_{4p} = 4Ap + B$$

$\therefore \quad T_p, T_{2p}, T_{4p}$ are in G P.

$$\therefore \quad (2Ap + B)^2 = (Ap + B)(4Ap + B)$$

$$\Rightarrow \quad ABp = 0$$

$$\therefore \quad B = 0,\ A \ne 0,\ p \ne 0$$

$$\Rightarrow \text{Common ratio, } r = \frac{T_{2p}}{T_p} = \frac{2Ap + 0}{Ap + 0} = 2$$

92. $a \neq 1, b \neq 0$ and $a \neq b$

Let $S = (a+b) + (a^2 + ab + b^2) + (a^3 + a^2b + ab^2 + b^3) + \ldots + n$ terms

$$= \frac{1}{(a-b)}[(a^2-b^2) + (a^3-b^3) + (a^4-b^4) + \ldots + n \text{ terms}]$$

$$= \frac{1}{(a-b)}[a^2(1 + a + \ldots + n \text{ terms}) - b^2(1 + b + b^2 + \ldots + n \text{ terms})]$$

$$= \frac{1}{(a-b)}\left[a^2 \cdot \frac{1\cdot(a^n-1)}{(a-1)} - b^2 \cdot \frac{1\cdot(b^n-1)}{(b-1)}\right]$$

$$= \frac{1}{(a-b)}\left[a^2\frac{(1-a^n)}{(1-a)} - b^2\frac{(1-b^n)}{(1-b)}\right]$$

93. Sequence of natural number is divided into group.

1, 3, 5, 7, 9, 11, ...

$\therefore$ nth row contains n elements

1st element of nth row $= n^2 - (n-1)$

Least element of nth row $= n^2 + (n-1)$

$\therefore$ Sum of the element in the nth row

$$= \frac{n}{2}(a+l) = \frac{n}{2}[n^2 - (n-1) + n^2 + (n-1)]$$

$$= \frac{n}{2}[n^2 - n + 1 + n^2 + n - 1] = \frac{n}{2}[2n^2] = n^3$$

94. $a = S_n = \dfrac{a(r^n - 1)}{r-1}$ ...(i)

$b = S_{2n} - S_n = \dfrac{a(r^{2n}-1)}{(r-1)} - \dfrac{a(r^n-1)}{(r-1)} = \dfrac{a(r^n-1)}{(r-1)}(r^n)$ ...(ii)

$c = S_{3n} - S_{2n} = \dfrac{a(r^{3n}-1)}{(r-1)} - \dfrac{a(r^{2n}-1)}{(r-1)}$

$= \dfrac{a(r^n-1)}{(r-1)}(r^{2n} + r^n + 1 - r^n - 1) = \dfrac{a(r^n-1)}{(r-1)}\cdot(r^n)^2$ ...(iii)

From Eqs. (i), (ii) and (iii), $b^2 = ac$, so a, b, c are in GP.

95. First four terms of an AP are a, $2a$, b and $(a-6-b)$.

So, $2a - a = a - 6 - b - b$

$\Rightarrow$ $a = a - 6 - 2b$

$\Rightarrow$ $-2b = 6 \Rightarrow b = -3$

and $2a - a = b - 2a$

$\Rightarrow$ $b = 3a \Rightarrow a = -1$

$\therefore$ First terms $a = -1$ and $d = a = -1$

$$S_{100} = \frac{100}{2}[2a + (100-1)d]$$

$$= 50[-2 + 99(-1)]$$

$$= 50(-2-99) = 50(-101) = -5050$$

96. (i) $\dfrac{1}{1^2} + \dfrac{1}{2^2} + \dfrac{1}{3^2} + \ldots + \infty = \dfrac{\pi^2}{6}$ ...(i)

$\therefore$ $\dfrac{1}{1^2} + \dfrac{1}{3^2} + \dfrac{1}{5^2} + \ldots + \infty$

$$= \left(\frac{1}{1^2} + \frac{1}{2^2} + \frac{1}{3^2} + \frac{1}{4^2} + \ldots + \infty\right) - \left(\frac{1}{2^2} + \frac{1}{4^2} + \frac{1}{6^2} + \ldots + \infty\right)$$

$$= \frac{\pi^2}{6} - \frac{1}{4}\frac{\pi^2}{6} = \frac{3}{4} \times \frac{\pi^2}{6} = \frac{\pi^2}{8}$$

(ii) $1 - \dfrac{1}{2^2} + \dfrac{1}{3^2} - \dfrac{1}{4^2} + \ldots + \infty = \left(\dfrac{1}{1^2} - \dfrac{1}{3^3} + \ldots\right) - \dfrac{1}{2^2}\left(\dfrac{1}{1^2} - \dfrac{1}{2^2} + \ldots + \infty\right)$

$= \dfrac{\pi^2}{8} - \dfrac{1}{4} \times \dfrac{\pi^2}{6} = \dfrac{\pi^2}{12}$ [by part (i)]

97. $\Sigma a_i b_i = \Sigma a_i(1 - a_i) = na - \Sigma a_i^2$

$= na - \Sigma(a_i - a + a)^2$

$= na - \Sigma[(a_i - a)^2 + a^2 + 2a(a_i - a)]$

$= na - \Sigma[(a_i - a)^2 - \Sigma a^2 - 2a\Sigma(a_i - a)$

$\therefore$ $\Sigma a_i b_i + \Sigma(a_i - a)^2 = na - na^2 - 2a(na - na)$

$= na(1-a) = nab$ $\left[\begin{array}{l}\because \Sigma b_i = \Sigma 1 - \Sigma a_i \\ \therefore nb = n - na \\ \text{or } a + b = 1\end{array}\right]$

98. $a_1 + a_2 + \ldots + a_{98} = 137$

$\dfrac{98}{2}(a_1 + a_{98}) = 137$

$a_1 + a_2 + 97 = \dfrac{137}{49}$; $2a_1 + 97 = \dfrac{137}{49}$

$2a_1 = \dfrac{137}{49} - 97$; $a_1 = \dfrac{1}{2}\dfrac{(137 - 4753}{49}$

$a_1 = -\dfrac{4616}{2 \times 49}$; $a_1 = \dfrac{2308}{49}$ ...(i)

Now, $a_2 + a_4 + \ldots + a_{98} = (a_1 + 1) + (a_1 + 3) + \ldots + (a_1 + 97)$ [$\because d = 1$]

$= 49a_1 + (1 + 3 + \ldots + 97)$

$= -49 \times \dfrac{2308}{49} + \dfrac{49}{2}(1 + 97)$

$= -2308 + 49^2$

$= -2308 + 2401 = 93$

99. $t_1 = 1$ and $t_r - t_{r-1} = 2^{r-1}, r \geq 2$

$t_2 - t_1 = 2$

$t_3 - t_2 = 2^2$

$t_4 - t_3 = 2^3$

$\vdots \quad \vdots \quad \vdots$

$t_n - t_{n-1} = 2^{n-1}$

Addiing columnwise, we get

$t_n - t_1 = 2 + 2^2 + \ldots + 2^{n-1}$

$t_n = 1 + 2 + 2^2 + \ldots + 2^{n-1}$

$t_n = \dfrac{1\cdot(2^n - 1)}{2-1} \Rightarrow t_n = 2^n - 1$

So, $\displaystyle\sum_{r=1}^{n} t_r = t_1 + t_2 + \ldots + t_n = (2-1) + (2^2 - 1) + \ldots + (2^n - 1)$

$= (2 + 2^2 + \ldots + 2^n) - n = \dfrac{2\cdot(2^n - 1)}{(2-1)} - n = 2^{n+1} - 2 - n$

$= 2^{n+1} - n - 2$

100. (i) $I_n = \int_0^{\pi} \frac{\sin 2nx}{\sin x} dx = \int_0^{\pi} \frac{\sin 2n(\pi - x)}{\sin x} dx$

$= \int_0^{\pi} \frac{\sin (2n\pi - 2nx)}{\sin x} dx$

$I_n = - \int_0^{\pi} \frac{\sin 2nx}{\sin x} dx$

$I_n = - I_n \Rightarrow 2I_n = 0 \Rightarrow I_n = 0$

$\therefore \quad I_1 = I_2 = I_3 = \ldots = 0$

which is a constant series.

$\therefore$ This series is AP with common difference 0 and first term o.

(ii) $I_n = \int_0^{\pi} \frac{\sin^2 nx}{\sin^2 x} dx$

Let $\quad f(x) = \frac{\sin^2 nx}{\sin^2 x}$

Hence, $f(\pi - x) = f(x)$

So, $\quad I_n = 2 \int_0^{\pi/2} \frac{\sin^2 nx}{\sin^2 x} dx$

Now, $I_{n+1} + I_{n-1} - 2I_n$

$$= 2\int_0^{\pi/2} \left\{ \frac{(\sin^2 (n+1)x - \sin^2 nx)}{\sin^2 x} + \frac{(\sin^2 (n-1)x - \sin^2 nx)}{\sin^2 x} \right\} dx$$

$= 2 \int_0^{\pi/2} \frac{\sin (2n+1) x \sin x - \sin (2n-1) x \sin x}{\sin^2 x} dx$

$= 2 \int_0^{\pi/2} \frac{\sin (2n+1) x - \sin (2n-1) x}{\sin x} dx$

$= 2 \int_0^{\pi/2} \frac{2 \cos 2nx \sin x}{\sin x} dx$

$= 4 \int_0^{\pi/2} \cos 2nx \, dx = \frac{4}{2n} [\sin 2nx]_0^{\pi/2} = \frac{2}{n} \cdot 0 = 0$

$\therefore I_{n+1} + I_{n-1} = 2I_n \therefore I_1, I_2, I_3, \ldots$ are in A P.

101. $S = 7 + 13 + 21 + 31 + \ldots + T_n$

$$\begin{array}{l} S = \quad 7 + 13 + 21 + \ldots + T_{n-1} + T_n \\ \underline{- \quad - \quad - \quad - \quad - \quad - \quad -} \\ 0 = 7 + 6 + 8 + 10 + \ldots + n \text{ terms} - T_n \end{array}$$

$T_n = 7 + 6 + 8 + 10 + \ldots + n$ terms

$T_n = 7 + \{6 + 8 + 10 + \ldots + (n-1) \text{ terms}\}$

$T_n = 7 + \frac{(n-1)}{2} (12 + (n-2)2)$

$T_n = 7 + \frac{(n-1)}{2} (8 + 2n)$

$T_n = 7 + (n-1)(4+n)$

$T_{70} = 7 + 69 \times 74 = 7 + 5106 = 5113$

102. $\left(x + \frac{1}{x}\right)^3 + \left(x^2 + \frac{1}{x^2}\right)^3 + \ldots + \left(x^n + \frac{1}{x^n}\right)^3 = \sum_{n=1}^{n} \left(x^n + \frac{1}{x^n}\right)^3$

$= \sum_{n=1}^{n} \left(x^{3n} + \frac{1}{x^{3n}} + 3\left(x^n + \frac{1}{x^n}\right) \right)$

$= \sum_{n=1}^{n} x^{3n} + \sum_{n=1}^{n} \frac{1}{x^{3n}} + 3 \sum_{n=1}^{n} x^n + 3 \sum_{n=1}^{n} \frac{1}{x^n}$

$= \frac{x^3 (1 - x^{3n})}{(1 - x^3)} + \frac{(1 - x^{3n})}{x^{3n} (1 - x^3)} + \frac{3x (1 - x^n)}{(1 - x)} + \frac{3 (1 - x^n)}{x^n (1 - x)}$

103. Let d be the common difference of AP.

LHS $= a_1^2 - a_2^2 + a_3^2 - a_4^2 + \ldots + a_{2n-1}^2 - a_{2n}^2$

$(a_1 - a_2)(a_1 + a_2) + (a_3 - a_4)(a_3 + a_4) + \ldots + (a_{2n-1} - a_{2n})(a_{2n-1} + a_{2n})$

$= - d (a_1 + a_2 + \ldots + a_{2n-1} + a_{2n})$

$= - d [(a_1 + a_{2n}) + (a_2 + a_{2n-1}) + \ldots + (a_n + a_{n+1})]$

$= - dn (a_1 + a_{2n})$

$= - dn \frac{(a_1^2 - a_{2n}^2)}{(a_1 - a_{2n})} = \frac{-dn(a_1^2 - a_{2n}^2)}{(1-2n)d}$ $[\because a_{2n} = a_1 + (2n-1) d]$

$= \frac{n}{2n-1} (a_1^2 - a_{2n}^2)$

104. Let a, b, c (unequal number) are in HP

$\therefore \quad b = \frac{2ac}{a+c}$

$\Rightarrow \quad \frac{b}{2} = \frac{ac}{a+c} = \lambda$ [say]

$\Rightarrow \quad b = 2\lambda$ and $ac = \lambda (a+c)$ ...(i)

Now, a^2, b^2, c^2 are in AP

So, $\quad b^2 = \frac{a^2 + c^2}{2} \Rightarrow 2b^2 = a^2 + c^2$

$\Rightarrow \quad 2(2\lambda)^2 = (a+c)^2 - 2ac$

$\Rightarrow \quad (a+c)^2 - 2\lambda (a+c) - 8\lambda^2 = 0$

$\Rightarrow \quad (a + c - 4\lambda)(a + c + 2\lambda) = 0$

$\Rightarrow \quad a + c = 4\lambda$ or $a + c = -2\lambda$

***Case* I** If $a + c = 4\lambda$

$\therefore \quad ac = 4\lambda^2$ [from Eq. (i)]

$\Rightarrow \quad (a-c)^2 = (a+c)^2 - 4ac$

$\Rightarrow \quad (a-c)^2 = 16\lambda^2 - 16\lambda^2$

$\Rightarrow \quad (a-c)^2 = 0 \Rightarrow a = c$

Let given that a, b, c are distinct, so $a + c = 4\lambda$ is not valid.

***Case* II** If $a + c = -2\lambda$

$\Rightarrow \quad ac = -2\lambda^2$ [from Eq. (i)]

$\therefore \quad (a-c)^2 = (a+c)^2 - 4ac$

$\Rightarrow \quad (a-c)^2 = 4\lambda^2 + 8\lambda^2 \Rightarrow (a-c) = \pm 2\sqrt{3}\lambda$ ...(ii)

If $\quad a - c = 2\sqrt{3}\lambda,$ ...(iii)

then $\quad a + c = 2\lambda$

From Eqs. (ii) and (iii), we get

$a = (\sqrt{3} - 1)\lambda$ and $c = -(1 + \sqrt{3})\lambda$

$\therefore \quad a : b : c = (\sqrt{3} - 1)\lambda : 2\lambda : -(\sqrt{3} + 1)\lambda$

$a : b : c = (\sqrt{3} - 1) : 2 : -(\sqrt{3} + 1)$

$\Rightarrow \quad a : b : c = (1 - \sqrt{3}) : -2 : (\sqrt{3} + 1)$

If $\quad a - c = -2\sqrt{3}\lambda,$ ...(iv)

then $\quad a + c = -2\lambda$ ...(v)

From Eqs. (iv) and (v), we get

$$a = -(\sqrt{3}+1)\lambda \text{ and } c = (\sqrt{3}-1)\lambda$$

$\therefore \quad a : b : c = -(\sqrt{3}+1)\lambda : 2\lambda : (\sqrt{3}-1)\lambda$

$\Rightarrow \quad a : b : c = (1+\sqrt{3}) : -2 : (1-\sqrt{3})$

105. $a_1, a_2, a, \ldots, a_n$ are in AP with $a_1 = 0$ and common difference d $[d \neq 0]$

$\therefore a_2 = d, a_3 = 2d, \ldots, a_n = (n-1)d$

$$\text{LHS} = \frac{a_3}{a_2} + \frac{a_4}{a_3} + \frac{a_5}{a_4} + \ldots + \frac{a_n}{a_{n-1}} - a_2\left(\frac{1}{a_2} + \frac{1}{a_3} + \ldots + \frac{1}{a_{n-2}}\right)$$

$$= \frac{1}{a_2}(a_3 - a_2) + \frac{1}{a_3}(a_4 - a_2) + \ldots + \frac{(a_{n-1} - a_2)}{a_{n-2}} + \frac{a_n}{a_{n-1}}$$

$$= \frac{1}{d}(2d - d) + \frac{1}{2d}(3d - d) + \ldots + \frac{[(n-2)d - d]}{(n-3)d} + \frac{(n-1)d}{(n-2)d}$$

$$= [1 + 1 + \ldots + (n-3) \text{ times}] + \frac{n-1}{n-2}$$

$$= (n-3) + \frac{(n-1)}{n-2} = (n-3) + \frac{(n-2)+1}{(n-2)}$$

$$= (n-3) + 1 + \frac{1}{n-2} = n - 2 + \frac{1}{n-2}$$

$$= \frac{a(n-2)d}{d} + \frac{d}{(n-2)d} = \frac{a_{n-1}}{a_2} + \frac{a_2}{a_{n-1}} = \text{RHS}$$

106. Let one side of equilateral triangle contains n balls. Then

Number of balls (initially) $= 1 + 2 + 3 + \ldots + n = \dfrac{n(n+1)}{2}$

According to the question, $\dfrac{n(n+1)}{2} + 669 = (n-8)^2$

$\Rightarrow \quad n^2 + n + 1338 = 2n^2 - 32n + 128$

$\Rightarrow \quad n^2 - 33n - 1210 = 0$

$\Rightarrow \quad (n-55)(n+22) = 0 \Rightarrow n = 55$ or $n = -22$

which is not possible

$\therefore \quad n = 55$

So, $\dfrac{n(n+1)}{2} = \dfrac{55 \times 56}{2} = 55 \times 28 = 1540$

107. $\theta_1, \theta_2, \theta_3, \ldots, \theta_n$ are in AP.

So, $\quad \theta_2 - \theta_1 = \theta_3 - \theta_2 = \ldots = \theta_n - \theta_{n-1} = d$

$\therefore$ LHS $= \sin d\,[\sec\theta_1 \sec\theta_2 + \sec\theta_2 \sec\theta_3 + \ldots + \sec\theta_{n-1}\sec\theta_n]$

$$= \sin d\left[\frac{1}{\cos\theta_1\cos\theta_2} + \frac{1}{\cos\theta_2\cos\theta_3} + \ldots + \frac{1}{\cos\theta_{n-1}\cos\theta_n}\right]$$

$$= \frac{\sin d}{\cos\theta_1\cos\theta_2} + \frac{\sin d}{\cos\theta_2\cos\theta_3} + \ldots + \frac{\sin d}{\cos\theta_{n-1}\cos\theta_n}$$

$$= \frac{\sin(\theta_2-\theta_1)}{\cos\theta_1\cos\theta_2} + \frac{\sin(\theta_3-\theta_2)}{\cos\theta_2\cos\theta_3} + \ldots + \frac{\sin(\theta_n-\theta_{n-1})}{\cos\theta_{n-1}\cos\theta_n}$$

$$= (\tan\theta_2 - \tan\theta_1) + (\tan\theta_3 - \tan\theta_2) + \ldots + (\tan\theta_n - \tan\theta_{n-1})$$

$$= \tan\theta_n - \tan\theta_1 = \text{RHS}$$

108. LHS $= (1+5^{-1})(1+5^{-2})(1+5^{-4})\ldots(1+5^{-2^n})$

$$= \left(1+\frac{1}{5}\right)\left(1+\frac{1}{5^2}\right)\left(1+\frac{1}{5^4}\right)\ldots\left(1+\frac{1}{5^{2^n}}\right)$$

$$= \frac{\left(1-\frac{1}{5}\right)}{\left(1-\frac{1}{5}\right)}\left(1+\frac{1}{5}\right)\left(1+\frac{1}{5^2}\right)\left(1+\frac{1}{5^4}\right)\ldots\left(1+\frac{1}{5^{2^n}}\right)$$

$$= \frac{5}{4}\left[\left(1+\frac{1}{5^2}\right)\left(1+\frac{1}{5^2}\right)\left(1+\frac{1}{5^4}\right)\ldots\left(1+\frac{1}{5^{2^n}}\right)\right]$$

$\vdots \qquad \vdots \qquad \vdots$

$$= \frac{5}{4}\left(1 - \frac{1}{5^{2^{n+1}}}\right) = \frac{5}{4}(1 - 5^{-2^{n+1}}) = \text{RHS}$$

109. $S = \displaystyle\sum_{n=0}^{\infty} \frac{2^n}{a^{2^n}+1}, (a > 1)$

$$S_n = \sum_{n=0}^{n} \frac{2^n}{a^{2^n}+1}$$

$$= \frac{1}{a+1} + \frac{2}{a^2+1} + \frac{4}{a^4+1} + \frac{8}{a^8+1} + \ldots + \frac{2^n}{a^{2^n}+1}$$

$$= \frac{1}{1+a} + \frac{2}{1+a^2} + \frac{4}{1+a^4} + \frac{8}{1+a^8} + \ldots + \frac{2^n}{1+a^{2^n}}$$

$$= \left(-\frac{1}{1-a} + \frac{1}{1-a}\right) + \frac{1}{1+a} + \frac{2}{1+a^2} + \frac{4}{1+a^4} + \ldots + \frac{2^n}{1+a^{2^n}}$$

$$= \frac{1}{a-1} + \left(\frac{1}{1-a} + \frac{1}{1+a}\right) + \frac{2}{1+a^2} + \frac{4}{1+a^4} + \ldots + \frac{2^n}{1+a^{2^n}}$$

$$= \frac{1}{a-1} + \left(\frac{2}{1-a^2} + \frac{2}{1+a^2}\right) + \frac{4}{1+a^4} + \ldots + \frac{2^n}{1+a^{2^n}}$$

$\vdots \qquad \vdots \qquad \vdots \qquad \vdots$

$$S_n = \frac{1}{a-1} + \frac{2^{n+1}}{1-a^{2^{n+1}}}$$

$$S = \lim_{n\to\infty} S_n = \lim_{n\to\infty}\left(\frac{1}{a-1} + \frac{2^{n+1}}{1-a^{2^{n+1}}}\right)$$

$$= \lim_{n\to\infty}\left(\frac{1}{a-1} + \frac{\frac{2^{n+1}}{a^{2^{n+1}}}}{\frac{1}{a^{2^{n+1}}} - 1}\right) = \frac{1}{a-1} + \frac{0}{0-1} = \frac{1}{a-1}$$

110. $T_n = \tan^{-1}\left(\dfrac{2^{n-1}}{1+2^{2n-1}}\right) = \tan^{-1}\left(\dfrac{2^{n-1}}{1+2^n \cdot 2^{n-1}}\right)$

$$= \tan^{-1}\left(\frac{2^n - 2^{n-1}}{1+2^n\cdot 2^{n-1}}\right) = \tan^{-1}2^n - \tan^{-1}2^{n-1}$$

$$S_n = T_1 + T_2 + \ldots + T_n$$

$$= (\tan^{-1}2^1 - \tan^{-1}2^0) + (\tan^{-1}2^2 - \tan^{-1}2^1) + \ldots + (\tan^{-1}2^n - \tan^{-1}2^{n-1})$$

$$= (\tan^{-1}2^n - \tan^{-1}1)$$

$$S_n = \tan^{-1}2^n - \frac{\pi}{4}$$

$$S = \lim_{n\to\infty} S_n = \lim_{n\to\infty}\left(\tan^{-1}2^n - \frac{\pi}{4}\right) = \frac{\pi}{2} - \frac{\pi}{4} = \frac{\pi}{4}$$

111. $T_n = \tan[\alpha + (n-1)\beta]\tan(\alpha + n\beta)$

$$\tan\beta = \tan[(\alpha + n\beta) - \{\alpha + (n-1)\beta\}]$$

$$\tan\beta = \frac{\tan(\alpha + n\beta) - \tan(\alpha + (n-1)\beta\}]}{1 + \tan(\alpha + n\beta)\tan\{\alpha + (n-1)\beta\}]}$$

$$\therefore 1 + T_n = \cot\beta[\tan(\alpha + n\beta) - \tan\{\alpha + (n-1)\beta\}]$$

$$T_n = \cot\beta[\tan(\alpha + n\beta) - \tan\{\alpha + (n-1)\beta\}] - 1$$

For $n = 1$,

$$T_1 = \cot\beta[\tan(\alpha + \beta) - \tan\alpha] - 1$$

For $n = 2$,

$$T_2 = \cot\beta[\tan(\alpha + 2\beta) - \tan(\alpha + \beta)] - 1$$

For $n = 3$,

$$T_3 = \cot\beta[\tan(\alpha + 3\beta) - \tan(\alpha + 2\beta)] - 1$$

$$\vdots \quad \vdots \quad \vdots \quad \vdots$$

For $n = n$,

$$T_n = \cot\beta[\tan(\alpha + n\beta) - \tan(\alpha + (n-1)\beta\}] - 1$$

Sum columnwise,

$$S_n = T_1 + T_2 + T_3 + \ldots + T_n = \cot\beta[\tan(\alpha + n\beta) - \tan\alpha] - n$$

$$= \frac{\dfrac{\sin(\alpha + n\beta)}{\cos(\alpha + n\beta)} + \dfrac{\sin\alpha}{\cos\alpha}}{\tan\beta} - n = \frac{\dfrac{\sin(\alpha + n\beta - \alpha)}{\cos\alpha\cos(\alpha + n\beta)}}{\tan\beta} - n$$

$$= \frac{\dfrac{\sin n\beta}{\cos(\alpha + n\beta)\cos\alpha}}{\tan\beta} - n\tan\beta$$

112. $S_n = \sum_{r=1}^{n} T_r = \dfrac{n(n+1)(n+2)(n+3)}{8}$

$$T_r = S_r - S_{r-1} = \frac{r(r+1)(r+2)(r+3)}{8} - \frac{(r-1)r(r+1)(r+2)}{8}$$

$$= \frac{r(r+1)(r+2)}{2}$$

$$\frac{1}{T_r} = \frac{2}{r(r+1)(r+2)} = \frac{(r+2) - r}{r(r+1)(r+2)} = \left(\frac{1}{r(r+1)} - \frac{1}{(r+1)(r+2)}\right)$$

$$\sum_{r=1}^{n}\frac{1}{T_r} = \sum_{r=1}^{n}\left(\frac{1}{r(r+1)} - \frac{1}{(r+1)(r+2)}\right)$$

$$= \sum_{r=1}^{n}\left\{\left(\frac{1}{r} - \frac{1}{r+1}\right) - \left(\frac{1}{r+1} - \frac{1}{r+2}\right)\right\}$$

$$= \left(\frac{1}{1} - \frac{1}{n+1}\right) - \left(\frac{1}{2} - \frac{1}{n+2}\right)$$

$$= \frac{1}{2} + \frac{1}{n+2} - \frac{1}{n+1} = \frac{n(n+3)}{2(n+1)(n+2)}$$

113. Let d_1, d_2 and d_3 be the common differences of the 3 arithmetic progressions.

$$\therefore \quad S_i = \frac{n}{2}[2 \times a + (n-1)d_i], \forall i = 1, 2, 3$$

$$\Rightarrow \quad S_i = \frac{n}{2}[2 + (n-1)d_i]$$

$$\Rightarrow \quad S_i = n + \frac{n(n-1)}{2}d_i \Rightarrow d_i = \frac{2(S_i - n)}{n(n-1)}$$

Given that d_1, d_2, d_3 are in HP.

$$\therefore \quad \frac{1}{d_1}, \frac{1}{d_2}, \frac{1}{d_3} \text{ are in AP.}$$

$$\therefore \quad \frac{2}{d_2} = \frac{1}{d_1} + \frac{1}{d_3}$$

$$\Rightarrow \quad \frac{2}{\dfrac{2(S_2 - n)}{n(n-1)}} = \frac{1}{\dfrac{2(S_1 - n)}{n(n-1)}} + \frac{1}{\dfrac{2(S_3 - n)}{n(n-1)}}$$

$$\Rightarrow \quad \frac{2}{S_2 - n} = \frac{1}{S_1 - n} + \frac{1}{S_3 - n}$$

$$\Rightarrow \quad \frac{2}{S_2 - n} = \frac{S_3 + S_1 - 2n}{(S_1 - n)(S_3 - n)}$$

$$\Rightarrow 2[S_1S_3 - (S_1 + S_3)n + n^2] = (S_2 - n)(S_1 + S_3 - 2n)$$

$$\Rightarrow 2S_1S_3 - 2(S_1 + S_3)n + 2n^2$$

$$= S_1S_2 + S_2S_3 - 2nS_2 - n(S_1 + S_3) + 2n^2$$

$$\Rightarrow \quad 2S_1S_3 - S_2S_3 - S_1S_2 = n(S_1 + S_3 - 2S_2)$$

$$\Rightarrow \quad n = \frac{(2S_1S_3 - S_2S_3 - S_1S_2)}{(S_1 - 2S_2 + S_3)}$$

114. Let their ages be a, ar, ar^2.

After 3 yr, their ages will be $a + 3$, $ar + 3$, $ar^2 + 3$.

Given, $2(a + 3) = ar^2 + 3$ ...(i)

Let x rupees be the sum of the money divided.

And let $y = a + ar + ar^2$ ...(ii)

Then, $y + 9 = a + 3 + (ar + 3) + (ar^2 + 3)$

We have, $\dfrac{x(a+3)}{(y+9)} = \dfrac{xa}{y} + 105$

$$\Rightarrow \quad x\left(\frac{a+3}{y+9} - \frac{a}{y}\right) = 105 \quad \text{...(iii)}$$

Also, $\dfrac{x(ar+3)}{(y+9)} = \dfrac{xar}{y} + 15$

$$\Rightarrow \quad x\left[\frac{ar+3}{y+9} - \frac{ar}{y}\right] = 15 \quad \text{...(iv)}$$

On dividing Eq. (iii) by Eq. (iv), we get

$$\frac{y(a+3) - a(y+9)}{y(ar+3) - ar(y+9)} = 7 \Rightarrow \frac{y - 3a}{y - 3ar} = 7$$

$$\Rightarrow \quad 6y = 21ar - 3a \Rightarrow y = \frac{a(7r-1)}{2}$$

From Eq. (ii),

$$\frac{a(7r-1)}{2} = a + ar + ar^2$$

$$\Rightarrow \quad 5ar = 3a + 2ar^2 \quad \text{...(v)}$$

From Eqs. (i) and (ii),

$$a = 12, r = \frac{3}{2}$$

Let ages of these friends are $12, 12 \times \frac{3}{2}, 12 \times \left(\frac{3}{2}\right)^2$ i.e. 12, 18, 27.

115. Clearly, $x = \dfrac{1}{1-a}$, $y = \dfrac{1}{1-b}$ and $z = \dfrac{1}{1-c}$.

Since, a, b, c are in AP.

$$\Rightarrow \quad 1 - a, 1 - b, 1 - c \text{ are also in AP.}$$

$$\Rightarrow \quad \frac{1}{1-a}, \frac{1}{1-b}, \frac{1}{1-c} \text{ are in HP.}$$

$\therefore x, y, z$ are in HP.

116. $\because$ $B_n = 1 - A_n > A_n \Rightarrow A_n < \frac{1}{2}$

Now, $A_n = \dfrac{\frac{3}{4}\left(1 - \left(-\frac{3}{4}\right)^n\right)}{1 + \frac{3}{4}} < \frac{1}{2} \Rightarrow \left(-\frac{3}{4}\right)^n > -\frac{1}{6}$

Obviously, it is true for all even values of n.

But for $n = 1, -\frac{3}{4} < -\frac{1}{6}$

$n = 3\left(-\frac{3}{4}\right)^3 = -\frac{27}{24} < -\frac{1}{6}$

$n = 5, \left(-\frac{3}{4}\right)^5 = -\frac{243}{1024} > -\frac{1}{6}$

which is true for $n = 7$ obviously, $n_0 = 7$

Aliter $B_n = 1 - A_n > A_n$

$\Rightarrow A_n < \frac{1}{2} \Rightarrow \dfrac{\frac{3}{4}\left(1 - \left(-\frac{3}{4}\right)^n\right)}{1 + \frac{3}{4}} < \frac{1}{2} \Rightarrow \left(-\frac{3}{4}\right)^n > -\frac{1}{6}$

Obviously, it is true for all even values of n.

But for $n = 1, -\frac{3}{4} < -\frac{1}{6}$

$n = 3, \left(-\frac{3}{4}\right)^3 = -\frac{27}{64} < -\frac{1}{6}$

$n = 5, \left(-\frac{3}{4}\right)^5 = -\frac{243}{1024} < -\frac{1}{6}$

and for $n = 7 \Rightarrow \left(-\frac{3}{4}\right)^7 = -\frac{2187}{12288} > -\frac{1}{6}$

Hence, minimum natural number $n_0 = 7$.

117. $\because$ $\dfrac{\frac{p}{2}[2a_1 + (p-1)d]}{\frac{q}{2}[2a_1 + (q-1)d]} = \dfrac{p^2}{q^2}$

$\Rightarrow \dfrac{2a_1 + (p-1)d}{2a_1 + (q-1)d} = \dfrac{p}{q} \Rightarrow \dfrac{a_1 + \left(\frac{p-1}{2}\right)d}{a_1 + \left(\frac{q-1}{2}\right)d} = \dfrac{p}{q}$

For $\frac{a_6}{a_{21}}$, $p = 11$ and $q = 41 \Rightarrow \frac{a_6}{a_{21}} = \frac{11}{41}$

118. $\frac{1}{a_2} - \frac{1}{a_1} = \frac{1}{a_3} - \frac{1}{a_2} = \ldots = \frac{1}{a_n} - \frac{1}{a_{n-1}} = d$ [say]

Then, $a_1a_2 = \frac{a_1 - a_2}{d}, a_2a_3 = \frac{a_2 - a_3}{d}, \ldots, a_{n-1}a_n = \frac{a_{n-1} - a_n}{d}$

$\therefore a_1a_2 + a_2a_3 + \ldots + a_{n-1}a_n = \frac{a_1 - a_n}{d}$

Also, $\frac{1}{a_n} = \frac{1}{a_1} + (n-1)d \Rightarrow \frac{a_1 - a_n}{d} = (n-1)a_1a_n$

$\therefore a_1a_2 + a_2a_3 + \ldots + a_{n-1}a_n = (n-1)a_1a_n$

119. (i) $V_r = \frac{r}{2}[(2r + (r-1)(2r-1)] = \frac{1}{2}(2r^3 - r^2 + r)$

$\therefore \sum_{r=1}^{n} V_r = \frac{1}{2}\left[2\sum_{r=1}^{n} r^3 - \sum_{r=1}^{n} r^3 + \sum_{r=1}^{n} r\right]$

$= \frac{1}{2}\left[2\left(\frac{n(n+1)}{2}\right)^2 - \frac{n(n+1)(2n+1)}{6} + \frac{n(n+1)}{2}\right]$

$= \frac{1}{12}n(n+1)(3n^2 + n + 2)$

(ii) $V_{r+1} - V_r = (r+1)^3 - r^3 - \frac{1}{2}[(r+1)^2 - r^2] + \frac{1}{2}(1)$

$= 3r^2 + 2r + 1$

$\therefore T_r = 3r^2 + 2r - 1$

$= (r+1)(3r-1)$, which is a composite number.

(iii) Since, $T_r = 3r^2 + 2r - 1$

$\therefore T_{r+1} = 3(r+1)^2 + 2(r+1) - 1$

$\therefore Q_r = T_{r+1} - T_r = 3[2r + 1] + 2[1]$

$\Rightarrow Q_r = 6r + 5$

$\Rightarrow Q_{r+1} = 6(r+1) + 5$

Common difference $= Q_{r+1} - Q_r = 6$

120. (i) $A_1 = \frac{a+b}{2}; G_1 = \sqrt{ab}; H_1 = \frac{2ab}{a+b}$

$A_n = \frac{A_{n-1} + H_{n-1}}{2}, G_n = \sqrt{A_{n-1}H_{n-1}}$ and $H_n = \frac{2A_{n-1}H_{n-1}}{A_{n-1} + H_{n-1}}$

Clearly, $G_1 = G_2 = G_3 = \ldots = \sqrt{ab}$

(ii) A_2 is AM of A_1 and H_1 and $A_1 > H_1$

$\Rightarrow A_1 > A_2 > H_1$

A_3 is AM of A_2 and H_2 and $A_2 > H_2$

$\Rightarrow A_2 > A_3 > H_2$

$\therefore A_1 > A_2 > A_3 > \ldots$

(iii) As above $A_1 > H_2 > H_1, A_1 > H_3 > H_2$

$\therefore H_1 < H_2 < H_3 < \ldots$

121. Let geometric progression is $a, ar, ar^2, \ldots,$ $[a, r > 0]$

$\because a = ar + ar^2$

$\Rightarrow r^2 + r - 1 = 0 \Rightarrow r = \frac{-1 \pm \sqrt{5}}{2}$

$\therefore r = \frac{\sqrt{5} - 1}{2}$

122. $b_1 = a_1, b_2 = b_1 + a_2 = a_1 + a_2, b_3 = b_2 + a_3 = a_1 + a_2 + a_3$

and $b_4 = b_3 + a_4 = a_1 + a_2 + a_3 + a_4$

Hence, b_1, b_2, b_3, b_4 are neither in AP nor in GP and nor in HP

123. Let $a, ar, ar^2, \ldots$

$a + ar = 12$ ...(i)

and $ar^2 + ar^3 = 48$ ...(ii)

On dividing Eq. (ii) by Eq. (i), we get

$r^2 = 4$, if $r \neq -1$

$\therefore r = -2$

[$\because$ terms are alternatively positive and negative]

Now, from Eq. (i), $a = -12$

124. $\because$ $S_n = cn^2$

$\therefore t_n = S_n - S_{n-1} = c(2n - 1)$

$\Sigma t_n^2 = c^2\Sigma(2n-1)^2$

$= c^2\Sigma(4n^2 - 4n + 1) = c^2\{4\Sigma n^2 - 4\Sigma n + \Sigma 1\}$

$= c^2\left\{\frac{4n(n+1)(2n+1)}{6} - \frac{4n(n+1)}{2} + n\right\}$

$$= c^2 n \left\{ \frac{2}{3}(2n^2 + 3n + 1) - 2n - 2 + 1 \right\}$$

$$= \frac{c^2 n}{3}(4n^2 - 1) = \frac{n(4n^2 - 1)c^2}{3}$$

125. Let $S = 1 + \frac{2}{3} + \frac{6}{3^2} + \frac{10}{3^3} + \frac{14}{3^4} + \dots$ ...(i)

$$\therefore \frac{1}{3}S = \frac{1}{3} + \frac{2}{3^2} + \frac{6}{3^3} + \frac{10}{3^4} + \dots \quad \text{...(ii)}$$

On subtracting Eq. (ii) from Eq. (i), we get

$$\frac{2}{3}S = 1 + \frac{1}{3} + \frac{4}{3^2} + \frac{4}{3^3} + \frac{4}{3^4} + \dots$$

$$= \frac{4}{3} + 4\left(\frac{1}{3^2} + \frac{1}{3^3} + \frac{1}{3^4} + \dots\right) = \frac{4}{3} + 4\left\{\frac{\frac{1}{3^2}}{1 - \frac{1}{3}}\right\} = \frac{4}{3} + \frac{2}{3} = 2$$

$$\therefore \quad S = 3$$

126. $S_k = \frac{a}{1-r} = \frac{\frac{k-1}{k!}}{1 - \frac{1}{k}} = \frac{k}{k!} = \frac{1}{(k-1)!}$

Now, $\sum_{k=2}^{100} |(k^2 - 3k + 1)S_k| = \sum_{k=2}^{100} \left|(k^2 - 3k + 1) \cdot \frac{1}{(k-1)!}\right|$

$$= \sum_{k=2}^{100} \left| \frac{(k-1)}{(k-2)} - \frac{k}{(k-1)!} \right|$$

$$= \left| \frac{1}{0!} - \frac{2}{1!} \right| + \left| \frac{2}{1!} - \frac{3}{2!} \right| + \left| \frac{3}{2!} - \frac{4}{3!} \right| + \dots + \left| \frac{99}{98!} - \frac{100}{99!} \right|$$

$$= \left(\frac{2}{1!} - \frac{1}{0!} \right) + \left(\frac{2}{1!} - \frac{3}{2!} \right) + \left(\frac{3}{2!} - \frac{4}{3!} \right) + \dots + \left(\frac{99}{98!} - \frac{100}{99!} \right)$$

$$= 3 - \frac{100}{99!} = 3 - \frac{(100)^2}{100!}$$

$$\therefore \frac{(100)^2}{100!} + \sum_{k=2}^{100} |(k^2 - 3k + 1)S_k| = 3$$

127. $\because \quad a_k = 2a_{k-1} - a_{k-2}$ or $a_{k-1} = \frac{a_{k-2} + a_k}{2}$

$\therefore \quad a_1, a_2, a_3, \dots$ are in AP.

$$\because \quad \frac{a_1^2 + a_2^2 + a_3^2 + \dots + a_{11}^2}{11} = 90 \Rightarrow \sum_{i=1}^{11} a_i^2 = 11 \times 90$$

$$\Rightarrow \quad \sum_{k=1}^{11} (a_1 + (i-1)d)^2 = 11 \times 90$$

$$\Rightarrow \quad \sum_{k=1}^{11} \{a_1^2 + 2a_1 d(i-1) + d^2 (i-1)^2\} = 11 \times 90$$

$$\Rightarrow \quad 11 \times a_1^2 + 2a_1 d(0 + 1 + 2 + 3 + \dots + 10) + d^2(0^2 + 1^2 + 2^2 + \dots + 10^2) = 11 \times 90$$

$$\Rightarrow \quad 11 \times 15^2 + 2 \times 15 \times d \cdot \left(\frac{10 \cdot 11}{2}\right) + d^2 \cdot \left(\frac{10 \cdot 11 \cdot 21}{6}\right) = 11 \times 90$$

$$\Rightarrow \quad 385d^2 + 1650d + 1485 = 0 \quad [\because a_1 = 15]$$

$$\Rightarrow \quad 7d^2 + 30d + 27 = 0$$

$$\Rightarrow \quad (7d + 9)(d + 3) = 0$$

$$\therefore \quad d = -3, d \neq -\frac{9}{7} \quad [\because 27 - 2a_2 > 0]$$

$$\therefore \quad \frac{a_1 + a_2 + a_3 + \dots + a_{11}}{11} = \frac{\frac{11}{2}\{2a_1 + (11-1)d\}}{11}$$

$$= a_1 + 5d = 15 - 15 = 0$$

128. Till 10th minute, number of counted notes = 1500

$$\therefore 3000 = \frac{n}{2}\{2 \times 148 + (n-1) \times -2\} = n(148 - n + 1)$$

$$\Rightarrow \quad n^2 - 149n + 3000 = 0$$

$$\Rightarrow \quad (n - 125)(n - 24) = 0$$

$$\therefore \quad n = 125, 24$$

$n = 125$ is not possible.

$$\therefore \quad n = 24$$

$\therefore$ Total time $= 10 + 24 = 34$ min

129. $\because$ AM $\geq$ GM

$$\therefore \quad \frac{a^{-5} + a^{-4} + a^{-3} + a^{-3} + a^{-3} + 1 + a^8 + a^{10}}{8}$$

$$\geq (a^{-5} \cdot a^{-4} \cdot a^{-3} \cdot a^{-3} \cdot a^{-3} \cdot 1 \cdot a^8 \cdot a^{10})^{1/8} = (1)^{1/8} = 1$$

$$\Rightarrow \quad \frac{a^{-5} + a^{-4} + 3a^{-3} + 1 + a^8 + a^{10}}{8} \geq 1$$

$$\therefore \quad a^{-5} + a^{-4} + 3a^{-3} + 1 + a^8 + a^{10} \geq 8$$

$\Rightarrow$ Required minimum value = 8

130. Let the time taken to save ₹ 11040 be $(n + 3)$ months.

For first 3 months, he saves ₹ 200 each month.

$\therefore$ In $(n + 3)$ month,

$$3 \times 200 + \frac{n}{2}[2(240) + (n-1) \times 40] = 11040$$

$$\Rightarrow \quad 600 + \frac{n}{2}[40(12 + n - 1)] = 11040$$

$$\Rightarrow \quad 600 + 20n(n + 11) = 11040$$

$$\Rightarrow \quad n^2 + 11n - 522 = 0$$

$$\Rightarrow \quad (n - 18)(n + 29) = 0$$

$$\therefore \quad n = 18, \text{ neglecting } n = -29$$

$\therefore$ Total time $= n + 3 = 21$ months

131. Given, $\quad a_2 + a_4 + a_6 + \dots + a_{200} = \alpha$ ...(i)

and $\quad a_1 + a_3 + a_5 + \dots + a_{199} = \beta$ ...(ii)

On subtracting Eq. (ii) from Eq. (i), we get

$$(a_2 - a_1) + (a_4 - a_3) + (a_6 - a_5) + \dots + (a_{200} - a_{199}) = \alpha - \beta$$

$$\Rightarrow \quad d + d + d + \dots + d = \alpha - \beta \Rightarrow 100d = \alpha - \beta$$

$$\therefore \quad d = \frac{(\alpha - \beta)}{100}$$

132. $\because a_1, a_2, a_3, \dots$ are in HP.

$$\therefore \quad \frac{1}{a_1}, \frac{1}{a_2}, \frac{1}{a_3}, \dots \text{ are in AP.}$$

Let D be the common difference of this AP, then

$$\frac{1}{a_{20}} = \frac{1}{a_1} + (20 - 1)D$$

$$\Rightarrow \quad D = \frac{\frac{1}{25} - \frac{1}{5}}{19} = -\frac{4}{25 \times 19}$$

and $\frac{1}{a_n}=\frac{1}{a_1}+(n-1)D=\frac{1}{5}-\frac{4(n-1)}{25\times 19}=\left(\frac{95-4n+4}{25\times 19}\right)$

$=\left(\frac{99-4n}{25\times 19}\right)<0$ $[\because a_n<0]$

$\Rightarrow \quad 99-4n<0 \Rightarrow n>24.75$

Hence, the least positive integer is $n=25$.

133. $\because \quad (1)=(1-0)(1^2+1\cdot 0+0^2)=1^3-0^3$

$(1+2+4)=(2-1)(2^2+2\cdot 1+1^2)=2^3-1^3$

$(4+6+9)=(3-2)(3^2+3\cdot 2+2^2)=3^3-2^3$

$\vdots \quad \vdots \quad \vdots$

$(361+380+400)=(20-19)(20^2+20\cdot 19+19^2)=20^3-19^3$

Required sum

$=(1^3-0^3)+(2^3-1^3)+(3^3-2^3)+\ldots+(20^2-19^3)=20^3=8000$

Also, $\sum_{k=1}^{n}k^3-(k-1)^3=\sum_{k=1}^{n}\{k-(k-1)\}\{k^2+k(k-1)+(k-1)^2\}$

$=\sum_{k=1}^{n}(3k^2-3k+1)=3\Sigma n^2-3\Sigma n+\Sigma 1$

$=\frac{3n(n+1)(2n+1)}{6}-\frac{3n(n+1)}{2}+n$

$=\frac{n}{2}(2n^2+3n+1-3n-3+2)=n^3$

Both statements are correct and Statement-2 is the correct explanation of Statement-1.

134. Let a be the first term and d be the common difference. Then,

$100\,T_{100}=50\,T_{50}$

$\Rightarrow \quad 100(a+99d)=50(a+49d)$

$\Rightarrow \quad 2(a+99d)=(a+49d) \Rightarrow a+149d=0$

$\therefore \quad T_{150}=0$

135. $\because$ x, y, z are in AP.

Let $x=y-d, z=y+d$ ...(i)

Also, given $\tan^{-1}x, \tan^{-1}y, \tan^{-1}z$ are in AP.

$\therefore \quad 2\tan^{-1}y=\tan^{-1}x+\tan^{-1}z$

$\Rightarrow \quad \tan^{-1}\left(\frac{2y}{1-y^2}\right)=\tan^{-1}\left(\frac{x+z}{1-xz}\right)$

$\Rightarrow \quad \frac{2y}{1-y^2}=\frac{x+z}{1-xz} \Rightarrow \frac{2y}{1-y^2}=\frac{2y}{1-(y^2-d^2)}$

$\Rightarrow \quad y^2=y^2-d^2$ [from Eq. (i)]

$\therefore \quad d=0$

From Eq. (i), $x=y$ and $z=y$

$\therefore \quad x=y=z$

Aliter

$\because$ x, y, z are in AP. ...(i)

$\therefore \quad 2y=x+z$ ...(ii)

Also, $\tan^{-1}x, \tan^{-1}y, \tan^{-1}z$ are in AP.

$\therefore \quad 2\tan^{-1}y=\tan^{-1}x+\tan^{-1}z$

$\Rightarrow \quad \tan^{-1}\left(\frac{2y}{1-y^2}\right)=\tan^{-1}\left(\frac{x+z}{1-xz}\right)$

$\Rightarrow \quad \frac{2y}{1-y^2}=\frac{x+z}{1-xz}=\frac{2y}{1-xz}$ [from Eq. (ii)]

$\Rightarrow \quad y^2=zx$

$\therefore$ x, y, z are in GP. ...(iii)

From Eqs. (i) and (ii) x, y, z are in AP and also in GP, then $x=y=z$.

136. $S=0.7+0.77+0.777+\ldots$ upto 20 terms

$=\frac{7}{9}(0.9+0.99+0.999+\ldots$ upto 20 terms$)$

$=\frac{7}{9}[(1-0.1)+(1-0.01)+(1-0.001)+\ldots$ upto 20 terms$]$

$=\frac{7}{9}[(1+1+1+\ldots$ upto 20 times$)$

$-\left(\frac{1}{10}+\frac{1}{10^2}+\frac{1}{10^3}+\ldots \text{ upto 20 terms}\right)]$

$=\frac{7}{9}\left[20-\frac{\frac{1}{10}\left(1-\left(\frac{1}{10}\right)^{20}\right)}{1-\frac{1}{10}}\right]=\frac{7}{9}\left[\frac{180-1+10^{-20}}{9}\right]$

$=\frac{7}{81}(179+10^{-20})$

137. $S_n=-1^2-2^2+3^2+4^2-5^2-6^2+7^2+8^2-\ldots+(4n-1)^2+(4n)^2$

$=(3^2-1^2)+(4^2-2^2)+(7^2-5^2)+(8^2-6^2)+\ldots$
$+[\{(4n-1)^2-(4n-3)^2\}+\{(4n)^2-(4n-2)^2\}]$

$=4[2+3+6+7+10+11+\ldots+(4n-2)+(4n-1)]$

$=8\{(1+3+5+\ldots+(2n-1)\}+4\{3+7+11+\ldots+(4n-1)\}$

$=16n^2+4n=4n(4n+1), n\in N$

Satisfied by (a) and (d), where $n=8, 9$, respectively.

138. Let two consecutive numbers are k and $k+1$ such that $1\le k\le n-1$, then

$(1+2+3+\ldots+n)-(k+k+1)=1224$

$\Rightarrow \quad \frac{n(n+1)}{2}-(2k+1)=1224$ or $k=\frac{n^2+n-2450}{4}$

Now, $1\le\frac{n^2+n-2450}{4}\le n-1 \Rightarrow 49<n<51$

$\therefore \quad n=50 \Rightarrow k=25$

Hence, $k-20=25-20=5$

139. The given series can be written as

$k=1+2\left(\frac{11}{10}\right)+3\left(\frac{11}{10}\right)^2+\ldots+9\left(\frac{11}{10}\right)^8+10\left(\frac{11}{10}\right)^9$ ...(i)

On multiplying both sides by $\left(\frac{11}{10}\right)$, then

$\frac{11k}{10}=\left(\frac{11}{10}\right)+2\left(\frac{11}{10}\right)^2+3\left(\frac{11}{10}\right)^3+\ldots+9\left(\frac{11}{10}\right)^9+10\left(\frac{11}{10}\right)^{10}$ ...(ii)

Now, on subtracting Eq. (ii) from Eq. (i), then

$-\frac{k}{10}=\underbrace{1+\left(\frac{11}{10}\right)+\left(\frac{11}{10}\right)^2+\ldots+\left(\frac{11}{10}\right)^2}_{10 \text{ times}}-10\left(\frac{11}{10}\right)^{10}$

$=\frac{1\cdot\left\{\left(\frac{11}{10}\right)^{10}-1\right\}}{\left(\frac{11}{10}-1\right)}-10\left(\frac{11}{10}\right)^{10}$

$$\Rightarrow \quad k = -100 \cdot \left\{\left(\frac{11}{10}\right)^{10} - 1\right\} + 100\left(\frac{11}{10}\right)^{10} = 100$$

140. Let a, ar, ar^2 are in GP. $\because$ GP is increasing.

$\therefore \quad r > 1$

New numbers $a, 2ar, ar^2$ are in AP.

$\therefore \quad 4ar = a + ar^2 \Rightarrow r^2 - 4r + 1 = 0$

Hence, $\quad r = \dfrac{4 \pm \sqrt{(16-4)}}{2} = 2 + \sqrt{3} \quad [\because r > 1]$

141. Let $\quad \dfrac{b}{a} = \dfrac{c}{b} = r$

$\therefore \quad b = ar, c = ar^2$

Given, $\quad \dfrac{a+b+c}{3} = b + 2 \Rightarrow 1 + \dfrac{b}{a} + \dfrac{c}{a} = 3\left(\dfrac{b}{a}\right) + \dfrac{6}{a}$

$\Rightarrow \quad 1 + r + r^2 = 3r + \dfrac{6}{a}$

Now, for $a = 6$, only we get $r = 0, 2$ [rational]

So, $\quad r = 2$

$\Rightarrow \quad (a, b, c) = (6, 12, 24)$

$\therefore \quad \dfrac{a^2 + a - 14}{a+1} = \dfrac{36 + 6 - 14}{6+1} = 4$

142. $T_n = \dfrac{1^3 + 2^3 + 3^3 + \ldots + n^3}{1 + 3 + 5 + \ldots + (2n-1)} = \dfrac{\left(\dfrac{n(n+1)}{2}\right)^2}{\dfrac{n(1+2n-1)}{2}} = \dfrac{(n+1)^2}{4}$

$= \dfrac{1}{4}(n^2 + 2n + 1)$

$\therefore S_n = \dfrac{1}{4}(\Sigma n^2 + 2\Sigma n + \Sigma 1) = \dfrac{1}{4}\left[\dfrac{n(n+1)(2n+1)}{6} + \dfrac{2n(n+1)}{2} + n\right]$

$S_9 = \dfrac{1}{4}[285 + 90 + 9] = 96$

143. Given, $m = \dfrac{l+n}{2} \Rightarrow l + n = 2m \quad \ldots(i)$

and l, G_1, G_2, G_3, n are in GP.

$\therefore \quad \dfrac{G_1}{l} = \dfrac{G_2}{G_1} = \dfrac{G_3}{G_2} = \dfrac{n}{G_3}$

$\Rightarrow \quad G_1G_3 = \ln, G_1^2 = lG_2, G_2^2 = G_3G_1, G_3^2 = nG_2 \quad \ldots(ii)$

Now, $G_1^4 + 2G_2^4 + G_3^4 = l^2G_2^2 + 2G_2^4 + n^2G_2^2$

$= G_2^2(l^2 + 2G_2^2 + n^2)$ [from Eq. (ii)]

$= G_3G_1(l^2 + 2G_3G_1 + n^2)$ [from Eq. (ii)]

$= \ln(l^2 + 2\ln + n^2)$ [from Eq. (ii)]

$= \ln(l+n)^2 = \ln(2m)^2$ [from Eq. (i)] $= 4lm^2n$

144. Let first term $= a$ and common difference $= d$

$\because \quad \dfrac{\text{sum of seven terms}}{\text{sum of eleven terms}} = \dfrac{6}{11}$

$\Rightarrow \quad \dfrac{\frac{7}{2}(a_1 + a_7)}{\frac{11}{2}(a_1 + a_{11})} = \dfrac{6}{11} \Rightarrow \dfrac{\frac{7}{2}(2a + 6d)}{\frac{11}{2}(2a + 10d)} = \dfrac{6}{11}$

or $\quad a = 9d$ and $130 < a_7 < 140$

$\Rightarrow \quad 130 < a_1 + 6d < 140 \Rightarrow 130 < 15d < 140$

$\therefore \quad 8\frac{2}{3} < d < 9\frac{1}{3} \quad \Rightarrow d = 9 \quad (\because a, d \in N)$

145. $\because$ $a + d, a + 4d, a + 8d$ are in GP $(d \neq 0)$

$\therefore \quad (a + 4d)^2 = (a + d)(a + 8d)$

$\Rightarrow \quad a = 8d$

$\therefore$ Common ratio $= \dfrac{a + 4d}{a + d} = \dfrac{8d + 4d}{8d + d} = \dfrac{4}{3} \quad (\because a = 8d)$

Aliter

Let the GP be a, ar, ar^2 and terms of AP and $A + d, A + 4d, A + 8d$, then

$$r = \frac{ar^2 - ar}{ar - a} = \frac{(A + 8d) - (A + 4d)}{(A + 4d) - (A + d)} = \frac{4}{3}$$

146. $\left(\dfrac{8}{5}\right)^2 + \left(\dfrac{12}{5}\right)^2 + \left(\dfrac{16}{5}\right)^2 + \left(\dfrac{20}{5}\right)^2 + \ldots + \left(\dfrac{44}{5}\right)^2$

$= \dfrac{16}{25}(2^2 + 3^2 + 4^2 + 5^2 + \ldots 11^2)$

$= \dfrac{16}{25}\left(\dfrac{11.(11+1).(22+1)}{6} - 1\right)$

$= \dfrac{16}{25} \times 505 = \dfrac{16}{5} \times 101 = \dfrac{16}{5}$ m (given)

$\therefore m = 101$

147. $\because$ $\log_e b_1, \log_e b_2, \log_e b_3, \ldots, \log_e b_{101}$ are in AP.

$\Rightarrow$ $b_1, b_2, b_3, \ldots, b_{101}$ are in GP with common ratio 2.

($\because$ common difference $= \log_e 2$)

Also, $a_1, a_2, a_3, \ldots a_{101}$ are in AP.

where, $a_1 = b_1$ and $a_{51} = b_{51}$

$\therefore$ $b_2, b_3, \ldots, b_{50}$ are GM's and $a_2, a_3, \ldots, a_{50}$ are AM's between b_1 and b_{51}.

$\because \quad$ GM < AM

$\Rightarrow \quad b_2 < a_2, b_3 < a_3, \ldots, b_{50} < a_{50}$

$\therefore \quad b_1 + b_2 + b_3 + \ldots + b_{51} < a_1 + a_2 + a_3 + \ldots + a_{51}$

$\Rightarrow t < s$

Also, $a_1, a_2, a_3, \ldots, a_{101}$ are in AP and $b_1, b_2, b_3, \ldots b_{101}$ are in GP.

$\because \quad a_1 = b_1$ and $a_{51} = b_{51}$

$\therefore \quad b_{101} > a_{101}$

148. $(15a)^2 + (3b)^2 + (5c)^2 - 45ab - 15bc - 75ac = 0$

$\Rightarrow \dfrac{1}{2}\{(15a - 3b)^2 + (3b - 5c)^2 + (5c - 15a)^2\} = 0$

$\Rightarrow \quad (15a - 3b)^2 + (3b - 5c)^2 + (5c - 15a)^2 = 0$

or $\quad 15a - 3b = 0, 3b - 5c = 0, 5c - 15a = 0$

$\because \quad b = 5a, c = 3a$

$\Rightarrow$ $5a, 3a, a$ are in AP i.e. b, c, a are in AP.

CHAPTER

04

Logarithms and Their Properties

Learning Part

Session 1

- Definition
- Characteristic and Mantissa

Session 2

- Principle Properties of Logarithm

Session 3

- Properties of Monotonocity of Logarithm
- Graphs of Logarithmic Functions

Practice Part

- JEE Type Examples
- Chapter Exercises

The technique of logarithms was introduced by **John Napier** (1550-1617). The logarithm is a form of indices which is used to simplify the algebraic calculations. The operations of multiplication, division of a very large number becomes quite easy and get converted into simple operations of addition and subtraction, respectively. The results obtained are correct upto some decimal places.

Session 1

Definition, Characteristic and Mantissa

Definition

The logarithm of any positive number, whose base is a number (> 0) different from 1, is the index or the power to which the base must be raised in order to obtain the given number.

i.e. if $a^x = b$ (where $a > 0, \neq 1$), then x is called the logarithm of b to the base a and we write $\log_a b = x$, clearly $b > 0$. Thus, $\log_a b = x \Leftrightarrow a^x = b, a > 0, a \neq 1$ and $b > 0$.

If $a = 10$, then we write $\log b$ rather than $\log_{10} b$. If $a = e$, we write $\ln b$ rather than $\log_e b$. Here, 'e' is called as **Napier's base** and has numerical value equal to 2.7182. Also, $\log_{10} e$ is known as **Napierian constant**.

i.e. $\log_{10} e = 0.4343$

$\therefore$ $\ln b = 2.303 \log_{10} b$

$$\left[\text{since, } \ln b = \log_{10} b \times \log_e 10 = \frac{1}{\log_{10} e} \times \log_{10} b = \frac{1}{0.4343} \log_{10} b = 2.303 \log_{10} b\right]$$

Remember

(i) $\log 2 = \log_{10} 2 = 0.3010$

(ii) $\log 3 = \log_{10} 3 = 0.4771$

(iii) $\ln 2 = 2.303 \log 2 = 0.693$

(iv) $\ln 10 = 2.303$

Corollary **I** From the definition of the logarithm of the number b to the base a, we have an identity

$$a^{\log_a b} = b, a > 0, a \neq 1 \text{ and } b > 0$$

which is known as the **Fundamental Logarithmic Identity**.

Corollary **II** The function defined by $f(x) = \log_a x, a > 0, a \neq 1$ is called logarithmic function. Its domain is $(0, \infty)$ and range is R (set of all real numbers).

Corollary **III** $a^x > 0, \forall x \in R$

(i) If $a > 1$, then a^x is monotonically increasing.

For example, $5^{2.7} > 5^{2.5}, 3^{222} > 3^{111}$

(ii) If $0 < a < 1$, then a^x is monotonically decreasing.

For example, $\left(\frac{1}{5}\right)^{2.7} < \left(\frac{1}{5}\right)^{2.5}, (0.7)^{222} < (0.7)^{212}$

Corollary **IV**

(i) If $a > 1$, then $a^{-\infty} = 0$

$\therefore$ $\log_a 0 = -\infty$ (if $a > 1$)

(ii) If $0 < a < 1$, then $a^{\infty} = 0$

$\therefore$ $\log_a 0 = +\infty$ (if $0 < a < 1$)

Corollary **V** (i) $\log_a b \to \infty$, if $a > 1, b \to \infty$

(ii) $\log_a b \to -\infty$, if $0 < a < 1, b \to \infty$

Remark

1. 'log' is the abbreviation of the word 'logarithm'.
2. **Common logarithm** (Brigg's logarithms) The base is 10.
3. If $x < 0, a > 0$ and $a \neq 1$, then $\log_a x$ is an imaginary.
4. If $a > 1$, $\log_a x = \begin{cases} +\text{ve}, & x > 1 \\ 0, & x = 1 \\ -\text{ve}, & 0 < x < 1 \end{cases}$

   And if $0 < a < 1$, $\log_a x = \begin{cases} +\text{ve}, & 0 < x < 1 \\ 0, & x = 1 \\ -\text{ve}, & x > 1 \end{cases}$
5. $\log_a 1 = 0\ (a > 0, a \neq 1)$

   $\log_a a = 1\ (a > 0, a \neq 1)$ and $\log_{(1/a)} a = -1\ (a > 0, a \neq 1)$

Example 1. Find the value of the following :

(i) $\log_9 27$ (ii) $\log_{3\sqrt{2}} 324$

(iii) $\log_{1/9}(27\sqrt{3})$ (iv) $\log_{(5+2\sqrt{6})}(5-2\sqrt{6})$

(v) $\log_{0.2} 0.008$ (vi) $2^{2\log_4 5}$

(vii) $(0.4)^{-\log_{2.5}\left\{\frac{1}{3}+\frac{1}{3^2}+\frac{1}{3^3}+\dots\right\}}$ (viii) $(0.05)^{\log_{\sqrt{20}}(0.\bar{3})}$

Sol. (i) Let $x = \log_9 27$

$\Rightarrow \quad 9^x = 27 \Rightarrow 3^{2x} = 3^3 \Rightarrow 2x = 3$

$\therefore \quad x = \frac{3}{2}$

(ii) Let $x = \log_{3\sqrt{2}} 324$

$\Rightarrow (3\sqrt{2})^x = 324 = 2^2 \cdot 3^4 \Rightarrow (3\sqrt{2})^x = (3\sqrt{2})^4$

$\therefore \quad x = 4$

(iii) Let $x = \log_{1/9}(27\sqrt{3})$

$\Rightarrow \quad \left(\frac{1}{9}\right)^x = 27\sqrt{3} \Rightarrow 3^{-2x} = 3^{7/2} \Rightarrow -2x = 7/2$

$\therefore \quad x = -\frac{7}{4}$

(iv) $\because (5+2\sqrt{6})(5-2\sqrt{6}) = 1$

or $5 + 2\sqrt{6} = \frac{1}{5-2\sqrt{6}}$ ...(i)

Now, let $x = \log_{(5+2\sqrt{6})}(5-2\sqrt{6})$

$= \log_{1/(5-2\sqrt{6})} 5 - 2\sqrt{6} = -1$ [from Eq. (i)]

(v) Let $x = \log_{0.2} 0.008$

$\Rightarrow \quad (0.2)^x = 0.008 \Rightarrow (0.2)^x = (0.2)^3 \Rightarrow x = 3$

(vi) Let $x = 2^{2\log_4 5} = 4^{\log_4 5} = 5$

(vii) Let $x = (0.4)^{-\log_{2.5}\left\{\frac{1}{3}+\frac{1}{3^2}+\frac{1}{3^3}+\dots\right\}}$

$$= \left(\frac{4}{10}\right)^{-\log_{2.5}\left\{\frac{\frac{1}{3}}{1-\frac{1}{3}}\right\}} = \left(\frac{2}{5}\right)^{-\log_{2.5}\left(\frac{1}{2}\right)} = \left(\frac{5}{2}\right)^{\log_{5/2}\left(\frac{1}{2}\right)} = \frac{1}{2}$$

(viii) Let $x = (0.05)^{\log_{\sqrt{20}}(0.\bar{3})} = (0.05)^{\log_{\sqrt{20}}(\lambda)}$ ...(i)

where, $\lambda = 0.\bar{3}$

Then, $\lambda = 0.33333\dots$ ...(ii)

$\Rightarrow \quad 10\lambda = 3.33333\dots$ ...(iii)

On subtracting Eq. (ii) from Eq. (iii), we get

$$9\lambda = 3 \Rightarrow \lambda = \frac{1}{3}$$

Now, from Eq. (i), $x = (0.05)^{\log_{\sqrt{20}}\left(\frac{1}{3}\right)}$

$$= \left(\frac{1}{20}\right)^{\log_{(20)^{1/2}}(3)^{-1}} = \left(\frac{1}{20}\right)^{-\frac{1}{1/2}\log_{20} 3}$$

$$= 20^{(2\log_{20} 3)} = 20^{\log_{20} 3^2} = 3^2 = 9$$

Example 2. Find the value of the following:

(i) $\log_{\tan 45^\circ} \cot 30^\circ$ (ii) $\log_{(\sec^2 60^\circ - \tan^2 60^\circ)} \cos 60^\circ$

(iii) $\log_{(\sin^2 30^\circ + \cos^2 30^\circ)} 1$ (iv) $\log_{30} 1$

Sol. (i) Here, base $= \tan 45^\circ = 1$ tan

$\therefore$ log is not defined.

(ii) Here, base $= \sec^2 60^\circ - \tan^2 60^\circ = 1$

$\therefore$ log is not defined.

(iii) $\because \log_{(\sin^2 30^\circ + \cos^2 30^\circ)} 1 = \log_1 1 \neq 1$

$\because$ Here, base = 1

$\therefore$ log is not defined.

(iv) $\log_{30} 1 = 0$

Characteristic and Mantissa

The integral part of a logarithm is called the **characteristic** and the fractional part (decimal part) is called **mantissa**.

i.e., $\log N$ = Integer + Fractional or decimal part (+ve)

↓ 

Characteristic Mantissa

The mantissa of log of a number is always kept positive.

i.e., if $\log 564 = 2.751279$, then 2 is the characteristic and 0.751279 is the mantissa of the given number 564.

And if $\log 0.00895 = -2.0481769$

$= -2 - 0.0481769$

$= (-2-1) + (1 - 0.0481769)$

$= -3 + 0.9518231$

Hence, -3 is the characteristic and 0.9518231 (not 0.0481769) is mantissa of log 0.00895.

In short, $-3 + 0.9518231$ is written as $\bar{3}.9518231$.

Remark

1. If $N > 1$, the characteristic of $\log N$ will be one less than the number of digits in the integral part of N.

   For example, If $\log 235.68 = 2.3723227$

   Here, $N = 235.68$

   $\therefore$ Number of digits in the integral part of $N = 3$

   $\Rightarrow$ Characteristic of $\log 235.68 = N - 1 = 3 - 1 = 2$

2. If $0 < N < 1$, the characteristic of $\log N$ is negative and numerically it is one greater than the number of zeroes immediately after the decimal part in N.

   For example, If $\log 0.0000279 = \bar{5}.4456042$

   Here, four zeroes immediately after the decimal point in the number 0.0000279 is $\overline{(4+1)}$, i.e. $\bar{5}$.

3. If the characteristics of $\log N$ be n, then number of digits in N is $(n+1)$ (Here, $N > 1$).

4. If the characteristics of $\log N$ be $-n$, then there exists $(n-1)$ number of zeroes after decimal part of N (here, $0 < N < 1$).

Example 3. If $\log 2 = 0.301$ and $\log 3 = 0.477$, find the number of digits in 6^{20}.

Sol. Let $P = 6^{20} = (2 \times 3)^{20}$

$$\therefore \quad \log P = 20 \log(2 \times 3) = 20\{\log 2 + \log 3\}$$
$$= 20\{0.301 + 0.477\}$$
$$= 20 \times 0.778 = 15.560$$

Since, the characteristic of $\log P$ is 15, therefore the number of digits in P will be 15 + 1, i.e. 16.

Example 4. Find the number of zeroes between the decimal point and first significant digit of $(0.036)^{16}$, where $\log 2 = 0.301$ and $\log 3 = 0.477$.

Sol. Let $P = (0.036)^{16} \Rightarrow \log P = 16 \log(0.036)$

$$= 16 \log\left(\frac{36}{1000}\right) = 16 \log\left(\frac{2^2 \cdot 3^2}{1000}\right)$$
$$= 16\{\log 2^2 + \log 3^2 - \log 10^3\}$$
$$= 16\{2\log 2 + 2\log 3 - 3\}$$
$$= 16\{2 \times 0.301 + 2 \times 0.477 - 3\}$$
$$= 16\{1.556 - 3\} = 24.896 - 48$$
$$= -48 + 24 + 0.896$$
$$= -24 + 0.896 = \overline{24} + 0.896$$

$\therefore$ The required number of zeroes $= 24 - 1 = 23$.

Exercise for Session 1

1. The value of $\log_{2\sqrt{3}} 1728$ is

(a) 6
(b) 8
(c) 3
(d) 5

2. The value of $\log_{(8-3\sqrt{7})}(8 + 3\sqrt{7})$ is

(a) –2
(b) –1
(c) 0
(d) Not defined

3. The value of $(0.16)^{\log_{2.5}\left\{\frac{1}{3} + \frac{1}{3^2} + \dots\right\}}$ is

(a) 2
(b) 4
(c) 6
(d) 8

4. If $\log 2 = 0.301$, the number of integers in the expansion of 4^{17} is

(a) 9
(b) 11
(c) 13
(d) 15

5. If $\log 2 = 0.301$, then the number of zeroes between the decimal point and the first significant figure of 2^{-34} is

(a) 9
(b) 10
(c) 11
(d) 12

Session 2

Principle Properties of Logarithm

Principle Properties of Logarithm

Let m and n be arbitrary positive numbers, $a > 0, a \neq 1, b > 0, b \neq 1$ and α, β be any real numbers, then

(i) $\log_a (mn) = \log_a m + \log_a n$

In general, $\log_a (x_1 x_2 x_3 \dots x_n) = \log_a x_1 + \log_a x_2 + \log_a x_3 + \dots + \log_a x_n$ (where, $x_1, x_2, x_3, \dots, x_n > 0$)

Or

$$\log_a \left(\prod_{i=1}^{n} x_i \right) = \sum_{i=1}^{n} \log_a x_i, \forall x_i > 0$$

where, $i = 1, 2, 3, \dots, n$.

(ii) $\log_a \left(\dfrac{m}{n} \right) = \log_a m - \log_a n$

(iii) $\log_a m^{\alpha} = \alpha \log_a m$

(iv) $\log_{a^{\beta}} m = \dfrac{1}{\beta} \log_a m$ (v) $\log_b m = \dfrac{\log_a m}{\log_a b}$

Remark

1. $\log_b a \cdot \log_a b = 1 \Leftrightarrow \log_b a = \dfrac{1}{\log_a b}$
2. $\log_b a \cdot \log_c b \cdot \log_a c = 1$
3. $\log_y x \cdot \log_z y \cdot \log_a z = \log_a x$
4. $e^{\ln a^x} = a^x$

Extra Properties of Logarithm

(i) $a^{\log_b x} = x^{\log_b a}$, $b \neq 1$, a, b, x are positive numbers.

(ii) $a^{\log_a x} = x, a > 0, a \neq 1, x > 0$

(iii) $\log_{a^k} x = \dfrac{1}{k} \log_a x, \ a > 0, a \neq 1, x > 0$

(iv) $\log_a x^{2k} = 2k \log_a |x|, \ a > 0, a \neq 1, k \in I$

(v) $\log_{a^{2k}} x = \dfrac{1}{2k} \log_{|a|} x, \ x > 0, a > 0, a \neq \pm 1$ and $k \in I \sim \{0\}$

(vi) $\log_{a^{\alpha}} x^{\beta} = \dfrac{\beta}{\alpha} \log_a x, \ x > 0, a > 0, a \neq 1, \alpha \neq 0$

(vii) $\log_a x^2 \neq 2 \log_a x, \ a > 0, a \neq 1$

Since, domain of $\log_a (x^2)$ is $R \sim \{0\}$ and domain of $\log_a x$ is $(0, \infty)$ are not same.

(viii) $a^{\log_b a} = \sqrt{a}$, if $b = a^2, a > 0, b > 0, b \neq 1$

(ix) $a^{\log_b a} = a^2$, if $b = \sqrt{a}, a > 0, b > 0, b \neq 1$

Example 5. Solve the equation $3 \cdot x^{\log_5 2} + 2^{\log_5 x} = 64$.

Sol. $\because \quad 3 \cdot x^{\log_5 2} + 2^{\log_5 x} = 64$

$\Rightarrow \quad 3 \cdot 2^{\log_5 x} + 2^{\log_5 x} = 64$ [by extra property (i)]

$\Rightarrow \quad 4 \cdot 2^{\log_5 x} = 64$

$\Rightarrow \quad 2^{\log_5 x} = 4^2 = 2^4$

$\therefore \quad \log_5 x = 4$

$\Rightarrow \quad x = 5^4 = 625$

Example 6. If $4^{\log_{16} 4} + 9^{\log_3 9} = 10^{\log_x 83}$, find x.

Sol. $\because \quad 4^{\log_{16} 4} = \sqrt{4} = 2$ [by extra property (ix)]

and $\quad 9^{\log_3 9} = 9^2 = 81$ [by extra property (viii)]

$\therefore \quad 4^{\log_{16} 4} + 9^{\log_3 9} = 2 + 81 = 83 = 10^{\log_x 83}$

$\Rightarrow \quad \log_{10} 83 = \log_x 83$

$\therefore \quad x = 10$

Example 7. Prove that $a^{\sqrt{\log_a b}} - b^{\sqrt{\log_b a}} = 0$.

Sol. $\because \quad a^{\sqrt{(\log_a b)}} = a^{\sqrt{\log_a b} \times \sqrt{\log_a b} \times \sqrt{\log_b a}}$

$= a^{\log_a b \cdot \sqrt{(\log_b a)}}$

$= b^{\sqrt{\log_b a}}$ [by extra property (ii)]

Hence, $a^{\sqrt{(\log_a b)}} - b^{\sqrt{(\log_b a)}} = 0$

Example 8. Prove that $\dfrac{\log_2 24}{\log_{96} 2} - \dfrac{\log_2 192}{\log_{12} 2} = 3$.

Sol. LHS $= \dfrac{\log_2 24}{\log_{96} 2} - \dfrac{\log_2 192}{\log_{12} 2}$

$= \log_2 24 \times \log_2 96 - \log_2 192 \times \log_2 12$

Now, let $12 = \lambda$, then

LHS $= \log_2 2\lambda \times \log_2 8\lambda - \log_2 16\lambda \times \log_2 \lambda$

$= (\log_2 2 + \log_2 \lambda)(\log_2 8 + \log_2 \lambda)$
$\qquad - (\log_2 16 + \log_2 \lambda)\log_2 \lambda$

$= (\log_2 2 + \log_2 \lambda)(\log_2 2^3 + \log_2 \lambda)$
$\qquad - (\log_2 2^4 + \log_2 \lambda)\log_2 \lambda$

$= (1 + \log_2 \lambda)(3\log_2 2 + \log_2 \lambda)$
$\qquad - (4\log_2 2 + \log_2 \lambda)\log_2 \lambda$

$= (1 + \log_2 \lambda)(3 + \log_2 \lambda) - \log_2 \lambda(4 + \log_2 \lambda)$

$= 3$

= RHS

Example 9. Solve for a, λ, if

$$\log_\lambda a \cdot \log_5 \lambda \cdot \log_\lambda 25 = 2.$$

Sol. Here, $\lambda > 0, \lambda \neq 1$

We have, $\log_\lambda a \cdot \{\log_5 \lambda \cdot \log_\lambda 25\} = 2$

$\Rightarrow (\log_\lambda a)\{\log_5 25\} = 2$

$\Rightarrow (\log_\lambda a)\{\log_5 5^2\} = 2$

$\Rightarrow (\log_\lambda a)\{2\log_5 5\} = 2$

$\Rightarrow (\log_\lambda a)\{2\} = 2$

$\therefore \log_\lambda (a) = 1$ or $a = \lambda$

Exercise for Session 2

1 If $a = \log_{24} 12$, $b = \log_{48} 36$ and $c = \log_{36} 24$, $1 + abc$ is equal to

(a) $2ab$ (b) $2bc$ (c) $2ca$ (d) $ba + bc$

2 The value of $\log_4[\log_2\{\log_2(\log_3 81)\}]$ is equal to

(a) -1 (b) 0 (c) 1 (d) 2

3 $\log_2 \log_2 (\underbrace{\sqrt{\sqrt{\ldots\sqrt{\sqrt{2}}}}}_{n \text{ times}})$ is equal to

(a) 0 (b) 1 (c) n (d) $-n$

4 If $a = \log_3 5$, $b = \log_{17} 25$, which one of the following is correct?

(a) $a < b$ (b) $a = b$ (c) $a > b$ (d) None of these

5 The value of $\log_{0.75} \log_2 \sqrt{\sqrt[-2]{(0.125)}}$ is equal to

(a) -1 (b) 0 (c) 1 (d) None of these

Session 3

Properties of Monotonocity of Logarithm, Graphs of Logarithmic Functions

Properties of Monotonocity of Logarithm

1. Constant Base

(i) $\log_a x > \log_a y \Leftrightarrow \begin{cases} x > y > 0, \text{ if } a > 1 \\ 0 < x < y, \text{ if } 0 < a < 1 \end{cases}$

(ii) $\log_a x < \log_a y \Leftrightarrow \begin{cases} 0 < x < y, \text{ if } a > 1 \\ x > y > 0, \text{ if } 0 < a < 1 \end{cases}$

(iii) $\log_a x > p \Leftrightarrow \begin{cases} x > a^p, \text{ if } a > 1 \\ 0 < x < a^p, \text{ if } 0 < a < 1 \end{cases}$

(iv) $\log_a x < p \Leftrightarrow \begin{cases} 0 < x < a^p, \text{ if } a > 1 \\ x > a^p, \text{ if } 0 < a < 1 \end{cases}$

2. Variable Base

(i) $\log_x a$ is defined, if $a > 0, x > 0, x \neq 1$.

(ii) If $a > 1$, then $\log_x a$ is monotonically decreasing in $(0, 1) \cup (1, \infty)$.

(iii) If $0 < a < 1$, then $\log_x a$ is monotonically increasing in $(0, 1) \cup (1, \infty)$.

Very Important Concepts

(i) If $a > 1, p > 1$, then $\log_a p > 0$

(ii) If $0 < a < 1, p > 1$, then $\log_a p < 0$

(iii) If $a > 1, 0 < p < 1$, then $\log_a p < 0$

(iv) If $p > a > 1$, then $\log_a p > 1$

(v) If $a > p > 1$, then $0 < \log_a p < 1$

(vi) If $0 < a < p < 1$, then $0 < \log_a p < 1$

(vii) If $0 < p < a < 1$, then $\log_a p > 1$

Graphs of Logarithmic Functions

1. Graph of $y = \log_a x$, if $a > 1$ and $x > 0$

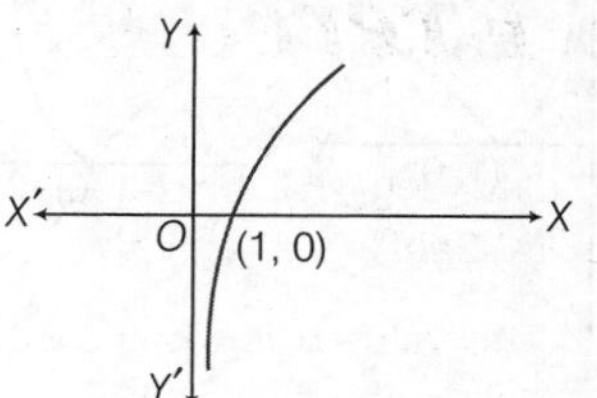

2. Graph of $y = \log_a x$, if $0 < a < 1$ and $x > 0$

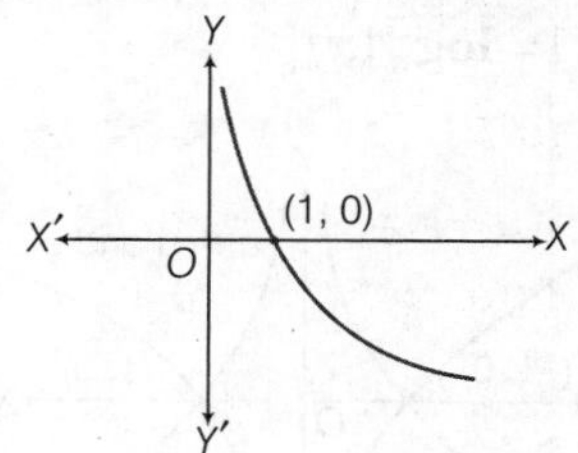

Remark

1. If the number x and the base 'a' are on the same side of the unity, then the logarithm is positive.

Case I $y = \log_a x, a > 1, x > 1$ ***Case II*** $y = \log_a x, 0 < a < 1, 0 < x < 1$

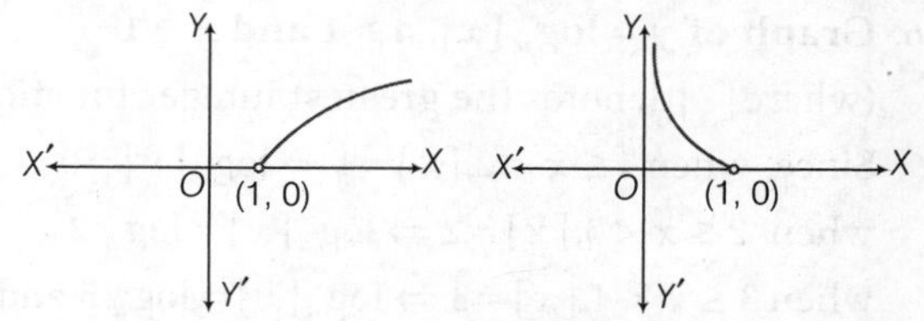

2. If the number x and the base a are on the opposite sides of the unity, then the logarithm is negative.

Case I $y = \log_a x, a > 1, 0 < x < 1$

Case II $y = \log_a x, 0 < a < 1, x > 1$

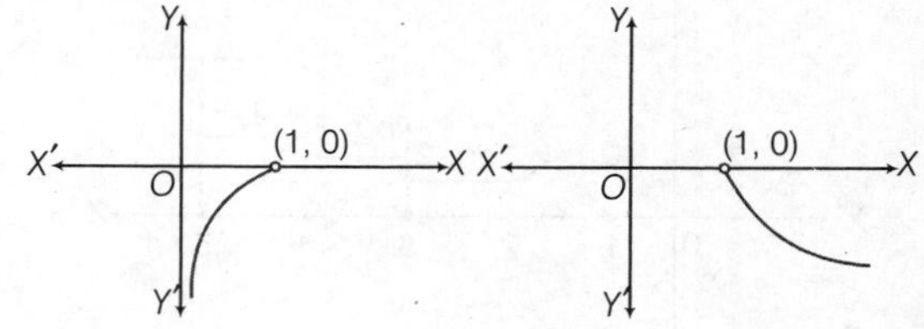

3. Graph of $y = \log_a |x|$

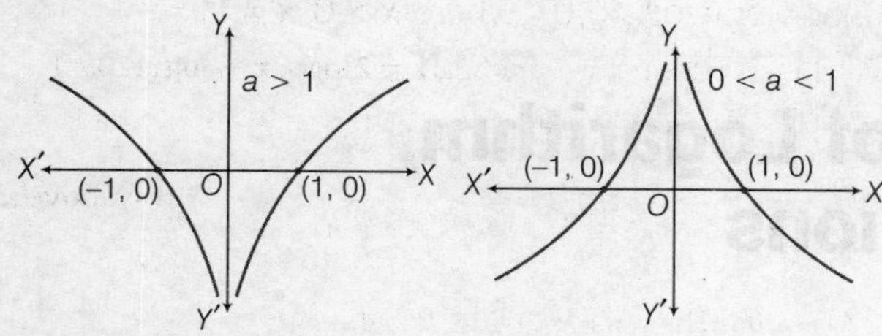

Remark

Graphs are symmetrical about Y-axis.

4. Graph of $y = |\log_a |x||$

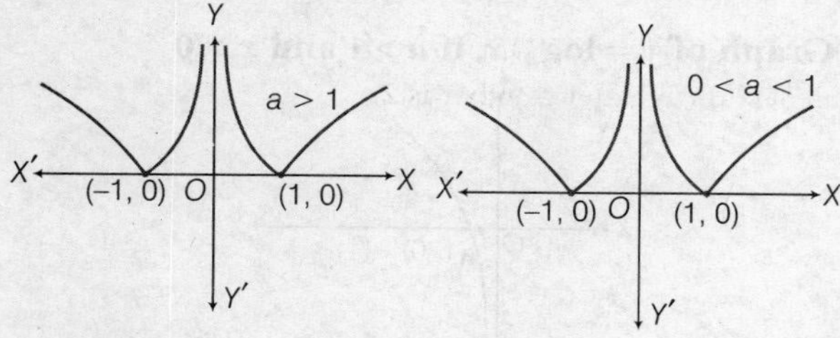

Remark

Graphs are same in both cases i.e., $a > 1$ and $0 < a < 1$.

5. Graph of $|y| = \log_a |x||$

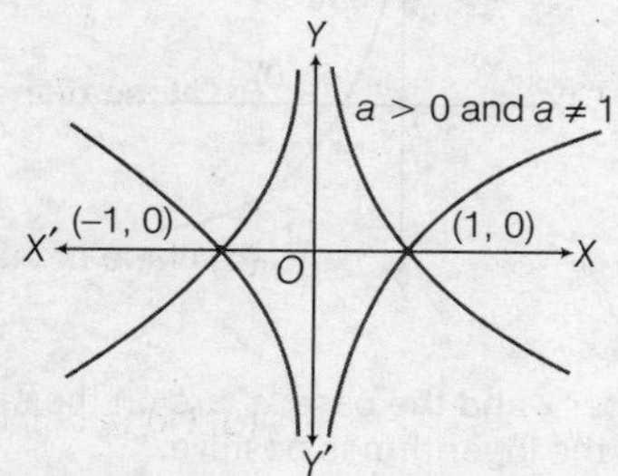

6. Graph of $y = \log_a [x]$, $a > 1$ and $x \geq 1$

(where $[\cdot]$ denotes the greatest integer function)

Since, when $1 \leq x < 2, [x] = 1 \Rightarrow \log_a [x] = 0$

when $2 \leq x < 3, [x] = 2 \Rightarrow \log_a [x] = \log_a 2$

when $3 \leq x < 4, [x] = 3 \Rightarrow \log_a [x] = \log_a 3$ and so on.

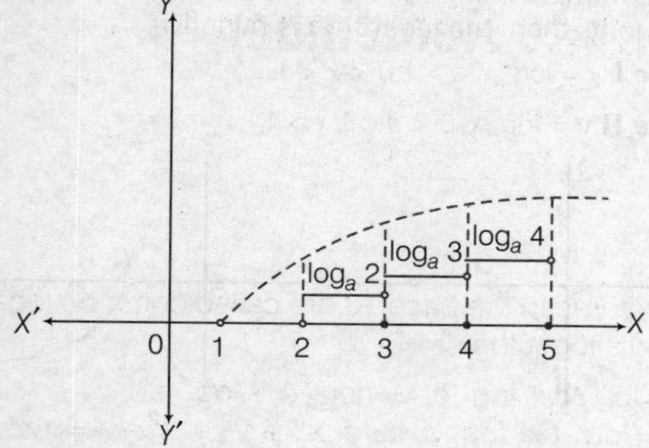

Example 10. Arrange in ascending order $\log_2(x), \log_3(x), \log_e(x), \log_{10}(x)$, if

(i) $x > 1$ (ii) $0 < x < 1$.

Sol. $\because 2 < e < 3 < 10$

(i) For $x > 1$, $\log_x 2 < \log_x e < \log_x 3 < \log_x 10$

$$\Rightarrow \frac{1}{\log_2(x)} < \frac{1}{\log_e(x)} < \frac{1}{\log_3(x)} < \frac{1}{\log_{10}(x)}$$

$$\Rightarrow \log_2(x) > \log_e(x) > \log_3(x) > \log_{10}(x)$$

Hence, ascending order is

$$\log_{10}(x) < \log_3(x) < \log_e(x) < \log_2(x)$$

(ii) For $0 < x < 1$, $\log_x 2 > \log_x e > \log_x 3 > \log_x 10$

$$\Rightarrow \frac{1}{\log_2(x)} > \frac{1}{\log_e(x)} > \frac{1}{\log_3(x)} > \frac{1}{\log_{10}(x)}$$

$$\therefore \log_2(x) < \log_e(x) < \log_3(x) < \log_{10}(x)$$

which is in ascending order.

Example 11. If $\log 11 = 1.0414$, prove that $10^{11} > 11^{10}$.

Sol. $\because \log 10^{11} = 11 \log 10 = 11$

and $\log 11^{10} = 10 \log 11 = 10 \times 1.0414 = 10.414$

It is clear that, $11 > 10.414$

$\Rightarrow \log 10^{11} > \log 11^{10}$ [$\because$ here, base = 10]

$\Rightarrow 10^{11} > 11^{10}$

Example 12. If $\log_2(x-2) < \log_4(x-2)$, find the interval in which x lies.

Sol. Here, $x - 2 > 0$

$\Rightarrow x > 2$ ...(i)

and $\log_2(x-2) < \log_{2^2}(x-2) = \frac{1}{2}\log_2(x-2)$

$\Rightarrow \log_2(x-2) < \frac{1}{2}\log_2(x-2)$

$\Rightarrow \frac{1}{2}\log_2(x-2) < 0 \Rightarrow \log_2(x-2) < 0$

$\Rightarrow x - 2 < 2^0 \Rightarrow x - 2 < 1$

$\Rightarrow x < 3$ ...(ii)

From Eqs. (i) and (ii), we get

$2 < x < 3$ or $x \in (2, 3)$

Example 13. Prove that $\log_n(n+1) > \log_{(n+1)}(n+2)$ for any natural number $n > 1$.

Sol. Since, $\frac{n+1}{n} = 1 + \frac{1}{n} > 1 + \frac{1}{n+1} = \left(\frac{n+2}{n+1}\right)$

For $n > 1$,

$$\log_n\left(\frac{n+1}{n}\right) > \log_{n+1}\left(\frac{n+1}{n}\right) > \log_{n+1}\left(\frac{n+2}{n+1}\right)$$

$\Rightarrow \quad \log_n(n+1) - \log_n n > \log_{(n+1)}(n+2) - \log_{(n+1)}(n+1)$

$\Rightarrow \quad \log_n(n+1) - 1 > \log_{(n+1)}(n+2) - 1$

$\therefore \quad \log_n(n+1) > \log_{(n+1)}(n+2)$ **Hence proved.**

How to Find Minimum Value of $\lambda_1 \log_a x + \lambda_2 \log_x a, a > 0, x > 0, a \neq 1, x \neq 1$ and $\lambda_1, \lambda_2 \in R_+$

$\because \quad AM \geq GM$

$$\Rightarrow \frac{\lambda_1 \log_a x + \lambda_2 \log_x a}{2} \geq \sqrt{(\lambda_1 \log_a x)(\lambda_2 \log_x a)} = \sqrt{\lambda_1 \lambda_2}$$

$$\Rightarrow \lambda_1 \log_a x + \lambda_2 \log_x a \geq 2\sqrt{\lambda_1 \lambda_2}$$

Hence, the minimum value of $\lambda_1 \log_a x + \lambda_2 \log_x a$ is $2\sqrt{\lambda_1 \lambda_2}$.

Example 14. Find the least value of the expression $2\log_{10} x - \log_x 0.01$, where $x > 0, x \neq 1$.

Sol. Let $P = 2\log_{10} x - \log_x 0.01 = 2\log_{10} x - \log_x(10^{-2})$

$= 2(\log_{10} x + \log_x 10)$

$\geq 2 \cdot 2 = 4$ [by above article]

$\therefore \quad P \geq 4$

Hence, the least value of P is 4.

Example 15. Which is smaller 2 or $(\log_\pi 2 + \log_2 \pi)$?

Sol. Let $P = \log_\pi 2 + \log_2 \pi > 2$ [by above article] $[\because \pi \neq 2]$

$\therefore \quad P > 2$

$\Rightarrow \quad (\log_\pi 2 + \log_2 \pi) > 2$

Hence, the smaller number is 2.

Exercise for Session 3

1 If $\log_{0.16}(a+1) < \log_{0.4}(a+1)$, then a satisfies

(a) $a > 0$ (b) $0 < a < 1$ (c) $-1 < a < 0$ (d) None of these

2 The value of x satisfying the inequation $x^{\frac{1}{\log_{10} x}} \cdot \log_{10} x < 1$, is

(a) $0 < x < 10$ (b) $0 < x < 10^{10}$ (c) $0 < x < 10^{1/10}$ (d) None of these

3 If $\log_{\text{cosec}\, x} \sin x > 0$, then

(a) $x > 0$ (b) $x < 0$ (c) $-1 < x < 1$ (d) None of these

4 The value of $\log_{10} 3$ lies in the interval

(a) $\left(\frac{2}{5}, \frac{1}{2}\right)$ (b) $\left(0, \frac{1}{2}\right)$ (c) $\left(0, \frac{2}{5}\right)$ (d) None of these

5 The least value of n in order that the sum of first n terms of the infinite series $1 + \frac{3}{4} + \left(\frac{3}{4}\right)^2 + \left(\frac{3}{4}\right)^3 + \dots$, should differ from the sum of the series by less than 10^{-6}, is (given, $\log 2 = 0.30103, \log 3 = 0.47712$)

(a) 14 (b) 27 (c) 53 (d) 57

Shortcuts and Important Results to Remember

1 For a non-negative number 'a' and $n \geq 2, n \in N$, $\sqrt[n]{a} = a^{1/n}$.

2 The number of positive integers having base a and characteristic n is $a^{n+1} - a^n$.

3 Logarithm of zero and negative real number is not defined.

4 $|\log_b a + \log_a b| \geq 2, \forall a > 0, a \neq 1, b > 0, b \neq 1$.

5 $\log_2 \log_2 \underbrace{\sqrt{\sqrt{\sqrt{\dots\sqrt{2}}}}}_{n \text{ times}} = -n$

6 $a^{\sqrt{\log_a b}} = b^{\sqrt{\log_b a}}$

7 Logarithms to the base 10 are called common logarithms (Brigg's logarithms).

8 If $x = \log_c b + \log_b c, y = \log_a c + \log_c a, z = \log_a b + \log_b a$, then $x^2 + y^2 + z^2 - 4 = xyz$.

JEE Type Solved Examples : Single Option Correct Type Questions

- This section contains **8 multiple choice examples.** Each example has four choices (a), (b), (c) and (d) out of which **ONLY ONE** is correct.

• Ex. 1 *The expression* $\log_2 5 - \sum_{k=1}^{4} \log_2\left(\sin\left(\frac{k\pi}{5}\right)\right)$ *reduces to* $\frac{p}{q}$, *where p and q are co-prime, the value of* $p^2 + q^2$ *is*

(a) 13 (b) 17 (c) 26 (d) 29

Sol. (b) Let $p = \log_2 5 - \sum_{k=1}^{4} \log_2\left(\sin\left(\frac{k\pi}{5}\right)\right)$

$$= \log_2 5 - \left\{\log_2\left(\sin\left(\frac{\pi}{5}\right)\right) + \log_2\left(\sin\left(\frac{2\pi}{5}\right)\right) + \log_2\left(\sin\left(\frac{3\pi}{5}\right)\right) + \log_2\left(\sin\left(\frac{4\pi}{5}\right)\right)\right\}$$

$$= \log_2 5 - \log_2\left\{\sin\frac{\pi}{5}\cdot\sin\frac{2\pi}{5}\cdot\sin\frac{3\pi}{5}\cdot\sin\frac{4\pi}{5}\right\}$$

$$= \log_2 5 - \log_2\left\{\sin^2\left(\frac{\pi}{5}\right)\cdot\sin^2\left(\frac{2\pi}{5}\right)\right\}$$

$$= \log_2 5 - \log_2\left\{\frac{(1-\cos 72^\circ)(1-\cos 144^\circ)}{4}\right\}$$

$$= \log_2 5 - \log_2\left\{\frac{(1-\sin 18^\circ)(1+\cos 36^\circ)}{4}\right\}$$

$$= \log_2 5 - \log_2\left\{\frac{\left(1-\frac{\sqrt{5}-1}{4}\right)\left(1+\frac{\sqrt{5}+1}{4}\right)}{4}\right\}$$

$$= \log_2 5 - \log_2\left\{\frac{(5-\sqrt{5})(5+\sqrt{5})}{64}\right\} = \log_2 5 - \log_2\left(\frac{5}{16}\right)$$

$$= \log_2\left(5\times\frac{16}{5}\right) = \log_2 2^4 = \frac{4}{1} = \frac{p}{q} \quad \text{[given]}$$

$\therefore \quad p = 4, q = 1$

Hence, $p^2 + q^2 = 4^2 + 1^2 = 17$

• Ex. 2 *If* $3 \le a \le 2015$, $3 \le b \le 2015$ *such that* $\log_a b + 6\log_b a = 5$, *the number of ordered pairs (a, b) of integers is*

(a) 48 (b) 50 (c) 52 (d) 54

Sol. (c) Let $x = \log_a b$ ...(i)

$\Rightarrow \quad x + \frac{6}{x} = 5 \Rightarrow x^2 - 5x + 6 = 0 \Rightarrow x = 2, 3$

From Eq. (i), we get $\log_a b = 2, 3$

$\Rightarrow \quad b = a^2$ or a^3

The pairs (a, b) are

$(3, 3^2), (4, 4^2), (5, 5^2), (6, 6^2), \ldots, (44, 44^2)$ and $(3, 3^3), (4, 4^3), (5, 5^3), \ldots, (12, 12^3)$.

Hence, there are $42 + 10 = 52$ pairs.

• Ex. 3 *The lengths of the sides of a triangle are* $\log_{10} 12$, $\log_{10} 75$ *and* $\log_{10} n$, *where* $n \in N$. *If a and b are the least and greatest values of n respectively, the value of* $b - a$ *is divisible by*

(a) 221 (b) 222 (c) 223 (d) 224

Sol. (c) In a triangle,

$\log_{10} 12 + \log_{10} 75 > \log_{10} n \Rightarrow n < 12 \times 75 = 900$

$\therefore \quad n < 900$ ...(i)

and $\log_{10} 12 + \log_{10} n > \log_{10} 75$

$\Rightarrow \quad n > \frac{75}{12} = \frac{25}{4}$

$\therefore \quad n > \frac{25}{4}$ ...(ii)

From Eqs. (i) and (ii), we get $\frac{25}{4} < n < 900$

$\therefore \quad n = 7, 8, 9, 10, \ldots, 899$

Hence, $a = 7, b = 899$

$\therefore \quad b - a = 892 = 4 \times 223$

Hence, $b - a$ is divisible by 223.

• Ex. 4 *If* $5\log_{abc}(a^3 + b^3 + c^3) = 3\lambda\left(\frac{1+\log_3(abc)}{\log_3(abc)}\right)$ *and* $(abc)^{a+b+c} = 1$ *and* $\lambda = \frac{m}{n}$, *where m and n are relative primes, the value of* $|m+n| + |m-n|$ *is*

(a) 8 (b) 10 (c) 12 (d) 14

Sol. (b) $\because \quad (abc)^{a+b+c} = 1 = (abc)^0$

$\therefore \quad a + b + c = 0 \Rightarrow a^3 + b^3 + c^3 = 3abc$

Now, LHS $= 5\log_{abc}(a^3 + b^3 + c^3) = 5\log_{abc}(3abc)$ ...(i)

and RHS $= 3\lambda\left(\frac{1+\log_3(abc)}{\log_3(abc)}\right) = 3\lambda\left(\frac{\log_3(3abc)}{\log_3(abc)}\right)$

$= 3\lambda\log_{abc}(3abc)$ ...(ii)

From Eqs. (i) and (ii), we get

$5\log_{abc}(3abc) = 3\lambda\log_{abc}(3abc)$

$\therefore \quad \lambda = \frac{5}{3} = \frac{m}{n}$ [given]

$\Rightarrow \quad m = 5, n = 3$

Hence, $|m+n| + |m-n| = 8 + 2 = 10$

● ***Ex. 5*** *If* $a^{\log_b c} = 3 \cdot 3^{\log_4 3} \cdot 3^{\log_4 3^{\log_4 3}} \cdot 3^{\log_4 3^{\log_4 3^{\log_4 3}}} \ldots \infty$, *where a, b, c ∈ Q, the value of abc is*

(a) 9 (b) 12 (c) 16 (d) 20

Sol. (c) $a^{\log_b c} = 3^{1 + \log_4 3 + (\log_4 3)^2 + (\log_4 3)^3 + \ldots \infty}$

$$= 3^{1/(1-\log_4 3)} = 3^{1/\log_4 (4/3)} = 3^{\log_{4/3} 4}$$

$$\therefore \quad a = 3, b = \frac{4}{3}, c = 4$$

Hence, $abc = 3 \cdot \frac{4}{3} \cdot 4 = 16$

● ***Ex. 6*** *Number of real roots of equation* $3^{\log_3 (x^2 - 4x + 3)} = (x - 3)$ *is*

(a) 0 (b) 1 (c) 2 (d) infinite

Sol. (a) $\because \quad 3^{\log_3 (x^2 - 4x + 3)} = (x - 3)$ ...(i)

Eq. (i) is defined, if $x^2 - 4x + 3 > 0$

$\Rightarrow \quad (x-1)(x-3) > 0$

$\Rightarrow \quad x < 1 \text{ or } x > 3$ ...(ii)

Eq. (i) reduces to $x^2 - 4x + 3 = x - 3 \Rightarrow x^2 - 5x + 6 = 0$

$\therefore \quad x = 2, 3$ ...(iii)

From Eqs. (ii) and (iii), use get $x \in \phi$

∴ Number of real roots = 0

● ***Ex. 7*** *If* $\log_6 a + \log_6 b + \log_6 c = 6$, *where a, b, c ∈ N and a, b, c are in GP and b − a is a square of an integer, then the value of a + b − c is*

(a) 21 (b) 15 (c) 9 (d) 3

Sol. (b) $\because \quad \log_6 a + \log_6 b + \log_6 c = 6$

$\Rightarrow \quad \log_6 (abc) = 6$

$\Rightarrow \quad abc = 6^6$

$\Rightarrow \quad b^3 = 6^6 \quad [\because b^2 = ac]$

$\Rightarrow \quad b = 36$

Also, $b - a = 36 - a$ is a square for $a = 35, 32, 27, 20, 11$

Now, $c = \frac{b^2}{a} = \frac{36^2}{a}$ is an integer for $a = 27$

$\therefore \quad a = 27, b = 36, c = 48$

Hence, $a + b - c = 27 + 36 - 48 = 15$

● ***Ex. 8*** *If* $x = \log_{2a}\left(\frac{bcd}{2}\right), y = \log_{3b}\left(\frac{acd}{3}\right)$, $z = \log_{4c}\left(\frac{abd}{4}\right)$ *and* $w = \log_{5d}\left(\frac{abc}{5}\right)$ *and* $\frac{1}{x+1} + \frac{1}{y+1} + \frac{1}{z+1} + \frac{1}{w+1} = \log_{abcd} N + 1$, *the value of N is*

(a) 40 (b) 80
(c) 120 (d) 160

Sol. (c) $\because \quad x = \log_{2a}\left(\frac{bcd}{2}\right)$

$\Rightarrow \quad x + 1 = \log_{2a}\left(\frac{2abcd}{2}\right) = \log_{2a}(abcd)$

$\therefore \quad \frac{1}{x+1} = \log_{abcd} 2a$

Similarly, $\frac{1}{y+1} = \log_{abcd} 3b, \frac{1}{z+1} = \log_{abcd} 4c$

and $\frac{1}{w+1} = \log_{abcd} 5d$

$\therefore \quad \frac{1}{x+1} + \frac{1}{y+1} + \frac{1}{z+1} + \frac{1}{w+1} = \log_{abcd}(2a \cdot 3b \cdot 4c \cdot 5d)$

$= \log_{abcd}(120abcd)$

$= \log_{abcd} 120 + 1$

$= \log_{abcd} N + 1$ [given]

Hence, $N = 120$

JEE Type Solved Examples : More than One Correct Option Type Questions

- This section contains **4 multiple choice examples.** Each example has four choices (a), (b), (c) and (d) out of **which more than one** may be correct.

● ***Ex. 9*** *The equation* $(\log_{10} x + 2)^3 + (\log_{10} x - 1)^3 = (2\log_{10} x + 1)^3$ *has*

(a) no natural solution (b) two rational solutions
(c) no prime solution (d) one irrational solution

Sol. (b, c, d) Let $\log_{10} x + 2 = a$ and $\log_{10} x - 1 = b$

$\therefore a + b = 2\log_{10} x + 1$, then given equation reduces to

$$a^3 + b^3 = (a+b)^3$$

$\Rightarrow \quad 3ab(a+b) = 0 \Rightarrow a = 0 \text{ or } b = 0 \text{ or } a + b = 0$

$\Rightarrow \quad \log_{10} x + 2 = 0 \text{ or } \log_{10} x - 1 = 0$

or $\quad 2\log_{10} x + 1 = 0$

$\Rightarrow \quad x = 10^{-2} \text{ or } x = 10 \text{ or } x = 10^{-1/2}$

Hence, $x = \frac{1}{100}$ or $x = 10$ or $x = \frac{1}{\sqrt{10}}$

● ***Ex. 10*** *The value of* $\frac{\log_5 9 \cdot \log_7 5 \cdot \log_3 7}{\log_3 \sqrt{6}} + \frac{1}{\log_4 \sqrt{6}}$ *is co-prime with*

(a) 1 (b) 3 (c) 4 (d) 5

Sol. (a, b, d) Let $P = \frac{\log_5 9 \cdot \log_7 5 \cdot \log_3 7}{\log_3 \sqrt{6}} + \frac{1}{\log_4 \sqrt{6}}$

$$= \frac{\log_3 9}{\log_3 \sqrt{6}} + \log_{\sqrt{6}} 4 = \log_{\sqrt{6}} 9 + \log_{\sqrt{6}} 4$$

$$= \log_{\sqrt{6}}(36) = \log_{\sqrt{6}}(\sqrt{6})^4 = 4 \Rightarrow P = 4$$

which is co-prime with 1, 3, 4 and 5.

• **Ex. 11** *Which of the following quantities are irrational for the quadratic equation* $(\log_{10} 8)x^2 - (\log_{10} 5)x = 2(\log_2 10)^{-1} - x$?

(a) Sum of roots (b) Product of roots
(c) Sum of coefficients (d) Discriminant

Sol. (c, d) $\because$ $(\log_{10} 8)x^2 - (\log_{10} 5)x = 2(\log_2 10)^{-1} - x$

$$\Rightarrow (3\log_{10} 2)x^2 + (1 - \log_{10} 5)x - 2\log_{10} 2 = 0$$

$$\Rightarrow (3\log_{10} 2)x^2 + (\log_{10} 2)x - 2\log_{10} 2 = 0$$

Now, Sum of roots $= -\frac{1}{3}$ = Rational

Product of roots $= -\frac{2}{3}$ = Rational

Sum of coefficients $= 3\log_{10} 2 + \log_{10} 2 - 2\log_{10} 2$

$= 2\log_{10} 2$ = Irrational

Discriminant $= (\log_{10} 2)^2 + 24(\log_{10} 2)^2$

$= 25 (\log_{10} 2)^2$ = Irrational

• **Ex. 12** *The system of equations*

$\log_{10}(2000xy) - \log_{10} x \cdot \log_{10} y = 4$

$\log_{10}(2yz) - \log_{10} y \cdot \log_{10} z = 1$

and $\log_{10}(zx) - \log_{10} z \cdot \log_{10} x = 0$

has two solutions (x_1, y_1, z_1) *and* (x_2, y_2, z_2), *then*

(a) $x_1 + x_2 = 101$ (b) $y_1 + y_2 = 25$
(c) $x_1 x_2 = 100$ (d) $z_1 z_2 = 100$

Sol. (a, b, c, d) Let $\log_{10} x = a$, $\log_{10} y = b$ and $\log_{10} z = c$

Then, given equations reduces to

$$a + b - ab = 4 - \log_{10} 2000 = \log_{10} 5 \quad ...(i)$$

$$b + c - bc = 1 - \log_{10} 2 = \log_{10} 5 \quad ...(ii)$$

and $c + a - ca = 0$ ...(iii)

From Eqs. (i) and (ii), we get

$$a + b - ab = b + c - bc$$

$$\Rightarrow (c - a) - b(c - a) = 0$$

$$\Rightarrow (c - a)(1 - b) = 0$$

$$1 - b \neq 0, c - a = 0 \Rightarrow c = a$$

From Eq. (iii), we get

$$2a - a^2 = 0 \Rightarrow a = 0, 2$$

Then, $c = a \Rightarrow c = 0, 2$

and $b = \log_{10} 5, 2 - \log_{10} 5$

$\therefore$ $\log_{10} x = 0, 2 \Rightarrow x = 10^0, 10^2$

$\Rightarrow$ $x = 1, 100$

$\Rightarrow$ $x_1 = 1, x_2 = 100$

and $\log_{10} y = \log_{10} 5, 2 - \log_{10} 5$

$= \log_{10} 5, \log_{10} 20$

$\Rightarrow$ $y = 5, 20$

$\Rightarrow$ $y_1 = 5, y_2 = 20$

and $\log_{10} z = 0, 2 \Rightarrow z = 10^0, 10^2$

$\Rightarrow$ $z = 1, 100$

$\Rightarrow$ $z_1 = 1, z_2 = 100$

Finally, $x_1 + x_2 = 1 + 100 = 101$, $y_1 + y_2 = 5 + 20 = 25$,

$x_1 x_2 = 1 \times 100 = 100$ and $z_1 z_2 = 1 \times 100 = 100$

JEE Type Solved Examples : Passage Based Questions

- This section contains **2 solved passages** based upon each of the passage **3 multiple choice** examples have to be answered. Each of these examples has four choices (a), (b), (c) and (d) out of which **ONLY ONE** is correct.

Passage I
(Ex. Nos. 13 to 15)

Suppose that $\log_{10}(x - 2) + \log_{10} y = 0$ and $\sqrt{x} + \sqrt{(y - 2)} = \sqrt{(x + y)}$.

13. The value of x is

(a) $2 + \sqrt{2}$ (b) $1 + \sqrt{2}$ (c) $2\sqrt{2}$ (d) $4 - \sqrt{2}$

14. The value of y is

(a) 2 (b) $2\sqrt{2}$ (c) $1 + \sqrt{2}$ (d) $2 + 2\sqrt{2}$

15. If $x^{2t^2 - 6} + y^{6 - 2t^2} = 6$, the value of $t_1 t_2 t_3 t_4$ is

(a) 1 (b) 2 (c) 4 (d) 8

Sol. (Ex. Nos. 13-15)

$\because$ $\log_{10}(x - 2) + \log_{10} y = 0$

$\therefore$ $x - 2 > 0, y > 0$

$\Rightarrow$ $x > 2, y > 0$ ...(i)

and $\log_{10}\{(x - 2)y\} = 0$

$\Rightarrow$ $(x - 2)y = 10^0 = 1$

$\therefore$ $(x - 2)y = 1$ ...(ii)

Also, given that $\sqrt{x} + \sqrt{(y - 2)} = \sqrt{(x + y)}$

$\therefore$ $x \geq 0, y - 2 \geq 0, x + y \geq 0$

$\Rightarrow \quad x \geq 0, y \geq 2$ ...(iii)

On squaring both sides, we get

$$x + y - 2 + 2\sqrt{x}\sqrt{(y-2)} = x + y$$

$\Rightarrow \quad \sqrt{x}\sqrt{y-2} = 1$

$\Rightarrow \quad x(y-2) = 1$ ...(iv)

From Eqs. (i) and (iii),we get

$$x > 2, y \geq 2$$

and from Eqs. (ii) and (iv), we get $y = x$

From Eq. (ii), $(x-2)x = 1$

$\Rightarrow \quad x^2 - 2x - 1 = 0$

$\therefore \quad x = \dfrac{2 \pm \sqrt{4+4}}{2}$ [neglect –ve sign, since $x > 2$]

13. (*b*) $x = (\sqrt{2} + 1)$.

14. (*c*) $y = x = \sqrt{1+1}$

15. (*d*) $\because \quad x^{2t^2-6} + y^{6-2t^2} = 6$

$\Rightarrow \quad x^{2t^2-6} + (x^{-1})^{2t^2-6} = 6$

$\Rightarrow \quad (x^2)^{t^2-3} + (x^{-2})^{t^2-3} = 6$

$\Rightarrow \quad (3+2\sqrt{2})^{t^2-3} + (3-2\sqrt{2})^{t^2-3} = 6$

Now, we get $\quad t^2 - 3 = \pm 1$

$\Rightarrow \quad t^2 = 4, 2$

$\therefore \quad t = \pm 2, \pm\sqrt{2}$

$\therefore \quad t_1 t_2 t_3 t_4 = (2)(-2)(\sqrt{2})(-\sqrt{2}) = 8$

Passage II

(Ex. Nos. 16 to 18)

If $10^{\log_p \{\log_q (\log_r x)\}} = 1$ and $\log_q \{\log_r (\log_p x)\} = 0$.

16. The value of x is

(a) q^r (b) r^q (c) r^p (d) rq

Sol. (*b*) $\because \quad 10^{\log_p [\log_q (\log_r x)]} = 1 = 10^0$

$\Rightarrow \quad \log_p \{\log_q (\log_r x)\} = 0$

$\Rightarrow \quad \log_q (\log_r x) = 1 \Rightarrow \log_r x = q$

$\Rightarrow \quad x = r^q$ ...(i)

and $\quad \log_q \{\log_r (\log_p x)\} = 0$

$\Rightarrow \quad \log_r (\log_p x) = 1 \Rightarrow \log_p x = r$

$\therefore \quad x = p^r$ ...(ii)

From Eqs. (i) and (ii), we get $\quad x = r^q = p^r$

17. The value of p is

(a) $r^{q/r}$ (b) rq (c) 1 (d) $r^{r/q}$

Sol. (*a*) $\because \quad r^q = p^r$ ...(iii)

$\Rightarrow \quad p = r^{q/r}$

18. The value of q is

(a) $r^{p/r}$ (b) $p\log_p r$ (c) $r\log_r p$ (d) $r^{r/p}$

Sol. (*c*) From Eq. (iii),

$$q \log r = r \log p \Rightarrow q = r\left(\frac{\log p}{\log r}\right) = r \log_r p$$

JEE Type Solved Examples : Single Integer Answer Type Questions

- This section contains **2 examples.** The answer to each example is a **single digit integer** ranging from **0** to **9** (both inclusive).

● **Ex. 19** *If x_1 and x_2 are the solutions of the equation $x^{\log_{10} x} = 100x$ such that $x_1 > 1$ and $x_2 < 1$, the value of $\dfrac{x_1 x_2}{2}$ is*

Sol. (5) $\because \quad x^{\log_{10} x} = 100x$

Taking logarithm on both sides on base 10, then we get

$$\log_{10} x \cdot \log_{10} x = \log_{10} 100 + \log_{10} x$$

$\Rightarrow \quad (\log_{10} x)^2 - \log_{10} x - 2 = 0$

$\Rightarrow \quad (\log_{10} x - 2)(\log_{10} x + 1) = 0$

$\therefore \quad \log_{10} x = 2, -1 \Rightarrow x = 10^2, 10^{-1}$

$\therefore \quad x_1 = 100, x_2 = \dfrac{1}{10}$

$\therefore \quad \dfrac{x_1 x_2}{2} = 5$

● **Ex. 20** *If $(31.6)^a = (0.0000316)^b = 100$, the value of $\dfrac{1}{a} - \dfrac{1}{b}$ is*

Sol. (3) $\because \quad (31.6)^a = (0.0000316)^b = 100$

$\Rightarrow \quad a\log_{10}(31.6) = b\log_{10}(0.0000316) = \log_{10} 100$

$\Rightarrow \quad a\log_{10}(31.6) = b\log_{10}(31.6 \times 10^{-6}) = 2$

$\Rightarrow \quad a\log_{10}(31.6) = b\log_{10}(31.6) - 6b = 2$

$\Rightarrow \quad \dfrac{2}{a} = \log_{10}(31.6)$

and $\quad \dfrac{2}{b} = \log_{10}(31.6) - 6$

$\therefore \quad \dfrac{2}{a} - \dfrac{2}{b} = 6$

$\Rightarrow \quad \dfrac{1}{a} - \dfrac{1}{b} = 3$

JEE Type Solved Examples : Matching Type Questions

- This section contains **2 examples.** Examples 24 and 25 have three statements (A, B and C) given in Column I and four statements (p, q, r and s) in **Column II.** Any given statement in **Column I** can have correct matching with one or more statement(s) given in **Column II.**

• Ex. 21

	Column I		Column II
(A)	If x_1 and x_2 satisfy the equation $(x+1)^{\log_{10}(x+1)} = 100(x+1)$, then the value of $(x_1+1)(x_2+1)+5$ is	(p)	irrational
(B)	The product of all values of x which make the following statement true $(\log_3 x)(\log_5 9) - \log_x 25 + \log_3 2 = \log_3 54$, is	(q)	rational
		(r)	prime
(C)	If $\log_b a = -3$, $\log_b c = 4$ and if the value of x satisfying the equation $a^{3x} = c^{x-1}$ is expressed in the form p/q, where p and q are relatively prime, then q is	(s)	composite
		(t)	twin prime

Sol. A → (q, s, t), B → (p), C → (q, r)

(A) $(x+1)^{\log_{10}(x+1)} = 100(x+1)$

Taking logarithm on both sides on base 10, then we get

$$\log_{10}(x+1)\cdot\log_{10}(x+1) = \log_{10}100 + \log_{10}(x+1)$$

$$\Rightarrow \quad \{\log_{10}(x+1)\}^2 = 2 + \log_{10}(x+1)$$

$$\Rightarrow \{\log_{10}(x+1)\}^2 - \log_{10}(x+1) - 2 = 0$$

$$\Rightarrow \{\log_{10}(x+1) - 2\}\{\log_{10}(x+1)+1\} = 0$$

$$\therefore \quad \log_{10}(x+1) = 2, -1$$

$$\Rightarrow \quad (x+1) = 10^2, 10^{-1}$$

$$\therefore \quad (x_1+1)(x_2+1) = 10^2 \times 10^{-1} = 10$$

$$\Rightarrow \quad (x_1+1)(x_2+1)+5 = 10+5$$

$$= 15 = 3 \times 5$$

(B) $\because (\log_3 x)(\log_5 9) - \log_x 25 + \log_3 2 = \log_3 54$

$$\Rightarrow \quad 2\log_5 x - 2\log_x 5 = \log_3 54 - \log_3 2$$

$$= \log_3(27) = 3$$

Let $\log_5 x = \lambda$, then

$$2\lambda - \frac{2}{\lambda} = 3$$

$$\Rightarrow \quad 2\lambda^2 - 3\lambda - 2 = 0$$

$$\Rightarrow \quad 2\lambda^2 - 4\lambda + \lambda - 2 = 0$$

$$2\lambda(\lambda-2) + 1(\lambda-2) = 0 \Rightarrow \lambda = -\frac{1}{2}, 2$$

$$\therefore \quad \log_5 x = -\frac{1}{2}, 2$$

$$\Rightarrow \quad x = 5^{-1/2}, 5^2 \text{ or } x = \frac{1}{\sqrt{5}}, 25$$

$$\therefore \text{ Product of the values of } x = \frac{1}{\sqrt{5}} \times 25 = 5\sqrt{5}$$

(C) $\because \quad \log_b a = -3$ and $\log_b c = 4$

$$\therefore \quad \log_c a = -\frac{3}{4} \qquad \text{...(i)}$$

and $\quad a^{3x} = c^{x-1}$

$$\Rightarrow \quad 3x\log a = (x-1)\log c$$

$$\Rightarrow \quad 3x\log_c a = x - 1$$

$$\Rightarrow \quad 3x \times -\frac{3}{4} = x - 1 \qquad \text{[from Eq. (i)]}$$

$$\Rightarrow \quad -9x = 4x - 4 \text{ or } x = \frac{4}{13}$$

$$\therefore \quad q = 13 \qquad \text{[prime and rational]}$$

• Ex. 22

	Column I		Column II
(A)	If α and β are the roots of $ax^2 + bx + c = 0$, where $a = 2^{\log_2 3} - 3^{\log_3 2}$, $b = 1 + 2^{\sqrt{\log_2 3}} - 3^{\sqrt{\log_3 2}}$	(p)	divisible by 2
	and $c = \log_2 \log_2 \sqrt{\sqrt{\sqrt{\sqrt{\sqrt{\sqrt{2}}}}}}$, then HM of α and β is	(q)	divisible by 4
(B)	The sum of the solutions of the equation	(r)	divisible by 6
	$\lvert x-1\rvert^{\log_2 x^2 - 2\log_x 4} = (x-1)^7$ is	(s)	divisible by 8
(C)	If $5(\log_y x + \log_x y) = 26$, $xy = 64$, then the value of $\lvert x - y\rvert$ is	(t)	divisible by 10

Sol. A → (p, q, r), B → (p, r), C → (p, r, t)

(A) $\because a = 3 - 2 = 1, b = 1, c = \log_2 \log_2 2^{2^{-6}}$

$$= \log_2(2^{-6}) = -6$$

The equation reduces to $x^2 + x - 6 = 0$

$$\therefore \quad \alpha + \beta = -1, \ \alpha\beta = -6$$

$$\therefore \quad \text{HM} = \frac{2\alpha\beta}{\alpha+\beta} = \frac{2(-6)}{(-1)} = 12$$

(B) Obviously, $x = 2$ is a solution. Since, LHS is positive, $x - 1 > 0$. The equation reduces to

$$\log_2 x^2 - 2\log_x 4 = 7$$

$$\Rightarrow \quad 2\lambda - \frac{4}{\lambda} = 7, \text{ where } \lambda = \log_2 x$$

$\Rightarrow \quad 2\lambda^2 - 7\lambda - 4 = 0 \Rightarrow \lambda = 4, -\frac{1}{2}$

$\therefore \quad \log_2 x = 4, -\frac{1}{2} \Rightarrow x = 2^4, 2^{-1/2}$

$\Rightarrow \quad x = 16, \frac{1}{\sqrt{2}}$

$\Rightarrow \quad x = 16, x \neq \frac{1}{\sqrt{2}} \qquad [\because x > 1]$

$\therefore$ Solutions are $x = 2, 16$

$\therefore$ Sum of solutions $= 2 + 16 = 18$

(C) If $\alpha = \log x, \beta = \log y$

$\therefore \quad \log_y x + \log_x y = \frac{\alpha}{\beta} + \frac{\beta}{\alpha}$

$\therefore \quad 5(\log_y x + \log_x y) = 26$

$\Rightarrow \quad \frac{\alpha}{\beta} + \frac{\beta}{\alpha} = \frac{26}{5}$

Let $\frac{\alpha}{\beta} = \lambda$, then $\lambda + \frac{1}{\lambda} = \frac{26}{5}$

$\Rightarrow \quad 5\lambda^2 - 26\lambda + 5 = 0$

$\Rightarrow \quad 5\lambda^2 - 25\lambda - \lambda + 5 = 0$

$\Rightarrow \quad (\lambda - 5)(5\lambda - 1) = 0$

$\Rightarrow \quad \lambda = 5, \frac{1}{5}$

$\therefore \quad \frac{\alpha}{\beta} = 5, \frac{1}{5} \Rightarrow \frac{\alpha}{\beta} = 5$

$\Rightarrow \quad \alpha = 5\beta \qquad \text{...(i)}$

and $\alpha + \beta = \log x + \log y = \log(xy) = \log(64)$

$\therefore \quad \alpha + \beta = 6\log 2 \qquad \text{...(ii)}$

From Eqs. (i) and (ii), we get

$\beta = \log 2$ and $\alpha = 5\log 2$

$\Rightarrow \quad y = 2, x = 32$ or $y = 32, x = 2$

$\therefore \quad |x - y| = 30$

JEE Type Solved Examples : Statement I and II Type Questions

- **Directions** Example numbers 23 to 24 are Assertion-Reason type examples. Each of these examples contains two statements:

Statement-1 (Assertion) and **Statement-2** (Reason)

Each of these examples also has four alternative choices, only one of which is the correct answer. You have to select the correct choice as given below.

(a) Statement-1 is true, Statement-2 is true; Statement-2 is a correct explanation for Statement-1

(b) Statement-1 is true, Statement-2 is true; Statement-2 is not a correct explanation for Statement-1

(c) Statement-1 is true, Statement-2 is false

(d) Statement-1 is false, Statement-2 is true

- ***Ex. 23*** **Statement-1** *If* $N = \left(\frac{1}{0.4}\right)^{20}$*, then N contains 7 digits before decimal.*

Statement-2 *Characteristic of the logarithm of N to the base 10 is 7.*

Sol. (*d*) $\because \quad N = \left(\frac{1}{0.4}\right)^{20} = \left(\frac{10}{2^2}\right)^{20}$

$\Rightarrow \log_{10} N = 20(1 - 2\log_{10} 2) = 20(1 - 2 \times 0.3010)$

$= 20 \times 0.3980 = 7.9660$

Since, characteristic of $\log_{10} N$ is 7, therefore the number of digits in N will be 7 + 1, i.e. 8.

Hence, Statement-1 is false and Statement-2 is true.

- ***Ex. 24*** **Statement-1** *If* $p, q \in N$ *satisfy the equation* $x^{\sqrt{x}} = (\sqrt{x})^x$ *and* $q > p$*, then q is a perfect number.*

Statement-2 *If a number is equal to the sum of its factor, then number is known as perfect number.*

Sol. (*d*) $\because \quad x^{\sqrt{x}} = (\sqrt{x})^x$

Taking logarithm on both sides on base e, then

$$\ln(x)^{\sqrt{x}} = \ln(\sqrt{x})^x$$

$\Rightarrow \quad \sqrt{x}\ln x = x\ln\sqrt{x} \Rightarrow \sqrt{x}\ln x = \frac{x}{2}\ln x$

$\Rightarrow \quad \ln x\left(\sqrt{x} - \frac{x}{2}\right) = 0$

$\Rightarrow \quad \ln x \cdot \sqrt{x} \cdot \left(1 - \frac{\sqrt{x}}{2}\right) = 0$

$\Rightarrow \quad \ln x = 0, \sqrt{x} = 0, 1 - \frac{\sqrt{x}}{2} = 0$

$\therefore \quad x = 1, 0, 4$

$\because \quad x \in N$

$\therefore \quad x = 1, 4 \Rightarrow p = 1$ and $q = 4$

$\because \quad 4 = 1 \times 2 \times 2 \Rightarrow 4 \neq 1 + 2 + 2$

$\therefore$ q is not a perfect number.

Hence, Statement-1 is false and Statement-2 is true.

Subjective Type Questions

- In this section, there are **21 subjective** solved examples.

Ex. 25 *Prove that* $\log_3 5$ *is an irrational.*

Sol. Let $\log_3 5$ is rational.

$\therefore \quad \log_3 5 = \frac{p}{q}$, where p and q are co-prime numbers.

$\Rightarrow \quad 5 = 3^{p/q} \Rightarrow 3^p = 5^q$

which is not possible, hence our assumption is wrong. Hence, $\log_3 5$ is an irrational.

Ex. 26 *Find the value of the expression*

$$(\log 2)^3 + \log 8 \cdot \log 5 + (\log 5)^3.$$

Sol. $\because \quad \log 2 + \log 5 = \log(2 \cdot 5) = \log 10 = 1 \quad \ldots(\text{i})$

$\Rightarrow \quad (\log 2 + \log 5)^3 = 1$

$\Rightarrow \quad (\log 2)^3 + (\log 5)^3 + 3 \log 2 \log 5 (\log 2 + \log 5) = 1^3$

$\Rightarrow \quad (\log 2)^3 + (\log 5)^3 + \log 2^3 \log 5(1) = 1 \quad$ [from Eq. (i)]

$\Rightarrow \quad (\log 2)^3 + \log 8 \log 5 + (\log 5)^3 = 1$

Ex. 27 *If* $\lambda^{\log_3 5} = 81$, *find the value of* $\lambda^{(\log_3 5)^2}$.

Sol. $\because \quad \lambda^{\log_3 5} = 81$

$\therefore (\lambda^{\log_3 5})^{\log_3 5} = (81)^{\log_3 5}$

$\Rightarrow \quad \lambda^{(\log_3 5)^2} = 3^{4 \log_3 5} = 3^{\log_3 5^4} = 5^4 = 625$

Ex. 28 *Find the product of the positive roots of the equation* $\sqrt{(2009)}(x)^{\log_{2009} x} = x^2$.

Sol. Given, $\sqrt{(2009)}(x)^{\log_{2009} x} = x^2$

Taking logarithm both sides on base 2009, then

$$\log_{2009} \sqrt{(2009)} + \log_{2009} x \cdot \log_{2009} x = \log_{2009} x^2$$

$\Rightarrow \quad \frac{1}{2} + (\log_{2009} x)^2 = 2 \log_{2009} x \quad$ [for $x > 0$]

$\Rightarrow \quad (\log_{2009} x)^2 - 2 \log_{2009} x + \frac{1}{2} = 0$

If roots are x_1 and x_2, then $\log_{2009} x_1 + \log_{2009} x_2 = 2$

$\Rightarrow \quad \log_{2009}(x_1 x_2) = 2$ or $x_1 x_2 = (2009)^2$

Ex. 29 *Prove that* $\log_7 11$ *is greater than* $\log_8 5$.

Sol. $\because \quad 11 > 5$

$\Rightarrow \quad \log 11 > \log 5 \quad \ldots(\text{i})$

and $\quad 8 > 7$

$\Rightarrow \quad \log 8 > \log 7 \quad \ldots(\text{ii})$

From Eqs. (i) and (ii), we get

$$\log 11 \cdot \log 8 > \log 7 \cdot \log 5$$

$\Rightarrow \quad \frac{\log 11}{\log 7} > \frac{\log 5}{\log 8} \Rightarrow \log_7 11 > \log_8 5$

Ex. 30 *Given,* $a^2 + b^2 = c^2$. *Prove that*

$$\log_{b+c} a + \log_{c-b} a = 2 \log_{c+b} a \cdot \log_{c-b} a, \forall a > 0, a \neq 1$$

$$c - b > 0, c + b > 0$$

$$c - b \neq 1, c + b \neq 1.$$

Sol. LHS $= \log_{b+c} a + \log_{c-b} a$

$$= \frac{1}{\log_a(c+b)} + \frac{1}{\log_a(c-b)}$$

$$= \frac{\log_a(c+b) + \log_a(c-b)}{\log_a(c+b)\log_a(c-b)}$$

$$= \frac{\log_a(c^2 - b^2)}{\log_a(c+b) \cdot \log_a(c-b)}$$

$$= \frac{\log_a a^2}{\log_a(c+b) \cdot \log_a(c-b)} \quad [\because c^2 - b^2 = a^2]$$

$$= \frac{2 \log_a a}{\log_a(c+b) \cdot \log_a(c-b)}$$

$$= \frac{2}{\log_a(c+b) \cdot \log_a(c-b)}$$

$$= 2 \log_{c+b} a \cdot \log_{c-b} a = \text{RHS}$$

Ex. 31 *Let* $a > 0, c > 0, b = \sqrt{ac}$, a, c *and* $ac \neq 1, N > 0$.

Prove that $\frac{\log_a N}{\log_c N} = \frac{\log_a N - \log_b N}{\log_b N - \log_c N}$.

Sol. RHS $= \frac{\log_a N - \log_b N}{\log_b N - \log_c N} = \frac{\frac{1}{\log_N a} - \frac{1}{\log_N b}}{\frac{1}{\log_N b} - \frac{1}{\log_N c}}$

$$= \frac{(\log_N b - \log_N a)}{(\log_N c - \log_N b)} \cdot \frac{\log_N c}{\log_N a}$$

$$= \frac{\log_N\left(\frac{b}{a}\right)}{\log_N\left(\frac{c}{b}\right)} \cdot \frac{\log_a N}{\log_c N} = \frac{\log_a N}{\log_c N} = \text{LHS}$$

$$\left[\because b = \sqrt{ac} \Rightarrow b^2 = ac \Rightarrow \frac{b}{a} = \frac{c}{b}\right]$$

Ex. 32 *If $a^x = b, b^y = c, c^z = a, x = \log_b a^{k_1}, y = \log_c b^{k_2}$, $z = \log_a c^{k_3}$, find the minimum value of $3k_1 + 6k_2 + 12k_3$.*

Sol. $\because \quad a = c^z = (b^y)^z \quad [\because c = b^y]$

$= b^{yz} = (a^x)^{yz} = a^{xyz} \quad [\because b = a^x]$

$\therefore \quad xyz = 1$

Also, $xyz = \log_b a^{k_1} \cdot \log_c b^{k_2} \cdot \log_a c^{k_3}$

$= k_1 \cdot k_2 \cdot k_3 \cdot \log_b a \cdot \log_c b \cdot \log_a c$

$1 = k_1 k_2 k_3$

$\because \quad$ AM $\geq$ GM

$$\therefore \quad \frac{3k_1 + 6k_2 + 12k_3}{3} \geq (3k_1 \cdot 6k_2 \cdot 12k_3)^{1/3}$$

$= (3 \cdot 6 \cdot 12 \cdot k_1 k_2 k_3)^{1/3}$

$= (3 \cdot 6 \cdot 12)^{1/3} \quad [\because k_1 k_2 k_3 = 1]$

$= (2^3 \cdot 3^3)^{1/3} = 6$

or $3k_1 + 6k_2 + 12k_3 \geq 18$

$\therefore$ Minimum value of $3k_1 + 6k_2 + 12k_3$ is 18.

Ex. 33 *If $x = 1 + \log_a bc, y = 1 + \log_b ca, z = 1 + \log_c ab$, prove that $xyz = xy + yz + zx$.*

Sol. $\because \quad x = 1 + \log_a bc = 1 + \dfrac{\log bc}{\log a} = 1 + \dfrac{\log b + \log c}{\log a}$

$$= \frac{\log a + \log b + \log c}{\log a}$$

or $\quad \dfrac{1}{x} = \dfrac{\log a}{\log a + \log b + \log c} \quad$ ...(i)

Similarly, $\quad \dfrac{1}{y} = \dfrac{\log b}{\log a + \log b + \log c} \quad$ ...(ii)

and $\quad \dfrac{1}{z} = \dfrac{\log c}{\log a + \log b + \log c} \quad$ ...(iii)

On adding Eqs. (i), (ii) and (iii), we get

$$\frac{1}{x} + \frac{1}{y} + \frac{1}{z} = 1$$

or $\quad xyz = xy + yz + zx$

Ex. 34 *If $\dfrac{\ln a}{(b-c)} = \dfrac{\ln b}{(c-a)} = \dfrac{\ln c}{(a-b)}$, prove that*

$$a^{b+c} \cdot b^{c+a} \cdot c^{a+b} = 1$$

Also, prove that $\quad a^{b+c} + b^{c+a} + c^{a+b} \geq 3.$

Sol. Since, $a > 0, b > 0, c > 0$

$$\frac{\ln a}{(b-c)} = \frac{\ln b}{(c-a)} = \frac{\ln c}{(a-b)}$$

$$= \frac{(b+c)\ln a + (c+a)\ln b + (a+b)\ln c}{0}$$

[using ratio and proportion]

$\therefore \quad (b+c)\ln a + (c+a)\ln b + (a+b)\ln c = 0$

$\Rightarrow \quad \ln a^{b+c} + \ln b^{c+a} + \ln c^{a+b} = 0$

$\Rightarrow \quad \ln \{a^{b+c} \cdot b^{c+a} \cdot c^{a+b}\} = 0$

$\Rightarrow \quad a^{b+c} \cdot b^{c+a} \cdot c^{a+b} = e^0 = 1 \quad$ ...(i)

Again, AM $\geq$ GM

$$\Rightarrow \quad \frac{a^{b+c} + b^{c+a} + c^{a+b}}{3} \geq (a^{b+c} \cdot b^{c+a} \cdot c^{a+b})^{1/3}$$

$= (1)^{1/3} = 1 \quad$ [from Eq. (i)]

or $\quad a^{b+c} + b^{c+a} + c^{a+b} \geq 3$

Ex. 35 *Simplify* $5^{\log_{1/5}(1/2)} + \log_{\sqrt{2}}\left(\dfrac{4}{\sqrt{7} + \sqrt{3}}\right) + \log_{1/2}\left(\dfrac{1}{10 + 2\sqrt{21}}\right)$.

Sol. $\because \quad 5^{\log_{1/5}\left(\frac{1}{2}\right)} = 5^{\log_5(2)} = 2$

$$\log_{\sqrt{2}}\left(\frac{4}{\sqrt{7}+\sqrt{3}}\right) = \log_{\sqrt{2}}\left(\frac{4(\sqrt{7}-\sqrt{3})}{(\sqrt{7}+\sqrt{3})(\sqrt{7}-\sqrt{3})}\right)$$

$= \log_{\sqrt{2}}(\sqrt{7} - \sqrt{3})$

$= \log_{2^{1/2}}(\sqrt{7} - \sqrt{3})^1$

$= \dfrac{1}{1/2}\log_2(\sqrt{7} - \sqrt{3})$

$= \log_2(\sqrt{7} - \sqrt{3})^2 = \log_2(10 - 2\sqrt{21})$

and $\log_{1/2}\left(\dfrac{1}{10 + 2\sqrt{21}}\right) = \log_2(10 + 2\sqrt{21})$

Hence,

$$5^{\log_{1/5}(1/2)} + \log_{\sqrt{2}}\left(\frac{4}{\sqrt{7}+\sqrt{3})}\right) + \log_{1/2}\left(\frac{1}{10+2\sqrt{21}}\right)$$

$= 2 + \log_2(10 - 2\sqrt{21}) + \log_2(10 + 2\sqrt{21})$

$= 2 + \log_2\{(10 - 2\sqrt{21})(10 + 2\sqrt{21})\}$

$= 2 + \log_2(100 - 84) = 2 + \log_2(2)^4 = 2 + 4 = 6$

Ex. 36 *Find the square of the sum of the roots of the equation $\log_2 x \cdot \log_3 x \cdot \log_5 x = \log_2 x \cdot \log_3 x + \log_3 x \cdot \log_5 x + \log_5 x \cdot \log_2 x$.*

Sol. Let $\log_2 x = A, \log_3 x = B$ and $\log_5 x = C$, then the given equation can be written as

$$ABC = AB + BC + CA = ABC\left(\frac{1}{C} + \frac{1}{A} + \frac{1}{B}\right)$$

$$\Rightarrow \quad ABC\left(\frac{1}{A} + \frac{1}{B} + \frac{1}{C} - 1\right) = 0$$

or $A = 0, B = 0, C = 0, \dfrac{1}{A} + \dfrac{1}{B} + \dfrac{1}{C} - 1 = 0$

$$\underbrace{\log_2 x = 0, \log_3 x = 0, \log_5 x = 0}_{x>0},\ \underbrace{\log_x 2 + \log_x 3 + \log_x 5 = 0}_{x>0,\ x\neq 1}$$

or $\quad x = 2^0, x = 3^0, x = 5^0, \log_x(2\cdot 3\cdot 5) = 0$

or $\quad x = 1, x = 1, x = 1, x = 30$

$\therefore$ Roots are 1 and 30.

Hence, the required value

$$= (1+30)^2 = (31)^2 = 961$$

• Ex. 37 *Given that* $\log_2 a = \lambda, \log_4 b = \lambda^2$ *and* $\log_{c^2}(8) = \dfrac{2}{\lambda^3+1}$, *write* $\log_2\left(\dfrac{a^2b^5}{c^4}\right)$ *as a function of 'λ' (a, b, c > 0, c ≠ 1).*

Sol. $\because \log_2 a = \lambda \Rightarrow a = 2^\lambda$

$\Rightarrow \quad \log_4 b = \lambda^2$

$\Rightarrow \quad b = 4^{\lambda^2} = 2^{2\lambda^2}$

and $\quad \log_{c^2}(8) = \dfrac{2}{\lambda^3+1}$

$\Rightarrow \quad \dfrac{3}{2}\log_c 2 = \dfrac{2}{\lambda^3+1}$

$\Rightarrow \quad \log_c 2 = \dfrac{4}{3(\lambda^3+1)}$

or $\quad \log_2 c = \dfrac{3(\lambda^3+1)}{4}$ or $c = 2^{\left\{\frac{3(\lambda^3+1)}{4}\right\}}$

$$\therefore \quad \log_2\left(\frac{a^2b^5}{c^4}\right) = \log_2(a^2b^5c^{-4})$$

$$= \log_2\{2^{2\lambda}\cdot 2^{10\lambda^2}\cdot 2^{-3(\lambda^3+1)}\}$$

$$= \log_2\{2^{2\lambda+10\lambda^2-3(\lambda^3+1)}\}$$

$$= 2\lambda + 10\lambda^2 - 3(\lambda^3+1)$$

• Ex. 38 *Given that* $\log_2 3 = a, \log_3 5 = b, \log_7 2 = c$, *express the logarithm of the number 63 to the base 140 in terms of a, b and c.*

Sol. $\because \log_2 3 = a$ ...(i)

$\Rightarrow \quad b = \log_3 5 = \dfrac{\log_2 5}{\log_2 3} = \dfrac{\log_2 5}{a}$ [from Eq. (i)]

$\therefore \quad \log_2 5 = ab$ ...(ii)

and $\quad \log_7 2 = c$

$\Rightarrow \quad \dfrac{1}{\log_2 7} = c$ or $\log_2 7 = \dfrac{1}{c}$ ...(iii)

Now, $\quad \log_{140} 63 = \dfrac{\log_2 63}{\log_2 140} = \dfrac{\log_2(3^2\times 7)}{\log_2(2^2\times 5\times 7)}$

$$= \frac{2\log_2 3 + \log_2 7}{2 + \log_2 5 + \log_2 7} = \frac{2a + \frac{1}{c}}{2 + ab + \frac{1}{c}}$$

[from Eqs. (i), (ii) and (iii)]

$$= \left(\frac{2ac+1}{2c+abc+1}\right)$$

• Ex. 39 *Show that the sum of the roots of the equation* $x+1 = 2\log_2(2^x+3) - 2\log_4(1980-2^{-x})$ *is* $\log_2 11$.

Sol. Given,

$$x + 1 = 2\log_2(2^x+3) - 2\log_4(1980-2^{-x})$$

$$= 2\log_2(2^x+3) - 2\log_{2^2}(1980-2^{-x})^1$$

$$= 2\log_2(2^x+3) - 2\cdot\frac{1}{2}\log_2(1980-2^{-x})$$

$$= \log_2(2^x+3)^2 - \log_2(1980-2^{-x})$$

$$= \log_2\left\{\frac{(2^x+3)^2}{1980-2^{-x}}\right\}$$

or $\quad 2^{x+1} = \dfrac{(2^x+3)^2}{1980-2^{-x}}$

$\Rightarrow \quad 1980(2^{x+1}) - 2 = 2^{2x} + 9 + 6\cdot 2^x$

$\Rightarrow \quad 2^{2x} - 3954\cdot 2^x + 11 = 0$ ...(i)

If x_1, x_2 are the roots of Eq. (i), then

$$2^{x_1}\cdot 2^{x_2} = 11 \text{ or } 2^{x_1+x_2} = 11$$

$\Rightarrow \quad x_1 + x_2 = \log_2 11$

• Ex. 40 *Solve the following equations for x and y* $\log_{100}|x+y| = \dfrac{1}{2}, \log_{10} y - \log_{10}|x| = \log_{100} 4.$

Sol. $\because \quad \log_{100}|x+y| = \dfrac{1}{2}$

$\Rightarrow \quad |x+y| = (100)^{1/2} = 10$

$\Rightarrow \quad |x+y| = 10$ ...(i)

and $\quad \log_{10} y - \log_{10}|x| = \log_{100} 4, y > 0$

$\Rightarrow \quad \log_{10}\left(\dfrac{y}{|x|}\right) = \log_{10^2} 2^2 = \dfrac{2}{2}\log_{10} 2$

$\Rightarrow \quad \log_{10}\left(\dfrac{y}{|x|}\right) = \log_{10} 2 \Rightarrow \dfrac{y}{|x|} = 2$

$\Rightarrow \quad y = 2|x|$ ...(ii)

From Eqs. (i) and (ii),we get

$$|x + 2|x|| = 10 \quad \text{...(iii)}$$

Case I If $x > 0$, then $|x| = x$

From Eq. (iii),

$$|x + 2x| = 10$$

$$\Rightarrow \quad 3|x| = 10 \Rightarrow |x| = \frac{10}{3}$$

$$\therefore \quad x = \frac{10}{3}, y = \frac{20}{3} \quad \text{[from Eq. (ii)]}$$

Case II If $x < 0$, then $|x| = -x$

From Eq. (iii),

$$|x - 2x| = 10$$

$$\Rightarrow \quad |-x| = 10 \Rightarrow |x| = 10$$

$$\therefore \quad -x = 10$$

$$\Rightarrow \quad x = -10$$

From Eq. (ii), $y = 20$

Hence, solutions are $\left\{\frac{10}{3}, \frac{20}{3}\right\}, \{-10, 20\}$.

Ex. 41 *Solve the following equation for x*

$$\frac{6}{5}a^{\log_a x \cdot \log_{10} a \cdot \log_a 5} - 3^{\log_{10}(x/10)} = 9^{\log_{100} x + \log_4 2}.$$

Sol. $\because \frac{6}{5} \cdot a^{\log_a x \cdot \log_{10} a \cdot \log_a 5} - 3^{\log_{10}(x/10)} = 9^{\log_{100} x + \log_4 2}$

$$\Rightarrow \quad \frac{6}{5} \cdot x^{\log_{10} 5} - 3^{(\log_{10} x - 1)} = 3^{2\left(\frac{1}{2}\log_{10} x + \frac{1}{2}\right)} \quad \text{[by property]}$$

$$\Rightarrow \quad \frac{6}{5} \cdot 5^{\log_{10} x} - \frac{3^{\log_{10} x}}{3} = 3^{\log_{10} x + 1} \quad \text{[by property]}$$

Let $\log_{10} x = \lambda$, then

$$\Rightarrow \quad \frac{6}{5} \cdot 5^{\lambda} - \frac{3^{\lambda}}{3} = 3 \cdot 3^{\lambda}$$

$$\Rightarrow \quad \frac{6}{5} \cdot 5^{\lambda} = 3^{\lambda}\left(\frac{1}{3} + 3\right) = \frac{10}{3} \cdot 3^{\lambda}$$

$$\Rightarrow \quad 5^{\lambda - 2} = 3^{\lambda - 2} \text{ which is possible only, where } \lambda = 2.$$

$$\Rightarrow \quad \log_{10} x = 2$$

$$\therefore \quad x = 10^2 = 100$$

Ex. 42 *Find the value of x satisfying the equation*

$$|x - 1|^{\log_3 x^2 - 2\log_x 9} = (x - 1)^7.$$

Sol. The given equation is,

$$|x - 1|^{\log_3 x^2 - 2\log_x 9} = (x - 1)^7 \quad \text{...(i)}$$

This equation is defined for

$$x^2 > 0, x > 0, x \neq 1 \text{ and } x - 1 \geq 1$$

$\Rightarrow \quad x \geq 2$, then Eq. (i) reduces to

$$(x - 1)^{\log_3 x^2 - 2\log_x 9} = (x - 1)^7$$

Taking log on both sides, then

$$(\log_3 x^2 - 2\log_x 9)\log(x - 1) = 7\log(x - 1)$$

$$\Rightarrow \quad \log(x - 1)\{\log_3 x^2 - 2\log_x 9 - 7\} = 0$$

$$\Rightarrow \quad \log(x - 1)\left\{2\log_3 x - \frac{4}{\log_3 x} - 7\right\} = 0$$

$$\Rightarrow \quad \log(x - 1)\{2(\log_3 x)^2 - 7\log_3 x - 4\} = 0$$

$$\Rightarrow \quad \log(x - 1)(\log_3 x - 4)(2\log_3 x + 1) = 0$$

$$\Rightarrow \quad \log(x - 1) = 0, \log_3 x = 4, \log_3 x = -\frac{1}{2}$$

$$\Rightarrow \quad x - 1 = (10)^0, x = 3^4, x = 3^{-1/2}$$

$$\Rightarrow \quad x - 1 = 1, x = 81, x = \frac{1}{\sqrt{3}}$$

$$\therefore \quad x = 2, 81 \quad \left[\because x \geq 2, \therefore x \neq \frac{1}{\sqrt{3}}\right]$$

Ex. 43 *Find all real numbers x which satisfy the equation* $2\log_2 \log_2 x + \log_{1/2} \log_2(2\sqrt{2}x) = 1$.

Sol. Given,

$$2\log_2 \log_2 x + \log_{1/2} \log_2(2\sqrt{2}x) = 1$$

$$\Rightarrow \quad 2\log_2 \log_2 x - \log_2 \log_2(2\sqrt{2}x) = 1$$

$$\Rightarrow \quad 2\log_2 \log_2 x - \log_2\{\log_2(2\sqrt{2}) + \log_2 x\} = 1$$

$$\Rightarrow \quad 2\log_2 \log_2 x - \log_2\left\{\frac{3}{2} + \log_2 x\right\} = 1$$

Let $\log_2 x = \lambda$, then $2\log_2 \lambda - \log_2\left(\frac{3}{2} + \lambda\right) = 1$

$$\Rightarrow \quad \log_2 \lambda^2 - \log_2\left(\frac{3}{2} + \lambda\right) = 1$$

$$\Rightarrow \quad \log_2\left\{\frac{\lambda^2}{\frac{3}{2} + \lambda}\right\} = 1 \Rightarrow \frac{\lambda^2}{\frac{3}{2} + \lambda} = 2^1$$

$$\Rightarrow \quad \lambda^2 = 3 + 2\lambda \Rightarrow \lambda^2 - 2\lambda - 3 = 0$$

$$\Rightarrow \quad (\lambda - 3)(\lambda + 1) = 0$$

$$\therefore \quad \lambda = 3, -1$$

$$\text{or} \quad \log_2 x = 3, -1$$

$$\Rightarrow \quad x = 2^3, 2^{-1}$$

$$\Rightarrow \quad x = 8, \frac{1}{2} \quad \text{...(i)}$$

But the given equation is valid only when,

$$x > 0, 2\sqrt{2}x > 0, \log_2 x > 0, \log_2(2\sqrt{2}x) > 0$$

$$\Rightarrow \quad x > 0, x > 0, x > 1, x > \frac{1}{2\sqrt{2}}$$

Hence, $x > 1$

From Eq. (i), the solution of the given equation is $x = 8$.

Ex. 44 *Solve for x,*

$$\log_{3/4} \log_8(x^2 + 7) + \log_{1/2} \log_{1/4}(x^2 + 7)^{-1} = -2.$$

Sol. Given,

$$\log_{3/4} \log_8(x^2 + 7) + \log_{1/2} \log_{1/4}(x^2 + 7)^{-1} = -2$$

$$\Rightarrow \log_{3/4} \log_{2^3} (x^2+7) + \log_{2^{-1}} \log_{2^{-2}} (x^2+7)^{-1} = -2$$

$$\Rightarrow \log_{3/4}\left\{\frac{1}{3}\log_2(x^2+7)\right\} - \log_2\left\{\frac{1}{2}\log_2(x^2+7)\right\} = -2$$

Let $\log_2(x^2+7) = 6\lambda$ ...(i)

Then, $\log_{3/4}(2\lambda) - \log_2(3\lambda) = -2$

$$\Rightarrow \frac{\log_2(2\lambda)}{\log_2(3/4)} - \log_2(3\lambda) = -2$$

$$\Rightarrow \frac{1+\log_2\lambda}{\log_2 3 - \log_2 4} - (\log_2 3 + \log_2\lambda) = -2$$

$$\Rightarrow \frac{1+\log_2\lambda}{\log_2 3 - 2} - (\log_2 3 + \log_2\lambda) = -2$$

Again, let $\log_2\lambda = A$ and $\log_2 3 = B$, then

$$\frac{1+A}{B-2} - (B+A) = -2$$

$$\Rightarrow 1 + A - B^2 - AB + 2B + 2A = -2B + 4$$

$$\Rightarrow A(3-B) = B^2 - 4B + 3 = (B-1)(B-3)$$

$$\Rightarrow A = -(B-1)$$

$[\because B - 3 \neq 0, \text{ i.e. } \log_2 3 \neq 3]$

$$\Rightarrow A + B = 1 \Rightarrow \log_2\lambda + \log_2 3 = 1$$

$$\Rightarrow \log_2(3\lambda) = 1$$

$$\Rightarrow 3\lambda = 2$$

$$\Rightarrow 3\cdot\frac{1}{6}\log_2(x^2+7) = 2 \text{ [from Eq. (i)]}$$

$$\Rightarrow \log_2(x^2+7) = 4$$

$$\Rightarrow x^2 + 7 = 2^4 = 16 \text{ or } x^2 = 9$$

$$\therefore x = \pm 3$$

• **Ex. 45** *Prove that*

$$2^{\left(\sqrt{\log_a \sqrt[4]{ab} + \log_b \sqrt[4]{ab}} - \sqrt{\log_a \sqrt[4]{b/a} + \log_b \sqrt[4]{a/b}}\right)\sqrt{\log_a b}} = \begin{cases} 2, & b \geq a > 1. \\ 2^{\log_a b}, & 1 < b < a \end{cases}$$

Sol. Since, $\sqrt{\log_a \sqrt[4]{ab} + \log_b \sqrt[4]{ab}} = \sqrt{\frac{1}{4}\log_a(ab) + \frac{1}{4}\log_b(ab)}$

$$= \sqrt{\frac{1}{4}(1 + \log_a b + \log_b a + 1)}$$

$$= \sqrt{\left(\frac{\log_a b + \frac{1}{\log_a b} + 2}{4}\right)} = \sqrt{\left(\frac{\sqrt{|\log_a b|} + \frac{1}{\sqrt{|\log_a b|}}}{2}\right)^2}$$

$$= \frac{1}{2}\left(\sqrt{|\log_a b|} + \frac{1}{\sqrt{|\log_a b|}}\right)$$

and $\sqrt{\log_a \sqrt[4]{(b/a)} + \log_b \sqrt[4]{(a/b)}}$

$$= \sqrt{\frac{1}{4}\log_a\left(\frac{b}{a}\right) + \frac{1}{4}\log_b\left(\frac{a}{b}\right)}$$

$$= \sqrt{\frac{1}{4}(\log_a b - 1 + \log_b a - 1)}$$

$$= \sqrt{\frac{\log_a b + \frac{1}{\log_a b} - 2}{4}}$$

$$= \frac{\left|\sqrt{|\log_a b|} - \frac{1}{\sqrt{|\log_a b|}}\right|}{2}$$

$$\therefore \sqrt{\log_a \sqrt[4]{ab} + \log_b \sqrt[4]{ab}} - \sqrt{\log_a \sqrt[4]{b/a} + \log_b \sqrt[4]{(a/b)}}$$

P (say)

$$= \frac{1}{2}\left\{\sqrt{|\log_a b|} + \frac{1}{\sqrt{|\log_a b|}} + \left|\sqrt{|\log_a b|} - \frac{1}{\sqrt{|\log_a b|}}\right|\right\}$$

***Case* I** If $b \geq a > 1$, then

$$P = \frac{1}{2}\left\{\sqrt{|\log_a b|} + \frac{1}{\sqrt{|\log_a b|}} - \sqrt{|\log_a b|} + \frac{1}{\sqrt{|\log_a b|}}\right\}$$

$$= \frac{1}{\sqrt{\log_a b}}$$

$$\therefore 2^{P\sqrt{\log_a b}} = 2^1 = 2$$

***Case* II** If $1 < b < a$, then

$$P = \frac{1}{2}\left\{\sqrt{|\log_a b|} + \frac{1}{\sqrt{|\log_a b|}} + \sqrt{|\log_a b|} - \frac{1}{\sqrt{|\log_a b|}}\right\}$$

$$= \sqrt{|\log_a b|}$$

$$\therefore 2^{P\sqrt{\log_a b}} = 2^{\log_a b}$$

Logarithms and Their Properties Exercise 1 :
Single Option Correct Type Questions

- This section contains **20 multiple choice questions.** Each question has four choices (a), (b), (c) and (d) out of which **ONLY ONE** is correct

1. If $\log_{10} 2 = 0.3010\ldots$, the number of digits in the number 2000^{2000} is

(a) 6601 (b) 6602 (c) 6603 (d) 6604

2. There exist a positive number λ, such that $\log_2 x + \log_4 x + \log_8 x = \log_\lambda x$, for all positive real numbers x.
If $\lambda = \sqrt[b]{a}$, where $a, b \in N$, the smallest possible value of $(a+b)$ is equal to

(a) 12 (b) 63 (c) 65 (d) 75

3. If a, b and c are the three real solutions of the equation

$$x^{\log_{10}^2 x + \log_{10} x^3 + 3} = \frac{2}{\dfrac{1}{\sqrt{x+1}-1} - \dfrac{1}{\sqrt{x+1}+1}}$$

where, $a > b > c$, then a, b, c are in

(a) AP (b) GP
(c) HP (d) $a^{-1} + b^{-1} = c^{-1}$

4. If $f(n) = \prod_{i=2}^{n-1} \log_i (i+1)$, the value of $\sum_{k=1}^{100} f(2^k)$ equals

(a) 5010 (b) 5050 (c) 5100 (d) 5049

5. If $\log_3 27 \cdot \log_x 7 = \log_{27} x \cdot \log_7 3$, the least value of x, is

(a) 7^{-3} (b) 3^{-7} (c) 7^3 (d) 3^7

6. If $x = \log_5 (1000)$ and $y = \log_7 (2058)$, then

(a) $x > y$ (b) $x < y$
(c) $x = y$ (d) None of these

7. If $\log_5 120 + (x-3) - 2\log_5 (1 - 5^{x-3}) = -\log_5 (0.2 - 5^{x-4})$, then x is

(a) 1 (b) 2 (c) 3 (d) 4

8. If $x_n > x_{n-1} > \ldots > x_2 > x_1 > 1$, the value of

$$\log_{x_1} \log_{x_2} \log_{x_3} \ldots \log_{x_n} x_n^{x_{n-1}^{\cdot^{\cdot^{\cdot^{x_1}}}}}$$ is

(a) 0 (b) 1
(c) 2 (d) undefined

9. If $\dfrac{x(y+z-x)}{\log x} = \dfrac{y(z+x-y)}{\log y} = \dfrac{z(x+y-z)}{\log z}$,
then $x^y y^x = z^y y^z$ is equal to

(a) $z^x x^z$ (b) $x^z y^x$ (c) $x^y y^z$ (d) $x^x y^y$

10. If $y = a^{\frac{1}{1-\log_a x}}$ and $z = a^{\frac{1}{1-\log_a y}}$, then x is equal to

(a) $a^{\frac{1}{1+\log_a z}}$ (b) $a^{\frac{1}{2+\log_a z}}$ (c) $a^{\frac{1}{1-\log_a z}}$ (d) $a^{\frac{1}{2-\log_a z}}$

11. If $\log_{0.3}(x-1) < \log_{0.09}(x-1)$, then x lies in the interval

(a) $(-\infty, 1)$
(b) $(1, 2)$
(c) $(2, \infty)$
(d) None of the above

12. The value of $a^x - b^y$ is (where $x = \sqrt{\log_a b}$ and $y = \sqrt{\log_b a}$, $a > 0, b > 0$ and $a, b \neq 1$)

(a) 1 (b) 2
(c) 0 (d) -1

13. If $x = 1 + \log_a bc$, $y = 1 + \log_b ca$, $z = 1 + \log_c ab$, then $\dfrac{xyz}{xy+yz+zx}$ is equal to

(a) 0 (b) 1
(c) -1 (d) 2

14. The value of $a^{\frac{\log_b(\log_b N)}{\log_b a}}$ is

(a) $\log_a N$ (b) $\log_b N$
(c) $\log_N a$ (d) $\log_N b$

15. The value of $49^A + 5^B$, where $A = 1 - \log_7 2$ and $B = -\log_5 4$ is

(a) 10.5 (b) 11.5
(c) 12.5 (d) 13.5

16. The number of real values of the parameter λ for which $(\log_{16} x)^2 - \log_{16} x + \log_{16} \lambda = 0$ with real coefficients will have exactly one solution is

(a) 1 (b) 2
(c) 3 (d) 4

17. The number of roots of the equation $x^{\log_x (x+3)^2} = 16$ is

(a) 1 (b) 0
(c) 2 (d) 4

18. The point on the graph $y = \log_2 \log_6 \{2^{\sqrt{(2x+1)}} + 4\}$, whose y-coordinate is 1 is

(a) (1, 1) (b) (6,1)
(c) (8, 1) (d) (12, 1)

19. Given, $\log 2 = 0.301$ and $\log 3 = 0.477$, then the number of digits before decimal in $3^{12} \times 2^8$ is

(a) 7 (b) 8
(c) 9 (d) 11

20. The number of solution(s) for the equation $2\log_x a + \log_{ax} a + 3\log_{a^2 x} a = 0$, is

(a) one (b) two
(c) three (d) four

Logarithms and Their Properties Exercise 2 : More than One Correct Option Type Questions

- This section contains **9 multiple choice questions**. Each question has four choices (a), (b), (c) and (d) out of which **MORE THAN ONE** may be correct.

21. If $x^{(\log_2 x)^2 - 6\log_2 x + 11} = 64$, then x is equal to

(a) 2 (b) 4 (c) 6 (d) 8

22. If $\log_\lambda x \cdot \log_5 \lambda = \log_x 5$, $\lambda \neq 1$, $\lambda > 0$, then x is equal to

(a) λ (b) 5 (c) $\frac{1}{5}$ (d) None of these

23. If $S = \{x : \sqrt{\log_x \sqrt{3x}}$, where $\log_3 x > -1\}$, then

(a) S is a finite set (b) $S \in \phi$

(c) $S \subset (0, \infty)$ (d) S properly contains $\left(\frac{1}{3}, \infty\right)$

24. If x satisfies $\log_2(9^{x-1} + 7) = 2 + \log_2(3^{x-1} + 1)$, then

(a) $x \in Q$

(b) $x \in N$

(c) $x \in \{x \in Q : x < 0\}$

(d) $x \in N_e$ (set of even natural numbers)

25. $\log_p \log_p \underbrace{\sqrt[p]{\sqrt[p]{\sqrt[p]{\ldots \sqrt[p]{p}}}}}_{n \text{ times}}$, $p > 0$ and $p \neq 1$ is equal to

(a) n (b) $-n$

(c) $\frac{1}{n}$ (d) $\log_{1/p}(p^n)$

26. If $\log_a x = \alpha$, $\log_b x = \beta$, $\log_c x = \gamma$ and $\log_d x = \delta$, $x \neq 1$ and $a, b, c, d \neq 0, > 1$, then $\log_{abcd} x$ equals

(a) $\leq \frac{\alpha + \beta + \gamma + \delta}{16}$ (b) $\geq \frac{\alpha + \beta + \gamma + \delta}{16}$

(c) $\frac{1}{\alpha^{-1} + \beta^{-1} + \gamma^{-1} + \delta^{-1}}$ (d) $\frac{1}{\alpha\beta\gamma\delta}$

27. If $\log_{10} 5 = a$ and $\log_{10} 3 = b$, then

(a) $\log_{10} 8 = 3(1 - a)$ (b) $\log_{40} 15 = \frac{(a + b)}{(3 - 2a)}$

(c) $\log_{243} 32 = \left(\frac{1 - a}{b}\right)$ (d) All of these

28. If x is a positive number different from 1, such that $\log_a x$, $\log_b x$ and $\log_c x$ are in AP, then

(a) $\log b = \frac{2(\log a)(\log c)}{(\log a + \log c)}$ (b) $b = \frac{a + c}{2}$

(c) $b = \sqrt{ac}$ (d) $c^2 = (ac)^{\log_a b}$

29. If $|a| < |b|$, $b - a < 1$ and a, b are the real roots of the equation $x^2 - |\alpha| x - |\beta| = 0$, the equation $\log_{|b|} \left|\frac{x}{a}\right| - 1 = 0$ has

(a) one root lying in interval $(-\infty, a)$

(b) one root lying in interval (b, ∞)

(c) one positive root

(d) one negative root

Logarithms and Their Properties Exercise 3 : Passage Based Questions

- This section contains **4 passages**. Based upon each of the passage **3 multiple choice questions** have to be answered. Each of these questions has four choices (a), (b), (c) and (d) out of which **ONLY ONE** is correct.

Passage I

(Q. Nos. 30 to 32)

Let $\log_2 N = a_1 + b_1$, $\log_3 N = a_2 + b_2$ *and* $\log_5 N = a_3 + b_3$, *where* $a_1, a_2, a_3 \in I$ *and* $b_1, b_2, b_3 \in [0, 1)$.

30. If $a_1 = 5$ and $a_2 = 3$, the number of integral values of N is

(a) 16 (b) 32 (c) 48 (d) 64

31. If $a_1 = 6$, $a_2 = 4$ and $a_3 = 3$, the largest integral value of N is

(a) 124 (b) 63

(c) 624 (d) 127

32. If $a_1 = 6$, $a_2 = 4$ and $a_3 = 3$, the difference of largest and smallest integral values of N, is

(a) 2 (b) 8

(c) 14 (d) 20

Passage II

(Q. Nos. 33 to 35)

Let 'S' denotes the antilog of 0.5 to the base 256 and 'K' denotes the number of digits in 6^{10} *(given* $\log_{10} 2 = 0.301$, $\log_{10} 3 = 0.477$*) and G denotes the number of positive integers, which have the characteristic 2, when the base of logarithm is 3.*

33. The value of G is

(a) 18 (b) 24 (c) 30 (d) 36

34. The value of KG is

(a) 72 (b) 144 (c) 216 (d) 288

35. The value of SKG is

(a) 1440 (b) 17280
(c) 2016 (d) 2304

Passage III
(Q. Nos. 36 to 38)

Suppose 'U' denotes the number of digits in the number $(60)^{100}$ and 'M' denotes the number of cyphers after decimal, before a significant figure comes in $(8)^{-296}$. If the fraction U/M is expressed as rational number in the lowest term as p/q (given $\log_{10} 2 = 0.301$ and $\log_{10} 3 = 0.477$).

36. The value of p is

(a) 1 (b) 2 (c) 3 (d) 4

37. The value of q is

(a) 5 (b) 2
(c) 3 (d) 4

38. The equation whose roots are p and q, is

(a) $x^2 - 3x + 2 = 0$ (b) $x^2 - 5x + 6 = 0$
(c) $x^2 - 7x + 12 = 0$ (d) $x^2 - 9x + 20 = 0$

Passage IV (Q. Nos. 39 to 41)

Let G, O, E and L be positive real numbers such that $\log(G\cdot L) + \log(G\cdot E) = 3$, $\log(E\cdot L) + \log(E\cdot O) = 4$, $\log(O\cdot G) + \log(O\cdot L) = 5$ (base of the log is 10).

39. If the value of the product $(GOEL)$ is λ, the value of $\sqrt{\log\lambda\sqrt{\log\lambda\sqrt{\log\lambda\ldots}}}$ is

(a) 3 (b) 4
(c) 5 (d) 7

40. If the minimum value of $3G + 2L + 2O + E$ is $2^{\lambda}3^{\mu}5^{\nu}$, where λ, μ and ν are whole numbers, the value of $\sum(\lambda^{\mu} + \mu^{\lambda})$ is

(a) 7 (b) 13
(c) 19 (d) None of these

41. If $\log\left(\frac{G}{O}\right)$ and $\log\left(\frac{O}{E}\right)$ are the roots of the equation

(a) $x^2 + x = 0$ (b) $x^2 - x = 0$
(c) $x^2 - 2x + 3 = 0$ (d) $x^2 - 1 = 0$

Logarithms and Their Properties Exercise 4 :
Single Integer Answer Type Questions

- This section contains **10 questions**. The answer to each question is a **single digit integer**, ranging from 0 to 9 (both inclusive).

42. If $x, y \in R^+$ and $\log_{10}(2x) + \log_{10} y = 2$ and $\log_{10} x^2 - \log_{10}(2y) = 4$ and $x + y = \frac{m}{n}$, where m and n are relative prime, the value of $m - 3n^6$ is

43. A line $x = \lambda$ intersects the graph of $y = \log_5 x$ and $y = \log_5(x + 4)$. The distance between the points of intersection is 0.5. Given $\lambda = a + \sqrt{b}$, where a and b are integers, the value of $(a + b)$ is

44. If the left hand side of the equation $a(b - c)x^2 + b(c - a)xy + c(a - b)y^2 = 0$ is a perfect square, the value of
$$\left\{\frac{\log(a + c) + \log(a - 2b + c)}{\log(a - c)}\right\}^2, (a, b, c \in R^+, a > c) \text{ is}$$

45. Number of integers satisfying the inequality $\left(\frac{1}{3}\right)^{\frac{|x+2|}{2-|x|}} > 9$ is

46. If $x > 2$ is a solution of the equation $|\log_{\sqrt{3}} x - 2| + |\log_3 x - 2| = 2$, then the value of x is

47. Number of integers satisfying the inequality $\log_2 \sqrt{x} - 2\log_{1/4}^2 x + 1 > 0$, is

48. The value of $b(> 0)$ for which the equation $2\log_{1/25}(bx + 28) = -\log_5(12 - 4x - x^2)$ has coincident roots, is

49. The value of $\dfrac{2^{\log_{2^{1/4}} 2} - 3^{\log_{27} 125} - 4}{7^{4\log_{49} 2} - 3}$ is

50. If x_1 and x_2 $(x_2 > x_1)$ are the integral solutions of the equation $(\log_5 x)^2 + \log_{5x}\left(\frac{5}{x}\right) = 1$, the value of $|x_2 - 4x_1|$ is

51. If $x = \log_{\lambda} a = \log_a b = \frac{1}{2}\log_b c$ and $\log_{\lambda} c = nx^{n+1}$, the value of n is

Logarithms and Their Properties Exercise 5 : Matching Type Questions

- This section contains **3 questions**. Questions 52 to 54 have four statements (A, B, C and D) given in **Column I** and four statements (p, q, r and s) in **Column II**. Any given statement in **Column I** can have correct matching with one or more statement(s) given in **Column II**.

52.

	Column I		Column II
(A)	$\dfrac{\log_3 243}{\log_2 \sqrt{32}}$	(p)	positive integer
(B)	$\dfrac{2 \log 6}{(\log 12 + \log 3)}$	(q)	negative integer
(C)	$\log_{1/3}\left(\dfrac{1}{9}\right)^{-2}$	(r)	rational but not integer
(D)	$\dfrac{\log_5 16 - \log_5 4}{\log_5 128}$	(s)	prime

53.

	Column I		Column II
(A)	The expression $\sqrt{\log_{0.5}^2 8}$ has the value equal to	(p)	1
(B)	The value of the expression $(\log_{10} 2)^3 + \log_{10} 8 \cdot \log_{10} 5 + (\log_{10} 5)^3 + 3$, is	(q)	2
(C)	Let $N = \log_2 15 \cdot \log_{1/6} 2 \cdot \log_3 \left(\dfrac{1}{6}\right)$. The value of $[N]$ is (where $[\cdot]$ denotes the greatest integer function)	(r)	3
(D)	If $(52.6)^a = (0.00526)^b = 100$, the value of $\dfrac{1}{a} - \dfrac{1}{b}$ is	(s)	4

54.

	Column I		Column II
(A)	If $\log_{1/x}\left\{\dfrac{2(x-2)}{(x+1)(x-5)}\right\} \geq 1$, then x can belongs to	(p)	$\left(0, \dfrac{1}{3}\right]$
(B)	If $\log_3 x - \log_3^2 x \leq \dfrac{3}{2} \log_{(1/2\sqrt{2})} 4$, then x can belongs to	(q)	$(1, 2]$
(C)	If $\log_{1/2}(4-x) \geq \log_{1/2} 2 - \log_{1/2}(x-1)$, then x belongs to	(r)	$[3, 4)$
(D)	Let α and β are the roots of the quadratic equation $(\lambda^2 - 3\lambda + 4)x^2 - 4(2\lambda - 1)x + 16 = 0$, if α and β satisfy the condition $\beta > 1 > \alpha$, then p can lie in	(s)	$(3, 8)$

Logarithms and Their Properties Exercise 6 : Statement I and II Type Questions

- **Directions** Question numbers 55 to 60 are Assertion-Reason type questions. Each of these questions contains two statements:
Statement-1 (Assertion) and **Statement-2** (Reason)
Each of these questions also has four alternative choices, only one of which is the correct answer. You have to select the correct choice as given below.
  (a) Statement-1 is true, Statement-2 is true; Statement-2 is a correct explanation for Statement-1
  (b) Statement-1 is true, Statement-2 is true; Statement-2 is not a correct explanation for Statement-1
  (c) Statement-1 is true, Statement-2 is false
  (d) Statement-1 is false, Statement-2 is true

55. Statement-1 $\log_{10} x < \log_3 x < \log_e x < \log_2 x$ $(x > 0, x \neq 1)$.

Statement-2 If $0 < x < 1$, then $\log_x a > \log_x b \Rightarrow 0 < a < b$.

56. Statement-1 The equation $7^{\log_7 (x^3+1)} - x^2 = 1$ has two distinct real roots.

Statement-2 $a^{\log_a N} = N$, where $a > 0, a \neq 1$ and $N > 0$.

57. Statement-1 $\left(\dfrac{1}{3}\right)^7 < \left(\dfrac{1}{3}\right)^4$

$$\Rightarrow \quad 7 \log\left(\frac{1}{3}\right) < 4 \log\left(\frac{1}{3}\right) \Rightarrow 7 < 4$$

Statement-2 If $ax < ay$, where $a < 0$, $x, y > 0$, then $x > y$.

58. Statement-1 The equation $x^{\log_x (1-x)^2} = 9$ has two distinct real solutions.

Statement-2 $a^{\log_a b} = b$, when $a > 0, a \neq 1, b > 0$.

59. Statement-1 The equation $(\log x)^2 + \log x^2 - 3 = 0$ has two distinct solutions.

Statement-2 $\log x^2 = 2 \log x$.

60. Statement-1 $\log_x 3 \cdot \log_{x/9} 3 = \log_{81}(3)$ has a solution.

Statement-2 Change of base in logarithms is possible.

Logarithms and Their Properties Exercise 7 : Subjective Type Questions

- In this section, there are **27 subjective** questions.

61. (i) If $\log_7 12 = a$, $\log_{12} 24 = b$, then find value of $\log_{54} 168$ in terms of a and b.

(ii) If $\log_3 4 = a$, $\log_5 3 = b$, then find the value of $\log_3 10$ in terms of a and b.

62. If $\dfrac{\ln a}{b-c} = \dfrac{\ln b}{c-a} = \dfrac{\ln c}{a-b}$, prove the following.

(i) $abc = 1$

(ii) $a^a \cdot b^b \cdot c^c = 1$

(iii) $a^{b^2+bc+c^2} \cdot b^{c^2+ca+a^2} \cdot c^{a^2+ab+b^2} = 1$

(iv) $a + b + c \geq 3$

(v) $a^a + b^b + c^c \geq 3$

(vi) $a^{b^2+bc+c^2} + b^{c^2+ca+a^2} + c^{a^2+ab+b^2} \geq 3$

63. Prove that $\log_{10} 2$ lies between $\dfrac{1}{3}$ and $\dfrac{1}{4}$.

64. If $\log 2 = 0.301$ and $\log 3 = 0.477$, find the number of integers in

(i) 5^{200} (ii) 6^{20}

(iii) the number of zeroes after the decimal is 3^{-500}.

65. If $\log 2 = 0.301$ and $\log 3 = 0.477$, find the value of $\log(3.375)$.

66. Find the least value of $\log_2 x - \log_x(0.125)$ for $x > 1$.

67. Without using the tables, prove that

$$\frac{1}{\log_3 \pi} + \frac{1}{\log_4 \pi} > 2.$$

68. Solve the following equations.

(i) $x^{1+\log_{10} x} = 10x$

(ii) $\log_2(9 + 2^x) = 3$

(iii) $2 \cdot x^{\log_4 3} + 3^{\log_4 x} = 27$

(iv) $\log_4 \log_3 \log_2 x = 0$

(v) $x^{\frac{\log_{10} x + 5}{3}} = 10^{5+\log_{10} x}$

(vi) $\log_3\left(\log_9 x + \dfrac{1}{2} + 9^x\right) = 2x$

(vii) $4^{\log_{10} x+1} - 6^{\log_{10} x} - 2 \cdot 3^{\log_{10} x^2 + 2} = 0$

(viii) $\dfrac{\log_{10}(x-3)}{\log_{10}(x^2-21)} = \dfrac{1}{2}$

(ix) $x^{\log_2 x + 4} = 32$

(x) $\log_a x = x$, where $a = x^{\log_4 x}$

(xi) $\log_{\sqrt{2}\sin x}(1 + \cos x) = 2$

69. Find a rational number, which is 50 times its own logarithm to the base 10.

70. Find the value of the expression

$$\frac{2}{\log_4(2000)^6} + \frac{3}{\log_5(2000)^6}.$$

71. Find the value of x satisfying $\log_a\{1 + \log_b\{1 + \log_c(1 + \log_p x)\}\} = 0.$

72. Find the value of $4^{5\log_{4\sqrt{2}}(3-\sqrt{6}) - 6\log_8(\sqrt{3}-\sqrt{2})}$.

73. Solve the following inequations.

(i) $\log_{(2x+3)} x^2 < 1$

(ii) $\log_{2x}(x^2 - 5x + 6) < 1$

(iii) $\log_2(2 - x) < \log_{1/2}(x + 1)$

(iv) $\log_{x^2}(x + 2) < 1$

(v) $3^{\log_3 \sqrt{(x-1)}} < 3^{\log_3(x-6)} + 3$

(vi) $\log_{1/2}(3x - 1)^2 < \log_{1/2}(x + 5)^2$

(vii) $\log_{10} x + 2 \leq \log_{10}^2 x$

(viii) $\log_{10}(x^2 - 2x - 2) \leq 0$

(ix) $\log_x\left(2x - \dfrac{3}{4}\right) > 2$

(x) $\log_{1/3} x < \log_{1/2} x$

(xi) $\log_{2x+3} x^2 < \log_{2x+3}(2x + 3)$

(xii) $\log_2^2 x + 3\log_2 x \geq \dfrac{5}{2}\log_{4\sqrt{2}} 16$

(xiii) $(x^2 + x + 1)^x < 1$

(xiv) $\log_{(3x^2+1)} 2 < \dfrac{1}{2}$

(xv) $x^{(\log_{10} x)^2 - 3\log_{10} x + 1} > 1000$

(xvi) $\log_4\{14 + \log_6(x^2 - 64)\} \leq 2$

(xvii) $\log_2(9 - 2^x) \leq 10^{\log_{10}(3-x)}$

(xviii) $\log_a\left(\dfrac{2x+3}{x}\right) \geq 0$ for

(a) $a > 1$, (b) $0 < a < 1$

(xix) $1 + \log_2(x - 1) \leq \log_{x-1} 4$

(xx) $\log_{5x+4}(x^2) \leq \log_{5x+4}(2x + 3)$

74. Solve $\sqrt{\log_x(ax)^{1/5} + \log_a(ax)^{1/5}} + \sqrt{\log_a\left(\dfrac{x}{a}\right)^{1/5} + \log_x\left(\dfrac{a}{x}\right)^{1/5}} = a.$

75. It is known that $x = 9$ is root of the equation,

$$\log_\pi(x^2 + 15a^2) - \log_\pi(a - 2) = \log_\pi \frac{8ax}{a-2}$$

find the other roots of this equation.

76. Solve $\log_4(\log_3 x) + \log_{1/4}(\log_{1/3} y) = 0$ and $x^2 + y^2 = \frac{17}{4}$.

77. Find the real value(s) of x satisfying the equation $\log_{2x}(4x) + \log_{4x}(16x) = 4$.

78. Find the sum and product of all possible values of x which makes the following statement true

$$\log_6 54 + \log_x 16 = \log_{\sqrt{2}} x - \log_{36}\left(\frac{4}{9}\right).$$

79. Solve the equation

$$\frac{3}{2}\log_4(x+2)^3 + 3 = \log_4(4-x)^3 + \log_4(x+6)^3.$$

80. Solve $\log_2(4^{x+1} + 4)\cdot\log_2(4^x + 1) = \log_{1/\sqrt{2}}\left(\frac{1}{\sqrt{8}}\right)$.

81. Solve the system of equations $2^{\sqrt{x}+\sqrt{y}} = 256$ and $\log_{10}\sqrt{xy} - \log_{10}\left(\frac{3}{2}\right) = 1$.

82. Solve the system of equations $\log_2 y = \log_4(xy-2)$, $\log_9 x^2 + \log_3(x-y) = 1$.

83. Find the solution set of the inequality

$$2\log_{1/4}(x+5) > \frac{9}{4}\log_{\frac{1}{3\sqrt{3}}}(9) + \log_{\sqrt{(x+5)}}(2).$$

84. Solve $\log_3(\sqrt{x} + |\sqrt{x} - 1|) = \log_9(4\sqrt{x} - 3 + 4|\sqrt{x} - 1|)$.

85. In the inequality

$$(\log_2 x)^4 - \left(\log_{1/2}\frac{x^5}{4}\right)^2 - 20\log_2 x + 148 < 0$$

holds true in (a, b), where $a, b \in N$. Find the value of $ab(a+b)$.

86. Find the value of x satisfying the equation

$$\sqrt{(\log_3 \sqrt[3]{3x} + \log_x \sqrt[3]{3x})\cdot\log_3 x^3} + \sqrt{\left(\log_3 \sqrt[3]{\left(\frac{x}{3}\right)} + \log_x \sqrt[3]{\left(\frac{3}{x}\right)}\right)\log_3 x^3} = 2.$$

87. If P is the number of natural numbers whose logarithm to the base 10 have the characteristic P and Q is the number of natural numbers reciprocals of whose 3 logarithms to the base 10 have the characteristic $-q$, show that $\log_{10} P - \log_{10} Q = p - q + 1$.

Logarithms and Their Properties Exercise 8 : Questions Asked in Previous 13 Year's Exam

- This section contains questions asked in **IIT-JEE, AIEEE, JEE Main & JEE Advanced** from year **2005** to year **2017**.

88. Let $a = \log_3\log_3 2$ and an integer k satisfying $1 < 2^{(-k+3^{-a})} < 2$, then k equals to **[IIT-JEE 2008, 1.5M]**

(a) 0
(b) 1
(c) 2
(d) 3

89. Let (x_0, y_0) be solution of the following equations $(2x)^{\ln 2} = (3y)^{\ln 3}$ and $3^{\ln x} = 2^{\ln y}$, then x_0 is **[IIT-JEE 2011, 3M]**

(a) $\frac{1}{6}$ (b) $\frac{1}{3}$ (c) $\frac{1}{2}$ (d) 6

90. The value of

$$6 + \log_{3/2}\left(\frac{1}{3\sqrt{2}}\sqrt{4 - \frac{1}{3\sqrt{2}}\sqrt{4 - \frac{1}{3\sqrt{2}}\sqrt{4 - \frac{1}{3\sqrt{2}}\ldots}}}\right) \text{ is}$$

[IIT-JEE 2012, 4M]

91. If $3^x = 4^{x-1}$, then x equals **[JEE Advanced 2013, 3M]**

(a) $\frac{2\log_3 2}{2\log_3 2 - 1}$
(b) $\frac{2}{2 - \log_2 3}$
(c) $\frac{1}{1 - \log_4 3}$
(d) $\frac{2\log_2 3}{2\log_2 3 - 1}$

Answers

Exercise for Session 1

1. (a) **2.** (b) **3.** (b) **4.** (b) **5.** (b)

Exercise for Session 2

1. (b) **2.** (b) **3.** (d) **4.** (c) **5.** (c)

Exercise for Session 3

1. (c) **2.** (c) **3.** (d) **4.** (a) **5.** (c)

Chapter Exercises

1. (c) **2.** (d) **3.** (b) **4.** (b) **5.** (a) **6.** (a)
7. (a) **8.** (b) **9.** (a) **10.** (c) **11.** (c) **12.** (c)
13. (b) **14.** (b) **15.** (c) **16.** (b) **17.** (b) **18.** (d)
19. (c) **20.** (b)
21. (a, b, d) **22.** (b, c) **23.** (c, d) **24.** (a, b) **25.** (b, d)
26. (a, c) **27.** (a, b, c, d) **28.** (a, d) **29.** (c, d)
30. (b) **31.** (d) **32.** (a) **33.** (a) **34.** (b) **35.** (d)
36. (b) **37.** (c) **38.** (b) **39.** (b) **40.** (a) **41.** (d)
42. (9) **43.** (6) **44.** (4) **45.** (3) **46.** (9) **47.** (3)
48. (4) **49.** (7) **50.** (1) **51.** (2)
52. (A) → (p, s), (B) → (p), (C) → (q), (D) → (r)
53. (A) → (r), (B) → (s), (C) → (q), (D) → (q)
54. (A) → (q), (B) → (p), (C) → (q, r), (D) → (s)
55. (d) **56.** (d) **57.** (d) **58.** (d) **59.** (c) **60.** (d)
61. (i) $\dfrac{ab+1}{a(8-5b)}$ (ii) $\dfrac{ab+2}{2b}$ **64.** (i) 140 (ii) 16 (iii) 238 **65.** 0.528
66. $2\sqrt{3}$ **68.** (i) 10, $\dfrac{1}{10}$ (ii) $x \in \phi$
(iii) $x = 16$ (iv) $x = 8$ (v) $\{10^{-5}, 10^{3}\}$
(vi) $x = \dfrac{1}{3}$ (vii) $x = \dfrac{1}{100}$ (viii) $x = 5$ (ix) $x = 2$ or $\dfrac{1}{32}$
(x) $x = 2$ (xi) $x = \dfrac{\pi}{3}$

69. 100 **70.** $\dfrac{1}{6}$ **71.** 1 **72.** 9
73. (i) $x \in \left(-\dfrac{3}{2}, 3\right) \cup \{-1, 0\}$ (ii) $x \in \left(0, \dfrac{1}{2}\right) \cup (1, 2) \cup (3, 6)$
(iii) $x \in \left(-1, \dfrac{1-\sqrt{5}}{2}\right) \cup \left(\dfrac{1+\sqrt{5}}{2}, 2\right)$
(iv) $x \in (-2, 1) \cup (2, \infty) \sim \{-1, 0\}$ (v) $x > 6$
(vi) $x \in (-\infty, -5) \cup (-5, -1) \cup (3, \infty)$
(vii) $x \in (0, 10^{-1}] \cup [10^{2}, \infty)$
(viii) $x \in [-1, 1-\sqrt{3}) \cup (1+\sqrt{3}, 3]$
(ix) $x \in \left(\dfrac{3}{8}, \dfrac{1}{2}\right) \cup \left(1, \dfrac{3}{2}\right)$ (x) $x \in (0, 1)$
(xi) $x \in \left(-\dfrac{3}{2}, -1\right) \cup (-1, 3)$ (xii) $x \in \left(0, \dfrac{1}{16}\right] \cup [2, \infty)$
(xiii) $x \in (-\infty, -1)$ (xiv) $x \in (-\infty, -1) \cup (1, \infty)$
(xv) $x \in (1000, \infty)$ (xvi) $x \in [-10, -8) \cup (8, 10]$
(xvii) $x \in (-\infty, 0]$
(xviii) (a) $x \in (-\infty, -3] \cup (0, \infty)$ (b) $x \in \left[-3, -\dfrac{3}{2}\right)$
(xix) $x \in (2, 3]$ (xx) $x \in \left(-\dfrac{3}{5}, -\dfrac{3}{2}\right) \cup [-1, 0) \cup (0, 3]$
74. $x = a^{4/5_{a2}}$ **75.** $x = 15$ for $a = 3$
76. $x = 2$ or $\dfrac{1}{2}$, $y = \dfrac{1}{2}$ or 2
77. $x = 1, 2^{-3/2}$ **78.** Sum $= \dfrac{9}{2}$, Product $= 2$
79. $x = 2$ **80.** $x = 0$ **81.** (9, 25) and (25, 9)
82. $x = 3$, $y = 2$ **83.** $x \in (-5, -4) \cup (-3, -1)$
84. $x = \dfrac{25}{64}$ **85.** 3456 **86.** $x \in (1, 3]$ **88.** (b)
89. (c) **90.** (4) **91.** (a, b, c)

Solutions

1. $\log_{10} 2 = 0.3010$

Let $y = 2000^{2000}$

$$\log_{10} y = 2000 \log_{10} 2000 = 2000 \times (\log_{10} 2 + 3)$$
$$= 2000 \times 3.3010 = 6602$$

So, the number of digits in $2000^{2000} = 6602 + 1 = 6603$.

2. $\because \lambda > 0$ and $\lambda \neq 1$ and $x > 0$

$$\log_2 x + \log_4 x + \log_8 x = \log_\lambda x$$
$$\Rightarrow \log_2 x + \frac{1}{2}\log_2 x + \frac{1}{3}\log_2 x = \log_\lambda x$$
$$\Rightarrow \frac{11}{6}\log_2 x = \log_\lambda x$$
$$\Rightarrow \frac{11}{6\log_x 2} = \frac{11}{\log_x \lambda}$$
$$\Rightarrow 11\log_x \lambda - 6\log_x 2 = 0$$
$$\Rightarrow \log_x\left(\frac{\lambda^{11}}{2^6}\right) = 0 \Rightarrow \frac{\lambda^{11}}{2^6} = 1$$
$$\Rightarrow \lambda^{11} = 2^6 \Rightarrow \lambda = 2^{6/11}$$
$$\Rightarrow \lambda = (2^6)^{1/11} \quad \text{...(i)}$$

Given that, $\lambda = \sqrt[b]{a}$ and $a, b \in N$

$$\Rightarrow \lambda = a^{\frac{1}{b}} \quad \text{...(ii)}$$

From Eqs. (i) and (ii), we get

$$a = 2^6 \text{ and } b = 11$$
$$\Rightarrow a + b = 64 + 11 = 75$$

3. $x^{\log_{10}^2 x + \log_{10} x^3 + 3} = \dfrac{2}{\dfrac{1}{\sqrt{x+1}-1} - \dfrac{1}{\sqrt{x+1}+1}}$

Given, a, b and c are real solution Eq. (i) and $a > b > c$ and for Eq. (i) to be defined $x > 0$, $x > -1 \Rightarrow x > 0$ from Eq. (i),

$$x^{\log_{10}^2 x + 3\log_{10} x + 3} = \frac{2x}{2}$$

On taking logarithm both sides on base 10, then

$$(\log_{10}^2 x + 3\log_{10} x + 3)\log_{10} x = \log_{10} x$$
$$\Rightarrow (\log_{10}^2 x + 3\log_{10} x + 2)\log_{10} x = 0$$
$$\Rightarrow (\log_{10} x + 1)(\log_{10} x + 2)\log_{10} x = 0$$
$$\therefore \log_{10} x = -2, -1, 0$$
$$\therefore x = 10^{-2}, 10^{-1}, 10^0$$
$$x = \frac{1}{100}, \frac{1}{10}, 1$$

So, a, b, c can take values $a = 1$, $b = \dfrac{1}{10}$, $c = \dfrac{1}{100}$ $\quad (\because a > b > c)$

$$\therefore a, b, c \in \text{GP}$$

4. $f(n) = \prod_{i=2}^{n-1} \dfrac{\log(i+1)}{\log(i)} = \dfrac{\log(n)}{\log(2)} = \log_2 n$

$$\therefore f(2^k) = k$$

Then, $\displaystyle\sum_{k=1}^{100} f(2^k) = \sum_{k=1}^{100} k = \frac{100 \cdot (100+1)}{2} = 5050$

5. $\log_3 27 \cdot \log_x 7 = \log_{27} x \cdot \log_7 3 \quad \text{... (i)}$

Eq. (i) valid for $x > 0$, $x \neq 1$

On solving Eq. (i),

$$\log_3(3^3) \cdot \log_x 7 = \frac{1}{3}\log_3 x \cdot \log_7 3$$
$$\Rightarrow 9 \cdot \log_x 7 = \log_7 x$$
$$\Rightarrow 9 = (\log_7 x)^2$$
$$\Rightarrow \log_7 x = \pm 3$$
$$\Rightarrow x = 7^3 \text{ or } x = 7^{-3}$$

Then, the least value of x is $\dfrac{1}{7^3}$ i.e., 7^{-3}.

6. $\because x = \log_5(5^3 \times 8) = 3 + \log_5 8$

$$\Rightarrow x - 3 = \log_5 8 \quad \text{...(i)}$$

and $y = \log_7(7^3 \times 6) = 3 + \log_7 6$

$$\Rightarrow y - 3 = \log_7 6 \quad \text{...(ii)}$$
$$\because 8 > 6 \text{ and } 7 > 5$$
$$\Rightarrow \log 8 > \log 6 \text{ and } \log 7 > \log 5$$

or $(\log 8)(\log 7) > (\log 6)(\log 5)$

$$\Rightarrow \log_5 8 > \log_7 6$$
$$\Rightarrow x - 3 > y - 3 \quad \text{[from Eqs. (i) and (ii)]}$$
$$\therefore x > y$$

7. $\because \log_5 120 + (x-3) - 2\log_5(1 - 5^{x-3}) = -\log_5(0.2 - 5^{x-4})$

$$\Rightarrow \log_5(5 \times 24) + (x-3)$$
$$= \log_5(1 - 5^{x-3})^2 - \log_5\left(\frac{1 - 5^{x-3}}{5}\right)$$
$$\Rightarrow 1 + \log_5 24 + (x-3) = \log_5\{5 \cdot (1 - 5^{x-3})\}$$
$$\Rightarrow 1 + \log_5(24 \cdot 5^{x-3}) = 1 + \log_5(1 - 5^{x-3})$$
$$\Rightarrow 24 \cdot 5^{x-3} = 1 - 5^{x-3}$$
$$\Rightarrow 25 \cdot 5^{x-3} = 1$$
$$\Rightarrow 5^{x-1} = 5^0$$
$$\therefore x - 1 = 0 \Rightarrow x = 1$$

8. Given, $x_n > x_{n-1} > \cdots > x_2 > x_1 > 1$

$$\therefore \log_{x_1} \log_{x_2} \log_{x_3} \cdots \log_{x_n} x_n^{x_{n-1}^{\cdot^{\cdot^{x_1}}}}$$
$$= \log_{x_1} \log_{x_2} \log_{x_3} \cdots \log x_{n-1}^{x_{n-1}^{x_{n-2}^{\cdot^{\cdot^{x_1}}}}}$$
$$= \log_{x_1} x_1 = 1 \quad (\because \log_a a = 1)$$

9. Let $\dfrac{x(y+z-x)}{\log x} = \dfrac{y(z+x-y)}{\log y} = \dfrac{z(x+y-z)}{\log z} = \dfrac{1}{n}$

Then, $\log x = nx(y+z-x) \quad \text{...(i)}$

$\log y = ny(z+x-y) \quad \text{...(ii)}$

and $\log z = nz(x+y-z) \quad \text{...(iii)}$

$\therefore \quad y\log x + x\log y = y\log z + z\log y$

$= z\log x + x\log z$

$\Rightarrow \quad \log(x^y \cdot y^x) = \log(y^z \cdot z^y) = \log(x^z \cdot x^x)$

$\Rightarrow \quad x^y \cdot y^x = y^z \cdot z^y = z^x \cdot x^z$

10. $\because \quad y = a^{\frac{1}{1-\log_a x}}$

$\Rightarrow \quad \log_a y = \dfrac{1}{1-\log_a x}$ ...(i)

and $\quad z = a^{\frac{1}{1-\log_a y}}$

or $\quad \log_a z = \dfrac{1}{1-\log_a y}$ ...(ii)

From Eqs. (i) and (ii), we get

$$\log_a z = \frac{1}{1-\left(\dfrac{1}{1-\log_a x}\right)} = 1 - \frac{1}{\log_a x}$$

$\Rightarrow \quad \dfrac{1}{\log_a x} = (1-\log_a z) \Rightarrow \log_a x = \dfrac{1}{(1-\log_a z)}$

$\therefore \quad x = a^{\frac{1}{1-\log_a z}}$

11. $\log_{0.3}(x-1) < \log_{0.09}(x-1)$ ...(i)

Eq. (i) defined for $x > 1$, ...(ii)

$\Rightarrow \quad \log_{0.3}(x-1) - \log_{(0.3)^2}(x-1) < 0$

$\Rightarrow \quad \log_{0.3}(x-1) - \dfrac{1}{2}\log_{0.3}(x-1) < 0$

$\Rightarrow \quad \dfrac{1}{2}\log_{0.3}(x-1) < 0$

$\Rightarrow \quad \log_{0.3}(x-1) < 0$

$\Rightarrow \quad (x-1) > (0.3)^0$

[$\because$ base of log is lie in (0, 1)]

$\Rightarrow \quad x > 2$ ...(iii)

From Eqs. (ii) and (iii), we get

$x > 2 \Rightarrow x \in (2, \infty)$

12. $\because \; a^x = a^{\sqrt{\log_a b}}$

$= a^{\sqrt{\log_a b} \cdot \sqrt{\log_a b}\sqrt{\log_b a}} = a^{\log_a b\sqrt{\log_b a} = b\sqrt{\log_b a}} = b^y$

$\therefore \; a^x - b^y = 0$

13. $\because \; x = 1 + \log_a bc = \log_a a + \log_a bc = \log_a(abc)$

$\therefore \quad \dfrac{1}{x} = \log_{abc} a$ ...(i)

Similarly, $\quad \dfrac{1}{y} = \log_{abc} b$ ...(ii)

and $\quad \dfrac{1}{z} = \log_{abc} c$ ...(iii)

On adding Eqs. (i), (ii) and (iii), we get

$\dfrac{1}{x} + \dfrac{1}{y} + \dfrac{1}{z} = \log_{abc} abc = 1$

$\Rightarrow \dfrac{xy + yz + zx}{xyz} = 1$ or $\dfrac{xyz}{xy + yz + zx} = 1$

14. $a^{\frac{\log_b(\log_b N)}{\log_b a}} = a^{\log_a(\log_b N)} = \log_b N$

15. $49^A + 5^B = ?$

$A = 1 - \log_7 2$

$A = \log_7 7 - \log_7 2$

$A = \log_7 \dfrac{7}{2} \Rightarrow 7^A = \dfrac{7}{2} \Rightarrow 49^A = \dfrac{49}{4}$

and $\quad B = -\log_5 4 = \log_5\left(\dfrac{1}{4}\right) \Rightarrow 5^B = \dfrac{1}{4}$

$\therefore \quad 49^A + 5^B = \dfrac{49}{4} + \dfrac{1}{4} = \dfrac{50}{4} = 12.5$

16. $(\log_{16} x)^2 - \log_{16} x + \log_{16}\lambda = 0$ ...(i)

Eq. (i) defined for $x > 0, \lambda > 0 \left(\log_{16} x - \dfrac{1}{2}\right)^2 - \dfrac{1}{4} + \log_{16}\lambda = 0$

For exactly one solution,

$\log_{16} x - \dfrac{1}{2} = 0$

$\therefore \quad -\dfrac{1}{4} + \log_{16}\lambda = 0 \Rightarrow \log_{16}\lambda = \dfrac{1}{4}$

or $\quad \lambda = (16)^{1/4} = 2$

17. $x^{\log_x (x+3)^2} = 16$ ...(i)

From Eq. (i), $x > 0$ and $x \neq 1$ ... (ii)

By Eq. (i), $\quad (x+3)^2 = 16$

$\Rightarrow \quad x + 3 = \pm 4$

$\Rightarrow \quad x = 1$ or $x = -7$

From Eq. (ii), no values of x satisfy Eq. (i).

$\therefore$ Number of values of x satisfy Eq. (i)

$\therefore$ Number of roots = 0

18. Given, $y = \log_2 \log_6(2^{\sqrt{2x+1}} + 4)$ ...(i)

From Eq. (i) to be defined,

$2x + 1 > 0 \Rightarrow x > -\dfrac{1}{2}$ ... (ii)

We find value of x for which $y = 1$

$\therefore \quad 1 = \log_2 \log_6(2^{\sqrt{2x+1}} + 4)$

$\Rightarrow \quad \log_6(2^{\sqrt{2x+1}} + 4) = 2$

$\Rightarrow \quad 2^{\sqrt{2x+1}} + 4 = 36$

$\Rightarrow \quad 2^{\sqrt{2x+1}} = 32 = 2^5 \Rightarrow \sqrt{2x+1} = 5$

$\Rightarrow \quad 2x + 1 = 25 \Rightarrow x = 12$

So, required point is (12, 1).

19. Given that, $\log 2 = 0.301$

$\log 3 = 0.477$

Let $\quad y = 3^{12} \times 2^8$

$\log y = 12\log 3 + 8\log 2$

$= 12 \times (0.477) + 8(0.301) = 8.132$

So, number of digits before decimal in $3^{12} \times 2^8 = 8 + 1 = 9$

20. Given, equation $2\log_x a + \log_{ax} a + 3\log_{a^2 x} a = 0$ ...(i)

$\Rightarrow \quad \dfrac{2}{\log_a x} + \dfrac{1}{1+\log_a x} + \dfrac{3}{2+\log_a x} = 0$ ...(ii)

Let $\log_a x = t$

Then, Eq. (ii),

$$\frac{2}{t} + \frac{1}{1+t} + \frac{3}{2+t} = 0 \Rightarrow 6t^2 + 11t + 4 = 0$$

$\Rightarrow \quad t = -\dfrac{4}{3}$ or $-\dfrac{1}{2}$

So, $x = a^{-4/3}$ or $x = a^{-1/2}$

Two value of x possible for which Eq. (i) is defined and satisfy.

21. Decimal on $x > 0$ and $x \neq 1$.

Taking logarithm on both sides on base 2, we get

$$\{(\log_2 x)^2 - 6\log_2 x + 11\}\log_2 x = 6$$

Let $\log_2 x = t$

$\therefore \quad t^3 - 6t^2 + 11t - 6 = 0$

$\Rightarrow \quad (t-1)(t-2)(t-3) = 0 \Rightarrow t = 1, 2, 3$

$\Rightarrow \quad \log_2 x = 1, 2, 3$

$\Rightarrow \quad x = 2, 2^2, 2^3$

22. $\log_\lambda x \cdot \log_5 \lambda = \log_x 5$ ...(i)

$\lambda \neq 1, \lambda > 0$ and $x > 0, \ x \neq 1$

$\Rightarrow \quad \log_5 x = \log_x 5 \quad \Rightarrow \quad (\log_5 x)^2 = 1$

$\Rightarrow \quad \log_5 x = \pm 1 \quad \Rightarrow \quad x = 5^1$ and 5^{-1}

$\therefore \quad x = 5$ and $\dfrac{1}{5}$

23. $S = \{x : \sqrt{\log_x \sqrt{3x}} : \log_3 x > -1\}$

$\log_3 x > -1$

$\Rightarrow \quad x > \dfrac{1}{3}$ ...(i)

Let $y = \sqrt{\log_x \sqrt{3x}}, x \neq 1$

To be defined $y, 3x > 0 \Rightarrow x > 0$ ...(ii)

and $\log_x \sqrt{3x} \geq 0$ ...(iii)

From Eqs. (i) and (iii),

for $x \in \left(\dfrac{1}{3}, 1\right) \Rightarrow \sqrt{3x} \leq 1$

$\Rightarrow \quad 3x \leq 1 \quad \Rightarrow \quad x \leq \dfrac{1}{3}$

No solution for this case.

Now, for $x > 1$, from Eq. (iii), $\sqrt{3x} \geq 1 \Rightarrow x \geq \dfrac{1}{3}$

$\therefore \quad x > 1$

24. Given equation,

$$\log_2(9^{x-1} + 7) = 2 + \log_2(3^{x-1} + 1)$$

$\Rightarrow \quad \log_2 \dfrac{\{3^{2(x-1)} + 7\}}{3^{(x-1)} + 1} = 2$

$\Rightarrow \quad 3^{2(x-1)} + 7 = 4 \cdot \{3^{(x-1)} + 1\}$

$\Rightarrow \quad \{3^{(x-1)}\}^2 - 4 \cdot 3^{(x-1)} + 3 = 0$

$\Rightarrow \quad (3^{x-1} - 3)(3^{x-1} - 1) = 0$

$\Rightarrow \quad x - 1 = 1$ or $x - 1 = 0$

$\Rightarrow \quad x = 2$ or $x = 1$

25. $y = \log_p \log_p (\underbrace{\sqrt[p]{\sqrt[p]{\sqrt[p]{\ldots \sqrt[p]{p}}}}}_{n \text{ times}})$ $[p > 0, p$

$$= \log_p \left\{\log_p (\underbrace{\sqrt[p]{\ldots \sqrt[p]{p}}}_{(n-1) \text{ times}})^{\frac{1}{p}}\right\} = \log_p \left\{\frac{1}{p}\log_p (\underbrace{\sqrt[p]{\sqrt[p]{\ldots \sqrt[p]{p}}}}_{(n-1) \text{ times}})\right\}$$

$$= \log_p \left\{\frac{1}{p} \cdot \frac{1}{p} \log_p (\underbrace{\sqrt[p]{\sqrt[p]{\ldots \sqrt[p]{p}}}}_{(n-2) \text{ times}})\right\}$$

$$= \log_p \left(\frac{1}{p^n}\right) = -n, \ \log_{1/p} p^n = -n$$

26. $\log_a x = \alpha, \log_b x = \beta, \log_c x = \gamma, \log_d x = \delta$

$\Rightarrow \quad \log_x a = \alpha^{-1}$

$\Rightarrow \quad \log_x b = \beta^{-1}$

$\Rightarrow \quad \log_x c = \gamma^{-1}$

$\Rightarrow \quad \log_x d = \delta^{-1}$

On adding Eqs. (i), (ii), (iii) and (iv) , we get

$$\log_x(abcd) = \frac{1}{\alpha} + \frac{1}{\beta} + \frac{1}{\gamma} + \frac{1}{\delta}$$

$\therefore \quad \log_{abcd} x = \dfrac{1}{a^{-1} + \beta^{-1} + \gamma^{-1} + \delta^{-1}}$

For $\alpha, \beta, \gamma, \delta$

$$\text{AM} \geq \text{HM} \Rightarrow \frac{\alpha + \beta + \gamma + \delta}{4} \geq \frac{4}{\alpha^{-1} + \beta^{-1} + \gamma^{-1} + \delta^{-1}}$$

or $\dfrac{1}{\alpha^{-1} + \beta^{-1} + \gamma^{-1} + \delta^{-1}} \leq \dfrac{\alpha + \beta + \gamma + \delta}{16}$

or $\log_{abcd} x \leq \dfrac{\alpha + \beta + \gamma + \delta}{16}$ [from Eq.

27. $\because \quad \log_{10} 5 = a$ and $\log_{10} 3 = b$

$\therefore \quad \log_{10} 2 = \log_{10}\left(\dfrac{10}{5}\right) = 1 - a$

Option (a)

$\therefore \quad \log_{10} 8 = 3\log_{10} 2 = 3(1 - a)$ [from Eq. (

Option (b) $\log_{40} 15 = \dfrac{\log_{10} 15}{\log_{10} 40} = \dfrac{\log_{10}(5 \times 3)}{\log_{10}(2^3 \times 5)}$

$$= \frac{\log_{10} 5 + \log_{10} 3}{\log_{10} 2^3 + \log_{10} 5}$$

$$= \frac{a + b}{3(1-a) + a} = \frac{(a+b)}{(3 - 2a)}$$

Option (c) $\log_{243} 32 = \log_{3^5} 2^5 = \dfrac{5}{5}\log_5 2 = \dfrac{\log_{10} 2}{\log_{10} 2}$

$= \dfrac{1-a}{a}$ [from Eqs. (i) and (

Hence, all options are correct.

28. $\because x > 0$ and $x \neq 1$

Given, $\log_a x$, $\log_b x$ and $\log_c x$ are in AP.

$\Rightarrow \quad 2\log_b x = \log_a x + \log_c x$

$\Rightarrow \quad \dfrac{2\log x}{\log b} = \dfrac{\log x}{\log a} + \dfrac{\log x}{\log c}$

$\Rightarrow \quad \dfrac{2}{\log b} = \dfrac{1}{\log a} + \dfrac{1}{\log c} \qquad \begin{bmatrix} \log x \neq 0 \\ \therefore x \neq 1 \end{bmatrix}$

$\Rightarrow \quad \log b = \dfrac{2(\log a)(\log c)}{(\log a + \log c)}$

Also, $\quad \dfrac{\log b}{\log a} = \dfrac{2\log c}{\log a + \log c}$

$\Rightarrow \quad \log_a b = \dfrac{\log c^2}{\log(ac)} = \log_{(ac)} c^2$

$\therefore \quad c^2 = (ac)^{\log_a b}$

29. $|a| < |b|$, $b - a < 1$

$a, b \in x^2 - |a|\, x - |\beta| = 0 \qquad$ ...(i)

So, $\quad \left.\begin{aligned} a + b &= |\alpha| \\ ab &= -|\beta| \end{aligned}\right\} \qquad$ ...(ii)

Given equation, $\log_{|b|}\left|\dfrac{x}{a}\right| - 1 = 0$, $\log_{|b|}\left|\dfrac{x}{a}\right| = 1$

$\Rightarrow \quad \left|\dfrac{x}{a}\right| = |b|^1$

$\Rightarrow \quad |x| = |ab|$

$\Rightarrow \quad |x| = |\beta| \qquad$ [from Eq. (ii)]

$\therefore \quad x = \pm\beta$

Sol. (Q. Nos. 30 to 32)

$\because \quad \log_2 N = a_1 + b_1$

$\Rightarrow \quad b_1 = \log_2 N - a_1$

Given, $\quad 0 \leq b_1 < 1 \Rightarrow 0 \leq \log_2 N - a_1 < 1$

$\Rightarrow \quad a_1 \leq \log_2 N < 1 + a_1$

$\Rightarrow \quad 2^{a_1} \leq N < 2^{1 + a_1} \qquad$ ...(i)

Similarly, $\quad 3^{a_2} \leq N \; 3^{1 + a_2} \qquad$ ...(ii)

and $\quad 5^{a_3} \leq N < 5^{1 + a_3} \qquad$ ...(iii)

30. Here, $a_1 = 5$ and $a_2 = 3$, then from Eqs. (i) and (ii),

$2^5 \leq N < 2^6$ and $3^3 \leq N < 3^4$

$\therefore$ Common values of N are 32, 33, 34, ..., 63

Number of integral values of N are 32.

31. Here, $a_1 = 6$, $a_2 = 4$ and $a_3 = 3$, then from Eqs. (i), (ii) and (iii),

$2^6 \leq N < 2^7, 3^4 \leq N < 3^5$ and $5^3 \leq N < 5^4$

$\Rightarrow$ 64, 65, 66, ..., 127, 81, 82, 83,..., 242 and 125, 126, ..., 624

$\therefore$ Largest common value = 127

32. Here, $a_1 = 6$, $a_2 = 4$ and $a_3 = 3$

From question number 31, we get

64, 65, 66,..., 127; 81, 82, 83, ..., 242 and 125, 126, ...,624

$\therefore$ Largest common value = 127

and smallest common value = 125

$\therefore$ Difference = 127 − 125 = 2

Sol. (Q. Nos. 33 to 35)

S = Antilog of (0.5) to the base 256

$\Rightarrow \quad \log_{256} S = 0.5$

$S = (256)^{0.5} = (2^8)^{1/2}$

$S = 2^4$

$S = 16 \qquad$ ...(i)

K = Number of digits in 6^{10}

$[\because \log_{10} 2 = 0.301, \log_{10} 3 = 0.477]$

Let $\quad \alpha = 6^{10}$

$\log \alpha = 10\log_{10} 6 = 10(0.301 + 0.477)$

$= 10(0.778)$

$\log(6^{10}) = 7.78$

So, $\quad x = 7 + 1$, $x = 8$

Number of positive integers which have characteristic 2, when the base of logarithm is 3

$= 3^{2+1} - 3^2 = 18$

$\therefore \quad G = 18$

33. The value of $G = 18$

34. The value of $KG = 8 \times 18 = 144$

35. The value of $SKG = 16 \times 8 \times 18 = 16 \times 144 = 2304$

Sol. (Q. Nos. 36 to 38)

U = Number of digits in $(60)^{100}$

Let $\quad \alpha = (60)^{100}$

$\log_{10} \alpha = 100 \log_{10} 60 = 100(1 + \log_{10} 2 + \log_{10} 3)$

$= 100\,(1.778)$

$\log_{10} \alpha = 177.8$

So, $\quad U = 177 + 1 \Rightarrow U = 178 \qquad$ ...(i)

M = Number of cyphers after decimal, before a significant figure comes in $(8)^{-296}$

Let $\quad \beta = (8)^{-296}$

$\log_{10}\beta = (-296)\log_{10} 8 = (-296) \times 3\log_{10} 2$

$\log_{10}\beta = (-296) \times 3 \times (0.301)$

$= -267.288 = -267 - 0.288$

$= -267 - 1 + (1 - 0.288) = -268 + 0.712$

$\log_{10}\beta = \overline{268}.712$

$\therefore \quad M = 268 - 1 = 267$

Now, $\quad \dfrac{U}{M} = \dfrac{178}{267}$

According to the question,

$\dfrac{U}{M} = \dfrac{2}{3}$

$\Rightarrow \quad \dfrac{U}{M} = \dfrac{p}{q}$

So, $\quad p = 2$

and $\quad q = 3$

36. The value of $p = 2$.

37. The value of $q = 3$.

38. The equation whose roots are p and q is $x^2 - 5x + 6 = 0$.

Sol. (Q. Nos. 39 to 41)

According to question, $G, O, E, L > 0$ and are real numbers.

Such that,

$\log_{10}(G\cdot L)+\log_{10}(G\cdot E)=3 \Rightarrow \log_{10} G^2LE=3$

$\Rightarrow \quad G^2LE=10^3 \quad$ ...(i)

and $\quad \log_{10}E\cdot L+\log_{10}E\cdot O=4$

$\Rightarrow \quad \log_{10}E^2\cdot L\cdot O=4$

$\Rightarrow \quad E^2\cdot L\cdot O=10^4 \quad$ ...(ii)

and $\log_{10}(O\cdot G)+\log_{10}(O\cdot L)=5$

$\Rightarrow \quad \log_{10}O^2GL=5 \Rightarrow O^2GL=10^5 \quad$ ...(iii)

From Eqs. (i), (ii) and (iii), we get

$$G^3O^3E^3L^3=10^{12}$$

$$GOEL=10^4 \quad \text{...(iv)}$$

$\Rightarrow \quad \lambda=10^4$

39. Now, let

$$y=\sqrt{\log\lambda\sqrt{\log\lambda\sqrt{\log\lambda\cdots}}}=(\log\lambda)^{\frac{1}{2}+\frac{1}{4}+\frac{1}{8}+\cdots}$$

$$=(\log\lambda)^{\frac{1/2}{1-1/2}}=(\log\lambda)$$

$$=\log 10^4=4\log 10=4$$

40. Minimum of $3G+2L+2O+E=2^\lambda 3^\mu 5^\upsilon$

where $\lambda,\mu,\upsilon\in W$

Apply AM $\geq$ GM for $3G, 2L, 2O, E$

$$\frac{3G+2L+2O+E}{8}\geq\sqrt[8]{G^3\times L^2\times O^2\times E}$$

So, $\quad 8\times\sqrt[8]{G^3L^2O^2E}=2^\lambda 3^\mu 5^\upsilon \quad$ ...(v)

(equality hold, if $G=L=O=E$)

From Eqs. (i) and (iii) of Q. 10, we get

$$G^3L^2O^2E=10^8$$

From Eq. (v), $\quad 8\times(10^8)^{1/8}=2^\lambda 3^\mu 5^\upsilon$

$$8\times 10=2^\lambda 3^\mu 5^\upsilon$$

$$2^4\times 5^1=2^\lambda 3^\mu 5^\upsilon$$

$\therefore \quad \lambda=4, \upsilon=1, \mu=0$

$$\Sigma(\lambda^\mu+\mu^\lambda)=(4^0+0^4)+(0^1+1^0)+(1^4+4^1)$$

$$=(1+0)+(0+1)+1+4=7$$

41. $\log_{10}\left(\dfrac{G}{O}\right)+\log_{10}\left(\dfrac{O}{E}\right)=\log_{10}\left(\dfrac{G}{E}\right)=\log_{10}1=0$

[divide Eq. (iv) and Eq. (ii) of Q. 39]

$$P=\log_{10}\frac{G}{O}\cdot\log_{10}\frac{O}{E}=\log\left(\frac{1}{10}\right)\log(10)=-1$$

[by dividing Eq. (i) by Eq. (ii) and dividing Eq. (iii) by Eq. (iv) in Q. 10]

$$=x^2-0\cdot x+(-1)=0=x^2-1$$

42. $\log_{10}(2x)+\log_{10}y=2 \Rightarrow 2xy=10^2 \quad$ ...(i)

and $\quad \log_{10}x^2-\log_{10}2y=4$

$\Rightarrow \quad \dfrac{x^2}{2y}=10^4 \quad$ ...(ii)

From Eqs. (i) and (ii), $\quad x^3=10^6 \Rightarrow x=100$

From Eq. (i), $\quad y=\dfrac{1}{2}$

$\therefore \quad x+y=100+\dfrac{1}{2}=\dfrac{201}{2}=\dfrac{m}{n} \quad$ (given)

$\therefore \quad m=201$ and $n=2$

$\Rightarrow \quad m-3n^6=201-3(2)^6=201-192=9$

43. Solving, $x=\lambda$ and $y=\log_5 x$, we get

$$A\equiv(\lambda,\log_5\lambda),\ \lambda>0$$

and solving $x=\lambda$ and $y=\log_5(x+4)$, we get

$$B\equiv\{\lambda,\log_5(\lambda+4)\},\ \lambda>-4$$

Given, $\quad AB=0.5$

$\Rightarrow \quad \log_5(\lambda+4)-\log_5\lambda=0.5$

$\Rightarrow \quad \dfrac{\lambda+4}{\lambda}=(5)^{1/2}=\sqrt{5}$

$\Rightarrow \quad \lambda=\dfrac{4}{\sqrt{5}-1}=4\dfrac{(\sqrt{5}+1)}{4}$

$$=1+\sqrt{5}=a+\sqrt{b} \quad \text{[given]}$$

$\therefore \quad a=1$ and $b=5$

Then, $\quad a+b=1+5=6$

44. $\therefore \quad a(b-c)x^2+b(c-a)xy+c(a-b)y^2=b, y\neq 0 \quad$ ...(i)

$$a(b-c)\left(\frac{x}{y}\right)^2+b(c-a)\left(\frac{x}{y}\right)+c(a-b)=0$$

Let $\quad \dfrac{x}{y}=X$

$\Rightarrow \quad a(b-c)X^2+b(c-a)X+c(a-b)=0$

$\because \quad a(b-c)+b(c-a)+c(a-b)=0$

$\therefore \quad X=1$

$\because$ Eq. (i) is perfect square.

$\therefore$ Roots are equal.

$\therefore \quad 1\times 1=\dfrac{c(a-b)}{a(b-c)}$

$\Rightarrow \quad b=\dfrac{2ac}{a+c} \quad$ ...(ii)

Now, $\log(a+c)+\log(a-2b+c)$

$$=\log\{(a+c)^2-2b(a+c)\}$$

$$=\log\{(a+c)^2-4ac\} \quad \text{[from Eq. (ii)]}$$

$$=\log(a-c)^2=2\log(a-c)$$

$\Rightarrow \quad \dfrac{\log(a+c)+\log(a-2b+c)}{\log(a-c)}=2$

$\therefore \quad \left\{\dfrac{\log(a+c)+\log(a-2b+c)}{\log(a-c)}\right\}^2=4$

45. According to the question, $x\in I$

Given equation, $\left(\dfrac{1}{3}\right)^{\frac{|x+2|}{2-|x|}}>9 \quad [x\neq\pm 2] \quad$ ...(i)

$\Rightarrow \quad 3^{\frac{|x+2|}{2-|x|}}>3^2 \Rightarrow -\dfrac{|x+2|}{2-|x|}>2$

$$\Rightarrow \quad \frac{|x+2|}{|x|-2} - 2 > 0$$

$$\Rightarrow \quad \frac{|x+2| - 2|x| + 4}{|x|-2} > 0 \quad \text{...(ii)}$$

Case I If $x < -2$, $-\frac{x-2+2x+4}{-x-2} > 0$

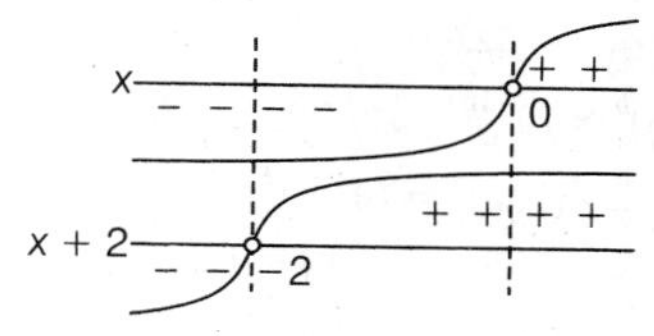

$$\frac{x+2}{-(x+2)} > 0 \Rightarrow -1 > 0$$

which is not possible.

***Case* II** $-2 < x < 0$, then Eq. (ii)

$$\Rightarrow \quad \frac{x+2+2x+4}{-x-2} > 0 \Rightarrow \frac{3x+6}{-(x+2)} > 0$$

$$\frac{-3(x+2)}{(x+2)} > 0 - 3 > 0$$

which is not possible.

***Case* III** when $x > 0$

From Eq. (ii),

$$\frac{x+2-2x+4}{x-2} > 0 \Rightarrow \frac{-x+6}{x-2} > 0$$

$$\frac{x-6}{x-2} < 0$$

$$2 < x < 6$$

So, the integer values of $x = 3, 4, 5$

So, the number of integer values of x is 3.

46. $x > 2$

$$|\log_{\sqrt{3}} x - 2| + |\log_3 x - 2| = 2$$

$$|2\log_3 x - 2| + |\log_3 x - 2| = 2$$

$$2|\log_3 x - 1| + |\log_3 x - 2| = 2$$

Let $\log_3 x = y$ ...(i)

Then, Eq. (i) $\Rightarrow 2|y-1| + |y-2| = 2$ ...(ii)

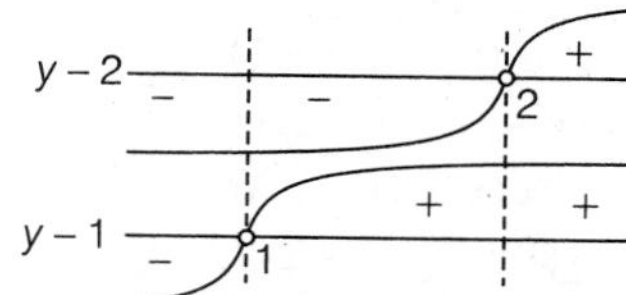

***Case* I** $y < 1$, then $x < 3$

Eq. (ii) becomes $-2y + 2 - y + 2 = 2$

$$-3y = -2, y = \frac{2}{3}$$

$$\log_3 x = \frac{2}{3} \quad \text{[from Eq. (i)]}$$

$$\Rightarrow \quad x = 3^{2/3}$$

which is less than 2, so not acceptable.

***Case* II** $1 < y < 2$, then $3 < x < 9$

From Eq. (ii), $2(y-1) - (y-2) = 2$

$\Rightarrow$ $y = 2$

$\Rightarrow$ $\log_3 x = 2$

$\therefore$ $x = 3^2 = 9$ [impossible]

***Case* III** $y \geq 2$, then $x \geq 9$

From Eq. (ii), $2(y-1) + (y-2) = 2$

$\therefore$ $y = 2, \log_3 x = 2$

$\therefore$ $x = 9$ [acceptable]

47. Given equation is

$$\log_2 \sqrt{x} - 2\log^2_{1/4} x + 1 > 0 \quad \text{...(i)}$$

From Eq. (i), $x > 0$

Eq. (i) $\Rightarrow \frac{1}{2}\log_2 x - \frac{2}{(-2)^2}\log^2_2 x + 1 > 0$

$$\Rightarrow \quad \frac{1}{2}\log_2 x - \frac{1}{2}\log^2_2 x + 1 > 0$$

$$\Rightarrow \quad (\log_2 x)^2 - (\log_2 x) - 2 < 0$$

$$\Rightarrow \quad (\log_2 x - 2)(\log_2 x + 1) < 0$$

$$\Rightarrow \quad -1 < \log_2 x < 2$$

$$\Rightarrow \quad 2^{-1} < x < 2^2$$

$$\Rightarrow \quad \frac{1}{2} < x < 4$$

$$\Rightarrow \quad x \in I, \text{ so } x = 1, 2, 3$$

So, number of integer value of x is 3.

48. Given that, $b > 0$

$$2\log_{1/25}(bx+28) = -\log_5(12-4x-x^2) \quad \text{...(i)}$$

$$\frac{2}{(-2)}\log_5(bx+28) = -\log_5(12-4x-x^2)$$

$\Rightarrow$ $bx + 28 = 12 - 4x - x^2$

and $bx + 28 > 0$

and $12 - 4x - x^2 > 0$

$\Rightarrow$ $x^2 + (4+b)x + 16 = 0$ ...(ii)

and $x > \frac{-28}{b}$ and $-6 < x < 2$

Since, Eq. (i) has coincident roots, so discriminant Eq. (ii) is zero.

$$(4+b)^2 - 64 = 0$$

$$b + 4 = \pm 8$$

$$b = 4 \text{ or } b = -12$$

Since, $b > 0$ so $b = 4$

for this value $x > -7$ and $-6 < x < 2$

49. $$\frac{2^{\log_{1/4} 2} - 3^{\log_{27} 125} - 4}{7^{4\log_{49} 2} - 3} = \frac{2^{4\log_2 2} - 3^{\log_{3^3} 5^3} - 4}{7^{4\log_{7^2} 2^1}}$$

$$= \frac{2^4 - 5 - 4}{7^{2\log_7 2} - 3} = \frac{16 - 9}{2^2 - 3} = 7$$

50. $(\log_5 x)^2 + \log_{5x}\left(\frac{5}{x}\right) = 1, x > 0, x \neq \frac{1}{5}$

$$\Rightarrow \quad (\log_5 x)^2 + \frac{\log_5\left(\frac{5}{x}\right)}{\log_5(5x)} = 1 \Rightarrow (\log_5 x)^2 + \frac{1 - \log_5 x}{1 + \log_5 x} = 1$$

Let $\log_5 x = t$, then

$$t^2 + \frac{1-t}{1+t} = 1$$

$\Rightarrow \quad t^3 + t^2 - 2t = 0$

$\Rightarrow \quad t(t+2)(t-1) = 0 \Rightarrow t = -2, 0, 1$

$\Rightarrow \quad x = 5^{-2}, 5^0, 5^1$

$\Rightarrow \quad x = \frac{1}{25}, 1, 5$

$x_1, x_2 \in I$

$\therefore \quad x_1 = 1, x_2 = 5$

$\therefore \quad |x_2 - 4x_1| = |5 - 4| = 1$

51. Given, $x = \log_\lambda a = \log_a b = \frac{1}{2}\log_b c$ and $\log_\lambda c = nx^{n+1}$

$x = \log_\lambda a = \log_a b = \log_b \sqrt{c}$ and $\log_\lambda c = nx^{n+1}$ ...(i)

From Eq. (i), $\log_\lambda a \times \log_a b + \log_b \sqrt{c} = x^3$

$\log_\lambda \sqrt{c} = x^3, \frac{1}{2}\log_\lambda c = x^3$

$\log_\lambda c = 2x^3$

Compare with $\quad \log_\lambda c = nx^{n+1}$

$\Rightarrow \quad n = 2$

52. (A) $\dfrac{\log_3 243}{\log_2 \sqrt{32}} = \dfrac{\log_3 3^5}{-\frac{1}{2}\log_2 2^5} = \dfrac{5 \times 2}{5} = 2$ (p,s)

(B) $\dfrac{2\log 6}{\log 12 + \log 3} = \dfrac{2\log 6}{\log 36} = \dfrac{2\log 6}{2\log 6} = 1$ (p)

(C) $\log_{1/3}\left(\frac{1}{9}\right)^{-2} = -\log_3 3^4 = -4$ (q)

(D) $\dfrac{\log_5 16 - \log_5 4}{\log_5 128} = \dfrac{\log_5\left(\frac{16}{4}\right)}{\log_5 (2)^7} = \dfrac{\log_5 (2)^2}{\log_5 (2)^7} = \dfrac{2}{7}$ (r)

53. (A) $\sqrt{\log^2_{(0.5)^2} 8} = \sqrt{\log^2_{1/2} 8} = \sqrt{(\log_{2^{-1}} 2^3)^2}$

$= \sqrt{\left(\frac{3}{-1}\log_2 2\right)^2} = \sqrt{(-3)^2} = \sqrt{9} = 3$ (r)

(B) $(\log_{10} 2)^3 + \log_{10} 8 \cdot \log_{10} 5 + (\log_{10} 5)^3$

$= (\log_{10} 2)^3 + 3\log_{10} 2 \log_{10} 5 + (\log_{10} 5)^3$

$= (\log_{10} 2)^3 + 3 \cdot \log_{10} 2 \cdot \log_{10} 5 \cdot (\log_{10} 2 + \log_{10} 5) + (\log_{10} 5)^3$

$[\because \log_{10} 2 + \log_{10} 5 = \log_{10} 10 = 1]$

$= (\log_{10} 2 + \log_{10} 5)^3 = (\log_{10} 10)^3 = (1)^3 = 1$

$3 + (\log_{10} 2)^3 + \log_{10} 8 \cdot \log_{10} 5 + (\log_{10} 5)^3$

$= 3 + 1 = 4$ (s)

(C) $N = \log_2 15 \cdot \log_{1/6} 2 \cdot \log_3 \frac{1}{6}$

$= \log_2 15 (-\log_6 2)(-\log_3 6)$

$= \dfrac{\log 15}{\log 2} \times \dfrac{\log 2}{\log 6} \times \dfrac{\log 6}{\log 3} = \log_3 15$

$9 < 15 < 27$

$2 < \log_3 15 < 3$

So, $[N] = 2$ (q)

(D) $(52.6)^a = (0.00526)^b = 100$

$(52.6)^a = 100$ and $(0.00526)^b = 100$

$52.6 = 10^{\frac{2}{a}}$ ...(i)

$(52.6)^b \times 10^{-4b} = 10^2$

$(52.6)^b = 10^{2+4b}$

$\Rightarrow \quad 52.6 = 10^{\left(\frac{2+4b}{b}\right)}$ ...(ii)

From Eqs. (i) and (ii), we get

$10^{\frac{2}{a}} = 10^{\frac{2+4b}{b}}$

$\Rightarrow \quad \frac{2}{a} = \frac{2}{b} + 4$

$\Rightarrow \quad \frac{1}{a} - \frac{1}{b} = 2$ (q)

54. (A) Given that, $\log_{1/x} \dfrac{2(x-2)}{(x+1)(x-5)} \geq 1$ ...(i)

for log to be defined $\dfrac{(x-2)}{(x+1)(x-5)} > 0,$

then $\quad x \in (-1, 2) \cup (5, \infty)$

Let $\quad x > 0$ and $x \neq 1$

So, $\quad x \in (0, 1) \cup (1, 2) \cup (5, \infty)$

***Case* I** $\quad x \in (0, 1)$ ...(ii)

$\frac{1}{x} > 1$

$\therefore$ By Eq. (i), $\log_{\frac{1}{x}} \dfrac{2(x-2)}{(x+1)(x-5)} \geq 1$

$\Rightarrow \quad \dfrac{2(x-2)}{(x+1)(x-5)} \geq \dfrac{1}{x}$

$\Rightarrow \quad \dfrac{2(x-2)}{(x+1)(x-5)} - \dfrac{1}{x} \geq 0$

$\Rightarrow \quad \dfrac{2x(x-2) - (x+1)(x+5)}{x(x+1)(x-5)} \geq 0$

$\Rightarrow \quad \dfrac{2x^2 - 4x - x^2 + 4x + 5}{x(x+1)(x-5)} \geq 0$

$\Rightarrow \quad \dfrac{x^2 + 5}{x(x+1)(x-5)} \geq 0$

$\Rightarrow \quad x(x+1)(x-5) > 0$

$\Rightarrow \quad x \in (-1, 0) \cup (5, \infty)$

But by Eq. (ii), $x \in (0, 1)$

So, no solution for this case.

***Case* II** Let $x \in (1, 2) \cup (5, \infty)$ ...(iii)

$$\frac{1}{x} < 1$$

Eq. (i) $\Rightarrow \log_{\frac{1}{x}} \frac{2(x-2)}{(x+1)(x-5)} \ge 1$

$$\frac{2(x-2)}{(x+1)(x-5)} \le \frac{1}{x}$$

$$\Rightarrow \frac{2(x-2)}{(x+1)(x-5)} - \frac{1}{x} \le 0$$

$$\Rightarrow \frac{x^2+5}{x(x+1)(x-5)} \le 0 \quad \text{[by case I]}$$

$$\Rightarrow x(x+1)(x-5) < 0$$

$$\Rightarrow x \in (-\infty, -1) \cup (0, 5) \quad \text{...(iv)}$$

Eq. (iii), $x \in (1, 2) \cup (5, \infty)$

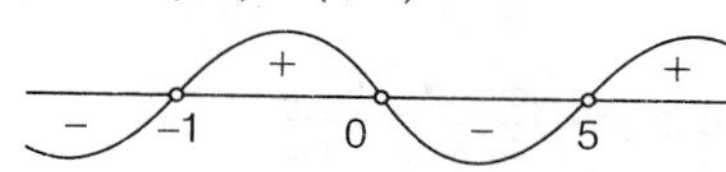

From Eqs. (iii) and (iv), $x \in (1, 2]$ (q)

(B) $\log_3 x - \log_3^2 x \le \frac{3}{2} \log_{\frac{1}{2\sqrt{2}}} 4$ ...(i)

defined, when $x > 0$

$$\log_3 x - \log_3^2 x \ge \frac{3}{2} \times \left(\frac{-2}{3}\right) \times 2 \times 1$$

$$\Rightarrow \log_3 x - \log_3^2 x + 2 \le 0$$

$$\Rightarrow \log_3^2 x - \log_3 x - 2 \ge 0$$

$$\Rightarrow (\log_3 x - 2)(\log_3 x + 1) \ge 0$$

$$\Rightarrow \log_3 x \le -1$$

or

$$\log_3 x \ge 2$$

$$\Rightarrow x \le \frac{1}{3} \text{ or } x \ge 9$$

From Eq. (i), $x > 0$

So, $x \in \left(0, \frac{1}{3}\right] \cup [9, \infty)$ (p)

(C) $\log_{\frac{1}{2}} (4-x) \ge \log_{\frac{1}{2}} 2 - \log_{\frac{1}{2}} (x-1)$ ...(i)

$$\Rightarrow \log_{\frac{1}{2}} \frac{(4-x)(x-1)}{2} \ge 0$$

$$\Rightarrow -\frac{(x-4)(x-1)}{2} \le 1$$

$$\Rightarrow (x-4)(x-1) \ge -2$$

$$\Rightarrow x^2 - 5x + 4 + 2 \ge 0$$

$$\Rightarrow x^2 - 5x + 6 \ge 0$$

$$(x-3)(x-2) \ge 0$$

$$x \le 2 \text{ or } x \ge 3 \quad \text{...(ii)}$$

From Eq. (i) to be defined, $4 - x > 0$ and $x - 1 > 0$

$$x < 4 \text{ and } x > 1 \quad \text{...(iii)}$$

From Eqs. (ii) and (iii),

$$x \in (1, 2] \cup [3, 4) \text{ (q, r)}$$

(D) Given equation is

$$(\lambda^2 - 3\lambda + 4)x^2 - 4(2\lambda - 1)x + 16 = 0 \quad \text{...(i)}$$

$$\lambda^2 - 3\lambda + 4 = \lambda^2 - 3\lambda + \left(\frac{3}{2}\right)^2 - \left(\frac{3}{2}\right)^2 + 4 = \left(\lambda - \frac{3}{2}\right)^2 + \frac{7}{4}$$

So, $\lambda^2 - 3\lambda + 4 > 0, \forall \lambda \in R$

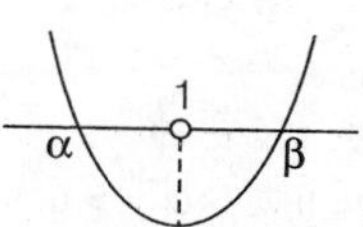

and $D > 0$

$\Rightarrow$ We get $\lambda > \frac{15}{8}$ ...(ii)

Let $f(x) = (\lambda^2 - 3\lambda + 4)x^2 = 4(2\lambda - 1)x + 16$

$\therefore$ $f(1) < 0$ by graph of $f(x)$

$$\lambda^2 - 11\lambda + 24 < 0$$

$$(\lambda - 3)(\lambda - 8) < 0$$

$$3 < \lambda < 8 \quad \text{...(iii)}$$

From Eqs. (ii) and (iii), we get

$$3 < \lambda < 8 \Rightarrow \lambda \in (3, 8) \text{ (s)}$$

55. If $0 < a < b$

Statement-1 If $x > 1$

$\Rightarrow$ $\log_x a < \log_x b$

$\therefore$ **Statement-2** If $0 < x < 1$

$\Rightarrow$ $\log_x a > \log_x b$

$\therefore$ Statement-2 is true, also

$$10 > 3 > e > 2$$

If $x > 1$,

then $\log_x 10 > \log_x 3 > \log_x e > \log_x 2$

$$\Rightarrow \frac{1}{\log_x 10} < \frac{1}{\log_x 3} < \frac{1}{\log_x e} < \frac{1}{\log_x 2}$$

$$\Rightarrow \log_{10} x < \log_3 x < \log_e x < \log_2 x$$

and for $0 < x < 1$

We get, $\log_{10} x > \log_3 x > \log_e x > \log_2 x$

It is clear that for $x > 0, x \ne 1$

Statement-1 is false.

56. **Statement-1** $7^{\log_7 (x^3+1)} - x^2 = 1$ ...(i)

$$\left.\begin{aligned} x^3 + 1 - x^2 &= 1 \\ x^3 - x^2 &= 0 \\ x^2(x-1) &= 0 \end{aligned}\right\} \begin{aligned} &\text{for this } x^3 + 1 > 0 \\ &\Rightarrow x^3 > -1 \\ &\Rightarrow x > -1 \end{aligned}$$

$x = 0$ (repeated) or $x = 1$

Thus, Eq. (i) has 2 repeated roots.

$\therefore$ Statement-1 is false.

Statement-2 $a^{\log_a N} = N, a > 0, a \ne 1$ and $N > 0$

which is true.

57. **Statement-1** $\left(\frac{1}{3}\right)^7 < \left(\frac{1}{3}\right)^4$. Taking log on both sides,

$$\log_e \left(\frac{1}{3}\right)^7 < \log_e \left(\frac{1}{3}\right)^4$$

$$7 \log_e \frac{1}{3} < 4 \log_e \frac{1}{3}$$

Now, $\log_e \frac{1}{3} < 0$ $[\because 2 < e < 3]$

So, $7 > 4$ ...(i)

Statement-1 is false.

Statement-2 $ax < ay$

and $a < 0, x > 0, y > 0$

Eq. (i) divide by a, we get $x > y$

Statement-2 is true.

58. **Statement-1** $x^{\log_x (1-x)^2} = 9$

$(1-x)^2 = 9$ $\left\{\begin{array}{l}\text{Eq. (i) is defined, if}\\ x \neq 1, x > 0\end{array}\right.$

$1 - x = \pm 3$

$\therefore$ $x = -2$ or 4

$x = 4$ [acceptable]

$\therefore$ Eq. (i) has only one solution.

Statement-1 is false.

Statement-2 $a^{\log_a b} = b$, where $a > 0, a \neq 1, b > 0$

which is true.

59. **Statement-1** $(\log x)^2 + \log x^2 - 3 = 0$ ...(i)

$\Rightarrow$ $(\log x)^2 + 2 \log x - 3 = 0$

$\Rightarrow$ $(\log x + 3)(\log x - 1) = 0$

$\Rightarrow$ $\log x = -3$ or $\log x = 1$

$\Rightarrow$ $x = 10^{-3}$ or $x = 10$

Eq. (i) is defined for $x > 0$.

So, Eq. (i) has 2 distinct solutions.

Statement-2 $\log x^2 \neq 2 \log x$

$\because$ LHS has domain $x \in R$ and RHS has domain $x \in (0, \infty)$

$\therefore$ Statement-2 is false.

60. **Statement-1**

$\log_x 3 \cdot \log_{x/9} 3 = \log_{81} 3$ ...(i)

Eq. (i) holds, if $x > 0, x \neq 1, x \neq 9$

By Eq. (i), $\frac{1}{\log_3 x} \cdot \frac{1}{(\log_3 x + 2)} = \frac{1}{4}$

$(\log_3 x)^2 + 2 \log_3 x - 4 = 0$

$(\log_3 x)^2 + 2 \log_3 x + 4 = 8$

$(\log_3 x + 2)^2 = 8$

$\log_3 x + 2 = \pm 2\sqrt{2}$

$\log_3 x = 2(-1 \pm \sqrt{2})$

$\therefore$ $x = 3^{2(-1 \pm \sqrt{2})}$

Two values of x satisfying Eq. (i)

So, Statement-1 is false.

Statement-2 Change of bases in logarithm is possible.

$\therefore$ Statement-2 is true.

61. (i) $\because a = \log_7 12 = \frac{\log 12}{\log 7} = \frac{2 \log 2 + \log 3}{\log 7}$

$a = \frac{2 + \log_2 3}{\log_2 7}$ ...(i)

and $b = \log_{12} 24 = \frac{\log 24}{\log 12} = \frac{3 \log 2 + \log 3}{2 \log 2 + \log 3}$

$= \frac{3 + \log_2 3}{2 + \log_2 3}$ ...(ii)

Let $\log_2 3 = \lambda$ and $\log_2 7 = \mu$

From Eq. (i), $a = \frac{2 + \lambda}{\mu}$

and from Eq. (ii), $b = \frac{3 + \lambda}{2 + \lambda}$, we get

$\lambda = \frac{3 - 2b}{b - 1}$ and $\mu = \frac{1}{a(b-1)}$

$\therefore$ $\log_{54} 168 = \frac{\log 168}{\log 54} = \frac{\log (2^3 \times 3 \times 7)}{\log (3^3 \times 2)}$

$= \frac{3 \log 2 + \log 3 + \log 7}{3 \log 3 + \log 2}$

$= \frac{3 + \log_2 3 + \log_2 7}{3 \log_2 3 + 1} = \frac{3 + \lambda + \mu}{3\lambda + 1}$

$= \frac{3 + \frac{3 - 2b}{b - 1} + \frac{1}{a(b-1)}}{\frac{3(3 - 2b)}{b - 1} + 1}$

$= \frac{(ab + 1)}{a(8 - 5b)}$

(ii) $\because$ $a = \log_3 4$ and $b = \log_5 3$

$\therefore$ $ab = \log_5 4$ ...(i)

Now, $\log_3 10 = \frac{\log_5 10}{\log_5 3} = \frac{2 \log_5 10}{2 \log_5 3}$

$= \frac{\log_5 (100)}{2b} = \frac{\log_5 (4 \times 25)}{2b}$

$= \frac{\log_5 4 + 2}{2b} = \frac{ab + 2}{2b}$ [from Eq. (i)]

62. $\because \frac{\ln a}{b - c} = \frac{\ln b}{c - a} = \frac{\ln c}{a - b}$ [by using law of proportion]

(i) $\because$ $\frac{\ln a}{b - c} = \frac{\ln b}{c - a} = \frac{\ln c}{a - b}$

$= \frac{\ln a + \ln b + \ln c}{b - c + c - a + a - b} = \frac{\ln (abc)}{0}$

$\Rightarrow \ln (abc) = 0 \Rightarrow abc = 1$

(ii) $\frac{\ln a}{b - c} + \frac{\ln b}{c - a} + \frac{\ln c}{a - b} = \frac{a \ln a + b \ln b + c \ln c}{a(b - c) + b(c - a) + c(a - b)}$

$= \frac{\ln a^a + \ln b^b + \ln c^c}{0} = \frac{\ln (a^a \cdot b^b \cdot c^c)}{0}$

$\Rightarrow$ $\ln (a^a b^b c^c) = 0$

$\Rightarrow$ $a^a b^b c^c = 1$

(iii) $\dfrac{\ln a}{b-c} = \dfrac{\ln b}{c-a} = \dfrac{\ln c}{a-b}$

$$= \frac{[(b^2+bc+c^2)\ln a + (c^2+ca+a^2)\ln b + (a^2+ab+b^2)\ln c]}{[(b^2+bc+c^2)(b-c)+(c^2+ca+a^2)(c-a)+(a^2+ab+b^2)(a-b)]}$$

$$= \frac{\ln a^{b^2+bc+c^2} + \ln b^{c^2+ca+a^2} + \ln c^{a^2+ab+b^2}}{(b^3-c^3)+(c^3-a^3)+(a^3-b^3)}$$

$$= \frac{\ln (a^{b^2+bc+c^2} \cdot b^{c^2+ca+a^2} \cdot c^{a^2+ab+b^2})}{0}$$

$$\Rightarrow \ln (a^{b^2+bc+c^2} \cdot b^{c^2+ca+a^2} \cdot c^{a^2+ab+b^2}) = 0$$

$$\therefore \quad a^{b^2+bc+c^2} \cdot b^{c^2+ca+a^2} \cdot c^{a^2+ab+b^2} = 1$$

(iv) $\because$ AM $\geq$ GM

$$\therefore \quad \frac{a+b+c}{3} \geq (abc)^{1/3} = (1)^{1/3} = 1 \quad \text{[from Eq. (i)]}$$

$$\therefore \quad \frac{a+b+c}{3} \geq 1 \Rightarrow a+b+c \geq 3$$

(v) $\because$ AM $\geq$ GM

$$\Rightarrow \quad \frac{a^a+b^b+c^c}{3} \geq (a^a \cdot b^b \cdot c^c)^{1/3}$$

$$= (1)^{1/3} = 1 \quad \text{[from Eq. (ii)]}$$

$$\Rightarrow \quad \frac{a^a+b^b+c^c}{3} \geq 1 \Rightarrow a^a+b^b+c^c \geq 3$$

(vi) $\because$ AM $\geq$ GM $\dfrac{a^{b^2+bc+c^2} + b^{c^2+ca+a^2} + c^{a^2+ab+b^2}}{3}$

$$\geq (a^{b^2+bc+c^2} \cdot b^{c^2+ca+a^2} \cdot c^{a^2+ab+b^2})^{1/3}$$

$$= (1)^{1/3} \quad \text{[from Eq. (iii)]}$$

$$= 1$$

$$\Rightarrow \quad \frac{a^{b^2+bc+c^2} + b^{c^2+ca+a^2} + c^{a^2+ab+b^2}}{3} \geq 1$$

$$\Rightarrow \quad a^{b^2+bc+c^2} + b^{c^2+ca+a^2} + c^{a^2+ab+b^2} \geq 3$$

63. To prove $\log_{10} 2$ lies between $\frac{1}{3}$ and $\frac{1}{4}$

$$2^{12} = 4096$$

$$1000 < 4096 < 10000$$

$$10^3 < 2^{12} < 10^4$$

Taking logarithm to the base 10,

$$\log_{10} 10^3 < \log_{10} 2^{12} < \log_{10} 10^4$$

$$3 < 12 \log_{10} 2 < 4 \Rightarrow \frac{1}{4} < \log_{10} 2 < \frac{1}{3}$$

64. $\log 2 = 0.301$

$\log 3 = 0.477$

(i) Let $\alpha = 5^{200}$

$$\log \alpha = 200 \log 5 = 200 (\log 10 - \log 2) = 200 (1 - 0.301)$$

$$= 200 \times 0.699 = 139.8$$

So, number of integers in $5^{200} = 139 + 1 = 140$.

(ii) $\alpha = 6^{20}$

$$\therefore \log \alpha = 20 \log 6 = 20 (\log 2 + \log 3)$$

$$= 20 (0.310 + 0.477)$$

$$= 20 \times 0.778 = 15.560$$

So, number of integers in $6^{20} = 15 + 1 = 16$

(iii) Let $\alpha = 3^{-500}$

$$\log \alpha = -500 \log 3 = -500 \times (0.477) = -238.5$$

$$= -239 + 0.5 = \overline{239}.5$$

So, number of zeroes after the decimal in

$$3^{-500} = 239 - 1 = 238$$

65. Given that, $\log_{10} 2 = 0.301$

and $\log_{10} 3 = 0.477$

$$\log 3.375 = \log(3375) - \log 10^3 = \log 5^3 \times 3^3 - 3 \log 5 \times 2$$

$$= 3 \log 5 + 3 \log 3 - 3 \log 5 - 3 \log 2$$

$$= 3 (0.477) - 3 (0.301) = 3 (0.176)$$

$$= 0.528$$

66. Let $P = \log_2 x - \log_x (0.125) = \log_2 x - \log_x \left(\frac{1}{8}\right)$

$$= \log_2 x + 3 \log_x 2$$

$\therefore$ AM $\geq$ GM

$$\Rightarrow \quad \frac{\log_2 x + 3 \log_x 2}{2} \geq \sqrt{(\log_2 x)(3 \log_x 2)} = \sqrt{3}$$

$$\therefore \quad \frac{P}{2} \geq \sqrt{3}$$

$$\Rightarrow \quad P \geq 2\sqrt{3}$$

$\therefore$ Least value of $\log_2 x - \log_x (0.125)$ is $2\sqrt{3}$.

67. Let $y = \dfrac{1}{\log_3 \pi} + \dfrac{1}{\log_4 \pi} = \log_\pi 3 + \log_\pi 4$

$$= \log_\pi 12$$

Now, $12 > \pi^2$

$$\log_\pi 12 > \log_\pi \pi^2 \quad \therefore \quad y > 2$$

68. (i) $\therefore \quad x^{1+\log_{10} x} = 10x \quad \text{...(i)}$

$$\Rightarrow \quad x \cdot x^{\log_{10} x} = 10x$$

$$\Rightarrow \quad x [x^{\log_{10} x} - 10] = 0$$

$$x \neq 0, \text{ so } x^{\log_{10} x} - 10 = 0$$

$$\Rightarrow \quad x^{\log_{10} x} = 10$$

$$\Rightarrow \quad \log_{10} x = \log_x 10$$

$$\Rightarrow \quad (\log_{10} x)^2 = 1$$

$$\Rightarrow \quad \log_{10} x = \pm 1$$

$$\Rightarrow \quad x = 10^{\pm 1}$$

$$\Rightarrow \quad x = 10 \text{ or } \frac{1}{10} \quad [\because x > 0]$$

(ii) $\log_2 (9 + 2^x) = 3$

$$\Rightarrow \quad 9 + 2^x = 8$$

$$\Rightarrow \quad 2^x = -1$$

which is not possible, so $x \in \phi$.

(iii) $2\cdot x^{\log_4 3} + 3^{\log_4 x} = 27$

$$2\cdot 3^{\log_4 x} + 3^{\log_4 x} = 27 \quad \left[\because a^{\log_b c} = c^{\log_b a}\right]$$

$$3^{\log_4 (x+1)} = 3^3$$

$$\log_4 (x+1) = 3$$

$$\log_4 x = 2$$

$$x = 16$$

(iv) $\log_4 \log_3 \log_2 x = 0$ ...(i)

Defined for $x > 0$, $\log_2 x > 0$ and $\log_3 \log_2 x > 0$

$\Rightarrow \quad x > 0, x > 1, x > 3$

$\therefore \quad x > 3$

$$\log_3 \log_2 x = 1$$

$$\log_2 x = 3, x = 8$$

which satisfy Eq. (i).

(v) $x^{\frac{\log_{10} x + 5}{3}} = 10^{5 + \log_{10} x}$ ...(i)

Defined for $x > 0$

Let $\quad \log_{10} x = y$

$\Rightarrow \quad x = 10^y$

By Eq. (i), $\quad 10^{y\left(\frac{y+5}{3}\right)} = 10^{5+y}$

$\Rightarrow \quad y^2 + 5y = 15 + 3y$

$\Rightarrow \quad y^2 + 2y - 15 = 0$

$\Rightarrow \quad (y+5)(y-3) = 0$

$\Rightarrow \quad y = -5$ or $y = 3$

$\Rightarrow \quad x = \frac{1}{10^5}$ or $x = 10^3$

$\therefore \quad x = \{10^{-5}, 10^3\}$

(vi) $\log_3 \left(\log_9 x + \frac{1}{2} + 9^x\right) = 2x$

Defined for $x > 0$,

$$\log_9 x + \frac{1}{2} + 9^x = 9^x$$

$\Rightarrow \quad \log_9 x = -\frac{1}{2} \Rightarrow x = 9^{-\frac{1}{2}}$

$\Rightarrow \quad x = 3^{-1}$

$\therefore \quad x = \frac{1}{3}$

(vii) $4^{\log_{10} x + 1} - 6^{\log_{10} x} - 2\cdot 3^{\log_{10} x^2 + 2} = 0$ ...(i)

$\Rightarrow \quad 2^{2\log_{10} x + 2} - (2\times 3)^{\log_{10} x} - 2\cdot 3^{2\log_{10} x + 2} = 0$

Let $\log_{10} x = \lambda$, then

$$2^{2\lambda + 2} - (2\times 3)^{\lambda} - 2\cdot 3^{2\lambda + 2} = 0$$

$\Rightarrow \quad 2^2 - \left(\frac{3}{2}\right)^{\lambda} - 2\cdot 3^2 \cdot \left(\frac{3}{2}\right)^{2\lambda} = 0$

Let $\quad \left(\frac{3}{2}\right)^{\lambda} = \mu$

$\therefore \quad 18\mu^2 + \mu - 4 = 0$

$\Rightarrow \quad 18\mu^2 + 9\mu - 8\mu - 4 = 0$

$\Rightarrow \quad 9\mu(2\mu + 1) - 4(2\mu + 1) = 0$

$\therefore \quad \mu = -\frac{1}{2}, \mu = \frac{4}{9}$

$$\mu \neq -\frac{1}{2}$$

$\therefore \quad \mu = \frac{4}{9}$

$$\left(\frac{3}{2}\right)^{\lambda} = \left(\frac{3}{2}\right)^{-2} \Rightarrow \lambda = -2$$

Hence, $x = 10^{\lambda} = 10^{-2} \frac{1}{100}$

(viii) $\frac{\log_{10}(x-3)}{\log_{10}(x^2 - 21)} = \frac{1}{2}$

is defined for $x > 1$ and $x^2 > 21$.

$\therefore \quad x > \sqrt{21}$ ...(i)

$\Rightarrow \quad 2\log_{10}(x-3) = \log_{10}(x^2 - 21)$

$\Rightarrow \quad \log_{10}(x-3)^2 = \log_{10}(x^2 - 21)$

$\Rightarrow \quad (x-3)^2 = x^2 - 21$

$$x^2 - 6x + 9 = x^2 - 21$$

$\therefore \quad x = 5$

satisfy Eq. (i), hence $x = 5$.

(ix) $x^{\log_2 x + 4} = 32$

Defined for $x > 0$,

$$\log_2 x + 4 = \log_x 2^5$$

$$\log_2 x + 4 = \frac{5}{\log_2 x}$$

$$(\log_2 x)^2 + 4\log_2 x - 5 = 0$$

$$(\log_2 x + 5)(\log_2 x - 1) = 0$$

$\Rightarrow \quad \log_2 x = -5$ or $\log_2 x = 1$

$\Rightarrow \quad x = 2^{-5}$ or $x = 2^1$

$\therefore \quad x = \frac{1}{32}$ or $x = 2$

which satisfy Eq. (i).

(x) $\quad \log_a x = x$ ...(i)

and $\quad a = x^{\log_4 x}$ ...(ii)

Defined for $x > 0$

From Eq. (i), $\quad x = a^x$

$$a^x = x, a = x^{1/x}$$

From Eq. (ii), $x^{\frac{1}{x}} = x^{\log_4 x}$

$\Rightarrow \quad \frac{1}{x} = \log_4 x$

$\Rightarrow \quad x = \log_x 4 \Rightarrow x^x = 4$

$\therefore \quad x = 2$

(xi) $\log_{\sqrt{2}\sin x}(1 + \cos x) = 2$ ...(i)

Defined for $1 + \cos x > 0$, $\sqrt{2}\sin x > 0$

and $\sqrt{2}\sin x \neq 1$, then

$$1 + \cos x = 2\sin^2 x$$

$$1 + \cos x = 2 - 2\cos^2 x$$

$$2\cos^2 x + \cos x - 1 = 0$$
$$(2\cos x - 1)(\cos x + 1) = 0$$
$$1 + \cos x \neq 0$$

So, $\cos x = \frac{1}{2}$

$x = \frac{\pi}{3}$, Eq. (i) is defined for that value of x.

69. Let rational number be x, then

$$x = 50\log_{10} x \Rightarrow 2x = 100 \cdot \log_{10} x$$

Taking logarithm to the base 10, then

$$\log_{10} 2 + \log_{10} x = 2 + \log_{10}(\log_{10} x)$$

Let $\log_{10} x = \lambda$

$\therefore$ $\log_{10} 2 + \lambda = 2 + \log_{10}(\lambda)$

$\Rightarrow$ $\log_{10}\left(\frac{\lambda}{2}\right) = \lambda - 2$

which is true for $\lambda = 2$.

$\therefore$ $\log_{10} x = 2$

$\Rightarrow$ $x = 10^2 = 100$

70. Let $y = \frac{2}{\log_4 (2000)^6} + \frac{3}{\log_5 (2000)^6}$

$= 2\log_{(2000)^6} 4 + 3\log_{(2000)^6} 5$

$= \log_{(2000)^6} 4^2 + \log_{(2000)^6} 5^3$

$= \log_{(2000)^6} (4^2 \times 5^3)$

$= \frac{1}{6}\log_{2000} 2000 = \frac{1}{6}$

71. $\log_a [1 + \log_b \{1 + \log_c (1 + \log_p x)\}] = 0$ ...(i)

$\Rightarrow$ $1 + \log_b \{1 + \log_c (1 + \log_p x)\} = 1$

$\Rightarrow$ $\log_b \{1 + \log_c (1 + \log_p x)\} = 0$

$\Rightarrow$ $1 + \log_c (1 + \log_p x) = 1$

$\Rightarrow$ $\log_c (1 + \log_p x) = 0$

$\Rightarrow$ $1 + \log_p x = 1$

$\Rightarrow$ $\log_p x = 0$

$\Rightarrow$ $x = p^0$

$\Rightarrow$ $x = 1$

Eq. (i) is satisfied for this value of x.

72. $\because 5\log_{4\sqrt{2}}(3-\sqrt{6}) - 6\log_8(\sqrt{3}-\sqrt{2})$

$= 5\log_{2^{5/2}}(3-\sqrt{6}) - 6\log_{2^3}(\sqrt{3}-\sqrt{2})$

$= 5 \times \frac{1}{5/2}\log_2(3-\sqrt{6}) - 6 \times \frac{1}{3}\log_2(\sqrt{3}-\sqrt{2})$

$= \log_2(3-\sqrt{6})^2 - \log_2(\sqrt{3}-\sqrt{2})^2$

$= \log_2\left(\frac{3-\sqrt{6}}{\sqrt{3}-\sqrt{2}}\right)^2 = \log_2\left(\frac{\sqrt{3}(\sqrt{3}-\sqrt{2})}{(\sqrt{3}-\sqrt{2})}\right)^2 = \log_2 3$

$\therefore$ $= 4^{5\log_{4\sqrt{2}}(3-\sqrt{6}) - 6\log_8(\sqrt{3}-\sqrt{2})}$

$= 4^{\log_2 3} = 2^{2\log_2 3} = 2^{\log_2 9} = 9$

73. (i) $\log_{2x+3} x^2 < 1$ ...(i)

***Case* I** $0 < 2x + 3 < 1$, i.e. $-\frac{3}{2} < x < -1$

Eq. (i), $x^2 > 2x + 3$

$$x^2 - 2x - 3 > 0$$
$$(x-3)(x+1) > 0$$
$$x < -1 \text{ or } x > 3$$

$\therefore$ $x \in \left(-\frac{3}{2}, -1\right)$ ...(ii)

***Case* II** $2x + 3 > 1 \Rightarrow x > -1$

Eq. (i), $x^2 < 2x + 3$

$(x-3)(x+1) < 0 \; -1 < x < 3$

$\Rightarrow$ $x \in (-1, 3]$ ...(iii)

Eq. (i), $x \neq 0$ ...(iv)

Eqs. (ii), (iii) and (iv), $x \in \left(-\frac{3}{2}, 3\right) \cup \{-1, 0\}$

(ii) $\log_{2x}(x^2 - 5x + 6) < 1$ ...(i)

For Eq. (i) to be defined $2x > 0$ and $2x \neq 1$

So, $x > 0$ and $x \neq \frac{1}{2}$

and $x^2 - 5x + 6 > 0 \Rightarrow x < 2$ or $x > 3$ ...(ii)

***Case* I** $0 < 2x < 1 \Rightarrow 0 < x < \frac{1}{2}$ ...(iii)

From Eq. (i), $\log_{2x}(x^2 - 5x + 6) < 1$

$$x^2 - 5x + 6 < 2x$$
$$x^2 - 7x + 5 > 0$$
$$(x-6)(x-1) > 0$$

$x < 1$ or $x > 6$ ...(iv)

From Eqs. (iii), (iv) and (ii)

$x \in \left(0, \frac{1}{2}\right)$ ...(A)

***Case* II** $2x > 1 \Rightarrow x > \frac{1}{2}$ ...(v)

From Eq. (i), $\log_{2x}(x^2 - 5x + 6) < 1$

$\Rightarrow$ $x^2 - 5x + 6 < 2x$

$\Rightarrow$ $x^2 - 7x + 6 < 0$

$\Rightarrow$ $1 < x < 6$ ...(vi)

From Eqs. (ii), (v) and (vi),

$x \in (1, 2) \cup (3, 6)$ ...(B)

From Eqs. (A) and (B), $x \in \left(0, \frac{1}{2}\right) \cup (1, 2) \cup (3, 6)$

(iii) $\log_2(2 - x) < \log_{1/2}(x + 1)$ ...(i)

From Eq. (i) to be defined $2 - x > 0 \Rightarrow x < 2$

and $x + 1 > 0 \Rightarrow x > -1$

So, $x \in (-1, 2)$ ...(ii)

Now, from Eq. (i), $\log_2(2 - x) + \log_2(x + 1) < 0$

$$(2-x)(x+1) < 1$$
$$(x-2)(x+1) + 1 > 0$$
$$x^2 - x - 2 + 1 > 0$$
$$x^2 - x - 1 > 0$$

$\Rightarrow \quad x < \dfrac{1-\sqrt{5}}{2}$

or $\quad x > \dfrac{1+\sqrt{5}}{2}$ ...(iii)

From Eqs. (ii) and (iii),

$$x \in \left(-1, \frac{1-\sqrt{5}}{2}\right) \cup \left(\frac{1+\sqrt{5}}{2}, 2\right)$$

(iv) $\log_{x^2}(x+2) < 1$ ...(i)

From Eq. (i) to be defined, $x + 2 > 0 \Rightarrow x > -2$
and $x \in R, x \neq 0$ and $x \neq 1$ ...(A)

***Case* I** $x \in (-1, 1) \sim \{0\}$ ...(ii)

Eq. (i), $(x+2) > x^2$

$$x^2 - x - 2 < 0$$

$$(x-2)(x+1) < 0$$

$$x - 1 < x < 2 \quad \text{...(iii)}$$

From Eqs. (ii), (iii) and (A),

$$x \in (-1, 0) \cup (0, 1) \quad \text{...(B)}$$

***Case* II** $x \in (-\infty, -1) \cup (1, \infty)$ ...(iv)

Eq. (i), $x + 2 < x^2$

$$x^2 - x - 2 > 0$$

$$x < -1 \text{ or } x > 2 \quad \text{...(v)}$$

From Eqs. (iv), (v) and (A),

$$x \in (-2, -1) \cup (2, \infty) \quad \text{...(C)}$$

From Eqs. (B) and (C),

$$x \in (-2, 1) \cup (2, \infty) \sim \{-1, 0\}$$

(v) $3^{\log_3 \sqrt{x-1}} < 3^{\log_3 (x-6)} + 3$ ...(i)

From Eq. (i) to be defined

$x - 1 > 0 \Rightarrow x > 1$ ...(ii)

and $x - 6 > 0 \Rightarrow x > 6$ ...(iii)

From Eqs. (ii) and (iii), $x > 6$ ...(iv)

Eq. (i), $\sqrt{x-1} - (x-6) - 3 < 0$

$$\sqrt{x-1} - x + 3 < 0$$

$$\sqrt{x-1} < (x-3)\ x - 1 < (x-3)^2$$

$$x^2 + 9 - 6x - x + 1 > 0$$

$$x^2 - 7x + 10 > 0$$

$$(x-5)(x-2) > 0$$

$$x < 2 \text{ or } x > 5 \quad \text{...(v)}$$

From Eqs. (iv) and (v), $x > 6$

(vi) $\log_{1/2}(3x-1)^2 < \log_{1/2}(x+5)^2$ ...(i)

From Eq. (i) to be defined $x \neq \dfrac{1}{3}, x \neq -5$ ...(ii)

Eq. (i), $(3x-1)^2 > (x+5)^2$

$$(3x - 1 - x - 5)(3x - 1 + x + 5) > 0$$

$$(2x-6)(4x+4) > 0$$

$$(x-3)(x+1) > 0$$

$$x < -1 \text{ or } x > 3 \quad \text{...(iii)}$$

From Eqs. (ii) and (iii),

$$x \in (-\infty, -5) \cup (-5, -1) \cup (3, \infty)$$

(vii) $\log_{10} x + 2 \leq \log_{10}^2 x$ ...(i)

From Eq. (i), $x > 0$ ...(ii)

$$\log_{10}^2 x + \log_{10} x - 2 \geq 0$$

$$(10_{10}\ x - 2)(\log_{10} x + 1) \geq 0$$

$$\log_{10} x \leq -1 \text{ or } \log_{10} x \geq 2$$

$$x \leq \frac{1}{10} \text{ or } x \geq 100 \quad \text{...(iii)}$$

From Eqs. (ii) and (iii),

$$x \in \left(0, \frac{1}{10}\right] \cup [100, \infty)$$

or $\quad x \in (0, 10^{-1}] \cup [10^2, \infty)$

(viii) $\log_{10}(x^2 - 2x - 2) \leq 0$ ...(i)

From Eq. (i), $x^2 - 2x - 2 > 0$

$$x^2 - 2x + 1 - 3 > 0$$

$$(x-1)^2 - (\sqrt{3})^2 > 0$$

$$[x - (1+\sqrt{3})][x - (1-\sqrt{3})] > 0$$

$\therefore \quad x \in (-\infty, 1-\sqrt{3}) \cup (1+\sqrt{3}, \infty)$ ...(ii)

$$x^2 - 2x - 2 \leq 1$$

$$x^2 - 2x - 3 \leq 0$$

$$(x-3)(x+1) \leq 0$$

$$-1 \leq x \leq 3 \quad \text{...(iii)}$$

From Eqs. (ii) and (iii), we get

$$x \in [-1, 1-\sqrt{3}) \cup (1+\sqrt{3}, 3]$$

(ix) $\log_x\left(2x - \dfrac{3}{4}\right) > 2$ ...(i)

From Eq. (i) to be defined $x > 0, x \neq 1, 2x - \dfrac{3}{4} > 0$

$$x > 0, x \neq 1, x > \frac{3}{8} \quad \text{...(ii)}$$

From Eq. (i), $\log_x\left(2x - \dfrac{3}{4}\right) > 2$

***Case* I** $\quad 0 < x < 1$ ...(iii)

$$2x - \frac{3}{4} < x^2$$

$$8x - 3 - 4x^2 < 0$$

$$4x^2 - 8x + 3 > 0$$

$$4x^2 - 6x - 2x + 3 > 0$$

$$(2x-1)(2x-3) > 0$$

$$x < \frac{1}{2} \text{ or } x > \frac{3}{2} \quad \text{...(iv)}$$

From Eqs. (ii), (iii) and (iv),

$$x \in \left(\frac{3}{8}, \frac{1}{2}\right) \quad \text{...(v)}$$

***Case* II** $\quad x > 1$ ...(vi)

Eq. (i) $\Rightarrow \quad 2x - \dfrac{3}{4} > x^2$

$$8x - 3 > 4x^2$$

$$4x^2 - 8x + 3 < 0$$

$$\frac{1}{2} < x < \frac{3}{2} \quad \text{...(vii)}$$

From Eqs. (ii), (vi) and (vii), we get

$$x \in \left(1, \frac{3}{2}\right) \quad \text{...(viii)}$$

From Eqs. (v) and (viii), we get

$$x \in \left(\frac{3}{8}, \frac{1}{2}\right) \cup \left(1, \frac{3}{2}\right)$$

(x) $\log_{1/3} x < \log_{1/2} x \ (x > 0)$

$$\Rightarrow \log_3 x > \log_2 x$$

$$\Rightarrow \frac{\log x}{\log 3} - \frac{\log x}{\log 2} > 0$$

$$\log x \left(\frac{\log 3 - \log 2}{\log 2 \log 3}\right) < 0$$

$$\Rightarrow \log x < 0 \Rightarrow x < 1$$

So, $x \in (0, 1)$

(xi) $\log_{2x+3} x^2 < \log_{2x+3} (2x+3)$ ...(i)

From Eq. (i) to be defined,

$$2x + 3 > 0$$

$$x > -\frac{3}{2}$$

$$2x + 3 \neq 1$$

$$x \neq -1$$

$$x \in R - \{0\} \quad \text{...(A)}$$

From Eq. (i), $\log_{2x+3} x^2 < 1$ ...(ii)

***Case* I** $0 < 2x + 3 < 1 \Rightarrow -\frac{3}{2} < x < -1$ ...(iii)

From Eq. (ii), $\log_{2x+3} x^2 < 1$

$$\Rightarrow x^2 > 2x + 3 \Rightarrow x^2 - 2x - 3 > 0$$

$$\Rightarrow (x-3)(x+1) > 0$$

$$\Rightarrow x < -1 \text{ or } x > 3 \quad \text{...(iv)}$$

From Eqs. (A), (iii) and (iv), $x \in \left(-\frac{3}{2}, -1\right)$ ...(B)

***Case* II** If $2x + 3 > 1 \Rightarrow x > -1$ ...(v)

$$\log_{2x+3} x^2 < 1$$

$$x^2 < 2x + 3$$

$$x^2 - 2x - 3 < 0$$

$$(x-3)(x+1) < 0$$

$$\Rightarrow -1 < x < 3 \quad \text{...(vi)}$$

So, Eqs. (A), (v) and (vi), $x \in (-1, 3)$ ...(C)

From Eqs. (B) and (C),

$$x \in \left(-\frac{3}{2}, -1\right) \cup (-1, 3)$$

(xii) $\log_2^2 x + 3\log_2 x \geq \frac{5}{2} \log_{4\sqrt{2}} 16$ ...(i)

$$\log_2^2 x + 3\log_2 x - \frac{5}{2} \times \frac{2}{5} \log_2 16 \geq 0$$

$$\log_2^2 x + 3\log_2 x - 4 \geq 0$$

$$(\log_2 x + 4)(\log_2 x - 1) \geq 0$$

$$\log_2 x \leq -4 \text{ or } \log_2 x \geq 1 \Rightarrow x \leq \frac{1}{16}$$

or $x \geq 2$ ...(ii)

From Eq. (i), $x > 0$ ...(iii)

From Eqs. (ii) and (iii), $x \in \left(0, \frac{1}{16}\right] \in [2, \infty)$

(xiii) $\because (x^2 + x + 1)^x < 1$

Taking logarithm on both sides, then

$$x \log (x^2 + x + 1) < 0$$

$$\because x^2 + x + 1 > 0, \forall x \in R$$

***Case* I** If $x > 0$ ...(i)

Then, $\log (x^2 + x + 1) < 0$

$$\therefore x^2 + x + 1 < 1$$

$$\Rightarrow x(x+1) < 0$$

$$\Rightarrow -1 < x < 0 \quad \text{...(ii)}$$

From Eqs. (i) and (ii), $x \in \phi$

***Case* II** If $x < 0$ ...(iii)

Then, $\log (x^2 + x + 1) > 0$

$$\Rightarrow x^2 + x + 1 > 1$$

$$\Rightarrow x(x+1) > 0$$

$$\therefore x \in (-\infty, -1) \cup (0, \infty) \quad \text{...(iv)}$$

From Eqs. (iii) and (iv), we get

$$x \in (-\infty, -1)$$

(xiv) $\log_{(3x^2+1)} 2 < \frac{1}{2}$

$$2 < (3x^2 + 1)^{1/2}$$

$$(3x^2 + 1 > 1, \forall x \in R)$$

$$4 < 3x^2 + 1$$

$$3x^2 > 3$$

$$x^2 > 1$$

$$x < -1 \text{ or } x > 1$$

$$\Rightarrow x \in (-\infty, -1) \cup (1, \infty)$$

(xv) $x^{(\log_{10} x)^2 - 3\log_{10} x + 1} > 1000$ ...(i)

From Eq. (i) to be defined, $x > 0$ and $x \neq 1$

Let $\log_{10} x = y \Rightarrow x = 10^y$

From Eq. (i), $10^{y(y^2 - 3y + 1)} > 10^3$

$$\Rightarrow y^3 - 3y^2 + y - 3 > 0$$

$$\Rightarrow y^2(y-3) + 1(y-3) > 0$$

$$\Rightarrow (y-3)(y^2+1) > 0$$

$$\Rightarrow y > 3$$

$$\Rightarrow \log_{10} x > 3$$

$$\Rightarrow x > 1000$$

$$\Rightarrow x \in (1000, \infty)$$

(xvi) $\log_4 \{14 + \log_6(x^2 - 64)\} \leq 2$ ...(i)

$$14 + \log_6(x^2 - 64) \leq 16$$

$$\log_6 (x^2 - 64) \leq 2$$

$$x^2 - 64 \leq 36$$
$$x^2 \leq 100$$
$$-10 \leq x \leq 10 \qquad \text{...(ii)}$$

From Eq. (i), $\quad x^2 - 64 > 0$

$\Rightarrow \quad x < -8$ or $x > 8 \qquad$ ...(iii)

From Eqs. (ii) and (iii),

$$x \in [-10, -8) \cup (8, 10]$$

(xvii) $\quad \log_2 (9 - 2^x) \leq 10^{\log_{10} (3 - x)} \qquad$ ...(i)

From Eq. (i) to be defined,

$$9 - 2^x > 0 \Rightarrow 9 > 2^x$$

$\Rightarrow \quad 2^x < 9 \Rightarrow x < \log_2 9$

$$3 - x > 0 \Rightarrow x < 3$$

Then, $\quad x < 3 \qquad$ ...(ii)

From Eq. (i), $\log_2 (9 - 2^x) \leq 3 - x$

$\Rightarrow \quad 9 - 2^x \leq 2^{3-x}$

$\Rightarrow \quad 9 - 2^x - 8 \cdot 2^{-x} \leq 0$

$\Rightarrow \quad (2^x)^2 - 92^x + 8 \geq 0$

$\Rightarrow \quad (2^x - 8)(2^x - 1) \geq 0$

$\Rightarrow \quad 2^x \leq 1$ or $2^x \geq 8$

$\Rightarrow \quad x \leq 0$ or $x \geq 3 \qquad$ ...(iii)

From Eqs. (ii) and (iii), $x \leq 0 \Rightarrow x \in (-\infty, 0]$

(xviii) $\log_a \left(\dfrac{2x + 3}{x}\right) \geq 0 \qquad$ ...(i)

From inequation (a), $\; a > 1$

By Eq. (i), $\quad \dfrac{2x + 3}{x} > 0$

$\Rightarrow \quad \left[\dfrac{x - \left(-\frac{3}{2}\right)}{x - 0}\right] > 0$

$\Rightarrow \quad x < -\dfrac{3}{2}$ or $x > 0 \qquad$ ...(ii)

From Eq. (i), $\quad \log_a \left(2 + \dfrac{3}{x}\right) \geq 0$

$$2 + \frac{3}{x} \geq 1$$
$$\frac{3 + x}{x} \geq 0$$
$$\frac{x - (-3)}{x - 0} \geq 0$$
$$x \leq -3 \text{ or } x \geq 0 \qquad \text{...(iii)}$$

From Eqs. (ii) and (iii),

$$x \leq -3 \text{ or } x > 0 \qquad \text{...(iv)}$$

$\Rightarrow \quad x \in (-\infty, -3] \cup (0, \infty)$

From inequation in (b), $\; 0 < a < 1$

From Eq. (i), $\quad \dfrac{2x + 3}{x} \leq 1$

$\Rightarrow \quad \dfrac{x + 3}{x} \leq 0$

$\Rightarrow \quad -3 \leq x \leq 0$

$\Rightarrow \quad x \in [-3, 0] \qquad$ ...(v)

From Eqs. (ii) and (v), we get $x \in \left[-3, -\dfrac{3}{2}\right)$

(xix) $\quad 1 + \log_2 (x - 1) \leq \log_{(x-1)} 4 \qquad$ ...(i)

From Eq. (i) to be defined, $x - 1 > 0 \Rightarrow x > 1$

and $\quad x - 1 \neq 1 \Rightarrow x \neq 2 \qquad$ ...(ii)

By Eq. (i), $1 + \log_2 (x - 1) \leq 2 \log_{(x-1)} 2$

Let $\log_2 (x - 1) = \lambda$, then

$$1 + \lambda \leq \frac{2}{\lambda}$$

$\Rightarrow \quad \dfrac{\lambda^2 + \lambda - 2}{\lambda} \leq 0$

$\Rightarrow \quad \dfrac{(\lambda + 2)(\lambda - 1)}{\lambda} \leq 0$

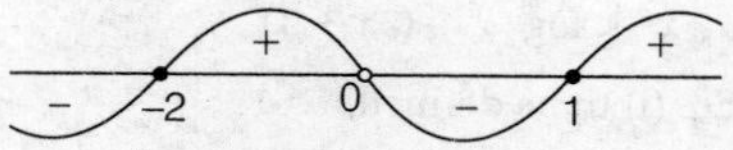

$\Rightarrow \quad \lambda \leq -2$ or $0 < \lambda \leq 1$

$\Rightarrow \quad \log_2 (x - 1) \leq -2$

or $\quad 0 < \log_2 (x - 1) \leq 1$

$\Rightarrow \quad x - 1 \leq 2^{-2}$ or $2^0 < x - 1 \leq 2^1$

$\Rightarrow \quad x \leq \dfrac{5}{4}$ or $2 < x \leq 3 \qquad$ ...(iii)

From Eqs. (ii) and (iii), we get

$$x \in (2, 3]$$

(xx) $\log_{5x+4} x^2 \leq \log_{5x+4} (2x + 3) \qquad$ ...(i)

From Eq. (i) to be defined, $5x + 4 > 0 \Rightarrow x > -\dfrac{4}{5}$

$$5x + 4 \neq 1 \Rightarrow x \neq -\frac{3}{5}$$
$$2x + 3 > 0 \Rightarrow x > -\frac{3}{2}$$

and $\quad x \in (-\infty, \infty) - \{0\}$

$\Rightarrow \quad x \in \left(-\dfrac{4}{5}, -\dfrac{3}{5}\right) \cup \left(-\dfrac{3}{5}, 0\right) \cup (0, \infty) \qquad$ ...(ii)

From Eq. (i), $\; \log_{5x+4} x^2 \leq \log_{5x+4} (2x + 3)$

$$\log_{5x+4} \frac{x^2}{2x + 3} \leq 0 \qquad \text{...(iii)}$$

***Case* I** $\quad 0 < 5x + 4 < 1$

$\Rightarrow \quad -\dfrac{4}{5} < x < -\dfrac{3}{5} \qquad$ ...(iv)

From Eq. (iii), $\dfrac{x^2}{2x + 3} \geq 1$

$$\frac{x^2 - 2x - 3}{2x + 3} \geq 0$$

$$\frac{(x-3)(x+1)}{\left[x-\left(-\frac{3}{2}\right)\right]} \geq 0$$

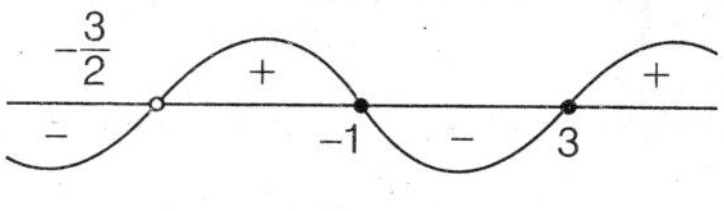

$$x \in \left(-\frac{3}{2}, -1\right] \cup [3, \infty) \quad ...(v)$$

From Eqs. (ii), (iv) and (v), $x \in \phi$ ...(vi)

***Case* II** $\quad 5x + 4 > 1 \Rightarrow x > -\frac{3}{5}$ ...(vii)

From Eq. (iii), $\frac{x^2}{2x+3} \leq 1$,

$$\left[\frac{(x-3)(x+1)}{\left\{x-\left(-\frac{3}{2}\right)\right\}}\right] \leq 0$$

$\Rightarrow \quad x < -\frac{3}{2}$ or $x \in [-1, 3]$ ...(viii)

From Eqs. (ii), (vii) and (viii),

$$x \in \left(-\frac{3}{5}, -\frac{3}{2}\right) \cup [-1, 0) \cup (0, 3] \quad ...(ix)$$

From Eqs. (vi) and (ix), we get

$$x \in \left(-\frac{3}{5}, -\frac{3}{2}\right) \cup [-1, 0) \cup (0, 3]$$

74. Given equation is

$$\sqrt{\log_x (ax)^{1/5} + \log_a (ax)^{1/5}} + \sqrt{\log_a \left(\frac{x}{a}\right)^{1/5} + \log_x \left(\frac{a}{x}\right)^{1/5}} = a \quad ...(i)$$

$$\frac{1}{\sqrt{5}}\sqrt{1 + \log_x a + 1 + \log_a x} + \frac{1}{\sqrt{5}}\sqrt{\log_a x - 1 + \log_x a - 1} = a$$

$$\sqrt{\log_a x + \frac{1}{\log_a x} + 2} + \sqrt{\log_a x + \frac{1}{\log_a x} - 2} = \sqrt{5}a$$

$$\left|\sqrt{|\log_a x|} + \frac{1}{\sqrt{|\log_a x|}}\right| + \left|\sqrt{|\log_a x|} - \frac{1}{\sqrt{|\log_a x|}}\right| = \sqrt{5}a \quad ...(ii)$$

Let $\quad \sqrt{|\log_a x|} = y \quad [y \geq 0]$

$$\left|y + \frac{1}{y}\right| + \left|y - \frac{1}{y}\right| = \sqrt{5}a \quad ...(iii)$$

***Case* I** $x \geq a > 1$ Eq. (iii) $\Rightarrow y + \frac{1}{y} + y - \frac{1}{y} = \sqrt{5}a$

$$\Rightarrow \quad 2y = \sqrt{5}a$$

$$2\sqrt{|\log_a x|} = \sqrt{5}a$$

$$\sqrt{|\log_a x|} = \frac{\sqrt{5}}{2}a$$

$$\log_a x = \frac{5}{4}a^2$$

$$x = a^{\frac{5}{4}a^2}$$

***Case* II** $1 < x < a$ ...(v)

By Eq. (iii), $\quad y + \frac{1}{y} - y + \frac{1}{y} = \sqrt{5}a$

$$\frac{2}{y} = \sqrt{5}a$$

$$y = \frac{2}{\sqrt{5}a}$$

$$\sqrt{|\log_a x|} = \frac{2}{\sqrt{5}a}$$

$$\Rightarrow \quad \log_a x = \frac{4}{5a^2}$$

$$x = a^{4/5a^2}$$

75. Given equation,

$$\log_\pi (x^2 + 15a^2) - \log_\pi (a-2) = \log_\pi \frac{8ax}{a-2} \quad ...(i)$$

Eq. (i) is defined, if $a - 2 > 0 \Rightarrow a > 2$ ...(ii)

$$\frac{8ax}{a-2} > 0$$

By Eq. (ii), $\quad a > 2$

So, $ax > 0$, then $x > 0$

Eq. (i) for $\quad x = 9, a > 0$

$$\log_\pi \frac{(x^2 + 15a^2)}{(a-2)} = \log_\pi \frac{8ax}{a-2}$$

$$x^2 + 15a^2 = 8ax \quad ...(iii)$$

$$(x - 3a)(x - 5a) = 0$$

$\therefore \quad x = 3a$ and $x = 5a$

For $\quad a = 3$, $x = 9$ and $x = 15$

$\Rightarrow \quad x = 15$ for $a = 3$

76. Given that,

$$\log_4 (\log_3 x) + \log_{1/4} (\log_{1/3} y) = 0 \quad ...(i)$$

$$\Rightarrow \frac{1}{2}\log_2 \log_3 x - \frac{1}{2}\log_2(-\log_3 y) = 0$$

$$\Rightarrow \frac{1}{2}\left[\log_2 \left(\frac{\log_3 x}{-\log_3 y}\right)\right] = 0$$

$$\Rightarrow -\frac{\log_3 x}{\log_3 y} = 1$$

$$\Rightarrow \log_3 x = -\log_3 y$$

$$\Rightarrow \log_3 x = \log_3 \left(\frac{1}{y}\right)$$

$$\Rightarrow x = \frac{1}{y} \quad ...(ii)$$

Also, given that, $\quad x^2 + y^2 = \frac{17}{4}$

$$x^2 + \frac{1}{x^2} = \frac{17}{4}$$

$$\left(x+\frac{1}{x}\right)^2=\frac{17}{4}+2$$

$$x+\frac{1}{x}=\frac{5}{2} \qquad \text{[by Eq. (i) } x>0, y>0]$$

$$x+\frac{1}{x}=2+\frac{1}{2}$$

$$\therefore \quad x=2 \text{ or } \frac{1}{2}$$

For these values of x, $y=\frac{1}{2}$ or 2 [by Eq. (ii)]

77. $\log_{2x} 4x+\log_{4x} 16x=4$ ...(i)

From Eq. (i) is defined for $x>0, x\neq\frac{1}{2}, x\neq\frac{1}{4}$ ...(ii)

$$\Rightarrow \quad \frac{\log 4x}{\log 2x}+\frac{\log 16x}{\log 4x}=4$$

$$\Rightarrow \quad \frac{2\log 2+\log x}{\log 2+\log x}+\frac{4\log 2+\log x}{2\log 2+\log x}=4$$

On dividing by log 2, then

$$\frac{2+\log_2 x}{1+\log_2 x}+\frac{4+\log_2 x}{2+\log_2 x}=4$$

Let $\log_2 x=\lambda$, then

$$(2+\lambda)^2+(1+\lambda)(4+\lambda)=4(1+\lambda)(2+\lambda)$$

$$\Rightarrow \quad 2\lambda^2+9\lambda+8=4\lambda^2+12\lambda+8$$

$$\Rightarrow \quad 2\lambda^2+3\lambda=0$$

$$\therefore \quad \lambda=0, \lambda=-\frac{3}{2}$$

$$\Rightarrow \quad \log_2 x=0, \log_2 x=-\frac{3}{2}$$

$$\therefore \quad x=2^0, x=2^{-3/2}$$

or $\quad x=1, x=2^{-3/2}$

78. Given equation,

$$\log_6 54+\log_x 16=\log_{\sqrt{2}} x-\log_{36}\frac{4}{9} \qquad \text{...(i)}$$

Eq. (i) holds, if $x>0, x\neq 1$

From Eq. (i),

$$1+\log_6 9+4\log_x 2=2\log_2 x-\log_6\frac{2}{3}$$

$$\Rightarrow \quad 1+\log_6 9+\log_6\frac{2}{3}+4\log_x 2-2\log_2 x=0$$

$$\Rightarrow \quad 2+4\log_x 2-2\log_2 x=0$$

$$\Rightarrow \quad (\log_2 x)^2-\log_2 x-2=0$$

$$\Rightarrow \quad \log_2 x=2 \text{ or } \log_2 x=-1$$

$$\Rightarrow \quad x=4 \text{ or } x=\frac{1}{2}$$

Sum of the values of x satisfy Eq. (i) $=4+\frac{1}{2}=\frac{9}{2}$

Product of the values of x satisfy Eq. (i) $=4\times\frac{1}{2}=2$

79. Let $\frac{3}{2}\log_4(x+2)^3+3=\log_4(4-x)^3+\log_4(x+6)^3$ ...(i)

Eq. (i) holds, if $4-x>0$ and $x+0>0$, $x+2>0$

i.e., $\quad -2<x<4$ ...(ii)

From Eq. (i),

$$\frac{3}{2}\times 2\times\frac{1}{2}\log_2|(x+2)|+3=\frac{1}{2}\times 3\log_2(4-x)+\frac{1}{2}\times 3\log_2(x+6)$$

$$\Rightarrow \quad \log_2(x+2)+2=\log_2(4-x)+\log_2(x+6)$$

$$\Rightarrow \quad \log_2\{4(x+2)\}=\log_2\{(4-x)(x+6)\}$$

$$\Rightarrow \quad 4(x+2)=(4-x)(x+6)$$

$$4x+8=-x^2-2x+24$$

$$x^2+6x-16=0$$

$$(x+8)(x-2)=0$$

$$\therefore \quad x=-8, x=2 \qquad \text{...(iii)}$$

From Eqs. (ii) and (iii), we get $x=2$

80. $\log_2(4^{x+1}+4)\cdot\log_2(4^x+1)=\log_{1/\sqrt{2}}\left(\frac{1}{\sqrt{8}}\right)$ ...(i)

Eq. (i) defined, for $4^x+1>0$ which is true for all $x\in R$.

$$\log_2[4(4^x+1)]\cdot\log_2(4^x+1)=\log_{\sqrt{2}}\sqrt{8}=3$$

$$[2+\log_2(4^x+1)]\log_2(4^x+1)=3$$

Let $\quad \log_2(4^x+1)=y$

$$\therefore \quad (y+2)y=3$$

$$y^2+2y-3=0$$

$$(y+3)(y-1)=0$$

$$y=1 \text{ or } y=-3$$

$\therefore \log_2(4^x+1)=1$ or $\log_2(4^x+1)=-3$

$$4^x+1=2 \text{ or } 4^x+1=\frac{1}{8}$$

$$4^x=1 \text{ or } 4^x=\frac{1}{8}-1$$

$x=0$ or $4^x=-\frac{7}{8}$ which is not possible.

$$\therefore \quad x=0$$

81. $2^{\sqrt{x}+\sqrt{y}}=256$

$$\Rightarrow \quad 2^{\sqrt{x}+\sqrt{y}}=2^8$$

$$\Rightarrow \quad \sqrt{x}+\sqrt{y}=8 \qquad \text{...(i)}$$

Also, given that, $\log_{10}\sqrt{xy}-\log_{10}\frac{3}{2}=1$ ...(ii)

which is defined, $xy>0$

So, Eq. (ii) $\Rightarrow$ $\log_{10}\sqrt{xy}=\log_{10}\left(10\times\frac{3}{2}\right)$

$$\Rightarrow \quad \sqrt{xy}=15$$

$$\Rightarrow \quad xy=225 \qquad \text{...(iii)}$$

From Eq. (i), $x+y+2\sqrt{xy}=64$

$$x+y=64-30$$

$$x+y=34$$

From Eq. (iii), $\quad xy=225$

After solving, we get $x=9$ or $x=25$, then $y=25$ or $y=9$

Hence, solutions are (9, 25) and (25, 9).

82. Given, $\log_2 y = \log_4 (xy - 2)$ ...(i)

Eq. (i) defined for $y > 0$ and $xy - 2 > 0$ ...(ii)

$$xy > 0 \quad ...(iii)$$

From Eqs. (ii) and (iii) $\Rightarrow$ $y > 0, x > 0$

By Eq. (i), $y = \sqrt{xy - 2}$

$$y^2 - xy + 2 = 0 \quad ...(iv)$$

$$y(x - y) = 2 \quad ...(v)$$

Also given that,

$$\log_9 x^2 + \log_3 (x - y) = 1 \quad ...(vi)$$

which is defined for $x \in R - \{0\}$ and $x - y > 0$

$$\Rightarrow \quad x > y$$

By Eq. (vi), $x(x-y) = 3 \Rightarrow x^2 - xy = 3$ ...(vii)

and $x(x-y) = 3$ ...(viii)

Form Eqs. (iv) and (vii), $y^3 + 2 = x^2 - 3$

$$x^2 - y^2 = 5 \quad ...(ix)$$

On dividing Eq. (v) by Eq. (viii),

$$\frac{y}{x} = \frac{2}{3} \Rightarrow y = \frac{2x}{3} \quad ...(x)$$

From Eqs. (ix) and (x),

$$x = 3 \text{ and } y = 2$$

83. Given that,

$$2\log_{1/4}(x+5) > \frac{9}{4}\log_{1/3\sqrt{3}} 9 + \log_{\sqrt{x+5}} 2 \quad ...(i)$$

By Eq. (i), $x + 5 > 0 \Rightarrow x > -5$

$$x + 5 \neq 1 \Rightarrow x \neq -4$$

So, $x \in (-5, -4) \cup (-4, \infty)$ ...(ii)

Now, by Eq. (i)

$$\frac{2}{-2}\log_2(x+5) - \frac{9}{4} \times \left(\frac{-2}{3}\right)\log_3 9 - 2\log_{x+5} 2 > 0$$

$$-\log_2(x+5) + 3 - 2\log_{x+5} 2 > 0$$

$$-\log_2(x+5) - \frac{2}{\log_2(x+5)} + 3 > 0 \quad ...(iii)$$

Now, let $\log_2(x+5) = y$, then Eq. (iii) becomes

$$-y - \frac{2}{y} + 3 > 0$$

$$\Rightarrow \frac{-y^2 + 3y - 2}{y} > 0$$

$$\Rightarrow \frac{y^2 - 3y + 2}{y} < 0$$

$$\Rightarrow \frac{(y-2)(y-1)}{y} < 0$$

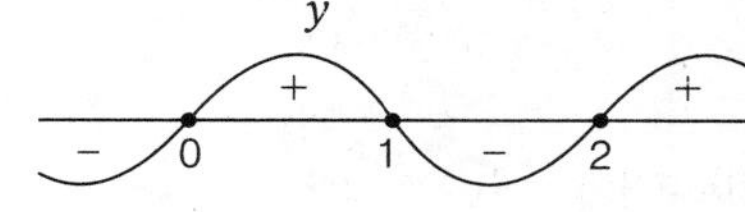

$$\Rightarrow \quad y < 0 \text{ or } 1 < y < 2$$

$$\Rightarrow \quad \log_2(x+5) < 0 \text{ or } 1 < \log_2(x+5) < 2$$

$$\Rightarrow \quad x + 5 < 1 \text{ or } 2 < x + 5 < 4$$

$$\Rightarrow \quad x < -4 \quad ...(iv)$$

or $\quad -3 < x < -1$ ...(v)

From Eqs. (ii), (iv) and (v),

$$x \in (-5, -4) \cup (-3, -1)$$

84. $\log_3(\sqrt{x} + |\sqrt{x} - 1|) = \log_9(4\sqrt{x} - 3 + 4|\sqrt{x} - 1|)$ ...(i)

From Eq. (i) is defined, if $x \geq 0$

then $\log_3(\sqrt{x} + |\sqrt{x} - 1|) = \log_{3^2}(4\sqrt{x} - 3 + 4|\sqrt{x} - 1|)$

$$\Rightarrow \quad 2(\sqrt{x} + |\sqrt{x} - 1|) = 4\sqrt{x} - 3 + 4|\sqrt{x} - 1|$$

$$\Rightarrow \quad 3 - 2\sqrt{x} = 2|\sqrt{x} - 1|$$

On squaring both sides, then

$$9 + 4x - 12\sqrt{x} = 4x + 4 - 4\sqrt{x}$$

$$\Rightarrow \quad 8\sqrt{x} = 5$$

$$\therefore \quad x = \frac{25}{64}$$

85. $(\log_2 x)^4 - \left(\log_{1/2}\frac{x^5}{4}\right)^2 - 20\log_2 x + 148 < 0$

From Eq. (i), $x > 0$

$\Rightarrow (\log_2 x)^4 - (5\log_2 x - 2)^2 - 20\log_2 x + 148 < 0$ ...(i)

$$(\log_2 x)^4 - 25\log_2^2 x - 4 + 20\log_x x - 20\log_2 x + 148 < 0$$

$$(\log_2 x)^4 - 25\log_2^2 x + 144 < 0$$

$$\{(\log_2 x)^2 - 16\}\{(\log_2 x)^2 - 9\} < 0$$

$$9 < (\log_2 x)^2 < 16$$

$$3 < \log_2 x < 4 \text{ or } -4 < \log_2 x < -3$$

$$8 < x < 16 \quad ...(ii)$$

or $$\frac{1}{16} < x < \frac{1}{8} \quad ...(iii)$$

According to the question in Eq. (i) holds, for $x \in (a, b)$ where $a, b \in N$

So, from Eq. (ii), $a = 8$, $b = 16$

$$\therefore \quad ab(a+b) = 8 \times 16(8+16)$$
$$= 144 \times 24 = 3456$$

86. $\sqrt{(\log_3 \sqrt[3]{3x}) + (\log_x \sqrt[3]{3x})\log_3 x^3}$

$$+ \sqrt{\left(\log_3 \sqrt[3]{\frac{x}{3}} + \log_x \sqrt[3]{\frac{3}{x}}\right)\log_3 x^3} = 2 \quad ...(i)$$

Eq. (i) is defined for $x > 0, x \neq 1$

From Eq. (i), $\sqrt{\frac{1}{3}(1 + \log_3 x + 1 + \log_x 3)\, 3\log_3 x}$

$$+ \sqrt{\frac{1}{3}(\log_3 x - 1 + \log_x 3 - 1)\, 3\log_3 x}$$

$$= 2\sqrt{\left(\log_3 x + \frac{1}{\log_3 x} + 2\right)} + \sqrt{\left(\log_3 x + \frac{1}{\log_3 x} - 2\right)}$$

$$= 2\sqrt{|\log_x 3|}$$

$$\Rightarrow \sqrt{|\log_3 x|} + \frac{1}{\sqrt{|\log_3 x|}} + \left|\sqrt{|\log_3 x|} - \frac{1}{\sqrt{|\log_3 x|}}\right| = 2\sqrt{|\log_x 3|} \quad ...(ii)$$

***Case* I** If $x \geq 3$, $\sqrt{\log_3 x} - \dfrac{1}{\sqrt{\log_3 x}} > 0$

$$2\sqrt{\log_3 x} = 2\sqrt{\log_x 3}$$

$$(\log_3 x)^2 = 1 \Rightarrow x = 3 \text{ or } \frac{1}{3}, \text{ so } x = 3$$

***Case* II** If $1 < x < 3$, $\dfrac{2}{\sqrt{\log_3 x}} = 2\sqrt{\log_x 3}$

$$\Rightarrow \quad \log_3 x \cdot \log_x 3 = 1$$

$$\Rightarrow \quad 1 = 1$$

which is true, for all $x \in (1, 3]$.

So, $x \in (1, 3]$

87. P = Number of natural numbers, whose logarithms to the base 10 have characteristic p.

Let 'x' represent the natural number, i.e.

$$x = \lambda \times 10^p \ [\lambda = \alpha_1 \cdot \alpha_2 \cdot \alpha_3 \ldots]$$

So, P = Number of natural numbers which have $(p + 1)$ digits

$$= 9 \cdot 10^p - 1 + 1 = 9 \cdot 10^p$$

Q = Number of natural numbers which have (q) digits.

$$Q = 9 \cdot 10^{q-1} - 1 + 1 = 9 \cdot 10^{q-1}$$

So, $\log_{10} P - \log_{10} Q = \log_{10}(9 \cdot 10^p) - \log_{10}(9 \cdot 10^{q-1})$

$$= (\log_{10} 9 + p) - (\log_{10} 9 + q - 1)$$

$$= p - q + 1$$

88. $\because \quad a = \log_3 \log_3 2$

$$\Rightarrow \quad 3^a = \log_3 2$$

$$\therefore \quad 3^{-a} = \log_2 3$$

Now, $\quad 1 < 2^{-k + 3^{-a}} < 2^1$

$$\Rightarrow \quad 2^0 < 2^{-k + 3^{-a}} < 2^1$$

$$\therefore \quad 0 < -k + 3^{-a} < 1$$

$$\Rightarrow \quad 0 < -k + \log_2 3 < 1$$

$$\Rightarrow \quad 0 > k - \log_2 3 > -1$$

$$\Rightarrow \quad \log_2 3 - 1 < k < \log_2 3$$

$$\therefore \quad k = 1$$

89. $\because (2x)^{\ln 2} = (3y)^{\ln 3}$

Taking log with base e on both sides, then

$$\ln 2\,(\ln 2 + \ln x) = \ln 3\,(\ln 3 + \ln y) \quad \ldots\text{(i)}$$

and $\quad 3^{\ln x} = 2^{\ln y}$

Taking log with base e on both sides, then

$$\ln x \cdot \ln 3 = \ln y \cdot \ln 2 \quad \ldots\text{(ii)}$$

From Eqs. (i) and (ii), we get

$$\ln 2\,(\ln 2 + \ln x) = \ln 3 \left(\ln 3 + \frac{\ln x \cdot \ln 3}{\ln 2} \right)$$

$$\Rightarrow \quad \ln x \left(\frac{(\ln 3)^2}{\ln 2} - \ln 2 \right) = -((\ln 3)^2 - (\ln 2)^2)$$

$$\therefore \quad \ln x = -\ln 2 = \ln\left(\frac{1}{2}\right)$$

$$\Rightarrow \quad x = \frac{1}{2}$$

$$\therefore \quad x_0 = \frac{1}{2}$$

90. Let $S = \dfrac{1}{3\sqrt{2}} \sqrt{4 - \dfrac{1}{3\sqrt{2}} \sqrt{4 - \dfrac{1}{3\sqrt{2}} \sqrt{4 - \dfrac{1}{3\sqrt{2}} \ldots \infty}}}$

$$\Rightarrow \quad S = \frac{1}{3\sqrt{2}} \sqrt{4 - S}$$

or $\quad (3\sqrt{2}\, S)^2 = 4 - S$

$$\Rightarrow \quad 18S^2 + S - 4 = 0$$

$$\Rightarrow \quad (9S - 4)(2S + 1) = 0$$

$$\therefore \quad 9S - 4 = 0 \qquad [\because 2S + 1 \neq 0]$$

or $\quad S = \dfrac{4}{9} = \left(\dfrac{3}{2}\right)^{-2}$

$$\Rightarrow \quad \log_{3/2} S = -2 \Rightarrow 6 + \log_{3/2} S = 6 - 2 = 4$$

Hence,

$$6 + \log_{3/2} \left(\frac{1}{3\sqrt{2}} \sqrt{4 - \frac{1}{3\sqrt{2}} \sqrt{4 - \frac{1}{3\sqrt{2}} \sqrt{4 - \frac{1}{3\sqrt{2}} \ldots}}} \right) = 4$$

91. $(3/4)^x = 1/4$

Taking log with base 2

$$\Rightarrow \quad x(\log_2 3 - 2) = -2$$

$$\therefore \quad x = \frac{2}{2 - \log_2 3} = \frac{1}{1 - \log_4 3} \Rightarrow \text{(b, c)}$$

and taking log with base 3

$$\Rightarrow \quad x(1 - \log_3 4) = -2\log_3 2$$

$$\therefore \quad x = \frac{2\log_3 2}{2\log_3 2 - 1}$$

CHAPTER

05

Permutations and Combinations

Learning Part

Session 1

- Fundamental Principle of Counting
- Factorial Notation

Session 2

- Divisibility Test
- Principle of Inclusion and Exclusion
- Permutation

Session 3

- Number of Permutations Under Certain Conditions
- Circular Permutations
- Restricted Circular Permutations

Session 4

- Combination
- Restricted Combinations

Session 5

- Combinations from Identical Objects

Session 6

- Arrangement in Groups
- Multinomial Theorem
- Multiplying Synthetically

Session 7

- Rank in a Dictionary
- Gap Method [when particular objects are never together]

Practice Part

- JEE Type Examples
- Chapter Exercises

In everyday life, we need to know about the number of ways of doing certain work from given number of available options. *For example,* Three persons A, B and C are applying for a job in which only one post is vacant. Clearly, vacant post can be filled either by A or B or C i.e., total number of ways doing this work is three.

Again, let two persons A and B are to be seated in a row, then only two possible ways of arrangement is AB or BA. In two arrangements, persons are same but their order is different. Thus, in arranging things, order of things is important.

Session 1

Fundamental Principle of Counting, Factorial Notation

Fundamental Principle of Counting

(i) Multiplication Principle

If an operation can be performed in 'm' different ways, following which a second operation can be performed in 'n' different ways, then the two operations in succession can be performed in $m \times n$ ways. This can be extended to any finite number of operations.

Note For AND → '×' (multiply)

Example 1. A hall has 12 gates. In how many ways can a man enter the hall through one gate and come out through a different gate?

Sol. Since, there are 12 ways of entering into the hall. After entering into the hall, the man come out through a different gate in 11 ways.

Hence, by the fundamental principle of multiplication, total number of ways is $12 \times 11 = 132$ ways.

Example 2. There are three stations A, B and C, five routes for going from station A to station B and four routes for going from station B to station C. Find the number of different ways through which a person can go from A to C via B.

Sol. Since, there are five routes for going from A to B. So, there are four routes for going from B to C.

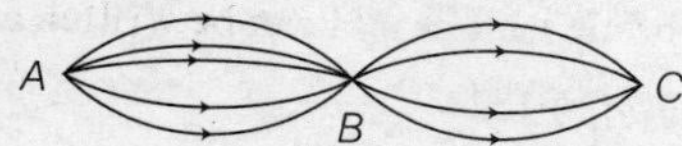

Hence, by the fundamental principle of multiplication, total number of different ways

$= 5 \times 4$ [i.e., A to B and then B to C]

$= 20$ ways

(ii) Addition Principle

If an operation can be performed in 'm' different ways and another operation, which is independent of the first operation, can be performed in 'n' different ways. Then, either of the two operations can be performed in $(m + n)$ ways. This can be extended to any finite number of mutually exclusive operation.

Note For OR → '+' (Addition)

Example 3. There are 25 students in a class in which 15 boys and 10 girls. The class teacher select either a boy or a girl for monitor of the class. In how many ways the class teacher can make this selection?

Sol. Since, there are 15 ways to select a boy, so there are 10 ways to select a girl.

Hence, by the fundamental principle of addition, either a boy or a girl can be performed in $15 + 10 = 25$ ways.

Example 4. There are 4 students for Physics, 6 students for Chemistry and 7 students for Mathematics gold medal. In how many ways one of these gold medals be awarded?

Sol. The Physics, Chemistry and Mathematics student's gold medal can be awarded in 4, 6 and 7 ways, respectively.

Hence, by the fundamental principle of addition, number ways of awarding one of the three gold medals.

$= 4 + 6 + 7 = 17$ ways.

Factorial Notation

Let n be a positive integer. Then, the continued product of first 'n' natural numbers is called factorial n, to be denoted by $n!$ or n i.e., $n! = n(n-1)(n-2) \ldots 3 \cdot 2 \cdot 1$

Note When n is negative or a fraction, $n!$ is not defined.

Some Important Properties

(i) $n! = n(n-1)! = n(n-1)(n-2)!$

(ii) $0! = 1! = 1$

(iii) $(2n)! = 2^n n![1\cdot 3\cdot 5\dots(2n-1)]$

(iv) $\dfrac{n!}{r!} = n(n-1)(n-2)\dots(r+1)$ $[r < n]$

(v) $\dfrac{n!}{(n-r)!} = n(n-1)(n-2)\dots(n-r+1)$ $[r < n]$

(vi) $\dfrac{1}{n!} + \dfrac{1}{(n+1)!} = \dfrac{\lambda}{(n+2)!}$, then $\lambda = (n+2)^2$

(vii) If $x! = y! \Rightarrow x = y$ or $x = 0, y = 1$ or $x = 1, y = 0$

Example 5. Find n, if $(n+2)! = 60 \times (n-1)!$.

Sol. $\because (n+2)! = (n+2)(n+1)n(n-1)!$

$$\Rightarrow \frac{(n+2)!}{(n-1)!} = (n+2)(n+1)n$$

$$\Rightarrow 60 = (n+2)(n+1)n \quad \text{[given]}$$

$$\Rightarrow 5\times 4\times 3 = (n+2)\times(n+1)\times n$$

$$\therefore n = 3$$

Example 6. Evaluate $\sum_{r=1}^{n} r \times r!$.

Sol. We have, $\sum_{r=1}^{n} r\times r! = \sum_{r=1}^{n}\{(r+1)-1\}r! = \sum_{r=1}^{n}(r+1)! - r!$

$= (n+1)! - 1!$ [put $r = n$ in $(r+1)!$ and $r = 1$ is $r!$]

$= (n+1)! - 1$

Example 7. Find the remainder when $\sum_{r=1}^{n} r!$ is divided by 15, if $n \ge 5$.

Sol. Let $N = \sum_{r=1}^{n} r! = 1! + 2! + 3! + 4! + 5! + 6! + 7! + \dots + n!$

$= (1! + 2! + 3! + 4!) + (5! + 6! + 7! + \dots + n!)$

$= 33 + (5! + 6! + 7! + \dots + n!)$

$$\Rightarrow \frac{N}{15} = \frac{33}{15} + \frac{(5! + 6! + 7! + \dots + n!)}{15}$$

$= 2 + \dfrac{3}{15}$ + Integer [as $5!, 6!, \dots$ are divisible by 15]

$= \dfrac{3}{15}$ + Integer

Hence, remainder is 3.

Exponent of prime p in $n!$

Exponent of prime p in $n!$ is denoted by $E_p(n!)$, where p is prime number and n is a natural number. The last integer amongst $1, 2, 3, \dots, (n-1), n$ which is divisible by p is $\left[\dfrac{n}{p}\right]p$, where $[\cdot]$ denotes the greatest integer function.

$$\therefore E_p(n!) = E_p(1\cdot 2\cdot 3\dots(n-1)\cdot n)$$

$$= E_p\left(p\cdot 2p\cdot 3p\dots(n-1)p\cdot\left[\frac{n}{p}\right]p\right)$$

[because the remaining natural numbers from 1 to n are not divisible by p]

$$= \left[\frac{n}{p}\right] + E_p\left(1\cdot 2\cdot 3\dots\left[\frac{n}{p}\right]\right) \quad \dots\text{(i)}$$

Now, the last integer amongs $1, 2, 3, \dots, \left[\dfrac{n}{p}\right]$ which is divisible by p is $\left[\dfrac{\frac{n}{p}}{p}\right] = \left[\dfrac{n}{p^2}\right]$. Now, from Eq. (i), we get

$$E_p(n!) = \left[\frac{n}{p}\right] + E_p\left(p, 2p, 3p, \dots, \left[\frac{n}{p^2}\right]p\right)$$

[because the remaining natural numbers from 1 to $\left[\dfrac{n}{p}\right]$ are not divisible by p]

$$\therefore E_p(n!) = \left[\frac{n}{p}\right] + \left[\frac{n}{p^2}\right] + E_p\left(1\cdot 2\cdot 3\dots\left[\frac{n}{p^2}\right]\right)$$

Similarly, we get

$$E_p(n!) = \left[\frac{n}{p}\right] + \left[\frac{n}{p^2}\right] + \left[\frac{n}{p^3}\right] + \dots + \left[\frac{n}{p^s}\right]$$

where, s is the largest natural number such that

$$p^s \le n < p^{s+1}$$

Note Number of zeroes at the end of $n! = E_5(n!)$.

Example 8. Find the exponent of 3 in 100! .

Sol. In terms of prime factors 100! can be written as $2^a\cdot 3^b\cdot 5^c\cdot 7^d\dots$

Now, $b = E_3(100!)$

$$= \left[\frac{100}{3}\right] + \left[\frac{100}{3^4}\right] + \left[\frac{100}{3^3}\right] + \left[\frac{100}{3^4}\right] + \dots$$

$= 33 + 11 + 3 + 1 + 0 + \dots = 48$

Hence, exponent of 3 is 48.

Aliter

$$\because \quad 100! = 1\times2\times3\times4\times5\times\ldots\times98\times99\times100$$

$$= (1\times2\times4\times5\times7\times\ldots\times98\times100)(3\times6\times9\times\ldots\times96\times99)$$

$$= k\times3^{33}(1\times2\times3\times\ldots\times32\times33)$$

$$= [k(1\times2\times4\times5\times\ldots\times31\times32)](3\times6\times9\times\ldots\times30\times33)$$

$$= 3^{33}k_1\times3^{11}(1\times2\times3\times\ldots\times10\times11)$$

$$= 3^{44}[k_1(1\times2\times4\times5\times\ldots\times10\times11)](3\times6\times9)$$

$$= k_2\times3^{44}\times3^4\times2 = k_3\times3^{48}$$

Hence, exponent of 3 in 100! is 48.

Example 9. Prove that 33! is divisible by 2^{19} and what is the largest integer n such that 33! is divisible by 2^n?

Sol. In terms of prime factors, 33! can be written as $2^a\cdot3^b\cdot5^c\cdot7^d\ldots$

$$\text{Now,}\quad E_2(33!) = \left[\frac{33}{2}\right]+\left[\frac{33}{2^2}\right]+\left[\frac{33}{2^3}\right]+\left[\frac{33}{2^4}\right]+\left[\frac{33}{2^5}\right]+\ldots$$

$$= 16+8+4+2+1+0+\ldots$$

$$= 31$$

Hence, the exponent of 2 in 33! is 31. Now, 33! is divisible by 2^{31} which is also divisible by 2^{19}.

$\therefore$ Largest value of n is 31.

Example 10. Find the number of zeroes at the end of 100!.

Sol. In terms of prime factors, 100! can be written as $2^a\cdot3^b\cdot5^c\cdot7^d\ \ldots$

$$\text{Now, } E_2(100!) = \left[\frac{100}{2}\right]+\left[\frac{100}{2^2}\right]+\left[\frac{100}{2^3}\right]+\left[\frac{100}{2^4}\right]+\left[\frac{100}{2^5}\right]+\left[\frac{100}{2^6}\right]$$

$$= 50+25+12+6+3+1 = 97$$

$$\text{and } E_5(100!) = \left[\frac{100}{5}\right]+\left[\frac{100}{5^2}\right]$$

$$= 20+4 = 24$$

$$\therefore \quad 100! = 2^{97}\cdot3^b\cdot5^{24}\cdot7^d\ldots = 2^{73}\cdot3^b\cdot(2\times5)^{24}\cdot7^d\ldots$$

$$= 2^{73}\cdot3^b\cdot(10)^{24}\cdot7^d\ \ldots$$

Hence, number of zeroes at the end of 100! is 24.

or Exponent of 10 in 100! = min (97, 24) = 24.

Aliter

Number of zeroes at the end of 100!

$$= E_5(100!) = \left[\frac{100}{5}\right]+\left[\frac{100}{5^2}\right]+\ldots$$

$$= 20+4+0+\ldots = 24$$

Example 11. For how many positive integral values of n does $n!$ end with precisely 25 zeroes?

Sol. $\because$ Number of zeroes at the end of $n!$ = 25 [given]

$$\Rightarrow \quad E_5(x!) = 25$$

$$\Rightarrow \quad \left[\frac{n}{5}\right]+\left[\frac{n}{25}\right]+\left[\frac{n}{125}\right]+\ldots = 25$$

It's easy to see that $n = 105$ is the smallest satisfactory value of n. The next four values of n will also work (i.e., n = 106, 107, 108, 109). Hence, the answer is 5.

Example 12. Find the exponent of 80 in 180!.

Sol. $\because\ 80 = 2^4\times5$

$$\therefore \quad E_2(180!) = \left[\frac{180}{2}\right]+\left[\frac{180}{2^2}\right]+\left[\frac{180}{2^3}\right]+\left[\frac{180}{2^4}\right]+\left[\frac{180}{2^5}\right]+\left[\frac{180}{2^6}\right]+\left[\frac{180}{2^7}\right]+\ldots$$

$$= 90+45+22+11+5+2+1 = 176$$

$$\text{and } E_5(180!) = \left[\frac{180}{5}\right]+\left[\frac{180}{5^2}\right]+\left[\frac{180}{5^3}\right]+\ldots$$

$$= 36+7+1+0+\ldots$$

$$= 44$$

Now, exponent of 16 in 180! is $\left[\frac{176}{4}\right] = 44$, where $[\cdot]$ denotes the greatest integer function. Hence, the exponent of 80 in 180! is 44.

Exercise for Session 1

1. There are three routes: air, rail and road for going from Chennai to Hyderabad. But from Hyderabad to Vikarabad, there are two routes, rail and road. The number of routes from Chennai to Vikarabad via Hyderabad is

(a) 4 (b) 5 (c) 6 (d) 7

2. There are 6 books on Mathematics, 4 books on Physics and 5 books on Chemistry in a book shop. The number of ways can a student purchase either a book on Mathematics or a book on Chemistry, is

(a) 10 (b) 11 (c) 9 (d) 15

3. If a, b and c are three consecutive positive integers such that $a < b < c$ and $\frac{1}{a!} + \frac{1}{b!} = \frac{\lambda}{c!}$, the value of $\sqrt{\lambda}$ is

(a) a (b) b (c) c (d) $a + b + c$

4. If $n!$, $3 \times n!$ and $(n+1)!$ are in GP, then $n!$, $5 \times n!$ and $(n+1)!$ are in

(a) AP (b) GP (c) HP (d) AGP

5. Sum of the series $\sum_{r=1}^{n} (r^2 + 1) r!$ is

(a) $(n+1)!$ (b) $(n+2)! - 1$ (c) $n \cdot (n+1)!$ (d) $n \cdot (n+2)!$

6. If $15! = 2^{\alpha} \cdot 3^{\beta} \cdot 5^{\gamma} \cdot 7^{\delta} \cdot 11^{\theta} \cdot 13^{\phi}$, the value of $\alpha - \beta + \gamma - \delta + \theta - \phi$ is

(a) 4 (b) 6 (c) 8 (d) 10

7. The number of naughts standing at the end of 125! is

(a) 29 (b) 30 (c) 31 (d) 32

8. The exponent of 12 in 100! is

(a) 24 (b) 25 (c) 47 (d) 48

9. The number 24! is divisible by

(a) 6^{24} (b) 24^6 (c) 12^{12} (d) 48^5

10. The last non-zero digit in 20! is

(a) 2 (b) 4 (c) 6 (d) 8

11. The number of prime numbers among the numbers $105! + 2, 105! + 3, 105! + 4, \ldots, 105! + 104$ and $105! + 105$ is

(a) 31 (b) 32 (c) 33 (d) None of these

Session 2

Divisibility Test, Principle of Inclusion and Exclusion, Permutation

Divisibility Test

In decimal system all numbers are formed by the digits 0, 1, 2, 3, ..., 9. If $a\,b\,c\,d\,e$ is a five-digit number in decimal system, then we can write that.

$a\,b\,c\,d\,e = 10^4 \cdot a + 10^3 \cdot b + 10^2 \cdot c + 10 \cdot d + e.$

Number $a\,b\,c\,d\,e$ will be divisible

(1) **by 2**, if e is divisible by 2.

(2) **by 4**, if $2d + e$ is divisible by 4.

(3) **by 8**, if $4c + 2d + e$ is divisible by 8.

(4) **by 2^t**, if number formed by last t digits is divisible by 2^t.

For example, Number 820101280 is divisible by 2^5 because 01280 is divisible by 2^5.

(5) **by 5**, if $e = 0$ or 5.

(6) **by 5^t**, if number formed by last t digits is divisible by 5^t.

For example, Number 1128375 is divisible by 5^3 because 375 is divisible by 5^3.

(7) **by 3**, if $a + b + c + d + e$(sum of digits) is divisible by 3.

(8) **by 9**, if $a + b + c + d + e$ is divisible by 9.

(9) **by 6**, if $e =$ even and $a + b + c + d + e$ is divisible by 3.

(10) **by 18**, if $e =$ even and $a + b + c + d + e$ is divisible by 9.

(11) **by 7**, if $abcd - 2e$ is divisible by 7.

For example, Number 6552 is divisible by 7 because $655 - 2 \times 2 = 651 = 93 \times 7$ is divisible by 7.

(12) **by 11**, if $\underbrace{a + c + e}_{\text{Sum of digits at odd places}} - \underbrace{b + d}_{\text{Sum of digits at even places}}$ is divisible by 11.

For example, Number 15222163 is divisible by 11 because $(1 + 2 + 2 + 6) - (5 + 2 + 1 + 3) = 0$ is divisible by 11.

(13) **by 13**, if $abcd + 4e$ is divisible by 13.

For example, Number 1638 is divisible by 13 because $163 + 4 \times 8 = 195 = 15 \times 13$ is divisible by 13.

Principle of Inclusion and Exclusion

1. If A and B are finite sets, from the Venn diagram (i), it is clear that

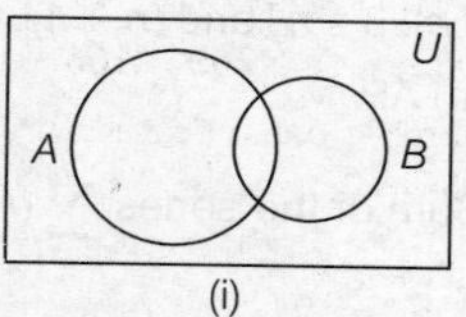

(i)

$$n(A \cup B) = n(A) + n(B) - n(A \cap B)$$
and $n(A' \cap B') = n(U) - n(A \cup B)$

2. If A, B and C are three finite sets, then from the Venn diagram (ii), it is clear that

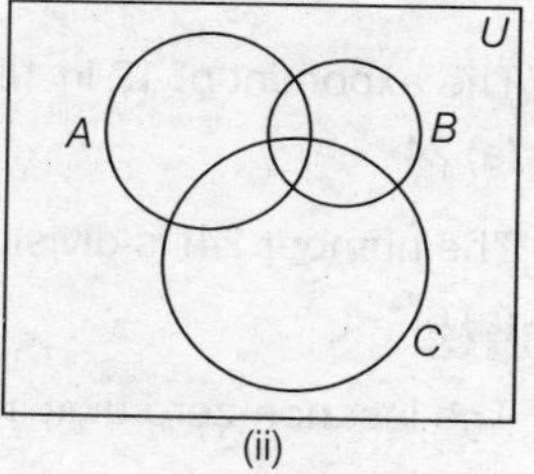

(ii)

$$n(A \cup B \cup C) = n(A) + n(B) + n(C) - n(A \cap B) - n(B \cap C) - n(C \cap A) + n(A \cap B \cap C)$$
and $n(A' \cap B' \cap C') = n(U) - n(A \cup B \cup C)$

Note If $A_1, A_2, A_3, \ldots, A_n$ are finite sets, then

$$n(A_1 \cup A_2 \cup \ldots \cup A_n) = \Sigma n(A_i) - \Sigma n(A_i \cap A_j) + \Sigma n(A_i \cap A_j \cap A_k) - \ldots + (-1)^n \Sigma n(A_1 \cap A_2 \cap \ldots \cap A_n)$$

and $n(A'_1 \cap A'_2 \cap \ldots \cap A'_n) = n(U) - n(A_1 \cup A_2 \cup \ldots \cup A_n)$.

Example 13. Find the number of positive integers from 1 to 1000, which are divisible by atleast 2, 3 or 5.

Sol. Let A_k be the set of positive integers from 1 to 1000, which is divisible by k. Obviously, we have to find $n(A_2 \cup A_3 \cup A_5)$. If $[\cdot]$ denotes the greatest integer function, then

$$n(A_2) = \left[\frac{1000}{2}\right] = [500] = 500$$

$$n(A_3) = \left[\frac{1000}{3}\right] = [333.33] = 333$$

$$n(A_5)=\left[\frac{1000}{5}\right]=[200]=200$$
$$n(A_2\cap A_3)=\left[\frac{1000}{6}\right]=[166.67]=166$$
$$n(A_3\cap A_5)=\left[\frac{1000}{15}\right]=[66.67]=66$$
$$n(A_2\cap A_5)=\left[\frac{1000}{10}\right]=[100]=100$$
and $n(A_2\cap A_3\cap A_5)=\left[\frac{1000}{30}\right]=[33.33]=33$

From Principle of Inclusion and Exclusion
$$n(A_2\cup A_3\cup A_5)=n(A_2)+n(A_3)+n(A_5)-n(A_2\cap A_3)$$
$$-n(A_3\cap A_5)-n(A_2\cap A_5)+n(A_2\cap A_3\cap A_5)$$
$$=500+333+200-166-66-100+33=734$$

Hence, the number of positive integers from 1 to 1000, which are divisible by atleast 2, 3 or 5 is 734.

Note

The number of positive integers from 1 to 1000, which are not divisible by 2, 3 or 5 is $n(A'_2\cap A'_3\cap A'_5)$.

$\therefore n(A'_2\cap A'_3\cap A'_5)=n(U)-n(A_2\cup A_3\cup A_5)$ [here, $n(U)=1000$]
$=1000-734=266$

Permutation

Each of the different arrangements which can be made by taking some or all of a number of things is called a permutation. In permutation, order of the arrangement is important.

Important Results

1. The number of permutations of n different things, taking r at a time is denoted by ^nP_r or $P(n,r)$ or $A(n,r)$, then

$$^nP_r=n(n-1)(n-2)\dots(n-r+1)$$
$$=\frac{n!}{(n-r)!}$$

where, $n\in N$, $r\in W$ and $0\le r\le n$.

Proof LHS $=\,^nP_r=$ Number of ways of filling up r vacant places simultaneously from n different things

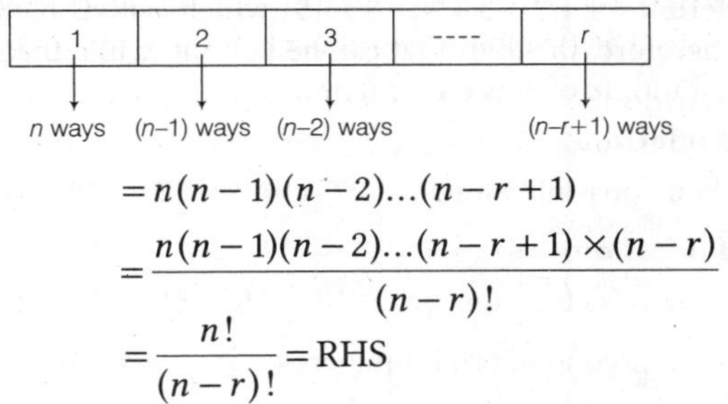

$$=n(n-1)(n-2)\dots(n-r+1)$$
$$=\frac{n(n-1)(n-2)\dots(n-r+1)\times(n-r)}{(n-r)!}$$
$$=\frac{n!}{(n-r)!}=\text{RHS}$$

Note

(i) The number of permutations of n different things taken all at a time $=\,^nP_n=n!$

(ii) $^nP_0=1$, $^nP_1=n$ and $^nP_{n-1}=\,^nP_n=n!$

(iii) $^nP_r=n(^{n-1}P_{r-1})=n(n-1)(^{n-2}P_{r-2})$
$=n(n-1)(n-2)(^{n-3}P_{r-3})=\dots$

(iv) $^{n-1}P_r=(n-r)\,^{n-1}P_{r-1}$

(v) $\frac{^nP_r}{^nP_{r-1}}=(n-r+1)$

Example 14. If $^{56}P_{r+6}:\,^{54}P_{r+3}=30800:1$, find $^rP_2$.

Sol. We have, $\frac{^{56}P_{r+6}}{^{54}P_{r+3}}=\frac{30800}{1}$

$\Rightarrow\ (56)(55)\frac{^{54}P_{r+4}}{^{54}P_{r+3}}=\frac{30800}{1}$ [from note (iii)]

$\Rightarrow\ \frac{^{54}P_{r+4}}{^{54}P_{r+3}}=10$

$\Rightarrow\ 54-(r+4)+1=10$ [from note (v)]

$r=41$

$\therefore\ ^rP_2=\,^{41}P_2=41\cdot40=1640$

Example 15. If $^{n+5}P_{n+1}=\frac{11(n-1)}{2}\cdot\,^{n+3}P_n$, find n.

Sol. We have, $\frac{^{n+5}P_{n+1}}{^{n+3}P_n}=\frac{11(n-1)}{2}$

$\Rightarrow\ \frac{(n+5)(n+4)\cdot\,^{n+3}P_{n-1}}{^{n+3}P_n}=\frac{11(n-1)}{2}$ [from note (iii)]

$\frac{(n+5)(n+4)}{(n+3-n+1)}=\frac{11(n-1)}{2}$ [from note (v)]

$\Rightarrow\ (n+5)(n+4)=22(n-1)$

$\Rightarrow\ n^2-13n+42=0$

$\Rightarrow\ (n-6)(n-7)=0$

$\therefore\ n=6,7$

Example 16. If $^{m+n}P_2=90$ and $^{m-n}P_2=30$, find the values of m and n.

Sol. $\because\ ^{m+n}P_2=90=10\times9=\,^{10}P_2$

$\therefore\ m+n=10$ ...(i)

and $^{m-n}P_2=30=6\times5=\,^6P_2$

$\therefore\ m-n=6$ ...(ii)

From Eqs. (i) and (ii), we get

$m=8$ and $n=2$.

Example 17. Find the value of r, if

(i) ${}^{11}P_r = 990$

(ii) ${}^8P_5 + 5\cdot{}^8P_4 = {}^9P_r$

(iii) ${}^{22}P_{r+1} : {}^{20}P_{r+2} = 11:52$

Sol. (i) $\because {}^{11}P_r = 990 = 11\times10\times9 = {}^{11}P_3$

$\therefore\ r = 3$

(ii) $\because\ {}^8P_5 + 5\cdot{}^8P_4 = {}^9P_r$

$$\Rightarrow {}^8P_4\left(\frac{{}^8P_5}{{}^8P_4} + 5\right) = {}^9P_r$$

$$\Rightarrow {}^8P_4(8-5+1+5) = {}^9P_r \quad \text{[from note (v)]}$$

$$\Rightarrow 9\cdot{}^8P_4 = {}^9P_r$$

$$\Rightarrow {}^9P_5 = {}^9P_r \quad \text{[from note (iii)]}$$

$$\therefore r = 5$$

(iii) $\because\ {}^{22}P_{r+1} : {}^{20}P_{r+2} = 11:52$

$$\Rightarrow \frac{{}^{22}P_{r+1}}{{}^{20}P_{r+2}} = \frac{11}{52}$$

$$\Rightarrow \frac{22\cdot21\cdot{}^{20}P_{r-1}}{(19-r)\cdot(20-r)\cdot(21-r)\cdot{}^{20}P_{r-1}} = \frac{11}{52}$$

[from note (iii) and (iv)]

$$\Rightarrow (21-r)\cdot(20-r)\cdot(19-r) = 52\times2\times21 = 14\times13\times12$$

$$\therefore r = 7$$

Example 18. Prove that ${}^1P_1 + 2\cdot{}^2P_2 + 3\cdot{}^3P_3 + \ldots + n\cdot{}^nP_n = {}^{n+1}P_{n+1} - 1.$

Sol. LHS $= {}^1P_1 + 2\cdot{}^2P_2 + 3\cdot{}^3P_3 + \ldots + n\cdot{}^nP_n$

$$= \sum_{r=1}^{n} r\cdot{}^rP_r = \sum_{r=1}^{n}\{(r+1)-1)\}\cdot{}^rP_r$$

$$= \sum_{r=1}^{n}\{(r+1)\cdot{}^rP_r - {}^rP_r)\}$$

$$= \sum_{r=1}^{n}({}^{r+1}P_{r+1} - {}^rP_r) \quad \text{[from note (iii)]}$$

$$= {}^{n+1}P_{n+1} - {}^1P_1 = {}^{n+1}P_{n+1} - 1$$

= RHS

Example 19. Determine the number of permutations of the letters of the word 'SIMPLETON' taken all at a time.

Sol. There are 9 letters in the word 'SIMPLETON' and all the 9 letters are different. Hence, the number of permutations taking all the letters at a time

$$= {}^9P_9 = 9! = 362880$$

Note Total number of letters in English alphabet = 26

(i) Number of vowels = 5
i.e., A, E, I, O, U [strong vowels]

(ii) *W* and *Y* an half vowels. [weak vowels]

(iii) Number of consonants = 21 [except vowels]
i.e., B, C, D, F, G, ..., Y, Z

(iv) Words which contains all vowels are
EDUCATION, EQUATION, ...

(iv) Words which do not contains any vowels are
SKY, FLY, TRY, ...

Example 20. How many different signals can be given using any number of flags from 4 flags of different colours?

Sol. The signals can be made by using one or more flags at a time. Hence, by the fundamental principle of addition, the total number of signals

$$= {}^4P_1 + {}^4P_2 + {}^4P_3 + {}^4P_4$$

$$= 4 + (4\times3) + (4\times3\times2) + (4\times3\times2\times1)$$

$$= 4 + 12 + 24 + 24 = 64$$

Example 21. Find the total number of 9-digit numbers which have all different digits.

Sol. Number of digits are 10 (0, 1, 2, 3, 4, 5, 6, 7, 8, 9)

Total number of 9-digit numbers $= {}^{10}P_9$

Out of these, the number of numbers having zero at the first place $= {}^9P_8$.

Hence, required number of numbers $= {}^{10}P_9 - {}^9P_8$

$$= 10\times{}^9P_8 - {}^9P_8 = 9\times{}^9P_8$$

$$= 9\times\frac{9!}{1!} = 9\times9!$$

Note Total number of n digit numbers $(1\le n\le 10)$, which have all different digits $= {}^{10}P_n - {}^9P_{n-1}$

Example 22. A 5-digit number divisible by 3 is to be formed using the numbers 0, 1, 2, 3, 4 and 5 without repetition. Find total number of ways in which this can be done.

Sol. A number will be divisible by 3, if sum of the digits in number be divisible by 3.

Here, $0+1+2+3+4+5 = 15$, which is divisible by 3. Therefore, the digit that can be left out, while the sum still is multiple of 3, is either 0 or 3.

If 0 left out

Then, possible numbers $= {}^5P_5 = 5! = 120$

If 3 left out

Then, possible numbers $= {}^5P_5 - {}^4P_4 = 5! - 4! = 120 - 24 = 96$

Hence, required total numbers $= 120 + 96 = 216$

Example 23. A 5-digit number is formed by the digits 1, 2, 3, 4, 5 without repetition. Find the number of the numbers, thus formed divisible by 4.

Sol. Let a 5-digit number be *abcde*.

It will be divisible by 4, if $2d + e$ is divisible by 4.

$\Rightarrow \quad \underbrace{2d + e}_{\text{Even}}$ is divisible by 4 $\quad \therefore$ *e* must be even.

$\Rightarrow \quad \underbrace{2\left(d + \frac{e}{2}\right)}_{\text{Should be even}}$ is divisible by 4

Then, $e = 2, d = 1, 3, 5$ and $e = 4, d = 2$ } Total four cases

$\therefore$ Required number of ways $= 4 \times \underbrace{3!}_{\text{Number of ways}} = 24$

filling *abc* after filling *de*.

Aliter A number will be divisible by 4, if the last two digits of the number is divisible by 4, then for divisible by 4, last two digits 12 or 24 or 32 or 52

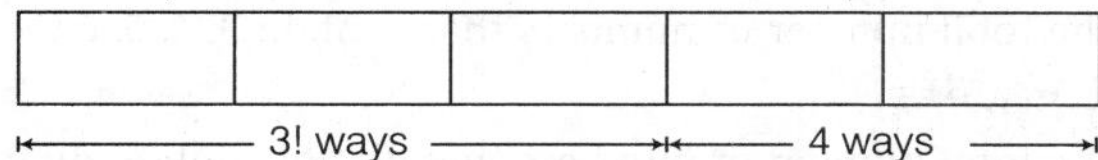

Hence, the number formed is divisible by $4 = 3! \times 4 = 24$.

Example 24. Find the number of permutations of letters *a b c d e f g* taken all together if neither *'beg'* nor *'cad'* pattern appear.

Sol. The total number of permutations without any restriction is 7!

$$n(U) = 7! = 5040$$

Let $n(A)$ be the number of permutations in which *'beg'* pattern always appears

$$b\,e\,g\,a\,c\,d\,f$$

i.e., $\quad n(A) = 5! = 120$

and let $n(B)$ be the number of permutations in which *'cad'* pattern always appears

$$c\,a\,d\,b\,e\,f\,g$$

i.e., $\quad n(B) = 5! = 120$

Now, $n(A \cap B) =$ Number of permutations in which *'beg'* and *'cad'* pattern appear

$$b\,e\,g\,c\,a\,d\,f$$

i.e., $\quad n(A \cap B) = 3! = 6$

Hence, the number of permutations in which *'beg'* and *'cad'* patterns do not appear is $n(A' \cap B')$.

or $\quad n(A' \cap B') = n(U) - n(A \cup B)$

$$= n(U) - [n(A) + n(B) - n(A \cap B)]$$

$$= 5040 - 120 - 120 + 6 = 4806$$

2. The number of permutations of n things taken all at a time, p are alike of one kind, q are alike of second kind and r are alike of a third kind and the rest $n - (p + q + r)$ are all different is $\dfrac{n!}{p!\,q!\,r!}$

Proof Let the required number of permutations be x. Since, p different things can be arranged among themselves in $p!$ ways, therefore if we replace p identical things by p different things, which are also different from the rest of things, the number of permutations will become $x \times p!$

Again, if we replace q identical things by q different things, the number of permutations will become $(x \times p!) \times q!$

Again, if we replace r identical things by r different things, the number of permutations will become $(x \times p! \times q!) \times r!$. Now, all the n things are different and therefore, number of permutations should be $n!$.

Thus, $x \times p! \times q! \times r! = n!$

$$\therefore \quad x = \frac{n!}{p!\,q!\,r!}$$

Remark

The above theorem can be extended further i.e. if there are n things taken all at a time, p_1 are alike of one kind, p_2 are alike of second kind, p_3 are alike of third kind, ..., p_r are alike of rth kind such that $p_1 + p_2 + p_3 + \dots + p_r = n$, the number of permutations of these n things is $\dfrac{n!}{p_1!\,p_2!\,p_3! \dots p_r!}$.

Example 25. How many words can be formed with the letters of the word 'ARIHANT' by rearranging them?

Sol. Here, total letters 7, in which 2A's but the rest are different. Hence, the number of words formed $= \dfrac{7!}{2!} = 2520$

Example 26. Find the number of permutations of the letters of the words 'DADDY DID A DEADLY DEED'.

Sol. Here, total letters 19, in which 9D's, 3A's, 2Y's, 3E's and rest occur only once.

$\therefore$ Required number of permutations $= \dfrac{19!}{9! \times 3! \times 2! \times 3!}$

Example 27. How many words can be formed with the letters of the words

(i) HIGH SCHOOL and

(ii) INTERMEDIATE by rearranging them?

Sol. (i) Here, total letters are 10, in which 3H's and 2O's, but the rest are different. Hence, the number of words formed $= \dfrac{10!}{3!\,2!}$

(ii) Here, total letters are 12, in which 2I's, 2T's and 3E's but the rest are different. Hence, the number of words formed $= \dfrac{12!}{2!\,2!\,3!}$

Note [For Remember]

High School = 10 th class = Total number of letters are 10

Intermediate = 12 th class = Total number of letters are 12

3. The number of permutations of n different things taken r at a time when each thing may be repeated any number of times is n^r.

Proof Since, the number of permutations of n different things taken r at a time = Number of ways in which r blank places can be filled by n different things.

Clearly, the first place can be filled in n ways. Since, each thing may be repeated, the second place can be filled in n ways. Similarly, each of the 3rd, 4th,..., rth place can be filled in n ways.

By multiplication principle, the number of permutations of n different things taken r at a time when each thing may be repeated any number of times

$$= n \times n \times n \times \ldots \times r \text{ factors}$$

$$= n^r$$

Corollary When $r = n$

i.e., the number of permutations of n different things, taken all at a time, when each thing may be repeated any number of times in each arrangements is n^n.

Example 28. A child has four pockets and three marbles. In how many ways can the child put the marbles in its pockets?

Sol. The first marble can be put into the pocket in 4 ways, so can the second. Thus, the number of ways in which the child can put the marbles $= 4 \times 4 \times 4 = 4^3 = 64$ ways

Example 29. There are m men and n monkeys $(n > m)$. If a man have any number of monkeys. In how many ways may every monkey have a master?

Sol. The first monkey can select his master by m ways and after that the second monkey can select his master again by m ways, so can the third and so on.

All monkeys can select master $= m \times m \times m \ldots$ upto n factors $= (m)^n$ ways

Example 30. How many four digit numbers can be formed by using the digits 1, 2, 3, 4, 5, 6, 7, if atleast one digit is repeated ?

Sol. The numbers that can be formed when repetition of digits is allowed are $7^4 = 2401$.

The numbers that can be formed when all the digits are distinct when repetition is not allowed are ${}^7P_4 = 840$.

Therefore, the numbers that can be formed when atleast one digit is repeated $= 7^4 - {}^7P_4$

$$= 2401 - 840 = 1561$$

Example 31. In how many ways can 4 prizes be distribute among 5 students, if no student gets all the prizes?

Sol. The number of ways in which the 4 prizes can be given away to the 5 students, if a student can get any number of prizes $= 5^4 = 625$.

Again, the number of ways in which a student gets all the 4 prizes = 5, since there are 5 students and any one of them may get all the four prizes.

Therefore, the required number of ways in which a student does not get all the prizes $= 625 - 5 = 620$.

Example 32. Find the number of n-digit numbers, which contain the digits 2 and 7, but not the digits 0, 1, 8, 9.

Sol. The total number without any restrictions containing digit 2, 3, 4, 5, 6, 7 is $n(U) = 6^n$.

The total number of numbers that contain 3, 4, 5, 6, 7 is $n(A) = 5^n$.

The total number of numbers that contain 2, 3, 4, 5, 6 is $n(B) = 5^n$.

The total number of numbers that contain 3, 4, 5, 6 is $n(A \cap B) = 4^n$.

The total number of numbers that do not contain digits 2 and 7 is $n(A \cup B)$

i.e., $n(A \cup B) = n(A) + n(B) - n(A \cap B)$

$$= 5^n + 5^n - 4^n = 2(5^n) - 4^n$$

Hence, the total number of numbers that contain 2 and 7 is $n(A' \cap B')$

$$\therefore \quad n(A' \cap B') = n(U) - n(A \cup B) = 6^n - 2 \cdot (5^n) + 4^n$$

Example 33. Show that the total number of permutations of n different things taken not more than r at a time, when each thing may be repeated any number of times is $\dfrac{n(n^r - 1)}{(n-1)}$.

Sol. Given, total different things $= n$

The number of permutations of n things taken one at a time $= {}^nP_1 = n$, now if we taken two at a time (repetition is allowed), then first place can be filled by n ways and second place can again be filled in n ways.

$\therefore$ The number of permutations of n things taken two at a time

$$= {}^nP_1 \times {}^nP_1 = n \times n = n^2$$

Similarly, the number of permutations of n things taken three at a time $= n^3$

$$\vdots \quad \vdots \quad \vdots \quad \vdots \quad \vdots$$

The number of permutations of n things taken r at a time $= n^r$. Hence, the total number of permutations

$$= n + n^2 + n^3 + \ldots + n^r$$

$$= \frac{n(n^r - 1)}{(n-1)} \qquad \text{[sum of } r \text{ terms of a GP]}$$

Exercise for Session 2

1. If ${}^nP_5 = 20 \cdot {}^nP_3$, then n equals

(a) 4 (b) 8 (c) 6 (d) 7

2. If ${}^9P_5 + 5 \cdot {}^9P_4 = {}^nP_r$, then $n + r$ equals

(a) 13 (b) 14 (c) 15 (d) 16

3. If ${}^{m+n}P_2 = 56$ and ${}^{m-n}P_3 = 24$, then $\dfrac{{}^mP_3}{{}^nP_2}$ equals

(a) 20 (b) 40 (c) 60 (d) 80

4. If ${}^{2n+1}P_{n-1} : {}^{2n-1}P_n = 7 : 10$, then ${}^nP_3$ equals

(a) 60 (b) 24 (c) 120 (d) 6

5. In a train, five seats are vacant, the number of ways three passengers can sit, is

(a) 10 (b) 20 (c) 30 (d) 60

6. If a denotes the number of permutations of $x + 2$ things taken all at a time, b the number of permutations of x things taken 11 at a time and c the number of permutations of $(x - 11)$ things taken all at a time such that $a = 182\,bc$, the value of x is

(a) 10 (b) 12 (c) 15 (d) 18

7. The number of nine non-zero digits such that all the digits in the first four places are less than the digit in the middle and all the digits in the last four places are greater than that in the middle, is

(a) 48 (b) 7560 (c) 10080 (d) 576

8. Total number of words that can be formed using all letters of the word 'DIPESH' that neither begins with 'I' nor ends with 'D' is equal to

(a) 504 (b) 480 (c) 624 (d) 696

9. The number of all five digit numbers which are divisible by 4 that can be formed from the digits 0, 1, 2, 3, 4 (without repetition), is

(a) 36 (b) 30 (c) 34 (d) None of these

10. The number of words can be formed with the letters of the word 'MATHEMATICS' by rearranging them, is

(a) $\dfrac{11!}{2!\,2!}$ (b) $\dfrac{11!}{2!}$ (c) $\dfrac{11!}{2!\,2!\,2!}$ (d) 11!

11. Six identical coins are arranged in a row. The number of ways in which the number of tails is equal to the number of heads, is

(a) 9 (b) 20 (c) 40 (d) 120

12. A train time table must be compiled for various days of the week so that two trains twice a day depart for three days, one train daily for two days and three trains once a day for two days. How many different time tables can be compiled?

(a) 140 (b) 210 (c) 133 (d) 72

13. Five persons entered the lift cabin on the ground floor of an 8 floor house. Suppose each of them can leave the cabin independently at any floor beginning with the first. The total number of ways in which each of the five persons can leave the cabin at any one of the floor, is

(a) 5^7 (b) 7^5 (c) 35 (d) 2520

14. Four die are rolled. The number of ways in which atleast one die shows 3, is

(a) 625 (b) 671 (c) 1256 (d) 1296

15. The number of 4-digit numbers that can be made with the digits 1, 2, 3, 4 and 5 in which atleast two digits are identical, is

(a) $4^5 - 5!$ (b) 505 (c) 600 (d) 120

16. There are unlimited number of identical balls of three different colours. How many arrangements of atmost 7 balls in a row can be made by using them?

(a) 2187 (b) 343 (c) 399 (d) 3279

Session 3

Number of Permutations Under Certain Conditions, Circular Permutations, Restricted Circular Permutations

Number of Permutations Under Certain Conditions

(i) Number of permutations of n different things, taken r at a time, when a particular thing is to be always included in each arrangement, is $r \cdot {}^{n-1}P_{r-1}$

Corollary Number of permutations of n different things, taken r at a time, when p particular things is to be always included in each arrangement, is

$$p!\,(r-(p-1))\,{}^{n-p}P_{r-p}.$$

(ii) Number of permutations of n different things, taken r at a time, when a particular thing is never taken in each arrangement, is

$${}^{n-1}P_r.$$

(iii) Number of permutations of n different things, taken all at a time, when m specified things always come together, is

$$m!\times(n-m+1)!$$

(iv) Number of permutations of n different things, taken all at a time, when m specified things never come together, is

$$n!-m!\times(n-m+1)!$$

| Example 34. How many permutations can be made out of the letters of the word 'TRIANGLE'? How many of these will begin with T and end with E?

Sol. The word 'TRIANGLE' has eight different letters, which can be arranged themselves in 8! ways.

$\therefore$ Total number of permutations $= 8! = 40320$

Again, when T is fixed at the first place and E at the last place, the remaining six can be arranged themselves in $6!$ ways.

$\therefore$ The number of permutations which begin with T and end with

$$E = 6! = 720.$$

| Example 35. In how many ways can the letters of the word 'INSURANCE' be arranged, so that the vowels are never separate?

Sol. The word 'INSURANCE' has nine different letters, combine the vowels into one bracket as (IUAE) and treating them as one letter we have six letters viz.

(IUAE) N S R N C and these can be arranged among themselves in $\dfrac{6!}{2!}$ ways and four vowels within the bracket can be arranged themselves in $4!$ ways.

$\therefore$ Required number of words $= \dfrac{6!}{2!}\times 4! = 8640$

| Example 36. How many words can be formed with the letters of the word 'PATALIPUTRA' without changing the relative positions of vowels and consonants?

Sol. The word 'PATALIPUTRA' has eleven letters, in which 2P's, 3A's, 2T's, 1L, 1U, 1R and 1I. Vowels are AAIUA

These vowels can be arranged themselves in $\dfrac{5!}{3!} = 20$ ways.

The consonants are PTLPTR these consonants can be arranged themselves in $\dfrac{6!}{2!\,2!} = 180$ ways

$\therefore$ Required number of words

$$= 20\times 180 = 3600 \text{ ways.}$$

| Example 37. Find the number of permutations that can be had from the letters of the word 'OMEGA'

(i) O and A occuping end places.

(ii) E being always in the middle.

(iii) Vowels occuping odd places.

(iv) Vowels being never together.

Sol. There are five letters in the word 'OMEGA'.

(i) When O and A occuping end places

i.e., M E G (OA)

the first three letters (M, E, G) can be arranged themselves by $3! = 6$ ways and last two letters (O, A) can be arranged themselves by $2! = 2$ ways.

$\therefore$ Total number of such words

$$= 6\times 2 = 12 \text{ ways.}$$

(ii) When E is the fixed in the middle, then there are four places left to be filled by four remaining letters O, M, G and A and this can be done in 4 ! ways.

$\therefore$ Total number of such words = 4 ! = 24 ways.

(iii) Three vowels (O, E, A) can be arranged in the odd places in 3 ! ways (1st, 3rd and 5th) and the two consonants (M, G) can be arranged in the even places in 2 ! ways (2nd and 4th)

$\therefore$ Total number of such words

$$= 3! \times 2! = 12 \text{ ways.}$$

(iv) Total number of words = 5 ! = 120

Combine the vowels into one bracket as (OEA) and treating them as one letter, we have

(OEA), M, G and these can be arranged themselves in 3 ! ways and three vowels with in the bracket can be arranged themselves in 3 ! ways.

$\therefore$ Number of ways when vowels come together

$$= 3! \times 3! = 36 \text{ ways.}$$

Hence, number of ways when vowels being never together = 120 − 36 = 84 ways.

Circular Permutations

(i) Arrangements round a circular table

Consider five persons *A*, *B*, *C*, *D* and *E* on the circumference of a circular table in order which has no head now, shifting *A*, *B*, *C*, *D* and E one position in anti-clockwise direction we will get arragements as follows

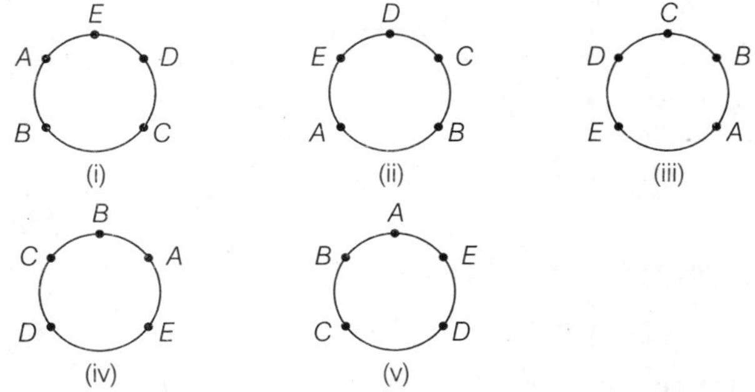

We see that, if 5 persons are sitting at a round table, they can be shifted five times and five different arrangements. Thus, obtained will be the same, because anti-clockwise order of *A*, *B*, *C*, *D* and *E* does not change.

But if *A*, *B*, *C*, *D* and *E* are sitting in a row and they are shifted in such an order that the last occupies the place of first, then the five arrangements will be different. Thus, if there are 5 things, then for each circular arrangement number of linear arrangements is 5.

Similarly, if *n* different things are arranged along a circle for each circular arrangement number of linear arrangements is *n*.

Therefore, the number of linear arrangements of *n* different things = $n \times$ number of circular arrangements of *n* different things

(ii) Arrangements of beads or flowers (all different) around a circular necklace or garland

Consider five beads *A*, *B*, *C*, *D* and *E* in a necklace or five flowers *A*, *B*, *C*, *D* and *E* in a garland, etc. If the necklace or garland on the left is turned over, we obtain the arrangement on the right i.e. anti-clockwise and clockwise order of arrangement is not different we will get arrangements as follows:

We see that arrangements in figures are not different.

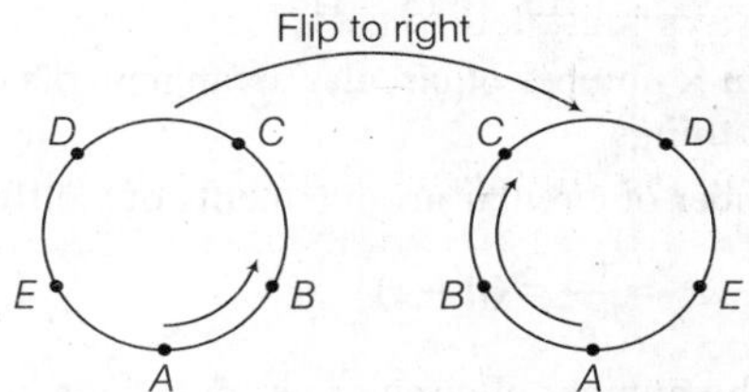

Then, the number of circular permutations of *n* different things taken all at a time is $\frac{1}{2}(n-1)!$, if clockwise and anti-clockwise orders are taken as not different.

Example 38. Find the number of ways in which 12 different beads can be arranged to form a necklace.

Sol. 12 different beads can be arranged among themselves in a circular order in $(12-1)! = 11!$ ways. Now, in the case of necklace, there is no distinction between clockwise and anti-clockwise arrangements. So, the required number of arrangements $= \frac{1}{2}(11!)$.

Example 39. Consider 21 different pearls on a necklace. How many ways can the pearls be placed in on this necklace such that 3 specific pearls always remain together?

Sol. After fixing the places of three pearls, treating 3 specific pearls = 1 unit. So, we have now

18 pearls + 1 unit = 19 and the number of arrangement will be $(19-1)! = 18!$

Also, the number of ways of 3 pearls can be arranged between themselves is $3! = 6$.

Since, there is no distinction between the clockwise and anti-clockwise arrangements.

So, the required number of arrangements $= \frac{1}{2} 18! \cdot 6 = 3(18!)$.

Restricted Circular Permutations

***Case* I** If clockwise and anti-clockwise orders are taken as different, then the number of circular permutations of n different things taken r at a time.

$$=\frac{{}^nP_r}{r}=\frac{1}{r}\cdot\frac{n!}{(n-r)!}$$

Note For checking correctness of formula, put $r = n$, then we get $(n-1)!$ [result (5) (i)]

Example 40. In how many ways can 24 persons be seated round a table, if there are 13 sets ?

Sol. In case of circular table, the clockwise and anti-clockwise orders are different, the required number of circular permutations $=\frac{{}^{24}P_{13}}{13}=\frac{24!}{13\times 11!}$

$\Rightarrow n! = n \times$ number of circular arrangements of n different things

$\Rightarrow$ Number of circular arrangements of n different things

$$=\frac{n!}{n}=(n-1)!$$

Hence, the number of circular permutations of n different things taken all at a time is $(n-1)!$, if clockwise and anti-clockwise orders are taken as different.

Example 41. Find the number of ways in which three Americans, two British, one Chinese, one Dutch and one Egyptian can sit on a round table so that persons of the same nationality are separated.

Sol. The total number of persons without any restrictions is

$$n(U)=(8-1)!$$
$$=7!=5040$$

When, three Americans (A_1, A_2, A_3) are sit together,

$$n(A)=5!\times 3!$$
$$=720$$

When, two British (B_1, B_2) are sit together

$$n(B)=6!\times 2!$$
$$=1440$$

When, three Americans (A_1, A_2, A_3) and two British (B_1, B_2) are sit together $n(A \cap B) = 4! \times 3! \times 2! = 288$

$$\therefore \quad n(A\cup B)=n(A)+nB)-n(A\cap B)$$
$$=720+1440-288=1872$$

Hence, $\quad n(A\cap B')=n(U)-n(A\cup B)$

$$=5040-1872$$
$$=3168$$

Example 42. In how many different ways can five boys and five girls form a circle such that the boys and girls alternate?

Sol. After fixing up one boy on the table, the remaining can be arranged in 4 ! ways but boys and girls are to alternate. There will be 5 places, one place each between two boys these five places can be filled by 5 girls in 5 ! ways.

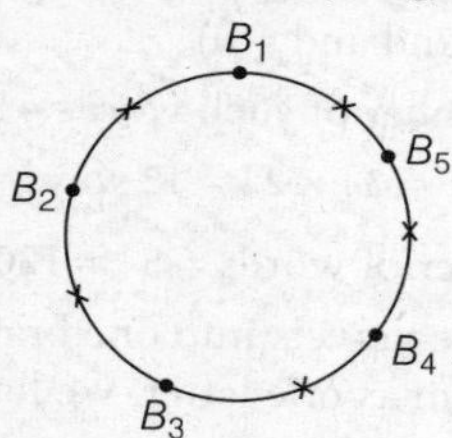

Hence, by the principle of multiplication, the required number of ways $= 4! \times 5! = 2880$.

Example 43. 20 persons were invited to a party. In how many ways can they and the host be seated at a circular table ? In how many of these ways will two particular persons be seated on either side of the host?

Sol. **I Part** Total persons on the circular table

$$= 20 \text{ guest} + 1 \text{ host} = 21$$

They can be seated in $(21-1)! = 20!$ ways.

II Part After fixing the places of three persons (1 host + 2 persons).

Treating (1 host + 2 persons) = 1 unit, so we have now {(remaining 18 persons + 1 unit) = 19} and the number of arrangement will be $(19-1)! = 18!$ also these two particular persons can be seated on either side of the host in $2!$ ways.

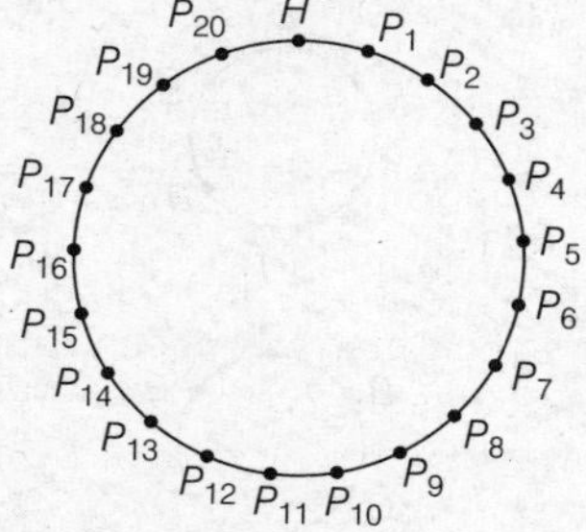

Hence, the number of ways of seating 21 persons on the circular table such that two particular persons be seated on either side of the host $= 18! \times 2! = 2 \times 18!$

***Case* II** If clockwise and anti-clockwise orders are taken as not different, then the number of circular permutations of n different things taken r at a time $=\frac{{}^nP_r}{2r}=\frac{1}{2r}\cdot\frac{n!}{(n-r)!}$

Note

For checking correctness of formula put $r = n$, then we get $\frac{(n-1)!}{2}$ [result (5) (ii)]

Example 44. How many necklace of 12 beads each can be made from 18 beads of various colours?

Sol. In the case of necklace, there is no distinction between the clockwise and anti-clockwise arrangements, the required number of circular permutations.

$$= \frac{{}^{18}P_{12}}{2 \times 12} = \frac{18!}{6! \times 24} = \frac{18 \times 17 \times 16 \times 15 \times 14 \times 13!}{6 \times 5 \times 4 \times 3 \times 2 \times 1 \times 24} = \frac{119 \times 13!}{2}$$

Exercise for Session 3

1. How many words can be formed from the letters of the word 'COURTESY' whose first letter is C and the last letter is Y ?

(a) 6! (b) 8! (c) 2(6)! (d) 2(7)!

2. The number of words that can be made by writing down the letters of the word 'CALCULATE' such that each word starts and ends with a consonant, is

(a) $\frac{3}{2}$ (7)! (b) 2(7)! (c) $\frac{5}{2}$ (7)! (d) 3(7)!

3. The number of words can be formed from the letters of the word 'MAXIMUM', if two consonants cannot occur together, is

(a) 4! (b) 3!× 4!

(c) 3! (d) $\frac{4!}{3!}$

4. All the letters of the word 'EAMCET' are arranged in all possible ways. The number of such arrangements in which two vowels are not adjacent to each other, is

(a) 54 (b) 72

(c) 114 (d) 360

5. How many words can be made from the letters of the word 'DELHI', if L comes in the middle in every word?

(a) 6 (b) 12 (c) 24 (d) 60

6. In how many ways can 5 boys and 3 girls sit in a row so that no two girls are sit together?

(a) 5!× 3! (b) ${}^4P_3 \times 5!$ (c) ${}^6P_3 \times 5!$ (d) ${}^5P_3 \times 3!$

7. There are n numbered seats around a round table. Total number of ways in which n_1 $(n_1 < n)$ persons can sit around the round table, is equal to

(a) ${}^nC_{n_1}$ (b) ${}^nP_{n_1}$ (c) ${}^nC_{n_1-1}$ (d) ${}^nP_{n_1-1}$

8. In how many ways can 7 men and 7 women can be seated around a round table such that no two women can sit together?

(a) 7! (b) 7!× 6! (c) $(6!)^2$ (d) $(7!)^2$

9. The number of ways that 8 beads of different colours be string as a necklace, is

(a) 2520 (b) 2880 (c) 4320 (d) 5040

10. If 11 members of a committee sit at a round table so that the President and secretary always sit together, then the number of arrangements, is

(a) 9! × 2 (b) 10! (c) 10!× 2 (d) 11!

11. In how many ways can 15 members of a council sit along a circular table, when the secretary is to sit on one side of the Chairman and the deputy secretary on the other side?

(a) 12!× 2 (b) 24 (c) 15!× 2 (d) 30

Session 4

Combination, Restricted Combinations

Combination

Each of the different groups or selections which can be made by some or all of a number of given things without reference to the order of the things in each group is called a combination.

Important Result

(1) The number of combinations of n different things taken r at a time is denoted by ^nC_r or $C(n, r)$ or $\binom{n}{r}$.

Then,

$$^nC_r = \frac{n!}{r!(n-r)!} \quad [0 \le r \le n]$$

$$= \frac{^nP_r}{r!}$$

$$= \frac{n(n-1)(n-2)\dots(n-r+1)}{r(r-1)(r-2)\dots 2\cdot 1}, n \in N \text{ and } r \in W$$

Proof Let the number of combinations of n different things taken r at a time be ^nC_r.

Now, each combination consists of r different things and these r things can be arranged among themselves in $r!$ ways.

Thus, for one combination of r different things, the number of arrangements is $r!$.

Hence, for ^nC_r combinations, number of arrangements is

$$r! \times {^nC_r} \quad \dots\text{(i)}$$

But number of permutations of n different things taken r at a time is ^nP_r. ...(ii)

From Eqs. (i) and (ii), we get

$$r! \times {^nC_r} = {^nP_r} = \frac{n!}{(n-r)!}$$

$$\therefore \quad ^nC_r = \frac{n!}{r!(n-r)!}, r \in W \text{ and } n \in N$$

Note the following facts:

(i) ^nC_r is a natural number

(ii) $^nC_r = 0$, if $r > n$

(iii) $^nC_0 = {^nC_n} = 1$, $^nC_1 = n$

(iv) $^nP_r = {^nC_r}$, if $r = 0$ or 1

(v) $^nC_r = {^nC_{n-r}}$, if $r > \frac{n}{2}$

(vi) If $^nC_x = {^nC_y} \Rightarrow x = y$ or $x + y = n$

(vii) $^nC_r + {^nC_{r-1}} = {^{n+1}C_r}$ [Pascal's rule]

(viii) $^nC_r = \frac{n}{r} \cdot {^{n-1}C_{r-1}}$

(ix) $n \cdot {^{n-1}C_{r-1}} = (n-r+1) \cdot {^nC_{r-1}}$

(x) $\frac{^nC_r}{^nC_{r-1}} = \frac{n-r+1}{r}$

(xi) (a) If n is even, ^nC_r is greatest for $r = \frac{n}{2}$

(b) If n is odd, ^nC_r is greatest for $r = \frac{n-1}{2}$ or $\frac{n+1}{2}$

(xii) $^nC_0 + {^nC_1} + {^nC_2} + \dots + {^nC_n} = 2^n$

(xiii) $^nC_0 + {^nC_2} + {^nC_4} + \dots = {^nC_1} + {^nC_3} + {^nC_5} + \dots = 2^{n-1}$

(xiv) $^{2n+1}C_0 + {^{2n+1}C_1} + {^{2n+1}C_2} + \dots + {^{2n+1}C_n} = 2^{2n}$

(xv) $^nC_n + {^{n+1}C_n} + {^{n+2}C_2} + {^{n+3}C_n} + \dots + {^{2n-1}C_n} = {^{2n}C_{n+1}}$

Example 45. If $^{15}C_{3r} = {^{15}C_{r+3}}$, find $^rC_2$.

Sol. We have, $^{15}C_{3r} = {^{15}C_{r+3}}$

$\Rightarrow \quad 3r = r + 3$

or $\quad 3r + r + 3 = 15$

$\Rightarrow \quad 2r = 3$ or $4r = 12$

$\Rightarrow \quad r = \frac{3}{2}$ or $r = 3$

but $r \in W$, so that $r \ne \frac{3}{2}$

$\therefore \quad r = 3$

Then, $\quad ^rC_2 = {^3C_2} = {^3C_1} = 3$

Example 46. If ${}^nC_9 = {}^nC_7$, find n.

Sol. We have, $${}^nC_9 = {}^nC_7 \Rightarrow n = 9 + 7 \quad [\because 9 \neq 7]$$
$$\therefore \quad n = 16$$

Example 47. Prove that
$$\binom{n}{r} + 2\binom{n}{r-1} + \binom{n}{r-2} = \binom{n+2}{r}$$

Sol. $\therefore \binom{n}{r} = {}^nC_r$

$$\therefore \text{LHS} = \binom{n}{r} + 2\binom{n}{r-1} + \binom{n}{r-2}$$
$$= {}^nC_r + 2\,{}^nC_{r-1} + {}^nC_{r-2}$$
$$= ({}^nC_r + {}^nC_{r-1}) + ({}^nC_{r-1} + {}^nC_{r-2})$$
$$= {}^{n+1}C_r + {}^{n+1}C_{r-1} = {}^{n+2}C_r$$
$$= \binom{n+2}{r} = \text{RHS}$$

Example 48. If ${}^{2n}C_3 : {}^nC_3 = 11:1$, find the value of n.

Sol. We have,
$${}^{2n}C_3 : {}^nC_3 = 11:1$$
$$\Rightarrow \quad \frac{{}^{2n}C_3}{{}^nC_3} = \frac{11}{1}$$
$$\Rightarrow \quad \frac{\dfrac{2n(2n-1)(2n-2)}{1\cdot 2\cdot 3}}{\dfrac{n(n-1)(n-2)}{1\cdot 2\cdot 3}} = 11 \Rightarrow \frac{4(2n-1)}{(n-2)} = 11$$
$$\Rightarrow \quad 8n - 4 = 11n - 22 \quad \Rightarrow 3n = 18$$
$$\therefore \quad n = 6$$

Example 49. If ${}^{n+1}C_{r+1} : {}^nC_r : {}^{n-1}C_{r-1} = 11:6:3$, find the values of n and r.

Sol. Here, $$\frac{{}^{n+1}C_{r+1}}{{}^nC_r} = \frac{11}{6}$$
$$\Rightarrow \quad \frac{n+1}{r+1}\cdot\frac{{}^nC_r}{{}^nC_r} = \frac{11}{6} \quad \left[\because {}^nC_r = \frac{n}{r}\cdot {}^{n-1}C_{r-1}\right]$$
$$\Rightarrow \quad \frac{n+1}{r+1} = \frac{11}{6}$$
$$\Rightarrow \quad 6n + 6 = 11r + 11$$
$$\Rightarrow \quad 6n - 11r = 5 \quad \ldots\text{(i)}$$
and $$\frac{{}^nC_r}{{}^{n-1}C_{r-1}} = \frac{6}{3}$$
$$\Rightarrow \quad \frac{n}{r}\cdot\frac{{}^{n-1}C_{r-1}}{{}^{n-1}C_{r-1}} = \frac{6}{3} \quad \left[\because {}^nC_r = \frac{n}{r}\cdot {}^{n-1}C_{r-1}\right]$$
$$\Rightarrow \quad \frac{n}{r} = 2$$
$$\Rightarrow \quad n = 2r \quad \ldots\text{(ii)}$$
On solving Eqs. (i) and (ii), we get $n = 10$ and $r = 5$.

Example 50. If ${}^nC_{r-1} = 36$, ${}^nC_r = 84$ and ${}^nC_{r+1} = 126$, find r.

Sol. Here, $$\frac{{}^nC_r}{{}^nC_{r-1}} = \frac{84}{36}$$
$$\Rightarrow \quad \frac{n-r+1}{r} = \frac{7}{3} \quad \left[\because \frac{{}^nC_r}{{}^nC_{r-1}} = \frac{n-r+1}{r}\right]$$
$$\Rightarrow \quad 3n - 3r + 3 = 7r$$
$$\Rightarrow \quad 10r - 3n = 3 \quad \ldots\text{(i)}$$
and $$\frac{{}^nC_{r+1}}{{}^nC_r} = \frac{n-(r+1)+1}{(r+1)} = \frac{126}{84} \quad \left[\because \frac{{}^nC_r}{{}^nC_{r-1}} = \frac{n-r+1}{r}\right]$$
$$\Rightarrow \quad \frac{n-r}{r+1} = \frac{3}{2}$$
$$\Rightarrow \quad 2n - 2r = 3r + 3$$
$$\Rightarrow \quad 5r - 2n = -3$$
or $$10r - 4n = -6 \quad \ldots\text{(ii)}$$
On subtracting Eq. (ii) from Eq. (i), we get
$$n = 9$$
From Eq. (i), we get
$$10r - 27 = 3 \Rightarrow 10r = 30$$
$$\therefore \quad r = 3$$

Example 51. Prove that product of r consecutive positive integers is divisible by $r!$.

Sol. Let r consecutive positive integers be (m), $(m+1), (m+2), \ldots, (m+r-1)$, where $m \in N$.

$$\therefore \text{Product} = m(m+1)(m+2)\ldots(m+r-1)$$
$$= \frac{(m-1)!\, m(m+1)(m+2)\ldots(m+r-1)}{(m-1)!}$$
$$= \frac{(m+r-1)!}{(m-1)!} = \frac{r!\cdot(m+r-1)!}{r!\,(m-1)!}$$
$$[\because {}^{m+r-1}C_r \text{ is natural number}]$$
$$= r!\cdot {}^{m+r-1}C_r,$$
which is divisible by $r!$.

Example 52. Evaluate
$${}^{47}C_4 + \sum_{j=0}^{3} {}^{50-j}C_3 + \sum_{k=0}^{5} {}^{56-k}C_{53-k}.$$

Sol. We have, $${}^{47}C_4 + \sum_{j=0}^{3} {}^{50-j}C_3 + \sum_{k=0}^{5} {}^{56-k}C_{53-k}$$

$$= {}^{47}C_4 + \sum_{j=0}^{3} {}^{50-j}C_3 + \sum_{k=0}^{5} {}^{56-k}C_3 \quad [\because {}^nC_r = {}^nC_{n-r}]$$

$$= {}^{47}C_4 + ({}^{50}C_3 + {}^{49}C_3 + {}^{48}C_3 + {}^{47}C_3)$$
$$+ ({}^{56}C_3 + {}^{55}C_3 + {}^{54}C_3 + {}^{53}C_3 + {}^{52}C_3 + {}^{51}C_3)$$
$$= {}^{47}C_4 + {}^{47}C_3 + {}^{48}C_3 + {}^{49}C_3 + {}^{50}C_3 + {}^{51}C_3$$
$$+ {}^{52}C_3 + {}^{53}C_3 + {}^{54}C_3 + {}^{55}C_3 + {}^{56}C_3$$
$$= ({}^{47}C_4 + {}^{47}C_3) + {}^{48}C_3 + {}^{49}C_3 + {}^{50}C_3 + {}^{51}C_3$$
$$+ {}^{52}C_3 + {}^{53}C_3 + {}^{54}C_3 + {}^{55}C_3 + {}^{56}C_3$$
$$= {}^{48}C_4 + {}^{48}C_3 + {}^{49}C_3 + {}^{50}C_3 + {}^{51}C_3 + \ldots + {}^{56}C_3$$
$$= {}^{49}C_4 + {}^{49}C_3 + {}^{50}C_3 + \ldots + {}^{56}C_3$$
$$\vdots \quad \vdots \quad \vdots \quad \vdots \quad \vdots$$
$$= {}^{56}C_4 + {}^{56}C_3 = {}^{57}C_4$$

Example 53. Prove that the greatest value of ${}^{2n}C_r \ (0 \le r \le 2n)$ is ${}^{2n}C_n$ (for $1 \le r \le n$).

Sol. We have, $\dfrac{{}^{2n}C_r}{{}^{2n}C_{r-1}} = \dfrac{2n-r+1}{r}$ $\left[\because \dfrac{{}^nC_r}{{}^nC_{r-1}} = \dfrac{n-r+1}{r}\right]$

$$= \frac{2(n-r)+(r+1)}{r} = \frac{1+2(n-r)+1}{r} > 1$$

$$\Rightarrow \quad \frac{{}^{2n}C_r}{{}^{2n}C_{r-1}} > 1 \qquad [\text{for } 1 \le r \le n]$$

$$\therefore \quad {}^{2n}C_{r-1} < {}^{2n}C_r$$

On putting $r = 1, 2, 3, \ldots, n$,

then ${}^{2n}C_0 < {}^{2n}C_1, {}^{2n}C_1 < {}^{2n}C_2, \ldots, {}^{2n}C_{n-1} < {}^{2n}C_n$

On combining all inequalities, we get

$$\Rightarrow \quad {}^{2n}C_0 < {}^{2n}C_1 < {}^{2n}C_2 < {}^{2n}C_3 < \ldots < {}^{2n}C_{n-1} < {}^{2n}C_n$$

but ${}^{2n}C_r = {}^{2n}C_{2n-r}$, it follows that

$${}^{2n}C_{2n} < {}^{2n}C_{2n-1} < {}^{2n}C_{2n-2} < {}^{2n}C_{2n-3} < \ldots < {}^{2n}C_{n+1} < {}^{2n}C_n$$

Hence, the greatest value of ${}^{2n}C_r$ is ${}^{2n}C_n$.

Example 54. Thirty six games were played in a football tournament with each team playing once against each other. How many teams were there?

Sol. Let the number of teams be n.

Then number of matches to be played is ${}^nC_2 = 36$

$$\Rightarrow \quad {}^nC_2 = \frac{9 \times 8}{1 \times 2} = {}^9C_2$$

$$\Rightarrow \quad n = 9$$

Restricted Combinations

(i) The number of selections (combinations) of r objects out of n different objects, when

(a) k particular things are always included $= {}^{n-k}C_{r-k}$.

(b) k particular things are never included $= {}^{n-k}C_r$.

(ii) The number of combinations of r things out of n different things, such that k particular things are not together in any selection $= {}^nC_r - {}^{n-k}C_{r-k}$

(iii) The number of combinations of n different objects taking r at a time when, p particular objects are always included and q particular objects are always excluded $= {}^{n-p-q}C_{r-p}$

Note

(i) The number of selections of r consecutive things out of n things in a row $= n - r + 1$.

(ii) The number of selections of r consecutive things out of n things along a circle $= \begin{cases} n, & \text{if } r < n \\ 1, & \text{if } r = n \end{cases}$

Example 55. In how many ways can a cricket, eleven players by chosen out of a batch 15 players, if

(i) a particular is always chosen.

(ii) a particular player is never chosen?

Sol. (i) Since, particular player is always chosen. It means that $11 - 1 = 10$ players are selected out of the remaining $15 - 1 = 14$ players.

$\therefore$ Required number of ways $= {}^{14}C_{10} = {}^{14}C_4$

$$= \frac{14 \cdot 13 \cdot 12 \cdot 11}{1 \cdot 2 \cdot 3 \cdot 4} = 1001$$

(ii) Since, particular player is never chosen. It means that 11 players are selected out of the remaining $15 - 1 = 14$ players.

$\therefore$ Required number of ways $= {}^{14}C_{11} = {}^{14}C_3$

$$= \frac{14 \cdot 13 \cdot 12}{1 \cdot 2 \cdot 3} = 364$$

Example 56. How many different selections of 6 books can be made from 11 different books, if

(i) two particular books are always selected.

(ii) two particular books are never selected?

Sol. (i) Since, two particular books are always selected. It means that $6 - 2 = 4$ books are selected out of the remaining $11 - 2 = 9$ books.

$\therefore$ Required number of ways $= {}^9C_4 = \dfrac{9 \cdot 8 \cdot 7 \cdot 6}{1 \cdot 2 \cdot 3 \cdot 4} = 126.$

(ii) Since, two particular books are never selected. It means that 6 books are selected out of the remaining $11 - 2 = 9$ books.

$\therefore$ Required number of ways $= {}^9C_6$

$$= {}^9C_3 = \frac{9 \cdot 8 \cdot 7}{1 \cdot 2 \cdot 3} = 84.$$

Example 57. A person tries to form as many different parties as he can, out of his 20 friends. Each party should consist of the same number. How many friends should be invited at a time? In how many of these parties would the same friends be found?

Sol. Let the person invite r number of friends at a time. Then, the number of parties are ${}^{20}C_r$, which is maximum, when $r = 10$.

If a particular friend will be found in p parties, then p is the number of combinations out of 20 in which this particular friend must be included. Therefore, we have to select 9 more from 19 remaining friends.

Hence, $p = {}^{19}C_9$

(2) The number of ways (or combinations) of n different things selecting atleast one of them is $2^n - 1$. This can also be stated as the total number of combinations of n different things.

Proof For each things, there are two possibilities, whether it is selected or not selected.

Hence, the total number of ways is given by total possibilities of all the things which is equal to $2 \times 2 \times 2 \times \ldots \times n$ factors $= 2^n$

But, this includes one case in which nothing is selected.

Hence, the total number of ways of selecting one or more of n different things $= 2^n - 1$

Aliter Number of ways of selecting one, two, three, ..., n things from n different things are

$${}^nC_1, {}^nC_2, {}^nC_3, \ldots, {}^nC_n, \text{ respectively.}$$

Hence, the total number of ways or selecting atleast one thing is

$${}^nC_1 + {}^nC_2 + {}^nC_3 + \ldots + {}^nC_n$$
$$= ({}^nC_0 + {}^nC_1 + {}^nC_2 + \ldots + {}^nC_n) - {}^nC_0 = 2^n - 1$$

Example 58. Mohan has 8 friends, in how many ways he invite one or more of them to dinner?

Sol. Mohan select one or more than one of his 8 friends. So, required number of ways

$$= {}^8C_1 + {}^8C_2 + {}^8C_3 + \ldots + {}^8C_8$$
$$= 2^8 - 1 = 255.$$

Example 59. A question paper consists of two sections having respectively, 3 and 5 questions. The following note is given on the paper "It is not necessory to attempt all the questions one question from each section is compulsory". In how many ways can a candidate select the questions?

Sol. Here, we have two sections A and B (say), the section A has 3 questions and section B has 5 questions and one question from each section is compulsory, according to the given direction.

$\therefore$ Number of ways selecting one or more than one question from section A is $2^3 - 1 = 7$

and number of ways selecting one or more than one question from section B is $2^5 - 1 = 31$

Hence, by the principle of multiplication, the required number of ways in which a candidate can select the questions

$$= 7 \times 31 = 217.$$

Example 60. A student is allowed to select atleast one and atmost n books from a collection of $(2n+1)$ books. If the total number of ways in which he can select books is 63, find the value of n.

Sol. Given, student select atleast one and atmost n books from a collection of $(2n + 1)$ books. It means that he select one book or two books or three books or ... or n books. Hence, by the given hypothesis.

$${}^{2n+1}C_1 + {}^{2n+1}C_2 + {}^{2n+1}C_3 + \ldots + {}^{2n+1}C_n = 63 \quad \ldots\text{(i)}$$

Also, the sum of binomial coefficients, is

$${}^{2n+1}C_0 + {}^{2n+1}C_1 + \ldots + {}^{2n+1}C_n + {}^{2n+1}C_{n+1} + \ldots + {}^{2n+1}C_{n+1}$$
$$= (1+1)^{2n+1} = 2^{2n+1}$$

$$\Rightarrow {}^{2n+1}C_0 + 2({}^{2n+1}C_1 + {}^{2n+1}C_2 + \ldots + {}^{2n+1}C_n) + {}^{2n+1}C_{2n+1} = 2^{2n+1} \quad [\because {}^nC_r = C_{n-r}]$$

$$\Rightarrow 1 + 2 \times 63 + 1 = 2^{2n+1} \Rightarrow 128 = 2^{2n+1}$$

$$\Rightarrow 2^7 = 2^{2n+1} \Rightarrow 7 = 2n + 1$$

$$\therefore n = 3$$

Example 61. There are three books of Physics, four of Chemistry and five of Mathematics. How many different collections can be made such that each collection consists of

(i) one book of each subject,

(ii) atleast one book of each subject,

(iii) atleast one book of Mathematics.

Sol. (i) ${}^3C_1 \times {}^4C_1 \times {}^5C_1 = 3 \times 4 \times 5 = 60$

(ii) $(2^3 - 1) \times (2^4 - 1) \times (2^5 - 1) = 7 \times 15 \times 31 = 3255$

(iii) $(2^5 - 1) \times 2^7 = 31 \times 128 = 3968$

Exercise for Session 4

1. If $^{43}C_{r-6} = {}^{43}C_{3r+1}$, the value of r is

(a) 6 (b) 8 (c) 10 (d) 12

2. If $^{18}C_{15} + 2\,(^{18}C_{16}) + {}^{17}C_{16} + 1 = {}^{n}C_3$, the value of n is

(a) 18 (b) 20 (c) 22 (d) 24

3. If $^{20}C_{n+2} = {}^{n}C_{16}$, the value of n is

(a) 7 (b) 10 (c) 13 (d) None of these

4. If $^{47}C_4 + \sum_{r=1}^{5} {}^{52-r}C_3$ is equal to

(a) $^{47}C_6$ (b) $^{52}C_5$ (c) $^{52}C_4$ (d) None of these

5. If $^{n}C_3 + {}^{n}C_4 > {}^{n+1}C_3$ then

(a) $n > 6$ (b) $n < 6$ (c) $n > 7$ (d) $n < 7$

6. The Solution set of $^{10}C_{x-1} > 2 \cdot {}^{10}C_x$ is

(a) {1, 2, 3} (b) {4, 5, 6} (c) {8, 9, 10} (d) {9, 10, 11}

7. If $^{2n}C_2 : {}^{n}C_2 = 9:2$ and $^{n}C_r = 10$, then r is equal to

(a) 2 (b) 3 (c) 4 (d) 5

8. If $^{2n}C_3 : {}^{n}C_2 = 44:3$, for which of the following value of r, the value of $^{n}C_r$ will be 15.

(a) $r = 3$ (b) $r = 4$ (c) $r = 5$ (d) $r = 6$

9. If $^{n}C_r = {}^{n}C_{r-1}$ and $^{n}P_r = {}^{n}P_{r+1}$, the value of n is

(a) 2 (b) 3 (c) 4 (d) 5

10. If $^{n}P_r = 840$, $^{n}C_r = 35$, the value of n is

(a) 1 (b) 3 (c) 5 (d) 7

11. If $^{n}P_3 + {}^{n}C_{n-2} = 14n$, the value of n is

(a) 5 (b) 6 (c) 8 (d) 10

12. There are 12 volleyball players in all in a college, out of which a team of 9 players is to be formed. If the captain always remains the same, in how many ways can the team be formed ?

(a) 36 (b) 99 (c) 108 (d) 165

13. In how many ways a team of 11 players can be formed out of 25 players, if 6 out of them are always to be included and 5 are always to be excluded

(a) 2002 (b) 2008 (c) 2020 (d) 8002

14. A man has 10 friends. In how many ways he can invite one or more of them to a party?

(a) 10! (b) 2^{10} (c) $10! - 1$ (d) $2^{10} - 1$

15. In an examination, there are three multiple choice questions and each question has four choices. Number of ways in which a student can fail to get all answers correct, is

(a) 11 (b) 12 (c) 27 (d) 63

16. In an election, the number of candidates is 1 greater than the persons to be elected . If a voter can vote in 254 ways, the number of candidates is

(a) 6 (b) 7 (c) 8 (d) 10

17. The number of groups that can be made from 5 different green balls, 4 different blue balls and 3 different red balls, if atleast one green and one blue ball is to be included

(a) 3700 (b) 3720 (c) 4340 (d) None of these

18. A person is permitted to select atleast one and atmost n coins from a collection of $(2n + 1)$ distinct coins. If the total number of ways in which he can select coins is 255, then n equals

(a) 4 (b) 8 (c) 16 (d) 32

Session 5

Combinations from Identical Objects

Combinations from Identical Objects

(i) The number of combinations of n identical objects taking r objects $(r \le n)$ at a time $= 1$.

(ii) The number of combinations of zero or more objects from n identical objects $= n + 1$.

(iii) The total number of combinations of atleast one out of $a_1 + a_2 + a_3 + \ldots + a_n$ objects, where a_1 are alike of one kind, a_2 are alike of second kind, a_3 are alike of third kind, ..., a_n are alike of nth kind

$$= (a_1 + 1)(a_2 + 1)(a_3 + 1) \ldots (a_n + 1) - 1$$

Example 62. How many selections of atleast one red ball from a bag containing 4 red balls and 5 black balls, balls of the same colour being identical?

Sol. Number of selections of atleast one red ball from 4 identical red balls = 4

Number of selections of any number of black balls from 5 identical black balls

$$= 5 + 1 = 6$$

$\therefore$ Required number of selections of balls

$$= 4 \times 6 = 24$$

Example 63. There are p copies each of n different books. Find the number of ways in which a non-empty selection can be made from them.

Sol. Since, copies of the same book are identical.

$\therefore$ Number of selections of any number of copies of a book is $p + 1$. Similarly, in the case for each book.

Therefore, total number of selections is $(p+1)^n$.

But this includes a selection, which is empty i.e., zero copy of each book. Excluding this, the required number of non-empty selections is $(p+1)^n - 1$.

Example 64. There are 4 oranges, 5 apples and 6 mangoes in a fruit basket and all fruits of the same kind are identical. In how many ways can a person make a selection of fruits from among the fruits in the basket?

Sol. Zero or more oranges can be selected out of 4 identical oranges $= 4 + 1 = 5$ ways.

Similarly, for apples number of selection $= 5 + 1 = 6$ ways and mangoes can be selected in $6 + 1 = 7$ ways.

$\therefore$ The total number of selections when all the three kinds of fruits are selected $= 5 \times 6 \times 7 = 210$

But, in one of these selection number of each kind of fruit is zero and hence this selection must be excluded.

$\therefore$ Required number $= 210 - 1 = 209$

Combinations when both Identical and Distinct Objects are Present

The number of combinations (selections) of one or more objects out of $a_1 + a_2 + a_3 + \ldots + a_n$ objects, where a_1 are alike of one kind, a_2 are alike of second kind, a_3 are alike of third kind, ..., a_n are alike of nth kind and k are distinct.

$$= \{(a_1 + 1)(a_2 + 1)(a_3 + 1) \cdots (a_n + 1)\} ({}^kC_0 + {}^kC_1 + {}^kC_2 + \ldots + {}^kC_k) - 1$$

$$= (a_1 + 1)(a_2 + 1)(a_3 + 1) + \ldots + (a_n + 1) 2^k - 1$$

Example 65. Find the number of ways in which one or more letters can be selected from the letters

AAAAA BBBB CCC DD EFG.

Sol. Here, $5A$'s are alike, $4\,B$'s are alike, $3\,C$'s are alike, $2D$'s are alike and E, F, G are different.

$\therefore$ Total number of combinations

$$= (5+1)(4+1)(3+1)(2+1)2^3 - 1$$

$$= 6 \cdot 5 \cdot 4 \cdot 3 \cdot 8 - 1$$

$$= 2879$$

[excluding the case, when no letter is selected]

Explanation Selection from $(AAAAA)$ can be made by 6 ways such include no A, include one A, include two A, include three A, include four A, include five A. Similarly, selections from $(BBBB)$ can be made in 5 ways, selections from (CCC) can be made in 4 ways, selections from (DD) can be made in 3 ways and from E, F, G can be made in $2 \times 2 \times 2$ ways.

Number of Divisors of *N*

Every natural number N can always be put in the form $N = p_1^{\alpha_1} \cdot p_2^{\alpha_2} \cdot p_3^{\alpha_3} \ldots p_k^{\alpha_k}$, where $p_1, p_2, p_3, \ldots, p_k$ are distinct primes and $\alpha_1, \alpha_2, \alpha_3, \ldots, \alpha_k \in W$.

(i) The total number of divisors of N including 1 and N
$=(\alpha_1+1)(\alpha_2+1)(\alpha_3+1)\ldots(\alpha_k+1)$

(ii) The total number of divisors of N excluding 1 and N
$=(\alpha_1+1)(\alpha_2+1)(\alpha_3+1)\ldots(\alpha_k+1)-2$

(iii) The total number of divisors of N excluding either 1 or $N=(\alpha_1+1)(\alpha_2+1)(\alpha_3+1)\ldots(\alpha_k+1)-1$

(iv) Sum of all divisors $=(p_1^0+p_1^1+p_1^2+p_1^3+\ldots+p_1^{\infty_1})$
$(p_2^0+p_2^1+p_2^2+p_2^3+\ldots+p_2^{\alpha_2})\ldots$
$(p_k^0+p_k^1+p_k^2+p_k^3+\ldots+p_k^{\alpha_k})$

$$=\left(\frac{1-p_1^{\alpha_1+1}}{1-p_1}\right)\cdot\left(\frac{1-p_2^{\alpha_2+1}}{1-p_2}\right)\ldots\left(\frac{1-p_k^{\alpha_k+1}}{1-p_k}\right)$$

(v) Sum of proper divisors (excluding 1 and the expression itself)
$=$ Sum of all divisors $-(N+1)$

(vi) The number of even divisors of N are possible only if $p_1=2$, otherwise there is no even divisor.

$\therefore$ Required number of **even** divisors
$=\alpha_1(\alpha_2+1)(\alpha_3+1)+\ldots+(\alpha_k+1)$

(vii) The number of **odd** divisors of N

***Case* I** If $p_1=2$, the number of odd divisors
$=(\alpha_2+1)(\alpha_3+1)\ldots(\alpha_k+1)$

***Case* II** If $p_1\neq 2$, the number of odd divisors
$=(\alpha_1+1)(\alpha_2+1)(\alpha_3+1)\ldots(\alpha_k+1)$

(viii) The number of ways in which N can be resolved as a product of two factors

$$=\begin{cases}\frac{1}{2}(\alpha_1+1)(\alpha_2+1)\ldots(\alpha_k+1), & \text{if } N \text{ is not a perfect square}\\ \frac{1}{2}\{(\alpha_1+1)(\alpha_2+1)\ldots(\alpha_k+1)+1\}, & \text{if } N \text{ is a perfect square}\end{cases}$$

(ix) The number of ways in which a composite number N can be resolved into two factors which are relatively prime (or coprime) to each other is equal to 2^{n-1}, where n is the number of different factors (or different primes) in N.

| Example 66. Find the number of proper factors of the number 38808. Also, find sum of all these divisors.

Sol. The number $38808=2^3\cdot 3^2\cdot 7^2\cdot 11$

Hence, the total number of proper factors (excluding 1 and itself i.e., 38808)

$=(3+1)(2+1)(2+1)(1+1)-2$
$=72-2=70$

And sum of all these divisors (proper)

$=(2^0+2^1+2^2+2^3)(3^0+3^1+3^2)$
$(7^0+7^1+7^2)(11^0+11^1)-1-38808$
$=(15)(13)(57)(12)-38809$
$=133380-38809$
$=94571$

| Example 67. Find the number of even proper divisor of the number 1008.

Sol. $\because 1008=2^4\times 3^2\times 7^1$

$\therefore$ Required number of even proper divisors
$=$ Total number of selections of atleast one 2 and any number of 3's or 7's.
$=4\times(2+1)\times(1+1)-1=23$

| Example 68. Find the number of odd proper divisors of the number 35700. Also, find sum of the odd proper divisors.

Sol. $\because 35700=2^2\times 3^1\times 5^2\times 7^1\times 17^1$

$\therefore$ Required number of odd proper divisors
$=$ Total number of selections of zero 2 and an number of 3's or 5's o 7's or 17'
$=(1+1)(2+1)(1+1)(1+1)-1=23$

$\therefore$ The sum of odd proper divisors
$=(3^0+3^1)(5^0+5^1+5^2)(7^0+7^1)(17^0+7^1)-$
$=4\times 31\times 8\times 18-1$
$=17856-1=17855$

| Example 69. If $N=10800$, find the

(i) the number of divisors of the form $4m+2,\ \forall\ m\in W$.

(ii) the number of divisors which are multiple of 10.

(iii) the number of divisors which are multiple of 15.

Sol. We have, $N=10800=2^4\times 3^3\times 5^2$

(i) $\because(4m+2)=2(2m+1)$, in any divisor of the form $4m+2$, 2 should be exactly 1.

So, the number of divisors of the form
$(4m+2)=1\times(3+1)\times(2+1)=1\times 4\times 3=12$

(ii) $\therefore$ The required number of proper divisors
$=$ Total number of selections of atleast one 2 and one 5 from 2, 2, 2, 2, 3, 3, 3, 5, 5
$=4\times(3+1)\times 2=32$

(iii) $\therefore$ The required number of proper divisors

= Total number of selections of atleast one 3 and one 5 from 2, 2, 2, 2, 3, 3, 3, 5, 5

$= (4 + 1) \times 3 \times 2 = 30$

| Example 70. Find the number of divisors of the number $N = 2^3 \cdot 3^5 \cdot 5^7 \cdot 7^9 \cdot 9^{11}$, which are perfect square.

Sol. $\because N = 2^3 \cdot 3^5 \cdot 5^7 \cdot 7^9 \cdot 9^{11}$

$= 2^3 \cdot 3^5 \cdot 5^7 \cdot 7^9 \cdot 3^{22}$

$= 2^3 \cdot 3^{27} \cdot 5^7 \cdot 7^9$

For perfect square of N, each prime factor must occur even number of times.

2 can be taken in 2 ways (i.e., 2^0 or 2^2)

3 can be taken in 14 ways (i.e., 3^0 or 3^2 or 3^4 or 3^6 or 3^8 or 3^{10} or 3^{12} or 3^{14} or 3^{16} or 3^{18} or 3^{20} or 3^{22} or 3^{24} or 3^{26})

5 can taken in 4 ways (i.e., 5^0 or 5^2 or 5^4 or 5^6)

and 7 can taken in 5 ways
(i.e., 7^0 or 7^2 or 7^4 or 7^4 or 7^6 or 7^8)

Hence, total divisors which are perfect squares

$= 2 \times 14 \times 4 \times 5 = 560$

| Example 71. In how many ways the number 10800 can be resolved as a product of two factors?

Sol. Let $N = 10800 = 2^4 \times 3^3 \times 5^2$

Here, N is not a perfect square [$\because$ power of 3 is odd]

Hence, the number of ways $= \frac{1}{2}(4 + 1)(3 + 1)(2 + 1) = 30$

| Example 72. In how many ways the number 18900 can be split in two factors which are relatively prime (or coprime)?

Sol. Let $N = 18900 = 2^2 \cdot 3^3 \cdot 5^2 \cdot 7^1$

Relatively prime or coprime Two numbers not necessarily prime are said to be relatively prime or coprime, if their HCF (highest common factor) is one as 2, 3, 5, 7 are relatively prime numbers.

$\therefore$ $n = 4$ [number of different primes in N]

Hence, number of ways in which a composite number N can be resolved into two factors which are relatively prime or coprime $= 2^{4-1} = 2^3 = 8$

Division of Objects Into Groups

(a) Division of Objects Into Groups of Unequal Size

Theorem Number of ways in which $(m+n)$ distinct objects can be divided into two unequal groups containing m and n objects is $\frac{(m+n)!}{m!\,n!}$.

Proof The number of ways in which $(m + n)$ distinct objects are divided into two groups of the size m and n
= The number of ways m objects are selected out of $(m + n)$ objects to form one of the groups, which can be done in ${}^{m+n}C_m$ ways. The other group of n objects is formed by the remaining n objects.

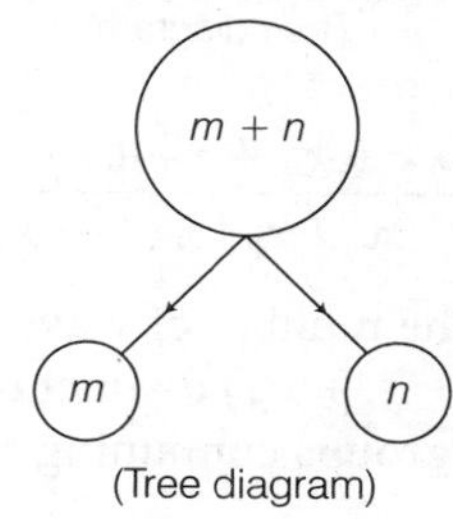

(Tree diagram)

$$= {}^{m+n}C_m \cdot {}^nC_n = \frac{(m+n)}{m!\,n!}$$

***Corollary* I** The number of ways to distribute $(m + n)$ distinct objects among 2 persons in the groups containing m and n objects
= (Number of ways to divide) × (Number of groups)

$$= \frac{(m+n)}{m!\,n!} \times 2!$$

***Corollary* II** The number of ways in which $(m + n + p)$ distinct objects can be divided into three unequal groups containing m, n and p objects, is

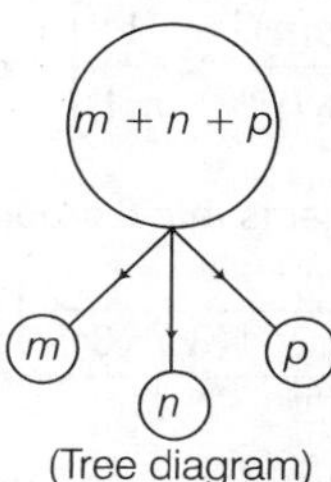

(Tree diagram)

$${}^{m+n+p}C_m \cdot {}^{n+p}C_n \cdot {}^pC_p = \frac{(m+n+p)!}{m!\,n!\,p!}$$

***Corollary* III** The number of ways to distribute $(m + n + p)$ distinct objects among 3 persons in the groups containing m, n and p objects
= (Number of ways to divide) × (Number of groups)

$$= \frac{(m+n+p)!}{m!\,n!\,p!} \times 3!$$

***Corollary* IV** The number of ways in which $(x_1 + x_2 + x_3 + \cdots + x_n)$ distinct objects can be divided into n unequal groups containing x_1, $x_2, x_3, \ldots, x_n$ objects, is

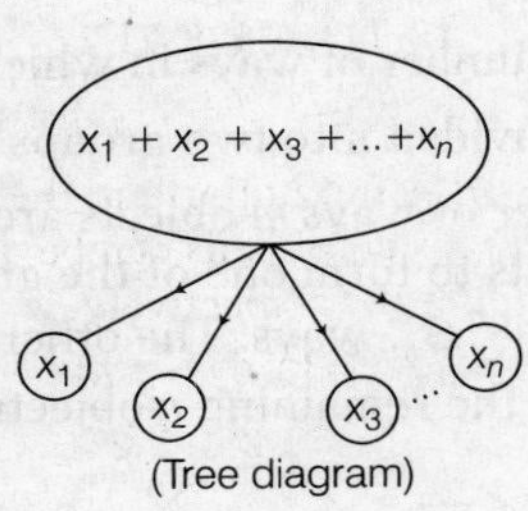

(Tree diagram)

$$\frac{(x_1+x_2+x_3+\cdots+x_n)!}{x_1!\,x_2!\,x_3!\cdots x_n!}.$$

***Corollary* V** The number of ways to distribute $(x_1+x_2+x_3+\ldots+x_n)$ distinct objects among n persons in the groups containing $x_1, x_2, \ldots, x_n$ objects

= (Number of ways to divide) × (Number of groups)

$$=\frac{(x_1+x_2+x_3+\ldots+x_n)!}{x_1!\,x_2!\,x_3!\ldots x_n!}\times n!$$

(b) Division of Objects Into Groups of Equal Size

The number of ways in which mn distinct objects can be divided equally into m groups, each containing n objects and

(i) If order of groups is not important is.

$$=\left(\frac{(mn)!}{(n!)^m}\right)\times\frac{1}{m!}.$$

(ii) If order of groups is important is.

$$\left(\frac{(mn)!}{(n!)^m}\times\frac{1}{m!}\right)\times m!=\frac{(mn)!}{(n!)^m}.$$

Note Division of $14n$ objects into 6 groups of $2n, 2n, 2n, 2n, 3n, 3n$, size is

$$\frac{\left(\frac{(14n)!}{(2n)!\,(2n)!\,(2n)!\,(2n)!\,(3n)!\,(3n)!}\right)}{4!\,2!}=\frac{(14n)}{((2n)!)^4\,((3n)!)^2}\times\frac{1}{4!\,2!}$$

Now, the distribution ways of these 6 groups among 6 persons is

$$\frac{(14n)!}{[(2n)!)]^4\,[(3n)!]^2}\times\frac{1}{4!\,2!}\times 6!=\frac{(14n)!}{[(2n)!]^4\,[(3n)!]^2}\times 15.$$

| Example 73. In how many ways can a pack of 52 cards be

(i) distributed equally among four players in order?

(ii) divided into four groups of 13 cards each?

(iii) divided into four sets, three of them having 17 cards each and fourth just one card?

Sol. (i) Here, order of group is important, then the numbers of ways in which 52 different cards can be divided equally into 4 players is

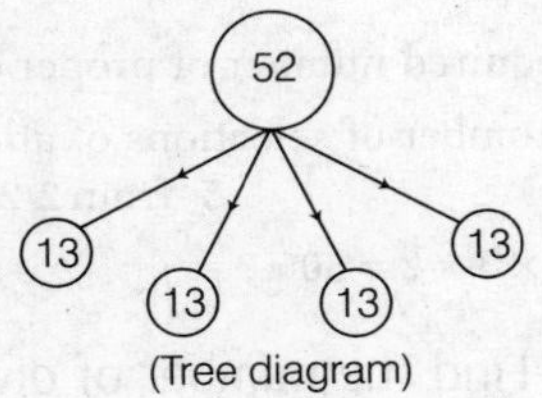

(Tree diagram)

$$\frac{52!}{4!\,(13!)^4}\times 4!=\frac{52!}{(13!)^4}$$

Aliter Each player will get 13 cards. Now, first player can be given 13 cards out of 52 cards in ${}^{52}C_{13}$ ways. Second player can be given 13 cards out of remaining 39 cards (i.e., $52-13=39$) in ${}^{39}C_{13}$ ways. Third player can be given 13 cards out of remaining 26 cards (i.e., $39-13=26$) in ${}^{26}C_{13}$ ways and fourth player can be given 13 cards out of remaining 13 cards (i.e., $26-13=13$) in ${}^{13}C_{13}$ ways.

Hence, required number of ways

$$={}^{52}C_{13}\times{}^{39}C_{13}\times{}^{26}C_{13}\times{}^{13}C_{13}$$

$$=\frac{52!}{13!\,39!}\times\frac{39!}{13!\,26!}\times\frac{26!}{13!\,13!}\times 1=\frac{52!}{(13!)^4}$$

(ii) Here, order of group is not important, then the number of ways in which 52 different cards can be divided equally into 4 groups is

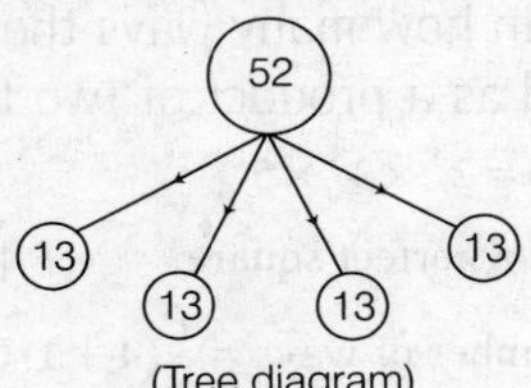

(Tree diagram)

$$\frac{52!}{4!\,(13!)^4}$$

Aliter Each group will get 13 cards. Now, first group can be given 13 cards out of 52 cards in ${}^{52}C_{13}$ ways. Second group can be given 13 cards out of remaining 39 cards (i.e., $52-13=39$) in ${}^{39}C_{13}$ ways. Third group can be given 13 cards out of remaining 26 cards (i.e., $39-13=26$) in ${}^{26}C_{13}$ ways and fourth group can be given 13 cards out of remaining 13 cards (i.e., $26-13=13$) in ${}^{13}C_{13}$ ways. But the all (four) groups can be interchanged in 4! ways. Hence, the required number of ways

$$={}^{52}C_{13}\times{}^{39}C_{13}\times{}^{26}C_{13}\times{}^{13}C_{13}\times\frac{1}{4!}$$

$$=\frac{52!}{13!\,39!}\times\frac{39!}{13!\,26!}\times\frac{26!}{13!\,13!}\times 1\times\frac{1}{4!}=\frac{52!}{(13!)^4\,4!}$$

(iii) First, we divide 52 cards into two sets which contains 1 and 51 cards respectively, is

$$\frac{52!}{1!\,51!}$$

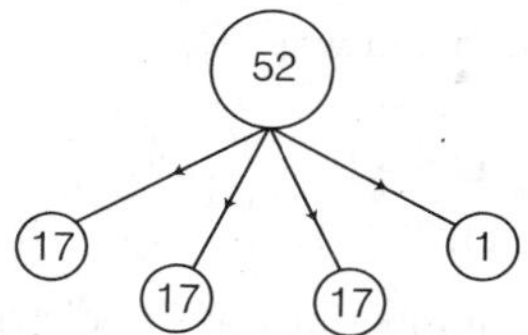

Now, 51 cards can be divided equally in three sets each contains 17 cards (here order of sets is not important) in $\frac{51!}{3!\,(17!)^3}$ ways.

Hence, the required number of ways

$$= \frac{52!}{1!\,51!} \times \frac{51!}{3!(17!)^3}$$

$$= \frac{52!}{1!\,3!(17)^3} = \frac{52!}{(17!)^3 3!}$$

Aliter First set can be given 17 cards out of 52 cards in ${}^{52}C_{17}$. Second set can be given 17 cards out of remaining 35 cards (i.e., $52 - 17 = 35$) in ${}^{35}C_{17}$. Third set can be given 17 cards out of remaining 18 cards (i.e., $35 - 17 = 18$) in ${}^{18}C_{17}$ and fourth set can be given 1 card out of 1 card in ${}^{1}C_1$. But the first three sets can interchanged in 3! ways. Hence, the total number of ways for the required distribution

$$= {}^{52}C_{17} \times {}^{35}C_{17} \times {}^{18}C_{17} \times {}^{1}C_1 \times \frac{1}{3}!$$

$$= \frac{52!}{17!\,35!} \times \frac{35!}{17!\,1!} \times \frac{18!}{17!\,18!} \times 1 \times \frac{1}{3!} = \frac{(52)!}{(17!)^3\,3!}$$

| Example 74. In how many ways can 12 different balls be divided between 2 boys, one receiving 5 and the other 7 balls? Also, in how many ways can these 12 balls be divided into groups of 5, 4 and 3 balls, respectively?

Sol. **I Part** Here, order is important, then the number of ways in which 12 different balls can be divided between two boys which contains 5 and 7 balls respectively, is

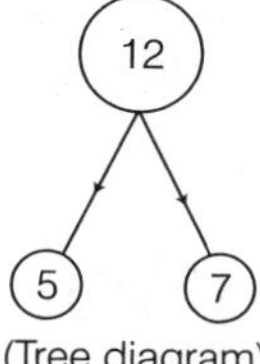

(Tree diagram)

$$= \frac{12!}{5!\,7!} \times 2! = \frac{12 \cdot 11 \cdot 10 \cdot 9 \cdot 8 \cdot 7!}{(5 \cdot 4 \cdot 3 \cdot 2 \cdot 1)7!} \cdot 2 = 1584$$

Aliter First boy can be given 5 balls out of 12 balls in ${}^{12}C_5$. Second boy can be given 7 balls out of 7 balls (i.e., $12 - 5 = 7$) but there order is important boys interchange by (2 types), then required number of ways

$$= {}^{12}C_5 \times {}^{7}C_7 \times 2! = \frac{12!}{5!\,7!} \times 1 \times 2!$$

$$= \frac{12! \times 2}{5! \times 7!} = \frac{12 \cdot 11 \cdot 10 \cdot 9 \cdot 8 \cdot 7! \cdot 2}{5 \cdot 4 \cdot 3 \cdot 2 \cdot 1 \cdot 7!} = 1584.$$

II Part Here, order is not important, then the number of ways in which 12 different balls can be divided into three groups of 5,4 and 3 balls respectively, is

$$= \frac{12!}{5!\,4!\,3!} = \frac{12 \cdot 11 \cdot 10 \cdot 9 \cdot 8 \cdot 7 \cdot 6 \cdot 5!}{5! \cdot 4 \cdot 3 \cdot 2 \cdot 1 \cdot 3 \cdot 2 \cdot 1} = 27720$$

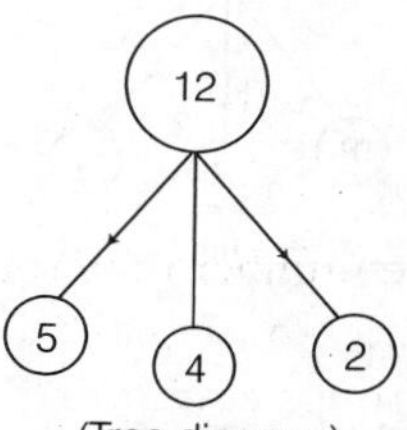

(Tree diagram)

Aliter First group can be given 5 balls out of 12 balls in ${}^{12}C_5$ ways. Second group can be given 4 balls out of remaining 7 balls $(12 - 5 = 7)$ in ${}^{7}C_4$ and 3 balls can be given out of remaining 3 balls in ${}^{3}C_3$.

Hence, the required number of ways (here order of groups are not important)

$$= {}^{12}C_5 \times {}^{7}C_4 \times {}^{3}C_3$$

$$= \frac{12!}{5!\,7!} \times \frac{7!}{4!\,3!} \times 1$$

$$= \frac{12!}{5!\,4!\,3!}$$

| Example 75. In how many ways can 16 different books be distributed among three students A, B, C so that B gets 1 more than A and C gets 2 more than B?

Sol. Let A gets n books, then B gets $n + 1$ and C gets $n + 3$.

Now, $n + (n + 1) + (n + 3) = 16$

$\Rightarrow \quad 3n = 12$

$\therefore \quad n = 4$

(Tree diagram)

$\Rightarrow$ A, B, C gets 4, 5 and 7 books, respectively.

Hence, the total number of ways for the required distribution

$$= \frac{16!}{4!\,5!\,7!}$$

Example 76. In how many ways can 9 different books be distributed among three students if each receives atleast 2 books?

Sol. If each receives atleast 2 books, then the division as shown by tree diagrams

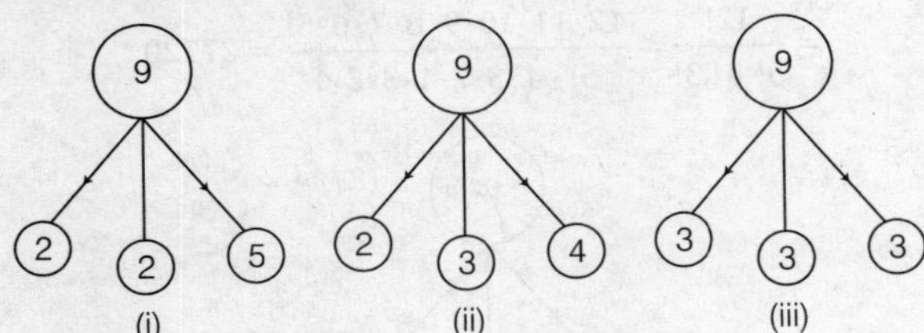

The number of division ways for tree diagrams (i), (ii) and (iii) are

$$\frac{9!}{(2!)^2\,(5!)} \times \frac{1}{2!}, \frac{9!}{2!\,3!\,4!} \text{ and } \frac{9!}{(3!)^3} \times \frac{1}{3!}, \text{ respectively.}$$

Hence, the total number of ways of distribution of these groups among 3 students is

$$\left[\frac{9!}{(2!)^2\,(5!)} \times \frac{1}{2!} + \frac{9!}{2!\,3!\,4!} + \frac{9!}{(3!)^3} \times \frac{1}{3!}\right] \times 3!$$

$$= [378 + 1260 + 280] \times 6$$
$$= 11508$$

Exercise for Session 5

1. There are 3 oranges, 5 apples and 6 mangoes in a fruit basket (all fruits of same kind are identical). Number of ways in which fruits can be selected from the basket, is

(a) 124 (b) 125 (c) 167 (d) 168

2. In a city no two persons have identical set of teeth and there is no person without a tooth. Also, no person has more than 32 teeth. If we disguard the shape and size of tooth and consider only the positioning of the teeth, the maximum population of the city is

(a) 2^{32} (b) $(32)^2 - 1$ (c) $2^{32} - 1$ (d) 2^{31}

3. If $a_1, a_2, a_3, \dots, a_{n+1}$ be $(n + 1)$ different prime numbers, then the number of different factors (other than 1) of $a_1^m \cdot a_2 \cdot a_3, \dots, a_{n+1}$, is

(a) $m + 1$ (b) $(m + 1)2^n$ (c) $m \cdot 2^n + 1$ (d) None of these

4. Number of proper factors of 2400 is equal to

(a) 34 (b) 35
(c) 36 (d) 37

5. The sum of the divisors of $2^5 \cdot 3^4 \cdot 5^2$ is

(a) $3^2 \cdot 7^1 \cdot 11^2$ (b) $3^2 \cdot 7^1 \cdot 11^2 \cdot 31$
(c) $3 \cdot 7 \cdot 11 \cdot 31$ (d) None of these

6. The number of proper divisors of $2^p \cdot 6^q \cdot 21^r, \forall\, p, q, r \in N$, is

(a) $(p + q + 1)(q + r + 1)(r + 1)$ (b) $(p + q + 1)(q + r + 1)(r + 1) - 2$
(c) $(p + q)(q + r)r - 2$ (d) $(p + q)(q + r)r$

7. The number of odd proper divisors of $3^p \cdot 6^q \cdot 15^r, \forall\, p, q, r \in N$, is

(a) $(p + 1)(q + 1)(r + 1) - 2$ (b) $(p + 1)(q + 1)(r + 1) - 1$
(c) $(p + q + r + 1)(r + 1) - 2$ (d) $(p + q + r + 1)(r + 1) - 1$

8. The number of proper divisors of 1800, which are also divisible by 10, is

(a) 18 (b) 27 (c) 34 (d) 43

9. Total number of divisors of 480 that are of the form $4n + 2, n \ge 0$, is equal to

(a) 2 (b) 3 (c) 4 (d) 5

10. Total number of divisors of $N = 2^5 \cdot 3^4 \cdot 5^{10} \cdot 7^6$ that are of the form $4n + 2, n \ge 1$, is equal to

(a) 54 (b) 55 (c) 384 (d) 385

11. Total number of divisors of $N = 3^5 \cdot 5^7 \cdot 7^9$ that are of the form $4n + 1, n \geq 0$ is equal to
(a) 15 (b) 30 (c) 120 (d) 240

12. Number of ways in which 12 different books can be distributed equally among 3 persons, is
(a) $\frac{12!}{(4!)^3}$ (b) $\frac{12!}{(3!)^4}$ (c) $\frac{12!}{(4!)^4}$ (d) $\frac{12!}{(3!)^3}$

13. Number of ways in which 12 different things can be distributed in 3 groups, is
(a) $\frac{12!}{(4!)^3}$ (b) $\frac{12!}{3!(4!)^3}$ (c) $\frac{12!}{4!(3!)^3}$ (d) $\frac{12!}{(3!)^4}$

14. Number of ways in which 12 different things can be distributed in 5 sets of 2, 2, 2, 3, 3, things is
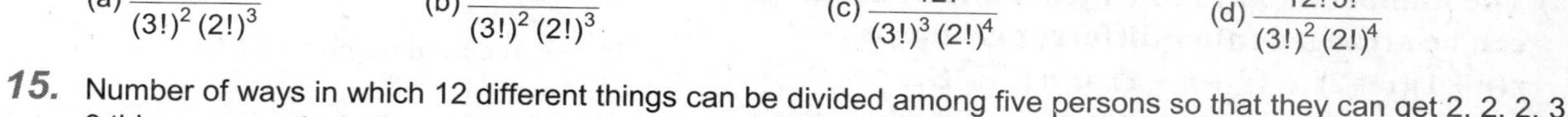
(a) $\frac{12!}{(3!)^2(2!)^3}$ (b) $\frac{12!5!}{(3!)^2(2!)^3}$ (c) $\frac{12!}{(3!)^3(2!)^4}$ (d) $\frac{12!5!}{(3!)^2(2!)^4}$

15. Number of ways in which 12 different things can be divided among five persons so that they can get 2, 2, 2, 3, 3 things respectively, is
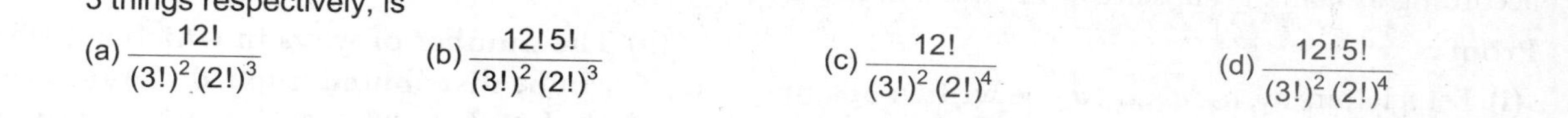
(a) $\frac{12!}{(3!)^2(2!)^3}$ (b) $\frac{12!5!}{(3!)^2(2!)^3}$ (c) $\frac{12!}{(3!)^2(2!)^4}$ (d) $\frac{12!5!}{(3!)^2(2!)^4}$

16. The total number of ways in which $2n$ persons can be divided into n couples, is
(a) $\frac{2n!}{(n!)^2}$ (b) $\frac{2n!}{(2n!)^n}$ (c) $\frac{2n!}{n!(2n!)^2}$ (d) None of these

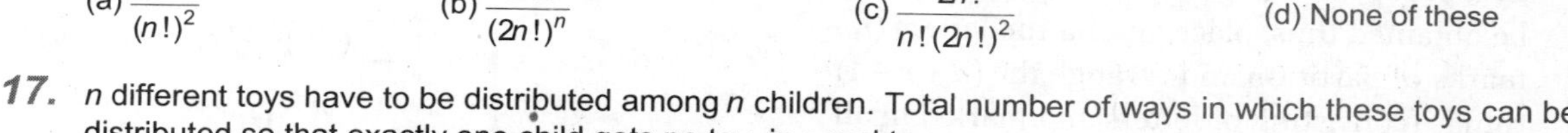
17. n different toys have to be distributed among n children. Total number of ways in which these toys can be distributed so that exactly one child gets no toy, is equal to
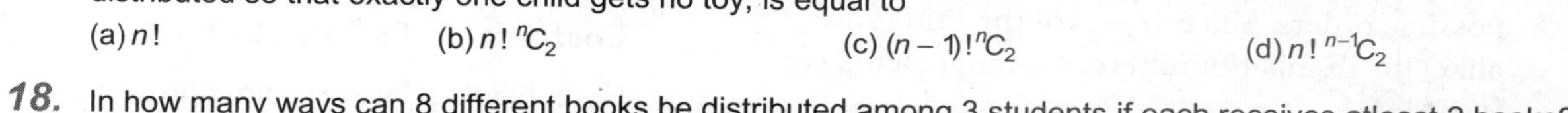
(a) $n!$ (b) $n!\,{}^nC_2$ (c) $(n-1)!\,{}^nC_2$ (d) $n!\,{}^{n-1}C_2$

18. In how many ways can 8 different books be distributed among 3 students if each receives atleast 2 books?
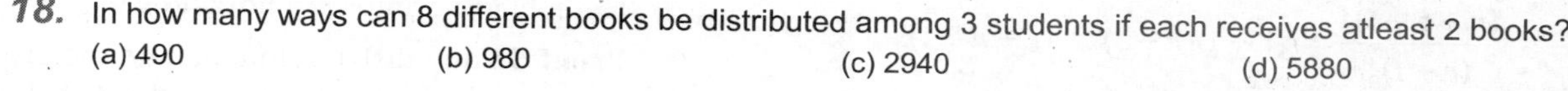
(a) 490 (b) 980 (c) 2940 (d) 5880

Session 6

Arrangement in Groups, Multinomial Theorem, Multiplying Synthetically

Arrangement in Groups

(a) The number of ways in which n different things can be arranged into r different groups is $r(r+1)(r+2)\ldots(r+n-1)$ or $n!\cdot {}^{n-1}C_{r-1}$ according as blank groups are or are not admissible.

Proof

(i) Let n letters $a_1, a_2, a_3, \ldots, a_n$ be written in a row in any order. All the arrangements of the letters in r, groups, blank groups being admissible, can be obtained thus, place among the letters $(r-1)$ marks of partition and arrange the $(n+r-1)$ things (consisting of letters and marks) in all possible orders. Since, $(r-1)$ of the things are alike, the number of different arrangements is $\dfrac{(n+r-1)!}{(r-1)!} = r(r+1)(r-2)\ldots(r+n-1)$.

(ii) All the arrangements of the letters in r groups, none of the groups being blank, can be obtained as follows:

(I) Arrange the letters in all possible orders. This can be done in $n!$ ways.

(II) In every such arrangement, place $(r-1)$ marks of partition in $(r-1)$ out of the $(n-1)$ spaces between the letters. This can be done in ${}^{n-1}C_{r-1}$ ways.

Hence, the required number is $n!\cdot {}^{n-1}C_{r-1}$.

| Example 77. In how many ways 5 different balls can be arranged into 3 different boxes so that no box remains empty?

Sol. The required number of ways $= 5!\cdot {}^{5-1}C_{3-1} = 5!\cdot {}^{4}C_2$

$$= (120)\cdot\left(\frac{4\cdot 3}{1\cdot 2}\right) = 720$$

Aliter

Each box must contain atleast one ball, since no box remains empty. Boxes can have balls in the following systems

Box	I	II	III
Number of balls	1	1	3

Or

Box	I	II	III
Number of balls	1	2	2

All 5 balls can be arranged by 5! ways and boxes can be arranged in each system by $\dfrac{3!}{2!}$.

Hence, required number of ways $= 5! \times \dfrac{3!}{2!} + 5! \times \dfrac{3!}{2!}$

$$= 120 \times 3 + 120 \times 3 = 720$$

(b) The number of ways in which n different things can be distributed into r different groups is

$$r^n - {}^rC_1(r-1)^n + {}^rC_2(r-2)^n - \ldots + (-1)^{r-1}\cdot {}^rC_{r-1}$$

Or

$$\sum_{p=0}^{r} (-1)^p \cdot {}^rC_p \cdot (r-p)^n$$

Or

Coefficient of x^n in $n!(e^x - 1)^r$.

Here, blank groups are not allowed.

Proof In any distribution, denote the groups by $g_1, g_2, g_3, \ldots, g_r$ and consider the distributions in which blanks are allowed.

The total number of these is r^n.

The number in which g_1 is blank, is $(r-1)^n$.

Therefore, the number in which g_1 is not blank, is

$$r^n - (r-1)^n$$

of these last, the number in which g_2 is blank, is

$$(r-1)^n - (r-2)^n$$

Therefore, the number in which g_1, g_2 are not blank, is

$$r^n - 2(r-1)^n + (r-2)^n$$

of these last, the number in which g_3 is blank, is

$$(r-1)^n - 2(r-2)^n + (r-3)^n$$

Therefore, the number in which g_1, g_2, g_3 are not blank, is

$$r^n - 3(r-1)^n + 3(r-2)^n - (r-3)^n$$

This process can be continued as far as we like and it is obvious that the coefficients are formed as in a binomial expansion.

Hence, the number of distributions in which no one of x assigned groups is blank, is

$$r^n - {}^xC_1(r-1)^n + {}^xC_2(r-2)^n - \ldots + (-1)^x(r-x)^n$$

when $x = r$, then

$$r^n - {}^rC_1(r-1)^n + {}^rC_2(r-2)^n - \ldots + (-1)^{r-1} \cdot {}^rC_{r-1}(r-(r-1))^n + (-1)^r \cdot {}^rC_r(r-r)^n$$

Or

$$r^n - {}^rC_1(r-1)^n + {}^rC_2(r-2)^n - \ldots + (-1)^{r-1} \cdot {}^rC_{r-1}$$

Aliter

By Principle of Inclusion and Exclusion

Let A_i denotes the set of distribution of things, if ith group gets nothing. Then, $n(A_i) = (r-1)^n$

[as n things can be distributed among $(r-1)$ groups in $(r-1)^n$ ways]

Then, $n(A_i \cap A_j)$ represents number of distribution ways in which groups i and j get no object. Then,

$$n(A_i \cap A_j) = (r-2)^n$$

Also, $n(A_i \cap A_j \cap A_k) = (r-3)^n$

This process can be continued, then the required number is

$$\begin{aligned} n(A_1' A_2' \cap \ldots \cap A_r') &= n(U) - n(A_1 \cup A_2 \cup \ldots \cup A_r) \\ &= r^n - \{\sum n(A_i) - \sum n(A_i \cap A_j) \\ &\quad + \sum n(A_i \cap A_j \cap A_k) \ldots \\ &\quad + (-1)^n \sum n(A_1 \cap A_2 \cap \ldots \cap A_r)\} \\ &= r^n - \{{}^rC_1(r-1)^n - {}^rC_2(r-2)^n \\ &\quad + {}^rC_3(r-3)^n - \ldots + (-1)^r \cdot {}^rC_{r-1}\} \\ &= r^n - {}^rC_1(r-1)^n + {}^rC_2(r-2)^n \\ &\quad - {}^rC_3(r-3)^n + \ldots + (-1)^{r-1} \cdot {}^rC_{r-1} \cdot 1 \end{aligned}$$

Note Coefficient of x^r in $e^{px} = \dfrac{p^r}{r!}$.

Example 78. In how many ways 5 different balls can be distributed into 3 boxes so that no box remains empty?

Sol. The required number of ways

$$= 3^5 - {}^3C_1(3-1)^5 + {}^3C_2(3-2)^5 - {}^3C_3(3-3)^5$$

$$= 243 - 96 + 3 - 0 = 150$$

Or

Coefficient of x^5 in $5!(e^x - 1)^3$

$= $ Coefficient of x^5 in $5!(e^{3x} - 3e^{2x} + 3e^x - 1)$

$$= 5!\left(\frac{3^5}{5!} - 3 \times \frac{2^5}{5!} + 3 \times \frac{1}{5!}\right) = 3^5 - 3 \cdot 2^5 + 3 = 243 - 96 + 3 = 150$$

Aliter

Each box must contain atleast one ball, since number box remains empty. Boxes can have balls in the following systems

Box	I	II	III
Number of balls	1	1	3

Or

Box	I	II	III
Number of balls	1	2	2

The number of ways to distribute the balls in I system

$$= {}^5C_1 \times {}^4C_1 \times {}^3C_3$$

$\therefore$ The total number of ways to distribute 1, 1, 3 balls to the boxes

$$= {}^5C_1 \times {}^4C_1 \times {}^3C_3 \times \frac{3!}{2!} = 5 \times 4 \times 1 \times 3 = 60$$

and the number of ways to distribute the balls in II system

$$= {}^5C_1 \times {}^4C_2 \times {}^2C_2$$

$\therefore$ The total number of ways to distribute 1, 2, 2 balls to the boxes

$$= {}^5C_1 \times {}^4C_2 \times {}^2C_2 \times \frac{3!}{2!}$$

$$= 5 \times 6 \times 1 \times 3 = 90$$

$\therefore$ The required number of ways $= 60 + 90 = 150$

Example 79. In how many ways can 5 different books be tied up in three bundles?

Sol. The required number of ways $= \dfrac{1}{3!}(3^5 - {}^3C_1 \cdot 2^5 + {}^3C_2 \cdot 1^5)$

$$= \frac{150}{6} = 25$$

Example 80. If $n(A) = 5$ and $n(B) = 3$, find number of onto mappings from A to B.

Sol. We know that in onto mapping, each image must be assigned atleast one pre-image.

This is equivalent to number of ways in which 5 different balls (pre-images) can be distributed in 3 different boxes (images), if no box remains empty. The total number of onto mappings from A to B

$$= 3^5 - {}^3C_1(3-1)^5 + {}^3C_2(3-2)^5$$

$$= 243 - 96 + 3 = 150$$

(c) The number of ways in which n identical things can be distributed into r different groups is ${}^{n+r-1}C_{r-1}$ or ${}^{n-1}C_{r-1}$

According, as blank groups are or are not admissible.

Proof

If blank groups are not allowed Any such distribution can be effected as follows: place the n things in a row and put marks of partition in a selection of $(r-1)$ out of the $(n-1)$ spaces between them. This can be done in ${}^{n-1}C_{r-1}$.

If blank groups are allowed The number of distribution is the same as that of $(n+r)$ things of the same sort into r groups with no blank groups. For such a distribution can be effected thus, put one of the

$(n+r)$ things into each of the r groups and distribute the remaining n things into r groups, blank lots being allowed. Hence, the required number is ${}^{n+r-1}C_{r-1}$.

Aliter The number of distribution of n identical things into r different groups is the coefficient of x^n in $(1+x+x^2+\ldots+\infty)^r$ or in $(x+x^2+x^3+\ldots+\infty)^r$ according as blank groups are or are not allowed.

These expressions are respectively equal to $(1-x)^{-r}$ and $x^r(1-x)^{-r}$

Hence, coefficient of x^n in two expressions are ${}^{n+r-1}C_{r-1}$ and ${}^{n-1}C_{r-1}$, respectively.

| Example 81. In how many ways 5 identical balls can be distributed into 3 different boxes so that no box remains empty?

Sol. The required number of ways $= {}^{5-1}C_{3-1} = {}^4C_2 = \dfrac{4\cdot 3}{1\cdot 2} = 6$

Aliter Each box must contain atleast one ball, since no box remains empty. Boxes can have balls in the following systems.

Box	I	II	III
Number of balls	1	1	3

Or

Box	I	II	III
Number of balls	1	2	2

Here, balls are identical but boxes are different the number of combinations will be 1 in each systems.

$\therefore$ Required number of ways $= 1 \times \dfrac{3!}{2!} + 1 \times \dfrac{3!}{2!} = 3 + 3 = 6$

| Example 82. Four boys picked up 30 mangoes. In how many ways can they divide them, if all mangoes be identical?

Sol. Clearly, 30 mangoes can be distributed among 4 boys such that each boy can receive any number of mangoes.

Hence, total number of ways $= {}^{30+4-1}C_{4-1}$

$$= {}^{33}C_3 = \frac{33\cdot 32\cdot 31}{1\cdot 2\cdot 3} = 5456$$

| Example 83. Find the positive number of solutions of $x+y+z+w=20$ under the following conditions

(i) Zero value of x, y, z and w are included.

(ii) Zero values are excluded.

Sol. (i) Since, $x+y+z+w=20$

Here, $x\ge 0, y\ge 0, z\ge 0, w\ge 0$

The number of Sols of the given equation in this case is same as the number of ways of distributing 20 things among 4 different groups.

Hence, total number of Sols $= {}^{20+4-1}C_{4-1}$

$$= {}^{23}C_3 = \frac{23\cdot 22\cdot 21}{1\cdot 2\cdot 3} = 1771$$

(ii) Since, $x+y+z+w=20$ ...(i)

Here, $x\ge 1, y\ge 1, z\ge 1, w\ge 1$

or $x-1\ge 0, y-1\ge 0, z-1\ge 0, w-1\ge 0$

Let $x_1 = x-1 \Rightarrow x = x_1+1$

$y_1 = y-1 \Rightarrow y = y_1+1$

$z_1 = z-1 \Rightarrow z = z_1+1$

$w_1 = w-1 \Rightarrow w = w_1+1$

Then, from Eq. (i), we get

$$x_1+1+y_1+1+z_1+1+w_1+1 = 20$$

$$\Rightarrow \quad x_1+y_1+z_1+w_1 = 16$$

and $x_1\ge 0, y_1\ge 0, z_1\ge 0, w_1\ge 0$

Hence, total number of Solutions $= {}^{16+4-1}C_{4-1}$

$$= {}^{19}C_3 = \frac{19\cdot 18\cdot 17}{1\cdot 2\cdot 3} = 57\cdot 17 = 969$$

Aliter

Part (ii) $\because$ $x+y+z+w=20$

$x\ge 1, y\ge 1, z\ge 1, w\ge 1$

Hence, total number of solutions

$$= {}^{20-1}C_{4-1} = {}^{19}C_3 = 969$$

| Example 84. How many integral solutions are there to $x+y+z+t=29$, when $x\ge 1$, $y>1$, $z\ge 3$ and $t\ge 0$?

Sol. Since, $x+y+z+t=29$ ...(i)

and x, y, z, t are integers

$\therefore$ $x\ge 1, y\ge 2, z\ge 3, t\ge 0$

$\Rightarrow$ $x-1\ge 0, y-2\ge 0, z-3\ge 0, t\ge 0$

Let $x_1 = x-1, x_2 = y-2, x_3 = z-3$

or $x = x_1+1, y = x_2+2, z = x_3+3$ and then $x_1\ge 0, x_2\ge 0, x_3\ge 0, t\ge 0$

From Eq. (i), we get

$$x_1+1+x_2+2+x_3+3+t = 29$$

$$\Rightarrow \quad x_1+x_2+x_3+t = 23$$

Hence, total number of solutions $= {}^{23+4-1}C_{4-1}$

$$= {}^{26}C_3 = \frac{26\cdot 25\cdot 24}{1\cdot 2\cdot 3} = 2600$$

Aliter

$\because$ $x+y+z+t=29$ ...(i)

and $x\ge 1, y-1\ge 1, z-2\ge 1, t+1\ge 1$

Let $x_1 = x, y_1 = y-1, z_1 = z-2, t_1 = t+1$

or $x = x_1, y = y_1+1, z = z_1+2, t = t_1-1$

and then $x_1\ge 1, y_1\ge 1, z_1\ge 1, t_1\ge 1$

From Eq. (i), $x_1+y_1+1+z_1+2+t_1-1 = 29$

$$\Rightarrow \quad x_1+y_1+z_1+t_1 = 27$$

Hence, total number of solutions $= {}^{27-1}C_{4-1} = {}^{26}C_3$

$$= \frac{26\cdot 25\cdot 24}{1\cdot 2\cdot 3} = 2600$$

Example 85. How many integral Solutions are there to the system of equations $x_1 + x_2 + x_3 + x_4 + x_5 = 20$ and $x_1 + x_2 = 15$, when $x_k \geq 0$?

Sol. We have, $x_1 + x_2 + x_3 + x_4 + x_5 = 20$ ...(i)

and $x_1 + x_2 = 15$ ...(ii)

Then, from Eqs. (i) and (ii), we get two equations

$$x_3 + x_4 + x_5 = 5 \quad \text{...(iii)}$$

$$x_1 + x_2 = 15 \quad \text{...(iv)}$$

and given $x_1 \geq 0, x_2 \geq 0, x_3 \geq 0, x_4 \geq 0$ and $x_5 \geq 0$

Then, number of solutions of Eq. (iii)

$$= {}^{5+3-1}C_{3-1} = {}^7C_2$$

$$= \frac{7 \cdot 6}{1 \cdot 2} = 21$$

and number of solutions of Eq. (iv)

$$= {}^{15+2-1}C_{2-1} = {}^{16}C_1 = 16$$

Hence, total number of solutions of the given system of equations

$$= 21 \times 16 = 336$$

Example 86. Find the number of non-negative integral solutions of $3x + y + z = 24$.

Sol. We have,

$$3x + y + z = 24 \text{ and given } x \geq 0, y \geq 0, z \geq 0$$

Let $x = k$

$\therefore$ $y + z = 24 - 3k$ ...(i)

Here, $24 \geq 24 - 3k \geq 0 [\because x \geq 0]$

Hence, $0 \leq k \leq 8$

The total number of integral solutions of Eq. (i) is

$$^{24-3k+2-1}C_{2-1} = {}^{25-3k}C_1 = 25 - 3k$$

Hence, the total number of Sols of the original equation

$$= \sum_{k=0}^{8}(25 - 3k) = 25\sum_{k=0}^{8}1 - 3\sum_{k=0}^{8}k$$

$$= 25 \cdot 9 - 3 \cdot \frac{8 \cdot 9}{2} = 225 - 108 = 117$$

(d) The number of ways in which n identical things can be distributed into r groups so that no group contains less than l things and more than m things $(l < m)$ is coefficient of x^{n-lr} in the expansion of $(1 - x^{m-l+1})^r (1 - x)^{-r}$.

Proof Required number of ways

= Coefficient of x^n in the expansion of

$$(x^l + x^{l+1} + x^{l+2} + \ldots + x^m)^r$$

[$\because$ no group contains less than l things and more than m things, here r groups]

= Coefficient of x^n in the expansion of $x^{lr}(1 + x + x^2 + \ldots + x^{m-l})^r$

= Coefficient of x^{n-lr} in the expansion of $(1 + x + x^2 + \ldots + x^{m-l})^r$

= Coefficient of x^{n-lr} in the expansion of

$$\left(\frac{1 \cdot (1 - x^{m-l+1})}{(1 - x)}\right)^r$$

[sum of $m - l + 1$ terms of GP]

= Coefficient of x^{n-lr} in the expansion of

$$(1 - x^{m-l+1})^r (1 - x)^{-r}$$

Example 87. In how many ways can three persons, each throwing a single dice once, make a sum of 15 ?

Sol. Number on the faces of the dice are 1, 2, 3, 4, 5, 6 (least number 1, greatest number 6)

Here, $l = 1, m = 6, r = 3$ and $n = 15$

$\therefore$ Required number of ways = Coefficient of $x^{15-1\times3}$ in the expansion of $(1 - x^6)^3(1 - x)^{-3}$

= Coefficient of x^{12} in the expansion of

$$(1 - 3x^6 + 3x^{12})(1 + {}^3C_1 x + {}^4C_2 x^2 + \ldots + {}^8C_6 x^6 + \ldots + {}^{14}C_{12} x^{12} + \ldots)$$

$$= {}^{14}C_{12} - 3 \times {}^8C_6 + 3 = {}^{14}C_2 - 3 \times {}^8C_2 + 3$$

$$= 91 - 84 + 3 = 10$$

Example 88. In how many ways in which an examiner can assign 30 marks to 8 questions, giving not less than 2 marks to any question.

Sol. If examiner given marks any seven question 2 (each) marks, then marks on remaining questions given by examiner $= -7 \times 2 + 30 = 16$

If x_i are the marks assigned to ith question, then $x_1 + x_2 + x_3 + \ldots + x_8 = 30$ and $2 \leq x_i \leq 16$ for $i = 1, 2, 3, \ldots, 8$.

Here, $l = 2, m = 16, r = 8$ and $n = 30$

$\therefore$ Required number of ways

= Coefficient of $x^{30-2\times8}$ in the expansion of

$$(1 - x^{16-2+1})^8(1 - x)^{-8}$$

= Coefficient of x^{14} in the expansion of

$$(1 - x^{15})^8(1 + {}^8C_1 x + {}^9C_2 x^2 + \ldots + {}^{21}C_{14} x^{14} + \ldots)$$

= Coefficient of x^{14} in the expansion of

$$(1 + {}^8C_1 x + {}^9C_2 x^2 + \ldots + {}^{21}C_{14} x^{14} + \ldots)$$

$$= {}^{21}C_{14} = {}^{21}C_7$$

Note Coefficient of x^r in the expansion of $(1 - x)^{-n}$ is ${}^{n+r-1}C_r$.

(e) If a group has n things in which p are identical, then the number of ways of selecting r things from a group is

$$\sum_{r=0}^{r} {}^{n-p}C_r \text{ or } \sum_{r=r-p}^{r} {}^{n-p}C_r, \text{according as } r \le p \text{ or } r \ge p.$$

Example 89. A bag has contains 23 balls in which 7 are identical. Then, find the number of ways of selecting 12 balls from bag.

Sol. Here, $n = 23,\ p = 7,\ r = 12\ (r > p)$

$\therefore$ Required number of selections $= \sum_{r=5}^{12} {}^{16}C_r$

$$= {}^{16}C_5 + {}^{16}C_6 + {}^{16}C_7 + {}^{16}C_8 + {}^{16}C_9 + {}^{16}C_{10} + {}^{16}C_{11} + {}^{16}C_{12}$$

$$= ({}^{16}C_5 + {}^{16}C_6) + ({}^{16}C_7 + {}^{16}C_8) + ({}^{16}C_9 + {}^{16}C_{10}) + ({}^{16}C_{11} + {}^{16}C_{12})$$

$$= {}^{17}C_6 + {}^{17}C_8 + {}^{17}C_{10} + {}^{17}C_{12} \quad [\because {}^nC_r + {}^nC_{r-1} = {}^{n+1}C_r]$$

$$= {}^{17}C_{11} + {}^{17}C_9 + {}^{17}C_{10} + {}^{17}C_{12} \quad [\because {}^nC_r = {}^nC_{n-r}]$$

$$= ({}^{17}C_{11} + {}^{17}C_{12}) + ({}^{17}C_9 + {}^{17}C_{10})$$

$$= {}^{18}C_{12} + {}^{18}C_{10} = {}^{18}C_6 + {}^{18}C_8$$

Derangements Any change in the order of the things in a group is called a derangement.

Or

When 'n' things are to be placed at 'n' specific places but none of them is placed on its specified position, then we say that the 'n' things are deranged.

Or

Assume $a_1, a_2, a_3, \ldots, a_n$ be n distinct things such that their positions are fixed in a row. If we now rearrange $a_1, a_2, a_3, \ldots, a_n$ in such a way that no one occupy its original position, then such an arrangement is called a derangement.

Consider 'n' letters and 'n' corresponding envelops. The number of ways in which letters can be placed in the envelopes (one letter in each envelope) so that no letter is placed in correct envelope is

$$n!\left(1 - \frac{1}{1!} + \frac{1}{2!} - \frac{1}{3!} + \ldots + (-1)^n \frac{1}{n!}\right)$$

Proof n letters are denoted by 1, 2, 3, …, n. Let A_i denote the set of distribution of letters in envelopes (one letter in each envelop) so that the i th letter is placed in the corresponding envelope, then

$$n(A_i) = 1 \times (n-1)!$$

[$\because$ the remaining $(n-1)$ letters can be placed in $(n-1)$ envelopes is $(n-1)!$]

and $n(A_i \cap A_j) = 1 \times 1 \times (n-2)!$ [$\because$ i and j can be placed in their corresponding envelopes and remaining $(n-2)$ letters can be placed in $(n-2)$ envelopes in $(n-2)!$ way]

Also, $n(A_i \cap A_j \cap A_k) = 1 \times 1 \times 1 \times (n-3)!$

Hence, the required number is

$$n(A_1' \cap A_2' \cap A_3' \cap \ldots \cap A_n')$$

$$= n(U) - n(A_1 \cup A_2 \cup A_3 \cup \ldots \cup A_n)$$

$$= n! - \left\{\sum n(A_i) - \sum n(A_i \cap A_j) + \sum n(A_i \cap A_j \cap A_k) - \ldots + (-1)^n \sum n(A_1 \cap A_2 \cap A_3 \cap \ldots \cap A_n)\right\}$$

$$= n! - \{{}^nC_1 \times (n-1)! - {}^nC_2 \times (n-2)! + {}^nC_3 \times (n-3)! - \ldots + (-1)^{n-1} \times {}^nC_n \times 1!\}$$

$$= n! - \left\{\frac{n \times (n-1)!}{1!} - \frac{n(n-1)}{2!} \times (n-2)! + \frac{n(n-1)(n-2)}{3!} \times (n-3)! - \ldots + (-1)^{n-1} \times 1\right\}$$

$$= n! - \left\{\frac{n!}{1!} - \frac{n!}{2!} + \frac{n!}{3!} - \ldots + (-1)^n \cdot 1\right\}$$

$$= n!\left[1 - \frac{1}{1!} + \frac{1}{2!} - \frac{1}{3!} + \ldots + \frac{(-1)^n}{n!}\right]$$

Maha Short Cut Method

If $\quad D_n = n!\left[1 - \frac{1}{1!} + \frac{1}{2!} - \frac{1}{3!} + \ldots + \frac{(-1)^n}{n!}\right]$

Then, $\boldsymbol{D_{n+1} = (n+1)D_n + (-1)^{n+1}, \forall x \in N}$

and $\quad \boldsymbol{D_{n+1} = n(D_n + D_{n-1}), \forall x \in N - \{1\}}$

where $\quad D_1 = 0$

For $n = 1$, from result I

$$D_2 = 2D_1 + (-1)^2 = 0 + 1 = 1$$

For $n = 2$, from result I

$$D_3 = 3D_2 + (-1)^3 = 3 \times 1 - 1 = 2$$

For $n = 3$, from result I

$$D_4 = 4D_3 + (-1)^4 = 4 \times 2 + 1 = 9$$

For $n = 4$, from result I

$$D_5 = 5D_4 + (-1)^5 = 5 \times 9 - 1 = 44$$

For $n = 5$, from result I

$$D_6 = 6D_5 + (-1)^6 = 6 \times 44 + 1 = 265$$

Note $D_1 = 0, D_2 = 1, D_3 = 2, D_4 = 9, D_5 = 44, D_6 = 265$ [Remember]

Remark

If r things goes to wrong place out of n things, then $(n-r)$ things goes to original place (here $r < n$).

If D_n = Number of ways, if all n things goes to wrong places.

and D_r = Number of ways, if r things goes to wrong places.

If r goes to wrong places out of n, then $(n-r)$ goes to correct places.

Then, $D_n = {}^nC_{n-r}\, D_r$

where, $D_r = r!\left(1 - \frac{1}{1!} + \frac{1}{2!}! - \frac{1}{3!} + \ldots + (-1)^r \frac{1}{r!}\right)$

If atleast p things goes to wrong places, then $D_n = \sum_{r=p}^{n} {}^nC_{n-r} \cdot D_r$

Example 90. A person writes letters to six friends and addresses the corresponding envelopes. In how many ways can the letters be placed in the envelopes so that (i) atleast two of them are in the wrong envelopes. (ii) all the letters are in the wrong envelopes.

Sol. (i) The number of ways in which atleast two of them in the wrong envelopes

$$= \sum_{r=2}^{6} {}^6C_{6-r} \cdot D_r$$

$$= {}^6C_4 \times D_2 + {}^6C_3 \times D_3 + {}^6C_2 \times D_4 + {}^6C_1 \times D_5 + {}^6C_0 \times D_6$$

$$= 15D_2 + 20D_3 + 15D_4 + 6D_5 + D_6 \quad \text{[from note]}$$

$$= 15 \times 1 + 20 \times 2 + 15 \times 9 + 6 \times 44 + 265$$

$$= 719$$

(ii) The number of ways in which all letters be placed in wrong envelopes $= D_6 = 265$ [from note]

Aliter

(i) The number of all the possible ways of putting 6 letters into 6 envelopes is $6!$.

Number of ways to place all letters correctly into corresponding envelopes = 1

and number of ways to place one letter in the wrong envelope and other 5 letters in the write envelope = 0

[∵ It is not possible that only one letter goes in the wrong envelope, when if 5 letters goes in the right envelope, then remaining one letter also goes in the write envelope]

Hence, number of ways to place atleast two letters goes in the wrong envelopes

$$= 6! - 0 - 1 = 6! - 1 = 720 - 1 = 719$$

(ii) The number of ways 1 letter in 1 address envelope, so that one letter is in wrong envelope = 0 ...(i)

[because it is not possible that only one letter goes in the wrong envelope]

The number of ways to put 2 letters in 2 addressed envelopes so that all are in wrong envelopes

= The number of ways without restriction – The number of ways in which all are in correct envelopes – The number of ways in which 1 letter is in the correct envelope

$$= 2! - 1 - 0 = 2 - 1$$

$$= 1 \quad \text{...(ii) [from Eq. (i)]}$$

The number of ways to put 3 letters in 3 addressed envelopes so that all are in wrong envelopes

= The number of ways without restriction – The number of ways in which all are in correct envelopes – The number of ways in which 1 letter is in the correct envelope – The number of ways in which 2 letter are in correct envelope

$$= 3! - 1 - {}^3C_1 \times 1 - 0 \quad \text{[from Eqs. (i) and (ii)]}$$

$$= 2$$

[${}^3C_1$ means that select one envelope to put the letter correctly]

The number of ways to put 4 letters in 4 addressed envelopes so that all are in wrong envelopes

= The number of ways without restriction – The number of ways in which all are in correct envelopes – The number of ways in which 1 letter is in the correct envelope – The number of ways in which 2 letters are in correct envelopes – The number of ways in which 3 letters are in correct envelopes

$$= 4! - 1 - {}^4C_1 \times 2 - {}^4C_2 \times 1 - {}^4C_3 \times 0$$

[from Eqs. (i), (ii) and (iii)]

$$= 24 - 1 - 8 - 6 - 0 = 9 \quad \text{...(iv)}$$

The number of ways to put 5 letters in 5 addressed envelopes so that all are in wrong envelopes

= The number of ways without restriction – The number of ways in which all are in correct envelopes – The number of ways in which 1 letter is in the correct envelopes – The number of ways in which 2 letters are in correct envelopes – The number of ways in which 3 letters are in correct envelopes – The number of ways in which 4 letters are in correct envelopes

$$= 5! - 1 - {}^5C_1 \times 9 - {}^5C_2 \times 2 - {}^5C_3 \times 1 - {}^5C_4 \times 0$$

[from Eqs. (i), (ii), (iii) and (iv)]

$$= 120 - 1 - 45 - 20 - 10 - 0 = 44$$

The number of ways to put 6 letters in 6 addressed envelopes so that all are in wrong envelopes

= The number of ways without restriction – The number of ways in which all are in correct envelopes – The number of ways in which 1 letter is in the correct envelope – The number of ways in which 2 letters are in correct envelopes – The number of ways in which 3 letters are in correct envelopes – The number of ways in which 4 letters are in correct envelopes – The number of ways in which 5 letters are in correct envelopes.

$$=6!-1-{}^6C_1\times 44-{}^6C_2\times 9-{}^6C_3\times 2 - {}^6C_4\times 1-{}^6C_5\times 0$$

[from Eqs. (i), (ii), (iii), (iv) and (v)]

$=720-1-264-135-40-15=720-455=265$

Multinomial Theorem

(i) If there are l objects of one kind, m objects of second kind, n objects of third kind and so on, then the number of ways of choosing r objects out of these objects (i.e., $l+m+n+\ldots$) is the coefficient of x^r in the expansion of

$$(1+x+x^2+x^3+\ldots+x^l)(1+x+x^2+\ldots+x^m)(1+x+x^2+\ldots+x^n)$$

Further, if one object of each kind is to be included, then the number of ways of choosing r objects out of these objects (i.e., $l+m+n+\ldots$) is the coefficient of x^r in the expansion of

$$(x+x^2+x^3+\ldots+x^l)(x+x^2+x^3+\ldots+x^m)(x+x^2+x^3+\ldots+x^n)\ldots$$

(ii) If there are l objects of one kind, m objects of second kind, n objects of third kind and so on, then the number of possible arrangements/permutations of r objects out of these objects (i.e., $l+m+n+\ldots$) is the coefficient of x^r in the expansion of

$$r!\left(1+\frac{x}{1!}+\frac{x^2}{2!}+\ldots+\frac{x^l}{l!}\right)\left(1+\frac{x}{1!}+\frac{x^2}{2!}+\ldots+\frac{x^m}{m!}\right)\left(1+\frac{x}{1!}+\frac{x^2}{2!}+\ldots+\frac{x^n}{n!}\right)\ldots$$

Different Cases of Multinomial Theorem

***Case* I If upper limit of a variable is more than or equal to the sum required, then the upper limit of that variable can be taken as infinite.**

| Example 91. In how many ways the sum of upper faces of four distinct die can be five?

Sol. Here, the number of required ways will be equal to the number of solutions of $x_1+x_2+x_3+x_4=5$ i.e., $1\le x_i\le 6$ for $i=1, 2, 3, 4$.

Since, upper limit is 6, which is greater than required sum, so upper limit taken as infiite. So, number of Sols is equal to coefficient of α^5 in the expansion of $(1+\alpha+\alpha^2+\ldots+\infty)^4$

$$= \text{Coefficient of } \alpha^5 \text{ in the expansion of } (1-\alpha)^{-4}$$

$$= \text{Coefficient of } \alpha^5 \text{ in the expansion of } (1+{}^4C_1\alpha+{}^5C_2\alpha^2+\ldots)$$

$$= {}^8C_5={}^8C_3=\frac{8\cdot 7\cdot 6}{1\cdot 2\cdot 3}=56$$

***Case* II If the upper limit of a variable is less than the sum required and the lower limit of all variables is non-negative, then the upper limit of that variable is that given in the problem.**

| Example 92. In an examination, the maximum marks each of three papers is 50 and the maximum mark for the fourth paper is 100. Find the number of ways in which the candidate can score 60% marks in aggregate.

Sol. Aggregate of marks $=50\times 3+100=250$

$\therefore$ 60% of the aggregate $=\dfrac{60}{100}\times 250=150$

Let the marks scored by the candidate in four papers be x_1, x_2, x_3 and x_4. Here, the number of required ways will be equal to the number of Sols of $x_1+x_2+x_3+x_4=150$ i.e., $0\le x_1, x_2, x_3\le 50$ and $0\le x_4\le 100$.

Since, the upper limit is 100 < required sum (150).

The number of solutions of the equation is equal to coefficient of α^{150} in the expansion of

$$(\alpha^0+\alpha^1+\alpha^2+\ldots+\alpha^{50})^3(\alpha^0+\alpha^1+\alpha^2+\ldots+\alpha^{100})$$

$$= \text{Coefficient of } \alpha^{150} \text{ in the expansion of } (1-\alpha^{51})^3(1-\alpha^{10})(1-\alpha)^{-4}$$

$$= \text{Coefficient of } \alpha^{150} \text{ in the expansion of } (1-3\alpha^{51}+3\alpha^{102})(1-\alpha^{101})(1+{}^4C_1\alpha+{}^5C_2\alpha^2+\ldots+\infty)$$

$$= \text{Coefficient of } \alpha^{150} \text{ in the expansion of } (1-3\alpha^{51}-\alpha^{101}+3\alpha^{102})(1+{}^4C_1\alpha+{}^5C_2\alpha^2+\ldots+\infty)$$

$$= {}^{153}C_{150}-3\times{}^{102}C_{99}-{}^{52}C_{49}+3\times{}^{51}C_{48}$$

$$= {}^{153}C_3-3\times{}^{102}C_3-{}^{52}C_3+3\times{}^{51}C_3$$

$$=110556$$

Very Important Trick

On multiplying $p_0 + p_1\alpha + p_2\alpha^2 + p_3\alpha^3 + \ldots + p_n\alpha^n$ by $(1+\alpha)$, we get

$$p_0 + (p_0 + p_1)\alpha + (p_1 + p_2)\alpha^2 + (p_2 + p_3)\alpha^3 + \ldots + (p_{n-2} + p_{n-1})\alpha^{n-1} + (p_{n-1} + p_n)\alpha^n + p_n\alpha^{n+1}$$

i.e., we just add coefficient of α^r with coefficient of α^{r-1} (i.e., previous term) to get coefficient α^r in product.

Now, coefficient of $\alpha^r = p_{r-1} + p_r$

On multiplying $p_0 + p_1\alpha + p_2\alpha^2 + p_3\alpha^3 + \ldots + p_n\alpha^n$ by $(1+\alpha+\alpha^2)$

we get, $p_0 + (p_0 + p_1)\alpha + (p_0 + p_1 + p_2)\alpha^2 + (p_1 + p_2 + p_3)\alpha^3 + (p_2 + p_3 + p_4)\alpha^4 + \ldots$

i.e., to find coefficient of α^r in product and add this with 2 preceding coefficients.

Now, coefficient of $\alpha^r = p_{r-2} + p_{r-1} + p_r$

Similarly, in product of $p_0 + p_1\alpha + p_2\alpha^2 + \ldots$ with $(1+\alpha+\alpha^2+\alpha^3)$, the coefficient of α^r in product will be

$$\underbrace{p_{r-3} + p_{r-2} + p_{r-1}}_{\text{3 preceding coefficients}} + p_r$$

and in product of $p_0 + p_1\alpha + p_2\alpha^2 + \ldots$ with $(1+\alpha+\alpha^2+\alpha^3+\alpha^4)$, the coefficient of α^r in product will be $\underbrace{p_{r-4} + p_{r-3} + p_{r-2} + p_{r-1}}_{\text{4 preceding coefficients}} + p_r$

Finally, in product of $p_0 + p_1\alpha + p_2\alpha^2 + \ldots$ with $(1+\alpha+\alpha^2+\alpha^3+\ldots+\text{upto}\,\infty)$, the coefficient of α^r in product will be $\underbrace{p_0 + p_1 + p_2 + \ldots + p_{r-1}}_{\text{all preceding coefficients}} + p_r$

| Example 93. Find the coefficient of α^6 in the product $(1+\alpha+\alpha^2)(1+\alpha+\alpha^2)(1+\alpha+\alpha^2+\alpha^3)(1+\alpha)(1+\alpha)(1+\alpha)$.

Sol. The given product can be written as

$$(1+\alpha+\alpha^2)(1+\alpha+\alpha^2)(1+\alpha+\alpha^2+\alpha^3)(1+\alpha)^3$$

$$\text{or } (1+\alpha+\alpha^2)(1+\alpha+\alpha^2)(1+\alpha+\alpha^2+\alpha^3)(1+3\alpha+3\alpha^2+\alpha^3)$$

Multiplying Synthetically

1	α	α^2	α^3	α^4	α^5	α^6	...
1	3	3	1	0	0	0	

... on multiplying by $1+\alpha+\alpha^2+\alpha^3 \rightarrow$ To each coefficient add 3 preceding coefficients

1	4	7	8	7	4	1	...

...on multiplying by $1+\alpha+\alpha^2 \rightarrow$ To each coefficient add 2 preceding coefficients.

1	5	12	19	22	19	12	...

...on multiplying by $1+\alpha+\alpha^2 \rightarrow$ To each coefficient add 2 preceding coefficients.

...	...	...	...	...	...	53	...

Hence, required coefficient is 53.

| Example 94. Find the number of different selections of 5 letters which can be made from 5A's, 4B's, 3C's, 2D's and 1E

Sol. All selections of 5 letters are given by 5th degree terms in

$$(1 + A + A^2 + A^3 + A^4 + A^5)(1 + B + B^2 + B^3 + B^4)$$
$$(1 + C + C^2 + C^3)(1 + D + D^2)(1 + E)$$

$\therefore$ Number of 5 letter selections

$$= \text{Coefficient of } \alpha^5 \text{ in } (1+\alpha+\alpha^2+\alpha^3+\alpha^4+\alpha^5)(1+\alpha+\alpha^2+\alpha^3+\alpha^4)(1+\alpha+\alpha^2+\alpha^3)(1+\alpha+\alpha^2)(1+\alpha)$$

Multiplying synthetically

1	α	α^2	α^3	α^4	α^5 ...
1	1	1	1	1	1
					$\times 1+\alpha+\alpha+\alpha^2+\alpha^3+\alpha^4$
1	2	3	4	5	5 ...
					$\times 1+\alpha+\alpha^2+\alpha^3$
1	3	6	10	14	17 ...
					$\times 1+\alpha+\alpha^2$
1	4	10	19	30	41 ...
					$\times 1+\alpha$
1	5	14	29	49	**71**

Hence, required coefficient is 71.

| Example 95. Find the number of combinations and permutations of 4 letters taken from the word EXAMINATION.

Sol. There are 11 letters

A, A, N, N, X, M, T, O.

Then, number of combinations

$= \text{coefficient of } x^4 \text{ in } (1 + x + x^2)^3(1 + x)^5$

[$\because$ 2A's, 2I 's, 2N's, 1E, 1X, 1M, 1T and 1O]

$= \text{Coefficient of } x^4 \text{ in } \{(1+x)^3 + x^6 + 3(1+x)^2 x^2 + 3(1+x)x^4\}(1+x)^5$

$= \text{Coefficient of } x^4 \text{ in}$

$\{(1+x)^8 + x^6(1+x)^5 + 3x^2(1+x)^7 + 3x^4(1+x)^6\}$

$= {}^8C_4 + 0 + 3\cdot{}^7C_2 + 3 = \frac{8\cdot7\cdot6\cdot5}{1\cdot2\cdot3\cdot4} + 3\cdot\frac{7\cdot6}{1\cdot2} + 3 = 70 + 63 + 3$

$= 136$

and number of permutations

$= \text{Coefficient of } x^4 \text{ in } 4!\left(1 + \frac{x}{1!} + \frac{x^2}{2!}\right)^3 \left(1 + \frac{x}{1!}\right)^5$

$= \text{Coefficient of } x^4 \text{ in } 4!\left(1 + x + \frac{x^2}{2}\right)^3 (1+x)^5$

$= \text{Coefficient of } x^4 \text{ in}$

$4!\left\{(1+x)^3 + \frac{x^6}{8} + \frac{3}{2}(1+x)^2 x^2 + \frac{3}{4}x^4(1+x)\right\}(1+x)^5$

$= \text{Coefficient of } x^4 \text{ in}$

$4!\left\{(1+x)^8 + \frac{x^6}{8}(1+x)^5 + \frac{3}{2}x^2(1+x)^7 + \frac{3}{4}x^4(1+x)^6\right\}$

$= 4!\left\{{}^8C_4 + 0 + \frac{3}{2}\cdot{}^7C_2 + \frac{3}{4}\right\} = 24\left\{\frac{8\cdot7\cdot6\cdot5}{1\cdot2\cdot3\cdot4} + \frac{3}{2}\cdot\frac{7\cdot6}{1\cdot2} + \frac{3}{4}\right\}$

$= 8\cdot7\cdot6\cdot5 + 6(3\cdot7\cdot6) + 6\cdot3 = 1680 + 756 + 18 = 2454$

Aliter There are 11 letters:

A, A, I, I, N, N, E, X, M, T, O

The following cases arise:

***Case* I All letters different** The required number of choosing 4 different letters from 8 different (A, I, N, E, X, M, T, O) types of the letters

$= {}^8C_4 = \frac{8\cdot7\cdot6\cdot5}{1\cdot2\cdot3\cdot4} = 70$

and number of permutations $= {}^8P_4 = 8\cdot7\cdot6\cdot5 = 1680$

***Case* II Two alike of one type and two alike of another type** This must be 2A's, 2I's or 2I's, 2N's, or 2N's, 2A's.

$\therefore$ Number of selections $= {}^3C_2 = 3$

For example, [for arrangements]

A	A	I	I

and number of permutations $= 3\cdot\frac{4!}{2!2!} = 18$

***Case* III Two alike and two different** This must be 2A's or 2I's or 2N's

and for each case 7 different letters.

For example, for 2A's, 7 differents's are I, N, E, X, M, T, O

For example, [for arrangements]

A	X	A	O

$\therefore$ Number of selections $= {}^3C_1 \times {}^7C_2 = 3 \times \frac{7\times6}{1\times2} = 63$

and number of permutations $= 63\cdot\frac{4!}{2!} = 756$

From Case I, II and III

The required number of combinations $= 70 + 3 + 63 = 136$

and number of permutations $= 1680 + 18 + 756 = 2454$

Note Number of combinations and permutations of 4 letters taken from the word MATHEMATICS are 136 and 2454 respectively, as like of EXAMINATION.

Number of Solutions with the Help of Multinomial Theorem

***Case* I** If the equation

$$\alpha + 2\beta + 3\gamma + \ldots + q\theta = n \qquad \ldots\text{(i)}$$

(a) If zero included, the number of solution of Eq. (i)

$= \text{Coefficient of } x^n \text{ in } (1 + x + x^2 + \ldots)$
$(1 + x^2 + x^4 + \ldots)(1 + x^3 + x^6 + \ldots)\ldots$
$(1 + x^q + x^{2q} + \ldots)$

$= \text{Coefficient of } x^n \text{ in}$
$(1-x)^{-1}(1-x^2)^{-1}(1-x^3)^{-1}\ldots(1-x^q)^{-1}$

(b) If zero excluded, then the number of solutions of Eq. (i)

$= \text{Coefficient of } x^n \text{ in } (x + x^2 + x^3 + \ldots)$
$(x^2 + x^4 + x^6 + \ldots)(x^3 + x^6 + x^9 + \ldots)$
$\ldots(x^q + x^{2q} + \ldots)$

$= \text{Coefficient of } x^n \text{ in } x^{1+2+3+\ldots+q}(1-x)^{-1}$
$(1-x^2)^{-1}(1-x^3)^{-1}\ldots(1-x^q)^{-1}$

$= \text{Coefficient of } x^{n - \frac{q(q+1)}{2}} \text{ in}$
$(1-x)^{-1}(1-x^2)^{-1}(1-x^3)^{-1}\ldots(1-x^q)^{-1}$

Example 96. Find the number of non-negative integral solutions of $x_1 + x_2 + x_3 + 4x_4 = 20$.

Sol. Number of non-negative integral solutions of the given equation

$= \text{Coefficient of } x^{20} \text{ in } (1-x)^{-1}(1-x)^{-1}(1-x)^{-1}(1-x^4)^{-1}$

$= \text{Coefficient of } x^{20} \text{ in } (1-x)^{-3}(1-x^4)^{-1}$

$= \text{Coefficient of } x^{20} \text{ in } (1 + {}^3C_1 + {}^4C_2x^2 + {}^5C_3x^3 + {}^6C_4x^4 + \ldots + {}^{10}C_8x^8 + \ldots + {}^{14}C_{12}x^{12} + \ldots + {}^{18}C_{16}x^{16} + \ldots + {}^{22}C_{20}x^{20} + \ldots)(1 + x^4 + x^8 + x^{12} + x^{16} + x^{20} + \ldots)$

$= 1 + {}^6C_4 + {}^{10}C_8 + {}^{14}C_{12} + {}^{18}C_{16} + {}^{22}C_{20}$

$$= 1 + {}^6C_2 + {}^{10}C_2 + {}^{14}C_2 + {}^{18}C_2 + {}^{22}C_2$$

$$= 1 + \left(\frac{6\cdot5}{1\cdot2}\right) + \left(\frac{10\cdot9}{1\cdot2}\right) + \left(\frac{14\cdot13}{1\cdot2}\right) + \left(\frac{18\cdot17}{1\cdot2}\right) + \left(\frac{22\cdot21}{1\cdot2}\right)$$

$$= 1 + 15 + 45 + 91 + 153 + 231 = 536$$

Example 97. Find the number of positive unequal integral solutions of the equation $x + y + z + w = 20$.

Sol. We have, $\qquad x + y + z + w = 20 \qquad$ ...(i)

Assume $x < y < z < w$. Here, $x, y, z, w \geq 1$

Now, let $x = x_1, y - x = x_2, z - y = x_3$ and $w - z = x_4$

$\therefore \quad x = x_1, y = x_1 + x_2, z = x_1 + x_2 + x_3$ and

$w = x_1 + x_2 + x_3 + x_4$

From Eq. (i), $4x_1 + 3x_2 + 2x_3 + x_4 = 20$

Then, $x_1, x_2, x_3, x_4 \geq 1$

$\because \quad 4x_1 + 3x_2 + 2x_3 + x_4 = 20 \qquad$ ...(ii)

$\therefore$ Number of positive integral solutions of Eq. (ii)

$= $ Coefficient of x^{20-10} in

$$(1 - x^4)^{-1}(1 - x^3)^{-1}(1 - x^2)^{-1}(1 - x)^{-1}$$

$= $ Coefficient of x^{10} in

$$(1 - x^4)^{-1}(1 - x^3)^{-1}(1 - x^2)^{-1}(1 - x)^{-1}$$

$= $ Coefficient of x^{10} in $(1 + x^4 + x^8 + x^{12} + \dots)$

$$\times (1 + x^3 + x^6 + x^9 + x^{12} + \dots) \times (1 + x^2 + x^4 + x^6 + x^8 + x^{10} + \dots) \times (1 + x + x^2 + x^3 + x^4 + x^5 + x^6 + x^7 + x^8 + x^9 + x^{10} + \dots)$$

$= $ Coefficient of x^{10} in

$$(1 + x^3 + x^6 + x^9 + x^4 + x^7 + x^{10} + x^8) \times (1 + x^2 + x^4 + x^6 + x^8 + x^{10})(1 + x + x^2 + x^3 + x^4 + x^5 + x^6 + x^7 + x^8 + x^9 + x^{10})$$

[neglecting higher powers]

$= $ Coefficient of x^{10} in

$$(1 + x^2 + x^4 + x^6 + x^8 + x^{10} + x^3 + x^5 + x^7 + x^9 + x^6 + x^8 + x^{10} + x^9 + x^4 + x^6 + x^8 + x^{10} + x^7 + x^9 + x^{10} + x^8 + x^{10})(1 + x + x^2 + x^3 + x^4 + x^5 + x^6 + x^7 + x^8 + x^9 + x^{10})$$

[neglecting higher powers]

$$= 1 + 1 + 1 + 1 + 1 + 1 + 1 + 1 + 1 + 1 + 1 + 1 + 1 + 1 + 1 + 1 + 1 + 1 + 1 + 1 + 1 + 1 + 1 = 23$$

But x, y, z and w can be arranged in ${}^4P_4 = 4! = 24$

Hence, required number of Sols $= (23)(24) = 552$

Example 98. In how many ways can 15 identical blankets be distributed among six beggars such that everyone gets atleast one blanket and two particular beggars get equal blankets and another three particular beggars get equal blankets.

Sol. The number of ways of distributing blankets is equal to the number of solutions of the equation $3x + 2y + z = 15$, where $x \geq 1, y \geq 1, z \geq 1$ which is equal to coefficient of α^{15} in

$$(\alpha^3 + \alpha^6 + \alpha^9 + \alpha^{12} + \alpha^{15} + \dots) \times (\alpha^2 + \alpha^4 + \alpha^6 + \alpha^8 + \alpha^{10} + \alpha^{12} + \alpha^{14} + \dots) \times (\alpha + \alpha^2 + \alpha^3 + \dots + \alpha^{15} + \dots)$$

$= $ Coefficient of α^9 in $(1 + \alpha^3 + \alpha^6 + \alpha^9)$

$$\times (1 + \alpha^2 + \alpha^4 + \alpha^6 + \alpha^8) \times (1 + \alpha + \alpha^2 + \alpha^3 + \alpha^4 + \alpha^5 + \alpha^6 + \alpha^7 + \alpha^8 + \alpha^9)$$

[neglecting higher powers]

$= $ Coefficient of α^9 in $(1 + \alpha^2 + \alpha^4 + \alpha^6 + \alpha^8 + \alpha^3 + \alpha^5 + \alpha^7 + \alpha^9 + \alpha^6 + \alpha^8 + \alpha^9) \times (1 + \alpha + \alpha^2 + \alpha^3 + \alpha^4 + \alpha^5 + \alpha^6 + \alpha^7 + \alpha^8 + \alpha^9)$

[neglecting higher powers]

$$= 1 + 1 + 1 + 1 + 1 + 1 + 1 + 1 + 1 + 1 + 1 + 1 = 12$$

***Case* II** If the inequation

$$x_1 + x_2 + x_3 + \dots + x_m \leq n \qquad \text{...(i)}$$

[when the required sum is not fixed]

In this case, we introduce a dummy variable x_{m+1}.

So that,

$$x_1 + x_2 + x_3 + \dots + x_m + x_{m+1} = n,$$

$$x_{m+1} \geq 0 \qquad \text{...(ii)}$$

Here, the number of Sols of Eqs. (i) and (ii) will be same.

Example 99. Find the number of positive integral solutions of the inequation $3x + y + z \leq 30$.

Sol. Let dummy variable w, then

$$3x + y + z + w = 30, w \geq 0 \qquad \text{...(i)}$$

Now, let $a = x - 1, b = y - 1, c = z - 1, d = w$, then

$$3a + b + c + d = 25, \text{ where } a, b, c, d \geq 0 \qquad \text{...(ii)}$$

$\therefore$ Number of positive integral solutions of Eq. (i)

$= $ Number of non-negative integral solutions of Eq. (ii)

$= $ Coefficient of α^{25} in $(1 + \alpha^3 + \alpha^6 + \dots)(1 + \alpha + \alpha^2 + \dots)^3$

$= $ Coefficient of α^{25} in $(1 + \alpha^3 + \alpha^6 + \dots)(1 - \alpha)^{-3}$

$= $ Coefficient of α^{25} in

$$(1 + \alpha^3 + \alpha^6 + \dots)(1 + {}^3C_1\alpha + {}^4C_2\alpha^2 + \dots)$$

$$= {}^{27}C_{25} + {}^{24}C_{22} + {}^{21}C_{19} + {}^{18}C_{16} + {}^{15}C_{13} + {}^{12}C_{10} + {}^9C_7 + {}^6C_4 + {}^3C_1$$

$$= {}^{27}C_2 + {}^{24}C_2 + {}^{21}C_2 + {}^{18}C_2 + {}^{15}C_2 + {}^{12}C_2 + {}^9C_2 + {}^6C_2 + {}^3C_1$$

$$= 351 + 276 + 210 + 153 + 105 + 66 + 36 + 15 + 3 = 1215$$

Aliter

From Eq. (ii), $3a + b + c + d = 25$, where $a, b, c, d \geq 0$

Clearly, $0 \leq a \leq 8$, if $a = k$, then

$$b + c + d = 25 - 3k \quad \text{...(iii)}$$

Hence, number of non-negative integral solutions of Eq. (iii) is

$$^{25 - 3k + 3 - 1}C_{3 - 1} = {}^{27 - 3k}C_2 = \frac{(27 - 3k)(26 - 3k)}{2}$$

$$= \frac{3}{2}(3k^2 - 53k + 234)$$

Therefore, required number is

$$\frac{3}{2}\sum_{k=0}^{8}(3k^2 - 53k + 234)$$

$$= \frac{3}{2}\left[3\cdot\left(\frac{8 \times 9 \times 17}{6}\right) - 53\cdot\left(\frac{8 \times 9}{2}\right) + 234 \times 9\right] = 1215$$

Example 100. In how many ways can we get a sum of atmost 15 by throwing six distinct dice ?

Sol. Let x_1, x_2, x_3, x_4, x_5 and x_6 be the number that appears on the six dice.

The number of ways = Number of solutions of the inequation

$$x_1 + x_2 + x_3 + x_4 + x_5 + x_6 \leq 15$$

Introducing a dummy variable $x_7 (x_7 \geq 0)$, the inequation becomes an equation

$$x_1 + x_2 + x_3 + x_4 + x_5 + x_6 + x_7 = 15$$

Here, $1 \leq x_i \leq 6$ for $i = 1, 2, 3, 4, 5, 6$ and $x_7 \geq 0$.

Therefore, number of solutions

$= \text{Coefficient of } x^{15} \text{ in } (x + x^2 + x^3 + x^4 + x^5 + x^6)^6 \times (1 + x + x^2 + \dots)$

$= \text{Coefficient of } x^9 \text{ in } (1 - x^6)^6 (1 - x)^{-7}$

$= \text{Coefficient of } x^9 \text{ in } (1 - 6x^6)(1 + {}^7C_1 x + {}^8C_2 x^2 + \dots)$ [neglecting higher powers]

$= {}^{15}C_9 - 6 \times {}^9C_3 = {}^{15}C_6 - 6 \times {}^9C_3$

$= 5005 - 504 = 4501$

***Case* III** If the inequation

$$x_1 + x_2 + x_3 + \dots + x_n \geq n$$

[when the values of $x_1, x_2, \dots, x_n$ are restricted]

In this case first find the number of solutions of $x_1 + x_2 + x_3 + \dots + x_n \leq n - 1$ and then subtract it from the total number of solutions.

Example 101. In how many ways can we get a sum greater than 15 by throwing six distinct dice?

Sol. Let x_1, x_2, x_3, x_4, x_5 and x_6 be the number that appears on the six dice.

The number of ways = Number of solutions of the inequation

$$x_1 + x_2 + x_3 + x_4 + x_5 + x_6 > 15$$

Here, $1 \leq x_i \leq 6$, $i = 1, 2, 3, 4, 5, 6$

Total number of cases $= 6^6 = 2^6 \times 3^6 = 64 \times 729 = 46656$

and number of ways to get the sum less than or equal to 15, which is 4501 [from Example 100]

Hence, the number of ways to get a sum greater than 15 is $46656 - 4501 = 42155$

***Case* IV** If the equation

$$x_1 x_2 x_3 \dots x_n = 2^{\alpha_1} \cdot 3^{\alpha_2} \cdot 5^{\alpha_3} \dots$$

where $\alpha_1, \alpha_2, \alpha_3, \dots$ are natural numbers.

In this case number of positive integral solutions $(x_1, x_2, x_3, \dots, x_n)$ are

$$({}^{\alpha_1 + n - 1}C_{n-1})({}^{\alpha_2 + n - 1}C_{n-1})({}^{\alpha_3 + n - 1}C_{n-1}) \dots$$

Example 102. Find the total number of positive integral solutions for (x, y, z) such that $xyz = 24$.

Sol. $\because$ $xyz = 24 = 2^3 \times 3^1$

Hence, total number of positive integral solutions

$$= ({}^{3 + 3 - 1}C_{3 - 1})({}^{1 + 3 - 1}C_{3 - 1})$$

$$= {}^5C_2 \times {}^3C_2 = 30$$

Aliter

$\because$ $xyz = 24 = 2^3 \times 3^1$

Now, consider three boxes x, y, z.

3 can be put in any of the three boxes.

Also, 2, 2, 2 can be distributed in the three boxes in ${}^{3+3-1}C_{3-1} = {}^5C_2 = 10$ ways. Hence, the total number of positive integral solutions = the number of distributions which is given by $3 \times 10 = 30$.

Geometrical Problems

(a) If there are n points in a plane out of these points no three are in the same line except m points which are collinear, then

(i) Total number of different lines obtained by joining these n points is ${}^nC_2 - {}^mC_2 + 1$

(ii) Total number of different triangles formed by joining these n points is ${}^nC_3 - {}^mC_3$

(iii) Total number of different quadrilateral formed by joining these n points is

$${}^nC_4 - ({}^mC_3 \cdot {}^nC_1 + {}^mC_4 \cdot {}^nC_0)$$

Example 103. There are 10 points in a plane out of these points no three are in the same straight line except 4 points which are collinear. How many

(i) straight lines (ii) trian-gles

(iii) quadrilateral, by joining them?

Sol. (i) Required number of straight lines

$$= {}^{10}C_2 - {}^4C_2 + 1 = \frac{10\cdot 9}{1\cdot 2} - \frac{4\cdot 3}{1\cdot 2} + 1 = 45 - 6 + 1 = 40$$

(ii) Required number of triangles

$$= {}^{10}C_3 - {}^4C_3 = \frac{10\cdot 9\cdot 8}{1\cdot 2\cdot 3} - {}^4C_1 = 120 - 4 = 116$$

(iii) Required number of quadrilaterals

$$= {}^{10}C_4 - ({}^4C_3\cdot {}^6C_1 + {}^4C_4\cdot {}^6C_0)$$

$$= \frac{10\cdot 9\cdot 8\cdot 7}{1\cdot 2\cdot 3\cdot 4} - ({}^4C_1\cdot {}^6C_1 + 1.1)$$

$$= 210 - (4\times 6 + 1) = 210 - 25 = 185$$

(b) If there are n points in a plane out of these points no any three are collinear, then

(i) Total points of intersection of the lines joining these n points $= {}^pC_2$, where $p = {}^nC_2$

(ii) If n points are the vertices of a polygon, then total number of diagonals $= {}^nC_2 - n = \frac{n(n-3)}{2}$

Example 104. How many number of points of intersection of n straight lines, if n satisfies ${}^{n+5}P_{n+1} = \frac{11(n-1)}{2} \times {}^{n+3}P_n$?

Sol. We have, $${}^{n+5}P_{n+1} = \frac{11(n-1)}{2}\times {}^{n+3}P_n$$

$$\Rightarrow \frac{(n+5)!}{4!} = \frac{11(n-1)}{2}\times\frac{(n+3)!}{3!}$$

$$\Rightarrow \frac{(n+5)(n+4)}{4} = \frac{11(n-1)}{2}$$

$$\Rightarrow n^2 - 13n + 42 = 0 \Rightarrow (n-6)(n-7) = 0$$

$$\Rightarrow n = 6 \text{ or } n = 7$$

The number of points of intersection of lines is ${}^6C_2$ or ${}^7C$

$$= 15 \text{ or } 21$$

Example 105. The interior angles of a regular polygon measure 150° each. Then, find the number of diagonals of the polygon.

Sol. Each exterior angle $= 30°$

$$\therefore \text{Number of sides} = \frac{360°}{30°} = \frac{360\times\frac{\pi}{180}}{30\times\frac{\pi}{180}} = 12$$

$$\therefore \text{Number of diagonals} = {}^{12}C_2 - 12 = 66 - 12 = 54$$

Example 106. In a polygon the number of diagonals is 77. Find the number of sides of the polygon.

Sol. Let number of sides of the polygon $= n$, then ${}^nC_2 - n = 77$

$$\Rightarrow \frac{n(n-1)}{2} - n = 77 \Rightarrow \frac{n(n-3)}{2} = \frac{14\times 11}{2}$$

we get, $n = 14$

(c) n straight lines are drawn in a plane such that no two of them are parallel and no three of them are concurrent. Then, number of parts into which these lines divides the plane is equal to

$$1 + \sum_{k=1}^{n} k, \text{ .e. } \frac{(n^2+n+2)}{2}$$

Example 107. If n lines are drawn in a plane such that no two of them are parallel and no three of them are concurrent, such that these lines divide the plane in 67 parts, then find number of different points at which these lines will cut.

Sol. Given number of straight lines $= n$, then

$$1 + \sum_{k=1}^{n} k = 67 \Rightarrow \frac{n^2+n+2}{2} = 67$$

$$\Rightarrow n^2 + n - 132 = 0 \Rightarrow (n+12)(n-11) = 0$$

$$\therefore n = 11, n \neq -12$$

Hence, required number of points $= {}^nC_2 = {}^{11}C_2 = \frac{11\cdot 10}{2}$

$$= 55$$

(d) If m parallel lines in a plane are intersected by a family of other n parallel lines. Then, total number of parallelograms so formed

$$= {}^mC_2\cdot {}^nC_2 \text{ i.e., } \frac{mn(m-1)(n-1)}{4}$$

Example 108. Find number of rectangles in a chess board, which are not a square.

Sol. Number of rectangles $= {}^9C_2\times {}^9C_2 = (36)^2 = 1296$

Number of squares $= 8\times 8 + 7\times 7 + 6\times 6 + \ldots + 1\times 1$

$$= 204$$

$\therefore$ Required number $= 1296 - 204 = 1092$

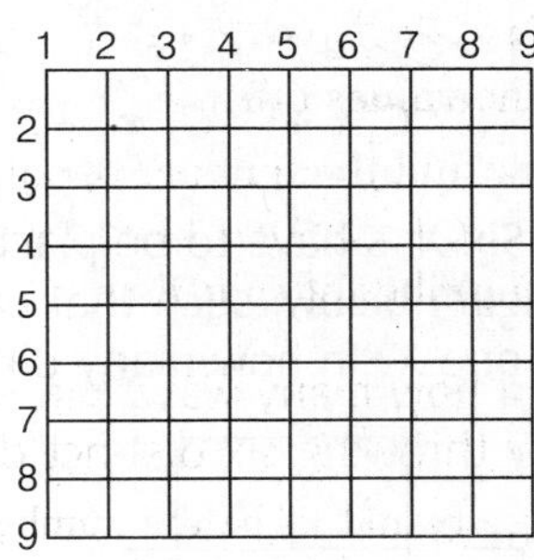

Square can be formed as follows :

To form the smallest square, select any two consecutive lines from the given (here 9) vertical and horizontal lines. This can be done in 8×8 ways (1-2, 2-3, 3-4, ..., 8-9)

Again, to form the square consists of four small squares, select the lines as follows (1-3, 2-4, 3-5,..., 7-9) from both vertical and horizontal lines, thus 7×7 squares are obtained. Proceed in the same way)

Note If n parallel lines are intersected by another n parallel lines, then number of rhombus $= \sum (n-1)^2 = \dfrac{(n-1)\,n\,(2n-1)}{6}$

(e) Number of Rectangles and Squares

(i) Number of rectangles of any size in a square of $n \times n$ is $\sum_{r=1}^{n} r^3$ and number of squares of any size is $\sum_{r=1}^{n} r^2$.

(ii) In a rectangle of $n \times p$ $(n < p)$ number of rectangles of any size is $\dfrac{np}{4}(n+1)(p+1)$ and number of squares of any size is

$$\sum_{r=1}^{n} (n+1-r)(p+1-r).$$

Example 109. Find the number of rectangles excluding squares from a rectangle of size 9×6.

Sol. Here, $n = 6$ and $p = 9$

$\therefore$ Number of rectangles excluding square

$$= \frac{6 \cdot 9}{4}(6+1)(9+1) - \sum_{r=1}^{6}(7-r)(10-r)$$

$$= 945 - \sum_{r=1}^{6}(70 - 17r + r^2) = 945 - 154 = 791$$

(f) If there are n rows, first row has α_1 squares, 2nd row has α_2 squares, 3rd row has α_3 squares, ... and nth row has α_n squares. If we have to filled up the squares with β X_s such that each row has atleast one X. The number of ways = Coefficient of x^{β} in

$$({}^{\alpha_1}C_1 x + {}^{\alpha_2}C_2 x^2 + \ldots + {}^{\alpha_1}C_{\alpha_1} x^{\alpha_1})$$
$$\times({}^{\alpha_2}C_1 x + {}^{\alpha_2}C_2 x^2 + \ldots + {}^{\alpha_2}C_{\alpha_2} x^{\alpha_2})$$
$$\times({}^{\alpha_3}C_1 x + {}^{\alpha_3}C_2 x^2 + \ldots + {}^{\alpha_3}C_{\alpha_3} x^{\alpha_3}) \times$$
$$\ldots \times({}^{\alpha_n}C_1 x + {}^{\alpha_n}C_2 x^2 + \ldots + {}^{\alpha_n}C_{\alpha_n} x^{\alpha_n})$$

Example 110. Six X's have to be placed in the squares of the figure below, such that each row contains atleast one X. In how many different ways can this be done?

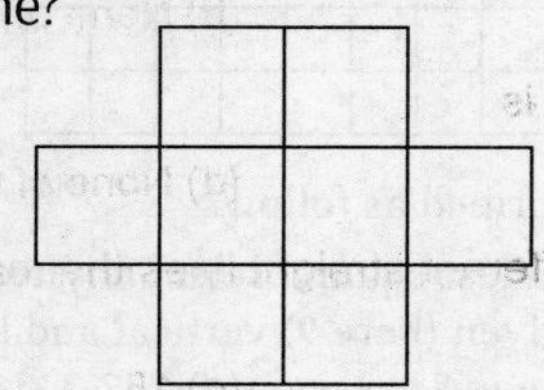

Sol. The required number of ways

$= $ Coefficient of x^6 in $({}^2C_1 x + {}^2C_2 x^2)({}^4C_1 x + {}^4C_2 x^2 + {}^4C_3 x^3 + {}^4C_4 x^4)({}^2C_1 x + {}^2C_2 x^2)$

$= $ Coefficient of x^3 in $(2+x)^2(4 + 6x + 4x^2 + x^3)$

$= $ Coefficient of x^3 in $(4 + 4x + x^2)(4 + 6x + 4x^2 + x^3)$

$= 4 + 16 + 6$

$= 26$

Aliter

In the given figure there are 8 squares and we have to place $6X$'s this can be done in

$${}^8C_6 = {}^8C_2 = \frac{8 \cdot 7}{1 \cdot 2} = 28 \text{ ways}$$

But these include the possibility that either headed row or lowest row may not have any X. These two possibilities are to be excluded.

$\therefore$ Required number of ways $= 28 - 2 = 26$

X X
X X X X OR X X X X
X X

Example 111. In how many ways the letters of the word DIPESH can be placed in the squares of the adjoining figure so that no row remains empty?

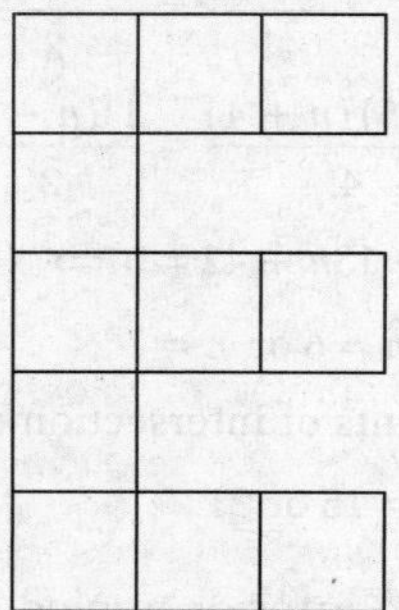

Sol. If all letters are same, then number of ways

$= $ Coefficient of x^6 in $({}^3C_1 x + {}^3C_2 x^2 + {}^3C_3 x^3)^3 ({}^1C_1 x)^2$

$= $ Coefficient of x in $(3 + 3x + x^2)^3$

$= $ Coefficient of x in $(3 + 3x)^3$

[neglecting higher degree term]

$= 27 \times {}^3C_1 = 81$

But in DIPESH all letters are different.

$\therefore$ Required number of ways $= 81 \times 6!$

Exercise for Session 6

1. If number of ways in which 7 different balls can be distributed into 4 different boxes, so that no box remains empty is 100 λ, the value of λ is
(a) 18 (b) 108 (c) 1008 (d) 10008

2. If number of ways in which 7 different balls can be distributed into 4 boxes, so that no box remains empty is 48 λ, the value of λ is
(a) 231 (b) 331 (c) 431 (d) 531

3. If number of ways in which 7 identical balls can be distributed into 4 boxes, so that no box remains empty is 4λ, the value of λ is
(a) 5 (b) 7 (c) 9 (d) 11

4. Number of non-negative integral solutions of the equation $a + b + c = 6$ is
(a) 28 (b) 32 (c) 36 (d) 56

5. Number of integral solutions of $a + b + c = 0$, $a \geq -5$, $b \geq -5$ and $c \geq -5$, is
(a) 272 (b) 136 (c) 240 (d) 120

6. If a, b and c are integers and $a \geq 1$, $b \geq 2$ and $c \geq 3$. If $a + b + c = 15$, the number of possible solutions of the equation is
(a) 55 (b) 66 (c) 45 (d) None of these

7. Number of integral solutions of $2x + y + z = 10$ $(x \geq 0, y \geq 0, Z \geq 0)$ is
(a) 18 (b) 27 (c) 36 (d) 51

8. A person writes letters to six friends and addresses the corresponding envelopes. Let x be the number of ways so that atleast two of the letters are in wrong envelopes and y be the number of ways so that all the letters are in wrong envelopes. Then, $x - y$ is equal to
(a) 719 (b) 265 (c) 454 (d) None of these

9. A person goes for an examination in which there are four papers with a maximum of m marks from each paper. The number of ways in which one can get $2m$ marks, is
(a) ${}^{2m+3}C_3$
(b) $\left(\frac{1}{3}\right)(m + 1)(2m^2 + 4m + 1)$
(c) $\left(\frac{1}{3}\right)(m + 1)(2m^2 + 4m + 3)$
(d) None of these

10. The number of selections of four letters from the letters of the word ASSASSINATION, is
(a) 72 (b) 71 (c) 66 (d) 52

11. The number of positive integral solutions of $2x_1 + 3x_2 + 4x_3 + 5x_4 = 25$, is
(a) 20 (b) 22 (c) 23 (d) None of these

12. If a, b, and c are positive integers such that $a + b + c \leq 8$, the number of possible values of the ordered triplet (a, b, c) is
(a) 84 (b) 56 (c) 83 (d) None of these

13. The total number of positive integral solutions of $15 < x_1 + x_2 + x_3 \leq 20$ is equal to
(a) 685 (b) 785 (c) 1125 (d) None of these

14. The total number of integral solutions for (x, y, z) such that $xyz = 24$, is
(a) 36 (b) 90 (c) 120 (d) None of these

15. There are 12 points in a plane in which 6 are collinear. Number of different straight lines that can be drawn by joining them, is
(a) 51 (b) 52 (c) 132 (d) 18

16. 4 points out of 11 points in a plane are collinear. Number of different triangles that can be drawn by joining them, is

(a) 165 (b) 161 (c) 152 (d) 159

17. The number of triangles that can be formed with 10 points as vertices, n of them being collinear, is 110. Then, n is

(a) 3 (b) 4 (c) 5 (d) 6

18. $ABCD$ is a convex quadrilateral. 3, 4, 5 and 6 points are marked on the sides AB, BC, CD and DA, respectively. The number of triangles with vertices on different sides, is

(a) 270 (b) 220 (c) 282 (d) None of these

19. There are 10 points in a plane of which no three points are collinear and 4 points are concyclic. The number of different circles that can be drawn through atleast 3 points of these points, is

(a) 116 (b) 120 (c) 117 (d) None of these

20. 4 points out of 8 points in a plane are collinear. Number of different quadrilateral that can be formed by joining them, is

(a) 56 (b) 60 (c) 76 (d) 53

21. There are $2n$ points in a plane in which m are collinear ($n > m > 4$). Number of quadrilateral formed by joining these lines

(a) is equal to ${}^{2n}C_4 - {}^{m}C_4$ (b) is greater than ${}^{2n}C_4 - {}^{m}C_4$
(c) is less than ${}^{2n}C_4 - {}^{m}C_4$ (d) None of these

22. In a polygon the number of diagonals is 54. The number of sides of the polygon, is

(a) 10 (b) 12 (c) 9 (d) None of these

23. In a polygon no three diagonals are concurrent. If the total number of points of intersection of diagonals interior to the polygon be 70, then the number of diagonals of the polygon, is

(a) 20 (b) 28 (c) 8 (d) None of these

24. n lines are drawn in a plane such that no two of them are parallel and no three of them are concurrent. The number of different points at which these lines will cut, is

(a) $\sum_{k=1}^{n-1} k$ (b) $n(n-1)$ (c) n^2 (d) None of these

25. Six straight lines are drawn in a plane such that no two lines are parallel and no three lines are concurrent. Then, the number of parts into which these lines divide the plane, is

(a) 15 (b) 22 (c) 29 (d) 36

26. A parallelogram is cut by two sets of m lines parallel to its sides. The number of parallelogram thus formed, is

(a) $({}^{m}C_2)^2$ (b) $({}^{m+1}C_2)^2$ (c) $({}^{m+2}C_2)^2$ (d) None of these

27. The number of rectangles excluding squares from a rectangle of size 11×8 is 48λ, then the value of λ is

(a) 13 (b) 23 (c) 43 (d) 53

28. The number of ways the letters of the word PERSON can be placed in the squares of the figure shown so that no row remains empty, is

R_1
R_2
R_3

(a) $24 \times 6!$ (b) $26 \times 6!$ (c) $26 \times 7!$ (d) $27 \times 7!$

Session 7

Rank in a Dictionary, Gap Method

Rank in a Dictionary

The dictionary format means words are arranged in alphabetical order.

Following Examples will help you learn how to find the rank in the dictionary.

Example 112. If the letters of the word are arranged as in dictionary, find the rank of the following words.

(i) RAJU (ii) UMANG

(iii) AIRTEL

Sol. **(i)** In a dictionary, the letters in alphabetical order are A, J, R, U

$\therefore$ The first word is AJRU.

Number of words beginning with A = Number of ways arranging J, R, U $= 3! = 6$

Number of words beginning with J $= 3! = 6$

The next word begin with R and it is RAJU.

$\therefore$ Number of words before RAJU = 12

$\therefore$ Rank of word RAJU = 13

(ii) The letters in alphabetical order are A, G, M, N, U

$\therefore$ The first word is AGMNU

Number of words beginning with A $= 4! = 24$

Number of words beginning with G $= 4! = 24$

Number of words beginning with M $= 4! = 24$

Number of words beginning with N $= 4! = 24$

Number of words beginning with UA $= 3! = 6$

Number of words beginning with UG $= 3! = 6$

Number of words beginning with UMAG $= 1! = 1$

Number of words beginning with UMANG = 1

$\therefore$ Rank of the word

UMANG $= 24 + 24 + 24 + 24 + 6 + 6 + 1 + 1 = 110$

(iii) The letters in alphabetical order are A, E, I, L, R, T

$\therefore$ The first word is AEILRT

Number of words beginning with AE $= 4! = 24$

Number of words beginning with AIE $= 3! = 6$

Number of words beginning with AIL $= 3! = 6$

Number of words beginning with AIRE $= 2! = 2$

Number of words beginning with AIRL $= 2! = 2$

Number of words beginning with AIRTEL = 1

$\therefore$ Rank of the word AIRTEL $= 24 + 6 + 6 + 2 + 2 + 1 = 41$

Example 113. If letters of the word are arranged as in dictionary, find the rank of the following words.

(i) INDIA (ii) SURITI (iii) DOCOMO

Sol. (i) The letters in alphabetical order are A, D, I, I, N

$\therefore$ The first word is ADIIN

Number of words beginning with A $= \dfrac{4!}{2!} = 12$

Number of words beginning with D $= \dfrac{4!}{2!} = 12$

Number of words beginning with IA $= 3! = 6$

Number of words beginning with ID $= 3! = 6$

Number of words beginning with II $= 3! = 6$

Number of words beginning with INA $= 2! = 2$

Number of words beginning with INDA $= 1! = 1$

Number of words beginning with INDIA = 1

$\therefore$ Rank of the word INDIA

$= 12 + 12 + 6 + 6 + 6 + 2 + 1 + 1 = 46$

(ii) The letters in alphabetical order are I, I, R, S, T, U

$\therefore$ The first word is IIRSTU

Number of words beginning with I $= 5! = 120$

Number of words beginning with R $= \dfrac{5!}{2!} = 60$

Number of words beginning with SI $= 4! = 24$

Number of words beginning with SR $= \dfrac{4!}{2!} = 12$

Number of words beginning with ST $= \dfrac{4!}{2!} = 12$

Number of words beginning with SUI $= 3! = 6$

Number of words beginning with SURII $= 1! = 1$

Number of words beginning with SURITI = 1

$\therefore$ Rank of the word SURITI

$= 120 + 60 + 24 + 12 + 12 + 6 + 1 + 1 = 236$

(iii) The letters in alphabetical order are C, D, M, O, O, O

$\therefore$ The first word is CDMOOO

Number of words beginning with C $= \dfrac{5!}{3!} = 20$

Number of words beginning with DC $= \dfrac{4!}{3!} = 4$

Number of words beginning with DM $= \dfrac{4!}{3!} = 4$

Number of words beginning with DOCM $= \dfrac{2!}{2!} = 1$

Number of words beginning with DOCOMO = 1

$\therefore$ Rank of the word DOCOMO $= 20 + 4 + 4 + 1 + 1 = 30$

Gap Method

[when particular objects are never together]

Example 114. There are 10 candidates for an examination out of which 4 are appearing in Mathematics and remaining 6 are appearing in different subjects. In how many ways can they be seated in a row so that no two Mathematics candidates are together?

Sol. In this method first arrange the remaining candidates

Here, remaining candidates = 6

$$\times 0 \times 0 \times 0 \times 0 \times 0 \times 0 \times$$

$\times$: Places available for Mathematics candidates

0 : Places for others

Remaining candidates can be arranged in $6!$ ways. There are seven places available for Mathematics candidates so that no two Mathematics candidates are together. Now, four candidates can be placed in these seven places in ${}^7P_4$ ways.

Hence, the total number of ways $= 6! \times {}^7P_4 = 720 \times 840$

$$= 604800$$

Example 115. In how many ways can 7 plus (+) and 5 minus (−) signs be arranged in a row so that no two minus (−) signs are together?

Sol. In this method, first arrange the plus (+) signs.

Here, minus (−) signs = 5

$$0 + 0 + 0 + 0 + 0 + 0 + 0 + 0$$

We can put minus (−) sign in any of the 8 places in the above arrangement i.e., we have to select 5 places out of 8 which can be done is ${}^8C_5$ ways $= {}^8C_3$ ways = 56 ways.

Example 116. Find the number of ways in which 5 girls and 5 boys can be arranged in a row, if no two boys are together.

Sol. In this example, there is no condition for arranging the girls. Now, 5 girls can be arranged in $5!$ ways.

$$\times G \times G \times G \times G \times G \times$$

When girls are arranged, six gaps are generated as shown above with '×'.

Now, boys must occupy the places with '×' marked, so that no two boys are together.

Therefore, five boys can be arranged in these six gaps in ${}^6P_5$ ways.

Hence, total number of arrangement is $5! \times {}^6P_5$.

Example 117. Find the number of ways in which 5 girls and 5 boys can be arranged in a row, if boys and girls are alternate.

Sol. First five girls can be arranged in $5!$ ways

i.e., $\times G \times G \times G \times G \times G$ or $G \times G \times G \times G \times G \times$

Now, if girls and boys are alternate, then boys can occupy places with '×' as shows above.

Hence, total number of arrangements is

$$5! \times 5! + 5! \times 5! = 2 \times (5!)^2$$

Use of Set Theory

A set is well defined collection of distinct objects.

Subset

If every element of a set A is also an element of a set B, then A is called the subset B, we write

$$A \subset B \Leftrightarrow \{x \in A \Rightarrow x \in B\}$$

Union

The union of two sets A and B is the set of all those elements which are either in A or in B or in both. This set is denoted by $A \cup B$ or $A + B$.

Symbolically, $A \cup B = \{x : x \in A \text{ or } x \in B\}$

Intersection

The intersection of two sets A and B is the set of all elements which are common in A and B. This set is denoted by $A \cap B$ or AB.

Symbolically, $A \cap B = \{x : x \in A \text{ and } x \in B\}$

Example 118. A is a set containing n elements. A subset P_1 of A is chosen. The set A is reconstructed by replacing the elements of P_1. Next, a subset P_2 of A is chosen and again the set is reconstructed by replacing the elements of P_2. In this way $m\ (>1)$ subsets $P_1, P_2, \ldots, P_m$ of A are chosen. Find the number of ways of choosing $P_1, P_2, \ldots, P_m$, so that

(i) $P_1 \cap P_2 \cap P_3 \cap \ldots \cap P_m = \phi$

(ii) $P_1 \cup P_2 \cup P_3 \cup \ldots \cup P_m = A$

Sol. Let $A = \{a_1, a_2, a_3, \ldots, a_n\}$

(i) For each a_i $(1 \le i \le n)$, we have either $a \in P_j$ or $a_i \notin P_j$ $(1 \le j \le m)$. i.e., there are 2^m choices in which $a_i (1 \le i \le n)$ may belong to the P_j's.

Out of these, there is only one choice, in which $a_i \in P_j$ for all $j = 1, 2, \ldots, m$ which is not favourable for $P_1 \cap P_2 \cap P_3 \cap \ldots \cap P_m$ to be ϕ. Thus, $a_i \notin P_1 \cap P_2 \cap \ldots \cap P_m$ in $(2^m - 1)$ ways. Since, there are n elements in the set A, the total number of choices is $(2^m - 1)^n$.

(ii) There is exactly one choice, in which, $a_i \in P_j$ for all $j = 1, 2, 3, \dots, m$ which is not favourable for $P_1 \cup P_2 \cup P_3 \cup \dots \cup P_m$ to be equal to A. Thus, a_i can belong to $P_1 \cup P_2 \cup P_3 \cup \dots \cup P_m$ in $(2^m - 1)$ ways.

Since, there are n elements in the set A, the number of ways in which $P_1 \cup P_2 \cup P_3 \cup \dots \cup P_m$ can be equal to A is $(2^m - 1)^n$.

Example 119. A is a set containing n elements. A subset P of A is chosen. The set A is reconstructed by replacing the elements of P. A subset of A is again chosen. Find the number of ways of choosing P and Q, so that

(i) $P \cap Q$ contains exactly r elements.

(ii) $P \cap Q$ contains exactly 2 elements.

(iii) $P \cap Q = \phi$

Sol. Let $A = \{a_1, a_2, a_3, \dots, a_n\}$

(i) The r elements in P and Q such that $P \cap Q$ can be chosen out of n is ${}^nC_r$ ways a general element of A must satisfy one of the following possibilities [here, general element be $a_i (1 \le i \le n)$]

(i) $a_i \in P$ and $a_i \in Q$

(ii) $a_i \in P$ and $a_i \notin Q$

(iii) $a_i \in P$ and $a_i \in Q$

(iv) $a_i \notin P$ and $a_i \notin Q$

Let $a_1, a_2, \dots, a_r \in P \cap Q$

There is only one choice each of them (i.e., (i) choice) and three choices (ii), (iii) and (iv) for each of remaining $(n - r)$ elements.

Hence, number of ways of remaining elements $= 3^{n-r}$

Hence, number of ways in which $P \cap Q$ contains exactly r elements $= {}^nC_r \times 3^{n-r}$

(i) Put $r = 2$, then ${}^nC_2 \times 3^{n-2}$

(iii) Put $r = 0$, then ${}^nC_0 \times 3^n = 3^n$

Sum of digits

(i) The sum of the digits in the unit's place of all numbers formed with the help of $a_1, a_2, \dots, a_n$ taken all at a time is $(n-1)!(a_1 + a_2 + \dots + a_n)$ (repetition of digits not allowed)

Example 120. Find the sum of the digits in the unit's place of all numbers formed with the help of 3, 4, 5, 6 taken all at a time.

Sol. Sum of the digits in the unit's place

$$= (4-1)!(3+4+5+6) = 6 \times 18 = 108$$

(ii) The sum of all digit numbers that can be formed using the digits $a_1, a_2, \dots, a_n$ (repetition of digits not allowed)

$$\text{is} = (n-1)!(a_1 + a_2 + \dots + a_n)\frac{(10^n - 1)}{9}$$

Example 121. Find the sum of all five digit numbers that can be formed using the digits 1, 2, 3, 4 and 5 (repetition of digits not allowed)

Sol. Required sum $= (5-1)!(1+2+3+4+5)\left(\dfrac{10^5 - 1}{9}\right)$

$$= 24 \cdot 15 \cdot 11111 = 3999960$$

Aliter

Since, one of the numbers formed with the 5 digits a, b, c, d and e is $10^4 a + 10^3 b + 10^2 c + 10d + e$;

Hence, $10^4 a$ will occur altogether in 4 ! ways similarly each of $10^4 b, 10^4 c, 10^4 d, 10^4 e$ will occur in 4 ! ways.

Hence, if all the numbers formed with the digits be written one below the other, thus

$$10^4 \cdot a + 10^3 \cdot b + 10^2 \cdot c + 10 \cdot d + e$$
$$10^4 \cdot b + 10^3 \cdot c + 10^2 \cdot d + 10 \cdot e + a$$
$$10^4 \cdot c + 10^3 \cdot d + 10^2 \cdot e + 10 \cdot a + b$$
$$10^4 \cdot d + 10^3 \cdot e + 10^2 \cdot a + 10 \cdot b + c$$
$$10^4 \cdot e + 10^3 \cdot a + 10^2 \cdot b + 10 \cdot c + d$$

Hence, the required sum

$$= 4! \times (a+b+c+d+e) \times (10^4 + 10^3 + 10^2 + 10 + 1)$$
$$= 4! \times (1+2+3+4+5)(11111) = 3999960$$

Difference between Permutation and Combination

Problems of permutations	Problems of combinations
1. Arrangements	Selections, choose
2. Standing in a line, seated in a row	Distributed group is formed
3. Problems on digits	Committee
4. Problems on letters from a word	Geometrical problems

Exercise for Session 7

1. The letters of the word "DELHI" are arranged in all possible ways as in a dictionary, the rank of the word "DELHI" is

(a) 4
(b) 5
(c) 6
(d) 7

2. The letters of the word "KANPUR" are arranged in all possible ways as in a dictionary, the rank of the word "KANPUR" from last is

(a) 121
(b) 122
(c) 598
(d) 599

3. The letters of the word "MUMBAI" are arranged in all possible ways as in a dictionary, the rank of the word "MUMBAI" is

(a) 297
(b) 295
(c) 299
(d) 301

4. The letters of the word "CHENNAI" are arranged in all possible ways as in a dictionary, then rank of the word "CHENNAI" from last is

(a) 2016
(b) 2017
(c) 2018
(d) 2019

5. If all permutations of the letters of the word "AGAIN" are arranged as in a dictionary, then 50th word is

(a) NAAGI
(b) NAGAI
(c) NAAIG
(d) NAIAG

Shortcuts and Important Results to Remember

1 When two dice are thrown, the number of ways of getting a total r (sum of numbers on upper faces), is

(i) $r-1$, if $2 \le r \le 7$

(ii) $13-r$, if $8 \le r \le 12$

2 When three dice are thrown, the number of ways of getting a total r (sum of numbers on upper faces), is

(i) ${}^{r-1}C_2$, if $3 \le r \le 8$

(ii) 25, if $r = 9$

(iii) 27, if $r = 10, 11$

(iv) 25, if $r = 12$

(v) ${}^{20-r}C_2$, if $13 \le r \le 18$

3 The product of k consecutive positive integers is divisible by $k\,!$.

4 Number of zeroes in $n\,! = E_5(n\,!)$

5 n straight lines are drawn in the plane such that no two lines are parallel and no three lines are concurrent. Then, the number of parts into which these lines divides the plane is equal to $\frac{(n^2+n+2)}{2}$.

6 ${}^nC_r$ is divisible by n only, if n is a prime number $(1 \le r \le n-1)$.

7 The number of diagonals in n-gon (n sides closed polygon) is $\frac{n(n-3)}{2}$.

8 In n-gon no three diagonals are concurrent, then the total number of points of intersection of diagonals interior to the polygon is ${}^nC_4$.

9 Consider a polygon of n sides, then number of triangles in which no side is common with that of the polygon are $\frac{1}{6}n(n-4)(n-5)$.

10 If m parallel lines in a plane are intersected by a family of other n parallel lines. The total number of parallelograms so formed $= {}^mC_2 \cdot {}^nC_2 = \frac{mn(m-1)(n-1)}{4}$

11 Highest power of prime p in ${}^nC_r$, since

$$ {}^nC_r = \frac{n\,!}{r\,!(n-r)!} $$

If $H_p(n\,!) = \alpha$,

$H_p(r\,!) = \beta$

and $H_p\{(n-r)!\} = \gamma$

Then, $H_p({}^nC_r) = \alpha - (\beta + \gamma)$

12 Highest power of prime p in ${}^nP_r$, since

$$ {}^nP_r = \frac{n\,!}{(n-r)!} $$

If $H_p(n\,!) = \lambda$, $H_p\{(n-r)!\} = \mu$. Then, $H_p({}^nP_r) = \lambda - \mu$

13 If there are n rows. Ist row has m_1 squares, IInd row has m_2 squares, IIIrd row has m_3 squares and so on. If we placed λ X's in the squares such that each row contains atleast one X. Then the number of ways = Coefficient of x^λ in

$$ ({}^{m_1}C_1x + {}^{m_1}C_2x^2 + \ldots + {}^{m_1}C_{m_1}x^{m_1}) $$
$$ \times({}^{m_2}C_1x + {}^{m_2}C_2x^2 + {}^{m_2}C_3x^3 + \ldots + {}^{m_2}C_{m_2}x^{m_2}) \times $$
$$ ({}^{m_3}C_1x + {}^{m_3}C_2x^2 + \ldots + {}^{m_3}C_{m_3}x^{m_3}) \times \ldots $$

14 If $\frac{1}{x} + \frac{1}{y} = \frac{1}{n}$, $\forall\, x, y, n \in N$

$\Rightarrow \quad (x-n)(y-n) = n^2$

$\therefore \quad x = n + \lambda,$

$$ y = n + \frac{n^2}{\lambda}, $$

where λ is divisor of n^2.

Then, number of integral solutions (x, y) is equal to number of divisors of n^2.

If $n = 3$, $n^2 = 9 = 3^2$, the equation has 3 solutions.

$(x, y) = (4, 12), (6, 6), (12, 4)$

JEE Type Solved Examples : Single Option Correct Type Questions

- This section contains **10 multiple choice examples.** Each example has four choices (a), (b), (c) and (d) out of which **ONLY ONE** is correct.

- ***Ex. 1*** *Number of words of 4 letters that can be formed with the letters of the word IIT JEE, is*

(a) 42 (b) 82 (c) 102 (d) 142

Sol. (c) There are 6 letters I, I, E, E, T, J

The following cases arise:

Case **I** All letters are different

$${}^4P_4 = 4! = 24$$

Case **II** Two alike and two different

$${}^2C_1 \times {}^3C_2 \times \frac{4!}{2!} = 72$$

Case **III** Two alike of one kind and two alike of another kind

$${}^2C_2 \times \frac{4!}{2!\,2!} = 6$$

Hence, number of words = 24 + 72 + 6 = 102

Aliter

Number of words = Coefficient of x^4 in

$$4!\left(1 + \frac{x}{1!} + \frac{x^2}{2!}\right)^2 (1 + x)^2$$

$= \text{Coefficient of } x^4 \text{ in } 6[(1 + x)^2 + 1]^2 (1 + x)^2$

$= \text{Coefficient of } x^4 \text{ in } 6[(1 + x)^6 + 2(1 + x)^4 + (1 + x)^2]$

$= 6[{}^6C_4 + 2 \cdot {}^4C_4 + 0] = 6(15 + 2) = 102$

- ***Ex. 2*** *Let y be element of the set* $A = \{1, 2, 3, 5, 6, 10, 15, 30\}$ *and* x_1, x_2, x_3 *be integers such that* $x_1 x_2 x_3 = y$, *the number of positive integral solutions of* $x_1 x_2 x_3 = y$, *is*

(a) 27 (b) 64 (c) 81 (d) 256

Sol. (b) Number of solutions of the given equations is the same as the number of solutions of the equation

$$x_1\, x_2\, x_3\, x_4 = 30 = 2 \times 3 \times 5$$

Here, x_4 is infact a dummy variable.

If $x_1\, x_2\, x_3 = 15$, then $x_4 = 2$ and if $x_1 x_2\, x_3 = 5$, then $x_4 = 6$, etc.

Thus, $x_1\, x_2\, x_3\, x_4 = 2 \times 3 \times 5$

Each of 2, 3 and 5 will be factor of exactly one of x_1, x_2, x_3, x_4 in 4 ways.

$\therefore$ Required number $= 4^3 = 64$

- ***Ex. 3*** *The number of positive integer solutions of* $a + b + c = 60$, *where a is a factor of b and c, is*

(a) 184 (b) 200 (c) 144 (d) 270

Sol. (c) $\because$ a is a factor of b and $c \Rightarrow a$ divides 60

$\therefore$ $a = 1, 2, 3, 4, 5, 6, 10, 12, 15, 30$ $[\because a \neq 60]$

and $b = ma$, $c = na$, when $m, n \geq 1$

$\because$ $a + b + c = 60$

$\Rightarrow a + ma + na = 60 \Rightarrow m + n = \left(\frac{60}{a} - 1\right)$

$\therefore$ Number of solutions $= {}^{\frac{60}{a} - 1 - 1}C_{2-1} = \left(\frac{60}{a} - 2\right)$

Hence, total number of solutions for all values of a

$= 58 + 28 + 18 + 13 + 10 + 8 + 4 + 3 + 2 + 0 = 144$

- ***Ex. 4*** *The number of times the digit 3 will be written when listing the integers from 1 to 1000, is*

(a) 269 (b) 271 (c) 300 (d) 302

Sol. (c) Since, 3 does not occur in 1000. So, we have to count the number of times 3 occurs, when we list the integers from 1 to 999.

Any number between 1 and 999 is of the form xyz, where $0 \leq x, y, z \leq 9$.

Let us first count the number in which 3 occurs exactly once. Since, 3 can occur at one place in ${}^3C_1$ ways, there are ${}^3C_1 \times 9 \times 9 = 243$ such numbers. Next 3 can occur in exactly two places in ${}^3C_2 \times 9 = 27$ such numbers. Lastly, 3 can occur in all three digits in one number only. Hence, the number of times, 3 occurs is $1 \times 243 + 2 \times 27 + 3 \times 1 = 300$

- ***Ex. 5*** *Number of points having position vector* $a\hat{\mathbf{i}} + b\hat{\mathbf{j}} + c\hat{\mathbf{k}}$, *where* $a, b, c \in \{1, 2, 3, 4, 5\}$ *such that* $2^a + 3^b + 5^c$ *is divisible by 4, is*

(a) 70 (b) 140
(c) 210 (d) 280

Sol. (a) $\because 2^a + 3^b + 5^c = 2^a + (4 - 1)^b + (4 + 1)^c$

$= 2^a + 4k + (-1)^b + (1)^c$

$= 2^a + 4k + (-1)^b + 1$

I. $a = 1$, $b =$ even, $c =$ any number

II. $a \neq 1$, $b =$ odd, $c =$ any number

$\therefore$ Required number of ways $= 1 \times 2 \times 5 + 4 \times 3 \times 5 = 70$

[$\because$ even numbers = 2, 4; odd numbers = 1, 3, 5 and any numbers = 1, 2, 3, 4, 5]

- ***Ex. 6*** *Number of positive unequal integral solutions of the equation* $x + y + z = 12$ *is*

(a) 21 (b) 42 (c) 63 (d) 84

Sol. (b) We have, $x + y + z = 12$ ...(i)

Assume $x < y < z$. Here, $x, y, z \geq 1$

$\therefore$ Solutions of Eq. (i) are
(1, 2, 9), (1, 3, 8), (1, 4, 7), (1, 5, 6), (2, 3, 7), (2, 4, 6) and (3, 4, 5).

Number of positive integral solutions of Eq. (i) = 7 but x, y, z can be arranged in $3! = 6$

Hence, required number of solutions $= 7 \times 6 = 42$

Aliter

Let $x = \alpha, y - x = \beta, z - y = \gamma$

$\therefore\ x = \alpha, y = \alpha + \beta, z = \alpha + \beta + \gamma$

From Eq. (i), $3\alpha + 2\beta + \gamma = 12; \alpha, \beta, \gamma \geq 1$

$\therefore$ Number of positive integral solutions of Eq. (i)

= Coefficient of λ^{12} in

$$(\lambda^3 + \lambda^6 + \lambda^9 + \lambda^{12} + \ldots)(\lambda^2 + \lambda^4 + \lambda^6 + \lambda^8 + \lambda^{10} + \lambda^{12} + \ldots)(\lambda + \lambda^2 + \lambda^3 + \ldots + \lambda^{12})$$

= Coefficient of λ^6 in $(1 + \lambda^3 + \lambda^6)(1 + \lambda^2 + \lambda^4 + \lambda^6)(1 + \lambda + \lambda^2 + \lambda^3 + \lambda^4 + \lambda^5 + \lambda^6)$

= Coefficient of λ^6 in $(1 + \lambda^2 + \lambda^4 + \lambda^6 + \lambda^3 + \lambda^5 + \lambda^6) \times (1 + \lambda + \lambda^2 + \lambda^3 + \lambda^4 + \lambda^5 + \lambda^6)$

$= 1 + 1 + 1 + 1 + 1 + 1 + 1 = 7$

but x, y, z can be arranged in $3! = 6$

Hence, required number of solutions $= 7 \times 6 = 42$

Ex. 7 *12 boys and 2 girls are to be seated in a row such that there are atleast 3 boys between the 2 girls. The number of ways this can be done is $\lambda \times 12!$, the value of λ is*

(a) 55 (b) 110 (c) 20 (d) 45

Sol. (*b*) Let $P =$ Number of ways, 12 boys and 2 girls are seated in a row

$$= 14! = 14 \times 13 \times 12! = 182 \times 12!$$

P_1 = Number of ways, the girls can sit together
$= (14 - 2 + 1) \times 2! \times 12! = 26 \times 12!$

P_2 = Number of ways, one boy sits between the girls
$= (14 - 3 + 1) \times 2! \times 12! = 24 \times 12!$

P_3 = Number of ways, two boys sit between the girls
$= (14 - 4 + 1) \times 2! \times 12! = 22 \times 12!$

$\therefore$ Required number of ways $= (182 - 26 - 24 - 22) \times 12!$
$= 110 \times 12! = \lambda \times 12!$ [given]

$\therefore\ \lambda = 110$

Ex. 8 *A is a set containing n elements. A subset P of A is chosen. The set A is reconstructed by replacing the elements of P. A subset Q of A is again chosen, the number of ways of choosing so that $(P \cup Q)$ is a proper subset of A, is*

(a) 3^n (b) 4^n (c) $4^n - 2^n$ (d) $4^n - 3^n$

Sol. (*d*) Let $A = \{a_1, a_2, a_3, \ldots, a_n\}$

a general element of A must satisfy one of the following possibilities.

[here, general element be $a_i (1 \leq i \leq n)$]

(i) $a_i \in P, a_i \in Q$ (ii) $a_i \in P, a_i \notin Q$
(iii) $a_i \notin P, a_i \in Q$ (iv) $a_i \notin P, a_i \notin Q$

Therefore, for one element a_i of A, we have four choices (i), (ii), (iii) and (iv).

$\therefore$ Total number of cases for all elements $= 4^n$

and for one element a_i of A, such that $a_i \in P \cup Q$, we have three choices (i), (ii) and (iii).

$\therefore$ Number of cases for all elements belong to $P \cup Q = 3^n$

Hence, number of ways in which atleast one element of A does not belong to

$$P \cup Q = 4^n - 3^n.$$

Ex. 9 *Let N be a natural number. If its first digit (from the left) is deleted, it gets reduced to $\frac{N}{29}$. The sum of all the digits of N is*

(a) 14 (b) 17
(c) 23 (d) 29

Sol. (*a*) Let $N = a_n\, a_{n-1}\, a_{n-2} \ldots a_3\, a_2\, a_1\, a_0$

$$= a_0 + 10a_1 + 10^2 a_2 + \ldots + 10^{n-1} a_{n-1} + 10^n a_n \quad \ldots \text{(i)}$$

Then, $\frac{N}{29} = a_{n-1}\, a_{n-2}\, a_{n-3} \ldots a_3\, a_2\, a_1\, a_0$

$$= a_0 + 10a_1 + 10^2 a_2 + \ldots + 10^{n-2} a_{n-2} + 10^{n-1} a_{n-1}$$

or $N = 29(a_0 + 10a_1 + 10^2 a_2 + \ldots + 10^{n-2} a_{n-2} + 10^{n-1} a_{n-1})$ ...(ii)

From Eqs. (i) and (ii), we get

$$10^n \cdot a_n = 28(a_0 + 10a_1 + 10^2 a_2 + \ldots + 10^{n-1} a_{n-1})$$

$\Rightarrow$ 28 divides $10^n \cdot a_n \Rightarrow a_n = 7, n \geq 2 \Rightarrow 5^2 = a_0 + 10a_1$

The required N is 725 or 7250 or 72500, etc.

$\therefore$ The sum of the digits is 14.

Ex. 10 *If the number of ways of selecting n cards out of unlimited number of cards bearing the number 0, 9, 3, so that they cannot be used to write the number 903 is 93, then n is equal to*

(a) 3 (b) 4
(c) 5 (d) 6

Sol. (*c*) We cannot write 903.

If in the selection of n cards, we get either

(9 or 3), (9 or 0), (0 or 3), (only 0), (only 3) or (only 9).

For (9 or 3) can be selected $= 2 \times 2 \times 2 \times \ldots \times n$ factors $= 2^n$

Similarly, (9 or 0) or (0 or 3) can be selected $= 2^n$

In the above selection (only 0) or (only 3) or (only 9) is repeated twice.

$\therefore$ Total ways $= 2^n + 2^n + 2^n - 3 = 93$

$\Rightarrow\ 3 \cdot 2^n = 96 \Rightarrow 2^n = 32 = 2^5$

$\therefore\ n = 5$

JEE Type Solved Examples : More than One Correct Option Type Questions

- This section contains **5 multiple choice examples.** Each example has four choices (a), (b), (c) and (d) out of **which more than one** may be correct.

Ex. 11 *In a plane, there are two families of lines $y = x + r, y = -x + r$, where $r \in \{0, 1, 2, 3, 4\}$. The number of squares of diagonals of the length 2 formed by the lines is*

(a) 9 (b) 16 (c) $\frac{3}{2} \cdot {}^4C_2$ (d) $5_{C_2} + {}^3P_2$

Sol. (*a, c*) There are two sets of five parallel lines at equal distances. Clearly, lines like l_1, l_3, m_1 and m_3 form a square whose diagonal's length is 2.

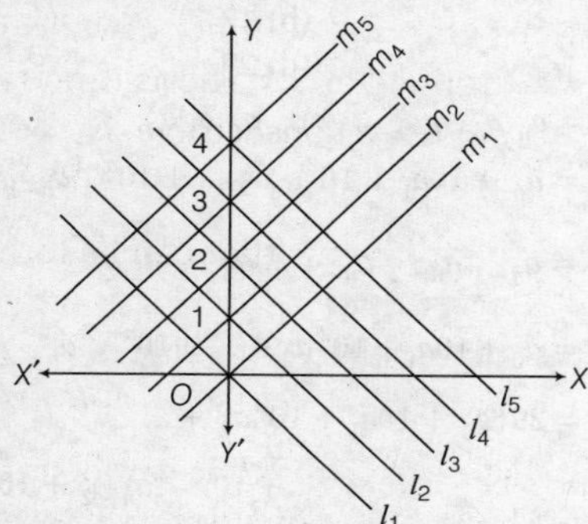

$\therefore$ The number of required squares $= 3 \times 3 = 9 = \frac{3}{2} \cdot {}^4C_2$

[$\because$ choices are (l_1, l_2), (l_2, l_4) and (l_3, l_5) for one set, etc.]

Ex. 12 *Number of ways in which three numbers in AP can be selected from 1, 2, 3, ..., n, is*

(a) $\left(\frac{n-1}{2}\right)^2$, if n is even (b) $\frac{n(n-2)}{4}$, if n is even

(c) $\frac{(n-1)^2}{4}$, if n is odd (d) $\frac{n(n+1)}{2}$, if n is odd

Sol. (*b, c*) If a, b, c are in AP, then $a + c = 2b$

a and c both are odd or both are even.

***Case* I If *n* is even**

Let $n = 2m$ in which m are even and m are odd numbers.

$\therefore$ Number of ways $= {}^mC_2 + {}^mC_2 = 2 \cdot {}^mC_2 = 2 \cdot \frac{m(m-1)}{2}$

$= \frac{n}{2}\left(\frac{n}{2} - 1\right) = \frac{n(n-2)}{4}$ [$\because n = 2m$]

***Case* II If *n* is odd**

Let $n = 2m + 1$ in which m are even and $m + 1$ are odd numbers.

$\therefore$ Number of ways $= {}^mC_2 + {}^{m+1}C_2$

$= \frac{m(m-1)}{2} + \frac{(m+1)m}{2} = m^2 = \frac{(n-1)^2}{4}$ [$\because n = 2m + 1$]

Ex. 13 *If n objects are arranged in a row, then number of ways of selecting three of these objects so that no two of them are next to each other, is*

(a) ${}^{n-2}C_3$ (b) ${}^{n-3}C_3 + {}^{n-3}C_2$

(c) $\frac{(n-2)(n-3)(n-4)}{6}$ (d) ${}^nC_2$

Sol. (*a, b, c*) Let a_0 be the number of objects to the left of the first object chosen, a_1 be the number of objects between the first and the second, a_2 be the number of objects between the second and the third and a_3 be the number of objects to the right of the third object. Then,

$$a_0, a_3 \geq 0 \text{ and } a_1, a_2 \geq 1$$

$\leftarrow a_0 \rightarrow \bullet \leftarrow a_1 \rightarrow \bullet \leftarrow a_2 \rightarrow \bullet \leftarrow a_3 \rightarrow$

also $a_0 + a_1 + a_2 + a_3 = n - 3$

Let $a = a_0 + 1, b = a_3 + 1$, then $a \geq 1, b \geq 1$ such that $a + a_1 + a_2 + b = n - 1$

The total number of positive integral solutions of this equation is ${}^{n-1-1}C_{4-1} = {}^{n-2}C_3 = {}^{n-3}C_3 + {}^{n-3}C_2$

$$= \frac{(n-2)(n-3)(n-4)}{1 \cdot 2 \cdot 3}$$

Ex. 14 *Given that the divisors of $n = 3^p \cdot 5^q \cdot 7^r$ are of the form $4\lambda + 1, \lambda \geq 0$. Then,*

(a) $p + r$ is always even (b) $p + q + r$ is even or odd

(c) q can be any integer (d) if p is even, then r is odd

Sol. (*a, b, c*)

$\because$ $3^p = (4-1)^p = 4\lambda_1 + (-1)^p$,

$5^q = (4+1)^q = 4\lambda_2 + 1$

and $7^r = (8-1)^r = 8\lambda_3 + (-1)^r$

Hence, both p and r must be odd or both must be even. Thus, $p + r$ is always even. Also, $p + q + r$ can be odd or even.

Ex. 15 *Number of ways in which 15 identical coins can be put into 6 different bags*

(a) is coefficient of x^{15} in $x^6(1 + x + x^2 + ... \infty)^6$, if no bag remains empty

(b) is coefficient of x^{15} in $(1-x)^{-6}$

(c) is same as number of the integral solutions of $a + b + c + d + e + f = 15$

(d) is same as number of non-negative integral solutions of $\sum_{i=1}^{6} x_i = 15$

Sol. (*a, b, d*) Let bags be x_1, x_2, x_3, x_4, x_5 and x_6, then $x_1 + x_2 + x_3 + x_4 + x_5 + x_6 = 15$.

$\therefore$ For no bags remains empty, number of ways

$= \text{Coefficient of } x^{15} \text{ in } (x^1 + x^2 + x^3 + ... \infty)^6$

$= \text{Coefficient of } x^{15} \text{ in } x^6(1 + x + x^2 + ... \infty)^6$

$= \text{Coefficient of } x^9 \text{ in } (1-x)^{-6}$

In option (c), it is not mentioned that solution is positive integral

JEE Type Solved Examples : Passage Based Questions

- This section contains **3 solved passages** based upon each of the passage **3 multiple choice** examples have to be answered. Each of these examples has four choices (a), (b), (c) and (d) out of which **ONLY ONE** is correct.

Passage I

(Ex. Nos. 16 to 18)

All the letters of the word 'AGAIN' be arranged and the words thus formed are known as 'Simple Words'. Further two new types of words are defined as follows:

(i) ***Smart word:*** *All the letters of the word 'AGAIN' are being used, but vowels can be repeated as many times as we need.*

(ii) ***Dull word:*** *All the letters of the word 'AGAIN' are being used, but consonants can be repeated as many times as we need.*

16. If a vowel appears in between two similar letters, the number of simple words is

(a) 12 (b) 6 (c) 36 (d) 14

17. Number of 7 letter smart words is

(a) 1500 (b) 1050 (c) 1005 (d) 150

18. Number of 7 letter dull words in which no two vowels are together, is

(a) 402 (b) 420 (c) 840 (d) 42

Sol.

16. (*b*)

N	A-I-A	G

$\therefore$ Required number of simple words $= 3! = 6$

17. (*b*)

A	G	A	I	N	A	A
					I	I
					A	I

$\therefore$ Number of 7 letter smart words

$$= \frac{7!}{4!} + \frac{7!}{2!\,3!} + \frac{7!}{3!\,2!} = 210 + 420 + 420 = 1050$$

18. (*b*) Now, 3 vowels A, I, A are to be placed in the five available places.

$$\begin{cases} \times\text{N}\times\text{G}\times\text{N}\times\text{N}\times \\ \text{OR} \\ \times\text{N}\times\text{G}\times\text{G}\times\text{G}\times \\ \text{OR} \\ \times\text{N}\times\text{G}\times\text{G}\times\text{N}\times \end{cases}$$

Hence, required number of ways

$$= {}^5C_3 \times \frac{3!}{2!} \times \left\{\frac{4!}{3!} + \frac{4!}{3!} + \frac{4!}{2!\,2!}\right\}$$

$$= 30(4 + 4 + 6) = 420$$

Passage II (Ex. Nos. 19 to 21)

Consider a polygon of sides 'n' which satisfies the equation $3 \cdot {}^nP_4 = {}^{n-1}P_5$.

19. Rajdhani express travelling from Delhi to Mumbai has n stations enroute. Number of ways in which a train can be stopped at 3 stations if no two of the stopping stations are consecutive, is

(a) 20 (b) 35 (c) 56 (d) 84

20. Number of quadrilaterals that can be formed using the vertices of a polygon of sides 'n' if exactly 1 side of the quadrilateral is common with side of the n-gon, is

(a) 96 (b) 100 (c) 150 (d) 156

21. Number of quadrilaterals that can be made using the vertices of the polygon of sides 'n' if exactly two adjacent sides of the quadrilateral are common to the sides of the n-gon, is

(a) 50 (b) 60 (c) 70 (d) 80

Sol. $\because$ $3 \cdot {}^nP_4 = {}^{n-1}P_5$

It is clear that $n \geq 6$.

$\therefore$ $3 \cdot n(n-1)(n-2)(n-3) = (n-1)(n-2)(n-3)(n-4)(n-5)$

$\Rightarrow$ $(n-1)(n-2)(n-3)(n^2 - 12n + 20) = 0$

$\Rightarrow$ $(n-1)(n-2)(n-3)(n-10)(n-2) = 0$

$\therefore$ $n = 10, n \neq 1, 2, 3$ $[\because n \geq 6]$

$\Rightarrow$ $n = 10$

19. (*d*) Let a_0 be the number of stations to the left of the station I chosen, a_1 be the number of stations between the station I and station II, a_2 be the number of stations between the station II and station III and a_3 be the number of stations to the right of the third station. Then,

$$a_0, a_3 \geq 0 \text{ and } a_1, a_2 \geq 1$$

Also, $a_0 + a_1 + a_2 + a_3 = n + 1 - 3$

Let $a = a_0 + 1, b = a_3 + 1$, then $a, b \geq 1$ such that

$$a + a_1 + a_2 + b = n$$

$\therefore$ Required number of ways $= {}^{n-1}C_{4-1} = {}^9C_3$ [here, $n = 10$]

$= 84$

20. (*c*) Number of quadrilaterals of which exactly one side is the side of the n-gon

$$= n \times {}^{n-4}C_2 = 10 \times {}^6C_2 = 150 \quad [\because n = 10]$$

21. (*a*) Number of quadrilaterals of which exactly two adjacent sides of the quadrilateral are common to the sides of the n-gon

$$= n \times {}^{n-5}C_1 = n(n-5) = 10 \times 5 \quad [\because n = 10]$$
$$= 50$$

Passage III
(Ex. Nos. 22 to 23)

Consider the number $N = 2016$.

22. Number of cyphers at the end of ${}^{N}C_{N/2}$ is

(a) 0 (b) 1
(c) 2 (d) 3

23. Sum of all even divisors of the number N is

(a) 6552 (b) 6448
(c) 6048 (d) 5733

Sol.

22. (*c*) $\because$ ${}^{N}C_{N/2} = {}^{2016}C_{1008} = \dfrac{(2016)!}{[(1008)!]^2}$

$$E_5(2016!) = \left[\frac{2016}{5}\right] + \left[\frac{2016}{5^2}\right] + \left[\frac{2016}{5^3}\right] + \left[\frac{2016}{5^4}\right]$$
$$= 403 + 80 + 16 + 3 = 502$$

and $E_5(1008!) = \left[\dfrac{1008}{5}\right] + \left[\dfrac{1008}{5^2}\right] + \left[\dfrac{1008}{5^3}\right] + \left[\dfrac{1008}{5^4}\right]$

$$= 201 + 40 + 8 + 1 = 250$$

Hence, the number of cyphers at the end of ${}^{2016}C_{1008}$

$$= 502 - 250 - 250 = 2$$

23. (*b*) $\because$ $N = 2016 = 2^5 \cdot 3^2 \cdot 7^1$

$\therefore$ Sum of all even divisors of the number N

$$= (2 + 2^2 + 2^3 + 2^4 + 2^5)(1 + 3 + 3^2)(1 + 7^1) = 6448$$

JEE Type Solved Examples : Single Integer Answer Type Questions

- This section contains **2 examples.** The answer to each example is a **single digit integer** ranging from **0** to **9** (both inclusive).

• **Ex. 24** *If* $\dbinom{18}{r-2} + 2\dbinom{18}{r-1} + \dbinom{18}{r} \ge \dbinom{20}{13}$, *then the number of values of r are*

Sol. (7) We have, $\dbinom{18}{r-2} + 2\dbinom{18}{r-1} + \dbinom{18}{r} \ge \dbinom{20}{13}$

It means that ${}^{18}C_{r-2} + 2 \cdot {}^{18}C_{r-1} + {}^{18}C_r \ge {}^{20}C_{13}$

$\Rightarrow$ $({}^{18}C_{r-2} + {}^{18}C_{r-1}) + ({}^{18}C_{r-1} + {}^{18}C_r) \ge {}^{20}C_7$

$\Rightarrow$ ${}^{19}C_{r-1} + {}^{19}C_r \ge {}^{20}C_7$

$\Rightarrow$ ${}^{20}C_r \ge {}^{20}C_7$

or ${}^{20}C_r \ge {}^{20}C_{13}$

$\Rightarrow$ $7 \le r \le 13$

$\therefore$ $r = 7, 8, 9, 10, 11, 12, 13$

Hence, the number of values of r are 7.

• **Ex. 25** *If* λ *be the number of 3-digit numbers are of the form xyz with* $x < y$, $z < y$ *and* $x \ne 0$, *the value of* $\dfrac{\lambda}{30}$ *is*

Sol. (8) Since, $x \ge 1$, then $y \ge 2$ $[\because x < y]$

If $y = n$, then x takes values form 1 to $n - 1$ and z can take the values from 0 to $n - 1$ (i.e., n values).

Thus, for each values of $y (2 \le y \le 9)$, x and z take $n(n-1)$ values.

Hence, the 3-digit numbers are of the form xyz

$$= \sum_{n=2}^{9} n(n-1) = \sum_{n=1}^{9} n(n-1) \quad [\because \text{at } n = 1, n(n-1) = 0]$$
$$= \sum_{n=1}^{9} n^2 - \sum_{n=1}^{9} n$$
$$= \frac{9(9+1)(18+1)}{6} - \frac{9(9+1)}{2}$$
$$= 285 - 45$$
$$= 240 = \lambda \quad \text{[given]}$$

$\therefore$ $\dfrac{\lambda}{30} = 8$

JEE Type Solved Examples : Matching Type Questions

- This section contains **2 examples.** Examples 26 and 27 have four statements (A, B and C) given in **Column I** and four statements (p, q, r and s) in **Column II.** Any given statement in **Column I** can have correct matching with one or more statement(s) given in **Column II.**

Ex. 26

	Column I		Column II
(A)	The sum of the factors of 8! which are odd and are the form $3\lambda + 2$, $\lambda \in N$, is	(p)	384
(B)	The number of divisors of $n = 2^7 \cdot 3^5 \cdot 5^3$ which are the form $4\lambda + 1$, $\lambda \in N$, is	(q)	240
(C)	Total number of divisors of $n = 2^5 \cdot 3^4 \cdot 5^{10} \cdot 7^6$ which are the form $4\lambda + 2$, $\lambda \geq 1$, is	(r)	11
(D)	Total number of divisors of $n = 3^5 \cdot 5^7 \cdot 7^9$ which are the form $4\lambda + 1$, $\lambda \geq 0$, is	(s)	40

Sol. (A) $\to$ s; (B) $\to$ r; (C) $\to$ p; (D) $\to$ q

(A) Here, $8! = 2^7 \cdot 3^2 \cdot 5^1 \cdot 7^1$

So, the factors may be 1, 5, 7, 35 of which 5 and 35 are of the form $3\lambda + 2$.

$\therefore$ Sum is 40.

(B) Number of odd numbers $= (5 + 1)(3 + 1) = 24$

Required number $= 12$, but 1 is included.

$\therefore$ Required number of numbers $= 12 - 1 = 11$ of the form $4\lambda + 1$.

(C) Here, $4\lambda + 2 = 2(2\lambda + 1)$

$\therefore$ Total divisors $= 1 \cdot 5 \cdot 11 \cdot 7 - 1 = 384$

[$\because$ one is subtracted because there will be case when selected powers of 3, 5 and 7 are zero]

(D) Here, any positive integer power of 5 will be in the form of $4\lambda + 1$ when even powers of 3 and 7 will be in the form of $4\lambda + 1$ and odd powers of 3 and 7 will be in the form of $4\lambda - 1$.

$\therefore$ Required divisors $= 8(3 \cdot 5 + 3 \cdot 5) = 240$

Ex. 27

	Column I		Column II
(A)	Four dice (six faced) are rolled. The number of possible outcomes in which atleast one die shows 2, is	(p)	210
(B)	Let A be the set of 4-digit numbers $a_1 a_2 a_3 a_4$, where $a_1 > a_2 > a_3 > a_4$. Then, $n(A)$ is equal to	(q)	480
(C)	The total number 3-digit numbers, the sum of whose digits is even, is equal to	(r)	671
(D)	The number of 4-digit numbers that can be formed from the digits 0, 1, 2, 3, 4, 5, 6, 7, so that each number contains digit 1, is	(s)	450

Sol. (A) $\to$ r; (B) $\to$ p; (C) $\to$ s; (D) $\to$ q

(A) The number of possible outcomes with 2 on atleast one die
= The total number of outcomes with 2 on atleast one die
= (The total number of outcomes) – (The number of outcomes in which 2 does not appear on any dice)
$= 6^4 - 5^4 = 1296 - 625 = 671$

(B) Any selection of four digits from the 10 digits 0, 1, 2, 3,..., 9 gives one number. So, the required number of numbers is ${}^{10}C_4$ i.e., 210.

(C) Let the number be $n = pqr$. Since, $p + q + r$ is even, p can be filled in 9 ways and q can be filled in 10 ways.
r can be filled in number of ways depending upon what is the sum of p and q.
If $(p + q)$ is odd, then r can be filled with any one of five odd digits.
If $(p + q)$ is even, then r can be filled with any one of five even digits.
In any case, r can be filled in five ways.
Hence, total number of numbers is $9 \times 10 \times 5 = 450$

(D) After fixing 1 at one position out of 4 places, 3 places can be filled by ${}^7P_3$ ways. But for some numbers whose fourth digit is zero, such type of ways is ${}^6P_2$. Therefore, total number of ways is ${}^7P_3 - {}^6P_2 = 480$

JEE Type Solved Examples : Statement I and II Type Questions

- **Directions** Example numbers 28 and 29 are Assertion-Reason type examples. Each of these examples contains two statements:
Statement-1 (Assertion) and **Statement-2** (Reason)
Each of these examples also has four alternative choices, only one of which is the correct answer. You have to select the correct choice as given below.
(a) Statement-1 is true, Statement-2 is true; Statement-2 is a correct explanation for Statement-1
(b) Statement-1 is true, Statement-2 is true; Statement-2 is not a correct explanation for Statement-1
(c) Statement-1 is true, Statement-2 is false
(d) Statement-1 is false, Statement-2 is true

- ***Ex. 28*** **Statement-1** *Number of rectangles on a chess-board is* $^8C_2 \times {}^8C_2$.

Statement-2 *To form a rectangle, we have to select any two of the horizontal lines and any two of the vertical lines.*

Sol. (*d*) In a chessboard, there are 9 horizontal lines and 9 vertical lines.

$\therefore$ Number of rectangles of any size are $^9C_2 \times {}^9C_2$.

Hence, Statement-1 is false and Statement-2 is true.

- ***Ex. 29*** **Statement-1** *If* $f:\{a_1,a_2,a_3,a_4,a_5\}\to\{a_1,a_2,a_3,a_4,a_5\}$, *f is onto and* $f(x)\neq x$ *for each* $x\in\{a_1,a_2,a_3,a_4,a_5\}$, *is equal to 44.*

- **Statement-2** *The number of derangement for n objects is* $n!\sum_{r=0}^{n}\frac{(-1)^r}{r!}$.

Sol. (*a*) $\because D_n = n!\sum_{r=0}^{n}\frac{(-1)^r}{r!} = n!\left(1-\frac{1}{1!}+\frac{1}{2!}-\frac{1}{3!}+\ldots+\frac{(-1)^n}{n!}\right)$

$$\therefore\quad D_5 = 5!\left(1-\frac{1}{1!}+\frac{1}{2!}-\frac{1}{3!}+\frac{1}{4!}-\frac{1}{5!}\right)$$
$$=120\left(\frac{1}{2}-\frac{1}{6}+\frac{1}{24}-\frac{1}{120}\right)$$
$$=6-20+5-1$$
$$=65-21$$
$$=44$$

Hence, Statement-1 is true, Statement-2 is true and Statement-2 is a correct explanation for Statement-1.

Subjective Type Examples

- In this section, there are **17 subjective** solved examples.

- ***Ex. 30*** *Solve the inequality*
$$^{x-1}C_4 - {}^{x-1}C_3 - \frac{5}{4}\,{}^{x-2}A_2 < 0, x\in N.$$

Sol. We have, $^{x-1}C_4 - {}^{x-1}C_3 - \frac{5}{4}\,{}^{x-2}A_2 < 0$

$$\Leftrightarrow \frac{(x-1)(x-2)(x-3)(x-4)}{1\cdot2\cdot3\cdot4}-\frac{(x-1)(x-2)(x-3)}{1\cdot2\cdot3}-\frac{5}{4}\cdot(x-2)(x-3)<0$$
$$\Leftrightarrow (x-1)(x-2)(x-3)(x-4)-4(x-1)(x-2)(x-3)-30(x-2)(x-3)<0$$
$$\Leftrightarrow (x-2)(x-3)\{(x-1)(x-4)-4(x-1)-30\}<0$$

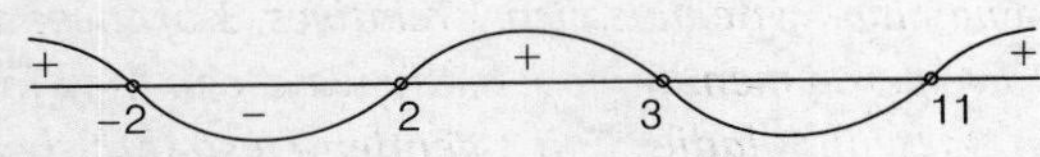

$$\Leftrightarrow (x-2)(x-3)\{x^2-9x-22\}<0$$
$$\Leftrightarrow (x-2)(x-3)(x+2)(x-11)<0$$

From wavy curve method

$$x\in(-2,2)\cup(3,11)$$

but $\quad x\in N$

$\therefore \quad x = 1, 4, 5, 6, 7, 8, 9, 10 \quad$ ...(i)

From inequality,

$$x-1\geq 4,\ x-1\geq 3,\ x-2\geq 2$$

or $\quad x\geq 5,\ x\geq 4,\ x\geq 4$

Hence, $\quad x\geq 5 \quad$ ...(ii)

From Eqs. (i) and (ii), solutions of the inequality are

$$x = 5, 6, 7, 8, 9, 10.$$

- ***Ex. 31*** *Find the sum of the series*
$(1^2+1)1!+(2^2+1)2!+(3^2+1)3!+\ldots+(n^2+1)n!$.

Sol. Let $S_n=(1^2+1)1!+(2^2+1)2!+(3^2+1)3!+\ldots+(n^2+1)n!$

$\therefore$ nth term $T_n=(n^2+1)n!$

$$=\{(n+1)(n+2)-3(n+1)+2\}n!$$
$$T_n=(n+2)!-3(n+1)!+2n!$$

Putting $n = 1, 2, 3, 4, \ldots, n$

Then, $T_1 = 3! - 3\cdot 2! + 2\cdot 1!$

$T_2 = 4! - 3\cdot 3! + 2\cdot 2!$

$T_3 = 5! - 3\cdot 4! + 2\cdot 3!$

$T_4 = 6! - 3\cdot 5! + 2\cdot 4!$

…………………

…………………

$T_{n-1} = (n+1)! - 3n! + 2(n-1)!$

$T_n = (n+2)! - 3(n+1)! + 2n!$

$\therefore \quad S_n = T_1 + T_2 + T_3 + \ldots + T_n$

$= (n+2)! - 2(n+1)!$ [the rest cancel out]

$= (n+2)(n+1)! - 2(n+1)!$

$= (n+1)!(n+2-2)$

$= n(n+1)!$

● ***Ex. 32*** *Find the negative terms of the sequence*

$$x_n = \frac{{}^{n+4}P_4}{P_{n+2}} - \frac{143}{4P_n}.$$

Sol. We have,

$$x_n = \frac{{}^{n+4}P_4}{P_{n+2}} - \frac{143}{4P_n}$$

$$\therefore \quad x_n = \frac{(n+4)(n+3)(n+2)(n+1)}{(n+2)!} - \frac{143}{4n!}$$

$$= \frac{(n+4)(n+3)(n+2)(n+1)}{(n+2)(n+1)n!} - \frac{143}{4n!}$$

$$= \frac{(n+4)(n+3)}{n!} - \frac{143}{4n!} = \frac{(4n^2+28n-95)}{4n!}$$

$\because$ x_n is negative

$$\therefore \quad \frac{(4n^2+28n-95)}{4n!} < 0$$

which is true for $n = 1, 2$.

Hence, $x_1 = -\frac{63}{4}$ and $x_2 = -\frac{23}{8}$ are two negative terms.

● ***Ex. 33*** *How many integers between* 1 *and* 1000000 *have the sum of the digits equal to* 18*?*

Sol. Integers between 1 and 1000000 will be 1, 2, 3, 4, 5 or 6 digits and given sum of digits = 18

Thus, we need to obtain the number of solutions of the equation

$$x_1 + x_2 + x_3 + x_4 + x_5 + x_6 = 18 \quad \ldots\text{(i)}$$

where, $0 \le x_i \le 9$, $i = 1, 2, 3, 4, 5, 6$

Therefore, the number of solutions of Eq. (i), will be

$= $ Coefficient of x^{18} in $(x^0 + x^1 + x^2 + x^3 + \ldots + x^9)^6$

$= $ Coefficient of x^{18} in $\left(\frac{1-x^{10}}{1-x}\right)^6$

$= $ Coefficient of x^{18} in $(1-x^{10})^6(1-x)^{-6}$

$= $ Coefficient of x^{18} in $(1-6x^{10})(1 + {}^6C_1x + {}^7C_2x^2 + \ldots + {}^{13}C_8x^8 + \ldots + {}^{23}C_{18}x^{18} + \ldots)$

$= {}^{23}C_{18} - 6\cdot{}^{13}C_8 = {}^{23}C_5 - 6\cdot{}^{13}C_5$

$$= \frac{23\cdot 22\cdot 21\cdot 20\cdot 19}{1\cdot 2\cdot 3\cdot 4\cdot 5} - 6\cdot\frac{13\cdot 12\cdot 11\cdot 10\cdot 9}{1\cdot 2\cdot 3\cdot 4\cdot 5}$$

$= 33649 - 7722 = 25927$

● ***Ex. 34*** *How many different car licence plates can be constructed, if the licences contain three letters of the English alphabet followed by a three digit number,*

(i) if repetition are allowed?

(ii) if repetition are not allowed?

Sol. (i) Total letters = 26 (i.e., $A, B, C, \ldots, X, Y, Z$)

and total digit number = 10 (i.e., 0, 1, 2, …, 9)

If three letters on plate is represented by, then first place can be filled = 26

Second place can again be filled = 26

[$\because$ repetition are allowed]

and third place can again be filled = 26

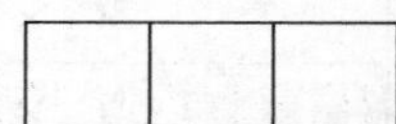

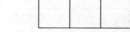

Hence, three letters can be filled $= 26 \times 26 \times 26 = (26)^3$ ways

and three digit numbers on plate by 999 ways (i.e., 001, 002, …, 999)

Hence, by the principle of multiplication, the required number of ways $= (26)^3(999)$ ways

(ii) Here, three letters out of 26 can be filled $= {}^{26}P_3$

[$\because$ repetition are not allowed]

and three digit can be filled out of $10 = {}^{10}P_3$

[$\because$ repetition are not allowed]

Hence, required number of ways $= ({}^{26}P_3)({}^{10}P_3)$ ways.

● ***Ex. 35*** *A man has* 7 *relatives,* 4 *of them are ladies and* 3 *gentlemen, has wife, has also* 7 *relatives,* 3 *of them are ladies and* 4 *are gentlemen. In how many ways can they invite a dinner party of* 3 *ladies and* 3 *gentlemen so that there are* 3 *of them man's relatives and* 3 *of the wife's relatives?*

Sol. The four possible ways of inviting 3 ladies and 3 gentlemen for the party with the help of the following table :

Man's relatives		Wife's relatives		Number of ways
4 Ladies	3 Gentlemen	3 Ladies	4 Gentlemen	
0	3	3	0	${}^4C_0 \times {}^3C_3 \times {}^3C_3 \times {}^4C_0 = 1$
1	2	2	1	${}^4C_1 \times {}^3C_2 \times {}^3C_2 \times {}^4C_1 = 144$
2	1	1	2	${}^4C_2 \times {}^3C_1 \times {}^3C_1 \times {}^4C_2 = 324$
3	0	0	3	${}^4C_3 \times {}^3C_0 \times {}^3C_0 \times {}^4C_3 = 16$

∴ Required number of ways to invite $= 1 + 144 + 324 + 16 = 485$

● **Ex. 36** *A team of ten is to be formed from 6 male doctors and 10 nurses of whom 5 are male and 5 are female. In how many ways can this be done, if the team must have atleast 4 doctors and atleast 4 nurses with atleast 2 male nurses and atleast 2 female nurses?*

Sol.

6 Doctors	5 Male nurses	5 Female nurses	Number of ways of selection
4	4	2	${}^6C_4 \times {}^5C_4 \times {}^5C_2 = 750$
4	3	3	${}^6C_4 \times {}^5C_3 \times {}^5C_3 = 1500$
4	2	4	${}^6C_4 \times {}^5C_2 \times {}^5C_4 = 750$
5	3	2	${}^6C_5 \times {}^5C_3 \times {}^5C_2 = 600$
5	2	3	${}^6C_5 \times {}^5C_2 \times {}^5C_3 = 600$
6	2	2	${}^6C_6 \times {}^5C_2 \times {}^5C_2 = 100$

∴ Total ways = 4300

● **Ex. 37** *A number of four different digits is formed with the help of the digits 1,2,3,4,5,6,7 in all possible ways.*

(i) How many such numbers can be formed?
(ii) How many of these are even?
(iii) How many of these are exactly divisible by 4?
(iv) How many of these are exactly divisible by 25?

Sol. Here total digit = 7 and no two of which are alike

(i) Required number of ways = Taking 4 out of 7

$$= {}^7P_4 = 7 \times 6 \times 5 \times 4 = 840$$

(ii) For even number last digit must be 2 or 4 or 6. Now the remaining three first places on the left of 4-digit numbers are to be filled from the remaining 6-digits and this can be done in

$${}^6P_3 = 6 \cdot 5 \cdot 4 = 120 \text{ ways}$$

and last digit can be filled in 3 ways.

∴ By the principle of multiplication, the required number of ways

$$= 120 \times 3 = 360$$

(iii) For the number exactly divisible by 4, then last two digit must be divisible by 4, the last two digits are *viz.*, 12, 16, 24, 32, 36, 52, 56, 64, 72, 76. Total 10 ways.

Now, the remaining two first places on the left of 4-digit numbers are to be filled from the remaining 5-digits and this can be done in ${}^5P_2 = 20$ ways.

Hence, by the principle of multiplication, the required number of ways

$$= 20 \times 10 = 200$$

(iv) For the number exactly divisible by 25, then last two digit must be divisible by 25, the last two digits are *viz.*, 25, 75. Total 2 ways.

Now, the remaining two first places on the left of 4-digit number are to be filled from the remaining 5-digits and this can be done in ${}^5P_2 = 20$ ways.

Hence, by the principle of multiplication, the required number of ways

$$= 20 \times 2 = 40$$

● **Ex. 38** *India and South Africa play One Day International Series until one team wins 4 matches. No match ends in a draw. Find in how many ways the series can be won?*

Sol. Taking I for India and S for South Africa. We can arrange I and S to show the wins for India and South Africa, respectively.

For example., *ISSSS* means first match is won by India which is followed by 4 wins by South Africa. This is one way in which series can be won.

Suppose, South Africa wins the series, then last match is always won by South Africa.

	Wins of I	Wins of S	Number of ways
(i)	0	4	1
(ii)	1	4	$\frac{4!}{3!} = 4$
(iii)	2	4	$\frac{5!}{2!3!} = 10$
(iv)	3	4	$\frac{6!}{3!3!} = 20$

∴ Total number of ways = 35

In the same number of ways, India can win the series.

∴ Total number of ways in which the series can be won

$$= 35 \times 2 = 70$$

Ex. 39 *Let n and k be positive integers such that $n \geq \frac{k(k+1)}{2}$. Find the number of solutions $(x_1, x_2, \ldots, x_k)$, $x_1 \geq 1, x_2 \geq 2, \ldots, x_k \geq k$ all integers satisfying $x_1 + x_2 + \ldots + x_k = n$.*

Sol. We have, $x_1 + x_2 + \ldots + x_k = n$ ...(i)

Now, let $y_1 = x_1 - 1,\ y_2 = x_2 - 2, \ldots, y_k = x_k - k$

$\therefore \quad y_1 \geq 0,\ y_2 \geq 0, \ldots, y_k \geq 0$

On substituting the values $x_1, x_2, \ldots, x_k$ in terms of $y_1, y_2, \ldots, y_k$ in Eq. (i), we get

$$y_1 + 1 + y_2 + 2 + \ldots + y_k + k = n$$

$$\Rightarrow \quad y_1 + y_2 + \ldots + y_k = n - (1 + 2 + 3 + \ldots + k)$$

$$\therefore \quad y_1 + y_2 + \ldots + y_k = n - \frac{k(k+1)}{2} = A \text{ (say)} \qquad \ldots\text{(ii)}$$

The number of non-negative integral solutions of the Eq. (ii) is

$$= {}^{k+A-1}C_A = \frac{(k+A-1)!}{A!(k-1)!}$$

where, $\quad A = n - \frac{k(k+1)}{2}$

Ex. 40 *Find the number of all whole numbers formed on the screen of a calculator which can be recognised as numbers with (unique) correct digits when they are read inverted. The greatest number formed on its screen is 999999.*

Sol. The number can use digits 0, 1, 2, 5, 6, 8 and 9 because they can be recognised as digits when they are see inverted.

A number can't begin with ,therefore all numbers having at unit's digit should no be counted. (when those numbers will be read inverted they will begin with).

No. of digits	Total numbers
1	7
2	$6^2 = 36$
3	$6 \times 7 \times 6 = 252$
4	$6 \times 7^2 \times 6 = 1764$
5	$6 \times 7^3 \times 6 = 12348$
6	$6 \times 7^4 \times 6 = 86436$
$\therefore$	Total = 100843

Ex. 41 *How many different numbers which are smaller than 2×10^8 and are divisible by 3, can be written by means of the digits 0, 1 and 2?*

Sol. 12, 21 ... 122222222 are form the required numbers we can assume all of them to be nine digit in the form $a_1, a_2, a_3, a_4, a_5, a_6, a_7, a_8, a_9$ and can use 0 for $a_1; a_2$ and a_0 and $a_0,\ a_1, a_2$ and $a_3 \ldots$ and so on to get 8-digit, 7-digit, 6-digit numbers etc. a_1 can assume one of the 2 values of 0 or 1. $a_2, a_3, a_4, a_5, a_6, a_7, a_8$ can assume any of 3 values 0, 1, 2. The number for which $a_1 = a_2 = a_3 = a_4 = a_5 = a_6 = a_7 = a_8 = a_9 = 0$ must be eleminated. The sum of first 8-digits i.e., $a_1 + a_2 + \ldots + a_8$ can be in the form of $3n - 2$ or $3n - 1$ or $3n$.

In each case a_9 can be chosen from 0,1,2 in only 1 way so that the sum of all 9-digits in equal to $3n$.

$\therefore \quad$ Total numbers $= 2 \times 3^7 \times 1 - 1 = 4374 - 1 = 4373.$

Ex. 42 *There are n straight lines in a plane such that n_1 of them are parallel in one direction, n_2 are parallel in different direction and so on, n_k are parallel in another direction such that $n_1 + n_2 + \ldots + n_k = n$. Also, no three of the given lines meet at a point. Prove that the total number of points of intersection is*

$$\frac{1}{2}\left\{n^2 - \sum_{r=1}^{k} n_r^2\right\}.$$

Sol. Total number of points of intersection when no two of n given lines are parallel and no three of them are concurrent, is ${}^nC_2$. But it is given that there are k sets of $n_1, n_2, n_3, \ldots, n_k$ parallel lines such that no line in one set is parallel to line in another set.

Hence, total number of points of intersection

$$= {}^nC_2 - ({}^{n_1}C_2 + {}^{n_2}C_2 + \ldots + {}^{n_k}C_2)$$

$$= \frac{n(n-1)}{2} - \left\{\frac{n_1(n_1-1)}{2} + \frac{n_2(n_2-1)}{2} + \ldots + \frac{n_k(n_k-1)}{2}\right\}$$

$$= \frac{n(n-1)}{2} - \frac{1}{2}\{(n_1^2 + n_2^2 + \ldots + n_k^2) - (n_1 + n_2 + \ldots + n_k)\}$$

$$= \frac{n(n-1)}{2} - \frac{1}{2}\left\{\sum_{r=1}^{k} n_r^2 - n\right\}$$

$$= \frac{n^2}{2} - \frac{1}{2}\sum_{r=1}^{k} n_r^2 = \frac{1}{2}\left\{n^2 - \sum_{r=1}^{k} n_r^2\right\}$$

Ex. 43 *There are p intermediate stations on a railway line from one terminus to another. In how many ways a train can stop at 3 of these interediate stations, if no two of these stopping stations are to be consecutive?*

Sol. A — S_1 — S_2 — S_3 — S_{n-1} — S_n — S_{n+1} — S_{p-1} — S_p — B

Let there be p intermediate stations between two terminus stations A and B as shown above.

Number of ways the train can stop in three intermediate stations $= {}^pC_3$

These are comprised of two exclusive cases *viz.*

(i) atleast two stations are consecutive.

(ii) now two of which is consecutive.

Now, there are $(p-1)$ pairs of consecutive intermediate stations.

In order to get a station trio in which atleast two stations are consecutive, each pair can be associated with a third station in $(p-2)$ ways. Hence, total number of ways in which 3 stations consisting of atleast two consecutive stations, can be chosen in $(p-1)(p-2)$ ways. Among these, each triplet of consecutive stations occur twice.

For example, the pair (S_n, S_{n-1}) when combined with S_{n+1} and the pair (S_n, S_{n+1}) when combined with S_{n-1} gives the same triplet and is counted twice. So, the number of three consecutive stations trio should be subtracted.

Now, number of these three consecutive stations trio is $(p-2)$.

Hence, the number of ways the triplet of stations consisting of atleast two consecutive stations can be chosen in

$$= \{(p-1)(p-2)-(p-2)\} \text{ ways}$$
$$= (p-2)^2 \text{ ways}$$

Therefore, number of ways the train can stop in three consecutive stations

$$= {}^pC_3 - (p-2)^2 = \frac{p(p-1)(p-2)}{1\cdot2\cdot3} - (p-2)^2$$

$$= (p-2)\left[\frac{p^2-p-6p+12}{6}\right] = \frac{(p-2)(p^2-7p+12)}{6}$$

$$= \frac{(p-2)(p-3)(p-4)}{1\cdot2\cdot3} = {}^{(p-2)}C_3$$

● **Ex. 44** *How many different 7-digit numbers are there and sum of whose digits is even?*

Sol. Let us consider 10 successive 7-digit numbers

$a_1a_2a_3a_4a_5a_6\,0,$

$a_1a_2a_3a_4a_5a_6\,1,$

$a_1a_2a_3a_4a_5a_6\,2,$

....

$a_1a_2a_3a_4a_5a_6\,9$

where, a_1, a_2, a_3, a_4, a_5 and a_6 are some digits. We see that half of these 10 numbers, i.e. 5 numbers have an even sum of digits.

The first digit a_1 can assume 9 different values and each of the digits a_2, a_3, a_4, a_5 and a_6 can assume 10 different values.

The last digit a_7 can assume only 5 different values of which the sum of all digits is even.

$\therefore$ There are $9\times10^5\times5 = 45\times10^5$, 7-digit numbers the sum of whose digits is even.

● **Ex. 45** *There are 2n guests at a dinner party. Supposing that the master and mistress of the house have fixed seats opposite one another and that there are two specified guests who must not be placed next to one another. Find the number of ways in which the company can be placed.*

Sol. Let the M and M' represent seats of the master and mistress respectively and let $a_1, a_2, a_3, \ldots, a_{2n}$ represent the $2n$ seats.

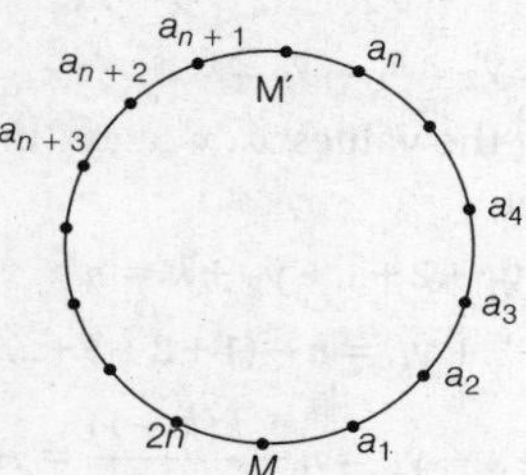

Let the guests who must not be placed next to one another be called P and Q.

Now, put P at a_1 and Q at any position, other than a_2, say at a_3, then remaining $(2n-2)$ guests can be arranged in the remaining $(2n-2)$ positions in $(2n-2)!$ ways. Hence, there will be altogether $(2n-2)(2n-2)!$ arrangements of the guests, when P is at a_1.

The same number of arrangements when P is at a_n or a_{n+1} or a_{2n}. Thus, for these positions $(a_1, a_n, a_{n+1}, a_{2n})$ of P, there are altogether $4(2n-2)(2n-2)!$ ways. ...(i)

If P is at a_2, then there are altogether $(2n-3)$ positions for Q. Hence, there will be altogether $(2n-3)(2n-2)!$ arrangements of the guests, when P is at a_2.

The same number of arrangements can be made when P is at any other position excepting the four positions

$a_1, a_n, a_{n+1}, a_{2n}$.

Hence, for these $(2n-4)$ positions of P, there will be altogether

$(2n-4)(2n-3)(2n-2)!$ arrangements of the guests ...(ii)

Hence, from Eqs. (i) and (ii), the total number of ways of arranging the guests

$$= 4(2n-2)(2n-2)! + (2n-4)(2n-3)(2n-2)!$$
$$= (4n^2-6n+4)(2n-2)!$$

● **Ex. 46** *Find the number of triangles whose angular points are at the angular points of a given polygon of n sides, but none of whose sides are the sides of the polygon.*

Sol. A polygon of n sides has n angular points. Number of triangles formed from these n angular points $= {}^nC_3$.

These are comprised of two exclusive cases *viz.*

(i) atleast one side of the triangle is a side of the polygon.

(ii) no side of the triangle is a side of the polygon.

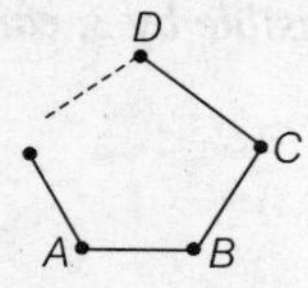

Let AB be one side of the polygon. If each angular point of the remaining $(n-2)$ points are joined with A and B, we get a triangle with one side AB.

$\therefore$ Number of triangles of which AB is one side $= (n-2)$

Likewise, number of triangles of which BC is one side $= (n-2)$ and of which atleast one side is the side of the polygon $= n(n-2)$.

Out of these triangle, some are counted twice. For example, the triangle when C is joined with AB is ΔABC, is taken when AB is taken as one side. Again triangle formed when A is joined with BC is counted when BC is taken as one side.

Number of such triangles $= n$

So, the number of triangles of which one side is the side of the triangle

$$= n(n-2) - n = n(n-3)$$

Hence, the total number of required triangles

$$= {}^nC_3 - n(n-3) = \frac{1}{6}n(n-4)(n-5)$$

• Ex. 47 *Prove that $(n!)!$ is divisible by $(n!)^{(n-1)!}$.*

Sol. First we show that the product of p consecutive positive integers is divisible by $p!$. Let the p consecutive integers be $m, m+1, m+2, \ldots, m+p-1$. Then,

$$m(m+1)(m+2)\ldots(m+p-1) = \frac{(m+p-1)!}{(m-1)!}$$

$$= p!\frac{(m+p-1)!}{(m-1)!\,p!}$$

$$= p!\,{}^{m+p-1}C_p$$

Since, ${}^{m+p-1}C_p$ is an integer.

$$\therefore \quad {}^{m+p-1}C_p = \frac{m(m+1)(m+2)\ldots(m+p-1)}{p!}$$

Now, $(n!)!$ is the product of the positive integers from 1 to $n!$. We write the integers from 1 to $n!$ is $(n-1)!$ rows as follows:

1	2	3	....	n
$n+1$	$n+2$	$n+3$	....	$2n$
$2n+1$	$2n+2$	$2n+3$	....	$3n$
:	:	:	:	:
$n!-n+1$	$n!-n+2$	$n!-n+3$	....	$n!$

Each of these $(n-1)!$ rows contain n consecutive positive integers. The product of the consecutive integers in each row is divisible by $n!$. Thus, the product of all the integers from 1 to $n!$ is divisible by $(n!)^{(n-1)!}$.

Permutations and Combinations Exercise 1 : Single Option Correct Type Questions

- This section contains **30 multiple choice questions.** Each question has four choices (a), (b), (c) and (d) out of which **ONLY ONE** is correct

1. A lady gives a dinner party to 5 guests to be selected from nine friends. The number of ways of forming the party of 5, given that two of the friends will not attend the party together, is
(a) 56 (b) 126 (c) 91 (d) None of these

2. If a, b, c and d are odd natural numbers such that $a+b+c+d=20$, the number of values of the ordered quadruplet (a, b, c, d) is
(a) 165 (b) 455 (c) 310 (d) None of these

3. If $l=$ LCM of 8!, 10! and 12! and $h=$ HCF of 8!, 10! and 12!, then $\frac{l}{h}$ is equal to
(a) 132 (b) 11800
(c) 11880 (d) None of these

4. The number of positive integers satisfying the inequality ${}^{n+1}C_{n-2} - {}^{n+1}C_{n-1} \le 100$ is
(a) 9 (b) 8
(c) 5 (d) None of these

5. The number of ways in which a score of 11 can be made from a through by three persons, each throwing a single die once, is
(a) 45 (b) 18 (c) 27 (d) 68

6. The number of positive integers with the property that they can be expressed as the sum of the cubes of 2 positive integers in two different ways is
(a) 1 (b) 100 (c) infinite (d) 0

7. In a plane there are 37 straight lines, of which 13 pass through the point A and 11 pass through the point B. Besides, no three lines pass through one point, no line passes through both points A and B and no two are parallel, the number of intersection points the lines have, is
(a) 535 (b) 601 (c) 728 (d) 963

8. If a denotes the number of permutations of $x+2$ things taken all at a time, b the number of permutations of x things taken 11 at a time and c the number of permutations of $x-11$ things taken all at a time such that $a=182bc$, the value of x is
(a) 15 (b) 12 (c) 10 (d) 18

9. The number of numbers less than 1000 that can be formed out of the digits 0, 1, 2, 3, 4 and 5, no digit being repeated, is
(a) 130 (b) 131 (c) 156 (d) 158

10. If the permutations of a, b, c, d and e taken all together are written down in alphabetical order as in dictionary and numbered, the rank of the permutation *debac* is
(a) 90 (b) 91 (c) 92 (d) 93

11. On a railway there are 20 stations. The number of different tickets required in order that it may be possible to travel from every station to every station, is
(a) 210 (b) 225 (c) 196 (d) 105

12. A set containing n elements. A subset P of A is chosen. The set A is reconstructed by replacing the element of P. A subset Q of A is again chosen the number of ways of choosing P and Q, so that $P \cap Q = \phi$, is
(a) $2^{2n} - {}^{2n}C_n$ (b) 2^n (c) $2^n - 1$ (d) 3^n

13. The straight lines I_1, I_2, I_3 are parallel and lie in the same plane. A total number of m points on I_1 ; n points on I_2 ; k points on I_3, the maximum number of triangles formed with vertices at these points is
(a) ${}^{m+n+k}C_3$ (b) ${}^{m+n+k}C_3 - {}^mC_3 - {}^nC_3 - {}^kC_3$
(c) ${}^mC_3 + {}^nC_3 + {}^kC_3$ (d) None of these

14. Let A be a set of $n(\ge 3)$ distinct elements. The number of triplets (x, y, z) of the set A in which atleast two coordinates are equal to
(a) ${}^nP_3$ (b) $n^3 - {}^nP_3$
(c) $3n^2 - 2n$ (d) $3n^2(n-1)$

15. The total number of five-digit numbers of different digits in which the digit in the middle is the largest, is
(a) $2^2 \cdot 3^2 \cdot 7^2$ (b) $2^3 \cdot 3 \cdot 7^3$
(c) $2^2 \cdot 3^3 \cdot 7^2$ (d) $2^3 \cdot 3^2 \cdot 7^3$

16. The total number of words that can be formed using all letters of the word 'RITESH' that neither begins with I nor ends with R, is
(a) 504 (b) 480
(c) 600 (d) 720

17. A man has three friends. The number of ways he can invite one friend everyday for dinner on six successive nights, so that no friend is invited more than three times, is
(a) 360 (b) 420 (c) 170 (d) 510

18. The number of three digit numbers of the form xyz such that $x < y, z \le y$ and $x \ne 0$, is
(a) 240 (b) 244 (c) 276 (d) 285

19. The letters of the word 'MEERUT' are arranged in all possible ways as in a dictionary, then the rank of the word 'MEERUT' is
(a) 119 (b) 120 (c) 121 (d) 122

20. The number of ways in which 10 candidates $A_1, A_2, \dots, A_{10}$ can be ranked so that A_1 is always above A_2, is

(a) 10! (b) $\frac{10!}{2}$
(c) 9! (d) None of these

21. Let A be the set of four digit numbers $a_1a_2\,a_3a_4$, where $a_1 > a_2 > a_3 > a_4$, then $n(A)$ is

(a) 126 (b) 84
(c) 210 (d) None of these

22. The number of distinct rational numbers x such that $0 < x < 1$ and $x = \frac{p}{q}$, where $p, q \in \{1, 2, 3, 4, 5, 6\}$ is

(a) 15 (b) 13 (c) 12 (d) 11

23. The total number of integral solutions of $xyz = 24$ is

(a) 30 (b) 36 (c) 90 (d) 120

24. If *ABCD* is a convex quadrilateral with 3, 4, 5 and 6 points, marked on sides *AB*, *BC*, *CD* and *DA* respectively, then the number of triangles with vertices on different sides, is

(a) 220 (b) 270 (c) 282 (d) 342

25. The number of ways can a team of six horses be selected out of a stud of 16, so that there shall always be three out of *A*, *B*, *C*, *D*, *E*, *F* but never *AD*, *BE* or *CF* together, is

(a) 720 (b) 840 (c) 960 (d) 1260

26. The number of polynomials of the form $x^3 + ax^2 + bx + c$ that are divisible by $x^2 + 1$, where $a, b, c \in \{1, 2, 3, 4, 5, 6, 7, 8, 9, 10\}$, is

(a) 10 (b) 15 (c) 5 (d) 8

27. Let $x_1, x_2, x_3, \dots, x_k$ be the divisors of positive integer 'n' (including 1 and x). If $x_1 + x_2 + \dots + x_k = 75$, then $\sum_{i=1}^{k} \frac{1}{x_i}$ is equal to

(a) $\frac{k^2}{75}$ (b) $\frac{75}{k}$ (c) $\frac{n^2}{75}$ (d) $\frac{75}{n}$

28. The total number of functions 'f' from the set $\{1, 2, 3\}$ into the set $\{1, 2, 3, 4, 5\}$ such that $f(i) \le f(j)$, $\forall\, i < j$, is

(a) 35 (b) 30 (c) 50 (d) 60

29. Ten persons numbered 1, 2, 3, ..., 10 play a chess tournament, each player playing against every player exactly one game. It is known that no game ends in a draw. Let $w_1, w_2, w_3, \dots, w_{10}$ be the number of games won by player 1, 2, 3, ..., 10 respectively and $l_1, l_2, l_3, \dots, l_{10}$ be the number of games lost by the players 1, 2, 3, ..., 10 respectively, then

(a) $\Sigma w_i^2 = 81 - \Sigma l_i^2$ (b) $\Sigma w_i^2 = 81 + \Sigma l_i^2$
(c) $\Sigma w_i^2 = \Sigma l_i^2$ (d) None of these

30. In the next world cup of cricket there will be 12 teams, divided equally in two groups. Teams of each group will play a match against each other. From each group 3 top teams will qualify for the next round. In this round each team will play against others once.
Four top teams of this round will qualify for the semi- final round, where each team will play against the others once. Two top teams of this round will go to the final round, where they will play the best of three matches. The minimum number of matches in the next world cup will be

(a) 54 (b) 53 (c) 38 (d) 37

Permutations and Combinations Exercise 2 :
More than One Correct Option Type Questions

- This section contains **10 multiple choice questions.** Each question has four choices (a), (b), (c) and (d) out of which **MORE THAN ONE** may be correct.

31. If $300! = 3^m \times$ an integer, then

(a) $m = 148$ (b) $m = 150$
(c) It is equivalent to number of n in $150! = 2^{n-2} \times$ an integer
(d) $m = {}^{150}C_2$

32. If $102! = 2^{\alpha} \cdot 3^{\beta} \cdot 5^{\gamma} \cdot 7^{\delta} \dots$, then

(a) $\alpha = 98$ (b) $\beta = 2\gamma + 1$ (c) $\alpha = 2\beta$ (d) $2\gamma = 3\delta$

33. The number of ways of choosing triplet (x, y, z) such that $z \ge \max\{x, y\}$ and $x, y, z \in \{1, 2, 3, \dots, n, n+1\}$, is

(a) ${}^{n+1}C_3 + {}^{n+2}C_3$ (b) $\frac{n(n+1)(2n+1)}{6}$
(c) $1^2 + 2^2 + 3^2 + \dots + n^2$ (d) $2({}^{n+2}C_3) - {}^{n+1}C_2$

34. Let n be 4-digit integer in which all the digits are different. If x is the number of odd integers and y is the number of even integers, then

(a) $x < y$ (b) $x > y$
(c) $x + y = 4500$ (d) $|x - y| = 56$

35. Let $S = \{1, 2, 3, \dots, n\}$. If X denotes the set of all subsets of S containing exactly two elements, then the value of $\sum_{A \in X} (\text{min. } A)$ is given by

(a) ${}^{n+1}C_3$ (b) ${}^{n}C_3$
(c) $\frac{n(n^2 - 1)}{6}$ (d) $\frac{n(n^2 - 3n + 2)}{6}$

36. Let $p = 2520$, $x =$ number of divisors of p which are multiple of 6, $y =$ number of divisors of p which are multiple of 9, then

(a) $x = 12$ (b) $x = 24$ (c) $y = 12$ (d) $y = 16$

37. If N denotes the number of ways of selecting r objects out of n distinct objects $(r \geq n)$ with unlimited repetition but with each object included atleast once in selection, then N is

(a) ${}^{r-1}C_{r-n}$ (b) ${}^{r-1}C_n$
(c) ${}^{r-1}C_{n-1}$ (d) ${}^{r-1}C_{r-n-1}$

38. There are three teams x, $x+1$ and y childrens and total number of childrens in the teams is 24. If two childrens of the same team do not fight,then

(a) maximum number of fights is 190
(b) maximum number of fights is 191
(c) maximum number of fights occur when $x = 7$
(d) maximum number of fights occur when $x = 8$

39. Let N denotes the number of ways in which $3n$ letters can be selected from $2n$ A's, $2nB$'s and $2nC$'s. Then,

(a) $3 \mid (N-1)$
(b) $n \mid (N-1)$
(c) $(n+1) \mid (N-1)$
(d) $3n(n+1) \mid (N-1)$

40. If $\alpha = x_1 x_2 x_3$ and $\beta = y_1 y_2 y_3$ are two 3-digit numbers, then the number of pairs of α and β can be formed so that α can be subtracted from β without borrowing, is

(a) $2! \times 10! \times 10!$ (b) $(45)(55)^2$
(c) $3^2 \cdot 5^3 \cdot 11^2$ (d) 136125

Permutations and Combinations Exercise 3 :
Passage Based Questions

- This section contains **5 passages**. Based upon each of the passage **3 multiple choice questions** have to be answered. Each of these questions has four choices (a), (b), (c) and (d) out of which **ONLY ONE** is correct.

Passage I (Q. Nos. 41 to 43)

Consider the word $W = TERRORIST$.

41. Number of four letter words that can be made using only the letters from the word W, if each word must contains atleast one vowel, is

(a) 588 (b) 504 (c) 294 (d) 600

42. Number of arrangements of the word W, if no two R's are together, is

(a) 11460 (b) 10400
(c) 12600 (d) 9860

43. Number of arrangements of the word W, if R's as well as T's are separated, is

(a) 9860 (b) 1080 (c) 10200 (d) 11400

Passage II (Q. Nos. 44 to 46)

Different words are formed by arranging the letters of the word 'SUCCESS'.

44. The number of words in which C's are together but S's are separated, is

(a) 120 (b) 96
(c) 24 (d) 420

45. The number of words in which no two C's and no two S's are together, is

(a) 120 (b) 96
(c) 24 (d) 180

46. The number of words in which the consonants appear in alphabetic order, is

(a) 42 (b) 40 (c) 420 (d) 480

Passage III (Q. Nos. 47 to 49)

Different words are being formed by arranging the letters of the word 'ARRANGE'.

47. The number of words in which the two R's are not together, is

(a) 1260 (b) 960
(c) 900 (d) 600

48. The number of words in which neither two R's nor two A's come together, is

(a) 1260 (b) 900
(c) 660 (d) 240

49. The rank of the word 'ARRANGE' in the dictionary is

(a) 340 (b) 341 (c) 342 (d) 343

Passage IV (Q. Nos. 50 to 52)

Let $S(n)$ denotes the number of ordered pairs (x, y) satisfying $\frac{1}{x} + \frac{1}{y} = \frac{1}{n}$, $\forall\, x, y, n \in N$.

50. $S(10)$ equals

(a) 3 (b) 6 (c) 9 (d) 12

51. $S(6) + S(7)$ equals

(a) $S(3) + S(4)$ (b) $S(5) + S(6)$ (c) $S(8) + S(9)$ (d) $S(1) + S(11)$

52. $\sum_{r=1}^{10} S(r)$ equals

(a) 47 (b) 48 (c) 49 (d) 50

Passage V (Q. Nos. 53 to 55)

Let $f(n)$ denotes the number of different ways, the positive integer n can be expressed as the sum of the 1's and 2's. For example, $f(4) = 5$

i.e., $4 = 1+1+1+1$

$= 1+1+2 = 1+2+1 = 2+1+1 = 2+2$

53. The value of $f\{f(6)\}$ is

(a) 376 (b) 377 (c) 321 (d) 370

54. The number of solutions of the equation $f(n) = n$, where $n \in N$ is

(a) 1 (b) 2 (c) 3 (d) 4

55. In a stage show, $f(4)$ superstars and $f(3)$ junior artists participate. Each one is going to present one item, then the number of ways the sequence of items can be planned, if no two junior artists present their items consecutively, is

(a) 144 (b) 360 (c) 4320 (d) 14400

Permutations and Combinations Exercise 4 :
Single Integer Answer Type Questions

- This section contains **10 questions**. The answer to each question is a **single digit integer**, ranging from 0 to 9 (both inclusive).

56. The ten's digit of $1! + 2! + 3! + \ldots + 97!$ is

57. The exponent of 7 in ${}^{100}C_{50}$ is

58. Let P_n denotes the number of ways in which three people can be selected out of n people sitting in a row, in two of them are consecutive. If $P_{n+1} - P_n = 15$, the value of n is

59. If the letters of the word are arranged as in a dictionary. m and n are the rank of the words BULBUL and NANNU respectively, then the value of $m - 4n$ is

60. An n-digit number is a positive number with exactly n digits. Nine hundred distinct n-digit numbers are to be formed using only the three digits 2, 5 and 7. The smallest value of n for which this is possible, is

61. If a, b, c are three natural numbers in AP such that $a + b + c = 21$ and if possible number of ordered triplet (a, b, c) is λ, then the vlaue of $(\lambda - 5)$ is

62. If 2λ is the number of ways of selecting 3 member subset of {1, 2, 3, ..., 29}, so that the numbers form of a GP with integer common ratio, then the value of λ is

63. In a certain test, there are n questions. In this test, 2^{n-k} students gave wrong answers to atleast k questions, where $k = 1, 2, 3, \ldots, n$. If the total number of wrong answers given is 127, then the value of n is

64. A 7-digit number made up of all distinct digits 8, 7, 6, 4, 2, x and y, is divisible by 3. The, possible number of ordered pair (x, y) is

65. There are five points A, B, C, D and E. No three points are collinear and no four are concyclic. If the line AB intersects of the circles drawn throught the five points. The number of points of intersection on the line apart from A and B is

Permutations and Combinations Exercise 5 :
Matching Type Questions

- This section contains **5 questions**. Questions 66 to 70 have four statements (A, B, C and D) given in **Column I** and four statements (p, q, r and s) in **Column II**. Any given statement in **Column I** can have correct matching with one or more statement(s) given in **Column II**.

66.

	Column I		Column II
(A)	${}^{n+4}C_{n+1} - {}^{n+3}C_n = 15(n+2)$, then n equals	(p)	19
(B)	$11 \cdot {}^nP_4 = 20 \cdot {}^{n-2}P_4$, then n equals	(q)	27
(C)	${}^{2n}C_3 = 11 \cdot {}^nC_3$, then n equals	(r)	16
(D)	${}^{n+2}C_8 : {}^{n-2}P_4 = 57 : 16$, then n equals	(s)	6

67.

	Column I		Column II
(A)	Number of increasing permutations of m symbols are there from the n set numbers $(a_1, a_2, \ldots, a_n)$, where the order among the numbers, is given by $a_1 < a_2 < a_3 < \ldots < a_{m-1} < a_m$ is	(p)	n^m
(B)	There are m men and n monkeys. Number of ways in which every monkey has a master, if a man can have any number of monkeys is	(q)	${}^mC_n$
(C)	Number of ways in which r red balls and $(m-1)$ green balls can be arranged in a line, so that no two red balls are together is (balls of the same colour are alike)	(r)	${}^nC_m$
(D)	Number of ways in which 'm' different toys can be distributed in n children, if every child may received any number of toys is	(s)	m^n

68.

	Column I		Column II
(A)	Number of straight lines joining any two of 10 points of which four point are collinear is	(p)	30
(B)	Maximum number of points of intersection of 10 straight lines in the plane is	(q)	60
(C)	Maximum number of points of intersection of 6 circles in the plane is	(r)	40
(D)	Maximum number of points of intersection of 6 parabolas is	(s)	45

69. Consider a 6×6 chessboard. Then, match the following columns.

	Column I		Column II
(A)	Number of rectangles is	(p)	${}^{10}C_5$
(B)	Number of squares is	(q)	441
(C)	Number of ways three squares can be selected, if they are not in same row or column is	(r)	91
(D)	In how many ways eleven '+' sign can be arranged in the squares, if no row remains empty	(s)	2400

70. 5 balls are to be placed in 3 boxes. Each box can hold all the 5 balls. Number of ways in which the balls can be placed so that no box remain empty, if

	Column I		Column II
(A)	balls are identical but boxes are different	(p)	2
(B)	balls are different but boxes are identical	(q)	25
(C)	balls as well as boxes are identical	(r)	50
(D)	balls as well as boxes are identical but boxes kept in a row	(s)	6

Permutations and Combinations Exercise 6 :
Statement I and II Type Questions

- **Directions** (Q. Nos. 71 to 82) are Assertion-Reason type questions. Each of these questions contains two statements:
Statement-1 (Assertion) and **Statement-2** (Reason)
Each of these questions also has four alternative choices, only one of which is the correct answer. You have to select the correct choice as given below.
  (a) Statement-1 is true, Statement-2 is true; Statement-2 is a correct explanation for Statement-1
  (b) Statement-1 is true, Statement-2 is true; Statement-2 is not a correct explanation for Statement-1
  (c) Statement1 is true, Statement-2 is false
  (d) Statement-1 is false, Statement-2 is true

71. Statement-1 The smallest positive integer n such that $n!$ can be expressed as a product of n-3 consecutive integers, is 6.

Statement-2 Product of three consecutive integers is divisible by 6.

72. Statement-1 A number of four different digits is formed with the help of the digits 1, 2, 3, 4, 5, 6, 7 in all possible ways. The number of ways which are exactly divisible by 4 is 200.

Statement-2 A number divisible by 4, if units place digit is also divisible by 4.

73. Statement-1 The number of divisors of 10! is 280.

Statement-2 $10! = 2^p \cdot 3^q \cdot 5^r \cdot 7^s$, where $p, q, r, s \in N$.

74. Statement-1 Number of permutations of 'n' dissimilar things taken 'n' at a time is $n!$.

Statement-2 If $n(A) = n(B) = n$, then the total number of functions from A to B are $n!$.

75. **Statement-1** If N the number of positive integral solutions of $x_1\ x_2\ x_3\ x_4 = 770$, then N is divisible by 4 distinct prime numbers.

Statement-2 Prime numbers are 2, 3, 5, 7, 11, 13, ...

76. **Statement-1** The total number of ways in which three distinct numbers in AP, can be selected from the set {1, 2, 3, ..., 21}, is equal to 100.

Statement-2 If a, b, c are in AP, then $a + c = 2b$.

77. **Statement-1** The number of even divisors of the numbers $N = 12600$ is 54.

Statement-2 0, 2, 4, 6, 8, ... are even integers.

78. **Statement-1** A 5-digit number divisible by 3 is to be formed using the digits 0, 1, 2, 3, 4, 5 and 6 without repetition, then the total number of ways this can be done is 216.

Statement-2A number is divisible by 3, if sum of its digits is divisible by 3.

79. **Statement-1** The sum of the digits in the ten's place of all numbers formed with the help of 3, 4, 5, 6 taken all at a time is 108.

Statement-2 The sum of the digits in the ten's places = The sum of the digits is the units's place.

80. **Statement-1** There are $p \ge 8$ points in space no four of which are in the same with exception of $q \ge 3$ points which are in the same plane, then the number of planes each containing three points is ${}^pC_3 - {}^qC_3$.

Statement-2 3 non-collinear points always determine unique plane.

81. **Statement-1** The highest power of 3 in ${}^{50}C_{10}$ is 4.

Statement-2 If p is any prime number, then power of p in $n!$ is equal to $\left[\frac{n}{p}\right] + \left[\frac{n}{p^2}\right] + \left[\frac{n}{p^3}\right] + \ldots$, where $[\cdot]$ denotes the greatest integer function.

82. **Statement-1** A convex quindecagon has 90 diagonals.

Statement-2 Number of diagonals in a polygon is ${}^nC_2 - n$.

Permutations and Combinations Exercise 7 : Subjective Type Questions

- In this section, there are **17 subjective** questions.

83. Given that ${}^nC_{n-r} + 3\,{}^nC_{n-r+1} + 3.$
${}^nC_{n-r+2} + {}^nC_{n-r+3} = {}^xC_r$. Find x

84. Solve the equation $3^{x+1}C_2 + P_2 x = 4^x A_2, x \in N$.

85. How many positive terms are there in the sequence (x_n) if $x_n = \dfrac{195}{4P_n} - \dfrac{{}^{n+3}A_3}{P_{n+1}}, n \in N$?

86. Prove that ${}^{n-1}C_3 + {}^{n-1}C_4 > {}^nC_3$ if $n > 7$.

87. In how many ways can a mixed doubles game in tennis be arranged from 5 married couples, if no husband and wife play in the same game?

88. In how many ways, we can choose two teams of mixed double for a tennis tournament from four couples such that if any couple participates, then it is in the same team?

89. A family consists of a grandfather, 5 sons and daughters and 8 grand child. They are to be seated in a row for dinner. The grand children wish to occupy the 4 seats at each end and the grandfather refuses to have a grand child on either side of him. In how many ways can the family be made to sit?

90. A tea party is arranged for 16 people along two sides of a large table with 8 chairs on each side. Four men sit on one particular side and two on the other side. In how many ways can they be seated?

91. Every man who has lived on earth has made a certain number of handshakes. Prove that the number of men who have made an odd number of handshakes is even.

92. A train is going from Cambridge to London stops at nine intermediate stations. Six persons enter the train during the journey with six different tickets. How many different sets of tickets they have had?

93. n different things are arranged around a circle. In how many ways can 3 objects be selected when no two of the selected objects are consecutive?

94. A boat 's crew consists of 8 men, 3 of whom can only row on one side and 2 only on the other. Find the number of ways in which the crew can be arranged.

95. In how many different ways can a set A of $3n$ elements be partitioned into 3 subsets of equal number of elements ? (The subsets P, Q, R form a partition if $P \cup Q \cup R = A, P \cap R = \phi, Q \cap R = \phi, R \cap P = \phi$.)

96. A square of n units by n units is divided into n^2 squares each of area 1 sq unit. Find the number of ways in which 4 points (out of $(n+1)^2$ vertices of the squares) can be chosen so that they form the vertices of a square.

97. How many sets of 2 and 3 (different) numbers can be formed by using numbers between 0 and 180 (both including) so that 60 is their average?

98. There are n straight lines in a plane, no two of which are parallel and no three passes through the same point. Their point of intersection are joined. Show that the number of fresh lines thus introduced, is $\frac{1}{8}n(n-1)(n-2)(n-3)$.

99. 6 balls marked as 1, 2, 3, 4, 5 and 6 are kept in a box. Two players A and B start to take out 1 ball at a time from the box one after another without replacing the ball till the game is over. The number marked on the ball is added each time to the previous sum to get the sum of numbers marked on the balls taken out. If this sum is even, then 1 point is given to the player. The first player to get 2 points is declared winner. At the start of the game, the sum is 0. If A starts to take out the ball, find the number of ways in which the game can be won.

Permutations and Combinations Exercise 8 : Questions Asked in Previous 13 Year's Exam

- This section contains questions asked in **IIT-JEE, AIEEE, JEE Main & JEE Advanced** from year **2005** to year **2017**.

100. There is a rectangular sheet of dimension $(2m-1)\times(2n-1)$, (where $m>0, n>0$). It has been divided into square of unit area by drawing line perpendicular to the sides. Find the number of rectangles having sides of odd unit length. **[IIT-JEE 2005, 3M]**

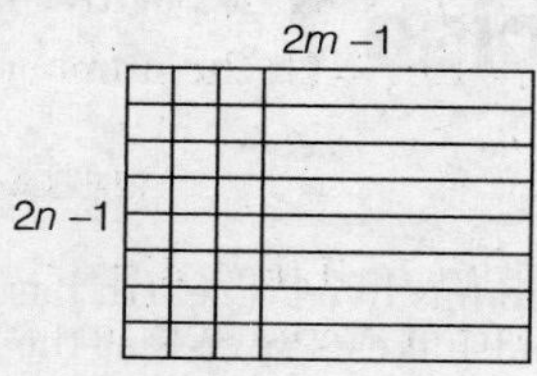

(a) $(m+n+1)^2$ (b) $mn(m+1)(n+1)$
(c) 4^{m+n-2} (d) m^2n^2

101. If the letters of the word SACHIN arranged in all possible ways and these words are written out as in dictionary, then the word SACHIN appears at series number **[AIEEE 2005, 3M]**
(a) 603 (b) 602 (c) 601 (d) 600

102. If r, s, t are prime numbers and p, q are the positive integers such that LCM of p, q is $r^2t^4s^2$, then the number of ordered pair (p, q) is **[IIT-JEE 2006, 3M]**
(a) 252 (b) 254 (c) 225 (d) 224

103. At an election, a voter may vote for any number of candidates, not greater than number to be elected. There are 10 candidates and 4 are to be selected. If a voter votes for atleast one candidate, then number of ways in which he can vote, is **[AIEEE 2006, 4.5M]**
(a) 5040 (b) 6210
(c) 385 (d) 1110

104. The letters of the word COCHIN are permuted and all the permutations are arranged in an alphabetical order as in English dictionary. The number of words that appear before the word COHIN is **[IIT-JEE 2007, 3M]**
(a) 360 (b) 192
(c) 96 (d) 48

105. The set $S=\{1,2,3,\ldots,12\}$ to be partitioned into three sets A, B, C of equal size. Thus, $A\cup B\cup C=S, A\cap B=B\cap C=A\cap C=\phi$. The number of ways to partition S, is **[AIEEE 2007, 3M]**
(a) $\frac{12!}{3!(4!)^3}$ (b) $\frac{12!}{3!(3!)^4}$
(c) $\frac{12!}{(4!)^3}$ (d) $\frac{12!}{(3!)^4}$

106. Consider all possible permutations of the letters of the word ENDEANOEL. Match the statements/ expressions in **Column I** with the statements/ expressions in **Column II.** **[IIT-JEE 2008, 6M]**

	Column I		Column II
(A)	The number of permutations containing the word ENDEA is	(p)	5!
(B)	The number of permutations in which the letters E occurs in the first and the last positions, is	(q)	$2\times5!$
(C)	The number of permutations in which none of the letters D, L, N occurs in the last five positions, is	(r)	$7\times5!$
(D)	The number of permutations in which the letters A, E, O occur only in odd positions, is	(s)	$21\times5!$

107. How many different words can be formed by Jumbling the letters in the word MISSISSIPPI in which no two S's are adjacent? **[AIEEE 2008, 3M]**
(a) $6\cdot7\cdot{}^8C_4$ (b) $6\cdot8\cdot{}^7C_4$
(c) $7\cdot{}^6C_4\cdot{}^8C_4$ (d) $8\cdot{}^6C_4\cdot{}^7C_4$

108. In a shop, there are five types of ice-creams available. A child buys six ice-creams. **[AIEEE 2008, 3M]**

Statement-1 The number of different ways the child can buy the six ice-creams is ${}^{10}C_4$.

Statement-2 The number of different ways the child can buy six ice-creams is equal to the number of different ways to arranging 6A's and 4B's in a row. **[AIEEE 2008, 3M]**

(a) Statement-1 is true, Statement-2 is true; Statement-2 is a correct explanation for Statement-1
(b) Statement-1 is true, Statement-2 is true; Statement-2 is not a correct explanation for Statement-1
(c) Statement-1 true, Statement-2 is false
(d) Statement-1 is false, Statement-2 is true

109. The number of 7-digit integers, with sum of the digits equal to10 and formed by using the digits 1, 2 and 3 only, is **[IIT-JEE 2009, 3M]**
(a) 55 (b) 66 (c) 77 (d) 88

110. From 6 different novels and 3 different dictionaries, 4 novels and 1 dictionary are to be selected and arranged in a row on a shelf so that the dictionary is always in the middle. Then, the number of such arrangements is **[AIEEE 2009, 4M]**
(a) atleast 1000
(b) less than 500
(c) atleast 500 but less than 750
(d) atleast 750 but less than 1000

111. There are two urns. Urn A has 3 distinct red balls and urn B has 9 distinct blue balls. From each urn, two balls are taken out at random and then transferred to the other. The number of ways in which this can be done, is **[AIEEE 2010, 4M]**
(a) 36 (b) 66 (c) 108 (d) 3

112. Statement-1 The number of ways distributing 10 identical balls in 4 distinct boxes such that no box is empty, is ${}^9C_3$.

Statement-2 The number of ways of choosing any 3 places from 9 different places is ${}^9C_3$ **[AIEEE 2011, 4M]**
(a) Statement-1 is true, Statement-2 is true; Statement-2 is a correct explanation for Statement-1
(b) Statement-1 is true, Statement-2 is true; Statement-2 is not a correct explanation for Statement-1
(c) Statement-1 is true, Statement-2 is false
(d) Statement-1 is false, Statement-2 is true

113. There are 10 points in a plane, out of these 6 are collinear. If N is the number of triangles formed by joining these points, then **[AIEEE 2011, 4M]**
(a) $N > 190$ (b) $N \le 100$
(c) $100 < N \le 140$ (d) $140 < N \le 190$

114. The total number of ways in which 5 balls of different colours can be distributed among 3 persons, so that each person gets atleast one ball is **[IIT-JEE 2012, 3M]**
(a) 75 (b) 150 (c) 210 (d) 243

- **Directions** (Q. Nos. 115 to 116) Let a_n denotes the number of all n-digits positive integer formed by the digits 0, 1 or both such that no consecutive digits in them are 0. Let b_n be the number of such n-digit integers ending with digit 1 and c_n be the number of such n digits integers ending with digit 0.

115. The value of b_6, is **[IIT-JEE 2012, 3+3M]**
(a) 7 (b) 8 (c) 9 (d) 11

116. Which of the following is correct?
(a) $a_{17} = a_{16} + a_{15}$ (b) $c_{17} \ne c_{16} + c_{15}$
(c) $b_{17} \ne b_{16} + c_{16}$ (d) $a_{17} = c_{17} + b_{16}$

117. Assuming the balls to be identical except for difference in colours, the number of ways in which one or more balls can be selected from 10 white, 9 green and 7 black balls, is **[AIEEE 2012, 4M]**
(a) 630 (b) 879 (c) 880 (d) 629

118. Let T_n be the number of all possible triangles formed by joining vertices of an n-sided regular polygon. If $T_{n+1} - T_n = 10$, the value of n is **[JEE Main 2013, 4M]**
(a) 5 (b) 10 (c) 8 (d) 7

119. Consider the set of eight vectors $V = [a\hat{i} + b\hat{j} + c\hat{k}: a, b, c \in \{-1, 1\}]$. Three non-coplanar vectors can be chosen from V in 2^p ways, then p is **[JEE Advanced 2013, 4M]**

120. Let $n_1 < n_2 < n_3 < n_4 < n_5$ be positive integers such that $n_1 + n_2 + n_3 + n_4 + n_5 = 20$, the number of such distinct arrangements $(n_1, n_2, n_3, n_4, n_5)$ is **[JEE Advanced 2014, 3M]**

121. For $n \ge 2$ be an integer. Take n distinct points on a circle and join each pair of points by a line segment. Colour the line segment joining every pair of adjacent points by blue and the rest by red. If the number of red and blue line segments are equal, the value of n is **[JEE Advanced 2014, 3M]**

122. Six cards and six envelopes are numbered 1, 2, 3, 4, 5, 6 and cards are to be placed in envelopes, so that each envelope contains exactly one card and no card is placed in the envelope bearing the same number and moreover the card numbered 1 is always placed in envelope numbered 2. Then the number of ways it can be done, is **[JEE Advanced 2014, 3M]**
(a) 264 (b) 265
(c) 53 (d) 67

123. The number of integers greater than 6000 that can be formed using the digits 3,5,6,7 and 8 without repetition, is **[JEE Main 2015, 4M]**
(a) 120 (b) 72
(c) 216 (d) 192

124. Let n be the number of ways in which 5 boys and 5 girls can stand in a queue in such away that all the girls stand consecutively in the queue. Let m be the number of ways in which 5 boys and 5 girls can stand in a queue in such a way that exactly four girls stand consecutively in the queue, the value of $\frac{m}{n}$ is **[JEE Advanced 2015, 3M]**

125. If all the words (with or without meaning having five letters, formed using the letters of the word SMALL and arranged as in a dictionary, then the position of the word SMALL is **[JEE Main 2016, 4M]**

(a) 59th (b) 52nd (c) 58th (d) 46th

126. A debate club consists of 6 girls and 4 boys. A team of 4 members is to be selected from this club including the selection of a captain (from among these 4 members) for the team. If the team has to include at most one boy, then the number of ways of selecting the team is **[JEE Advanced 2016, 3M]**

(a) 380 (b) 320
(c) 260 (d) 95

127. A man X has 7 friends, 4 of them are ladies and 3 are men. His wife Y also has 7 friends, 3 of them are ladies and 4 are men. Assume X and Y have no common friends. Then the total number of ways in which X and Y together can throw a party inviting 3 ladies and 3 men, so that 3 friends of each of X and Y are in this party, is **[JEE Main 2017, 4M]**

(a) 484 (b) 485
(c) 468 (d) 469

Answers

Exercise for Session 1

1. (c) 2. (b) 3. (c) 4. (a) 5. (c) 6. (b)
7. (c) 8. (c) 9. (b) 10. (b) 11. (d)

Exercise for Session 2

1. (b) 2. (c) 3. (c) 4. (d) 5. (d) 6. (b)
7. (d) 8. (a) 9. (b) 10. (c) 11. (b) 12. (b)
13. (b) 14. (b) 15. (b) 16. (d)

Exercise for Session 3

1. (a) 2. (c) 3. (a) 4. (b) 5. (c) 6. (c)
7. (b) 8. (b) 9. (a) 10. (a) 11. (a)

Exercise for Session 4

1. (d) 2. (b) 3. (d) 4. (c) 5. (a) 6. (c)
7. (a) 8. (b) 9. (b) 10. (d) 11. (a) 12. (d)
13. (a) 14. (d) 15. (d) 16. (c) 17. (b) 18. (a)

Exercise for Session 5

1. (c) 2. (c) 3. (d) 4. (a) 5. (b) 6. (b)
7. (d) 8. (a) 9. (c) 10. (c) 11. (d) 12. (a)
13. (b) 14. (c) 15. (d) 16. (c) 17. (b) 18. (c)

Exercise for Session 6

1. (c) 2. (c) 3. (a) 4. (a) 5. (b) 6. (a)
7. (c) 8. (c) 9. (c) 10. (a) 11. (d) 12. (b)
13. (a) 14. (c) 15. (b) 16. (b) 17. (c) 18. (d)
19. (c) 20. (d) 21. (c) 22. (b) 23. (a) 24. (a)
25. (b) 26. (c) 27. (c) 28. (b)

Exercise for Session 7

1. (b) 2. (d) 3. (a) 4. (c) 5. (c)

Chapter Exercises

1. (c) 2. (a) 3. (c) 4. (b) 5. (c) 6. (c)
7. (a) 8. (b) 9. (b) 10. (d) 11. (a) 12. (d)
13. (b) 14. (b) 15. (c) 16. (a) 17. (d) 18. (c)
19. (d) 20. (b) 21. (c) 22. (d) 23. (d) 24. (d)
25. (c) 26. (a) 27. (d) 28. (a) 29. (c) 30. (b)
31. (a, c) 32. (a,b,c,d) 33. (a,b,c,d) 34. (a,d) 35. (a, c)
36. (b,d) 37. (a, c) 38. (b,c) 39. (a,b,c,d) 40. (b,c,d)
41. (a) 42. (c) 43. (c) 44. (c) 45. (b) 46. (a)
47. (c) 48. (c) 49. (c) 50. (c) 51. (c) 52. (b)
53. (b) 54. (c) 55. (d) 56. (1) 57. (0) 58. (8)
59. (3) 60. (7) 61. (8) 62. (6) 63. (7) 64. (8)
65. (8) 66. (A) → (q); (B) → (r); (C) → (s); (D) → (p)
67. (A) → (r); (B) → (s); (C) → (q); (D) → (p)
68. (A) → (r); (B) → (s); (C) → (p); (D) → (q)
69. (A) → (s); (B) → (r); (C) → (s); (D) → (p)
70. (A) → (s); (B) → (q); (C) → (p); (D) → (s)
71. (b) 72. (c) 73. (d) 74. (c) 75. (d) 76. (b)
77. (b) 78. (d) 79. (a) 80. (d) 81. (d) 82. (a)
83. $x = n + 3$ 84. $x = 3$ 85. 4 87. 60 88. 42
89. 11520 90. ${}^8P_4 \times {}^8P_2 \times 10!$ 92. ${}^{45}C_6$
93. $\frac{n(n-4)(n-5)}{6}$ 94. 1728 95. $\frac{(3n)!}{6(n!)^3}$ 96. $\frac{n^2(n+1)}{2}$
97. 4530 99. 96 100. (d) 101. (c) 102. (d)
103. (c) 104. (c) 105. (c)
106. (A) → (p); (B) → (s); (C) → (q); (D) → (q)
107. (c) 108. (a) 109. (c) 110. (a) 111. (c) 112. (a)
113. (b) 114. (b) 115. (b) 116. (a) 117. (b) 118. (a)
119. (5) 120. (7) 121. (5) 122. (c) 123. (d) 124. (5)
125. (c) 126. (a) 127. (b)

Solutions

1. $^9C_5 - {}^{9-2}C_{5-2} = {}^9C_4 - {}^7C_3$

$= 126 - 35 = 91$

2. Let $a = 2x - 1, b = 2y - 1, c = 2z - 1, d = 2w - 1$

where, $x, y, z, w \in N$

Then, $a + b + c + d = 20$

$\Rightarrow \quad x + y + z + w = 12$

$\therefore$ Number of ordered quadruplet $= {}^{12-1}C_{4-1}$

$$= {}^{11}C_3 = \frac{11 \cdot 10 \cdot 9}{1 \cdot 2 \cdot 3} = 165$$

3. $l =$ LCM of 8!, 10! and 12! = 12!

and $h =$ HCF of 8!, 10! and 12! = 8!

$\therefore \quad \dfrac{l}{h} = \dfrac{12!}{8!} = 12 \cdot 11 \cdot 10 \cdot 9 = 11880$

4. $^{n+1}C_{n-2} - {}^{n+1}C_{n-1} \le 100$

$\Rightarrow \quad {}^{n+1}C_3 - {}^{n+1}C_2 \le 100$

$\Rightarrow \quad \dfrac{(n+1)n(n-1)}{6} - \dfrac{(n+1)n}{2} \le 100$

$\Rightarrow \quad n(n+1)(n-4) \le 600$

It is true for $n = 2, 3, 4, 5, 6, 7, 8, 9$

5. Coefficient of x^{11} in $(x + x^2 + x^3 + x^4 + x^5 + x^6)^3$

= Coefficient of x^8 in

$(1 + x + x^2 + x^3 + x^4 + x^5)^3$

= Coefficient of x^8 in$(1 - x^6)^3(1 - x)^{-3}$

= Coefficient of x^8 in $(1 - 3x^6)(1 + {}^3C_1x + \dots)$

$= {}^{10}C_2 - 3 \times {}^4C_2 = 45 - 18 = 27$

6. $^nC_2, n \in N$, infinite numbers.

7. $\because$ 13 lines pass through A and 11 lines pass through B.

$\therefore$ Number of intersection points

$= {}^{37}C_2 - {}^{13}C_2 - {}^{11}C_2 + 2 \quad$ [$\because$ two points A and B]

$= 535$

8. $\because \quad a = 182bc$

$\Rightarrow \quad (x+2)! = 182 \times {}^xP_{11} \times (x - 11)!$

$\Rightarrow \quad (x+2)! = 182 \times x!$

$\Rightarrow \quad (x+2)(x+1) = 14 \times 13$

$\Rightarrow \quad x + 1 = 13$

$\therefore \quad x = 12$

9. $6 + 5 \times 5 + 5 \times 5 \times 4 = 131$

10. The letters in alphabetical order are *abcde*

$a \to 4! = 24 \qquad db \to 3! = 6$

$b \to 4! = 24 \qquad dc \to 3! = 6$

$c \to 4! = 24 \qquad dea \to 2! = 2$

$da \to 3! = 6 \qquad debac \to 1$

$\therefore$ The rank of *debac* $= 24 + 24 + 24 + 6 + 6 + 6 + 2 + 1 = 93$

11. Number of different tickets

$= 20 + 19 + 18 + 17 + \dots + 3 + 2 + 1 = 210$

12. Let $A = \{a_1, a_2, a_3, \dots, a_n\}$

(i) $a_i \in P, a_i \in Q$ (ii) $a_i \in P, a_i \notin Q$

(iii) $a_i \notin P, a_i \in Q$ (iv) $a_i \notin P, a_i \notin Q$, where $1 \le i \le n$

$\because \quad P \cap Q = \phi$ [cases in favour 3 i.e., (ii), (iii), (iv)]

$\therefore$ Required number of ways $= 3^n$

13. Total points on all three lines $= m + n + k$

$\therefore$ Maximum number of triangles $= {}^{m+n+k}C_3 - {}^mC_3 - {}^nC_3 - {}^kC_3$

14. Required number of triplets = Total number of triplets without restrictions − Number of triplets with all different coordinates

$= n^3 - {}^nP_3$

15. Let middle largest digit be r, then digits available for remaining four places are $0, 1, 2, 3, \dots, r - 1$.

Number of ways filling remaining four places

$$= \sum_{r=4}^{9} ({}^rP_4 - {}^{r-1}P_3) = \sum_{r=4}^{9} (r-1) \times {}^{r-1}P_3$$

$$= 3 \times {}^3P_3 + 4 \times {}^4P_3 + 5 \times {}^5P_3 + 6 \times {}^6P_3 + 7 \times {}^7P_3 + 8 \times {}^8P_3$$

$$= 5292 = 2^2 \cdot 3^3 \cdot 7^2$$

16. Required number of words $= 6! - 5! - 5! + 4! = 504$

17. Let x, y, z be the friends and a, b, c denote the case when x is invited a times, y is invited b times and z is invited c times. Now, we have the following possibilities $(a, b, c) = (1, 2, 3)$ or $(2, 2, 2)$ or $(3, 3, 0)$ [grouping of 6 days of week]

Hence, the total number of ways

$$= \frac{6!}{1!\,2!\,3!} \times 3! + \frac{6!}{2!\,2!\,2!} \times \frac{3!}{3!} + \frac{6!}{3!\,3!\,0!} \times \frac{3!}{2!}$$

$$= 360 + 90 + 60 = 510$$

18. If $y = n$, then x takes values from 1 to $n - 1$ and z can take values from 0 to n (i.e., $(n + 1)$ values). Thus, for each value of y $(2 \le y \le 9)$, x and z take $(n - 1)(n + 1)$ values.

Hence, the 3-digit numbers are of the form xyz

$$= \sum_{x=2}^{9} (n-1)(n+1) = \sum_{x=2}^{9} (n^2 - 1) = 276$$

19. The letters in alphabetical order are EEMRTU

$\text{E} \to 5! = 120$

$\text{MEERTU} \to 1! = 1$

$\text{MEERUT} \to 1$

$\therefore$ Rank of MEERUT $= 120 + 1 + 1 = 122$

20. The candidates can be ranked in 10! ways. In half of these ways, A_1 is above A_2 and in another half, A_2 is above A_1. So, required number of ways $= \dfrac{10!}{2}$.

21. Any selection of four digits from the ten digits $0, 1, 2, 3, \dots, 9$ gives one number.

So, the required number of numbers $= {}^{10}C_4 = 210$

22. As $0 < x < 1$, we have $p < q$

The number of rational numbers $= 5 + 4 + 3 + 2 + 1 = 15$

When p, q have a common factor, we get some rational numbers which are not different from those already counted.

There are 4 such numbers $\frac{2}{4}, \frac{2}{6}, \frac{3}{6}, \frac{4}{6}$.

$\therefore$ The required number of rational numbers $= 15 - 4 = 11$

23. We have,

$$24 = 2 \times 3 \times 4 = 2 \times 2 \times 6$$
$$= 1 \times 6 \times 4 = 1 \times 3 \times 8$$
$$= 1 \times 2 \times 12 = 1 \times 1 \times 24$$

The number of positive integral solutions of $xyz = 24$ is

$$3! + \frac{3!}{2!} + 3! + 3! + 3! + \frac{3!}{2!} = 30$$

and number of integral solutions having two negative factors is ${}^3C_2 \times 30 = 90$.

Hence, number of integral solutions $= 30 + 90 = 120$

24. Total number of triangles = Number of triangles with vertices on sides $[(AB, BC, CD) + (AB, BC, DA) + (AB, CD, DA) + (BC, CD, DA)]$

$$= {}^3C_1 \times {}^4C_1 \times {}^5C_1 + {}^3C_1 \times {}^4C_1 \times {}^6C_1 + {}^3C_1 \times {}^5C_1 \times {}^6C_1 + {}^4C_1 \times {}^5C_1 \times {}^6C_1$$

$$= 60 + 72 + 90 + 120 = 342$$

25. $\because$ 16 horses = 10 horses + (A, B, C, D, E, F)

$\therefore$ The number of ways $= {}^{10}C_3 \times$ (Number of ways of choosing out of A, B, C, D, E, F, so that AD, BE and CF are not together)

$= {}^{10}C_3 \times$ (One from each of pairs AD, BE, CF)

$= {}^{10}C_3 \times {}^2C_1 \times {}^2C_1 \times {}^2C_1 = 960$

26. We have, $\quad i^3 + ai^2 + bi + c = 0$

and $(-i)^3 + a(-i)^2 + b(-i) + c = 0$

$\Rightarrow \quad (c - a) + (b - 1)i = 0$

and $\quad (c - a) - i(b - 1) = 0$

$\Rightarrow \quad b = 1, a = c$

Thus, total number of such polynomials $= {}^{10}C_1 = 10$

27. $$\sum_{i=1}^{k} \frac{1}{x_i} = \frac{1}{x_1} + \frac{1}{x_2} + \ldots + \frac{1}{x_k} = \frac{\sum_{i=1}^{k} x_i}{n} = \frac{75}{n}$$

[as LCM of $x_1, x_2, x_3, \ldots, x_k$ is n]

28. Let '1' be associated with 'r', $r \in \{1, 2, 3, 4, 5\}$, then '2' can be associated with $r, r + 1, \ldots, 5$. Let '2' be associated with 'j' then 3 can be associated with $j, j + 1, \ldots, 5$. Thus, required number of functions

$$\sum_{r=1}^{5} \left(\sum_{j=r}^{5} (6 - j) \right) = \sum_{r=1}^{5} \frac{(6 - r)(7 - r)}{2} = 35$$

29. Clearly, each player will play 9 games.

$\therefore$ Total number of games $= {}^{10}C_2 = 45$

Clearly, $w_i + l_i = 9$ and $\Sigma w_i = \Sigma l_i = 45$

$\Rightarrow \quad w_i = 9 - l_i \Rightarrow w_i^2 = 81 - 18 l_i + l_i^2$

$\Rightarrow \quad \Sigma w_i^2 = \Sigma 81 - 18 \Sigma l_i + \Sigma l_i^2$

$= 81 \times 10 - 18 \times 45 + \Sigma l_i^2 = \Sigma l_i^2$

30. The number of matches in the first round $= {}^6C_2 + {}^6C_2 = 30$

The number of matches in the next round $= {}^6C_2 = 15$

and the number of matches in the semi-final round $= {}^4C_2 = 6$

$\therefore$ The required number of matches $= 30 + 15 + 6 + 2 = 53$

[$\because$ for 'best of three' atleast two matches are played]

31. $$E_3(300!) = \left[\frac{300}{3}\right] + \left[\frac{300}{3^2}\right] + \left[\frac{300}{3^3}\right] + \left[\frac{300}{3^4}\right] + \left[\frac{300}{3^5}\right]$$

$$= 100 + 33 + 11 + 3 + 1 = 148$$

$\therefore \quad m = 148$

and $$E_2(150!) = \left[\frac{150}{2}\right] + \left[\frac{150}{2^2}\right] + \left[\frac{150}{2^3}\right] + \ldots + \left[\frac{150}{2^7}\right]$$

$$= 75 + 37 + 18 + 9 + 4 + 2 + 1 = 146$$

$\therefore \quad n - 2 = 146$

$\Rightarrow \quad n = 148$

32. $\because \quad E_2(102!) = 98$, $E_3(102!) = 49$,

$E_5(102!) = 24$ and $E_7(102!) = 16$

$\therefore \ \alpha = 98, \beta = 49, \gamma = 24$ and $\delta = 16$

33. Triplets with

(i) $x = y < z$ (ii) $x < y < z$

(iii) $y < x < z$

can be chosen in ${}^{n+1}C_2, {}^{n+1}C_3, {}^{n+1}C_3$ ways.

$$\therefore \quad {}^{n+1}C_2 + {}^{n+1}C_3 + {}^{n+1}C_3 = {}^{n+2}C_3 + {}^{n+1}C_3$$
$$= 2({}^{n+2}C_3) - {}^{n+1}C_2$$
$$= \frac{n(n + 1)(2n + 1)}{6}$$

34. When x is odd

Unit's place filled by 1, 3, 5, 7, 9.

$\therefore \quad x = 8 \times 8 \times 7 \times 5 = 2240$

When x is even

Unit's place filled by 0, 2, 4, 6, 8.

$\therefore \quad y = 8 \times 8 \times 7 \times 4 + 9 \times 8 \times 7 \times 1 = 2296$

$\Rightarrow \quad x < y$ and $|x - y| = 56$

35. $$\sum_{A \in X} \min A$$

$$\sum_{r=1}^{n-1} r(n - r) = n \sum_{r=1}^{n-1} r - \sum_{r=1}^{n-1} r^2$$

$$= \frac{n(n - 1)n}{2} - \frac{(n - 1)n(2n - 1)}{6}$$

$$= \frac{(n + 1) \cdot n \cdot (n - 1)}{1 \cdot 2 \cdot 3} = {}^{n+1}C_3 = \frac{n(n^2 - 1)}{6}$$

36. $\because p = 2520 = 2^3 \cdot 3^2 \cdot 5^1 \cdot 7^1$

$= 6 \cdot 2^2 \cdot 3^1 \cdot 5^1 \cdot 7^1 = 9 \cdot 2^3 \cdot 5^1 \cdot 7^1$

$\therefore \quad x = (2 + 1)(1 + 1)(1 + 1)(1 + 1) = 24$

and $\quad y = (3 + 1)(1 + 1)(1 + 1) = 16.$

37. $\because x_1 + x_2 + x_3 + \ldots + x_n = r, \forall x_i \geq 1, (1 \leq i \leq n)$

Total number of such solutions $= {}^{r-1}C_{n-1} = {}^{r-1}C_{r-n}$

38. $\because x + x + 1 + y = 24$

$\Rightarrow \quad y = 23 - 2x$

Let N = Total number of fights subject to the condition that any two children of one team do not fight.

$\therefore \quad N = {}^{24}C_2 - ({}^xC_2 + {}^{x+1}C_2 + {}^yC_2)$

$= {}^{24}C_2 - ({}^xC_2 + {}^{x+1}C_2 + {}^{23-2x}C_2)$

$= 23 - 3x^2 + 45x$

$\therefore \quad \dfrac{dN}{dx} = 0 - 6x + 45$

For maximum or minimum, put $\dfrac{dN}{dx} = 0 \Rightarrow x = 7.5$

$\Rightarrow \quad x = 7 \quad [\because x \in I]$

Now, $\quad \dfrac{d^2N}{dx^2} < 0$

$\therefore$ N will be maximum when $x = 7$

and $\quad N = 23 - 3(7)^2 + 45 \times 7 = 191$

39. $\because x + y + z = 3n$

$\Rightarrow \quad N$ = Coefficient of α^{3n} in $(1 + \alpha + \alpha^2 + \ldots + \alpha^{2n})^3$

= Coefficient of α^{3n} in $(1 - \alpha^{2n+1})^3(1-\alpha)^{-3}$

= Coefficient of α^{3n} in $(1 - 3\alpha^{2n+1})\ (1 + {}^3C_1\,\alpha + \ldots)$

$= {}^{3n+2}C_{3n} - 3 \cdot {}^{n+1}C_{n-1}$

$= {}^{3n+2}C_2 - 3 \cdot {}^{n+1}C_2 = 3n^2 + 3n + 1$

$\therefore \quad N - 1 = 3n(n+1)$

40. Since, α can be subtracted from β without borrowing, if $y_i \geq x_i$, for $i = 1, 2, 3$.

Let $x_i = \lambda$

If $i = 1$, then $\lambda = 1, 2, 3, \ldots, 9$

and if $i = 2$ and 3, then $\lambda = 0, 1, 2, 3, \ldots, 9$

Hence, total number of ways of choosing the pair α, β

$$= \left(\sum_{\lambda=1}^{9}(10-\lambda)\right)\left(\sum_{\lambda=0}^{9}(10-\lambda)\right)^2 = (45)(55)^2$$

41. There are 9 letters

T, T, R, R, R, E, O, I, S

λ = Number of four lettered words (no restriction)

= Coefficient of x^4 in

$$4!\left(1 + \frac{x}{1!} + \frac{x^2}{2!}\right)\left(1 + \frac{x}{1!} + \frac{x^2}{2!} + \frac{x^3}{3!}\right)(1+x)^4 = 626$$

μ = Number of four lettered words (no vowels)

= Coefficient of x^4 in

$$4!\left(1 + \frac{x}{1!} + \frac{x^2}{2!}\right)\left(1 + \frac{x}{1!} + \frac{x^2}{2!} + \frac{x^3}{3!}\right)(1+x) = 38$$

$\therefore$ Required ways (atleast one vowel) $= 626 - 38 = 588$

42. × T × E × O × I × S × T ×

There are 7 available places for RRR.

$\therefore$ Required ways $= {}^7C_3 \times \dfrac{6!}{2!} = 12600$

43. × E × TT × O × I × S ×

Number of ways having TT together and RRR separated

$= {}^6C_3 \times 5! = 2400$

Hence, number of arrangements of the word W, if R's as well as T's are separated $= 12600 - 2400 = 10200$

44. × U × CC × E ×

Hence, required number of ways $= {}^4C_3 \times 3! = 24$

45. × U × C × C × E ×

There are five available places for three SSS.

$\therefore$ Total number of ways no two S's together $= {}^5C_3 \times \dfrac{4!}{2!} = 120$

Hence, number of words having CC separated and SSS separated $= 120 - 24 = 96$

46. Total number of ways $= \dfrac{7!}{2!3!} = 420$

Consonants in SUCCESS are S, C, C, S, S

Number of ways arranging consonants $= \dfrac{5!}{2!3!} = 10$

Hence, number of words in which consonants appear in alphabetic order $= \dfrac{420}{10} = 42$

47. ×A × A × N × G × E ×

Hence, required number of ways $= {}^6C_2 \times \dfrac{5!}{2!} = 900$

48. The number of ways in which two A's are together

i.e., × A A × N × G × E × is ${}^5C_2 \times 4! = 240$

Hence, number of ways in which neither two R's no two A's come together $= 900 - 240 = 660$

49. The letters in alphabetical order are AAEGNRR

AA $\rightarrow \dfrac{5!}{2!} = 60$ ARA $\rightarrow 4! = 24$

AE $\rightarrow \dfrac{5!}{2!} = 60$ ARE $\rightarrow 4! = 24$

AG $\rightarrow \dfrac{5!}{2!} = 60$ ARG $\rightarrow 4! = 24$

AN $\rightarrow \dfrac{5!}{2!} = 60$ ARN $\rightarrow 4! = 24$

ARRAE $\rightarrow 2! = 2$ ARRAG $\rightarrow 2! = 2$

ARRANEG $\rightarrow 1$ ARRANGE $\rightarrow 1$

$\therefore$ Rank in dictionary

$= 60 + 60 + 60 + 60 + 24 + 24 + 24 + 24 + 2 + 2 + 1 + 1 = 342$

- ***Sol.*** (Q. Nos. 50-52)

$$\frac{1}{x} + \frac{1}{y} = \frac{1}{n} \Rightarrow (x-n)(y-n) = n^2$$

$$\therefore \quad x = n + \lambda,\ y = n + \frac{n^2}{\lambda}$$

where, λ is divisor of n^2.

The number of integral solutions (x, y) is equal to the number of divisors of n^2.

If $n = 3, n^2 = 9 = 3^2$, then the equation has 3 solutions.

$(x, y) = (4, 12), (6, 6), (12, 4)$

50. $\because \quad 10^2 = 2^2 \cdot 5^2$

$\therefore \quad S(10) = 3 \times 3 = 9$

51. $\because \quad 6^2 = 2^2 \cdot 3^2$

$\Rightarrow \quad S(6) = 3 \times 3 = 9$ and $7^2 \Rightarrow S(7) = 3$

$\therefore \quad S(6) + S(7) = 12$

Also, $\quad 8^2 = 2^6$

$\Rightarrow \quad S(8) = 7$ and $9^2 = 3^4 \quad \Rightarrow S(9) = 5$

$\therefore \quad S(8) + S(9) = 12$

$\Rightarrow \quad S(6) + S(7) = S(8) + S(9) = 12$

52. $\because \; 1^2 \to S(1) = 1, 2^2 \to S(2) = 3, 3^2 \to S(3) = 3,$

$4^2 \to 2^4 \to S(4) = 5, 5^2 \to S(5) = 3, S(6) = 9$

$S(7) = 3, S(8) = 7, S(9) = 5$ and $S(10) = 9$ [from above]

$$\therefore \quad \sum_{r=1}^{10} S(r) = S(1) + S(2) + S(3) + S(4) + S(5) + S(6) + S(7) + S(8) + S(9) + S(10)$$

$$= 1 + 3 + 3 + 5 + 3 + 9 + 3 + 7 + 5 + 9 = 48$$

53. $\because \; f(6) = {}^6C_0 + {}^5C_1 + {}^4C_2 + {}^3C_3 = 13$

$\therefore f\{f(6)\} = f(13) = {}^{13}C_0 + {}^{12}C_1 + {}^{11}C_2 + {}^{10}C_3 + {}^9C_4 + {}^8C_5 + {}^7C_6$

$= 1 + 12 + 55 + 120 + 126 + 56 + 7 = 377$

54. $\because \; f(1) = {}^1C_0 = 1, f(2) = {}^2C_0 + {}^1C_1 = 2, f(3) = {}^3C_0 + {}^2C_1 = 3,$

$f(4) = 5$ [given]

and $f(5) = {}^5C_0 + {}^4C_1 + {}^3C_2 = 8$

Thus, we say that $f(n) > n$ for $n = 4, 5, 6, \ldots$

Hence, number of solutions for $f(n) = n$ is 3.

55. Number of superstars $= f(4) = 5$

and number of junior artists $= f(3) = 3$

$\times S_1 \times S_2 \times S_3 \times S_4 \times S_5 \times$ [S_i for superstars]

$\therefore$Required number of ways $= {}^6C_3 \times 5! \times 3! = 14400$

56. For $n \ge 10$, the number of zeros in $n! \ge 2$

$\therefore \quad 1! + 2! + 3! + 4! + \ldots + 97! = \ldots 13$

$\therefore$ Ten's digit $= 1$

57. $\because \quad {}^{100}C_{50} = \dfrac{100!}{(50!)^2}$

$$\therefore \quad E_7(100!) = \left[\frac{100}{7}\right] + \left[\frac{100}{7^2}\right] = 14 + 2 = 16$$

$$\text{and} \quad E_7(50!) = \left[\frac{50}{7}\right] + \left[\frac{50}{7^2}\right] = 7 + 1 = 8$$

$\therefore \; E_7$ in $({}^{100}C_{50}) = 16 - 2 \times 8 = 0$

58. ${}^{n-1}C_3 - {}^{n-2}C_3 = 15$

$\Rightarrow \quad n = 8$ [$\because P_n = {}^{n-2}C_3$]

59. For BULBUL, the letters in alphabetical order are BBLLUU

BB $\to \dfrac{4!}{2!2!} = 6$ BULBLU $\to 1$

BL $\to \dfrac{4!}{2!} = 12$ BULBUL $\to 1$

BU $\to \dfrac{3!}{2!} = 39$

$\therefore \quad m = 6 + 12 + 3 + 1 + 1 = 23$

For NANNU

The letters in alphabetical order are ANNNU

A $\to \dfrac{4!}{3!} = 4$ NANNU $\to 1$

$\therefore \quad n = 4 + 1 = 5$

Hence, $m - 4n = 23 - 20 = 3$

60. Each of the n digits can be anyone of the three 2, 5 or 7.

$\therefore$ The number of n-digit numbers is 3^n.

$\Rightarrow \quad 3^n > 900$

$\Rightarrow \quad n = 7, 8, 9 \ldots$

Hence, smallest value of n is 7.

61. $a + b + c = 21 \Rightarrow 3b = 21 \Rightarrow b = 7$ [$\because a + c = 2b$]

$\Rightarrow \quad a + b + c = 21 \Rightarrow a + c = 14$

$\Rightarrow \quad \lambda = {}^{14-1}C_{2-1} = {}^{13}C_1 = 13$

Hence, $\lambda - 5 = 13 - 5 = 8$

62. $2\lambda =$ Number of selecting 3 member subsets of $\{1, 2, 3, \ldots, 29\}$ which are in

GP with common ratio (2 or 3 or 4 or 5).

$$= \left[\frac{29}{2^2}\right] + \left[\frac{29}{3^2}\right] + \left[\frac{29}{4^2}\right] + \left[\frac{29}{5^2}\right]$$

$$= 7 + 3 + 1 + 1 = 12$$

$\therefore \quad \lambda = 6$

63. The number of students answering exactly $i (1 \le i \le n - 1)$ questions wrongly is $2^{n-i} - 2^{n-i-1}$. The number of students answering all n questions wrongly is 2^0.

Hence, the total number of wrong answers

$$\sum_{i=1}^{n-1} i(2^{n-i} - 2^{n-i-1}) + n(2^0) = 127$$

$\Rightarrow 2^{n-1} + 2^{n-2} + 2^{n-3} + \ldots + 2^1 + 2^0 = 127$

$\Rightarrow \quad 2^n - 1 = 127$

$\Rightarrow \quad 2^n = 128 = 2^7$

$\therefore \quad n = 7$

64. The sum of digits is divisible by 3.

i.e., $8 + 7 + 6 + 4 + 2 + x + y$ or $27 + x + y$ is divisible by 3

$\therefore \; x + y$ must be divisible by 3.

Then, possible ordered pairs are

(0, 3), (3, 0), (1, 5), (5, 1), (0, 9), (9, 0), (3, 9), (9, 3)

$\therefore$ Number of ordered pairs $= 8$

65. Number of circles through ACD, ACE, ADE intersect the line $AB = 3$ and

Number of circles through BCD, BCE, BDE intersect the line $AB = 3$ and

Number of circles through CDE intersects the line $AB = 2$

Hence, number of points of intersection $= 3 + 3 + 2 = 8$

66. (A) ${}^{n+4}C_{n+1} - {}^{n+3}C_n = 15(n + 2)$

$\Rightarrow \quad {}^{n+3}C_{n+1} + {}^{n+3}C_n - {}^{n+3}C_n = 15(n + 2)$

$\Rightarrow \quad {}^{n+3}C_{n+1} = 15(n + 2)$

$\Rightarrow \quad {}^{n+3}C_2 = 15(n + 2)$

$\Rightarrow \quad \dfrac{(n + 3)}{2} = 15 \Rightarrow n = 27$

(B) $11 \cdot {}^nP_4 = 20 \cdot {}^{n-2}P_4$

$\Rightarrow 11.n(n-1)(n-2)(n-3) = 20(n-2)(n-3)(n-4)(n-5)$

$\Rightarrow \quad 11n(n-1) = 20(n-4)(n-5) \quad [\because n \neq 2, 3]$

$\Rightarrow \quad 9n^2 - 169n + 400 = 0$

$\therefore \quad n = 16 \Rightarrow n \neq \frac{25}{9}$

(C) ${}^{2n}C_3 = 11 \cdot {}^nC_3$

$\Rightarrow \quad \frac{2n(2n-1)(2n-2)}{1\cdot 2\cdot 3} = \frac{11\cdot n(n-1)(n-2)}{1\cdot 2\cdot 3}$

$\therefore \quad n = 6$

(D) ${}^{n+2}C_8 : {}^{n-2}P_4 = 57:16 \Rightarrow \frac{{}^{n+2}C_8}{{}^{n-2}P_4} = \frac{57}{16}$

$\Rightarrow \quad \frac{(n+2)}{8}\cdot\frac{n+1}{7}\cdot\frac{(n)}{6}\cdot\frac{(n-1)}{5}\cdot\frac{{}^{n-2}C_4}{{}^{n-2}P_4} = \frac{57}{16}$

$\Rightarrow \quad (n+2)(n+1)\,n(n-1) = 21\cdot 20\cdot 19\cdot 18$

$\therefore \quad n = 19$

67. (A) $\frac{{}^nP_m}{m!} = {}^nC_m$

(B) Required ways $= \underbrace{m \times m \times m \times \ldots \times m}_{n \text{ times}} = m^n$

(C) $\times G \times G \times G \times G \times \ldots \times G \times$

Here, number of gaps for red balls $= m - 1 + 1 = m$

$\therefore$ Required ways $= {}^mC_n$

(D) Required ways $= \frac{n \times n \times n \times \ldots \times n}{m \text{ times}} = n^m$

68. (A) Required lines $= {}^{10}C_2 - {}^4C_2 + 1 = 40$

(B) Maximum number of points $= {}^{10}C_2 = 45$

(C) Maximum number of points $= {}^6C_2 \times 2 = 30$

(D) Maximum number of points $= {}^6C_2 \times 4 = 60$

69. (A) Number of rectangles $= {}^7C_2 \times {}^7C_2 = 441$

[select two vertical and two horizontal lines]

(B) Number of squares $= 1^2 + 2^2 + 3^2 + 4^2 + 5^2 + 6^2 = 91$

(C) First square can be selected in 36 ways, second square can be selected in $(36-6-5) = 25$ ways and third square can be selected in $(25-5-4) = 16$ ways.

$\therefore$ Required ways $= 36 \times 25 \times 15 = 2400$

(D) $a_1 + a_2 + a_3 + a_4 + a_5 + a_6 = 11$

where, $a_1, a_2, a_3, a_4, a_5, a_6, \geq 1$

$\therefore$ Required ways $= {}^{11-1}C_{6-1} = {}^{10}C_5$

70. (A) ☐☐☐ or ☐☐☐ Required ways

$= 1 \times 1 \times 1 \times \frac{3!}{2!} + 1 \times 1 \times 1 \times \frac{3!}{2!} = 6$

(B) ☐☐☐ or ☐☐☐ Required ways

$= \frac{{}^5C_3 \times {}^2C_1 \times {}^1C_1}{2} + \frac{{}^5C_2 \times {}^3C_2 \times {}^1C_1}{2} = 25$

(C) ☐☐☐ or ☐☐☐ Required ways $= 1 \times 1 \times 1 + 1 \times 1 \times 1 = 2$

(D) ☐☐☐ or ☐☐☐ Required ways $= 3 + 3 = 6$

71. Statement-1 is True

$\because 6! = 720 = 8 \times 9 \times 10$ i.e., Product of $6 - 3 = 3$ consecutive integers and Statement-2 is also true, but Statement-2 is not a correct explanation for Statement-1

72. For the number exactly divisible by 4, then last two digits must be divisible by 4, the last two digits are 12, 16, 24, 32, 36, 52, 56, 64, 72, 76. Total 10 ways.

Now, the remaining two first places on the left of 4 digit numbers are to be filled from remaining 5 digits and this can be done in ${}^5P_2 = 20$ ways.

$\therefore$ Required number of ways $= 20 \times 10 = 200$

Hence, Statement-1 is true and Statement-2 is false.

73. $\because 10! = 2^8 \cdot 3^4 \cdot 5^2 \cdot 7^1$

$\therefore$ Total number of divisors

$= (8+1)(4+1)(2+1)(1+1) = 270$

Hence, Statement-1 is false and Statement-2 is true.

74. $\because$ Number of permutations of n dissimilar things taken n at a time $= {}^nP_n = n!$

$\therefore$ Statement-1 is true and Statement-2 is false.

[$\because$ number of function $= n^n$]

75. $\because x_1 x_2 x_3 x_4 = 2 \cdot 5 \cdot 7 \cdot 11$

Each of 2, 5, 7, 11 can assign in 4 ways.

$\therefore$ Required number of solutions $= 4 \times 4 \times 4 \times 4 = 4^4 = 2^8 = 256$

Hence, Statement-1 is false and Statement-2 is true.

76. $\because a + c = 2b$

i.e., sum of two numbers is even, then both numbers are even or odd. In {1,2,3,4,...,21}, 11 numbers are odd and 10 numbers are even.

Then, total number of ways $= {}^{11}C_2 + {}^{10}C_2 = 55 + 45 = 100$

Hence, both statements are true but Statement-2 is not a correct explanation for Statement-1.

77. $\because N = 12600 = 2^3 \cdot 3^2 \cdot 5^2 \cdot 7^1$

$\therefore$ Number of even divisors $= 3\cdot(2+1)\cdot(2+1)\cdot(1+1) = 54$

Both statements are true but Statement-2 is not a correct explanation for Statement-1.

78. We know that a number is divisible by 3, if the sum of its digits is divisible by 3. Now, out of 0, 1, 2, 3, 4, 5, 6 if we take 1,2,4,5,6 or 1,2,3,4,5 or 0,3,4,5,6 or 0,2,3,4,6 or 0,1,3,5,6 or 0,1,2,4,5 or 0,1,2,3,6

$\therefore \quad$ Total number of ways $= 2 \times {}^5P_5 + 5 \times ({}^5P_5 - {}^4P_4)$

$= 240 + 480$

$= 720$

Statement-1 is false, Statement-2 is true.

79. The sum of the digits in the ten's place

= The sum of the digits in the unit's place

$= (4-1)!(3+4+5+6) = 108$

Both statements are true and Statement-2 is a correct explanation for Statement-1.

80. Number of planes each containing three points

$= {}^pC_3 - {}^qC_3 + 1$

$\therefore \quad$ Statement-1 is false and Statement-2 is always true.

81. $\because \quad {}^{50}C_{10} = \dfrac{50!}{10!40!}$

$\therefore \quad E_3(50!) = \left[\dfrac{50}{3}\right]+\left[\dfrac{50}{9}\right]+\left[\dfrac{50}{27}\right]+\left[\dfrac{50}{81}\right]+...$

$= 16+5+1+0+...= 22$

$E_3(40!) = \left[\dfrac{40}{3}\right]+\left[\dfrac{40}{9}\right]+\left[\dfrac{40}{27}\right]+\left[\dfrac{40}{81}\right]+...$

$= 13+4+1+0 = 18$

and $E_3(10!) = \left[\dfrac{10}{3}\right]+\left[\dfrac{10}{9}\right]+\left[\dfrac{10}{27}\right]+... = 3+1+0 = 4$

Hence, highest power of 3 in ${}^{50}C_{10} = 22-(18+4) = 0$

$\therefore$ Statement-1 is false, Statement-2 is true.

82. Number of diagonals in quindecagon $= {}^{15}C_2 - 15 = 105-15 = 90$

Both statements are true and Statement-2 is a correct explanation for Statement-1.

83. We have, ${}^nC_{n-r} + 3\,{}^nC_{n-r+1} + 3\,{}^nC_{n-r+2} + {}^nC_{n-r+3} = {}^xC_r$

$\Leftrightarrow ({}^nC_{n-r}+{}^nC_{n-r+1}) + 2({}^nC_{n-r+1}+{}^nC_{n-r+2}) + ({}^nC_{n-r+2}+{}^nC_{n-r+3}) = {}^xC_r$

$\Leftrightarrow \quad {}^{n+1}C_{n-r+1} + 2.\,{}^{n+1}C_{n-r+2} + {}^{n+1}C_{n-r+3} = {}^xC_r$

$\Leftrightarrow ({}^{n+1}C_{n-r+1}+{}^{n+1}C_{n-r+2}) + ({}^{n+1}C_{n-r+2}+{}^{n+1}C_{n-r+3}) = {}^xC_r$

$\Leftrightarrow \quad {}^{n+2}C_{n-r+2} + {}^{n+2}C_{n-r+3} = {}^xC_r$

$\Leftrightarrow \quad {}^{n+3}C_{n-r+3} = {}^xC_r$

$\Leftrightarrow \quad {}^{n+3}C_r = {}^xC_r \qquad [\because {}^nC_r = {}^nC_{n-r}]$

Hence, $\quad x = n+3$

84. We have, $\quad 3\,{}^{x+1}C_2 + P_2 \cdot x = 4\,{}^xA_2$

$\Leftrightarrow \quad \dfrac{3(x+1)x}{1\cdot 2} + 2!x = 4\cdot x(x-1)$

$\Leftrightarrow \quad 3x^2 + 3x + 4x = 8x^2 - 8x$

$\Leftrightarrow \quad 5x^2 - 15x = 0$

$\Leftrightarrow \quad 5x(x-3) = 0$

$\therefore \quad x \neq 0 \qquad [\because x \in N]$

Hence, $x = 3$ is the solution of the given equation.

85. We have, $x_n = \dfrac{195}{4P_n} - \dfrac{{}^{n+3}A_3}{P_{n+1}}$

$\therefore \quad x_n = \dfrac{195}{4\cdot n!} - \dfrac{(n+3)(n+2)(n+1)}{(n+1)!}$

$= \dfrac{195}{4\cdot n!} - \dfrac{(n+3)(n+2)}{n!}$

$= \dfrac{195-4n^2-20n-24}{4\cdot n!} = \dfrac{171-4n^2-20n}{4\cdot n!}$

$\because \quad x_n$ is positive.

$\therefore \quad \dfrac{171-4n^2-20n}{4\cdot n!} > 0$

$\Rightarrow \quad 4n^2 + 20n - 171 < 0$

which is true for $n = 1,2,3,4$

Hence, the given sequence (x_n) has 4 positive terms.

86. We have, $\quad {}^{n-1}C_3 + {}^{n-1}C_4 > {}^nC_3 \qquad [\because {}^nC_r + {}^nC_{r-1} = {}^{n+1}C_r]$

$\Leftrightarrow \quad {}^nC_4 > {}^nC_3$

$\Leftrightarrow \quad \dfrac{n!}{4!(n-4)!} > \dfrac{n!}{3!(n-3)!}$

$\Leftrightarrow \quad \dfrac{1}{4(n-4)!} > \dfrac{1}{(n-3)(n-4)!} \qquad [\because m! = m(m-1)!]$

$\Leftrightarrow \quad n-3 > 4 \Leftrightarrow n > 7$

87. Now, let sides of game be A and B. Given 5 married couples, i.e., 5 husbands and 5 wives. Now 2 husbands for two sides A and B be selected out of $5 = {}^5C_2 = 10$ ways.

After choosing the two husbands their wives are to be excluded (since no husband and wife play in the same game). So, we are to choose 2 wives out of remaining $5-2 = 3$ wives i.e., ${}^3C_2 = 3$ ways. Again two wives can interchange their sides A and B in $2! = 2$ ways.

By the principle of multiplication.

The required number of ways $= 10\times 3\times 2 = 60$.

88. ***Case* I When no couple is chosen**

We can choose 2 men in ${}^4C_2 = 6$ ways and hence two teams can be formed in $2\times 6 = 12$ ways.

***Case* II When only one couple is chosen**

A couple can be chosen in ${}^4C_1 = 4$ ways and the other team can be chosen in ${}^3C_1 \times {}^2C_1 = 6$ ways. Hence, two teams can be formed in $4\times 6 = 24$ ways.

***Case* III When two couples are chosen**

Then team can be chosen in ${}^4C_2 = 6$ ways.

Hence, total ways $= 12+24+6 = 42$.

89. The total number of seats

$= 1$ grandfather $+5$ sons and daughters $+8$ grand children $= 14$

The grand children with to occupy the 4 seats on either side of the table $4!$ ways $= 24$ ways

and grandfather can occupy a seat in $(5-1)$ ways $= 4$ ways

[Since 4 gaps between 5 sons and daughters]

and the remaining seat can be occupied in $5!$ ways

$= 120$ ways [5 seats for sons and daughters]

Hence, required number of ways, By the principle of multiplication law $= 24\times 4\times 120 = 11520$

90. There are 8 chairs on each side of the table. Let sides be represented by A and B. Let four persons sit on side A, then number of ways arranging 4 persons on 8 chairs on side $A = {}^8P_4$ and then two persons sit on side B, then number of ways arranging 2 persons on 8 chairs on side $B = {}^8P_2$ and arranging the remaining 10 persons in remaining 10 chairs in $10!$ ways.

Hence, the total number of ways in which the persons can be arranged $= {}^8P_4 \times {}^8P_2 \times 10! = \dfrac{8!\cdot 8!\,10!}{4!\,6!}$

91. The total number of handshake participations by all men what so ever is an even number, which is twice the number of handshakes.

The sum of all participations by men having an even number of handshakes is an even number, which is the sum of several even numbers.

The sum of all participations by men having an odd number of handshakes is an even number, which is an even number minus an even number.

The number of men having an odd number of handshakes must be even for the sum of the odd numbers of their participations be even.

92. C—S_1 S_2 S_3 S_4 S_5 S_6 S_7 S_8 S_9—L

For S_1, 9 different tickets are available, one for each of the remaining 9 stations, similarly at S_2, 8 different tickets are available and so on.

Thus, total number of different tickets

$$= 9 + 8 + 7 + 6 + 5 + 4 + 3 + 2 + 1 = 45$$

So, the six different tickets must be any six of these 45 and there are evidently as many different sets of 6 tickets as there are combinations of 45 things taken 6 at a time.

Hence, the required number $= {}^{45}C_6$.

93. Let the object be denoted by $a_1, a_2, a_3, \ldots, a_n$ arranged in a circle, we have to select 3 objects so that no two of them are consecutive. For this, we first find the number of ways in which 2 or 3 objects are consecutive. Now, number of ways in which 2 or 3 objects are consecutive, is obtained as follows with a_1. The number of such triples is

$a_1a_2a_3, a_1a_2a_4, a_1a_2a_5, \ldots, a_1a_2a_{n-1}$.

[Since, we have excluded $a_1a_2a_n$, so it will be repeated again. If we start with a_n, then we shall get triples : $a_na_1a_2$, $a_na_1a_3$]

So, number of such triples when we start with a_1, is $(n-3)$. Similarly, with $a_2, a_3, a_4, \ldots$, we shall get the numbers of triples that is $(n-3)$.

But total number of triples is ${}^nC_3$.

Hence, required number of ways $= {}^nC_3 - n(n-3)$

$$= \frac{n(n-1)(n-2)}{1\cdot 2\cdot 3} - n(n-3) = \frac{n}{6}[n^2 - 3n + 2 - 6n + 18]$$

$$= \frac{n}{6}(n^2 - 9n + 20) = \frac{n}{6}(n-4)(n-5)$$

94. Let the men P, Q, R, S, T, U, V, W and suppose P, Q, R remain only on one side and S, T on the other as represented in figure.

P Q R / S T

Then, since 4 men must row on each side, of the remaining 3, one must be placed on the side of P, Q, R and the other two on the side of S, T and this can evidently be done in 3 ways, for we can place any one of the three on the side of P, Q, R.

Now, 3 ways of distributing the crew let us first consider one, say that in which U is on the side of P, Q, R as shown in figure.

P Q R U / S T V W

Now, P, Q, R, U can be arranged in $4!$ ways and S, T, V, W can be arranged in $4!$ ways. Hence, total number of ways arranging the men $= 4! \times 4! = 576$

Hence, the number of ways of arranging the crew

$$= 3 \times 576$$
$$= 1728$$

95. The required number of ways = The number of ways in which $3n$ different things can be divided in 3 equal groups = The number of ways to distribute $3n$ different things equally among three persons $= \dfrac{3n!}{3!(n!)^3} = \dfrac{3n!}{6(n!)^3}$

96. Number of squares of area n^2 square units $= 1^2$

Number of squares of area $(n-1)^2$ square units $= 2^2$

Number of squares of area $(n-2)^2$ square units $= 3^2$

....

Number of squares of area 1^2 square units $= n^2$

Adding gives $N_1 = 1^2 + 2^2 + 3^2 + \ldots + n^2 = \dfrac{n(n+1)(2n+1)}{6}$

When n is even

Number of squares of area $\dfrac{n^2}{2}$ square units $= 1^2$

Number of squares of area $\dfrac{(n-2)^2}{2}$ square units $= 3^2$

....

Number of squares of area $\dfrac{2^2}{2}$ square units $= (n-1)^2$

Adding gives $N_2 = 1^2 + 3^2 + 5^2 + \ldots + (n-1)^2 = \dfrac{n(n-1)(n+1)}{6}$

When n is odd

Number of squares of area $\dfrac{(n-1)^2}{2}$ square units $= 2^2$

Number of squares of area $\dfrac{(n-3)^2}{2}$ square units $= 4^2$

Number of squares of area $\dfrac{(n-5)^2}{2}$ square units $= 6^2$

....

Number of squares of area $\dfrac{2^2}{2}$ square units $= (n-1)^2$

Adding gives $N_2 = 2^2 + 4^2 + 6^2 + \ldots + (n-1)^2 = \dfrac{n(n-1)(n+1)}{6}$

$\therefore$ Total number of squares formed which can be obtained by taking 4 points out of $(n+1)^2$ points $= N_1 + N_2$

$$= \frac{n(n+1)(2n+1)}{6} + \frac{n(n-1)(n+1)}{6} = \frac{n^2(n+1)}{2}$$

97. **(i) Set of 2 numbers**

Let a and b be 2 numbers $\dfrac{a+b}{2} = 60 \Rightarrow a + b = 120$

a and b both cannot be equal to or greater than 60

[$\because$ 60 cannot be used twice]

Let $0 \le a \le 59$ and $61 \le b \le 120$

The total number of ways in which a can be chosen

$$= {}^{60}C_1 = 60$$

The value of b depends on the value of a and there is 1 value of b corresponding to 1 of a.

$\therefore$ Total number of sets having 2 numbers $= 60$

(ii) Set of 3 numbers

Let a,b,c be the three numbers

Then, $\frac{a+b+c}{3}=60 \Rightarrow a+b+c=180$

***Case* I** Let $0 \le a \le 59$, $0 \le b \le 59$ and $c \ge 60$

a can be chosen in ${}^{60}C_1 = 60$ ways

b can be chosen in ${}^{59}C_1 = 59$ ways

[$\because$ b cannot use the value of a]

$\therefore$ Number of ways in which a and b can be chosen

$= 60 \times 59 = 3540$

Now, $1 \le a+b \le 117$ and there is only one value of c for 1 value of $a+b$ so that $a+b+c=180$.

$\therefore$ Number of ways in which a,b,c can be chosen

$= 60 \times 59 = 3540$

***Case* II** $a = 60$

$\therefore$ $b+c=120$

The number of ways in which b and c can assume values

$= 60$ [from Eq. (i)]

$\therefore$ Number of ways in which a, b, c can be chosen $= 60$

***Case* III** $61 \le a \le 90, 61 \le b \le 90$ and $c \le 60$

a can assume values in ${}^{30}C_1 = 30$ ways

b can assume values in ${}^{29}C_1 = 29$ ways

The value of c depends on the value of a and b

$\therefore$ Number of ways in which a,b,c can be chosen

$= 30 \times 29 = 870$

$\therefore$ Total number of ways in which sets of 3 numbers can be chosen

$= 3540 + 60 + 870 = 4470$

$\therefore$ Total number of ways in which sets of 2 and 3 numbers can be chosen

$= 4470 + 60 = 4530$

98. Let AB be any one of n straight lines and suppose it is intersected by some other straight line CD at P.

A ——•P—— B

Then, it is clear that AB contains $(n-1)$ of the points of intersection because it is intersected by the remaining $(n-1)$ $(n-1)$ straight lines in $(n-1)$ different points. So, the aggregate number of points contained in the n straight lines is $n(n-1)$. But in making up this aggregate, each point has evidently been counted twice. For instance, the point P has been counted once among the points situated on AB and again among those on CD.

Hence, the actual number of points $= \frac{n(n-1)}{2}$

Now, we have to find the number of new lines formed by joining these points. The number of new lines passing through P is evidently equal to the number of points lying outside the lines AB and CD for getting a new line joining P with each of these points only.

Since, each of the lines AB and CD contained $(n-2)$ points besides the point P, the number of points situated on AB and CD

$= 2(n-2) - 1$

$= (2n-3)$

$\therefore$ The number of points outside AB and CD

$= \frac{n(n-1)}{2} - (2n-3)$

The number of new lines passing through P and similarly through each other points.

$\therefore$ The aggregate number of new lines passing through the points

$$= \frac{n(n-1)}{2}\left\{\frac{n(n-1)}{2} - (2n-3)\right\}$$

But in making up this aggregate, every new line is counted twice. For instance, if Q is one of the points outside AB and CD, the line PQ is counted once among the lines passing through P and again among these passing through Q.

Hence, actual number of fresh lines introduced

$$= \frac{1}{2}\left[\frac{n(n-1)}{2}\left\{\frac{n(n-1)}{2} - (2n-3)\right\}\right]$$

$$= \frac{1}{8}n(n-1)(n-2)(n-3)$$

99. Denoting A_1, B_1, A_2 and B_2 for their taking out the ball, a chart is made to denote the winner.

S. No.		A_1	B_1	A_2	B_2	Number of ways
1.	**Points** Number on the ball Sum	1 Even (1 of 3) Even	1 Even (1 of 2) Even	0 Odd (1 of 3) Odd	2 Odd (1 of 2) Even	${}^3C_1 \times {}^2C_1 \times {}^3C_1 \times {}^2C_1 = 36$
2.	**Points** Number on the ball Sum	–1 Odd (1 of 3)Odd	1 Odd (1 of 2) Even	0 Even (1 of 3)Even	2 Even (1 of 2) Even	${}^3C_1 \times {}^2C_1 \times {}^3C_1 \times {}^2C_1 = 36$
3.	**Points** Number on the ball Sum	1 Even (1 of 3) Even	2 Odd (1 of 3) Odd	0 Odd (1 of 3) Even		${}^3C_1 \times {}^3C_1 \times {}^2C_1 = 18$
4.	**Points** Number on the ball Sum	1 Even (1 of 3) Even	1 Even (1 of 2) Even	2 Even (1 of 1)Even		${}^3C_1 \times {}^2C_1 \times {}^1C_1 = 6$

$\therefore$ Total number of ways in which the game can be won when A starts the game $= 36 + 36 + 18 + 6 = 96$

100. Along horizontal side one unit can be taken in $(2m-1)$ ways and 3 unit side can be taken in $(2m-3)$ ways. The number of ways of selecting a side horizontally is

$$(2m-1+2m-3+2m-5+...+3+1)=\frac{m}{2}(2m-1+1)=m^2$$

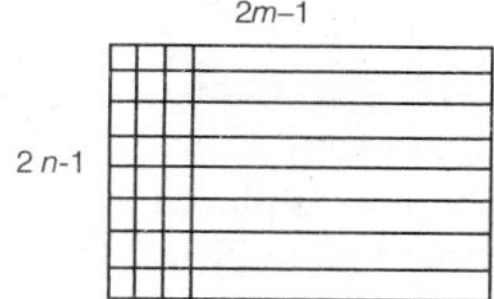

Similarly, the number of ways along vertical side is

$$(2n-1+2n-3+...+5+3+1)=\frac{n}{2}(2n-1+1)=n^2$$

$\therefore$ Total number of rectangles $= m^2n^2$

101. Words starting with A, C, H, I, N are each equals to 5!

$\therefore$ Total words $= 5\times 5! = 600$

The first word starting with S is SACHIN.

$\therefore$ SACHIN appears in dictionary at serial number 601.

102. Required number of ordered pair (p,q) is

$(2\times 3-1)(2\times 5-1)(2\times 3-1)-1=224$

103. ${}^{10}C_1+{}^{10}C_2+{}^{10}C_3+{}^{10}C_4=10+45+120+210=385$

104. In a word COCHIN, the second place can be filled in ${}^4C_1$ ways and the remaining four alphabets can be arranged in 4! ways in four different places. The next 97th word will be COCHIN.

Hence, the number of words that appear before the word COCHIN is 96.

105. 12 different objects are to be divided into 3 groups of equal size, which are named as A, B and C.

Number of ways $={}^{12}C_4\times{}^8C_4\times{}^4C_4=\dfrac{12!}{(4!)^3}$

106. (A) $\to$ (p); (B) $\to$ (s); (C) $\to$ (q); (D) $\to$ (q)

(A) ENDEA, N, O, E, L are five different letters, then permutations $=5!$.

(B) If E is in the first and last position, then permutations

$$=\frac{7!}{2!}=\frac{7\times 6\times 5!}{2}=21\times 5!$$

(C) For first four letters $=\dfrac{4!}{2!}=4\times 3=12$ and for last five letters $=\dfrac{5!}{3!}=\dfrac{5!}{6}$, then permutations $=12\times\dfrac{5!}{6}=2\times 5!$

(D) For A, E and O $=\dfrac{5!}{3!}$ and for others $=\dfrac{4!}{2!}=12$, then permutations $=\dfrac{5!}{3!}\times 12=\dfrac{5!}{6}\times 12=2\times 5!$.

107. Other than S seven letters M, I, I, I, P, P, I can be arranged in

$$\frac{7!}{2!4!}=\frac{7\cdot 6\cdot 5}{1\cdot 2}=7\cdot{}^6C_2=7\cdot{}^6C_4$$

Now, four S can be placed in 8 spaces in ${}^8C_4$ ways.

Hence, required number of ways $=7\cdot{}^6C_4\cdot{}^8C_4$

108. $x_1+x_2+x_3+x_4+x_5=6\Rightarrow{}^{6+5-1}C_{5-1}={}^{10}C_4$

109. Coefficient of x^{10} in $(x+x^2+x^3)^7$

$\Rightarrow$ Coefficient of x^3 in $(1+x+x^2)^7$

$\Rightarrow$ Coefficient of x^3 in $\left(\dfrac{1-x^3}{1-x}\right)^7=(1-x^3)^7(1-x)^{-7}$

$\Rightarrow$ Coefficient of x^3 in $(1-7x^3)(1+{}^7C_1x+{}^8C_2x^2+{}^9C_3x^3+...)$

$$={}^9C_3-7=\frac{9\cdot 8\cdot 7}{1\cdot 2\cdot 3}-7=77$$

Aliter

The digits are 1, 1, 1, 1, 1, 2, 3, or 1, 1, 1, 1, 2, 2, 2

Hence, number of seven digit numbers formed $=\dfrac{7!}{5!}+\dfrac{7!}{4!3!}$

$=42+35=77$

110. 4 novels can be selected from 6 novels in ${}^6C_4$ ways. 1 dictionary can be selected from 3 dictionaries in ${}^3C_1$ ways.

As the dictionary selected is fixed in the middle, the remaining 4 novels can be arranged in 4! ways.

$\therefore$ The required number of ways of arrangement.

$={}^6C_4\times{}^3C_1\times 4!=1080$

111. Total number of ways $={}^3C_2\times{}^9C_2={}^3C_1\times{}^9C_2=3\times\dfrac{9\times 8}{1\times 2}$

$=3\times 9\times 4=108$

112. The number of ways of distributing 10 identical balls in 4 different boxes such that no box is empty $={}^{10-1}C_{4-1}={}^9C_3$

Statement-1 is true.

The number of ways of choosing any 3 places from 9 different places $={}^9C_3$

Statement-2 is true.

Both statements are true but statement-2 is not a correct explanation for statement-1.

Aliter Let a, b, c, d are the balls in four boxes, then $a+b+c+d=10$ and $a\ge 1, b\ge 1, c\ge 1, d\ge 1$ [$\because$ no box is empty]

$\therefore$ Number of solutions $={}^{10-1}C_{4-1}={}^9C_3$

113. Number of triangles $={}^{10}C_3-{}^6C_3$

$\Rightarrow\quad N=\dfrac{10\cdot 9\cdot 8}{1\cdot 2\cdot 3}-\dfrac{6\cdot 5\cdot 4}{1\cdot 2\cdot 3}\Rightarrow N=120-20\Rightarrow N=100$

$\therefore\quad N\le 100$

114. $\because$ Each person gets atleast one ball.

$\therefore$ 3 persons can have 5 balls in the following systems

Person	I	II	III
No. of balls	1	1	3

or

Person	I	II	III
No. of balls	1	2	2

The number of ways to distribute the balls in first system

$$={}^5C_1\times{}^4C_1\times{}^3C_3$$

$\therefore$ The total number of ways to distribute 1,1,3 balls to the persons $={}^5C_1\times{}^4C_1\times{}^3C_3\times\dfrac{3!}{2!}=60$

and the number of ways to distribute the balls in second system $={}^5C_1\times{}^4C_2\times{}^2C_2$

Hence, the total number of ways to distribute 1,2,2 balls to the persons $={}^5C_1\times{}^4C_2\times{}^2C_2\times\dfrac{3!}{2!}=90$

$\therefore$ The required number of ways $=60+90=150$

Aliter The required number of ways

$$=3^5-{}^3C_1(3-1)^5+{}^3C_2(3-2)^5-{}^3C_3(3-3)^5$$

$$=243-96+3-0=150$$

115. $\because a_n =$ number of all n-digit positive integers formed by the digits 0,1 or both such that no consecutive digits in them are zero.

and $b_n =$ number of such n-digit integers ending with 1

$c_n =$ number of such n-digit integers ending with 0.

Clearly $a_n = b_n + c_n$ [$\because a_n$ can end with 0 or 1]

Also, $b_n = a_{n-1}$ and $c_n = a_{n-2}$

[$\because$ if last digit is 0, second last has to be 1]

$\therefore$ We get $a_n = a_{n-1} + a_{n-2}, n \geq 3$

Also, $a_1 = 1, a_2 = 2$

By the recurring formula $a_3 = a_2 + a_1 = 3$

$a_4 = a_3 + a_2 = 3 + 2 = 5$

$a_5 = a_4 + a_3 = 5 + 3 = 8$

Also, $b_6 = a_5 = 8$

116. By recurring formula, $a_{17} = a_{16} + a_{15}$ is correct.

Also, $C_{17} \neq C_{16} + C_{15} \Rightarrow a_{15} \neq a_{14} + a_{13}$ [$\because C_n = a_{n-2}$]

$\therefore$ Incorrect. Similarly, other parts are also incorrect.

117. Required number of ways

$$= (10+1)(9+1)(7+1) - 1 = 880 - 1 = 879$$

118. $\because T_{n+1} - T_n = 10 \Rightarrow {}^{n+1}C_3 - {}^nC_3 = 10 \Rightarrow {}^nC_2 + {}^nC_3 - {}^nC_3 = 10$

$$\Rightarrow {}^nC_2 = 10 = \frac{20}{2} = \frac{5 \cdot 4}{1 \cdot 2} = {}^5C_2 \Rightarrow n = 5$$

119. Given 8 vectors are $(1,1,1), (-1,1,1), (1,-1,1), (1,1,-1), (-1,-1,1), (1,-1,-1), (-1,1,-1), (-1,-1,-1)$ there are 4 diagonals of a cube.

Now, for 3 non-coplanar vectors first we select 3 groups of diagonals and its opposite in ${}^4C_3 = 4$ ways. Then one vector from each group can be selected in $2 \times 2 \times 2 = 8$ ways.

$\therefore$ Total ways $= 4 \times 8 = 32 = 2^5 = 2^p$ (given)

Hence, $p = 5$

120. If n_1, n_2, n_3, n_4 take minimum values 1,2,3,4 respectively, then n_5 will be maximum 10.

$\therefore$ Corresponding to $n_5 = 10$, there is only one solution

$n_1 = 1, n_2 = 2, n_3 = 3, n_4 = 4$

Corresponding to $n_5 = 9$, we can have,

$n_1 = 1, n_2 = 2, n_3 = 3, n_4 = 5$ i.e., one solution

Corresponding to $n_5 = 8$, we can have,

$n_1 = 1, n_2 = 2, n_3 = 3, n_4 = 6$

or $n_1 = 1, n_2 = 2, n_3 = 4, n_4 = 5$ i.e., two solutions

Corresponding to $n_5 = 7$, we can have

$n_1 = 1, n_2 = 2, n_3 = 4, n_4 = 6$

or $n_1 = 1, n_2 = 3, n_3 = 4, n_4 = 5$ i.e., two solutions

Corresponding to $n_5 = 6$, we can have

$n_1 = 2, n_2 = 3, n_3 = 4, n_4 = 5$ i.e., one solution

Thus, there can be 7 solutions.

121. Number of adjacent lines $= n$

Number of non-adjacent lines $= {}^nC_2 - n = \dfrac{n(n-3)}{2}$

$$\therefore \frac{n(n-3)}{2} = n \Rightarrow \frac{n(n-5)}{2} = 0 \Rightarrow n = 0 \text{ or } 5$$

But $n \geq 2 \Rightarrow n = 5$

122. $\because$ Card numbered 1 is always placed in envelope numbered 2, we can consider two cases.

***Case* I** Card numbered 2 is placed in envelope numbered 1, then it is derangement of 4 objects, which can be done in

$$4!\left(1 - \frac{1}{1!} + \frac{1}{2!} - \frac{1}{3!} + \frac{1}{4!}\right) = 9 \text{ ways}$$

***Case* II** Card numbered 2 is not placed in envelope numbered 1, then it is derangement of 5 objects, which can be done in

$$5!\left(1 - \frac{1}{1!} + \frac{1}{2!} - \frac{1}{3!} + \frac{1}{4!} - \frac{1}{5!}\right) = 44 \text{ ways}$$

$\therefore$ Total ways $= 9 + 44 = 53$ ways

123. Four digit numbers can be arranged in $3 \times 4! = 72$ ways and five digit numbers can be arranged in $5! = 120$ ways

$\therefore$ Number of integers $= 72 + 120 = 192$

124. $n = 5! \times 6!$

For m: 5 boys can stand in a row in 5!, creating 6 alternate space for girls. A group of 4 girls can be selected in ${}^5C_4$ ways. A group of 4 and single girl can be arranged at 2 places out of 6 in ${}^6P_2$ ways. Also, 4 girls can arrange themselves in 4! ways.

$$\therefore m = 5! \times {}^6P_2 \times {}^5C_4 \times 4! = 5! \times 30 \times 5 \times 4! = 5! \times 6! \times 5$$

$$\Rightarrow \frac{m}{n} = \frac{5! \times 6! \times 5}{5! \times 6!} = 5$$

125. Words starting with A, L, M $= \dfrac{4!}{2!} + 4! + \dfrac{4!}{2!} = 48$

Words starting with SA, SL $= \dfrac{3!}{2!} + 3! = 9$

Rank of the word SMALL $= 48 + 9 + 1 = 58$

126. Either one boy will be selected or no boy will be selected. Also out of four members one captain is to be selected.

$\therefore$ Required number of ways $= ({}^4C_1 \times {}^6C_3 + {}^6C_4) \times {}^4C_1$

$$= (4 \times 20 + 15) \times 4 = 95 \times 4 = 380$$

127.

X: 4L	X: 3M	Y: 3L	Y: 4M	
3	0	0	3	$= {}^4C_3 \times {}^3C_0 \times {}^3C_0 \times {}^4C_3 = 16$
2	1	1	2	$= {}^4C_2 \times {}^3C_1 \times {}^3C_1 \times {}^4C_2 = 324$
1	2	2	1	$= {}^4C_1 \times {}^3C_2 \times {}^3C_2 \times {}^4C_1 = 144$
0	3	3	0	$= {}^4C_0 \times {}^3C_3 \times {}^3C_3 \times {}^4C_0 = 1$

485

CHAPTER

06

Binomial Theorem

Learning Part

Session 1

- Binomial Theorem for Positive Integral Index
- Pascal's Triangle

Session 2

- General Term
- Middle Terms
- Greatest Term
- Trinomial Expansion

Session 3

- Two Important Theorems
- Divisibility Problems

Session 4

- Use of Complex Numbers in Binomial Theorem
- Multinomial Theorem
- Use of Differentiation
- Use of Integration
- When Each Term is Summation Contains the Product of Two Binomial Coefficients or Square of Binomial Coefficients
- Binomial Inside Binomial
- Sum of the Series

Practice Part

- JEE Type Examples
- Chapter Exercises

Arihant on Your Mobile !

Exercises with the symbol can be practised on your mobile. See inside cover page to activate for free.

Session 1

Binomial Theorem for Positive Integral Index, Pascal's Triangle

An algebraic expression consisting of two dissimilar terms with positive or negative sign between them is called a binomial expressions.

For example, $x + a, x^2 a - \frac{a}{x}, \frac{p}{x^2} - \frac{q}{x^4}, 5 - x,$

$(x^2+1)^{1/3} - \frac{1}{\sqrt{(x^3+1)}}$, etc., are called binomial expressions.

Remarks

1. An algebraic expression consisting of three dissimilar terms is called a trinomial. e.g. $a + 2b + c, x - 2y + 3z, 2\alpha - \frac{3}{\beta} + \gamma,$ etc. are called the trinomials.
2. In general, expressions consisting more than two dissimilar terms are known as multinomial expressions.

Binomial Theorem for Positive Integral Index

If $x, a \in C$ and $n \in N$, then

$$(x+a)^n = {}^nC_0\, x^{n-0}\, a^0 + {}^nC_1\, x^{n-1} a^1 + {}^nC_2\, x^{n-2}\, a^2 + \dots + {}^nC_r\, x^{n-r}\, a^r + \dots + {}^nC_{n-1}\, x^1\, a^{n-1} + {}^nC_n\, x^0\, a^n \quad \text{...(i)}$$

or $$(x+a)^n = \sum_{r=0}^{n} {}^nC_r\, x^{n-r}\, a^r$$

Hence, ${}^nC_0, {}^nC_1, {}^nC_2, \dots, {}^nC_n$ are called binomial coefficients.

Remark

1. In each term, the degree is n and the coefficient of $x^{n-r} a^r$ is equal to the number of ways $\underbrace{x, x, x, \dots, x}_{(n-r)\text{ times}}, \underbrace{a, a, a, \dots, a}_{r\text{ times}}$ can be arranged, which is given by $\frac{n!}{(n-r)!\,r!} = {}^nC_r$

   For example, $(x+a)^5 = \frac{5!}{5!\,0!} x^5 a^0 + \frac{5!}{4!\,1!} x^4 a + \frac{5!}{3!\,2!} x^3 a^2 + \frac{5!}{2!\,3!} x^2 a^3 + \frac{5!}{1!\,4!} x a^4 + \frac{5!}{0!\,5!} x^0 a^5$

   $= {}^5C_0 x^5 + {}^5C_1 x^4 a + {}^5C_2 x^3 a^2 + {}^5C_3 x^2 a^3 + {}^5C_4 x a^4 + {}^5C_5 a^5$

2. Let $S = (x+a)^n = \sum_{r=0}^{n} {}^nC_r\, x^{n-r}\, a^r$

   Replacing r by $n - r$, we have

   $S = (x+a)^n = \sum_{r=0}^{n} {}^nC_{n-r}\, x^{n-(n-r)}\, a^{n-r} = \sum_{r=0}^{n} {}^nC_{n-r}\, x^r\, a^{n-r}$

   $= {}^nC_n\, a^n + {}^nC_{n-1}\, a^{n-1} x + {}^nC_{n-2}\, a^{n-2} x^2 + \dots + {}^nC_0\, x^n$

   Thus, replacing r by $n - r$, we are infact writing the binomial expansion in reverse order.

Some Important Points

1. Replacing a by $(-a)$ in Eq. (i), we get

   $$(x-a)^n = {}^nC_0\, x^{n-0}\, a^0 - {}^nC_1\, x^{n-1}\, a^1 + {}^nC_2\, x^{n-2}\, a^2 - \dots + \dots + (-1)^r\, {}^nC_r\, x^{n-r}\, a^r + \dots + (-1)^n\, {}^nC_n\, x^0\, a^n \quad \text{...(ii)}$$

   or $$(x-a)^n = \sum_{r=0}^{n} (-1)^r\, {}^nC_r\, x^{n-r}\, a^r$$

2. On adding Eqs. (i) and (ii), we get

   $$(x+a)^n + (x-a)^n = 2\{{}^nC_0\, x^{n-0}\, a^0 + {}^nC_2\, x^{n-2}\, a^2 + {}^nC_4\, x^{n-4}\, a^4 + \dots\}$$
   $$= 2\ \{\text{Sum of terms at odd places}\}$$

   The last term is ${}^nC_n\, a^n$ or ${}^nC_{n-1}\, x\, a^{n-1}$, according as n is even or odd, respectively.

3. On subtracting Eq. (ii) from Eq. (i), we get

   $$(x+a)^n - (x-a)^n = 2\{{}^nC_1\, x^{n-1}\, a^1 + {}^nC_3\, x^{n-3}\, a^3 + {}^nC_5\, x^{n-5}\, a^5 + \dots\}$$
   $$= 2\ \{\text{Sum of terms at even places}\}$$

   The last term is ${}^nC_{n-1}\, x\, a^{n-1}$ or ${}^nC_n\, a^n$, according as n is even or odd, respectively.

4. Replacing x by 1 and a by x in Eq. (i), we get

   $$(1+x)^n = {}^nC_0\, x^0 + {}^nC_1\, x^1 + {}^nC_2\, x^2 + \dots + {}^nC_r\, x^r + \dots + {}^nC_{n-1}\, x^{n-1} + {}^nC_n\, x^n \quad \text{...(iii)}$$

   or $$(1+x)^n = \sum_{r=0}^{n} {}^nC_r\, x^r$$

5. Replacing x by $(-x)$ in Eq. (iii), we get

$$(1-x)^n = {}^nC_0\, x^0 - {}^nC_1\, x^1 + {}^nC_2\, x^2 - \dots + (-1)^r\, {}^nC_r\, x^r + \dots + {}^nC_n (-1)^n x^n$$

or $$(1-x)^n = \sum_{r=0}^{n} (-1)^r\, {}^nC_r\, x^r$$

| Example 1. Expand $\left(2a - \frac{3}{b}\right)^5$ by binomial theorem.

Sol. Using binomial theorem, we get

$$\left(2a-\frac{3}{b}\right)^5 = {}^5C_0\,(2a)^{5-0}\left(-\frac{3}{b}\right)^0 + {}^5C_1(2a)^{5-1}\left(-\frac{3}{b}\right)^1 + {}^5C_2\,(2a)^{5-2}\left(-\frac{3}{b}\right)^2 + {}^5C_3\,(2a)^{5-3}\left(-\frac{3}{b}\right)^3 + {}^5C_4\,(2a)^{5-4}\left(-\frac{3}{b}\right)^4 + {}^5C_5\,(2a)^{5-5}\left(-\frac{3}{b}\right)^5$$

$$= {}^5C_0\,(2a)^5 - {}^5C_1\,(2a)^4\left(\frac{3}{b}\right) + {}^5C_2\,(2a)^3\left(\frac{3}{b}\right)^2 - {}^5C_3\,(2a)^2\left(\frac{3}{b}\right)^3 + {}^5C_4\,(2a)^1\left(\frac{3}{b}\right)^4 - {}^5C_5\left(\frac{3}{b}\right)^5$$

$$= 32a^5 - \frac{240\,a^4}{b} + \frac{720\,a^3}{b^2} - \frac{1080\,a^2}{b^3} + \frac{810\,a}{b^4} - \frac{243}{b^5}$$

| Example 2. Simplify

$$(x+\sqrt{(x^2-1)})^6 + (x-\sqrt{(x^2-1})^6.$$

Sol. Let $\sqrt{(x^2-1)} = a$

Then, $$(x+a)^6 + (x-a)^6 = 2\{{}^6C_0\, x^{6-0}\, a^0 + {}^6C_2\, x^{6-2}\, a^2 + {}^6C_4\, x^{6-4}\, a^4 + {}^6C_6\, x^{6-6}\, a^6\}$$

$$= 2\{x^6 + 15x^4a^2 + 15x^2a^4 + a^6\} \qquad \text{[from point (2)]}$$

$$= 2\{x^6 + 15x^4(x^2-1) + 15x^2(x^2-1)^2 + (x^2-1)^3\} \qquad [\because a = \sqrt{x^2-1}]$$

$$= 2(32x^6 - 48x^4 + 18x^2 - 1)$$

| Example 3. In the expansion of $(x+a)^n$, if sum of odd terms is P and sum of even terms is Q, prove that

(i) $P^2 - Q^2 = (x^2 - a^2)^n$

(ii) $4PQ = (x+a)^{2n} - (x-a)^{2n}$

Sol. $$\because (x+a)^n = {}^nC_0\, x^{n-0} a^0 + {}^nC_1\, x^{n-1}\, a^1 + {}^nC_2\, x^{n-2}\, a^2 + {}^nC_3\, x^{n-3}\, a^3 + \dots + \dots + {}^nC_n\, x^{n-n}\, a^n$$

$$= ({}^nC_0\, x^n + {}^nC_2\, x^{n-2}\, a^2 + {}^nC_4\, x^{n-4}\, a^4 + \dots) + ({}^nC_1\, x^{n-1}\, a^1 + {}^nC_3\, x^{n-3}\, a^3 + {}^nC_5\, x^{n-5}\, a^5 + \dots)$$

$$= P + Q \text{ (given)} \qquad \dots\text{(i)}$$

and $$(x-a)^n = {}^nC_0\, x^{n-0}\, a^0 - {}^nC_1\, x^{n-1}\, a^1 + {}^nC_2\, x^{n-2}\, a^2 - {}^nC_3\, x^{n-3}\, a^3 + \dots + {}^nC_n\, x^{n-n}\, a^n$$

$$= ({}^nC_0\, x^n + {}^nC_2\, x^{n-2}\, a^2 + {}^nC_4\, x^{n-4}\, a^4 + \dots) - ({}^nC_1\, x^{n-1}\, a + {}^nC_3\, x^{n-3}\, a^3 + {}^nC_5\, x^{n-5}\, a^5 + \dots)$$

$$= P - Q \text{ (given)} \qquad \dots\text{(ii)}$$

(i) $$P^2 - Q^2 = (P+Q)(P-Q) = (x+a)^n \cdot (x-a)^n = (x^2-a^2)^n \qquad \text{[from Eqs. (i) and (ii)]}$$

(ii) $$(x+a)^{2n} - (x-a)^{2n} = [(x+a)^n]^2 - [(x-a)^n]^2 = (P+Q)^2 - (P-Q)^2 = 4PQ \qquad \text{[from Eqs. (i) and (ii)]}$$

| Example 4. Show that $(101)^{50} > (100)^{50} + (99)^{50}$.

Sol. Since, $$(101)^{50} - (99)^{50} = (100+1)^{50} - (100-1)^{50}$$

$$= 2\{{}^{50}C_1\,(100)^{49} + {}^{50}C_3\,(100)^{47} + {}^{50}C_5\,(100)^{45} + \dots\}$$

$$= 2 \times {}^{50}C_1\,(100)^{49} + 2\{{}^{50}C_3\,(100)^{47} + {}^{50}C_5\,(100)^{45} + \dots\}$$

$$= (100)^{50} + (\text{a positive number}) > (100)^{50}$$

Hence, $$(101)^{50} - (99)^{50} > (100)^{50}$$

$$\Rightarrow (101)^{50} > (100)^{50} + (99)^{50}$$

| Example 5. If $a_n = \sum_{r=0}^{n} \frac{1}{{}^nC_r}$, find the value of $\sum_{r=0}^{n} \frac{r}{{}^nC_r}$.

Sol. Let $$P = \sum_{r=0}^{n} \frac{r}{{}^nC_r} \qquad \dots\text{(i)}$$

Replacing r by $(n-r)$ in Eq. (i), we get

$$P = \sum_{r=0}^{n} \frac{(n-r)}{{}^nC_{n-r}} = \sum_{r=0}^{n} \frac{(n-r)}{{}^nC_r} \qquad [\because {}^nC_r = {}^nC_{n-r}] \dots\text{(ii)}$$

On adding Eqs. (i) and (ii), we get

$$2P = \sum_{r=0}^{n} \frac{n}{{}^nC_r} = n\sum_{r=0}^{n} \frac{1}{{}^nC_r} = na_n \qquad \text{[given]}$$

$$\therefore \quad P = \frac{n}{2}\, a_n$$

Hence, $$\sum_{r=0}^{n} \frac{r}{{}^nC_r} = \frac{n}{2}\, a_n$$

Properties of Binomial Expansion $(x+a)^n$

(i) This expansion has $(n+1)$ terms.

(ii) Since, ${}^nC_r = {}^nC_{n-r}$, we have

$$ {}^nC_0 = {}^nC_n = 1 $$
$$ {}^nC_1 = {}^nC_{n-1} = n $$
$$ {}^nC_2 = {}^nC_{n-2} = \frac{n(n-1)}{2!} \text{ and so on.} $$

(iii) In any term, the suffix of C is equal to the index of a and the index of $x = n -$ (suffix of C).

(iv) In each term, sum of the indices of x and a is equal to n.

Properties of Binomial Coefficient

(i) ${}^nC_r$ can also be represented by $C(n,r)$ or $\binom{n}{r}$

(ii) ${}^nC_x = {}^nC_y$, then either $x=y$ or $n = x+y$.

So, ${}^nC_r = {}^nC_{n-r} = \dfrac{n!}{r!(n-r)!}$

(iii) ${}^nC_r + {}^nC_{r-1} = {}^{n+1}C_r$

(iv) $\dfrac{{}^nC_r}{{}^nC_{r-1}} = \dfrac{n-r+1}{r}$

(v) ${}^nC_r = \dfrac{n}{r} \cdot {}^{n-1}C_{r-1}$

Pascal's Triangle

Coefficients of binomial expansion can also be easily determined by Pascal's triangle.

$(x+a)^0$	1
$(x+a)^1$	1 1
$(x+a)^2$	1 2 1
$(x+a)^3$	1 3 3 1
$(x+a)^4$	1 4 6 4 1
$(x+a)^5$	1 5 10 10 5 1

Pascal triangle gives the direct binomial coefficients.

For example,

$$ (x+a)^4 = 1\cdot x^4 + 4\cdot x^3\cdot a + 6\cdot x^2a^2 + 4\cdot x a^3 + 1\cdot a^4 $$
$$ = x^4 + 4x^3a + 6x^2a^2 + 4xa^3 + a^4 $$

How to Construct a Pascal's Triangle

Binomial coefficients in the expansion of $(x+a)^3$ are

1 3 3 1

	1	3	3		1
	1	$(1+3)$	$(3+3)$	$(3+1)$	1
Then,	1	4	6	4	1

are the binomial coefficients in the expansion of $(x+a)^4$.

Example 6. Find the number of dissimilar terms in the expansion of $(1-3x+3x^2-x^3)^{33}$.

Sol. $(1-3x+3x^2-x^3)^{33} = [(1-x)^3]^{33} = (1-x)^{99}$

Therefore, number of dissimilar terms in the expansion of $(1-3x+3x^2-x^3)^3$ is 100.

Example 7. Find the value of $\displaystyle\sum_{r=1}^{n} \frac{r\cdot {}^nC_r}{{}^nC_{r-1}}$.

Sol. $\because \dfrac{{}^nC_r}{{}^nC_{r-1}} = \dfrac{n-r+1}{r}$

$$ \therefore \frac{r\cdot {}^nC_r}{{}^nC_{r-1}} = (n-r+1) $$

$$ \therefore \sum_{r=1}^{n} \frac{r\cdot {}^nC_r}{{}^nC_{r-1}} = \sum_{r=1}^{n}(n-r+1) = \sum_{r=1}^{n}(n+1) - \sum_{r=1}^{n} r $$
$$ = (n+1)\sum_{r=1}^{n} 1 - (1+2+3+\ldots+n) $$
$$ = (n+1)\cdot n - \frac{n(n+1)}{2} = \frac{n(n+1)}{2} $$

Example 8. Let C_r stands for ${}^nC_r$, prove that
$$ (C_0+C_1)(C_1+C_2)(C_2+C_3)\ldots(C_{n-1}+C_n) = \frac{(n+1)^n}{n!}(C_0C_1C_2\ldots C_{n-1}). $$

Sol. LHS $= (C_0+C_1)(C_1+C_2)(C_2+C_3)\ldots(C_{n-1}+C_n)$

$$ = \prod_{r=1}^{n}(C_{r-1}+C_r) = \prod_{r=1}^{n}({}^{n+1}C_r) \quad [\because {}^nC_r + {}^nC_{r-1} = {}^{n+1}C_r] $$
$$ = \prod_{r=1}^{n}\left(\frac{n+1}{r}\right){}^nC_{r-1} \quad \left[\because {}^nC_r = \frac{n}{r}\cdot {}^{n-1}C_{r-1}\right] $$
$$ = \prod_{r=1}^{n}(n+1)\cdot \prod_{r=1}^{n}\frac{1}{r}\cdot \prod_{r=1}^{n} C_{r-1} $$
$$ = (n+1)^n \cdot \frac{1}{n!}\cdot(C_0C_1C_2\ldots C_{n-1}) $$
$$ = \frac{(n+1)^n}{n!}(C_0\,C_1\,C_2\ldots C_{n-1}) = \text{RHS} $$

| Example 9. Find the sum of the series

$$\sum_{r=0}^{n}(-1)^r\,{}^nC_r\left\{\frac{1}{2^r}+\frac{3^r}{2^{2r}}+\frac{7^r}{2^{3r}}+\frac{15^r}{2^{4r}}+\ldots\text{ upto } m \text{ terms}\right\}.$$

Sol. $\because (1-x)^n=\sum_{r=0}^{n}(-1)^r\,{}^nC_r\,x^r$ ...(i)

Let $P=\sum_{r=0}^{n}(-1)^r\,{}^nC_r\left\{\left(\frac{1}{2}\right)^r+\left(\frac{3}{4}\right)^r+\left(\frac{7}{8}\right)^r+\left(\frac{15}{16}\right)^r+\ldots\text{ upto } m\text{ terms}\right\}$

$$=\sum_{r=0}^{n}(-1)^r\,{}^nC_r\cdot\left(\frac{1}{2}\right)^r+\sum_{r=0}^{n}(-1)^r\,{}^nC_r\cdot\left(\frac{3}{4}\right)^r+\sum_{r=0}^{n}(-1)^r\,{}^nC_r\cdot\left(\frac{7}{8}\right)^r+\sum_{r=0}^{n}(-1)^r\,{}^nC_r\cdot\left(\frac{15}{16}\right)^r+\ldots\text{ upto } m\text{ terms}$$

$$=\left(1-\frac{1}{2}\right)^n+\left(1-\frac{3}{4}\right)^n+\left(1-\frac{7}{8}\right)^n+\left(1-\frac{15}{16}\right)^n+\ldots\text{ upto } m\text{ terms}$$

$$=\left(\frac{1}{2}\right)^n+\left(\frac{1}{2}\right)^{2n}+\left(\frac{1}{2}\right)^{3n}+\left(\frac{1}{2}\right)^{4n}+\ldots\text{ upto } m\text{ terms}$$

$$=\frac{\left(\frac{1}{2}\right)^n\left[1-\left\{\left(\frac{1}{2}\right)^n\right\}^m\right]}{1-\left(\frac{1}{2}\right)^n}$$

$$=\frac{(2^{mn}-1)}{2^{mn}(2^n-1)}$$

Exercise for Session 1

1. The value of $\sum_{r=0}^{10} r\cdot{}^{10}C_r\cdot 3^r\cdot(-2)^{10-r}$ is

(a) 10 (b) 20 (c) 30 (d) 300

2. The number of dissimilar terms in the expansion of $\left(x+\frac{1}{x}+x^2+\frac{1}{x^2}\right)^{15}$ are

(a) 61 (b) 121 (c) 255 (d) 16

3. The expansion $\{x+(x^3-1)^{1/2}\}^5+\{x-(x^3-1)^{1/2}\}^5$ is a polynomial of degree

(a) 5 (b) 6 (c) 7 (d) 8

4. $(\sqrt{2}+1)^6-(\sqrt{2}-1)^6$ is equal to

(a) 101 (b) $70\sqrt{2}$ (c) $140\sqrt{2}$ (d) $120\sqrt{2}$

5. The total number of dissimilar terms in the expansion of $(x+a)^{100}+(x-a)^{100}$ after simplification will be

(a) 202
(b) 51
(c) 50
(d) 101

6. The number of non-zero terms in the expansion of $(1+3\sqrt{2}x)^9+(1-3\sqrt{2}x)^9$, is

(a) 0
(b) 5
(c) 9
(d) 10

7. If $(1+x)^n=\sum_{r=0}^{n}C_r\,x^r$, $\left(1+\frac{C_1}{C_0}\right)\left(1+\frac{C_2}{C_1}\right)\ldots\left(1+\frac{C_n}{C_{n-1}}\right)$ is equal to

(a) $\frac{n^{n-1}}{(n-1)!}$
(b) $\frac{(n+1)^{n-1}}{(n-1)!}$
(c) $\frac{(n+1)^n}{n!}$
(d) $\frac{(n+1)^{n+1}}{n!}$

8. If ${}^{n+1}C_{r+1}:{}^nC_r:{}^{n-1}C_{r-1}=11:6:3$, nr is equal to

(a) 20
(b) 30
(c) 0
(d) 50

Session 2

General Term, Middle Terms, Greatest Term, Trinomial Expansion

General Term

The term ${}^nC_r\ x^{n-r}\ a^r$ is the $(r+1)$ th term from beginning in the expansion of $(x+a)^n$. It is usually called the general term and it is denoted by T_{r+1}.
i.e., $T_{r+1} = {}^nC_r\ x^{n-r}\ a^r$

Example 10. Find the 7th term in the expansion of $\left(4x - \frac{1}{2\sqrt{x}}\right)^{13}$.

Sol. Seventh term, $T_7 = T_{6+1} = {}^{13}C_6\,(4x)^{13-6}\left(-\frac{1}{2\sqrt{x}}\right)^6$

$$= {}^{13}C_6 \cdot 4^7 \cdot x^7 \cdot \frac{1}{2^6 \cdot x^3}$$

$$= {}^{13}C_6 \cdot 2^8 \cdot x^4$$

Example 11. Find the coefficient of x^8 in the expansion of $\left(x^2 - \frac{1}{x}\right)^{10}$.

Sol. Here, $T_{r+1} = {}^{10}C_r\,(x^2)^{10-r}\left(-\frac{1}{x}\right)^r$

$$= {}^{10}C_r\, x^{20-2r} \cdot (-1)^r \cdot \frac{1}{x^r}$$

$$= {}^{10}C_r\,(-1)^r \cdot x^{20-3r} \quad \text{...(i)}$$

Now, in order to find out the coefficient of x^8, $20-3r$ must be 8.

i.e. $20 - 3r = 8$

$\therefore$ $r = 4$

Hence, putting $r = 4$ in Eq. (i), we get

Required coefficient $= (-1)^4 \cdot {}^{10}C_4 = \frac{10\cdot 9\cdot 8\cdot 7}{1\cdot 2\cdot 3\cdot 4} = 210$

Example 12. Find

(i) the coefficient of x^7 in the expansion of $\left(ax^2 + \frac{1}{bx}\right)^{11}$.

(ii) the coefficient of x^{-7} in the expansion of $\left(ax - \frac{1}{bx^2}\right)^{11}$.

Also, find the relation between a and b, so that these coefficients are equal.

Sol. (i) Here, $T_{r+1} = {}^{11}C_r\,(ax^2)^{11-r}\left(\frac{1}{bx}\right)^r$

$$= {}^{11}C_r \cdot \frac{a^{11-r}}{b^r} \cdot x^{22-3r} \quad \text{...(i)}$$

Now, in order to find out the coefficient of x^7, $22-3r$ must be 7,

i.e. $22 - 3r = 7$

$\therefore$ $r = 5$

Hence, putting $r = 5$ in Eq. (i), we get

Required coefficient $= {}^{11}C_5 \cdot \frac{a^6}{b^5}$

(ii) Here, $T_{R+1} = {}^{11}C_R\,(ax)^{11-R}\left(-\frac{1}{bx^2}\right)^R$

$$= {}^{11}C_R\,(a)^{11-R}\left(-\frac{1}{b}\right)^R \cdot x^{11-3R}$$

$$= (-1)^R \cdot {}^{11}C_R \cdot \frac{a^{11-R}}{b^R} \cdot x^{11-3R} \quad \text{...(ii)}$$

Now, in order to find out the coefficient of x^{-7}, $11-3R$ must be -7.

i.e., $11 - 3R = -7 \Rightarrow R = 6$. Hence, putting $R = 6$ in Eq. (ii), we get

Required coefficient

$$= (-1)^6 \cdot {}^{11}C_6 \cdot \frac{a^5}{b^6} = {}^{11}C_5 \cdot \frac{a^5}{b^6} \quad [\because {}^nC_r = {}^nC_{n-r}]$$

Also given, coefficient of x^7 in

$\left(ax^2 + \frac{1}{bx}\right)^{11}$ = coefficient of x^{-7} in $\left(ax - \frac{1}{bx^2}\right)^{11}$

$$\Rightarrow {}^{11}C_5 \cdot \frac{a^6}{b^5} = {}^{11}C_5 \cdot \frac{a^5}{b^6} \Rightarrow ab = 1$$

which is the required relation between a and b.

Example 13. Find the term independent of x in the expansion of $\left(\frac{3}{2}x^2 - \frac{1}{3x}\right)^9$.

Sol. Here, $T_{r+1} = {}^9C_r \left(\frac{3}{2}x^2\right)^{9-r} \left(-\frac{1}{3x}\right)^r$

$$= (-1)^r \cdot {}^9C_r \cdot \left(\frac{3}{2}\right)^{9-r} \cdot \left(\frac{1}{3}\right)^r \cdot x^{18-3r} \quad ...(i)$$

If this term is independent of x, then the index of x must be zero, i.e., $18 - 3r = 0 \Rightarrow r = 6$

Therefore, $(r+1)$ th term, i.e., 7th term is independent of x and its value by putting $r = 6$ in Eq. (i)

$$= (-1)^6 \cdot {}^9C_6 \cdot \left(\frac{3}{2}\right)^3 \cdot \left(\frac{1}{3}\right)^6 = {}^9C_3 \cdot \frac{1}{2^3 \cdot 3^3}$$

$$= \frac{9 \cdot 8 \cdot 7}{(1 \cdot 2 \cdot 3)\, 2^3 \cdot 3^3} = \frac{7}{18}$$

$(p+1)$ th Term From End in the Expansion of $(x+a)^n$

$(p+1)$ th term from end in the expansion of $(x+a)^n$

$= (p+1)$ th term from beginning in the expansion of $(a+x)^n$

$= {}^nC_p\, a^{n-p}\, x^p$

Example 14. Find the 4th term from the end in the expansion of $\left(\frac{x^3}{2} - \frac{2}{x^2}\right)^7$.

Sol. 4th term from the end in the expansion of $\left(\frac{x^3}{2} - \frac{2}{x^2}\right)^7$

$=$ 4th term from beginning in the expansion of $\left(-\frac{2}{x^2} + \frac{x^3}{2}\right)^7$

$$= {}^7C_3 \left(-\frac{2}{x^2}\right)^{7-3} \left(\frac{x^3}{2}\right)^3 = \frac{7 \cdot 6 \cdot 5}{1 \cdot 2 \cdot 3} \cdot \frac{2^4}{x^8} \cdot \frac{x^9}{2^3} = 70x$$

Example 15. Find the $(n+1)$th term from the end in the expansion of $\left(2x - \frac{1}{x}\right)^{3n}$.

Sol. $(n+1)$th term from the end in the expansion of $\left(2x - \frac{1}{x}\right)^{3n}$

$= (n+1)$ th term from beginning in the expansion of $\left(-\frac{1}{x} + 2x\right)^{3n}$

$$= T_{n+1} = {}^{3n}C_n \left(-\frac{1}{x}\right)^{3n-n} (2x)^n = {}^{3n}C_n \cdot 2^n \cdot x^{-n}$$

How to Find Free from Radical Terms or Rational Terms in the Expansion of $(a^{1/p} + b^{1/q})^N, \forall\, a, b \in$ Prime Numbers

First, find $T_{r+1} = {}^NC_r\, (a^{1/p})^{N-r}\, (b^{1/q})^r$

$\therefore \quad T_{r+1} = {}^NC_r \cdot a^{(N-r)/p} \cdot b^{r/q}$

By inspection, putting the values of $0 \le r \le N$, when indices of a and b are integers.

Remark

1. If indices of a and b are positive integers.
   Then, free from radical terms = Terms which are integers
   $\therefore$ Number of non-integral terms = Total terms – Number of integral terms
2. If indices of a and b both are not positive integers.
   Then, free from radical terms = Rational terms – Integral terms
3. Number of irrational terms = Total terms – Number of rational terms

Example 16. Find the number of terms in the expansion of $(\sqrt[4]{9} + \sqrt[6]{8})^{500}$ which are integers.

Sol. Since, $(\sqrt[4]{9} + \sqrt[6]{8})^{500} = (9^{1/4} + 8^{1/6})^{500} = (3^{1/2} + 2^{1/2})^{500}$

[$\because a, b \in$ prime numbers]

$\therefore$ General term, $T_{r+1} = {}^{500}C_r\, (3^{1/2})^{500-r} \cdot (2^{1/2})^r$

$$= {}^{500}C_r \cdot 3^{\frac{500-r}{2}} \cdot 2^{r/2}$$

$$= {}^{500}C_r \cdot 3^{250-r/2} \cdot 2^{r/2}$$

Now, $\quad 0 \le r \le 500$

For $r = 0, 2, 4, 6, 8, \dots, 500$, indices of 3 and 2 are positive integers.

Hence, number of terms which are integers $= 250 + 1 = 251$

Example 17. Find the sum of all rational terms in the expansion of $(3^{1/5} + 2^{1/3})^{15}$.

Sol. The general term in the expansion of $(3^{1/5} + 2^{1/3})^{15}$ is

$$T_{r+1} = {}^{15}C_r\, (3^{1/5})^{15-r} \cdot (2^{1/3})^r$$

$$= {}^{15}C_r \cdot 3^{3-\frac{r}{5}} \cdot 2^{\frac{r}{3}}$$

Now, $\quad 0 \le r \le 15$

For $r = 0, 15$

Rational terms are T_{0+1} and T_{15+1}.

Then, $\quad T_{0+1} = {}^{15}C_0 \cdot 3^3 \cdot 2^0 = 27$

and $\quad T_{15+1} = {}^{15}C_{15} \cdot 3^0 \cdot 2^5 = 32$

$\therefore$ Sum of all rational terms $= 27 + 32 = 59$

Example 18. Find the number of irrational terms in the expansion of $(\sqrt[8]{5}+\sqrt[6]{2})^{100}$.

Sol. Since, $(\sqrt[8]{5}+\sqrt[6]{2})^{100}=(5^{1/8}+2^{1/6})^{100}$

$\therefore$ General term, $T_{r+1}={}^{100}C_r\,(5^{1/8})^{100-r}\,(2^{1/6})^r$

$$={}^{100}C_r\,(5)^{(100-r)/8}\cdot(2)^{r/6}$$

As, 2 and 5 are coprime.

$\therefore$ T_{r+1} will be rational, if $(100-r)$ is a multiple of 8 and r is a multiple of 6.

Also, $\quad 0\le r\le 100$

$\therefore \quad r=0,6,12,18,\ldots,96$

Now, $\quad 100-r=4,10,16,\ldots,100 \quad$ ...(i)

and $\quad 100-r=0,8,16,24,\ldots,100 \quad$ ...(ii)

The common terms in Eqs. (i) and (ii) are 16, 40, 64 and 88.

$\therefore$ $r=84,60,36,12$ gives rational terms.

$\therefore$ The number of irrational terms $=101-4=97$

Problems Regarding Three/Four Consecutive Terms or Coefficients

(i) If consecutive coefficients are given

In this case, divide consecutive coefficients pairwise, we get equations and then solve them.

Example 19. Let n be a positive integer. If the coefficients of rth, $(r+1)$th and $(r+2)$th terms in the expansion of $(1+x)^n$ are in AP, then find the relation between n and r.

Sol. $\because \quad T_r=T_{(r-1)+1}={}^nC_{r-1}\,x^{r-1}$

$T_{r+1}={}^nC_r\,x^r$ and $T_{r+2}=T_{(r+1)+1}={}^nC_{r+1}\,x^{r+1}$

$\therefore$ Coefficients of rth, $(r+1)$th and $(r+2)$th terms in the expansion of

$(1+x)^n$ are ${}^nC_{r-1},{}^nC_r,{}^nC_{r+1}$.

$\because$ Given, ${}^nC_{r-1},{}^nC_r,{}^nC_{r+1}$ are in AP.

and $\quad n\ge r+1$

$\therefore \quad \dfrac{{}^nC_{r-1}}{{}^nC_r},1,\dfrac{{}^nC_{r+1}}{{}^nC_r}$ are also in AP.

$\Rightarrow \quad \dfrac{r}{n-r+1},1,\dfrac{n-r}{r+1}$ are in AP.

$$\Rightarrow 1-\frac{r}{n-r+1}=\frac{n-r}{r+1}-1 \Rightarrow \frac{n-2r+1}{n-r+1}=\frac{n-2r-1}{r+1}$$

$$\Rightarrow nr-2r^2+r+n-2r+1$$

$$=n^2-2nr-n-nr+2r^2+r+n-2r-1$$

$$\Rightarrow \quad n^2-4nr+4r^2=n+2\Rightarrow (n-2r)^2=n+2$$

***Corollary* I** For $r=2,n=7$ $\quad [\because n\ge 3]$

***Corollary* II** For $r=5,n=7,14$ $\quad [\because n\ge 6]$

Example 20. If a,b,c and d are any four consecutive coefficients in the expansion of $(1+x)^n$, then prove that:

(i) $\dfrac{a}{a+b}+\dfrac{c}{c+d}=\dfrac{2b}{b+c}$.

(ii) $\left(\dfrac{b}{b+c}\right)^2>\dfrac{ac}{(a+b)(c+d)}$, if $x>0$.

Sol. Let a,b,c and d be the coefficients of the r th, $(r+1)$th, $(r+2)$th and $(r+3)$th terms respectively, in the expansion of $(1+x)^n$. Then,

$$T_r=T_{r-1+1}={}^nC_{r-1}\,x^{r-1}$$

$\therefore \quad a={}^nC_{r-1} \quad$ ...(i)

$\because \quad T_{r+1}={}^nC_r\,x^r$

$\therefore \quad b={}^nC_r \quad$ ...(ii)

$\because \quad T_{r+2}=T_{(r+1)+1}={}^nC_{r+1}\,x^{r+1}$

$\therefore \quad c={}^nC_{r+1} \quad$ ...(iii)

and $\quad T_{r+3}=T_{(r+2)+1}={}^nC_{r+2}\,x^{r+2}$

$\therefore \quad d={}^nC_{r+2} \quad$ ...(iv)

From Eqs. (i) and (ii), we get

$$a+b={}^nC_{r-1}+{}^nC_r={}^{n+1}C_r$$

$$=\frac{n+1}{r}\cdot{}^nC_{r-1}=\left(\frac{n+1}{r}\right)a$$

$\therefore \quad \dfrac{a}{a+b}=\dfrac{r}{n+1} \quad$ ...(v)

From Eqs. (ii) and (iii), we get

$$b+c={}^nC_r+{}^nC_{r+1}={}^{n+1}C_{r+1}$$

$$=\left(\frac{n+1}{r+1}\right){}^nC_r=\left(\frac{n+1}{r+1}\right)b$$

$\therefore \quad \dfrac{b}{b+c}=\dfrac{r+1}{n+1} \quad$ ...(vi)

From Eqs. (iii) and (iv), we get

$$c+d={}^nC_{r+1}+{}^nC_{r+2}={}^{n+1}C_{r+2}$$

$$=\left(\frac{n+1}{r+2}\right){}^nC_{r+1}=\left(\frac{n+1}{r+2}\right)c$$

$\therefore \quad \dfrac{c}{c+d}=\dfrac{r+2}{n+1} \quad$ ...(vii)

From Eqs. (v), (vi) and (vii), we get

$$\frac{a}{a+b},\frac{b}{b+c}\text{ and }\frac{c}{c+d}\text{ are in AP.}$$

(i) $\dfrac{a}{a+b}+\dfrac{c}{c+d}=2\left(\dfrac{b}{b+c}\right)$

or $\quad \dfrac{a}{a+b}+\dfrac{c}{c+d}=\dfrac{2b}{b+c}$

(ii) AM > GM

$$\therefore \quad \left(\frac{b}{b+c}\right) > \sqrt{\left(\frac{a}{a+b}\right)\left(\frac{c}{c+d}\right)}$$

$$\Rightarrow \quad \left(\frac{b}{b+c}\right)^2 > \frac{ac}{(a+b)(c+d)}$$

Remembering Method

$\because$

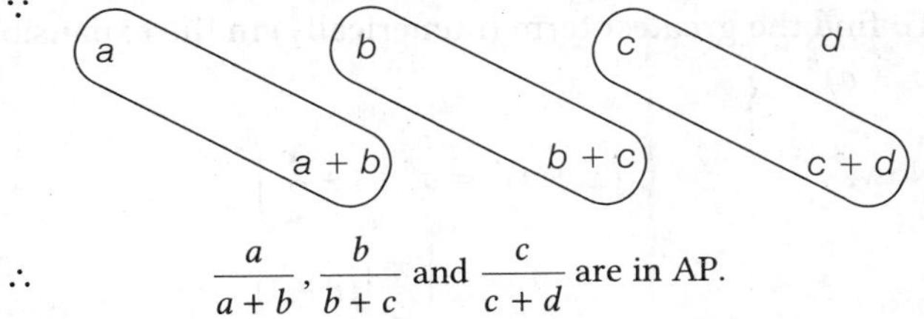

$$\therefore \quad \frac{a}{a+b}, \frac{b}{b+c} \text{ and } \frac{c}{c+d} \text{ are in AP.}$$

(ii) If consecutive terms are given

In this case, divide consecutive terms pairwise. i.e., If four consecutive terms are $T_r, T_{r+1}, T_{r+2}, T_{r+3}$. Then, find $\frac{T_{r+1}}{T_r}, \frac{T_{r+2}}{T_{r+1}}, \frac{T_{r+3}}{T_{r+2}} \Rightarrow \lambda_1, \lambda_2, \lambda_3$ (say). Then, divide λ_2 by λ_1 and λ_3 by λ_2 and solve.

Example 21. If the 2nd, 3rd and 4th terms in the expansion of $(x+y)^n$ are 240, 720 and 1080 respectively, find x, y and n.

Sol. Given, $T_2 = T_{1+1} = {}^nC_1 \cdot x^{n-1} \cdot y = 240$ ...(i)

$$T_3 = T_{2+1} = {}^nC_2 \cdot x^{n-2} \cdot y^2 = 720 \quad \text{...(ii)}$$

and $T_4 = T_{3+1} = {}^nC_3 \cdot x^{n-3} \cdot y^3 = 1080$ ...(iii)

On dividing Eq. (ii) by Eq. (i), we get

$$\frac{{}^nC_2 \cdot x^{n-2} \cdot y^2}{{}^nC_1 \cdot x^{n-1} \cdot y} = \frac{720}{240}$$

$$\Rightarrow \quad \left(\frac{n-2+1}{2}\right) \cdot \frac{y}{x} = 3 \Rightarrow \frac{y}{x} = \frac{6}{n-1} \quad \text{...(iv)}$$

Also, dividing Eq. (iii) by Eq. (ii), we get

$$\frac{{}^nC_3 \cdot x^{n-3} \cdot y^3}{{}^nC_2 \cdot x^{n-2} \cdot y^2} = \frac{1080}{720}$$

$$\Rightarrow \quad \left(\frac{n-3+1}{3}\right) \cdot \frac{y}{x} = \frac{3}{2} \Rightarrow \frac{y}{x} = \frac{9}{2(n-2)} \quad \text{...(v)}$$

From Eqs. (iv) and (v), we get

$$\frac{6}{n-1} = \frac{9}{2(n-2)}$$

$$\Rightarrow \quad 12n - 24 = 9n - 9$$

$$\Rightarrow \quad 3n = 15$$

$$\therefore \quad n = 5$$

From Eq. (iv), we get $y = \frac{3}{2}x$ ...(vi)

From Eqs. (i) and (vi), we get

$${}^5C_1 \cdot x^4 \cdot y = 240 \quad \Rightarrow 5 \cdot x^4 \cdot \frac{3}{2}x = 240$$

$$\therefore \quad x^5 = 32 = 2^5 \Rightarrow x = 2$$

From Eq. (vi), we get $y = 3$

Hence, $x = 2, y = 3$ and $n = 5$

Middle Terms

The middle term depends upon the value of n.

(i) **When n is even** The total number of terms in the expansion of $(x+a)^n$ is $n+1$ (odd). So, there is only one middle term, i.e., $\left(\frac{n}{2}+1\right)$th term is the middle term. It is given by $T_{n/2+1} = {}^nC_{n/2}\, x^{n/2}\, a^{n/2}$

(ii) **When n is odd** The total number of terms in the expansion of $(x+a)^n$ is $n+1$ (even). So, there are two middle terms, i.e., $\left(\frac{n+1}{2}\right)$th and $\left(\frac{n+3}{2}\right)$th are two middle terms. They are given by

$$T_{\frac{n+1}{2}} = T_{\left(\frac{n-1}{2}\right)+1} = {}^nC_{\frac{n-1}{2}} \cdot x^{\frac{n+1}{2}} \cdot a^{\frac{n-1}{2}}$$

and $$T_{\frac{n+3}{2}} = T_{\left(\frac{n+1}{2}\right)+1} = {}^nC_{\frac{n+1}{2}} \cdot x^{\frac{n-1}{2}} \cdot a^{\frac{n+1}{2}}$$

Example 22. Find the middle term in the expansion of $\left(\frac{a}{x}+bx\right)^{12}$.

Sol. The number of terms in the expansion of $\left(\frac{a}{x}+bx\right)^{12}$ is 13 (odd), its middle term is $\left(\frac{12}{2}+1\right)$th, i.e., 7th term.

$$\therefore \text{ Required term, } T_7 = T_{6+1} = {}^{12}C_6 \left(\frac{a}{x}\right)^6 (bx)^6$$

$$= {}^{12}C_6\, a^6\, b^6 = 924\, a^6\, b^6$$

Example 23. Find the middle term in the expansion of $\left(3x - \frac{x^3}{6}\right)^9$.

Sol. The number of terms in the expansion of $\left(3x - \frac{x^3}{6}\right)^9$ is 10 (even). So, there are two middle terms, i.e. $\left(\frac{9+1}{2}\right)$th and $\left(\frac{9+3}{2}\right)$th terms. They are given by T_5 and T_6.

$$\therefore \quad T_5 = T_{4+1} = {}^9C_4 (3x)^5 \left(-\frac{x^3}{6}\right)^4$$

$$= \frac{9 \cdot 8 \cdot 7 \cdot 6}{1 \cdot 2 \cdot 3 \cdot 4} \cdot 3^5 x^5 \cdot \frac{x^{12}}{6^4} = \frac{189}{8} x^{17}$$

and $$T_6 = T_{5+1} = {}^9C_5 (3x)^4 \left(-\frac{x^3}{6}\right)^5$$

$$= -{}^9C_4 \cdot 3^4 \cdot x^4 \cdot \frac{x^{15}}{6^5}$$

$$= -\frac{9 \cdot 8 \cdot 7 \cdot 6}{1 \cdot 2 \cdot 3 \cdot 4} \cdot 3^4 \cdot \frac{x^{19}}{6^5} = -\frac{21}{16} x^{19}$$

Example 24. Show that the middle term in the expansion of $(1+x)^{2n}$ is

$$\frac{1 \cdot 3 \cdot 5 \ldots (2n-1)}{n!} \cdot 2^n x^n, n \text{ being a positive integer.}$$

Sol. The number of terms in the expansion of $(1+x)^{2n}$ is $2n+1$ (odd), its middle term is $(n+1)$th term.

$\therefore$ Required term $= T_{n+1}$

$$= {}^{2n}C_n x^n = \frac{2n!}{n!\,n!} x^n = \frac{(1 \cdot 2 \cdot 3 \cdot 4 \ldots (2n-1) \cdot 2n)}{n!\,n!} x^n$$

$$= \frac{\{1 \cdot 3 \cdot 5 \ldots (2n-1)\}\{2 \cdot 4 \cdot 6 \ldots 2n\}}{n!\,n!} x^n$$

$$= \frac{\{1 \cdot 3 \cdot 5 \ldots (2n-1)\} 2^n (1 \cdot 2 \cdot 3 \ldots n)}{n!\,n!} x^n$$

$$= \frac{\{1 \cdot 3 \cdot 5 \ldots (2n-1)\} 2^n n!}{n!\,n!} x^n = \frac{1 \cdot 3 \cdot 5 \ldots (2n-1)}{n!} 2^n x^n$$

Greatest Term

If T_r and T_{r+1} are the rth and $(r+1)$th terms in the expansion of $(x+a)^n$, then

$$\frac{T_{r+1}}{T_r} = \frac{{}^nC_r \cdot x^{n-r} \cdot a^r}{{}^nC_{r-1} \cdot x^{n-r+1} \cdot a^{r-1}} = \left(\frac{n-r+1}{r}\right) \cdot \frac{a}{x}$$

Let numerically, T_{r+1} be the greatest term in the above expansion. Then,

$$T_{r+1} \geq T_r \text{ or } \frac{T_{r+1}}{T_r} \geq 1 \Rightarrow \left(\frac{n-r+1}{r}\right)\left|\frac{a}{x}\right| \geq 1$$

[$\because$ a may be + ve or − ve]

or $$r \leq \frac{(n+1)}{\left(1 + \left|\frac{x}{a}\right|\right)} \quad \ldots\text{(i)}$$

Now, on substituting values of n, x and a in Eq. (i), we get

$$r \leq m + f \text{ or } r \leq m$$

where, $m \in N$ and $0 < f < 1$

In the first case, T_{m+1} is the greatest term, while in the second case, T_m and T_{m+1} are the greatest terms and both are equal (numerically).

Shortcut Method

To find the greatest term (numerically) in the expansion of $(x+a)^n$.

Now, $$(x+a)^n = a^n \left(1 + \frac{x}{a}\right)^n$$

Calculate $$m = \frac{\left|\frac{x}{a}\right|(n+1)}{\left(\left|\frac{x}{a}\right| + 1\right)}$$

***Case* I** If $m \in$ Integer, then T_m and T_{m+1} are the greatest terms and both are equal (numerically).

***Case* II** If $m \notin$ Integer, then $T_{[m]+1}$ is the greatest term, where $[\cdot]$ denotes the greatest integer function.

Example 25. Find numerically the greatest term in the expansion of $(2+3x)^9$, when $x = 3/2$.

Sol. Let T_{r+1} be the greatest term in the expansion of $(2+3x)^9$, we have

$$\frac{T_{r+1}}{T_r} = \left(\frac{9-r+1}{r}\right)\left|\frac{3x}{2}\right| = \left(\frac{10-r}{r}\right)\left|\frac{3}{2} \times \frac{3}{2}\right| = \frac{90-9r}{4r}$$

[$\because x = 3/2$]

$$\therefore \quad \frac{T_{r+1}}{T_r} \geq 1$$

$$\Rightarrow \quad \frac{90-9r}{4r} \geq 1 \Rightarrow 90 \geq 13r$$

$$\therefore \quad r \leq \frac{90}{13} = 6\frac{12}{13}$$

or $$r \leq 6\frac{12}{13}$$

$\therefore$ Maximum value of r is 6.

So, greatest term $= T_{6+1} = {}^9C_6 (2)^{9-6} (3x)^6$

$$= {}^9C_3 \cdot 2^3 \cdot \left(3 \times \frac{3}{2}\right)^6$$

$$= \frac{9 \cdot 8 \cdot 7}{1 \cdot 2 \cdot 3} \cdot \frac{2^3 \cdot 3^{12}}{2^6} = \frac{7 \times 3^{13}}{2}$$

Aliter Since, $(2+3x)^9 = 2^9 \left(1 + \frac{3x}{2}\right)^9$

Now, $m = \dfrac{(9+1)\left|\dfrac{3x}{2}\right|}{\left|\dfrac{3x}{2}\right|+1} = \dfrac{10 \times \dfrac{9}{4}}{\dfrac{9}{4}+1}$ $[\because x = 3/2]$

$= \dfrac{90}{13} = 6\dfrac{12}{13} \neq$ Integer

$\therefore$ The greatest term in the expansion is

$T_{[m]+1} = T_{6+1}$ in $(2+3x)^9$

$= {}^9C_6\,(2)^{9-6}\,(3x)^6 = {}^9C_3 \cdot 2^3 \cdot \left(\dfrac{3^2}{2}\right)^6$ $[\because x = 3/2]$

$= \dfrac{9 \cdot 8 \cdot 7}{1 \cdot 2 \cdot 3} \cdot \dfrac{3^{12}}{2^3} = \dfrac{7 \times 3^{13}}{2}$

Example 26. Find numerically the greatest term in the expansion of $(3-5x)^{11}$, when $x = \dfrac{1}{5}$.

Sol. Let T_{r+1} be the greatest term in the expansion of $(3-5x)^{11}$, we have

$\dfrac{T_{r+1}}{T_r} = \left(\dfrac{11-r+1}{r}\right)\left|-\dfrac{5x}{3}\right|$

$= \left(\dfrac{12-r}{r}\right)\left|-\dfrac{1}{3}\right| = \dfrac{12-r}{3r}$ $[\because x = 1/5]$

$\therefore \quad \dfrac{T_{r+1}}{T_r} \geq 1 \Rightarrow \dfrac{12-r}{3r} \geq 1 \Rightarrow 12 \geq 4r$

$\therefore \quad r \leq 3 \Rightarrow r = 2, 3$

So, the greatest terms are T_{2+1} and T_{3+1}.

$\therefore$ Greatest term (when $r=2$) $= T_{2+1} = {}^{11}C_2\,(3)^9\,(-5x)^2$

$= \dfrac{11 \cdot 10}{1 \cdot 2} \cdot 3^9 \cdot (1)^2 = 55 \times 3^9$ $[\because x = 1/5]$

and greatest term (when $r=3$) $= T_{3+1}$

$= \left|{}^{11}C_3\,(3)^8\,(-5x)^3\right| = \left|{}^{11}C_3\,(3)^8\,(-1)^3\right|$ $[\because x = 1/5]$

$= {}^{11}C_3 \cdot 3^8 = \dfrac{11 \cdot 10 \cdot 9}{1 \cdot 2 \cdot 3} \cdot 3^8 = 55 \times 3^9$

From above, we say that the values of both greatest terms are equal.

Aliter

Since, $(3-5x)^{11} = 3^{11}\left(1 - \dfrac{5x}{3}\right)^{11}$

Now, $m = \dfrac{(11+1)\left|-\dfrac{5x}{3}\right|}{\left|-\dfrac{5x}{3}\right|+1} = \dfrac{12 \times \left|-\dfrac{1}{3}\right|}{\left|-\dfrac{1}{3}\right|+1}$ $\left[\because x = \dfrac{1}{5}\right]$

$= \dfrac{4}{\dfrac{1}{3}+1} = 3$

Since, the greatest terms in the expansion are T_3 and T_4.

$\therefore$ Greatest term (when $r=2$) $= {}^{11}C_2\,(3)^9\,(-5x)^2$

$= {}^{11}C_2\,(3)^9\,(-1)^2$ $\left[\because x = \dfrac{1}{5}\right]$

$= \dfrac{11 \cdot 10}{1 \cdot 2} \cdot 3^9 = 55 \times 3^9$

and greatest term (when $r=3$) $= \left|{}^{11}C_3\,(3)^8\,(-5x)^3\right|$

$= \left|{}^{11}C_3\,(3)^8\,(-1)^3\right|$ $\left[\because x = \dfrac{1}{5}\right]$

$= \dfrac{11 \cdot 10 \cdot 9}{1 \cdot 2 \cdot 3} \cdot 3^8 = 55 \times 3^9$

Greatest Coefficient

(i) If n is even, then greatest coefficient is ${}^nC_{n/2}$.

(ii) If n is odd, then greatest coefficients are ${}^nC_{(n-1)/2}$ and ${}^nC_{(n+1)/2}$.

Example 27. Show that, if the greatest term in the expansion of $(1+x)^{2n}$ has also the greatest coefficient, then x lies between $\dfrac{n}{n+1}$ and $\dfrac{n+1}{n}$.

Sol. In the expansion of $(1+x)^{2n}$, the middle term is $\left(\dfrac{2n}{2}+1\right)$th

i.e., $(n+1)$th term, we know that from binomial expansion, middle term has greatest coefficient.

$[\because$ Terms $T_1, T_2, T_3, \ldots, T_n, T_{n+1}, T_{n+2}, \ldots]$

$\therefore \quad T_n < T_{n+1} > T_{n+2}$

$\Rightarrow \quad \dfrac{T_{n+1}}{T_n} = \dfrac{{}^{2n}C_n \cdot x^n}{{}^{2n}C_{n-1} \cdot x^{n-1}} = \dfrac{2n-n+1}{n} \cdot x$

$\Rightarrow \quad \dfrac{T_{n+1}}{T_n} > 1$ or $\dfrac{n+1}{n} \cdot x > 1$

or $\quad x > \dfrac{n}{n+1}$ ...(i)

and $\quad \dfrac{T_{n+2}}{T_{n+1}} = \dfrac{{}^{2n}C_{n+1}\,x^{n+1}}{{}^{2n}C_n\,x^n} = \dfrac{2n-(n+1)+1}{n+1} \cdot x$

$= \dfrac{n}{n+1} \cdot x$

$\Rightarrow \quad \dfrac{T_{n+2}}{T_{n+1}} < 1 \Rightarrow \dfrac{n}{n+1} \cdot x < 1$ or $x < \dfrac{n+1}{n}$ ...(ii)

From Eqs. (i) and (ii), we get

$$\dfrac{n}{n+1} < x < \dfrac{n+1}{n}$$

Corollary For $n = 5$

$$\dfrac{5}{6} < x < \dfrac{6}{5}$$

Important Properties of the Binomial Coefficients

In the binomial expansion of $(1+x)^n$. Let us denote the coefficients ${}^nC_0, {}^nC_1, {}^nC_2, \ldots, {}^nC_r, \ldots, {}^nC_n$ by $C_0, C_1, C_2, \ldots, C_r, \ldots, C_n$, respectively.

(i) The coefficients of the terms equidistant from the beginning and the end are equal

The $(r+1)$th term from the beginning in the expansion of $(1+x)^n$ is ${}^nC_r\, x^r$.

$\therefore$ The coefficient of the $(r+1)$th term from the beginning is ${}^nC_r$ and the $(r+1)$th term from the end in the expansion of $(1+x)^n = (r+1)$ th term from the beginning in the expansion of $(x+1)^n = {}^nC_r\, x^{n-r}$

$\therefore$ The coefficient of the $(r+1)$th term from the end is ${}^nC_r$.

Hence, the coefficients of $(r+1)$th term from the beginning and the end are equal.

(ii) The sum of the binomial coefficients in the expansion of $(1+x)^n$

$\because \quad (1+x)^n = {}^nC_0 + {}^nC_1\, x + {}^nC_2\, x^2 + {}^nC_3\, x^3 + \ldots + {}^nC_n\, x^n$

Putting $x = 1$, we get

$$2^n = {}^nC_0 + {}^nC_1 + {}^nC_2 + \ldots + {}^nC_n$$

or $\quad C_0 + C_1 + C_2 + \ldots + C_n = 2^n$

$\therefore$ Sum of binomial coefficients $= 2^n$

(iii) The sum of the coefficients of the odd terms = The sum of the coefficients of the even terms

$\because \quad (1+x)^n = {}^nC_0 + {}^nC_1\, x + {}^nC_2\, x^2 + {}^nC_3\, x^3 + \ldots + {}^nC_n\, x^n$

Putting $x = -1$, we get

$$0 = {}^nC_0 - {}^nC_1 + {}^nC_2 - {}^nC_3 + {}^nC_4 - {}^nC_5 + \ldots$$

or $\quad {}^nC_1 + {}^nC_3 + {}^nC_5 + \ldots = {}^nC_0 + {}^nC_2 + {}^nC_4 + \ldots$

Since, the sum of all the coefficients is 2^n, therefore each side is equal to $\dfrac{2^n}{2}$ i.e. 2^{n-1}.

Hence, $C_1 + C_3 + C_5 + \ldots = C_0 + C_2 + C_4 + \ldots = 2^{n-1}$

Remark

1. In the expansion of $(x - 2y + 3z)^n$, putting $x = y = z = 1$, then we get the sum of coefficients $= (1 - 2 + 3)^n = 2^n$.
2. In the expansion of $(1 + x + x^2)^n$, putting $x = 1$, we get the sum of coefficients $= (1 + 1 + 1)^n = 3^n$.

Trinomial Expansion

For $n \in N, (1 + x + x^2)^n = \sum_{r=0}^{2n} a_r x^r$

$$= a_0 + a_1 x + a_2 x^2 + \ldots + a_n x^n + \ldots + a_{2n} x^{2n} \qquad \ldots\text{(i)}$$

There are $(2n+1)$ terms. The middle coefficient is a_n which is also the greatest.

$$a_0 = a_{2n}, a_1 = a_{2n-1}, \ldots, a_r = a_{2n-r}$$

The coefficients of $(1 + x + x^2)^n$ for $n = 0, 1, 2, \ldots$ can be arranged in a triangle.

```
                  1
               1  1  1
            1  2  3  2  1
         1  3  6  7  6  3  1
      1  4 10 16 19 16 10  4  1
   1  5 15 30 45 51 45 30 15  5  1
   :  :  :  :  :  :  :  :  :  :  :
```

i.e., The rows contains the coefficients for $n = 0, 1, 2, 3, \ldots$.

Each entry other than two entries at the ends is the sum of three entries above it.

$$15 = 1 + 4 + 10, 30 = 16 + 10 + 4, \text{ etc.}$$

Putting $x = 1$ and $x = -1$ in Eq. (i), we get

$$a_0 + a_1 + a_2 + a_3 + \ldots + a_{2n} = 3^n$$

[sum of all coefficients] ...(ii)

and $\quad a_0 - a_1 + a_2 - a_3 + \ldots + a_{2n} = 1 \qquad \ldots$(iii)

On adding Eqs. (ii) and (iii), we get

$$a_0 + a_2 + a_4 + \ldots + a_{2n} = \frac{3^n + 1}{2}$$

[sum of coefficients of even powers of x]

On subtracting Eq. (ii) from Eq. (i), we get

$$a_1 + a_3 + a_5 + \ldots + a_{2n-1} = \frac{3^n - 1}{2}$$

[sum of coefficients of odd powers of x]

Putting $x = i\,(\sqrt{-1})$ in Eq. (i), we get

$$a_0 + a_1 i + a_2 i^2 + a_3 i^3 + a_4 i^4 + a_5 i^5 + \ldots + a_{2n} i^{2n} = i^n$$

$$\Rightarrow \quad (a_0 - a_2 + a_4 - \ldots) + i(a_1 - a_3 + a_5 - \ldots) = i^n$$

$$(a_0 - a_2 + a_4 - \ldots) + i(a_1 - a_3 + a_5 - \ldots) = \left(\cos\frac{\pi}{2} + i\sin\frac{\pi}{2}\right)^n = \cos\left(\frac{n\pi}{2}\right) + i\sin\left(\frac{n\pi}{2}\right)$$

On comparing real and imaginary parts, we get

$$a_0 - a_2 + a_4 - \ldots = \cos\left(\frac{n\pi}{2}\right)$$

and $$a_1 - a_3 + a_5 - \ldots = \sin\left(\frac{n\pi}{2}\right)$$

Putting $x = \omega$ and ω^2 (cube roots of unity) in Eq. (i), we get

$$a_0 + a_1\,\omega + a_2\,\omega^2 + a_3\,\omega^3 + a_4\,\omega^4 + \ldots = 0 \quad \ldots\text{(iv)}$$

and $$a_0 + a_1\,\omega^2 + a_2\,\omega^4 + a_3\,\omega^6 + a_4\,\omega^8 + \ldots = 0 \quad \ldots\text{(v)}$$

On adding Eqs. (ii), (iv) and (v) and then dividing by 3, we get

$$a_0 + a_3 + a_6 + \ldots = 3^{n-1}$$

Note

(i) $a_1 + a_4 + a_7 + \ldots = a_2 + a_5 + a_8 + \ldots = 3^{n-1}$

(ii) $a_0 + a_4 + a_8 + \ldots = \frac{1}{4}\left\{3^n + 1 + 2\cos\left(\frac{n\pi}{2}\right)\right\}$

(iii) $a_1 + a_5 + a_9 + \ldots = \frac{1}{4}\left\{3^n - 1 + 2\sin\left(\frac{n\pi}{2}\right)\right\}$

(iv) $a_0 + a_6 + a_{12} + \ldots = \frac{1}{6}\left\{3^n + 1 + 2^{n+1}\cos\left(\frac{n\pi}{3}\right)\right\}$

(v) $\sum_{r=1}^{2n} r\cdot a_r = n\cdot 3^n$ (vi) $\sum_{r=1}^{2n}(-1)^{r-1}\cdot r\cdot a_r = -n$

Example 28. Find the sum of coefficients in the expansion of the binomial $(5p - 4q)^n$, where n is a positive integer.

Sol. Putting $p = q = 1$ in $(5p - 4q)^n$, the required sum of coefficients $= (5-4)^n = 1^n = 1$

Example 29. In the expansion of $(3^{-x/4} + 3^{5x/4})^n$, if the sum of binomial coefficients is 64 and the term with the greatest binomial coefficient exceeds the third by $(n-1)$, find the value of x.

Sol. Given sum of the binomial coefficients in the expansion of $(3^{-x/4} + 3^{5x/4})^n = 64$

Then, putting $3^{-x/4} = 3^{5x/4} = 1$

$$\therefore \quad (1+1)^n = 64 \Rightarrow 2^n = 2^6$$

$$\therefore \quad n = 6$$

We know that, middle term has the greatest binomial coefficients. Here, $n = 6$

$\therefore$ Middle term $= \left(\frac{n}{2}+1\right)$th term = 4th term $= T_4$

and given that $T_4 = (n-1) + T_3$

$$\Rightarrow \quad T_{3+1} = (6-1) + T_{2+1}$$

$$\Rightarrow \quad {}^6C_3\,(3^{-x/4})^3\,(3^{5x/4})^3 = 5 + {}^6C_2\,(3^{-x/4})^4\,(3^{5x/4})^2$$

$$\Rightarrow \quad 20\cdot 3^{3x} = 5 + 15\cdot 3^{3x/2}$$

Let $3^{3x/2} = t$

$$\therefore \quad 20t^2 = 5 + 15t$$

$$\Rightarrow \quad 4t^2 - 3t - 1 = 0$$

$$\Rightarrow \quad (4t+1)(t-1) = 0$$

$$\therefore \quad t = 1,\ t \ne -\frac{1}{4} \Rightarrow 3^{3x/2} = 1 = 3^0$$

$$\therefore \quad \frac{3x}{2} = 0 \text{ or } x = 0$$

Example 30. Find the values of

(i) $\frac{1}{(n-1)!} + \frac{1}{(n-3)!\,3!} + \frac{1}{(n-5)!\,5!} + \ldots$

(ii) $\frac{1}{12!} + \frac{1}{10!\,2!} + \frac{1}{8!\,4!} + \ldots + \frac{1}{12!}$

Sol. (i) $\because 1! = 1$

$\therefore$ The given series can be written as

$$\frac{1}{(n-1)!\,1!} + \frac{1}{(n-3)!\,3!} + \frac{1}{(n-5)!\,5!} + \ldots \quad \ldots\text{(i)}$$

$\because$ Sum of values of each terms in factorial are equal.

i.e. $(n-1)+1 = (n-3)+3 = (n-5)+5 = \ldots = n$

From Eq. (i),

$$\frac{1}{n!}\left[\frac{n!}{(n-1)!\,1!} + \frac{n!}{(n-3)!\,3!} + \frac{n!}{(n-5)!\,5!} + \ldots\right]$$

$$= \frac{1}{n!}({}^nC_1 + {}^nC_3 + {}^nC_5 + \ldots) = \frac{2^{n-1}}{n!}$$

(ii) $\because 0! = 1$

$\therefore$ The given series can be written as

$$\frac{1}{12!\,0!} + \frac{1}{10!\,2!} + \frac{1}{8!\,4!} + \ldots + \frac{1}{0!\,12!} \quad \ldots\text{(ii)}$$

$\because$ Sum of values of each terms in factorial are equal

i.e., $12 + 0 = 10 + 2 = 8 + 4 = \ldots = 12$

From Eq. (ii), $$\frac{1}{12!}\left[\frac{12!}{12!\,0!} + \frac{12!}{10!\,2!} + \frac{12!}{8!\,4!} + \ldots + \frac{12!}{0!\,12!}\right]$$

$$= \frac{1}{12!}({}^{12}C_0 + {}^{12}C_2 + {}^{12}C_4 + \ldots + {}^{12}C_{12}) = \frac{2^{12-1}}{12!} = \frac{2^{11}}{12!}$$

Example 31. Prove that the sum of the coefficients in the expansion of $(1 + x - 3x^2)^{2163}$ is -1.

Sol. Putting $x = 1$ in $(1 + x - 3x^2)^{2163}$, the required sum of coefficients $= (1+1-3)^{2163} = (-1)^{2163} = -1$

Example 32. If the sum of the coefficients in the expansion of $(\alpha x^2 - 2x + 1)^{35}$ is equal to the sum of the coefficients in the expansion of $(x - \alpha y)^{35}$, find the value of α.

Sol. Given, sum of the coefficients in the expansion of $(\alpha x^2 - 2x + 1)^{35}$

= Sum of the coefficients in the expansion of $(x - \alpha y)^{35}$

Putting $x = y = 1$, we get

$$(\alpha - 1)^{35} = (1 - \alpha)^{35}$$

$$\Rightarrow \quad (\alpha - 1)^{35} = -(\alpha - 1)^{35}$$

$$\Rightarrow \quad 2(\alpha - 1)^{35} = 0$$

$$\Rightarrow \quad \alpha - 1 = 0$$

$$\therefore \quad \alpha = 1$$

Example 33. If $(1 + x - 2x^2)^{20} = \sum_{r=0}^{40} a_r x^r$, then find the value of $a_1 + a_3 + a_5 + \ldots + a_{39}$.

Sol. $\because \quad (1 + x - 2x^2)^{20} = \sum_{r=0}^{40} a_r x^r \quad \ldots(i)$

Putting $x = 1$, we get $0 = \sum_{r=0}^{40} a_r$

or $\quad a_0 + a_1 + a_2 + a_3 + a_4 + a_5 + \ldots + a_{39} + a_{40} = 0 \quad \ldots(ii)$

Putting $x = -1$ in Eq. (i), we get

$$(-2)^{20} = \sum_{r=0}^{40} (-1)^r a_r$$

or $a_0 - a_1 + a_2 - a_3 + a_4 - a_5 + \ldots - a_{39} + a_{40} = 2^{20} \quad \ldots(iii)$

On subtracting Eq. (iii) from Eq. (ii), we get

$$2[a_1 + a_3 + a_5 + \ldots + a_{39}] = -2^{20}$$

or $\quad a_1 + a_3 + a_5 + \ldots + a_{39} = -2^{19}$

Corollary On adding Eqs. (ii) and (iii) and then dividing by 2, we get $a_0 + a_2 + a_4 + \ldots + a_{40} = 2^{19}$

Exercise for Session 2

1. If the rth term in the expansion of $(1 + x)^{20}$ has its coefficient equal to that of the $(r + 4)$th term, then r is
(a) 7 (b) 9 (c) 11 (d) 13

2. If the fourth term in the expansion of $\left(px + \frac{1}{x}\right)^n$ is $\frac{5}{2}$, then $n + p$ is equal to
(a) $\frac{9}{2}$ (b) $\frac{11}{2}$ (c) $\frac{13}{2}$ (d) $\frac{15}{2}$

3. If in the expansion of $\left(\sqrt[3]{2} + \frac{1}{\sqrt[3]{3}}\right)^n$, the ratio of 7th term from the beginning to the 7th term from the end is $\frac{1}{6}$, then n is
(a) 3 (b) 5 (c) 7 (d) 9

4. The number of integral terms in the expansion of $(5^{1/2} + 7^{1/8})^{1024}$ is
(a) 128 (b) 129 (c) 130 (d) 131

5. In the expansion of $(7^{1/3} + 11^{1/9})^{6561}$, the number of terms free from radicals is
(a) 715 (b) 725 (c) 730 (d) 750

6. If the coefficients of three consecutive terms in the expansion of $(1 + x)^n$ are 165, 330 and 462 respectively, the value of n is
(a) 7 (b) 9 (c) 11 (d) 13

7. If the coefficients of 5th, 6th and 7th terms in the expansion of $(1 + x)^n$ are in AP, then n is equal to
(a) 7 only (b) 14 only (c) 7 or 14 (d) None of these

8. If the middle term in the expansion of $\left(x^2 + \frac{1}{x}\right)^n$ is $924x^6$, the value of n is
(a) 8 (b) 12 (c) 16 (d) 20

9. If the sum of the binomial coefficients in the expansion of $\left(x^2 + \frac{2}{x^3}\right)^n$ is 243, the term independent of x is equal to
(a) 40 (b) 30 (c) 20 (d) 10

10. In the expansion of $(1 + x)(1 + x + x^2)\ldots(1 + x + x^2 + \ldots + x^{2n})$, the sum of the coefficients is
(a) 1 (b) $2n!$ (c) $2n! + 1$ (d) $(2n + 1)!$

Session 3

Two Important Theorems, Divisibility Problems

Two Important Theorems

Theorem 1 If $(\sqrt{P}+Q)^n = I + f$, where I and n are positive integers, n being odd and $0 \le f < 1$, then show that $(I+f)f = k^n$, where $P - Q^2 = k > 0$ and $\sqrt{P} - Q < 1$.

Proof Given, $\sqrt{P} - Q < 1 \quad \therefore \quad 0 < (\sqrt{P}-Q)^n < 1$

Now, let $(\sqrt{P}-Q)^n = f'$, where $0 < f' < 1$

Also
$$I + f = (\sqrt{P}+Q)^n \quad \text{...(i)}$$
$$0 \le f < 1 \quad \text{...(ii)}$$
$$f' = (\sqrt{P}-Q)^n \quad \text{...(iii)}$$
and
$$0 < f' < 1 \quad \text{...(iv)}$$

On subtracting Eq. (iii) from Eq. (i), we get
$$I + f - f' = (\sqrt{P}+Q)^n - (\sqrt{P}-Q)^n$$
$$= 2[{}^nC_1 (\sqrt{P})^{n-1} \cdot Q + {}^nC_3 (\sqrt{P})^{n-3} \cdot Q^3 + \dots]$$
$$= 2 \text{ (integer)} = \text{Even integer} \quad \text{...(v)}$$

[Since, n is odd, RHS contains even powers of $\sqrt{P}$, so RHS is an even integer]

$\therefore$ LHS is also an integer.

$\because$ I is an integer.

$\therefore$ $(f - f')$ is also an integer.

$\Rightarrow \quad f - f' = 0 \quad [\because -1 < (f - f') < 1]$

or $\quad f = f'$

From Eq. (v), I is an even integer and
$$(I+f)f = (I+f)f' = (\sqrt{P}+Q)^n (\sqrt{P}-Q)^n$$
$$= (P - Q^2)^n = k^n$$

Remark

If n is even integer, then $(\sqrt{P}+Q)^n + (\sqrt{P}-Q)^n = I + f + f'$

Since, LHS and I are integers.

$\therefore \quad (f + f')$ is also an integer.

$\Rightarrow \quad f + f' = 1 \quad [\because 0 < (f + f') < 2]$

$\therefore \quad f' = 1 - f$

Hence, $\quad (I+f)(1-f) = (I+f)f' = (\sqrt{P}+Q)^n (\sqrt{P}-Q)^n$
$$= (P - Q^2)^n = k^n$$

Theorem 2 If $(P+\sqrt{Q})^n = I + f$, where I and n are positive integers and $0 \le f < 1$, show that $(I+f)(1-f) = k^n$, where $P^2 - Q = k > 0$ and $P - \sqrt{Q} < 1$.

Proof Given, $\quad P - \sqrt{Q} < 1$

$\therefore \quad 0 < (P - \sqrt{Q})^n < 1$

Now, let $(P - \sqrt{Q})^n = f'$, where $0 < f' < 1$

Also,
$$I + f = (P + \sqrt{Q})^n \quad \text{...(i)}$$
$$0 \le f < 1 \quad \text{...(ii)}$$
$$f' = (P - \sqrt{Q})^n \quad \text{...(iii)}$$
and
$$0 < f' < 1 \quad \text{...(iv)}$$

On adding Eqs. (i) and (iii), we get
$$I + f + f' = (P+\sqrt{Q})^n + (P-\sqrt{Q})^n$$
$$= 2[{}^nC_0 P^n + {}^nC_2 P^{n-2} (\sqrt{Q})^2 + {}^nC_4 P^{n-4} (\sqrt{Q})^4 + \dots]$$
$$= 2 \text{ (integer)} = \text{Even integer} \quad \text{...(v)}$$

[Since, RHS contains even power of $\sqrt{Q}$, so RHS is an even integer]

$\therefore$ LHS is also an integer.

$\because$ I is an integer.

$\Rightarrow$ $f + f'$ is also an integer.

$\therefore \quad f + f' = 1 \quad [\because 0 < (f + f') < 2]$

or $\quad f' = 1 - f$

From Eq. (v), I = even integer $- 1$ = odd integer and
$$(I+f)(1-f) = (I+f)f'$$
$$= (P+\sqrt{Q})^n (P-\sqrt{Q})^n = (P^2 - Q)^n = k^n$$

Example 34. Show that the integral part of $(5+2\sqrt{6})^n$ is odd, where n is natural number.

Sol. $(5+2\sqrt{6})^n$ can be written as $(5+\sqrt{24})^n$

Now, let
$$I + f = (5+\sqrt{24})^n \quad \text{...(i)}$$
$$0 \le f < 1 \quad \text{...(ii)}$$
and let
$$f' = (5-\sqrt{24})^n \quad \text{...(iii)}$$
$$0 < f' < 1 \quad \text{...(iv)}$$

On adding Eqs. (i) and (iii), we get
$$I + f + f' = (5+\sqrt{24})^n + (5-\sqrt{24})^n$$
$$I + 1 = 2p,$$
$$\forall\, p \in N = \text{Even integer} \quad \text{[from theorem 2]}$$
$$\therefore \quad I = 2p - 1 = \text{Odd integer}$$

Example 35. Show that the integral part of $(5\sqrt{5}+11)^{2n+1}$ is even, where $n \in N$.

Sol. $(5\sqrt{5}+11)^{2n+1}$ can be written as $(\sqrt{125}+11)^{2n+1}$

Now, let
$$I + f = (\sqrt{125}+11)^{2n+1} \quad \text{...(i)}$$
$$0 \le f < 1 \quad \text{...(ii)}$$
and let
$$f' = (\sqrt{125}-11)^{2n+1} \quad \text{...(iii)}$$
$$0 < f' < 1 \quad \text{...(iv)}$$

On subtracting Eq. (iii) from Eq. (i), we get

$$I + f - f' = (\sqrt{125} + 11)^{2n+1} - (\sqrt{125} - 11)^{2n+1}$$

$$I + 0 = 2p, \forall\ p \in N = \text{Even integer} \quad \text{[from theorem 1]}$$

$$\therefore \quad I = 2p = \text{Even integer}$$

Example 36. Let $R = (6\sqrt{6} + 14)^{2n+1}$ and $f = R - [R]$, where $[\cdot]$ denotes the greatest integer function. Find the value of $Rf, n \in N$.

Sol. $(6\sqrt{6} + 14)^{2n+1}$ can be written as $(\sqrt{216} + 14)^{2n+1}$ and given that $f = R - [R]$

and $\quad R = (6\sqrt{6} + 14)^{2n+1} = (\sqrt{216} + 14)^{2n+1}$

$$\therefore \quad [R] + f = (\sqrt{216} + 14)^{2n+1} \quad \ldots\text{(i)}$$

$$0 \le f < 1 \quad \ldots\text{(ii)}$$

Let $\quad f' = (\sqrt{216} - 14)^{2n+1} \quad \ldots$(iii)

$$0 < f' < 1 \quad \ldots\text{(iv)}$$

On subtracting Eq. (iii) from Eq. (i), we get

$$[R] + f - f' = (\sqrt{216} + 14)^{2n+1} - (\sqrt{216} - 14)^{2n+1}$$

$$[R] + 0 = 2p, \forall\ p \in N = \text{Even integer [from theorem 1]}$$

$$\therefore \quad f - f' = 0 \text{ or } f = f'$$

Now, $\quad Rf = Rf' = (\sqrt{216} + 14)^{2n+1} (\sqrt{216} - 14)^{2n+1}$

$$= (216 - 196)^{2n+1} = (20)^{2n+1}$$

Example 37. If $(7 + 4\sqrt{3})^n = s + t$, where n and s are positive integers and t is a proper fraction, show that $(1 - t)(s + t) = 1$.

Sol. $(7 + 4\sqrt{3})^n$ can be written as $(7 + \sqrt{48})^n$

$$\therefore \quad s + t = (7 + \sqrt{48})^n \quad \ldots\text{(i)}$$

$$0 < t < 1 \quad \ldots\text{(ii)}$$

Now, let $\quad t' = (7 - \sqrt{48})^n \quad \ldots$(iii)

$$0 < t' < 1 \quad \ldots\text{(iv)}$$

On adding Eqs. (i) and (iii), we get

$$s + t + t' = (7 + \sqrt{48})^n + (7 - \sqrt{48})^n$$

$$s + 1 = 2p, \forall\ p \in N = \text{Even integer [from theorem 2]}$$

$$\therefore \quad t + t' = 1 \text{ or } 1 - t = t'$$

Then, $(1 - t)(s + t) = t'(s + t) = (7 - \sqrt{48})^n (7 + \sqrt{48})^n$ [from Eqs. (i) and (iii)]

$$= (49 - 48)^n = (1)^n = 1$$

Example 38. If $x = (8 + 3\sqrt{7})^n$, where n is a natural number, prove that the integral part of x is an odd integer and also show that $x - x^2 + x[x] = 1$, where $[\cdot]$ denotes the greatest integer function.

Sol. $(8 + 3\sqrt{7})^n$ can be written as $(8 + \sqrt{63})^n$

$$\therefore \quad x = [x] + f$$

or $\quad [x] + f = (8 + \sqrt{63})^n \quad \ldots$(i)

$$0 \le f < 1 \quad \ldots\text{(ii)}$$

Now, let $\quad f' = (8 - \sqrt{63})^n \quad \ldots$(iii)

$$0 < f' < 1 \quad \ldots\text{(iv)}$$

On adding Eqs. (i) and (iii), we get

$$[x] + f + f' = (8 + \sqrt{63})^n + (8 - \sqrt{63})^n$$

$$[x] + 1 = 2p, \forall\ p \in N = \text{Even integer} \quad \text{[from theorem 2]}$$

$$\therefore \quad [x] = 2p - 1 = \text{Odd integer}$$

i.e., Integral part of x = Odd integer

$$\because \quad f + f' = 1 \Rightarrow 1 - f = f' \quad \ldots\text{(v)}$$

$$\text{LHS} = x - x^2 + x[x] = x - x(x - [x]) = x - xf \quad [\because x = [x] + f]$$

$$= x(1 - f) = xf' \quad \text{[from Eq.(v)]}$$

$$= (8 + \sqrt{63})^n (8 - \sqrt{63})^n \text{ [from Eqs.(i) and (iii)]}$$

$$= (64 - 63)^n = (1)^n = 1 = \text{RHS}$$

Remark

Sometimes, students find it difficult to decide whether a problem is on addition or subtraction. Now, if $x = [x] + f$ and $0 < f' < 1$ and if $[x] + f + f'$ = Integer. Then, addition and if $[x] + f - f'$ = Integer, the subtraction and values of $(f + f')$ and $(f - f')$ are 1 and 0, respectively.

Divisibility Problems

Type I

(i) $(x^n - a^n)$ is divisible by $(x - a)$, $\forall\ n \in N$.

(ii) $(x^n + a^n)$ is divisible by $(x + a)$, $\forall\ n \in$ Only odd natural numbers.

Example 39. Show that $1992^{1998} - 1955^{1998} - 1938^{1998} + 1901^{1998}$ is divisible by 1998.

Sol. Here, $n = 1998$ (Even)

$\therefore$ Only result (i) applicable.

Let $\quad P = 1992^{1998} - 1955^{1998} - 1938^{1998} + 1901^{1998}$

$$= \underbrace{(1992^{1998} - 1955^{1998})}_{\text{divisible by } (1992 - 1955) \text{ i.e. } 37} - \underbrace{(1938^{1998} - 1901^{1998})}_{\text{divisible by } (1938 - 1901) \text{ i.e. } 37}$$

$\therefore$ P is divisible by 37.

Also, $P = \underbrace{(1992^{1998} - 1938^{1998})}_{\text{divisible by } (1992 - 1938) \text{ i.e., } 54} - \underbrace{(1955^{1998} - 1901^{1998})}_{\text{divisible by } (1955 - 1901) \text{ i.e., } 54}$

$\therefore$ P is also divisible by 54.

Hence, P is divisible by 37×54, i.e., 1998.

Example 40. Prove that $2222^{5555} + 5555^{2222}$ is divisible by 7.

Sol. We have, $2222^{5555} + 5555^{2222}$

$$= (2222^{5555} + 4^{5555}) + (5555^{2222} - 4^{2222}) - (4^{5555} - 4^{2222}) \ldots\text{(i)}$$

The number $(2222^{5555}+4^{5555})$ is divisible by $2222+4$ $=2226=7\times318$, which is divisible by 7 and the number $(5555^{2222}-4^{2222})$ is divisible by

$5555-4=5551=7\times793$, which is divisible by 7 and the number

$(4^{5555}-4^{2222})=4^{2222}(4^{3333}-1)=4^{2222}(64^{1111}-1^{1111})$ is divisible by $64-1=63=7\times9$, which is divisible by 7.

Therefore, each brackets of Eq. (i) are divisible by 7. Hence, $2222^{5555}+5555^{2222}$ is divisible by 7.

Type II To show that an Expression is Divisible by An Integer

Solution Process

(i) If a, p, n and r are positive integers, first of all write $a^{pn+r}=a^{pn}\cdot a^r=(a^p)^n\cdot a^r$

(ii) If we will show that the given expression is divisible by c. Then, expression $a^p=\{1+(a^p-1)\}$, if some power of (a^p-1) has c as a factor.

or $a^p=\{2+(a^p-2)\}$, if some power of (a^p-2) has c as a factor.

or $a^p=\{3+(a^p-3)\}$, if some power of (a^p-3) has c as a factor.

⋮ ⋮ ⋮ ⋮ ⋮

or $a^p=\{k+(a^p-k)\}$, if some power of (a^p-k) has c as a factor.

Example 41. If n is any positive integer, show that $2^{3n+3}-7n-8$ is divisible by 49.

Sol. Given expression

$$=2^{3n+3}-7n-8=2^{3n}\cdot2^3-7n-8$$
$$=8^n\cdot8-7n-8=8(1+7)^n-7n-8$$
$$=8(1+{}^nC_1\cdot7+{}^nC_2\cdot7^2+\ldots+{}^nC_n\cdot7^n)-7n-8$$
$$=8+56n+8({}^nC_2\cdot7^2+\ldots+{}^nC_n\cdot7^n)-7n-8$$
$$=49n+8({}^nC_2\cdot7^2+\ldots+{}^nC_n\cdot7^n)$$
$$=49\{n+8({}^nC_2+\ldots+{}^nC_n\cdot7^{n-2})\}$$

Hence, $2^{3n+3}-7n-8$ is divisible by 49.

Example 42. If 10^n divides the number $101^{100}-1$, find the greatest value of n.

Sol. We have, $101^{100}-1=(1+100)^{100}-1$

$$=1+{}^{100}C_1\cdot100+{}^{100}C_2\cdot100^2+\ldots+{}^{100}C_{100}\,100^{100}-1$$
$$={}^{100}C_1\cdot100+{}^{100}C_2\cdot100^2+\ldots+{}^{100}C_{100}\cdot10^{100}$$
$$=(100)(100)+{}^{100}C_2\cdot100^2+\ldots+{}^{100}C_{100}\cdot100^{100}$$
$$=(100)^2[1+{}^{100}C_2+\ldots+100^{98}]$$
$$=100^2\,k,\text{ where } k \text{ is a positive integer}$$

Therefore, $101^{100}-1$ is divisible by 100^2 i.e., 10^4.

$\therefore \quad n=4$

How to Find Remainder by Using Binomial Theorem

If a, p, n and r are positive integers, then to find the remainder when a^{pn+r} is divided by b, we adjust power of a to a^{pn+r} which is very close to b, say with difference 1 i.e., $b\pm1$. Also, the remainder is always positive. When number of the type $5n-2$ is divided by 5, then we have

$$5)\,5n-2\,(n$$
$$\underline{-\;5n}$$
$$-2$$

We can write $-2=-2-3+3=-5+3$

or $\dfrac{5n-2}{5}=\dfrac{5n-5+3}{5}=n-1+\dfrac{3}{5}$

Hence, the remainder is 3.

Example 43. If 7^{103} is divided by 25, find the remainder.

Soln. We have, $7^{103}=7\cdot7^{102}=7\cdot(7^2)^{51}=7\,(49)^{51}=7\,(50-1)^{51}$

$$=7\,[(50)^{51}-{}^{51}C_1(50)^{50}+{}^{51}C_2(50)^{49}-\ldots-1]$$
$$=7\,[(50)^{51}-{}^{51}C_1(50)^{50}+{}^{51}C_2(50)^{49}-\ldots+{}^{51}C_{50}(50)]-7-18+18$$
$$=7\,[50((50)^{50}-{}^{51}C_1(50)^{49}+{}^{51}C_2(50)^{48}-\ldots+{}^{51}C_{50})]-25+18$$
$$=7\,[50k]-25+18,\text{ where } k \text{ is an integer.}$$
$$=25\,[14k-1]+18=25p+18 \quad [\text{where } p \text{ is an integer}]$$

Now, $\dfrac{7^{103}}{25}=p+\dfrac{18}{25}$. Hence, the remainder is 18.

Example 44. Find the remainder, when $5^{5^{5^{\cdot^{\cdot^{5}}}}}$ (24 times 5) is divided by 24.

Sol. Here, $5^{5^{\cdot^{\cdot^{5}}}}$ (23 times 5) is an odd natural number.

Let $5^{5^{\cdot^{\cdot^{5}}}}$ (23 times 5) $=2m+1$

Now, let $x=5^{5^{5^{\cdot^{\cdot^{5}}}}}$ (24 times 5) $=5^{2m+1}=5\cdot5^{2m}$, where m is a natural number.

$$\therefore \quad x=5\cdot(5^2)^m=5\,(24+1)^m$$
$$=5\,[{}^mC_0(24)^m+{}^mC_1(24)^{m-1}+\ldots+{}^mC_{m-1}(24)+1]$$
$$=5\,(24k+1)=24\,(5k)+5$$
$$\therefore \quad \frac{x}{24}=5k+\frac{5}{24}$$

Hence, the remainder is 5.

Example 45. If 7 divides $32^{32^{32}}$, then find the remainder.

Solution. We have, $32=2^5$

$$\therefore \quad 32^{32}=(2^5)^{32}=2^{160}=(3-1)^{160}$$
$$={}^{160}C_0(3)^{160}-{}^{160}C_1(3)^{159}+\ldots-{}^{160}C_{159}(3)+1$$
$$=3\,(3^{159}-{}^{160}C_1(3)^{158}+\ldots-{}^{160}C_{159})+1$$
$$=3m+1,\; m\in I^+$$

Now, $32^{32^{32}} = 32^{3m+1} = 2^{5(3m+1)} = 2^{15m+5}$

$= 2^2 \cdot 2^{3(5m+1)} = 4(8)^{5m+1} = 4(7+1)^{5m+1}$

$= 4[{}^{5m+1}C_0 (7)^{5m+1} + {}^{5m+1}C_1 (7)^{5m} + {}^{5m+1}C_2 (7)^{5m-1} + \dots + {}^{5m+1}C_{5m} (7) + 1]$

$= 4[7({}^{5m+1}C_0 (7)^{5m} + {}^{5m+1}C_1 (7)^{5m-1} + \dots + {}^{5m+1}C_{5m}) + 1]$

$= 4[7k+1]$, where k is positive integer $= 28k + 4$

$\therefore \quad \dfrac{32^{32^{32}}}{7} = 4k + \dfrac{4}{7}$

Hence, the remainder is 4.

How to Find Last Digit, Last Two Digits, Last Three Digits, ... and so on.

If a, p, n and r are positive integers, then a^{pn+r} is adjust of the form $(10k \pm 1)^m$, where k and m are positive integers. For last digit, take 10 common. For last two digits, take 100 common, for last three digits, take 1000 common, ... and so on.

i.e. $(10k \pm 1)^m = (10k)^m + {}^mC_1 (10k)^{m-1} (\pm 1) + {}^mC_2 (10k)^{m-2} (\pm 1)^2 + \dots + {}^mC_{m-2} (10k)^2 (\pm 1)^{m-2} + {}^mC_{m-1} (10k)(\pm 1)^{m-1} + (\pm 1)^m$

For last digit $= 10\lambda + (\pm 1)^m$

For last two digits $= 100\mu + {}^mC_{m-1} (10k)(\pm 1)^{m-1} + (\pm 1)^m$

For last three digits $= 1000\nu + {}^mC_{m-2} (10k)^2 (\pm 1)^{m-2} + {}^mC_{m-1} (10k)(\pm 1)^{m-1} + (\pm 1)^m$ and so on where $\lambda, \mu, \nu \in I$.

Example 46. Find the last two digits of 3^{400}.

Sol. We have, $3^{400} = (3^2)^{200} = (9)^{200} = (10-1)^{200}$

$= (10)^{200} - {}^{200}C_1 (10)^{199} + {}^{200}C_2 (10)^{198} - {}^{200}C_3 (10)^{197} + \dots + {}^{200}C_{198} (10)^2 - {}^{200}C_{199} (10) + 1$

$= 100\mu - {}^{200}C_{199} (10) + 1$, where $\mu \in I$

$= 100\mu - {}^{200}C_1 (10) + 1 = 100\mu - 2000 + 1$

$= 100(\mu - 20) + 1 = 100p + 1$, where p is an integer.

Hence, the last two digits of 3^{400} is $00 + 1 = 01$.

Example 47. If the number is 17^{256}, find the

(i) last digit. (ii) last two digits.

(iii) last three digits of 17^{256}.

Sol. Since, $17^{256} = (17^2)^{128} = (289)^{128} = (290-1)^{128}$

$\therefore 17^{256} = {}^{128}C_0 (290)^{128} - {}^{128}C_1 (290)^{127} + {}^{128}C_2 (290)^{126} - {}^{128}C_3 (290)^{125} + \dots - {}^{128}C_{125} (290)^3 + {}^{128}C_{126} (290)^2 - {}^{128}C_{127} (290) + 1$

(i) **For last digit**

$17^{256} = 290[{}^{128}C_0 (290)^{127} - {}^{128}C_1 (290)^{126} + {}^{128}C_2 (290)^{125} - \dots - {}^{128}C_{127} (1)] + 1$

$= 290(k) + 1$, where k is an integer.

$\therefore$ Last digit $= 0 + 1 = 1$

(ii) **For last two digits,**

$17^{256} = (290)^2 [{}^{128}C_0 (290)^{126} - {}^{128}C_1 (290)^{125} + {}^{128}C_2 (290)^{124} - \dots + {}^{128}C_{126} (1)] - {}^{128}C_{127} (290) + 1$

$= 100m - {}^{128}C_{127} (290) + 1$, where m is an integer.

$= 100m - {}^{128}C_1 (290) + 1 = 100m - 128 \times 290 + 1$

$= 100m - 128 \times (300 - 10) + 1$

$= 100(m - 384) + 1281$

$= 100n + 1281$, where n is an integer.

$\therefore$ Last two digits $= 00 + 81 = 81$

(iii) **For last three digits,**

$17^{256} = (290)^3 [{}^{128}C_0 (290)^{125} - {}^{128}C_1 (290)^{124} + {}^{128}C_2 (290)^{123} - \dots - {}^{128}C_{125} (1)] + {}^{128}C_{126} (290)^2 - {}^{128}C_{127} (290) + 1$

$= 1000m + {}^{128}C_{126} (290)^2 - {}^{128}C_{127} (290) + 1$

where, m is an integer

$= 1000m + {}^{128}C_2 (290)^2 - {}^{128}C_1 (290) + 1$

$= 1000m + \dfrac{(128)(127)}{2} (290)^2 - 128 \times 290 + 1$

$= 1000m + (128)(127)(290)(145) - (128)(290) + 1$

$= 1000m + (128)(290)(127 \times 145 - 1) + 1$

$= 1000m + (128)(290)(18414) + 1$

$= 1000m + 683527680 + 1$

$= 1000m + 683527000 + 680 + 1$

$= 1000(m + 683527) + 681$

$\therefore$ Last three digits $= 000 + 681 = 681$

Two Important Results

(i) $2 \le \left(1 + \dfrac{1}{n}\right)^n < 3, n \ge 1, n \in N$

(ii) If $n > 6$, then $\left(\dfrac{n}{3}\right)^n < n! < \left(\dfrac{n}{2}\right)^n$

Example 48. Find the positive integer just greater than $(1 + 0.0001)^{10000}$.

Sol. $(1 + 0.0001)^{10000} = \left(1 + \dfrac{1}{10000}\right)^{10000}$

We know that, $2 \le \left(1 + \frac{1}{n}\right)^n < 3,\ n \ge 1,\ n \in N$ [Result (i)]

Hence, positive integer just greater than $(1 + 0.0001)^{10000}$ is 3.

Example 49. Find the greater number is 100^{100} and $(300)!$.

Sol. Using Result (ii), We know that, $\left(\frac{n}{3}\right)^n < n!$

Putting $n = 300$, we get

$$(100)^{300} < (300)! \quad \ldots(i)$$

But $\quad (100)^{100} < (100)^{300} \quad \ldots(ii)$

From Eqs. (i) and (ii), we get

$$(100)^{100} < (100)^{300} < (300)!$$

$$\Rightarrow \quad (100)^{100} < (300)!$$

Hence, the greater number is $(300)!$.

Example 50. Find the greater number in $300!$ and $\sqrt{300^{300}}$.

Sol. Since, $(100)^{150} > 3^{150}$

$$\Rightarrow \quad (100)^{150} \cdot (100)^{150} > 3^{150} \cdot (100)^{150}$$

$$\Rightarrow \quad (100)^{300} > (300)^{150}$$

or $\quad (100)^{300} > \sqrt{300^{300}} \quad \ldots(i)$

Using result (ii), $\left(\frac{n}{3}\right)^n < n!$

Putting $n = 300$, we get $(100)^{300} < 300! \quad \ldots(ii)$

From Eqs. (i) and (ii), we get

$$\sqrt{300^{300}} < (100)^{300} < 300!$$

$$\Rightarrow \quad \sqrt{300^{300}} < 300!$$

Hence, the greater number is $300!$.

Exercise for Session 3

1. If $x = (7 + 4\sqrt{3})^{2n} = [x] + f$, where $n \in N$ and $0 \le f < 1$, then $x(1 - f)$ is equal to

(a) 1 (b) 0 (c) -1 (d) even integer

2. If $(5 + 2\sqrt{6})^n = I + f;\ n, I \in N$ and $0 \le f < 1$, then I equals

(a) $\frac{1}{f} - f$ (b) $\frac{1}{1+f} - f$ (c) $\frac{1}{1-f} - f$ (d) $\frac{1}{1+f} + f$

3. If $n > 0$ is an odd integer and $x = (\sqrt{2} + 1)^n,\ f = x - [x]$, then $\frac{1 - f^2}{f}$ is

(a) an irrational number (b) a non-integer rational number (c) an odd number (d) an even number

4. Integral part of $(\sqrt{2} + 1)^6$ is

(a) 196 (b) 197 (c) 198 (d) 199

5. $(103)^{86} - (86)^{103}$ is divisible by

(a) 7 (b) 13 (c) 17 (d) 23

6. Fractional part of $\frac{2^{78}}{31}$ is

(a) $\frac{2}{31}$ (b) $\frac{4}{31}$ (c) $\frac{8}{31}$ (d) $\frac{16}{31}$

7. The unit digit of $17^{1983} + 11^{1983} - 7^{1983}$ is

(a) 1 (b) 2 (c) 3 (d) 0

8. The last two digits of the number $(23)^{14}$ are

(a) 01 (b) 03 (c) 09 (d) 27

9. The last four digits of the number 3^{100} are

(a) 2001 (b) 3211 (c) 1231 (d) 0001

10. The remainder when 23^{23} is divided by 53 is

(a) 17 (b) 21 (c) 30 (d) 47

Session 4

Use of Complex Numbers in Binomial Theorem, Multinomial Theorem, Use of Differentiation, Use of Integration, Binomial Inside Binomial, Sum of the Series

Use of Complex Numbers in Binomial Theorem

If $\theta \in R, n \in N$ and $i = \sqrt{-1}$, then

$$(\cos\theta + i\sin\theta)^n = {}^nC_0 (\cos\theta)^{n-0} (i\sin\theta)^0 + {}^nC_1 (\cos\theta)^{n-1} (i\sin\theta)^1 + {}^nC_2 (\cos\theta)^{n-2} (i\sin\theta)^2 + {}^nC_3 (\cos\theta)^{n-3} (i\sin\theta)^3 + \dots$$

or $$\cos n\theta + i\sin n\theta = \cos^n\theta + i\cdot {}^nC_1 (\cos\theta)^{n-1}\sin\theta - {}^nC_2 (\cos\theta)^{n-2}\sin^2\theta - i\cdot {}^nC_3 (\cos\theta)^{n-3}\sin^3\theta + \dots$$

On comparing real and imaginary parts, we get

$$\cos n\theta = \cos^n\theta - {}^nC_2 (\cos\theta)^{n-2}\sin^2\theta - {}^nC_4 (\cos\theta)^{n-4}\sin^4\theta - \dots$$

and $$\sin n\theta = {}^nC_1 (\cos\theta)^{n-1}\sin\theta - {}^nC_3 (\cos\theta)^{n-3}\sin^3\theta + {}^nC_5 (\cos\theta)^{n-5}\sin^5\theta - \dots$$

Example 51. If $(1+x)^n = C_0 + C_1x + C_2x^2 + C_3x^3 + C_4x^4 + \dots$, find the values of

(i) $C_0 - C_2 + C_4 - C_6 + \dots$

(ii) $C_1 - C_3 + C_5 - C_7 + \dots$

(iii) $C_0 + C_3 + C_6 + \dots$

Sol. $\because (1+x)^n = C_0 + C_1x + C_2x^2 + C_3x^3 + C_4x^4 + C_5x^5 + \dots$

Putting $x = i$, where $i = \sqrt{-1}$, then

$$(1+i)^n = C_0 + C_1 i + C_2 i^2 + C_3 i^3 + C_4 i^4 + C_5 i^5 + \dots$$
$$= (C_0 - C_2 + C_4 - \dots) + i(C_1 - C_3 + C_5 - \dots) \quad \text{...(i)}$$

Also, $$(1+i)^n = \left[\sqrt{2}\left(\frac{1}{\sqrt{2}} + \frac{i}{\sqrt{2}}\right)\right]^n$$
$$= 2^{n/2}\left(\cos\frac{\pi}{4} + i\sin\frac{\pi}{4}\right)^n$$
$$= 2^{n/2}\left(\cos\frac{n\pi}{4} + i\sin\frac{n\pi}{4}\right) \quad \text{...(ii)}$$

From Eqs. (i) and (ii), we get

$$(C_0 - C_2 + C_4 - \dots) + i(C_1 - C_3 + C_5 - \dots) = 2^{n/2}\cos\left(\frac{n\pi}{4}\right) + i\cdot 2^{n/2}\sin\left(\frac{n\pi}{4}\right)$$

On comparing real and imaginary parts, we get

$$C_0 - C_2 + C_4 - \dots = 2^{n/2}\cos\left(\frac{n\pi}{4}\right) \quad \text{[part (i)]}$$

$$C_1 - C_3 + C_5 - \dots = 2^{n/2}\sin\left(\frac{n\pi}{4}\right) \quad \text{[part (ii)]}$$

We have, $(1+x)^n = C_0 + C_1x + C_2x^2 + C_3x^3 + C_4x^4 + C_5x^5 + C_6x^6 + \dots$

Putting $x = 1, \omega, \omega^2$ (cube roots of unity) and adding, we get

$$3(C_0 + C_3 + C_6 + \dots) = 2^n + (1+\omega)^n + (1+\omega^2)^n$$
$$= 2^n + (-\omega^2)^n + (-\omega)^n = 2^n + (-1)^n(\omega^{2n} + \omega^n)$$
$$= 2^n + (-1)^n\left\{e^{\frac{4\pi i n}{3}} + e^{\frac{2\pi i n}{3}}\right\}$$
$$= 2^n + (-1)^n \cdot e^{n\pi i}\cdot 2\cos\left(\frac{n\pi}{3}\right)$$
$$= 2^n + (-1)^n\cdot(-1)^n\cdot 2\cos\left(\frac{n\pi}{3}\right)$$
$$= 2^n + (-1)^{2n}\cdot 2\cos\left(\frac{n\pi}{3}\right) = 2^n + 2\cos\left(\frac{n\pi}{3}\right)$$
$$\therefore C_0 + C_3 + C_6 + \dots = \frac{1}{3}\left\{2^n + 2\cos\left(\frac{n\pi}{3}\right)\right\}$$

Example 52. Find the value of ${}^{4n}C_0 + {}^{4n}C_4 + {}^{4n}C_8 + \dots + {}^{4n}C_{4n}$.

Sol. $\because 4 - 0 = 8 - 4 = \dots = 4$

$\therefore$ Four roots of unity $(1)^{1/4}$ are $1, -1, i, -i$, we have

$$(1+x)^{4n} = {}^{4n}C_0 + {}^{4n}C_1x + {}^{4n}C_2x^2 + {}^{4n}C_3x^3 + \dots$$

Putting $x = 1, -1, i, -i$ and then adding, we get

$$4({}^{4n}C_0 + {}^{4n}C_4 + {}^{4n}C_8 + \dots) = 2^{4n} + 0 + (1+i)^{4n} + (1-i)^{4n}$$
$$= 2^{4n} + (2i)^{2n} + (-2i)^{2n}$$

$$= 2^{4n} + 2^{2n}(-1)^n + 2^{2n}(-1)^n$$

$$= 2^{4n} + (-1)^n \cdot 2^{2n+1}$$

$$\therefore \ {}^{4n}C_0 + {}^{4n}C_4 + {}^{4n}C_8 + \dots = 2^{4n-2} + (-1)^n \cdot 2^{2n-1}$$

Remark

If $(1+x)^n = C_0 + C_1x + C_2x^2 + C_3x^3 + \dots + C_nx^n$, then

(i) $C_0 + C_4 + C_8 + C_{12} + \dots = \frac{1}{2}\left\{2^{n-1} + 2^{n/2}\cos\left(\frac{n\pi}{4}\right)\right\}$

(ii) $C_1 + C_5 + C_9 + C_{13} + \dots = \frac{1}{2}\left\{2^{n-1} + 2^{n/2}\sin\left(\frac{n\pi}{4}\right)\right\}$

(iii) $C_0 + C_6 + C_{12} + \dots = \frac{1}{3}\left\{2^{n-1}\cos\left(\frac{n\pi}{4}\right) + 3^{n/2}\cos\left(\frac{n\pi}{6}\right)\right\}$

Multinomial Theorem

If n is a positive integer and $x_1, x_2, x_3, \dots, x_k \in C$, then

$$(x_1 + x_2 + x_3 + \dots + x_k)^n = \sum \frac{n!}{(\alpha_1!)(\alpha_2!)(\alpha_3!)\dots(\alpha_k!)} x_1^{\alpha_1} x_2^{\alpha_2} x_3^{\alpha_3} \dots x_k^{\alpha_k}$$

where, $\alpha_1, \alpha_2, \alpha_3, \dots, \alpha_k$ are all non-negative integers such that $\alpha_1 + \alpha_2 + \alpha_3 + \dots + \alpha_k = n$.

Remark

The coefficient of $x_1^{\alpha_1} \cdot x_2^{\alpha_2} \cdot x_3^{\alpha_3} \dots x_k^{\alpha_k}$ in the expansion of $(x_1 + x_2 + x_3 + \dots + x_k)^n$ is $\sum \frac{n!}{(\alpha_1!)(\alpha_2!)(\alpha_3!)\dots(\alpha_k!)}$.

In Particular

(i) $(a+b+c)^n = \sum \frac{n!}{(\alpha!)(\beta!)(\gamma!)} a^\alpha b^\beta c^\gamma$ such that $\alpha + \beta + \gamma = n$

(ii) $(a+b+c+d)^n = \sum \frac{n!}{(\alpha!)(\beta!)(\gamma!)(\delta!)} a^\alpha b^\beta c^\gamma d^\delta$ such that $\alpha + \beta + \gamma + \delta = n$

Example 53. Find the coefficient of $a^4 b^3 c^2 d$ in the expansion of $(a-b+c-d)^{10}$.

Sol. The coefficient of $a^4 b^3 c^2 d$ in the expansion of $(a-b+c-d)^{10}$ is $(-1)^4 \frac{10!}{4!\,3!\,2!\,1!} = 12600$

[powers of b and d are 3 and 1 $\therefore (-1)^3(-1)$]

Example 54. Find the coefficient of $a^3b^4c^5$ in the expansion of $(bc+ca+ab)^6$.

Sol. In this case, write $a^3b^4c^5 = (ab)^x (bc)^y (ca)^z$ say

$$\therefore \quad a^3b^4c^5 = a^{z+x} \cdot b^{x+y} \cdot c^{y+z}$$

$$\Rightarrow \quad z + x = 3, \ x + y = 4$$

$$y + z = 5$$

On adding all, we get $2(x+y+z) = 12$

$$\therefore \quad x + y + z = 6$$

Then, $x = 1, y = 3, z = 2$

Therefore, the coefficient of $a^3b^4c^5$ in the expansion of $(bc+ca+ab)^6$ or the coefficient of $(ab)^1(bc)^3(ca)^2$ in the expansion of $(bc+ca+ab)^6$ is $\frac{6!}{1!\,3!\,2!}$, i.e. 60.

Aliter

Coefficient of $a^3b^4c^5$ in the expansion of $(bc+ca+ab)^6$

= Coefficient of $a^3b^4c^5$ in the expansion of $(abc)^6\left(\frac{1}{a} + \frac{1}{b} + \frac{1}{c}\right)^6$

= Coefficient of $\left(\frac{1}{a}\right)^3\left(\frac{1}{b}\right)^2\left(\frac{1}{c}\right)^1$ in the expansion of $\left(\frac{1}{a} + \frac{1}{b} + \frac{1}{c}\right)^6$ is $\frac{6!}{3!\,2!\,1!} = 60$

Number of Distinct or Dissimilar Terms in the Multinomial Expansion

Statement The number of distinct or dissimilar terms in the multinomial expansion of $(x_1 + x_2 + x_3 + \dots + x_k)^n$ is ${}^{n+k-1}C_{k-1}$.

Proof We have, $(x_1 + x_2 + x_3 + \dots + x_k)^n$

$$= \sum \frac{n!}{(\alpha_1!)(\alpha_2!)(\alpha_3!)\dots(\alpha_k!)} x_1^{\alpha_1} x_2^{\alpha_2} x_3^{\alpha_3} \dots x_k^{\alpha_k}$$

where, $\alpha_1, \alpha_2, \alpha_3, \dots, \alpha_k$ are non-negative integers such that

$$\alpha_1 + \alpha_2 + \alpha_3 + \dots + \alpha_k = n \quad \text{...(i)}$$

Here, the number of terms in the expansion of $(x_1 + x_2 + x_3 + \dots + x_k)^n$

= The number of non-negative integral solutions of the Eq. (i)

$= {}^{n+k-1}C_{k-1}$

Example 55. Find the total number of distinct or dissimilar terms in the expansion of $(x+y+z+w)^n$, $n \in N$.

Sol. The total number of distinct or dissimilar terms in the expansion of $(x+y+z+w)^n$ is

$$= {}^{n+4-1}C_{4-1} = {}^{n+3}C_3 = \frac{(n+3)(n+2)(n+1)}{1\cdot2\cdot3}$$

$$= \frac{(n+1)(n+2)(n+3)}{6}$$

I. Aliter

We know that, $(x+y+z+w)^n = \{(x+y)+(z+w)\}^n$

$$= (x+y)^n + {}^nC_1 (x+y)^{n-1}(z+w) + {}^nC_2 (x+y)^{n-2}(z+w)^2 + \ldots + {}^nC_n (z+w)^n$$

$\therefore$ Number of terms in RHS

$$= (n+1) + n\cdot 2 + (n-1)\cdot 3 + \ldots + 1\cdot(n+1)$$

$$= \sum_{r=0}^{n} (n-r+1)(r+1)$$

$$= \sum_{r=0}^{n} (n+1) + nr - r^2 = (n+1)\sum_{r=0}^{n} 1 + n\sum_{r=0}^{n} r - \sum_{r=0}^{n} r^2$$

$$= (n+1)\cdot(n+1) + n\cdot\frac{n(n+1)}{2} - \frac{n(n+1)(2n+1)}{6}$$

$$= \frac{(n+1)(n+2)(n+3)}{6}$$

II. Aliter

$$(x+y+z+w)^n = \sum \frac{n!}{n_1!\, n_2!\, n_3!\, n_4!} x^{n_1} y^{n_2} z^{n_3} w^{n_4}$$

where, n_1, n_2, n_3, n_4 are non-negative integers subject to the condition $n_1 + n_2 + n_3 + n_4 = n$

Hence, number of the distinct terms

$= $ Coefficient of x^n in $(x^0 + x^1 + x^2 + \ldots + x^n)^4$

$= $ Coefficient of x^n in $\left(\dfrac{1-x^{n+1}}{1-x}\right)^4$

$= $ Coefficient of x^n in $(1-x^{n+1})^4 (1-x)^{-4}$

$= $ Coefficient of x^n in $(1-x)^{-4}$ $\quad [\because x^{n+1} > x^n]$

$$= {}^{n+3}C_n = {}^{n+3}C_3 = \frac{(n+3)(n+2)(n+1)}{6}$$

Greatest Coefficient in Multinomial Expansion

The greatest coefficient in the expansion of $(x_1 + x_2 + x_3 + \ldots + x_k)^n$ is $\dfrac{n!}{(q!)^{k-r}((q+1)!)^r}$, where q is the quotient and r is the remainder when n is divided by k i.e.

$$k\,)\,n\,(q \\ \underline{\quad} \\ r$$

Example 56. Find the greatest coefficient in the expansion of $(a+b+c+d)^{15}$.

Sol. Here, $n = 15$ and $k = 4$ $\quad [\because a, b, c, d$ are four terms$]$

$$4\,)\,15\,(3 \\ \underline{12} \\ 3$$

$\therefore \quad q = 3$ and $r = 3$

Hence, greatest coefficient $= \dfrac{15!}{(3!)^1 (4!)^3}$

Coefficient of x^r in Multinomial Expansion

If n is a positive integer and $a_1, a_2, a_3, \ldots, a_k \in C$, then coefficient of x^r in the expansion of $(a_1 + a_2 x + a_3 x^2 + \ldots + a_k x^{k-1})^n$, is

$$\sum \frac{n!}{(\alpha_1!)(\alpha_2!)(\alpha_3!)\ldots(\alpha_k!)} a_1^{\alpha_1} a_2^{\alpha_2} a_3^{\alpha_3} \ldots a_k^{\alpha_k}$$

where, $\alpha_1, \alpha_2, \alpha_3, \ldots, \alpha_k$ are non-negative integers such that $\alpha_1 + \alpha_2 + \alpha_3 + \ldots + \alpha_k = n$

and $\quad \alpha_2 + 2\alpha_3 + 3\alpha_4 + \ldots + (k-1)\alpha_k = r$

Example 57. Find the coefficient of x^7 in the expansion of $(1+3x-2x^3)^{10}$.

Sol. Coefficient of x^7 in the expansion of $(1+3x-2x^3)^{10}$ is

$$= \sum \frac{10!}{\alpha!\,\beta!\,\gamma!} (1)^\alpha (3)^\beta (-2)^\gamma$$

where, $\alpha + \beta + \gamma = 10$ and $\beta + 3\gamma = 7$

The possible values of α, β and γ are given below

α	β	γ
3	7	0
5	4	1
7	1	2

$\therefore$ Coefficient of x^7

$$= \frac{10!}{3!\,7!\,0!}(1)^3(3)^7(-2)^0 + \frac{10!}{5!\,4!\,1!}(1)^5(3)^4(-2)^1 + \frac{10!}{7!\,1!\,2!}(1)^7(3)^1(-2)^2$$

$$= 262440 - 204120 + 4320 = 62640$$

Use of Differentiation

This method applied only when the numericals occur as the product of the binomial coefficients, if

$$(1+x)^n = C_0 + C_1 x + C_2 x^2 + C_3 x^3 + \ldots + C_n x^n$$

Solution Process

(i) If last term of the series leaving the plus or minus sign is m, then divide m by n. If q is the quotient and r is the remainder.

i.e. $\quad m = nq + r \quad$ or $\quad n\,)\,m\,(q$

$$\underline{nq} \\ r$$

Then, replace x by x^q in the given series and multiplying both sides of the expression by x^r.

(ii) After this, differentiate both sides w.r.t. x and put $x = 1$ or -1 or $i(i = \sqrt{-1})$, etc. According to the given series.

(iii) If product of two numericals (or square of numericals) or three numericals (or cube of numericals), then differentiate twice or thrice.

Example 58. If $(1+x)^n = C_0 + C_1 x + C_2 x^2 + \ldots + C_n x^n$, prove that $C_1 + 2C_2 + 3C_3 + \ldots + nC_n = n \cdot 2^{n-1}$.

Sol. Here, last term of $C_1 + 2C_2 + 3C_3 + \ldots + nC_n$ is nC_n i.e., n and last term with positive sign.

Then, $n = n \cdot 1 + 0$ or $n)\, n\, (1$

$\underline{n}$

$\underline{0}$

Here, $q = 1$ and $r = 0$

Then, the given series is

$$(1+x)^n = C_0 + C_1 x + C_2 x^2 + C_3 x^3 + \ldots + C_n x^n$$

Differentiating both sides w.r.t. x, we get

$$n(1+x)^{n-1} = 0 + C_1 + 2C_2 x + 3C_3 x^2 + \ldots + nC_n x^{n-1}$$

Putting $x = 1$, we get

$$n \cdot 2^{n-1} = C_1 + 2C_2 + 3C_3 + \ldots + nC_n$$

or $$C_1 + 2C_2 + 3C_3 + \ldots + nC_n = n \cdot 2^{n-1}$$

I. Aliter

$$C_1 + 2C_2 + 3C_3 + \ldots + nC_n$$

$$= n + 2 \cdot \frac{n(n-1)}{1 \cdot 2} + 3 \cdot \frac{n(n-1)(n-2)}{1 \cdot 2 \cdot 3} + \ldots + n \cdot 1$$

$$= n\left\{1 + (n-1) + \frac{(n-1)(n-2)}{1 \cdot 2} + \ldots + 1\right\}$$

Let $n - 1 = N$, then

$$\text{LHS} = (1+N)\left\{1 + N + \frac{N(N-1)}{1 \cdot 2} + \ldots + 1\right\}$$

$$= (1+N)\{1 + {}^N C_1 + {}^N C_2 + \ldots + {}^N C_N\}$$

$$= (1+N)\, 2^N = n \cdot 2^{n-1} = \text{RHS}$$

II. Aliter

$$\text{LHS} = C_1 + 2C_2 + 3C_3 + \ldots + nC_n = \sum_{r=1}^{n} r \cdot {}^n C_r$$

$$= \sum_{r=1}^{n} r \cdot \frac{n}{r} \cdot {}^{n-1}C_{r-1} \qquad \left[\because {}^n C_r = \frac{n}{r} \cdot {}^{n-1}C_{r-1}\right]$$

$$= n \sum_{r=1}^{n} {}^{n-1}C_{r-1}$$

$$= n({}^{n-1}C_0 + {}^{n-1}C_1 + {}^{n-1}C_2 + \ldots + {}^{n-1}C_{n-1}]$$

$$= n \cdot 2^{n-1} = \text{RHS}$$

Example 59. If $(1+x)^n = C_0 + C_1 x + C_2 x^2 + \ldots + C_n x^n$, prove that $C_0 + 2C_1 + 3C_2 + \ldots + (n+1)C_n = (n+2)2^{n-1}$.

Sol. Here, last term of $C_0 + 2C_1 + 3C_2 + \ldots + (n+1)C_n$ is $(n+1)C_n$ i.e., $(n+1)$ and last term with positive sign.

and $n + 1 = n \cdot 1 + 1$

or $n)\, n + 1\, (1$

$\underline{-n}$

$\underline{1}$

Here, $q = 1$ and $r = 1$

The given series is

$$(1+x)^n = C_0 + C_1 x + C_2 x^2 + \ldots + C_n x^n$$

Now, replacing x by x^1 and multiplying both sides by x, we get

$$x(1+x)^n = C_0 x + C_1 x^2 + C_2 x^3 + \ldots + C_n x^{n+1}$$

Differentiating both sides w.r.t. x, we get

$$x \cdot n(1+x)^{n-1} + (1+x)^n \cdot 1 = C_0 + 2C_1 x + 3C_2 x^2 + \ldots + (n+1)C_n x^n$$

Putting $x = 1$, we get

$$n(2)^{n-1} + 2^n = C_0 + 2C_1 + 3C_2 + \ldots + (n+1)C_n$$

or $$C_0 + 2C_1 + 3C_2 + \ldots + (n+1)C_n = (n+2)2^{n-1}$$

I. Aliter

$$\text{LHS} = C_0 + 2C_1 + 3C_2 + \ldots + (n+1)C_n$$

$$= C_0 + (1+1)C_1 + (1+2)C_2 + \ldots + (1+n)C_n$$

$$= (C_0 + C_1 + C_2 + \ldots + C_n) + (C_1 + 2C_2 + \ldots + nC_n)$$

[use example 58]

$$= 2^n + n \cdot 2^{n-1} = (n+2)2^{n-1} = \text{RHS}$$

II. Aliter

$$\text{LHS} = C_0 + 2C_1 + 3C_2 + \ldots + (n+1)C_n$$

$$= \sum_{r=1}^{n+1} r \cdot {}^n C_{r-1} = \sum_{r=1}^{n+1} (r - 1 + 1) \cdot {}^n C_{r-1}$$

$$= \sum_{r=1}^{n+1} (r-1) \cdot {}^n C_{r-1} + {}^n C_{r-1}$$

$$= \sum_{r=1}^{n+1} n \cdot {}^{n-1}C_{r-2} + \sum_{r=1}^{n+1} {}^n C_{r-1}$$

$$\left[\because {}^n C_{r-1} = \frac{n}{r-1} \cdot {}^{n-1}C_{r-2}\right]$$

$$= n(0 + {}^{n-1}C_0 + {}^{n-1}C_1 + {}^{n-1}C_2 + \ldots + {}^{n-1}C_{n-1}) + ({}^n C_0 + {}^n C_1 + {}^n C_2 + \ldots + {}^n C_n)$$

$$= n \cdot 2^{n-1} + 2^n = (n+2) \cdot 2^{n-1} = \text{RHS}$$

Example 60. If $(1+x)^n = C_0 + C_1x + C_2x^2 + \ldots + C_nx^n$, prove that $C_0 + 3C_1 + 5C_2 + \ldots + (2n+1)C_n = (n+1)2^n$.

Sol. Here, last term of $C_0 + 3C_1 + 5C_2 + \ldots + (2n+1)C_n$ is $(2n+1)C_n$ i.e., $(2n+1)$ and last term with positive sign.

Then, $2n+1 = n \cdot 2 + 1$

or $n)\,2n+1\,(2$
$\quad -2n$
$\quad \overline{\quad 1 \quad}$

Here, $q = 2$ and $r = 1$

The given series is

$$(1+x)^n = C_0 + C_1x + C_2x^2 + \ldots + C_nx^n$$

Now, replacing x by x^2, we get

$$(1+x^2)^n = C_0 + C_1x^2 + C_2x^4 + \ldots + C_nx^{2n}$$

On multiplying both sides by x^1, we get

$$x(1+x^2)^n = C_0x + C_1x^3 + C_2x^5 + \ldots + C_nx^{2n+1}$$

On differentiating both sides w.r.t. x, we get

$$x \cdot n(1+x^2)^{n-1} \cdot 2x + (1+x^2)^n \cdot 1 = C_0 + 3C_1x^2 + 5C_2x^4 + \ldots + (2n+1)C_nx^{2n}$$

Putting $x = 1$, we get

$$n \cdot 2^{n-1} \cdot 2 + 2^n = C_0 + 3C_1 + 5C_2 + \ldots + (2n+1)C_n$$

or $\quad C_0 + 3C_1 + 5C_2 + \ldots + (2n+1)C_n = (n+1)2^n$

I. Aliter

$$\begin{aligned}
\text{LHS} &= C_0 + 3C_1 + 5C_2 + \ldots + (2n+1)C_n \\
&= C_0 + (1+2)C_1 + (1+4)C_2 + \ldots + (1+2n)C_n \\
&= (C_0 + C_1 + C_2 + \ldots + C_n) + 2(C_1 + 2C_2 + \ldots + nC_n) \\
&= 2^n + 2 \cdot n \cdot 2^{n-1} = 2^n + n \cdot 2^n \qquad \text{[from Illusration 58]} \\
&= (n+1)2^n = \text{RHS}
\end{aligned}$$

II. Aliter

$$\begin{aligned}
\text{LHS} &= C_0 + 3C_1 + 5C_2 + \ldots + (2n+1)C_n \\
&= \sum_{r=0}^{n} (2r+1)\,{}^nC_r = \sum_{r=0}^{n} 2r \cdot {}^nC_r + \sum_{r=0}^{n} {}^nC_r \\
&= 2\sum_{r=0}^{n} r \cdot {}^nC_r + \sum_{r=0}^{n} {}^nC_r \\
&= 2\sum_{r=0}^{n} r \cdot \frac{n}{r} \cdot {}^{n-1}C_{r-1} + \sum_{r=0}^{n} {}^nC_r \quad \left[\because {}^nC_r = \frac{n}{r} \cdot {}^{n-1}C_{r-1}\right] \\
&= 2n \sum_{r=0}^{n} {}^{n-1}C_{r-1} + \sum_{r=0}^{n} {}^nC_r \\
&= 2n(0 + {}^{n-1}C_0 + {}^{n-1}C_1 + {}^{n-1}C_2 + \ldots + {}^{n-1}C_{n-1}) \\
&\quad + ({}^nC_0 + {}^nC_1 + {}^nC_2 + \ldots + {}^nC_n) \\
&= 2n \cdot 2^{n-1} + 2^n = (n+1) \cdot 2^n = \text{RHS}
\end{aligned}$$

Example 61. If $(1+x)^n = C_0 + C_1x + C_2x^2 + \ldots + C_nx^n$, prove that $+ 3^2 \cdot C_3 + \ldots + n^2 \cdot C_n$ $1^2 \cdot C_1 + 2^2 \cdot C_2 = n(n+1) \cdot 2^{n-2}$.

Sol. Here, last term of $1^2 \cdot C_1 + 2^2 \cdot C_2 + 3^2 \cdot C_3 + \ldots + n^2 \cdot C_n$ is $n^2 \cdot C_n$ i.e., n^2. Linear factors of n^2 are n and n; [start always with greater factor] and last term with positive sign.

and $n = n \cdot 1 + 0$ or $n)\,n\,(1$
$\quad -n$
$\quad \overline{\quad 0 \quad}$

Here, $q = 1$ and $r = 0$

Then, the given series is

$$(1+x)^n = C_0 + C_1x + C_2x^2 + C_3x^3 + \ldots + C_nx^n$$

On differentiating both sides w.r.t. x, we get

$$nx(1+x)^{n-1} = C_1 + 2C_2x + 3C_3x^2 + \ldots + nC_nx^{n-1} \quad \ldots \text{(i)}$$

and in last term, numerical is nC_n i.e., n and power of $(1+x)$ is $n-1$.

Then, $n = (n-1) \cdot 1 + 1$ or $n-1)\,n\,(1$
$\quad n-1$
$\quad -+$
$\quad \overline{\quad 1 \quad}$

Here, $q = 1$ and $r = 1$

Now, multiplying both sides by x in Eq. (i), then

$$nx(1+x)^{n-1} = C_1x + 2C_2x^2 + 3C_3x^3 + \ldots + nC_nx^n$$

Differentiating on both sides w.r.t. x, we get

$$n\{x \cdot (n-1)(1+x)^{n-2} + (1+x)^{n-1} \cdot 1\} = C_1 \cdot 1 + 2^2C_2x + 3^2C_3x^2 + \ldots + n^2C_nx^{n-1}$$

Putting $x = 1$, we get

$$n\{1 \cdot (n-1) \cdot 2^{n-2} + 2^{n-1}\} = 1^2 \cdot C_1 + 2^2 \cdot C_2 + 3^2 \cdot C_3 + \ldots + n^2 \cdot C_n$$

or $1^2 \cdot C_1 + 2^2 \cdot C_2 + 3^2 \cdot C_3 + \ldots + n^2 \cdot C_n = n(n+1)2^{n-2}$

Aliter

$$\begin{aligned}
\text{LHS} &= 1^2 \cdot C_1 + 2^2 \cdot C_2 + 3^2 \cdot C_3 + \ldots + n^2 \cdot C_n \\
&= \sum_{r=1}^{n} r^2 \cdot {}^nC_r = \sum_{r=1}^{n} r^2 \cdot \frac{n}{r} \cdot {}^{n-1}C_{r-1} \\
&\qquad \left[\because {}^nC_r = \frac{n}{r} \cdot {}^{n-1}C_{r-1}\right] \\
&= n\sum_{r=1}^{n} r \cdot {}^{n-1}C_{r-1} = n\sum_{r=1}^{n} \{(r-1)+1\} \cdot {}^{n-1}C_{r-1} \\
&= n\sum_{r=1}^{n} (r-1) \cdot {}^{n-1}C_{r-1} + n\sum_{r=1}^{n} {}^{n-1}C_{r-1} \\
&= n\sum_{r=1}^{n} (n-1) \cdot {}^{n-2}C_{r-2} + n\sum_{r=1}^{n} {}^{n-1}C_{r-1}
\end{aligned}$$

$$= n(n-1)\sum_{r=1}^{n} {}^{n-2}C_{r-2} + n\sum_{r=1}^{n} {}^{n-1}C_{r-1}$$

$$= n(n-1)(0 + {}^{n-2}C_0 + {}^{n-2}C_1 + {}^{n-2}C_2 + \dots + {}^{n-2}C_{n-2}) + n({}^{n-1}C_0 + {}^{n-1}C_1 + {}^{n-1}C_2 + \dots + {}^{n-1}C_{n-1})$$

$$= n(n-1)\cdot 2^{n-2} + n\cdot 2^{n-1} = n(n+1)2^{n-2} = \text{RHS}$$

Example 62. If $(1+x)^n = C_0 + C_1 x + C_2 x^2 + \dots + C_n x^n$, prove that $(1\cdot 2)C_2 + (2\cdot 3)C_3 + \dots + \{(n-1)\cdot n\}C_n = n(n-1)2^{n-2}$.

Sol. Here, last term of

$(1\cdot 2)C_2 + (2\cdot 3)C_3 + \dots + \{(n-1)\cdot n\}C_n$ is $(n-1)nC_n$

i.e. $(n-1)n$

[start with greater factor here greater factor is n] and last term with positive sign, then $n = n\cdot 1 + 0$

or $\quad n)\,n\,(1$

$\quad\;\; -n$

$\quad\;\; \overline{\;\;0\;\;}$

Here, $q = 1$ and $r = 0$

The given series is

$$(1+x)^n = C_0 + C_1 x + C_2 x^2 + C_3 x^3 + \dots + C_n x^n$$

Differentiating on both sides w.r.t. x, we get

$$n(1+x)^{n-1} = 0 + C_1 + 2C_2 x + 3C_3 x^2 + \dots + nC_n x^{n-1}$$

Again, differentiating on both sides w.r.t. x, we get

$$n(n-1)(1+x)^{n-2} = 0 + 0 + (1\cdot 2)C_2 + (2\cdot 3)C_3 x + \dots + \{(n-1)\cdot n\}C_n x^{n-2}$$

Putting $x = 1$, we get

$$n(n-1)(1+1)^{n-2} = (1\cdot 2)C_2 + (2\cdot 3)C_3 + \dots + \{(n-1)n\}\cdot C_n$$

or $(1\cdot 2)C_2 + (2\cdot 3)C_3 + \dots + \{(n-1)n\}\cdot C_n = n(n-1)2^{n-2}$

I. Aliter

$$\text{LHS} = (1\cdot 2)C_2 + (2\cdot 3)C_3 + (3\cdot 4)C_4 + \dots + \{(n-1)n\}\cdot C_n$$

$$= (1\cdot 2)\frac{n(n-1)}{1\cdot 2} + (2\cdot 3)\frac{n(n-1)(n-2)}{1\cdot 2\cdot 3} + (3\cdot 4)\frac{n(n-1)(n-2)(n-3)}{1\cdot 2\cdot 3\cdot 4} + \dots + (n-1)n\cdot 1$$

$$= n(n-1)\left\{1 + \frac{(n-2)}{1} + \frac{(n-2)(n-3)}{1\cdot 2} + \dots + 1\right\}$$

Now, in bracket, let $n-2 = N$, then

$$= n(n-1)\left\{1 + \frac{N}{1} + \frac{N(N-1)}{2!} + \dots + 1\right\}$$

$$= n(n-1)\{{}^N C_0 + {}^N C_1 + \dots + {}^N C_N\}$$

$$= n(n-1)2^N = n(n-1)2^{n-2} = \text{RHS}$$

II. Aliter

$$\text{LHS} = (1\cdot 2)C_2 + (2\cdot 3)C_3 + \dots + \{(n-1)\cdot n\}C_n$$

$$= \sum_{r=2}^{n}(r-1)\cdot r\cdot {}^nC_r$$

$$= \sum_{r=2}^{n}(r-1)\cdot r\cdot \frac{n}{r}\cdot\frac{n-1}{(r-1)}\cdot {}^{n-2}C_{r-2}$$

$$= (n-1)n\sum_{r=2}^{n} {}^{n-2}C_{r-2}$$

$$= (n-1)n({}^{n-2}C_0 + {}^{n-2}C_1 + {}^{n-2}C_2 + \dots + {}^{n-2}C_{n-2})$$

$$= (n-1)n\cdot 2^{n-2} = \text{RHS}$$

Example 63. If $(1+x)^n = C_0 + C_1 x + C_2 x^2 + C_3 x^3 + \dots + C_n x^n$, prove that $C_0 - 2C_1 + 3C_2 - 4C_3 + \dots + (-1)^n(n+1)C_n = 0$.

Sol. Numerical value of last term of

$C_0 - 2C_1 + 3C_2 - 4C_3 + \dots + (-1)^n(n+1)C_n$ is $(n+1)C_n$ i.e., $(n+1)$, then

$n+1 = n\cdot 1 + 1 \quad$ or $\quad n)\,n+1\,(1$

$\quad\;\; -n$

$\quad\;\; \overline{\;\;1\;\;}$

Here, $q = 1$ and $r = 1$

The given series is

$$(1+x)^n = C_0 + C_1 x + C_2 x^2 + C_3 x^3 + \dots + C_n x^n$$

On multiplying both sides by x, we get

$$x(1+x)^n = C_0 x + C_1 x^2 + C_2 x^3 + C_3 x^4 + \dots + C_n x^{n+1}$$

On differentiating both sides w.r.t. x, we get

$$x\cdot n(1+x)^{n-1} + (1+x)^n\cdot 1 = C_0 + 2C_1 x + 3C_2 x^2 + 4C_3 x^3 + \dots + (n+1)C_n x^n$$

Putting $x = -1$, we get

$$0 = C_0 - 2C_1 + 3C_2 - 4C_3 + \dots + (-1)^n(n+1)C_n$$

or $\quad C_0 - 2C_1 + 3C_2 - 4C_3 + \dots + (-1)^n(n+1)C_n = 0$

I. Aliter

$$\text{LHS} = C_0 - 2C_1 + 3C_2 - 4C_3 + \dots + (-1)^n(n+1)C_n$$

$$= C_0 - (C_1 + C_1) + (C_2 + 2C_2) - (C_3 + 3C_3) + \dots + (-1)^n\{C_n + nC_n\}$$

$$= \{C_0 - C_1 + C_2 - C_3 + \dots + (-1)^n C_n\} + \{-C_1 + 2C_2 - 3C_3 + \dots + (-1)^n nC_n\}$$

$$= (1-1)^n + \left\{-n + 2\cdot\frac{n(n-1)}{1\cdot 2} - 3\frac{n(n-1)(n-2)}{1\cdot 2\cdot 3} + \dots + (-1)^n\cdot n\right\}$$

$$= 0 + n\left\{-1 + (n-1) - \frac{(n-1)(n-2)}{1\cdot 2} + \dots + (-1)^n\right\}$$

$$= 0 - n\left\{1 - (n-1) + \frac{(n-1)(n-2)}{1\cdot 2} - \dots + (-1)^{n-1}\right\}$$

Let in bracket, put $n - 1 = N$, we get

$$\text{LHS} = 0 - n\left\{1 - N + \frac{N(N-1)}{1\cdot 2} - \dots + (-1)^N\right\}$$

$$= 0 - n\{{}^NC_0 - {}^NC_1 + {}^NC_2 - \dots + (-1)^N\, {}^NC_N\}$$

$$= 0 - n(1-1)^N = 0 - 0 = 0 = \text{RHS}$$

II. Aliter

$$\text{LHS} = C_0 - 2C_1 + 3C_2 - 4C_3 + \dots + (-1)^n (n+1) C_n$$

$$= \sum_{r=0}^{n} (-1)^r (r+1)\, {}^nC_r = \sum_{r=0}^{n} (-1)^r [r\cdot {}^nC_r + {}^nC_r]$$

$$= \sum_{r=0}^{n} (-1)^r [n\cdot {}^{n-1}C_{r-1} + {}^nC_r] \quad \left[\because {}^nC_r = \frac{n}{r}\, {}^{n-1}C_{r-1}\right]$$

$$= n\sum_{r=0}^{n} (-1)^r\cdot {}^{n-1}C_{r-1} + \sum_{r=0}^{n} (-1)^r\cdot {}^nC_r$$

$$= -n\sum_{r=0}^{n} (-1)^{r-1}\cdot {}^{n-1}C_{r-1} + \sum_{r=0}^{n} (-1)^r\cdot {}^nC_r$$

$$= -n(1-1)^{n-1} + (1-1)^n = 0 + 0 = 0 = \text{RHS}$$

Example 64. If $(1+x)^n = C_0 + C_1 x + C_2 x^2 + C_3 x^3 + \dots + C_n x^n$, prove that $C_1 - 2C_2 + 3C_3 - \dots + (-1)^{n-1}\, nC_n = 0$.

Sol. Numerical value of last term of $C_1 - 2C_2 + 3C_3 - \dots + (-1)^{n-1}\, nC_n$ is nC_n i.e., n, then

and $\quad n = n\cdot 1 + 0$ or $n)\,n\,(1$

$$\frac{-n}{1}$$

Here, $q = 1$ and $r = 0$

The given series is

$$(1+x)^n = C_0 + C_1 x + C_2 x^2 + C_3 x^3 + \dots + C_n x^n$$

On differentiating both sides w.r.t. x, we get

$$n(1+x)^{n-1} = 0 + C_1 + 2C_2 x + 3C_3 x^2 + \dots + nC_n x^{n-1}$$

Putting $\quad x = -1$, we get

$$0 = C_1 - 2C_2 + 3C_3 - \dots + (-1)^{n-1}\, nC_n$$

or $\quad C_1 - 2C_2 + 3C_3 - \dots + (-1)^{n-1}\, nC_n = 0$

I. Aliter

$$\text{LHS} = C_1 - 2C_2 + 3C_3 - \dots + (-1)^{n-1}\, n\cdot C_n$$

$$= n - 2\cdot\frac{n(n-1)}{1\cdot 2} + 3\frac{n(n-1)(n-2)}{1\cdot 2\cdot 3} - \dots + (-1)^{n-1}\cdot n\cdot 1$$

$$= n\left\{1 - \frac{(n-1)}{1} + \frac{(n-1)(n-2)}{1\cdot 2} - \dots + (-1)^{n-1}\right\}$$

In bracket, put $n - 1 = N$, then

$$\text{LHS} = n\left\{1 - \frac{N}{1} + \frac{N(N-1)}{1\cdot 2} - \dots + (-1)^N\right\}$$

$$= n\{{}^NC_0 - {}^NC_1 + {}^NC_2 - \dots + (-1)^N\, {}^NC_N\}$$

$$= n(1-1)^N = 0 = \text{RHS}$$

II. Aliter

$$\text{LHS} = C_1 - 2C_2 + 3C_3 - \dots + (-1)^{n-1}\cdot nC_n$$

$$= \sum_{r=1}^{n} (-1)^{r-1}\cdot r\cdot {}^nC_r$$

$$= \sum_{r=1}^{n} (-1)^{r-1}\cdot n\cdot {}^{n-1}C_{r-1} \quad \left[\because {}^nC_r = \frac{n}{r}\cdot {}^{n-1}C_{r-1}\right]$$

$$= n\sum_{r=1}^{n} (-1)^{r-1}\cdot {}^{n-1}C_{r-1}$$

$$= n(1-1)^{n-1} = 0 = \text{RHS}$$

Example 65. If $(1+x)^n = C_0 + C_1 x + C_2 x^2 + C_3 x^3 + \dots + C_n x^n$, prove that $C_0 - 3C_1 + 5C_2 - \dots + (-1)^n (2n+1) C_n = 0$.

Sol. The numerical value of last term of

$C_0 - 3C_1 + 5C_2 - \dots + (-1)^n (2n+1) C_n$ is $(2n+1) C_n$

i.e. $\quad (2n+1)$

and $\quad 2n + 1 = 2\cdot n + 1$ or $n)\,2n+1\,(2$

$$\frac{-2n}{1}$$

Here, $q = 2$ and $r = 1$

The given series is

$(1+x)^n = C_0 + C_1 x + C_2 x^2 + C_3 x^3 + \dots + C_n x^n$ now, replacing x by x^2, then we get

$$(1+x^2)^n = C_0 + C_1 x^2 + C_2 x^4 + \dots + C_n x^{2n}$$

On multiplying both sides by x, we get

$$x(1+x^2)^n = C_0 x + C_1 x^3 + C_2 x^5 + \dots + C_n x^{2n+1}$$

On differentiating both sides w.r.t. x, we get

$$x\cdot n(1+x^2)^{n-1} 2x + (1+x^2)^n\cdot 1 = C_0 + 3C_1 x^2 + 5C_2 x^4 + \dots + (2n+1) C_n x^{2n}$$

Putting $x = i$ in both sides, we get

$$0 + 0 = C_0 - 3C_1 + 5C_2 - \dots + (2n+1)(-1)^n C_n$$

or $\quad C_0 - 3C_1 + 5C_2 - \dots + (-1)^n (2n+1) C_n = 0$

I. Aliter

$$\text{LHS} = C_0 - 3C_1 + 5C_2 - \dots + (-1)^n (2n+1) C_n$$

$$= C_0 - (1+2) C_1 + (1+4) C_2 - \dots + (-1)^n (1+2n) C_n$$

$$= (C_0 - C_1 + C_2 - \dots + (-1)^n C_n) - 2(C_1 - 2C_2 + \dots + (-1)^{n-1}\, n\cdot C_n$$

$= (1-1)^n - 2\cdot 0$ [from Example 64]

$= 0 = \text{RHS}$

II. Aliter

$$\text{LHS} = C_0 - 3C_1 + 5C_2 - \ldots + (-1)^n (2n+1) C_n$$

$$= \sum_{r=1}^{n} (-1)^r (2r+1)\, {}^nC_r = \sum_{r=1}^{n} (-1)^r [2r \cdot {}^nC_r + {}^nC_r]$$

$$= 2\sum_{r=1}^{n} n \cdot {}^{n-1}C_{r-1} + \sum_{r=1}^{n} (-1)^r \cdot {}^nC_r$$

$$= 2n(1-1)^{n-1} + (1-1)^n = 0 + 0 = 0 = \text{RHS}$$

Use of Integration

This method is applied only when the numericals occur as the denominator of the binomial coefficient.

Solution Process

If $(1+x)^n = C_0 + C_1 x + C_2 x^2 + C_3 x^3 + \ldots + C_n x^n$, then integrate both sides between the suitable limits which gives the required series.

1. If the sum contains $C_0, C_1, C_2, \ldots, C_n$ are all positive signs, then integrate between limits 0 to 1.
2. If the sum contains alternate signs (i.e., +, −), then integrate between limits −1 to 0.
3. If the sum contains odd coefficients (i.e., $C_0, C_2, C_4, \ldots$), then integrate between −1 to +1.
4. If the sum contains even coefficients (i.e., $C_1, C_3, C_5, \ldots$), then subtracting (2) from (1) and then dividing by 2.
5. If in denominator of binomial coefficient product of two numericals, then integrate two times first times taken limits between 0 to x and second times take suitable limits.

Example 66. If $(1+x)^n = C_0 + C_1 x + C_2 x^2 + \ldots + C_n x^n$, prove that

$$C_0 + \frac{C_1}{2} + \frac{C_2}{3} + \ldots + \frac{C_n}{n+1} = \frac{2^{n+1}-1}{n+1}.$$

Sol. $\because (1+x)^n = C_0 + C_1 x + C_2 x^2 + \ldots + C_n x^n$ ...(i)

Integrating both sides of Eq. (i) within limits 0 to 1, then we get

$$\int_0^1 (1+x)^n\, dx = \int_0^1 (C_0 + C_1 x + C_2 x^2 + \ldots + C_n x^n)\, dx$$

$$\left[\frac{(1+x)^{n+1}}{n+1}\right]_0^1$$

$$\Rightarrow \quad = \left[C_0 x + \frac{C_1 x^2}{2} + \frac{C_2 x^3}{3} + \ldots + \frac{C_n x^{n+1}}{n+1}\right]_0^1$$

$$\Rightarrow \quad \frac{2^{n+1}-1}{n+1} = C_0 + \frac{C_1}{2} + \frac{C_2}{3} + \ldots + \frac{C_n}{n+1}$$

or $C_0 + \dfrac{C_1}{2} + \dfrac{C_2}{3} + \ldots + \dfrac{C_n}{n+1} = \dfrac{2^{n+1}-1}{n+1}$

I. Aliter

$$\text{LHS} = C_0 + \frac{C_1}{2} + \frac{C_2}{3} + \ldots + \frac{C_n}{n+1}$$

$$= 1 + \frac{n}{1\cdot 2} + \frac{n(n-1)}{1\cdot 2\cdot 3} + \ldots + \frac{1}{n+1}$$

$$= \frac{1}{n+1}\left[(n+1) + \frac{(n+1)n}{1\cdot 2} + \frac{(n+1)\,n\,(n-1)}{1\cdot 2\cdot 3} + \ldots + 1\right]$$

Put $n+1 = N$, then

$$\text{LHS} = \frac{1}{N}\left[N + \frac{N(N-1)}{2!} + \frac{N(N-1)(N-2)}{3!} + \ldots + 1\right]$$

$$= \frac{1}{N}[{}^NC_1 + {}^NC_2 + {}^NC_3 + \ldots + {}^NC_N]$$

$$= \frac{1}{N}[(1+1)^N - 1] = \frac{2^N - 1}{N} = \frac{2^{n+1}-1}{n+1} = \text{RHS}$$

II. Aliter

$$\text{LHS} = C_0 + \frac{C_1}{2} + \frac{C_2}{3} + \ldots + \frac{C_n}{n+1} = \sum_{r=0}^{n} \frac{C_r}{r+1}$$

$$= \sum_{r=0}^{n} \frac{{}^nC_r}{(r+1)} = \sum_{r=0}^{n} \frac{{}^{n+1}C_{r+1}}{(n+1)} \quad \left[\because \frac{{}^{n+1}C_{r+1}}{n+1} = \frac{{}^nC_r}{r+1}\right]$$

$$= \frac{1}{(n+1)} \sum_{r=0}^{n} {}^{n+1}C_{r+1}$$

$$= \frac{1}{(n+1)} ({}^{n+1}C_1 + {}^{n+1}C_2 + {}^{n+1}C_3 + \ldots + {}^{n+1}C_{n+1})$$

$$= \frac{1}{n+1}(2^{n+1} - 1) = \frac{2^{n+1}-1}{n+1} = \text{RHS}$$

Example 67. If $(1+x)^n = C_0 + C_1 x + C_2 x^2 + C_3 x^3 + \ldots + C_n x^n$, prove that

$$C_0 - \frac{C_1}{2} + \frac{C_2}{3} - \ldots + (-1)^n \frac{C_n}{n+1} = \frac{1}{n+1}.$$

Sol. $\because (1+x)^n = C_0 + C_1 x + C_2 x^2 + \ldots + C_n x^n$ ...(i)

Integrating on both sides of Eq. (i) within limits − 1 to 0, then we get

$$\int_{-1}^{0} (1+x)^n\, dx = \int_{-1}^{0} (C_0 + C_1 x + C_2 x^2 + \ldots + C_n x^n)\, dx$$

$$\Rightarrow \left[\frac{(1+x)^n}{n+1}\right]_{-1}^{0} = \left[C_0 x + \frac{C_1 x^2}{2} + \frac{C_2 x^3}{3} + \ldots + \frac{C_n x^{n+1}}{n+1}\right]_{-1}^{0}$$

$$\Rightarrow \quad \frac{1-0}{n+1} = 0 - \left(-C_0 + \frac{C_1}{2} - \frac{C_2}{3} + \ldots + (-1)^{n+1}\frac{C_n}{n+1}\right)$$

$$\Rightarrow \quad \frac{1}{n+1} = C_0 - \frac{C_1}{2} + \frac{C_2}{3} - \ldots + (-1)^{n+2}\frac{C_n}{n+1}$$

$$\Rightarrow \quad \frac{1}{n+1} = C_0 - \frac{C_1}{2} + \frac{C_2}{3} - \ldots + (-1)^n \frac{C_n}{n+1}$$

$$[\because (-1)^{n+2} = (-1)^n (-1)^2 = (-1)^n]$$

Hence, $C_0 - \frac{C_1}{2} + \frac{C_2}{3} - \ldots + (-1)^n \frac{C_n}{n+1} = \frac{1}{n+1}$

I. Aliter

$$\text{LHS} = C_0 - \frac{C_1}{2} + \frac{C_2}{3} - \ldots + (-1)^n \frac{C_n}{n+1}$$

$$= 1 - \frac{n}{2} + \frac{n(n-1)}{1\cdot 2\cdot 3} - \ldots + (-1)^n \frac{1}{n+1} = \frac{1}{(n+1)}$$

$$\left[(n+1) - \frac{(n+1)n}{1\cdot 2} + \frac{(n+1)n(n-1)}{1\cdot 2\cdot 3} - \ldots + (-1)^n\right]$$

Put $n+1 = N$, we get

$$= \frac{1}{N}\left[N - \frac{N(N-1)}{1\cdot 2} + \frac{N(N-1)(N-2)}{1\cdot 2\cdot 3} - \ldots + (-1)^{N-1}\right]$$

$$= \frac{1}{N}[\,{}^N C_1 - {}^N C_2 + {}^N C_3 - \ldots + (-1)^{N-1}]$$

$$= -\frac{1}{N}[-{}^N C_1 + {}^N C_2 - {}^N C_3 + \ldots + (-1)^N\, {}^N C_N]$$

$$= -\frac{1}{N}[\,{}^N C_0 - {}^N C_1 + {}^N C_2 - {}^N C_3 + \ldots + (-1)^N\, {}^N C_N - {}^N C_0]$$

$$= -\frac{1}{N}[(1-1)^N - {}^N C_0] = -\frac{1}{N}[0-1] = \frac{1}{N}$$

$$= \frac{1}{n+1} = \text{RHS}$$

II. Aliter

$$\text{LHS} = C_0 - \frac{C_1}{2} + \frac{C_2}{3} - \ldots + (-1)^n \frac{C_n}{n+1} = \sum_{r=0}^{n} \frac{(-1)^r \cdot C_r}{r+1}$$

$$= \sum_{r=0}^{n} \frac{(-1)^r \cdot {}^n C_r}{r+1}$$

$$= \sum_{r=0}^{n} (-1)^r \cdot \frac{{}^{n+1}C_{r+1}}{(n+1)} \qquad \left[\because \frac{{}^{n+1}C_{r+1}}{n+1} = \frac{{}^n C_r}{r+1}\right]$$

$$= \frac{1}{(n+1)} \sum_{r=0}^{n} (-1)^r \cdot {}^{n+1}C_{r+1}$$

$$= \frac{1}{(n+1)}(\,{}^{n+1}C_1 - {}^{n+1}C_2 + {}^{n+1}C_3 - \ldots + (-1)^n \cdot {}^{n+1}C_{n+1})$$

$$= \frac{1}{(n+1)}\{\,{}^{n+1}C_0 - (\,{}^{n+1}C_0 - {}^{n+1}C_1 + {}^{n+1}C_2 - {}^{n+1}C_3 + \ldots + (-1)^{n+1}\, {}^{n+1}C_{n+1})\}$$

$$= \frac{1}{(n+1)}[1 - (1-1)^{n+1}] = \frac{1}{(n+1)}[1-0] = \frac{1}{n+1} = \text{RHS}$$

Example 68. If $(1+x)^n = C_0 + C_1 x + C_2 x^2 + C_3 x^3 + \ldots + C_n x^n$, prove that

$$\frac{C_0}{1} + \frac{C_2}{3} + \frac{C_4}{5} + \ldots = \frac{2^n}{n+1}.$$

Sol. $\because (1+x)^n = C_0 + C_1 x + C_2 x^2 + C_3 x^3 + C_4 x^4 + \ldots + C_n x^n \quad \ldots \text{(i)}$

Integrating on both sides of Eq. (i) within limits -1 to 1, then we get

$$\int_{-1}^{1} (1+x)^n\, dx = \int_{-1}^{1} (C_0 + C_1 x + C_2 x^2 + C_3 x^3 + C_4 x^4 + \ldots + C_n x^n)\, dx$$

$$= \int_{-1}^{1} (C_0 + C_2 x^2 + C_4 x^4 + \ldots)\, dx + \int_{-1}^{1} (C_1 x + C_3 x^3 + \ldots)\, dx$$

$$= 2\int_0^1 (C_0 + C_2 x^2 + C_4 x^4 + \ldots)\, dx + 0$$

[by property of definite integral]

[since, second integral contains odd function]

$$\left[\frac{(1+x)^{n+1}}{n+1}\right]_{-1}^{1} = 2\left[\left(C_0 x + \frac{C_2 x^3}{3} + \frac{C_4 x^5}{5} + \ldots\right)\right]_0^1$$

$$\Rightarrow \quad \frac{2^{n+1}}{n+1} = 2\left(C_0 + \frac{C_2}{3} + \frac{C_4}{5} + \ldots\right)$$

or $C_0 + \frac{C_2}{3} + \frac{C_4}{5} + \ldots = \frac{2^n}{n+1}$

I. Aliter

$$\text{LHS} = C_0 + \frac{C_2}{3} + \frac{C_4}{5} + \ldots$$

$$= 1 + \frac{n(n-1)}{1\cdot 2\cdot 3} + \frac{n(n-1)(n-2)(n-3)}{1\cdot 2\cdot 3\cdot 4\cdot 5} + \ldots$$

$$= \frac{1}{(n+1)}\left\{\frac{n+1}{1} + \frac{(n+1)n(n-1)}{1\cdot 2\cdot 3} + \frac{(n+1)n(n-1)(n-2)(n-3)}{1\cdot 2\cdot 3\cdot 4\cdot 5} + \ldots\right\}$$

$$= \frac{1}{n+1}\{\,{}^{n+1}C_1 + {}^{n+1}C_3 + {}^{n+1}C_5 + \ldots\}$$

$$= \frac{1}{(n+1)}[\text{sum of even binomial coefficients of } (1+x)^{n+1}]$$

$$= \frac{2^{n+1-1}}{n+1} = \frac{2^n}{n+1} = \text{RHS}$$

II. Aliter LHS $= \dfrac{C_0}{1} + \dfrac{C_2}{3} + \dfrac{C_4}{5} + \dots$

***Case* I** If n is odd say $n = 2m+1$, $\forall\ m \in W$, then

$$\text{LHS} = \sum_{r=0}^{m} \frac{{}^{2m+1}C_{2r}}{2r+1} = \sum_{r=0}^{m} \frac{{}^{2m+2}C_{2r+1}}{(2m+1)}$$

$$\left[\because \frac{{}^{2m+1}C_{2r}}{2r+1} = \frac{{}^{2m+2}C_{2r+1}}{2m+1}\right]$$

$$= \frac{1}{(2m+1)} \cdot 2^{2m+2-1} = \frac{2^n}{n+1} = \text{RHS}$$

$$[\because n = 2m+1]$$

***Case* II** If n is even say $n = 2m$, $\forall\ m \in N$, then

$$\text{LHS} = \sum_{r=0}^{m} \frac{{}^{2m}C_{2r}}{2r+1} = \sum_{r=0}^{m} \frac{{}^{2m+1}C_{2r+1}}{(2m+1)}$$

$$\left[\because \frac{{}^{2m+1}C_{2r+1}}{2m+1} = \frac{{}^{2m}C_{2r}}{2r+1}\right]$$

$$= \frac{2^{2m+1-1}}{2m+1} = \frac{2^n}{n+1} = \text{RHS} \qquad [\because n = 2m]$$

Example 69. If $(1+x)^n = C_0 + C_1x + C_2x^2 + C_3x^3 + \dots + C_nx^n$, prove that $\dfrac{C_1}{2} + \dfrac{C_3}{4} + \dfrac{C_5}{6} + \dots = \dfrac{2^n - 1}{n+1}$.

Sol. We know that, from Examples (66) and (67)

$$C_0 + \frac{C_1}{2} + \frac{C_2}{3} + \frac{C_3}{4} + \frac{C_4}{5} + \frac{C_5}{6} + \dots = \frac{2^{n+1} - 1}{n+1} \qquad \dots\text{(i)}$$

and $$C_0 - \frac{C_1}{2} + \frac{C_2}{3} - \frac{C_3}{4} + \frac{C_4}{5} - \frac{C_5}{6} + \dots = \frac{1}{n+1} \qquad \dots\text{(ii)}$$

On subtracting Eq. (ii) from Eq. (i), we get

$$2\left(\frac{C_1}{2} + \frac{C_3}{4} + \frac{C_5}{6} + \dots\right) = \frac{2^{n+1} - 2}{n+1}$$

On dividing each sides by 2, we get

$$\frac{C_1}{2} + \frac{C_3}{4} + \frac{C_5}{6} + \dots = \frac{2^n - 1}{n+1}$$

I. Aliter LHS $= \dfrac{C_1}{2} + \dfrac{C_3}{4} + \dfrac{C_5}{6} + \dots$

$$= \frac{n}{1\cdot 2} + \frac{n(n-1)(n-2)}{1\cdot 2\cdot 3\cdot 4} + \frac{n(n-1)(n-2)(n-3)(n-4)}{1\cdot 2\cdot 3\cdot 4\cdot 5\cdot 6} + \dots$$

$$= \frac{1}{n+1}\left[\frac{(n+1)n}{1\cdot 2} + \frac{(n+1)n(n-1)(n-2)}{1\cdot 2\cdot 3\cdot 4} + \frac{(n+1)n(n-1)(n-2)(n-3)(n-4)}{1\cdot 2\cdot 3\cdot 4\cdot 5\cdot 6} + \dots\right]$$

Put $n + 1 = N$, then

$$\text{LHS} = \frac{1}{N}\left[\frac{N(N-1)}{2!} + \frac{N(N-1)(N-2)(N-3)}{4!} + \frac{N(N-1)(N-2)(N-3)(N-4)(N-5)}{6!} + \dots\right]$$

$$= \frac{1}{N}[{}^NC_2 + {}^NC_4 + {}^NC_6 + \dots]$$

$$= \frac{1}{N}[({}^NC_0 + {}^NC_2 + {}^NC_4 + {}^NC_6 + \dots) - {}^NC_0]$$

$$= \frac{1}{N}[2^{N-1} - 1] = \frac{2^n - 1}{n+1} = \text{RHS}$$

II. Aliter

$$\text{LHS} = \frac{C_1}{2} + \frac{C_3}{4} + \frac{C_5}{6} + \dots$$

***Case* I** If n is odd say $n = 2m+1$, $\forall\ m \in W$, then

$$\text{LHS} = \sum_{r=0}^{m} \frac{{}^{2m+1}C_{2r+1}}{2r+2} = \sum_{r=0}^{m} \frac{{}^{2m+2}C_{2r+2}}{(2m+2)}$$

$$\left[\because \frac{{}^{2m+2}C_{2r+2}}{2m+2} = \frac{{}^{2m+1}C_{2r+1}}{2r+2}\right]$$

$$= \frac{1}{(2m+2)}({}^{2m+2}C_2 + {}^{2m+2}C_4 + \dots + {}^{2m+2}C_{2m+2})$$

$$= \frac{1}{(2m+2)} \cdot (2^{2m+2-1} - {}^{2m+1}C_0) = \frac{2^n - 1}{n+1} \qquad [\because 2m+1 = n]$$

$= \text{RHS}$

***Case* II** If n is even say $n = 2m$, $\forall\ m \in N$, then

$$\text{LHS} = \sum_{r=0}^{m-1} \frac{{}^{2m}C_{2r+1}}{(2r+2)} = \sum_{r=0}^{m-1} \frac{{}^{2m+1}C_{2r+2}}{(2m+1)}$$

$$\left[\because \frac{{}^{2m+1}C_{2r+2}}{2m+1} = \frac{{}^{2m}C_{2r+1}}{2r+2}\right]$$

$$= \frac{1}{(2m+1)} \sum_{r=0}^{m-1} {}^{2m+1}C_{2r+2}$$

$$= \frac{1}{(2m+1)}({}^{2m+1}C_2 + {}^{2m+1}C_4 + {}^{2m+1}C_6 + \dots + {}^{2m+1}C_{2n})$$

$$= \frac{1}{(2m+1)} \cdot (2^{2m+1-1} - {}^{2m+1}C_0)$$

$$= \frac{2^n - 1}{n+1} = \text{RHS} \qquad [\because n = 2m]$$

Example 70. If $(1+x)^n = C_0 + C_1x + C_2x^2 + \dots + C_nx^n$, prove that

$$3C_0 + 3^2\frac{C_1}{2} + \frac{3^3C_2}{3} + \frac{3^4C_3}{4} + \dots + \frac{3^{n+1}C_n}{n+1} = \frac{4^{n+1} - 1}{n+1}.$$

Sol. $\because \quad (1+x)^n = C_0 + C_1x + C_2x^2 + C_3x^3 + \ldots + C_nx^n \quad \ldots(i)$

Integrating on both sides of Eq. (i) within limits 0 to 3, we get

$$\int_0^3 (1+x)^n dx = \int_0^3 (C_0 + C_1x + C_2x^2 + C_3x^3 + \ldots + C_nx^n)dx$$

$$\Rightarrow \left[\frac{(1+x)^{n+1}}{n+1}\right]_0^3 = \left[C_0x + \frac{C_1x^2}{2} + \frac{C_2x^3}{3} + \frac{C_3x^4}{4} + \ldots + \frac{C_nx^{n+1}}{n+1}\right]_0^3$$

$$\Rightarrow \frac{4^{n+1}-1}{n+1} = 3C_0 + \frac{3^2C_1}{2} + \frac{3^3C_2}{3} + \frac{3^4C_3}{4} + \ldots + \frac{3^{n+1}C_n}{n+1}$$

Hence,

$$3C_0 + \frac{3^2C_1}{2} + \frac{3^3C_2}{3} + \frac{3^4C_3}{4} + \ldots + \frac{3^{n+1}C_n}{n+1} = \frac{4^{n+1}-1}{n+1}$$

I. Aliter

$$\text{LHS} = 3C_0 + \frac{3^2C_1}{2} + \frac{3^3C_2}{3} + \frac{3^4C_3}{4} + \ldots + \frac{3^{n+1}C_n}{n+1}$$

$$= 3\cdot 1 + \frac{3^2\cdot n}{2} + \frac{3^3\cdot n(n-1)}{1\cdot 2\cdot 3} + \frac{3^4\cdot n(n-1)(n-2)}{1\cdot 2\cdot 3\cdot 4} + \ldots + \frac{3^{n+1}}{n+1}$$

$$= \frac{1}{(n+1)}\left[3\cdot(n+1) + \frac{3^2(n+1)n}{1\cdot 2} + \frac{3^3(n+1)n(n-1)}{1\cdot 2\cdot 3} + \frac{3^4(n+1)n(n-1)(n-2)}{1\cdot 2\cdot 3\cdot 4} + \ldots + 3^{n+1}\right]$$

Put $n+1 = N$, then

$$\text{LHS} = \frac{1}{N}\left[3N + \frac{3^2N(N-1)}{2!} + \frac{3^3N(N-1)(N-2)}{3!} + \frac{3^4N(N-1)(N-2)(N-3)}{4!} + \ldots + 3^N\right]$$

$$= \frac{1}{N}[{}^NC_1(3) + {}^NC_2(3)^2 + {}^NC_3(3)^3 + \ldots + {}^NC_N(3)^N]$$

$$= \frac{1}{N}[{}^NC_0 + {}^NC_1(3) + {}^NC_2(3)^2 + {}^NC_3(3)^3 + \ldots + {}^NC_N(3)^N - {}^NC_0]$$

$$= \frac{1}{N}\{(1+3)^N - 1\} = \frac{4^N-1}{N} = \frac{4^{n+1}-1}{n+1} = \text{RHS}$$

II. Aliter

$$\text{LHS} = 3C_0 + 3^2\frac{C_1}{2} + \frac{3^3C_2}{3} + \frac{3^4C_3}{4} + \ldots + \frac{3^{n+1}C_n}{n+1}$$

$$= \sum_{r=0}^{n}\frac{3^{r+1}\cdot {}^nC_r}{(r+1)} = \sum_{r=0}^{n}\frac{3^{r+1}\cdot {}^{n+1}C_{r+1}}{(n+1)}$$

$$\left[\because \frac{{}^{n+1}C_{r+1}}{n+1} = \frac{{}^nC_r}{r+1}\right]$$

$$= \frac{1}{(n+1)}\sum_{r=0}^{n}{}^{n+1}C_{r+1}\cdot 3^{r+1}$$

$$= \frac{1}{(n+1)}({}^{n+1}C_1\cdot 3 + {}^{n+1}C_2\cdot 3^2 + {}^{n+1}C_3\cdot 3^3 + \ldots + {}^{n+1}C_{n+1}\cdot 3^{n+1})$$

$$= \frac{1}{(n+1)}[(1+3)^{n+1} - {}^{n+1}C_0]$$

$$= \frac{4^{n+1}-1}{n+1} = \text{RHS}$$

Example 71. If $(1+x)^n = C_0 + C_1x + C_2x^2 + \ldots + C_nx^n$, show that $\frac{2^2}{1\cdot 2}C_0 + \frac{2^3}{2\cdot 3}C_1 + \frac{2^4}{3\cdot 4}C_2 + \ldots + \frac{2^{n+2}C_n}{(n+1)(n+2)} = \frac{3^{n+2}-2n-5}{(n+1)(n+2)}$.

Sol. Given,

$$(1+x)^n = C_0 + C_1x + C_2x^2 + C_3x^3 + \ldots + C_nx^n \quad \ldots(i)$$

Integrating both sides of Eq. (i) within limits 0 to x, we get

$$\int_0^x (1+x)^n dx = \int_0^x (C_0 + C_1x + C_2x^2 + \ldots + C_nx^n)dx$$

$$\Rightarrow \left[\frac{(1+x)^{n+1}}{n+1}\right]_0^x = \left[C_0x + \frac{C_1x^2}{2} + \frac{C_2x^3}{3} + \ldots + \frac{C_nx^{n+1}}{n+1}\right]_0^x$$

$$\Rightarrow \frac{(1+x)^{n+1}-1}{(n+1)} = C_0x + \frac{C_1x^2}{2} + \frac{C_2x^3}{3} + \ldots + \frac{C_nx^{n+1}}{n+1} \quad \ldots(ii)$$

Again, integrating both sides of Eq. (ii) within limits 0 to 2, we get

$$\int_0^2 \frac{(1+x)^{n+1}-1}{(n+1)}dx = \int_0^2\left(C_0x + \frac{C_1x^2}{2} + \frac{C_2x^3}{3} + \ldots + \frac{C_nx^{n+1}}{n+1}\right)dx$$

$$\Rightarrow \frac{1}{(n+1)}\left(\frac{(1+x)^{n+2}}{n+2} - x\right)_0^2 = \left[\frac{C_0x^2}{1\cdot 2} + \frac{C_1x^3}{2\cdot 3} + \frac{C_2x^4}{3\cdot 4} + \ldots + \frac{C_nx^{n+2}}{(n+1)(n+2)}\right]_0^2$$

$$\Rightarrow \frac{1}{(n+1)}\left\{\frac{3^{n+2}}{n+2} - 2 - \frac{1}{n+2}\right\} = \frac{2^2}{1\cdot 2}C_0 + \frac{2^3}{2\cdot 3}C_1 + \frac{2^4}{3\cdot 4}C_2 + \ldots + \frac{2^{n+2}C_n}{(n+1)(n+2)}$$

Hence, $\frac{2^2}{1\cdot 2}C_0 + \frac{2^3}{2\cdot 3}C_1 + \frac{2^4}{3\cdot 4}C_2 + \dots + \frac{2^{n+2}C_n}{(n+1)(n+2)}$

$$= \frac{3^{n+2} - 2n - 5}{(n+1)(n+2)}$$

I. Aliter

$$\text{LHS} = \frac{2^2}{1\cdot 2}C_0 + \frac{2^3}{2\cdot 3}C_1 + \frac{2^4}{3\cdot 4}C_2 + \dots + \frac{2^{n+2}C_n}{(n+1)(n+2)}$$

$$= \frac{2^2}{1\cdot 2}(1) + \frac{2^3}{2\cdot 3}\cdot n + \frac{2^4}{3\cdot 4}\frac{n(n-1)}{1\cdot 2} + \dots + \frac{2^{n+2}\cdot 1}{(n+1)(n+2)}$$

$$= \frac{1}{(n+1)(n+2)}\left\{\frac{(n+2)(n+1)}{1\cdot 2}2^2 + \frac{(n+2)(n+1)n}{1\cdot 2\cdot 3}2^3 + \frac{(n+2)(n+1)n(n-1)}{1\cdot 2\cdot 3\cdot 4}2^4 + \dots + 2^{n+2}\right\}$$

Put $n+2 = N$, then we get

$$= \frac{1}{N(N-1)}\left\{\frac{N(N-1)}{1\cdot 2}2^2 + \frac{N(N-1)(N-2)}{1\cdot 2\cdot 3}2^3 + \frac{N(N-1)(N-2)(N-3)}{1\cdot 2\cdot 3\cdot 4}2^4 + \dots + 2^N\right\}$$

$$= \frac{1}{N(N-1)}\{{}^NC_2(2)^2 + {}^NC_3(2)^3 + {}^NC_4(2)^4 + \dots + {}^NC_N(2)^N]$$

$$= \frac{1}{N(N-1)}\{{}^NC_0 + {}^NC_1(2) + {}^NC_2(2)^2 + {}^NC_3(2)^3 + {}^NC_4(2)^4 + \dots + {}^NC_N(2)^N - {}^NC_0 - {}^NC_1(2)]$$

$$= \frac{1}{N(N-1)}\{(1+2)^N - 1 - 2N\}$$

$$= \frac{3^{n+2} - 1 - 2(n+2)}{(n+2)(n+1)} = \frac{3^{n+2} - 2n - 5}{(n+1)(n+2)} = \text{RHS}$$

II. Aliter

$$\text{LHS} = \frac{2^2}{1\cdot 2}\cdot C_0 + \frac{2^3}{2\cdot 3}\cdot C_1 + \frac{2^4}{3\cdot 4}\cdot C_2 + \dots + \frac{2^{n+2}\cdot C_n}{(n+1)(n+2)}$$

$$= \sum_{r=1}^{n+1}\frac{2^{r+1}}{r(r+1)}\cdot {}^nC_{r-1}$$

$$= \sum_{r=1}^{n+1}\frac{2^{r+1}\cdot {}^{n+2}C_{r+1}}{(n+1)(n+2)} \quad \left[\because \frac{{}^{n+2}C_{r+1}}{(n+1)(n+2)} = \frac{{}^nC_{r-1}}{r(r+1)}\right]$$

$$= \frac{1}{(n+1)(n+2)}\sum_{r=1}^{n+1}{}^{n+2}C_{r+1}\cdot 2^{r+1}$$

$$= \frac{1}{(n+1)(n+2)}[{}^{n+2}C_2\cdot 2^2 + {}^{n+2}C_3\cdot 2^3 + \dots + {}^{n+2}C_{n+2}\cdot 2^{n+2}]$$

$$= \frac{1}{(n+1)(n+2)}[(1+2)^{n+2} - {}^{n+2}C_0 - {}^{n+2}C_1\cdot 2^1]$$

$$= \frac{(3^{n+2} - 2n - 5)}{(n+1)(n+2)} = \text{RHS}$$

When Each Term in Summation Contains the Product of Two Binomial Coefficients or Square of Binomial Coefficients

Solution Process

1. **If difference of the lower suffixes of binomial coefficients in each term is same.**

i.e. ${}^nC_0\,{}^nC_2 + {}^nC_1\cdot{}^nC_3 + {}^nC_2\cdot{}^nC_4 + \dots$

Here, $2 - 0 = 3 - 1 = 4 - 2 = \dots = 2$

***Case* I If each term of series is positive, then**

$$(1+x)^n = C_0 + C_1x + C_2x^2 + \dots + C_nx^n \quad \dots\text{(i)}$$

Interchanging 1 and x, we get

$$(x+1)^n = C_0x^n + C_1x^{n-1} + C_2x^{n-2} + \dots + C_n \quad \dots\text{(ii)}$$

Then, multiplying Eqs. (i) and (ii) and equate the coefficients of suitable power of x on both sides.

Replacing x by $\frac{1}{x}$ in Eq. (i), then we get

$$\left(1+\frac{1}{x}\right)^n = C_0 + \frac{C_1}{x} + \frac{C_2}{x^2} + \dots + \frac{C_n}{x^n} \quad \dots\text{(iii)}$$

Then, multiplying Eqs. (i) and (iii) and equate the coefficients of suitable power of x on both sides.

Example 72. If $(1+x)^n = C_0 + C_1x + C_2x^2 + C_3x^3 + \dots + C_nx^n$, prove that

$$C_0C_r + C_1C_{r+1} + C_2C_{r+2} + \dots + C_{n-r}C_n = \frac{2n!}{(n-r)!(n+r)!}.$$

Sol. Here, differences of lower suffixes of binomial coefficients in each term is r.

i.e., $r - 0 = r + 1 - 1 = r + 2 - 2 = \dots = n - (n-r) = r$

Given,

$$(1+x)^n = C_0 + C_1x + C_2x^2 + \dots + C_{n-r}x^{n-r} + \dots + C_nx^n \quad \dots\text{(i)}$$

Now,

$$(x+1)^n = C_0x^n + C_1x^{n-1} + C_2x^{n-2} + \dots + C_rx^{n-r} + C_{r+1}x^{n-r-1} + C_{r+2}x^{n-r-2} + \dots + C_n \quad \dots\text{(ii)}$$

On multiplying Eqs. (i) and (ii), we get

$$(1+x)^{2n} = (C_0 + C_1x + C_2x^2 + \dots + C_{n-r}x^{n-r} + \dots + C_nx^n)\times(C_0x^n + C_1x^{n-1} + C_2x^{n-2} + \dots + C_rx^{n-r} + C_{r+1}x^{n-r-1} + C_{r+2}x^{n-r-2} + \dots + C_n) \quad \dots\text{(iii)}$$

Now, coefficient of x^{n-r} on LHS of Eq. (iii) $= {}^{2n}C_{n-r}$

$$= \frac{2n!}{(n-r)!(n+r)!}$$

and coefficient of x^{n-r} on RHS of Eq. (iii)

$$= C_0C_r + C_1C_{r+1} + C_2C_{r+2} + \dots + C_{n-r}C_n$$

But Eq. (iii) is an identity, therefore coefficient of x^{n-r} in RHS = coefficient of x^{n-r} in LHS.

$$\Rightarrow C_0C_r + C_1C_{r+1} + C_2C_{r+2} + \dots + C_{n-r}C_n = \frac{2n!}{(n-r)!(n+r)!}$$

Aliter

Given,

$$(1+x)^n = C_0 + C_1x + C_2x^2 + \dots + C_rx^r + C_{r+1}x^{r+1} + C_{r+2}x^{r+2} + \dots + C_{n-r}x^r + \dots + C_nx^n \quad \dots\text{(i)}$$

$$\text{Now, } \left(1+\frac{1}{x}\right)^n = C_0 + \frac{C_1}{x} + \frac{C_2}{x^2} + \dots + \frac{C_r}{x^r} + \frac{C_{r+1}}{x^{r+1}} + \frac{C_{r+2}}{x^{r+2}} + \dots + \frac{C_{n-r}}{x^{n-r}} + \dots + \frac{C_n}{x^n} \quad \dots\text{(ii)}$$

On multiplying Eqs. (i) and (ii), we get

$$\frac{(1+x)^{2n}}{x^n} = (C_0 + C_1x + C_2x^2 + \dots + C_rx^r + C_{r+1}x^{r+1} + C_{r+2}x^{r+2} + \dots + C_{n-r}x^{n-r} + \dots + C_nx^n)$$
$$\times \left(C_0 + \frac{C_1}{x} + \frac{C_2}{x^2} + \dots + \frac{C_r}{x^r} + \frac{C_{r+1}}{x^{r+1}} + \frac{C_{r+2}}{x^{r+2}} + \dots + \frac{C_{n-r}}{x^{n-r}} + \dots + \frac{C_n}{x^n}\right) \quad \dots\text{(iii)}$$

Now, coefficient of $\frac{1}{x^r}$ in RHS

$$= (C_0C_r + C_1C_{r+1} + C_2C_{r+2} + \dots + C_{n-r}C_n)$$

$\therefore$ Coefficient of $\frac{1}{x^r}$ in LHS = Coefficient of x^{n-r} in

$$(1+x)^{2n} = {}^{2n}C_{n-r} = \frac{2n!}{(n-r)!(n+r)!}$$

But Eq. (iii) is an identity, therefore coefficient of $\frac{1}{x^r}$ in RHS = coefficient of $\frac{1}{x^r}$ in LHS.

$$\Rightarrow C_0C_r + C_1C_{r+1} + C_2C_{r+2} + \dots + C_{n-r}C_n = \frac{2n!}{(n-r)!(n+r)!}$$

***Corollary* I** For $r = 0$,

$$C_0^2 + C_1^2 + C_2^2 + \dots + C_n^2 = \frac{2n!}{(n!)^2}$$

***Corollary* II** For $r = 1$,

$$C_0C_1 + C_1C_2 + C_2C_3 + \dots + C_{n-1}C_n = \frac{2n!}{(n-1)!(n+1)!}$$

***Corollary* III** For $r = 2$,

$$C_0C_2 + C_1C_3 + C_2C_4 + \dots + C_{n-2}C_n = \frac{2n!}{(n-2)!(n+2)!}$$

Example 73. If $(1+x)^n = C_0 + C_1x + C_2x^2 + \dots + C_nx^n$, prove that $C_0^2 + C_1^2 + C_2^2 = \frac{2n!}{n!\,n!} = \frac{1\cdot3\cdot5\dots(2n-1)}{n!}\cdot 2^n$.

Sol. Given, $(1+x)^n = C_0 + C_1x + C_2x^2 + \dots + C_nx^n \quad \dots\text{(i)}$

Now, $(x+1)^n = C_0x^n + C_1x^{n-1} + C_2x^{n-2} + \dots + C_n \quad \dots\text{(ii)}$

On multiplying Eqs. (i) and (ii), we get

$$(1+x)^{2n} = (C_0 + C_1x + C_2x^2 + \dots + C_nx^n) \times (C_0x^n + C_1x^{n-1} + C_2x^{n-2} + \dots + C_n) \quad \dots\text{(iii)}$$

Now, coefficient of x^n in RHS

$$= C_0^2 + C_1^2 + C_2^2 + \dots + C_n^2$$

And coefficient of x^n in LHS $= {}^{2n}C_n = \frac{2n!}{n!\,n!}$

$$= \frac{1\cdot2\cdot3\cdot4\cdot5\dots(2n-1)\,2n}{n!\,n!} = \frac{1\cdot3\cdot5\dots(2n-1)\,2^n\,n!}{n!\,n!}$$

But Eq. (iii) is an identity, therefore coefficient of x^n in RHS = coefficient of x^n in LHS.

$$\Rightarrow C_0^2 + C_1^2 + C_2^2 + \dots + C_n^2 = \frac{2n!}{n!\,n!} = \frac{1\cdot3\cdot5\dots(2n-1)}{n!}\cdot 2^n$$

Aliter

Given, $(1+x)^n = C_0 + C_1x + C_2x^2 + \dots + C_nx^n \quad \dots\text{(i)}$

$$\text{Now, } \left(1+\frac{1}{x}\right)^n = C_0 + \frac{C_1}{x} + \frac{C_2}{x^2} + \dots + \frac{C_n}{x^n} \quad \dots\text{(ii)}$$

On multiplying Eqs. (i) and (ii), we get

$$\frac{(1+x)^{2n}}{x^n} = (C_0 + C_1x + C_2x^2 + \dots + C_nx^n) \times \left(C_0 + \frac{C_1}{x} + \frac{C_2}{x^2} + \dots + \frac{C_n}{x^n}\right) \quad \dots\text{(iii)}$$

Now, constant term in RHS $= C_0^2 + C_1^2 + C_2^2 + \dots + C_n^2$

Constant term in LHS = Constant term in $\frac{(1+x)^{2n}}{x^n}$

$$= \text{Coefficient of } x^n \text{ in } (1+x)^{2n} = {}^{2n}C_n = \frac{2n!}{n!\,n!}$$

$$= \frac{n!\,2^n\,[1\cdot3\cdot5\dots(2n-1)]}{n!\,n!} = \frac{2^n\,[1\cdot3\cdot5\dots(2n-1)]}{n!}$$

But Eq. (iii) is an identity, therefore the constant term in RHS = constant term in LHS.

$$\Rightarrow C_0^2 + C_1^2 + C_2^2 + \dots + C_n^2 = \frac{2n!}{n!\,n!} = \frac{\{1\cdot 3\cdot 5\dots(2n-1)\}}{n!}2^n$$

Case II If terms of the series alternately positive and negative, then

$$(1-x)^n = C_0 - C_1 x + C_2 x^2 - \dots + (-1)^n C_n x^n \quad \dots\text{(i)}$$

$$\text{and } (x+1)^n = C_0 x^n + C_1 x^{n-1} + C_2 x^{n-2} + \dots + C_n \quad \dots\text{(ii)}$$

Then, multiplying Eqs. (i) and (ii) and equate the coefficient of suitable power of x on both sides.

Or

Replacing x by $\frac{1}{x}$ in Eq. (i), we get

$$\left(1-\frac{1}{x}\right)^n = C_0 - \frac{C_1}{x} + \frac{C_2}{x^2} - \dots + (-1)^n \frac{C_n}{x^n} \quad \dots\text{(iii)}$$

Then, multiplying Eqs. (i) and (iii) and equate the coefficient of suitable power of x on both sides.

Example 74. Prove that $({}^{2n}C_0)^2 - ({}^{2n}C_1)^2 + ({}^{2n}C_2)^2 - \dots + ({}^{2n}C_{2n})^2 = (-1)^n \cdot {}^{2n}C_n$.

Sol. Since, $(1-x)^{2n} = {}^{2n}C_0 - {}^{2n}C_1 x + {}^{2n}C_2 x^2 - \dots + (-1)^{2n} \cdot {}^{2n}C_{2n} x^{2n}$

or $(1-x)^{2n} = {}^{2n}C_0 - {}^{2n}C_1 x + {}^{2n}C_2 x^2 - \dots + {}^{2n}C_{2n} x^{2n}$ ...(i)

and $(x+1)^{2n} = {}^{2n}C_0 x^{2n} + {}^{2n}C_1 x^{2n-1} + {}^{2n}C_2 x^{2n-2} + \dots + {}^{2n}C_{2n}$ ...(ii)

On multiplying Eqs. (i) and (ii), we get

$$(x^2-1)^{2n} = ({}^{2n}C_0 - {}^{2n}C_1 x + {}^{2n}C_2 x^2 - \dots + {}^{2n}C_{2n} x^{2n}) \times ({}^{2n}C_0 x^{2n} + {}^{2n}C_1 x^{2n-1} + {}^{2n}C_2 x^{2n-2} + \dots + {}^{2n}C_{2n}) \quad \dots\text{(iii)}$$

Now, coefficient of x^{2n} in RHS

$$= ({}^{2n}C_0)^2 - ({}^{2n}C_1)^2 + ({}^{2n}C_2)^2 - \dots + ({}^{2n}C_{2n})^2$$

Now, LHS can also be written as $(1-x^2)^{2n}$.

$\therefore$ General term in LHS, $T_{r+1} = {}^{2n}C_r(-x^2)^r$

Putting $r = n$, we get $T_{n+1} = (-1)^n \cdot {}^{2n}C_n x^{2n}$

$\Rightarrow$ Coefficient of x^{2n} in LHS $= (-1)^n \cdot {}^{2n}C_n$

But Eq. (iii) is an identity, therefore coefficient of x^{2n} in RHS = coefficient of x^{2n} in LHS

$$\Rightarrow ({}^{2n}C_0)^2 - ({}^{2n}C_1)^2 + ({}^{2n}C_2)^2 - \dots + ({}^{2n}C_{2n})^2 = (-1)^n \cdot {}^{2n}C_n$$

Aliter

Since, $(1+x)^{2n} = {}^{2n}C_0 + {}^{2n}C_1 x + {}^{2n}C_2 x^2 + \dots + {}^{2n}C_{2n} x^{2n}$ ...(i)

and $\left(1-\frac{1}{x}\right)^{2n} = {}^{2n}C_0 - \frac{{}^{2n}C_1}{x} + \frac{{}^{2n}C_2}{x^2} - \dots + \frac{{}^{2n}C_{2n}}{x^{2n}}$ ...(ii)

On multiplying Eqs. (i) and (ii), we get

$$\frac{(x^2-1)^{2n}}{x^{2n}} = ({}^{2n}C_0 + {}^{2n}C_1 x + {}^{2n}C_2 x^2 + \dots + {}^{2n}C_{2n} x^{2n}) \times \left({}^{2n}C_0 - \frac{{}^{2n}C_1}{x} + \frac{{}^{2n}C_2}{x^2} - \dots + \frac{{}^{2n}C_{2n}}{x^{2n}}\right) \quad \dots\text{(iii)}$$

Now, constant term in RHS

$$= ({}^{2n}C_0)^2 - ({}^{2n}C_1)^2 + ({}^{2n}C_2)^2 - \dots + ({}^{2n}C_{2n})^2$$

Constant term in LHS = Constant term in $\frac{(x^2-1)^{2n}}{x^{2n}}$

$= $ Coefficient of x^{2n} in $(x^2-1)^{2n}$

$= $ Coefficient of x^{2n} in $(1-x^2)^{2n}$

$= {}^{2n}C_n(-1)^n = (-1)^n \cdot {}^{2n}C_n$

But Eq. (iii) is an identity, therefore the constant term in RHS = constant term in LHS.

$$\Rightarrow ({}^{2n}C_0)^2 - ({}^{2n}C_1)^2 + ({}^{2n}C_2)^2 - \dots + ({}^{2n}C_{2n})^2 = (-1)^n \cdot {}^{2n}C_n$$

Example 75. If $(1+x)^n = C_0 + C_1 x + C_2 x^2 + \dots + C_n x^n$, prove that $C_0^2 - C_1^2 + C_2^2 - \dots + (-1)^n \cdot C_n^2 = 0$ or $(-1)^{n/2} \cdot \frac{n!}{(n/2)!\,(n/2)!}$, according as n is odd or even. Also, evaluate $C_0^2 + C_1^2 + C_2^2 - \dots + (-1)^n \cdot C_n^2$ for $n = 10$ and $n = 11$

Sol. Since, $(1-x)^n = C_0 - C_1 x + C_2 x^2 - \dots + (-1)^n C_n x^n$ ...(i)

and $(x+1)^n = C_0 x^n + C_1 x^{n-1} + C_2 x^{n-2} + \dots + C_n$ ...(ii)

On multiplying Eqs. (i) and (ii), we get

$$(1-x^2)^n = \{C_0 - C_1 x + C_2 x^2 - \dots + (-1)^n C_n x^n\} \times (C_0 x^n + C_1 x^{n-1} + C_2 x^{n-2} + \dots + C_n) \quad \dots\text{(iii)}$$

Now, coefficient of x^n in RHS

$$= C_0^2 - C_1^2 + C_2^2 - \dots + (-1)^n C_n^2$$

General term in LHS $= T_{r+1} = {}^nC_r(-x^2)^r = {}^nC_r(-1)^r x^{2r}$

Putting $2r = n$, we get $r = n/2$

$\therefore \quad T_{(n/2)+1} = {}^nC_{n/2}(-1)^{n/2} x^n$

$\therefore$ Coefficient of x^n in LHS $= {}^nC_{n/2}(-1)^{n/2}$

$$= (-1)^{n/2} \cdot \frac{n!}{(n/2)!\,(n/2)!}$$

$$= \begin{cases} 0, & \text{if } n \text{ is odd} \\ (-1)^{n/2}\dfrac{n!}{(n/2)!\,(n/2)!}, & \text{if } n \text{ is even} \end{cases} \quad \left[\because \left(\frac{\text{odd}}{2}\right)! = \infty\right]$$

But Eq. (iii) is an identity, therefore coefficient of x^n in RHS = coefficient of x^n in LHS.

$$\Rightarrow C_0^2 - C_1^2 + C_2^2 - \dots + (-1)^n C_n^2 = \begin{cases} 0 & ,\text{if } n \text{ is odd} \\ (-1)^{n/2} \dfrac{n!}{(n/2)!\,(n/2)!}, & \text{if } n \text{ is even} \end{cases}$$

Now, for $n = 10$,

$$C_0^2 - C_1^2 + C_2^2 - \dots + C_{10}^2 = (-1)^{10/2} \frac{10!}{5!\,5!} = -252$$

[$\because$ 10 is even]

and from $n = 11$,

$$C_0^2 - C_1^2 + C_2^2 - \dots - C_{11}^2 = 0 \quad [\because 11 \text{ is odd}]$$

Aliter

Since, $(1+x)^n = C_0 + C_1 x + C_2 x^2 + \dots + C_n x^n$ ...(i)

Replacing x by $-\frac{1}{x}$, then we get

$$\left(1 - \frac{1}{x}\right)^n = C_0 - \frac{C_1}{x} + \frac{C_2}{x^2} - \dots + (-1)^n \frac{C_n}{x^n} \quad \text{...(ii)}$$

On multiplying Eqs. (i) and (ii), we get

$$\frac{(x^2-1)^n}{x^n} = (C_0 + C_1 x + C_2 x^2 + \dots + C_n x^n) \times \left(C_0 - \frac{C_1}{x} + \frac{C_2}{x^2} - \dots + (-1)^n \frac{C_n}{x^n}\right) \quad \text{...(iii)}$$

Now, constant term in RHS

$$= C_0^1 - C_1^2 + C_2^2 - \dots + (-1)^n C_n^2$$

$\therefore$ Constant term in LHS

$$= \text{Constant term in } \frac{(x^2-1)^n}{x^n}$$

$$= \text{Coefficient of } x^n \text{ in } (x^2-1)^n$$

$$= \text{Coefficient of } x^n \text{ in } {}^nC_{n/2} (x^2)^{n-(n/2)} (-1)^{n/2}$$

$$= (-1)^{n/2} \cdot {}^nC_{n/2}$$

$$= (-1)^{n/2} \cdot \frac{n!}{(n/2)!\,(n/2)!}$$

$$= \begin{cases} 0, & \text{if } n \text{ is odd} \\ (-1)^{n/2} \cdot \dfrac{n!}{(n/2)!\,(n/2)!}, & \text{if } n \text{ is even} \end{cases}$$

But Eq. (iii) is an identity, therefore the constant term in RHS = constant term in LHS.

$$\Rightarrow C_0^2 - C_1^2 + C_2^2 - \dots + (-1)^n C_n^2 = \begin{cases} 0, & \text{if } n \text{ is odd} \\ (-1)^{n/2} \cdot \dfrac{n!}{(n/2)!\,(n/2)!}, & \text{if } n \text{ is even} \end{cases}$$

2. If sum of the lower suffixes of binomial coefficients in each term is same.

i.e., $C_0 C_n + C_1 C_{n-1} + C_2 C_{n-2} + \dots + C_n C_0$

Here, $0 + n = 1 + (n-1) = 2 + (n-2) = \dots = n + 0 = n$

***Case* I** If each term of series is positive, then

$$(1+x)^n = C_0 + C_1 x + C_2 x^2 + \dots + C_n x^n \quad \text{...(}$$

and $(1+x)^n = C_0 + C_1 x + C_2 x^2 + \dots + C_n x^n$ ...(i

Then, multiplying Eqs. (i) and (ii) and equate the coefficient of suitable power of x on both sides.

Example 76. Prove that ${}^{m+n}C_r = {}^mC_r + {}^mC_{r-1}\,{}^nC_1 + {}^mC_{r-2}\,{}^nC_2 + \dots + {}^nC_r$ if $r < m, r < n$ and m, n, r are positive integers.

Sol. Here, sum of lower suffixes of binomial coefficients in each term is r.

i.e. $r = r - 1 + 1 = r - 2 + 2 = \dots = r = r$

Since,

$$(1+x)^m = {}^mC_0 + {}^mC_1 x + \dots + {}^mC_{r-2} x^{r-2} + {}^mC_{r-1} x^{r-1} + {}^mC_r x^r + \dots + {}^mC_m x^m \quad \text{...(}$$

and $(1+x)^n = {}^nC_0 + {}^nC_1 x + {}^nC_2 x^2 + \dots + {}^nC_r x^r + \dots + {}^nC_n x^n$ ...(i

On multiplying Eqs. (i) and (ii), we get

$$(1+x)^{m+n} = ({}^mC_0 + {}^mC_1 x + \dots + {}^mC_{r-2} x^{r-2} + {}^mC_{r-1} x^{r-1} + {}^mC_r x^r + \dots + {}^mC_m x^m) \times ({}^nC_0 + {}^nC_1 x + {}^nC_2 x^2 + \dots + {}^nC_r x^r + \dots + {}^nC_n x^n) \quad \text{...(iii)}$$

Now, coefficient of x^r in RHS

$$= {}^mC_r \cdot {}^nC_0 + {}^mC_{r-1} \cdot {}^nC_1 + {}^mC_{r-2} \cdot {}^nC_2 + \dots + {}^mC_0 \cdot {}^nC_r$$

$$= {}^mC_r + {}^mC_{r-1} \cdot {}^nC_1 + {}^mC_{r-2} \cdot {}^nC_2 + \dots + {}^nC_r$$

Coefficient of x^r in LHS $= {}^{m+n}C_r$

But Eq. (iii) is an identity, therefore coefficient of x^r in LHS = coefficient of x^r in RHS.

$$\Rightarrow {}^{m+n}C_r = {}^mC_r + {}^mC_{r-1} \cdot {}^nC_1 + {}^mC_{r-2} \cdot {}^nC_2 + \dots + {}^nC_r$$

***Case* II** If terms of the series alternately positive and negative, then

$$(1-x)^n = C_0 - C_1 x + C_2 x^2 - \dots + (-1)^n C_n x^n \quad \text{...(i}$$

and $(1+x)^n = C_0 + C_1 x + C_2 x^2 + \dots + C_n x^n$ ...(ii

Then, multiplying Eqs. (i) and (ii) and equate the coefficient of suitable power of x on both sides.

Example 77. If $(1+x)^n = C_0 + C_1 x + C_2 x^2 + \dots + C_n x^n$, prove that $C_0 C_n - C_1 C_{n-1} + C_2 C_{n-2} - \dots + (-1)^n C_n C_0 = 0$ or $(-1)^{n/2} \dfrac{n!}{(n/2)!\,(n/2)!}$, according as n is odd or even.

Sol. Given, $(1+x)^n = C_0 + C_1x + C_2x^2 + \ldots + C_{n-2}x^{n-2} + C_{n-1}x^{n-1} + C_n x^n \quad \ldots(i)$

and $(1-x)^n = C_0 - C_1x + C_2x^2 - \ldots + (-1)^n C_n x^n \quad \ldots(ii)$

On multiplying Eqs. (i) and (ii), we get

$$(1-x^2)^n = (C_0 + C_1x + C_2x^2 + \ldots + C_{n-2}x^{n-2} + C_{n-1}x^{n-1} + C_n x^n) \times (C_2 - C_1x + C_2x^2 - \ldots + (-1)^n C_n x^n) \quad \ldots(iii)$$

Now, coefficient of x^n in RHS

$$= C_0C_n - C_1C_{n-1} + C_2C_{n-2} - \ldots + (-1)^n C_nC_0$$

Now, general term in LHS,

$$T_{r+1} = {}^nC_r(-x^2)^r = (-1)^r \cdot {}^nC_r x^{2r}$$

Putting $2r = n$, we get

$$r = n/2$$

Now, $T_{n/2+1} = (-1)^{n/2} \cdot {}^nC_{n/2} x^n$

$\therefore$ Coefficient of x^n in LHS $= (-1)^{n/2} \cdot {}^nC_{n/2}$

$$= (-1)^{n/2} \cdot \frac{n!}{(n/2)!(n/2)!}$$

$$= \begin{cases} 0 & \text{if } n \text{ is odd} \\ (-1)^{n/2} \cdot \dfrac{n!}{(n/2)!(n/2)!}, & \text{if } n \text{ is even} \end{cases}$$

But Eq. (iii) is an identity, therefore the coefficient of x^n in RHS = coefficient of x^n in LHS.

$$\Rightarrow C_0C_n - C_1C_{n-1} + C_2C_{n-2} - \ldots + (-1)^n C_nC_0$$

$$= \begin{cases} 0, & \text{if } n \text{ is odd} \\ (-1)^{n/2} \cdot \dfrac{n!}{(n/2)!(n/2)!}, & \text{if } n \text{ is even} \end{cases}$$

3. If each term is the product of two binomial coefficient divided or multiplied by an integer, then integrating or differentiating by preceeding method. Then, multiplying two series and equate the coefficient of suitable power of x on both sides.

Example 78. If $(1+x)^n = C_0 + C_1x + C_2x^2 + C_3x^3 + \ldots + C_n x^n$, prove that $C_1^2 + 2C_2^2 + 3C_3^2 + \ldots + nC_n^2 = \dfrac{(2n-1)!}{((n-1)!)^2}$.

Sol. Given, $(1+x)^n = C_0 + C_1x + C_2x^2 + C_3x^3 + \ldots + C_n x^n$

Differentiating both sides w.r.t. x, we get

$$n(1+x)^{n-1} = 0 + C_1 + 2C_2x + 3C_3x^2 + \ldots + nC_n x^{n-1}$$

$$\Rightarrow n(1+x)^{n-1} = C_1 + 2C_2x + 3C_3x^2 + \ldots + nC_n x^{n-1} \quad \ldots(i)$$

and $(x+1)^n = C_0x^n + C_1x^{n-1} + C_2x^{n-2} + C_3x^{n-3} + \ldots + C_n \quad \ldots(ii)$

On multiplying Eqs. (i) and (ii), then we get

$$n(1+x)^{2n-1} = (C_1 + 2C_2x + 3C_3x^2 + \ldots + nC_n x^{n-1}) \times (C_0x^n + C_1x^{n-1} + C_2x^{n-2} + C_3x^{n-3} + \ldots + C_n) \quad \ldots(iii)$$

Now, coefficient of x^{n-1} on RHS

$$= C_1^2 + 2C_2^2 + 3C_3^2 + \ldots + nC_n^2$$

and coefficient of x^{n-1} on LHS

$$= n \cdot {}^{2n-1}C_{n-1} = n \cdot \frac{(2n-1)!}{(n-1)!\,n!}$$

$$= \frac{(2n-1)!}{(n-1)!(n-1)!} = \frac{(2n-1)!}{\{(n-1)!)^2\}}$$

But Eq. (iii) is an identity, therefore the coefficient of x^{n-1} in RHS = coefficient of x^{n-1} in LHS.

$$\Rightarrow \quad C_1^2 + 2C_2^2 + 3C_3^2 + \ldots + nC_n^2 = \frac{(2n-1)!}{\{(n-1)!\}}$$

Example 79. If $(1+x)^n = C_0 + C_1x + C_2x^2 + \ldots + C_n x^n$, prove that $C_0^2 + \dfrac{C_1^2}{2} + \dfrac{C_2^2}{3} + \ldots + \dfrac{C_n^2}{n+1} = \dfrac{(2n+1)!}{\{(n+1)!\}^2}$.

Sol. Given, $(1+x)^n = C_0 + C_1x + C_2x^2 + \ldots + C_n x^n$

Integrating both sides w.r.t. x within limits 0 to x, then we get

$$\int_0^x (1+x)^n\,dx = \int_0^x (C_0 + C_1x + C_2x^2 + \ldots + C_n x^n)\,dx$$

$$\frac{(1+x)^{n+1} - 1}{(1+n)} = C_0x + \frac{C_1x^2}{2} + \frac{C_2x^3}{3} + \ldots + \frac{C_n x^{n+1}}{n+1} \quad \ldots(i)$$

and $(x+1)^n = C_0x^n + C_1x^{n-1} + C_2x^{n-2} + \ldots + C_n \quad \ldots(ii)$

Multiplying Eqs. (i) and (ii), we get

$$\frac{1}{(n+1)}\{(1+x)^{2n+1} - (1+x)^n\}$$

$$= \left(C_0x + \frac{C_1x^2}{2} + \frac{C_2x^3}{3} + \ldots + \frac{C_n x^{n+1}}{n+1}\right)$$

$$\times (C_0x^n + C_1x^{n-1} + C_2x^{n-2} + \ldots + C_n) \quad \ldots(iii)$$

Now, coefficient of x^{n-1} in RHS of Eq. (iii)

$$= C_0^2 + \frac{C_1^2}{2} + \frac{C_2^2}{3} + \ldots + \frac{C_n^2}{n+1}$$

and coefficient of x^{n+1} in LHS of Eq. (iii)

$$= \frac{1}{(n+1)}\{{}^{2n+1}C_{n+1} - 0\}$$

$$= \frac{1}{(n+1)} \cdot \frac{(2n+1)!}{(n+1)!\,n!}$$

$$= \frac{(2n+1)!}{(n+1)!(n+1)!} = \frac{(2n+1)!}{\{(n+1)!\}^2}$$

But Eq. (iii) is an identity, therefore coefficient of x^{n+1} in RHS of Eq. (iii) = coefficient of x^{n+1} in LHS of Eq. (iii).

$$\Rightarrow C_0^2 + \frac{C_1^2}{2} + \frac{C_2^2}{3} + \dots + \frac{C_n^2}{n+1} = \frac{(2n+1)!}{\{(n+1)!\}^2}$$

Binomial Inside Binomial

The upper suffices of binomial coefficients are different but lower suffices are same.

| Example 80. Evaluate $\sum_{r=0}^{n} {}^{n+r}C_n$.

Sol. $\sum_{r=0}^{n} {}^{n+r}C_n = {}^nC_n + {}^{n+1}C_n + {}^{n+2}C_n + \dots + {}^{2n}C_n$

$= $ Coefficient of x^n in

$[(1+x)^n + (1+x)^{n+1} + (1+x)^{n+2} + \dots + \dots + (1+x)^{2n}]$

$= $ Coefficient of x^n in $\left[\frac{(1+x)^n[(1+x)^{n+1}-1]}{(1+x)-1}\right]$

$= $ Coefficient of x^{n+1} in $[(1+x)^{2n+1} - (1+x)^n]$

$= {}^{2n+1}C_{n+1} - 0 = {}^{2n+1}C_n$

| Example 81. If $(1+x)^n = C_0 + C_1x + C_2x^2 + \dots + C_nx^n$, prove that $C_0 \cdot {}^{2n}C_n - C_1 \cdot {}^{2n-2}C_n + C_2 \cdot {}^{2n-4}C_n - \dots = 2^n$

Sol. LHS $= C_0 \cdot {}^{2n}C_n - C_1 \cdot {}^{2n-2}C_n + C_2 \cdot {}^{2n-4}C_n - \dots$

$= $ Coefficient of x^n in

$[C_0(1+x)^{2n} - C_1(1+x)^{2n-2} + C_2(1+x)^{2n-4} - \dots]$

$= $ Coefficient of x^n in

$[C_0(1+x)^2]^n - C_1[(1+x)^2]^{n-1} + C_2[(1+x)^2]^{n-2} - \dots]$

$= $ Coefficient of x^n in $[[(1+x)^2 - 1]^n]$

$= $ Coefficient of x^n in $(2x + x^2)^n$

$= $ Constant term in $(2+x)^n = 2^n = $ RHS

| Example 82. If $(1+x)^n = C_0 + C_1x + C_2x^2 + C_3x^3 + \dots + C_nx^n$, prove that

$C_0 \cdot {}^{2n}C_n - C_1 \cdot {}^{2n-1}C_n + C_2 \cdot {}^{2n-2}C_n - C_3 \cdot {}^{2n-3}C_n + \dots + (-1)^n C_n \cdot {}^nC_n = 1$

Sol. LHS $= C_0 \cdot {}^{2n}C_n - C_1 \cdot {}^{2n-1}C_n + C_2 \cdot {}^{2n-2}C_n - C_3 \cdot {}^{2n-3}C_n + \dots + (-1)^n C_n \cdot {}^nC_n$

$= $ Coefficient of x^n in

$[C_0(1+x)^{2n} - C_1(1+x)^{2n-1} + C_2(1+x)^{2n-2} - C_3(1+x)^{2n-3} + \dots + (-1)^n C_n \cdot (1+x)^n]$

$= $ Coefficient of x^n in

$(1+x)^n[C_0(1+x)^n - C_1(1+x)^{n-1} + C_2(1+x)^{n-2} - C_3(1+x)^{n-3} + \dots + (-1)^n C_n \cdot 1]$

$= $ Coefficient of x^n in $(1+x)^n[((1+x)-1)^n]$

$= $ Coefficient of x^n in $(1+x)^n \cdot x^n$d

$= $ Constant term in $(1+x)^n = 1 = $ RHS

Sum of the Series

***Case* I When *i* and *j* are independent.**

In this summation, three types of terms occur, when $i < j, i = j$ and $i > j$,

i.e., $\sum_{i=0}^{n}\sum_{j=0}^{n} a_i a_j = \sum_{i=0}^{n}\left\{a_i\left(\sum_{j=0}^{n} a_j\right)\right\}$

$= \sum_{i=0}^{n} a_i \sum_{j=0}^{n} a_j = \left(\sum_{i=0}^{n} a_i\right)^2$ or $\left(\sum_{j=0}^{n} a_j\right)^2$

***Corollary* I** $\sum_{i=0}^{n}\sum_{j=0}^{n} {}^nC_i\,{}^nC_j = \left(\sum_{i=0}^{n} {}^nC_i\right)^2$

$= (2^n)^2 = 2^{2n}$

| Example 83. If $(1+x)^n = C_0 + C_1x + C_2x^2 + \dots + C_nx^n$, find the values of the following.

(i) $\sum_{i=0}^{n}\sum_{j=0}^{n}(C_i + C_j)$

(ii) $\sum_{i=0}^{n}\sum_{j=0}^{n}(i+j)C_iC_j$

Sol. (i) $\sum_{i=0}^{n}\sum_{j=0}^{n}(C_i + C_j) = \sum_{i=0}^{n}\sum_{j=0}^{n} C_i + \sum_{i=0}^{n}\sum_{j=0}^{n} C_j$

$= \sum_{j=0}^{n}\left(\sum_{i=0}^{n} C_i\right) + \sum_{i=0}^{n}\left(\sum_{j=0}^{n} C_j\right)$

$= \sum_{j=0}^{n}(2^n) + \sum_{i=0}^{n}(2^n) = (n+1)\cdot 2^n + (n+1)\cdot 2^n$

$= 2(n+1)2^n = (n+1)2^{n+1}$

(ii) $\sum_{i=0}^{n}\sum_{j=0}^{n}(i+j)C_iC_j = \sum_{i=0}^{n}\sum_{j=0}^{n} iC_iC_j + \sum_{i=0}^{n}\sum_{j=0}^{n} jC_iC_j$

$= \sum_{i=0}^{n} iC_i\left(\sum_{j=0}^{n} C_j\right) + \sum_{j=0}^{n} jC_j\left(\sum_{i=0}^{n} C_i\right)$

$$= \sum_{i=0}^{n} i\, C_i\, (2^n) + \sum_{j=0}^{n} j\, C_j\, (2^n)$$

$$= 2^n \sum_{i=0}^{n} i\, {}^nC_i + 2^n \sum_{j=0}^{n} j\, {}^nC_j$$

$$= 2^n \sum_{i=0}^{n} i \cdot \frac{n}{i} \cdot {}^{n-1}C_{i-1} + 2^n \sum_{j=0}^{n} j \cdot \frac{n}{j} \cdot {}^{n-1}C_{j-1}$$

$$= n \cdot 2^n \sum_{i=0}^{n} {}^{n-1}C_{i-1} + n \cdot 2^n \sum_{j=0}^{n} {}^{n-1}C_{j-1}$$

$$= n \cdot 2^n \cdot 2^{n-1} + n \cdot 2^n \cdot 2^{n-1}$$

$$= n \cdot 2 \cdot 2^{2n-1} = n \cdot 2^{2n}$$

***Case* II When *i* and *j* are dependent.**

In this summation, when $i < j$ is equal to the sum of the terms when $i > j$, if a_i and a_j are symmetrical. So, in this case

$$\sum_{i=0}^{n} \sum_{j=0}^{n} a_i\, a_j = \sum\sum_{0 \le i < j \le n} a_i\, a_j + \sum\sum_{i=j} a_i a_j + \sum\sum_{0 \le j < i \le n} a_i a_j$$

$$= 2 \sum\sum_{0 \le i < j \le n} a_i\, a_j + \sum\sum_{i=j} a_i\, a_j$$

$$\Rightarrow \quad \sum\sum_{0 \le i < j \le n} a_i\, a_j = \frac{\sum_{i=0}^{n} \sum_{j=0}^{n} a_i\, a_j - \sum\sum_{i=j} a_i\, a_j}{2}$$

When a_i and a_j are not symmetrical, we find the sum by listing all the terms.

***Corollary* I**

$$\sum\sum_{0 \le i < j \le n} {}^nC_i\, {}^nC_j = \frac{\sum_{i=0}^{n} \sum_{j=0}^{n} {}^nC_i {}^nC_j - \sum\sum_{i=j} {}^nC_i \cdot {}^nC_j}{2}$$

$$= \frac{(2^n)^2 - \sum_{i=0}^{n} ({}^nC_i)^2}{2} = \frac{2^{2n} - {}^{2n}C_n}{2} = 2^{2n-1} - \frac{2n!}{2(n!)^2}$$

| Example 84. If $(1+x)^n = C_0 + C_1 x + C_2 x^2 + \ldots + C_n x^n$, find the values of the following.

(i) $\sum\sum_{0 \le i < j \le n} C_i$ (ii) $\sum\sum_{0 \le i < j \le n} j C_i$

(iii) $\sum\sum_{i \ne j} C_i\, C_j$ (iv) $\sum\sum_{0 \le i \le j \le n} C_i\, C_j$

(v) $\sum\sum_{0 \le i < j \le n} (C_i \pm C_j)^2$

(vi) $\sum\sum_{0 \le i < j \le n} (i + j) C_i\, C_j$

(vii) $\sum\sum_{0 \le i < j \le n} (i \cdot j) C_i\, C_j$

Sol. (i) $$\sum\sum_{0 \le i < j \le n} C_i = \frac{\left(\sum_{i=0}^{n} \sum_{j=0}^{n} C_i\right) - \sum\sum_{i=j} C_i}{2}$$

$$= \frac{(n+1) \sum_{i=0}^{n} C_i - \sum_{i=0}^{n} C_i}{2} = n \cdot 2^{n-1}$$

(ii) $$\sum\sum_{0 \le i < j \le n} j\, C_i = \sum_{r=0}^{n-1} {}^nC_r \{(r+1) + (r+2) + (r+3) + \ldots + n\}$$

$$= \sum_{r=0}^{n-1} {}^nC_r \cdot \frac{(n-r)(n+r+1)}{2}$$

$$= \frac{1}{2} \sum_{r=0}^{n-1} {}^nC_r\, (n^2 - r^2 + n - r)$$

$$= \frac{1}{2}(n^2 + n) \sum_{r=0}^{n-1} {}^nC_r - \frac{1}{2} \sum_{r=0}^{n-1} r \cdot {}^nC_r - \frac{1}{2} \sum_{r=0}^{n-1} r^2 \cdot {}^nC_r$$

$$= \frac{1}{2}(n^2 + n)(2^n - 1) - \frac{1}{2} \cdot n \cdot (2^{n-1} - 1) - \frac{1}{2} \cdot n\, [(n-1)(2^{n-2} - 1) + 2^{n-1} - 1]$$

$$= n\,(3n+1) \cdot 2^{n-3}$$

Remark

Here, j and C_i are not symmetrical.

(iii) Here, $i \ne j$ i.e., $i > j$ or $i < j$

But C_i and C_j are symmetrical.

$$\therefore \quad \sum\sum_{i \ne j} C_i\, C_j = 2 \sum\sum_{0 \le i < j \le n} C_i\, C_j$$

$$= 2\left(\frac{2^{2n} - {}^{2n}C_n}{2}\right) \quad \text{[from corollary I]}$$

$$= 2^{2n} - {}^{2n}C_n$$

(iv) $$\sum\sum_{0 \le i \le j \le n} C_i C_j = \sum\sum_{0 \le i < j \le n} C_i C_j + \sum\sum_{i=j} C_i C_j$$

$$= \frac{1}{2}(2^{2n} - {}^{2n}C_n) + {}^{2n}C_n \quad \text{[from corollary I]}$$

$$= \frac{1}{2}(2^{2n} + {}^{2n}C_n)$$

(v) $$\sum\sum_{0 \le i < j \le n} (C_i \pm C_j)^2 = \sum\sum_{0 \le i < j \le n} (C_i^2 + C_j^2 \pm 2\, C_i C_j)$$

$$= \sum\sum_{0 \le i < j \le n} (C_i^2 + C_j^2) \pm 2 \sum\sum_{0 \le i < j \le n} C_i\, C_j$$

$$\because \quad \sum\sum_{0 \le i < j \le n} (C_i^2 + C_j^2)$$

$$= \frac{\sum_{i=0}^{n} \sum_{j=0}^{n} (C_i^2 + C_j^2) - 2 \sum_{i=0}^{n} C_i^2}{2}$$

$$= \frac{\sum_{i=0}^{n} \left(\sum_{j=0}^{n} C_i^{\,2} + \sum_{j=0}^{n} C_j^2 \right) - 2 \cdot {}^{2n}C_n}{2}$$

$$= \frac{\sum_{i=0}^{n} ((n+1) C_i^{\,2} + {}^{2n}C_n) - 2 \cdot {}^{2n} C_n}{2}$$

$$= \frac{(n+1) \sum_{i=0}^{n} C_i^{\,2} + {}^{2n}C_n \sum_{i=0}^{n} 1 - 2 \cdot {}^{2n}C_n}{2}$$

$$= \frac{(n+1) \cdot {}^{2n}C_n + {}^{2n}C_n \cdot (n+1) - 2 \cdot {}^{2n}C_n}{2}$$

$$= n \cdot {}^{2n}C_n$$

$$\therefore \quad \sum_{0 \le i < j \le n}\sum (C_i \pm C_j)^2 = n \cdot {}^{2n}C_n \pm (2^{2n} - {}^{2n}C_n)$$

[from corollary 1]

$$= (n \mp 1)\, {}^{2n}C_n \pm 2^{2n};$$

$$\sum_{0 \le i < j \le n}\sum (i+j) C_i C_j$$

Remark

$$\sum_{0 \le i < j \le n}\sum (C_i + C_j) = n \cdot 2^n$$

(vi) $\sum_{0 \le i < j \le n}\sum (i+j) C_i C_j$

Let $P = \sum_{0 \le i < j \le n}\sum (i+j)\, C_i\, C_j$ ...(i)

Replacing i by $n - i$ and j by $n - j$ in Eq. (i), then we get

$$P = \sum_{0 \le i < j \le n}\sum (n - i + n - j)\, C_{n-i}\, C_{n-j}$$

[∵ sum of binomial expansion does not change if we replace r by $n - r$]

$$P = \sum_{0 \le i < j \le n}\sum (2n - i - j)\, C_i\, C_j$$

$[\because {}^nC_r = {}^nC_{n-r}]$ ...(ii)

On adding Eqs. (i) and (ii), we get

$$2P = 2n \sum_{0 \le i < j \le n}\sum C_i\, C_j$$

or $P = n \sum_{0 \le i < j \le n}\sum C_i\, C_j = \frac{n}{2}(2^{2n} - {}^{2n}C_n)$

[from corollary I]

(vii) $\sum_{0 \le i < j \le n}\sum (i \cdot j)\, C_i\, C_j = \sum_{0 \le i < j \le n}\sum (i\, {}^nC_i)(j \cdot {}^nC_j)$

$$= n^2 \sum_{0 \le i < j \le n}\sum {}^{n-1}C_{i-1}\; {}^{n-1}C_{j-1}$$

$$= n^2 \left[\frac{2^{2(n-1)} - {}^{2n-2}C_{n-1}}{2} \right] \text{[from corollary I]}$$

$$= n^2 \left(2^{2n-3} - \frac{1}{2} \cdot {}^{2n-2}C_{n-1} \right)$$

Exercise for Session 4

1. The coefficient of $a^4 b^8 c^9 d^9$ in the expansion of $(abc + abd + acd + bcd)^{10}$ is

(a) $10!$ (b) $\frac{10!}{4!8!9!9!}$ (c) 2520 (d) None of these

2. If $(1+2x+3x^2)^{10} = a_0 + a_1 x + a_2 x^2 + \ldots + a_{20} x^{20}$, then a_1 equals

(a) 210 (b) 20 (c) 10 (d) None of these

3. If $(1+x+x^2+x^3)^5 = a_0 + a_1 x + a_2 x^2 + \ldots + a_{15} x^{15}$, then a_{10} equals

(a) 99 (b) 100 (c) 101 (d) 110

4. Coefficient of x^{15} in $(1+x+x^3+x^4)^n$ is

(a) $\sum_{r=0}^{5} {}^nC_{5-r} \cdot {}^nC_{3r}$ (b) $\sum_{r=0}^{5} {}^nC_{5r}$ (c) $\sum_{r=0}^{5} {}^nC_{2r}$ (d) $\sum_{r=0}^{3} {}^nC_{3-r} \cdot {}^nC_{5r}$

5. The number of terms in the expansion of $\left(x^2 + 1 + \frac{1}{x^2}\right)^n, n \in N$ is

(a) ${}^{n+2}C_2$ (b) ${}^{n+3}C_2$ (c) ${}^{2n+1}C_{2n}$ (d) ${}^{3n+1}C_{3n}$

6. If $(1+x)^{10} = a_0 + a_1 x + a_2 x^2 + \ldots + a_{10} x^{10}$, then $(a_0 - a_2 + a_4 - a_6 + a_8 - a_{10})^2 + (a_1 - a_3 + a_5 - a_7 + a_9)^2$ is equal to

(a) 2^9 (b) 3^9 (c) 2^{10} (d) 3^{10}

7. If $(1+x)^n = C_0 + C_1 x + C_2 x^2 + C_3 x^3 + \ldots + C_n x^n$, n being even the value of $C_0 + (C_0 + C_1) + (C_0 + C_1 + C_2) + \ldots + (C_0 + C_1 + C_2 + \ldots + C_{n-1})$ is equal to

(a) $n \cdot 2^n$ (b) $n \cdot 2^{n-1}$ (c) $n \cdot 2^{n-2}$ (d) $n \cdot 2^{n-3}$

8. The value of $\frac{C_0}{1 \cdot 3} - \frac{C_1}{2 \cdot 3} + \frac{C_2}{3 \cdot 3} - \frac{C_3}{4 \cdot 3} + \ldots + (-1)^n \frac{C_n}{(n+1) \cdot 3}$ is

(a) $\frac{3}{n+1}$ (b) $\frac{n+1}{3}$ (c) $\frac{1}{3(n+1)}$ (d) None of these

9. The value of $\binom{50}{0}\binom{50}{1} + \binom{50}{1}\binom{50}{2} + \ldots + \binom{50}{49}\binom{50}{50}$, where ${}^nC_r = \binom{n}{r}$, is

(a) $\binom{100}{50}$ (b) $\binom{100}{51}$ (c) $\binom{50}{25}$ (d) $\binom{50}{25}^2$

10. If C_r stands for ${}^4C_r$, then $C_0 C_4 - C_1 C_3 + C_2 C_2 - C_3 C_1 + C_4 C_0$ is equal to

(a) C_1 (b) C_2 (c) C_3 (d) C_4

11. The sum $\sum_{r=0}^{n} (r+1)({}^nC_r)^2$ is equal to

(a) $\frac{(n+2)(2n-1)!}{n!(n-1)!}$ (b) $\frac{(n+2)(2n+1)!}{n!(n-1)!}$ (c) $\frac{(n+2)(2n+1)!}{n!(n+1)!}$ (d) $\frac{(n+2)(2n-1)!}{n!(n+1)!}$

12. $\sum_{r=1}^{n} \left(\sum_{p=0}^{r-1} {}^nC_r \, {}^rC_p \, 2^p \right)$ is equal to

(a) $4^n - 3^n + 1$ (b) $4^n - 3^n - 1$ (c) $4^n - 3^n + 2$ (d) $4^n - 3^n$

13. $\left(\sum_{r=0}^{10} {}^{10}C_r \right) \left(\sum_{m=0}^{10} (-1)^m \frac{{}^{10}C_m}{2^m} \right)$ is equal to

(a) 1 (b) 2^5 (c) 2^{10} (d) 2^{20}

14. The value of $\sum\sum\sum\sum_{0 \le i < j < k < l \le n} 2$ is equal to

(a) $2(n+1)^3$ (b) $2 \cdot {}^{n+1}C_4$ (c) $2(n+1)^4$ (d) $2 \cdot {}^{n+2}C_3$

Shortcuts and Important Results to Remember

1 $(r + 1)$th term from end in the expansion of $(x + y)^n = (r + 1)$th term from beginning in the expansion of $(y + x)^n$.

2 If ${}^nC_{r-1}, {}^nC_r, {}^nC_{r+1}$ are in AP, then $(n - 2r)^2 = n + 2$ or $r = \frac{1}{2}(n \pm \sqrt{(n+2)})$ for $r = 2,\ n = 7$ and for $r = 5, n = 7, 14$.

3 Four consecutive binomial coefficients can never be in AP.

4 Three consecutive binomial coefficients can never be in GP or HP.

5 If a, b, c, d are four consecutive coefficients in the expansion of $(1 + x)^n$, then $\frac{a}{a+b}, \frac{b}{b+c}, \frac{c}{c+d}$ are in AP.

(i) $\frac{a}{a+b} + \frac{c}{c+d} = 2\left(\frac{b}{b+c}\right)$

(ii) $\left(\frac{b}{b+c}\right)^2 > \frac{ac}{(a+b)(c+d)}$

6 If greatest term in $(1 + x)^{2n}$ has the greatest coefficient, then $\frac{n}{n+1} < x < \frac{n+1}{n}$.

7 (a) The coefficient of x^{n-1} in the expansion of

$$(x-1)(x-2)(x-3)\ldots(x-n) = -(1+2+3+\ldots+n) = -\frac{n(n+1)}{2} = -{}^{n+1}C_2$$

(b) The coefficient of x^{n-1} in the expansion of

$$(x+1)(x+2)(x+3)\ldots(x+n) = (1+2+3+\ldots+n) = \frac{n(n+1)}{2} = {}^{n+1}C_2$$

8 The number of terms in the expansion of

$$(x+a)^n + (x-a)^n = \begin{cases} \frac{n+2}{2}, & \text{if } n \text{ is even} \\ \frac{n+1}{2}, & \text{if } n \text{ is odd} \end{cases}$$

9 The number of terms in the expansion of

$$(x+a)^n - (x-a)^n = \begin{cases} \frac{n}{2}, & \text{if } n \text{ is even} \\ \frac{n+1}{2}, & \text{if } n \text{ is odd} \end{cases}$$

10 The number of terms in the expansion of multinomial $(x_1 + x_2 + x_3 + \ldots + x_m)^n$, when $x_1, x_2, x_3, \ldots, x_m \in C$ and $n \in N$, is ${}^{n+m-1}C_{m-1}$.

11 The number of terms in the expansion of $\left(ax^p + \frac{b}{x^p} + c\right)^n$, where $n, p \in N$ and a, b, c are constants, is $2n + 1$.

12 If the coefficients of pth and qth terms in the expansion of $(1 + x)^n$ are equal, then $p + q = n + 2$, where $p, q, n \in N$.

13 If the coefficients of x^r, x^{r+1} in the expansion of $\left(a + \frac{x}{b}\right)^n$ are equal, then $n = (r + 1)(ab + 1) - 1$, where $n, r \in N$ and a, b are constants.

14 Coefficient of x^m in the expansion of $\left(ax^p + \frac{b}{x^q}\right)^n$ = Coefficient of T_{r+1}, where $r = \frac{np - m}{p + q}$, where $p, q, n \in N$ and a, b are constants.

15 The term independent of x in the expansion of $\left(ax^p + \frac{b}{x^q}\right)^n$ is T_{r+1}, where $r = \frac{np}{p+q}$, where $n, p, q \in N$ and a, b are constants.

16 Sum of the coefficients in the expansion of $(ax + by)^n$ is $(a + b)^n$, where $n \in N$ and a, b are constants.

17 If $(1 + x)^n = C_0 + C_1x + C_2x^2 + \ldots + C_nx^n$ and $p + q = 1$, then

(i) $\sum_{r=0}^{n} r \cdot C_r \cdot p^r \cdot q^{n-r} = np$

(ii) $\sum_{r=0}^{n} r^2 \cdot C_r \cdot p^r \cdot q^{n-r} = n^2p^2 + npq$

18 If $(1 + x)^n = C_0 + C_1x + C_2x^2 + \ldots + C_nx^n$, then

(i) $\sum_{r=0}^{n} r \cdot C_r = n \cdot 2^{n-1}$ (ii) $\sum_{r=0}^{n} \frac{C_r}{r+1} = \frac{2^{n+1} - 1}{n+1}$

(iii) $\sum_{r=0}^{n} r^2 \cdot C_r = n(n+1)2^{n-2}$ (iv) $\sum_{r=0}^{n} (-1)^r \cdot r \cdot C_r = 0$

(v) $\sum_{r=0}^{n} \frac{(-1)^r C_r}{r+1} = \frac{1}{n+1}$

(vi) $\sum_{r=0}^{n} (-1)^r \frac{C_r}{r} = 1 + \frac{1}{2} + \frac{1}{3} + \ldots + \frac{1}{n}$

(vii) $\sum_{r=0}^{n} (-1)^r \cdot r^2 \cdot C_r = 0$

(viii) $\sum_{r=0}^{n} (-1)^r \cdot (a - r)(b - r) C_r = 0, \forall n > 3$

(ix) $\sum_{r=0}^{n} (-1)^r (a - r)(b - r)(c - r) C_r = 0, \forall n > 3$

(x) $\sum_{r=0}^{n} (-1)^r (a - r)^3 C_r = 0, \forall n > 3$

(xi) $\sum_{r=0}^{n} r(r-1)(r-2)\ldots(r-k+1) C_r x^{r-k} = \frac{d^k}{dx^k}(1+x)^n$

for $k = 2$, $\sum_{r=0}^{n} r(r-1) C_r = \frac{d^2}{dx^2}[(1+x)^n]_{x=1} = n(n-1)2^{n-2}$

and for $k = 3$, $\sum_{r=0}^{n} r(r-1)(r-2)(-1)^{r-3} C_r$

$$= \frac{d^3}{dx^3}[(1+x)^n]_{x=-1} = 0$$

JEE Type Solved Examples : Single Option Correct Type Questions

- This section contains **10 multiple choice examples.** Each example has four choices (a), (b), (c) and (d) out of which **ONLY ONE** is correct.

• Ex. 1 *If* $\binom{2n+1}{0}+\binom{2n+1}{3}+\binom{2n+1}{6}+\ldots=170$, *then n equals*

(a) 2 (b) 4 (c) 6 (d) 8

Sol. (b) $\because\ (1+x)^{2n+1}={}^{2n+1}C_0+{}^{2n+1}C_1x+{}^{2n+1}C_2x^2+{}^{2n+1}C_3x^3$
$+{}^{2n+1}C_4x^4+{}^{2n+1}C_5x^5+{}^{2n+1}C_6x^6+\ldots$

Putting $x=1,\omega,\omega^2$ (where ω is cube root of unity) and adding, we get

$$2^{2n+1}+(1+\omega)^{2n+1}+(1+\omega^2)^{2n+1}=3({}^{2n+1}C_0+{}^{2n+1}C_3+{}^{2n+1}C_6+\ldots$$

$$\Rightarrow\ 2^{2n+1}-\omega^{2(2n+1)}-\omega^{2n+1}=3({}^{2n+1}C_0+{}^{2n+1}C_3+{}^{2n+1}C_6+\ldots)\ [\because 1+\omega+\omega^2=0]$$

$$\Rightarrow\ {}^{2n+1}C_0+{}^{1+2n}C_3+{}^{2n+1}C_6+\ldots=\frac{1}{3}(2^{2n+1}-\omega^{2(2n+1)}-\omega^{2n+1})$$

$$\Rightarrow\ \binom{2n+1}{0}+\binom{2n+1}{3}+\binom{2n+1}{6}+\ldots=\frac{1}{3}(2^{2n+1}-\omega^{2(2n+1)}-\omega^{2n+1})$$

$$\Rightarrow\ 170=\frac{1}{3}(2^{2n+1}-\omega^{2(2n+1)}-\omega^{2n+1})$$

For $n=4, 170=\frac{1}{3}(512-1-1)=170$ $[\because \omega^3=1]$

Hence, $n=4$

• Ex. 2 $({}^mC_0+{}^mC_1-{}^mC_2-{}^mC_3)+({}^mC_4+{}^mC_5-{}^mC_6-{}^mC_7)+\ldots=0$ *if and only if for some positive integer k, m is equal to*

(a) $4k$ (b) $4k+1$ (c) $4k-1$ (d) $4k+2$

Sol. (c) If $\theta\in R$ and $i=\sqrt{-1}$, then $(\cos\theta+i\sin\theta)^n$

$$={}^mC_0(\cos\theta)^m+{}^mC_1(\cos\theta)^{m-1}(i\sin\theta)+{}^mC_2(\cos\theta)^{m-2}(i\sin\theta)^2+\ldots+{}^mC_m(i\sin\theta)^m$$

$$(\cos m\theta+i\sin m\theta)=[{}^mC_0(\cos\theta)^m-{}^mC_2(\cos\theta)^{m-2}\cdot\sin^2\theta+{}^mC_4(\cos\theta)^{m-4}\sin^4\theta-\ldots]+i[{}^mC_1(\cos\theta)^{m-1}\cdot\sin\theta-{}^mC_3(\cos\theta)^{m-3}\sin^3\theta+\ldots]$$

[using Demoivre's theorem]

Comparing real and imaginary parts, we get

$$\cos m\theta={}^mC_0(\cos\theta)^m-{}^mC_2(\cos\theta)^{m-2}\sin^2\theta+{}^mC_4(\cos\theta)^{m-4}\sin^4\theta-\ldots \quad \text{...(i)}$$

$$\sin m\theta={}^mC_1(\cos\theta)^{m-1}\cdot\sin\theta-{}^mC_3(\cos\theta)^{m-3}\cdot\sin^3\theta+\ldots \quad \text{...(ii)}$$

On adding Eqs. (i) and (ii), we get

$$\cos m\theta+\sin m\theta={}^mC_0(\cos\theta)^m+{}^mC_1(\cos\theta)^{m-1}\cdot\sin\theta-{}^mC_2(\cos\theta)^{m-2}\sin^2\theta-{}^mC_3(\cos\theta)^{m-3}\sin^3\theta+{}^mC_4(\cos\theta)^{m-4}\sin^4\theta+\ldots\sin\left(m\theta+\frac{\pi}{4}\right)$$

$$=(\cos\theta)^m\left\{\begin{array}{l}{}^mC_0+{}^mC_1\tan\theta-{}^mC_2\tan^2\theta-{}^mC_3\tan^3\theta\\+{}^mC_4\tan^4\theta+{}^mC_5\tan^5\theta-\ldots\end{array}\right\}$$

Putting $\theta=\frac{\pi}{4}$, $\sqrt{2}\sin\left(\frac{(m+1)\pi}{4}\right)=\frac{1}{2^{m/2}}$

$$\left\{\begin{array}{l}({}^mC_0+{}^mC_1-{}^mC_2-{}^mC_3)+({}^mC_4+{}^mC_5-{}^mC_6-{}^mC_7)\\+\ldots+({}^mC_{m-3}+{}^mC_{m-2}-{}^mC_{m-1}-{}^mC_m)\end{array}\right\}$$

$$\because({}^mC_0+{}^mC_1-{}^mC_2-{}^mC_3)+({}^mC_4+{}^mC_5-{}^mC_6-{}^mC_7)+\ldots=0\ \text{[given]}$$

$$\therefore\ \sin\left(\frac{(m+1)\pi}{4}\right)=0\Rightarrow\frac{(m+1)\pi}{4}=k\pi$$

or $m=4k-1, \forall k\in I$

• Ex. 3 *If coefficient of* x^n *in the expansion of* $(1+x)^{101}(1-x+x^2)^{100}$ *is non-zero, then n cannot be of the form*

(a) $3\lambda+1$ (b) 3λ (c) $3\lambda+2$ (d) $4\lambda+1$

Sol. (c) $\because (1+x)^{101}(1-x+x^2)^{100}=(1+x)((1+x)(1-x+x^2))^{100}$
$=(1+x)(1+x^3)^{100}$
$=(1+x)(1+{}^{100}C_1x^3+{}^{100}C_2x^6+{}^{100}C_3x^9+\ldots+\ldots+{}^{100}C_{10}x^{300})$

Clearly, in this expression x^3 will present if $n=3\lambda$ or $n=3\lambda+1$. So, n cannot be of the form $3\lambda+2$.

• Ex. 4 *The sum* $\sum_{i=0}^{m}\binom{10}{i}\binom{20}{m-i}$, *(where* $\frac{p}{q}=0$, *if* $p<q$*) is maximum when m is*

(a) 5 (b) 10 (c) 15 (d) 20

Sol. (c) $\sum_{i=0}^{m}\binom{10}{i}\binom{20}{m-i}=\sum_{i=0}^{m}{}^{10}C_i\,{}^{20}C_{m-i}$

$={}^{10}C_0\cdot{}^{20}C_m+{}^{10}C_1\cdot{}^{20}C_{m-1}+{}^{10}C_2\cdot{}^{20}C_{m-2}+\ldots+{}^{10}C_m\cdot{}^{20}C_0$

= Coefficient of x^m in the expansion of product $(1+x)^{10}(1+x)^{20}$

= Coefficient of x^m in the expansion of $(1+x)^{30}={}^{30}C_m$

To get maximum value of the given sum, ${}^{30}C_m$ should be maximum. Which is so, when $m=\frac{30}{2}=15$

● **Ex. 5** *If* $^{n-1}C_r = (k^2-3)\cdot {}^nC_{r+1}$ *then k belongs to*

(a) $(-\infty, -2]$ (b) $[2, \infty)$
(c) $[-\sqrt{3}, \sqrt{3}]$ (d) $(\sqrt{3}, 2]$

Sol. (d) $\because {}^{n-1}C_r = (k^2-3)\cdot {}^nC_{r+1}$

$$\Rightarrow \quad k^2 - 3 = \frac{^{n-1}C_r}{^nC_{r+1}} = \frac{r+1}{n} \quad \text{...(i)}$$

$$\Rightarrow \quad 0 \le r \le n-1$$

$$\Rightarrow \quad 1 \le r+1 \le n$$

$$\Rightarrow \quad \frac{1}{n} \le \frac{r+1}{n} \le 1$$

$$\Rightarrow \quad \frac{1}{n} \le (k^2-3) \le 1$$

$$\Rightarrow \quad 3 + \frac{1}{n} \le k^2 \le 4 \quad \text{or} \quad 3 < k^2 \le 4 \qquad [\text{here, } n \ge 2]$$

$$\therefore \quad k \in [-2, \sqrt{3}) \cup (\sqrt{3}, 2]$$

● **Ex. 6** *If* $\left(x + \frac{1}{x} + 1\right)^6 = a_0 + \left(a_1 x + \frac{b_1}{x}\right) + \left(a_2 x^2 + \frac{b_2}{x^2}\right) + \ldots + \left(a_6 x^6 + \frac{b_6}{x^6}\right)$, *the value of* a_0 *is*

(a) 121 (b) 131
(c) 141 (d) 151

Sol. (c) $\because \left(x + \frac{1}{x} + 1\right)^6 = \sum_{r=0}^{6} {}^6C_r \left(x + \frac{1}{x}\right)^r$ for constant term r must be even integer.

$$\therefore a_0 = {}^6C_0 + {}^6C_2 \times {}^2C_1 + {}^6C_4 \times {}^4C_2 + {}^6C_6 \times {}^6C_3$$

$$= 1 + 30 + 90 + 20 = 141$$

● **Ex. 7** *The coefficient of* x^{50} *in the series* $\sum_{r=1}^{101} r x^{r-1}(1+x)^{101-r}$ *is*

(a) $^{100}C_{50}$ (b) $^{101}C_{50}$
(c) $^{102}C_{50}$ (d) $^{103}C_{50}$

Sol. (c) Let $S = \sum_{r=1}^{101} r x^{r-1}(1+x)^{101-r}$

$$= (1+x)^{100} + 2x(1+x)^{99} + 3x^2(1+x)^{98} + \ldots + 101x^{100}$$

$$S = (1+x)^{100}\left\{1 + 2\left(\frac{x}{1+x}\right) + 3\left(\frac{x}{1+x}\right)^2 + \ldots + 101\left(\frac{x}{1+x}\right)^{100}\right\} \quad \text{...(i)}$$

$$\therefore \frac{Sx}{(1+x)} = (1+x)^{100}\left\{\left(\frac{x}{1+x}\right) + 2\left(\frac{x}{1+x}\right)^2 + 3\left(\frac{x}{1+x}\right)^3 + \ldots + 101\left(\frac{x}{1+x}\right)^{101}\right\} \quad \text{...(ii)}$$

On subtracting Eq. (ii) from Eq. (i), then we get

$$\frac{S}{(1+x)} = (1+x)^{100}\left\{1 + \left(\frac{x}{1+x}\right) + \left(\frac{x}{1+x}\right)^2 + \ldots + \left(\frac{x}{1+x}\right)^{100} - 101\left(\frac{x}{1+x}\right)^{101}\right\}$$

$$= (1+x)^{100}\left\{\frac{1\cdot\left(1 - \left(\frac{x}{1+x}\right)^{101}\right)}{1 - \left(\frac{x}{1+x}\right)} - 101\left(\frac{x}{1+x}\right)^{101}\right\}$$

$$\therefore \quad S = (1+x)^{102} - x^{101}(1+x) - 101x^{101}$$

and coefficient of x^{50} in $S = {}^{102}C_{50}$.

● **Ex. 8** *The largest integer* λ *such that* 2^λ *divides* $3^{2^n} - 1$, $n \in N$ *is*

(a) $n-1$ (b) n (c) $n+1$ (d) $n+2$

Sol. (d) $\because 3^{2^n} - 1 = (4-1)^{2^n} - 1$

$$= (4^{2^n} - {}^{2^n}C_1 \cdot 4^{2^n - 1} + {}^{2^n}C_2 \cdot 4^{2^n-2} - \ldots - {}^{2^n}C_{2^n-1} \cdot 4 + 1) - 1$$

$$= 4^{2^n} - 2^n \cdot 4^{2^n-1} + \frac{2^n(2^n-1)}{2} \cdot 4^{2^n-2} - \ldots - 2^n \cdot 4$$

$$= 2^{n+2}(2^{2^{n+1}-n-2} - 2^{2^{n+1}-4} + \ldots - 1) = 2^{n+2}(\text{Integer})$$

Hence, $3^{2^n} - 1$ is divisible by 2^{n+2}. $\lambda = n+2$

● **Ex. 9** The last term in the binomial expansion of $\left(\sqrt[3]{2} - \frac{1}{\sqrt{2}}\right)^n$ is $\left(\frac{1}{3\sqrt[3]{9}}\right)^{\log_3 8}$, the 5th term from beginning is

(a) $^{10}C_6$ (b) $2\,{}^{10}C_4$
(c) $\frac{1}{2}\cdot{}^{10}C_4$ (d) None of the above

Sol. (a) Since, last term in the expansion of $\left(\sqrt[3]{2} - \frac{1}{\sqrt{2}}\right)^n$

$$= \left(\frac{1}{3\cdot\sqrt[3]{9}}\right)^{\log_3 8} \Rightarrow {}^nC_n\left(-\frac{1}{\sqrt{2}}\right)^n = \left(\frac{1}{3\cdot\sqrt[3]{9}}\right)^{\log_3 8}$$

$$\Rightarrow \quad (-1)^n \cdot \left(\frac{1}{2}\right)^{n/2} = \left(\frac{1}{3^{5/3}}\right)^{\log_3 8} = (3^{-5/3})^{\log_3 2^3}$$

$$= 3^{-\frac{5}{3}\times 3 \times \log_3 2} = 3^{-5\log_3 2} = 3^{\log_3 2^{-5}} = 2^{-5} = \left(\frac{1}{2}\right)^5$$

$$\Rightarrow (-1)^n \cdot \left(\frac{1}{2}\right)^{n/2} = \left(\frac{1}{2}\right)^5 \therefore \; n = 10$$

Now, 5th term from beginning $= {}^{10}C_4(\sqrt[3]{2})^6\left(-\frac{1}{\sqrt{2}}\right)^4$

$$= {}^{10}C_4 \cdot 2^2 \cdot \frac{1}{2^2} = {}^{10}C_4 = {}^{10}C_6$$

• **Ex. 10** If $f(x)=\sum_{r=1}^{n}\{r^2({}^nC_r-{}^nC_{r-1})+(2r+1){}^nC_r\}$ *and* $f(30)=30(2)^{\lambda}$, *then the value of* λ *is*

(a) 3 (b) 4 (c) 5 (d) 6

Sol. (c) Here, $f(x)=\sum_{r=1}^{n}\{r^2({}^nC_r-{}^nC_{r-1})+(2r+1){}^nC_r\}$

$$=\sum_{r=1}^{n}(r^2+2r+1){}^nC_r-r^2\cdot{}^nC_{r-1}$$

$$=\sum_{r=1}^{n}((r+1)^2\cdot{}^nC_r-r^2\cdot{}^nC_{r-1})$$

$$=(n+1)^2\cdot{}^nC_n-1^2\cdot{}^nC_0$$

$$=(n+1)^2-1=(n^2+2n)$$

$\therefore \quad f(30)=(30)^2+2(30)=960$

$=30\times32=30(2)^5=30(2)^{\lambda}$ [given]

Hence, $\lambda=5$

JEE Type Solved Examples : More than One Correct Option Type Questions

- This section contains **5 multiple choice examples.** Each example has four choices (a), (b), (c) and (d) out of **which more than one** may be correct.

• **Ex. 11** *Let* $a_n=\left(1+\frac{1}{n}\right)^n$. *Then for each* $n\in N$

(a) $a_n\geq2$ (b) $a_n<3$ (c) $a_n<4$ (d) $a_n<2$

Sol. (a, b, c)

$$\because a_n=\left(1+\frac{1}{n}\right)^n={}^nC_0+{}^nC_1\cdot\left(\frac{1}{n}\right)+\sum_{r=2}^{n}{}^nC_r\left(\frac{1}{n}\right)^2$$

$$=2+\sum_{r=2}^{n}{}^nC_r\left(\frac{1}{n}\right)^2$$

$\therefore \quad a_n\geq2$ for all $n\in N$

Also, $\lim_{n\to\infty}\left(1+\frac{1}{n}\right)^n=e=2.7182\ldots$

$\therefore \quad a_n<e$

Finally, $2\leq a_n<e$

• **Ex. 12** *Let* $S_n(x)=\sum_{k=0}^{n}{}^nC_k\sin(kx)\cos((n-k)x)$ *then*

(a) $S_5\left(\frac{\pi}{2}\right)=16$ (b) $S_7\left(\frac{-\pi}{2}\right)=64$

(c) $S_{50}(\pi)=0$ (d) $S_{51}(-\pi)=-2^{50}$

Sol. (a, b, c)

$$\because \quad S_n(x)=\sum_{k=0}^{n}{}^nC_k\sin(kx)\cos((n-k)x) \quad \ldots\text{(i)}$$

Replace k by $n-k$ in Eq. (i), then

$$S_n(x)=\sum_{k=0}^{n}{}^nC_{n-k}\sin((n-k)x)\cos(kx)$$

or
$$S_n(x)=\sum_{k=0}^{n}{}^nC_k\sin((n-k)x)\cos(kx) \quad \ldots\text{(ii)}$$

On adding Eqs. (i) and (ii), we get

$$2S_n(x)=\sum_{k=0}^{n}{}^nC_k\cdot\sin(nx)=2^n\cdot\sin(nx)$$

$$\Rightarrow \quad S_n(x)=2^{n-1}\cdot\sin(nx)$$

$$\therefore \quad S_5\left(\frac{\pi}{2}\right)=2^4\cdot\sin\left(\frac{5\pi}{2}\right)=16,$$

$$S_7\left(-\frac{\pi}{2}\right)=2^6\cdot\sin\left(-\frac{7\pi}{2}\right)=2^6\times-1\times-1=64$$

$$S_{50}(\pi)=2^{49}\cdot\sin(50\pi)=0$$

and $S_{51}(-\pi)=2^{50}\cdot\sin(-51\pi)=0$

• **Ex. 13** *If* $a+b=k$, *when* $a,b>0$ *and* $S(k,n)=\sum_{r=0}^{n}r^2({}^nC_r)a^r\cdot b^{n-r}$, *then*

(a) $S(1,3)=3(3a^2+ab)$ (b) $S(2,4)=16(4a^2+ab)$

(c) $S(3,5)=25(5a^2+ab)$ (d) $S(4,6)=36(6a^2+ab)$

Sol. (a, b)

$$\because \quad S(k,n)=\sum_{r=0}^{n}r^2\cdot({}^nC_r)a^r\cdot b^{n-r}$$

$$=b^n\sum_{r=0}^{n}r^2\cdot\left(\frac{n}{r}\cdot{}^{n-1}C_{r-1}\right)\cdot\left(\frac{a}{b}\right)^r$$

$$=nb^n\sum_{r=0}^{n}((r-1)+1)^{n-1}C_{r-1}\cdot\left(\frac{a}{b}\right)^r$$

$$=nb^n\sum_{r=0}^{n}((n-1)\cdot{}^{n-2}C_{r-2}+{}^{n-1}C_{r-1})\left(\frac{a}{b}\right)^r$$

$$=nb^n\cdot(n-1)\cdot\left(\frac{a}{b}\right)^2\sum_{r=0}^{n}{}^{n-2}C_{r-2}\left(\frac{a}{b}\right)^{r-2}+nb^n\cdot\left(\frac{a}{b}\right)\sum_{r=0}^{n}{}^{n-1}C_{r-}\left(\frac{a}{b}\right)^{r-1}$$

$$=nb^n\cdot(n-1)\left(\frac{a}{b}\right)^2\left(1+\frac{a}{b}\right)^{n-2}+nb^n\cdot\left(\frac{a}{b}\right)\left(1+\frac{a}{b}\right)^{n-1}$$

$$=n(n-1)a^2k^{n-2}+nak^{n-1}$$

$$=n^2a^2k^{n-2}+nak^{n-2}(k-a)=n^2a^2k^{n-2}+nabk^{n-2}$$

$\therefore S(1,3)=9a^2+3ab=3(3a^2+ab)$ $[\because a+b=k]$

$S(2,4)=16(4a^2+ab)$

$S(3,5)=135(5a^2+ab)$

$S(4,6)=1536(6a^2+ab)$

• **Ex. 14** *The value of x, for which the ninth term in the expansion of* $\left\{\frac{\sqrt{10}}{(\sqrt{x})^{5\log_{10}x}} + x\cdot x^{\frac{1}{2\log_{10}x}}\right\}^{10}$ *is 450 is equal to*

(a) 10 (b) 10^2 (c) $\sqrt{10}$ (d) $10^{-2/5}$

Sol. (b, d) Let $\log_{10} x = \lambda \Rightarrow x = 10^{\lambda}$ ...(i)

Given, $T_9 = 450$

$$\Rightarrow {}^{10}C_8 \cdot \left(\frac{\sqrt{10}}{10^{\frac{5\lambda^2}{2}}}\right)^2 \cdot (10^{\lambda}\cdot 10^{1/2})^8 = 450$$

$$\Rightarrow {}^{10}C_2 \cdot \frac{10}{10^{5\lambda^2}} \cdot 10^{8\lambda}\cdot 10^4 = 450$$

$$\Rightarrow 10^{8\lambda+4-5\lambda^2} = 1 = 10^0$$

$$\Rightarrow 8\lambda + 4 - 5\lambda^2 = 0$$

$$\Rightarrow 5\lambda^2 - 8\lambda - 4 = 0$$

$$\Rightarrow \lambda = 2, -2/5$$

$$\Rightarrow x = 10^2, 10^{-2/5} \quad \text{[from Eq. (i)]}$$

• **Ex. 15** *For a positive integer n, if the expansion of* $\left(\frac{5}{x^2} + x^4\right)$ *has a term independent of x, then n can be*

(a) 18 (b) 27 (c) 36 (d) 45

Sol. (a, b, c, d) Let $(r+1)$th term of $\left(\frac{5}{x^2} + x^4\right)^n$ be independent of x. We have, $T_{r+1} = {}^nC_r\left(\frac{5}{x^2}\right)^{n-r}(x^4)^r = {}^nC_r \cdot 5^{n-r}\cdot x^{6r-2n}$

For this term to be independent of x,

$$6r - 2n = 0 \text{ or } n = 3r$$

For $r = 6, 9, 12, 15,$

$$n = 18, 27, 36, 45.$$

JEE Type Solved Examples : Passage Based Questions

- This section contains **2 solved passages** based upon each of the passage **3 multiple choice** examples have to be answered. Each of these examples has four choices (a), (b), (c) and (d) out of which **ONLY ONE** is correct.

Passage I (Ex. Nos. 16 to 18)

Consider $(1 + x + x^2)^n = \sum_{r=0}^{2n} a_r x^r$, *where* $a_0, a_1, a_2, \dots, a_{2n}$ *are real numbers and n is a positive integer.*

16. The value of $\sum_{r=0}^{n-1} a_{2r}$ is

(a) $\frac{9^n - 2a_{2n} - 1}{4}$ (b) $\frac{9^n - 2a_{2n} + 1}{4}$

(c) $\frac{9^n + 2a_{2n} - 1}{4}$ (d) $\frac{9^n + 2a_{2n} + 1}{4}$

17. The value of $\sum_{r=1}^{n} a_{2r-1}$ is

(a) $\frac{9^n - 1}{2}$ (b) $\frac{9^n - 1}{4}$ (c) $\frac{9^n + 1}{2}$ (d) $\frac{9^n + 1}{4}$

18. The value of a_2 is

(a) ${}^{4n+1}C_2$ (b) ${}^{3n+1}C_2$

(c) ${}^{2n+1}C_2$ (d) ${}^{n+1}C_2$

Sol.

We have, $(1 + x + x^2)^{2n} = \sum_{r=0}^{4n} a_r x^r$ ...(i)

Replacing x by $\frac{1}{x}$ in Eq. (i), we get

$$\left(1 + \frac{1}{x} + \frac{1}{x^2}\right)^{2n} = \sum_{r=0}^{4n} a_r \left(\frac{1}{x}\right)^r$$

$$\Rightarrow (1 + x + x^2)^{2n} = \sum_{r=0}^{4n} a_r x^{4n-r} \quad \text{...(ii)}$$

From Eqs. (i) and (ii), we get $\sum_{r=0}^{4n} a_r x^r = \sum_{r=0}^{4n} a_r x^{4n-r}$

Equating the coefficient of x^{4n-r} on both sides, we get

$$a_{4n-r} = a_r \text{ for } 0 \le r \le 4n$$

Hence, $a_r = a_{4n-r}$

Putting $x = 1$ in Eq. (i), then

$$\sum_{r=0}^{4n} a_r = 3^{2n} = 9^n \quad \text{...(iii)}$$

Putting $x = -1$ in Eq. (i), then $\sum_{r=0}^{4n} (-1)^r a_r = 1$ ...(iv)

16. (b) On adding Eqs. (iii) and (iv), we get

$2(a_0 + a_2 + a_4 + \dots + a_{2n-2} + a_{2n} + \dots + a_{4n}) = 9^n + 1$

$\Rightarrow 2[2(a_0 + a_2 + a_4 + \dots + a_{2n-2}) + a_{2n}) = 9^n + 1$

$[\because a_r = a_{4n-r}]$

$$\therefore a_0 + a_2 + a_4 + \dots + a_{2n-2} = \frac{9^n - 2a_{2n} + 1}{4}$$

$$\Rightarrow \sum_{r=0}^{n-1} a_{2r} = \frac{9^n - 2a_{2n} + 1}{4}$$

17. (b) On subtracting Eq. (iv) from Eq. (iii), we get

$2(a_1 + a_3 + a_5 + \dots + a_{2n-1} + a_{2n+1} + \dots + a_{4n-1}) = 9^n - 1$

$\Rightarrow 2[2(a_1 + a_3 + a_5 + \dots + a_{2n-1}] = 9^n - 1 \quad [\because a_r = a_{4n-r}]$

$$\therefore\ a_1 + a_3 + a_5 + \ldots + a_{2n-1} = \frac{9^n - 1}{4}$$

$$\Rightarrow \sum_{r=1}^{n} a_{2r-1} = \frac{9^n - 1}{4}$$

18. (c) $\because a_2 =$ Coefficient of x^2 in $(1 + x + x^2)^{2n}$

$$\therefore (1 + x + x^2)^{2n} = \sum_{\alpha+\beta+\gamma=2n} \frac{2n!}{\alpha!\beta!\gamma!}(1)^\alpha (x)^\beta (x^2)^\gamma$$

$$= \sum_{\alpha+\beta+\gamma=2n} \frac{2n!}{\alpha!\beta!\gamma!} x^{\beta+2\gamma}$$

For a_2, $\beta + 2\gamma = 2$

Possible values of α, β, γ are $(2n-2, 2, 0)$ and $(2n-1, 0, 1)$.

$$\therefore \quad a_2 = \frac{2n!}{(2n-2)!\,2!\,0!} + \frac{2n!}{(2n-1)!\,0!\,1!}$$

$$= {}^{2n}C_2 + {}^{2n}C_1 = {}^{2n+1}C_2$$

Passage II

(Ex. Nos. 19 to 21)

Let $\quad S = \sum_{r=1}^{30} \frac{{}^{30+r}C_r\,(2r-1)}{{}^{30}C_r\,(30+r)},\ K = \sum_{r=0}^{30} ({}^{30}C_r)^2$

and $\quad G = \sum_{r=0}^{60} (-1)^r\,({}^{60}C_r)^2$

19. The value of $(G - S)$ is

(a) 0 (b) 1 (c) 2^{30} (d) 2^{60}

20. The value of $(SK - SG)$ is

(a) 0 (b) 1
(c) 2^{30} (d) 2^{60}

21. The value of $K + G$ is

(a) $2S - 2$ (b) $2S - 1$
(c) $2S + 1$ (d) $2S + 2$

Sol.

$$\because S = \sum_{r=1}^{30} \frac{{}^{30+r}C_r\,(2r-1)}{{}^{30}C_r\,(30+r)} = \sum_{r=1}^{30} \frac{{}^{30+r}C_r}{{}^{30}C_r}\left(1 - \frac{30-r+1}{30+r}\right)$$

$$= \sum_{r=1}^{30}\left[\frac{{}^{30+r}C_r}{{}^{30}C_r} - \frac{{}^{30+r}C_r}{{}^{30}C_r}\cdot\frac{(30-r+1)}{(30+r)}\right]$$

$$= \sum_{r=1}^{30}\left[\frac{{}^{30+r}C_r}{{}^{30}C_r} - \frac{\frac{(30+r)}{r}\cdot{}^{29+r}C_{r-1}}{{}^{30}C_r}\cdot\frac{(31-r)}{30+r}\right]$$

$$= \sum_{r=1}^{30}\left[\frac{{}^{30+r}C_r}{{}^{30}C_r} - \frac{{}^{29+r}C_{r-1}}{{}^{30}C_{r-1}}\right] \quad \left[\because \frac{{}^nC_r}{{}^nC_{r-1}} = \frac{n-r+1}{r}\right]$$

For $n = 30\left(\frac{31-r}{r}\right)\cdot{}^{30}C_r = {}^{30}C_{r-1}$

$$= \frac{{}^{30+30}C_{30}}{{}^{30}C_{30}} - \frac{{}^{29+1}C_0}{{}^{30}C_0} = {}^{60}C_{30} - 1$$

$$K = \sum_{r=0}^{30} ({}^{30}C_r)^2 = {}^{60}C_{30} \text{ and } G = \sum_{r=0}^{60} (-1)^r\,({}^{60}C_r)^2$$

$$= ({}^{60}C_0)^2 - ({}^{60}C_1)^2 + ({}^{60}C_2)^2 - \ldots + ({}^{60}C_{60})^2 = {}^{60}C_{30}$$

$[\because n = 60$ is even$]$

19. (b) $G - S = {}^{60}C_{30} - ({}^{60}C_{30} - 1) = 1$

20. (a) $SK - SG = S(K - G) = S(G - G) = 0 \quad [\because K = G]$

21. (d) $K + G = 2\cdot{}^{60}C_{30} = 2(S + 1) = 2S + 2$

JEE Type Solved Examples : Single Integer Answer Type Questions

- This section contains **2 examples.** The answer to each example is a **single digit integer** ranging from **0** to **9** (both inclusive).

● ***Ex. 22*** *The digit at unit's place in* $2^{9^{100}}$ *is*

Sol. (2) $\because 9^{100} = (2\cdot 4 + 1)^{100} = 4n + 1$ [say]

[where n is positive integer]

$$\therefore \quad 2^{9^{100}} = 2^{4n+1} = 2^{4n}\cdot 2 = (16)^n\cdot 2$$

The digit at unit's place in $(16)^n = 6$.

$\therefore$ The digit at unit's place in $(16)^n\cdot 2 = 2$

● ***Ex. 23*** *If* $(1 + x)^n = \sum_{r=0}^{n} a_r x^r,\ b_r = 1 + \frac{a_r}{a_{r-1}}$ *and* $\prod_{r=1}^{n} b_r = \frac{(101)^{100}}{100!}$, *then the value of* $\frac{n}{20}$ *is*

Sol. (5) Here, $a_r = {}^nC_r$

$$\therefore \quad b_r = 1 + \frac{a_r}{a_{r-1}} = 1 + \frac{{}^nC_r}{{}^nC_{r-1}}$$

$$= 1 + \frac{n-r+1}{r} = \frac{(n+1)}{r}$$

$$\Rightarrow \prod_{r=1}^{n} b_r = \prod_{r=1}^{n} \frac{(n+1)}{r}$$

$$= \frac{(n+1)}{1}\cdot\frac{(n+1)}{2}\cdot\frac{(n+1)}{3}\cdots\frac{(n+1)}{n} = \frac{(n+1)^n}{n!}$$

$$= \frac{(101)^{100}}{100!} \quad \text{[given]}$$

$$\therefore \quad n = 100 \Rightarrow \frac{n}{20} = 5$$

JEE Type Solved Examples : Matching Type Questions

- This section contains **2 examples.** Examples 24 and 25 have three statements (A, B and C) given in Column I and four statements (p, q, r and s) in **Column II.** Any given statement in **Column I** can have correct matching with one or more statement(s) given in **Column II.**

• Ex. 24

	Column I		Column II
(A)	If m and n are the numbers of rational terms in the expansions of $(\sqrt{2}+3^{1/5})^{10}$ and $(\sqrt{3}+5^{1/8})^{256}$ respectively, then	(p)	$n-m=6$
(B)	If m and n are the numbers of irrational terms in the expansions of $(2^{1/2}+3^{1/5})^{40}$ and $(5^{1/10}+2^{1/6})^{100}$ respectively, then	(q)	$m+n=20$
(C)	If m and n are the numbers of rational terms in the expansions of $(1+\sqrt{2}+3^{1/3})^6$ and $(1+\sqrt[3]{2}+\sqrt[5]{3})^{15}$ respectively, then	(r)	$n-m=31$
		(s)	$m+n=35$
		(t)	$n-m=39$

Sol. (A) → (r, s); (B) → (t); (C) → (p, q)

(A) ∵ $(\sqrt{2}+3^{1/5})^{10}=(2^{1/2}+3^{1/5})^{10}$

$$\therefore \quad T_{r+1}={}^{10}C_r\cdot 2^{\frac{10-r}{2}}\cdot 3^{\frac{r}{5}}$$

For rational terms, $r=0, 10$ $\quad [\because 0\le r\le 10]$

∴ Number of rational terms = 2

i.e., $m=2$ and $(\sqrt{3}+5^{1/8})^{256}=(3^{1/2}+5^{1/8})^{256}$

$$\therefore \; T_{R+1}={}^{256}C_R\cdot 3^{\frac{256-R}{2}}\cdot 5^{R/8}$$

For rational terms, $r=0, 8, 16, 24, 32, \ldots, 256$ $[\because 0\le r\le 256]$

∴ Number of rational terms = 1 + 32 = 33

i.e., $n=33 \Rightarrow m+n=35$ (s) and $n-m=31$

(B) T_{r+1} in $(2^{1/3}+3^{1/5})^{40}={}^{40}C_r\cdot 2^{\frac{40-r}{3}}\cdot 3^{r/5}$

For rational terms, $r=10, 25, 40$ $[\because 0\le r\le 40]$

∵ Number of rational terms = 3

∴ Number of irrational terms

= Total terms – Number of rational terms

= 41 – 3 = 38 i.e. $m=38$

and T_{R+1} in $(5^{1/10}+2^{1/6})^{100}={}^{100}C_R\cdot 5^{\frac{100-R}{10}}\cdot 2^{R/6}$

rational terms, $R=0, 30, 60, 90$ $\quad [\because 0\le R\le 100]$

∵ Number of rational terms = 4

∴ Number of irrational terms = 101 – 4 = 97

i.e. $n=97 \Rightarrow m+n=100, n-m=97-38=39$

(C) ∵ $(1+\sqrt{2}+3^{1/3})^6=(1+2^{1/2}+3^{1/3})^6$

$$=\sum_{\alpha+\beta+\gamma=6}\frac{6!}{\alpha!\,\beta!\,\gamma!}(1)^{\alpha}(2^{1/2})^{\beta}(3^{1/3})^{\gamma}$$

$$=\sum_{\alpha+\beta+\gamma=6}\frac{6!}{\alpha!\,\beta!\,\gamma!}2^{\beta/2}\cdot 3^{\gamma/3}$$

Values of (α, β, γ) for rational terms are (0, 0, 6), (1, 2, 3), (3, 0, 3), (0, 6, 0), (2, 4, 0), (4, 2, 0), (6, 0, 0).

∴ Number of rational terms = 7 i.e., $m=7$

and $(1+\sqrt[3]{2}+\sqrt[5]{3})^{15}=(1+2^{1/3}+3^{1/5})^{15}$

$$=\sum_{\alpha+\beta+\gamma=15}\frac{15!}{\alpha!\,\beta!\,\gamma!}(1)^{\alpha}(2^{1/3})^{\beta}(3^{1/5})^{\gamma}$$

$$=\sum_{\alpha+\beta+\gamma=15}\frac{15!}{\alpha!\,\beta!\,\gamma!}2^{\beta/3}\cdot 3^{\gamma/5}$$

of (α, β, γ) for rational terms are

(5, 0, 10), (2, 3, 10), (10, 0, 5), (7, 3, 5), (4, 6, 5), (1, 9, 5), (15, 0, 0), (12, 3, 0), (9, 6, 0), (6, 9, 0), (3, 12, 0), (15, 0, 0).

∴ Number of rational terms = 13 i.e. $n=13$

Hence, $\quad m+n=20$ and $n-m=6$

• Ex. 25 *If* $(1+x)^n=\sum_{r=0}^{n}C_r x^r$, *match the following.*

	Column I		Column II
(A)	If $S=\sum_{r=0}^{n}\lambda\, C_r$ and values of S are a, b, c for $\lambda=1, r, r^2$ respectively, then	(p)	$a=b+c$
(B)	If $S=\sum_{r=0}^{n}(-1)^r\,\lambda\, C_r$ and values of S are a, b, c for $\lambda=1, r, r^2$ respectively, then	(q)	$a+b=c+2$
(C)	If $S=\sum_{r=0}^{n}\frac{\lambda\, C_r}{(r+1)}$ and values of S are a, b, c for $\lambda=1, r, r^2$ respectively, then	(r)	$a^3+b^3+c^3=3abc$
		(s)	$b^{c-a}+(c-a)^b=1$
		(t)	$a+c=4b$

Sol. (A) → (p, q); (B) → (p, r, t); (C) →(s, t)

(A) For $\lambda=1, a=\sum_{r=0}^{n}C_r=2^n$

For $\lambda=r, b=\sum_{r=0}^{n}r\,C_r=\sum_{r=0}^{n}r\cdot\frac{n}{r}\cdot{}^{n-1}C_{r-1}$

$$=n\sum_{r=0}^{n}{}^{n-1}C_{r-1}=n\cdot 2^{n-1}$$

and for $\lambda=r^2$, $c=\sum_{r=0}^{n}r^2\,C_r=\sum_{r=0}^{n}r^2\cdot\frac{n}{r}\cdot{}^{n-1}C_{r-1}$

$$=n\sum_{r=0}^{n}r\cdot{}^{n-1}C_{r-1}=n\sum_{r=1}^{n}r\cdot{}^{n-1}C_{r-1}$$

$$= n\left[\sum_{r=1}^{n} \{(r-1)+1\}^{n-1}C_{r-1}\right]$$

$$= n\left[\sum_{r=1}^{n} (r-1)\cdot {}^{n-1}C_{r-1} + \sum_{r=1}^{n} {}^{n-1}C_{r-1}\right]$$

$$= n\left[\sum_{r=1}^{n} (r-1)\frac{(n-1)}{(r-1)}\cdot {}^{n-2}C_{r-2} + 2^{n-1}\right]$$

$$= n\left[(n-1)\sum_{r=1}^{n} {}^{n-2}C_{r-2} + 2^{n-1}\right]$$

$$= n\left[(n-1)\cdot 2^{n-2} + 2^{n-1}\right] = n(n+1)\,2^{n-2}$$

For $n = 1, a = 2, b = 1, c = 1$ and for $n = 2, a = 4, b = 4, c = 6$ $\Big\}$ $a = b + c$, $a + b = c + 2$

(B) For $\lambda = 1$, $a = \sum_{r=0}^{n} (-1)^r \cdot C_r = 0$

For $\lambda = r$,

$$b = \sum_{r=0}^{n} (-1)^r \cdot r \cdot C_r = \sum_{r=0}^{n} (-1)^r \cdot r \cdot \frac{n}{r}\, {}^{n-1}C_{r-1}$$

$$= n\sum_{r=1}^{n} (-1)^r \cdot {}^{n-1}C_{r-1} = n(1-1)^{n-1} = 0$$

and for $\lambda = r^2$, $c = \sum_{r=0}^{n} (-1)^r \cdot r^2 \cdot C_r$

$$= \sum_{r=0}^{n} (-1)^r \cdot r^2 \cdot \frac{n}{r} \cdot {}^{n-1}C_{r-1}$$

$$= n\sum_{r=0}^{n} (-1)^r \cdot r \cdot {}^{n-1}C_{r-1}$$

$$= n\sum_{r=0}^{n} (-1)^r \{(r-1)+1\}\, {}^{n-1}C_{r-1}$$

$$= n\sum_{r=0}^{n} (-1)^r (r-1)\, {}^{n-1}C_{r-1} + n\sum_{r=0}^{n} (-1)^r \cdot {}^{n-1}C_{r-1}$$

$$= 0 + 0 = 0$$

$\therefore a = b = c = 0 \Rightarrow a = b + c$

$\Rightarrow a^3 + b^3 + c^3 = 3abc \Rightarrow a + c = 4b$

(C) For $\lambda = 1$, $a = \sum_{r=0}^{n} \frac{C_r}{(r+1)} = \frac{1}{(n+1)} \sum_{r=0}^{n} \left(\frac{n+1}{r+1}\right) \cdot {}^nC_r$

$$= \frac{1}{(n+1)} \sum_{r=0}^{n} {}^{n+1}C_{r+1} = \frac{1}{n+1}(2^{n+1} - 1)$$

$$= \frac{2^{n+1}-1}{n+1}$$

For $\lambda = r$, $b = \sum_{r=0}^{n} \frac{r \cdot C_r}{(r+1)} = \sum_{r=0}^{n}\left(1 - \frac{1}{r+1}\right) C_r$

$$= 2^n - \left(\frac{2^{n+1}-1}{n+1}\right) = \frac{(n-1)\,2^n + 1}{n+1}$$

For $\lambda = r^2$, $c = \sum_{r=0}^{n} \frac{r^2 \cdot C_r}{(r+1)} = \sum_{r=0}^{n}\left((r-1) + \frac{1}{r+1}\right) C_r$

$$= \sum_{r=0}^{n} r \cdot C_r - \sum_{r=0}^{n} C_r + \sum_{r=0}^{n} \frac{C_r}{r+1}$$

$$= n \cdot 2^{n-1} - 2^n + \frac{2^{n+1}-1}{n+1}$$

$$= \frac{(n^2 - n + 2)\,2^{n-1} - 1}{(n+1)}$$

For $n = 1, a = \frac{3}{2}, b = \frac{1}{2}, c = \frac{1}{2}$ and for $n = 2, a = \frac{7}{3}, b = \frac{5}{3}, c = \frac{7}{3}$; $\Big\}$ $a + c = 4b$, $b^{c-a} + (c-a)^b = 1$

JEE Type Solved Examples : Statement I and II Type Questions

- **Directions** Example numbers 26 and 27 are Assertion-Reason type examples. Each of these examples contains two statements:
Statement-1 (Assertion) and **Statement-2** (Reason)
Each of these examples also has four alternative choices, only one of which is the correct answer. You have to select the correct choice as given below.
  (a) Statement-1 is true, Statement-2 is true; Statement-2 is a correct explanation for Statement-1
  (b) Statement-1 is true, Statement-2 is true; Statement-2 is not a correct explanation for Statement-1
  (c) Statement-1 is true, Statement-2 is false
  (d) Statement-1 is false, Statement-2 is true

• ***Ex. 26*** **Statement-1** $(7^9 + 9^7)$ *is divisible by 16*

Statement-2 $(x^y + y^x)$ *is divisible by* $(x + y), \forall\, x, y$.

Sol. (c) $7^9 + 9^7 = (8-1)^9 + (8+1)^7$

$$= (8^9 - {}^9C_1 \cdot 8^8 + {}^9C_2 \cdot 8^7 - {}^9C_3 \cdot 8^6 + \dots + {}^9C_8 \cdot 8 - 1)$$
$$+ (8^7 + {}^7C_1 \cdot 8^6 + {}^7C_2 \cdot 8^5 + \dots + {}^7C_6 \cdot 8 + 1)$$
$$= 8^9 - 9 \cdot 8^8 + 8^7 \cdot ({}^9C_2 + 1) + 8^6(-{}^9C_3 + 7)$$
$$+ 8^5({}^9C_4 + {}^7C_2) + \dots + 8({}^9C_8 + {}^7C_6)$$

$= 64\,\lambda$ [λ is an integer]

$\therefore 7^9 + 9^7$ is divisible by 16.

$\therefore$ Statement-1 is true. Statement-2 is false.

• ***Ex. 27.*** **Statement-1** *Number of distinct terms in the sum of expansion* $(1 + ax)^{10} + (1 - ax)^{10}$ *is 22.*

Statement-2 *Number of terms in the expansion of* $(1 + x)^n$ *is* $n + 1, \forall\, n \in N$.

Sol. (d) $\because (1 + ax)^{10} + (1 - ax)^{10} = 2\{1 + {}^{10}C_2 (ax)^2$
$+ {}^{10}C_4 (ax)^4 + {}^{10}C_6 (ax)^6 + {}^{10}C_8 (ax)^8 + {}^{10}C_{10} (ax)^{10}\}$

$\therefore$ Number of distinct terms $= 6$

$\Rightarrow$ Statement-1 is false but Statement-2 is obviously true.

Subjective Type Examples

• **Ex. 28** *Find the coefficient independent of x in the expansion of* $(1+x+2x^3)\left(\frac{3}{2}x^2-\frac{1}{3x}\right)^9$.

Sol. $(r+1)$ th term in the expansion of $\left(\frac{3}{2}x^2-\frac{1}{3x}\right)^9$

i.e., $T_{r+1} = {}^9C_r\left(\frac{3}{2}x^2\right)^{9-r}\left(-\frac{1}{3x}\right)^r$

$$= {}^9C_r\left(\frac{3}{2}\right)^{9-r}\cdot x^{18-2r}\cdot\left(-\frac{1}{3}\right)^r\cdot x^{-r}$$

$$= {}^9C_r\left(\frac{3}{2}\right)^{9-r}\cdot\left(-\frac{1}{3}\right)^r\cdot x^{18-3r}$$

Hence, general term in the expansion of $(1+x+2x^3)$ $\left(\frac{3}{2}x^2-\frac{1}{3x}\right)^9 = {}^9C_r\left(\frac{3}{2}\right)^{9-r}\left(-\frac{1}{3}\right)^r\cdot x^{18-3r}$

$$+ {}^9C_r\left(\frac{3}{2}\right)^{9-r}\left(-\frac{1}{3}\right)^r\cdot x^{19-3r}$$

$$+2\,{}^9C_r\left(\frac{3}{2}\right)^{9-r}\left(-\frac{1}{3}\right)^r\cdot x^{21-3r}$$

For independent term, putting $18-3r=0, 19-3r=0$, $21-3r=0$ respectively, we get $r=6, r=19/3$ [impossible] $r=7$, second term do not given the independent term.

Hence, coefficient independent of x

$$= {}^9C_6\cdot\left(\frac{3}{2}\right)^3\cdot\left(-\frac{1}{3}\right)^6+0+2\cdot{}^9C_7\cdot\left(\frac{3}{2}\right)^2\left(-\frac{1}{3}\right)^7$$

$$= {}^9C_3\cdot\frac{27}{8.729}-2.{}^9C_2\cdot\frac{9}{4}\cdot\frac{1}{2187}=\frac{7}{18}-\frac{2}{27}=\frac{17}{54}$$

• **Ex. 29** *If* $(1+x)^n = C_0+C_1x+C_2x^2+\ldots+C_nx^n$, *show that* $\sum_{r=0}^{n} C_r{}^3$ *is equal to the coefficient of* x^ny^n *in the expansion of* $\{(1+x)(1+y)(x+y)\}^n$.

Sol. $(1+x)^n(y+1)^n(x+y)^n = \sum_{r=0}^{n} C_r x^r$

$$\sum_{s=0}^{n} C_s y^{n-s}\sum_{t=0}^{n} C_t x^{n-t}y^t \quad \ldots\text{(i)}$$

Since, $C_0{}^3$ is the coefficient of $x^0y^{n-0}x^{n-0}y^0$

i.e., $x^ny^n\ (r=s=t=0)$

Now, $C_1{}^3$ is the coefficient of $x^1y^{n-1}x^{n-1}y$

i.e., $x^ny^n\ (r=s=t=1)$

And $C_k{}^3$ is the coefficient of $x^ky^{n-k}x^{n-k}y^k$

i.e., $x^ny^n\ (r=s=t=k)$

Hence, the coefficient of x^ny^n in $(1+x)^n(y+1)^n(x+y)^n$

$$= C_0{}^3+C_1{}^3+C_2{}^3+\ldots+C_n{}^3 = \sum_{r=0}^{n} C_r{}^3$$

• **Ex. 30** *Let* $(1+x^2)^2(1+x)^n = \sum_{k=0}^{n+4} a_k x^k$. *If* a_1, a_2 *and* a_3 *are in AP, find n.*

Sol. We have,

$$(1+x^2)^2(1+x)^n = (1+2x^2+x^4)\times({}^nC_0+{}^nC_1x+{}^nC_2x^2+{}^nC_3x^3+\ldots)$$

$$= a_0+a_1x+a_2x^2+a_3x^3+\ldots \quad \text{[say]}$$

Now, comparing the coefficients of x, x^2 and x^3, we get

$$a_1 = {}^nC_1,\ a_2 = 2\cdot{}^nC_0+{}^nC_2,\ a_3 = 2\cdot{}^nC_1+{}^nC_3 \quad \ldots\text{(i)}$$

In a_1, $n\ge 1$, in a_2, $n\ge 2$ and in a_3, $n\ge 3$

$\therefore$ $n\ge 3$ ...(ii)

From Eq. (i),

$$a_1 = n,\ a_2 = 2+\frac{n(n-1)}{1\cdot 2}=\frac{n^2-n+4}{2}$$

and $$a_3 = 2n+\frac{n(n-1)(n-2)}{1\cdot 2\cdot 3}=\frac{n^3-3n^2+14n}{6}$$

Since, a_1, a_2, a_3 are in AP.

Therefore, $2a_2 = a_1+a_3$

$$\Rightarrow\quad n^2-n+4 = n+\frac{n^3-3n^2+14n}{6}$$

$$\Rightarrow\quad n^3-9n^2+26n-24=0$$

or $(n-2)(n-3)(n-4)=0$

$\therefore$ $n=2,3,4$

Hence, $n=3,4$ [from Eq. (ii)]

• **Ex. 31** *If* $(1-x^3)^n = \sum_{r=0}^{n} a_r x^r(1-x)^{3n-2r}$, *find* a_r, *where* $n\in N$.

Sol. We have, $(1-x^3)^n = \sum_{r=0}^{n} a_r x^r(1-x)^{3n-2r}$

$$\Rightarrow (1-x)^n(1+x+x^2)^n = \sum_{r=0}^{n}\frac{a_r\cdot x^r(1-x)^{3n}}{(1-x)^{2r}}$$

$$\Rightarrow \frac{(1-x)^n(1+x+x^2)^n}{(1-x)^{3n}} = \sum_{r=0}^{n}\frac{a_r\cdot x^r}{(1-x)^{2r}}$$

$$\Rightarrow \left[\frac{1+x+x^2}{(1-x)^2}\right]^n = \sum_{r=0}^{n} a_r\cdot\frac{x^r}{(1-x)^{2r}}$$

$$\Rightarrow \left[\frac{(1-x)^2+3x}{(1-x)^2}\right]^n = \sum_{r=0}^{n} a_r \left[\frac{x}{(1-x)^2}\right]^r$$

$$\Rightarrow \left[1+3\left(\frac{x}{(1-x)^2}\right)\right]^n = \sum_{r=0}^{n} a_r \left[\frac{x}{(1-x)^2}\right]^r \quad \text{...(i)}$$

Let $A = \dfrac{x}{(1-x)^2}$

Then, Eq. (i) becomes $(1+3A)^n = \sum_{r=0}^{n} a_r A^r$

On comparing the coefficient of A^r, we get

$${}^nC_r \cdot 3^r = a_r$$

Hence, $a_r = {}^nC_r \cdot 3^r$

Ex. 32 *If $a_0, a_1, a_2, \ldots, a_{2n}$ are the coefficients in the expansion of $(1+x+x^2)^n$ in ascending powers of x, show that $a_0^2 - a_1^2 - a_2^2 - \ldots + a_{2n}^2 = a_n$.*

Sol. We have, $(1+x+x^2)^n = a_0 + a_1x + a_2x^2 + a_{2n}x^{2n}$ ...(i)

Replacing x by $\left(-\dfrac{1}{x}\right)$ in Eq. (i), we get

$$\left(1-\frac{1}{x}+\frac{1}{x^2}\right)^n = a_0 - \frac{a_1}{x} + \frac{a_2}{x^2} - \ldots + \frac{a_{2n}}{x^{2n}} \quad \text{...(ii)}$$

On multiplying Eqs. (i) and (ii), we get

$$(1+x+x^2)^n \times \left(1-\frac{1}{x}+\frac{1}{x^2}\right)^n = (a_0 + a_1x + a_2x^2 + \ldots + a_{2n}x^{2n}) \times \left(a_0 - \frac{a_1}{x} + \frac{a_2}{x^2} - \ldots + \frac{a_{2n}}{x^{2n}}\right)$$

$$\Rightarrow \frac{(1+x^2+x^4)^n}{x^{2n}} = (a_0 + a_1x + a_2x^2 + \ldots + a_{2n}x^{2n}) \times \left(a_0 - \frac{a_1}{x} + \frac{a_2}{x^2} - \ldots + \frac{a_{2n}}{x^{2n}}\right) \quad \text{...(iii)}$$

Constant term in RHS $= a_0^2 - a_1^2 + a_2^2 - \ldots + a_{2n}^2$

Now, constant term in $\dfrac{(1+x^2+x^4)^n}{x^{2n}}$ = Coefficient of x^{2n} in $(1+x^2+x^4)^n = a_n$ [replacing x by x^2 in Eq. (i)]

But Eq. (iii) is an identity, therefore, the constant term in RHS = constant term in LHS.

$$a_0^2 - a_1^2 + a_2^2 - \ldots + a_{2n}^2 = a_n$$

Ex. 33 *Show that no three consecutive binomial coefficients can be in (i) GP and (ii) HP.*

Sol. (i) Suppose that the r th, $(r+1)$th and $(r+2)$th coefficients of $(1+x)^n$ are in GP.

i.e., ${}^nC_{r-1}, {}^nC_r, {}^nC_{r+1}$ are in GP.

Then, $\dfrac{{}^nC_r}{{}^nC_{r-1}} = \dfrac{{}^nC_{r+1}}{{}^nC_r}$

$$\Rightarrow \frac{n-r+1}{r} = \frac{n-r}{r+1} \quad \left[\because \frac{{}^nC_r}{{}^nC_{r-1}} = \frac{n-r+1}{r}\right]$$

$$\Rightarrow (n-r+1)(r+1) = r(n-r)$$

$$\Rightarrow nr + n - r^2 - r + r + 1 = nr - r^2$$

$$\Rightarrow n+1 = 0$$

$$\Rightarrow n = -1$$

which is not possible, since n is a positive integer.

(ii) Suppose that rth, $(r+1)$th and $(r+2)$th coefficients of $(1+x)^n$ are in HP,

i.e. ${}^nC_{r-1}, {}^nC_r, {}^nC_{r+1}$ are in HP.

Then, $\dfrac{2}{{}^nC_r} = \dfrac{1}{{}^nC_{r-1}} + \dfrac{1}{{}^nC_{r+1}}$

$$\Rightarrow 2 = \frac{{}^nC_r}{{}^nC_{r-1}} + \frac{{}^nC_r}{{}^nC_{r+1}} \quad \left[\because \frac{{}^nC_r}{{}^nC_{r-1}} = \frac{n-r+1}{r}\right]$$

$$\Rightarrow 2 = \frac{n-r+1}{r} + \frac{r+1}{n-r}$$

$$\Rightarrow 2r(n-r) = (n-r+1)(n-r) + r(r+1)$$

$$\Rightarrow 2nr - 2r^2 = n^2 - nr - nr + r^2 + n - r + r^2 + r$$

$$\Rightarrow n^2 - 4nr + 4r^2 + n = 0 \Rightarrow (n-2r)^2 + n = 0$$

which is not possible, as $(n-2r)^2 \geq 0$ and n is a positive integer.

Ex. 34 *Evaluate $\sum_{i=0}^{n} \sum_{j=1}^{n} {}^nC_j \cdot {}^jC_i, i \leq j$.*

Sol. We have, $\sum_{i=0}^{n} \sum_{j=1}^{n} {}^nC_j \cdot {}^jC_i$

$$= {}^nC_1({}^1C_0 + {}^1C_1) + {}^nC_2({}^2C_0 + {}^2C_1 + {}^2C_2) + {}^nC_3({}^3C_0 + {}^3C_1 + {}^3C_2 + {}^3C_3) + {}^nC_4({}^4C_0 + {}^4C_1 + {}^4C_2 + {}^4C_3 + {}^4C_4) + \ldots + {}^nC_n({}^nC_0 + {}^nC_1 + {}^nC_2 + \ldots + {}^nC_n)$$

$$= {}^nC_1(2) + {}^nC_2(2)^2 + {}^nC_3(2)^3 + \ldots + {}^nC_n(2)^n = (1+2)^n - 1$$

$$= 3^n - 1$$

Ex. 35 *Find the remainder, when 27^{40} is divided by 12.*

Sol. We have, $27^{40} = (3^3)^{40} = 3^{120} = 3 \cdot (3)^{119} = 3 \cdot (4-1)^{119}$

$= 3(4n-1)$, where n is some integer

$= 12n - 3 = 12n - 12 + 9 = 12(n-1) + 9$

$= 12m + 9$, where m is some integer.

$$\therefore \frac{27^{40}}{12} = m + \frac{9}{12}$$

Hence, the remainder is 9.

Ex. 36 *Show that* $[(\sqrt{3}+1)^{2n}]+1$ *is divisible by* 2^{n+1}, $\forall n \in N$, *where* $[\cdot]$ *denotes the greatest integer function.*

Sol. Let $x = (\sqrt{3}+1)^{2n} = [x] + f$ ...(i)

where, $0 \le f < 1$

and $(\sqrt{3}-1)^{2n} = f'$ ...(ii)

where, $0 < f' < 1$

On adding Eqs. (i) and (ii), we get

$$[x] + f + f' = (\sqrt{3}+1)^{2n} + (\sqrt{3}-1)^{2n}$$
$$= (4+2\sqrt{3})^n + (4-2\sqrt{3})^n$$
$$= 2^n \{(2+\sqrt{3})^n + (2-\sqrt{3})^n\}$$
$$= 2^n \cdot 2\{{}^nC_0(2)^n + {}^nC_2(2)^{n-2}(\sqrt{3})^2 + {}^nC_4(2)^{n-4}(\sqrt{3})^4 + \dots\}$$

$\therefore$ $[x] + f + f' = 2^{n+1}k$, where k is an integer. ...(iii)

Hence, $(f + f')$ is an integer.

i.e., $f + f' = 1$ $[\because 0 < (f + f') < 2]$

From Eq. (iii), we get

$$[x] + 1 = 2^{n+1}k$$

$\Rightarrow$ $[(\sqrt{3}+1)^{2n}] + 1 = 2^{n+1}k$ [from Eq. (i)]

which shows that $[(\sqrt{3}+1)^{2n}]+1$ divisible by 2^{n+1}, $\forall n \in N$.

Ex. 37 *Find the number of rational terms and also find the sum of rational terms in* $(\sqrt{2}+\sqrt[3]{3}+\sqrt[6]{5})^{10}$.

Sol. We have, $(\sqrt{2}+\sqrt[3]{3}+\sqrt[6]{5})^{10} = (2^{1/2}+3^{1/3}+5^{1/6})^{10}$

$$= \sum_{\alpha+\beta+\gamma=10} \frac{10!}{\alpha!\,\beta!\,\gamma!} 2^{\alpha/2} \cdot 3^{\beta/3} \cdot 5^{\gamma/6}$$

For rational terms,

$\alpha = 0, 2, 4, 6, 8, 10$, $\beta = 0, 3, 6, 9$, $\gamma = 0, 6$

Since, $0 \le \alpha, \beta, \gamma \le 10$.

$\therefore$ Possible triplets are $(4, 0, 6), (4, 6, 0), (10, 0, 0)$.

There exists three rational terms.

$\therefore$ Required sum

$$= \frac{10!}{4!\,0!\,6!} 2^2 \cdot 5 + \frac{10!}{4!\,6!\,0!} 2^2 \cdot 3^2 + \frac{10!}{10!\,0!\,0!} 2^5$$

$= 4200 + 7560 + 32 = 11792$

Ex. 38 *Find the remainder, when* $(1690^{2608} + 2608^{1690})$ *is divided by 7.*

Sol. We have, $1690^{2608} + 2608^{1690} = (1690^{2608} - 3^{2608}) + (2608^{1690} - 4^{1690}) + (3^{2608} + 4^{1690})$

The number $(1690^{2608} - 3^{2608})$ is divisible by $1690 - 3 = 1687 = 7 \times 241$ which is divisible by 7, the difference $(2608^{1690} - 4^{1690})$ is also divisible by 7, since it is divisible by $2608 - 4 = 2604 = 7 \times 372$.

As to sum $3^{2608} + 4^{1690}$, it can be rewritten as

$$3 \cdot (3^3)^{869} + 4 \cdot (4^3)^{563}$$
$$= 3(28-1)^{869} + 4(63+1)^{563}$$
$$= 3(7m-1) + 4(7n+1)$$

[where, m and n are some positive integers]

where p is some positive integer.

Hence, the remainder is 1.

Ex. 39 *If* $C_0, C_1, C_2, \dots, C_n$ *are the binomial coefficients in the expansion of* $(1+x)^n$, *prove that*

$$(C_0 + 2C_1 + C_2)(C_1 + 2C_2 + C_3)\dots(C_{n-1} + 2C_n + C_{n+1}) = \frac{(n+2)^n}{(n+1)!} \prod_{r=1}^{n} (C_{r-1} + C_r).$$

Sol. LHS $= (C_0 + 2C_1 + C_2)(C_1 + 2C_2 + C_3)\dots(C_{n-1} + 2C_n + C_{n+1})$

$$= \prod_{r=1}^{n} ({}^nC_{r-1} + 2\,{}^nC_r + {}^nC_{r+1})$$
$$= \prod_{r=1}^{n} \{({}^nC_{r-1} + {}^nC_r) + ({}^nC_r + {}^nC_{r+1})\}$$
$$= \prod_{r=1}^{n} ({}^{n+1}C_r + {}^{n+1}C_{r+1}) \quad \text{[by Pascal's rule]}$$
$$= \prod_{r=1}^{n} ({}^{n+2}C_{r+1}) = \prod_{r=1}^{n} \left(\frac{n+2}{r+1}\right) {}^{n+1}C_r \quad \left[\because {}^nC_r = \frac{n}{r} \cdot {}^{n-1}C_{r-1}\right]$$
$$= \prod_{r=1}^{n} \left(\frac{n+2}{r+1}\right) ({}^nC_{r-1} + {}^nC_r) = \prod_{r=1}^{n} \left(\frac{n+2}{r+1}\right) \prod_{r=1}^{n} (C_{r-1} + C_r)$$
$$= \frac{(n+2)}{2} \cdot \frac{(n+2)}{3} \cdot \frac{(n+2)}{4} \cdots \frac{(n+2)}{(n+1)} \prod_{r=1}^{n} (C_{r-1} + C_r)$$
$$= \frac{(n+2)^n}{(n+1)!} \prod_{r=1}^{n} (C_{r-1} + C_r) = \text{RHS}$$

Ex. 40 *If* $\sum_{r=0}^{2n} a_r (x-2)^r = \sum_{r=0}^{2n} b_r (x-3)^r$ *and* $a_k = 1$, $\forall k \ge n$, *show that* $b_n = {}^{2n+1}C_{n+1}$.

Sol. $\because$ $\sum_{r=0}^{2n} a_r (x-2)^r = \sum_{r=0}^{2n} b_r (x-3)^r$

Let $y = x - 3 \Rightarrow y + 1 = x - 2$

So, the given expression reduces to

$$\sum_{r=0}^{2n} a_r (1+y)^r = \sum_{r=0}^{2n} b_r y^r$$

$$\Rightarrow \quad a_0 + a_1(1+y) + a_2(1+y)^2 + \ldots + a_{2n}(1+y)^{2n} = b_0 + b_1 y + \ldots + b_{2n} y^{2n}$$

Using $a_k = 1, \forall k \ge n$, we get

$$a_0 + a_1(1+y) + a_2(1+y)^2 + \ldots + a_{n-1}(1+y)^{n-1} + (1+y)^n + (1+y)^{n+1} + \ldots + (1+y)^{2n}$$
$$= b_0 + b_1 y + \ldots + b_n y^n + \ldots + b_{2n} y^{2n}$$

On comparing the coefficient of y^n on both sides, we get

$${}^nC_n + {}^{n+1}C_n + {}^{n+2}C_n + \ldots + {}^{2n}C_n = b_n$$
$$\Rightarrow \quad {}^{n+1}C_{n+1} + {}^{n+1}C_n + {}^{n+2}C_n + \ldots + {}^{2n}C_n = b_n$$
$$[\because {}^nC_r + {}^nC_{r-1} = {}^{n+1}C_r]$$
$$\Rightarrow {}^{n+2}C_{n+1} + {}^{n+2}C_n + \ldots + {}^{2n}C_n = b_n$$

[adding first two terms]

If we combine terms on LHS finally, we get

$${}^{2n+1}C_{n+1} = b_n$$

• Ex. 41 *(i) If n is an odd natural number, prove that*

$$\sum_{r=0}^{n} \frac{(-1)^r}{{}^nC_r} = 0.$$

(ii) If n is an even natural number, find the value of

$$\sum_{r=0}^{n} \frac{(-1)^r}{{}^nC_r}.$$

Sol. (i) We have, $\displaystyle\sum_{r=0}^{n} \frac{(-1)^r}{{}^nC_r} = \sum_{r=0}^{\frac{n+1}{2}} \left[\frac{(-1)^r}{{}^nC_r} + \frac{(-1)^{n-r}}{{}^nC_{n-r}}\right]$

$$= \sum_{r=0}^{\frac{n+1}{2}} (-1)^r \left[\frac{1}{{}^nC_r} + \frac{(-1)^n}{{}^nC_{n-r}}\right] = \sum_{r=0}^{\frac{n+1}{2}} (-1)^r \left[\frac{1}{{}^nC_r} - \frac{1}{{}^nC_r}\right]$$

$= 0$ $\quad [\because n \text{ is odd and } {}^nC_r = {}^nC_{n-r}]$

(ii) We have,

$$\sum_{r=0}^{n} \frac{(-1)^r}{{}^nC_r} = \sum_{r=0}^{\frac{n}{2}-1} \left[\frac{(-1)^r}{{}^nC_r} + \frac{(-1)^{n-r}}{{}^nC_{n-r}}\right] + \frac{(-1)^{n/2}}{{}^nC_{n/2}}$$

$$= \sum_{r=0}^{\frac{n}{2}-1} (-1)^r \left[\frac{1}{{}^nC_r} + \frac{(-1)^n}{{}^nC_r}\right] + \frac{(-1)^{n/2}}{{}^nC_{n/2}}$$

$$= \sum_{r=0}^{\frac{n}{2}-1} (-1)^r \left[\frac{1}{{}^nC_r} + \frac{1}{{}^nC_r}\right] + \frac{(-1)^{n/2}}{{}^nC_{n/2}}$$

$$= \left[\sum_{r=0}^{\frac{n}{2}-1} (-1)^r \cdot \frac{2}{{}^nC_r}\right] + \frac{(-1)^{n/2}}{{}^nC_{n/2}}$$

• Ex. 42 *If $(1+x)^n = C_0 + C_1 x + C_2 x^2 + C_3 x^3 + \ldots + C_n x^n$, show that*

$$C_1 - \frac{C_2}{2} + \frac{C_3}{3} - \ldots (-1)^{n-1} \frac{C_n}{n} = 1 + \frac{1}{2} + \frac{1}{3} + \ldots + \frac{1}{n}.$$

Sol. We know that,

$$(1-x)^n = C_0 - C_1 x + C_2 x^2 - \ldots + (-1)^n C_n x^n$$

or $C_0 - (1-x)^n = C_1 x - C_2 x^2 + C_3 x^3 - \ldots + (-1)^{n-1} C_n x^n$

$$\Rightarrow 1 - (1-x)^n = C_1 x - C_2 x^2 + C_3 x^3 - \ldots + (-1)^{n-1} C_n x^n$$

Dividing in each side by x, then

$$\frac{1-(1-x)^n}{x} = C_1 - C_2 x + C_3 x^2 - \ldots + (-1)^{n-1} C_n x^{n-1}$$

On integrating within limits 0 to 1, we have

$$\int_0^1 \frac{1-(1-x)^n}{x}\, dx = \int_0^1 (C_1 - C_2 x + C_3 x^2 - \ldots + (-1)^{n-1} C_n x^{n-1})\, dx$$

$$= \left[C_1 x - \frac{C_2 x^2}{2} + \frac{C_3 x^3}{3} - \ldots + (-1)^{n-1} C_n \frac{x^n}{n}\right]_0^1$$

$$\int_0^1 \frac{1-(1-x)^n}{x}\, dx = C_1 - \frac{C_2}{2} + \frac{C_3}{3} - \ldots + \frac{(-1)^{n-1}}{n} C_n$$

Putting $1 - x = t$ in integral,

$\Rightarrow \quad dx = -dt$

when $x \to 1, t \to 0$ and when $x \to 0, t \to 1$

$$\therefore \int_0^1 \frac{(1-t^n)}{(1-t)}(-dt) = C_1 - \frac{C_2}{2} + \frac{C_3}{3} - \ldots + (-1)^{n-1} \frac{C_n}{n}$$

$$\Rightarrow \quad \int_0^1 \frac{(1-t^n)}{(1-t)}\, dt = C_1 - \frac{C_2}{2} + \frac{C_3}{3} - \ldots + (-1)^{n-1} \frac{C_n}{n}$$

$$\Rightarrow \int_0^1 (1 + t + t^2 + \ldots + t^{n-1})\, dt = C_1 - \frac{C_2}{2} + \frac{C_3}{3} - \ldots + (-1)^{n-1} \frac{C_n}{n}$$

$$\Rightarrow \left[t + \frac{t^2}{2} + \frac{t^3}{3} + \ldots + \frac{t^n}{n}\right]_0^1 = C_1 - \frac{C_2}{2} + \frac{C_3}{3} - \ldots + (-1)^{n-1} \frac{C_n}{n}$$

$$\Rightarrow 1 + \frac{1}{2} + \frac{1}{3} + \ldots + \frac{1}{n} = C_1 - \frac{C_2}{2} + \frac{C_3}{3} - \ldots + (-1)^{n-1} \frac{C_n}{n}$$

Hence, $\displaystyle C_1 - \frac{C_2}{2} + \frac{C_3}{3} - \ldots + (-1)^{n-1} \frac{C_n}{n} = 1 + \frac{1}{2} + \frac{1}{3} + \ldots + \frac{1}{n}.$

• Ex. 43 *If $(1+x)^n = C_0 + C_1 x + C_2 x^2 + C_3 x^3 + \ldots + C_n x^n$, find the sum of the seriesd*

$$\frac{C_0}{2} - \frac{C_1}{6} + \frac{C_2}{10} - \frac{C_3}{14} + \ldots + (-1)^n \frac{C_n}{4n+2}.$$

Sol. Let $S=\frac{C_0}{2}-\frac{C_1}{6}+\frac{C_2}{10}-\frac{C_3}{14}+\ldots+(-1)^n\frac{C_n}{4n+2}$

$$=\frac{1}{2}\left(\frac{C_0}{1}-\frac{C_1}{3}+\frac{C_2}{5}-\frac{C_3}{7}+\ldots+(-1)^n\frac{C_n}{2n+1}\right) \quad \ldots(i)$$

Consider, $(1-x^2)^n=C_0-C_1x^2+C_2x^4-C_3x^6+\ldots+(-1)^nC_nx^{2n}$

$$\Rightarrow \int_0^1(1-x^2)^n\,dx=\int_0^1(C_0-C_1x^2+C_2x^4-C_3x^6+\ldots+(-1)^nC_nx^{2n})\,dx$$

$$\Rightarrow \int_0^1(1-x^2)^n\,dx=\left[C_0x-\frac{C_1x^3}{3}+\frac{C_2x^5}{5}-\frac{C_3x^7}{7}+\ldots+(-1)^n\frac{C_nx^{2n+1}}{2n+1}\right]$$

$$\Rightarrow \int_0^1(1-x^2)^n\,dx=C_0-\frac{C_1}{3}+\frac{C_2}{5}-\frac{C_3}{7}+\ldots+(-1)^n\frac{C_n}{2n+1}$$

From Eq. (i),

$$\int_0^1(1-x^2)^n\,dx=2S \quad\text{or}\quad S=\frac{1}{2}\int_0^1(1-x^2)^n\,dx$$

Put $x=\sin\theta$ i.e., $dx=\cos\theta\,d\theta$

$$S=\frac{1}{2}\int_0^{\pi/2}\cos^{2n+1}\theta\,d\theta$$

By using Walli's formula,

$$S=\frac{1}{2}\cdot\frac{2n(2n-2)(2n-4)\ldots4\cdot2}{(2n+1)(2n-1)(2n-3)\ldots3\cdot1}\cdot1$$

$$=\frac{1}{2}\cdot\frac{\{2n(2n-2)(2n-4)\ldots4\cdot2\}^2}{(2n+1)!}$$

$$=\frac{1}{2}\cdot\frac{(2^n\,n!)^2}{(2n+1)!}=2^{2n-1}\frac{(n!)^2}{(2n+1)!}$$

• **Ex. 44** *If* $(1+x)^n=\sum_{r=0}^{n}C_r\,x^r$, *then prove that*

$$\sum\sum_{0\le i<j\le n}\left(\frac{i}{C_i}+\frac{j}{C_j}\right)=\frac{n^2}{2}\sum_{r=0}^{n}\frac{1}{C_r}.$$

Sol. Let $S=\sum\sum_{0\le i<j\le n}\left(\frac{i}{C_i}+\frac{j}{C_j}\right) \quad \ldots(i)$

Replacing i by $n-i$ and j by $n-j$, we get

$$S=\sum\sum_{0\le i<j\le n}\left(\frac{n-i}{C_{n-i}}+\frac{n-j}{C_{n-j}}\right)=\sum\sum_{0\le i<j\le n}\left(\frac{n-i}{C_i}+\frac{n-j}{C_j}\right)$$

$[\because C_r=C_{n-r}]$ ...(ii)

On adding Eqs. (i) and (ii), we get

$$2S=n\sum\sum_{0\le i<j\le n}\left(\frac{1}{C_i}+\frac{1}{C_j}\right)$$

$$\therefore\quad S=\frac{n}{2}\sum\sum_{0\le i<j\le n}\left(\frac{1}{C_i}+\frac{1}{C_j}\right)=\frac{n}{2}\left(\sum_{r=0}^{n-1}\frac{n-r}{C_r}+\sum_{r=1}^{n}\frac{r}{C_r}\right)$$

$$=\frac{n}{2}\left(\sum_{r=0}^{n}\frac{n-r}{C_r}+\sum_{r=0}^{n}\frac{r}{C_r}\right)=\frac{n}{2}\left(\sum_{r=0}^{n}\frac{n}{C_r}\right)=\frac{n^2}{2}\sum_{r=0}^{n}\frac{1}{C_r}$$

• **Ex. 45** *If* $(1+x)^n=C_0+C_1x+C_2x^2+C_3x^3+\ldots+C_nx^n$, *show that*

$$\sum_{r=0}^{n}\frac{C_r\,3^{r+4}}{(r+1)(r+2)(r+3)(r+4)}=\frac{1}{(n+1)(n+2)(n+3)(n+4)}\left(4^{n+4}-\sum_{t=0}^{3}{}^{n+4}C_t\,3^t\right).$$

Sol. LHS $=\sum_{r=0}^{n}\frac{C_r\cdot3^{r+4}}{(r+1)(r+2)(r+3)(r+4)}$

$$=\sum_{r=0}^{n}\frac{C_r\cdot3^{r+4}}{\frac{(r+1)(r+2)(r+3)(r+4)}{4!}4!}$$

$$=\sum_{r=0}^{n}\frac{C_r\,3^{r+4}}{{}^{r+4}C_4\cdot4!}=\sum_{r=0}^{n}\frac{n!}{r!(n-r)!}\cdot\frac{3^{r+4}}{\frac{(r+4)!}{4!r!}\cdot4!}$$

$$=\sum_{r=0}^{n}\frac{n!\cdot3^{r+4}}{(n-r)!\cdot(n+4)!}$$

$$=\sum_{r=0}^{n}\frac{n!\cdot3^{r+4}}{(n-r)!\cdot(r+4)!}\cdot\frac{(n+1)(n+2)(n+3)(n+4)}{(n+1)(n+2)(n+3)(n+4)}$$

$$=\sum_{r=0}^{n}\frac{(n+4)!\,3^{r+4}}{(n-r)!\,(r+4)!\,(n+1)(n+2)(n+3)(n+4)}$$

$$=\frac{1}{(n+1)(n+2)(n+3)(n+4)}\left[\sum_{r=0}^{n}\frac{(n+4)!\cdot3^{r+4}}{(n-r)!\cdot(r+4)!}\right]$$

$$=\frac{1}{(n+1)(n+2)(n+3)(n+4)}\left[\sum_{r=0}^{n}{}^{n+4}C_{r+4}\,3^{r+4}\right]$$

$$=\frac{1}{(n+1)(n+2)(n+3)(n+4)}\left\{\sum_{t=4}^{n+4}{}^{n+4}C_t\,3^t\right\}$$

[put $r+4=t$]

$$=\frac{1}{(n+1)(n+2)(n+3)(n+4)}\left\{\sum_{t=0}^{n+4}{}^{n+4}C_t\,3^t-\sum_{t=0}^{3}{}^{n+4}C_t\,3^t\right\}$$

$$=\frac{1}{(n+1)(n+2)(n+3)(n+4)}\left\{(1+3)^{n+4}-\sum_{t=0}^{3}{}^{n+4}C_t\,3^t\right\}$$

$$=\frac{1}{(n+1)(n+2)(n+3)(n+4)}\left\{4^{n+4}-\sum_{t=0}^{3}{}^{n+4}C_t\,3^t\right\}$$

= RHS

Ex. 46 *Prove that* $\sum_{k=0}^{9} x^k$ *divides* $\sum_{k=0}^{9} x^{kkkk}$.

Sol. Let $S_1 = \sum_{k=0}^{9} x^{kkkk} = x^0 + x^{1111} + x^{2222} + \dots + x^{9999}$

and $S_2 = \sum_{k=0}^{9} x^k = x^0 + x^1 + x^2 + \dots + x^9$

Now, $S_1 - S_2 = \sum_{k=0}^{9} (x^{kkkk} - x^k) = \sum_{k=0}^{9} x^k ((x^{10})^{kkk} - 1)$

$= [(x^{10})^{kkk} - 1] \sum_{k=0}^{9} x^k = \lambda \sum_{k=0}^{9} x^k$

$\Rightarrow S_1 - S_2 = \lambda S_2 \Rightarrow S_1 = (1+\lambda) S_2$

Hence, $\sum_{k=0}^{9} x^{kkkk}$ is divisible by $\sum_{k=0}^{9} x^k$.

Ex. 47 *Prove that* $\sum_{r=1}^{k} (-3)^{r-1} \cdot {}^{3n}C_{2r-1} = 0$, *where* $k = \frac{3n}{2}$ *and n is an even positive integer.*

Sol. Given, n is an even positive integer.

Let $n = 2m$; $\therefore k = 3m$, $m \in N$

$$\text{LHS} = \sum_{r=1}^{k} (-3)^{r-1}\, {}^{3n}C_{2r-1} = \sum_{r=1}^{3m} (-3)^{r-1}\, {}^{6m}C_{2r-1}$$

$$= {}^{6m}C_1 - 3 \cdot {}^{6m}C_3 + 3^2 \cdot {}^{6m}C_5 - \dots + (-3)^{3m-1}\, {}^{6m}C_{6m-1} \quad \text{...(i)}$$

Consider $(1+i\sqrt{3})^{6m} = {}^{6m}C_0 + {}^{6m}C_1 (i\sqrt{3}) + {}^{6m}C_2 (i\sqrt{3})^2 + {}^{6m}C_3 (i\sqrt{3})^3 + {}^{6m}C_4 (i\sqrt{3})^4 + {}^{6m}C_5 (i\sqrt{3})^5 + \dots + {}^{6m}C_{6m-1} (i\sqrt{3})^{6m-1} + {}^{6m}C_{6m} (i\sqrt{3})^{6m}$ ...(ii)

Now, $(1+i\sqrt{3})^{6m} = \left\{(-2)\left(\frac{-1-i\sqrt{3}}{2}\right)\right\}^{6m} = (-2\omega^2)^{6m}$

$= 2^{6m}$, where ω^2 is cube root of unity.

Then, Eq. (ii) can be written as

$2^{6m} = \{{}^{6m}C_0 - {}^{6m}C_2 \cdot 3 + {}^{6m}C_4 \cdot 3^2 - \dots + (-3)^{3m} \cdot {}^{6m}C_{6m}\} + i\sqrt{3}\,\{{}^{6m}C_1 - {}^{6m}C_3 \cdot 3 + {}^{6m}C_5 \cdot 3^2 - \dots + (-3)^{3m-1} \cdot {}^{6m}C_{6m-1}\}$

On comparing the imaginary part on both sides, we get

$\sqrt{3}({}^{6m}C_1 - 3 \cdot {}^{6m}C_3 + 3^2 \cdot {}^{6m}C_5 - \dots + (-3)^{3m-1} \cdot {}^{6m}C_{6m-1}) = 0$

or ${}^{6m}C_1 - 3 \cdot {}^{6m}C_3 + 3^2 \cdot {}^{6m}C_5 - \dots + (-3)^{3m-1} \cdot {}^{6m}C_{6m-1} = 0$

$$\Rightarrow \sum_{r=1}^{3m} (-3)^{r-1} \cdot {}^{6m}C_{2r-1} = 0$$

or $\sum_{r=1}^{k} (-3)^{r-1} \cdot {}^{3n}C_{2r-1} = 0$, where $n = 2m$ and $k = 3m$

Ex. 48 *Prove that*

$${}^nC_3 + {}^nC_7 + {}^nC_{11} + \dots = \frac{1}{2}\left\{2^{n-1} - 2^{n/2} \sin \frac{n\pi}{4}\right\}$$

Sol. In given series difference in lower suffices is 4.

i.e., $7 - 3 = 11 - 7 = \dots = 4$

Now, $(1)^{1/4} = (\cos 0 + i \sin 0)^{1/4}$

$= (\cos 2r\pi + i \sin 2r\pi)^{1/4}$

$= \cos \frac{r\pi}{2} + i \sin \frac{r\pi}{2}$, where $r = 0, 1, 2, 3$

Four roots of unity $= 1, i, -1, -i = 1, \alpha, \alpha^2, \alpha^3$ [say]

and $(1+x)^n = \sum_{r=0}^{n} {}^nC_r x^r$

Putting $x = 1, \alpha, \alpha^2, \alpha^3$, we get $2^n = \sum_{r=0}^{n} {}^nC_r$ ...(i)

$$(1+\alpha)^n = \sum_{r=0}^{n} {}^nC_r \alpha^r \quad \text{...(ii)}$$

$$(1+\alpha^2)^n = \sum_{r=0}^{n} {}^nC_r \alpha^{2r} \quad \text{...(iii)}$$

and $(1+\alpha^3)^n = \sum_{r=0}^{n} {}^nC_r \alpha^{3r}$ ...(iv)

On multiplying Eq. (i) by 1, Eq. (ii) by α, Eq. (iii) by α^2 and Eq. (iv) by α^3 and adding, we get

$\Rightarrow 2^n + \alpha(1+\alpha)^n + \alpha^2(1+\alpha^2)^n + \alpha^3(1+\alpha^3)^n$

$$= \sum_{r=0}^{n} {}^nC_r (1 + \alpha^{r+1} + \alpha^{2r+2} + \alpha^{3r+3}) \quad \text{...(v)}$$

For $r = 3, 7, 11, \dots$ RHS of Eq. (v)

$= {}^nC_3(1 + \alpha^4 + \alpha^8 + \alpha^{12}) + {}^nC_7(1 + \alpha^8 + \alpha^{16} + \alpha^{24}) + {}^nC_{11}(1 + \alpha^{12} + \alpha^{24} + \alpha^{36}) + \dots$

$= 4({}^nC_3 + {}^nC_7 + {}^nC_{11} + \dots)$ $[\because \alpha^4 = 1]$

and LHS of Eq. (v)

$= 2^n + i(1+i)^n + i^2(1+i^2)^n + i^3(1+i^3)^n$

$= 2^n + i(1+i)^n + 0 - i(1-i)^n$

$= 2^n + i\{(1+i)^n - (1-i)^n\}$

$\left[\text{Since, } (1+i)^n = \left[\sqrt{2}\left(\frac{1}{\sqrt{2}} + \frac{i}{\sqrt{2}}\right)\right]^n = 2^{n/2}\left\{\cos\frac{\pi}{4} + i \sin\frac{\pi}{4}\right\}^n = 2^{n/2}\left\{\cos\frac{n\pi}{4} + i\sin\frac{n\pi}{4}\right\}\right]$

$= 2^n + i2^{n/2} \cdot 2i \sin \frac{n\pi}{4}$

$= 2^n - 2^{n/2} \cdot 2 \sin \frac{n\pi}{4}$

Hence, $4({}^nC_3 + {}^nC_7 + {}^nC_{11} + \dots) = 2\left(2^{n-1} - 2^{n/2} \sin \frac{n\pi}{4}\right)$

$$\Rightarrow {}^nC_3 + {}^nC_7 + {}^nC_{11} + \dots = \frac{1}{2}\left(2^{n-1} - 2^{n/2} \sin \frac{n\pi}{4}\right)$$

Ex. 49 *Evaluate* $\sum_{i=0}^{n-1}\sum_{j=1+i}^{n+1} {}^nC_i\ {}^{n+1}C_j$.

Sol. Let $P = \sum_{i=0}^{n-1}\sum_{j=1+i}^{n+1} {}^nC_i\ {}^{n+1}C_j$

$$= \sum_{j=1}^{n+1} {}^nC_0\ {}^{n+1}C_j + \sum_{j=2}^{n+1} {}^nC_1\ {}^{n+1}C_j + \sum_{j=3}^{n+1} {}^nC_2\ {}^{n+1}C_j + \dots + \sum_{j=n}^{n+1} {}^nC_{n-1}\ {}^{n+1}C_j$$

$$= {}^nC_0 \sum_{j=1}^{n+1} {}^{n+1}C_j + {}^nC_1 \sum_{j=2}^{n+1} {}^{n+1}C_j + {}^nC_2 \sum_{j=3}^{n+1} {}^{n+1}C_j + \dots + {}^nC_{n-1} \sum_{j=n}^{n+1} {}^{n+1}C_j$$

$$= {}^nC_0 ({}^{n+1}C_1 + {}^{n+1}C_2 + {}^{n+1}C_3 + \dots + {}^{n+1}C_{n+1}) + {}^nC_1({}^{n+1}C_2 + {}^{n+1}C_3 + {}^{n+1}C_4 + \dots + {}^{n+1}C_{n+1}) + {}^nC_2 ({}^{n+1}C_3 + {}^{n+1}C_4 + {}^{n+1}C_5 + \dots + {}^{n+1}C_{n+1}) + \dots + {}^nC_{n-1} ({}^{n+1}C_n + {}^{n+1}C_{n+1})$$

$$= {}^{n+1}C_1 \cdot {}^nC_0 + {}^{n+1}C_2 ({}^nC_0 + {}^nC_1) + {}^{n+1}C_3 ({}^nC_0 + {}^nC_1 + {}^nC_2) + \dots + {}^{n+1}C_{n+1} ({}^nC_0 + {}^nC_1 + {}^nC_2 + \dots + {}^nC_{n-1})$$

$$= ({}^nC_0 + {}^nC_1) \cdot {}^nC_0 + ({}^nC_1 + {}^nC_2)({}^nC_0 + {}^nC_1) + ({}^nC_2 + {}^nC_3)({}^nC_0 + {}^nC_1 + {}^nC_2) + \dots + ({}^nC_n + {}^nC_{n-1})({}^nC_0 + {}^nC_1 + {}^nC_2 + \dots + {}^nC_{n-1}) + n$$

$$= ({}^nC_0)^2 + ({}^nC_1)^2 + ({}^nC_2)^2 + \dots + ({}^nC_{n-1})^2 + 2\{{}^nC_0 \cdot {}^nC_1 + {}^nC_0 \cdot {}^nC_2 + {}^nC_0 \cdot {}^nC_3 + \dots + {}^nC_0 \cdot {}^nC_{n-1} + \dots + {}^nC_{n-2}\ {}^nC_{n-1}\} + 2^n - 1 + n$$

$$= ({}^nC_0 + {}^nC_1 + {}^nC_2 + \dots + {}^nC_{n-1})^2 + 2^n - 1 + n$$

$$= (2^n - 1)^2 + 2^n - 1 + n = 2^{2n} - 2^n + n$$

Ex. 50 *If* $(9 + 4\sqrt{5})^n = I + f$, *n and I being positive integers and f is a proper fraction, show that* $(I - 1) f + f^2$ *is an even integer.*

Sol. $(9 + 4\sqrt{5})^n = I + f$ ...(i)

$0 \le f < 1$ ...(ii)

Let $f' = (9 - 4\sqrt{5})^n$ ...(iii)

and $0 < f' < 1$ ...(iv)

From Eqs. (i) and (iii), we get

$$I + f + f' = (9 + 4\sqrt{5})^n + (9 - 4\sqrt{5})^n$$
$$= 2\{9^n + {}^nC_2\ 9^{n-2}\ (4\sqrt{5})^2 + \dots\}$$
$$= 2N, \text{ where } N \text{ is a positive integer.}$$

and from Eqs. (ii) and (iii), we get $0 < f + f' < 2$

Since, $f + f'$ is an integer.

$\therefore \quad f + f' = 1$

Now, $\quad I + 1 = 2N \Rightarrow 1 = 2N - 1$ ...(v)

$\because \quad (I + f)(1 - f) = (9 + 4\sqrt{5})^n f'$

$$= (9 + 4\sqrt{5})^n (9 - 4\sqrt{5})^n = 1^n = 1$$

$\therefore \quad (I - 1) f + f^2 = I - 1 = 2N - 1 - 1 = 2N - 2$ [from Eq. (v)]

$= \text{An even integer}$

Ex. 51 *If* P_r *is the coefficient of* x^r *in the expansion of* $(1+x)^2\left(1+\frac{x}{2}\right)^2\left(1+\frac{x}{2^2}\right)^2\left(1+\frac{x}{2^3}\right)^2 \dots$, *prove that* $P_r = \frac{2^2}{(2^r - 1)}(P_{r-1} + P_{r-2})$ *and* $P_4 = \frac{1072}{315}$.

Sol. Let $(1 + x)^2\left(1+\frac{x}{2}\right)^2\left(1+\frac{x}{2^2}\right)^2\left(1+\frac{x}{2^3}\right)^2 \dots,$

$$= 1 + P_1 x + P_2 x^2 + P_3 x^3 + P_4 x^4 + \dots + P_{r-1} x^{r-1} + P_r x^r + \dots \quad \text{...(i)}$$

Replacing x by $\frac{x}{2}$, we get

$$\left(1+\frac{x}{2}\right)^2\left(1+\frac{x}{2^2}\right)^2\left(1+\frac{x}{2^3}\right)^2\left(1+\frac{x}{2^4}\right)^2 \dots = \left[1 + P_1\left(\frac{x}{2}\right) + P_2\left(\frac{x}{2}\right)^2 + P_3\left(\frac{x}{2}\right)^3 + \dots\right]$$

On multiplying both sides by $(1 + x)^2$, we get

$$(1+x)^2\left(1+\frac{x}{2}\right)^2\left(1+\frac{x}{2^2}\right)^2\left(1+\frac{x}{2^3}\right)^2 \dots = (1+x)^2\left[1 + P_1\left(\frac{x}{2}\right) + P_2\left(\frac{x}{2}\right)^2 + P_3\left(\frac{x}{2}\right)^3 + \dots\right] \quad \text{...(ii)}$$

From Eqs. (i) and (ii), we get

$$1 + P_1 x + P_2 x^2 + P_3 x^3 + P_4 x^4 + \dots + P_{r-1} x^{r-1} + P_r x^r + \dots = (1+x)^2\left[1 + P_1\left(\frac{x}{2}\right) + P_2\left(\frac{x}{2}\right)^2 + P_3\left(\frac{x}{2}\right)^3 + \dots\right]$$

On equating coefficient of x^r, we get

$$P_r = P_r\left(\frac{1}{2^r}\right) + 2P_{r-1}\left(\frac{1}{2^{r-1}}\right) + P_{r-2}\left(\frac{1}{2^{r-2}}\right)$$

$$\Rightarrow \quad P_r\left(1 - \frac{1}{2^r}\right) = \frac{1}{2^{r-2}}(P_{r-1} + P_{r-2})$$

$$\Rightarrow \quad P_r = \frac{2^2}{(2^r - 1)}(P_{r-1} + P_{r-2})$$

Now, $\quad P_0 = 1,\ P_1 = 2 + 1 + \frac{1}{2} + \frac{1}{2^2} + \dots = 4$

$$P_2 = \frac{2^2(P_1 + P_0)}{2^2 - 1} = \frac{20}{3},$$

$$P_3 = \frac{2^2(P_2 + P_1)}{2^3 - 1} = \frac{128}{21}$$

and $\quad P_4 = \frac{2^2(P_3 + P_2)}{2^4 - 1} = \frac{4\left(\frac{128}{21} + \frac{20}{3}\right)}{15} = \frac{1072}{315}$

Binomial Theorem Exercise 1 :
Single Option Correct Type Questions

- This section contains **30 multiple choice questions.** Each question has four choices (a), (b), (c) and (d) out of which **ONLY ONE** is correct

1. If $\sum_{r=0}^{n} (-1)^r \, {}^nC_r \left[\frac{1}{2^r} + \frac{3^r}{2^{2r}} + \frac{7^r}{2^{3r}} + \dots \text{upto } m \text{ terms}\right] = f(n)\left(1 - \frac{1}{2^{mn}}\right)$,

$\int_{-3}^{3} f(x^3 \ln x)\, d(x^3 \ln x)$ is equal to

(a) -6 (b) -3
(c) 3 (d) Cannot be determined

2. The coefficient of $(a^3 \cdot b^6 \cdot c^8 \cdot d^9 \cdot e \cdot f)$ in the expansion of $(a + b + c - d - e - f)^{31}$ is

(a) 123210 (b) 23110
(c) 3110 (d) None of these

3. The sum of rational terms in $(\sqrt{2} + \sqrt{3} + \sqrt[6]{5})^{10}$, is

(a) 12632 (b) 1260
(c) 126 (d) None of these

4. If $(1 + x - 3x^2)^{2145} = a_0 + a_1 x + a_2 x^2 + \dots$, then $a_0 - a_1 + a_2 - a_3 + \dots$ ends with

(a) 1 (b) 3
(c) 7 (d) 9

5. In the expansion of $\left(\sqrt{\frac{q}{p}} + \sqrt[10]{\frac{p^7}{q^3}}\right)^n$, there is a term similar to pq, then that term is equal to

(a) $45pq$ (b) $120\, pq$
(c) $210\, pq$ (d) $252\, pq$

6. Let $(5 + 2\sqrt{6})^n = I + f$, where $n, I \in N$ and $0 < f < 1$, then the value of $f^2 - f + I \cdot f - I$, is

(a) a natural number (b) a negative integer
(c) a prime number (d) an irrational number

7. If $x + \frac{1}{x} = 1$ and $p = x^{4000} + \frac{1}{x^{4000}}$ and q is the digit at unit place in the number $2^{2^n} + 1$, $n \in N$ and $n > 1$, then $p + q$, is

(a) 8 (b) 6
(c) 7 (d) None of these

8. If the number of terms in $\left(x + 1 + \frac{1}{x}\right)^n$ $(n \in I^+)$ is 401, then n is greater than

(a) 201 (b) 200
(c) 199 (d) None of these

9. $\sum_{r=0}^{n-1} \frac{{}^nC_r}{{}^nC_r + {}^nC_{r+1}}$ is equal to

(a) $\frac{n}{2}$ (b) $\frac{n+1}{2}$
(c) $\frac{n(n+1)}{2}$ (d) $\frac{n(n-1)}{2(n+1)}$

10. The largest term in the expansion of $\left(\frac{b}{2} + \frac{b}{2}\right)^{100}$ is

(a) b^{100} (b) $\left(\frac{b}{2}\right)^{100}$
(c) ${}^{100}C_{50}\left(\frac{b}{2}\right)^{100}$ (d) ${}^{100}C_{50} b^{100}$

11. If the fourth term of $\left(\sqrt{x^{\left(\frac{1}{1+\log x}\right)}} + \sqrt[12]{x}\right)^6$ is equal to 200 and $x > 1$, x is equal to

(a) $10\sqrt{2}$ (b) 10 (c) 10^4 (d) $\frac{10}{\sqrt{2}}$

12. The coefficient of x^m in $(1 + x)^m + (1 + x)^{m+1} + \dots + (1 + x)^n$, $m \le n$, is

(a) ${}^{n+1}C_{m+1}$ (b) ${}^{n-1}C_{m-1}$
(c) ${}^nC_m$ (d) ${}^nC_{m+1}$

13. The number of values of 'r' satisfying the equation ${}^{39}C_{3r-1} - {}^{39}C_{r^2} = {}^{39}C_{r^2-1} - {}^{39}C_{3r}$ is

(a) 1 (b) 2
(c) 3 (d) 4

14. The sum $S = {}^{20}C_2 + 2 \cdot {}^{20}C_3 + 3 \cdot {}^{20}C_4 + \dots + 19 \cdot {}^{20}C_{20}$ is equal to

(a) $1 + 5 \cdot 2^{20}$ (b) $1 + 2^{21}$
(c) $1 + 9 \cdot 2^{20}$ (d) 2^{20}

15. The remainder, if $1 + 2 + 2^2 + 2^3 + \dots + 2^{1999}$ is divided by 5, is

(a) 0 (b) 1
(c) 2 (d) 3

16. Coefficient of $\frac{1}{x}$ in the expansion of $(1 + x)^n (1 + 1/x)^n$ is

(a) $\frac{n!}{(n-1)!(n+1)!}$ (b) $\frac{2n!}{(n-1)!(n+1)!}$
(c) $\frac{n!}{(2n-1)!(2n+1)!}$ (d) $\frac{2n!}{(2n-1)!(2n+1)!}$

17. The last two digits of the number 19^{9^4} is
(a) 19 (b) 29
(c) 39 (d) 81

18. If the second term in the expansion of $\left(\sqrt[13]{a}+\frac{a}{\sqrt{a^{-1}}}\right)^n$ is $14a^{5/2}$, the value of $\frac{{}^nC_3}{{}^nC_2}$ is
(a) 4 (b) 3
(c) 12 (d) 6

19. If $6^{83}+8^{83}$ is divided by 49, the remainder is
(a) 0 (b) 14
(c) 35 (d) 42

20. The sum of all the rational terms in the expansion of $(3^{1/4}+4^{1/3})^{12}$ is
(a) 91 (b) 251
(c) 273 (d) 283

21. Last four digits of the number $N=7^{100}-3^{100}$ is
(a) 2000 (b) 4000
(c) 6000 (d) 8000

22. If 5^{99} is divided by 13, the remainder is
(a) 2 (b) 4 (c) 6 (d) 8

23. The value of $\left\{\frac{3^{2003}}{28}\right\}$, where {.} denotes the fractional part function is
(a) 17/28 (b) 19/28
(c) 23/28 (d) 5/28

24. The value of $\sum_{r=0}^{20} r(20-r)({}^{20}C_r)^2$ is equal to
(a) $400\,{}^{37}C_{20}$ (b) $400\,{}^{40}C_{19}$
(c) $400\,{}^{38}C_{19}$ (d) $400\,{}^{38}C_{20}$

25. If $(3+x^{2008}+x^{2009})^{2010}=a_0+a_1x+a_2x^2+\ldots+a_nx^n$, the value of $a_0-\frac{a_1}{2}-\frac{a_2}{2}+a_3-\frac{a_4}{2}-\frac{a_5}{2}+a_6-\ldots$ is
(a) 1 (b) 2^{2010}
(c) 5^{2010} (d) 3^{2010}

26. The total number of terms which depend on the value of x in the expansion of $\left(x^2-2+\frac{1}{x^2}\right)^n$ is
(a) $2n+1$ (b) $2n$
(c) $n+1$ (d) n

27. The coefficient of x^{10} in the expansion of $(1+x^2-x^3)^8$, is
(a) 420 (b) 476
(c) 532 (d) 588

28. The number of real negative terms in the binomial expansion of $(1+ix)^{4n-2}$, $n\in N, n>0, i=\sqrt{-1}$, is
(a) n (b) $n+1$
(c) $n-1$ (d) $2n$

29. $\sum_{p=1}^{n}\sum_{m=p}^{n}\binom{n}{m}\binom{m}{p}$ is equal to
(a) 3^n (b) 2^n
(c) 3^n+2^n (d) 3^n-2^n

30. The largest real value of x, such that $\sum_{r=0}^{4}\left(\frac{5^{4-r}}{(4-r)!}\right)\left(\frac{x^r}{r!}\right)=\frac{8}{3}$ is
(a) $2\sqrt{2}-5$ (b) $2\sqrt{2}+5$
(c) $-2\sqrt{2}-5$ (d) $-2\sqrt{2}+5$

Binomial Theorem Exercise 2:
More than One Correct Option Type Questions

- This section contains **15 multiple choice questions.** Each question has four choices (a), (b), (c) and (d) out of which **MORE THAN ONE** may be correct.

31. If in the expansion of $(1+x)^m(1-x)^n$, the coefficients of x and x^2 are 3 and -6 respectively, the values of m and n are
(a) 3 (b) 6 (c) 9 (d) 12

32. If the coefficients of rth, $(r+1)$th and $(r+2)$th terms in the expansion of $(1+x)^{14}$ are in AP, then r is /are
(a) 5 (b) 9
(c) 10 (d) 12

33. If n is a positive integer and $(3\sqrt{3}+5)^{2n+1}=\alpha+\beta$, where α is an integer and $0<\beta<1$, then
(a) α is an even integer
(b) $(\alpha+\beta)^2$ is divisible by 2^{2n+1}
(c) the integer just below $(3\sqrt{3}+5)^{2n+1}$ divisible by 3
(d) α is divisible by 10

34. If $(8+3\sqrt{7})^n=P+F$, where P is an integer and F is a proper fraction, then
(a) P is an odd integer (b) P is an even integer
(c) $F(P+F)=1$ (d) $(1-F)(P+F)=1$

35. The value of x for which the 6th term in the expansion of

$$\left\{2^{\log_2\sqrt{(9^{x-1}+7)}} + \frac{1}{2^{\left(\frac{1}{5}\right)\log_2(3^{x-1}+1)}}\right\}^7$$ is 84, is

(a) 4 (b) 3
(c) 2 (d) 1

36. Consider the binomial expansion of $\left(\sqrt{x}+\frac{1}{2\cdot\sqrt[4]{x}}\right)^n$, $n \in N$, where the terms of the expansion are written in decreasing powers of x. If the coefficients of the first three terms form an arithmetic progression, then the statement(s) which hold good is /are

(a) Total number of terms in the expansion of the binomial is 8
(b) Number of terms in the expansion with integral power of x is 3
(c) There is no term in the expansion which is independent of x
(d) Fourth and fifth are the middle terms of the expansion

37. Let $(1+x^2)^2 (1+x)^n = a_0 + a_1 x + a_2 x^2 + \ldots$, if a_1, a_2 and a_3 are in AP, the value of n is

(a) 2 (b) 3
(c) 4 (d) 7

38. 10th term of $\left(3-\sqrt{\frac{17}{4}+3\sqrt{2}}\right)^{20}$ is

(a) an irrational number (b) a rational number
(c) a positive integer (d) a negative integer

39. If $(1+x)^n = C_0 + C_1 x + C_2 x^2 + C_3 x^3 + \ldots + C_n x^n$, then

$$C_0 - (C_0 + C_1) + (C_0 + C_1 + C_2) - (C_0 + C_1 + C_2 + C_3) + \ldots + (-1)^{n-1}(C_0 + C_1 + C_2 + \ldots + C_{n-1}),$$ when n is even integer is

(a) a positive value (b) a negative value
(c) divisible by 2^{n-1} (d) divisible by 2^n

40. If $f(n) = \sum_{i=0}^{n} \binom{30}{30-i}\binom{20}{30-i}$, then

(a) maximum value of $f(n)$ is ${}^{50}C_{25}$
(b) $f(0) + f(1) + f(2) + \ldots + f(50) = 2^{50}$
(c) $f(n)$ is always divisible by 50
(d) $f^2(0) + f^2(1) + f^2(2) + \ldots + f^2(50) = {}^{100}C_{50}$

41. Number of values of r satisfying the equation ${}^{69}C_{3r-1} - {}^{69}C_{r^2} = {}^{69}C_{r^2-1} - {}^{69}C_{3r}$ is

(a) 1 (b) 2
(c) 3 (d) 7

42. If the middle term of $\left(x+\frac{1}{x}\sin^{-1}x\right)^8$ is equal to $\frac{630}{16}$, the values of x is/are

(a) $-\frac{\pi}{3}$ (b) $-\frac{\pi}{6}$
(c) $\frac{\pi}{6}$ (d) $\frac{\pi}{3}$

43. If $b^2 < ac$, the sum of the coefficients in the expansion of $(a\alpha^2 x^2 + 2b\alpha x + c)^n, (a, b, c, \alpha \in R, n \in N)$, is

(a) + ve, if $a > 0$ (b) + ve, if $c > 0$
(c) − ve, if $a < 0$, n is odd (d) + ve, if $c < 0$, n is even

44. In the expansion of $\left(x^2+1+\frac{1}{x^2}\right)^n$, $n \in N$, then

(a) number of terms $= 2n+1$
(b) term independent of $x = 2^{n-1}$
(c) coefficient of $x^{2n-2} = n$
(d) coefficient of $x^2 = n$

45. The coefficient of the $(r+1)$th term of $\left(x+\frac{1}{x}\right)^{20}$, when expanded in the descending powers of x, is equal to the coefficient of the 6th term of $\left(x^2+2+\frac{1}{x^2}\right)^{10}$ when expanded in ascending powers of x. The value of r is

(a) 5 (b) 6
(c) 14 (d) 15

Binomial Theorem Exercise 3 : Passage Based Questions

- This section contains **7 passages**. Based upon each of the passage **3 multiple choice questions** have to be answered. Each of these questions has four choices (a), (b), (c) and (d) out of which **ONLY ONE** is correct.

Passage I (Q. Nos. 46 to 48)

Consider $(1+x+x^2)^n = \sum_{r=0}^{2n} a_r x^r$, *where* $a_0, a_1, a_2, \dots, a_{2n}$ *are real numbers and n is a positive integer.*

46. The value of $\sum_{r=0}^{n-1} a_r$ is

(a) $\frac{-3^n - a_n}{2}$ (b) $\frac{3^n - a_n}{2}$ (c) $\frac{a_n - 3^n}{2}$ (d) $\frac{3^n + a_n}{2}$

47. If n is even, the value of $\sum_{r=0}^{n/2-1} a_{2r}$ is

(a) $\frac{3^n - 1 + a_n}{2}$ (b) $\frac{3^n - 1 - a_n}{4}$

(c) $\frac{3^n + 1 + a_n}{2}$ (d) $\frac{3^n + 1 - 2a_n}{4}$

48. If n is odd, the value of $\sum_{r=1}^{\frac{n+1}{2}} a_{2r-1}$ is

(a) $\frac{3^n - 1 + 2a_n}{2}$ (b) $\frac{3^n - 1 + 2a_n}{4}$

(c) $\frac{3^n + 1 + 2a_n}{2}$ (d) $\frac{3^n + 1 - 2a_n}{4}$

Passage II (Q. Nos. 49 to 51)

If $(1+x+2x^2)^{20} = a_0 + a_1 x + a_2 x^2 + \dots + a_{40} x^{40}$.

49. The value of $a_0 + a_2 + a_4 + \dots + a_{38}$ is

(a) $2^{19}(2^{19}-1)$ (b) $2^{20}(2^{19}-1)$

(c) $2^{19}(2^{20}-1)$ (d) $2^{20}(2^{20}-1)$

50. The value of $a_1 + a_3 + a_5 + \dots + a_{37}$ is

(a) $2^{19}(2^{19}-20)$ (b) $2^{19}(2^{20}-21)$

(c) $2^{19}(2^{19}-21)$ (d) $2^{19}(2^{19}-19)$

51. The value of $\frac{a_{39}}{a_{40}}$, is

(a) 2^{20} (b) (c) 10 (d) 1

Passage III (Q. Nos. 52 to 54)

Suppose, m divided by n, then quotient q and remainder r

i.e. $n)m(q$
$\underline{\quad - \quad}$
$\underline{\ r\ }$

or $m = nq + r, \quad \forall\, m, n, q, r \in I$ *and* $n \neq 0$

52. If a is the remainder when 5^{40} is divided by 11 and b is the remainder when 2^{2011} is divided by 17, the value of $a+b$ is

(a) 7 (b) 8

(c) 9 (d) 10

53. If $19^{93} - 13^{99}$ is divided by 162, the remainder is

(a) 8 (b) 4

(c) 1 (d) 0

54. If 13^{99} is divided by 81, the remainder is

(a) 13 (b) 23

(c) 39 (d) 55

Passage IV (Q. Nos. 55 to 57)

Consider the binomial expansion $R = (1+2x)^n = I + f$, *where I is the integral part of R and f is the fractional part of R,* $n \in N$. *Also, the sum of coefficients of R is 2187.*

55. The value of $(n + Rf)$ for $x = \frac{1}{\sqrt{2}}$ is

(a) 7 (b) 8 (c) 9 (d) 10

56. If ith term is the greatest term for $x = 1/3$, then i equals

(a) 4 (b) 5 (c) 6 (d) 7

57. If kth term is having greatest coefficient, the sum of all possible values of k, is

(a) 7 (b) 9

(c) 11 (d) 13

Passage V (Q. Nos. 58 to 60)

If $(x+a_1)(x+a_2)(x+a_3)\dots(x+a_n) = x^n + S_1 x^{n-1} + S_2 x^{n-2} + \dots + S_n$

where, $S_1 = \sum_{i=1}^{n} a_i,\ S_2 = \sum\sum_{1 \le i < j \le n} a_i a_j,\ S_3 = \sum\sum\sum_{1 \le i < j < k \le n} a_i a_j a_k$

and so on.

58. If $(1+x)^n = C_0 + C_1 x + C_2 x^2 + \dots + C_n x^n$, the coefficient of x^n in the expansion of $(x+C_0)(x+3C_1)(x+5C_2)\dots(x+(2n+1)C_n)$, is

(a) $n \cdot 2^n$ (b) $(n+1) \cdot 2^n$

(c) $n \cdot 2^{n+1}$ (d) $n \cdot 2^n + 1$

59. If $(1+x)^n = C_0 + C_1 x + C_2 x^2 + \dots + C_n x^n$, the coefficient of x^{n-1} in the expansion of $(x+C_0)(x+C_1)(x+C_2)\dots(x+C_n)$ is

(a) $2^{2n-1} - \frac{1}{2}\, {}^{2n}C_{n-1}$ (b) $2^{2n-1} - \frac{1}{2}\, {}^{2n}C_n$

(c) $2^{2n-1} - \frac{1}{2}\, {}^{2n+1}C_n$ (d) $2^{2n-1} - \frac{1}{2}\, {}^{2n+1}C_{n-1}$

60. Coefficient of x^7 in the expansion of $(1+x)^2\ (3+x)^3\ (5+x)^4$ is

(a) 112 (b) 224 (c) 342 (d) 416

Passage VI (Q. Nos. 61 to 63)

Let us consider the binomial expression

$$A=\left(x^2+\frac{3}{x}\right)^m \text{ and } B=\left(\frac{5x}{2}+\frac{x^{-2}}{2}\right)^n$$

Sum of coefficients of expansion of B is 6561. The difference of the coefficient of third term to the second term in the expansion of A is equal to 117.

61. The value of m is

(a) 4 (b) 5 (c) 6 (d) 7

62. If n^m is divided by 7, the remainder is

(a) 1 (b) 2 (c) 3 (d) 5

63. The ratio of the coefficient of second term from the beginning and the end in the expansion of B, is

(a) 125 (b) 625
(c) 3125 (d) 15625

Passage VII (Q. Nos. 64 to 66)

Let us consider the binomial expression $(1+x)^n=\sum_{r=0}^{n} a_r x^r$, *where* a_4, a_5 and a_6 *are in AP,* $(n<10)$. *Consider another binomial expression of* $A=(\sqrt[3]{2}+\sqrt[4]{3})^{13n}$, *the expression of A contains some rational terms* $T_{a_1}, T_{a_2}, T_{a_3}, \ldots, T_{a_m}$ $(a_1<a_2<a_3<\ldots<a_m)$.

64. The value of $\sum_{i=1}^{n} a_i$ is

(a) 63 (b) 127
(c) 255 (d) 511

65. The value of a_m is

(a) 87 (b) 88
(c) 89 (d) 90

66. The common difference of the arithmetic progression $a_1, a_2, a_3, \ldots, a_m$ is

(a) 6 (b) 8
(c) 10 (d) 12

Binomial Theorem Exercise 4 :
Single Integer Answer Type Questions

- This section contains **10 questions**. The answer to each question is a **single digit integer**, ranging from 0 to 9 (both inclusive).

67. For integer $n>1$, the digit at unit's place in the number $\sum_{r=0}^{100} r!+2^{2^n}$ is

68. If $(1+x+x^2+x^3)^n=\sum_{r=0}^{3n} a_r x^r$ and $\sum_{r=0}^{3n} a_r=k$ and if $\sum_{r=0}^{3n} r\,a_r=\frac{\lambda n k}{2}$, the value of λ is

69. The number of rational terms in the expansion of $\left(\sqrt[3]{4}+\frac{1}{\sqrt[4]{6}}\right)^{20}$ is

70. If $2^{2006}+2006$ is divided by 7, the remainder is

71. The last two digits of the natural number 19^{9^4} is ab, the value of $b-3a$ is

72. If $\frac{\left[{}^nC_r+4\cdot{}^nC_{r+1}+6\cdot{}^nC_{r+2}+4\cdot{}^nC_{r+3}+{}^nC_{r+4}\right]}{\left[{}^nC_r+3\cdot{}^nC_{r+1}+3\cdot{}^nC_{r+2}+{}^nC_{r+3}\right]}=\frac{n+\lambda}{r+\lambda}$, the value of λ is

73. The value of $99^{50}-99\cdot 98^{50}+\frac{99\cdot 98}{1\cdot 2}(97)^{50}-\ldots+99$ is

74. If the greatest term in the expansion of $(1+x)^{2n}$ has the greatest coefficient if and only if $x\in\left(\frac{10}{11},\frac{11}{10}\right)$ and the fourth term in the expansion of $\left(\lambda x+\frac{1}{x}\right)^m$ is $\frac{n}{4}$, the value of $m\lambda$ is

75. If the value of $(n+2)\cdot{}^nC_0\cdot 2^{n+1}-(n+1)\cdot{}^nC_1\cdot 2^n+n\cdot{}^nC_2\cdot 2^{n-1}-\ldots$ is equal to $k(n+1)$, the value of k is

76. If $(1+x+x^2+\ldots+x^9)^4\,(x+x^2+x^3+\ldots+x^9)=\sum_{r=1}^{45} a_r x^r$ and the value of $a_2+a_6+a_{10}+\ldots+a_{42}$ is λ, the sum of all digits of λ is

Binomial Theorem Exercise 5 : Matching Type Questions

- This section contains **5 questions**. Questions 77, 78 and 79 have three statements (A, B and C) given in **Column** and five statements (p, q, r, s and t) in **Column II** and questions 80 and 81 have four statements (A, B, C and D given in **Column I** and four statements (p, q, r and s) in **Column II**. Any given statement in **Column I** can hav correct matching with one or more statement(s) given in **Column II**.

77.

	Column I		Column II
(A)	If λ and μ are the unit's place digit in m^n and n^m respectively, where m and n are the number of rational and irrational terms in the expansion of $(7^{1/3} + 11^{1/9})^{6561}$ respectively, then	(p)	$\lambda^2 + \mu^2 = 1$
(B)	If λ and μ are the unit's place digit in m^n and n^m respectively, where m and n are the number of terms with integral coefficients and number of terms with non-integral coefficients in the expansion of $(7^{1/3} + 5^{1/2} \cdot x)^{600}$ respectively, then	(q)	$\lambda^\mu + \mu^\lambda = 1$
(C)	If λ and μ are the unit's place digit in m^n and n^m respectively, where m and n are the number of rational and irrational terms in the expansion of $(\sqrt{2} + \sqrt[3]{3} + \sqrt[6]{7})^{10}$ respectively, then	(r)	$\lambda + \mu = 4$
		(s)	$\sqrt{\lambda\sqrt{\lambda\sqrt{\lambda\sqrt{\lambda \ldots \infty}}}} = \mu$
		(t)	$\lambda + \mu = \lambda^\mu$

78.

	Column I		Column II
(A)	If $\binom{18}{r-2} + 2\binom{18}{r-1} + \binom{18}{r} \geq \binom{20}{13}$, then the values of r is /are	(p)	5
(B)	The digit in the unit's place of the number $183! + 3^{183}$ is less than	(q)	6
(C)	If the 4th term in the expansion of $\left(ax + \frac{1}{x}\right)^n$ is 5 / 2, then na is less than	(r)	7
		(s)	8
		(t)	9

79.

	Column I		Column II
(A)	The sum of binomial coefficients of terms containing power of x more than x^{30} in $(1 + x)^{61}$ is divisible by	(p)	2^{57}
(B)	The sum of binomial coefficients of rational terms in the expansion of $(1 + \sqrt{3})^{62}$ is divisible by	(q)	2^{58}
(C)	If $\left(x + \frac{1}{x} + x^2 + \frac{1}{x^2}\right)^{31} = a_0 x^{-62} + a_1 x^{-61} + a_2 x^{-60} + \ldots + a_{124} x^{62}$, then $a_1 + a_3 + a_5 + \ldots + a_{123}$ is divisible by	(r)	2^{59}
		(s)	2^{60}
		(t)	2^{61}

80.

	Column I		Column II
(A)	If $11^n + 21^n$ is divisible by 16, then n can be	(p)	4
(B)	The remainder, when 3^{37} is divided by 80, is less than	(q)	5
(C)	In the expansion of $(1 + x)^{29}$ coefficient of $(r + 1)$th term is equal to that of $(r + k)$th term, then the value of k cannot be	(r)	6
(D)	If the ratio of 2nd and 3rd terms in the expansion of $(a + b)^n$ is equal to ratio of 3rd and 4th terms in the expansion of $(a + b)^{n+3}$, then n is less than	(s)	7

81.

	Column I		Column II
(A)	If number of dissimilar terms in the expansion of $(x + 2y + 3z)^n$ $(n \in N)$ is $an^2 + bn + c$, then	(p)	$a + b + c = 3$
(B)	If number of dissimilar terms in the expansion of $(x + y + z)^{2n+1} - (x + y - z)^{2n+1}$ $(n \in N)$ is $an^2 + bn + c$, then	(q)	$a + b + c = 4$
(C)	If number of dissimilar terms in the expansion of $(x - y + z)^n + (x + y - z)^n$ ($n \in$ is even natural number) is $an^2 + bn + c$, then	(r)	$a + b = 2c$
(D)	If number of dissimilar terms in the expansion of $\left(\frac{x^2 + 1 + x^4}{x^2}\right)^{\Sigma n}$ $(n \in N)$ is $an^2 + bn + c$, then	(s)	$b + c = 8a$

Binomial Theorem Exercise 6 : Statement I and II Type Questions

- **Directions** (Q. Nos. 71 to 82) are Assertion-Reason type questions. Each of these questions contains two statements:
Statement-1 (Assertion) and **Statement-2** (Reason) Each of these questions also has four alternative choices, only one of which is the correct answer. You have to select the correct choice as given below.
(a) Statement-1 is true, Statement-2 is true; Statement-2 is a correct explanation for Statement-1
(b) Statement-1 is true, Statement-2 is true; Statement-2 is not a correct explanation for Statement-1
(c) Statement1 is true, Statement-2 is false
(d) Statement-1 is false, Statement-2 is true

82. **Statement-1** Greatest coefficient in the expansion of $(1+3x)^6$ is ${}^6C_3 \cdot 3^3$.

Statement-2 Greatest coefficient in the expansion of $(1+x)^{2n}$ is the middle term.

83. **Statement-1** The term independent of x in the expansion of $\left(x^2+\dfrac{1}{x^2}+2\right)^{25}$ is ${}^{50}C_{25}$.

Statement-2 In a binomial expansion middle term is independent of x.

84. **Statement-1** In the expansion of $(1+x)^n$, if coefficient of 31st and 32nd terms are equal, then $n=61$.

Statement-2 Middle term in the expansion of $(1+x)^n$, has greatest coefficient.

85. **Statement-1** The number of terms in the expansion of $\left(x+\dfrac{1}{x}+1\right)^n$ is $(2n+1)$.

Statement-2 The number of terms in the expansion of $(x_1+x_2+x_3+\ldots+x_m)^n$ is ${}^{n+m-1}C_{m-1}$.

86. **Statement-1** 4^{101} when divided by 101 leaves the remainder 4.

Statement-2 (n^p-n) when divided by 'p' leaves remainder zero when $n \geq 2, n \in N$ and p is a prime number.

87. **Statement-1** $11^{25}+12^{25}$ when divided by 23 leaves the remainder zero.

Statement-2 a^n+b^n is always divisible by $(a+b), \forall\, n \in N$.

88. **Statement-1** The maximum value of the term independent of x in the expansion of $(ax^{1/6}+bx^{1/3})^9$ is 84.

Statement-2 $a^2+b=2$.

Binomial Theorem Exercise 7 : Subjective Type Questions

- In this section, there are **24 subjective** questions.

89. Determine the value of x in the expression of $(x+x^{\log_{10} x})^5$, if the third term in the expansion is 1000000.

90. Find the value of
$$\frac{18^3+7^3+3\cdot 18\cdot 7\cdot 25}{(3^6+6\cdot 243\cdot 2+15\cdot 81\cdot 4+20\cdot 27\cdot 8+15\cdot 9\cdot 16+6\cdot 3\cdot 32+64)}.$$

91. Simplify $\left(\dfrac{a+1}{a^{2/3}-a^{1/3}+1}-\dfrac{a-1}{a-a^{1/2}}\right)^{10}$ into a binomial and determine the terms independent of a.

92. Show that there will be a term independent of x in the expansion of $(x^a+x^{-b})^n$ only, if an is a multiple of $(a+b)$.

93. If a, b and c are the three consecutive coefficients in the expansion of a power of $(1+x)$, prove that the index of the power is $\dfrac{2ac+b(a+c)}{b^2-ac}$.

94. Find n in the binomial $\left[\sqrt[3]{2}+\dfrac{1}{\sqrt[3]{3}}\right]^n$, if the ratio of 7th term from beginning to 7th term from the end is 1/6.

95. If $S_n={}^nC_0{}^nC_1+{}^nC_1{}^nC_2+\ldots+{}^nC_{n-1}{}^nC_n$ and if $\dfrac{S_{n+1}}{S_n}=\dfrac{15}{4}$, find n.

96. If $(1+x)^n=C_0+C_1x+C_2x^2+\ldots+C_nx^n$, prove that $\dfrac{C_1}{C_0}+2\dfrac{C_2}{C_1}+3\dfrac{C_3}{C_2}+\ldots+n\dfrac{C_n}{C_{n-1}}=\dfrac{n(n+1)}{2}$

97. Which term in the expansion of $\left[\sqrt[3]{\left(\dfrac{a}{\sqrt{b}}\right)}+\sqrt{\left(\dfrac{b}{\sqrt[3]{a}}\right)}\right]^{21}$ contains a and b to one and same power.

98. Find the coefficient of x^r in the expansion of $(x+3)^{n-1}+(x+3)^{n-2}(x+2)+(x+3)^{n-3}(x+2)^2+\ldots+(x+2)^{n-1}$.

99. Prove that, if p is a prime number greater than 2, the difference $[(2+\sqrt{5})^p]-2^{p+1}$ is divisible by p, where $[.]$ denotes greatest integer.

100. If $((x))$ represents the least integer greater than x, prove that $((\{(\sqrt{3}+1)^{2n}\})), n \in N$ is divisible by 2^{n+1}.

101. Solve the equation

$$^{11}C_1 x^{10} - {^{11}C_3} x^8 + {^{11}C_5} x^6 - {^{11}C_7} x^4 + {^{11}C_9} x^2 - {^{11}C_{11}} = 0.$$

102. If $g(x) = \sum_{r=0}^{200} \alpha_r \cdot x^r$ and $f(x) = \sum_{r=10}^{200} \beta_r x^4, \beta_r = 1$ for $r \ge 100$ and $g(x) = f(1+x)$, show that the greatest coefficient in the expansion of $(1+x)^{201}$ is α_{100}.

103. If $(1+x)^n = C_0 + C_1 x + C_2 x^2 + \ldots + C_n x^n$, find the value of

$$\sum\sum_{0 \le i < j \le n} (i+j)(C_i + C_j + C_i C_j).$$

104. Evaluate $\sum\sum_{0 \le i \ne j \le 10} {^{21}C_i} \cdot {^{21}C_j}$.

105. Find the coefficients of x^4 in the expansions of

(i) $(1+x+x^2+x^3)^{11}$.

(ii) $(2-x+3x^2)^6$.

106. Prove the identity

$$\frac{1}{^{2n+1}C_r} + \frac{1}{^{2n+1}C_{r+1}} = \frac{2n+2}{2n+1} \cdot \frac{1}{^{2n}C_r},$$

use it to prove $\sum_{r=1}^{r=2n-1} \frac{(-1)^{r-1} r}{^{2n}C_r} = \frac{n}{n+1}$.

107. Let $a_0, a_1, a_2, \ldots$ are the coefficients in the expansion of $(1+x+x^2)^n$ arranged order of x. Find the value of $a_r - {^nC_1} a_{r-1} + {^nC_r} a_{r-2} - \ldots + (-1)^r {^nC_r} a_0$, where r is not divisible by 3.

108. If for z as real or complex.

$$(1+z^2+z^4)^8 = C_0 + C_1 z^2 + C_2 z^4 + \ldots + C_{16} z^{32},$$

prove that

(i) $C_0 - C_1 + C_2 - C_3 + \ldots + C_{16} = 1$

(ii) $C_0 + C_3 + C_6 + C_9 + C_{12} + C_{15} + (C_2 + C_5 + C_8 + C_{11} + C_{14})\omega + (C_1 + C_4 + C_7 + C_{10} + C_{13} + C_{16})\omega^2 = 0$,

where ω is a cube root of unity.

109. Let $f(x) = a_0 + a_1 x + a_2 x^2 + \ldots + a_{2n} x^{2n}$ and $g(x) = b_0 + b_1 x + b_2 x^2 + \ldots + b_{n-1} x^{n-1} + x^n + x^{n+1} + \ldots + x^{2n}$.

If $f(x) = g(x+1)$, find a_n in terms of n.

110. If $a_0, a_1, a_2, \ldots$ are the coefficients in the expansion of $(1+x+x^2)^n$ in ascending powers of x, prove that

(i) $a_0 a_1 - a_1 a_2 + a_2 a_3 - \ldots = 0$

(ii) $a_0 a_2 - a_1 a_3 + a_2 a_4 - \ldots + a_{2n-2} a_{2n} = a_{n+1}$

(iii) if $E_1 = a_0 + a_3 + a_6 + \ldots; E_2 = a_1 + a_4 + a_7 + \ldots$ and $E_3 = a_2 + a_5 + a_8 + \ldots$, then $E_1 = E_2 = E_3 = 3^{n-1}$

111. Prove that $(n-1)^2 C_1 + (n-3)^2 C_3 + (n-5)^2 C_5 + \ldots = n(n+1)2^{n-3}$, where C_r stands for ${^nC_r}$.

112. Show that $\frac{C_0}{1} - \frac{C_1}{4} + \frac{C_2}{7} - \ldots + (-1)^n \frac{C_n}{3n+1} = \frac{3^n \cdot n!}{1 \cdot 4 \cdot 7 \ldots (3n+1)}$, where C_r stands for ${^nC_r}$.

Binomial Theorem Exercise 8 :
Questions Asked in Previous 13 Year's Exams

- This section contains questions asked in **IIT-JEE, AIEEE, JEE Main & JEE Advanced** from year **2005** to year **2017**.

113. The value of $\binom{30}{0}\binom{30}{10} - \binom{30}{1}\binom{30}{11} + \binom{30}{2}\binom{30}{12} + \ldots + \binom{30}{20}\binom{30}{30}$ is **[IIT JEE 2005, 3M]**

(a) $^{60}C_{20}$ (b) $^{30}C_{10}$ (c) $^{60}C_{30}$ (d) $^{40}C_{30}$

114. If the coefficients of pth, $(p+1)$th and $(p+2)$th terms in expansion of $(1+x)^n$ are in AP, then **[AIEEE 2005, 3M]**

(a) $n^2 - 2np + 4p^2 = 0$

(b) $n^2 - n(4p+1) + 4p^2 - 2 = 0$

(c) $n^2 - n(4p+1) + 4p^2 = 0$

(d) None of the above

115. If the coefficient of x^7 in $\left(ax^2 + \frac{1}{bx}\right)^{11}$ is equal to the coefficient of x^{-7} in $\left(ax - \frac{1}{bx^2}\right)^{11}$, then ab is equal to **[AIEEE 2005, 3M]**

(a) 1 (b) 1 / 2

(c) 2 (d) 3

116. For natural numbers m and n, if $(1-y)^m (1+y)^n = 1 + a_1 y + a_2 y^2 + \dots$ and $a_1 = a_2 = 10$, then (m, n) is **[AIEEE 2006, 3M]**

(a) (20, 45) (b) (35, 20)
(c) (45, 35) (d) (35, 45)

117. In the binomial expansion of $(a-b)^n, n \geq 5$, the sum of 5th and 6th terms is zero, $\frac{a}{b}$ equals **[AIEEE 2007, 3M]**

(a) $\frac{5}{n-4}$ (b) $\frac{6}{n-5}$
(c) $\frac{n-5}{6}$ (d) $\frac{n-4}{5}$

118. The sum of the series $^{20}C_0 - {}^{20}C_1 + {}^{20}C_2 - {}^{20}C_3 + \dots + {}^{20}C_{10}$ is **[AIEEE 2007, 3M]**

(a) $-{}^{20}C_{10}$ (b) $\frac{1}{2}\,{}^{20}C_{10}$
(c) 0 (d) $^{20}C_{10}$

119. **Statement-1** $\sum_{r=0}^{n} (r+1)\,{}^nC_r = (n+2)\cdot 2^{n-1}$

Statement-2 $\sum_{r=0}^{n} (r+1)\,{}^nC_r\, x^r = (1+x)^n + nx(1+x)^{n-1}$. **[AIEEE 2007]**

(a) Statement-1 is true, Statement-2 is true; Statement-2 is a correct explanation for Statement-1
(b) Statement-1 is true, Statement-2 is true; Statement-2 is not a correct explanation for Statement-1
(c) Statement-1 is true, Statement-2 is false
(d) Statement-1 is false, Statement-2 is true

120. The remainder left out when $8^{2n} - (62)^{2n+1}$ is divided by 9, is **[AIEEE 2009, 4M]**

(a) 8 (b) 0 (c) 2 (d) 7

121. For $r = 0, 1, 2, \dots, 10$, let A_r, B_r and C_r denote respectively, the coefficients of x^r in the expansion of $(1+x)^{10}, (1+x)^{20}$ and $(1+x)^{30}$, $\sum_{r=1}^{10} A_r (B_{10}B_r - C_{10}A_r)$ is equal to **[IIT-JEE 2010, 5M]**

(a) $B_{10} - C_{10}$ (b) $A_{10}(B_{10} - C_{10}A_{10})$
(c) 0 (d) $C_{10} - B_{10}$

122. Let $S_1 = \sum_{j=1}^{10} j(j-1)\cdot {}^{10}C_j$, $S_2 = \sum_{j=1}^{10} j\cdot {}^{10}C_j$ and $S_3 = \sum_{j=1}^{10} j^2 \cdot {}^{10}C_j$ **[IIT-JEE 2010]**

Statement-1 $S_3 = 55 \times 2^9$

Statement-2 $S_1 = 90 \times 2^8$ and $S_2 = 10 \times 2^8$

(a) Statement-1 is true, Statement-2 is true; Statement-2 is a correct explanation for Statement-1
(b) Statement-1 is true, Statement-2 is true; Statement-2 is not a correct explanation for Statement-1
(c) Statement-1 is true, Statement-2 is false
(d) Statement-1 is false, Statement-2 is true

123. The coefficient of x^7 in the expansion of $(1 - x - x^2 + x^3)^6$, is **[AIEEE 2011, 4M]**

(a) -132 (b) -144
(c) 132 (d) 144

124. If n is a positive integer, then $(\sqrt{3}+1)^{2n} - (\sqrt{3}-1)^{2n}$ is **[AIEEE 2012, 4M]**

(a) an odd positive integer
(b) an even positive integer
(c) a rational number other than positive integer
(d) an irrational number

125. The term independent of x in the expansion of $\left(\frac{x+1}{x^{2/3} - x^{1/3} + 1} - \frac{x-1}{x - x^{1/2}}\right)^{10}$ is **[JEE Main, 2013, 4M]**

(a) 120 (b) 210
(c) 310 (d) 4

126. The coefficients of three consecutive terms of $(1+x)^{n+5}$ are in the ratio 5 : 10 : 14, the value of n is **[JEE Advanced 2013M]**

127. If the coefficients of x^3 and x^4 in the expansion of $(1 + ax + bx^2)(1-2x)^{18}$ in powers of x are both zero, then (a, b) is equal to **[JEE Main 2014, 3M]**

(a) $\left(14, \frac{272}{3}\right)$ (b) $\left(16, \frac{272}{3}\right)$
(c) $\left(14, \frac{251}{3}\right)$ (d) $\left(16, \frac{251}{3}\right)$

128. Coefficient of x^{11} in the expansion of $(1+x^2)^4 (1+x^3)^7 (1+x^4)^{12}$ is **[JEE Advanced 2014, 3M]**

(a) 1051 (b) 1106 (c) 1113 (d) 1120

129. The sum of coefficients of integral powers of x in the binomial expansion of $(1 - 2\sqrt{x})^{50}$, is **[JEE Main 2015, 4M]**

(a) $\frac{1}{2}(2^{50}+1)$ (b) $\frac{1}{2}(3^{50}+1)$
(c) $\frac{1}{2}(3^{50})$ (d) $\frac{1}{2}(3^{50}-1)$

130. The coefficients of x^9 in the expansion of $(1+x)(1+x^2)(1+x^3)\dots(1+x^{100})$ is **[JEE Advanced 2015, 4M]**

131. If the number of terms in the expansion of $\left(1 - \frac{2}{x} + \frac{4}{x^2}\right)^n$, $x \neq 0$ is 28, then the sum of the coefficients of all the terms in this expansion, is **[JEE Main 2016, 4M]**

(a) 243 (b) 729 (c) 64 (d) 2187

132. Let m be the smallest positive integer such that the coefficient of x^2 in the expansion of $(1+x)^2+(1+x)^3+\ldots+(1+x)^{49}+(1+mx)^{50}$ is $(3n+1)\,{}^{51}C_3$ for some positive integer n. Then the value of n is **[JEE Advanced 2016, 3M]**

133. The value of $({}^{21}C_1-{}^{10}C_1)+({}^{21}C_2-{}^{10}C_2)+({}^{21}C_3-{}^{10}C_3)+({}^{21}C_4-{}^{10}C_4)+\ldots+({}^{21}C_{10}-{}^{10}C_{10})$ is **[JEE Advanced 2017, 4M]**

(a) $2^{20}-2^{10}$ (b) $2^{21}-2^{11}$
(c) $2^{21}-2^{10}$ (d) $2^{20}-2^{9}$

Answers

Exercise for Session 1

1. (c) 2. (a) 3. (c) 4. (c) 5. (b) 6. (b)
7. (c) 8. (d)

Exercise for Session 2

1. (b) 2. (c) 3. (d) 4. (b) 5. (c) 6. (c)
7. (c) 8. (b) 9. (a) 10. (d)

Exercise for Session 3

1. (a) 2. (c) 3. (d) 4. (b) 5. (c) 6. (c)
7. (a) 8. (c) 9. (a) 10. (c)

Exercise for Session 4

1. (c) 2. (b) 3. (c) 4. (a) 5. (a) 6. (c)
7. (b) 8. (c) 9. (b) 10. (b) 11. (a) 12. (d)
13. (a) 14. (b)

Chapter Exercises

1. (d) 2. (d) 3. (a) 4. (b) 5. (d) 6. (b)
7. (b) 8. (c) 9. (a) 10. (c) 11. (b) 12. (a)
13. (b) 14. (c) 15. (a) 16. (b) 17. (a) 18. (a)
19. (c) 20. (d) 21. (d) 22. (d) 23. (b) 24. (d)
25. (b) 26. (b) 27. (b) 28. (a) 29. (d) 30. (a)
31. (c,d) 32. (a,b) 33. (a,d) 34. (a,d) 35. (c,d) 36. (b,c)
37. (b,c) 38. (a,d) 39. (b,c) 40. (a,b,d) 41. (c,d) 42. (a,d)
43. (a,b,c,d) 44. (a,c) 45. (a,d)

46. (b) 47. (d) 48. (b) 49. (c) 50. (b) 51. (c)
52. (c) 53. (d) 54. (d) 55. (b) 56. (a) 57. (b)
58. (b) 59. (b) 60. (d) 61. (c) 62. (a) 63. (d)
64. (b) 65. (c) 66. (d)
67. (0) 68. (3) 69. (3) 70. (8) 71. (6) 72. (4)
73. (0) 74. (3) 75. (4) 76. (9)

77. (A) $\to$ (q, r); (B) $\to$ (p, q, t); (C) $\to$ (s)

78. (A) $\to$ (r, s, t); (B) $\to$ (s, t); (C) $\to$ (p, q, r, s, t)

79. (A) $\to$ (p, q, r, s); (B) $\to$ (p, q, r, s, t); (C) $\to$ (p, q, r, s, t)

80. (A) $\to$ (q, s); (B) $\to$ (p, q, r, s); (C) $\to$ (q, s); (D) $\to$ (r, s)

81. (A) $\to$ (p, r); (B) $\to$ (q); (C) $\to$ (s); (D) $\to$ (p, r)

82. (d) 83. (c) 84. (b) 85. (b) 86. (d) 87. (c)
88. (a)

89. $x=10$ or $10^{-5/2}$ 90. 1 91. 210 94. 9 95. 4,2

97. 10 98. ${}^nC_r(3^{n-r}-2^{n-r})$ 101. $x=\cot\left(\frac{r\pi}{11}\right)$, $r=\pm1,\pm2,\ldots,\pm5$

103. $n^2\cdot 2^n+n\left\{2^{2n-1}-\frac{2n!}{2(n!)^2}\right\}$ 104. $\frac{1}{2}\left[2^{40}-\frac{42!}{2(21!)^2}\right]$

105. (i) 990 (ii) 3660 107. 0 109. ${}^{2n+1}C_{n+1}$

113. (b) 114. (b) 115. (a) 116. (d) 117. (d) 118. (b)
119. (a) 120. (c) 121. (d) 122. (b) 123. (b) 124. (d)
125. (b) 126. (6) 127. (b) 128. (c) 129. (b) 130. (8)
131. (b) 132. (5) 133. (a)

Solutions

1. $\because \sum_{r=0}^{n}(-1)^r\, {}^nC_r\left[\left(\frac{1}{2}\right)^r+\left(\frac{3}{4}\right)^r+\left(\frac{7}{8}\right)^r+\cdots \text{upto } m \text{ terms}\right]$

$$=\left(1-\frac{1}{2}\right)^n+\left(1-\frac{3}{4}\right)^n+\left(1-\frac{7}{8}\right)^n+\cdots \text{ upto } m \text{ terms}$$

$$=\frac{1}{2^n}+\frac{1}{2^{2n}}+\frac{1}{2^{3n}}+\cdots \text{upto } m \text{ terms}$$

$$=\frac{\frac{1}{2^n}\left[1-\left(\frac{1}{2^n}\right)^m\right]}{\left(1-\frac{1}{2^n}\right)}=\left(\frac{1}{2^n-1}\right)\left(1-\frac{1}{2^{mn}}\right)$$

$\therefore f(n)=\frac{1}{2^n-1}$

$\therefore \int_{-3}^{3} f(x^3 \ln x)\cdot d(x^3 \ln x)$

$$=\int_{-3}^{3}\frac{1}{(2^{x^3 \ln x}-1)}\cdot(3x^2\ln x+x^2)dx$$

Since, ln x cannot be defined for $x<0$.

$\therefore$ Above integral cannot be calculated.

2. Coefficient of $(a^3\cdot b^6\cdot c^8\cdot d^9\cdot e\cdot f)$ in given expansion

$$=(-1)^9\cdot(-1)^1\cdot(-1)^1\cdot\frac{31!}{3!6!8!9!1!1!}$$

3. General term of given expression

$$=\frac{10!}{\alpha!\,\beta!\,\gamma!}2^{\alpha/2}.3^{\beta/3}.5^{\gamma/6} \quad \text{...(i)}$$

α, β, γ satisfying two following property

$$0\le \alpha, \beta, \gamma \le 10;\ \alpha+\beta+\gamma=10$$

$\therefore \quad \alpha=0,2,4,6,8,10;\ \beta=0,3,6;\ \gamma=0,6$

Hence, possible pairs of $(\alpha, \beta, \gamma)=(4,6,0);(4,0,6);(10,0,0)$

$\therefore$ There exists three rational terms.

So, sum of rational terms

$$=\frac{10!}{4!6!}\cdot 2^2\cdot 3^2+\frac{10!}{4!6!}2^2\cdot 5^1+\frac{10!}{10!}2^5=12632$$

4. We have,

$$(1+x-3x^2)^{2145}=a_0+a_1x+a_2x^2+\cdots$$

On putting $x=-1$, we get

$$a_0-a_1+a_2-\ldots=(-3)^{2145}$$

But we know that,

$$3^1=3, 3^2=9, 3^3=27, 3^4=81$$

$\therefore \quad a_0-a_1+a_2+\ldots=[(-3)^4]^{536}(-3)^1$

$\therefore \quad$ End digit of $(-3)^{2145}$

$=$ End digit of $[(-3)^4]^{536}\times$ End digit of $(-3)^1$

$=1\times 3=3$

5. We have,

$$T_{r+1}={}^nC_r\left(\sqrt{\frac{q}{p}}\right)^{n-r}\left(\sqrt[10]{\frac{p^7}{q^3}}\right)^r={}^nC_r(q)^{\frac{n-r}{2}-\frac{3r}{10}}\times(p)^{\frac{r-n}{2}+\frac{7r}{10}}$$

$$={}^nC_r\cdot q^{\frac{5n-8r}{10}}\cdot p^{\frac{12r-5n}{10}}$$

For coefficient of pq, we put

$$\frac{5n-8r}{10}=1,\ \frac{12r-5n}{10}=1$$

$\Rightarrow \quad 5n-8r-10=0,\ 12r-5n-10=0$

$\Rightarrow \quad r=5, n=10$

$\therefore \quad T_6={}^{10}C_5\, pq=252\, pq$

6. We have,

$$(5+2\sqrt{6})^n=(5+\sqrt{24})^n$$

Now, let $\quad I+f=(5+\sqrt{24})^n \quad$ ...(i)

$0\le f<1 \quad$ ...(ii)

and $\quad f'=(5-\sqrt{24})^n \quad$ ...(iii)

$0<f'<1 \quad$ ...(iv)

On adding Eqs. (i) and (iii), we get

$$I+f+f'=2k \text{ (even integer)}$$

$\Rightarrow \quad f'+f'=1$

$\Rightarrow \quad f'=1-f$

$\therefore \quad f^2-f+If-I=f(f-1)+I(f-1)$

$=(f-1)(I+f)$

$=-(1-f)(I+f)=-f'(I+f)$

$=-(5-\sqrt{24})^n(5+\sqrt{24})^n$

$=-(25-24)^n=-1$

$=$ a negative integer

7. Given, $\quad x+\frac{1}{x}=1 \Rightarrow x^2-x+1=0$

$\Rightarrow \quad (x+\omega)(x+\omega^2)=0$

$\Rightarrow \quad x=-\omega, -\omega^2$

$\therefore \quad p=(-\omega)^{4000}+\frac{1}{(-\omega)^{4000}}=\omega^{4000}+\frac{1}{\omega^{4000}}$

$$=\omega+\frac{1}{\omega}=\frac{\omega^2+1}{\omega}=-\frac{\omega}{\omega}=-1$$

Also, for $\quad x=-\omega^2, p=-1$

For $\quad n>1, 2^n=4k, k\in N$

$\therefore \quad 2^{2^n}=2^{4k}=(16)^k=$ last digit number is 6

Now, $q=$ unit digit at unit place in the number $(2^{2^n}+1)$

$=6+1=7$

$\therefore \quad p+q=-1+7=6$

8. Now, $\left(x+1+\frac{1}{x}\right)^n=\frac{(1+x+x^2)^n}{x^n}$

Since, $(1+x+x^2)^n$ is of the form

$a_0+a_1x+a_2x^2+\cdots+a_{2n}x^{2n}$ which contains $2n+1$ terms.

$\therefore \quad 2n+1=401 \Rightarrow 2n=400 \Rightarrow n=200$

which is greater than 199.

9. We have, $\sum_{r=0}^{n-1} \frac{{}^nC_r}{{}^nC_r + {}^nC_{r+1}} = \sum_{r=0}^{n-1} \frac{{}^nC_r}{{}^{n+1}C_{r+1}}$

$$= \sum_{r=0}^{n-1} \frac{{}^nC_r}{\frac{n+1}{r+1}\,{}^nC_r} = \sum_{r=0}^{n-1} \frac{r+1}{n+1}$$

$$= \frac{1}{n+1}[1+2+\cdots+n] = \frac{n(n+1)}{2(n+1)} = \frac{n}{2}$$

10. Here, $n = 100$, so the total number of terms is 101.

$\therefore$ Largest term = Middle term = 51th term

$$= {}^{100}C_{50}\left(\frac{b}{2}\right)^{50}\left(\frac{b}{2}\right)^{50} = {}^{100}C_{50}\left(\frac{b}{2}\right)^{100}$$

11. We have, $T_4 = {}^6C_3\left(\sqrt{x^{\left(\frac{1}{1+\log x}\right)}}\right)^3 (x^{1/12})^3 = 200$ [given]

$$\Rightarrow \quad 20\,(x^{\frac{3}{2(1+\log x)}})\, x^{1/4} = 200$$

$$\Rightarrow \quad x^{\frac{3}{2(1+\log x)} + \frac{1}{4}} = 10$$

On taking logarithm on base 10, we get

$$\left[\frac{3}{2(1+\log x)} + \frac{1}{4}\right]\log x = 1$$

$$\Rightarrow \quad \frac{(6+1+\log x)\log x}{4(1+\log x)} = 1$$

$$\Rightarrow \quad (\log x)^2 + 3\log x - 4 = 0$$

$$\Rightarrow \quad (\log x + 4)(\log x - 1) = 0$$

$$\Rightarrow \quad \log x = -4, 1$$

$$\therefore \quad x = 10^{-4}, 10$$

But $\quad x > 1$

$$\therefore \quad x = 10$$

12. $\because (1+x)^m + (1+x)^{m+1} + \cdots + (1+x)^n$

$$= \frac{(1+x)^m\{(1+x)^{n-m+1} - 1\}}{(1+x)-1} = \frac{(1+x)^{n+1} - (1+x)^m}{x}$$

$\therefore$ Coefficient of x^m in $(1+x)^m + (1+x)^{m+1} + \cdots + (1+x)^n$

or coefficient of x^m in $\frac{(1+x)^{n+1} - (1+x)^m}{x}$

or coefficient of x^{m+1} in $(1+x)^{n+1} - (1+x)^m$

$$= {}^{n+1}C_{m+1} - 0 = {}^{n+1}C_{m+1}$$

13. We have, ${}^{39}C_{3r-1} + {}^{39}C_{3r} = {}^{39}C_{r^2} + {}^{39}C_{r^2-1}$

$$\Rightarrow \quad {}^{40}C_{3r} = {}^{40}C_{r^2}$$

$$\Rightarrow \quad 3r = r^2 \text{ or } 40 - 3r = r^2$$

$$\Rightarrow \quad r = 0, 3 \text{ or } r^2 + 3r - 40 = 0$$

$$\Rightarrow \quad (r+8)(r-5) = 0 \Rightarrow r = 0, 3, 5, -8$$

But $r = 0, -8$ do not satisfy the given equation

$\therefore \quad r = 3, 5$

14. We have, $(1+x)^{20} = {}^{20}C_0 + {}^{20}C_1\,x + {}^{20}C_2\,x^2 + \cdots + {}^{20}C_{20}\,x^{20}$

On dividing by x, we get

$$\frac{(1+x)^{20}}{x} = \frac{{}^{20}C_0}{x} + {}^{20}C_1 + {}^{20}C_2 x + {}^{20}C_3 x^2 + \cdots + {}^{20}C_{20}\,x^{19}$$

On differentiating w.r.t. x, we get

$$\frac{20(1+x)^{19}\cdot x - (1+x)^{20}}{x^2} = \frac{-{}^{20}C_0}{x^2} + 0 + {}^{20}C_2 + 2\cdot{}^{20}C_3 x + \cdots + 19\cdot{}^{20}C_{20}\,x^{18}$$

On putting $x = 1$, we get

$$20(2)^{19} - (2)^{20} = -\frac{1}{1} + {}^{20}C_2 + 2\cdot{}^{20}C_3 + \cdots + 19\cdot{}^{20}C_{20}$$

$$\therefore \quad {}^{20}C_2 + 2\cdot{}^{20}C_3 + \cdots + 19\cdot{}^{20}C_{20} = 1 + 10\cdot 2^{20} - 2^{20} = 1 + 9\cdot 2^{20}$$

15. We have, $S = \frac{1\,(2^{2000} - 1)}{2-1} = 2^{2000} - 1 = (2^2)^{1000} - 1$

$$= (5-1)^{1000} - 1$$

$$= (5^{1000} - {}^{1000}C_1\cdot 5^{999} + {}^{1000}C_2\cdot 5^{998} \cdots + {}^{1000}C_{998}\cdot 5^2 - {}^{1000}C_{999}\cdot 5 + 1) - 1$$

$$= 5(5^{999} - {}^{1000}C_1\cdot 5^{998} + {}^{1000}C_2\cdot 5^{997} - \cdots - {}^{1000}C_{999})$$

$\therefore$ Remainder is 0.

16. Now, $(1+x)^n\left(1+\frac{1}{x}\right)^n = \frac{(1+x)^{2n}}{x^n}$

$\therefore$ Coefficient of x^{-1} in $(1+x)^n\left(1+\frac{1}{x}\right)^n$

$$= \text{Coefficient of } x^{n-1} \text{ in } (1+x)^{2n} = {}^{2n}C_{n-1} = \frac{(2n)!}{(n-1)!\,(n+1)!}$$

17. $\because \quad 19^{9^4} = (20-1)^{9^4} = (20-1)^{6521} = -1 + (6521)\times 20 +$ multiple of 100

$$= -1 + 20 + \text{multiple of } 100$$

$$= 19 + \text{multiple of } 100$$

$\therefore$ Last two digits of the number 19^{9^4} is 19.

18. $T_2 = {}^nC_1\,(\sqrt[13]{a})^{n-1}\left(\frac{a}{\sqrt{a^{-1}}}\right)^1 = 14a^{5/2}$ [given]

$$\Rightarrow \quad n(a)^{\frac{n-1}{13}}\, a^{1+\frac{1}{2}} = 14a^{5/2}$$

$$\Rightarrow \quad na^{\frac{n-1}{13}}\, a^{3/2} = 14a^{5/2}$$

When we put $n = 14$, then it satisfies the above equation

$$\therefore \quad \frac{{}^nC_3}{{}^nC_2} = \frac{{}^{14}C_3}{{}^{14}C_2} = \frac{14-3+1}{3} = 4$$

19. $6^{83} + 8^{83} = (7-1)^{83} + (7+1)^{83}$

$$= 2(7^{83} + {}^{83}C_2\cdot 7^{81} + {}^{83}C_4\cdot 7^{79} + \ldots + {}^{83}C_{80}7^3 + {}^{83}C_{82}7)$$

$$= 2\{49m + {}^{83}C_{82}\cdot 7\}$$

where, m is an integer

$$= 98m + 2\cdot{}^{83}C_1\cdot 7 = 98m + 2\cdot 83\cdot 7$$

$$= 98m + 2(77+6)\cdot 7 = 49(2m+22) + 84$$

$= 49(2m+22) + 49 + 35$
$= 49(2m+23) + 35 = 49n + 35$

where n is an integer.

Hence, the remainder is 35.

20. In the expansion of $(3^{1/4} + 2^{2/3})^{12}$, the general term is

$$T_{r+1} = {}^{12}C_r (3^{1/4})^{12-r} (2^{2/3})^r = {}^{12}C_r 3^{3-\frac{r}{4}} 2^{\frac{2r}{3}}$$

Now, $0 \le r \le 12$

$\therefore$ $r = 0, 12$

Rational terms are T_{0+1} and T_{12+1}

Now, $T_1 = {}^{12}C_0 3^3 2^0 = 27$

$\Rightarrow$ $T_{13} = {}^{12}C_{12} 3^0 \cdot 2^8 = 256$

$\therefore$ Required sum $= T_1 + T_{13}$
$= 27 + 256 = 283$

21. $N = 7^{100} - 3^{100} = (7^2)^{50} - (3^2)^{50}$

$= (50-1)^{50} - (10-1)^{50}$

$= [(50)^{50} - {}^{50}C_1 (50)^{49} + {}^{50}C_2 (50)^{48} - {}^{50}C_3 (50)^{47} + \cdots + {}^{50}C_{48} (50)^2 - {}^{50}C_{49}(50) + 1]$

$- [10^{50} - {}^{50}C_1 \cdot 10^{49} + {}^{50}C_2 (10)^{48} - {}^{50}C_3 (10)^{47} + \cdots + {}^{50}C_{48} (10)^2 - {}^{50}C_{49}(10) + 1]$

$= [10^4 m - {}^{50}C_{47}(50)^3 + {}^{50}C_{48}(50)^2 - {}^{50}C_{49}(50) + 1]$
$- [10^4 n - {}^{50}C_{47}(10)^3 + {}^{50}C_{48}(10)^2 - {}^{50}C_{49}(10) + 1]$

when m and n are integers.

$= 10^4 p - {}^{50}C_3[(50)^3 - (10)^3] + {}^{50}C_2[(50)^2 - (10)^2] - {}^{50}C_1[(50) - (10)]$

When p is an integer.

$= 10^4 p - 124 \times 196 \times 10^5 + 294 \times 10^4 - 2000 = 10^4 q - 2000$

When q is an integer.

$= 10^4 q - 10^4 + 10^4 - 2000 = 10^4(q-1) + 8000$

$\therefore$ Last four digits $= 0000 + 8000 = 8000$

22. Let $P = 5^{99} = 5 \times 5^{98} = 5(25)^{49} = 5(26-1)^{49}$

$= 5[{}^{49}C_0(26)^{49} - {}^{49}C_1(26)^{48} + {}^{49}C_2(26)^{47} - \cdots + {}^{49}C_{48}(26) - {}^{49}C_{49} \cdot 1]$

$= 5 \times 26k - 5$, when k is an integer.

$\therefore$ $\frac{P}{13} = 10k - \frac{5}{13} = 10k - 1 + \frac{8}{13}$

Hence, the remainder is 8.

23. Now, $\frac{3^{2003}}{28} = \frac{3^2 \times 3^{2001}}{28} = \frac{9}{28}(3^3)^{667} = \frac{9}{28}(28-1)^{667}$

$= \frac{9}{28}\{(28)^{667} - {}^{667}C_1(28)^{666} + {}^{667}C_2(28)^{665} - \cdots + {}^{667}C_{666}(28) - 1\}$

$= 9k - \frac{9}{28}$, where k is an integer.

$= (9k-1) + \frac{19}{98}$

or $\left\{\frac{3^{2003}}{28}\right\} = \left\{(9k-1) + \frac{19}{28}\right\} = \frac{19}{28}$

24. $\sum_{r=0}^{20} r(20-r) \times ({}^{20}C_r)^2$

$= \sum_{r=0}^{20} r \times {}^{20}C_r (20-r) \times {}^{20}C_{20-r} = \sum_{r=0}^{20} 20 \cdot {}^{19}C_{r-1} \times 20 \times {}^{19}C_{19-r}$

$= 400 \sum_{r=0}^{20} {}^{19}C_{r-1} \times {}^{19}C_{19-r}$

$= 400 \times$ Coefficient of x^{18} in $(1+x)^{19}(1+x)^{19}$

$= 400 \times {}^{38}C_{18} = 400 \times {}^{38}C_{20}$

25. Given, $(3 + x^{2008} + x^{2009})^{2010} = a_0 + a_1 x + a_2 x^2 + \cdots + a_n x^n$

On putting $x = \omega$ and ω^2 respectively, we get

$(3 + \omega^{2008} + \omega^{2009})^{2010} = a_0 + a_1\omega + a_2\omega^2 + a_3\omega^3 + \cdots$

or $(3 + \omega + \omega^2)^{2010} = a_0 + a_1\omega + a_2\omega^2 + a_3\omega^3 + \cdots$

or $2^{2010} = a_0 + a_1\omega + a_2\omega^2 + a_3\omega^3 + a_4\omega^4 + a_5\omega^5 + a_6\omega^6 + \cdots$ ...(i)

and $[3 + (\omega^2)^{2008} + (\omega^2)^{2009}]^{2010}$
$= a_0 + a_1\omega^2 + a_2\omega^4 + a_3\omega^6 + a_4\omega^8 + a_5\omega^{10} + a_6\omega^{12} + \cdots$

or $(3 + \omega^2 + \omega)^{2010}$
$= a_0 + a_1\omega^2 + a_2\omega^4 + a_3\omega^6 + a_4\omega^8 + a_5\omega^{10} + a_6\omega^{12} + \cdots$

$\Rightarrow 2^{2010} = a_0 + a_1\omega^2 + a_2\omega^4 + a_3\omega^6 + a_4\omega^8 + a_5\omega^{10} + a_6\omega^{12}$ ...(ii)

On adding Eqs. (i) and (ii), we get

$2 \times 2^{2010} = 2a_0 + a_1(\omega + \omega^2) + a_2(\omega^2 + \omega^4) + a_3(\omega^3 + \omega^6) + a_4(\omega^4 + \omega^8) + a_5(\omega^5 + \omega^{10}) + a_6(\omega^6 + \omega^{12}) + \cdots$

$= 2a_0 - a_1 - a_2 + 2a_3 - a_4 - a_5 + 2a_6 - \cdots$

$\Rightarrow$ $2^{2010} = a_0 - \frac{1}{2}a_1 - \frac{1}{2}a_2 + a_3 - \frac{1}{2}a_4 - \frac{1}{2}a_5 + a_6 - \cdots$

26. Now, $\left(x^2 - 2 + \frac{1}{x^2}\right)^n = \frac{(x^4 - 2x^2 + 1)^n}{x^{2n}} = \frac{(x^2-1)^{2n}}{x^{2n}}$

$\therefore$ Total number of terms that are dependent of x is equal to number of terms in the expansion of $(x^2-1)^{2n}$ that have degree of x different from $2n$, which is given by $(2n+1) - 1 = 2n$.

27. Given expansion can be rewritten as $[1 + x^2(1-x)]^8$

$= {}^8C_0 + {}^8C_1 x^2(1-x) + {}^8C_2 x^4(1-x)^2 + {}^8C_3 x^6(1-x)^3 + {}^8C_4 x^8(1-x)^4 + {}^8C_5 x^{10}(1-x)^5 + \cdots$

There are only two terms, which we get the coefficient of x^{10}.

$\therefore$ Coefficient of $x^{10} = {}^8C_4$[Coefficient of x^2 in $(1-x)^4$] $+ {}^8C_5$ [Coefficient of x^0 in $(1-x)^5$]

$= {}^8C_4({}^4C_2) + {}^8C_5(1)$

$= ({}^8C_4)({}^4C_2) + {}^8C_3 = (70)(6) + 56 = 476$

28. $(1+ix)^{4n-2} = {}^{4n-2}C_0 + {}^{4n-2}C_1(ix) + {}^{4n-2}C_2(ix)^2 + \cdots + {}^{4n-2}C_{4n-2}(ix)^{4n-2}$

Here, we see that Ist negative term is T_3 and the next term is T_7 and the last negative term is T_{4n-1}.

Now, 3, 7, ⋯, $4n-1$

It is an AP.

$\because \quad l = a + (N-1)d$

$\therefore \quad 4n - 1 = 3 + (N-1)4$

$\Rightarrow \quad n - 1 = N - 1 \Rightarrow N = n$

29. $\because \quad \binom{n}{m}\binom{m}{p} = \dfrac{n!}{m!(n-m)!} \times \dfrac{m!}{p!(m-p)!}$

$$= \frac{n!}{(n-m)!\,p!(m-p)!} = \binom{n}{p}\binom{n-p}{m-p}$$

$$\therefore \sum_{p=1}^{n}\sum_{m=p}^{n}\binom{n}{m}\binom{m}{p} = \sum_{p=1}^{n}\sum_{m=p}^{n}\binom{n}{p}\binom{n-p}{m-p}$$

$$= \sum_{p=1}^{n}\binom{n}{p}\sum_{m=p}^{n}\binom{n-p}{m-p}$$

$$= \sum_{p=1}^{n}\binom{n}{p}\sum_{t=0}^{n-p}\binom{n-p}{t} \quad [\text{where, } t = m - p]$$

$$= 2^n \sum_{p=1}^{n}\binom{n}{p} 2^{n-p}$$

$$= 2^n \sum_{p=1}^{n}\binom{n}{p}\frac{1}{2^p} = 2^n\left[\left(1+\frac{1}{2}\right)^n - 1\right] = 3^n - 2^n$$

30. Given, $\displaystyle\sum_{r=0}^{4}\frac{5^{4-r}}{(4-r)!}\left(\frac{x^r}{r!}\right) = \frac{8}{3}$

$\Rightarrow \quad \dfrac{(5+x)^4}{4!} = \dfrac{8}{3}$

$\Rightarrow \quad (5+x)^4 = 64 = (2\sqrt{2})^4 \Rightarrow 5 + x = \pm 2\sqrt{2}$

$\therefore \quad x = 2\sqrt{2} - 5$ or $x = -2\sqrt{2} - 5$

Hence, largest real value of x is $2\sqrt{2} - 5$.

31. We have,

Coefficient of x in $(1+x)^m(1-x)^n = {}^mC_1 - {}^nC_1$

and coefficient of x^2 in $(1+x)^m(1-x)^n = {}^mC_2 - {}^mC_1\,{}^nC_1 + {}^nC_2$

According to the question, ${}^mC_1 - {}^nC_1 = 3$

$\Rightarrow \quad m - n = 3 \quad \ldots(\text{i})$

and $\quad {}^mC_2 - {}^mC_1\,{}^nC_1 + {}^nC_2 = -6$

$\Rightarrow \quad \dfrac{m(m-1)}{2} - mn + \dfrac{n(n-1)}{2} = -6$

$\Rightarrow \quad (m-n)^2 - (m+n) = -12$

$\Rightarrow \quad 9 - (m+n) = -12 \quad$ [from Eq. (i)]

or $\quad m + n = 21 \quad \ldots(\text{ii})$

From Eqs. (i) and (ii), we get

$$m = 12 \text{ and } n = 9$$

32. Coefficient of rth, $(r+1)$ th and $(r+2)$th terms in $(1+x)^{14}$ are ${}^{14}C_{r-1}$, ${}^{14}C_r$ and ${}^{14}C_{r+1}$, respectively.

Now, according to the question, $2({}^{14}C_r) = {}^{14}C_{r-1} + {}^{14}C_{r+1}$

On dividing both sides by ${}^{14}C_r$, we get

$$2 = \frac{{}^{14}C_{r-1}}{{}^{14}C_r} + \frac{{}^{14}C_{r+1}}{{}^{14}C_r}$$

$\Rightarrow \quad 2 = \dfrac{r}{14 - r + 1} + \dfrac{14 - (r+1) + 1}{r+1}$

$\Rightarrow \quad 2 = \dfrac{r}{15 - r} + \dfrac{14 - r}{r+1}$

$\Rightarrow \quad 2(15-r)(r+1) = r(r+1) + (15-r)(14-r)$

$\Rightarrow \quad -2r^2 + 28r + 30 = 2r^2 - 28r + 210$

$\Rightarrow \quad 4r^2 - 56r + 180 = 0 \Rightarrow r^2 - 14r + 45 = 0$

$\Rightarrow \quad (r-9)(r-5) = 0$

$\Rightarrow \quad r = 5, 9$

33. $(3\sqrt{3} + 5)^{2n+1} = (\sqrt{27} + 5)^{2n+1}$

Now, let $\alpha + \beta = (\sqrt{27} + 5)^{2n+1} \quad \ldots(\text{i})$

$0 < \beta < 1 \quad \ldots(\text{ii})$

and let $\quad \beta' = (\sqrt{27} - 5)^{2n+1} \quad \ldots(\text{iii})$

$0 < \beta' < 1 \quad \ldots(\text{iv})$

On subtracting Eq. (iii) from Eq. (i), we get

$\alpha + \beta - \beta' = (\sqrt{27} + 5)^{2n+1} - (\sqrt{27} - 5)^{2n+1} \quad \ldots(\text{v})$

$\Rightarrow \quad \alpha + 0 = 2p$ (even integer), $\forall\, p \in N$

$\Rightarrow \quad \alpha = 2p =$ even integer

Also, from Eq. (v), we get

$\alpha = (\sqrt{27} + 5)^{2n+1} - (\sqrt{27} - 5)^{2n+1}$ divisible by $(\sqrt{27} + 5) - (\sqrt{27} - 5)$, i.e. divisible by 10.

34. We have, $(8 + 3\sqrt{7})^n = (8 + \sqrt{63})^n$

Now, let $\quad P + F = (8 + \sqrt{63})^n \quad \ldots(\text{i})$

$0 < F < 1 \quad \ldots(\text{ii})$

and let $\quad F' = (8 - \sqrt{63})^n \quad \ldots(\text{iii})$

$0 < F' < 1 \quad \ldots(\text{iv})$

On adding Eqs. (i) and (iii), we get

$P + F + F' = (8 + \sqrt{63})^n + (8 - \sqrt{63})^n \quad \ldots(\text{v})$

$\Rightarrow \quad P + 1 = 2p$ (even integer), $\forall\, p \in N$

$\Rightarrow \quad P = 2p - 1 =$ odd integer

$\therefore \quad F' = 1 - F$

$\therefore \quad (1 - F)(P + F) = F'(P + F) = (8 - \sqrt{63})^n (8 + \sqrt{63})^n$

$$= (64 - 63)^n = 1^n = 1$$

35. We have, 6th term in the expansion of

$$\left\{2^{\log_2\sqrt{(9^{x-1}+7)}} + \frac{1}{2^{(1/5)\log_2(3^{x-1}+1)}}\right\}^7$$

or $\left\{\sqrt{(9^{x-1}+7)} + \dfrac{1}{(3^{x-1}+1)^{1/5}}\right\}^7$ is $T_6 = T_{5+1}$

$$= {}^7C_5\left(\sqrt{9^{x-1}+7}\right)^2\left\{\frac{1}{(3^{x-1}+1)^{1/5}}\right\}^5$$

$$= {}^7C_2 \cdot \frac{(9^{x-1}+7)}{(3^{x-1}+1)} = 21 \cdot \frac{(9^{x-1}+7)}{(3^{x-1}+1)} = 84 \quad [\text{given}]$$

$\Rightarrow \quad (9^{x-1}+7)=4(3^{x-1}+1)$

Let $3^{x-1}=\lambda$, then

$$\lambda^2-4\lambda+3=0$$

or $\quad (\lambda-3)(\lambda-1)=0$

$\therefore \quad \lambda=3,1$

$\Rightarrow \quad 3^{x-1}=3^1, 3^0$

or $\quad x-1=1, 0$ or $x=2, 1$

36. $\left(\sqrt{x}+\dfrac{1}{2\cdot\sqrt[4]{x}}\right)^n$ or $\left(x^{1/2}+\dfrac{1}{2}x^{-1/4}\right)^n$

$$={}^nC_0\cdot x^{\frac{n}{2}}+{}^nC_1\cdot\left(\frac{1}{2}\right)\cdot x^{\frac{2n-3}{4}}+{}^nC_2\cdot\left(\frac{1}{2}\right)^2\cdot x^{\frac{n-3}{2}}+\cdots$$

According to the question,

$${}^nC_0, {}^nC_1\left(\frac{1}{2}\right), {}^nC_2\left(\frac{1}{2}\right)^2 \text{ are in AP.}$$

$\therefore \quad {}^nC_1={}^nC_0+{}^nC_2\left(\dfrac{1}{2}\right)^2$

$\Rightarrow \quad n=1+\dfrac{n(n-1)}{4\cdot 2}$

$\Rightarrow \quad n^2-9n+8=0$

$\Rightarrow \quad (n-8)(n-1)=0$

$\therefore \quad n=8, n\neq 1$

option (a) Number of terms $=8+1=9$

option (b) Now, $T_{r+1}={}^8C_r\cdot x^{4-\frac{r}{2}}\cdot\left(\dfrac{1}{2}\right)^r\cdot x^{-\frac{r}{4}}$

$\because \quad 0\leq r\leq 8$

For integral powers of x, $r=0, 4, 8$

$\therefore$ Number of terms in the expansion with integral power of x is 3.

option (c) From option (b),

$$T_{r+1}={}^8C_r\cdot x^{4-\frac{3r}{4}}\cdot\left(\frac{1}{2}\right)^r$$

For independent of x,

$$4-\frac{3r}{4}=0$$

$$r=\frac{16}{3}\notin W$$

$\therefore$ No terms in the given expansion which is independent of x.

option (d) Middle term is

$$T_5={}^8C_4\cdot x\cdot\left(\frac{1}{2}\right)^4$$

i.e. only one middle term.

37. We have,

Coefficient of x, x^2 and x^3 in $(1+x^2)^2(1+x)^n$

i.e., values of a_1, a_2 and a_3 in $(1+2x^2+x^4)(1+x)^n$

$\Rightarrow \quad a_1={}^nC_1$, $a_2={}^nC_2+2$ and $a_3={}^nC_3+2\,{}^nC_1$

According to the question,

$$2a_2=a_1+a_3$$

$\Rightarrow \quad 2({}^nC_2+2)={}^nC_1+({}^nC_3+2\,{}^nC_1)$

$\Rightarrow \quad \left[2\dfrac{n(n-1)}{2}\right]+4=3n+\dfrac{n(n-1)(n-2)}{6}$

$\Rightarrow \quad n^3-9n^2+26n-24=0$

$\Rightarrow \quad (n-2)(n^2-7n+12)=0$

$\Rightarrow \quad (n-2)(n-3)(n-4)=0$

$\Rightarrow \quad n=2, 3, 4$

Hence, $n=3, 4$ ($n\neq 2, \because {}^nC_3$ is not defined)

38. We have, $\dfrac{17}{4}+3\sqrt{2}=\dfrac{1}{4}(9+8+12\sqrt{2})=\dfrac{1}{4}(3+2\sqrt{2})^2$

$\Rightarrow \quad 3-\sqrt{\dfrac{17}{4}+3\sqrt{2}}=3-\dfrac{1}{2}(3+2\sqrt{2})=\left(\dfrac{3}{2}-\sqrt{2}\right)$

$\therefore$ 10th term in $\left(3-\sqrt{\dfrac{17}{4}+3\sqrt{2}}\right)^{20}$ is

$$T_{9+1}={}^{20}C_9\left(\frac{3}{2}\right)^{20-9}(-\sqrt{2})^9$$

$$={}^{20}C_9(-1)^9 3^{11}\cdot 2^{-11+\frac{9}{2}}$$

$$=-{}^{20}C_9 3^{11} 2^{-\frac{13}{2}}$$

which is a negative and an irrational number.

39. We have, $C_0-(C_0+C_1)+(C_0+C_1+C_2)-(C_0+C_1+C_2+C_3)+\cdots(-1)^{n-1}(C_0+C_1+\cdots+C_{n-1})$

For even integer, take $n=2m$, we get

$$=C_0-(C_0+C_1)+(C_0+C_1+C_2)-(C_0+C_1+C_2+C_3)+\cdots-(C_0+C_1+\cdots+C_{2m-1})$$

$$=-(C_1+C_3+C_5+\cdots+C_{2m-1})$$

$$=-(C_1+C_3+C_5+\cdots+C_{n-1}) \qquad [\because n=2m]$$

$$=-2^{n-1}$$

40. We have,

$$f(n)=\sum_{i=0}^{n}\binom{30}{30-i}\binom{20}{n-i}=\sum_{i=0}^{n}\binom{30}{i}\binom{20}{n-i}={}^{50}C_n$$

$\therefore f(n)$ is greatest, when $n=25$

$\therefore$ Maximum value of $f(n)$ is ${}^{50}C_{25}$.

Also, $\quad f(0)+f(1)+\cdots+f(50)$

$$={}^{50}C_0+{}^{50}C_1+{}^{50}C_2+\cdots+{}^{50}C_{50}=2^{50}$$

Also, ${}^{50}C_n$ is not divisible by 50 for any n as 50 is not a prime number.

$$\sum_{n=0}^{50}(f(n))^2=({}^{50}C_0)^2+({}^{50}C_1)^2+\cdots+({}^{50}C_{50})^2={}^{100}C_{50}$$

41. ${}^{69}C_{3r-1}+{}^{69}C_{3r}={}^{69}C_{r^2-1}+{}^{69}C_{r^2}$

$\Rightarrow \quad {}^{70}C_{3r}={}^{70}C_{r^2}$

$\Rightarrow \quad r^2=3r$ or $70-3r=r^2$

$\Rightarrow \quad r=0, 3$ or $r^3+3r-70=0$

$\Rightarrow \quad r=0, 3$ or $(r+10)(r-7)=0$

$\Rightarrow \quad r=0, 3, 7, -10$

But $r = 0, -10$ do not satisfies the given equation.

Hence, two values of r satisfies,

i.e. $r = 3, 7$

42. Here, n is even, so middle term is $\left(\frac{8}{2}+1\right)$th, i.e. 5th term.

$$\therefore \quad T_5 = {}^8C_4(x)^4\left(\frac{\sin^{-1} x}{x}\right)^4 = \frac{630}{16} \quad \text{[given]}$$

$$\Rightarrow \quad 70(\sin^{-1} x)^4 = \frac{630}{10} \Rightarrow (\sin^{-1} x)^4 = \frac{9}{16}$$

$$\Rightarrow \quad (\sin^{-1} x)^2 = \frac{3}{4} \Rightarrow \sin^{-1} x = \pm\frac{\sqrt{3}}{2}$$

$$\Rightarrow \quad x = -\frac{\pi}{3}, \frac{\pi}{3} \quad \left[\because \sin^{-1} x \in \left(-\frac{\pi}{2}, \frac{\pi}{2}\right)\right]$$

43. Sum of coefficients $= (a\alpha^2 + 2b\alpha + c)^n$

Let $f(\alpha) = a\alpha^2 + 2b\alpha + c$

Now, $D = 4b^2 - 4ac = 4(b^2 - ac) < 0$

$\therefore$ $f(\alpha) < 0$ or $f(\alpha) > 0, \forall \alpha \in R$

If $a > 0$, then $f(\alpha) > 0$

$\Rightarrow (a\alpha^2 + 2b\alpha + c)^n > 0$

If $c > 0$, i.e. $f(0) > 0 \Rightarrow f(\alpha) > 0$

$\Rightarrow$ $(a\alpha^2 + 2b\alpha + c)^n > 0$

If $a < 0$, then $f(\alpha) < 0$

$\Rightarrow$ $(a\alpha^2 + 2b\alpha + c)^n < 0$, if n is odd

If $c < 0$, then $f(0) < 0 \Rightarrow f(\alpha) < 0$

$\Rightarrow$ $(a\alpha^2 + 2b\alpha + c)^n > 0$, if n is even.

44. $\because \left(x^2 + 1 + \frac{1}{x^2}\right)^n = \frac{(1 + x^2 + x^4)^n}{x^{2n}}$

$$= \frac{a_0 + a_1x^2 + a_2x^4 + \ldots + a_{2n}x^{4n}}{x^{2n}}$$

$\therefore$ Number of terms $= 2n + 1$

Term independent of $x = a_n$ = Constant term in $\left(x^2 + 1 + \frac{1}{x^2}\right)^n$

= Coefficient of x^{2n} in $(1 + x^2 + x^4)^n$

= Coefficient of x^n in $(1 + x + x^2)^n$

$$= \frac{d^n}{dx^n}(1 + x + x^2)^n \neq 2^{n-1}$$

Coefficient of x^{2n-2} in $\left(x^2 + 1 + \frac{1}{x^2}\right)^n$

= Coefficient of x^{4n-2} in $(1 + x^2 + x^4)^n$

= Coefficient of x^{2n-1} in $(1 + x + x^2)^n$

Now, let $(1 + x + x^2)^n = \lambda_0 + \lambda_1 x + \lambda_2 x^2 + \ldots$

$$+ \lambda_{2n-1}x^{2\lambda-1} + \lambda_{2n}x^{2n}$$

On replacing x by $\frac{1}{x}$, we get

$$\left(1 + \frac{1}{x} + \frac{1}{x^2}\right)^n = \lambda_0 + \frac{\lambda_1}{x} + \frac{\lambda_2}{x^2} + \ldots + \frac{\lambda_{2n-1}}{x^{2n-1}} + \frac{\lambda_{2n}}{x^{2n}}$$

or $\quad (1 + x + x^2)^n = \lambda_{2n} + \lambda_{2n-1}x + \ldots + \lambda_1 x^{2n-1} + \lambda_0 x^{2n}$

On differentiating both sides w.r.t. x, we get

$$n(1 + x + x^2)^n \cdot (1 + 2x) = \lambda_{2n-1} + \ldots + 2n\lambda_0 x^{2n-1}$$

On putting $x = 0$, we get $\lambda_{2n-1} = n$

Hence, coefficient of $x^{2n-2} = n$

and coefficient of x^2 in $\left(x^2 + 1 + \frac{1}{x^2}\right)^n$

= Coefficient of x^{2n+2} in $(1 + x^2 + x^4)^n$

= Coefficient of x^{n+1} in $(1 + x + x^2)^n$

$$= \frac{d^{n+1}}{dx^{n+1}}(1 + x + x^2)^n \neq n$$

45. Now, $\left(x + \frac{1}{x}\right)^{20} = {}^{20}C_0 x^{20} + {}^{20}C_1 x^{18} + {}^{20}C_2 x^{16}$

$$+ {}^{20}C_3 x^{14} + \ldots$$

$$+ {}^{20}C_9 x^2 + {}^{20}C_{10} + {}^{20}C_{11}x^{-2} + \ldots + {}^{20}C_{20}x^{-20}$$

$$T_{r+1} = {}^{20}C_r \cdot x^{20-2r} \quad \ldots\text{(i)}$$

and $\left(x^2 + 2 + \frac{1}{x^2}\right)^{10} = \left(\frac{1}{x} + x\right)^{20}$

$$= {}^{20}C_0 x^{-20} + {}^{20}C_1 x^{-18} + {}^{20}C_2 x^{-16}$$

$$+ \ldots + {}^{20}C_{10} + {}^{20}C_{11}x^2 + {}^{20}C_{12}x^4$$

$$+ \ldots + {}^{20}C_{20}x^{20}$$

$$\therefore \quad T_6 = T_{5+1} = {}^{20}C_5 x^{-10} \quad \ldots\text{(ii)}$$

According to the question, ${}^{20}C_r = {}^{20}C_5$

$\therefore$ $r = 5$ or $20 = r + 5 \Rightarrow Sr = 5, 15$

■ ***Sol.*** (Q. Nos. 46 to 48)

46. We have, $(1 + x + x^2)^n = \sum_{r=0}^{2n} a_r x^r \quad \ldots\text{(i)}$

On replacing x by $\frac{1}{x}$, we get

$$\left(1 + \frac{1}{x} + \frac{1}{x^2}\right)^n = \sum_{r=0}^{2n} a_r \left(\frac{1}{x}\right)^r$$

$$\Rightarrow \quad (1 + x + x^2)^n = \sum_{r=0}^{2n} a_r x^{2n-r} \quad \ldots\text{(ii)}$$

From Eqs. (i) and (ii), we get

$$\sum_{r=0}^{2n} a_r x^r = \sum_{r=0}^{2n} a_r x^{2n-r}$$

Equating the coefficient of x^{2n-r} on both sides, we get

$$a_{2n-r} = a_r \quad \ldots\text{(iii)}$$

$$0 \le r \le 2n$$

On putting $r = 0, 1, 2, 3, \ldots, n-1, n$, we get

$$a_{2n} = a_0$$
$$a_{2n-1} = a_1$$
$$a_{2n-2} = a_2$$
$$a_{2n-3} = a_3$$
$$\vdots \quad \vdots \quad \vdots$$
$$a_{n+1} = a_{n-1}, a_n = a_n$$

Then, $a_0 + a_1 + a_2 + \ldots + a_{n-1}$

$$= a_{n+1} + a_{n+2} + \ldots + a_{2n} \quad \ldots(\text{iv})$$

and on putting $x = 1$ in Eq. (i), we get

$$\sum_{r=0}^{2n} a_r = 3^n$$

$$\Rightarrow (a_0 + a_1 + a_2 + \ldots + a_{n-1}) + a_n + (a_{n+1} + a_{n+2} + \ldots + a_{2n}) = 3^n$$

From Eq.(iv), we get

$$2(a_0 + a_1 + a_2 + \ldots + a_{n-1}) = 3^n - a_n$$

or $\displaystyle\sum_{r=0}^{n-1} a_r = \frac{(3^n - a_n)}{2}$

47. On putting $x = 1$ and $x = -1$ in Eq. (i), we get

$$3^n = a_0 + a_1 + a_2 + \ldots + a_{2n} \quad \ldots(\text{v})$$

$$1 = a_0 - a_1 + a_2 - a_3 + \ldots + a_{2n} \quad \ldots(\text{vi})$$

On adding and subtracting Eqs. (v) and (vi), we get

$$\frac{3^n + 1}{2} = (a_0 + a_2 + \ldots + a_{2n}) \quad \ldots(\text{vii})$$

$$\frac{3^n - 1}{2} = (a_1 + a_3 + a_5 + \ldots + a_{2n-1}) \quad \ldots(\text{viii})$$

Also, $a_r = a_{2n-r}$

Put $r = 0, 2, 4, 6, \ldots, n-1$

$$a_0 = a_{2n}, a_2 = a_{2n-2}, a_4 = a_{2n-4}, \ldots$$

$$a_{n-1} = a_{n+1}$$

From Eq. (vii), we get

$$\frac{3^n + 1}{2} = 2(a_0 + a_2 + \ldots + a_{n-2}) + a_n$$

$$\frac{3^n + 1 - 2a_n}{4} = a_0 + a_2 + \ldots + a_{n-1}$$

48. From Eq. (viii), we get

$$\frac{3^n - 1}{2} = 2(a_1 + a_3 + \ldots + a_n) - a_n$$

$$\frac{3^n - 1 + 2a_n}{4} = (a_1 + a_3 + \ldots + a_n)$$

■ ***Sol.*** (Q. Nos. 49 to 51)

Given, $(1 + x + 2x^2)^{20} = a_0 + a_1 x + a_2 x^2 + \ldots + a_{40} x^{40}$

On putting $x = 1$ and $x = -1$ respectively, we get

$$a_0 + a_1 + a_2 + \ldots + a_{40} = 4^{20} = 2^{40} \quad \ldots(\text{i})$$

and $$a_0 - a_1 + a_2 - \ldots + a_{40} = 2^{20} \quad \ldots(\text{ii})$$

From Eqs. (i) and (ii), we get

$$a_0 + a_2 + a_4 + \ldots + a_{38} + a_{40} = 2^{19}(2^{20} + 1) \quad \ldots(\text{iii})$$

and $$a_1 + a_3 + a_5 + \ldots + a_{37} + a_{39} = 2^{19}(2^{20} - 1) \quad \ldots(\text{iv})$$

Also, replacing x by $\frac{1}{x}$ in given expression, we get

$$\left(1 + \frac{1}{x} + \frac{2}{x^2}\right)^{20} = a_0 + \frac{a_1}{x} + \frac{a_2}{x^2} + \ldots + \frac{a_{38}}{x^{38}} + \frac{a_{39}}{x^{39}} + \frac{a_{40}}{x^{40}}$$

$$\Rightarrow \quad (2 + x + x^2)^{20} = a_0 x^{40} + a_1 x^{39} + \ldots + a_{38} x^2 + a_{39} x + a_{40} \quad \ldots(\text{v})$$

On putting $x = 0$, we get $a_{40} = 2^{20}$ ...(vi)

On differentiating both sides of Eq. (v) w.r.t. x and put $x = 0$, we get

$$a_{39} = 20(2)^{19} \quad \ldots(\text{vii})$$

49. $a_0 + a_2 + a_4 + \ldots + a_{38} + a_{40} = 2^{19}(2^{20} + 1)$ [from Eq. (iii)]

$$\Rightarrow \quad a_0 + a_2 + a_4 + \ldots + a_{38} = 2^{19}(2^{20} + 1) - a_{40}$$

$$= 2^{19}(2^{20} + 1) - 2^{20} \quad [\text{from Eq. (vi)}]$$

$$= 2^{19}(2^{20} - 1)$$

50. $a_1 + a_3 + a_5 + \ldots + a_{37} + a_{39} = 2^{19}(2^{20} - 1)$ [from Eq. (iv)]

$$\Rightarrow \quad a_1 + a_3 + a_5 + \ldots + a_{37} = 2^{19}(2^{20} - 1) - a_{39}$$

$$= 2^{19}(2^{20} - 1) - 20(2)^{19} \quad [\text{from Eq. (vii)}]$$

$$= 2^{19}(2^{20} - 21)$$

51. From Eqs. (vi) and (vii), we get $\dfrac{a_{39}}{a_{40}} = \dfrac{20(2)^{19}}{2^{20}} = 10$

■ ***Sol.*** (Q. Nos. 52 to 54)

52. $5^{40} = (5^2)^{20} = (22 + 3)^{20} = 22\lambda + 3^{20}, \lambda \in N$

Also, $3^{20} = (3^2)^{10} = (11 - 2)^{10} = 11\mu + 2^{10}, \mu \in N$

Now, $2^{10} = 1024 = 11 \times 93 + 1$

$\therefore$ Remainder, $a = 1$

Also, $2^{2011} = 2^3(2^4)^{502} = 2^3(17 - 1)^{502}$

$$= 8[(17)^{502} - {}^{502}C_1(17)^{501} + \ldots - {}^{502}C_{501}(17) + 1]$$

$$= 8(17\lambda + 1), \lambda \in N = 8 \times 17\lambda + 8$$

$\therefore$ Remainder, $b = 8$

Hence, $a + b = 1 + 8 = 9$

53. $19^{93} - 13^{99}$ = (odd number) − (odd number) = even number

$\therefore$ $19^{93} - 13^{99}$ is divisible by 2.

Now, $19^{93} - 13^{99} = (18 + 1)^{93} - (12 + 1)^{99}$

$$= [(18)^{93} + {}^{93}C_1(18)^{92} + {}^{93}C_2(18)^{91} \ldots + \ldots + {}^{93}C_{92}(18) + 1]$$

$$- [(12)^{99} + {}^{99}C_1(12)^{98} + {}^{99}C_2(12)^{97} + \ldots + {}^{99}C_{98}(12) + 1]$$

$$= (18)^2\lambda + {}^{93}C_1 \times 18 - (12)^2\mu - {}^{99}C_1(12)$$

When λ and μ are integers

$$= (18)^2\lambda - (12)^2\mu + 486$$

$$= 81 \times 4\lambda - 12^2({}^{99}C_2 + 12 \cdot {}^{99}C_3) + 81p + 486$$

= 81 (integer), where p is an integer.

But 2 and 81 are co-prime.

$\therefore$ $19^{93} - 13^{99}$ is divisible by 162.

54. $13^{99} = (12 + 1)^{99} = (12)^{99} + {}^{99}C_1(12)^{98} + {}^{99}C_2(12)^{97} + \ldots + {}^{99}C_{97}(12)^2 + {}^{99}C_{98}(12) + 1$

$$= \{(12)^{99} + {}^{99}C_1(12)^{98} + {}^{99}C_2(12)^{97} + \ldots + {}^{99}C_{97}(12)^2\} + {}^{99}C_1(12) + 1$$

$= 81\lambda + 99 \times 12 + 1$, where λ is an integer

$$= 81\lambda + 81 \times 14 + 55$$

$\therefore$ Remainder = 55

■ ***Sol.*** (Q. Nos. 55 to 57)

Here, $(1+2)^n = 2187$

$$3^n = 2187 = 3^7 \Rightarrow n = 7$$

At $\quad x = \dfrac{1}{\sqrt{2}},\ R = (\sqrt{2}+1)^7 = I + f$

55. Let $f' = (\sqrt{2}-1)^7,\ 0 < f' < 1$

$\therefore \quad Rf' = (\sqrt{2}+1)^7(\sqrt{2}-1)^7 = (1)^7 = 1$

$\therefore \quad (n + Rf) = 7 + 1 = 8$

56. Here, $m = \left|\dfrac{(n+1)(x)}{1+x}\right|$

$$= \left|\frac{(7+1)\left(2\times\frac{1}{3}\right)}{1+2\times\frac{1}{3}}\right| = -\frac{8\times\frac{2}{3}}{\frac{5}{3}} = \frac{16}{5} = 3.2$$

$$T_{[m]+1} = T_{3+1} = T_4$$

57. Here, $n = 7$

$\therefore$ Greatest coefficient $= \dfrac{^7C_{7-1}}{2}$ or $^7C_3$

and $\dfrac{^7C_{7+1}}{2}$, i.e. $^7C_4$

Sum of values of $k = (3+1) + (4+1) = 9$

■ ***Sol.*** (Q. Nos. 58 to 60)

58. $(x + C_0)(x + 3\cdot C_1)(x + 5\cdot C_2) + \dots \{x + (2n+1)\cdot C_n\}$

$= x^{n+1} + x^n\{C_0 + 3\cdot C_1 + 5\cdot C_2 + \dots + (2n+1)\cdot C_n\}$

$\therefore$ Coefficient of $x^n = C_0 + 3\cdot C_1 + 5\cdot C_2 + \dots + (2n+1)\cdot C_n$

$$= (C_0 + C_1 + C_2 + \dots + C_n) + 2\{C_1 + 2\cdot C_2 + \dots n\cdot C_n\}$$

$$= 2^n + 2\left\{n + 2\cdot\frac{n(n-1)}{2} + \dots + n\right\}$$

$$= 2^n + 2n\left\{1 + (n-1) + \frac{(n-1)(n-2)}{1\cdot 2} + \dots + 1\right\}$$

$$= 2^n + 2n\{^{n-1}C_0 + {^{n-1}C_1} + {^{n-1}C_2} + \dots + {^{n-1}C_{n-1}}\}$$

$$= 2^n + 2n(1+1)^{n-1} = 2^n + n\cdot 2^n = (n+1)2^n$$

59. $(x + C_0)(x + C_1)(x + C_2) + \dots + (x + C_n)$

$$= x^{n+1} + \left(\sum_{r=0}^{n} C_r\right)^n x^n + \left(\sum_{0\le i}\sum_{j\le n} C_iC_j\right)x^{n-1} + \dots$$

$\therefore$ Coefficient of x^{n-1} in $\displaystyle\sum_{0\le i\le j\le n}\sum C_iC_j$

$$= \frac{1}{2}\left\{\left(\sum_{r=0}^{n} C_r\right)^2 - \left(\sum_{r=0}^{n} C_r^2\right)\right\} = \frac{1}{2}\{2^{2n} - {^{2n}C_n}\}$$

$$= 2^{2n-1} - \frac{1}{2}\cdot{^{2n}C_n}$$

60. $(x+1)^2(x+3)^3(x+5)^4$

$= (x+1)(x+1)(x+3)(x+3)(x+3)(x+5)(x+5)(x+5)(x+5)$

$= x^9 + (1+1+3+3+3+5+5+5+5)x^8$

$+ (1\cdot 1 + 1\cdot 3 + 1\cdot 3 + 1\cdot 3 + 1\cdot 5 + \dots + 1\cdot 5 + 3\cdot 3 + 3\cdot 3 + 3\cdot 5 + \dots + 5\cdot 5)x^7 + \dots$

$\therefore$ Coefficient of $x^7 = \dfrac{(1+1+3+3+3+5+5+5+5)^2 - (1^2+1^2+3^2+3^2+3^2+5^2+5^2+5^2+5^2)}{2}$

$$= \frac{(31)^2 - (129)}{2} = \frac{961 - 129}{2} = 416$$

■ ***Sol.*** (Q. Nos. 61 to 83)

Since, sum of coefficient of B is 6561.

$\therefore \quad \left(\dfrac{5}{2} + \dfrac{1}{2}\right)^n = 6561$

$\Rightarrow \quad 3^n = 6561 \Rightarrow 3^n = 3^8$

$\therefore \quad n = 8$

61. Coefficient $(T_3 - T_2) = 117$

$$^mC_2 3^2 - {^mC_1} 3^1 = 117$$

$\Rightarrow \quad m = 6$

62. $n^m = 8^6 = (1+7)^6 = (1 + 7k)$

Hence, remainder is 1.

63. $\dfrac{\text{Coefficient of } T_2 \text{ in } \left(\dfrac{5x}{2} + \dfrac{x^{-2}}{2}\right)^8}{\text{Coefficient of } T_2 \text{ in } \left(\dfrac{x^{-2}}{2} + \dfrac{5x}{2}\right)^8} = \dfrac{^8C_1\left(\frac{5}{2}\right)^7\left(\frac{1}{2}\right)}{^8C_1\left(\frac{1}{2}\right)^7\left(\frac{5}{2}\right)} = 5^6 = 15625$

■ ***Sol.*** (Q. Nos. 64 to 66)

$\because a_4, a_5, a_6$ i.e., $^nC_4, {^nC_5}, {^nC_6}$ are in AP, then

$$2\cdot{^nC_5} = {^nC_4} + {^nC_6}$$

$\Rightarrow \quad 2 = \dfrac{^nC_4}{^nC_5} + \dfrac{^nC_6}{^nC_5} = \dfrac{5}{n-5+1} + \dfrac{n-6+1}{6}$

$\Rightarrow \quad 2 = \dfrac{5}{n-4} + \dfrac{n-5}{6}$

$\Rightarrow \quad 12n - 48 = 30 + n^2 - 9n + 20$

$\Rightarrow \quad n^2 - 21n + 98 = 0 \Rightarrow n = 7, 14$

Hence, $\quad n = 7 \quad [\because n < 10]$

Also, $\quad A = (\sqrt[3]{2} + \sqrt[4]{3})^{13n} = (2^{1/3} + 3^{1/4})^{91}$

$\therefore \quad T_{r+1} = {^{91}C_r}(2^{1/3})^{91-r}\cdot(3^{1/4})^r$

$$= {^{91}C_r}\cdot 2^{\frac{91-r}{3}}\cdot 3^{r/4} \quad \text{...(i)}$$

64. $\displaystyle\sum_{i=1}^{n} a_i = \sum_{i=1}^{7} a_i = a_1 + a_2 + a_3 + \dots + a_7$

$$= {^7C_1} + {^7C_2} + {^7C_3} + \dots + {^7C_7} = 2^7 - 1 = 127$$

65. From Eq. (i), we get

$$0 \le r \le 91$$

For rational terms, $r = 4, 16, 28, 40, 52, 64, 76, 88$

Rational terms are $T_5, T_{17}, T_{29}, T_{41}, T_{53}, T_{65}, T_{77}, T_{89}$

$\therefore \quad a_m = 89$

66. Also, 5, 17, 29, 41 53,..., 89 are in AP with common difference 12.

67. The unit digit of 2^{2^n} is always 6 for $n > 1$.

Now, $\sum_{r=0}^{100} r! = 0! + 1! + 2! + 3! + 4! + 10(k); k \in N$

$$= 1 + 1 + 2 + 6 + 24 + 10k = 34 + 10k$$

$\therefore$ Unit digit of $\sum_{r=0}^{100} r! + 2^{2^n}$

$$= \text{Unit place of } \sum_{r=0}^{100} r! + \text{Unit place of } 2^{2^n}$$

$$= 4 + 0 + 6 = 10, \text{ its unit place is } 0.$$

68. Given, $\sum_{r=0}^{3n} a_r x^r = (1 + x + x^2 + x^3)^n$

It is clear that a_r is the coefficient of x^r in the expansion of $(1 + x + x^2 + x^3)^n$.

On replacing x by $\frac{1}{x}$ in the given equation, we get

$$\sum_{r=0}^{3n} a_r \left(\frac{1}{x}\right)^r = \frac{(1 + x + x^2 + x^3)^n}{x^{3n}}$$

Here, a_r represents the coefficient of 3^{3n-r} in $(1 + x + x^2 + x^3)^n$.

Thus, $a_r = a_{3n-r}$ ...(i)

Let $I = \sum_{r=0}^{3n} r \times a_r = \sum_{r=0}^{3n} (3n - r)\, a_{3n-r}$ [replacing r by $3n - r$]

$= \sum_{r=0}^{3n} (3n - r)\, a_r$ [from Eq. (i)]

$= 3n \sum_{r=0}^{3n} - \sum_{r=0}^{3n} rar$

$\Rightarrow 2I = 3nk \Rightarrow I = \frac{3nk}{2} \quad \therefore \lambda = 3$

69. We have, $T_{r+1} = {}^{20}C_r \cdot 4^{\frac{20-r}{3}} \cdot 6^{-r/4}$

$= {}^{20}C_r \cdot 2^{\frac{40-2r}{3}} \cdot 2^{-r/4} \cdot 3^{-r/4}$

$= {}^{20}C_r \cdot 2^{\frac{160-11r}{12}} \cdot 3^{-r/4}$

For rational terms, $\frac{r}{4}$ and $\frac{160 - 11r}{12}$ must be integers and $0 \le r \le 20$.

$\therefore$ $\frac{r}{4}$ is an integer.

$\Rightarrow r = 0, 4, 8, 12, 16, 20$

Clearly, for $r = 8, 16$ and 20 $\frac{160 - 11r}{12}$ is also an integer.

$\therefore$ The number of rational terms is 3.

70. We have, $2^{2006} = 2^2 (2^3)^{668}$

$$= 4(1 + 7)^{668} = 4(1 + 7k) = 4 + 28k$$

$\therefore 2^{2006} + 2006 = 4 + 28k + 7 \times (286) + 4$

Hence, remainder is 8.

71. We have, $19^{9^4} = (20 - 1)^{6561}$

$= (20)^{6561} - {}^{6561}C_1 (20)^{6560} + {}^{6561}C_2 (20)^{6559}$
$- \ldots - {}^{6561}C_{6559} (20)^2 + {}^{6561}C_{6560} (20)^2 - 1$

$= 1000k - {}^{6561}C_2 (400) + {}^{6561}C_1 (20) - 1$

where, k is an integer.

$= 1000p + 6561 \times 20 - 1 = 1000p + 131220 - 1$

where, p is an integer.

$= 1000p + 131219$

$\therefore$ $ab = 19$

i.e. $a = 1, b = 9$

Hence, $b - 3a = 9 - 3 = 6$

72. ${}^nC_r + 4 \cdot {}^nC_{r+1} + 6 \cdot {}^nC_{r+2} + 4 \cdot {}^nC_{r+3} + {}^nC_{r+4}$

$= ({}^nC_r + {}^nC_{r+1}) + 3({}^nC_{r+1} + {}^nC_{r+2})$
$+ 3({}^nC_{r+2} + {}^nC_{r+3}) + ({}^nC_{r+3} + {}^nC_{r+4})$

$= {}^{n+1}C_{r+1} + 3 \cdot {}^{n+1}C_{r+2} + 3 \cdot {}^{n+1}C_{r+3} + {}^{n+1}C_{r+4}$

$= ({}^{n+1}C_{r+1} + {}^{n+1}C_{r+2}) + 2({}^{n+1}C_{r+2}$
$+ {}^{n+1}C_{r+3}) + ({}^{n+1}C_{r+3} + {}^{n+1}C_{r+4})$

$= {}^{n+2}C_{r+2} + 2 \cdot {}^{n+2}C_{r+3} + {}^{n+2}C_{r+4}$

$= ({}^{n+2}C_{r+2} + {}^{n+2}C_{r+3}) + ({}^{n+2}C_{r+3} + {}^{n+2}C_{r+4})$

$= {}^{n+3}C_{r+3} + {}^{n+3}C_{r+4}$

$= {}^{n+4}C_{r+4} = \frac{n+4}{r+4}\, {}^{n+3}C_{r+3}$

Similarly, ${}^nC_r + 3 \cdot {}^nC_{r+1} + 3 \cdot {}^nC_{r+2} + {}^nC_{r+3} = {}^{n+3}C_{r+3}$

$\therefore \frac{n+4}{r+4} = \frac{n+\lambda}{r+\lambda} \Rightarrow \lambda = 4$

73. $99^{50} - 99 \cdot 98^{50} + \frac{99 \cdot 98}{1 \cdot 2} (97)^{50} - \ldots + 99$

$= 99^{50} - {}^{99}C_1 (98)^{50} + {}^{99}C_2 (97)^{50} - \ldots + {}^{99}C_{98} \cdot 1$

$= {}^{99}C_0 (99)^{50} - {}^{99}C_1 (99 - 1)^{50} + {}^{99}C_2 (99 - 2)^{50} - \ldots$
$+ {}^{99}C_{98} (99 - 98)^{50} - {}^{99}C_{99} (99 - 99)^{50}$

$= (99)^{50} \{{}^{99}C_0 - {}^{99}C_1 + {}^{99}C_2 - \ldots + {}^{99}C_{98} - {}^{99}C_{99}\}$
$+ {}^{50}C_1 (99)^{49} \{{}^{99}C_1 - 2 \cdot {}^{99}C_2 + 3 \cdot {}^{99}C_3 - \ldots\}$

$= 0 + 0 = 0$

74. Given,

$\because$ Greatest term in the expansion of $(1 + x)^{2n}$ has the greatest coefficient.

$\therefore$ $T_{n+1} = {}^{2n}C_n x^n$ (greatest term)

$\therefore$ $T_n < T_{n+1} > T_{n+2}$

$\Rightarrow {}^{2n}C_{n-1} \cdot x^{n-1} < {}^{2n}C_n \cdot x^n > {}^{2n}C_{n+1} \cdot x^{n+1}$

$\Rightarrow \frac{{}^{2n}C_{n-1}}{{}^{2n}C_n} \cdot \frac{1}{x} < 1 > \frac{{}^{2n}C_{n+1}}{{}^{2n}C_n} \cdot x$

$\Rightarrow \frac{n}{n+1} \cdot \frac{1}{x} < 1 > \frac{n}{n+1}\, x$

$\Rightarrow x > \frac{n}{n+1}$ and $x < \frac{n+1}{n}$

i.e., $x \in \left(\frac{n}{n+1}, \frac{n+1}{n}\right)$

Given, $x \in \left(\frac{10}{11}, \frac{11}{10}\right)$

$\therefore$ $n = 10$

Also, T_4 in $\left(\lambda x + \frac{1}{x}\right)^m = {}^mC_3(\lambda x)^{m-3}\left(\frac{1}{x}\right)^3 = \frac{n}{4}$ [given]

$${}^mC_3 \cdot \lambda^{m-3} \cdot x^{m-6} = \frac{n}{4} \quad \text{[given]}$$

$$= \frac{10}{4} \quad [\because n = 10]$$

$$= \frac{5}{2}$$

Put $m - 6 = 0$, we get

$$m = 6$$

$\therefore$ ${}^6C_3 \cdot \lambda^3 = \frac{5}{2}$

$\Rightarrow$ $\lambda^3 = \frac{5}{2} \times \frac{1}{20} = \frac{1}{8} = \left(\frac{1}{2}\right)^3$

$\therefore$ $\lambda = \frac{1}{2}$

Hence, $m\lambda = 6 \times \frac{1}{2} = 3$

75. We know that, $(x-1)^n = {}^nC_0x^n - {}^nC_1x^{n-1} + {}^nC_2x^{n-2} - \dots$

$\therefore$ $x^2(x-1)^n = {}^nC_0x^{n+2} - {}^nC_1x^{n+1} + {}^nC_2\,x^n - \dots$

On differentiating w.r.t. x, we get

$$2x\,(x-1)^n + x^2 \cdot n(x-1)^{n-1}$$

$$= (n+2)\,{}^nC_0\,x^{n+1} - (n+1)\,{}^nC_1x^n + n \cdot {}^nC_2\,x^{n-1} - \dots$$

On putting $x = 2$, we get

$$(n+2)\,{}^nC_0\,2^{n+1} - (n+1) \cdot {}^nC_1 \cdot 2^n + n \cdot {}^nC_2 2^{n-1} - \dots$$

$$= 4 + 4n = 4(1+n)$$

$\therefore$ $k = 4$

76. On putting $x = 1, -1, i, -i$ in the given expression, we get

$$10^4 \times 9 = a_1 + a_2 + a_3 + a_4 + \dots + a_{45} \quad \text{...(i)}$$

$$0 = -a_1 + a_2 - a_3 + a_4 + \dots - a_{45} \quad \text{...(ii)}$$

$$(1+i)^4 \cdot i = a_1 i - a_2 - a_3 i + a_4 + \dots$$

$\Rightarrow$ $-i\,(2i)^2 = -a_1 i + a_2 + a_3 i - a_4 - \dots$

$\Rightarrow$ $4i = -a_1 i + a_2 + a_3 i - a_4 - \dots$ ...(iii)

and $-4i = a_1 i + a_2 - a_3 i - a_4 - \dots$ ...(iv)

On adding Eqs. (i), (ii), (iii) and (iv), we get

$4(a_2 + a_6 + a_{10} + a_{14} + \dots + a_{42}) = 9 \times 10^4$

or $a_2 + a_6 + a_{10} + \dots + a_{42} = 22500 = \lambda$ [given]

$\therefore$ Required sum $= 2 + 2 + 5 + 0 + 0 = 9$

77. **(A)** General term, $T_{r+1} = {}^{6561}C_r\,(7^{1/3})^{6561-r}\,(11^{1/9})^r$

$$= {}^{6561}C_r 7^{\left(\frac{6561-r}{3}\right)} 11^{(r/9)}$$

For rational term, r should be a multiple of 9, i.e., $r = 0, 9, 18, \dots, 6561$

Total rational terms, $m = 730$

and irrational terms, $n = 6562 - 730 = 5832$

Let $\lambda =$ unit digit of $(730)^{5832} = 0$

and $\mu =$ unit digit of $(5832)^{730}0$.

$$= \text{unit digit of } (2^5)^{145} \cdot 2^5$$

$$= (2)(2) = 4$$

$\therefore$ $\lambda^\mu + \mu^\lambda = (0)^4 + (4)^0 = 1$

and $\lambda + \mu = 0 + 4 = 4$.

(B) General term, $t_{r+1} = {}^{600}C_r\,(7^{1/3})^{600-r}\,(x5^{1/2})^r$

$$= {}^{600}C_r\,(7)^{\frac{600-r}{3}}\,5^{r/2}\,x^r$$

For rational term, r should be multiple of 6.

i.e. $r = 0, 6, \dots, 600$

$\therefore$ Total rational terms, $m = 101$

and total irrational terms,

$$n = 601 - 101 = 500$$

Let $\lambda =$ unit digit of $(m)^n$

$$= \text{unit digit of } (101)^{500} = 1$$

and $\mu =$ unit digit of $(500)^{101} = 0$

$\therefore$ $\lambda^2 + \mu^2 = (1)^2 + (0)^2 = 1$

$$\lambda^\mu + \mu^\lambda = (1)^0 + (0)^1 = 1$$

and $\lambda + \mu = 1 + 0 = 1 = \lambda^\mu$

(C) $(\sqrt{2} + \sqrt[3]{3} + \sqrt[6]{7})^{10} = \Sigma \frac{10!}{\alpha!\beta!\gamma!}(\sqrt{2})^\alpha (\sqrt[3]{3})^\beta (\sqrt[6]{7})^\gamma$

$$= \Sigma \frac{10!}{\alpha!\beta!\gamma!}\, 2^{\alpha/2} \cdot 3^{\beta/3} \cdot 3^{\gamma/6}$$

$\because$ $\alpha + \beta + \gamma = 10$

For rational terms, $\alpha = 0, 2, 4, 6, 8, 10$, $\beta = 0, 3, 6, 9$ and $\gamma = 0, 6$

Possible triplets are $(4, 6, 0), (10, 0, 0), (4, 0, 6)$.

$\therefore$ Total rational terms, $m = 3$

Total irrational term, $n = {}^{10+2}C_2 - 3 = 63$

Let $\lambda =$ unit's place digit of $3^{63} = (3^4)^{15} \cdot 3^3 = 1 \times 27 = 7$

and $\mu =$ unit's place digit of $63^3 =$ unit digit of $3^3 = 7$

Now, $\sqrt{\lambda\sqrt{\lambda\sqrt{\lambda\sqrt{\lambda\sqrt{\lambda \dots \infty}}}}} = \mu$

$\Rightarrow$ $\lambda^{\left\{\frac{1}{2} + \frac{1}{4} + \frac{1}{8} + \dots\right\}} = \mu\,\lambda^{\frac{1/2}{1-1/2}} = \mu$ $\therefore$ $\lambda = \mu = 7$

78. **(A)** Given, $\binom{18}{r-2} + 2\binom{18}{r-1} + \binom{18}{r} \geq \binom{20}{13}$

$\Rightarrow$ $\binom{18}{r-2} + \binom{18}{r-1} + \binom{18}{r-1} + \binom{18}{r} \geq \binom{20}{13}$

$\Rightarrow$ $\binom{19}{r-1} + \binom{19}{r} \geq \binom{20}{13}$

$\Rightarrow \quad \binom{20}{r} \geq \binom{20}{7} \Rightarrow 7 \leq r \leq 13$

$\therefore \quad r = 7, 8, 9, 10, 11, 12, 13$

(B) The unit digit of 183! is 0.

Now, $\quad 3^{183} = (3^4)^{45}(3)^3$

Unit digit of 3^{183} = Unit digit of $(81)^{45}$ × Unit digit of 27

$= 1 \times 7 = 7$

∴ Unit digit of 183! + $3^{183} = 0 + 7 = 7$

which is less than 8 and 9.

(C) $T_4 = {}^nC_3 (ax)^{n-3}\left(\frac{1}{x}\right)^3 = \frac{5}{2}$

$\Rightarrow {}^nC_3\, a^{n-3} x^{n-6} = \frac{5}{2} \Rightarrow n = 6$ and $a = \frac{1}{3}$

$\therefore \quad na = 6 \times \frac{1}{3} = 2$

79. **(A)** The coefficient of power of x more than x^{30} in $(1 + x)^{61}$ is

$${}^{61}C_{31} + {}^{61}C_{32} + \ldots + {}^{61}C_{61}$$

We know that, $(1 + 1)^{61} = {}^{61}C_0 + {}^{61}C_1 + {}^{61}C_2 + \ldots + {}^{61}C_{61}$

$\Rightarrow \quad 2^{61} = 2({}^{61}C_{31} + {}^{61}C_{32} + \ldots + {}^{61}C_{61})$

$\Rightarrow \quad {}^{61}C_{31} + {}^{61}C_{32} + \ldots + {}^{61}C_{61} = 2^{60}$

Hence, 2^{60} is divisible by $2^{57}, 2^{58}, 2^{59}, 2^{60}$.

(B) General term is, $T_{r+1} = {}^{62}C_r (\sqrt{3})^r = {}^{62}C_r 3^{r/2}$

For rational term = r should be multiple of 2.

i.e. $\quad r = 0, 2, 4, 6, \ldots, 62$

∴ Required sum $= T_1 + T_3 + \ldots + T_{63}$

$= {}^{62}C_0 + {}^{62}C_2 + \ldots + {}^{62}C_{62} = 2^{62-1} = 2^{61}$

Hence, 2^{61} is divisible by $2^{57}, 2^{58}, 2^{59}, 2^{60}, 2^{61}$.

(C) Put $x = 1$ and $x = -1$ in given expression, then we get

$4^{31} = a_0 + a_1 + a_2 + a_3 + \ldots + a_{124}$ ...(i)

and $\quad 0 = a_0 - a_1 + a_2 - a_3 + \ldots + a_{124}$ ...(ii)

On subtracting Eq. (ii) from Eq. (i), we get

$2^{62} = 2(a_1 + a_3 + \ldots + a_{123})$

$\Rightarrow \quad 2^{61} = (a_1 + a_s + \ldots + a_{123})$

$\therefore a_1 + a_3 + \ldots + a_{123}$ is divisible by $2^{57}, 2^{58}, 2^{59}, 2^{60}, 2^{61}$.

80. **(A)** $(11)^n + (21)^n = (16 - 5)^n + (16 + 5)^n$

$= 2\,[{}^nC_0 (16)^n + {}^nC_2 (16)^{n-2} (5)^2 + {}^nC_4 (16)^{n-4}(5)^4 + {}^nC_6 (16)^{n-6}(5)^6 + \ldots]$

Hence, given expression is divisible by 16, if

$n = 1, 3, 5, 7$

(B) $3^{37} = (3^4)^9 \cdot 3 = (81)^9 \cdot 3 = 3\,(80 + 1)^9]$

$= 3\,[{}^9C_1 (80)^8 + {}^9C_2 (80)^7 + \ldots + 1]$

∴ Remainder of 3^{37} is 3.

(C) $\quad T_{r+1} = T_{r+k} \Rightarrow {}^{29}C_r = {}^{29}C_{r+k-1}$

$\Rightarrow 29 - r = r + k - 1 \Rightarrow 30 = 2r + k \quad [\because r \leq 29]$

For even values of k, i.e., $k = 0, 2, 4, 6, 8, \ldots, 28$,

(D) Given, $\frac{T_2}{T_3} = \frac{T'_3}{T'_4}$

$\Rightarrow \quad \frac{{}^nC_1 (a)^{n-1} (b)^1}{{}^nC_2 (a)^{n-2} (b)^2} = \frac{{}^{n+3}C_2 (a)^{n+1} (b)^2}{{}^{n+3}C_3 (a)^n (b)^3}$

$\Rightarrow \quad \frac{{}^nC_1}{{}^nC_2} \times \frac{a}{b} = \frac{{}^{n+3}C_2}{{}^{n+3}C_3} \cdot \frac{a}{b}$

$\Rightarrow \quad \frac{{}^nC_2}{{}^nC_1} = \frac{{}^{n+3}C_3}{{}^{n+3}C_2}$

$\Rightarrow \quad \frac{n - 2 + 1}{2} = \frac{n + 3 - 3 + 1}{3}$

$\Rightarrow \quad 3n - 3 = 2n + 2$

$\therefore \quad n = 5$

81. **(A)** Number of dissimilar terms in the expansion of $(x + 2y + 3z)^n \; (n \in N)$

$= {}^{n+3-1}C_{3-1} = {}^{n+2}C_2 = \frac{1}{2}n^2 + \frac{3}{2}n + 1$

$\therefore \quad a = \frac{1}{2}, b = \frac{3}{2}, c = 1$

Hence, $\quad a + b + c = \frac{1}{2} + \frac{3}{2} + 1 = 3$

and $\quad a + b = \frac{1}{2} + \frac{3}{2} = 2 = 2c$

(B) We have,

$(x + y + z)^{2n+1} = \{(x + y) + z\}^{2n+1}$

$= (x + y)^{2n+1} + {}^{2n+1}C_1 (x + y)^{2n} z + {}^{2n+1}C_2 (x + y)^{2n-1} z^2 + {}^{2n+1}C_3 (x + y)^{2n-2} z^3 + \ldots$

${}^{2n+1}C_{2n} (x + y)\, z^{2n} + {}^{2n+1}C_{2n+1} z^{2n+1}$

and $(x + y - z)^{2n+1} = \{(x + y) - z\}^{2n+1}$

$= (x + y)^{2n+1} - {}^{2n+1}C_1 (x + y)^{2n} z + {}^{2n+1}C_2 (x + y)^{2n-1} z^2$

$- {}^{2n+1}C_3 (x + y)^{2n-2} z^3 + \ldots + {}^{2n+1}C_{2n} (x + y) z^{2n} - {}^{2n+1}C_{2n+1} z^{2n+1}$

$\therefore (x + y + z)^{2n+1} - (x + y - z)^{2n+1}$

$= 2\,\{{}^{2n+1}C_1 (x + y)^{2n} z + {}^{2n+1}C_3 (x + y)^{2n-2} z^3 + \ldots + z^{2n+1}\}$

∴ The number of dissimilar terms in the expansion of $(x + y + z)^{2n+1} - (x + y - z)^{2n+1}$

$= (2n + 1) + (2n - 1) + (2n - 3) + \ldots 5 + 3 + 1$

$= \frac{(n + 1)}{2} (2n + 1 + 1) = (n + 1)^2$

$= n^2 + 2n + 1$

$\therefore \quad a = 1, b = 2, c = 1$

Hence, $\quad a + b + c = 1 + 2 + 1 = 4$

(C) We have, $(x - y + z)^n = \{x - (y - z)\}^n$

$= x^n - {}^nC_1 x^{n-1} (y - z) + {}^nC_2 x^{n-2} (y - z)^2 + {}^nC_3 x^{n-3} (y - z)^3 + \ldots - {}^nC_{n-1} x (y - z)^{n-1} + {}^nC_n (y - z)^n$

and $\quad (x + y - z)^n = (x + y - z)^n$

$$= x^n + {}^nC_1 x^{n-1}(y-z) + {}^nC_2 x^{n-2}(y-z)^2 + {}^nC_3 x^{n-3}(y-z)^3 + \ldots + {}^nC_{n-1} x(y-z)^{n-1} + (y-z)^n$$

$$\therefore (x-y+z)^n + (x+y-z)^n$$

$$= 2[x^n + {}^nC_2 x^{n-2}(y-z)^2 + {}^nC_4 x^{n-4}(y-z)^n + \ldots + (y-z)^n]$$

$\therefore$ The number of dissilmilar terms in the expansion of $(x-y+z)^n + (x+y-z)^n = 1+3+5+\ldots+(n+1)$

$$= \frac{\frac{(n+2)}{2}}{2}(1+n+1) = \frac{(n+2)^2}{4} = \frac{1}{4}(n^2+n+1)$$

$$\therefore \quad a = \frac{1}{4}, b = 1, c = 1$$

Hence, $b + c = 1 + 1 = 2 = 8a$

(D) $\because \left(\frac{x^2+1+x^4}{x^2}\right)^{\Sigma n}$

$$= \frac{a_0 + a_2x^2 + a_4x^4 + \ldots + a_{2n(n+1)}x^{2n(n+1)}}{x^{n(n+1)}}$$

$\therefore$ Number of terms $= \frac{1}{2} \cdot 2n(n+1) + 1 = n^2 + n + 1$

$$\therefore \quad a = 1, b = 1, c = 1$$

Hence, $\quad a + b + c = 1 + 1 + 1 = 3$

and $\quad a + b = 1 + 1 = 2 = 2c$

82. Statement-2 is obviously correct.

Now, we have $(1+3x)^6 = {}^6C_0 + {}^6C_1(3x) + {}^6C_2(3x)^2 + {}^6C_3(3x)^3 + {}^6C_4(3x)^4 + {}^6C_5(3x)^5 + {}^6C_6(3x)^6$

$\therefore$ Greatest coefficient in $(1+3x)^6$ is ${}^6C_6 3^6$.

So, Statement-1 is wrong.

83. We have, $\left(x^2 + \frac{1}{x^2} + 2\right)^{25} = \left(x + \frac{1}{x}\right)^{50}$

$$\therefore \quad T_{r+1} = {}^{50}C_r \cdot C^{50-r} \cdot \left(\frac{1}{x}\right)^r = {}^{50}C_r x^{50-2r}$$

For independent of x, we put

$$50 - 2r = 0 \Rightarrow r = 25$$

$$\therefore \quad T_{25+1} = {}^{50}C_{25}$$

But in binomial expansion of $(x+a)^n$, middle terms is independent of x, iff $x \cdot a = 1$.

84. We have,

Coefficient of 31st term in $(1+x)^n$ = Coefficient of 32nd term in $(1+x)^n$

$\Rightarrow$ Coefficient of T_{30+1} = Coefficient of T_{31+1}

$\Rightarrow$ ${}^nC_{30} = {}^nC_{31} \Rightarrow n = 30 + 31 = 61$

Hence, both statements are correct but Statement-2 is not the correct Explanation of Statement-1.

85. We have, $\left(x + \frac{1}{x} + 1\right)^n = 1 + {}^nC_1\left(x + \frac{1}{x}\right) + {}^nC_2\left(x + \frac{1}{x}\right)^2 + \ldots + {}^nC_n\left(x + \frac{1}{x}\right)^n$

$\therefore$ Number of terms $= 1 + n + n = 2n + 1$

$\therefore$ Both the statements are correct but Statement-2 is not the correct explanation of Statement-1.

86. $4^{101} - 4 = 4(4^{100} - 1) = 4(16^{50} - 1)$

$$= 4(16^{25} + 1)(16^{25} - 1)$$

$$= 4 \text{ (divisible by } 16+1) \text{ (divisible by } 16-1)$$

$$= \text{divisible by } 102$$

$\therefore 4^{101} - 4$ is divisible by 102.

or if 4^{101} is divisible by 102, then remainder is 4.

$\therefore$ Statement-1 is false but Statement-2 is obviously true.

87. $\because (x^n + a^n)$ is always divisible by $(x + a)$ when n is odd natural number. Therefore, $(11^{25} + 12^{25})$ is divisible by $11 + 12 = 23$.

$\therefore$ Statement-1 is always true but Statement-2 is false. for n even natural number.

88. $T_{r+1} = {}^9C_r (ax^{1/6})^{9-r}(bx^{-1/3})^r = {}^9C_r \cdot a^{9-r} \cdot b^r \cdot x^{\frac{9-r}{6} - \frac{r}{3}}$

For independent of x, put $\frac{9-r}{6} - \frac{5}{3} = 0$

$$\Rightarrow \quad 9 - r - 2r = 0$$

$$\Rightarrow \quad r = 3$$

$$\therefore \quad T_{3+1} = {}^9C_3 \cdot a^6b^3 = 84a^6b^3$$

Now using A M $\geq$ GM

$$\Rightarrow \quad \frac{a^2 + b}{2} \geq (a^2b)^{1/2} \Rightarrow \frac{2}{2} \geq (a^2b)^{1/2} \quad [\because a^2 + b = 2]$$

$$\therefore \quad a^2b \leq 1 \Rightarrow (a^2b)^3 \leq 1^3 \Rightarrow 84a^6b^3 \leq 84$$

$$\therefore \quad T_4 \leq 84$$

Hence, both statements are true and Statement-2 is the correct explanation of Statement-1.

89. We have, $10000 = T_3 = T_{2+1} = {}^5C_2 x^{(5-2)}(x^{\log_{10} x})^2$

$$\Rightarrow \quad 100000 = x^3 \cdot x^{2\log_{10} x} = x^{3 + 2\log_{10} x}$$

$$\Rightarrow 3 + 2\log_{10} x = \log_x 100000 = 5\log_x 10 = \frac{5}{\log_{10} x}$$

$$\Rightarrow 2(\log_{10} x)^2 + 3\log_{10} x - 5 = 0$$

Put $\log_{10} x = y$, we get

$$2y^2 + 3y - 5 = 0 \Rightarrow y = -\frac{5}{2} \text{ or } 1$$

$$\therefore \quad \log_{10} x = -\frac{5}{2} \text{ or } 1$$

$$\Rightarrow \quad x = 10 \text{ or } 10^{-5/2}$$

90. We have, $\frac{18^3 + 7^3 + 3 \cdot 18 \cdot 7 \cdot 25}{\left[\begin{array}{l}3^6 + 6 \cdot 243 \cdot 2 + 15 \cdot 81 \cdot 4 + 20 \cdot 27 \cdot 8 \\ + 15 \cdot 9 \cdot 16 + 6 \cdot 3 \cdot 32 + 64\end{array}\right]}$

$$= \frac{(18+7)^3}{(3+2)^6} = \frac{(25)^3}{(5)^6} = \frac{(25)^3}{(25)^3} = 1$$

91. We have, $\left(\frac{a+1}{a^{2/3} - a^{1/3} + 1} - \frac{a-1}{a - a^{1/2}}\right)^{10}$

$$= \left[\frac{(a^{1/3})^3 + 1^3}{a^{2/3} - a^{1/3} + 1} - \frac{(a^{1/2})^2 - 1^2}{a^{1/2}(a^{1/2} - 1)}\right]^{10}$$

$$= \left((a^{1/3}+1) - \frac{a^{1/2}+1}{a^{1/2}}\right)^{10} = (a^{1/3} - a^{-1/2})^{10}$$

Now, $\quad T_{r+1} = {}^{10}C_r (a^{1/3})^{10-r} (-a^{-1/2})^r \qquad$ ...(i)

$$= {}^{10}C_r a^{\frac{10-r}{3} - \frac{r}{2}} (-1)^r$$

It will be independent of a, if

$$\frac{10-r}{3} - \frac{r}{2} = 0 \Rightarrow 20 - 2r - 3r = 0$$

$$\Rightarrow \qquad r = 4$$

Putting $r = 4$ in Eq. (i), we get

$$T_5 = {}^{10}C_4 (-1)^4 = {}^{10}C_4 = 210$$

92. The general term in $(x^a + x^{-b})^n$ is

$$T_{r+1} = {}^nC_r (x^a)^{n-r} (x^{-b})^r = {}^nC_r x^{a(n-r)-br} = {}^nC_r x^{an-(a+b)r}$$

For independent of x, we must have $an - (a+b) = r = 0$

$$\Rightarrow \qquad r = \frac{an}{a+b} \Rightarrow an = (a+b)r, r \in N$$

$\Rightarrow$ an is multiple of $(a+b)$.

93. Let n be the index of power in $(1+x)$. Then, ${}^nC_r = a \qquad$ ...(i)

$${}^nC_{r+1} = b \qquad \text{...(ii)}$$

and $\qquad {}^nC_{r+2} = c \qquad$ ...(iii)

From Eqs. (i) and (ii), we get

$$\frac{{}^nC_r}{{}^nC_{r+1}} = \frac{a}{b}$$

$$\Rightarrow \qquad \frac{r+1}{n-r} = \frac{a}{b} \Rightarrow r = \frac{an-b}{a+b} \qquad \text{...(iv)}$$

From Eqs. (ii) and (iii), we get

$$\frac{{}^nC_{r+1}}{{}^nC_{r+2}} = \frac{b}{c}$$

$$\Rightarrow \qquad \frac{r+2}{n-r-1} = \frac{b}{c} \Rightarrow r = \frac{bn-b-2c}{b+c} \qquad \text{...(v)}$$

From Eqs. (iv) and (v), we get

$$\frac{bn-b-2c}{b+c} = \frac{an-b}{a+b}$$

$$\Rightarrow \qquad (b^2 - ac)n = 2ac + b(a+c)$$

$$\Rightarrow \qquad n = \frac{2ac + b(a+c)}{(b^2 - ac)}$$

94. Given expansion is $\left[\sqrt[3]{2} + \frac{1}{\sqrt[3]{3}}\right]^n$.

$\therefore$ 7th term from the beginning

$$= {}^nC_6 (2)^{\frac{n-6}{3}} \cdot (3^{-1/3})^6 = {}^nC_6 2^{\frac{n-6}{3}} \cdot 3^{-2}$$

$\therefore$ Again, 7th term from end in $\left[\sqrt[3]{2} + \frac{1}{\sqrt[3]{3}}\right]^n$

$= $ 7th term from beginning in $\left[\frac{1}{\sqrt[3]{3}} + \sqrt[3]{3}\right]^n$

$$= {}^nC_6 (3^{-1/3})^{n-6} (2)^2 = {}^nC_6 3^{\frac{6-n}{3}} \cdot 4$$

According to the question, we have

$$\frac{{}^nC_6 \cdot 2^{\frac{n-6}{3}} \cdot 3^{-2}}{{}^nC_6 \cdot 4 \cdot 3^{\frac{6-n}{3}}} = \frac{1}{6} \Rightarrow 2^{\frac{n-12}{3}} \cdot 3^{\frac{n-12}{3}} = \frac{1}{6}$$

$$\Rightarrow \qquad (6)^{\frac{n-12}{3}} = 6^{-1} \Rightarrow \frac{n-12}{2} = -1, n = 9$$

95. We know that, $(1+x)^n (x+1)^n$

$$= [{}^nC_0 + {}^nC_1 x + {}^nC_2 x^2 + \ldots + {}^nC_n x^n]$$
$$\times [{}^nC_0 x^n + {}^nC_1 x^{n-1} + {}^nC_2 x^{n-2} + \ldots + {}^nC_n]$$

Equating coefficient of x^{n+1} on both sides, we get

$${}^{2n}C_{n+1} = [{}^nC_0 {}^nC_1 + {}^nC_1 {}^nC_2 + \ldots + {}^nC_{n-1} {}^nC_n]$$

$$\therefore \qquad S_n = {}^{2n}C_{n+1}$$

But $\quad \frac{S_{n+1}}{S_n} = \frac{15}{4} \Rightarrow \frac{{}^{2n+2}C_{n+2}}{{}^{2n}C_{n+1}} = \frac{15}{4}$

$$\Rightarrow \qquad \frac{(2n+2)}{(n+2)} \cdot \frac{{}^{2n+1}C_{n+1}}{{}^{2n}C_{n+1}} = \frac{15}{4}$$

$$\Rightarrow \qquad \frac{2(n+1)}{(n+2)} \cdot \frac{{}^{2n+1}C_n}{{}^{2n}C_{n-1}} = \frac{15}{4}$$

$$\Rightarrow \qquad \frac{2(n+1)}{(n+2)} \cdot \frac{2n+1}{n} = \frac{15}{4}$$

$$\Rightarrow \qquad 8(2n^2 + 3n + 1) = 15n^2 + 30n$$

$$\Rightarrow \qquad n^2 - 6n + 8 = 0$$

$$\therefore \qquad n = 4, 2$$

96. $\frac{C_1}{C_0} + 2 \cdot \frac{C_2}{C_1} + 3 \cdot \frac{C_3}{C_2} + \ldots + n \cdot \frac{C_n}{C_{n-1}}$

$$= \frac{n}{1} + 2 \cdot \frac{n(n-1)}{2n} + 3 \cdot \frac{n(n-1)(n-2)}{3!} \times \frac{2!}{n(n-1)} + \ldots + n \cdot \frac{1}{n}$$

$$= n + (n-1) + (n-2) + \ldots + 1 \frac{n(n+1)}{2}$$

97. We have, $\left[\sqrt[3]{\left(\frac{a}{\sqrt{b}}\right)} + \sqrt{\left(\frac{b}{\sqrt[3]{a}}\right)}\right]^{21} = [ab^{-1/2}]^{1/3} + (ba^{-1/3})^{1/2}]^{21}$

Let T_{r+1} contain a and b to one and the same power.

$$\therefore \qquad T_{r+1} = {}^{21}C_r (ab^{-1/2})^{\frac{21-r}{3}} (ba^{-1/3})^{r/2}$$

$$= {}^{21}C_r \cdot a^{\frac{21-r}{3} - \frac{r}{6}} \cdot b^{\frac{r}{2} - \frac{21-r}{6}}$$

$$\because \quad \frac{21-r}{3} - \frac{r}{6} = \frac{r}{2} - \frac{21-r}{6} \quad \therefore \quad \frac{21-r}{2} = \frac{2r}{3}$$

$$\Rightarrow \qquad 63 - 3r = 4r \Rightarrow 63 = 7r \Rightarrow r = 9$$

$\therefore$ Required term $= r + 1 = 10$

98. Given series is a GP.

$$\therefore S = (x+3)^{n-1} \frac{\left[1 - \left(\frac{x+2}{x+3}\right)^n\right]}{1 - \frac{x+2}{x+3}} = (x+3)^n \frac{[(x+3)^n - (x+2)^n]}{(x+3)^n}$$

$$= (x+3)^n - (x+2)^n = (3+x)^n - (2+x)^n$$

$\therefore$ Coefficient of x^r in $S = {}^nC_r\, 3^{n-r} - {}^nC_r 2^{n-r}$

$$= {}^nC_r\,(3^{n-r} - 2^{n-r})$$

99. Let $(2+\sqrt{5})^p$ or $(\sqrt{5}+2)^p = I + f$ ...(i)

$$0 \le f < 1 \quad ...(ii)$$

$$(\sqrt{5}-2)^p = f' \quad ...(iii)$$

and $\quad 0 < f' < 1$ ...(iv)

On subtracting Eq. (iii) from Eq. (i), we get

$$I + f - f' = (\sqrt{5}+2)^p - (\sqrt{5}-2)^p$$

$$= 2\{{}^pC_1(\sqrt{5})^{p-1}\cdot 2^1 + {}^pC_3(\sqrt{5})^{p-3}\cdot 2^3 + \ldots + {}^pC_p\,(\sqrt{5})^0 2^p\}$$

[$\because$ integer value of $f - f' = 0$]

$\therefore\quad [(\sqrt{5}+2)^p] + 0 - 2^{p+1}$

$$= 2\,\{{}^pC_1\,(\sqrt{5})^{p-1}\cdot 2 + {}^pC_3\,(\sqrt{5})^{p-3}\cdot 2^3 + \ldots + {}^pC_{p-2}(\sqrt{5})^2\cdot 2^{p-2}\}$$

$= p\lambda = p$ (integer)

$\therefore\quad [(\sqrt{5}+2)^p] - 2^{p+1}$ is divisible by P.

100. Let $\quad (\sqrt{3}+1)^{2n} = I + f,\ 0 \le f < 1$

and $\quad f' = (\sqrt{3}-1)^{2n}$

$\therefore I + f + f' = (\sqrt{3}+1)^{2n} + (\sqrt{3}-1)^{2n}$

$$= [(\sqrt{3}+1)^2]^n + [(\sqrt{3}-1)^2]^n$$

$$= (4+2\sqrt{3})^n + (4-2\sqrt{3})^n$$

$$= 2^n\,(2+\sqrt{3})^n + 2^n\,(2-\sqrt{3})^n$$

$$= 2^n\cdot 2\{{}^nC_0 2^n + {}^nC_2(2^{n-2})\,(3) + {}^nC_4(2^{n-4})\,(3^2) + \ldots\}$$

$\therefore\quad I + 1 = 2^{n+1},\ k \in I$ $\quad$ [$\because f + f' = 1$]

or $\quad [(\{(\sqrt{3}+1)^{2n}\})] = 2^{n+1}k$

Hence, $[(\{(\sqrt{3}+1)^{2n}\})],\ n \in N$ is divisible by 2^{n+1}.

101. ${}^{11}C_1\cdot x^{10} - {}^{11}C_3\cdot x^8 + {}^{11}C_5\cdot x^6 - {}^{11}C_7 x^4 + {}^{11}C_9\, x^2 - {}^{11}C_{11} = 0$

Now, $\quad (1+ix)^{11} = {}^{11}C_0 + {}^{11}C_1 ix + {}^{11}C_2\,(ix)^2 + {}^{11}C_3\,(ix)^3 + {}^{11}C_4\,(ix)^4 + {}^{11}C_5\,(ix)^5 + {}^{11}C_6\,(ix)^6 + {}^{11}C_7\,(ix)^7 + \ldots + {}^{11}C_{11}\,(ix)^{11}$

$\Rightarrow\quad (1+ix)^{11} = ({}^{11}C_0 - {}^{11}C_2\, x^2 + {}^{11}C_4\, x^4 - {}^{11}C_6\, x^6 + {}^{11}C_8\, x^8 + {}^{11}C_{10}\, x^{10}) + i\,({}^{11}C_1\, x - {}^{11}C_3\, x^3 + {}^{11}C_5\, x^5 - {}^{11}C_7\, x^7 + {}^{11}C_9\, x^9 - {}^{11}C_{11}\, x^{11})$

Comparing real part on both sides, we get

$$(1+ix)^{11} = ({}^{11}C_{11} - {}^{11}C_9\, x^2 + {}^{11}C_7\, x^4 - {}^{11}C_5\, x^6 + {}^{11}C_3\, x^8 - {}^{11}C_1\, x^{10}) \quad [\because {}^nC_r = {}^nC_{n-r}]$$

$\Rightarrow \text{Re}\,\{(1+ix)^{11}\} = -({}^{11}C_1\, x^{10} - {}^{11}C_3\, x^8 + {}^{11}C_5\, x^6 - {}^{11}C_7\, x^4 + {}^{11}C_9\, x^2 - {}^{11}C_{11})$

$\Rightarrow\quad {}^{11}C_1 x^{10} - {}^{11}C_3\, x^8 + {}^{11}C_5\, x^6 - {}^{11}C_7\, x^4 + {}^{11}C_9\, x^2 - {}^{11}C_{11}$

$$= -\,\text{Re}\,\{1+ix\}^{11}\}$$

Let $\quad x = \cot\theta = -\text{Re}\{1 - i\cot\theta\}''$

$$= -\,\text{Re}\left[\left\{\frac{\sin\theta + i\cos\theta}{\sin\theta}\right\}^{11}\right] = -\,\text{Re}\left\{\frac{(i)^{11}\,(\cos\theta - i\sin\theta)}{\sin\theta}\right\}^{11}$$

$$= -\text{Re}\left\{\frac{-\,i\,(\cos 11\theta - i\sin 11\theta)}{\sin^{11}\theta}\right\} = \frac{\sin 11\theta}{\sin^{11}\theta} = 0 \quad \text{[given]}$$

$$\theta \ne 0$$

$\therefore\quad \sin 11\theta = r\pi$

or $\quad \theta = \dfrac{r\pi}{11},\ r = \pm 1, \pm 2, \pm 3, \pm 4, \pm 5$

$\therefore\quad x = \cot\theta = \cot\left(\dfrac{r\pi}{11}\right)$

$$r = \pm 1, \pm 2, \ldots, \pm 5$$

102. Since, $\quad g(x) = f(1+x)$

$$g(x) = \sum_{r=0}^{200} \alpha_r x^r \text{ and } f(x) = \sum_{r=0}^{200} \beta_r x^r$$

$$\therefore\quad \sum_{r=0}^{200} \alpha_r\, x^r = \sum_{r=0}^{200} \beta_r\,(1+x)^r$$

Now, $\quad \alpha_0 + \alpha_1 x + \alpha_2 x^2 + \ldots + \alpha_{200}\, x^{200}$

$$= \beta_0 + \beta_1\,(1+x) + \beta_2\,(1+x)^2 + \ldots + \beta_{100}\,(1+x)^{100} + \beta_{101}\,(1+x)^{101} + \ldots + \beta_{200}\,(1+x)^{200}$$

$\Rightarrow\quad \alpha_0 + \alpha_1 x + \alpha_2 x^2 + \ldots + \alpha_{200}\, x^{200}$

$$= \beta_0 + \beta_1\,(1+x) + \beta_2\,(1+x)^2 + \ldots + (1+x)^{100} + (1+x)^{101} + \ldots + (1+x)^{200} \quad [\because \beta_{100} = \beta_{101} = \ldots = \beta_{200} = 1]$$

Equating the coefficient of x^{100}, we get

$$\alpha_{100} = {}^{100}C_{100} + {}^{101}C_{100} + {}^{102}C_{100} + \ldots + {}^{200}C_{100}$$

$$= {}^{101}C_{101} + {}^{101}C_{100} + {}^{102}C_{100} + \ldots + {}^{200}C_{100}$$

$$= {}^{102}C_{101} + {}^{102}C_{100} + \ldots + {}^{200}C_{100}$$

$$\vdots \qquad \vdots \qquad \vdots$$

$$= {}^{200}C_{101} + {}^{200}C_{100} = {}^{201}C_{101} \quad ...(i)$$

Again, greatest coefficient in the expansion of $(1+x)^{201}$

= Coefficient of middle term

= Coefficient of T_{101} or coefficient of T_{102}

$$= {}^{201}C_{100} \text{ or } {}^{201}C_{101} = {}^{201}C_{100} \quad ...(ii)$$

From Eqs. (i) and (ii), we get

The greatest coefficient in the expansion of $(1+x)^{201}$.

103. $P = \sum\sum_{0 \le i < j \le n} (i+j)\,(C_i + C_j + C_iC_j)$ ...(i)

Replacing i by $n-i$ and j by $n-j$ in Eq. (i), we get

$$P = \sum\sum_{0 \le i < j \le n} (n-i+n-j)\,(C_{n-i} + C_{n-j} + C_{n-i}\,C_{n-j})$$

$$= \sum\sum_{0 \le i < j \le n} (2n-i-j)\,(C_i + C_j + C_iC_j)\,[\because {}^nC_r = {}^nC_{n-r}] \quad ...(ii)$$

On adding Eqs. (i) and (ii), then we get

$$2P = 2n \sum\sum_{0 \le i < j \le n} (C_i + C_j + C_iC_j)$$

$$\therefore\quad P = n \sum\sum_{0 \le i < j \le n} (C_i + C_j) + n \sum\sum_{0 \le i < j \le n} C_iC_j$$

$$= n \cdot n\,(C_0 + C_1 + C_2 + \ldots + C_n) + \frac{n}{2}(2^{2n} - {}^{2n}C_n)$$

$$= n^2 \cdot 2^n + n \cdot 2^{2n-1} - \frac{n}{2} \cdot {}^{2n}C_n$$

$$= n^2 \cdot 2^n + n\left\{2^{2n-1} - \frac{2n!}{2(n!)^2}\right\}$$

104. $\sum_{0 \le i \ne j \le 10}\sum {}^{21}C_i \cdot {}^{21}C_j$

$$= \frac{1}{2}\left[\sum_{i=0}^{10}\sum_{j=0}^{10} {}^{21}C_i\, {}^{21}C_j\right] - \sum_{i=0}^{10} ({}^{21}C_i)^2$$

$$= \frac{1}{2}\left[\sum_{i=0}^{10} {}^{21}C_i 2^{21-r}\right] - \frac{1}{2}\sum_{i=0}^{10} ({}^{21}C_i)^2$$

$$= \frac{2^{20} \cdot 2^{20}}{2} - \frac{{}^{42}C_{21}}{2 \times 2} = \frac{1}{2}\left[2^{40} - \frac{(42)!}{2\,(21!)^2}\right]$$

105. (i) We have, $(1 + x + x^2 + x^3)^{11} = (1+x)^{11}(1+x^2)^{11}$

$$= (1 + {}^{11}C_1 x + {}^{11}C_2 x^2 + {}^{11}C_3 x^3 + {}^{11}C_4 x^4 + \ldots) \times (1 + {}^{11}C_1 x^2 + {}^{11}C_2 x^4 + \ldots)$$

$\therefore$ Coefficient of $x^4 = {}^{11}C_2 + {}^{11}C_2 \times {}^{11}C_1 + {}^{11}C_4$

$$= 55 + 605 + 330 = 990$$

(ii) $[(2 - x) + 3x^2]^6$

$$= {}^6C_0(2-x)^6 + {}^6C_1(2-x)^5(3x)^2 + {}^6C_2(2-x)^4(3x^2)^2 + \ldots$$

$$= {}^6C_0\,[{}^6C_4(2)^2] + {}^6C_1 \times 3\,[{}^5C_2(2)^3] + {}^6C_2 \times 9\,[{}^4C_0(2)^4]$$

[equating coefficient of x^4]

$$= 60 + 1440 + 2160 = 3660$$

106. LHS $= \dfrac{1}{{}^{2n+1}C_r} + \dfrac{1}{{}^{2n+1}C_{r+1}}$

$$= \frac{(2n+1-r)!\,r!}{(2n+1)!} + \frac{(2n-r)!\,(r+1)!}{(2n+1)!}$$

$$= (2n-r)!\,(r)!\left[\frac{(2n+1-r)+r+1}{(2n+1)!}\right]$$

$$= \frac{(2n-r)!\,(r)!\,(2n+2)}{(2n+1)\,(2n)!} = \frac{2n+2}{2n+1} \cdot \frac{1}{{}^{2n}C_r}$$

Now, $$\sum_{r=1}^{2n-1} \frac{(-1)^{r-1} \cdot r}{{}^{2n}C_r} = \sum_{r=1}^{2n-1} (-1)^{r-1}\left(\frac{2n+1}{2n+2}\right)\left[\frac{1}{{}^{2n+1}C_r} + \frac{1}{{}^{2n+1}C_{r+1}}\right] \times r$$

$$= \left(\frac{2n+1}{2n+2}\right)\sum_{r=1}^{2n-1} (-1)^{r-1}\left(\frac{1}{{}^{2n+1}C_r} + \frac{1}{{}^{2n+1}C_{r+1}}\right) \times r$$

$$= \left(\frac{2n+1}{2n+2}\right)\left[\left(\frac{1}{{}^{2n+1}C_1} + \frac{1}{{}^{2n+1}C_2}\right) - 2\left(\frac{1}{{}^{2n+1}C_2} + \frac{1}{{}^{2n+1}C_3}\right) + 3\left(\frac{1}{{}^{2n+1}C_3} + \frac{1}{{}^{2n+1}C_4}\right) - 4\left(\frac{1}{{}^{2n+1}C_4} + \frac{1}{{}^{2n+1}C_5}\right) + \ldots + (2n-1)\left(\frac{1}{{}^{2n+1}C_{2n-1}} + \frac{1}{{}^{2n+1}C_{2n}}\right)\right]$$

$$= \left(\frac{2n+1}{2n+2}\right)\left[\frac{1}{{}^{2n+1}C_1} - \frac{1}{{}^{2n+1}C_2} + \frac{1}{{}^{2n+1}C_3} - \frac{1}{{}^{2n+1}C_4} + \ldots + \frac{(2n-1)}{{}^{2n+1}C_{2n}}\right]$$

$$= \left(\frac{2n+1}{2n+2}\right)\left[\frac{1}{{}^{2n+1}C_1} - \frac{1}{{}^{2n+1}C_2} + \frac{1}{{}^{2n+1}C_3} - \frac{1}{{}^{2n+1}C_4} + \ldots - \frac{1}{{}^{2n+1}C_{2n}} + \frac{2n}{{}^{2n+1}C_{2n}}\right]$$

$$= \left(\frac{2n+1}{2n+2}\right)\left[\left(\frac{1}{{}^{2n+1}C_1} - \frac{1}{{}^{2n+1}C_{2n}}\right) - \left(\frac{1}{{}^{2n+1}C_2} - \frac{1}{{}^{2n+1}C_{2n-1}}\right) + \ldots + \frac{2n}{{}^{2n+1}C_{2n}}\right]$$

$$= \left(\frac{2n+1}{2n+2}\right)\left[0 + \frac{2n}{{}^{2n+1}C_{2n}}\right] = \left(\frac{2n+1}{2n+2}\right)\left(\frac{2n}{2n+1}\right)$$

$$= \frac{2n}{2n+2} = \frac{n}{n+1}$$

107. Given, $(1 + x + x^2)^n = a_0 + a_1 x + a_2 x^2 + \ldots + a_{r-2} x^{r-2} + a_{r-1} x^{r-1} + a_r x^r + \ldots + a_{2n} x^{2n}$ ...(i)

and $(1-x)^n = {}^nC_0 - {}^nC_1 x + {}^nC_2 x^2 - \ldots + (-1)^r\, {}^nC_r x^r + \ldots + (-1)^n\, {}^nC_n$ ...(ii)

On multiplying Eqs. (i) and (ii) and equating coefficient of x^r on both sides, we get

Coefficient of x^r in $(1 - x^3)^n$

$$= {}^nC_0\, a_r - {}^nC_1 a_{r-1} + {}^nC_2 a_{r-2} - \ldots + (-1)^r\, {}^nC_r a_r$$

Since, r is not a multiple of 3, therefore the expression $(1 - x^3)^n$ does not contain x^r in any term.

$\therefore$ Coefficient of x^r in $(1 - x^3)^n = 0$

Hence, $a_r - {}^nC_1\, a_{r-1} + {}^nC_2\, a_{r-2} - \ldots + (-1)^r\, {}^nC_r\, a_0 = 0$

108. Given, $(1 + z^2 + z^4)^8 = C_0 + C_1 z^2 + C_2 z^4 + \ldots + C_{16} z^{32}$

(i) Put $z = i$, we get

$$(1 - 1 + 1)^8 = C_0 - C_1 + C_2 - C_3 + \ldots + C_{16}$$

$$C_0 - C_1 + C_2 - C_3 + \ldots + C_{16} = 1$$

(ii) Put $z = \omega$, we get

$$(1 + \omega^2 + \omega^4)^8 = C_0 + C_1\omega^2 + C_2\omega^4 + C_3\omega^6 + \ldots + C_{16}\omega^{32}$$

$$\Rightarrow (1 + \omega^2 + \omega)^8 = C_0 + C_1\omega^2 + C_2\omega + C_3 + C_4\omega^2 + C_5\omega + \ldots + C_{16}\omega^2$$

$$\Rightarrow 0 = (C_0 + C_3 + C_6 + \ldots + C_{15}) + (C_2 + C_5 + \ldots + C_{14})\,\omega + (C_1 + C_4 + \ldots + C_{16})\,\omega^2$$

109. Given, $f(x) = g(x+1)$

$$\therefore a_0 x^0 + a_1 x + a_2 x^2 + \ldots + a_{2n} x^{2n}$$

$$= b_0 + b_1(x+1) + b_2(x+1)^2 + \ldots + b_{n-1}(x+1)^{n-1} + (x+1)^n + (x+1)^{n+1} + (x+1)^{n+2} + \ldots + (x+1)^{2n}$$

Equating coefficient of x^n on both sides, we get

$$a_n = {}^nC_n + {}^{n+1}C_n + \ldots + {}^{2n}C_n$$

$= {}^{n+1}C_{n+1} + {}^{n+1}C_n + \ldots + {}^{2n}C_n \quad [\because {}^nC_n = {}^{n+1}C_{n+1}]$

$= {}^{n+2}C_{n+1} + \ldots + {}^{2n}C_n = {}^{2n}C_{n+1} + {}^{2n}C_n$

$[\because {}^nC_r + {}^nC_{r-1} = {}^{n+1}C_r]$

$= {}^{2n+1}C_{n+1}$

110. Let $(1 + x + x^2)^n = a_0 + a_1 x + a_2 x^2 + \ldots + a_{2n} x^{2n}$ ...(i)

Replacing x by $\left(-\frac{1}{x}\right)$, we get

$$\left(1 - \frac{1}{x} + \frac{1}{x^2}\right)^n = a_0 - \frac{a_1}{x} + \frac{a_2}{x^2} - \ldots + \frac{a_{2n}}{x^{2n}}$$

$\Rightarrow (1 - x + x^2)^n = a_0 x^{2n} - a_1 x^{2n-1} + a_2 x^{2n-2} - \ldots + a_{2n} x^{2n}$ ...(ii)

(i) Multiplying Eqs. (i) and (ii) and equating the coefficient of x^{2n+1}, then we get

Coefficient of x^{2n+1} in $(1 + x^2 + x^4)^n$

$= a_0 a_1 - a_1 a_2 + a_2 a_3 - \ldots$

In RHS, put $x^2 = y$, we get

$a_0 a_1 - a_1 a_2 + a_2 a_3 - \ldots = 0$ (only even powers contains)

(ii) Multiplying Eqs. (i) and (ii) and equating the coefficient of x^{2n+2}

Coefficient of x^{2n+2} in $(1 + x^2 + x^4)^n$

= Coefficient of y^{n+1} in $(1 + y + y^2)^n$

$= a_0 a_2 - a_1 a_3 + a_2 a_4 - \ldots + a_{2n-2} \cdot a_{2n}$

$[\because$ put $x^2 = y]$

$= a_{n+1}$

(iii) Put $x = 1, \omega$ and ω^2 in Eq. (i), we get

$3^n = a_0 + a_1 + a_2 + a_3 + \ldots + a_{2n}$ ...(iii)

$\Rightarrow (1 + \omega + \omega^2)^n = a_0 + a_1 \omega + a_2 \omega^2 + a_3 \omega^3 + \ldots + a_{2n} \omega^{2n}$

$\Rightarrow \quad 0 = a_0 + a_1 \omega + a_2 \omega^2 + a_3 + \ldots$ ...(iv)

and $(1 + \omega^2 + \omega^4)^n = a_0 + a_1 \omega^2 + a_2 \omega^4 + a_3 \omega^6 + \ldots$

$\Rightarrow \quad 0 = a_0 + a_1 \omega^2 + a_2 \omega + a_3 + \ldots$ ...(v)

on adding Eqs. (iii), (iv) and (v), we get

$3^n = 3a_0 + a_1 (1 + \omega + \omega^2)$

$+ a_2 (1 + \omega^2 + \omega) + 3a_3 + \ldots +$

$\Rightarrow \quad 3^n = 3(a_0 + a_3 + a_6 + \ldots) \Rightarrow a_0 + a_3 + a_6 + \ldots = 3^{n-1}$

On multiplying Eqs. (iv) and (v) by ω^2 and ω, respectively and then adding Eqs. (iii), (iv) and (v), we get

$3^n = a_0 (1 + \omega^2 + \omega) + a_1 (1 + \omega^3 + \omega^3)$

$+ a_2 (1 + \omega^4 + \omega^3) + a_3 (1 + \omega + \omega^2) + \ldots$

$= 3(a_1 + a_4 + \ldots)$

$\Rightarrow a_1 + a_4 + \ldots = 3^{n-1}$

Again, multiplying Eq. (iv) by ω and Eq. (v) by ω^2, respectively and then adding Eqs. (iii), (iv) and (v), we get

$3^n = 3(a_2 + a_5 + a_8 + \ldots)$

$\Rightarrow \quad a_2 + a_5 + a_8 + \ldots = 3^{n-1}$

Hence, $a_0 + a_3 + a_6 + \ldots = a_1 + a_4 + a_7 + \ldots$

$= a_2 + a_5 + a_8 + \ldots = 3^{n-1}$

111. LHS $= (n-1)^2 C_1 + (n-3)^2 C_3 + (n-5)^2 C_5 + \ldots$

$= n^2 (C_1 + C_3 + C_5 + \ldots) - 2n (C_1 + 3C_3 + 5C_5 + \ldots)$

$+ (1^2 C_1 + 3^2 C_3 + 5^2 C_5 + \ldots)$

$= n^2 (2^{n-1}) (-2n)$

$\left(\frac{n}{1} \cdot {}^{n-1}C_0 + \frac{n}{3} \cdot 3 \cdot {}^{n-1}C_2 + \frac{n}{5} \cdot 5 \cdot {}^{n-1}C_4 + \ldots\right)$

$+ \left(1^2 \cdot \frac{n}{1} \cdot {}^{n-1}C_0 + 3^2 \cdot \frac{n}{3} \cdot {}^{n-1}C_2 + 5^2 \cdot \frac{n}{5} \cdot {}^{n-1}C_4 + \ldots\right)$

$= n^2 \cdot 2^{n-1} - 2n^2 ({}^{n-1}C_0 + {}^{n-1}C_2 + {}^{n-1}C_4 + \ldots)$

$+ n (1 \cdot {}^{n-1}C_0 + 3 \cdot {}^{n-1}C_2 + 5 \cdot {}^{n-1}C_4 + \ldots)$

$= n^2 \cdot 2^{n-1} - 2n^2 \cdot 2^{n-2}$

$+ n[{}^{n-1}C_0 + (2+1) \cdot {}^{n-1}C_2 + (4+1) \cdot {}^{n-1}C_4 + \ldots]$

$= n^2 \cdot 2^{n-2}(2-2) + n[({}^{n-1}C_0 + {}^{n-1}C_2 + {}^{n-1}C_4 + \ldots)]$

$+ (2 \cdot {}^{n-1}C_2 + 4 \cdot {}^{n-1}C_4 + \ldots)]$

$= 0 + n\,[2^{n-2} + (n-1)\,\{{}^{n-2}C_1 + {}^{n-2}C_3 + \ldots\}]$

$= n\,[2^{n-2} + (n-1) \cdot 2^{n-3}] = n \cdot 2^{n-3}\,(2 + n - 1)$

$= n(n+1)\,2^{n-3} =$ RHS

112. $(1 - x^3)^n = C_0 - C_1 x^3 + C_2 x^6 - C_3 x^9 + \ldots + (-1)^n C_n x^{3n}$

Then, $\int_0^1 (1 - x^3)^n \, dx$

$$= \int_0^1 (C_0 - C_1 x^3 + C_2 x^6 - \ldots + (-1)^n C_n (x^{3n})\, dx$$

$$= \left[\frac{C_0 x}{1} - \frac{C_1 x^4}{4} + \frac{C_2 x^7}{7} - \ldots + (-1)^n \frac{C_n x^{3n+1}}{3n+1}\right]_0^1$$

$$= \frac{C_0}{1} - \frac{C_1}{4} + \frac{C_2}{7} - \ldots + (-1)^n \frac{C_n}{3n+1}$$

Let $I_n = \int_0^1 (1 - x^3)^n \cdot 1 \, dx$

$= [(1 - x^3)^n \cdot x]_0^1 - \int_0^1 n (1 - x^3)^{n-1} \cdot (-3x^2) \cdot x \, dx$

$= 0 - 3n \int_0^1 (1 - x^3)^{n-1} (1 - x^3 - 1) \, dx$

$= -3n (I_n - I_{n-1})$

$\Rightarrow \quad I_n = \frac{3n}{(3n+1)} I_{n-1}; \quad I_{n-1} = \frac{3(n-1)}{(3n-2)} I_{n-2}$

$I_{n-2} = \frac{3(n-2)}{(3n-5)} I_{n-3}$

$\vdots \quad \vdots \quad \vdots$

$I_3 = \frac{3 \cdot 3}{10} I_2; \quad I_2 = \frac{3 \cdot 2}{7} I_1; \quad I_1 = \frac{3 \cdot 1}{4} I_0 = \frac{3 \cdot 1}{3} (1)$

$$\therefore \quad I_n = \frac{(3 \cdot 1)(3 \cdot 2)(3 \cdot 3) \ldots (3 \cdot n)}{1 \cdot 4 \cdot 7 \cdot 10 \ldots (3n+1)} \cdot 1 = \frac{3^n \cdot n!}{1 \cdot 4 \cdot 7 \cdot 10 \ldots (3n+1)}$$

Hence, $\frac{C_0}{1} - \frac{C_1}{4} + \frac{C_2}{7} - \ldots + (-1)^n \frac{C_n}{3n+1} = \frac{3^n \cdot n!}{1 \cdot 4 \cdot 7 \ldots (3n+1)}$

113. $(1-x)^{30} = {}^{30}C_0 x^0 - {}^{30}C_1 x^1 + {}^{30}C_2 x^2 + \dots$ ...(i)

$(x+1)^{30} = {}^{30}C_0 x^{30} + {}^{30}C_1 x^{29} + {}^{30}C_2 x^{28} + \dots + {}^{30}C_{10} x^{20} + \dots + {}^{30}C_{30} x^0$ ...(ii)

On multiplying Eqs. (i) and (ii) and equating the coefficient of x^{20} on both sides, we get

required sum = coefficient of x^{20} in $(1-x^2)^{30} = {}^{30}C_{10}$

114. Coefficients of p th, $(p+1)$ th and $(p+2)$ th terms in expansion of $(1+x)^n$ are ${}^nC_{p-1}, {}^nC_p, {}^nC_{p+1}$.

Then, $2\cdot{}^nC_p = {}^nC_{p-1} + {}^nC_{p+1}$

$$2 = \frac{{}^nC_{p-1}}{{}^nC_p} + \frac{{}^nC_{p+1}}{{}^nC_p}$$

$$2 = \frac{p}{n-p+1} + \frac{n-p}{p+1}$$

$\Rightarrow \quad 2(n-p+1)(p+1) = p(p+1) + (n-p)(n-p+1)$

$\Rightarrow n^2 - n(4p+1) + 4p^2 - 2 = 0$

115. In the expansion of $\left(ax^2 + \frac{1}{bx}\right)^{11}$, the general term is

$$T_{r+1} = {}^{11}C_r (ax^2)^{11-r}\left(\frac{1}{bx}\right)^r = {}^{11}C_r a^{11-r}\frac{1}{b^r}x^{22-3r}$$

For x^7, we must have $22 - 3r = 7 \Rightarrow r = 5$ and then the

coefficient of $x^7 = {}^{11}C_5 \cdot a^{11-5}\frac{1}{b^5} = {}^{11}C_5 \frac{a^6}{b^5}$

Similarly, in the expansion of $\left(ax - \frac{1}{bx^2}\right)^{11}$, the general term is

$$T_{r+1} = {}^{11}C_r(-1)^r \frac{a^{11-r}}{b^r}\cdot x^{11-3r}$$

For x^{-7} we must have, $11 - 3r = -7$

$\Rightarrow r = 6$ and then coefficient of x^{-7} is ${}^{11}C_6 \frac{a^5}{b^6} = {}^{11}C_5 \frac{a^5}{b^6}$

As given, $\quad {}^{11}C_5 \frac{a^6}{b^5} = {}^{11}C_5 \frac{a^5}{b^6} \Rightarrow ab = 1$

116. $\because (1-y)^m (1+y)^n = (1 - {}^mC_1 y + {}^mC_2 y^2 \dots)$

$\times (1 + {}^nC_1 y + {}^nC_2 y^2 + \dots)$

$= 1 + (n-m)y + ({}^mC_2 + {}^nC_2 - mn) + \dots$

Then $\quad a_1 = n - m = 10$ [given]...(i)

and $\quad {}^mC_2 + {}^nC_2 - mn = a_2 = 10$ (given)

$\Rightarrow \quad \frac{m(m-1)}{2} + \frac{n(n-1)}{2} - mn = 10$

$\Rightarrow \quad m^2 + n^2 - m - n - 2mn = 20$

$\Rightarrow \quad (n-m)^2 - (m+n) = 20$ $\quad [\because n - m = 10]$

or $\quad 100 - (m - n = 20$

$\therefore \quad m + n = 80$ ...(ii)

On solving Eqs. (i) and (ii), we get

$n = 45, m = 35$

Hence, $\quad (m, n) = (35, 45)$

117. $\because T_5 + T_6 = 0 \Rightarrow \frac{T_6}{T_5} = -1$

$\Rightarrow \quad \frac{{}^nC_5 (a)^{n-5}(-b)^5}{{}^nC_4 (a)^{n-4}(-b)^4} = -1 \Rightarrow \left(\frac{n-5+1}{5}\right) = \frac{a}{b}$

$\therefore \quad \frac{a}{b} = \frac{n-4}{5}$

118. ${}^{20}C_0 - {}^{20}C_1 + {}^{20}C_2 - {}^{20}C_3 + \dots$

${}^{20}C_9 + {}^{20}C_{10} - {}^{20}C_{11} + {}^{20}C_{12} - \dots + {}^{20}C_{20} = 0$

$\Rightarrow 2\{{}^{20}C_0 - {}^{20}C_1 + {}^{20}C_2 - {}^{20}C_3 + \dots - {}^{20}C_9\} + {}^{20}C_{10} = 0$

$\Rightarrow 2\{{}^{20}C_0 - {}^{20}C_1 + {}^{20}C_2 - {}^{20}C_3 + \dots + {}^{20}C_9 + {}^{20}C_{10}\} = {}^{20}C_{10}$

$\Rightarrow {}^{20}C_0 - {}^{20}C_1 + {}^{20}C_2 - {}^{20}C_3 + \dots - {}^{20}C_9 + {}^{20}C_{10} = \frac{1}{2}\,{}^{20}C_{10}$

119. $\sum_{r=0}^{n}(r+1)\,{}^nC_r = \sum_{r=0}^{n} r\cdot{}^nC_r + \sum_{r=0}^{n}{}^nC_r$

$= \sum_{r=0}^{n} r\cdot\frac{n}{r}\cdot{}^{n-1}C_{r-1} + \sum_{r=0}^{n}{}^nC_r$

$= n\sum_{r=0}^{n}{}^{n-1}C_{r-1} + \sum_{r=0}^{n}{}^nC_r$

$= n\cdot 2^{n-1} + 2^n = (n+2)\,2^{n-1}$

Statement-1 is true.

and $\sum_{r=0}^{n}(r+1)\,{}^nC_r\,x^r = \sum_{r=0}^{n} r\cdot{}^nC_r\cdot x^r + \sum_{r=0}^{n}{}^nC_r\cdot x^r$

$= \sum_{r=0}^{n} r\cdot\frac{n}{r}\cdot{}^{n-1}C_{r-1}\cdot x^r + \sum_{r=0}^{n}{}^nC_r\cdot x^r$

$= n\sum_{r=0}^{n}{}^{n-1}C_{r-1}\cdot x^r + \sum_{r=0}^{n}{}^nC_r\cdot x^r$

$= nx(1+x)^{n-1} + (1+x)^n$

On substituting $x = 1$, then we get

$\sum_{r=0}^{n}(r+1)\,{}^nC_r = n\cdot 2^{n-1} + 2^n = (n+2)\,2^{n-1}$

Hence, Statement-2 is also true and it is a correct explanation for Statement-1.

120. $8^{2n} - (62)^{2n+1} = (64)^n - (62)^{2n+1}$

$= (63+1)^n - (63-1)^{2n+1}$

$= (1+63)^n + (1-63)^{2n+1}$

$= \{1 + {}^nC_1\cdot 63 + {}^nC_2(63)^2 + \dots + {}^nC_n(63)^n\}$
$+ \{1 - {}^{2n+1}C_1(63) + {}^{2n+1}C_2(63)^2 \dots - {}^{2n+1}C_{2n+1}(62)^{2n+1}\}$

$= 2 + 63\{{}^nC_1 + {}^nC_2\cdot 63 + \dots + {}^nC_n(63)^{n-1} - {}^{2n+1}C_1$
$+ {}^{2n+1}C_2\cdot 63 \dots - {}^{2n+1}C_{2n+1}(63)^{2n}\}$

$\therefore$ Remainder is 2.

121. $\because \quad A_r = {}^{10}C_r, B_r = {}^{20}C_r$ and $C_r = {}^{30}C_r$

$\therefore \quad \sum_{r=1}^{10} A_r(B_{10}B_r - C_{10}A_r) = \sum_{r=1}^{10}{}^{10}C_r({}^{20}C_{10}\cdot{}^{20}C_r - {}^{30}C_{10}\cdot{}^{10}C_r)$

$= {}^{20}C_{10}\sum_{r=1}^{10}({}^{10}C_r)({}^{20}C_r) - {}^{30}C_{10}\sum_{r=1}^{10}({}^{10}C_r)^2$

$= {}^{20}C_{10}({}^{30}C_{10} - 1) - {}^{30}C_{10}({}^{20}C_{10} - 1) = C_{10} - B_{10}$

122. Use ${}^nC_r = \frac{n}{r}\cdot{}^{n-1}C_{r-1}$, then $S_1 = \sum_{C=1}^{10} C(C-1)\cdot{}^{10}C_C$

$= \sum_{C=1}^{10} C(C-1)\cdot\frac{10.9}{C(C-1)}\cdot{}^8C_{C-2} = 90\sum_{C=1}^{10}{}^8C_{C-2} = 90\times 2^8$

$$S_2 = \sum_{C=1}^{10} C \cdot {}^{10}C_C = \sum_{C=1}^{10} C \cdot \frac{10}{C} \cdot {}^9C_{C-1} = 10 \sum_{C=1}^{10} {}^9C_{C-1} = 10 \times 2^9$$

$$\text{and} S_3 = \sum_{C=1}^{10} C^2 \cdot {}^{10}C_C = \sum_{C=1}^{10} C^2 \cdot \frac{10}{C} \cdot {}^9C_{C-1}$$

$$= 10 \sum_{C=1}^{10} ((C-1)+1) \cdot {}^9C_{C-1}$$

$$= 10 \sum_{C=1}^{10} (9 \cdot {}^8C_{C-2} + {}^9C_{C-1}) = 10(9.2^8 + 2^9) = 55 \times 2^9$$

Both statements are true but Statement-2 is not correct Explanation for Statement-1.

123. Here, $(1 - x - x^2 + x^3)^6 = (1-x)^6 (1-x^2)^6 = (1-x^2)^6(1-x)^6$

$$= (1 - {}^6C_1 x^2 + {}^6C_2 x^4 - {}^6C_3 x^6 + \dots) \times (1 - {}^6C_1 x + {}^6C_2 x^2 - {}^6C_3 x^3 + {}^6C_4 x^4 - {}^6C_5 x^5 + {}^6C_6 x^6)$$

$\therefore$ Coefficient of x^7 in $(1 - x - x^2 + x^3)^6$

$$= {}^6C_1 \times {}^6C_5 + ({}^6C_2 \times (-{}^6C_3) + \{(-{}^6C_3) \times (-{}^6C_1)\}$$

$$= 36 - 300 + 120 = -144$$

124. $(\sqrt{3}+1)^{2n} - (\sqrt{3}-1)^{2n} = 2\{{}^{2n}C_1(\sqrt{3})^{2n-1} + {}^{2n}C_3 (\sqrt{3})^{2n-3} + \dots + {}^{2n}C_{2n-1}(\sqrt{3})\}$

$$= 2\sqrt{3}\{{}^{2n}C_1(\sqrt{3})^{2n-2} + {}^{2n}C_3(\sqrt{3})^{2n-4} + \dots + {}^{2n}C_{2n-1}\}$$

$$= 2\sqrt{3}\{{}^{2n}C_1 (3)^{n-1} + {}^{2n}C_3(3)^{n-2} + \dots {}^{2n}C_{2n-1}\}$$

$$= \sqrt{3} \times \text{even integer}$$

125. $\because \quad x + 1 = (x^{1/3})^3 + 1^3 = (x^{1/3}+1)(x^{2/3} - x^{1/3} + 1)$

$$\therefore \quad \frac{x+1}{x^{2/3} - x^{1/3} + 1} = x^{1/3} + 1$$

and $\quad x - 1 = (x^{1/2})^2 - 1^2 = (x^{1/2}+1)(x^{1/2}-1)$

Now, $\dfrac{x-1}{x - x^{1/2}} = \dfrac{(x-1)}{x^{1/2}(x^{1/2}-1)} = \dfrac{x^{1/2}+1}{x^{1/2}} = 1 + x^{-1/2}$,

then $\left(\dfrac{x+1}{x^{2/3} - x^{1/3} + 1} - \dfrac{x-1}{x - x^{1/2}}\right)^{10} = (x^{1/3} - x^{-1/2})^{10}$

$$\therefore \; T_{r+1} = {}^{10}C_r (x^{1/3})^{10-r} (-x^{-1/2})^r$$

For independent of x, $\dfrac{10-r}{3} - \dfrac{r}{2} = 0 \Rightarrow r = 4$

$$\therefore \quad T_{4+1} = {}^{10}C_4 = \frac{10 \cdot 9 \cdot 8 \cdot 7}{1 \cdot 2 \cdot 3 \cdot 4} = 210$$

126. Since, ${}^{n+5}C_r : {}^{n+5}C_{r-1} = 2 \Rightarrow 3r = n + 6$ ...(i)

and ${}^{n+5}C_{r+1} : {}^{n+5}C_r = \dfrac{7}{5} \Rightarrow 12r = 5n + 18$ ...(ii)

From Eqs. (i) and (ii), we get

$$4(n+6) = 5n + 18 \Rightarrow n = 6$$

127. $(1 + ax + bx^2)(1-2x)^{18}$

$$= (1 + ax + bx^2)[1 - {}^{18}C_1(2x) + {}^{18}C_2(2x)^2 - {}^{18}C_3(2x)^3 + {}^{18}C_4(2x)^4 - \dots]$$

According to the question, Coefficient of x^3

$$= -{}^{18}C_3 \cdot 8 + a \cdot {}^{18}C_2 \cdot 2^2 - b \cdot {}^{18}C_1 \cdot 2 = 0$$

$\Rightarrow 17a - b = \dfrac{544}{3}$ ...(i)

and coefficient of $x^4 = {}^{18}C_4 \cdot 2^4 - {}^{18}C_3 \cdot 2^3 \cdot a + {}^{18}C_2 \cdot 2^2 \cdot b = 0$

$\Rightarrow \quad 32a - 3b = 240$ ...(ii)

On solving Eqs. (i) and (ii), we get

$$a = 16, \; b = \frac{272}{3}$$

$$\therefore \quad (a, b) = \left(16, \frac{272}{3}\right)$$

128. $\because (1+x^2)^4 (1+x^3)^7 (1+x^4)^{12}$

$$= (1 + {}^4C_1 x^2 + {}^4C_2 x^4 + {}^4C_3 x^6 + {}^4C_4 x^8) \times (1 + {}^7C_1 x^3 + {}^7C_2 x^6 + {}^7C_3 x^9 + \dots) \times (1 + {}^{12}C_1 x^4 + {}^{12}C_2 x^8 + \dots)$$

Required coefficient

$$= {}^{12}C_2 \cdot {}^7C_1 \cdot 1 + {}^{12}C_1 \cdot {}^7C_1 \cdot {}^4C_2 + {}^7C_1 \cdot {}^4C_4 + {}^7C_3 \cdot {}^4C_1$$

$$= 462 + 504 + 7 + 140 = 1113$$

129. $\because \quad T_{r+1} = {}^{50}C_r (-2\sqrt{x})^r = {}^{50}C_r (-2)^r \cdot x^{r/2}$

For integral powers of x, $r = 0, 2, 4, 6, \dots, 50$

$\therefore$ Required sum $= {}^{50}C_0 + 2^2 \cdot {}^{50}C_2 + 2^4 \cdot {}^{50}C_4 + \dots + 2^{50} \cdot {}^{50}C_{50}$

$$= \frac{1}{2}[(1+2)^{50} + (1-2)^{50}] = \frac{1}{2}(3^{50} + 1)$$

130. In the Expansion of $(1+x)(1+x^2)(1+x^3)\dots(1+x^{100})$.

x^9 can be found in the following ways

$x^9, x^{1+8}, x^{2+7}, x^{3+6}, x^{4+5}, x^{1+2+6}, x^{1+3+5}, x^{2+3+4}$

There are 8 cases

The coenfficient of x^9 in each cases is 1

$\therefore$ Required coefficient = 8

131. Total number of terms $= {}^{n+2}C_2 = 28$

$\Rightarrow (n+2)(n+1) = 56 = (6+2)(6+1)$

$\therefore \quad n = 6$

Sum of coefficients $= (1 - 2 + 4)^n = 3^6 = 729$

[**Note** In the solution it is considered that different terms in the expansion having same powers are not merged, as such it should be a bonus question]

132. Coefficient of x^2 in the expansion

$$= {}^2C_2 + {}^3C_2 + {}^4C_2 + {}^5C_2 + \dots + {}^{49}C_2 + {}^{50}C_2 \cdot m^2$$

$$= {}^3C_3 + {}^3C_2 + {}^4C_2 + {}^5C_2 + \dots + {}^{49}C_2 + {}^{50}C_2 \cdot m^2$$

$$= {}^4C_3 + {}^4C_2 + {}^5C_2 + \dots + {}^{49}C_2 + {}^{50}C_2 \cdot m^2$$

$= {}^{50}C_3 + {}^{50}C_2 \cdot m^2$ (Applying again and again Pascal's rule)

$$= ({}^{50}C_3 + {}^{50}C_2) + {}^{50}C_2(m^2 - 1)$$

$= {}^{51}C_3 + {}^{50}C_2(m^2-1) = (3n+1)\, {}^{51}C_3$ (given)

or $\quad {}^{50}C_2(m^2 - 1) = 3n \cdot {}^{51}C_3$

or $\quad \dfrac{m^2-1}{3n} = \dfrac{51}{3} = 17$ or $\dfrac{m^2-1}{51} = n$

for $m = 16, n = 5$

133. $({}^{21}C_1 + {}^{21}C_2 + {}^{21}C_3 + {}^{21}C_4 + \dots + {}^{21}C_{10}) - ({}^{10}C_1 + {}^{10}C_2 + {}^{10}C_3 + \dots + {}^{10}C_{10})$

$$= \frac{1}{2}(2^{21} - 2) - (2^{10} - 1) = (2^{20} - 1) - (2^{10} - 1)$$

$$= 2^{20} - 2^{10}$$

CHAPTER

07

Determinants

Learning Part

Session 1

- Definition of Determinants
- Expansion of Determinant
- Sarrus Rule for Expansion
- Window Rule for Expansion

Session 2

- Minors and Cofactors
- Use of Determinants in Coordinate Geometry
- Properties of Determinants

Session 3

- Examples on Largest Value of a Third Order Determinant
- Multiplication of Two Determinants of the Same Order
- System of Linear Equations
- Cramer's Rule
- Nature of Solutions of System of Linear Equations
- System of Homogeneous Linear Equations

Session 4

- Differentiation of Determinant
- Integration of a Determinant
- Walli's Formula
- Use of Σ in Determinant

Practice Part

- JEE Type Examples
- Chapter Exercises

Arihant on Your Mobile !

Exercises with the symbol can be practised on your mobile. See inside cover page to activate for free.

Session 1

Definition of Determinants, Expansion of Determinant, Sarrus Rule for Expansion, Window Rule for Expansion

Determinants were invented independently by **Gabriel Cramer**, whose now well-known rule for solving linear system was published in 1750, although not in present day notation. The now-standard "Vertical line notation", i.e. "| |" was given in 1841 by **Arthur Cayley**. The working knowledge of determinants is a basic necessity for a student. Determinants have wide applications in Engineering, Science, Economics, Social science, etc.

Definition of Determinants

Consider the system of two homogeneous linear equations

$$a_1 x + b_1 y = 0 \quad \text{...(i)}$$
$$a_2 x + b_2 y = 0 \quad \text{...(ii)}$$

in the two variables x and y. From these equations, we obtain

$$-\frac{a_1}{b_1} = \frac{y}{x} = -\frac{a_2}{b_2} \Rightarrow \frac{a_1}{b_1} = \frac{a_2}{b_2}$$

$$\Rightarrow \quad a_1 b_2 - a_2 b_1 = 0$$

The result $a_1 b_2 - a_2 b_1$ is represented by $\begin{vmatrix} a_1 & b_1 \\ a_2 & b_2 \end{vmatrix}$

which is known as determinant of order two. The quantities a_1, b_1, a_2 and b_2 are called constituents or elements of the determinant and $a_1 b_2 - a_2 b_1$ is called its value.

The horizontal lines are called rows and vertical lines are called columns. Here, this determinant consists two rows and two columns.

For example, The value of the determinant

$$\begin{vmatrix} 2 & 3 \\ 4 & -5 \end{vmatrix} = 2 \times (-5) - 3 \times 4 = -10 - 12 = -22$$

Now, let us consider the system of three homogeneous linear equations

$$a_1 x + b_1 y + c_1 z = 0 \quad \text{...(i)}$$
$$a_2 x + b_2 y + c_2 z = 0 \quad \text{...(ii)}$$
$$a_3 x + b_3 y + c_3 z = 0 \quad \text{...(iii)}$$

On solving Eqs. (ii) and (iii) for x, y and z by cross-multiplication, we get

$$\frac{x}{b_2 c_3 - b_3 c_2} = \frac{y}{c_2 a_3 - c_3 a_2} = \frac{z}{a_2 b_3 - a_3 b_2} = k \quad \text{[say]}$$

$$\Rightarrow \quad x = k(b_2 c_3 - b_3 c_2),\ y = k(c_2 a_3 - c_3 a_2)$$

and $\quad z = k(a_2 b_3 - a_3 b_2)$

On putting these values of x, y and z in Eq. (i), we get

$$a_1(b_2 c_3 - b_3 c_2) + b_1(c_2 a_3 - c_3 a_2) + c_1(a_2 b_3 - a_3 b_2) = 0$$

or $\quad a_1(b_2 c_3 - b_3 c_2) - b_1(c_3 a_2 - c_2 a_3) + c_1(a_2 b_3 - a_3 b_2) = 0 \quad \text{...(iv)}$

or $\quad a_1 \begin{vmatrix} b_2 & c_2 \\ b_3 & c_3 \end{vmatrix} - b_1 \begin{vmatrix} c_2 & a_2 \\ c_3 & a_3 \end{vmatrix} + c_1 \begin{vmatrix} a_2 & b_2 \\ a_3 & b_3 \end{vmatrix} = 0 \quad \text{...(v)}$

Usually this is written as $\begin{vmatrix} a_1 & b_1 & c_1 \\ a_2 & b_2 & c_2 \\ a_3 & b_3 & c_3 \end{vmatrix} = 0$

Here, the expression $\begin{vmatrix} a_1 & b_1 & c_1 \\ a_2 & b_2 & c_2 \\ a_3 & b_3 & c_3 \end{vmatrix}$ consisting of three rows and three columns, is called determinant of order three.

The quantities $a_1, b_1, c_1, a_2, b_2, c_2, a_3, b_3$ and c_3 are called constituents or elements of the determinant.

Remark

1. A determinant is generally denoted by D or Δ.
2. A determinant of the nth order consists of n rows and n columns and its expansion contains $n!$ terms.
3. A determinant of nth order consists of n rows and n columns.
   $\therefore$ Number of constituents in determinant $= n^2$
4. In a determinant the horizontal lines counting from top to bottom 1st, 2nd, 3rd, … respectively, known as rows and denoted by $R_1, R_2, R_3, \dots$ and vertical lines from left to right 1st, 2nd, 3rd, … respectively, known as columns and denoted by $C_1, C_2, C_3, \dots$.
5. Shape of every determinant is square.
6. Sign system for order 2, order 3, order 4, … are given by

$$\begin{vmatrix} + & - \\ - & + \end{vmatrix}, \begin{vmatrix} + & - & + \\ - & + & - \\ + & - & + \end{vmatrix}, \begin{vmatrix} + & - & + & - \\ - & + & - & + \\ + & - & + & - \\ - & + & - & + \end{vmatrix}, \dots$$

Expansion of Determinant

(i) Expansion of two order

$$\begin{vmatrix} a_1 & b_1 \\ a_2 & b_2 \end{vmatrix} = \begin{vmatrix} a_1 \searrow & \\ & b_2 \end{vmatrix} - \begin{vmatrix} & \swarrow b_1 \\ a_2 & \end{vmatrix} = a_1 b_2 - b_1 a_2$$

For example, $\begin{vmatrix} 5 & -4 \\ -3 & 2 \end{vmatrix} = \begin{vmatrix} 5 & \\ & 2 \end{vmatrix} - \begin{vmatrix} & -4 \\ -3 & \end{vmatrix}$

$$= 10 - 12 = -2$$

(ii) Expansion of third order

(a) *With respect to first row.*

$$\begin{vmatrix} a_1 \cdots & b_1 \cdots & c_1 \\ a_2 & b_2 & c_2 \\ a_3 & b_3 & c_3 \end{vmatrix} = a_1 \begin{vmatrix} b_2 & c_2 \\ b_3 & c_3 \end{vmatrix} - b_1 \begin{vmatrix} a_2 & c_2 \\ a_3 & c_3 \end{vmatrix} + c_1 \begin{vmatrix} a_2 & b_2 \\ a_3 & b_3 \end{vmatrix}$$

$$= a_1 (b_2 c_3 - b_3 c_2) - b_1 (a_2 c_3 - a_3 c_2) + c_1 (a_2 b_3 - a_3 b_2)$$

(b) *With respect to second column.*

$$\begin{vmatrix} a_1 & b_1 & c_1 \\ & \vdots & \\ a_2 & b_2 & c_2 \\ & \vdots & \\ a_3 & b_3 & c_3 \end{vmatrix} = -b_1 \begin{vmatrix} a_2 & c_2 \\ a_3 & c_3 \end{vmatrix} + b_2 \begin{vmatrix} a_1 & c_1 \\ a_3 & c_3 \end{vmatrix} - b_3 \begin{vmatrix} a_1 & c_1 \\ a_2 & c_2 \end{vmatrix}$$

$$= -b_1 (a_2 c_3 - a_3 c_2) + b_2 (a_1 c_3 - a_3 c_1) - b_3 (a_1 c_2 - a_2 c_1)$$

Remark

A determinant can be expanded along any of its row or column. Value of the determinant remains same in any of the cases.

Example 1. Find the value of the determinant $\begin{vmatrix} 1 & 2 & 4 \\ 3 & 4 & 9 \\ 2 & -1 & 6 \end{vmatrix}$

Sol. Expanding the determinant along the first row

$$\Delta_1 = 1 \begin{vmatrix} 4 & 9 \\ -1 & 6 \end{vmatrix} - 2 \begin{vmatrix} 3 & 9 \\ 2 & 6 \end{vmatrix} + 4 \begin{vmatrix} 3 & 4 \\ 2 & -1 \end{vmatrix}$$

$$= 1(24 + 9) - 2(18 - 18) + 4(-3 - 8)$$

$$= 33 - 0 - 44$$

$$= -11$$

and expanding the determinant along third column

$$\Delta_2 = 4 \begin{vmatrix} 3 & 4 \\ 2 & -1 \end{vmatrix} - 9 \begin{vmatrix} 1 & 2 \\ 2 & -1 \end{vmatrix} + 6 \begin{vmatrix} 1 & 2 \\ 3 & 4 \end{vmatrix}$$

$$= 4(-3 - 8) - 9(-1 - 4) + 6(4 - 6)$$

$$= -44 + 45 - 12$$

$$= 1 - 12$$

$$= -11$$

and expanding the determinant along second column

$$\Delta_3 = -2 \begin{vmatrix} 3 & 9 \\ 2 & 6 \end{vmatrix} + 4 \begin{vmatrix} 1 & 4 \\ 2 & 6 \end{vmatrix} - (-1) \begin{vmatrix} 1 & 4 \\ 3 & 9 \end{vmatrix}$$

$$= -2(18 - 18) + 4(6 - 8) + 1(9 - 12)$$

$$= 0 - 8 - 3$$

$$= -11$$

Hence, $\Delta_1 = \Delta_2 = \Delta_3$

Example 2. If $\Delta = \begin{vmatrix} 1 & \sin\theta & 1 \\ -\sin\theta & 1 & \sin\theta \\ -1 & -\sin\theta & 1 \end{vmatrix}$, prove that $2 \le \Delta \le 4$.

Sol. Given, $\Delta = \begin{vmatrix} 1 & \sin\theta & 1 \\ -\sin\theta & 1 & \sin\theta \\ -1 & -\sin\theta & 1 \end{vmatrix}$

Expanding along first row, we get

$$\Delta = 1 \begin{vmatrix} 1 & \sin\theta \\ -\sin\theta & 1 \end{vmatrix} - \sin\theta \begin{vmatrix} -\sin\theta & \sin\theta \\ -1 & 1 \end{vmatrix} + 1 \begin{vmatrix} -\sin\theta & 1 \\ -1 & -\sin\theta \end{vmatrix}$$

$$= (1 + \sin^2\theta) - \sin\theta(-\sin\theta + \sin\theta) + (\sin^2\theta + 1)$$

$$= 2(1 + \sin^2\theta)$$

Again, $0 \le \sin^2\theta \le 1$

$\Rightarrow \quad 1 \le (1 + \sin^2\theta) \le 1 + 1$

$\Rightarrow \quad 2 \le 2(1 + \sin^2\theta) \le 4$

$\therefore \quad 2 \le \Delta \le 4$

Sarrus Rule for Expansion

Sarrus gave a rule for a determinant of order 3.

Rule Write down the three rows of the Δ and rewrite the first two rows. The three diagonals sloping down to the right given the three terms and the three diagonals sloping down to the left also given the three terms.

If $\quad \Delta = \begin{vmatrix} a_1 & b_1 & c_1 \\ a_2 & b_2 & c_2 \\ a_3 & b_3 & c_3 \end{vmatrix}$

Rule

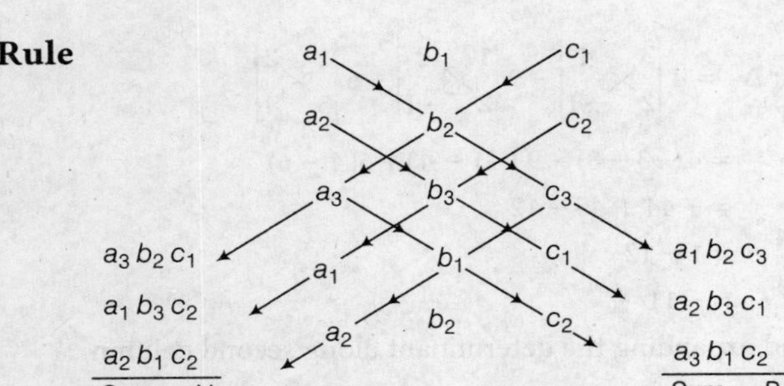

$\therefore \quad \Delta = P - N$

Example 3. Expand $\begin{vmatrix} 3 & 2 & 5 \\ 9 & -1 & 4 \\ 2 & 3 & -5 \end{vmatrix}$ by Sarrus rule.

Sol. Let $\Delta = \begin{vmatrix} 3 & 2 & 5 \\ 9 & -1 & 4 \\ 2 & 3 & -5 \end{vmatrix}$

Rule

3 2 5
9 −1 4
2 3 −5
3 2 5
9 −9 4

−10, 36, −90; $N = -64$

15, 135, 16; $P = 166$

$\therefore \quad \Delta = P - N = 166 - (-64) = 230$

Example 4. If $a, b, c \in R$, find the number of real roots of the equation $\begin{vmatrix} x & c & -b \\ -c & x & a \\ b & -a & x \end{vmatrix} = 0$

Sol. Let $\Delta = \begin{vmatrix} x & c & -b \\ -c & x & a \\ b & -a & x \end{vmatrix}$

Rule

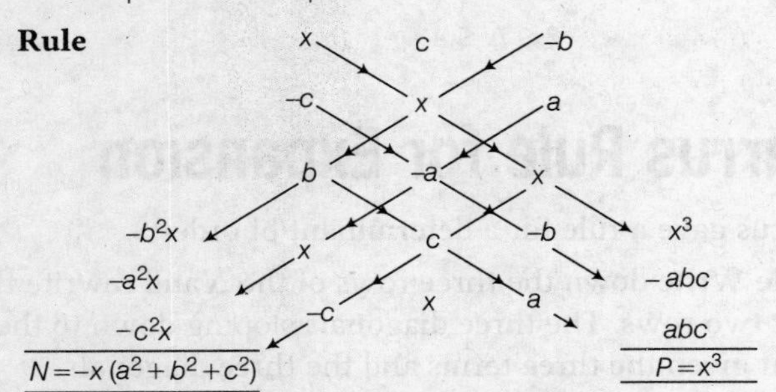

$$\therefore \quad \Delta = P - N$$
$$= x^3 + x(a^2 + b^2 + c^2) = 0 \qquad \text{[given]}$$

$\therefore \quad x = 0$ or $x^2 = -(a^2 + b^2 + c^2)$

$\Rightarrow \quad x = 0$ or $x = \pm i\sqrt{(a^2 + b^2 + c^2)}$, where $i = \sqrt{-1}$

Hence, number of real roots is one.

Window Rule for Expansion

Window rule valid only for third order determinant.

Let $\quad \Delta = \begin{vmatrix} a_1 & b_1 & c_1 \\ a_2 & b_2 & c_2 \\ a_3 & b_3 & c_3 \end{vmatrix}$

In this method, rewrite first two elements of second row and third row, then

Rule

$$\begin{matrix} a_1 & b_1 & c_1 & & \\ a_2 & b_2 & c_2 & a_2 & b_2 \\ a_3 & b_3 & c_3 & a_3 & b_3 \end{matrix}$$

Now, taking positive sign with a_1, b_1 and c_1.

$$\Delta = a_1(b_2 c_3 - b_3 c_2) + b_1(c_2 a_3 - c_3 a_2) + c_1(a_2 b_3 - a_3 b_2)$$

Example 5. Expand $\begin{vmatrix} 1 & 2 & 3 \\ 4 & 6 & 2 \\ 5 & 9 & 4 \end{vmatrix}$ by window rule.

Sol. Let $\Delta = \begin{vmatrix} 1 & 2 & 3 \\ 4 & 6 & 2 \\ 5 & 9 & 4 \end{vmatrix}$

Rule:

$$\begin{matrix} 1 & 2 & 3 & & \\ 4 & 6 & 2 & 4 & 6 \\ 5 & 9 & 4 & 5 & 9 \end{matrix}$$

$$\therefore \quad \Delta = 1(24 - 18) + 2(10 - 16) + 3(36 - 30)$$
$$= 6 - 12 + 18 = 12$$

Example 6. Find the value of the determinant $\begin{vmatrix} -1 & 2 & 1 \\ 3+2\sqrt{2} & 2+2\sqrt{2} & 1 \\ 3-2\sqrt{2} & 2-2\sqrt{2} & 1 \end{vmatrix}$.

Sol. Let $\Delta = \begin{vmatrix} -1 & 2 & 1 \\ 3+2\sqrt{2} & 2+2\sqrt{2} & 1 \\ 3-2\sqrt{2} & 2-2\sqrt{2} & 1 \end{vmatrix}$ and let $2\sqrt{2} = \lambda$,

then $\quad \Delta = \begin{vmatrix} -1 & 2 & 1 \\ 3+\lambda & 2+\lambda & 1 \\ 3-\lambda & 2-\lambda & 1 \end{vmatrix}$

Rule

$$\begin{matrix} -1 & 2 & 1 & & \\ 3+\lambda & 2+\lambda & 1 & 3+\lambda & 2+\lambda \\ 3-\lambda & 2-\lambda & 1 & 3-\lambda & 2-\lambda \end{matrix}$$

Now, $\quad \Delta = -1(2 + \lambda - 2 + \lambda) + 2(3 - \lambda - 3 - \lambda) + 1[(3 + \lambda)(2 - \lambda) - (3 - \lambda)(2 + \lambda)]$

$$= -2\lambda - 4\lambda + (-2\lambda) = -8\lambda = -16\sqrt{2}$$

$[\because \lambda = 2\sqrt{2}]$

Exercise for Session 1

1 Sum of real roots of the equation $\begin{vmatrix} 1 & 4 & 20 \\ 1 & -2 & 5 \\ 1 & 2x & 5x^2 \end{vmatrix} = 0$ is

(a) -2 (b) -1 (c) 0 (d) 1

2 If $\begin{vmatrix} 6i & -3i & 1 \\ 4 & 3i & -1 \\ 20 & 3 & i \end{vmatrix} = x + iy, i = \sqrt{-1}$, then

(a) $x = 3, y = 1$ (b) $x = 1, y = 3$
(c) $x = 0, y = 3$ (d) $x = 0, y = 0$

3 If $p\lambda^4 + q\lambda^3 + r\lambda^2 + s\lambda + t = \begin{vmatrix} \lambda^2 + 3\lambda & \lambda - 1 & \lambda + 3 \\ \lambda^2 + 1 & 2 - \lambda & \lambda - 3 \\ \lambda^2 - 3 & \lambda + 4 & 3\lambda \end{vmatrix}$, then t is equal to

(a) 7 (b) 14
(c) 21 (d) 28

4 If one root of the equation $\begin{vmatrix} 7 & 6 & x^2 - 13 \\ 2 & x^2 - 13 & 2 \\ x^2 - 13 & 3 & 7 \end{vmatrix} = 0$ is $x = 2$, the sum of all other five roots is

(a) $2\sqrt{15}$ (b) -2
(c) $\sqrt{20} + \sqrt{15} - 2$ (d) None of these

5 If A, B and C are the angles of a non-right angled ΔABC, the value of $\begin{vmatrix} \tan A & 1 & 1 \\ 1 & \tan B & 1 \\ 1 & 1 & \tan C \end{vmatrix}$ is

(a) 0 (b) 1 (c) 2 (d) 3

6 If $\Delta = \begin{vmatrix} 1 & 3\cos\theta & 1 \\ \sin\theta & 1 & 3\cos\theta \\ 1 & \sin\theta & 1 \end{vmatrix}$, the maximum value of Δ is

(a) -10 (b) $-\sqrt{10}$ (c) $\sqrt{10}$ (d) 10

7 If the value of the determinant $\begin{vmatrix} a & 1 & 1 \\ 1 & b & 1 \\ 1 & 1 & c \end{vmatrix}$ is positive, then $(a, b, c > 0)$

(a) $abc > 1$ (b) $abc > -8$ (c) $abc < -8$ (d) $abc > -2$

Session 2

Minors and Cofactors, Use of Determinants in Coordinate Geometry, Properties of Determinants

Minors and Cofactors

Let $$\Delta = \begin{vmatrix} a_{11} & a_{12} & a_{13} & \cdots & a_{1n} \\ a_{21} & a_{21} & a_{23} & \cdots & a_{2n} \\ a_{31} & a_{32} & a_{33} & \cdots & a_{3n} \\ \cdots & \cdots & \cdots & \cdots & \cdots \\ a_{n1} & a_{n2} & a_{n3} & \cdots & a_{nn} \end{vmatrix}$$

be a determinant of order n, $n \geq 2$, then the determinant of order $n-1$ obtained from the determinant Δ after deleting the ith row and jth column is called the **minor of the element a_{ij}** and it is usually denoted by M_{ij}, where $i = 1, 2, 3, \ldots, n$ and $j = 1, 2, 3, \ldots, n$.

If M_{ij} is the minor of the element a_{ij} in the determinant Δ, then $(-1)^{i+j} M_{ij}$ is called the **cofactor of the element a_{ij}**. It is usually denoted by C_{ij}.

Thus, $$C_{ij} = (-1)^{i+j} M_{ij} = \begin{cases} M_{ij}, & \text{if } i+j \text{ is an even integer} \\ -M_{ij}, & \text{if } i+j \text{ is an odd integer} \end{cases}$$

(i) Let $\Delta = \begin{vmatrix} a_{11} & a_{12} \\ a_{21} & a_{22} \end{vmatrix}$, then

$M_{11} = |a_{22}| = a_{22}$, $M_{12} = |a_{21}| = a_{21}$,

$M_{21} = |a_{12}| = a_{12}$, $M_{22} = |a_{11}| = a_{11}$ and

$C_{11} = (-1)^{1+1} M_{11} = a_{22}$,

$C_{12} = (-1)^{1+2} M_{12} = -a_{21}$,

$C_{21} = (-1)^{2+1} M_{21} = -a_{12}$

and $C_{22} = (-1)^{2+2} M_{22} = a_{11}$

(ii) Let $\Delta = \begin{vmatrix} a_{11} & a_{12} & a_{13} \\ a_{21} & a_{22} & a_{23} \\ a_{31} & a_{32} & a_{33} \end{vmatrix}$

Determinants of minors and cofactors are

$$\Delta^M = \begin{vmatrix} M_{11} & M_{12} & M_{13} \\ M_{21} & M_{22} & M_{23} \\ M_{31} & M_{32} & M_{33} \end{vmatrix}, \quad \Delta^c = \begin{vmatrix} C_{11} & C_{12} & C_{13} \\ C_{21} & C_{22} & C_{23} \\ C_{31} & a_{32} & a_{33} \end{vmatrix}$$

where

$$M_{11} = \begin{vmatrix} a_{22} & a_{23} \\ a_{32} & a_{33} \end{vmatrix}, C_{11} = (-1)^{1+1} M_{11} = M_{11}$$

$$M_{12} = \begin{vmatrix} a_{21} & a_{23} \\ a_{31} & a_{33} \end{vmatrix}, C_{12} = (-1)^{1+2} M_{12} = -M_{12}$$

$$M_{13} = \begin{vmatrix} a_{21} & a_{22} \\ a_{31} & a_{32} \end{vmatrix}, C_{13} = (-1)^{1+3} M_{13} = M_{13}$$

$$M_{21} = \begin{vmatrix} a_{12} & a_{13} \\ a_{32} & a_{33} \end{vmatrix}, C_{21} = (-1)^{2+1} M_{21} = -M_{21}$$

$$M_{22} = \begin{vmatrix} a_{11} & a_{13} \\ a_{31} & a_{33} \end{vmatrix}, C_{22} = (-1)^{2+2} M_{22} = M_{22}$$

$$M_{23} = \begin{vmatrix} a_{11} & a_{12} \\ a_{31} & a_{32} \end{vmatrix}, C_{23} = (-1)^{2+3} M_{23} = -M_{23}$$

$$M_{31} = \begin{vmatrix} a_{12} & a_{13} \\ a_{22} & a_{23} \end{vmatrix}, C_{31} = (-1)^{3+1} M_{31} = M_{31}$$

$$M_{32} = \begin{vmatrix} a_{11} & a_{13} \\ a_{21} & a_{23} \end{vmatrix}, C_{32} = (-1)^{3+2} M_{32} = -M_{32}$$

$$M_{33} = \begin{vmatrix} a_{11} & a_{12} \\ a_{21} & a_{22} \end{vmatrix}, C_{33} = (-1)^{3+3} M_{33} = M_{33}$$

Important Results for Cofactors

1. The sum of products of the elements of any row or column with their corresponding cofactors is equal to the value of the determinant.

i.e., $$\Delta = a_{11}C_{11} + a_{12}C_{12} + a_{13}C_{13} = a_{11}C_{11} + a_{21}C_{21} + a_{31}C_{31}$$
$$= a_{21}C_{21} + a_{22}C_{22} + a_{23}C_{23} = a_{12}C_{12} + a_{22}C_{22} + a_{32}C_{32}$$
$$= a_{31}C_{31} + a_{32}C_{32} + a_{33}C_{33} = a_{13}C_{13} + a_{23}C_{23} + a_{33}C_{33}$$

Now, value of n order determinant

$$\Delta = \begin{vmatrix} a_{11} & a_{12} & a_{13} & \cdots & \cdots & a_{1n} \\ a_{21} & a_{22} & a_{23} & \cdots & \cdots & a_{2n} \\ a_{31} & a_{32} & a_{33} & \cdots & \cdots & a_{3n} \\ \cdots & \cdots & \cdots & \cdots & \cdots & \cdots \\ \cdots & \cdots & \cdots & \cdots & \cdots & \cdots \\ a_{n1} & a_{n2} & a_{n3} & \cdots & \cdots & a_{nn} \end{vmatrix}$$
$$= a_{11}C_{11} + a_{12}C_{12} + a_{13}C_{13} + \ldots + a_{1n}C_{1n}$$

(when expanded along first row)

2. The sum of the product of element of any row (or column) with corresponding cofactors of another row (or column) is equal to zero.

i.e., $a_{11}C_{21} + a_{12}C_{22} + a_{13}C_{23} = 0$,

$a_{11}C_{13} + a_{21}C_{23} + a_{31}C_{33} = 0$, etc.

3. If the value of a n order determinant is Δ, then the value of the determinant formed by the cofactors of corresponding elements of the given determinant is given by

$$\Delta^c = \Delta^{n-1}$$

i.e., in case of second order determinant

$$\Delta^c = \Delta$$

and third order determinant $\Delta^c = \Delta^2$.

Example 7. Find the determinants of minors and cofactors of the determinant $\begin{vmatrix} 2 & 3 & 4 \\ 7 & 2 & -5 \\ 8 & -1 & 3 \end{vmatrix}$.

Sol. Here, $M_{11} = \begin{vmatrix} 2 & -5 \\ -1 & 3 \end{vmatrix} = 6 - 5 = 1$ [delete 1st row and 1st column]

$\therefore \quad C_{11} = (-1)^{1+1}M_{11} = M_{11} = 1$

$M_{12} = \begin{vmatrix} 7 & -5 \\ 8 & 3 \end{vmatrix} = 21 + 40 = 61$ [delete 1st row and 2nd column]

$\therefore \quad C_{12} = (-1)^{1+2}M_{12} = -M_{12} = -61$

$M_{13} = \begin{vmatrix} 7 & 2 \\ 8 & -1 \end{vmatrix} = -7 - 16 = -23$ [delete 1st row and 3rd column]

$\therefore \quad C_{13} = (-1)^{1+3} M_{13} = M_{13} = -23$

$M_{21} = \begin{vmatrix} 3 & 4 \\ -1 & 3 \end{vmatrix}$ [delete 2nd row and 1st column]

$= 9 + 4 = 13$

$\therefore \quad C_{21} = (-1)^{2+1}M_{21} = -M_{21} = -13$

$M_{22} = \begin{vmatrix} 2 & 4 \\ 8 & 3 \end{vmatrix}$ [delete 2nd row and 2nd column]

$= 6 - 32 = -26$

$\therefore \quad C_{22} = (-1)^{2+2}M_{22} = M_{22} = -26$

$M_{23} = \begin{vmatrix} 2 & 3 \\ 8 & -1 \end{vmatrix}$ [delete 2nd row and 3rd column]

$= -2 - 24 = -26$

$\therefore \quad C_{23} = (-1)^{2+3}M_{23} = -M_{23} = 26$

$M_{31} = \begin{vmatrix} 3 & 4 \\ 2 & -5 \end{vmatrix}$ [delete 3rd row and 1st column]

$= -15 - 8 = -23$

$\therefore \quad C_{31} = (-1)^{3+1}M_{31} = M_{31} = -23$

$M_{32} = \begin{vmatrix} 2 & 4 \\ 7 & -5 \end{vmatrix}$ [delete 3rd row and 2nd column]

$= -10 - 28 = -38$

$\therefore \quad C_{32} = (-1)^{3+2}M_{32} = -M_{32} = 38$

and $M_{33} = \begin{vmatrix} 2 & 3 \\ 7 & 2 \end{vmatrix} = 4 - 21 = -17$ [delete 3rd row and 3rd column]

$\therefore \quad C_{33} = (-1)^{3+3}M_{33} = M_{33} = -17$

Hence, determinants of minors and cofactors are

$$\begin{vmatrix} 1 & 61 & -23 \\ 13 & -26 & -26 \\ -23 & -38 & -17 \end{vmatrix} \text{ and } \begin{vmatrix} 1 & -61 & -23 \\ -13 & -26 & 26 \\ -23 & 38 & -17 \end{vmatrix}, \text{ respectively.}$$

Goyal's Method for Cofactors

(Direct Method)

This method applied only for third order determinant.

Method If $\Delta = \begin{vmatrix} a_1 & a_2 & a_3 \\ b_1 & b_2 & b_3 \\ c_1 & c_2 & c_3 \end{vmatrix}$

***Step* I** Write down the three rows of the Δ and rewrite first two rows.

i.e.
$$\begin{matrix} a_1 & a_2 & a_3 \\ b_1 & b_2 & b_3 \\ c_1 & c_2 & c_3 \\ a_1 & a_2 & a_3 \\ b_1 & b_2 & b_3 \end{matrix}$$

***Step* II** Alter Step I, rewrite first two columns.

i.e.,
$$\begin{matrix} a_1 & a_2 & a_3 & a_1 & a_2 \\ b_1 & b_2 & b_3 & b_1 & b_2 \\ c_1 & c_2 & c_3 & c_1 & c_2 \\ a_1 & a_2 & a_3 & a_1 & a_2 \\ b_1 & b_2 & b_3 & b_1 & b_2 \end{matrix}$$

***Step* III** After step II, deleting first row and first column, then we get all cofactors i.e.

$$\begin{matrix} b_2 & b_3 & b_1 & b_2 \\ c_2 & c_3 & c_1 & c_2 \\ a_2 & a_3 & a_1 & a_2 \\ b_2 & b_3 & b_1 & b_2 \end{matrix}$$

or
$$\Delta^c = \begin{vmatrix} b_2c_3 - b_3c_2 & b_3c_1 - b_1c_3 & b_1c_2 - b_2c_1 \\ c_2a_3 - c_3a_2 & c_3a_1 - c_1a_3 & c_1a_2 - c_2a_1 \\ a_2b_3 - a_3b_2 & a_3b_1 - a_1b_3 & a_1b_2 - a_2b_1 \end{vmatrix}$$

| Example 8. Find the determinant of cofactors of the determinant $\begin{vmatrix} 1 & 2 & 3 \\ -4 & 3 & 6 \\ 2 & -7 & 9 \end{vmatrix}$ by Direct Method.

Sol. Let $\Delta = \begin{vmatrix} 1 & 2 & 3 \\ -4 & 3 & 6 \\ 2 & -7 & 9 \end{vmatrix}$

***Step* I** Write down the three rows of the Δ and rewrite first two rows.

i.e.,
$$\begin{matrix} 1 & 2 & 3 \\ -4 & 3 & 6 \\ 2 & -7 & 9 \\ 1 & 2 & 3 \\ -4 & 3 & 6 \end{matrix}$$

***Step* II** After step I, rewrite first two columns

i.e.,
$$\begin{matrix} 1 & 2 & 3 & 1 & 2 \\ -4 & 3 & 6 & -4 & 3 \\ 2 & -7 & 9 & 2 & -7 \\ 1 & 2 & 3 & 1 & 2 \\ -4 & 3 & 6 & -4 & 3 \end{matrix}$$

***Step* III** After Step II, deleting first row and first column, then we get all cofactors i.e.,

$$\begin{matrix} 3 & 6 & -4 & 3 \\ -7 & 9 & 2 & -7 \\ 2 & 3 & 1 & 2 \\ 3 & 6 & -4 & 3 \end{matrix} \quad \text{or} \quad \Delta^c = \begin{vmatrix} 69 & 48 & 22 \\ -39 & 3 & 11 \\ 3 & -18 & 11 \end{vmatrix}$$

| Example 9. If the value of a third order determinant is 11, find the value of the square of the determinant formed by the cofactors.

Sol. Here, $n = 3$ and $\Delta = 11$

$\therefore \quad (\Delta^c)^2 = (\Delta^2)^2 = \Delta^4 = 11^4 = 14641$

Use of Determinants in Coordinate Geometry

(i) Area of triangle whose vertices are $(x_1, y_1), (x_2, y_2)$ and (x_3, y_3) is given by

$$\Delta = \frac{1}{2}\begin{vmatrix} x_1 & y_1 & 1 \\ x_2 & y_2 & 1 \\ x_3 & y_3 & 1 \end{vmatrix}$$

(ii) If points $(x_1, y_1), (x_2, y_2)$ and (x_3, y_3) and collinear, then

$$\begin{vmatrix} x_1 & y_1 & 1 \\ x_2 & y_2 & 1 \\ x_3 & y_3 & 1 \end{vmatrix} = 0$$

(iii) If $a_r x + b_r y + c_r = 0$; $r = 1, 2, 3$ are the sides of a triangle, then the area of the triangle is given by

$$\Delta = \frac{1}{|2C_1C_2C_3|}\begin{vmatrix} a_1 & b_1 & c_1 \\ a_2 & b_2 & c_2 \\ a_3 & b_3 & c_3 \end{vmatrix}^2$$

where C_1, C_2 and C_3 are the cofactors of the elements c_1, c_2 and c_3 respectively, in the determinant

$$\begin{vmatrix} a_1 & b_1 & c_1 \\ a_2 & b_2 & c_2 \\ a_3 & b_3 & c_3 \end{vmatrix}$$

(iv) Equation of straight line passing through two points (x_1, y_1) and (x_2, y_2) is

$$\begin{vmatrix} x & y & 1 \\ x_1 & y_1 & 1 \\ x_2 & y_2 & 1 \end{vmatrix} = 0$$

(v) If three lines $a_r x + b_r y + c_r = 0$; $r = 1, 2, 3$ are concurrent, then

$$\begin{vmatrix} a_1 & b_1 & c_1 \\ a_2 & b_2 & c_2 \\ a_3 & b_3 & c_3 \end{vmatrix} = 0$$

(vi) If $ax^2 + 2hxy + by^2 + 2gx + 2fy + c = 0$ represents a pair of straight lines, then

$$\begin{vmatrix} a & h & g \\ h & b & f \\ g & f & c \end{vmatrix} = 0$$

(vii) Equation of circle through three non-collinear points $(x_1, y_1), (x_2, y_2)$ and (x_3, y_3) is given by

$$\begin{vmatrix} x^2 + y^2 & x & y & 1 \\ x_1^2 + y_1^2 & x_1 & y_1 & 1 \\ x_2^2 + y_2^2 & x_2 & y_2 & 1 \\ x_3^2 + y_3^2 & x_3 & y_3 & 1 \end{vmatrix} = 0$$

Some Useful Operations

(i) The interchange of ith row and jth row is denoted by $R_i \leftrightarrow R_j$. (In case of column $C_i \leftrightarrow C_j$)

(ii) The addition of m times the elements of jth row to the corresponding elements of ith row is denoted by $R_i \to R_i + mR_j$.
(In case of column $C_i \to C_i + mC_j$)

(iii) The addition of m times the elements of jth row and n times the elements of k th row to the corresponding elements of ith row is denoted by $R_i \to R_i + mR_j + nR_k$.
(In case of column $C_i \to C_i + mC_j + nC_k$)

Properties of Determinants

We shall establish certain properties of a determinant of the third order but reader should note that these are capable of application to a determinant of any order.

Property I The value of a determinant remains unaltered when rows are changed into corresponding columns and columns are changed into corresponding rows.

Proof Let $\Delta = \begin{vmatrix} a_1 & b_1 & c_1 \\ a_2 & b_2 & c_2 \\ a_3 & b_3 & c_3 \end{vmatrix}$

Expanding the determinant along the first row, then

$$\Delta = a_1(b_2c_3 - b_3c_2) - b_1(a_2c_3 - a_3c_2) + c_1(a_2b_3 - a_3b_2)$$
$$= a_1(b_2c_3 - b_3c_2) - a_2(b_1c_3 - b_3c_1) + a_3(b_1c_2 - b_2c_1)$$
$$= \begin{vmatrix} a_1 & a_2 & a_3 \\ b_1 & b_2 & b_3 \\ c_1 & c_2 & c_3 \end{vmatrix}$$

$= \Delta'$, where Δ' be the value of the determinant when rows of determinant Δ are changed into corresponding columns.

Property II If any two rows (or two columns) of a determinant are interchanged, then the sign of determinant is changed and the numerical value remains unaltered.

Proof Let $\Delta = \begin{vmatrix} a_1 & b_1 & c_1 \\ a_2 & b_2 & c_2 \\ a_3 & b_3 & c_3 \end{vmatrix}$

Expanding the determinant along the first row, then

$$\Delta = a_1(b_2c_3 - b_3c_2) - b_1(a_2c_3 - a_3c_2) + c_1(a_2b_3 - a_3b_2)$$
$$= -a_2(b_1c_3 - b_3c_1) + b_2(a_1c_3 - a_3c_1) - c_2(a_1b_3 - a_3b_1)$$
$$= -[a_2(b_1c_3 - b_3c_1) - b_2(a_1c_3 - a_3c_1) + c_2(a_1b_3 - a_3b_1)]$$
$$= -\begin{vmatrix} a_2 & b_2 & c_2 \\ a_1 & b_1 & c_1 \\ a_3 & b_3 & c_3 \end{vmatrix} \quad [\text{by } R_1 \leftrightarrow R_2]$$

Hence, $\begin{vmatrix} a_1 & b_1 & c_1 \\ a_2 & b_2 & c_2 \\ a_3 & b_3 & c_3 \end{vmatrix} = -\begin{vmatrix} a_2 & b_2 & c_2 \\ a_1 & b_1 & c_1 \\ a_3 & b_3 & c_3 \end{vmatrix}$

Remark

If any row (or column) of a determinant Δ be passed over m rows (or columns), then the resulting determinant $= (-1)^m \Delta$.

Property III If two rows (or columns) of a determinant are identical, then the value of the determinant is zero.

Proof Let $\Delta = \begin{vmatrix} a_1 & b_1 & c_1 \\ a_2 & b_2 & c_2 \\ a_1 & b_1 & c_1 \end{vmatrix} = -\begin{vmatrix} a_1 & b_1 & c_1 \\ a_2 & b_2 & c_2 \\ a_1 & b_1 & c_1 \end{vmatrix} = -\Delta$

[by $R_1 \leftrightarrow R_3$]

$\Rightarrow \quad 2\Delta = 0$

$\therefore \quad \Delta = 0$

Property IV If the elements of any row (or any column) of a determinant be each multiplied by the same factor k, then the value of the determinant is multiplied by k.

Proof Let $\Delta = \begin{vmatrix} a_1 & b_1 & c_1 \\ a_2 & b_2 & c_2 \\ a_3 & b_3 & c_3 \end{vmatrix} = a_1C_{11} + b_1C_{12} + c_1C_{13}$

Then, $\begin{vmatrix} ka_1 & kb_1 & kc_1 \\ a_2 & b_2 & c_2 \\ a_3 & b_3 & c_3 \end{vmatrix} = ka_1C_{11} + kb_1C_{12} + kc_1C_{13}$

(where C_{11}, C_{12} and C_{13} are the cofactors of a_1, b_1 and c_1 in Δ)

$$= k(a_1C_{11} + b_1C_{12} + c_1C_{13}) = k\Delta$$

Property V If every element of some column (or row) is the sum of two items, then the determinant is equal to the sum of two determinants; one containing one the first term in place of each sum, the other only the second term. The remaining elements of both determinants are the same as in the given determinant i.e.,

$$\begin{vmatrix} a_1 + x & b_1 & c_1 \\ a_2 + y & b_2 & c_2 \\ a_3 + z & b_3 & c_3 \end{vmatrix} = \begin{vmatrix} a_1 & b_1 & c_1 \\ a_2 & b_2 & c_2 \\ a_3 & b_3 & c_3 \end{vmatrix} + \begin{vmatrix} x & b_1 & c_1 \\ y & b_2 & c_2 \\ z & b_3 & c_3 \end{vmatrix}$$

Proof Let $\Delta = \begin{vmatrix} a_1 + x & b_1 & c_1 \\ a_2 + y & b_2 & c_2 \\ a_3 + z & b_3 & c_3 \end{vmatrix}$

Expanding the determinant along first column, then

$$\Delta=(a_1+x)\begin{vmatrix} b_2 & c_2 \\ b_3 & c_3 \end{vmatrix}-(a_2+y)\begin{vmatrix} b_1 & c_1 \\ b_3 & c_3 \end{vmatrix}+(a_3+z)\begin{vmatrix} b_1 & c_1 \\ b_2 & c_2 \end{vmatrix}$$

$$=a_1\begin{vmatrix} b_2 & c_2 \\ b_3 & c_3 \end{vmatrix}-a_2\begin{vmatrix} b_1 & c_1 \\ b_3 & c_3 \end{vmatrix}+a_3\begin{vmatrix} b_1 & c_1 \\ b_2 & c_2 \end{vmatrix}+x\begin{vmatrix} b_2 & c_2 \\ b_3 & c_3 \end{vmatrix}-y\begin{vmatrix} b_1 & c_1 \\ b_3 & c_3 \end{vmatrix}+z\begin{vmatrix} b_1 & c_1 \\ b_2 & c_2 \end{vmatrix}$$

$$=\begin{vmatrix} a_1 & b_1 & c_1 \\ a_2 & b_2 & c_2 \\ a_3 & b_3 & c_3 \end{vmatrix}+\begin{vmatrix} x & b_1 & c_1 \\ y & b_2 & c_2 \\ z & b_3 & c_3 \end{vmatrix}$$

Remark

1. $$\begin{vmatrix} a_1+b_1+c_1 & d_1+e_1 & f_1 \\ a_2+b_2+c_2 & d_2+e_2 & f_2 \\ a_3+b_3+c_3 & d_3+e_3 & f_3 \end{vmatrix}=\begin{vmatrix} a_1 & d_1 & f_1 \\ a_2 & d_2 & f_2 \\ a_3 & d_3 & f_3 \end{vmatrix}+\begin{vmatrix} a_1 & e_1 & f_1 \\ a_2 & e_2 & f_2 \\ a_3 & e_3 & f_3 \end{vmatrix}+\begin{vmatrix} b_1 & d_1 & f_1 \\ b_2 & d_2 & f_2 \\ b_3 & d_3 & f_3 \end{vmatrix}+\begin{vmatrix} b_1 & e_1 & f_1 \\ b_2 & e_2 & f_2 \\ b_3 & e_3 & f_3 \end{vmatrix}+\begin{vmatrix} c_1 & d_1 & f_1 \\ c_2 & d_2 & f_2 \\ c_3 & d_3 & f_3 \end{vmatrix}+\begin{vmatrix} c_1 & e_1 & f_1 \\ c_2 & e_2 & f_2 \\ c_3 & e_3 & f_3 \end{vmatrix}$$
2. If each element of first row of a determinant consists of algebraic sum of p elements, second row consists of algebraic sum of q elements, third row consists of algebraic sum of r elements and so on.
   Then, given determinant is equivalent to the sum of $p \times q \times r \times \ldots$ other determinants in each of which the elements consists of single term.

Property VI The value of the determinant does not change, if the elements of any row (or column) are increased or diminished by equimultiples of the corresponding elements of any other row (or column) of the determinant.

i.e., $$\begin{vmatrix} a_1+mb_1+nc_1 & b_1 & c_1 \\ a_2+mb_2+nc_2 & b_2 & c_2 \\ a_3+mb_3+nc_3 & b_3 & c_3 \end{vmatrix}=\begin{vmatrix} a_1 & b_1 & c_1 \\ a_2 & b_2 & c_2 \\ a_3 & b_3 & c_3 \end{vmatrix}$$

Proof $$\begin{vmatrix} a_1+mb_1+nc_1 & b_1 & c_1 \\ a_2+mb_2+nc_2 & b_2 & c_2 \\ a_3+mb_3+nc_3 & b_3 & c_3 \end{vmatrix}=\begin{vmatrix} a_1 & b_1 & c_1 \\ a_2 & b_2 & c_2 \\ a_3 & b_3 & c_3 \end{vmatrix}+m\begin{vmatrix} b_1 & b_1 & c_1 \\ b_2 & b_2 & c_2 \\ b_3 & b_3 & c_3 \end{vmatrix}+n\begin{vmatrix} c_1 & b_1 & c_1 \\ c_2 & b_2 & c_2 \\ c_3 & b_3 & c_3 \end{vmatrix}$$

$$=\begin{vmatrix} a_1 & b_1 & c_1 \\ a_2 & b_2 & c_2 \\ a_3 & b_3 & c_3 \end{vmatrix}+m\cdot 0+n\cdot 0=\begin{vmatrix} a_1 & b_1 & c_1 \\ a_2 & b_2 & c_2 \\ a_3 & b_3 & c_3 \end{vmatrix}$$

Property VII If each element on one side or other side or both side of the principal diagonal of determinant is zero, then the value of the determinant is the product of the diagonal element.

i.e., $$\begin{vmatrix} a & 0 & 0 \\ f & b & 0 \\ e & d & c \end{vmatrix}=\begin{vmatrix} a & i & h \\ 0 & b & g \\ 0 & 0 & c \end{vmatrix}=\begin{vmatrix} a & 0 & 0 \\ 0 & b & 0 \\ 0 & 0 & c \end{vmatrix}=abc$$

Proof Let $\Delta=\begin{vmatrix} a\cdots & 0\cdots & 0 \\ f & b & 0 \\ e & d & c \end{vmatrix}$

Expanding along R_1, we get $a\begin{vmatrix} b & 0 \\ d & c \end{vmatrix}=a(bc)=abc$

Property VIII If determinant Δ becomes zero on putting $x=\alpha$, then we say that $(x-\alpha)$ is a factor of Δ.

i.e., if $$\Delta=\begin{vmatrix} x & 5 & 2 \\ x^2 & 9 & 4 \\ x^3 & 16 & 8 \end{vmatrix}$$

at $x=2, \Delta=0$ [because C_1 and C_3 are identical at $x=2$]

and at $x=0, \Delta=0$ [because all elements of C_1 are zero]

Hence, $(x-0)$ and $(x-2)$ are the factors of Δ.

Remark

1. It should be noted that while applying operations on determinant that atleast one row (or column) must remain unchanged.
2. Maximum number of operations at a time = order – 1
3. It should be noted that, if the row (or column) which is changed by multiplied a non-zero number, then the determinant will be divided by that number.

Examples on Properties

| Example 10. Evaluate $\begin{vmatrix} 13 & 16 & 19 \\ 14 & 17 & 20 \\ 15 & 18 & 21 \end{vmatrix}$.

Sol. Let $\Delta=\begin{vmatrix} 13 & 16 & 19 \\ 14 & 17 & 20 \\ 15 & 18 & 21 \end{vmatrix}$

Applying $R_2 \to R_2-R_1$ and $R_3 \to R_3-R_1$, then

$$\Delta=\begin{vmatrix} 13 & 16 & 19 \\ 1 & 1 & 1 \\ 2 & 2 & 2 \end{vmatrix}=2\begin{vmatrix} 13 & 16 & 19 \\ 1 & 1 & 1 \\ 1 & 1 & 1 \end{vmatrix}=0$$

[$\because R_2$ and R_3 are identical]

Example 11. Prove that $\begin{vmatrix} \alpha & \beta & \gamma \\ \theta & \phi & \psi \\ \lambda & \mu & \nu \end{vmatrix} = \begin{vmatrix} \beta & \mu & \phi \\ \alpha & \lambda & \theta \\ \gamma & \nu & \psi \end{vmatrix}$.

Sol. LHS $= \begin{vmatrix} \alpha & \beta & \gamma \\ \theta & \phi & \psi \\ \lambda & \mu & \nu \end{vmatrix} = \begin{vmatrix} \alpha & \theta & \lambda \\ \beta & \phi & \mu \\ \gamma & \psi & \nu \end{vmatrix}$

[interchanging rows and columns]

$$= (-1)\begin{vmatrix} \alpha & \lambda & \theta \\ \beta & \mu & \phi \\ \gamma & \nu & \psi \end{vmatrix} \quad [C_2 \leftrightarrow C_3]$$

$$= (-1)^2 \begin{vmatrix} \beta & \mu & \phi \\ \alpha & \lambda & \theta \\ \gamma & \nu & \psi \end{vmatrix} \quad [R_1 \leftrightarrow R_2]$$

$$= \begin{vmatrix} \beta & \mu & \phi \\ \alpha & \lambda & \theta \\ \gamma & \nu & \psi \end{vmatrix} = \text{RHS}$$

Example 12. Use the properties of determinant and without expanding, prove that

$$\begin{vmatrix} b+c & q+r & y+z \\ c+a & r+p & z+x \\ a+b & p+q & x+y \end{vmatrix} = 2\begin{vmatrix} a & p & x \\ b & q & y \\ c & r & z \end{vmatrix}.$$

Sol. Let LHS $= \Delta = \begin{vmatrix} b+c & q+r & y+z \\ c+a & r+p & z+x \\ a+b & p+q & x+y \end{vmatrix}$

Applying $R_1 \to R_1 + R_2 + R_3$, then

$$\Delta = \begin{vmatrix} 2(a+b+c) & 2(p+q+r) & 2(x+y+z) \\ c+a & r+p & z+x \\ a+b & p+q & x+y \end{vmatrix}$$

$$= 2\begin{vmatrix} a+b+c & p+q+r & x+y+z \\ c+a & r+p & z+x \\ a+b & p+q & x+y \end{vmatrix}$$

Applying $R_2 \to R_2 - R_1$ and $R_3 \to R_3 - R_1$, then

$$\Delta = 2\begin{vmatrix} a+b+c & p+q+r & x+y+z \\ -b & -q & -y \\ -c & -r & -z \end{vmatrix}$$

Applying $R_1 \to R_1 + R_2 + R_3$, then

$$\Delta = 2\begin{vmatrix} a & p & x \\ -b & -q & -y \\ -c & -r & -z \end{vmatrix} = 2(-1)(-1)\begin{vmatrix} a & p & x \\ b & q & y \\ c & r & z \end{vmatrix}$$

$$= 2\begin{vmatrix} a & p & x \\ b & q & y \\ c & r & z \end{vmatrix} = \text{RHS}$$

Example 13. Without expanding as far as possible, prove that

$$\begin{vmatrix} 1 & 1 & 1 \\ x & y & z \\ x^3 & y^3 & z^3 \end{vmatrix} = (x-y)(y-z)(z-x)(x+y+z).$$

Sol. Let $\Delta = \begin{vmatrix} 1 & 1 & 1 \\ x & y & z \\ x^3 & y^3 & z^3 \end{vmatrix}$

for $x = y, \Delta = 0$ [$\because C_1$ and C_2 are identical]

Hence, $(x-y)$ is a factor of Δ. Similarly, $(y-z)$ and $(z-x)$ are factors of Δ. But Δ is a homogeneous expression of the 4 th degree in x, y and z.

There must be one more factor of the 1st degree in x, y and z say $k(x+y+z)$, where k is a constant.

Let $\Delta = k(x-y)(y-z)(z-x)(x+y+z)$

On putting $x = 0, y = 1$ and $z = 2$, then

$$\begin{vmatrix} 1 & 1 & 1 \\ 0 & 1 & 2 \\ 0 & 1 & 8 \end{vmatrix} = k(0-1)(1-2)(2-0)(0+1+2)$$

$\Rightarrow \quad 1 \cdot (8-2) = k(-1)(-1)(2)(3) \quad \therefore k = 1$

$\Rightarrow \quad \Delta = (x-y)(y-z)(z-x)(x+y+z) = \text{RHS}$

Example 14. Solve for x,

$$\begin{vmatrix} 4x & 6x+2 & 8x+1 \\ 6x+2 & 9x+3 & 12x \\ 8x+1 & 12x & 16x+2 \end{vmatrix} = 0.$$

Sol. Applying $C_2 \to C_2 - \frac{3}{2}C_1$ and $C_3 \to C_3 - 2C_1$

Then, $\begin{vmatrix} 4x & 2 & 1 \\ 6x+2 & 0 & -4 \\ 8x+1 & -(3/2) & 0 \end{vmatrix} = 0$

$\Rightarrow 4x(0-6) - (6x+2)\left(0+\frac{3}{2}\right) + (8x+1)(-8-0) = 0$

$\Rightarrow \quad -97x - 11 = 0 \Rightarrow x = -\frac{11}{97}$

Example 15. Prove that

$$\begin{vmatrix} a^2+1 & ab & ac \\ ab & b^2+1 & bc \\ ac & bc & c^2+1 \end{vmatrix} = 1 + a^2 + b^2 + c^2.$$

Sol. Let LHS $= \Delta = \begin{vmatrix} a^2+1 & ab & ac \\ ab & b^2+1 & bc \\ ac & bc & c^2+1 \end{vmatrix}$

On taking common a, b and c from R_1, R_2 and R_3 respectively, then

$$\Delta = abc\begin{vmatrix} \frac{a^2+1}{a} & b & c \\ a & \frac{b^2+1}{b} & c \\ a & b & \frac{c^2+1}{c} \end{vmatrix}$$

Now, multiplying in C_1, C_2 and C_3 by a, b and c respectively, then

$$\Delta = \begin{vmatrix} a^2+1 & b^2 & c^2 \\ a^2 & b^2+1 & c^2 \\ a^2 & b^2 & c^2+1 \end{vmatrix}$$

Applying $C_1 \to C_1 + C_2 + C_3$, then

$$\Delta = \begin{vmatrix} 1+a^2+b^2+c^2 & b^2 & c^2 \\ 1+a^2+b^2+c^2 & b^2+1 & c^2 \\ 1+a^2+b^2+c^2 & b^2 & c^2+1 \end{vmatrix}$$

$$= (1+a^2+b^2+c^2)\begin{vmatrix} 1 & b^2 & c^2 \\ 1 & b^2+1 & c^2 \\ 1 & b^2 & c^2+1 \end{vmatrix}$$

Applying $R_2 \to R_2 - R_1$ and $R_3 \to R_3 - R_1$, then

$$\Delta = (1+a^2+b^2+c^2)\begin{vmatrix} 1 & b^2 & c^2 \\ 0 & 1 & 0 \\ 0 & 0 & 1 \end{vmatrix}$$

$$= (1+a^2+b^2+c^2)\cdot 1\cdot 1\cdot 1 = (1+a^2+b^2+c^2) = \text{RHS}$$

Example 16. If a, b and c are all different and if $\begin{vmatrix} a & a^2 & 1+a^3 \\ b & b^2 & 1+b^3 \\ c & c^2 & 1+c^3 \end{vmatrix} = 0$, prove that $abc = -1$.

Sol. Let $\Delta = \begin{vmatrix} a & a^2 & 1+a^3 \\ b & b^2 & 1+b^3 \\ c & c^2 & 1+c^3 \end{vmatrix} = \begin{vmatrix} a & a^2 & 1 \\ b & b^2 & 1 \\ c & c^2 & 1 \end{vmatrix} + \begin{vmatrix} a & a^2 & a^3 \\ b & b^2 & b^3 \\ c & c^2 & c^3 \end{vmatrix}$

$$= \begin{vmatrix} a & a^2 & 1 \\ b & b^2 & 1 \\ c & c^2 & 1 \end{vmatrix} + abc\begin{vmatrix} 1 & a & a^2 \\ 1 & b & b^2 \\ 1 & c & c^2 \end{vmatrix}$$

$$= (-1)\begin{vmatrix} 1 & a^2 & a \\ 1 & b^2 & b \\ 1 & c^2 & c \end{vmatrix} + abc\begin{vmatrix} 1 & a & a^2 \\ 1 & b & b^2 \\ 1 & c & c^2 \end{vmatrix} \quad [\text{by } C_1 \leftrightarrow C_3]$$

$$= (-1)^2\begin{vmatrix} 1 & a & a^2 \\ 1 & b & b^2 \\ 1 & c & c^2 \end{vmatrix} + abc\begin{vmatrix} 1 & a & a^2 \\ 1 & b & b^2 \\ 1 & c & c^2 \end{vmatrix} \quad [\text{by } C_2 \leftrightarrow C_3]$$

$$= \begin{vmatrix} 1 & a & a^2 \\ 1 & b & b^2 \\ 1 & c & c^2 \end{vmatrix}(1+abc)$$

Applying $R_2 \to R_2 - R_1$ and $R_3 \to R_3 - R_1$, then

$$\Delta = \begin{vmatrix} 1 & a & a^2 \\ 0 & b-a & b^2-a^2 \\ 0 & c-a & c^2-a^2 \end{vmatrix}(1+abc)$$

$$= (b-a)(c-a)(1+abc)\begin{vmatrix} 1 & a & a^2 \\ 0 & 1 & b+a \\ 0 & 1 & c+a \end{vmatrix}$$

Applying $R_3 \to R_3 - R_2$, then

$$= (b-a)(c-a)(1+abc)\begin{vmatrix} 1 & a & a^2 \\ 0 & 1 & b+a \\ 0 & 0 & c-b \end{vmatrix}$$

$$= (b-a)(c-b)(c-a)(1+abc)$$
$$= (a-b)(b-c)(c-a)(1+abc)$$

But given that, $\Delta = 0$

$\therefore \quad (a-b)(b-c)(c-a)(1+abc) = 0$

$\Rightarrow \quad 1+abc = 0$

[since a, b and c are different, so $a \neq b, b \neq c, c \neq a$]

Hence, $abc = -1$

Exercise for Session 2

1 If λ and μ are the cofactors of 3 and -2 respectively, in the determinant $\begin{vmatrix} 1 & 0 & -2 \\ 3 & -1 & 2 \\ 4 & 5 & 6 \end{vmatrix}$, the value of $\lambda + \mu$ is

(a) 5 (b) 7 (c) 9 (d) 11

2 If a, b and c are distinct and $D = \begin{vmatrix} a & b & c \\ b & c & a \\ c & a & b \end{vmatrix}$, then the square of the determinant of its cofactors is divisible by

(a) $(a^2 + b^2 + c^2)^2$ (b) $(ab + bc + ca)^2$ (c) $(a + b + c)^2$ (d) $(a + b + c)^4$

3 An equilateral triangle has each of its sides of length 4 cm. If $(x_r, y_r)(r = 1, 2, 3)$ are its vertices, the value of $\begin{vmatrix} x_1 & y_1 & 1 \\ x_2 & y_2 & 1 \\ x_3 & y_3 & 1 \end{vmatrix}^2$ is

(a) 192 (b) 768 (c) 1024 (d) 128

4 If the lines $ax + y + 1 = 0$, $x + by + 1 = 0$ and $x + y + c = 0$ (a, b and c being distinct and different from 1) are concurrent, the value of $\frac{a}{a-1} + \frac{b}{b-1} + \frac{c}{c-1}$ is

(a) 0 (b) 1 (c) 2 (d) 3

5 If $p + q + r = 0 = a + b + c$, the value of the determinant $\begin{vmatrix} pa & qb & rc \\ qc & ra & pb \\ rb & pc & qa \end{vmatrix}$ is

(a) 0 (b) $pa + qb + rc$ (c) 1 (d) None of the above

6 If p, q and r are in AP, the value of determinant $\begin{vmatrix} a^2 + 2^{n+1} + 2p & b^2 + 2^{n+2} + 3q & c^2 + p \\ 2^n + p & 2^{n+1} + q & 2q \\ a^2 + 2^n + p & b^2 + 2^{n+1} + 2q & c^2 - r \end{vmatrix}$ is

(a) 1 (b) 0 (c) $a^2b^2c^2 - 2^n$ (d) $(a^2 + b^2 + c^2) - 2^n q$

7 Let $\{D_1, D_2, D_3, \ldots, D_n\}$ be the set of third order determinants that can be made with the distinct non-zero real numbers $a_1, a_2, \ldots, a_9$. Then,

(a) $\sum_{i=1}^{n} D_i = 1$ (b) $\sum_{i=1}^{n} D_i = 0$ (c) $D_i = D_j, \forall i, j$ (d) None of these

8 If $\begin{vmatrix} x & 3 & 6 \\ 3 & 6 & x \\ 6 & x & 3 \end{vmatrix} = \begin{vmatrix} 2 & x & 7 \\ x & 7 & 2 \\ 7 & 2 & x \end{vmatrix} = \begin{vmatrix} 4 & 5 & x \\ 5 & x & 4 \\ x & 4 & 5 \end{vmatrix} = 0$, then x is equal to

(a) 0 (b) -9 (c) 3 (d) None of these

9 If $a + b + c = 0$, the one root of $\begin{vmatrix} a - x & c & b \\ c & b - x & a \\ b & a & c - x \end{vmatrix} = 0$ is

(a) 1 (b) 2 (c) $a^2 + b^2 + c^2$ (d) 0

10 If $a^2 + b^2 + c^2 = -2$ and $f(x) = \begin{vmatrix} 1 + a^2x & (1 + b^2)x & (1 + c^2)x \\ (1 + a^2)x & 1 + b^2x & (1 + c^2)x \\ (1 + a^2)x & (1 + b^2)x & 1 + c^2x \end{vmatrix}$, the $f(x)$ is a polynomial of degree

(a) 0 (b) 1 (c) 2 (d) 3

11 If a, b, c, d, e and f are in GP, the value of $\begin{vmatrix} a^2 & d^2 & x \\ b^2 & e^2 & y \\ c^2 & f^2 & z \end{vmatrix}$, is

(a) depends on x and y (b) depends on x and z (c) depends on y and z (d) independent of x, y and z

Session 3

Examples on Largest Value of a Third Order Determinant, Multiplication of Two Determinants of the Same Order, System of Linear Equations, Cramer's Rule, Nature of Solutions of System of Linear Equations, System of Homogeneous Linear Equations

Examples on Largest Value of a Third Order Determinant

| Example 17. Find the largest value of a third order determinant whose elements are 0 or 1.

Sol. Let $\Delta = \begin{vmatrix} a_1 & b_1 & c_1 \\ a_2 & b_2 & c_2 \\ a_3 & b_3 & c_3 \end{vmatrix}$

$$\Delta = a_1(b_2c_3 - b_3c_2) - b_1(a_2c_3 - a_3c_2) + c_1(a_2b_3 - a_3b_2)$$
$$= (a_1b_2c_3 + a_2b_3c_1 + a_3b_1c_2) - (b_1c_3a_2 + b_2c_1a_3 + b_3c_2a_1)$$

Since, each element of Δ is either 0 or 1, therefore the value of the Δ cannot exceed 3. But to attain this value, each expression with a positive sign must equal 1, while those with a negative sign must be 0. However, if $a_1b_2c_3 = a_2b_3c_1 = a_3b_1c_2 = 1$, every element of the determinant must be 1, making its value zero. Thus, noting that

$$\begin{vmatrix} 0 & 1 & 1 \\ 1 & 0 & 1 \\ 1 & 1 & 0 \end{vmatrix} = 2$$

The largest value of Δ is 2.

| Example 18. Find the largest value of a third order determinant, whose elements are 1 or –1.

Sol. Let $\Delta = \begin{vmatrix} a_1 & b_1 & c_1 \\ a_2 & b_2 & c_2 \\ a_3 & b_3 & c_3 \end{vmatrix}$

$$\therefore \Delta = a_1(b_2c_3 - b_3c_2) - b_1(a_2c_3 - a_3c_2) + c_1(a_2b_3 - a_3b_2)$$
$$= (a_1b_2c_3 + a_2b_3c_1 + a_3b_1c_2) - (b_1c_3a_2 + b_2c_1a_3 + b_3c_2a_1)$$

Since, each element of Δ is either 1 or –1, therefore the value of the Δ cannot exceed 6. But it can be 6 only if

$$a_1b_2c_3 = a_2b_3c_1 = a_3b_1c_2 = 1 \quad \text{...(i)}$$

and $$b_1c_3a_2 = b_2c_1a_3 = b_3c_2a_1 = -1 \quad \text{...(ii)}$$

In the first case, the product of the nine elements of the determinant equals 1, while it is –1 in the second case, so the two cannot occur simultaneously i.e., the determinant cannot equal 6. The following determinant satisfies the given conditions and equals the largest value

$$\begin{vmatrix} -1 & 1 & 1 \\ 1 & -1 & 1 \\ 1 & 1 & -1 \end{vmatrix} = -1(1-1) - 1(-1-1) + 1(1+1) = 4$$

| Example 19. Show that the value of a third order determinant whose all elements are 1 or –1 is an even number.

Sol. Let $\Delta = \begin{vmatrix} a_1 & b_1 & c_1 \\ a_2 & b_2 & c_2 \\ a_3 & b_3 & c_3 \end{vmatrix}$

Applying $R_2 \to R_2 - \frac{a_2}{a_1}R_1$ and $R_3 \to R_3 - \frac{a_3}{a_1}R_1$, then

$$\Delta = \begin{vmatrix} a_1 & b_1 & c_1 \\ 0 & b_2 - \frac{a_2}{a_1}b_1 & c_2 - \frac{a_2}{a_1}c_1 \\ 0 & b_3 - \frac{a_3}{a_1}b_1 & c_3 - \frac{a_3}{a_1}c_1 \end{vmatrix}$$

Expanding along C_1, we get

$$\Delta = a_1\left\{\left(b_2 - \frac{a_2}{a_1}b_1\right)\left(c_3 - \frac{a_3}{a_1}c_1\right) - \left(b_3 - \frac{a_3}{a_1}b_1\right)\left(c_2 - \frac{a_2}{a_1}c_1\right)\right\} \quad \text{...(i)}$$

Since, $a_1, a_2, a_3, b_1, b_2, b_3, c_1, c_2, c_3$ are 1 or –1.

$\therefore \quad b_2, \frac{a_2}{a_1}b_1, c_3, \frac{a_3}{a_1}c_1, b_3, \frac{a_3}{a_1}b_1, c_2, \frac{a_2}{a_1}c_1$ are 1 or –1

$\Rightarrow b_2 - \frac{a_2}{a_1}b_1, c_3 - \frac{a_3}{a_1}c_1, b_3 - \frac{a_3}{a_1}b_1, c_2 - \frac{a_2}{a_1}c_1$ are 2, –2 or 0.

$\therefore \quad \left(b_2 - \frac{a_2}{a_1}b_1\right)\left(c_3 - \frac{a_3}{a_1}c_1\right)$

and $\quad \left(b_3 - \frac{a_3}{a_1}b_1\right)\left(c_2 - \frac{a_2}{a_1}c_1\right)$ are 4, – 4

or $\quad 0 =$ an even number

From Eq. (i), $\Delta =$ an even number ($a_1 = 1$ or -1)

Multiplication of Two Determinants of the Same Order

Let the two determinants of third order be

$$\Delta_1 = \begin{vmatrix} a_1 & b_1 & c_1 \\ a_2 & b_2 & c_2 \\ a_3 & b_3 & c_3 \end{vmatrix} \text{ and } \Delta_2 = \begin{vmatrix} \alpha_1 & \beta_1 & \gamma_1 \\ \alpha_2 & \beta_2 & \gamma_2 \\ \alpha_3 & \beta_3 & \gamma_3 \end{vmatrix}$$

Let Δ be their product.

Method of Multiplication (Row by Row)

Take the first row of Δ_1 and the first row of Δ_2 i.e., a_1, b_1, c_1 and $\alpha_1, \beta_1, \gamma_1$ multiplying the corresponding elements and add. The result is $a_1\alpha_1 + b_1\beta_1 + c_1\gamma_1$ is the first element of first row of Δ.

Now, similar product first row of Δ_1 and second row of Δ_2 gives $a_1\alpha_2 + b_1\beta_2 + c_1\gamma_2$ is the second element of first row of Δ and the product of first row of Δ_1 and third row of Δ_2 gives $a_1\alpha_3 + b_1\beta_3 + c_1\gamma_3$ is the third element of first row of Δ. The second row and third row of Δ is obtained by multiplying second row and third row of Δ_1 with 1st, 2nd, 3rd row of Δ_2 in the above manner.

$$\text{Hence, } \Delta = \Delta_1 \times \Delta_2 = \begin{vmatrix} a_1 & b_1 & c_1 \\ a_2 & b_2 & c_2 \\ a_3 & b_3 & c_3 \end{vmatrix} \times \begin{vmatrix} \alpha_1 & \beta_1 & \gamma_1 \\ \alpha_2 & \beta_2 & \gamma_2 \\ \alpha_3 & \beta_3 & \gamma_3 \end{vmatrix}$$

$$= \begin{vmatrix} a_1\alpha_1 + b_1\beta_1 + c_1\gamma_1 & a_1\alpha_2 + b_1\beta_2 + c_1\gamma_2 & a_1\alpha_3 + b_1\beta_3 + c_1\gamma_3 \\ a_2\alpha_1 + b_2\beta_1 + c_2\gamma_1 & a_2\alpha_2 + b_2\beta_2 + c_2\gamma_2 & a_2\alpha_3 + b_2\beta_3 + c_2\gamma_3 \\ a_3\alpha_1 + b_3\beta_1 + c_3\gamma_1 & a_3\alpha_2 + b_3\beta_2 + c_3\gamma_2 & a_3\alpha_3 + b_3\beta_3 + c_3\gamma_3 \end{vmatrix}$$

Multiplication can also be performed row by column or column by row or column by column as required in the problem.

Example 20. Evaluate $\begin{vmatrix} 1 & 2 & 3 \\ -2 & 3 & 2 \\ 3 & 4 & -4 \end{vmatrix} \times \begin{vmatrix} -2 & 1 & 3 \\ 3 & -2 & 1 \\ 2 & 1 & -2 \end{vmatrix}$.

Using the concept of multiplication of determinants.

Sol. Let $\Delta = \begin{vmatrix} 1 & 2 & 3 \\ -2 & 3 & 2 \\ 3 & 4 & -4 \end{vmatrix} \times \begin{vmatrix} -2 & 1 & 3 \\ 3 & -2 & 1 \\ 2 & 1 & -2 \end{vmatrix}$

On multiplying row by row, we get

$$\Delta = \begin{vmatrix} -2+2+9 & 3-4+3 & 2+2-6 \\ 4+3+6 & -6-6+2 & -4+3-4 \\ -6+4-12 & 9-8-4 & 6+4+8 \end{vmatrix}$$

$$= \begin{vmatrix} 9 & 2 & -2 \\ 13 & -10 & -5 \\ -14 & -3 & 18 \end{vmatrix}$$

Applying $C_1 \to C_1 + C_3$ and $C_2 \to C_2 + C_3$, then

$$\Delta = \begin{vmatrix} 7 & 0 & -2 \\ 8 & -15 & -5 \\ 4 & 15 & 18 \end{vmatrix}$$

Applying $R_2 \to R_2 + R_3$, then

$$\Delta = \begin{vmatrix} 7 & 0 & -2 \\ 12 & 0 & 13 \\ 4 & 15 & 18 \end{vmatrix}$$

Expanding along C_2, we get

$$-15\begin{vmatrix} 7 & -2 \\ 12 & 13 \end{vmatrix} = -15(91+24) = -15 \times 115 = -1725$$

Example 21. If $ax_1^2 + by_1^2 + cz_1^2 = ax_2^2 + by_2^2 + cz_2^2 = ax_3^2 + by_3^2 + cz_3^2 = d$, $ax_2x_3 + by_2y_3 + cz_2z_3 = ax_3x_1 + by_3y_1 + cz_3z_1 = ax_1x_2 + by_1y_2 + cz_1z_2 = f$, then prove that

$$\begin{vmatrix} x_1 & y_1 & z_1 \\ x_2 & y_2 & z_2 \\ x_3 & y_3 & z_3 \end{vmatrix} = (d-f)\left\{\frac{(d+2f)}{abc}\right\}^{1/2}$$

Sol. Let LHS $= \Delta = \begin{vmatrix} x_1 & y_1 & z_1 \\ x_2 & y_2 & z_2 \\ x_3 & y_3 & z_3 \end{vmatrix}$

$$\therefore \Delta^2 = \Delta \times \Delta = \begin{vmatrix} x_1 & y_1 & z_1 \\ x_2 & y_2 & z_2 \\ x_3 & y_3 & z_3 \end{vmatrix} \times \begin{vmatrix} x_1 & y_1 & z_1 \\ x_2 & y_2 & z_2 \\ x_3 & y_3 & z_3 \end{vmatrix}$$

$$= \frac{1}{abc}\begin{vmatrix} x_1 & y_1 & z_1 \\ x_2 & y_2 & z_2 \\ x_3 & y_3 & z_3 \end{vmatrix} \times \begin{vmatrix} ax_1 & by_1 & cz_1 \\ ax_2 & by_2 & cz_2 \\ ax_3 & by_3 & cz_3 \end{vmatrix}$$

$$= \frac{1}{abc}\begin{vmatrix} ax_1^2 + by_1^2 + cz_1^2 & ax_1x_2 + by_1y_2 + cz_1z_2 & ax_3x_1 + by_3y_1 + cz_3z_1 \\ ax_1x_2 + by_1y_2 + cz_1z_2 & ax_2^2 + by_2^2 + cz_2^2 & ax_2x_3 + by_2y_3 + cz_2z_3 \\ ax_3x_1 + by_3y_1 + cz_3z_1 & ax_2x_3 + by_2y_3 + cz_2z_3 & ax_3^2 + by_3^2 + cz_3^2 \end{vmatrix}$$ [multiplying row by row]

$$= \frac{1}{abc}\begin{vmatrix} d & f & f \\ f & d & f \\ f & f & d \end{vmatrix}$$ [given]

Applying $C_1 \to C_1 + C_2 + C_3$, then

$$= \frac{1}{abc}\begin{vmatrix} d+2f & f & f \\ d+2f & d & f \\ d+2f & f & d \end{vmatrix} = \frac{(d+2f)}{abc}\begin{vmatrix} 1 & f & f \\ 1 & d & f \\ 1 & f & d \end{vmatrix}$$

Applying $R_2 \to R_2 - R_1$ and $R_3 \to R_3 - R_1$, then

$$= \frac{(d+2f)}{abc}\begin{vmatrix} 1 & f & f \\ 0 & d-f & 0 \\ 0 & 0 & d-f \end{vmatrix} = \frac{(d+2f)}{abc}(d-f)^2$$

$$\therefore \Delta = (d-f)\left\{\frac{d+2f}{abc}\right\}^{1/2} = \text{RHS}$$

An Important Property

If A_1, B_1 and $C_1, \ldots$ are respectively the cofactors of the elements a_1, b_1 and $c_1, \ldots$ of the determinant.

$$\Delta = \begin{vmatrix} a_1 & b_1 & c_1 \\ a_2 & b_2 & c_2 \\ a_3 & b_3 & c_3 \end{vmatrix}, \Delta \neq 0, \text{ then } \begin{vmatrix} A_1 & B_1 & C_1 \\ A_2 & B_2 & C_2 \\ A_3 & B_3 & C_3 \end{vmatrix} = \Delta^2$$

Proof Consider

$$\begin{vmatrix} a_1 & b_1 & c_1 \\ a_2 & b_2 & c_2 \\ a_3 & b_3 & c_3 \end{vmatrix} \times \begin{vmatrix} A_1 & B_1 & C_1 \\ A_2 & B_2 & C_2 \\ A_3 & B_3 & C_3 \end{vmatrix}$$

$$= \begin{vmatrix} a_1A_1 + b_1B_1 + c_1C_1 & a_1A_2 + b_1B_2 + c_1C_2 & a_1A_3 + b_1B_3 + c_1C_3 \\ a_2A_1 + b_2B_1 + c_2C_1 & a_2A_2 + b_2B_2 + c_2C_2 & a_2A_3 + b_2B_3 + c_2C_3 \\ a_3A_1 + b_3B_1 + c_3C_1 & a_3A_2 + b_3B_2 + c_3C_2 & a_3A_3 + b_3B_3 + c_3C_3 \end{vmatrix}$$

[multiplying row by row]

$$= \begin{vmatrix} \Delta & 0 & 0 \\ 0 & \Delta & 0 \\ 0 & 0 & \Delta \end{vmatrix} = \Delta^3 \quad \left(\text{as } a_iA_j + b_iB_j + c_iC_j = \begin{cases} \Delta, & i = j \\ 0, & i \neq j \end{cases} \right)$$

$$\Rightarrow \Delta \begin{vmatrix} A_1 & B_1 & C_1 \\ A_2 & B_2 & C_2 \\ A_3 & B_3 & C_3 \end{vmatrix} = \Delta^3 \text{ or } \begin{vmatrix} A_1 & B_1 & C_1 \\ A_2 & B_2 & C_2 \\ A_3 & B_3 & C_3 \end{vmatrix} = \Delta^2$$

$[\because \Delta \neq 0]$

Note Let $\Delta \neq 0$ and Δ^c denotes the determinant formed by the cofactors of Δ and n is order of determinant, then

$$\Delta^c = \Delta^{n-1}$$

This is known as **power cofactor formula.**

| Example 22. Show that

$$\begin{vmatrix} a^2 + x^2 & ab - cx & ac + bx \\ ab + cx & b^2 + x^2 & bc - ax \\ ac - bx & bc + ax & c^2 + x^2 \end{vmatrix} = \begin{vmatrix} x & c & -b \\ -c & x & a \\ b & -a & x \end{vmatrix}^2.$$

Sol. Let $\Delta = \begin{vmatrix} x & c & -b \\ -c & x & a \\ b & -a & x \end{vmatrix}$

Cofactors of 1st row of Δ are $x^2 + a^2, cx + ab, ac - bx$, cofactors of 2nd row of Δ are $ab - cx, x^2 + b^2, ax + bc$ and cofactors of 3rd row of Δ are $ac + bx, bc - ax, x^2 + c^2$. Hence, the determinant of the cofactors of Δ is

$$\Delta^c = \begin{vmatrix} a^2 + x^2 & ab + cx & ac - bx \\ ab - cx & b^2 + x^2 & bc + ax \\ ac + bx & bc - ax & c^2 + x^2 \end{vmatrix}$$

Interchanging rows into columns, we get

$$\Delta^c = \begin{vmatrix} a^2 + x^2 & ab - cx & ac + bx \\ ab + cx & b^2 + x^2 & bc - ax \\ ac - bx & bc + ax & c^2 + x^2 \end{vmatrix} = \begin{vmatrix} x & c & -b \\ -c & x & a \\ b & -a & x \end{vmatrix}^2 \quad [\because \Delta^c = \Delta^2]$$

| Example 23. Prove the following by multiplication of determinants and power cofactor formula

$$\begin{vmatrix} 0 & c & b \\ c & 0 & a \\ b & a & 0 \end{vmatrix}^2 = \begin{vmatrix} b^2 + c^2 & ab & ac \\ ab & c^2 + a^2 & bc \\ ac & bc & a^2 + b^2 \end{vmatrix}$$

$$= \begin{vmatrix} -a^2 & ab & ac \\ ab & -b^2 & bc \\ ac & bc & -c^2 \end{vmatrix} = 4a^2b^2c^2$$

Sol. Let $\Delta = \begin{vmatrix} 0 & c & b \\ c & 0 & a \\ b & a & 0 \end{vmatrix}$. Expanding along R_1, then

$$\Delta = 0 - c(0 - ab) + b(ac - 0) = 2abc$$

$$\therefore \begin{vmatrix} 0 & c & b \\ c & 0 & a \\ b & a & 0 \end{vmatrix}^2 = \Delta^2 = (2abc)^2 = 4a^2b^2c^2 \quad \ldots\text{(i)}$$

Also, $$\begin{vmatrix} 0 & c & b \\ c & 0 & a \\ b & a & 0 \end{vmatrix}^2 = \begin{vmatrix} 0 & c & b \\ c & 0 & a \\ b & a & 0 \end{vmatrix} \times \begin{vmatrix} 0 & c & b \\ c & 0 & a \\ b & a & 0 \end{vmatrix}$$

$$= \begin{vmatrix} b^2 + c^2 & ab & ac \\ ab & c^2 + a^2 & bc \\ ac & bc & a^2 + b^2 \end{vmatrix} \quad \ldots\text{(ii)}$$

[multiplying row by row]

and $\Delta^c = \begin{vmatrix} -a^2 & ab & ac \\ ab & -b^2 & bc \\ ac & bc & -c^2 \end{vmatrix} = \Delta^{3-1} = \Delta^2$

$$= \begin{vmatrix} 0 & c & b \\ c & 0 & a \\ b & a & 0 \end{vmatrix}^2 \quad \text{...(iii)}$$

From Eqs. (i), (ii) and (iii), we get

$$\begin{vmatrix} 0 & c & b \\ c & 0 & a \\ b & a & 0 \end{vmatrix}^2 = \begin{vmatrix} b^2+c^2 & ab & ac \\ ab & c^2+a^2 & bc \\ ac & bc & a^2+b^2 \end{vmatrix}$$

$$= \begin{vmatrix} -a^2 & ab & ac \\ ab & -b^2 & bc \\ ac & bc & -c^2 \end{vmatrix} = 4a^2b^2c^2$$

Express a Determinant Into Product of Two Determinants

Consider the determinant $\begin{vmatrix} a_1\alpha_1 + b_1\beta_1 & a_1\alpha_2 + b_1\beta_2 \\ a_2\alpha_1 + b_2\beta_1 & a_2\alpha_2 + b_2\beta_2 \end{vmatrix}$

Let $\Delta = \begin{vmatrix} a_1\alpha_1 + b_1\beta_1 & a_1\alpha_2 + b_1\beta_2 \\ a_2\alpha_1 + b_2\beta_1 & a_2\alpha_2 + b_2\beta_2 \end{vmatrix}$

By the property of determinant, Δ can be written as

$$\Delta = \begin{vmatrix} a_1\alpha_1 & a_1\alpha_2 + b_1\beta_2 \\ a_2\alpha_1 & a_2\alpha_2 + b_2\beta_2 \end{vmatrix} + \begin{vmatrix} b_1\beta_1 & a_1\alpha_2 + b_1\beta_2 \\ b_2\beta_1 & a_2\alpha_2 + b_2\beta_2 \end{vmatrix}$$

$$= \begin{vmatrix} a_1\alpha_1 & a_1\alpha_2 \\ a_2\alpha_1 & a_2\alpha_2 \end{vmatrix} + \begin{vmatrix} a_1\alpha_1 & b_1\beta_2 \\ a_2\alpha_1 & b_2\beta_2 \end{vmatrix} + \begin{vmatrix} b_1\beta_1 & a_1\alpha_2 \\ b_2\beta_1 & a_2\alpha_2 \end{vmatrix} + \begin{vmatrix} b_1\beta_1 & b_1\beta_2 \\ b_2\beta_1 & b_2\beta_2 \end{vmatrix}$$

$$= \alpha_1\alpha_2 \begin{vmatrix} a_1 & a_1 \\ a_2 & a_2 \end{vmatrix} + \alpha_1\beta_2 \begin{vmatrix} a_1 & b_1 \\ a_2 & b_2 \end{vmatrix} + \beta_1\alpha_2 \begin{vmatrix} b_1 & a_1 \\ b_2 & a_2 \end{vmatrix} + \beta_1\beta_2 \begin{vmatrix} b_1 & b_1 \\ b_2 & b_2 \end{vmatrix}$$

$$= 0 + \alpha_1\beta_2 \begin{vmatrix} a_1 & b_1 \\ a_2 & b_2 \end{vmatrix} - \beta_1\alpha_2 \begin{vmatrix} a_1 & b_1 \\ a_2 & b_2 \end{vmatrix} + 0$$

$$= \begin{vmatrix} a_1 & b_1 \\ a_2 & b_2 \end{vmatrix} (\alpha_1\beta_2 - \alpha_2\beta_1)$$

$$= \begin{vmatrix} a_1 & b_1 \\ a_2 & b_2 \end{vmatrix} \times \begin{vmatrix} \alpha_1 & \beta_1 \\ \alpha_2 & \beta_2 \end{vmatrix}$$

$$\therefore \begin{vmatrix} a_1\alpha_1 + b_1\beta_1 & a_1\alpha_2 + b_1\beta_2 \\ a_2\alpha_1 + b_2\beta_1 & a_2\alpha_2 + b_2\beta_2 \end{vmatrix} = \begin{vmatrix} a_1 & b_1 \\ a_2 & b_2 \end{vmatrix} \times \begin{vmatrix} \alpha_1 & \beta_1 \\ \alpha_2 & \beta_2 \end{vmatrix}$$

Example 24. Prove that

$$\begin{vmatrix} a_1\alpha_1 + b_1\beta_1 & a_1\alpha_2 + b_1\beta_2 & a_1\alpha_3 + b_1\beta_3 \\ a_2\alpha_1 + b_2\beta_1 & a_2\alpha_2 + b_2\beta_2 & a_2\alpha_3 + b_2\beta_3 \\ a_3\alpha_1 + b_3\beta_1 & a_3\alpha_2 + b_3\beta_2 & a_3\alpha_3 + b_3\beta_3 \end{vmatrix} = 0.$$

Sol. LHS $= \begin{vmatrix} a_1\alpha_1 + b_1\beta_1 & a_1\alpha_2 + b_1\beta_2 & a_1\alpha_3 + b_1\beta_3 \\ a_2\alpha_1 + b_2\beta_1 & a_2\alpha_2 + b_2\beta_2 & a_2\alpha_3 + b_2\beta_3 \\ a_3\alpha_1 + b_3\beta_1 & a_3\alpha_2 + b_3\beta_2 & a_3\alpha_3 + b_3\beta_3 \end{vmatrix}$

$$= \begin{vmatrix} a_1 & b_1 & 0 \\ a_2 & b_2 & 0 \\ a_3 & b_3 & 0 \end{vmatrix} \times \begin{vmatrix} \alpha_1 & \beta_1 & 0 \\ \alpha_2 & \beta_2 & 0 \\ \alpha_3 & \beta_3 & 0 \end{vmatrix} \quad \text{[row by row]}$$

$= 0 \times 0 = 0 =$ RHS

Example 25. Prove that

$$\begin{vmatrix} 2 & \alpha+\beta+\gamma+\delta & \alpha\beta+\gamma\delta \\ \alpha+\beta+\gamma+\delta & 2(\alpha+\beta)(\gamma+\delta) & \alpha\beta(\gamma+\delta)+\gamma\delta(\alpha+\beta) \\ \alpha\beta+\gamma\delta & \alpha\beta(\gamma+\delta)+\gamma\delta(\alpha+\beta) & 2\alpha\beta\gamma\delta \end{vmatrix} = 0.$$

Sol. LHS $= \begin{vmatrix} 2 & \alpha+\beta+\gamma+\delta & \alpha\beta+\gamma\delta \\ \alpha+\beta+\gamma+\delta & 2(\alpha+\beta)(\gamma+\delta) & \alpha\beta(\gamma+\delta)+\gamma\delta(\alpha+\beta) \\ \alpha\beta+\gamma\delta & \alpha\beta(\gamma+\delta)+\gamma\delta(\alpha+\beta) & 2\alpha\beta\gamma\delta \end{vmatrix}$

$$= \begin{vmatrix} 1 & 1 & 0 \\ \alpha+\beta & \gamma+\delta & 0 \\ \alpha\beta & \gamma\delta & 0 \end{vmatrix} \times \begin{vmatrix} 1 & 1 & 0 \\ \gamma+\delta & \alpha+\beta & 0 \\ \gamma\delta & \alpha\beta & 0 \end{vmatrix} \quad \text{[row by row]}$$

$= 0 \times 0 = 0 =$ RHS

Example 26. Prove that

$$\begin{vmatrix} \cos(A-P) & \cos(A-Q) & \cos(A-R) \\ \cos(B-P) & \cos(B-Q) & \cos(B-R) \\ \cos(C-P) & \cos(C-Q) & \cos(C-R) \end{vmatrix} = 0.$$

Sol. LHS $= \begin{vmatrix} \cos(A-P) & \cos(A-Q) & \cos(A-R) \\ \cos(B-P) & \cos(B-Q) & \cos(B-R) \\ \cos(C-P) & \cos(C-Q) & \cos(C-R) \end{vmatrix}$

$$= \begin{vmatrix} \cos A & \sin A & 0 \\ \cos B & \sin B & 0 \\ \cos C & \sin C & 0 \end{vmatrix} \times \begin{vmatrix} \cos P & \sin P & 0 \\ \cos Q & \sin Q & 0 \\ \cos R & \sin R & 0 \end{vmatrix} \quad \text{[row by row]}$$

$= 0 \times 0 = 0 =$ RHS

| Example 27. If α, β and γ are real numbers, without expanding at any stage, prove that

$$\begin{vmatrix} 1 & \cos(\beta-\alpha) & \cos(\gamma-\alpha) \\ \cos(\alpha-\beta) & 1 & \cos(\gamma-\beta) \\ \cos(\alpha-\gamma) & \cos(\beta-\gamma) & 1 \end{vmatrix} = 0.$$

Sol. LHS $= \begin{vmatrix} 1 & \cos(\beta-\alpha) & \cos(\gamma-\alpha) \\ \cos(\alpha-\beta) & 1 & \cos(\gamma-\beta) \\ \cos(\alpha-\gamma) & \cos(\beta-\gamma) & 1 \end{vmatrix}$

$$= \begin{vmatrix} \cos(\alpha-\alpha) & \cos(\beta-\alpha) & \cos(\gamma-\alpha) \\ \cos(\alpha-\beta) & \cos(\beta-\beta) & \cos(\gamma-\beta) \\ \cos(\alpha-\gamma) & \cos(\beta-\gamma) & \cos(\gamma-\gamma) \end{vmatrix}$$

$$= \begin{vmatrix} \cos\alpha & \sin\alpha & 0 \\ \cos\beta & \sin\beta & 0 \\ \cos\gamma & \sin\gamma & 0 \end{vmatrix} \times \begin{vmatrix} \cos\alpha & \sin\alpha & 0 \\ \cos\beta & \sin\beta & 0 \\ \cos\gamma & \sin\gamma & 0 \end{vmatrix}$$

$= 0 \times 0 = 0 =$ RHS

| Example 28. If $a, b, c, x, y, z \in R$, prove that

$$\begin{vmatrix} (a-x)^2 & (b-x)^2 & (c-x)^2 \\ (a-y)^2 & (b-y)^2 & (c-y)^2 \\ (a-z)^2 & (b-z)^2 & (c-z)^2 \end{vmatrix} = \begin{vmatrix} (1+ax)^2 & (1+bx)^2 & (1+cx)^2 \\ (1+ay)^2 & (1+by)^2 & (1+cy)^2 \\ (1+az)^2 & (1+bz)^2 & (1+cz)^2 \end{vmatrix}.$$

Sol. LHS $= \begin{vmatrix} (a-x)^2 & (b-x)^2 & (c-x)^2 \\ (a-y)^2 & (b-y)^2 & (c-y)^2 \\ (a-z)^2 & (b-z)^2 & (c-z)^2 \end{vmatrix}$

$$= \begin{vmatrix} a^2-2ax+x^2 & b^2-2bx+x^2 & c^2-2cx+x^2 \\ a^2-2ay+y^2 & b^2-2by+y^2 & c^2-2cy+y^2 \\ a^2-2az+z^2 & b^2-2bz+z^2 & c^2-2cz+z^2 \end{vmatrix}$$

$$= \begin{vmatrix} 1 & 2x & x^2 \\ 1 & 2y & y^2 \\ 1 & 2z & z^2 \end{vmatrix} \times \begin{vmatrix} a^2 & -a & 1 \\ b^2 & -b & 1 \\ c^2 & -c & 1 \end{vmatrix} \quad \text{[row by row]}$$

$$= \begin{vmatrix} 1 & 2x & x^2 \\ 1 & 2y & y^2 \\ 1 & 2z & z^2 \end{vmatrix} \times (-1)(-1) \begin{vmatrix} 1 & a & a^2 \\ 1 & b & b^2 \\ 1 & c & c^2 \end{vmatrix}$$

[$C_1 \leftrightarrow C_3$ and taking (-1) common from second determinant]

$$= \begin{vmatrix} 1 & 2x & x^2 \\ 1 & 2y & y^2 \\ 1 & 2z & z^2 \end{vmatrix} \times \begin{vmatrix} 1 & a & a^2 \\ 1 & b & b^2 \\ 1 & c & c^2 \end{vmatrix}$$

$$= \begin{vmatrix} 1+2ax+a^2x^2 & 1+2bx+b^2x^2 & 1+2cx+c^2x^2 \\ 1+2ay+a^2y^2 & 1+2by+b^2y^2 & 1+2cy+c^2y^2 \\ 1+2az+a^2z^2 & 1+2bz+b^2z^2 & 1+2cz+c^2z^2 \end{vmatrix}$$

[multiplying row by row]

$$= \begin{vmatrix} (1+ax)^2 & (1+bx)^2 & (1+cx)^2 \\ (1+ay)^2 & (1+by)^2 & (1+cy)^2 \\ (1+az)^2 & (1+bz)^2 & (1+cz)^2 \end{vmatrix} = \text{RHS}$$

System of Linear Equations

(i) Consistent equations *Definite and unique solution* [Intersecting lines]

A system of (linear) equations is said to be consistent, if it has atleast one solution.

For example, System of equations $\left.\begin{matrix} x+y=2 \\ x-y=6 \end{matrix}\right\}$ is consistent because it has a solution $x = 4, y = -2$. Here, two lines intersect at one point. i.e., intersecting lines.

(ii) Inconsistent equations *No solution* [Parallel lines]

A system of (linear) equations is said to be inconsistent, if it has no solution.

Let $a_1x + b_1y + c_1 = 0$ and $a_2x + b_2y + c_2 = 0$, then $\frac{a_1}{a_2} = \frac{b_1}{b_2} \neq \frac{c_1}{c_2}$

$\Rightarrow$ Given equations are inconsistent.

For example, System of equations $\left.\begin{matrix} x+y=2 \\ 2x+2y=5 \end{matrix}\right\}$ is inconsistent because it has no solution i.e., there is no value of x and y which satisfy both the equations. Here, the two lines are parallel.

(iii) Dependent equations *Infinite solutions* [Identical lines]

A system of (linear) equations is said to be dependent, if it has infinite solutions.

Let $a_1x + b_1y + c_1 = 0$ and $a_2x + b_2y + c_2 = 0$, then $\frac{a_1}{a_2} = \frac{b_1}{b_2} = \frac{c_1}{c_2} \Rightarrow$ Given equations are dependent.

For example, System of equations $\left.\begin{matrix} x+2y=3 \\ 2x+4y=6 \end{matrix}\right\}$ is dependent because it has infinite solutions i.e., there are infinite values of x and y satisfy both the equations. Here, the two lines are identical.

Cramer's Rule

System of linear equations in two variables

Let us consider a system of equations be

$$\left.\begin{aligned} a_1x + b_1y + c_1 &= 0 \\ a_2x + b_2y + c_2 &= 0 \end{aligned}\right\} \text{ where } \frac{a_1}{a_2} \neq \frac{b_1}{b_2}$$

On solving by cross-multiplication, we get

$$\frac{x}{(b_1c_2 - b_2c_1)} = \frac{y}{(c_1a_2 - c_2a_1)} = \frac{1}{(a_1b_2 - a_2b_1)}$$

or $$\frac{x}{\begin{vmatrix} b_1 & c_1 \\ b_2 & c_2 \end{vmatrix}} = \frac{y}{\begin{vmatrix} c_1 & a_1 \\ c_2 & a_2 \end{vmatrix}} = \frac{1}{\begin{vmatrix} a_1 & b_1 \\ a_2 & b_2 \end{vmatrix}}$$

or $$x = \frac{\begin{vmatrix} b_1 & c_1 \\ b_2 & c_2 \end{vmatrix}}{\begin{vmatrix} a_1 & b_1 \\ a_2 & b_2 \end{vmatrix}}, y = \frac{\begin{vmatrix} c_1 & a_1 \\ c_2 & a_2 \end{vmatrix}}{\begin{vmatrix} a_1 & b_1 \\ a_2 & b_2 \end{vmatrix}}$$

System of Linear Equations in Three Variables

Let us consider a system of linear equations be

$$a_1x + b_1y + c_1z = d_1 \quad \text{...(i)}$$
$$a_2x + b_2y + c_2z = d_2 \quad \text{...(ii)}$$
$$a_3x + b_3y + c_3z = d_3 \quad \text{...(iii)}$$

Here, $$\Delta = \begin{vmatrix} a_1 & b_1 & c_1 \\ a_2 & b_2 & c_2 \\ a_3 & b_3 & c_3 \end{vmatrix}, \Delta_1 = \begin{vmatrix} d_1 & b_1 & c_1 \\ d_2 & b_2 & c_2 \\ d_3 & b_3 & c_3 \end{vmatrix},$$

$$\Delta_2 = \begin{vmatrix} a_1 & d_1 & c_1 \\ a_2 & d_2 & c_2 \\ a_3 & d_3 & c_3 \end{vmatrix} \text{ and } \Delta_3 = \begin{vmatrix} a_1 & b_1 & d_1 \\ a_2 & b_2 & d_2 \\ a_3 & b_3 & d_3 \end{vmatrix}$$

If $\Delta \neq 0$, then

$$\Delta_1 = \begin{vmatrix} d_1 & b_1 & c_1 \\ d_2 & b_2 & c_2 \\ d_3 & b_3 & c_3 \end{vmatrix} = \begin{vmatrix} a_1x + b_1y + c_1z & b_1 & c_1 \\ a_2x + b_2y + c_2z & b_2 & c_2 \\ a_3x + b_3y + c_3z & b_3 & c_3 \end{vmatrix}$$

Applying $C_1 \to C_1 - yC_2 - zC_3$, then

$$\Delta_1 = \begin{vmatrix} a_1x & b_1 & c_1 \\ a_2x & b_2 & c_2 \\ a_3x & b_3 & c_3 \end{vmatrix} = x\begin{vmatrix} a_1 & b_1 & c_1 \\ a_2 & b_2 & c_2 \\ a_3 & b_3 & c_3 \end{vmatrix} = x\Delta$$

$\therefore$ $$x = \frac{\Delta_1}{\Delta}, \text{ where } \Delta \neq 0$$

Similarly, $\Delta_2 = y\Delta$ and $\Delta_3 = z\Delta$

$\therefore$ $$y = \frac{\Delta_2}{\Delta} \text{ and } z = \frac{\Delta_3}{\Delta}$$

Thus, $$x = \frac{\Delta_1}{\Delta}, y = \frac{\Delta_2}{\Delta}, z = \frac{\Delta_3}{\Delta}, \text{ where } \Delta \neq 0 \quad \text{...(iv)}$$

The rule given in Eq. (iv) to find the values of x, y and z is called the **CRAMER'S RULE**.

Remark

1. Δ_i is obtained by replacing elements of ith columns by d_1, d_2, d_3, where $i = 1, 2, 3$
2. Cramer's rule can be used only when $\Delta \neq 0$.

Nature of Solution of System of Linear Equations

Let us consider a system of linear equations be

$$a_1x + b_1y + c_1z = d_1$$
$$a_2x + b_2y + c_2z = d_2$$
$$a_3x + b_3y + c_3z = d_3$$

Now, there are two cases arise:

***Case* I** If $\Delta \neq 0$

In this case, $x = \frac{\Delta_1}{\Delta}, y = \frac{\Delta_2}{\Delta}, z = \frac{\Delta_3}{\Delta}$

Then, system will have unique finite solutions and so equations are **consistent**.

***Case* II** If $\Delta = 0$

(a) **When atleast one of $\Delta_1, \Delta_2, \Delta_3$ be non-zero**

(i) Let $\Delta_1 \neq 0$, then from $\Delta_1 = x\Delta$ will not be satisfied for any value of x because $\Delta = 0$ and $\Delta_1 \neq 0$ and hence no value of x is possible.

(ii) Let $\Delta_2 \neq 0$, then from $\Delta_2 = y\Delta$ will not be satisfied for any value of y because $\Delta = 0$ and $\Delta_2 \neq 0$ and hence no value of y is possible.

(iii) Let $\Delta_3 \neq 0$, then from $\Delta_3 = z\Delta$ will not be satisfied for any value of z because $\Delta = 0$ and $\Delta_3 \neq 0$ and hence no value of z is possible.

Thus, if $\Delta = 0$ and any of $\Delta_1, \Delta_2, \Delta_3$ is non-zero. Then, the system has no solution i.e., equations are **inconsistent.**

(b) **When $\Delta_1 = \Delta_2 = \Delta_3 = 0$**

In this case, $\left.\begin{aligned} \Delta_1 &= x\Delta \\ \Delta_2 &= y\Delta \\ \Delta_3 &= z\Delta \end{aligned}\right\}$ will be true for all values of x, y and z.

But, since $a_1x + b_1y + c_1z = d_1$, therefore only two of x, y and z will be independent and third will be dependent on the other two.

Thus, the system will have infinite number of solutions i.e., equations are **consistent**.

Remark

1. If $\Delta \neq 0$, the system will have unique finite solution and so equations are consistent.
2. If $\Delta = 0$ and atleast one of $\Delta_1, \Delta_2, \Delta_3$ be non-zero, then the system has no solution i.e., equations are inconsistent.
3. If $\Delta = \Delta_1 = \Delta_2 = \Delta_3 = 0$, the equations will have infinite number of solutions i.e. equations are consistent.

Example 29. Solve the following system of equations by Cramer's rule.

$$x + y = 4 \text{ and } 3x - 2y = 9$$

Sol. Here, $\Delta = \begin{vmatrix} 1 & 1 \\ 3 & -2 \end{vmatrix} = -2 - 3 = -5 \neq 0$

$\Delta_1 = \begin{vmatrix} 4 & 1 \\ 9 & -2 \end{vmatrix} = -8 - 9 = -17$

and $\Delta_2 = \begin{vmatrix} 1 & 4 \\ 3 & 9 \end{vmatrix} = 9 - 12 = -3$

Then, by Cramer's rule

$$x = \frac{\Delta_1}{\Delta} = \frac{-17}{-5} = \frac{17}{5} \text{ and } y = \frac{\Delta_2}{\Delta} = \frac{-3}{-5} = \frac{3}{5}$$

$$\therefore \quad x = \frac{17}{5}, y = \frac{3}{5}$$

Example 30. Solve the following system of equations by Cramer's rule.

$$x + y + z = 9$$
$$2x + 5y + 7z = 52$$
$$2x + y - z = 0$$

Sol. Here, $\Delta = \begin{vmatrix} 1 & 1 & 1 \\ 2 & 5 & 7 \\ 2 & 1 & -1 \end{vmatrix}$

Applying $C_2 \to C_2 - C_1$ and $C_3 \to C_3 - C_1$, then

$$= \begin{vmatrix} 1 & 0 & 0 \\ 2 & 3 & 5 \\ 2 & -1 & -3 \end{vmatrix}$$

Expanding along R_1, then

$\Delta = 1\begin{vmatrix} 3 & 5 \\ -1 & -3 \end{vmatrix} = -9 + 5 = -4 \neq 0$, $\Delta_1 = \begin{vmatrix} 9 & 1 & 1 \\ 52 & 5 & 7 \\ 0 & 1 & -1 \end{vmatrix}$

Applying $C_2 \to C_2 + C_3$, then

$$\Delta_1 = \begin{vmatrix} 9 & 2 & 1 \\ 52 & 12 & 7 \\ 0 & 0 & -1 \end{vmatrix}$$

Expanding along R_3, then

$$\Delta_1 = (-1)\begin{vmatrix} 9 & 2 \\ 52 & 12 \end{vmatrix} = -(108 - 104) = -4$$

$$\Rightarrow \quad \Delta_2 = \begin{vmatrix} 1 & 9 & 1 \\ 2 & 52 & 7 \\ 2 & 0 & -1 \end{vmatrix}$$

Applying $C_1 \to C_1 + 2C_3$, then

$$\Delta_2 = \begin{vmatrix} 3 & 9 & 1 \\ 16 & 52 & 7 \\ 0 & 0 & -1 \end{vmatrix}$$

Expanding along R_3, then

$\Delta_2 = (-1)\begin{vmatrix} 3 & 9 \\ 16 & 52 \end{vmatrix} = -(156 - 144) = -12$ and $\Delta_3 = \begin{vmatrix} 1 & 1 & 9 \\ 2 & 5 & 52 \\ 2 & 1 & 0 \end{vmatrix}$

Applying $C_1 \to C_1 - 2C_2$, then

$$\Delta_3 = \begin{vmatrix} -1 & 1 & 9 \\ -8 & 5 & 52 \\ 0 & 1 & 0 \end{vmatrix}$$

Expanding along R_3, then

$$\Delta_3 = (-1)\begin{vmatrix} -1 & 9 \\ -8 & 52 \end{vmatrix}$$
$$= -(-52 + 72) = -20$$

Then, by Cramer's rule

$$x = \frac{\Delta_1}{\Delta} = \frac{-4}{-4} = 1, y = \frac{-12}{-4} = 3$$

and $z = \dfrac{\Delta_3}{\Delta} = \dfrac{-20}{-4} = 5$

$$\therefore \quad x = 1, y = 3, z = 5$$

Example 31. For what values of p and q, the system of equations

$$x + y + z = 6$$
$$x + 2y + 3z = 10$$
$$x + 2y + pz = q \text{ has}$$

(i) unique solution?
(ii) an infinitely many solutions?
(iii) no solution?

Sol. Given equations are

$$x + y + z = 6 \quad \Rightarrow \quad x + 2y + 3z = 10$$
$$x + 2y + pz = q$$

$$\therefore \quad \Delta = \begin{vmatrix} 1 & 1 & 1 \\ 1 & 2 & 3 \\ 1 & 2 & p \end{vmatrix} = (p-3) \Rightarrow \Delta_1 = \begin{vmatrix} 6 & 1 & 1 \\ 10 & 2 & 3 \\ q & 2 & p \end{vmatrix}$$

$$= 6(2p-6) - 1(10p-3q) + (20-2q)$$

$$= 2p + q - 16$$

$$\Delta_2 = \begin{vmatrix} 1 & 6 & 1 \\ 1 & 10 & 3 \\ 1 & q & p \end{vmatrix}$$

$$= 1(10p-3q) - 6(p-3) + 1(q-10) = 4p - 2q + 8$$

$$\text{and } \Delta_3 = \begin{vmatrix} 1 & 1 & 6 \\ 1 & 2 & 10 \\ 1 & 2 & q \end{vmatrix}$$

$$= 1(2q-20) - 1(q-10) + 6(2-2) = q - 10$$

(i) For unique solution, $A \neq 0 \Rightarrow p \neq 3, q \in R$

(ii) For infinitely many solutions, $\Delta = \Delta_1 = \Delta_2 = \Delta_3 = 0$

$$\therefore \quad p = 3, q = 10$$

(iii) For no solution, $\Delta = 0$ and atleast one of $\Delta_1, \Delta_2, \Delta_3$ is non-zero is $p = 3$ and $q \neq 10$.

Condition for Consistency of Three Linear Equations in Two Unknowns

Let us consider a system of linear equations in x and y

$$a_1 x + b_1 y + c_1 = 0 \quad \text{...(i)}$$

$$a_2 x + b_2 y + c_2 = 0 \quad \text{...(ii)}$$

$$a_3 x + b_3 y + c_3 = 0 \quad \text{...(iii)}$$

will be consistent, the values of x and y obtained from any two equations satisfy the third equation.

On solving Eqs. (ii) and (iii) by Cramer's rule, we have

$$\frac{x}{\begin{vmatrix} b_2 & c_2 \\ b_3 & c_3 \end{vmatrix}} = \frac{y}{\begin{vmatrix} c_2 & a_2 \\ c_3 & a_3 \end{vmatrix}} = \frac{1}{\begin{vmatrix} a_2 & b_2 \\ a_3 & b_3 \end{vmatrix}}$$

These values of x and y will satisfy Eq. (i), then

$$a_1 \begin{vmatrix} b_2 & c_2 \\ b_3 & c_3 \end{vmatrix} + b_1 \begin{vmatrix} c_2 & a_2 \\ c_3 & a_3 \end{vmatrix} + c_1 \begin{vmatrix} a_2 & b_2 \\ a_3 & b_3 \end{vmatrix} = 0$$

$$\Rightarrow \quad a_1 \begin{vmatrix} b_2 & c_2 \\ b_3 & c_3 \end{vmatrix} - b_1 \begin{vmatrix} a_2 & c_2 \\ a_3 & c_3 \end{vmatrix} + c_1 \begin{vmatrix} a_2 & b_2 \\ a_3 & b_3 \end{vmatrix} = 0$$

$$\therefore \quad \begin{vmatrix} a_1 & b_1 & c_1 \\ a_2 & b_2 & c_2 \\ a_3 & b_3 & c_3 \end{vmatrix} = 0$$

which is the required condition.

Remark

For consistency of three linear equations in two knowns, the number of solution is one.

Example 32. Find the value of λ, if the following equations are consistent

$$x + y - 3 = 0$$

$$(1+\lambda)x + (2+\lambda)y - 8 = 0$$

$$x - (1+\lambda)y + (2+\lambda) = 0$$

Sol. The given equations in two unknowns are consistent, then

$$\begin{vmatrix} 1 & 1 & -3 \\ (1+\lambda) & (2+\lambda) & -8 \\ 1 & -(1+\lambda) & (2+\lambda) \end{vmatrix} = 0$$

Applying $C_2 \to C_2 - C_1$ and $C_3 \to C_3 + 3C_1$, then

$$\begin{vmatrix} 1 & \cdots & 0 & \cdots & 0 \\ \vdots & & & & \\ (1+\lambda) & & 1 & & (3\lambda-5) \\ \vdots & & & & \\ 1 & & -(2+\lambda) & & (5+\lambda) \end{vmatrix} = 0$$

Expanding along R_1, then

$$1 \cdot \begin{vmatrix} 1 & 3\lambda - 5 \\ -(2+\lambda) & (5+\lambda) \end{vmatrix} = 0$$

$$\Rightarrow \quad (5+\lambda) + (2+\lambda)(3\lambda - 5) = 0$$

$$\Rightarrow \quad 3\lambda^2 + 2\lambda - 5 = 0 \text{ or } (3\lambda+5)(\lambda-1) = 0$$

$$\therefore \quad \lambda = 1, -5/3$$

System of Homogeneous Linear Equations

Let us consider a system of homogeneous linear equations in three unknown x, y and z be

$$a_1 x + b_1 y + c_1 z = 0 \quad \text{...(i)}$$

$$a_2 x + b_2 y + c_2 z = 0 \quad \text{...(ii)}$$

$$a_3 x + b_3 y + c_3 z = 0 \quad \text{...(iii)}$$

Here, $$\Delta = \begin{vmatrix} a_1 & b_1 & c_1 \\ a_2 & b_2 & c_2 \\ a_3 & b_3 & c_3 \end{vmatrix}$$

***Case* I** If $\Delta \neq 0$, then $x = 0, y = 0, z = 0$ is the only solution of above system. This solution is called a **Trivial solution.**

***Case* II** If $\Delta = 0$, atleast one of x, y and z is non-zero. This solution is called a **Non-trivial solution.**

Explanation From Eqs. (ii) and (iii), we get

$$\frac{x}{(b_2 c_3 - b_3 c_2)} = \frac{y}{(c_2 a_3 - c_3 a_2)} = \frac{z}{(a_2 b_3 - a_3 b_2)}$$

or $$\frac{x}{\begin{vmatrix} b_2 & c_2 \\ b_3 & c_3 \end{vmatrix}} = \frac{y}{\begin{vmatrix} c_2 & a_2 \\ c_3 & a_3 \end{vmatrix}} = \frac{z}{\begin{vmatrix} a_2 & b_2 \\ a_3 & b_3 \end{vmatrix}} = k[\text{say}] \ (\neq 0)$$

$$\therefore \quad x = k \begin{vmatrix} b_2 & c_2 \\ b_3 & c_3 \end{vmatrix}, y = k \begin{vmatrix} c_2 & a_2 \\ c_3 & a_3 \end{vmatrix} \text{ and } z = k \begin{vmatrix} a_2 & b_2 \\ a_3 & b_3 \end{vmatrix}$$

On putting these values of x, y and z in Eq. (i), we get

$$a_1\left\{k\begin{vmatrix} b_2 & c_2 \\ b_3 & c_3 \end{vmatrix}\right\}+b_1\left\{k\begin{vmatrix} c_2 & a_2 \\ c_3 & a_3 \end{vmatrix}\right\}+c_1\left\{k\begin{vmatrix} a_2 & b_2 \\ a_3 & b_3 \end{vmatrix}\right\}=0$$

$$\Rightarrow \quad a_1\begin{vmatrix} b_2 & c_2 \\ b_3 & c_3 \end{vmatrix}-b_1\begin{vmatrix} a_2 & c_2 \\ a_3 & c_3 \end{vmatrix}+c_1\begin{vmatrix} a_2 & b_2 \\ a_3 & b_3 \end{vmatrix}=0 \quad [\because k \neq 0]$$

or
$$\begin{vmatrix} a_1 & b_1 & c_1 \\ a_2 & b_2 & c_2 \\ a_3 & b_3 & c_3 \end{vmatrix}=0 \text{ or } \Delta=0$$

This is the condition for system have **Non-trivial solution.**

Remark

1. If $\Delta \neq 0$, the given system of equations has **only zero** solution for all its variables, then the given equations are said to have **Trivial solution**.
2. If $\Delta = 0$, the given system of equations has **no solution** or **infinite solutions** for all its variables, then the given equations are said to have **Non-trivial solution**.

Example 33. Find all values of λ for which the equations

$$(\lambda-1)x+(3\lambda+1)y+2\lambda z=0$$
$$(\lambda-1)x+(4\lambda-2)y+(\lambda+3)z=0$$
$$2x+(3\lambda+1)y+3(\lambda-1)z=0$$

possess non-trivial solution and find the ratios $x:y:z$, where λ has the smallest of these values.

Sol. The given system of linear equations has non-trivial solution, then we must have

$$\begin{vmatrix} \lambda-1 & 3\lambda+1 & 2\lambda \\ \lambda-1 & 4\lambda-2 & \lambda+3 \\ 2 & 3\lambda+1 & 3(\lambda-1) \end{vmatrix}=0$$

Applying $R_2 \to R_2 - R_1$ and $R_3 \to R_3 - R_1$, then

$$\begin{vmatrix} \lambda-1 & 3\lambda+1 & 2\lambda \\ 0 & \lambda-3 & -\lambda+3 \\ 3-\lambda & 0 & \lambda-3 \end{vmatrix}=0$$

Applying $C_3 \to C_3 + C_2$, then

$$\begin{vmatrix} \lambda-1 & 3\lambda+1 & 5\lambda+1 \\ 0 & \lambda-3 & 0 \\ 3-\lambda & 0 & \lambda-3 \end{vmatrix}=0$$

Expanding along R_2, we get

$$(\lambda-3)\begin{vmatrix} \lambda-1 & 5\lambda+1 \\ 3-\lambda & \lambda-3 \end{vmatrix}=0$$

$$\Rightarrow \quad (\lambda-3)[(\lambda-1)(\lambda-3)-(3-\lambda)(5\lambda+1)]=0$$

$$\Rightarrow \quad (\lambda-3)^2 \cdot 6\lambda=0$$

$$\therefore \quad \lambda=0,3$$

Here, smallest value of λ is 0.

$\therefore$ The first two equations can be written as $x-y=0$ and $x+2y-3z=0$.

Using Cramer's rule, we get

$$\frac{x}{\begin{vmatrix} -1 & 0 \\ 2 & -3 \end{vmatrix}}=\frac{y}{\begin{vmatrix} 0 & 1 \\ -3 & 1 \end{vmatrix}}=\frac{z}{\begin{vmatrix} 1 & -1 \\ 1 & 2 \end{vmatrix}}$$

$$\Rightarrow \quad \frac{x}{3}=\frac{y}{3}=\frac{z}{3} \Rightarrow \frac{x}{1}=\frac{y}{1}=\frac{z}{1}$$

$$\therefore \quad x:y:z=1:1:1$$

Example 34. Given, $x=cy+bz$, $y=az+cx$ and $z=bx+ay$, where x, y and z are not all zero, prove that $a^2+b^2+c^2+2abc=1$.

Sol. The given equation can be rewritten as

$$x-cy-bz=0$$
$$-cx+y-az=0$$
$$-bx-ay+z=0$$

Since, x, y and z are not all zero, the system will have non-trivial solution, if

$$\begin{vmatrix} 1 & -c & -b \\ -c & 1 & -a \\ -b & -a & 1 \end{vmatrix}=0$$

Applying $C_2 \to C_2 + cC_1$ and $C_3 \to C_3 + bC_1$, then

$$\begin{vmatrix} 1 & 0 & 0 \\ -c & 1-c^2 & -a-bc \\ -b & -a-bc & 1-b^2 \end{vmatrix}=0$$

Expanding along R_1, we get

$$1\begin{vmatrix} 1-c^2 & -a-bc \\ -a-bc & 1-b^2 \end{vmatrix}=0$$

$$\Rightarrow \quad (1-c^2)(1-b^2)-(a+bc)^2=0$$

$$\Rightarrow \quad 1-b^2-c^2+b^2c^2-a^2-b^2c^2-2abc=0$$

$$\Rightarrow \quad a^2+b^2+c^2+2abc=1$$

Exercise for Session 3

1. Number of second order determinants which have maximum values whose each entry is either −1or 1 is equal to
(a) 2 (b) 4 (c) 6 (d) 8

2. Minimum value of a second order determinant whose each entry is either 1 or 2 is equal to
(a) 0 (b) −1 (c) −2 (d) −3

3. If $l_i^2 + m_i^2 + n_i^2 = 1, (i = 1, 2, 3)$ and $l_i l_j + m_i m_j + n_i n_j = 0, (i \neq j; i, j = 1, 2, 3)$ and $\Delta = \begin{vmatrix} l_1 & m_1 & n_1 \\ l_2 & m_2 & n_2 \\ l_3 & m_3 & n_3 \end{vmatrix}$, then
(a) $|\Delta| = 3$ (b) $|\Delta| = 2$ (c) $|\Delta| = 1$ (d) $|\Delta| = 0$

4. Let $\Delta_0 = \begin{vmatrix} a_{11} & a_{12} & a_{13} \\ a_{21} & a_{22} & a_{23} \\ a_{31} & a_{32} & a_{33} \end{vmatrix}$ and Δ_1 denotes the determinant formed by the cofactors of elements of Δ_0 and Δ_2 denote the determinant formed by the cofactors of Δ_1 and so on. Δ_n denotes the determinant formed by the cofactors of Δ_{n-1}, the determinant value of Δ_n is
(a) Δ_0^{2n} (b) $\Delta_0^{2^n}$ (c) $\Delta_0^{n^2}$ (d) Δ_0^2

5. If $\begin{vmatrix} 1 & x & x^2 \\ x & x^2 & 1 \\ x^2 & 1 & x \end{vmatrix} = 3$, then the value of $\begin{vmatrix} x^3 - 1 & 0 & x - x^4 \\ 0 & x - x^4 & x^3 - 1 \\ x - x^4 & x^3 - 1 & 0 \end{vmatrix}$, is
(a) 6 (b) 9 (c) 18 (d) 27

6. The value of the determinant $\begin{vmatrix} (a_1 - b_1)^2 & (a_1 - b_2)^2 & (a_1 - b_3)^2 & (a_1 - b_4)^2 \\ (a_2 - b_1)^2 & (a_2 - b_2)^2 & (a_2 - b_3)^2 & (a_2 - b_4)^2 \\ (a_3 - b_1)^2 & (a_3 - b_2)^2 & (a_3 - b_3)^2 & (a_3 - b_4)^2 \\ (a_4 - b_1)^2 & (a_4 - b_2)^2 & (a_4 - b_3)^2 & (a_4 - b_4)^2 \end{vmatrix}$, is
(a) depends on $a_i, i = 1, 2, 3, 4$ (b) depends on $b_i, i = 1, 2, 3, 4$ (c) depends on $c_i, i = 1, 2, 3, 4$ (d) 0

7. Value of $\begin{vmatrix} 1 + x_1 & 1 + x_1 x & 1 + x_1 x^2 \\ 1 + x_2 & 1 + x_2 x & 1 + x_2 x^2 \\ 1 + x_3 & 1 + x_3 x & 1 + x_3 x^2 \end{vmatrix}$ depends upon
(a) only x (b) only x_1 (c) only x_2 (d) None of these

8. If the system of linear equations $x + y + z = 6$, $x + 2y + 3z = 14$ and $2x + 5y + \lambda z = \mu$ $(\lambda, \mu \in R)$ has a unique solution, then
(a) $\lambda \neq 8$ (b) $\lambda = 8$ and $\mu \neq 36$ (c) $\lambda = 8$ and $\mu = 36$ (d) None of these

9. The system of equations $ax - y - z = a - 1$, $x - ay - z = a - 1$, $x - y - az = a - 1$ has no solution, if a is
(a) either −2 or 1 (b) −2 (c) 1 (d) not (−2)

10. The system of equations $x + 2y - 4z = 3$, $2x - 3y + 2z = 5$ and $x - 12y + 16z = 1$ has
(a) inconsistent solution (b) unique solution (c) infinitely many solutions (d) None of these

11. If $c < 1$ and the system of equations $x + y - 1 = 0$, $2x - y - c = 0$ and $-bx + 3by - c = 0$ is consistent, then the possible real values of b are
(a) $b \in \left(-3, \frac{3}{4}\right)$ (b) $b \in \left(-\frac{3}{2}, 4\right)$ (c) $b \in \left(-\frac{3}{4}, 3\right)$ (d) None of these

12. The equations $x + 2y = 3$, $y - 2x = 1$ and $7x - 6y + a = 0$ are consistent for
(a) $a = 7$ (b) $a = 1$ (c) $a = 11$ (d) None of these

13. Values of k for which the system of equations $x + ky + 3z = 0$, $kx + 2y + 2z = 0$ and $2x + 3y + 4z = 0$ possesses non-trivial solution
(a) $\left\{2, \frac{5}{4}\right\}$ (b) $\left\{-2, \frac{5}{4}\right\}$ (c) $\left\{2, -\frac{5}{9}\right\}$ (d) $\left\{-2, -\frac{5}{4}\right\}$

Session 4

Differentiation of Determinant, Integration of a Determinant, Walli's Formula, Use of Σ in Determinant

Differentiation of Determinant

Let $\Delta(x)$ be a determinant of order n. If we write $\Delta(x)=[C_1\ C_2\ C_3 \dots C_n]$, where $C_1, C_2, C_3, \dots, C_n$ denotes 1st, 2nd, 3rd, …, nth columns respectively, then

$$\Delta'(x)=[C_1'\ C_2\ C_3 \cdots C_n]+[C_1\ C'_2\ C_3 \cdots C_n] +[C_1\ C_2\ C_3' \cdots C_n]+\cdots+[C_1\ C_2\ C_3 \cdots C_n']$$

$$=\Sigma\,[C_1{}'\ C_2\ C_3 \cdots C_n]$$

where C_i' denotes the column which contains the derivative of all the functions in the ith column C_i. Also, if

$$\Delta(x)=\begin{bmatrix} R_1 \\ R_2 \\ R_3 \\ \vdots \\ R_n \end{bmatrix}$$

where $R_1, R_2, R_3, \dots, R_n$ denote 1st, 2nd, 3rd, …, nth rows respectively, then

$$\Delta'(x)=\begin{bmatrix} R_1' \\ R_2 \\ R_3 \\ \vdots \\ R_n \end{bmatrix}+\begin{bmatrix} R_1 \\ R_2' \\ R_3 \\ \vdots \\ R_n \end{bmatrix}+\begin{bmatrix} R_1 \\ R_2 \\ R_3' \\ \vdots \\ R_n \end{bmatrix}+\cdots+\begin{bmatrix} R_1 \\ R_2 \\ R_3 \\ \vdots \\ R_n' \end{bmatrix}=\Sigma\begin{bmatrix} R_1' \\ R_2 \\ R_3 \\ \vdots \\ R_n \end{bmatrix}$$

where R_i' denotes the row which contains the derivative of all the functions in the ith row R_i.

***Corollary* I** For $n=2$,

$$\Delta(x)=[C_1\ C_2], \text{ then } \Delta'(x)=[C_1'\ C_2]+[C_1\ C_2']$$

Also, if $\Delta(x)=\begin{bmatrix} R_1 \\ R_2 \end{bmatrix}$, then $\Delta'(x)=\begin{bmatrix} R'_1 \\ R_2 \end{bmatrix}+\begin{bmatrix} R_1 \\ R'_2 \end{bmatrix}$

For example, Let $\Delta(x)=\begin{vmatrix} a_1(x) & b_1(x) \\ a_2(x) & b_2(x) \end{vmatrix}$, then

$$\Delta'(x)=\begin{vmatrix} a_1'(x) & b_1'(x) \\ a_2(x) & b_2(x) \end{vmatrix}+\begin{vmatrix} a_1(x) & b_1(x) \\ a_2'(x) & b_2'(x) \end{vmatrix}$$

[derivative according to rowwise]

***Corollary* II** For $n=3$, $\Delta(x)=[C_1\ C_2\ C_3]$, then

$$\Delta'(x)=[C_1'\ C_2\ C_3]+[C_1\ C_2'\ C_3]+[C_1\ C_2\ C_3']$$

Also, if $\Delta(x)=\begin{bmatrix} R_1 \\ R_2 \\ R_3 \end{bmatrix}$, then $\Delta'(x)=\begin{bmatrix} R'_1 \\ R_2 \\ R_3 \end{bmatrix}+\begin{bmatrix} R_1 \\ R'_2 \\ R_3 \end{bmatrix}+\begin{bmatrix} R_1 \\ R_2 \\ R'_3 \end{bmatrix}$

For example, Let $\Delta(x)=\begin{vmatrix} a_1(x) & a_2(x) & a_3(x) \\ b_1(x) & b_2(x) & b_3(x) \\ c_1(x) & c_2(x) & c_3(x) \end{vmatrix}$, then

$$\Delta'(x)=\begin{vmatrix} a_1'(x) & a_2'(x) & a_3'(x) \\ b_1(x) & b_2(x) & b_3(x) \\ c_1(x) & c_2(x) & c_3(x) \end{vmatrix}+\begin{vmatrix} a_1(x) & a_2(x) & a_3(x) \\ b_1'(x) & b_2'(x) & b_3'(x) \\ c_1(x) & c_2(x) & c_3(x) \end{vmatrix}+\begin{vmatrix} a_1(x) & a_2(x) & a_3(x) \\ b_1(x) & b_2(x) & b_3(x) \\ c_1'(x) & c_2'(x) & c_3'(x) \end{vmatrix}$$

[derivative according to rowwise]

Remark

1. In a third order determinant, if two rows (columns) consist functions of x and third row (column) is constant, let

$$\Delta(x)=\begin{vmatrix} a_1(x) & a_2(x) & a_3(x) \\ b_1(x) & b_2(x) & b_3(x) \\ c_1 & c_2 & c_3 \end{vmatrix}, \text{ then}$$

$$\Delta'(x)=\begin{vmatrix} a_1'(x) & a_2'(x) & a_3'(x) \\ b_1(x) & b_2(x) & b_3(x) \\ c_1 & c_2 & c_3 \end{vmatrix}+\begin{vmatrix} a_1(x) & a_2(x) & a_3(x) \\ b_1'(x) & b_2'(x) & b_3'(x) \\ c_1 & c_2 & c_3 \end{vmatrix}$$

2. In a third order determinant, if only one row (column) consists functions of x and other rows (columns) are constant, let

$$\Delta(x)=\begin{vmatrix} a_1(x) & a_2(x) & a_3(x) \\ b_1 & b_2 & b_3 \\ c_1 & c_2 & c_3 \end{vmatrix}, \text{ then } \Delta'(x)=\begin{vmatrix} a_1'(x) & a_2'(x) & a_3'(x) \\ b_1 & b_2 & b_3 \\ c_1 & c_2 & c_3 \end{vmatrix}$$

and in general

$$\frac{d^n}{dx^n}\{\Delta(x)\}=\begin{vmatrix} \frac{d^n}{dx^n}\{a_1(x)\} & \frac{d^n}{dx^n}\{a_2(x)\} & \frac{d^n}{dx^n}\{a_3(x)\} \\ b_1 & b_2 & b_3 \\ c_1 & c_2 & c_3 \end{vmatrix}$$

Important Derivatives (Committed to Memory)

If a and b are constants and $n \in N$, then

1. if $y = (ax+b)^n$, then $\dfrac{d^n y}{dx^n} = n!\, a^n$
2. if $y = \sin(ax+b)$, then $\dfrac{d^n y}{dx^n} = \sin\left(\dfrac{n\pi}{2} + ax + b\right) \cdot a^n$
3. if $y = \cos(ax+b)$, then $\dfrac{d^n y}{dx^n} = \cos\left(\dfrac{n\pi}{2} + ax + b\right) \cdot a^n$

Example 35. If $f(x) = \begin{vmatrix} \sin x & \cos x & \sin x \\ \cos x & -\sin x & \cos x \\ x & 1 & 1 \end{vmatrix}$, find the value of $2^{f'(0)} + \{f'(1)\}^2$.

Sol. $f'(x) = \begin{vmatrix} \cos x & -\sin x & \cos x \\ \cos x & -\sin x & \cos x \\ x & 1 & 1 \end{vmatrix} + \begin{vmatrix} \sin x & \cos x & \sin x \\ -\sin x & -\cos x & -\sin x \\ x & 1 & 1 \end{vmatrix}$

$+ \begin{vmatrix} \sin x & \cos x & \sin x \\ \cos x & -\sin x & \cos x \\ 1 & 0 & 0 \end{vmatrix}$ [derivative according to rowwise]

$= 0 + 0 + 1 \begin{vmatrix} \cos x & \sin x \\ -\sin x & \cos x \end{vmatrix} = \cos^2 x + \sin^2 x = 1$

$\therefore f'(x) = 1 \Rightarrow f'(0) = 1$ and $f'(1) = 1$

$\Rightarrow \quad 2^{f'(0)} + \{f'(1)\}^2 = 2^1 + 1^2 = 3$

Example 36. Let $f(x) = \begin{vmatrix} \cos x & \sin x & \cos x \\ \cos 2x & \sin 2x & 2\cos 2x \\ \cos 3x & \sin 3x & 3\cos 3x \end{vmatrix}$, then find the value of $f'\left(\dfrac{\pi}{2}\right)$.

Sol. Given, $f(x) = \begin{vmatrix} \cos x & \sin x & \cos x \\ \cos 2x & \sin 2x & 2\cos 2x \\ \cos 3x & \sin 3x & 3\cos 3x \end{vmatrix}$

$\therefore \quad f'(x) = \begin{vmatrix} -\sin x & \sin x & \cos x \\ -2\sin 2x & \sin 2x & 2\cos 2x \\ -3\sin 3x & \sin 3x & 3\cos 3x \end{vmatrix}$

$+ \begin{vmatrix} \cos x & \cos x & \cos x \\ \cos 2x & 2\cos 2x & 2\cos 2x \\ \cos 3x & 3\cos 3x & 3\cos 3x \end{vmatrix} + \begin{vmatrix} \cos x & \sin x & -\sin x \\ \cos 2x & \sin 2x & -4\sin 2x \\ \cos 3x & \sin 3x & -9\sin 3x \end{vmatrix}$

[derivative according to columnwise]

$\Rightarrow f'\left(\dfrac{\pi}{2}\right) = \begin{vmatrix} -1 & 1 & 0 \\ 0 & 0 & -2 \\ 3 & -1 & 0 \end{vmatrix} + 0 + \begin{vmatrix} 0 & 1 & -1 \\ -1 & 0 & 0 \\ 0 & -1 & 9 \end{vmatrix}$

[$\because C_2 = C_3$ in second determinant]

$= 2(1-3) + 1(9-1) = -4 + 8 = 4$

Example 37. Let α be a repeated root of a quadratic equation $f(x) = 0$ and $A(x)$, $B(x)$ and $C(x)$ be polynomials of degree 3, 4, and 5 respectively, show that $\begin{vmatrix} A(x) & B(x) & C(x) \\ A(\alpha) & B(\alpha) & C(\alpha) \\ A'(\alpha) & B'(\alpha) & C'(\alpha) \end{vmatrix}$ is divisible by $f(x)$, where prime (′) denotes the derivatives.

Sol. Since, α is a repeated root of the quadratic equation $f(x) = 0$, then $f(x)$ can be written as $f(x) = a(x-\alpha)^2$, where a is some non-zero constant.

Let $\quad g(x) = \begin{vmatrix} A(x) & B(x) & C(x) \\ A(\alpha) & B(\alpha) & C(\alpha) \\ A'(\alpha) & B'(\alpha) & C'(\alpha) \end{vmatrix}$

$g(x)$ is divisible by $f(x)$, if it is divisible by $(x-a)^2$ i.e., $g(\alpha) = 0$ and $g'(\alpha) = 0$. As $A(x)$, $B(x)$ and $C(x)$ are polynomials of degree 3, 4 and 5, respectively.

$\therefore$ Degree of $g(x) \ge 2$

Now, $\quad g(\alpha) = \begin{vmatrix} A(\alpha) & B(\alpha) & C(\alpha) \\ A(\alpha) & B(\alpha) & C(\alpha) \\ A'(\alpha) & B'(\alpha) & C'(\alpha) \end{vmatrix} = 0$

[$\because R_1$ and R_2 are identical]

Also, $\quad g'(x) = \begin{vmatrix} A'(x) & B'(x) & C'(x) \\ A(\alpha) & B(\alpha) & C(\alpha) \\ A'(\alpha) & B'(\alpha) & C'(\alpha) \end{vmatrix}$

$\therefore \quad g'(\alpha) = \begin{vmatrix} A'(\alpha) & B'(\alpha) & C'(\alpha) \\ A(\alpha) & B(\alpha) & C(\alpha) \\ A'(\alpha) & B'(\alpha) & C'(\alpha) \end{vmatrix} = 0$

[$\because R_1$ and R_3 are identical]

This implies that $f(x)$ divides $g(x)$.

Example 38. Find the coefficient of x in the determinant $\begin{vmatrix} (1+x)^{a_1 b_1} & (1+x)^{a_1 b_2} & (1+x)^{a_1 b_3} \\ (1+x)^{a_2 b_1} & (1+x)^{a_2 b_2} & (1+x)^{a_2 b_3} \\ (1+x)^{a_3 b_1} & (1+x)^{a_3 b_2} & (1+x)^{a_3 b_3} \end{vmatrix}$

Sol. We know that, if $f(x)$ be a polynomial, then coefficient of x^n in $f(x) = \dfrac{1}{n!} f^n(0)$.

Let $\quad f(x) = \begin{vmatrix} (1+x)^{a_1 b_1} & (1+x)^{a_1 b_2} & (1+x)^{a_1 b_3} \\ (1+x)^{a_2 b_1} & (1+x)^{a_2 b_2} & (1+x)^{a_2 b_3} \\ (1+x)^{a_3 b_1} & (1+x)^{a_3 b_2} & (1+x)^{a_3 b_3} \end{vmatrix}$

$\therefore f'(x) = \begin{vmatrix} a_1 b_1 (1+x)^{a_1 b_1 - 1} & a_1 b_2 (1+x)^{a_1 b_2 - 1} & a_1 b_3 (1+x)^{a_1 b_3 - 1} \\ (1+x)^{a_2 b_1} & (1+x)^{a_2 b_2} & (1+x)^{a_2 b_3} \\ (1+x)^{a_3 b_1} & (1+x)^{a_3 b_2} & (1+x)^{a_3 b_3} \end{vmatrix}$

$$+\begin{vmatrix} (1+x)^{a_1b_1} & (1+x)^{a_1b_2} & (1+x)^{a_1b_3} \\ a_2b_1(1+x)^{a_2b_1-1} & a_2b_2(1+x)^{a_2b_2-1} & a_2b_3(1+x)^{a_2b_3-1} \\ (1+x)^{a_3b_1} & (1+x)^{a_3b_2} & (1+x)^{a_3b_3} \end{vmatrix}$$

$$+\begin{vmatrix} (1+x)^{a_1b_1} & (1+x)^{a_1b_2} & (1+x)^{a_1b_3} \\ (1+x)^{a_2b_1} & (1+x)^{a_2b_2} & (1+x)^{a_2b_3} \\ a_3b_1(1+x)^{a_3b_1-1} & a_3b_2(1+x)^{a_3b_2-1} & a_3b_3(1+x)^{a_3b_3-1} \end{vmatrix}$$

$$\therefore\ f'(0)=\begin{vmatrix} a_1b_1 & a_1b_2 & a_1b_3 \\ 1 & 1 & 1 \\ 1 & 1 & 1 \end{vmatrix}+\begin{vmatrix} 1 & 1 & 1 \\ a_2b_1 & a_2b_2 & a_3b_3 \\ 1 & 1 & 1 \end{vmatrix}+\begin{vmatrix} 1 & 1 & 1 \\ 1 & 1 & 1 \\ a_3b_1 & a_3b_2 & a_3b_3 \end{vmatrix}$$

$$=0+0+0=0$$

$\therefore$ Coefficient of x in $f(x)=\dfrac{f'(0)}{1!}=0$

Aliter

Let $\begin{vmatrix} (1+x)^{a_1b_1} & (1+x)^{a_1b_2} & (1+x)^{a_1b_3} \\ (1+x)^{a_2b_1} & (1+x)^{a_2b_2} & (1+x)^{a_2b_3} \\ (1+x)^{a_3b_1} & (1+x)^{a_3b_2} & (1+x)^{a_3b_3} \end{vmatrix}=A+Bx+Cx^2+\cdots$

On differentiating both sides w.r.t. x and then put $x=0$ in both sides, we get

$$B=\begin{vmatrix} a_1b_1 & a_1b_2 & a_1b_3 \\ 1 & 1 & 1 \\ 1 & 1 & 1 \end{vmatrix}+\begin{vmatrix} 1 & 1 & 1 \\ a_2b_1 & a_2b_2 & a_2b_3 \\ 1 & 1 & 1 \end{vmatrix}+\begin{vmatrix} 1 & 1 & 1 \\ 1 & 1 & 1 \\ a_3b_1 & a_3b_2 & a_3b_3 \end{vmatrix}$$

$$=0+0+0=0$$

Hence, coefficient of x in given determinant is 0.

Example 39. If $\Delta(x)=\begin{vmatrix} \alpha+x & \theta+x & \lambda+x \\ \beta+x & \phi+x & \mu+x \\ \gamma+x & \psi+x & \gamma+x \end{vmatrix}$, show that $\Delta''(x)=0$ and $\Delta(x)=\Delta(0)+Sx$, where S denotes the sum of all the cofactors of all elements in $\Delta(0)$ and dash denotes the derivative.

Sol. We have, $\Delta'(x)=\begin{vmatrix} 1 & \theta+x & \lambda+x \\ 1 & \phi+x & \mu+x \\ 1 & \psi+x & \nu+x \end{vmatrix}+\begin{vmatrix} \alpha+x & 1 & \lambda+x \\ \beta+x & 1 & \mu+x \\ \gamma+x & 1 & \nu+x \end{vmatrix}+\begin{vmatrix} \alpha+x & \theta+x & 1 \\ \beta+x & \phi+x & 1 \\ \gamma+x & \psi+x & 1 \end{vmatrix}$

Applying $C_2\to C_2-xC_1$ and $C_3\to C_3-xC_1$ in first, $C_1\to C_1-xC_2$ and $C_3\to C_3-xC_2$ in second and $C_1\to C_1-xC_3$ and $C_2\to C_2-xC_3$ in third, then

$$\Delta'(x)=\begin{vmatrix} 1 & \theta & \lambda \\ 1 & \phi & \mu \\ 1 & \psi & \nu \end{vmatrix}+\begin{vmatrix} \alpha & 1 & \lambda \\ \beta & 1 & \mu \\ \gamma & 1 & \nu \end{vmatrix}+\begin{vmatrix} \alpha & \theta & 1 \\ \beta & \phi & 1 \\ \gamma & \psi & 1 \end{vmatrix}$$

$$=\left\{\text{sum of all cofactors in }\Delta(0),\text{ where }\Delta(0)=\begin{vmatrix} \alpha & \theta & \lambda \\ \beta & \phi & \mu \\ \gamma & \psi & \nu \end{vmatrix}\right\}$$

$\therefore\quad \Delta''(x)=0$ [$\because S$ is constant]

Since, $\Delta'(x)=S$

On integrating $\Delta(x)=Sx+C$

$\therefore\quad \Delta(0)=0+C$

Hence, $\Delta(x)=Sx+\Delta(0)$

Example 40. If $f(x)=\begin{vmatrix} x^n & \sin x & \cos x \\ n! & \sin\left(\dfrac{n\pi}{2}\right) & \cos\left(\dfrac{n\pi}{2}\right) \\ \pi & \pi^2 & \pi^3 \end{vmatrix}$, then find the value of $\dfrac{d^n}{dx^n}\{f(x)\}$ at $x=0$, $n\in I$.

Sol. $\dfrac{d^n}{dx^n}\{f(x)\}=\begin{vmatrix} \dfrac{d^n}{dx^n}(x^n) & \dfrac{d^n}{dx^n}(\sin x) & \dfrac{d^n}{dx^n}(\cos x) \\ n! & \sin\left(\dfrac{n\pi}{2}\right) & \cos\left(\dfrac{n\pi}{2}\right) \\ \pi & \pi^2 & \pi^3 \end{vmatrix}$

$$=\begin{vmatrix} n! & \sin\left(\dfrac{n\pi}{2}+x\right) & \cos\left(\dfrac{n\pi}{2}+x\right) \\ n! & \sin\left(\dfrac{n\pi}{2}\right) & \cos\left(\dfrac{n\pi}{2}\right) \\ \pi & \pi^2 & \pi^3 \end{vmatrix}$$

$$\therefore\ \frac{d^n}{dx^n}\{f(x)\}\text{ at }(x=0)=\begin{vmatrix} n! & \sin\left(\dfrac{n\pi}{2}\right) & \cos\left(\dfrac{n\pi}{2}\right) \\ n! & \sin\left(\dfrac{n\pi}{2}\right) & \cos\left(\dfrac{n\pi}{2}\right) \\ \pi & \pi^2 & \pi^3 \end{vmatrix}$$

$=0$ [$\because R_1$ and R_2 are identical]

Integration of a Determinant

Let $\Delta(x)=\begin{vmatrix} f(x) & g(x) & h(x) \\ p & q & r \\ l & m & n \end{vmatrix}$

where p,q,r,l,m and n are constants, then

$$\int_a^b \Delta(x)\,dx=\begin{vmatrix} \int_a^b f(x)dx & \int_a^b g(x)dx & \int_a^b h(x)\,dx \\ p & q & r \\ l & m & n \end{vmatrix}$$

Remark

If in a determinant, the elements of more than one columns or rows are functions of x, then the integration can be done only after evaluation or expansion of the determinant.

Important Integrals (Committed to Memory)

1. (i) $\int_0^{\pi/2} \frac{\sin^n x}{\sin^n x + \cos^n x} dx = \frac{\pi}{4}$

$= \int_0^{\pi/2} \frac{\cos^n x}{\sin^n x + \cos^n x} dx, \forall n \in R$

(ii) $\int_0^{\pi/2} \frac{\tan^n x}{1+\tan^n x} dx = \frac{\pi}{4} = \int_0^{\pi/2} \frac{dx}{1+\tan^n x}, \forall n \in R$

(iii) $\int_0^{\pi/2} \frac{dx}{1+\cot^n x} = \frac{\pi}{4} = \int_0^{\pi/2} \frac{\cot^n x}{1+\cot^n x} dx, \forall n \in R$

2. (i) $\int_0^{\pi/2} \ln \sin x\, dx = \int_0^{\pi/2} \ln \cos x\, dx = -\frac{\pi}{2}\ln 2$

or $\frac{\pi}{2}\ln\left(\frac{1}{2}\right)$

(ii) $\int_0^{\pi/2} \ln \tan x\, dx = \int_0^{\pi/2} \ln \cot x\, dx = 0$

(iii) $\int_0^{\pi/2} \ln \sec x\, dx = \int_0^{\pi/2} \ln \operatorname{cosec} x\, dx = \frac{\pi}{2}\ln 2$

Walli's Formula

(An easy way to evaluate $\int_0^{\pi/2} \sin^m x \cos^n x\, dx$, where $m, n \in W$) We have, $\int_0^{\pi/2} \sin^m x \cos^n x\, dx$

$$= \frac{\{(m-1)(m-3)\ldots 2 \text{ or } 1\}\{(n-1)(n-3)\ldots 2 \text{ or } 1\}}{\{(m+n)(m+n-2)(m+n-4)\ldots 2 \text{ or } 1\}}$$

where, p is $\pi/2$, if m and n are both even, otherwise $p = 1$. The last factor in each of three products is either 1 or 2. In case any of m or n is 1, we simply write 1 as the only factor to replace its product. If any of m or n is zero provided, we put 1 as the only factor in its product and we regard 0 as even.

For example,

1. $\int_0^{\pi/2} \sin^6 x \cos^4 x\, dx = \frac{[5\cdot 3\cdot 1][3\cdot 1]}{[10\cdot 8\cdot 6\cdot 4\cdot 2]}\cdot\frac{\pi}{2} = \frac{3\pi}{512}$

2. $\int_0^{\pi/2} \sin^6 x \cos^3 x\, dx = \frac{[5\cdot 3\cdot 1][2]}{[9\cdot 7\cdot 5\cdot 3\cdot 1]}\cdot 1 = \frac{2}{63}$

3. $\int_0^{\pi/2} \sin^5 x \cos^7 x\, dx = \frac{[4\cdot 2][6\cdot 4\cdot 2]}{[12\cdot 10\cdot 8\cdot 6\cdot 4\cdot 2]}\cdot 1 = \frac{1}{120}$

4. $\int_0^{\pi/2} \sin^8 x\, dx = \frac{[7\cdot 5\cdot 3\cdot 1]}{[8\cdot 6\cdot 4\cdot 2]}\cdot\frac{\pi}{2} = \frac{35\pi}{256}$

5. $\int_0^{\pi/2} \cos^7 x\, dx = \frac{[6\cdot 4\cdot 2]}{[7\cdot 5\cdot 3\cdot 1]}\cdot 1 = \frac{16}{35}$

6. $\int_0^{\pi/2} \sin^{10} x \cos x\, dx = \frac{[9\cdot 7\cdot 5\cdot 3\cdot 1][1]}{[11\cdot 9\cdot 7\cdot 5\cdot 3\cdot 1]}\cdot 1 = \frac{1}{11}$

Example 41. If $\Delta(x) = \begin{vmatrix} a & b & c \\ 6 & 4 & 3 \\ x & x^2 & x^3 \end{vmatrix}$, then find $\int_0^1 \Delta(x)\, dx$.

Sol. $\int_0^1 \Delta(x)\, dx = \begin{vmatrix} a & b & c \\ 6 & 4 & 3 \\ \int_0^1 x\,dx & \int_0^1 x^2 dx & \int_0^1 x^3 dx \end{vmatrix}$

$$= \begin{vmatrix} a & b & c \\ 6 & 4 & 3 \\ \left[\frac{x^2}{2}\right]_0^1 & \left[\frac{x^3}{3}\right]_0^1 & \left[\frac{x^4}{4}\right]_0^1 \end{vmatrix} = \begin{vmatrix} a & b & c \\ 6 & 4 & 3 \\ \frac{1}{2} & \frac{1}{3} & \frac{1}{4} \end{vmatrix}$$

Applying $R_2 \to R_2 - 12R_3$, then $\int_0^1 \Delta(x)dx = \begin{vmatrix} a & b & c \\ 0 & 0 & 0 \\ \frac{1}{2} & \frac{1}{3} & \frac{1}{4} \end{vmatrix} = 0$

Example 42. If

$$f(x) = \begin{vmatrix} \sin^5 x & \ln \sin x & \frac{\sqrt{\sin x}}{\sqrt{\sin x}+\sqrt{\cos x}} \\ n & \sum_{k=1}^{n} k & \prod_{k=1}^{n} k \\ \frac{8}{15} & \frac{\pi}{2}\ln\left(\frac{1}{2}\right) & \frac{\pi}{4} \end{vmatrix},$$

then find the value of $\int_0^{\pi/2} f(x)dx$.

Sol. $\int_0^{\pi/2} f(x)\,dx$

$$= \begin{vmatrix} \int_0^{\pi/2} \sin^5 x\,dx & \int_0^{\pi/2} \ln \sin x\,dx & \int_0^{\pi/2} \frac{\sqrt{\sin x}}{\sqrt{\sin x}+\sqrt{\cos x}} \\ n & \sum_{k=1}^{n} k & \prod_{k=1}^{n} k \\ \frac{8}{15} & \frac{\pi}{2}\ln\left(\frac{1}{2}\right) & \frac{\pi}{4} \end{vmatrix},$$

$$= \begin{vmatrix} \frac{4}{5}\cdot\frac{2}{3} & -\frac{\pi}{2}\ln 2 & \frac{\pi}{4} \\ n & \sum_{k=1}^{n} k & \prod_{k=1}^{n} k \\ \frac{8}{15} & \frac{\pi}{2}\ln\left(\frac{1}{2}\right) & \frac{\pi}{4} \end{vmatrix}$$ [by Walli's formula]

$$= \begin{vmatrix} \frac{8}{15} & \frac{\pi}{2}\ln\left(\frac{1}{2}\right) & \frac{\pi}{4} \\ n & \sum_{k=1}^{n} k & \prod_{k=1}^{n} k \\ \frac{8}{15} & \frac{\pi}{2}\ln\left(\frac{1}{2}\right) & \frac{\pi}{4} \end{vmatrix} = 0$$ [since R_1 and R_3 are identical]

Example 43. Let $f(x)$

$$= \begin{vmatrix} \sec x & \cos x & \sec^2 x + \cot x \operatorname{cosec} x \\ \cos^2 x & \cos^2 x & \operatorname{cosec}^2 x \\ 1 & \cos^2 x & \cos^2 x \end{vmatrix}$$, then find

the value of $\int_0^{\pi/2} f(x)\,dx$.

Sol. Applying $C_2 \to C_2 - \cos^2 x C_1$, then

$$f(x) = \begin{vmatrix} \sec x & 0 & \sec^2 x + \cot x \operatorname{cosec} x \\ \cos^2 x & \cos^2 x - \cos^4 x & \operatorname{cosec}^2 x \\ 1 & 0 & \cos^2 x \end{vmatrix}$$

[expanding along C_2]

$$= (\cos^2 x - \cos^4 x) \begin{vmatrix} \sec x & \sec^2 x + \cot x \operatorname{cosec} x \\ 1 & \cos^2 x \end{vmatrix}$$

$$= (\cos^2 x - \cos^4 x)(\cos x - \sec^2 x - \cot x \operatorname{cosec} x)$$

$$= \cos^2 x (1 - \cos^2 x)\left(\cos x - \frac{1}{\cos^2 x} - \frac{\cos x}{\sin^2 x}\right)$$

$$= \cos^2 x \sin^2 x \left(\cos x - \frac{1}{\cos^2 x} - \frac{\cos x}{\sin^2 x}\right)$$

$$= \cos^3 x \sin^2 x - \sin^2 x - \cos^3 x$$

$$= -\cos^3 x (1 - \sin^2 x) - \sin^2 x$$

$$f(x) = -\cos^5 x - \sin^2 x$$

$$\therefore \int_0^{\pi/2} f(x)\,dx = -\int_0^{\pi/2} \cos^5 x\,dx - \int_0^{\pi/2} \sin^2 x\,dx$$

$$= -\left(\frac{4}{5}\cdot\frac{2}{3}\cdot 1\right) - \left(\frac{1}{2}\cdot\frac{\pi}{2}\right) = -\left(\frac{8}{15} + \frac{\pi}{4}\right)$$

[by Walli's formula]

Use of Σ in Determinant

If $\Delta(r) = \begin{vmatrix} f(r) & g(r) & h(r) \\ a & b & c \\ a_1 & b_1 & c_1 \end{vmatrix}$

where a, b, c, a_1, b_1 and c_1 are constants, independent of r, then

$$\sum_{r=1}^{n} \Delta(r) = \begin{vmatrix} \sum_{r=1}^{n} f(r) & \sum_{r=1}^{n} g(r) & \sum_{r=1}^{n} h(r) \\ a & b & c \\ a_1 & b_1 & c_1 \end{vmatrix}$$

Remark

If in a determinant, the elements of more than one columns or rows are function of r, then the Σ can be done only after evaluation or expansion of the determinant.

Important Summation

(Committed to Memory)

1. $\sum_{r=1}^{n} r = \Sigma n = 1 + 2 + 3 + \ldots + n = \frac{n(n+1)}{2}$

2. $\sum_{r=1}^{n} r^2 = \Sigma n^2 = 1^2 + 2^2 + 3^2 + \ldots + n^2 = \frac{n(n+1)(2n+1)}{6}$

3. $\sum_{r=1}^{n} r^3 = \Sigma n^3 = 1^3 + 2^3 + 3^3 + \ldots + n^3$

$$= \left[\frac{n(n+1)}{2}\right]^2 = (\Sigma n)^2$$

4. $\sum_{r=1}^{n} a = \Sigma a = \underbrace{a + a + a + \ldots + a}_{n \text{ times}} = an$

5. $\sum_{r=1}^{n} (\lambda - 1)\lambda^{r-1} = \lambda^n - 1, \forall \lambda \neq 1$ and $\lambda > 1$

6. $\sum_{r=1}^{n} \sin[\alpha + (r-1)\beta] = \frac{\sin\left\{\alpha + \frac{(n-1)\beta}{2}\right\} \sin\left(\frac{n\beta}{2}\right)}{\sin\left(\frac{\beta}{2}\right)}$

Particular For $\alpha = \beta = \theta$.

$$\sum_{r=1}^{n} \sin r\theta = \frac{\sin\left\{\left(\frac{n+1}{2}\right)\theta\right\} \cdot \sin\left(\frac{n\theta}{2}\right)}{\sin\left(\frac{\theta}{2}\right)}$$

7. $\sum_{r=1}^{n} \cos\{\alpha + (r-1)\beta\} = \frac{\cos\left\{\alpha + \frac{(n-1)}{2}\beta\right\} \sin\left(\frac{n\beta}{2}\right)}{\sin\left(\frac{\beta}{2}\right)}$

Particular For $\alpha = \beta = \theta$.

$$\sum_{r=1}^{n} \cos r\theta = \frac{\cos\left\{\left(\frac{n+1}{2}\right)\theta\right\} \sin\left(\frac{n\theta}{2}\right)}{\sin\left(\frac{\theta}{2}\right)}$$

8. $\sum_{r=1}^{n} \{f(r+1) - f(r)\} = f(n+1) - f(1)$

Particular $\sum_{r=1}^{n} \frac{1}{r(r+1)} = \sum_{r=1}^{n} \left(\frac{1}{r} - \frac{1}{r+1}\right)$

$$= \frac{1}{1} - \frac{1}{n+1} = \frac{n}{n+1}$$

9. $\sum_{r=1}^{n} {}^nC_r = 2^n$

Remark

Capital pie Π is not direct applicable in determint i.e.,

$$\prod_{r=1}^{n} \Delta(r) \neq \begin{vmatrix} \prod_{r=1}^{n} f(r) & \prod_{r=1}^{n} g(r) & \prod_{r=1}^{n} h(r) \\ a & b & c \\ a_1 & b_1 & c_1 \end{vmatrix}$$

Explanation $\prod_{r=1}^{n} \Delta(r) = \Delta(1) \times \Delta(2) \times \ldots \times \Delta(n)$

$$= \begin{vmatrix} f(1) & g(1) & h(1) \\ a & b & c \\ a_1 & b_1 & c_1 \end{vmatrix} \times \begin{vmatrix} f(2) & g(2) & h(2) \\ a & b & c \\ a_1 & b_1 & c_1 \end{vmatrix} \times \ldots \times \begin{vmatrix} f(n) & g(n) & h(n) \\ a & b & c \\ a_1 & b_1 & c_1 \end{vmatrix}$$

$$\neq \begin{vmatrix} \prod_{r=1}^{n} f(r) & \prod_{r=1}^{n} g(r) & \prod_{r=1}^{n} h(r) \\ a & b & c \\ a_1 & b_1 & c_1 \end{vmatrix}$$

| Example 44. Let n be a positive integer and

$$\Delta_r = \begin{vmatrix} 2r-1 & {}^nC_r & 1 \\ n^2-1 & 2^n & n+1 \\ \cos^2 n^2 & \cos^2 n & \cos^2(n+1) \end{vmatrix}, \text{ prove that}$$

$\sum_{r=0}^{n} \Delta_r = 0.$

Sol. We have, $\Delta_r = \begin{vmatrix} 2r-1 & {}^nC_r & 1 \\ n^2-1 & 2^n & n+1 \\ \cos^2(n^2) & \cos^2 n & \cos^2(n+1) \end{vmatrix}$

$$\therefore \quad \sum_{r=0}^{n} \Delta_r = \begin{vmatrix} \sum_{r=0}^{n} (2r-1) & \sum_{r=0}^{n} {}^nC_r & \sum_{r=0}^{n} 1 \\ n^2-1 & 2^n & n+1 \\ \cos^2(n^2) & \cos^2 n & \cos^2(n+1) \end{vmatrix}$$

Now, $\sum_{r=0}^{n} (2r-1) = 2\sum_{r=0}^{n} r - \sum_{r=0}^{n} 1$

$$= 2(0+1+2+3+\ldots+n) - \underbrace{(1+1+1+\ldots+1)}_{(n+1)\text{ times}}$$

$$= \frac{2n(n+1)}{2} - (n+1) = (n+1)(n-1) = n^2 - 1$$

$$\sum_{r=0}^{n} \Delta_r = \begin{vmatrix} n^2-1 & 2^n & n+1 \\ n^2-1 & 2^n & n+1 \\ \cos^2(n^2) & \cos^2 n & \cos^2(n+1) \end{vmatrix} = 0$$

[since R_1 and R_2 are identical]

| Example 45. Let n be a positive integer and

$$\Delta_r = \begin{vmatrix} r^2+r & r+1 & r-2 \\ 2r^2+3r-1 & 3r & 3r-3 \\ r^2+2r+3 & 2r-1 & 2r-1 \end{vmatrix} \text{ and}$$

$\sum_{r=1}^{n} \Delta_r = an^2 + bn + c$, find the value of $a+b+c$.

Sol. We have, $\Delta_r = \begin{vmatrix} r^2+1r & r+1 & r-2 \\ 2r^2+3r-1 & 3r & 3r-3 \\ r^2+2r+3 & 2r-1 & 2r-1 \end{vmatrix}$

Applying $R_2 \to R_2 - (R_1 + R_3)$, then

$$\Delta_r = \begin{vmatrix} r^2+r & r+1 & r-2 \\ \vdots & & \\ -4 & \ldots\ 0 & \ldots\ 0 \\ \vdots & & \\ r^2+2r+3 & 2r-1 & 2r-1 \end{vmatrix}$$

Expanding along R_2, we get

$$= 4\begin{vmatrix} r+1 & r-2 \\ 2r-1 & 2r-1 \end{vmatrix}$$

$$= 4[(r+1)(2r-1) - (r-2)(2r-1)]$$

$$= 24r - 12$$

Now, $\sum_{r=1}^{n} \Delta_r = 24\sum_{r=1}^{n} r - 12\sum_{r=1}^{n} 1$

$$= 24\frac{n(n+1)}{2} - 12n = 12n(n+1-1)$$

$$= 12n^2 = an^2 + bn + c \quad \text{[given]}$$

For $n = 1$, we have

$a + b + c = 12$

Exercise for Session 4

1. If $f(x)=\begin{vmatrix} x & x^2 & x^3 \\ 1 & 2 & 3 \\ 0 & 1 & x \end{vmatrix}$, $f'(1)$ is equal to

(a) -1 (b) 0 (c) 1 (d) 2

2. Let $f(x)=\begin{vmatrix} \sec x & x^2 & x \\ 2\sin x & x^3 & 2x^2 \\ \tan 3x & x^2 & x \end{vmatrix}$, $\lim_{x\to 0}\frac{f(x)}{x^4}$ is equal to

(a) 0 (b) -1 (c) 2 (d) 3

3. Let $\begin{vmatrix} x & 2 & x \\ x^2 & x & 6 \\ x & x & 6 \end{vmatrix}=Ax^4+Bx^3+Cx^2+Dx+E$, the value of $5A+4B+3C+2D+E$ is equal to

(a) -16 (b) -11 (c) 0 (d) 16

4. Let $f(x)=\begin{vmatrix} x^3 & \sin x & \cos x \\ 6 & -1 & 0 \\ p & p^2 & p^3 \end{vmatrix}$, where p is a constant. Then $\frac{d^3}{dx^3}\{f(x)\}$ at $x=0$ is

(a) p (b) $p+p^2$ (c) $p+p^3$ (d) independent of p

5. If $y=\sin mx$, the value of the determinant $\begin{vmatrix} y & y_1 & y_2 \\ y_3 & y_4 & y_5 \\ y_6 & y_7 & y_8 \end{vmatrix}$, where $y_n=\frac{d^ny}{dx^n}$, is

(a) m^2 (b) m^3 (c) m^9 (d) None of these

6. Let $f(x)=\begin{vmatrix} 2\cos^2 x & \sin 2x & -\sin x \\ \sin 2x & 2\sin^2 x & \cos x \\ \sin x & -\cos x & 0 \end{vmatrix}$, the value of $\int_0^{\pi/2}\{f(x)+f'(x)\}\,dx$, is

(a) $\frac{\pi}{2}$ (b) π (c) $\frac{3\pi}{2}$ (d) 2π

7. If $f(x)=\begin{vmatrix} \cos x & e^{x^2} & 2x\cos^2\left(\frac{x}{2}\right) \\ x^2 & \sec x & \sin x+x^3 \\ 1 & 2 & x+\tan x \end{vmatrix}$, the value of $\int_{-\pi/2}^{\pi/2}(x^2+1)[f(x)+f'(x)]\,dx$, is

(a) -1 (b) 0 (c) 1 (d) 2

8. If $f(x)=\begin{vmatrix} \sin^2 x+ & \cos^4 x\ln\cos x & \frac{1}{1+(\tan x)^{\sqrt{2}}} \\ \pi & \pi^2 & \pi^4 \\ \frac{7}{16} & -\frac{1}{2}\ln 2 & \frac{1}{4} \end{vmatrix}$, the value of $\int_0^{\pi/2}f(x)\,dx$ is

(a) 2 (b) -1 (c) 0 (d) None of these

9. If $\Delta_k=\begin{vmatrix} 1 & n & n \\ 2k & n^2+n+1 & n^2+n \\ 2k-1 & n^2 & n^2+n+1 \end{vmatrix}$ and $\sum_{k=1}^{n}\Delta_k=56$, then n is equal to

(a) 4 (b) 6 (c) 8 (d) None of these

10. The value of $\sum_{r=2}^{n}(-2)^r\begin{vmatrix} {}^{n-2}C_{r-2} & {}^{n-2}C_{r-1} & {}^{n-2}C_r \\ -3 & 1 & 1 \\ 2 & -1 & 0 \end{vmatrix}$ $(n>2)$ is

(a) $2n-1+(-1)^n$ (b) $2n+1+(-1)^n$ (c) $2n-3+(-1)^n$ (d) None of these

Shortcuts and Important Results to Remember

1 Symmetric Determinant The elements situated at equal distance from the diagonal are equal both in magnitude and sign. i.e. $\begin{vmatrix} a & h & g \\ h & b & f \\ g & f & c \end{vmatrix} = abc + 2fgh - af^2 - bg^2 - ch^2$

2 Skew-symmetric Determinant All the diagonal elements are zero and the elements situated at equal distance from the diagonal are equal in magnitude but opposite in sign. The value of skew-symmetric determinant of even order is always a perfect square and that of odd order is always zero i.e. $\begin{vmatrix} 0 & a \\ -a & 0 \end{vmatrix} = a^2$ and $\begin{vmatrix} 0 & c & -b \\ -c & 0 & a \\ b & -a & 0 \end{vmatrix} = 0$

3 Circulant Determinant The elements of the rows (or columns) are in cyclic order. i.e.,

(i) $\begin{vmatrix} 1 & a & a^2 \\ 1 & b & b^2 \\ 1 & c & c^2 \end{vmatrix} = (a-b)(b-c)(c-a)$

(ii) $\begin{vmatrix} a & b & c \\ a^2 & b^2 & c^2 \\ bc & ca & ab \end{vmatrix} = \begin{vmatrix} 1 & 1 & 1 \\ a^2 & b^2 & c^2 \\ a^3 & b^3 & c^3 \end{vmatrix}$

$= (a-b)(b-c)(c-a)(ab+bc+ca)$

(iii) $\begin{vmatrix} a & bc & abc \\ b & ca & abc \\ c & ab & abc \end{vmatrix} = \begin{vmatrix} a & a^2 & a^3 \\ b & b^2 & b^3 \\ c & c^2 & c^3 \end{vmatrix} = abc(a-b)(b-c)(c-a)$

(iv) $\begin{vmatrix} 1 & 1 & 1 \\ a & b & c \\ a^3 & b^3 & c^3 \end{vmatrix} = (a-b)(b-c)(c-a)(a+b+c)$

(v) $\begin{vmatrix} a & b & c \\ b & c & a \\ c & a & b \end{vmatrix} = -(a^3 + b^3 + c^3 - 3abc)$

Remark

These results direct applicable in lengthy questions as behaviour of standard results.

4 (i) If $\Delta = 0$, then $\Delta^c = 0$, where Δ^c denotes the determinant of cofactors of elements of Δ.

(ii) If $\Delta \neq 0$, then $\Delta^c = \Delta^{n-1}$, where n is order of Δ.

(iii) Let $\Delta = \begin{vmatrix} a_{11} & a_{12} & a_{13} \\ a_{21} & a_{22} & a_{23} \\ a_{31} & a_{32} & a_{33} \end{vmatrix}$

The sum of products of the elements of any row or column with the corresponding cofactors is equal to the value of determinant, i.e.

$$a_{11}C_{11} + a_{12}C_{12} + a_{13}C_{13} = a_{21}C_{21} + a_{22}C_{22} + a_{23}C_{23}$$
$$= a_{31}C_{31} + a_{32}C_{32} + a_{33}C_{33} = \Delta$$

and sum of products of the elements of any row or column with the cofactors of the corresponding elements of any other row or column is zero, i.e.,

$$a_{11}C_{21} + a_{12}C_{22} + a_{13}C_{23} = a_{11}C_{31} + a_{12}C_{32} + a_{13}C_{33}$$
$$= 0$$

5 A homogeneous system of equations is never consistent.

6 Conjugate of a Determinant If a_i, b_i and $c_i \in C$ $(i = 1, 2, 3)$ and $\Delta = \begin{vmatrix} a_1 & b_1 & c_1 \\ a_2 & b_2 & c_2 \\ a_3 & b_3 & c_3 \end{vmatrix}$, then $\overline{\Delta} = \begin{vmatrix} \overline{a_1} & \overline{b_1} & \overline{c_1} \\ \overline{a_2} & \overline{b_2} & \overline{c_2} \\ \overline{a_3} & \overline{b_3} & \overline{c_3} \end{vmatrix}$

(i) If Δ is purely real, then $\Delta = \Delta$

(ii) If Δ is purely imaginary, then $\overline{\Delta} = -\Delta$

7 (i) If $x_1, x_2, x_3, \ldots$ are in AP or $a^{x_1}, a^{x_2}, a^{x_3}, \ldots$ are in GP,

then $\begin{vmatrix} x_1 & x_2 & x_3 \\ x_{n+1} & x_{n+2} & x_{n+3} \\ x_{2n+1} & x_{2n+2} & x_{2n+3} \end{vmatrix} = 0$

(ii) If $a_1, a_2, a_3, \ldots$ are in GP and $a_i > 0, i = 1, 2, 3, \ldots,$

then $\begin{vmatrix} \log a_n & \log a_{n+1} & \log \alpha_{n+2} \\ \log a_{n+3} & \log a_{n+4} & \log a_{n+5} \\ \log a_{n+6} & \log a_{n+7} & \log a_{n+8} \end{vmatrix} = 0$

JEE Type Solved Examples : Single Option Correct Type Questions

- This section contains **10 multiple choice examples.** Each example has four choices (a), (b), (c) and (d) out of which **ONLY ONE** is correct.

• Ex. 1 *If* $(x_1 - x_2)^2 + (y_1 - y_2)^2 = a^2$, $(x_2 - x_3)^2 + (y_2 - y_3)^2 = b^2$ *and* $(x_3 - x_1)^2 + (y_3 - y_1)^2 = c^2$ *and* $k \begin{vmatrix} x_1 & y_1 & 1 \\ x_2 & y_2 & 1 \\ x_3 & y_3 & 1 \end{vmatrix}^2 = (a+b+c)(b+c-a)(c+a-b)(a+b-c)$, *the value of k is*

(a) 1 (b) 2 (c) 4 (d) 8

Sol. (c) Consider the triangle with vertices $B(x_1, y_1)$, $C(x_2, y_2)$ and $A(x_3, y_3)$ and

$$AB = c,\ BC = a \text{ and } CA = b$$

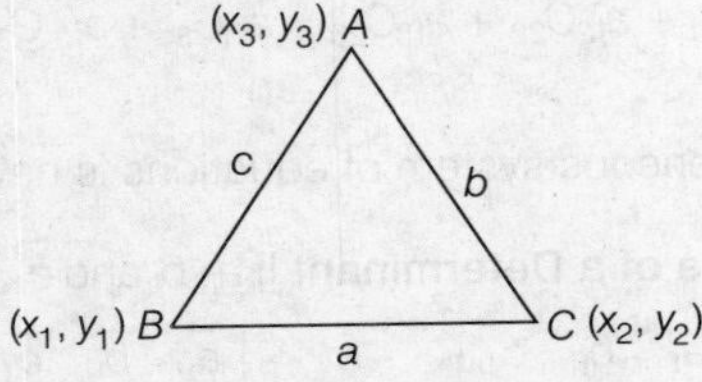

$\therefore$ Area of $\Delta ABC = \dfrac{1}{2}\begin{vmatrix} x_1 & y_1 & 1 \\ x_2 & y_2 & 1 \\ x_3 & y_3 & 1 \end{vmatrix}$ ...(i)

Also, area of $\Delta ABC = \sqrt{s(s-a)(s-b)(s-c)}$,

where $2s = a + b + c$ ...(ii)

From Eqs. (i) and (ii), we get

$$\frac{1}{2}\begin{vmatrix} x_1 & y_1 & 1 \\ x_2 & y_2 & 1 \\ x_3 & y_3 & 1 \end{vmatrix} = \sqrt{s(s-a)(s-b)(s-c)}$$

On squaring and simplifying, we get

$$4\begin{vmatrix} x_1 & y_1 & 1 \\ x_2 & y_2 & 1 \\ x_3 & y_3 & 1 \end{vmatrix}^2 = (a+b+c)(b+c-a)(c+a-b)(a+b-c)$$

Hence, the value of k is 4.

• Ex. 2 *If a, b and c are complex numbers, the determinant*

$$\Delta = \begin{vmatrix} 0 & -b & -c \\ \bar{b} & 0 & -a \\ \bar{c} & \bar{a} & 0 \end{vmatrix} \text{ is}$$

(a) a non-zero real number (b) purely imaginary
(c) 0 (d) None of these

Sol. (b) We observe that,

$$\bar{\Delta} = \begin{vmatrix} 0 & -\bar{b} & -\bar{c} \\ b & 0 & -\bar{a} \\ c & a & 0 \end{vmatrix}$$

$$\Rightarrow \bar{\Delta} = \begin{vmatrix} 0 & b & c \\ -\bar{b} & 0 & a \\ -\bar{c} & -\bar{a} & 0 \end{vmatrix}$$

[interchanging rows and columns]

$$= -\begin{vmatrix} 0 & -b & -c \\ \bar{b} & 0 & -a \\ \bar{c} & \bar{a} & 0 \end{vmatrix}$$

[taking (– 1) common from each row]

$$\Rightarrow \bar{\Delta} = -\Delta$$

Hence, Δ is purely imaginary.

• Ex. 3 *The equation*

$$\begin{vmatrix} (1+x)^2 & (1-x)^2 & -(2+x^2) \\ 2x+1 & 3x & 1-5x \\ x+1 & 2x & 2-3x \end{vmatrix} + \begin{vmatrix} (1+x)^2 & 2x+1 & x+1 \\ (1-x)^2 & 3x & 2x \\ 1-2x & 3x-2 & 2x-3 \end{vmatrix} = 0 \text{ has}$$

(a) no real solution
(b) 4 real solutions
(c) two real and two non-real solutions
(d) infinite number of solutions, real or non-real

Sol. (d) Interchanging rows and columns in first determinant, then

$$\begin{vmatrix} (1+x)^2 & 2x+1 & x+1 \\ (1-x)^2 & 3x & 2x \\ -(2+x^2) & 1-5x & 2-3x \end{vmatrix} + \begin{vmatrix} (1+x)^2 & 2x+1 & x+1 \\ (1-x)^2 & 3x & 2x \\ 1-2x & 3x-2 & 2x-3 \end{vmatrix} = 0$$

$$\Rightarrow \begin{vmatrix} (1+x)^2 & 2x+1 & x+1 \\ (1-x)^2 & 3x & 2x \\ -(1+x)^2 & -2x-1 & -x-1 \end{vmatrix} = 0$$

Applying $R_3 \to R_3 + R_1$, then

$$\Rightarrow \begin{vmatrix} (1+x)^2 & 2x+1 & x+1 \\ (1-x)^2 & 3x & 2x \\ 0 & 0 & 0 \end{vmatrix} = 0$$

$$\Rightarrow \quad 0 = 0$$

which is true for all values of x.

Hence, given equation has infinite number of solutions, real or non-real.

• Ex. 4 *If X, Y and Z are positive numbers such that Y and Z have respectively 1 and 0 at their unit's place and*

$$\Delta = \begin{vmatrix} X & 4 & 1 \\ Y & 0 & 1 \\ Z & 1 & 0 \end{vmatrix}$$

If $(\Delta + 1)$ is divisible by 10, then X has at its unit's place

(a) 0 (b) 1
(c) 2 (d) 3

Sol. (c) Let $X = 10x + \lambda$, $Y = 10y + 1$ and $Z = 10z$, where $x, y, z \in N$, then

$$\Delta = \begin{vmatrix} X & 4 & 1 \\ Y & 0 & 1 \\ Z & 1 & 0 \end{vmatrix} = \begin{vmatrix} 10x+\lambda & 4 & 1 \\ 10y+1 & 0 & 1 \\ 10z & 1 & 0 \end{vmatrix}$$

$$= \begin{vmatrix} 10x & 4 & 1 \\ 10y & 0 & 1 \\ 10z & 1 & 0 \end{vmatrix} + \begin{vmatrix} \lambda & 4 & 1 \\ 1 & 0 & 1 \\ 0 & 1 & 0 \end{vmatrix}$$

$$= 10 \begin{vmatrix} x & 4 & 1 \\ y & 0 & 1 \\ z & 1 & 0 \end{vmatrix} + (1 - \lambda)$$

$\Rightarrow \Delta + 1 = 10k + (2 - \lambda)$,

where $k = \begin{vmatrix} x & 4 & 1 \\ y & 0 & 1 \\ z & 1 & 0 \end{vmatrix}$.

It is given that $(\Delta + 1)$ is divisible by 10. Therefore, $2 - \lambda = 0$ i.e., $\lambda = 2$

$$\therefore \quad X = 10x + 2$$

$\Rightarrow$ 2 is at unit's place of X.

• Ex. 5 *The number of distinct values of a 2×2 determinant whose entries are from the set $\{-1, 0, 1\}$, is*

(a) 3 (b) 4 (c) 5 (d) 6

Sol. (c) Possible values are $-2, -1, 0, 1, 2$

i.e., $\begin{vmatrix} 1 & 0 \\ -1 & 1 \end{vmatrix} = 1$, $\begin{vmatrix} 1 & -1 \\ 0 & 0 \end{vmatrix} = 0$, $\begin{vmatrix} 0 & 1 \\ 1 & -1 \end{vmatrix} = -1$,

$\begin{vmatrix} 1 & -1 \\ 1 & 1 \end{vmatrix} = 2$, $\begin{vmatrix} -1 & 1 \\ 1 & 1 \end{vmatrix} = -2$

• Ex. 6 *If* $f(x) = \begin{vmatrix} (1+x)^a & (1+2x)^b & 1 \\ 1 & (1+x)^a & (1+2x)^b \\ (1+2x)^b & 1 & (1+x)^a \end{vmatrix}$; *$a, b$ being positive integers, then*

(a) constant term in $f(x)$ is 4
(b) coefficient of x in $f(x)$ is 0
(c) constant term in $f(x)$ is $(a - b)$
(d) constant term in $f(x)$ is $(a + b)$

Sol. (b) Let $\begin{vmatrix} (1+x)^a & (1+2x)^b & 1 \\ 1 & (1+x)^a & (1+2x)^b \\ (1+2x)^b & 1 & (1+x)^a \end{vmatrix}$

$$= A + Bx + Cx^2 + \ldots$$

Put $x = 0$, then $A = 0$

On differentiating both sides w.r.t. x and then put $x = 0$

$$\begin{vmatrix} a & 2b & 0 \\ 1 & 1 & 1 \\ 1 & 1 & 1 \end{vmatrix} + \begin{vmatrix} 1 & 1 & 1 \\ 0 & a & 2b \\ 1 & 1 & 1 \end{vmatrix} + \begin{vmatrix} 1 & 1 & 1 \\ 1 & 1 & 1 \\ 2b & 0 & a \end{vmatrix} = B$$

$$\therefore \quad 0 + 0 + 0 = B$$

$$\Rightarrow \quad B = 0$$

Hence, constant term in $f(x)$ is zero and coefficient of x in $f(x)$ is 0.

• Ex. 7 *If $f_j = \sum_{i=0}^{2} a_{ij} x^i$, $j = 1, 2, 3$ and f_j' and f_j'' are denoted by $\frac{df_j}{dx}$ and $\frac{d^2 f_j}{dx^2}$ respectively, then $g(x) = \begin{vmatrix} f_1 & f_2 & f_3 \\ f_1' & f_2' & f_3' \\ f_1'' & f_2'' & f_3'' \end{vmatrix}$ is*

(a) a constant (b) a linear in x
(c) a quadratic in x (d) a cubic in x

Sol. (a) $\because g'(x) = \begin{vmatrix} f_1' & f_2' & f_3' \\ f_1' & f_2' & f_3' \\ f_1'' & f_2'' & f_3'' \end{vmatrix} + \begin{vmatrix} f_1 & f_2 & f_3 \\ f_1'' & f_2'' & f_3'' \\ f_1'' & f_2'' & f_3'' \end{vmatrix} + \begin{vmatrix} f_1 & f_2 & f_3 \\ f_1' & f_2' & f_3' \\ f_1''' & f_2''' & f_3''' \end{vmatrix}$

$= 0 + 0 + 0$ $[\because f_j$ is a quadratic function$]$

$\therefore \quad g(x) = c =$ constant

• Ex. 8 *Let* $\Delta_a = \begin{vmatrix} (a-1) & n & 6 \\ (a-1)^2 & 2n^2 & 4n-2 \\ (a-1)^3 & 3n^3 & 3n^2 - 3n \end{vmatrix}$, *the value of $\sum_{a=1}^{n} \Delta_a$ is*

(a) 0 (b) $\frac{(n-1)n}{2}$

(c) $\frac{(n-1)n^2}{2}$ (d) $\frac{(n-1)n(2n-1)}{3}$

Sol. (a) $$\sum_{a=1}^{n}\Delta_a = \begin{vmatrix} \sum_{a=1}^{n}(a-1) & n & 6 \\ \sum_{a=1}^{n}(a-1)^2 & 2n^2 & 4n-2 \\ \sum_{a=1}^{n}(a-1)^3 & 3n^3 & 3n^2-3n \end{vmatrix}$$

$$= \begin{vmatrix} \frac{(n-1)n}{2} & n & 6 \\ \frac{(n-1)n(2n-1)}{6} & 2n^2 & 4n-2 \\ \frac{(n-1)^2n^2}{4} & 3n^3 & 3n^2-3n \end{vmatrix}$$

$$= \frac{(n-1)n^2}{2}\begin{vmatrix} 1 & 1 & 6 \\ \frac{2n-1}{3} & 2n & 4n-2 \\ \frac{(n-1)n}{2} & 3n^2 & 3n^2-3n \end{vmatrix}$$

[taking $\frac{(n-1)n}{2}$ and n common from C_1 and C_2]

Applying $C_3 \to C_3 - 6C_1$, then

$$\sum_{a=1}^{n}\Delta_a = \frac{(n-1)n^2}{2}\begin{vmatrix} 1 & 1 & 0 \\ \frac{2n-1}{3} & 2n & 0 \\ \frac{(n-1)n}{2} & 3n^2 & 0 \end{vmatrix} = 0$$

● ***Ex. 9*** *If* $\Delta(x) = \begin{vmatrix} 1 & \cos x & 1-\cos x \\ 1+\sin x & \cos x & 1+\sin x-\cos x \\ \sin x & \sin x & 1 \end{vmatrix}$, *then*

$\int_0^{\pi/2}\Delta(x)\,dx$ *is equal to*

(a) $-\frac{1}{2}$ (b) 0 (c) $\frac{1}{4}$ (d) $\frac{1}{2}$

Sol. (a) Applying $C_3 \to C_3 + C_2 - C_1$, then

$$\Delta(x) = \begin{vmatrix} 1 & \cos x & 0 \\ 1+\sin x & \cos x & 0 \\ \sin x & \sin x & 1 \end{vmatrix}$$

$$= 1(\cos x - \cos x - \cos x\sin x) = -\frac{1}{2}\sin 2x$$

$$\therefore \int_0^{\pi/2}\Delta(x)\,dx = -\frac{1}{2}\int_0^{\pi/2}\sin 2x\,dx$$

$$= \frac{1}{4}[\cos 2x]_0^{\pi/2} = \frac{1}{4}(-1-1) = -\frac{1}{2}$$

● ***Ex. 10*** *Number of values of a for which the system of equations* $a^2x+(2-a)y = 4+a^2$ *and* $ax+(2a-1)y = a^5-2$ *possess no solution, is*

(a) 0 (b) 1
(c) 2 (d) infinite

Sol. (c) $\because \Delta = \begin{vmatrix} a^2 & 2-a \\ a & 2a-1 \end{vmatrix} = a^2(2a-1) - a(2-a)$

$= 2a(a+1)(a-1)$

For no solution, $\Delta = 0$

$\therefore \quad a = -1, 0, 1$

$\Rightarrow \quad \Delta_1 = \begin{vmatrix} 4+a^2 & 2-a \\ a^5-2 & 2a-1 \end{vmatrix}$

Values of Δ_1 at $a = -1, 0, 1$ are $-6, 0, 6$ respectively and

$$\Delta_2 = \begin{vmatrix} a^2 & 4+a^2 \\ a & a^5-2 \end{vmatrix}$$

Values of Δ_2 at $a = -1, 0, 1$ are $2, 0, -6$, respectively.

For no solution,

$\Delta = 0$ and atleast one of Δ_1, Δ_2 is non-zero.

$\therefore \quad a = -1, 1$

JEE Type Solved Examples : More than One Correct Option Type Questions

- This section contains **5 multiple choice examples.** Each example has four choices (a), (b), (c) and (d) out of which **more than one** may be correct.

● ***Ex. 11*** *The determinant* $\begin{vmatrix} a^2 & a^2-(b-c)^2 & bc \\ b^2 & b^2-(c-a)^2 & ca \\ c^2 & c^2-(a-b)^2 & ab \end{vmatrix}$ *is divisible by*

(a) $a+b+c$ (b) $(a+b)(b+c)(c+a)$
(c) $a^2+b^2+c^2$ (d) $(a-b)(b-c)(c-a)$

Sol. (a,c,d) Applying $C_2 \to C_2 - C_1 - 2C_3$, then

$$\begin{vmatrix} a^2 & -(b^2+c^2) & bc \\ b^2 & -(c^2+a^2) & ca \\ c^2 & -(a^2+b^2) & ab \end{vmatrix} = -\begin{vmatrix} a^2 & b^2+c^2 & bc \\ b^2 & c^2+a^2 & ca \\ c^2 & a^2+b^2 & ab \end{vmatrix}$$

Applying $C_2 \to C_2 + C_1$, then

$$= -\begin{vmatrix} a^2 & a^2+b^2+c^2 & bc \\ b^2 & a^2+b^2+c^2 & ca \\ c^2 & a^2+b^2+c^2 & ab \end{vmatrix}$$

Applying $R_2 \to R_2 - R_1$ and $R_3 \to R_3 - R_1$, then

$$= -\begin{vmatrix} a^2 & a^2+b^2+c^2 & bc \\ b^2-a^2 & 0 & c(a-b) \\ c^2-a^2 & 0 & -b(c-a) \end{vmatrix}$$

$$= (a^2+b^2+c^2)\begin{vmatrix} -(a+b)(a-b) & c(a-b) \\ (c+a)(c-a) & -b(c-a) \end{vmatrix}$$

$$= (a-b)(c-a)(a^2+b^2+c^2)\begin{vmatrix} -(a+b) & c \\ c+a & -b \end{vmatrix}$$

Applying $C_1 \to C_1 - C_2$, then

$$= (a-b)(c-a)(a^2+b^2+c^2)\begin{vmatrix} -(a+b+c) & c \\ (a+b+c) & -b \end{vmatrix}$$

$$= (a-b)(b-c)(c-a)(a+b+c)(a^2+b^2+c^2)$$

- **Ex. 12** *The value of θ lying between $-\frac{\pi}{4}$ and $\frac{\pi}{2}$ and $0 \le A \le \frac{\pi}{2}$ and satisfying the equation*

$$\begin{vmatrix} 1+\sin^2 A & \cos^2 A & 2\sin 4\theta \\ \sin^2 A & 1+\cos^2 A & 2\sin 4\theta \\ \sin^2 A & \cos^2 A & 1+2\sin 4\theta \end{vmatrix} = 0, \text{ are}$$

(a) $A = \frac{\pi}{4}, \theta = -\frac{\pi}{8}$ (b) $A = \frac{3\pi}{8} = \theta$

(c) $A = \frac{\pi}{5}, \theta = -\frac{\pi}{8}$ (d) $A = \frac{\pi}{6}, \theta = \frac{3\pi}{8}$

Sol. (a, b, c, d)

$$\because \begin{vmatrix} 1+\sin^2 A & \cos^2 A & 2\sin 4\theta \\ \sin^2 A & 1+\cos^2 A & 2\sin 4\theta \\ \sin^2 A & \cos^2 A & 1+2\sin 4\theta \end{vmatrix} = 0$$

Applying $R_2 \to R_2 - R_1$ and $R_3 \to R_3 - R_1$, then

$$\begin{vmatrix} 1+\sin^2 A & \cos^2 A & 2\sin 4\theta \\ -1 & 1 & 0 \\ -1 & 0 & 1 \end{vmatrix} = 0$$

Applying $C_1 \to C_1 + C_2$, then

$$\begin{vmatrix} 2 & \cos^2 A & 2\sin 4\theta \\ 0 & 1 & 0 \\ -1 & 0 & 1 \end{vmatrix} = 0$$

$$\Rightarrow \quad 1(2 + 2\sin 4\theta) = 0$$

$$\therefore \quad \sin 4\theta = -1$$

$$\Rightarrow \quad 4\theta = (2n-1)\frac{\pi}{2} \Rightarrow \theta = (2n-1)\frac{\pi}{8}$$

For $n = 0, 2$, then $\theta = -\frac{\pi}{8}, \frac{3\pi}{8}$ and $A \in R$

- **Ex. 13** *The digits A, B, C are such that the three digit numbers A88, 6B8, 86C are divisible by 72, the determinant $\begin{vmatrix} A & 6 & 8 \\ 8 & B & 6 \\ 8 & 8 & C \end{vmatrix}$ is divisible by*

(a) 72 (b) 144 (c) 288 (d) 216

Sol. (a, b, c)

$\because$ $A88, 6B8, 86C$ are divisible by 72.

$\therefore$ $A88, 6B8, 86C$ are also divisible by 9.

$\Rightarrow$ $A+8+8, 6+B+8, 8+6+C$

are divisible by 9, then $A = 2, B = 4, C = 4$

$$\text{Let} \quad \Delta = \begin{vmatrix} A & 6 & 8 \\ 8 & B & 6 \\ 8 & 8 & C \end{vmatrix} = \begin{vmatrix} 2 & 6 & 8 \\ 8 & 4 & 6 \\ 8 & 8 & 4 \end{vmatrix}$$

$$= 2(16-48) - 6(32-48) + 8(64-32) = 288$$

Hence, Δ is divisible by 72, 144 and 288.

- **Ex. 14** *If p, q, r and s are in AP and*

$$f(x) = \begin{vmatrix} p+\sin x & q+\sin x & p-r+\sin x \\ q+\sin x & r+\sin x & -1+\sin x \\ r+\sin x & s+\sin x & s-q+\sin x \end{vmatrix}$$

such that $\int_0^1 f(x)\,dx = -2$, the common difference of the AP can be

(a) -1 (b) 1/2 (c) 1 (d) 2

Sol. (a, c)

$$\because f(x) = \frac{1}{2}\begin{vmatrix} p+\sin x & q+\sin x & p-r+\sin x \\ 2q+2\sin x & 2r+2\sin x & -2+2\sin x \\ r+\sin x & s+\sin x & s-q+\sin x \end{vmatrix}$$

Applying $R_2 \to R_2 - (R_1 + R_3)$, then

$$f(x) = \frac{1}{2}\begin{vmatrix} p+\sin x & q+\sin x & p-r+\sin x \\ 0 & 0 & -2 \\ r+\sin x & s+\sin x & s-q+\sin x \end{vmatrix}$$

$[\because 2q = p+r, 2r = q+s \text{ and } p+s = q+r]$

$$= -\frac{(-2)}{2}\begin{vmatrix} p+\sin x & q+\sin x \\ r+\sin x & s+\sin x \end{vmatrix}$$

Applying $C_2 \to C_2 - C_1$, then

$$f(x) = \begin{vmatrix} p + \sin x & D \\ p + 2D + \sin x & D \end{vmatrix}$$

[where D = common difference]

$$= D[p + \sin x - p - 2D - \sin x] = -2D^2$$

and $\int_0^1 f(x)dx = -4$

$\Rightarrow \int_0^1 (-2D^2)dx = -4 \Rightarrow -2D^2 = -2$

$\therefore D^2 = 1 \Rightarrow D = \pm 1$

• **Ex. 15** *If the system of equations $a^2x - by = a^2 - b$ and $bx - b^2y = 2 + 4b$ possess an infinite number of solutions, the possible values of a and b are*

(a) $a = 1, b = -1$ (b) $a = 1, b = -2$
(c) $a = -1, b = -1$ (d) $a = -1, b = -2$

Sol. (a, b, c, d)

Here, $\Delta = \begin{vmatrix} a^2 & -b \\ b & -b^2 \end{vmatrix} = -a^2b^2 + b^2 = -(a^2 - 1)b^2$

If $\Delta = 0$, then $a^2 = 1, b = 0$

Now, $\Delta_1 = \begin{vmatrix} a^2 - b & -b \\ 2 + 4b & -b^2 \end{vmatrix}$

For $a^2 = 1, \Delta_1 = \begin{vmatrix} 1 - b & -b \\ 2 + 4b & -b^2 \end{vmatrix} = b(b+1)(b+2)$

and $\Delta_2 = \begin{vmatrix} a^2 & a^2 - b \\ b & 2 + 4b \end{vmatrix}$

For $a^2 = 1, \Delta_2 = \begin{vmatrix} 1 & 1 - b \\ b & 2 + 4b \end{vmatrix} = (b+1)(b+2)$

For infinite number of solutions, $\Delta = \Delta_1 = \Delta_2 = 0$

$\therefore a^2 = 1, b = -1, -2 \Rightarrow a = \pm 1, b = -1, b = -2$

JEE Type Solved Examples : Passage Based Questions

- This section contains **2 solved passages** based upon each of the passage **3 multiple choice** examples have to be answered. Each of these examples has four choices (a), (b), (c) and (d) out of which **ONLY ONE** is correct.

Passage I
(Ex. Nos. 16 to 18)

Consider the system of equations

$$2x + ay + 6z = 8; \quad x + 2y + bz = 5$$
$$x + y + 3z = 4$$

16. The system has unique solution, if

(a) $a = 2, b = 3$ (b) $a = 2, b \neq 3$
(c) $a \neq 2, b = 3$ (d) $a \neq 2, b \neq 3$

17. The system has infinite solutions, if

(a) $a = 2, b \in R$ (b) $a = 3, b \in R$
(c) $a \in R, b = 2$ (d) $a \in R, b = 3$

18. The system has no solution, if

(a) $a = 2, b = 3$ (b) $a = 2, b \neq 3$
(c) $a \neq 2, b = 3$ (d) $a \neq 2, b \neq 3$

Sol. $\Delta = \begin{vmatrix} 2 & a & 6 \\ 1 & 2 & b \\ 1 & 1 & 3 \end{vmatrix} = 2(6 - b) - a(3 - b) + 6(1 - 2)$

$= ab - 3a - 2b + 6 = (a - 2)(b - 3)$

$\Delta_1 = \begin{vmatrix} 8 & a & 6 \\ 5 & 2 & b \\ 4 & 1 & 3 \end{vmatrix} = 8(6 - b) - a(15 - 4b) + 6(5 - 8)$

$= 4ab - 15a - 8b + 30 = (a - 2)(4b - 15)$

$\Delta_2 = \begin{vmatrix} 2 & 8 & 6 \\ 1 & 5 & b \\ 1 & 4 & 3 \end{vmatrix} = 0$ $[\because R_1 = 2R_3]$

$\Delta_3 = \begin{vmatrix} 2 & a & 8 \\ 1 & 2 & 5 \\ 1 & 1 & 4 \end{vmatrix} = 2(8 - 5) - a(4 - 5) + 8(1 - 2)$

$= 6 + a - 8 = a - 2$

16. (*d*) The system has unique solution, if

$\Delta \neq 0$

$\Rightarrow (a - 2)(b - 3) \neq 0$

$\Rightarrow a \neq 2, b \neq 3$

17. (*a*) The system has infinite solution, if

$\Delta = \Delta_1 = \Delta_2 = \Delta_3 = 0$

$\Rightarrow a - 2 = 0$

or $a = 2, b \in R$

18. (*c*) The system has no solution, if

$\Delta = 0$ and atleast one of Δ_1, Δ_2 and Δ_3 is non-zero.

$\Rightarrow a \neq 2, b = 3$

Passage II

(Ex. Nos. 19 to 20)

Let ${}^xC_i$, ${}^{x^2}C_i$ and ${}^{x^3}C_i$ $(i = 1, 2, 3)$ be Binomial coefficients, where $x \in N$

and $f(x) = 12\begin{vmatrix} {}^xC_1 & {}^xC_2 & {}^xC_3 \\ {}^{x^2}C_1 & {}^{x^2}C_2 & {}^{x^2}C_3 \\ {}^{x^3}C_1 & {}^{x^3}C_2 & {}^{x^3}C_3 \end{vmatrix}$, *then*

19. $f(x)$ is a polynomial of degree

(a) 6 (b) 10

(c) 14 (d) 18

20. If $f(x) = (x-1)^m x^n (x+1)^p$, where $m, n, p \in N$, then the value of Σmn is

(a) 32 (b) 43

(c) 44 (d) 56

Sol.

$$\because f(x) = 12\begin{vmatrix} {}^xC_1 & {}^xC_2 & {}^xC_3 \\ {}^{x^2}C_1 & {}^{x^2}C_2 & {}^{x^2}C_3 \\ {}^{x^3}C_1 & {}^{x^3}C_2 & {}^{x^3}C_3 \end{vmatrix}$$

$$= 12\begin{vmatrix} x & \dfrac{x(x-1)}{2} & \dfrac{x(x-1)(x-2)}{6} \\ x^2 & \dfrac{x^2(x^2-1)}{2} & \dfrac{x^2(x^2-1)(x^2-2)}{6} \\ x^3 & \dfrac{x^3(x^3-1)}{2} & \dfrac{x^3(x^3-1)(x^3-2)}{6} \end{vmatrix}$$

Taking x, x^2 and x^3 common from R_1, R_2 and R_3, then

$$f(x) = x \cdot x^2 \cdot x^3 \begin{vmatrix} 1 & (x-1) & (x-1)(x-2) \\ 1 & (x^2-1) & (x^2-1)(x^2-2) \\ 1 & (x^3-1) & (x^3-1)(x^3-2) \end{vmatrix}$$

$$= x^6(x-1)^2\begin{vmatrix} 1 & 1 & x-2 \\ 1 & x+1 & (x+1)(x^2-2) \\ 1 & x^2+x+1 & (x^2+x+1)(x^3-2) \end{vmatrix}$$

Applying $R_1 \to R_1 - R_2$ and $R_3 \to R_3 - R_2$, then

$$f(x) = x^6(x-1)^2\begin{vmatrix} 0 & -x & x(3-x-x^2) \\ \vdots & & \\ 1 \cdots & x+1 \cdots & (x+1)(x^2-2) \\ \vdots & & \\ 0 & x^2 & x^2(x^2+x^3-3) \end{vmatrix}$$

Expanding along C_1, then

$$= -x^6(x-1)^2\begin{vmatrix} -x & x(3-x-x^2) \\ x^2 & x^2(x^2+x^3-3) \end{vmatrix}$$

$$= -x^9(x-1)^2\begin{vmatrix} -1 & 3-x-x^2 \\ 1 & x^2+x^3-3 \end{vmatrix}$$

$$= -x^9(x-1)^2(-x^2-x^3+3-3+x+x^2)$$

$$= x^{10}(x-1)^2(x^2-1) = x^{10}(x-1)^3(x+1)$$

19. (c) $f(x)$ is a polynomial of degree 14.

20. (b) Here, $m = 3, n = 10$ and $p = 1$

$\therefore \Sigma mn = mn + np + pm = 30 + 10 + 3 = 43$

JEE Type Solved Examples : Single Integer Answer Type Questions

- This section contains **2 examples.** The answer to each example is a **single digit integer** ranging from **0** to **9** (both inclusive).

● ***Ex. 21*** *If* $\Delta_r = \begin{vmatrix} r & r-1 \\ r-1 & r \end{vmatrix}$, *where r is a natural number, the value of* $\sqrt[10]{\sum_{r=1}^{1024} \Delta_r}$ *is*

Sol. (4) $\because \quad \Delta_r = r^2 - (r-1)^2$

$$\therefore \quad \sum_{r=1}^{1024} \Delta_r = (1024)^2 - (1-1)^2 = (1024)^2 = 2^{20}$$

$$\Rightarrow \quad \sqrt[10]{\sum_{r=1}^{1024} \Delta_r} = 2^2 = 4$$

● ***Ex. 22*** *If P, Q and R are the angles of a triangle, the value of* $\begin{vmatrix} \tan P & 1 & 1 \\ 1 & \tan Q & 1 \\ 1 & 1 & \tan R \end{vmatrix}$ *is*

Sol. (2) $\begin{vmatrix} \tan P & 1 & 1 \\ 1 & \tan Q & 1 \\ 1 & 1 & \tan R \end{vmatrix} = \tan P(\tan Q \tan R - 1)$

$$-1(\tan R - 1) + 1(1 - \tan Q)$$

$$= \tan P \tan Q \tan R - (\tan P + \tan Q + \tan R) + 2$$

$$= 0 + 2$$

$[\because$ In ΔPQR, $\tan P + \tan Q + \tan R = \tan P \tan Q \tan R]$

$$= 2$$

JEE Type Solved Examples : Matching Type Questions

- This section contains 2 eamples. Example 23 have four statements (A, B, C and D) given in **Column I** and four statement (p, q, r and s) in **Column II** and example 24 have three statements (A, B and C) given in **Column I** and four statements (p, q, r and s) in **Column II**. Any given statement in **Column I** can have correct matching with one or more statements(s) given in **Column II.**

• ***Ex. 23*** *Let $f(x)$ denotes the determinant*

$$f(x)=\begin{vmatrix} x^2 & 2x & 1+x^2 \\ x^2+1 & x+1 & 1 \\ x & -1 & x-1 \end{vmatrix}.$$

On expansion $f(x)$ is seen to be a 4th degree polynomial given by $f(x)=a_0x^4+a_1x^3+a_2x^2+a_3x+a_4$.
Using differentiation of determinant or otherwise match the entries in Column I with one or more entries of the elements of Column II.

	Column I		Column II
(A)	$a_0^2+a_1$ is divisible by	(p)	2
(B)	$a_2^2+a_4$ is divisible by	(q)	3
(C)	$a_0^2+a_2$ is divisible by	(r)	4
(D)	$a_4^2+a_3^2+a_1^2$ is divisible by	(s)	5

Sol. (A) → (p, s); (B) → (p, r); (C) → (p, q); (D) → (q)

$$\because \quad f(x)=\begin{vmatrix} x^2 & 2x & 1+x^2 \\ x^2+1 & x+1 & 1 \\ x & -1 & x-1 \end{vmatrix}$$

Applying $C_1 \to C_1 - C_3$, then

$$f(x)=\begin{vmatrix} -1 & 2x & 1+x^2 \\ x^2 & x+1 & 1 \\ 1 & -1 & x-1 \end{vmatrix}$$

Expanding along R_1, then

$$f(x)=-(x^2-1+1)-2x(x^3-x^2-1)+(1+x^2)(-x^2-x-1)$$

$$=-3x^4+x^3\ 3x^2+x-1 \qquad \text{...(i)}$$

According to the question, we get

$$f(x)=a_0x^4+a_1x^3+a_2x^2+a_3x+a_4 \qquad \text{...(ii)}$$

From Eqs. (i) and (ii), we get

$$a_0=-3, a_1=1, a_2=-3, a_3=1, a_4=-1$$

(A) $a_0^2+a_1=(-3)^2+1=9+1=10=2\times 5$

(B) $a_2^2+a_4=(-3)^2-1=9-1=8=2\times 4$

(C) $a_0^2+a_2=(-3)^2-3=9-3=6=2\times 3$

(D) $a_4^2+a_3^2+a_1^2=(-1)^2+(1)^2+(1)^2=1+1+1=3$

• ***Ex. 24*** *Suppose a, b and c are distinct and x, y and z are connected by the system of equations $x+ay+a^2z=a^3$, $x+by+b^2z=b^3$ and $x+cy+c^2z=c^3$.*

	Column I		Column II
(A)	For $x=1$, $y=2$ and $z=3$, $(a+b+c)^{-(ab+bc+ca)}$ is divisible by	(p)	3
(B)	For $x=4$, $y=3$ and $z=2$, $(ab+bc+ca)^{abc}$ is divisible by	(q)	6
(C)	For $x=6$, $y=4$ and $z=2$, $(abc)^{a+b+c}$ is divisible by	(r)	9
		(s)	12

Sol. (A) → (p, r) (B) → (p, r); (C) → (p, q, r, s)

$$a\neq b\neq c$$

$$\Delta=\begin{vmatrix} 1 & a & a^2 \\ 1 & b & b^2 \\ 1 & c & c^2 \end{vmatrix}=(a-b)(b-c)(c-a)$$

$$\Delta_1=\begin{vmatrix} a^3 & a & a^2 \\ b^3 & b & b^2 \\ c^3 & c & c^2 \end{vmatrix}=\begin{vmatrix} a & a^2 & a^3 \\ b & b^2 & b^3 \\ c & c^2 & c^3 \end{vmatrix}=abc\begin{vmatrix} 1 & a & a^2 \\ 1 & b & b^2 \\ 1 & c & c^2 \end{vmatrix}$$

$$=abc(a-b)(b-c)(c-a)$$

$$\Delta_2=\begin{vmatrix} 1 & a^3 & a^2 \\ 1 & b^3 & b^2 \\ 1 & c^3 & c^2 \end{vmatrix}=-\begin{vmatrix} 1 & a^2 & a^3 \\ 1 & b^2 & b^3 \\ 1 & c^2 & c^3 \end{vmatrix}$$

$$=-(a-b)(b-c)(c-a)(ab+bc+ca)$$

$$\text{and } \Delta_3=\begin{vmatrix} 1 & a & a^3 \\ 1 & b & b^3 \\ 1 & c & c^3 \end{vmatrix}=(a-b)(b-c)(c-a)(a+b+c)$$

By Cramer's rule, we get

$$x=\frac{\Delta_1}{\Delta}=abc$$

$$y=\frac{\Delta^2}{\Delta}=-(ab+bc+ca),\ z=\frac{\Delta_3}{\Delta}=a+b+c$$

(A) $(a+b+c)^{-(ab+bc+ca)}=z^y=3^2=9$, which is divisible by 3 and 9.

(B) $(ab+bc+ca)^{abc}=(-y)^x=(-3)^4=81$, which is divisible by 3 and 9.

(C) $(abc)^{a+b+c}=x^3=6^2=36$, which is divisible by 3, 6, 9 and 12.

JEE Type Solved Examples : Statement I and II Type Questions

■ **Directions** Example numbers 25 and 26 are Assertion-Reason type examples. Each of these examples contains two statements:

Statement-1 (Assertion) and **Statement-2** (Reason)

Each of these examples also has four alternative choices, only one of which is the correct answer. You have to select the correct choice as given below.

(a) Statement-1 is true, Statement-2 is true; Statement-2 is a correct explanation for Statement-1
(b) Statement-1 is true, Statement-2 is true; Statement-2 is not a correct explanation for Statement-1
(c) Statement-1 is true, Statement-2 is false
(d) Statement-1 is false, Statement-2 is true

● ***Ex. 25*** **Statement-1** *Let*

$$\Delta_r = \begin{vmatrix} (r-1) & n! & 6 \\ (r-1)^2 & (n!)^2 & 4n-2 \\ (r-1)^3 & (n!)^3 & 3n^2-2n \end{vmatrix}, \text{ then } \prod_{r=2}^{n+1} \Delta_r = 0.$$

Statement-2 $\prod_{r=2}^{n+1} \Delta_r = \Delta_2 \cdot \Delta_3 \cdot \Delta_4 \dots \Delta_{n+1}$

Sol. (*d*) $\because \prod_{r=2}^{n+1} \Delta_r = \Delta_2 \cdot \Delta_3 \cdot \Delta_4 \dots \Delta_{n+1}$

$$= \begin{vmatrix} 1 & n! & 6 \\ 1 & (n!)^2 & 4n-2 \\ 1 & (n!)^3 & 3n^3-2n \end{vmatrix} \times \begin{vmatrix} 2 & n! & 6 \\ 4 & (n!)^2 & 4n-2 \\ 8 & (n!)^3 & 3n^2-2n \end{vmatrix} \times \dots \times \begin{vmatrix} n & n! & 6 \\ n^2 & (n!)^2 & 4n-2 \\ n^3 & (n!)^3 & (3n^2-2n) \end{vmatrix} \neq 0$$

$\therefore$ Statement-1 is false and Statement-2 is true.

● ***Ex. 26*** *Consider the determinant*

$$f(x) = \begin{vmatrix} 0 & x^2-a & x^3-b \\ x^2+a & 0 & x^2+c \\ x^4+b & x-c & 0 \end{vmatrix}.$$

Statement-1 *$f(x)=0$ has one root $x=0$.*

Statement-2 *The value of skew-symmetric determinant of odd order is always zero.*

Sol. (a) For $x = 0$, the determinant reduces to the determinant of a skew-symmetric of odd order which is always zero. Hence, $x = 0$ is the solution of given equation $f(x) = 0$.

Subjective Type Examples

■ In this section, there are **20 subjective** solved examples.

● ***Ex. 27*** *A determinant of second order is made with the elements 0 and 1. Find the number of determinants with non-negative values.*

Sol. The number of determinants that can be made with 0 and 1

$$= 2 \times 2 \times 2 \times 2 = 16$$

and there are only three determinants of second order with negative values

i.e., $\begin{vmatrix} 1 & 1 \\ 1 & 0 \end{vmatrix}, \begin{vmatrix} 0 & 1 \\ 1 & 1 \end{vmatrix}, \begin{vmatrix} 0 & 1 \\ 1 & 0 \end{vmatrix}$

Therefore, number of determinants with non-negative values $= 16 - 3 = 13$

● ***Ex. 28*** *Prove that* $\begin{vmatrix} 1+a & 1 & 1 \\ 1 & 1+b & 1 \\ 1 & 1 & 1+c \end{vmatrix}$

$= abc\left(1+\frac{1}{a}+\frac{1}{b}+\frac{1}{c}\right)$, *hence find the value of the determinant, if a, b and c are the roots of the equation $px^3 - qx^2 + rx - s = 0$.*

Sol. Let
$$\Delta = \begin{vmatrix} 1+a & 1 & 1 \\ 1 & 1+b & 1 \\ 1 & 1 & 1+c \end{vmatrix}$$

Since, the answer contain abc, then taking a, b and c common from R_1, R_2 and R_3 respectively, then

$$\Delta = abc \begin{vmatrix} \frac{1}{a}+1 & \frac{1}{a} & \frac{1}{a} \\ \frac{1}{b} & \frac{1}{b}+1 & \frac{1}{b} \\ \frac{1}{c} & \frac{1}{c} & \frac{1}{c}+1 \end{vmatrix}$$

But answer also contains $\left(1+\frac{1}{a}+\frac{1}{b}+\frac{1}{c}\right)$,

then applying $R_1 \to R_1 + R_2 + R_3$

$$\therefore \quad \Delta = abc \begin{vmatrix} 1+\frac{1}{a}+\frac{1}{b}+\frac{1}{c} & 1+\frac{1}{a}+\frac{1}{b}+\frac{1}{c} & 1+\frac{1}{a}+\frac{1}{b}+\frac{1}{c} \\ \frac{1}{b} & \frac{1}{b}+1 & \frac{1}{b} \\ \frac{1}{c} & \frac{1}{c} & \frac{1}{c}+1 \end{vmatrix}$$

Taking $\left(1+\frac{1}{a}+\frac{1}{b}+\frac{1}{c}\right)$ common from R_1, then

$$\Delta = abc\left(1+\frac{1}{a}+\frac{1}{b}+\frac{1}{c}\right)\begin{vmatrix} 1 & 1 & 1 \\ \frac{1}{b} & \frac{1}{b}+1 & \frac{1}{b} \\ \frac{1}{c} & \frac{1}{c} & \frac{1}{c}+1 \end{vmatrix}$$

Applying $C_2 \to C_2 - C_1$, then

$$\Delta = abc\left(1+\frac{1}{a}+\frac{1}{b}+\frac{1}{c}\right)\begin{vmatrix} 1 & 0 & 1 \\ \frac{1}{b} & 1 & \frac{1}{b} \\ \frac{1}{c} & 0 & \frac{1}{c}+1 \end{vmatrix}$$

Expanding along C_2, then

$$\Delta = abc\left(1+\frac{1}{a}+\frac{1}{b}+\frac{1}{c}\right)\begin{vmatrix} 1 & 1 \\ \frac{1}{c} & \frac{1}{c}+1 \end{vmatrix}$$

Hence, $\Delta = abc\left(1+\frac{1}{a}+\frac{1}{b}+\frac{1}{c}\right)$

2nd Part $\Delta = abc\left(1+\frac{1}{a}+\frac{1}{b}+\frac{1}{c}\right) = abc + bc + ca + ab$

$$= \frac{s}{p} + \frac{r}{p} = \left(\frac{s+r}{p}\right)$$

● ***Ex. 29*** *If a, b and c are positive and are the pth, qth and rth terms, respectively of a GP. Show without expanding that*

$$\begin{vmatrix} \log a & p & 1 \\ \log b & q & 1 \\ \log c & r & 1 \end{vmatrix} = 0.$$

Sol. Let A be the first term and R be the common ratio of GP, then

$$a = p\text{th term} = AR^{p-1}$$
$$b = q\text{th term} = AR^{q-1}$$
$$c = r\text{th term} = AR^{r-1}$$

$\therefore$ $\log a = \log A + (p-1)\log R$,
$\log b = \log A + (q-1)\log R$ and
$\log c = \log A + (r-1)\log R$

$$\therefore \quad \text{LHS} = \begin{vmatrix} \log a & p & 1 \\ \log b & q & 1 \\ \log c & r & 1 \end{vmatrix}$$

$$= \begin{vmatrix} \log A + (p-1)\log R & p & 1 \\ \log A + (q-1)\log R & q & 1 \\ \log A + (r-1)\log R & r & 1 \end{vmatrix}$$

Applying $C_1 \to C_1 - (\log A)C_3$, then

$$= \begin{vmatrix} (p-1)\log R & p & 1 \\ (q-1)\log R & q & 1 \\ (r-1)\log R & r & 1 \end{vmatrix} = \log R\begin{vmatrix} (p-1) & p & 1 \\ (q-1) & q & 1 \\ (r-1) & r & 1 \end{vmatrix}$$

Applying $C_1 \to C_1 + C_3$, then

$$= \log R\begin{vmatrix} p & p & 1 \\ q & q & 1 \\ r & r & 1 \end{vmatrix} = 0 \text{ [since } C_1 \text{ and } C_2 \text{ are identical]}$$

$= \text{RHS}$

● ***Ex. 30*** *Prove that*

$$\begin{vmatrix} -2a & a+b & a+c \\ b+a & -2b & b+c \\ c+a & c+b & -2c \end{vmatrix} = 4(b+c)(c+a)(a+b).$$

Sol. Let $\Delta = \begin{vmatrix} -2a & a+b & a+c \\ b+a & -2b & b+c \\ c+a & c+b & -2c \end{vmatrix}$

On putting $a+b=0$, $b=-a$

$$\text{Then,} \quad \Delta = \begin{vmatrix} -2a & 0 & a+c \\ 0 & 2a & c-a \\ c+a & c-a & -2c \end{vmatrix}$$

Expanding along R_1, then

$\Delta = -2a\{-4ac-(c-a)^2\} - 0 + (a+c)\{0-2a(c+a)\}$

$= 2a(c+a)^2 - 2a(c+a)^2 = 0$

Hence, $(a+b)$ is a factor of Δ, similarly $(b+c)$ and $(c+a)$ are the factors of Δ.

On expansion of determinant we can see that each term of the determinant is a homogeneous expression in a, b and c of degree 3 and also RHS is a homogeneous expression of degree 3.

Let $\quad \Delta = k(a+b)(b+c)(c+a)$

$$\text{or} \quad \begin{vmatrix} -2a & a+b & a+c \\ b+a & -2b & b+c \\ c+a & c+b & -2c \end{vmatrix} = k(a+b)(b+c)(c+a)$$

On putting $a=0$, $b=1$ and $c=2$, we get

$$\begin{vmatrix} 0 & 1 & 2 \\ 1 & -2 & 3 \\ 2 & 3 & -4 \end{vmatrix} = k(0+1)(1+2)(2+0)$$

$\Rightarrow \quad 0 - 1(-4-6) + 2(3+4) = 6k$

$\Rightarrow \quad 24 = 6k$

$\therefore \quad k = 4$

$$\text{Hence,} \quad \begin{vmatrix} -2a & a+b & a+c \\ b+a & -2b & b+c \\ c+a & c+b & -2c \end{vmatrix} = 4(a+b)(b+c)(c+a)$$

● ***Ex. 31*** *If* $bc+qr = ca+rp = ab+pq = -1$,

$$\textit{show that} \begin{vmatrix} ap & bp & cr \\ a & b & c \\ p & q & r \end{vmatrix} = 0.$$

Sol. Given equations can be rewritten as

$$bc + qr + 1 = 0 \quad \text{...(i)}$$
$$ca + rp + 1 = 0 \quad \text{...(ii)}$$
$$ab + pq + 1 = 0 \quad \text{...(iii)}$$

On multiplying Eqs. (i), (ii) and (iii) by ap, bq and cr respectively, we get

$$(abc)p + (pqr)a + ap = 0$$
$$(abc)q + (pqr)b + bq = 0$$
$$(abc)r + (pqr)c + cr = 0$$

These equations are consistent, given equations three but abc and pqr are two.

Hence, $$\begin{vmatrix} p & a & ap \\ q & b & bq \\ r & c & cr \end{vmatrix} = 0$$

$$\Rightarrow \quad \begin{vmatrix} p & q & r \\ a & b & c \\ ap & bq & cr \end{vmatrix} = 0$$

[interchanging rows into columns]

$$\Rightarrow \quad (-1)\begin{vmatrix} ap & bq & cr \\ a & b & c \\ p & q & r \end{vmatrix} = 0 \quad [R_1 \leftrightarrow R_3]$$

Hence, $$\begin{vmatrix} ap & bq & cr \\ a & b & c \\ p & q & r \end{vmatrix} = 0$$

• **Ex. 32** *If α and β are the roots of the equations $x^2 - 2x + 4 = 0$, find the value of* $\begin{vmatrix} \Sigma\alpha & \Sigma\alpha^2 & \Sigma\alpha^3 \\ \Sigma\alpha^2 & \Sigma\alpha^3 & \Sigma\alpha^4 \\ \Sigma\alpha^3 & \Sigma\alpha^4 & \Sigma\alpha^5 \end{vmatrix}$.

Sol. Given, $x^2 - 2x + 4 = 0$

$\therefore \quad x = 1 \pm i\sqrt{3}$

$\therefore \quad \alpha = 1 + i\sqrt{3}$

and $\quad \beta = 1 - i\sqrt{3}$

$$\Rightarrow \quad \alpha = -2\left(\frac{-1 - i\sqrt{3}}{2}\right) \text{ and } \beta = -2\left(\frac{-1 + i\sqrt{3}}{2}\right)$$

$\alpha = -2\omega^2$ and $\beta = -2\omega$, where ω is the cube root of unity.

$$\Sigma\alpha = \alpha + \beta = -2(\omega + \omega)^2 = -2(-1) = 2$$
$$\Sigma\alpha^2 = \alpha^2 + \beta^2 = 4\omega^4 + 4\omega^2 = 4(\omega + \omega)^2 = 4(-1) = -4$$
$$\Sigma\alpha^3 = \alpha^3 + \beta^3 = -8\omega^6 - 8\omega^3 = -8 - 8 = -16$$
$$\Sigma\alpha^4 = \alpha^4 + \beta^4 = 16\omega^8 + 16\omega^4 = 16(\omega^2 + \omega)$$
$$= 16(-1) = -16$$

and $\quad \Sigma\alpha^5 = \alpha^5 + \beta^5 = -32\omega^{10} - 32\omega^5$

$$= -32(\omega + \omega^2) = -32(-1) = 32$$

Let $$\Delta = \begin{vmatrix} \Sigma\alpha & \Sigma\alpha^2 & \Sigma\alpha^3 \\ \Sigma\alpha^2 & \Sigma\alpha^3 & \Sigma\alpha^4 \\ \Sigma\alpha^3 & \Sigma\alpha^4 & \Sigma\alpha^5 \end{vmatrix} = \begin{vmatrix} 2 & -4 & -16 \\ -4 & -16 & -16 \\ -16 & -16 & 32 \end{vmatrix}$$

$$= 2(-4)(-16)\begin{vmatrix} 1 & -2 & -8 \\ 1 & 4 & 4 \\ 1 & 1 & -2 \end{vmatrix} = 128\begin{vmatrix} 1 & -2 & -8 \\ 1 & 4 & 4 \\ 1 & 1 & -2 \end{vmatrix}$$

Applying $R_2 \to R_2 - R_1$ and $R_3 \to R_3 - R_1$, then

$$\Delta = 128\begin{vmatrix} 1 & -2 & -8 \\ 0 & 6 & 12 \\ 0 & 3 & 6 \end{vmatrix}$$

Expanding along C_1, we get

$$\Delta = 128 \cdot 1 \cdot \begin{vmatrix} 6 & 12 \\ 3 & 6 \end{vmatrix} = 128(36 - 36) = 0$$

• **Ex. 33** *If $a^2 + b^2 + c^2 = 1$, prove that*

$$\begin{vmatrix} a^2 + (b^2 + c^2)\cos\phi & ab(1 - \cos\phi) & ac(1 - \cos\phi) \\ ba(1 - \cos\phi) & b^2 + (c^2 + a^2)\cos\phi & bc(1 - \cos\phi) \\ ca(1 - \cos\phi) & cb(1 - \cos\phi) & c^2 + (a^2 + b^2)\cos\phi \end{vmatrix}$$

is independent of a, b and c.

Sol. Let

$$\Delta = \begin{vmatrix} a^2 + (b^2 + c^2)\cos\phi & ab(1 - \cos\phi) & ac(1 - \cos\phi) \\ ba(1 - \cos\phi) & b^2 + (c^2 + a^2)\cos\phi & bc(1 - \cos\phi) \\ ca(1 - \cos\phi) & cb(1 - \cos\phi) & c^2 + (a^2 + b^2)\cos\phi \end{vmatrix}$$

On multiplying C_1, C_2 and C_3 by a, b and c respectively and taking a, b and c common from R_1, R_2 and R_3 respectively, we get

$$\Delta = \frac{abc}{abc}\begin{vmatrix} a^2 + (b^2 + c^2)\cos\phi & b^2(1 - \cos\phi) & c^2(1 - \cos\phi) \\ a^2(1 - \cos\phi) & b^2 + (c^2 + a^2)\cos\phi & c^2(1 - \cos\phi) \\ a^2(1 - \cos\phi) & b^2(1 - \cos\phi) & c^2 + (a^2 + b^2)\cos\phi \end{vmatrix}$$

Applying $C_1 \to C_1 + C_2 + C_3$, then

$$\Delta = \begin{vmatrix} a^2+b^2+c^2 & b^2 1-\cos\phi) & c^2(1-\cos\phi) \\ a^2+b^2+c^2 & b^2+(c^2+a^2)\cos\phi & c^2(1-\cos\phi) \\ a^2+b^2+c^2 & b^2(1-\cos\phi) & c^2+(a^2+b^2)\cos\phi \end{vmatrix}$$

Taking $a^2+b^2+c^2$ common from C_1, then

$$\Delta = (a^2+b^2+c^2)\begin{vmatrix} 1 & b^2(1-\cos\phi) & c^2(1-\cos\phi) \\ 1 & b^2+(c^2+a^2)\cos\phi & c^2(1-\cos\phi) \\ 1 & b^2(1-\cos\phi) & c^2+(a^2+b^2)\cos\phi \end{vmatrix}$$

Applying $R_1 \to R_2 - R_1$ and $R_3 \to R_3 - R_1$, then

$$\Delta = 1\begin{vmatrix} 1 & b^2(1-\cos\phi) & c^2(1-\cos\phi) \\ 0 & (a^2+b^2+c^2)\cos\phi & 0 \\ 0 & 0 & (a^2+b^2+c^2)\cos\phi \end{vmatrix}$$

$$= (a^2+b^2+c^2)^2\cos^2\phi$$

[by property, since all elements zero below leading diagonal]

$$= 1^2\cdot\cos\phi = \cos^2\phi \qquad [\because a^2+b^2+c^2=1]$$

which is independent of a, b and c.

• Ex. 34 *If $a \neq 0$ and $a \neq 1$, show that*

$$\begin{vmatrix} x+1 & x & x \\ x & x+a & x \\ x & x & x+a^2 \end{vmatrix} = a^3\left[1+\frac{x(a^3-1)}{a^2(a-1)}\right].$$

Sol. Let

$$\text{LHS} = \Delta = \begin{vmatrix} x+1 & x & x \\ x & x+a & x \\ x & x & x+a^2 \end{vmatrix} = \begin{vmatrix} x+1 & x & x \\ x+0 & x+a & x \\ x+0 & x & x+a^2 \end{vmatrix}$$

$$= \begin{vmatrix} x & x & x \\ x & x+a & x \\ x & x & x+a^2 \end{vmatrix} + \begin{vmatrix} 1 & x & x \\ 0 & x+a & x \\ 0 & x & x+a^2 \end{vmatrix}$$

Applying $R_2 \to R_2 - R_1$ and $R_3 \to R_3 - R_1$ in first determinant, then

$$\Delta = \begin{vmatrix} x & x & x \\ 0 & a & 0 \\ 0 & 0 & a^2 \end{vmatrix} + \begin{vmatrix} 1 & x & x \\ 0 & x+a & x \\ 0 & x & x+a^2 \end{vmatrix}$$

Expanding first determinant by property, since all elements below leading diagonal are zero and expanding second determinant along C_1, then

$$\Delta = x\cdot a\cdot a^2 + 1\cdot\begin{vmatrix} x+a & x \\ x & x+a^2 \end{vmatrix}$$

$$= xa^3 + \{(x+a)(x+a^2) - x^2\}$$

$$= xa^3 + (x^2 + a^2x + ax + a^3 - x^2)$$

$$= xa^3 + a^2x + ax + a^3 = a^3 + x(a^3+a^2+a)$$

$$= a^3 + \frac{x\cdot a(a^3-1)}{(a-1)} = a^3\left[1+\frac{x(a^3-1)}{a^2(a-1)}\right] = \text{RHS}$$

• Ex. 35 (i) *Prove that* $\begin{vmatrix} bc-a^2 & ca-b^2 & ab-c^2 \\ ca-b^2 & ab-c^2 & bc-a^2 \\ ab-c^2 & bc-a^2 & ca-b^2 \end{vmatrix}$

$$= \begin{vmatrix} \alpha^2 & \beta^2 & \beta^2 \\ \beta^2 & \alpha^2 & \beta^2 \\ \beta^2 & \beta^2 & \alpha^2 \end{vmatrix},$$

where $\alpha^2 = a^2+b^2+c^2$ *and* $\beta^2 = ab+bc+ca$.

(ii) *Prove that* $\begin{vmatrix} bc-a^2 & ca-b^2 & ab-c^2 \\ ca-b^2 & ab-c^2 & bc-a^2 \\ ab-c^2 & bc-a^2 & ca-b^2 \end{vmatrix}$ *is divisible by* $(a+b+c)^2$. *Find the quotient.*

(iii) *Prove that* $\begin{vmatrix} bc-a^2 & ca-b^2 & ab-c^2 \\ ca-b^2 & ab-c^2 & bc-a^2 \\ ab-c^2 & bc-a^2 & ca-b^2 \end{vmatrix}$

$$= \begin{vmatrix} a^2 & c^2 & 2ac-b^2 \\ 2ab-c^2 & b^2 & a^2 \\ b^2 & 2bc-a^2 & c^2 \end{vmatrix}.$$

(iv) *Prove that* $\begin{vmatrix} 2bc-a^2 & c^2 & b^2 \\ c^2 & 2ca-b^2 & a^2 \\ b^2 & a^2 & 2ab-c^2 \end{vmatrix}$

$$= (a^3+b^3+c^3-3abc)^2.$$

Sol. (i) Let $\Delta = \begin{vmatrix} a & b & c \\ b & c & a \\ c & a & b \end{vmatrix}$

$\therefore$ Determinant of cofactors of Δ is

$$\Delta^c = \begin{vmatrix} bc-a^2 & ca-b^2 & ab-c^2 \\ ca-b^2 & ab-c^2 & bc-a^2 \\ ab-c^2 & bc-a^2 & ca-b^2 \end{vmatrix} = \Delta^{3-1} = \Delta^2$$

$$= \begin{vmatrix} a & b & c \\ b & c & a \\ c & a & b \end{vmatrix}^2 \qquad \text{...(i)}$$

$$= \begin{vmatrix} a & b & c \\ b & c & a \\ c & a & b \end{vmatrix} \times \begin{vmatrix} a & b & c \\ b & c & a \\ c & a & b \end{vmatrix}$$

$$= \begin{vmatrix} a^2+b^2+c^2 & ab+bc+ca & ab+bc+ca \\ ab+bc+ca & a^2+b^2+c^2 & ab+bc+ca \\ ab+bc+ca & ab+bc+ca & a^2+b^2+c^2 \end{vmatrix} \quad \text{[row by row]}$$

$$= \begin{vmatrix} \alpha^2 & \beta^2 & \beta^2 \\ \beta^2 & \alpha^2 & \beta^2 \\ \beta^2 & \beta^2 & \alpha^2 \end{vmatrix}$$

Hence, $\begin{vmatrix} bc-a^2 & ca-b^2 & ab-c^2 \\ ca-b^2 & ab-c^2 & bc-a^2 \\ ab-c^2 & bc-a^2 & ca-b^2 \end{vmatrix} = \begin{vmatrix} \alpha^2 & \beta^2 & \beta^2 \\ \beta^2 & \alpha^2 & \beta^2 \\ \beta^2 & \beta^2 & \alpha^2 \end{vmatrix}$

(ii) From Eq. (i), we get

$$\begin{vmatrix} bc-a^2 & ca-b^2 & ab-c^2 \\ ca-b^2 & ab-c^2 & bc-a^2 \\ ab-c^2 & bc-a^2 & ca-b^2 \end{vmatrix} = \begin{vmatrix} a & b & c \\ b & c & a \\ c & a & b \end{vmatrix}^2$$

$$= (a^3+b^3+c^3-3abc)^2$$
$$= (a+b+c)^2(a^2+b^2+c^2-ab-bc-ca)^2$$

Therefore, $\begin{vmatrix} bc-a^2 & ca-b^2 & ab-c^2 \\ ca-b^2 & ab-c^2 & bc-a^2 \\ ab-c^2 & bc-a^2 & ca-b^2 \end{vmatrix}$ is divisible by $(a+b+c)^2$.

Hence, the quotient is $(a^2+b^2+c^2-ab-bc-ca)^2$.

(iii) From Eq. (i), we get

$$\begin{vmatrix} bc-a^2 & ca-b^2 & ab-c^2 \\ ca-b^2 & ab-c^2 & bc-a^2 \\ ab-c^2 & bc-a^2 & ca-b^2 \end{vmatrix} = \begin{vmatrix} a & b & c \\ b & c & a \\ c & a & b \end{vmatrix}^2$$

Let $\Delta = \begin{vmatrix} a & b & c \\ b & c & a \\ c & a & b \end{vmatrix}^2 = \begin{vmatrix} a & b & c \\ b & c & a \\ c & a & b \end{vmatrix} \times \begin{vmatrix} a & b & c \\ b & c & a \\ c & a & b \end{vmatrix}$

$$= \begin{vmatrix} a & b & c \\ b & c & a \\ c & a & b \end{vmatrix} \times \begin{vmatrix} a & -c & b \\ b & -a & c \\ c & -b & a \end{vmatrix}$$

$$= \begin{vmatrix} a^2 & c^2 & 2ac-b^2 \\ 2ab-c^2 & b^2 & a^2 \\ b^2 & 2bc-a^2 & c^2 \end{vmatrix} \quad \text{[row by row]}$$

Hence, $\begin{vmatrix} bc-a^2 & ca-b^2 & ab-c^2 \\ ca-b^2 & ab-c^2 & bc-a^2 \\ ab-c^2 & bc-a^2 & ca-b^2 \end{vmatrix}$

$$= \begin{vmatrix} a^2 & c^2 & 2ac-b^2 \\ 2ab-c^2 & b^2 & a^2 \\ b^2 & 2bc-a^2 & c^2 \end{vmatrix}$$

(iv) LHS $= \begin{vmatrix} 2bc-a^2 & c^2 & b^2 \\ c^2 & 2ca-b^2 & a^2 \\ b^2 & a^2 & 2ab-c^2 \end{vmatrix}$

$$= \begin{vmatrix} a & b & c \\ b & c & a \\ c & a & b \end{vmatrix} \times \begin{vmatrix} -a & c & b \\ -b & a & c \\ -c & b & a \end{vmatrix} \quad \text{[row by row]}$$

$$= \begin{vmatrix} a & b & c \\ b & c & a \\ c & a & b \end{vmatrix} \times \begin{vmatrix} a & b & c \\ b & c & a \\ c & a & b \end{vmatrix} = \begin{vmatrix} a & b & c \\ b & c & a \\ c & a & b \end{vmatrix}^2$$

$$=(a+b+c)^2(a^2+b^2+c^2-ab-bc-ca)^2 \quad \text{[from Eq. (ii)]}$$
$$=[-(a^3+b^3+c^3-3abc)]^2$$
$$=(a^3+b^3+c^3-3abc)^2 = \text{RHS}$$

- **Ex. 36** *Let α and β be the roots of the equation $ax^2+bx+c=0$. Let $S_n=\alpha^n+\beta^n$ for $n \geq 1$. Evaluate the determinant* $\begin{vmatrix} 3 & 1+S_1 & 1+S_2 \\ 1+S_1 & 1+S_2 & 1+S_3 \\ 1+S_2 & 1+S_3 & 1+S_4 \end{vmatrix}$.

Sol. Since, α and β are the roots of the equation $ax^2+bx+c=0$.

$$\therefore \alpha+\beta = -\frac{b}{a}, \alpha\beta = \frac{c}{a} \text{ and } \alpha-\beta = \frac{\sqrt{D}}{a}$$

Let $\Delta = \begin{vmatrix} 3 & 1+S_1 & 1+S_2 \\ 1+S_1 & 1+S_2 & 1+S_3 \\ 1+S_2 & 1+S_3 & 1+S_4 \end{vmatrix}$

$$= \begin{vmatrix} 3 & 1+\alpha+\beta & 1+\alpha^2+\beta^2 \\ 1+\alpha+\beta & 1+\alpha^2+\beta^2 & 1+\alpha^3+\beta^3 \\ 1+\alpha^2+\beta^2 & 1+\alpha^3+\beta^3 & 1+\alpha^4+\beta^4 \end{vmatrix}$$

$$= \begin{vmatrix} 1 & 1 & 1 \\ 1 & \alpha & \beta \\ 1 & \alpha^2 & \beta^2 \end{vmatrix} \times \begin{vmatrix} 1 & 1 & 1 \\ 1 & \alpha & \beta \\ 1 & \alpha^2 & \beta^2 \end{vmatrix} = \Delta_1 \times \Delta_1 \quad \text{[say]}$$

$$\therefore \quad \Delta = \Delta_1^2 \qquad \text{...(i)}$$

$$\therefore \quad \Delta_1 = \begin{vmatrix} 1 & 1 & 1 \\ 1 & \alpha & \beta \\ 1 & \alpha^2 & \beta^2 \end{vmatrix}$$

Applying $C_2 \to C_2 - C_1$ and $C_3 \to C_3 - C_1$, then

$$\Delta_1 = \begin{vmatrix} 1 & 0 & 0 \\ 1 & \alpha-1 & \beta-1 \\ 1 & \alpha^2-1 & \beta^2-1 \end{vmatrix}$$

Expanding along R_1, then

$$\Delta_1 = \begin{vmatrix} \alpha - 1 & \beta - 1 \\ \alpha^2 - 1 & \beta^2 - 1 \end{vmatrix} = (\alpha - 1)(\beta - 1) \begin{vmatrix} 1 & 1 \\ \alpha + 1 & \beta + 1 \end{vmatrix}$$

$$= \{\alpha\beta - (\alpha + \beta) + 1\}(\beta - \alpha)$$

$$\therefore \quad \Delta = \Delta_1^2 = [\alpha\beta - (\alpha + \beta) + 1]^2 (\beta - \alpha)^2$$

$$= \left(\frac{c}{a} + \frac{b}{a} + 1\right)^2 \cdot \frac{D}{a^2} = \frac{(a + b + c)^2(b^2 - 4ac)}{a^4}$$

• **Ex. 37** *If A, B and C are the angles of a triangle, show that*

(i) $\begin{vmatrix} \sin 2A & \sin C & \sin B \\ \sin C & \sin 2B & \sin A \\ \sin B & \sin A & \sin 2C \end{vmatrix} = 0.$

(ii) $\begin{vmatrix} -1 + \cos B & \cos C + \cos B & \cos B \\ \cos C + \cos A & -1 + \cos A & \cos A \\ -1 + \cos B & -1 + \cos A & -1 \end{vmatrix} = 0.$

Sol. (i) LHS $= \begin{vmatrix} \sin 2A & \sin C & \sin B \\ \sin C & \sin 2B & \sin A \\ \sin B & \sin A & \sin 2C \end{vmatrix}$

$$= \begin{vmatrix} 2ka \cos A & kc & kb \\ kc & 2kb \cos B & ka \\ kb & ka & 2kc \cos C \end{vmatrix} \quad \text{[from sine rule]}$$

$$= k^3 \begin{vmatrix} 2a \cos A & c & b \\ c & 2b \cos B & a \\ b & a & 2c \cos C \end{vmatrix}$$

$$= k^3 \begin{vmatrix} a \cos A + a \cos A & a \cos B + b \cos A & a \cos C + c \cos A \\ a \cos B + b \cos A & b \cos B + b \cos B & b \cos C + c \cos B \\ a \cos C + c \cos A & c \cos B + b \cos C & c \cos C + c \cos C \end{vmatrix}$$

$$= k^3 \begin{vmatrix} \cos A & a & 0 \\ \cos B & b & 0 \\ \cos C & c & 0 \end{vmatrix} \times \begin{vmatrix} a & \cos A & 0 \\ b & \cos B & 0 \\ c & \cos C & 0 \end{vmatrix} = 0 \times 0 = 0 = \text{RHS}$$

(ii) LHS $= \begin{vmatrix} -1 + \cos B & \cos C + \cos B & \cos B \\ \cos C + \cos A & -1 + \cos A & \cos A \\ -1 + \cos B & -1 + \cos A & -1 \end{vmatrix}$

Applying $C_1 \to C_1 - C_3$ and $C_2 \to C_2 - C_3$, then

$$= \begin{vmatrix} -1 & \cos C & \cos B \\ \cos C & -1 & \cos A \\ \cos B & \cos A & -1 \end{vmatrix}$$

$$= \frac{1}{a} \begin{vmatrix} -a & \cos C & \cos B \\ a \cos C & -1 & \cos A \\ a \cos B & \cos A & -1 \end{vmatrix}$$

Applying $C_1 \to C_1 + bC_2 + cC_3$, then

$$= \frac{1}{a} \begin{vmatrix} 0 & \cos C & \cos B \\ 0 & -1 & \cos A \\ 0 & \cos A & -1 \end{vmatrix} = 0 = \text{RHS}$$

• **Ex. 38** *Without expanding at any stage, evaluate the value of the determinant*

$$\begin{vmatrix} 2 & \tan A \cot B + \cot A \tan B & \tan A \cot C + \cot A \tan C \\ \tan B \cot A + \cot B \tan A & 2 & \tan B \cot C + \cot B \tan C \\ \tan C \cot A + \cot C \tan A & \tan C \cot B + \cot C \tan B & 2 \end{vmatrix}.$$

Sol. The given determinant can be written as the product of two determinants

$$\begin{vmatrix} \tan A & \cot A & 0 \\ \tan B & \cot B & 0 \\ \tan C & \cot C & 0 \end{vmatrix} \times \begin{vmatrix} \cot A & \tan A & 0 \\ \cot B & \tan B & 0 \\ \cot C & \tan C & 0 \end{vmatrix} = 0 \times 0 = 0$$

• **Ex. 39** *Suppose that digit numbers A28, 3B9 and 62C, where A, B and C are integers between 0 and 9 are divisible by a fixed integer k, prove that the determinant* $\begin{vmatrix} A & 3 & 6 \\ 8 & 9 & C \\ 2 & B & 2 \end{vmatrix}$ *is also divisible by k.*

Sol. Given, $A28, 3B9$ and $62C$ are divisible by k, then

$$A28 = 100A + 20 + 8 = n_1 k \quad \text{...(i)}$$

$$3B9 = 300 + 10B + 9 = n_2 k \quad \text{...(ii)}$$

and $$62C = 600 + 20 + C = n_3 k \quad \text{...(iii)}$$

where $n_1, n_2, n_3 \in I$ (integers).

Let $$\Delta = \begin{vmatrix} A & 3 & 6 \\ 8 & 9 & C \\ 2 & B & 2 \end{vmatrix}.$$

Applying $R_2 \to R_2 + 10R_3 + 100R_1$, then

$$A = \begin{vmatrix} A & 3 & 6 \\ 100A + 20 + 8 & 300 + 10B + 9 & 600 + 20 + C \\ 2 & B & 2 \end{vmatrix}$$

$$= \begin{vmatrix} A & 3 & 6 \\ n_1 k & n_2 k & n_3 k \\ 2 & B & 2 \end{vmatrix} \quad \text{[using Eqs. (i), (ii) and (iii)]}$$

$$= k \begin{vmatrix} A & 3 & 6 \\ n_1 & n_2 & n_3 \\ 2 & B & 2 \end{vmatrix}$$

Hence, Δ is divisible by k.

● **Ex. 40** *If* $\Delta = \begin{vmatrix} \sin x & \sin(x+h) & \sin(x+2h) \\ \sin(x+2h) & \sin x & \sin(x+h) \\ \sin(x+h) & \sin(x+2h) & \sin x \end{vmatrix}$, *find* $\lim_{h \to 0} \left(\frac{\Delta}{h^2} \right)$.

Sol. Let $a = \sin x$, $b = \sin(x+h)$ and $c = \sin(x+2h)$

$$\Delta = \begin{vmatrix} a & b & c \\ c & a & b \\ b & c & a \end{vmatrix} = \begin{vmatrix} a & b & c \\ b & c & a \\ c & a & b \end{vmatrix} = (a^3 + b^3 + c^3 - 3abc)$$

$$= \frac{1}{2}(a+b+c)[(a-b)^2 + (b-c)^2 + (c-a)^2]$$

Now, $a - b = \sin x - \sin(x+h) = -2\cos\left(x + \frac{h}{2}\right)\sin\frac{h}{2}$

$b - c = \sin(x+h) - \sin(x+2h) = -2\cos\left(x + \frac{3h}{2}\right)\sin\frac{h}{2}$

and $c - a = \sin(x+2h) - \sin x = 2\cos(x+h)\sin h$

$$\therefore \quad \frac{\Delta}{h^2} = \frac{1}{2}(a+b+c)\left[\left(\frac{a-b}{h}\right)^2 + \left(\frac{b-c}{h}\right)^2 + \left(\frac{c-a}{h}\right)^2\right]$$

$$= \frac{1}{2}[\sin x + \sin(x+h) + \sin(x+2h)] \times \left[\left(\frac{-2\cos\left(x+\frac{h}{2}\right)\sin\frac{h}{2}}{h}\right)^2 + \left(\frac{-2\cos\left(x+\frac{3h}{2}\right)\sin\frac{h}{2}}{h}\right)^2 + \left(\frac{2\cos(x+h)\sin h}{h}\right)^2\right]$$

$$\therefore \quad \lim_{h \to 0} \frac{\Delta}{h^2} = \frac{1}{2}(3\sin x)(\cos^2 x + \cos^2 x + 4\cos^2 x)$$

$$\therefore \quad = 9\sin x \cos^2 x$$

● **Ex. 41** *If* $f(x) = \begin{vmatrix} x+c_1 & x+a & x+a \\ x+b & x+c_2 & x+a \\ x+b & x+b & x+c_3 \end{vmatrix}$, *show that* $f(x)$ *is linear in x. Hence, deduce that* $f(0) = \frac{bg(a) - ag(b)}{(b-a)}$, *where* $g(x) = (c_1 - x)(c_2 - x)(c_3 - x)$.

Sol. Since, $f(x) = \begin{vmatrix} x+c_1 & x+a & x+a \\ x+b & x+c_2 & x+a \\ x+b & x+b & x+c_3 \end{vmatrix}$

Applying $C_2 \to C_2 - C_1$ and $C_3 \to C_3 - C_2$, then

$$f(x) = \begin{vmatrix} x+c_1 & a-c_1 & 0 \\ x+b & c_2-b & a-c_2 \\ x+b & 0 & c_3-b \end{vmatrix}$$

$$f(x) = x\begin{vmatrix} 1 & a-c_1 & 0 \\ 1 & c_2-b & a-c_2 \\ 1 & 0 & c_3-b \end{vmatrix} + \begin{vmatrix} c_1 & a-c_1 & 0 \\ b & c_2-b & a-c_2 \\ b & 0 & c_3-b \end{vmatrix}$$

So, $f(x)$ is linear.

Let $\quad f(x) = Px + Q$

Then, $\quad f(-a) = -aP + Q$, $f(-b) = -bP + Q$

$$f(0) = 0 \cdot P + Q = Q$$

$$= \frac{bf(-a) - af(-b)}{(b-a)} \quad \text{...(ii)}$$

From Eq. (i), we get

$$f(-a) = \begin{vmatrix} c_1 - a & 0 & 0 \\ b-a & c_2-a & 0 \\ b-a & b-a & c_3-a \end{vmatrix}$$

$$= (c_1 - a)(c_2 - a)(c_3 - a)$$

Similarly, $f(-b) = (c_1 - b)(c_2 - b)(c_3 - b)$

and $\quad g(x) = (c_1 - x)(c_2 - x)(c_3 - x)$

$$g(a) = f(-a)$$

$$\therefore \quad g(b) = f(-b)$$

Now, from Eq. (ii), we get

$$f(0) = \frac{bg(a) - ag(b)}{(b-a)}$$

● **Ex. 42** *If* $f(x)$ *is a polynomial of degree* < 3, *prove that*

$$\begin{vmatrix} 1 & a & f(a)/(x-a) \\ 1 & b & f(b)/(x-b) \\ 1 & c & f(c)/(x-c) \end{vmatrix} \div \begin{vmatrix} 1 & a & a^2 \\ 1 & b & b^2 \\ 1 & c & c^2 \end{vmatrix} = \frac{f(x)}{(x-a)(x-b)(x-c)}.$$

Sol. $\frac{f(x)}{(x-a)(x-b)(x-c)} = \frac{A}{(x-a)} + \frac{B}{(x-b)} + \frac{C}{(x-c)}$ [let] ...(i)

On comparing the various powers of x, we get

$$\Rightarrow \begin{cases} A = \frac{f(a)}{(a-b)(a-c)} = -\frac{f(a)}{(a-b)(c-a)} \\ B = \frac{f(b)}{(b-a)(b-c)} = -\frac{f(b)}{(a-b)(b-c)} \\ C = \frac{f(c)}{(c-a)(c-b)} = -\frac{f(c)}{(b-c)(c-a)} \end{cases}$$

Now, from Eq. (i), we get

$$\frac{f(x)}{(x-a)(x-b)(x-c)}$$

$$=\frac{(c-b)\dfrac{f(a)}{(x-a)}-(c-a)\dfrac{f(b)}{(x-b)}+(b-a)\dfrac{f(c)}{(x-c)}}{(a-b)(b-c)(c-a)}$$

$$=\frac{\begin{vmatrix}1 & a & f(a)/(x-a)\\ 1 & b & f(b)/(x-b)\\ 1 & c & f(c)/(x-c)\end{vmatrix}}{\begin{vmatrix}1 & a & a^2\\ 1 & b & b^2\\ 1 & c & c^2\end{vmatrix}}$$

• ***Ex. 43*** *If* $f(a,b)=\dfrac{f(b)-f(a)}{b-a}$ *and*

$f(a,b,c)=\dfrac{f(b,c)-f(a,b)}{(c-a)}$, *prove that*

$$f(a,b,c)=\begin{vmatrix}f(a) & f(b) & f(c)\\ 1 & 1 & 1\\ a & b & c\end{vmatrix}\div\begin{vmatrix}1 & 1 & 1\\ a & b & c\\ a^2 & b^2 & c^2\end{vmatrix}.$$

Sol. LHS $=f(a,b,c)=\dfrac{f(b,c)-f(a,b)}{(c-a)}$

$$=\frac{\dfrac{f(c)-f(b)}{(c-b)}-\dfrac{f(b)-f(a)}{(b-a)}}{(c-a)}$$

$$=\frac{(b-a)\{f(c)-f(b)\}-(c-b)\{f(b)-f(a)\}}{(b-a)(c-b)(c-a)}$$

$$=\frac{(f(a)\cdot(c-b)-f(b)\cdot(c-a)+f(c)\cdot(b-a))}{(a-b)(b-c)(c-a)}$$

$$=\frac{f(a)\begin{vmatrix}1 & 1\\ b & c\end{vmatrix}-f(b)\begin{vmatrix}1 & 1\\ a & c\end{vmatrix}+f(c)\begin{vmatrix}1 & 1\\ a & b\end{vmatrix}}{\begin{vmatrix}1 & 1 & 1\\ a & b & c\\ a^2 & b^2 & c^2\end{vmatrix}}$$

$$=\frac{\begin{vmatrix}f(a) & f(b) & f(c)\\ 1 & 1 & 1\\ a & b & c\end{vmatrix}}{\begin{vmatrix}1 & 1 & 1\\ a & b & c\\ a^2 & b^2 & c^2\end{vmatrix}}$$

$$=\begin{vmatrix}f(a) & f(b) & f(c)\\ 1 & 1 & 1\\ a & b & c\end{vmatrix}\div\begin{vmatrix}1 & 1 & 1\\ a & b & c\\ a^2 & b^2 & c^2\end{vmatrix}=\text{RHS}$$

• ***Ex. 44*** *Let S be the sum of all possible determinants of order 2 having 0, 1, 2 and 3 as their elements. Find the common root α of the equations*

$$x^2+ax+[m+1]=0,$$
$$x^2+bx+[m+4]=0$$

and $x^2-cx+[m+15]=0$,

such that $\alpha>S$, *where* $a+b+c=0$ *and*

$$m=\lim_{n\to\infty}\frac{1}{n}\sum_{r=1}^{2n}\frac{r}{\sqrt{(n^2+r^2)}}$$

and [.] denotes the greatest integer function.

Sol. Let α be a common root of the given equations, then

$$\alpha^2+a\alpha+[m+1]=0$$

$$\Rightarrow \quad \alpha^2+a\alpha+[m]+1=0 \quad \text{...(i)}$$

$$\alpha^2+b\alpha+[m+4]=0$$

$$\Rightarrow \quad \alpha^2+b\alpha+[m]+4=0 \quad \text{...(ii)}$$

and $\quad \alpha^2-c\alpha+[m+15]=0$

$$\Rightarrow \quad \alpha^2-c\alpha+[m]+15=0 \quad \text{...(iii)}$$

On adding Eqs. (i) and (ii) and subtracting Eq. (iii), we get

$$a^2+(a+b+c)\alpha+[m]-10=0$$

$$\alpha^2+0+[m]-10=0 \quad [\because a+b+c=0]$$

$$\Rightarrow \quad \alpha^2+[m]-10=0 \quad \text{...(iv)}$$

Also, $\quad m=\lim\limits_{n\to\infty}\dfrac{1}{n}\sum\limits_{r=1}^{2n}\dfrac{r}{\sqrt{n^2+r^2}}$

$$=\lim_{n\to\infty}\sum_{r=1}^{2n}\frac{1}{n}\cdot\frac{r/n}{\sqrt{1+(r/n)^2}}=\int_0^2\frac{x}{\sqrt{(1+x^2)}}dx$$

$$[\sqrt{(1+x^2)}]_0^2=\sqrt{5}-1$$

Now, $\quad [m]=[\sqrt{5}-1]=1$

From Eq. (iv), we get

$$\alpha^2+1-10=0\Rightarrow\alpha^2=9$$

$\therefore \quad \alpha=\pm 3$

Now, number of determinants of order 2 having

$$0, 1, 2, 3 = 4! = 24$$

Let $\Delta_1=\begin{vmatrix}a_1 & a_2\\ a_3 & a_4\end{vmatrix}$ be one such determinant and their exists another determinant.

Let $\Delta_2=\begin{vmatrix}a_3 & a_4\\ a_1 & a_2\end{vmatrix}$ [obtained on interchanging R_1 and R_2]

such that $\Delta_1+\Delta_2=0$

$\because S=$ Sum of all the 24 determinants $=0$

Since, $\quad \alpha>S\Rightarrow\alpha>0$

$\therefore \quad \alpha=3$

• Ex. 45 *If a_1, a_2, a_3 and $b_1, b_2, b_3 \in R$ and are such that $a_i b_j \neq 1$ for $1 \le i, j \le 3$,*

$$\begin{vmatrix} \frac{1-a_1^3b_1^3}{1-a_1b_1} & \frac{1-a_1^3b_2^3}{1-a_1b_2} & \frac{1-a_1^3b_3^3}{1-a_1b_3} \\ \frac{1-a_2^3b_1^3}{1-a_2b_1} & \frac{1-a_2^3b_2^3}{1-a_2b_2} & \frac{1-a_2^3b_3^3}{1-a_2b_3} \\ \frac{1-a_3^3b_1^3}{1-a_3b_1} & \frac{1-a_3^3b_2^3}{1-a_3b_2} & \frac{1-a_3^3b_3^3}{1-a_3b_3} \end{vmatrix} > 0 \text{ provided either}$$

$a_1 < a_2 < a_3$ and $b_1 < b_2 < b_3$ or $a_1 > a_2 > a_3$ and $b_1 > b_2 > b_3$.

Sol. Since, $\dfrac{x^3 - y^3}{x - y} = \dfrac{(x-y)(x^2+xy+y^2)}{(x-y)} = x^2 + xy + y^2$

Hence, the given determinant becomes

$$\begin{vmatrix} 1 + a_1b_1 + a_1^2 b_1^2 & 1 + a_1b_2 + a_1^2 b_2^2 & 1 + a_1 b_3 + a_1^2 b_3^2 \\ 1 + a_2 b_1 + a_2^2 b_1^2 & 1 + a_2 b_2 + a_2^2 b_2^2 & 1 + a_2 b_3 + a_2^2 b_3^2 \\ 1 + a_3 b_1 + a_3^2 b_1^2 & 1 + a_3 b_2 + a_3^2 b_2^2 & 1 + a_3 b_3 + a_3^2 b_3^2 \end{vmatrix} > 0$$

$$\Rightarrow \quad \begin{vmatrix} 1 & a_1 & a_1^2 \\ 1 & a_2 & a_2^2 \\ 1 & a_3 & a_3^2 \end{vmatrix} \times \begin{vmatrix} 1 & b_1 & a_1^2 \\ 1 & b_2 & b_2^2 \\ 1 & b_3 & b_3^2 \end{vmatrix} > 0$$

$$\Rightarrow \quad (a_1 - a_2)(a_2 - a_3)(a_3 - a_1)(b_1 - b_2)(b_2 - b_3)(b_3 - b_1) > 0$$

$$\left\{ \because \begin{vmatrix} 1 & a & a^2 \\ 1 & b & b^2 \\ 1 & c & c^2 \end{vmatrix} = (a-b)(b-c)(c-a) \right\}$$

***Case* I** If $a_1 < a_2 < a_3$ and $b_1 < b_2 < b_3$, then

$(a_1 - a_2) < 0, (a_2 - a_3) < 0$

and $(b_1 - b_2) < 0, (b_2 - b_3) < 0$

$(a_1 - a_3) < 0$

and $(b_1 - b_3) < 0$

$\therefore$ $(a_3 - a_1) > 0$

$\therefore$ $(b_3 - b_1) > 0$

Then, $(a_1 - a_2)(a_2 - a_3)(a_3 - a_1) > 0$

and $(b_1 - b_2)(b_2 - b_3)(b_3 - b_1) > 0$

$\therefore$ $(a_1 - a_2)(a_2 - a_3)(a_3 - a_1)(b_1 - b_2)(b_2 - b_3)(b_3 - b_1) > 0$

which is true.

***Case* II** If $a_1 > a_2 > a_3$ and $b_1 > b_2 > b_3$

$\therefore$ $a_1 - a_2 > 0, a_2 - a_3 > 0$

and $b_1 - b_2 > 0, b_2 - b_3 > 0$

$a_1 - a_3 > 0 \Rightarrow a_3 - a_1 < 0$

and $b_1 - b_3 > 0 \Rightarrow b_3 - b_1 < 0$

Hence, $(a_1 - a_2)(a_2 - a_3)(a_3 - a_1) < 0$

and $(b_1 - b_2)(b_2 - b_3)(b_3 - b_1) < 0$

$\therefore$ $(a_1 - a_2)(a_2 - a_3)(a_3 - a_1)(b_1 - b_2)(b_2 - b_3)(b_3 - b_1) > 0$

which is true.

• Ex. 46 *Show that a six-digit number abcdef is divisible by 11, if and only if ab + cd + ef is divisible by 11. Hence or otherwise, find one set of values of two-digit numbers x, y and z, so that the value of the determinant* $\begin{vmatrix} x & 23 & 42 \\ 13 & 37 & y \\ 19 & z & 34 \end{vmatrix}$ *is divisible by 99 (without expanding the determinant).*

Sol. Since, $abcdef = ab0000 + cd00 + ef$

$= (9999 + 1)\, ab + (99 + 1)\, cd + ef$

$= 9999\, ab + 99\, cd + ab + cd + ef$

Given, $abcdef$ is divisible by 11, if and only if $ab + cd + ef$ is divisible by 11. Now, let $x = ab, y = cd$ and $z = ef$.
[each being a two-digit number]

Again, let $\Delta = \begin{vmatrix} x & 23 & 42 \\ 13 & 37 & y \\ 19 & z & 34 \end{vmatrix} = \begin{vmatrix} ab & 23 & 42 \\ 13 & 37 & cd \\ 19 & ef & 34 \end{vmatrix}$

Applying $R_1 \to R_1 + 100\, R_2 + 10000\, R_3$, we get

$$\Delta = \begin{vmatrix} 1913ab & ef3723 & 34cd42 \\ 13 & 37 & cd \\ 19 & ef & 34 \end{vmatrix}$$

Now, $1913ab$ is divisible by 11, if and only if $19 + 13 + ab = 32 + ab$ is divisible by $11 \Rightarrow ab = 01, 12, 23, \ldots$

Again, $1913ab$ is divisible by 9, if and only if $1 + 9 + 1 + 3 + a + b = 14 + a + b$ is divisibe by 9.

The above two conditions are satisfied for $a = 6, b = 7$. Thus, $x = 67$. Similarly, $y = 23$ and $z = 39$.

Determinants Exercise 1 : Single Option Correct Type Questions

- This section contains **30 multiple choice questions.** Each question has four choices (a), (b), (c) and (d) out of which **ONLY ONE** is correct

1. If $f(n)=\alpha^n+\beta^n$ and $\begin{vmatrix} 3 & 1+f(1) & 1+f(2) \\ 1+f(1) & 1+f(2) & 1+f(3) \\ 1+f(2) & 1+f(3) & 1+f(4) \end{vmatrix}$ $=k\,(1-\alpha)^2\,(1-\beta)^2\,(\alpha-\beta)^2, k^2$ d is equal to

(a) 1 (b) -1
(c) $\alpha\beta$ (d) $\alpha\beta\gamma$

2. Let $\Delta(x)=\begin{vmatrix} x+a & x+b & x+a-c \\ x+b & x+c & x-1 \\ x+c & x+d & x-b+d \end{vmatrix}$ and $\int_0^2 \Delta(x)\,dx=-16$, where a, b, c and d are in AP, then the common difference of the AP is equal to

(a) ± 1 (b) ± 2 (c) ± 3 (d) ± 4

3. If $\Delta(x)=\begin{vmatrix} x & 1+x^2 & x^3 \\ \log_e(1+x^2) & e^x & \sin x \\ \cos x & \tan x & \sin^2 x \end{vmatrix}$, then

(a) $\Delta(x)$ is divisible by x (b) $\Delta(x)=0$
(c) $\Delta'(x)=0$ (d) None of these

4. If a, b and c are sides of a triangle and

$\begin{vmatrix} a^2 & b^2 & c^2 \\ (a+1)^2 & (b+1)^2 & (c+1)^2 \\ (a-1)^2 & (b-1)^2 & (c-1)^2 \end{vmatrix}=0$, then

(a) ΔABC is an equilateral triangle
(b) ΔABC is a right angled isosceles triangle
(c) ΔABC is an isosceles triangle
(d) None of the above

5. If $\begin{vmatrix} \alpha & x & x & x \\ x & \beta & x & x \\ x & x & \gamma & x \\ x & x & x & \delta \end{vmatrix}=f(x)-xf'(x)$, then $f(x)$ is equal to

(a) $(x-\alpha)(x-\beta)(x-\gamma)(x-\delta)$
(b) $(x+\alpha)(x+\beta)(x+\gamma)(x+\delta)$
(c) $2(x-\alpha)(x-\beta)(x-\gamma)(x-\delta)$
(d) None of the above

6. If $\begin{vmatrix} a & b-c & c+b \\ a+c & b & c-a \\ a-b & a+b & c \end{vmatrix}=0$, the line $ax+by+c=0$ passes through the fixed point which is

(a) (1, 2) (b) (1, 1) (c) $(-2, 1)$ (d) (1, 0)

7. If $f(x)=a+bx+cx^2$ and α, β and γ are the roots of the equation $x^3=1$, then $\begin{vmatrix} a & b & c \\ b & c & a \\ c & a & b \end{vmatrix}$ is equal to

(a) $f(\alpha)+f(\beta)+f(\gamma)$
(b) $f(\alpha)\,f(\beta)+f(\beta)\,f(\gamma)+f(\gamma)\,f(\alpha)$
(c) $f(\alpha)\,f(\beta)\,f(\gamma)$
(d) $-f(\alpha)\,f(\beta)\,f(\gamma)$

8. When the determinant $\begin{vmatrix} \cos 2x & \sin^2 x & \cos 4x \\ \sin^2 x & \cos 2x & \cos^2 x \\ \cos 4x & \cos^2 x & \cos 2x \end{vmatrix}$ is expanded in powers of $\sin x$, the constant term in that expression is

(a) 1 (b) 0 (c) -1 (d) 2

9. If [ ] denotes the greatest integer less than or equal to the real number under consideration and $-1\le x<0, 0\le y<1, 1\le z<2$, the value of the determinant $\begin{vmatrix} [x]+1 & [y] & [z] \\ [x] & [y]+1 & [z] \\ [x] & [y] & [z]+1 \end{vmatrix}$ is

(a) $[x]$ (b) $[y]$
(c) $[z]$ (d) None of these

10. The determinant $\begin{vmatrix} y^2 & -xy & x^2 \\ a & b & c \\ a' & b' & c' \end{vmatrix}$ is equal to

(a) $\begin{vmatrix} bx+ay & cx+by \\ b'x+a'y & c'x+b'y \end{vmatrix}$ (b) $\begin{vmatrix} a'x+b'y & bx+cy \\ ax+by & b'x+c'y \end{vmatrix}$

(c) $\begin{vmatrix} bx+cy & ax+by \\ b'x+c'y & a'x+b'y \end{vmatrix}$ (d) $\begin{vmatrix} ax+by & bx+cy \\ a'x+b'y & b'x+c'y \end{vmatrix}$

11. If A, B and C are angles of a triangle, the value of $\begin{vmatrix} e^{2iA} & e^{-iC} & e^{-iB} \\ e^{-iC} & e^{2iB} & e^{-iA} \\ e^{-iB} & e^{-iBA} & e^{2iC} \end{vmatrix}$ is (where $i=\sqrt{-1}$)

(a) 1 (b) -1 (c) -2 (d) -4

12. If $\begin{vmatrix} x^n & x^{n+2} & x^{2n} \\ 1 & x^a & a \\ x^{n+5} & x^{a+6} & x^{2n+5} \end{vmatrix}=0, \forall\, x\in R$, where $n\in N$, the value of a is

(a) n (b) $n-1$
(c) $n+1$ (d) None of these

13. If x, y and z are the integers in AP lying between 1 and 9 and $x51$, $y41$ and $z31$ are three digits number, the value of $\begin{vmatrix} 5 & 4 & 3 \\ x51 & y41 & z31 \\ x & y & z \end{vmatrix}$ is

(a) $x+y+z$
(b) $x-y+z$
(c) 0
(d) None of the above

14. If $a_1 b_1 c_1$, $a_2 b_2 c_2$ and $a_3 b_3 c_3$ are three digit even natural numbers and $\Delta = \begin{vmatrix} c_1 & a_1 & b_1 \\ c_2 & a_2 & b_2 \\ c_3 & a_3 & b_3 \end{vmatrix}$, then Δ is

(a) divisible by 2 but not necessarily by 4
(b) divisible by 4 but not necessarily by 8
(c) divisible by 8
(d) None of the above

15. If a, b and c are sides of ΔABC such that

$$\begin{vmatrix} c & b\cos B + c\beta & a\cos A + b\alpha + c\gamma \\ a & c\cos B + a\beta & b\cos A + c\alpha + a\gamma \\ b & a\cos B + b\beta & c\cos A + a\alpha + b\gamma \end{vmatrix} = 0$$

$\left(\text{where } \alpha, \beta, \gamma \in R^+ \text{ and } \angle A, \angle B, \angle C \neq \frac{\pi}{2}\right)$, ΔABC is

(a) an isosceles
(b) an equilateral
(c) can't say
(d) None of these

16. If x_1, x_2 and y_1, y_2 are the roots of the equations $3x^2 - 18x + 9 = 0$ and $y^2 - 4y + 2 = 0$, the value of the determinant $\begin{vmatrix} x_1x_2 & y_1y_2 & 1 \\ x_1 + x_2 & y_1 + y_2 & 2 \\ \sin(\pi x_1x_2) & \cos(\pi/2y_1y_2) & 1 \end{vmatrix}$ is

(a) 0
(b) 1
(c) 2
(d) None of these

17. If the value of $\Delta = \begin{vmatrix} {}^{10}C_4 & {}^{10}C_5 & {}^{11}C_m \\ {}^{11}C_6 & {}^{11}C_7 & {}^{12}C_{m+2} \\ {}^{12}C_8 & {}^{12}C_9 & {}^{13}C_{m+4} \end{vmatrix}$ is equal to zero, then m is equal to

(a) 6
(b) 4
(c) 5
(d) None of these

18. The value of the determinant $\begin{vmatrix} 1 & \sin(\alpha-\beta)\theta & \cos(\alpha-\beta)\theta \\ a & \sin\alpha\theta & \cos\alpha\theta \\ a^2 & \sin(\alpha-\beta)\theta & \cos(\alpha-\beta)\theta \end{vmatrix}$ is independent of

(a) α
(b) β
(c) θ
(d) a

19. If $f(x), g(x)$ and $h(x)$ are polynomials of degree 4 and $\begin{vmatrix} f(x) & g(x) & h(x) \\ a & b & c \\ p & q & r \end{vmatrix} = mx^4 + nx^3 + rx^2 + sx + t$ be an identity in x, then

$$\begin{vmatrix} f'''(0) - f''(0) & g'''(0) - g''(0) & h'''(0) - h''(0) \\ a & b & c \\ p & q & r \end{vmatrix}$$

is equal to

(a) $2(3n+r)$
(b) $3(2n-r)$
(c) $3(2n+r)$
(d) $2(3n-r)$

20. If $f(x) = \begin{vmatrix} \cos(x+\alpha) & \cos(x+\beta) & \cos(x+\gamma) \\ \sin(x+\alpha) & \sin(x+\beta) & \sin(x+\gamma) \\ \sin(\beta-\gamma) & \sin(\gamma-\alpha) & \sin(\alpha-\beta) \end{vmatrix}$, then $f(\theta) - 2f(\phi) + f(\psi)$ is equal to

(a) 0
(b) $\alpha - \beta$
(c) $\alpha + \beta + \gamma$
(d) $\alpha + \beta - \gamma$

21. If $\begin{vmatrix} 1 & 1 & 1 \\ a & b & c \\ a^3 & b^3 & c^3 \end{vmatrix} = (a-b)(b-c)(c-a)(a+b+c)$, where a, b and c are all different, then the determinant

$$\begin{vmatrix} 1 & 1 & 1 \\ (x-a)^2 & (x-b)^2 & (x-c)^2 \\ (x-b)(x-c) & (x-c)(x-a) & (x-a)(x-b) \end{vmatrix}$$ vanishes when

(a) $a+b+c=0$
(b) $x = \frac{1}{3}(a+b+c)$
(c) $x = \frac{1}{2}(a+b+c)$
(d) $x = a+b+c$

22. Let $a, b, c \in R$ such that no two of them are equal and satisfy $\begin{vmatrix} 2a & b & c \\ b & c & 2a \\ c & 2a & b \end{vmatrix} = 0$, the equation $24ax^2 + 4bx + c = 0$ has

(a) atleast one root in $\left[0, \frac{1}{2}\right]$
(b) atleast one root in $\left[-\frac{1}{2}, \frac{1}{2}\right]$
(c) atleast one root in $[-1, 0]$
(d) atleast two roots in $[0, 2]$

23. The number of positive integral solution of the equation $\begin{vmatrix} x^3+1 & x^2y & x^2z \\ xy^2 & y^3+1 & y^2z \\ xz^2 & yz^2 & z^3+1 \end{vmatrix} = 11$ is

(a) 0
(b) 3
(c) 6
(d) 12

24. If $f(x) = ax^2 + bx + c$, $a, b, c \in R$ and equation $f(x) - x = 0$ has imaginary roots α, β γ and δ be the roots of $f(f(x)) - x = 0$, then $\begin{vmatrix} 2 & \alpha & \delta \\ \beta & 0 & \alpha \\ \gamma & \beta & 1 \end{vmatrix}$ is

(a) 0 (b) purely real
(c) purely imaginary (d) None of these

25. If the system of equations $2x - y + z = 0$, $x - 2y + z = 0$, $tx - y + 2z = 0$ has infinitely many solutions and $f(x)$ be a continuous function, such that $f(5 + x) + f(x) = 2$, then $\int_0^{-2t} f(x)\,dx$ is equal to

(a) 0 (b) $-2t$ (c) 5 (d) t

26. If $(1 + ax + bx^2)^4 = a_0 + a_1 x + a_2 x^2 + \ldots + a_8 x^8$, where $a, b, a_0, a_1, \ldots, a_8 \in R$ such that $a_0 + a_1 + a_2 \neq 0$ and $\begin{vmatrix} a_0 & a_1 & a_2 \\ a_1 & a_2 & a_0 \\ a_2 & a_0 & a_1 \end{vmatrix} = 0$, then

(a) $a = \frac{3}{4}, b = \frac{5}{8}$ (b) $a = \frac{1}{4}, b = \frac{5}{32}$
(c) $a = 1, b = \frac{2}{3}$ (d) None of these

27. Given, $f(x) = \log_{10} x$ and $g(x) = e^{\pi i x}$.
If $\phi(x) = \begin{vmatrix} f(x)\cdot g(x) & (f(x))^{g(x)} & 1 \\ f(x^2)\cdot g(x^2) & (f(x^2))^{g(x^2)} & 0 \\ f(x^3)\cdot g(x^3) & (f(x^3))^{g(x^3)} & 1 \end{vmatrix}$, the value of $\phi(10)$, is

(a) 1 (b) 2 (c) 0 (d) None of these

28. The value of the determinant
$\begin{vmatrix} 1 & (\alpha^{2x} - \alpha^{-2x})^2 & (\alpha^{2x} + \alpha^{-2x})^2 \\ 1 & (\beta^{2x} - \beta^{-2x})^2 & (\beta^{2x} + \beta^{-2x})^2 \\ 1 & (\gamma^{2x} - \gamma^{-2x})^2 & (\gamma^{2x} + \gamma^{-2x})^2 \end{vmatrix}$, is

(a) 0 (b) $(\alpha\beta\gamma)^{2x}$ (c) $(\alpha\beta\gamma)^{-2x}$ (d) None of these

29. If a, b and c are non-zero real numbers and if the equations $(a - 1)x = y + z$, $(b - 1)y = z + x$, $(c - 1)z = x + y$ has a non-trivial solution, then $ab + bc + ca$ equals to

(a) $a + b + c$ (b) abc (c) 1 (d) None of these

30. The set of equations $\lambda x - y + (\cos\theta)z = 0$, $3x + y + 2z = 0$, $(\cos\theta)x + y + 2z = 0$, $0 \le \theta \le 2\pi$, has non-trivial solution(s)

(a) for no value of λ and θ
(b) for all value of λ and θ
(c) for all values of λ and only two values of θ
(d) for only one value of λ and all values of θ

Determinants Exercise 2 : More than One Correct Option Type Questions

- This section contains **15 multiple choice questions.** Each question has four choices (a), (b), (c) and (d) out of which **MORE THAN ONE** may be correct.

31. The determinant $\Delta = \begin{vmatrix} a^2 + x^2 & ab & ac \\ ab & b^2 + x^2 & bc \\ ac & bc & c^2 + x^2 \end{vmatrix}$ is divisible by

(a) x (b) x^2 (c) x^3 (d) x^4

32. The value of the determinant
$\begin{vmatrix} \sqrt{6} & 2i & 3 + \sqrt{6} \\ \sqrt{12} & \sqrt{3} + \sqrt{8}i & 3\sqrt{2} + \sqrt{6}\,i \\ \sqrt{18} & \sqrt{2} + \sqrt{12}\,i & \sqrt{27} + 2i \end{vmatrix}$, is (where $i = \sqrt{-1}$)

(a) complex (b) real (c) irrational (d) rational

33. If $D_k = \begin{vmatrix} 2^{k-1} & \frac{1}{k(k+1)} & \sin k\theta \\ x & y & z \\ 2^n - 1 & \frac{n}{n+1} & \frac{\sin\left(\frac{n+1}{2}\right)\theta \sin\frac{n}{2}\theta}{\sin\frac{\theta}{2}} \end{vmatrix}$, then $\sum_{k=1}^{n} D_k$ is equal to

(a) 0 (b) independent of n
(c) independent of θ (d) independent of x, y and z

34. The determinant $\begin{vmatrix} a & b & a\alpha + b \\ b & c & b\alpha + c \\ a\alpha + b & b\alpha + c & 0 \end{vmatrix}$ is equal to zero, if

(a) a, b and c are in AP
(b) a, b, c, are in GP
(c) a, b and c are in HP
(d) $(x - \alpha)$ is a factor of $ax^2 + 2bx + c$

35. Let $f(x) = \begin{vmatrix} 2\cos x & 1 & 0 \\ 1 & 2\cos x & 1 \\ 0 & 1 & 2\cos x \end{vmatrix}$, then

(a) $f\left(\frac{\pi}{3}\right) = -1$
(b) $f'\left(\frac{\pi}{3}\right) = \sqrt{3}$
(c) $\int_0^{\pi} f(x)\,dx = 0$
(d) $\int_{-\pi}^{\pi} f(x)\,dx = 0$

36. If $\Delta(x)=\begin{vmatrix} x^2-5x+3 & 2x-5 & 3 \\ 3x^2+x+4 & 6x+1 & 9 \\ 7x^2-6x+9 & 14x-6 & 21 \end{vmatrix}$

$= ax^3+bx^2+cx+d$, then

(a) $a=0$ (b) $b=0$ (c) $c=0$ (d) $d=47$

37. If a, b and c are the sides of a triangle and A, B and C are the angles opposite to a, b and c respectively, then

$\Delta=\begin{vmatrix} a^2 & b\sin A & C\sin A \\ b\sin A & 1 & \cos A \\ C\sin A & \cos A & 1 \end{vmatrix}$ is independent of

(a) a (b) b (c) c (d) A, B, C

38. Let $f(a,b)=\begin{vmatrix} a & a^2 & 0 \\ 1 & (2a+b) & (a+b)^2 \\ 0 & 1 & (2a+3b) \end{vmatrix}$, then

(a) $(a+b)$ is a factor of $f(a,b)$
(b) $(a+2b)$ is a factor of $f(a,b)$
(c) $(2a+b)$ is a factor of $f(a,b)$
(d) a is a factor of $f(a,b)$

39. If $f(x)=\begin{vmatrix} \sec^2 x & 1 & 1 \\ \cos^2 x & \cos^2 x & \operatorname{cosec}^2 x \\ 1 & \cos^2 x & \cot^2 x \end{vmatrix}$, then

(a) $\int_{-\pi/4}^{\pi/4} f(x)\,dx=\frac{1}{16}(3\pi+8)$

(b) $f'\left(\frac{\pi}{2}\right)=0$

(c) maximum value of $f(x)$ is 1
(d) minimum value of $f(x)$ is 0

40. If $\begin{vmatrix} a & a+x^2 & a+x^2+x^4 \\ 2a & 3a+2x^2 & 4a+3x^2+2x^4 \\ 3a & 6a+3x^2 & 10a+6x^2+3x^4 \end{vmatrix}$

$=a_0+a_1x+a_2x^2+a_3x^3+a_4x^4+a_5x^5+a_6x^6+a_7x^7$ and

$f(x)=+a_0x^2+a_3x+a_6$, then

(a) $f(x)\ge 0,\ \forall\ x\in R$ if $a>0$
(b) $f(x)=0$, only if $a=0$
(c) $f(x)=0$, has two equal roots
(d) $f(x)=0$, has more than two root if $a=0$

41. If $\Delta(x)=\begin{vmatrix} 4x-4 & (x-2)^2 & x^3 \\ 8x-4\sqrt{2} & (x-2\sqrt{2})^2 & (x+1)^3 \\ 12x-4\sqrt{3} & (x-2\sqrt{3})^2 & (x-1)^3 \end{vmatrix}$, then

(a) term independent of x in $\Delta(x)=16(5-\sqrt{2}-\sqrt{3})$
(b) coefficient of x in $\Delta(x)=48(1+\sqrt{2}-\sqrt{3})$
(c) coefficient of x in $\Delta(x)=16(5+\sqrt{2}-\sqrt{3})$
(d) coefficient of x in $\Delta(x)$ is divisible by 16

42. If

$f(x)=\begin{vmatrix} 3 & 3x & 3x^2+2a^2 \\ 3x & 3x^2+2a^2 & 3x^3+6a^2x \\ 3x^2+2a^3 & 3x^3+6a^2x & 3x^4+12a^2x^2+2a^4 \end{vmatrix}$,

then

(a) $f'(x)=0$
(b) $y=f(x)$ is a straight line parallel to X-axis
(c) $\int_0^2 f(x)\,dx=32a^4$
(d) None of the above

43. If $a>b>c$ and the system of equations $ax+by+cz=0$, $bx+cy+az=0$, $cx+ay+bz=0$ has a non-trivial solution, then both the roots of the quadratic equation at^2+bt+c, are

(a) real
(b) of opposite sign
(c) positive
(d) complex

44. The values of λ and b for which the equations $x+y+z=3$, $x+3y+2z=6$ and $x+\lambda y+3z=b$ have

(a) a unique solution, if $\lambda\ne 5$, $b\in R$
(b) no solution, if $\lambda\ne 5$, $b=9$
(c) infinite many solution, $\lambda=5$, $b=9$
(d) None of the above

45. Let λ and α be real. Let S denote the set of all values of λ for which the system of linear equations

$\lambda x+(\sin\alpha)y+(\cos\alpha)z=0$
$x+(\cos\alpha)y+(\sin\alpha)z=0$
$-x+(\sin\alpha)y-(\cos\alpha)z=0$

has a non-trivial solution, then S contains

(a) $(-1, 1)$ (b) $[-\sqrt{2}, -1]$
(c) $[1, \sqrt{2}]$ (d) $(-2, 2)$

Determinants Exercise 3 :
Passage Based Questions

- This section contains **7 passages**. Based upon each of the passage **3 multiple choice questions** have to be answered. Each of these questions has four choices (a), (b), (c) and (d) out of which **ONLY ONE** is correct.

Passage I
(Q. Nos. 46 to 48)

Consider the system of equations

$$x+y+z=5;\ x+2y+3z=9;\ x+3y+\lambda z=\mu$$

The system is called smart, brilliant, good and lazy according as it has solution, unique solution, infinitely many solutions and no solution, respectively.

46. The system is smart, if
(a) $\lambda \neq 5$ or $\lambda = 5$ and $\mu = 13$ (b) $\lambda \neq 5$ and $\mu = 13$
(c) $\lambda \neq 5$ and $\mu \neq 13$ (d) $\lambda \neq 5$ or $\lambda = 5$ and $\mu \neq 13$

47. The system is good, if
(a) $\lambda \neq 5$ or $\lambda = 5$ and $\mu = 13$ (b) $\lambda = 5$ and $\mu = 13$
(c) $\lambda = 5$ and $\mu \neq 13$
(d) $\lambda \neq 5$, μ is any real number

48. The system is lazy, if
(a) $\lambda \neq 5$ or $\lambda = 5$ and $\mu = 13$ (b) $\lambda = 5$ and $\mu = 13$
(c) $\lambda = 5$ and $\mu \neq 13$ (d) $\lambda \neq 5$ or $\lambda = 5$ and $\mu \neq 13$

Passage II
(Q. Nos. 49 to 51)

If $\Delta = \begin{vmatrix} a_{11} & a_{12} & a_{13} \\ a_{21} & a_{22} & a_{23} \\ a_{31} & a_{32} & a_{33} \end{vmatrix}$ *and* $C_{ij} = (-1)^{i+j} M_{ij}$, *where* M_{ij} *is a determinant obtained by deleting ith row and jth column, then* $\begin{vmatrix} C_{11} & C_{12} & C_{13} \\ C_{21} & C_{22} & C_{23} \\ C_{31} & C_{32} & C_{33} \end{vmatrix} = \Delta^2$.

49. If $\begin{vmatrix} 1 & x & x^2 \\ x & x^2 & 1 \\ x^2 & 1 & x \end{vmatrix} = 5$ and $\Delta = \begin{vmatrix} x^3-1 & 0 & x-x^4 \\ 0 & x-x^4 & x^3-1 \\ x-x^4 & x^3-1 & 0 \end{vmatrix}$, then sum of digits of Δ^2, is
(a) 7 (b) 8 (c) 13 (d) 11

50. Suppose $a, b, c \in R$, $a+b+c>0$, $A = bc - a^2$, $B = ca - b^2$ and $C = ab - c^2$ and $\begin{vmatrix} A & B & C \\ B & C & A \\ C & A & B \end{vmatrix} = 49$, then the value of $a^3+b^3+c^3-3abc$, is
(a) −7 (b) 7 (c) −2401 (d) 2401

51. If $a^3+b^3+c^3-3abc=-3$ and $A = bc-a^2$, $B = ca-b^2$ and $C = ab-c^2$, then the value of $aA+bB+cC$, is
(a) −3 (b) 3 (c) −9 (d) 9

Passage III
(Q. Nos. 52 to 54)

If α, β, γ *are the roots of* $x^3+2x^2-x-3=0$

52. The value of $\begin{vmatrix} \alpha & \beta & \gamma \\ \gamma & \alpha & \beta \\ \beta & \gamma & \alpha \end{vmatrix}$ is equal to
(a) 14 (b) −2 (c) 10 (d) 14

53. If the absolute value of the expression $\frac{\alpha-1}{\alpha+2}+\frac{\beta-1}{\beta+2}+\frac{\gamma-1}{\gamma+2}$ can be expressed as $\frac{m}{n}$, where m and n are co-prime, the value of $\begin{vmatrix} m & n^2 \\ m-n & m+n \end{vmatrix}$ is
(a) 17 (b) 27 (c) 37 (d) 47

54. If $a = \alpha^2+\beta^2+\gamma^2$, $b = \alpha\beta+\beta\gamma+\gamma\alpha$, the value of $\begin{vmatrix} a & b & b \\ b & a & b \\ b & b & a \end{vmatrix}$, is
(a) 14 (b) 49 (c) 98 (d) 196

Passage IV
(Q. Nos. 55 to 57)

Suppose $f(x)$ *is a function satisfying the following conditions:*

(i) $f(0)=2$, $f(1)=1$

(ii) $f(x)$ *has a minimum value at* $x=\frac{5}{2}$

(iii) For all x, $f'(x) = \begin{vmatrix} 2ax & 2ax-1 & 2ax+b+1 \\ b & b+1 & -1 \\ 2(ax+b) & 2ax+2b+1 & 2ax+b \end{vmatrix}$.

55. The value of $f(2)+f(3)$ is
(a) 1 (b) $\frac{3}{2}$ (c) 2 (d) $\frac{5}{2}$

56. The number of solutions of the equation $f(x)+1=0$ is
(a) 0 (b) 1 (c) 2 (d) infinite

57. Range of $f(x)$ is
(a) $\left(-\infty, \frac{7}{16}\right]$ (b) $\left[\frac{3}{4}, \infty\right)$ (c) $\left[\frac{7}{16}, \infty\right)$ (d) $\left(-\infty, \frac{3}{4}\right]$

Passage V
(Q. Nos. 58 to 60)

If $\begin{vmatrix} x & e^{x-1} & (x-1)^3 \\ x-\ln x & \cos(x-1) & (x-1)^2 \\ \tan x & \sin^2 x & \cos^2 x \end{vmatrix} = a_0 + a_1(x-1) + a_2(x-1)^2 + \dots$

58. The value of $\cos^{-1}(a_1)$, is

(a) 0 (b) $\frac{\pi}{4}$ (c) $\frac{\pi}{2}$ (d) π

59. The value of $\lim_{x \to a_0} (\sin x)^x$ is

(a) 1 (b) e (c) $e-1$ (d) None of these

60. The equation whose roots are a_0 and a_1, is

(a) $x^2 - x = 0$ (b) $x^2 - 2x = 0$
(c) $x^2 - 3x = 0$ (d) None of these

Passage VI
(Q. Nos. 61 to 63)

Let $\Delta = \begin{vmatrix} -bc & b^2+bc & c^2+bc \\ a^2+ac & -ac & c^2+ac \\ a^2+ab & b^2+ab & -ab \end{vmatrix}$ *and the equation* $x^3 - px^2 + qx - r = 0$ *has roots a, b, c, where* $a, b, c \notin R^+$.

61. The value of Δ is

(a) $\le 9r^3$ (b) $\ge 27r^2$ (c) $\le 27r^2$ (d) $\ge 81r^3$

62. If a, b, c are in GP, then

(a) $r^3 = p^3q$ (b) $p^3 = r^3q$ (c) $p^3 = q^3r$ (d) $q^3 = p^3r$

63. If $\Delta = 27$ and $a^2 + b^2 + c^2 = 2$, then the value of $\sum a^2 b$, is

(a) $3(2\sqrt{2} - p)$ (b) $3(2\sqrt{2} - r)$
(c) $3(2\sqrt{2} - q)$ (d) $3(2\sqrt{2} - p - q)$

Passage VII
(Q. Nos. 64 to 66)

If $\Delta n = \begin{vmatrix} a^2+n & ab & ac \\ ab & b^2+n & bc \\ ac & bc & c^2+n \end{vmatrix}$, $n \in N$ *and the equation* $x^3 - \lambda x^2 + 11x - 6 = 0$ *has roots a, b, c and a, b, c are in AP.*

64. The value of $\sum_{r=1}^{7} \Delta_n$ is

(a) $(12)^3$ (b) $(14)^3$ (c) $(26)^3$ (d) $(28)^3$

65. The value of $\frac{\Delta 2_n}{\Delta_n}$ is

(a) < 8 (b) = 8
(c) > 8 (d) None of these

66. The value of $\sum_{r=1}^{30} \left(\frac{27\Delta_r - \Delta 3_r}{27r^2} \right)$ is

(a) 130 (b) 190 (c) 280 (d) 340

Determinants Exercise 4 :
Single Integer Answer Type Questions

- This section contains **10 questions**. The answer to each question is a **single digit integer**, ranging from 0 to 9 (both inclusive).

67. If $\begin{vmatrix} 3^2+k & 4^2 & 3^2+3+k \\ 4^2+k & 5^2 & 4^2+4+k \\ 5^2+k & 6^2 & 5^2+5+k \end{vmatrix} = 0$,

the value of $\sqrt{2^k \sqrt{2^k \sqrt{2^k \dots \infty}}}$ is

68. Let α, β and γ are three distinct roots of

$\begin{vmatrix} x-1 & -6 & 2 \\ -6 & x-2 & -4 \\ 2 & -4 & x-6 \end{vmatrix} = 0$, the value of $\left(\frac{1}{\alpha} + \frac{1}{\beta} + \frac{1}{\gamma} \right)^{-1}$ is

69. If $\begin{vmatrix} x & e^{x-1} & (x-1)^3 \\ x-\ln x & \cos(x-1) & (x-1)^2 \\ \tan x & \sin^2 x & \cos^2 x \end{vmatrix} = \sum_{r=0}^{n} a_r (x-1)^r$,

the value of $(2^{a_0} + 3^{a_1})^{a_1+1}$ is

70. If $\begin{vmatrix} 1 & \cos\alpha & \cos\beta \\ \cos\alpha & 1 & \cos\gamma \\ \cos\beta & \cos\gamma & 1 \end{vmatrix} = \begin{vmatrix} 0 & \cos\alpha & \cos\beta \\ \cos\alpha & 0 & \cos\gamma \\ \cos\beta & \cos\gamma & 0 \end{vmatrix}$,

$\cos^2\alpha + \cos^2\beta + \cos^2\gamma$ is equal to

71. Let $f(a, b, c) = \begin{vmatrix} (b+c)^2 & a^2 & a^2 \\ b^2 & (c+a)^2 & b^2 \\ c^2 & c^2 & (a+b)^2 \end{vmatrix}$, the greatest integer $n \in N$ such that $(a+b+c)^{n'}$ divides $f(a, b, c)$ is

72. If $0 \le \theta \le \pi$ and the system of equations

$$x = (\sin\theta)\, y + (\cos\theta)\, z$$
$$y = z + (\cos\theta)\, x$$
$$z = (\sin\theta)\, x + y$$

has a non-trivial solution, then $\frac{8\theta}{\pi}$ is equal to

73. The value of the determinant $\begin{vmatrix} 1 & 1 & 1 & 1 \\ 1 & 2 & 3 & 4 \\ 1 & 3 & 6 & 10 \\ 1 & 4 & 10 & 20 \end{vmatrix}$ is

74. If a, b, c and d are the roots of the equation $x^4 + 2x^3 + 4x^2 + 8x + 16 = 0$, the value of the determinant $\begin{vmatrix} 1+a & 1 & 1 & 1 \\ 1 & 1+b & 1 & 1 \\ 1 & 1 & 1+c & 1 \\ 1 & 1 & 1 & 1+d \end{vmatrix}$ is

75. If $a \neq 0, b \neq 0, c \neq 0$ and $\begin{vmatrix} 1+a & 1 & 1 \\ 1+b & 1+2b & 1 \\ 1+c & 1+c & 1+3c \end{vmatrix} = 0$, the value of $|a^{-1} + b^{-1} + c^{-1}|$ is equal to

76. If the system of equations

$$ax + hy + g = 0;\ hx + by + f = 0$$

and $ax^2 + 2hxy + by^2 + 2gx + 2fy + c + \lambda = 0$ has a unique solution and

$$\frac{abc + 2fgh - af^2 - bg^2 - ch^2}{h^2 - ab} = 8,$$ the value of λ is

Determinants Exercise 5 : Matching Type Questions

- This section contains **5 questions**. Questions 77 to 81 have three statements (A, B and C) given in **Column I** and four statements (p, q, r and s) in **Column II**. Any given statement in **Column I** can have correct matching with one or more statement(s) given in **Column II**.

77.

	Column I		Column II
(A)	If a,b,c are three complex numbers such that $a^2 + b^2 + c^2 = 0$ and $\begin{vmatrix} b^2+c^2 & ab & ac \\ ab & c^2+a^2 & bc \\ ac & bc & a^2+b^2 \end{vmatrix} = \lambda a^2b^2c^2$, then λ is divisible by	(p)	2
(B)	If $a,b,c \in R$ and $\begin{vmatrix} a & a+b & a+b+c \\ 2a & 5a+2b & 7a+5b+2c \\ 3a & 7a+3b & 9a+7b+3c \end{vmatrix} = -1024$, then a is divisible by	(q)	3
(C)	Let $\Delta(x) = \begin{vmatrix} x-1 & 2x^2-5 & x^3-1 \\ 2x^2+5 & 2x+2 & x^3+3 \\ x^3-1 & x+1 & 3x^2-2 \end{vmatrix}$ and $ax+b$ be the remainder, when $\Delta(x)$ is divided by x^2-1, then $4a+2b$ is divisible by	(r)	4
		(s)	5
		(t)	6

78.

	Column I		Column II
(A)	Let $f_1(x) = x + a_1$, $f_2(x) = x^2 + b_1x + b_2$, $x_1 = 2$, $x_2 = 3$ and $x_3 = 5$ and $\Delta = \begin{vmatrix} 1 & 1 & 1 \\ f_1(x_1) & f_1(x_2) & f_1(x_3) \\ f_2(x_1) & f_2(x_2) & f_2(x_3) \end{vmatrix}$, then Δ is	(p)	Even number
(B)	If $|a_1 - b_1| = 6$ and $f(x) = \begin{vmatrix} 1 & b_1 & a_1 \\ 1 & b_1 & 2a_1 - x \\ 1 & 2b_1 - x & a_1 \end{vmatrix}$, then the minimum value of $f(x)$ is	(q)	Prime number
(C)	If coefficient of x in $f(x) = \begin{vmatrix} x-2 & (x-1)^2 & x^3 \\ x-1 & x^2 & (x+1)^3 \\ x & (x+1)^2 & (x+2)^3 \end{vmatrix}$ is λ, then $|\lambda|$ is	(r)	Odd number
		(s)	Composite number
		(t)	Perfect number

79.

	Column I		Column II
(A)	If $\begin{vmatrix} x^2+3x & x-1 & x+3 \\ x^2+1 & 2+3x & x-3 \\ x^2-3 & x+4 & 3x \end{vmatrix} = ax^4+bx^3+cx^2+dx+e$, then $e+a$ is divisible by	(p)	2
(B)	If $\begin{vmatrix} x-1 & 5x & 7 \\ x^2-1 & x-1 & 8 \\ 2x & 3x & 0 \end{vmatrix} = ax^3+bx^2+cx+d$, then $(e+a-3)$ is divisible by	(q)	3
(C)	If $\begin{vmatrix} x^3+4x & x+3 & x-2 \\ x-2 & 5x & x-1 \\ x-3 & x+2 & 4x \end{vmatrix} = ax^5+bx^4+cx^3+dx^2+ex+f$, then $(f+e)$ is divisible by	(r)	5
		(s)	6
		(t)	7

80.

	Column I		Column II
(A)	If $a^2+b^2+c^2=1$ and $\Delta = \begin{vmatrix} a^2+(b^2+c^2)d & ab(1-d) & ca(1-d) \\ ab(1-d) & b^2+(c^2+a^2)d & bc(1-d) \\ ca(1-d) & bc(1-d) & c^2+(a+b^2)d \end{vmatrix}$, then Δ is	(p)	independent of a
(B)	If $\Delta = \begin{vmatrix} \frac{1}{c} & \frac{1}{c} & \frac{-(a+b)}{c^2} \\ \frac{-(b+c)}{a^2} & \frac{1}{a} & \frac{1}{a} \\ \frac{-bd(b+c)}{a^2c} & \frac{(ad+2bd+cd)}{ac} & \frac{-(a+b)bd}{ac^2} \end{vmatrix}$, then Δ is	(q)	independent of b
(C)	If $\Delta = \begin{vmatrix} \sin a & \cos a & \sin(a+d) \\ \sin b & \cos b & \sin(b+d) \\ \sin c & \cos c & \sin(c+d) \end{vmatrix}$, then Δ is	(r)	independent of c
		(s)	independent of d
		(t)	zero

81.

	Column I		Column II
(A)	If n be the number of distinct values of 2×2 determinant whose entries are from the set $\{-1,0,1\}$, then $(n-1)^2$ is divisible by	(p)	2
(B)	If n be the number of 2×2 determinants with non-negative values whose entries from the set $\{0,1\}$, then $(n-1)$ is divisible by	(q)	3
(C)	If n be the number of 2×2 determinants with negative values whose entries from the set $\{-1, 1\}$, then $n(n+1)$ is divisible by	(r)	4
		(s)	5
		(t)	6

Determinants Exercise 6 :
Statement I and II Type Questions

- **Directions** (Q. Nos. 82 to 87) are Assertion-Reason type questions. Each of these questions contains two statements:

Statement-1 (Assertion) and **Statement-2** (Reason) Each of these questions also has four alternative choices, only one of which is the correct answer. You have to select the correct choice as given below.

(a) Statement-1 is true, Statement-2 is true; Statement-2 is a correct explanation for Statement-1
(b) Statement-1 is true, Statement-2 is true; Statement-2 is not a correct explanation for Statement-1
(c) Statement1 is true, Statement-2 is false
(d) Statement-1 is false, Statement-2 is true

82. **Statement-1** If $\Delta(r) = \begin{vmatrix} r & r+1 \\ r+3 & r+4 \end{vmatrix}$ then $\sum_{r=1}^{n} \Delta(r) = -3n$

Statement-2 If $\Delta(r) = \begin{vmatrix} f_1(r) & f_2(r) \\ f_3(r) & f_4(r) \end{vmatrix}$

then $\sum_{r=1}^{n} \Delta(r) = \begin{vmatrix} \sum_{r=1}^{n} f_1(r) & \sum_{r=1}^{n} f_2(r) \\ \sum_{r=1}^{n} f_3(r) & \sum_{r=1}^{n} f_4(r) \end{vmatrix}$

83. Consider the determinant

$$\Delta = \begin{vmatrix} a_1 + b_1x^2 & a_1x^2 + b_1 & c_1 \\ a_2 + b_2 x^2 & a_2x^2 + b_2 & c_2 \\ a_3 + b_3x^2 & a_3 x^2 + b_3 & c_3 \end{vmatrix} = 0,$$

where $a_i, b_i, c_i \in R (i = 1, 2, 3)$ and $x \in R$.

Statement-1 The value of x satisfying $\Delta = 0$ are $x = 1, -1$

Statement-2 If $\begin{vmatrix} a_1 & b_1 & c_1 \\ a_2 & b_2 & c_2 \\ a_3 & b_3 & c_3 \end{vmatrix} = 0$, then $\Delta = 0$.

84. **Statement-1** The value of determinant

$$\begin{vmatrix} \sin \pi & \cos\left(x + \frac{\pi}{4}\right) & \tan\left(x - \frac{\pi}{4}\right) \\ \sin\left(x - \frac{\pi}{4}\right) & -\cos\left(\frac{\pi}{2}\right) & \ln\left(\frac{x}{y}\right) \\ \cot\left(\frac{\pi}{4} + x\right) & \ln\left(\frac{y}{x}\right) & \tan \pi \end{vmatrix} \text{ is zero.}$$

Statement-2 The value of skew-symmetric determinant of odd order equals zero.

85. **Statement-1** $f(x) = \begin{vmatrix} (1+x)^{11} & (1+x)^{12} & (1+x)^{13} \\ (1+x)^{21} & (1+x)^{22} & (1+x)^{23} \\ (1+x)^{31} & (1+x)^{32} & (1+x)^{33} \end{vmatrix}$,

the coefficient of x in $f(x) = 0$

Statement-2 If $P(x) = a_0 + a_1x + a_2 x^2 + a_3x^3 + \ldots + a_n x^n$, then $a_1 = P'(0)$, where dash denotes the differential coefficient.

86. **Statement-1** If system of equations $2x + 3y = a$ and $bx + 4y = 5$ has infinite solution, then $a = \frac{15}{4}, b = \frac{8}{5}$

Statement-2 Straight lines $a_1x + b_1y + c_1 = 0$ and $a_2 x + b_2 y + c_2 = 0$ are parallel, if $\frac{a_1}{a_2} = \frac{b_1}{b_2} \neq \frac{c_1}{c_2}$

87. **Statement-1** The value of the determinant $\begin{vmatrix} 1 & 2 & 3 \\ 4 & 5 & 6 \\ 7 & 8 & 0 \end{vmatrix} \neq 0$

Statement-2 Neither of two rows or columns of $\begin{vmatrix} 1 & 2 & 3 \\ 4 & 5 & 6 \\ 7 & 8 & 0 \end{vmatrix}$ is identical.

88. **Statement-1** The digits A, B and C re such that the three digit numbers $A88$, $6B8$, $86C$ are divisible by 72, then the determinant $\begin{vmatrix} A & 6 & 8 \\ 8 & B & 6 \\ 8 & 8 & C \end{vmatrix}$ is divisible by 288.

Statement-2 $A = B = ?$

Determinants Exercise 7 : Subjective Type Questions

- In this section, there are **20 subjective** questions.

89. Prove that $\begin{vmatrix} b+c & c & b \\ c & c+a & a \\ b & a & a+b \end{vmatrix} = 4abc.$

90. Prove that $\begin{vmatrix} a-b-c & 2a & 2a \\ 2b & b-c-a & 2b \\ 2c & 2c & c-a-b \end{vmatrix} = (a+b+c)^3.$

91. Find the value of determinant $\begin{vmatrix} \sqrt{13}+\sqrt{3} & 2\sqrt{5} & \sqrt{5} \\ \sqrt{15}+\sqrt{26} & 5 & \sqrt{10} \\ 3+\sqrt{65} & \sqrt{15} & 5 \end{vmatrix}.$

92. Find the value of the determinant $\begin{vmatrix} bc & ca & ab \\ p & q & r \\ 1 & 1 & 1 \end{vmatrix}$, where a, b and c respectively are the pth, qth and rth terms of a harmonic progression.

93. Without expanding the determinant at any stage, prove that $\begin{vmatrix} -5 & 3+5i & \frac{3}{2}-4i \\ 3-5i & 8 & 4+5i \\ \frac{3}{2}+4i & 4-5i & 9 \end{vmatrix}$ has a purely real value.

94. Prove without expanding that $\begin{vmatrix} ah+bg & g & ab+ch \\ bf+ba & f & hb+bc \\ af+bc & c & bg+fc \end{vmatrix} = a \begin{vmatrix} ah+bg & a & h \\ bf+ba & h & b \\ af+bc & g & f \end{vmatrix}.$

95. If A, B and C are the angles of a triangle and

$$\begin{vmatrix} 1 & 1 & 1 \\ 1+\sin A & 1+\sin B & 1+\sin C \\ \sin A+\sin^2 A & \sin B+\sin^2 B & \sin C+\sin^2 C \end{vmatrix} = 0,$$

then prove that ΔABC must be isosceles.

96. Prove that $\begin{vmatrix} \beta\gamma & \beta\gamma'+\beta'\gamma & \beta'\gamma' \\ \gamma\alpha & \gamma\alpha'+\gamma'\alpha & \gamma'\alpha' \\ \alpha\beta & \alpha\beta'+\alpha'\beta & \alpha'\beta' \end{vmatrix}$

$$= (\alpha\beta'-\alpha'\beta)(\beta\gamma'-\beta'\gamma)(\gamma\alpha'-\gamma'\alpha).$$

97. If $y = \frac{u}{v}$, where u and v are functions of x, show that

$$v^3 \frac{d^2y}{dx^2} = \begin{vmatrix} u & v & 0 \\ u' & v & v \\ u'' & v'' & 2v' \end{vmatrix}.$$

98. Show that the determinant $\Delta(x)$ is given by $\Delta(x) = \begin{vmatrix} \sin(x+\alpha) & \cos(x+\alpha) & a+x\sin\alpha \\ \sin(x+\beta) & \cos(x+\beta) & b+x\sin\beta \\ \sin(x+\gamma) & \cos(x+\gamma) & c+x\sin\gamma \end{vmatrix}$. is independent of x.

99. Evaluate $\begin{vmatrix} {}^xC_1 & {}^xC_2 & {}^xC_3 \\ {}^yC_1 & {}^yC_2 & {}^yC_3 \\ {}^zC_1 & {}^zC_2 & {}^zC_3 \end{vmatrix}.$

100. (i) Find maximum value of

$$f(x) = \begin{vmatrix} 1+\sin^2 x & \cos^2 x & 4\sin 2x \\ \sin^2 x & 1+\cos^2 x & 4\sin 2x \\ \sin^2 x & \cos^2 x & 1+4\sin 2x \end{vmatrix}.$$

(ii) Let A, B and C be the angles of a triangle, such that $A \geq B \geq C$.

Find the minimum value of Δ, where

$$\Delta = \begin{vmatrix} \sin^2 A & \sin A\cos A & \cos^2 A \\ \sin^2 B & \sin B\cos B & \cos^2 B \\ \sin^2 C & \sin C\cos C & \cos^2 C \end{vmatrix}.$$

101. If $f(x) = \begin{vmatrix} x^2-4x+6 & 2x^2+4x+10 & 3x^2-2x+16 \\ x-2 & 2x+2 & 3x-1 \\ 1 & 2 & 3 \end{vmatrix}$,

then find the value of $\int_{-3}^{3} \frac{x^2\sin x}{1+x^6} f(x)dx$.

102. If $Y = sX$ and $Z = tX$ all the variables beings functions of x, then prove that $\begin{vmatrix} X & Y & Z \\ X_1 & Y_1 & Z_1 \\ X_2 & Y_2 & Z_2 \end{vmatrix} = X^3 \begin{vmatrix} s_1 & t_1 \\ s_2 & t_2 \end{vmatrix}$,

where suffixes denote the order of differentiation with respect to x.

103. If f, g and h are differentiable functions of x and

$$\Delta = \begin{vmatrix} f & g & h \\ (xf)' & (xg)' & (xh)' \\ (x^2f)'' & (x^2g)'' & (x^2h)'' \end{vmatrix},$$ then prove that

$$\Delta' = \begin{vmatrix} f & g & h \\ f' & g' & h' \\ (x^3f'')' & (x^3g'')' & (x^3h'')' \end{vmatrix}.$$

104. If $|a_1| > |a_2| + |a_3|, |b_2| > |b_1| + |b_3|$ and $|c_3| > |c_1| + |c_2|$, then show that $\begin{vmatrix} a_1 & a_2 & a_3 \\ b_1 & b_2 & b_3 \\ c_1 & c_2 & c_3 \end{vmatrix} \neq 0.$

105. Show that $\begin{vmatrix} (a-a_1)^{-2} & (a-a_1)^{-1} & a_1^{-1} \\ (a-a_2)^{-2} & (a-a_2)^{-1} & a_2^{-1} \\ (a-a_3)^{-2} & (a-a_3)^{-1} & a_3^{-1} \end{vmatrix} =$

$\pm \dfrac{a^2\,\Pi(a_i - a_j)}{\Pi a_i\,\Pi(a-a_i)^2}$. Write out the terms of the product in the numerator and give the resulting expression its correct sign.

106. Show that in general there are three values of t for which the following system of equations has a non-trivial solution $(a-t)x + by + cz = 0$, $bx + (c-t)y + az = 0$ and $cx + ay + (b-t)z = 0$.

Express the product of these values of t in the form of a determinant.

107. Eliminates

(i) a, b and c

(ii) x, y, z from the equations

$$-a + \frac{by}{z} + \frac{cz}{y} = 0,\ -b + \frac{cz}{x} + \frac{ax}{z} = 0$$

and $$-c + \frac{ax}{y} + \frac{by}{x} = 0.$$

108. If x, z and y are not all zero and if

$ax + by + cz = 0,\ bx + cy + az = 0$
and $cx + ay + bz = 0$, then

prove that $x : y : z = 1 : 1 : 1$ or $1 : \omega : \omega^2$ or $1 : \omega^2 : \omega$

Determinants Exercise 8 :
Questions Asked in Previous 13 Year's Exam

- This section contains questions asked in **IIT-JEE, AIEEE, JEE Main & JEE Advanced** from year **2005** to year **2017**.

109. If $a^2 + b^2 + c^2 = -2$ and

$$f(x) = \begin{vmatrix} 1+a^2x & (1+b^2)x & (1+c^2)x \\ (1+a^2)x & 1+b^2x & (1+c^2)x \\ (1+a^2)x & (1+b^2)x & 1+c^2x \end{vmatrix}$$, then $f(x)$ is a polynomial of degree **[AIEEE 2005, 3M]**

(a) 3 (b) 2 (c) 1 (d) 0

110. The system of equations

$\alpha x + y + z = \alpha - 1,$
$x + \alpha y + z = \alpha - 1$
and $x + y + \alpha z = \alpha - 1$

has no solution, if α is **[AIEEE 2005, 3M]**

(a) not -2 (b) 1
(c) -2 (d) Either -2 or 1

111. If $a_1, a_2, a_3, \ldots, a_n, \ldots$ are in GP, then the determinant

$$\Delta = \begin{vmatrix} \log a_n & \log a_{n+1} & \log a_{n+2} \\ \log a_{n+3} & \log a_{n+4} & \log a_{n+5} \\ \log a_{n+6} & \log a_{n+7} & \log a_{n+8} \end{vmatrix}$$ is equal to **[AIEEE 2005, 3M]**

(a) 1 (b) 0 (c) 4 (d) 2

112. If $D = \begin{vmatrix} 1 & 1 & 1 \\ 1 & 1+x & 1 \\ 1 & 1 & 1+y \end{vmatrix}$ for $x \neq 0$, $y \neq 0$, then D is **[AIEEE 2007, 3M]**

(a) divisible by neither x nor y
(b) divisible by both x and y
(c) divisible by x but not y
(d) divisible by y but not x

113. Consider the system of equations

$$x - 2y + 3z = -1$$
$$-x + y - 2z = k$$
$$x - 3y + 4z = 1$$

Statement-1 The system of equations has no solutions for $k \neq 3$. **[IIT-JEE 2008, 3M]**

and

Statement-2 The determinant $\begin{vmatrix} 1 & 3 & -1 \\ -1 & -2 & k \\ 1 & 4 & 1 \end{vmatrix} \neq 0$, for $k \neq 3$.

(a) Statement-1 is true, Statement-2 is true and Statement-2 is a correct explanation for Statement-1.
(b) Statement-1 is true, Statement-2 is true and Statement-2 is not a correct explanation for Statement-1.
(c) Statement-1 is true, Statement-2 is false.
(d) Statement-1 is false, Statement-2 is true.

114. Let a, b, c be any real numbers. Suppose that there are real numbers x, y, z not all zero such that $x = cy + bz$, $y = az + cx$ and $z = bx + ay$. Then, $a^2 + b^2 + c^2 + 2abc$ is equal to **[AIEEE 2008, 3M]**

(a) -1 (b) 0 (c) 1 (d) 2

115. Let a, b, c be such that $b(a+c) \neq 0$. If

$$\begin{vmatrix} a & a+1 & a-1 \\ -b & b+1 & b-1 \\ c & c-1 & c+1 \end{vmatrix} + \begin{vmatrix} a+1 & b+1 & c-1 \\ a-1 & b-1 & c+1 \\ (-1)^{n+2}a & (-1)^{n+1}b & (-1)^n c \end{vmatrix} = 0,$$

then the value of n is **[AIEEE 2009, 4M]**

(a) any integer (b) zero
(c) an even integer (d) any odd integer

116. If $f(\theta)=\begin{vmatrix} 1 & \tan\theta & 1 \\ -\tan\theta & 1 & \tan\theta \\ -1 & -\tan\theta & 1 \end{vmatrix}$, then the set

$\left\{f(\theta): 0 \le \theta < \dfrac{\pi}{2}\right\}$ is **[IIT-JEE 2011, 2M]**

(a) $(-\infty,-1)\cup(1,\infty)$ (b) $[2,\infty)$
(c) $(-\infty,0]\cup[2,\infty)$ (d) $(-\infty,-1]\cup[1,\infty)$

117. The number of values of k for which the linear equations

$$4x+ky+2z=0$$
$$kx+4y+z=0$$
$$2x+2y+z=0$$

Possess a non-zero solution is **[AIEEE 2011,4M]**

(a) zero (b) 3 (c) 2 (d) 1

118. If the trivial solution is the only solution of the system of equations

$$x-ky+z=0$$
$$kx+3y-kz=0$$
$$3x+y-z=0$$

Then, the set of values of k is

(a) $\{2,-3\}$ (b) $R-\{2,-3\}$
(c) $R-\{2\}$ (d) $R-\{-3\}$ **[AIEEE 2011, 4M]**

119. The number of values of k for which the system of equations $(k+1)x+8y=4k$; $kx+(k+3)y=3k-1$ has no solution, is

(a) 1 (b) 2
(c) 3 (d) infinite **[JEE Main 2013, 4M]**

120. If $\alpha, \beta \ne 0$ and $f(n)=\alpha^n+\beta^n$ and

$$\begin{vmatrix} 3 & 1+f(1) & 1+f(2) \\ 1+f(1) & 1+f(2) & 1+f(3) \\ 1+f(2) & 1+f(3) & 1+f(4) \end{vmatrix} = k(1-\alpha)^2(1-\beta)^2(\alpha-\beta)^2,$$

then k is equal to **[JEE Main 2014, 4M]**

(a) 1 (b) -1
(c) $\alpha\beta$ (d) $1/\alpha\beta$

121. The set of all values of λ for which the system of linear equations

$$2x_1-2x_2+x_3=\lambda x_1$$
$$2x_1-3x_2+2x_3=\lambda x_2$$
$$-x_1+2x_2=\lambda x_3$$

has a non-trivial solution **[JEE Main 2015, 4M]**

(a) contains two elements
(b) contains more than two elements
(c) is an empty set
(d) is a singleton

122. Which of the following values of α satisfy the equation

$$\begin{vmatrix} (1+\alpha)^2 & (1+2\alpha)^2 & (1+3\alpha)^2 \\ (2+\alpha)^2 & (2+2\alpha)^2 & (2+3\alpha)^2 \\ (3+\alpha)^2 & (3+2\alpha)^2 & (3+3\alpha)^2 \end{vmatrix} = -648\alpha\,?$$

[JEE Advanced 2015, 4M]

(a) -4 (b) 9
(c) -9 (d) 4

123. The system of linear equations

$$x+\lambda y-z=0$$
$$\lambda x-y-z=0$$
$$x+y-\lambda z=0$$

has a non-trivial solution for **[JEE Main 2016, 4M]**

(a) exactly one-value of λ
(b) exactly two values of λ
(c) exactly three values of λ
(d) infinitely many values of λ.

124. The total number of distinct $x \in R$ for which

$$\begin{vmatrix} x & x^2 & 1+x^3 \\ 2x & 4x^2 & 1+8x^3 \\ 3x & 9x^2 & 1+27x^3 \end{vmatrix} = 10 \text{ is}$$

[JEE Advanced 2016, 3M]

125. Let $a, \lambda, \mu \in R$. Consider the system of linear equations

$$ax+2y=\lambda$$
$$3x-2y=\mu$$

Which of the following statement(s) is (are) correct?

[JEE Advanced 2016, 4M]

(a) If $a=-3$, then the system has infinitely many solutions for all values of λ and μ
(b) If $a \ne -3$, then the system has a unique solution for all values of λ and μ
(c) If $\lambda+\mu=0$, then the system has infinitely many solutions for $a=-3$
(d) If $\lambda+\mu \ne 0$, then the system has no solution for $a=-3$

126. If S is the set of distinct values of 'b' for which the following system of linear equations

$$x+y+z=1$$
$$x+ay+z=1$$
$$ax+by+z=0$$

has no solution, then S is **[JEE Main 2017, 4M]**

(a) an infinite set
(b) a finite set containing two or more elements
(c) a singleton
(d) an empty set

Answers

Exercise for Session 1

1. (d) 2. (d) 3. (c) 4. (b) 5. (c) 6. (d)
7. (b)

Exercise for Session 2

1. (c) 2. (d) 3. (a) 4. (c) 5. (a) 6. (b)
7. (b) 8. (b) 9. (d) 10. (c) 11. (d)

Exercise for Session 3

1. (b) 2. (c) 3. (c) 4. (b) 5. (b) 6. (d)
7. (d) 8. (a) 9. (b) 10. (c) 11. (c) 12. (a)
13. (a) 14. (a)

Exercise for Session 4

1. (c) 2. (b) 3. (b) 4. (d) 5. (d) 6. (b)
7. (b) 8. (c) 9. (d) 10. (a)

Chapter Exercises

1. (a) 2. (b) 3. (a) 4. (c) 5. (a) 6. (b)
7. (d) 8. (c) 9. (c) 10. (d) 11. (d) 12. (c)
13. (c) 14. (a) 15. (b) 16. (a) 17. (c) 18. (a)
19. (d) 20. (a) 21. (b) 22. (a) 23. (b) 24. (b)
25. (b) 26. (b) 27. (c) 28. (a) 29. (b) 30. (a)
31. (a, b, c, d) 32. (b, d) 33. (a, b, c, d) 34.(b, d)
35. (a, c, d) 36. (a, b, c) 37. (a, b, c, d) 38. (a, b, d)
39. (a, b, c, d) 40. (a, c, d) 41. (a, b) 42. (a, b)
43. (a, b) 44. (a, c) 45. (a, b, c) 46. (a)
47. (b) 48. (c) 49. (c) 50. (b) 51. (b)
52. (c) 53. (c) 54. (d) 55. (a) 56. (a) 57. (c)
58. (c) 59. (a) 60. (d) 61. (b) 62. (d) 63. (b)
64. (b) 65. (a) 66. (c) 67. (2) 68. (9) 69. (2)
70. (1) 71. (3) 72. (6) 73. (1) 74. (8) 75. (3)
76.(8) 77. (A) $\rightarrow$ (p,r); (B) $\rightarrow$ (p,r); (C) $\rightarrow$ (p,q,s,t)
78. (A) $\rightarrow$ (p,s,t); (B) $\rightarrow$ (r,t); (C) $\rightarrow$ (p,q)
79. (A) $\rightarrow$ (r); (B) $\rightarrow$ (r,t); (C) $\rightarrow$ (p,q,s)
80. (A) $\rightarrow$ (p,q,r); (B) $\rightarrow$ (p,q,r,s,t); (C) $\rightarrow$ (p,q,r,s,t)
81. (A) $\rightarrow$ (p,r); (B) $\rightarrow$ (p,q,r,t); (C) $\rightarrow$ (p,r,s)
82. (c) 83. (b) 84. (a) 85. (a) 86. (b) 87. (b)
88. (c) 91. $15\sqrt{2}-25\sqrt{3}$
92. 0 99. $\frac{1}{12}xyz(x-y)(y-z)(z-x)$
100. (i) 6 (ii) 0 101. 0
105. $-a^2(a_1-a_2)(a_2-a_3)(a_3-a_1)$
106. $\begin{vmatrix} a & b & c \\ b & c & a \\ c & a & b \end{vmatrix}$
107. (i) $\frac{yz}{x^2}+\frac{zx}{y^2}+\frac{xy}{z^2}+1=0$ (ii) $a^3+b^3+c^3=5\,abc$
109. (b) 110. (c) 111. (b) 112. (b) 113. (a) 114. (c)
115. (d) 116. (b) 117. (c) 118. (b) 119. (a) 120. (a)
121. (a) 122. (b, c) 123. (c) 124. (2) 125. (b,c,d)
126. (c)

Solutions

1. $\because f(n) = \alpha^n + \beta^n$

Let $\Delta = \begin{vmatrix} 3 & 1+f(1) & 1+f(2) \\ 1+f(1) & 1+f(2) & 1+f(3) \\ 1+f(2) & 1+f(3) & 1+f(4) \end{vmatrix}$

$$= \begin{vmatrix} 3 & 1+\alpha+\beta & 1+\alpha^2+\beta^2 \\ 1+\alpha+\beta & 1+\alpha^2+\beta^2 & 1+\alpha^3+\beta^3 \\ 1+\alpha^2+\beta^2 & 1+\alpha^3+\beta^3 & 1+\alpha^4+\beta^4 \end{vmatrix}$$

$$= \begin{vmatrix} 1 & 1 & 1 \\ 1 & \alpha & \beta \\ 1 & \alpha^2 & \beta^2 \end{vmatrix} \times \begin{vmatrix} 1 & 1 & 1 \\ 1 & \alpha & \beta \\ 1 & \alpha^2 & \beta^2 \end{vmatrix} = \begin{vmatrix} 1 & 1 & 1 \\ 1 & \alpha & \beta \\ 1 & \alpha^2 & \beta^2 \end{vmatrix}^2$$

Applying $C_2 \to C_2 - C_1$ and $C_3 \to C_3 - C_1$, then

$$\Delta = \begin{vmatrix} 1 & 0 & 0 \\ 1 & \alpha-1 & \beta-1 \\ 1 & \alpha^2-1 & \beta^2-1 \end{vmatrix}^2$$

Expanding along R_1, we get

$$\Delta = \begin{vmatrix} \alpha-1 & \beta-1 \\ \alpha^2-1 & \beta^2-1 \end{vmatrix}^2 = (\alpha-1)^2(\beta-1)^2 \begin{vmatrix} 1 & 1 \\ \alpha+1 & \beta+1 \end{vmatrix}^2$$

$$= (\alpha-1)^2(\beta-1)^2(\beta-\alpha)^2 = (1-\alpha)^2(1-\beta)^2(\alpha-\beta)^2$$

$$= k(1-\alpha)^2(1-\beta)^2(\alpha-\beta)^2 \qquad \text{[given]}$$

$\therefore \quad k = 1$

2. $\because a, b, c$ and d are in AP. Let D be the common difference, then

$$b = a + D, c = a + 2D, d = a + 3D \qquad \text{...(i)}$$

and $\Delta(x) = \begin{vmatrix} x+a & x+b & x+a-c \\ x+b & x+c & x-1 \\ x+c & x+d & x-b+d \end{vmatrix}$

On putting the values of b, c and d from Eq.(i) in $\Delta(x)$, then

$$\Delta(x) = \begin{vmatrix} x+a & x+a+D & x-2D \\ x+a+D & x+a+2D & x-1 \\ x+a+2D & x+a+3D & x+2D \end{vmatrix}$$

Applying $R_2 \to R_2 - \frac{1}{2}(R_1 + R_3)$, then

$$\Delta(x) = \begin{vmatrix} x+a & x+a+D & x-2D \\ 0 & 0 & -1 \\ x+a+2D & x+a+3D & x+2D \end{vmatrix}$$

Expanding along R_2, then

$$\Delta(x) = \begin{vmatrix} x+a & x+a+D \\ x+a+2D & x+a+3D \end{vmatrix}$$

Applying $R_2 \to R_2 - R_1$, then

$$\Delta(x) = \begin{vmatrix} x+a & x+a+D \\ 2D & 2D \end{vmatrix}$$

$$= 2D(x+a-x-a-D) = -2D^2$$

Also, $\quad \int_0^2 \Delta(x)\,dx = -16$

$\Rightarrow \quad -2D^2(2) = -16$

$\therefore \quad D^2 = 4 \;\text{ or }\; D = \pm 2$

3. Let $\Delta(x) = \begin{vmatrix} x & 1+x^2 & x^3 \\ \log_e(1+x^2) & e^x & \sin x \\ \cos x & \tan x & \sin^2 x \end{vmatrix}$

$$= a + bx + cx^2 + \ldots$$

On putting $x = 0$, we get

$$\begin{vmatrix} 0 & 1 & 0 \\ 0 & 1 & 0 \\ 1 & 0 & 0 \end{vmatrix} = a$$

$\therefore \quad 0 = a$

or $\quad a = 0$, then

$$\Delta(x) = bx + cx^2 + \ldots$$

Hence, $\Delta(x)$ is divisible by x.

4. Given, $\begin{vmatrix} a^2 & b^2 & c^2 \\ (a+1)^2 & (b+1)^2 & (c+1)^2 \\ (a-1)^2 & (b-1)^2 & (c-1)^2 \end{vmatrix} = 0$

$$\Rightarrow \begin{vmatrix} a^2 & b^2 & c^2 \\ a^2+2a+1 & b^2+2b+1 & c^2+2c+1 \\ a^2-2a+1 & b^2-2b+1 & c^2-2c+1 \end{vmatrix} = 0$$

Applying $R_2 \to R_2 - R_3$, then

$$\begin{vmatrix} a^2 & b^2 & c^2 \\ 4a & 4b & 4c \\ a^2-2a+1 & b^2-2b+1 & c^2-2c+1 \end{vmatrix} = 0$$

Applying $R_3 \to R_3 - R_1 + \frac{1}{2}R_2$, then

$$4\begin{vmatrix} a^2 & b^2 & c^2 \\ a & b & c \\ 1 & 1 & 1 \end{vmatrix} = 0$$

$$\Rightarrow -\begin{vmatrix} 1 & 1 & 1 \\ a & b & c \\ a^2 & b^2 & c^2 \end{vmatrix} = 0 \qquad [\because R_1 \to R_3]$$

$$\Rightarrow \begin{vmatrix} 1 & 1 & 1 \\ a & b & c \\ a^2 & b^2 & c^2 \end{vmatrix} = 0$$

$\Rightarrow \quad (a-b)(b-c)(c-a) = 0$

$\therefore \quad a-b = 0 \text{ or } b-c = 0 \text{ or } c-a = 0$

$\Rightarrow \quad a = b \text{ or } b = c \text{ or } c = a$

Hence, ΔABC is an isosceles triangle.

5. Let $\Delta = \begin{vmatrix} \alpha & x & x & x \\ x & \beta & x & x \\ x & x & \gamma & x \\ x & x & x & \delta \end{vmatrix}$

Applying $C_2 \to C_2 - C_1, C_3 \to C_3 - C_1$ and $C_4 \to C_4 - C_1$, then

$$\Delta = \begin{vmatrix} \alpha & x-\alpha & x-\alpha & x-\alpha \\ x & \beta - x & 0 & 0 \\ x & 0 & \gamma - x & 0 \\ x & 0 & 0 & \delta - x \end{vmatrix}$$

Expanding along first column, then

$$\Delta = \alpha(\beta - x)(\gamma - x)(\delta - x) - x(x-\alpha)(\gamma - x)(\delta - x) + x(\delta - x)(x-\alpha)(x-\beta) - x(x-\alpha)(\beta - x)(\gamma - x)$$

$$= (x-\alpha)(x-\beta)(x-\gamma)(x-\delta) - x[(x-\alpha)(x-\gamma)(x-\delta) + (x-\beta)(x-\gamma)(x-\delta) + (x-\alpha)(x-\beta)(x-\delta) + (x-\alpha)(x-\beta)(x-\gamma)] \quad \text{[given]}$$

$$= f(x) - xf'(x)$$

$\therefore \quad f(x) = (x-\alpha)(x-\beta)(x-\gamma)(x-\delta)$

6. Given, $\begin{vmatrix} a & b-c & c+b \\ a+c & b & c-a \\ a-b & a+b & c \end{vmatrix} = 0$

$$\Rightarrow \quad \frac{1}{a}\begin{vmatrix} a^2 & b-c & c+b \\ a^2+ac & b & c-a \\ a^2-ab & a+b & c \end{vmatrix} = 0$$

Applying $C_1 \to C_1 + bC_2 + cC_3$, then

$$\Rightarrow \quad \frac{1}{a}\begin{vmatrix} a^2+b^2+c^2 & b-c & c+b \\ a^2+b^2+c^2 & b & c-a \\ a^2+b^2+c^2 & a+b & c \end{vmatrix} = 0$$

Applying $R_2 \to R_2 - R_1$ and $R_3 \to R_3 - R_1$, then

$$\Rightarrow \quad \frac{1}{a}\begin{vmatrix} a^2+b^2+c^2 & b-c & c-b \\ 0 & c & -b-a \\ 0 & a+c & -b \end{vmatrix} = 0$$

Expanding along C_1, then

$$\Rightarrow \quad \frac{(a^2+b^2+c^2)}{a}\begin{vmatrix} c & -b-a \\ a+c & -b \end{vmatrix} = 0$$

$$\Rightarrow \quad \frac{(a^2+b^2+c^2)}{a}[(-bc + (b+a)(a+c)] = 0$$

$$\Rightarrow \quad \frac{(a^2+b^2+c^2)(-bc+ab+bc+a^2+ac)}{a} = 0$$

$$\Rightarrow \quad (a^2+b^2+c^2)(a+b+c) = 0$$

$\because \quad a^2+b^2+c^2 \neq 0$

$\therefore \quad a+b+c = 0$

Therefore, line $ax + by + c = 0$ passes through the fixed point (1, 1).

7. $\because \begin{vmatrix} a & b & c \\ b & c & a \\ c & a & b \end{vmatrix} = -(a^3+b^3+c^3-3abc)$

$$= -(a+b+c)(a+b\omega+c\omega^2)(a+b\omega^2+c\omega)$$

[where ω is cube roots of unity]

$$= -f(\alpha)f(\beta)f(\gamma) \quad [\because \alpha = 1, \beta = \omega, \gamma = \omega^2$$

8. Let $\Delta = \begin{vmatrix} \cos 2x & \sin^2 x & \cos 4x \\ \sin^2 x & \cos 2x & \cos^2 x \\ \cos 4x & \cos^2 x & \cos 2x \end{vmatrix}$

$$= \begin{vmatrix} 1-2\sin^2 x & \sin^2 x & 1-8\sin^2 x(1-\sin^2 x) \\ \sin^2 x & 1-2\sin^2 x & 1-\sin^2 x \\ 1-8\sin^2 x(1-\sin^2 x) & 1-\sin^2 x & 1-2\sin^2 x \end{vmatrix}$$

The required constant term is $\begin{vmatrix} 1 & 0 & 1 \\ 0 & 1 & 1 \\ 1 & 1 & 1 \end{vmatrix}$

Applying $C_3 \to C_3 - C_1$, then

$$\begin{vmatrix} 1 & 0 & 0 \\ 0 & 1 & 1 \\ 1 & 1 & 0 \end{vmatrix} = 1(0-1) = -1$$

9. $\because \quad -1 \le x < 0 \Rightarrow [x] = -1$

$0 \le y < 1 \Rightarrow [y] = 0$

$1 \le z < 2 \Rightarrow [z] = 1$

Let $\Delta = \begin{vmatrix} [x]+1 & [y] & [z] \\ [x] & [y]+1 & [z] \\ [x] & [y] & [z]+1 \end{vmatrix} = \begin{vmatrix} 0 & 0 & 1 \\ -1 & 1 & 1 \\ -1 & 0 & 2 \end{vmatrix}$

Expanding along C_2, then $\Delta = \begin{vmatrix} 0 & 1 \\ -1 & 2 \end{vmatrix} = 1 = [z]$

10. Let $\Delta = \begin{vmatrix} y^2 & -xy & x^2 \\ a & b & c \\ a' & b' & c' \end{vmatrix} = \frac{1}{xy}\begin{vmatrix} xy^2 & -xy & x^2y \\ ax & b & cy \\ a'x & b' & c'y \end{vmatrix}$

Applying $C_1 \to C_1 + yC_2$ and $C_3 \to C_3 + xC_2$, then

$$\Delta = \frac{1}{xy}\begin{vmatrix} 0 & -xy & 0 \\ ax+by & b & bx+cy \\ a'x+b'y & b' & b'x+c'y \end{vmatrix}$$

Expanding along R_1, then

$$= \frac{1}{xy} \cdot xy \cdot \begin{vmatrix} ax+by & bx+cy \\ a'x+b'y & b'x+c'y \end{vmatrix}$$

$$= \begin{vmatrix} ax+by & bx+cy \\ a'x+b'y & b'x+c'y \end{vmatrix}$$

11. $\because$ In a triangle $A + B + C = \pi$ and $e^{\pi} = \cos\pi + i\sin\pi = -1$

$$e^{i(B+C)} = e^{i(\pi - A)} = e^{i\pi}\cdot e^{iA} = -e^{-iA}$$

$$\Rightarrow \quad e^{-i(B+C)} = -e^{iA}$$

Similarly, $\quad e^{-i(A+B)} = -e^{iC}$ and $e^{-i(C+A)} = -e^{iB}$

Taking e^{iA}, e^{iB}, e^{iC} common from R_1, R_2 and R_3 respectively, we get

$$\Delta = e^{iA}\cdot e^{iB}\cdot e^{iC}\begin{vmatrix} e^{iA} & e^{-i(A+C)} & e^{-i(A+B)} \\ e^{-i(B+C)} & e^{iB} & e^{-i(A+B)} \\ e^{-i(B+C)} & e^{-i(A+C)} & e^{iC}\end{vmatrix}$$

$$= e^{i\pi} = \begin{vmatrix} e^{iA} & -e^{iB} & -e^{iC} \\ -e^{iA} & e^{iB} & -e^{iC} \\ -e^{iA} & -e^{iB} & e^{iC}\end{vmatrix}$$

Taking e^{iA}, e^{iB}, e^{iC} common from C_1, C_2 and C_3 respectively, we get

$$\Delta = (-1)\, e^{iA}\cdot e^{iB}\cdot e^{iC}\begin{vmatrix} 1 & -1 & -1 \\ -1 & 1 & -1 \\ -1 & -1 & 1\end{vmatrix}$$

$$= (-1)\, e^{i\pi}\begin{vmatrix} 1 & -1 & -1 \\ -1 & 1 & -1 \\ -1 & -1 & 1\end{vmatrix}$$

$$= (-1)(-1)\begin{vmatrix} 1 & -1 & -1 \\ -1 & 1 & -1 \\ -1 & -1 & 1\end{vmatrix} = \begin{vmatrix} 1 & -1 & -1 \\ -1 & 1 & -1 \\ -1 & -1 & 1\end{vmatrix}$$

Applying $C_2 \to C_2 + C_1$ and $C_3 \to C_3 + C_1$, then

$$\Delta = \begin{vmatrix} 1 & 0 & 0 \\ -1 & 0 & -2 \\ -1 & -2 & 0\end{vmatrix} = 1\,(0-4) = -4$$

12. Taking x^5 common from R_3, then

$$x^5\begin{vmatrix} x^n & x^{n+2} & x^{2n} \\ 1 & x^a & a \\ x^n & x^{a+1} & x^{2n}\end{vmatrix} = 0, \forall\, x \in R$$

$$\Rightarrow \quad a + 1 = n + 2 \Rightarrow a = n + 1$$

13. Since, x, y and z are in AP.

$$\therefore \quad 2y = x + z \quad \text{...(i)}$$

$$\text{Let } \Delta = \begin{vmatrix} 5 & 4 & 3 \\ x51 & y41 & z31 \\ x & y & z\end{vmatrix}$$

$$= \begin{vmatrix} 5 & 4 & 3 \\ 100x + 50 + 1 & 100y + 40 + 1 & 100z + 30 + 1 \\ x & y & z\end{vmatrix}$$

Applying $R_2 \to R_2 - \frac{1}{2}(R_1 + R_3)$, then

$$= \begin{vmatrix} 5 & 0 & 3 \\ 100x + 50 + 1 & 0 & 100z + 30 + 1 \\ x & 0 & z\end{vmatrix} \quad \text{[from Eq. (i)]}$$

$$= 0 \quad [\because \text{all elements of } C_2 \text{ are zeroes}]$$

14. As $a_1 b_1 c_1$, $a_2 b_2 c_2$ and $a_3 b_3 c_3$ are even natural numbers each of c_1, c_2, c_3 is divisible by 2.

Let $C_i = 2\lambda_i$ for $i = 1, 2, 3$ and $\lambda_i \in N$, then

$$\Delta = \begin{vmatrix} 2\lambda_1 & a_1 & b_1 \\ 2\lambda_2 & a_2 & b_2 \\ 2\lambda_3 & a_3 & b_3\end{vmatrix} = 2\begin{vmatrix} \lambda_1 & a_1 & b_1 \\ \lambda_2 & a_2 & b_2 \\ \lambda_3 & a_3 & b_3\end{vmatrix} = 2m$$

where m is some natural number. Thus, Δ is divisible by 2. That Δ may not be divisible by 4 can be seen by taking the three numbers as 112, 122 and 134.

$$\Delta = \begin{vmatrix} 2 & 1 & 1 \\ 2 & 1 & 2 \\ 4 & 1 & 3\end{vmatrix} = 2(3-2) - 1(6-8) + 1(2-4) = 2$$

which is divisible by 2 but not by 4.

15. $$\text{Let } \Delta = \begin{vmatrix} c & b\cos B + c\beta & a\cos A + b\alpha + c\gamma \\ a & c\cos B + a\beta & b\cos A + c\alpha + a\gamma \\ b & a\cos B + b\beta & c\cos A + a\alpha + b\gamma\end{vmatrix}$$

Applying $C_2 \to C_2 - \beta C_1$ and $C_3 \to C_3 - \gamma C_1$, then

$$\Delta = \begin{vmatrix} c & b\cos B & a\cos A + b\alpha \\ a & c\cos B & b\cos A + c\alpha \\ b & a\cos B & c\cos A + a\alpha\end{vmatrix}$$

Applying $C_3 \to C_3 - \alpha\sec B\, C_2$, then

$$\Delta = \begin{vmatrix} c & b\cos B & a\cos A \\ a & c\cos B & b\cos A \\ b & a\cos B & c\cos A\end{vmatrix} = \cos A\cos B\begin{vmatrix} c & b & a \\ a & c & b \\ b & a & c\end{vmatrix}$$

Applying $C_1 \leftrightarrow C_3$, then $\Delta = -\cos A\cos B\begin{vmatrix} a & b & c \\ b & c & a \\ c & a & b\end{vmatrix}$

$$= -\cos A\cos B\,(a+b+c)\cdot\frac{1}{2}[(a-b)^2 + (b-c)^2 + (c-a)^2]$$

Given, $\quad \cos A \ne 0, \cos B \ne 0$ and $a + b + c \ne 0$

$\because \quad \Delta = 0$

$\therefore \quad (a-b)^2 + (b-c)^2 + (c-a)^2 = 0$

which is independent, when $a - b = 0$, $b - c = 0$ and $c - a = 0$

i.e., $\quad a = b = c$

Hence, ΔABC is an equilateral.

16. Here, $\quad \left.\begin{matrix} x_1 + x_2 = 6, & x_1x_2 = 3 \\ y_1 + y_2 = 4, & y_1y_2 = 2\end{matrix}\right\}$ and ...(i)

$$\text{Let } \Delta = \begin{vmatrix} x_1x_2 & y_1y_2 & 1 \\ x_1 + x_2 & y_1 + y_2 & 2 \\ \sin(\pi\, x_1x_2) & \cos\left(\frac{\pi}{2}y_1y_2\right) & 1\end{vmatrix}$$

$$= \begin{vmatrix} 3 & 2 & 1 \\ 6 & 4 & 2 \\ \sin 3\pi & \cos\left(\frac{\pi}{4}\right) & 1\end{vmatrix} \quad \text{[from Eq. (i)]}$$

Applying $R_2 \to R_2 - 2R_1$, then $\Delta = \begin{vmatrix} 3 & 2 & 1 \\ 0 & 0 & 0 \\ 0 & \frac{1}{\sqrt{2}} & 1\end{vmatrix} = 0$

17. $\because \Delta = \begin{vmatrix} {}^{10}C_4 & {}^{10}C_5 & {}^{11}C_m \\ {}^{11}C_6 & {}^{11}C_7 & {}^{12}C_{m+2} \\ {}^{12}C_8 & {}^{12}C_9 & {}^{13}C_{m+4} \end{vmatrix}$

Applying $C_2 \to C_2 + C_1$ and use Pascal's rule $({}^nC_r + {}^nC_{r-1} = {}^{n+1}C_r)$, then

$$\Delta = \begin{vmatrix} {}^{10}C_4 & {}^{11}C_5 & {}^{11}C_m \\ {}^{11}C_6 & {}^{12}C_7 & {}^{12}C_{m+2} \\ {}^{12}C_8 & {}^{13}C_9 & {}^{13}C_{m+4} \end{vmatrix} = 0 \quad \text{[given]}$$

$\therefore \quad m = 5$

18. Let $\Delta = \begin{vmatrix} 1 & \sin(\alpha-\beta)\theta & \cos(\alpha-\beta)\theta \\ a & \sin\alpha\theta & \cos\alpha\theta \\ a^2 & \sin(\alpha-\beta)\theta & \cos(\alpha-\beta)\theta \end{vmatrix}$

Applying $R_1 \to R_1 - R_3$, then

$$\Delta = \begin{vmatrix} 1-a^2 & 0 & 0 \\ a & \sin\alpha\theta & \cos\alpha\theta \\ a^2 & \sin(\alpha-\beta)\theta & \cos(\alpha-\beta)\theta \end{vmatrix}$$

Expanding along R_1, then

$$\Delta = (1-a^2)\begin{vmatrix} \sin\alpha\theta & \cos\alpha\theta \\ \sin(\alpha-\beta)\theta & \cos(\alpha-\beta)\theta \end{vmatrix}$$

$$= (1-a^2)[\sin\alpha\theta \cdot \cos(\alpha-\beta)\theta - \cos\alpha\theta \cdot \sin(\alpha-\beta)\theta]$$

$$= (1-a^2)\sin(\alpha\theta - \alpha\theta + \beta\theta) = (1-a^2)\sin\beta\theta$$

19. Let $F(x) = \begin{vmatrix} f(x) & g(x) & h(x) \\ a & b & c \\ p & q & r \end{vmatrix} = mx^4 + nx^3 + rx^2 + sx + t$ ...(i)

On differentiating twice and thrice of Eq. (i) w.r.t. x, then

$$F''(x) = \begin{vmatrix} f''(x) & g''(x) & h''(x) \\ a & b & c \\ p & q & r \end{vmatrix} = 12mx^2 + 6nx + 2r \quad \text{...(ii)}$$

$$F'''(x) = \begin{vmatrix} f'''(x) & g'''(x) & h'''(x) \\ a & b & c \\ p & q & r \end{vmatrix} = 24mx + 6n \quad \text{...(iii)}$$

On putting $x = 0$ in Eqs. (ii) and (iii), we get

$$\begin{vmatrix} f''(0) & g''(0) & h''(0) \\ a & b & c \\ p & q & r \end{vmatrix} = 2r \quad \text{...(iv)}$$

and $$\begin{vmatrix} f''(0) & g''(0) & h''(0) \\ a & b & c \\ p & q & r \end{vmatrix} = 6n \quad \text{...(v)}$$

Now, subtracting Eq. (iv) from Eq. (v), we get

$$\begin{vmatrix} f'''(0) - f''(0) & g'''(0) - g''(0) & h'''(0) - h''(0) \\ a & b & c \\ p & q & r \end{vmatrix} = 6n - 2r = 2(3n - r)$$

20. $\because f(x) = \begin{vmatrix} \cos(x+\alpha) & \cos(x+\beta) & \cos(x+\gamma) \\ \sin(x+\alpha) & \sin(x+\beta) & \sin(x+\gamma) \\ \sin(\beta-\gamma) & \sin(\gamma-\alpha) & \sin(\alpha-\beta) \end{vmatrix}$

On differentiating both sides w.r.t. x, then

$$f'(x) = \begin{vmatrix} -\sin(x+\alpha) & -\sin(x+\beta) & -\sin(x+\gamma) \\ \sin(x+\alpha) & \sin(x+\beta) & \sin(x+\gamma) \\ \sin(\beta-\gamma) & \sin(\gamma-\alpha) & \sin(\alpha-\beta) \end{vmatrix} + \begin{vmatrix} \cos(x+\alpha) & \cos(x+\beta) & \cos(x+\gamma) \\ \cos(x+\alpha) & \cos(x+\beta) & \cos(x+\gamma) \\ \sin(\beta-\gamma) & \sin(\gamma-\alpha) & \sin(\alpha-\beta) \end{vmatrix}$$

$$= -\begin{vmatrix} \sin(x+\alpha) & \sin(x+\beta) & \sin(x+\gamma) \\ \sin(x+\alpha) & \sin(x+\beta) & \sin(x+\gamma) \\ \sin(\beta-\gamma) & \sin(\gamma-\alpha) & \sin(\alpha-\beta) \end{vmatrix} + \begin{vmatrix} \cos(x+\alpha) & \cos(x+\beta) & \cos(x+\gamma) \\ \cos(x+\alpha) & \cos(x+\beta) & \cos(x+\gamma) \\ \sin(\beta-\gamma) & \sin(\gamma-\alpha) & \sin(\alpha-\beta) \end{vmatrix}$$

$= 0 + 0$ [$\because R_1$ and R_2 are identical]

$= 0$

$\therefore f(x) = c$ [constant]

Now, $f(\theta) - 2f(\phi) + f(\psi) = c - 2c + c = 0$

21. Let $\Delta = \begin{vmatrix} 1 & 1 & 1 \\ a & b & c \\ a^3 & b^3 & c^3 \end{vmatrix}$

Taking a, b, c common from C_1, C_2, C_3, then $= abc\begin{vmatrix} \frac{1}{a} & \frac{1}{b} & \frac{1}{c} \\ 1 & 1 & 1 \\ a^2 & b^2 & c^2 \end{vmatrix}$

On multiplying in R_1 by abc, then

$$\Delta = \begin{vmatrix} bc & ca & ab \\ 1 & 1 & 1 \\ a^2 & b^2 & c^2 \end{vmatrix} = -\begin{vmatrix} 1 & 1 & 1 \\ bc & ca & ab \\ a^2 & b^2 & c^2 \end{vmatrix} \quad [R_1 \leftrightarrow R_2]$$

$$= \begin{vmatrix} 1 & 1 & 1 \\ a^2 & b^2 & c^2 \\ bc & ca & ab \end{vmatrix} \quad [R_2 \leftrightarrow R_3]$$

$$= (a-b)(b-c)(c-a)(a+b+c)$$

Now, $D = \begin{vmatrix} 1 & 1 & 1 \\ (x-a)^2 & (x-b)^2 & (x-c)^2 \\ (x-b)(x-c) & (x-c)(x-a) & (x-a)(x-b) \end{vmatrix}$

$$= (b-a)(c-b)(a-c)(3x-a-b-c)$$

Now, given that a, b and c are all different, then $D = 0$

$\therefore \quad 3x - a - b - c = 0$

$\Rightarrow \quad x = \frac{1}{3}(a+b+c)$

22. Given, determinant

$$2a(bc-4a^2)-b(b^2-2ac)+c(2ab-c^2)=0$$

$$\Rightarrow \quad -[(2a)^3+b^3+c^3-3\cdot 2a\cdot b\cdot c]=0$$

$$\Rightarrow \frac{1}{2}(2a+b+c)[(2a-b)^2+(b-c)^2+(c-2a)^2]=0$$

$$\Rightarrow \quad 2a+b+c=0 \quad \text{...(i) } [\because b\neq c]$$

Let $f(x)=8ax^3+2bx^2+cx+d$

$\therefore f(0)=d$ and for $\left(\frac{1}{2}\right)=a+\frac{b}{2}+\frac{c}{2}+d=\frac{2a+b+c}{2}+d$

$$=\frac{0}{2}+d=d \quad \text{[from Eq. (i)]}$$

$$\Rightarrow \quad f(0)=f\left(\frac{1}{2}\right)$$

So, $f(x)$ satisfies Rolle's theorem and hence $f'(x)=0$ has atleast one root in $\left[0,\frac{1}{2}\right]$.

23. Given, $\begin{vmatrix} x^3+1 & x^2y & x^2z \\ xy^2 & y^3+1 & y^2z \\ xz^2 & yz^2 & z^3+1 \end{vmatrix}=11$

Taking x, y, z common from C_1, C_2, C_3 respectively, then

$$\Rightarrow \quad xyz\begin{vmatrix} \frac{x^3+1}{x} & x^2 & x^2 \\ y^2 & \frac{y^3+1}{y} & y^2 \\ z^2 & z^2 & \frac{z^3+1}{z} \end{vmatrix}=11$$

On multiplying R_1 by x, R_2 by y and R_3 by z, we get

$$\Rightarrow \begin{vmatrix} x^3+1 & x^3 & x^3 \\ y^3 & y^3+1 & y^3 \\ z^3 & z^3 & z^3+1 \end{vmatrix}=11$$

Applying $R_1 \to R_1+R_2+R_3$, then

$$\begin{vmatrix} x^3+y^3+z^3+1 & x^3+y^3+z^3+1 & x^3+y^3+z^3+1 \\ y^3 & y^3+1 & y^3 \\ z^3 & z^3 & z^3+1 \end{vmatrix}=11$$

Applying $C_2 \to C_2-C_1$ and $C_3 \to C_3-C_1$, then

$$\begin{vmatrix} x^3+y^3+z^3+1 & 0 & 0 \\ y^3 & 1 & 0 \\ z^3 & 0 & 1 \end{vmatrix}=11$$

$$\Rightarrow \quad x^3+y^3+z^3+1=11$$

$$\Rightarrow \quad x^3+y^3+z^3=10$$

Therefore, the ordered triplets are (2, 1, 1), (1, 2, 1) and (1, 1, 2).

24. $\because f(x)-x=0$ has imaginary roots.

Then, $\quad f(x)-x>0$ or $f(x)-x, 0, \forall x\in R$

for $\quad f(x)-x>0, \forall x\in R$,

then $\quad f[f(x)]-f(x)>0, \forall x\in R$

On adding, we get

$$f[f(x)]-x>0, \forall x\in R$$

Similarly, $f[f(x)]-x<0, \forall x\in R$

Thus, roots of the equation $f[f(x)]-x=0$ are imaginary

Let $\quad z=\begin{vmatrix} 2 & \alpha & \delta \\ \beta & 0 & \alpha \\ \gamma & \beta & 1 \end{vmatrix}$

Then, $\quad \bar{z}=\begin{vmatrix} 2 & \bar{\alpha} & \bar{\delta} \\ \bar{\beta} & 0 & \bar{\alpha} \\ \bar{\gamma} & \bar{\beta} & 1 \end{vmatrix}=\begin{vmatrix} 2 & \beta & \gamma \\ \alpha & 0 & \beta \\ \delta & \alpha & 1 \end{vmatrix}=\begin{vmatrix} 2 & \alpha & \delta \\ \beta & 0 & \alpha \\ \gamma & \beta & 1 \end{vmatrix}=z$

Hence, z is purely real.

25. For infinitely many solutions

$$\Delta=\Delta_1=\Delta_2=\Delta_3=0$$

$$\Delta=0 \Rightarrow \begin{vmatrix} 2 & -1 & 1 \\ 1 & -2 & 1 \\ t & -1 & 2 \end{vmatrix}=0 \Rightarrow t=5$$

For $\quad t=5, \Delta_1=\Delta_2=\Delta_3=0$

Now, $\displaystyle\int_0^{-2t} f(x)\,dx=\int_0^{-10} f(x)\,dx=\int_0^{-5} f(x)\,dx+\int_{-5}^{-10} f(x)\,dx$

$$=\int_5^{-10} f(x+5)\,dx+\int_{-5}^{-10} f(x)\,dx$$

$$=\int_{-5}^{-10}[f(x+5)+f(x)]\,dx$$

$$=\int_{-5}^{-10} 2dx=2(-10+5)$$

$$=-10=-2t$$

26. On putting $x=0$, we get $a_0=1$

On differentiating both sides w.r.t. x and putting $x=0$, we get

$$a_1=4a$$

On differentiating again w.r.t. x and putting $x=0$, we get

$$2a_2=12a^2+8b$$

or $\quad a_2=6a^2+4b$

Also, given $\begin{vmatrix} a_1 & a_1 & a_2 \\ a_0 & a_2 & a_0 \\ a_2 & a_0 & a_1 \end{vmatrix}=0$

$$\Rightarrow \quad -(a_0^3+a_1^3+a_2^3-3a_0a_1a_2)=0$$

$$\Rightarrow \quad \frac{1}{2}(a_0+a_1+a_2)[(a_0-a_1)^2+(a_1-a_2)^2+(a_2-a_0)^2]=0$$

$$\because \quad a_0+a_1+a_2\neq 0$$

$$\therefore \quad (a_0-a_1)^2+(a_1-a_2)^2+(a_2-a_0)^2=0$$

$$\Rightarrow \quad a_0-a_1=0, a_1-a_2=0, a_2-a_0=0$$

$$\therefore \quad a_0=a_1=a_2$$

$$\Rightarrow \quad 1=4a=6a^2+4b$$

$$\Rightarrow \quad a=\frac{1}{4} \text{ and } b=\frac{5}{32}$$

27. $\because f(x)=\log_{10} x$ and $g(x)=e^{\pi i x}$

$$\therefore \quad f(10)=\log_{10} 10=1$$

and $\quad g(10)=e^{10\pi i}=(-1)^{10}=1$

$$f(10^2) = \log_{10} 10^2 = 2$$

and $$g(10^2) = e^{100\pi i} = (-1)^{100} = 1$$

$$f(10^3) = \log_{10} 10^3 = 3$$

and $$g(10^3) = e^{1000\pi i} = (-1)^{1000} = 1$$

Given, $$\phi(x) = \begin{vmatrix} f(x)\cdot g(x) & [f(x)]^{g(x)} & 1 \\ f(x^2)\cdot g(x^2) & [f(x^2)]^{g(x^2)} & 0 \\ f(x^3)\cdot g(x^3) & [f(x^3)]^{g(x^3)} & 1 \end{vmatrix}$$

$$\therefore \quad \phi(10) = \begin{vmatrix} f(10)\cdot g(10) & [f(10)]^{g(10)} & 1 \\ f(10^2)\cdot g(10^2) & [f(10^2)]^{g(10^2)} & 0 \\ f(10^3)\cdot g(10^3) & [f(10^3)]^{g(10^3)} & 1 \end{vmatrix}$$

$$= \begin{vmatrix} 1 & 1 & 1 \\ 2 & 2 & 0 \\ 3 & 3 & 1 \end{vmatrix} = 0$$

28. Let $$\Delta = \begin{vmatrix} 1 & (\alpha^{2x} - \alpha^{-2x})^2 & (\alpha^{2x} + \alpha^{-2x})^2 \\ 1 & (\beta^{2x} - \beta^{-2x})^2 & (\beta^{2x} + \beta^{-2x})^2 \\ 1 & (\gamma^{2x} - \gamma^{-2x})^2 & (\gamma^{2x} + \gamma^{-2x})^2 \end{vmatrix}$$

Applying $C_3 \to C_3 - C_2$, then $$\Delta = \begin{vmatrix} 1 & (\alpha^{2x} - \alpha^{-2x})^2 & 4 \\ 1 & (\beta^{2x} - \beta^{-2x})^2 & 4 \\ 1 & (\gamma^{2x} - \gamma^{-2x})^2 & 4 \end{vmatrix} = 0$$

29. The given equations can be written as

$$(a-1)x - y - z = 0,$$
$$-x + (b-1)y - z = 0$$
and $$-x - y + (c-1)z = 0$$

For non-trivial solution

$$\begin{vmatrix} a-1 & -1 & -1 \\ -1 & b-1 & -1 \\ -1 & -1 & c-1 \end{vmatrix} = 0$$

Applying $C_1 \to C_1 - C_3$ and $C_2 \to C_2 - C_3$, then

$$\begin{vmatrix} a & 0 & -1 \\ 0 & b & -1 \\ -c & -c & c-1 \end{vmatrix} = 0$$

Expanding along R_1, then

$$\Rightarrow \quad a(bc - b - c) - 0 - 1(0 + bc) = 0$$
$$\Rightarrow \quad ab + bc + ca = abc$$

30. For non-trivial solution $$\begin{vmatrix} \lambda & -1 & \cos\theta \\ 3 & 1 & 2 \\ \cos\theta & 1 & 2 \end{vmatrix} = 0$$

Applying $R_3 \to R_3 - R_2$, then

$$\begin{vmatrix} \lambda & -1 & \cos\theta \\ 3 & 1 & 2 \\ \cos\theta - 3 & 0 & 0 \end{vmatrix} = 0$$

Expanding along R_3, then

$$\Rightarrow \quad (\cos\theta - 3)(-2 - \cos\theta) = 0$$

$$\Rightarrow \quad (\cos\theta - 3)(2 + \cos\theta) = 0$$

$\cos\theta = 3, -2$, where -2 is neglected.

Hence, $\begin{vmatrix} \lambda & -1 & \cos\theta \\ 3 & 1 & 2 \\ \cos\theta & 1 & 2 \end{vmatrix} > 0$ only trivial solution is possible.

31. $$\because \Delta = \begin{vmatrix} a^2 + x^2 & ab & ac \\ ab & b^2 + x^2 & bc \\ ac & bc & c^2 + x^2 \end{vmatrix}$$

Taking a, b, c common from R_1, R_2, R_3 respectively, then

$$\Delta = abc \begin{vmatrix} \dfrac{a^2 + x^2}{a} & b & c \\ a & \dfrac{b^2 + x^2}{b} & c \\ a & b & \dfrac{c^2 + x^2}{c} \end{vmatrix}$$

On multiplying in C_1, C_2, C_3 by a, b, c respectively, then

$$\Delta = \begin{vmatrix} a^2 + x^2 & b^2 & c^2 \\ a^2 & b^2 + x^2 & c^2 \\ a^2 & b^2 & c^2 + x^2 \end{vmatrix}$$

Now, applying $C_1 \to C_1 + C_2 + C_3$, then

$$\Delta = \begin{vmatrix} x^2 + a^2 + b^2 + c^2 & b^2 & c^2 \\ x^2 + a^2 + b^2 + c^2 & b^2 + x^2 & c^2 \\ x^2 + a^2 + b^2 + c^2 & b^2 & c^2 + x^2 \end{vmatrix}$$

Applying $R_2 \to R_2 - R_1$ and $R_3 \to R_3 - R_1$, then

$$\Delta = \begin{vmatrix} x^2 + a^2 + b^2 + c^2 & b^2 & c^2 \\ 0 & x^2 & 0 \\ 0 & 0 & x^2 \end{vmatrix}$$

$$= x^4(x^2 + a^2 + b^2 + c^2)$$

32. Let $$\Delta = \begin{vmatrix} \sqrt{6} & 2i & 3 + \sqrt{6} \\ \sqrt{12} & \sqrt{3} + \sqrt{8}\,i & 3\sqrt{2} + \sqrt{6}\,i \\ \sqrt{18} & \sqrt{2} + \sqrt{12}\,i & \sqrt{27} + 2i \end{vmatrix}$$

Applying $R_2 \to R_2 - \sqrt{2}\,R_1$ and $R_3 \to R_3 - \sqrt{3}\,R_1$, then

$$\Delta = \begin{vmatrix} \sqrt{6} & 2i & 3 + \sqrt{6} \\ 0 & \sqrt{3} & -2\sqrt{3} + 6i \\ 0 & \sqrt{2} & -3\sqrt{2} + 2i \end{vmatrix}$$

Expanding along C_1, we get

$$= \sqrt{6} \begin{vmatrix} \sqrt{3} & -2\sqrt{3} + \sqrt{6}i \\ \sqrt{2} & -3\sqrt{2} + 2i \end{vmatrix}$$

$$= \sqrt{6}\,[-3\sqrt{6} + 2i\sqrt{3} + 2\sqrt{6} - 2i\sqrt{3}]$$

$$= \sqrt{6}(-\sqrt{6}) = -6$$ [real and rational]

33. $$\sum_{k=1}^{n} 2^{k-1} = 1 + 2 + 2^2 + \ldots + 2^n = 2^n - 1$$

$$\sum_{k=1}^{n}\frac{1}{k(k+1)} = \sum_{k=1}^{n}\left(\frac{1}{k}-\frac{1}{k+1}\right)$$

$$= \frac{1}{1}-\frac{1}{n+1} = \frac{n}{n+1}$$

and $$\sum_{k=1}^{n}\sin k\theta = \frac{\sin\left(\frac{n+1}{2}\right)\theta\,\sin\left(\frac{n\theta}{2}\right)}{\sin\left(\frac{\theta}{2}\right)}$$

Given, $$D_k = \begin{vmatrix} 2^{k-1} & \frac{1}{k(k+1)} & \sin k\theta \\ x & y & z \\ 2^n-1 & \frac{n}{n+1} & \frac{\sin\left(\frac{n+1}{2}\right)\theta\,\sin\left(\frac{n\theta}{2}\right)}{\sin\left(\frac{\theta}{2}\right)} \end{vmatrix}$$

$$\therefore \sum_{k=1}^{n} D_k = \begin{vmatrix} \sum_{k=1}^{n}2^{k-1} & \sum_{k=1}^{n}\frac{1}{k(k+1)} & \sum_{k=1}^{n}\sin k\theta \\ x & y & z \\ 2^n-1 & \frac{n}{n+1} & \frac{\sin\left(\frac{n+1}{2}\right)\theta\,\sin\left(\frac{n\theta}{2}\right)}{\sin\left(\frac{\theta}{2}\right)} \end{vmatrix}$$

$$= \begin{vmatrix} 2^n-1 & \frac{n}{n+1} & \frac{\sin\left(\frac{n+1}{2}\right)\theta\,\sin\left(\frac{n\theta}{2}\right)}{\sin\left(\frac{\theta}{2}\right)} \\ x & y & z \\ 2^n-1 & \frac{n}{n+1} & \frac{\sin\left(\frac{n+1}{2}\right)\theta\,\sin\left(\frac{n\theta}{2}\right)}{\sin\left(\frac{\theta}{2}\right)} \end{vmatrix} = 0$$

34. We have, $$\begin{vmatrix} a & b & a\alpha+b \\ b & c & b\alpha+c \\ a\alpha+b & b\alpha+c & 0 \end{vmatrix} = 0$$

Applying $C_3 \to C_3 - \alpha C_1 - C_2$, then

$$\begin{vmatrix} a & b & 0 \\ b & c & 0 \\ a\alpha+b & b\alpha+c & -(a\alpha^2+2b\alpha+c) \end{vmatrix} = 0$$

Expanding along C_3, we get

$$-(a\alpha^2+2b\alpha+c)(ac-b^2)=0$$

$$\Rightarrow \quad (a\alpha^2+2b\alpha+c)(b^2-ac)=0$$

$$\Rightarrow \quad b^2-ac=0 \text{ and } a\alpha^2+2b\alpha+c=0$$

i.e. a, b and c are in GP and $(x-\alpha)$ is a factor of $ax^2+2bx+c=0$.

35. $\because \quad f(x) = \begin{vmatrix} 2\cos x & 1 & 0 \\ 1 & 2\cos x & 1 \\ 0 & 1 & 2\cos x \end{vmatrix}$

$$= 2\cos x(4\cos^2 x - 1) - 1(2\cos x - 0) + 0$$
$$= 2\cos x(4\cos^2 x - 1 - 1)$$
$$= 4\cos x(2\cos^2 x - 1)$$
$$= 4\cos x\cos 2x$$
$$= 2(\cos 3x + \cos x)$$

Option (a)

$$f\left(\frac{\pi}{3}\right) = 2\left(\cos\frac{3\pi}{3} + \cos\frac{\pi}{3}\right) = 2\left(-1+\frac{1}{2}\right) = -1$$

Option (b)

$$f'(x) = 2(-3\sin 3x - \sin x)$$

$$\therefore \quad f'\left(\frac{\pi}{3}\right) = 2\left(-3\sin\pi - \sin\frac{\pi}{3}\right) = 2\left(0-\frac{\sqrt{3}}{2}\right) = -\sqrt{3}$$

Option (c)

$$\int_0^{\pi} f(x)\,dx = 2\int_0^{\pi}(\cos 3x + \cos x)\,dx = 2\left[\frac{\sin 3x}{3} + \sin x\right]_0^{\pi}$$

$$= 2[(0+0)-(0+0)] = 0$$

Option (d)

$$\int_0^{\pi} f(x)\,dx = 2\int_{-\pi}^{\pi}(\cos 3x + \cos x)\,dx = 4\int_0^{\pi}(\cos 3x + \cos x)\,dx$$

$$= 0 \qquad \text{[from option (c)]}$$

36. $\because \Delta(x) = \begin{vmatrix} x^2-5x+3 & 2x-5 & 3 \\ 3x^3+x+4 & 6x+1 & 9 \\ 7x^2-6x+9 & 14x-6 & 21 \end{vmatrix}$

Applying $R_2 \to R_2 - 3R_1$ and $R_3 \to R_3 - 7R_1$, then

$$= \begin{vmatrix} x^2-5x+3 & 2x-5 & 3 \\ 16x-5 & 16 & 0 \\ 29x-12 & 29 & 0 \end{vmatrix}$$

Expanding along C_3, we get $= 3\begin{vmatrix} 16x-5 & 16 \\ 29x-12 & 29 \end{vmatrix}$

Applying $C_1 \to C_1 - xC_2$, then

$$\Delta(x) = 3\begin{vmatrix} -5 & 16 \\ -12 & 29 \end{vmatrix} = 3(-145+192) = 3\times 47$$

$$= 141 = ax^3+bx^2+cx+d \text{ [given]}$$

$$\therefore \quad a=0, b=0, c=0, d=141$$

37. $\because \Delta = \begin{vmatrix} a^2 & b\sin A & c\sin A \\ b\sin A & 1 & \cos A \\ c\sin A & \cos A & 1 \end{vmatrix}$

Taking common a from each R_1 and C_1, then

$$\Delta = \begin{vmatrix} 1 & \frac{b \sin A}{a} & \frac{c \sin A}{a} \\ \frac{b \sin A}{a} & 1 & \cos A \\ \frac{c \sin A}{a} & \cos A & 1 \end{vmatrix} = \begin{vmatrix} 1 & \sin B & \sin C \\ \sin B & 1 & \cos A \\ \sin C & \cos A & 1 \end{vmatrix}$$

[by sine rule]

Applying $C_2 \to C_2 - \sin B C_1$ and $C_3 \to C_3 - \sin C C_1$, then

$$\Delta = \begin{vmatrix} 1 & 0 & 0 \\ \sin B & 1 - \sin^2 B & \cos A - \sin B \sin C \\ \sin C & \cos A - \sin B \sin C & 1 - \sin^2 C \end{vmatrix}$$

Expanding along R_1, then

$$\Delta = \begin{vmatrix} \cos^2 B & \cos[\pi - (B+C)] - \sin B \sin C \\ \cos[\pi - (B+C)] - \sin B \sin C & \cos^2 C \end{vmatrix}$$

$[\because A + B + C = \pi]$

$$= \begin{vmatrix} \cos^2 B & -\cos(B+C) - \sin B \sin C \\ -\cos(B+C) - \sin B \sin C & \cos^2 C \end{vmatrix}$$

$$= \begin{vmatrix} \cos^2 B & -\cos B \cos C \\ -\cos B \cos C & \cos^2 C \end{vmatrix}$$

$$= \cos^2 B \cos^2 C - \cos^2 B \cos^2 C = 0$$

38. $\because f(a, b) = \begin{vmatrix} a & a^2 & 0 \\ 1 & (2a+b) & (a+b)^2 \\ 0 & 1 & (2a+3b) \end{vmatrix}$

Applying $C_2 \to C_2 - aC_1$, then

$$f(a, b) = \begin{vmatrix} a & 0 & 0 \\ 1 & (a+b) & (a+b)^2 \\ 0 & 1 & (2a+3b) \end{vmatrix}$$

Expanding along R_1, then

$$f(a, b) = a \begin{vmatrix} (a+b) & (a+b)^2 \\ 1 & (2a+3b) \end{vmatrix}$$

$$= a(a+b) \begin{vmatrix} 1 & (a+b) \\ 1 & (2a+3b) \end{vmatrix}$$

$$= a(a+b)(2a + 3b - a - b)$$

$$= a(a+b)(a+2b)$$

39. $\because f(x) = \begin{vmatrix} \sec^2 x & 1 & 1 \\ \cos^2 x & \cos^2 x & \operatorname{cosec}^2 x \\ 1 & \cos^2 x & \cot^2 x \end{vmatrix}$

Applying $C_2 \to C_2 - \cos^2 x\, C_1$, then

$$f(x) = \begin{vmatrix} \sec^2 x & 0 & 1 \\ \cos^2 x & \cos^2 x - \cos^4 x & \operatorname{cosec}^2 x \\ 1 & 0 & \cot^2 x \end{vmatrix}$$

Expanding along C_2, then

$$f(x) = \sin^2 x \cos^2 x \begin{vmatrix} \sec^2 x & 1 \\ 1 & \cot^2 x \end{vmatrix}$$

$$= \sin^2 x \cos^2 x (\operatorname{cosec}^2 x - 1)$$

$$= \sin^2 x \cos^2 x \cot^2 x = \cos^4 x$$

option (a)

$$\int_{-\pi/4}^{\pi/4} f(x)\, dx = \int_{-\pi/4}^{\pi/4} \cos^4 x\, dx = 2 \int_0^{\pi/4} \cos^4 x\, dx$$

$$= 2 \int_0^{\pi/4} \left(\frac{1 + \cos 2x}{2} \right)^2 dx$$

$$= 2 \times \frac{1}{2} \int_0^{\pi/2} \left(\frac{1 + \cos x}{2} \right)^2 dx$$

$$= \frac{1}{4} \int_0^{\pi/2} (1 + 2 \cos x + \cos^2 x)\, dx$$

$$= \frac{1}{4} \int_0^{\pi/2} 1 \cdot dx + \frac{1}{2} \int_0^{\pi/2} \cos x\, dx + \frac{1}{4} \int_0^{\pi/2} \cos^2 x\, dx$$

$$= \frac{1}{4} \left(\frac{\pi}{2} - 0 \right) + \frac{1}{2} (\sin x)_0^{\pi/2} + \frac{1}{4} \cdot \frac{1}{2} \cdot \frac{\pi}{2}$$

$$= \frac{\pi}{8} + \frac{1}{2}(1 - 0) + \frac{\pi}{16} = \frac{1}{16}(2\pi + 8 + \pi) = \frac{1}{16}(3\pi + 8)$$

option (b)

$\because \quad f'(x) = 4 \cos^3 x \cdot (-\sin x)$

$\therefore \quad f'\left(\frac{\pi}{2}\right) = 0$

option (c) and (d)

$\because \quad 0 \le \cos^4 x \le 1$

$\because$ Maximum value of $f(x)$ is 1.

and minimum value of $f(x)$ is 0.

40. Let $\Delta = \begin{vmatrix} a & a + x^2 & a + x^2 + x^4 \\ 2a & 3a + 2x^2 & 4a + 3x^2 + 2x^4 \\ 3a & 6a + 3x^2 & 10a + 6x^2 + 3x^4 \end{vmatrix}$

Applying $R_2 \to R_2 - 2R_1$ and $R_3 \to R_3 - 3R_1$, then

$$\Delta = \begin{vmatrix} a & a + x^2 & a + x^2 + x^4 \\ 0 & a & 2a + x^2 \\ 0 & 3a & 7a + 3x^2 \end{vmatrix}$$

Applying $R_3 \to R_3 - 3R_2$, then

$$\Delta = \begin{vmatrix} a & a + x^2 & a + x^2 + x^4 \\ 0 & a & 2a + x^2 \\ 0 & 0 & a \end{vmatrix}$$

$$= a^3 = a_0 + a_1 x + a_2 x^2 + a_3 x^3 + a_4 x^4 + a_5 x^5 + a_6 x^6 + a_7 x^7 \quad \text{[given]}$$

$\therefore\ a_0 = a^3, a_1 = 0, a_2 = 0, a_3 = 0, a_4 = 0, a_5 = 0, a_6 = 0, a_7 = 0$

and $\quad f(x) = a_0 x^2 + a_3 x + a_6 = a^3 x^2$

option (a) $f(x) \geq 0 \Rightarrow a^3 x^2 \geq 0$

If $a^3 > 0$, then $x^2 \geq 0$

$\therefore \quad a > 0, x \in R$

option (b) If $a = 0$, then $f(x) = 0$

and $\quad$ If $x = 0$, then $f(x) = 0$

$\therefore$ Aliter (b) is fail

option (c) $f(x) = 0$

$\Rightarrow \quad a^3 x^2 = 0$ or $x^2 = 0$

$\therefore \quad x = 0, 0$

option (d) For $a = 0$, $f(x) = 0$ is an identity, then it has more than two roots.

41. Let $\Delta(x) = \begin{vmatrix} 4x - 4 & (x-2)^2 & x^3 \\ 8x - 4\sqrt{2} & (x - 2\sqrt{2})^2 & (x+1)^3 \\ 12x - 4\sqrt{3} & (x - 2\sqrt{3})^2 & (x-1)^3 \end{vmatrix}$

$$= a_0 + a_1 x + a_2 x^2 + \ldots \quad \ldots(\text{i})$$

On putting $x = 0$ in Eq. (i), then

$$\begin{vmatrix} -4 & 4 & 0 \\ -4\sqrt{2} & 8 & 1 \\ -4\sqrt{3} & 12 & -1 \end{vmatrix} = a_0$$

or $\quad a_0 = -4(-8-12) - 4(4\sqrt{2} + 4\sqrt{3})$

$= 16(5 - \sqrt{2} - \sqrt{3}) =$ term independent of x in Δ.

Also, on differentiating Eq. (i) w.r.t. x and then put $x = 0$, we get

$$\begin{vmatrix} 4 & -4 & 0 \\ -4\sqrt{2} & 8 & 1 \\ -4\sqrt{3} & 12 & -1 \end{vmatrix} + \begin{vmatrix} -4 & 4 & 0 \\ 8 & -4\sqrt{2} & 3 \\ -4\sqrt{3} & 12 & -1 \end{vmatrix} + \begin{vmatrix} -4 & 4 & 0 \\ -4\sqrt{2} & 8 & 1 \\ 12 & -4\sqrt{3} & 3 \end{vmatrix} = a_1$$

$\therefore \quad a_1 = 4(-8-12) + 4(4\sqrt{2} + 4\sqrt{3})$

$\quad - 4(4\sqrt{2} - 36) - 4(-8 + 12\sqrt{3})$

$\quad - 4(24 + 4\sqrt{3}) - 4(-12\sqrt{2} - 12)$

$= 48 + 48\sqrt{2} - 48\sqrt{3} = 48(1 + \sqrt{2} - \sqrt{3})$

$=$ Coefficient of x in $\Delta(x)$

42. $\because\ f(x) = \begin{vmatrix} 3 & 3x & 3x^2 + 2a^2 \\ 3x & 3x^2 + 2a^2 & 3x^3 + 6a^2 x \\ 3x^2 + 2a^2 & 3x^3 + 6a^2 x & 3x^4 + 12a^2 x^2 + 2a^4 \end{vmatrix}$

Applying $C_3 \to C_3 - xC_2$ and $C_2 \to C_2 - xC_1$, then

$$f(x) = \begin{vmatrix} 3 & 0 & 2a^2 \\ 3x & 2a^2 & 4a^2 x \\ 3x^2 + 2a^2 & 4a^2 x & 6a^2 x^2 + 2a^4 \end{vmatrix}$$

Applying $C_3 \to C_3 - x\,C_2$, then

$$= \begin{vmatrix} 3 & 0 & 2a^2 \\ 3x & 2a^2 & 2a^2 x \\ 3x^2 + 2a^2 & 4a^2 x & 2a^2 x^2 + 2a^4 \end{vmatrix}$$

$$= 4a^4 \begin{vmatrix} 3 & 0 & 1 \\ 3x & 1 & x \\ 3x^2 + 2a^2 & 2x & x^2 + a^2 \end{vmatrix}$$

Applying $C_1 \to C_1 - 3\,C_3$, then

$$f(x) = 4a^4 \begin{vmatrix} 0 & 0 & 1 \\ 0 & 1 & x \\ -a^2 & 2x & x^2 + a^2 \end{vmatrix}$$

Expanding along C_1, we get

$$= 4a^4 [-a^2(0-1)] = 4a^6$$

$\therefore \quad f'(x) = 0$

i.e. $y = f(x)$ is a straight line parallel to X-axis.

43. $\because a > b > c$ and given equations are

$$ax + by + cz = 0,$$
$$bx + cy + az = 0$$

and $\quad cx + ay + bz = 0$

For non-trivial solution

$$\begin{vmatrix} a & b & c \\ b & c & a \\ c & a & b \end{vmatrix} = 0$$

$\Rightarrow \quad 3abc - (a^3 + b^3 + c^3) = 0$

$\therefore \quad a + b + c = 0$

If α and β be the roots of $at^2 + bt + c = 0$

$\therefore \quad \alpha + \beta = -\dfrac{b}{a}$ and $\alpha\beta = \dfrac{c}{a}$

and $\quad D = b^2 - 4ac = (-a-c)^2 - 4ac = (a-c)^2 > 0$

For opposite sign $|\alpha - \beta| > 0$

$\Rightarrow \quad (\alpha - \beta)^2 > 0 \Rightarrow (\alpha + \beta)^2 - 4\alpha\beta > 0$

$\Rightarrow \quad \dfrac{b^2}{a^2} - \dfrac{4c}{a} > 0 \Rightarrow (-a-c)^2 - 4ac > 0$

$\Rightarrow \quad (a-c)^2 > 0$, true

Hence, the roots are real and have opposite sign.

44. Here, $\Delta = \begin{vmatrix} 1 & 1 & 1 \\ 1 & 3 & 2 \\ 1 & \lambda & 3 \end{vmatrix} = 1(9 - 2\lambda) - 1(3-2) + 1(\lambda - 3)$

$= -(\lambda - 5)$

$\Delta_1 = \begin{vmatrix} 3 & 1 & 1 \\ 6 & 3 & 2 \\ b & \lambda & 3 \end{vmatrix} = 3(9 - 2\lambda) - 1(18 - 2b) + 1(6\lambda - 3b)$

$= -(b - 9)$

$$\Delta_2 = \begin{vmatrix} 1 & 3 & 1 \\ 1 & 6 & 2 \\ 1 & b & 3 \end{vmatrix} = 1$$

$$(18 - 2b) - 3(3 - 2) + 1(b - 6) = -(b - 9)$$

and $\Delta_3 = \begin{vmatrix} 1 & 1 & 3 \\ 1 & 3 & 6 \\ 1 & \lambda & b \end{vmatrix} = 1$

$$(3b - 6\lambda) - 1(b - 6) + 3(\lambda - 3) = (2b - 3\lambda - 3)$$

Aliter (a) for unique solution $\Delta \neq 0$

i.e. $\lambda \neq 5, b \in R$

Aliter (b) for no solution

$D = 0$ and atleast one of $\Delta_1, \Delta_2, \Delta_3$ is non-zero

$\therefore \quad \lambda = 5, b \neq 9$

Aliter (c) For infinite many solution

$$\Delta = \Delta_1 = \Delta_2 = \Delta_3 = 0$$

$\therefore \quad \lambda = 5, b = 9$

45. For non-trivial solutions

$$\begin{vmatrix} \lambda & \sin\alpha & \cos\alpha \\ 1 & \cos\alpha & \sin\alpha \\ -1 & \sin\alpha & -\cos\alpha \end{vmatrix} = 0$$

Expanding along C_1, we get

$$\Rightarrow \lambda(-\cos^2\alpha - \sin^2\alpha) - 1(-\sin\alpha\cos\alpha - \sin\alpha\cos\alpha) - 1(\sin^2\alpha - \cos^2\alpha) = 0$$

$\Rightarrow \quad -\lambda + \sin 2\alpha + \cos 2\alpha = 0$

$\Rightarrow \quad \lambda = (\sin 2\alpha + \cos 2\alpha)$

$\because \quad -\sqrt{2} \leq \sin 2\alpha + \cos 2\alpha \leq \sqrt{2}$

$\therefore \quad -\sqrt{2} \leq \lambda \leq \sqrt{2}$

$\Rightarrow \quad S = [-\sqrt{2}, \sqrt{2}]$

Sol. (Q. Nos. 46 to 48)

$$\Delta = \begin{vmatrix} 1 & 1 & 1 \\ 1 & 2 & 3 \\ 1 & 3 & \lambda \end{vmatrix} = (\lambda - 5),$$

$$\Delta_1 = \begin{vmatrix} 5 & 1 & 1 \\ 9 & 2 & 3 \\ \mu & 3 & \lambda \end{vmatrix} = (\lambda + \mu - 18),$$

$$\Delta_2 = \begin{vmatrix} 1 & 5 & 1 \\ 1 & 9 & 3 \\ 1 & \mu & \lambda \end{vmatrix} = (4\lambda - 2\mu + 6)$$

and $\Delta_3 = \begin{vmatrix} 1 & 1 & 5 \\ 1 & 2 & 9 \\ 1 & 3 & \mu \end{vmatrix} = (\mu - 13)$

46. The system is smart, if

$$\Delta \neq 0 \Rightarrow \lambda \neq 5$$

or $\quad \Delta = \Delta_1 = \Delta_2 = \Delta_3 = 0$

$\Rightarrow \quad \lambda = 5$ and $\mu = 13$

47. The system is good, if

$$\Delta = \Delta_1 = \Delta_2 = \Delta_3 = 0$$

$\Rightarrow \quad \lambda = 5$ and $\mu = 13$

48. The system is lazy, if

$\Delta = 0$ and atleast one of $\Delta_1, \Delta_2, \Delta_3 \neq 0$

$\Rightarrow \quad \lambda = 5$ and $\mu \neq 13$

Sol. (Q. Nos. 49 to 51)

$$\because \begin{vmatrix} bc - a^2 & ca - b^2 & ab - c^2 \\ ca - b^2 & ab - c^2 & bc - a^2 \\ ab - c^2 & bc - a^2 & ca - b^2 \end{vmatrix} = \begin{vmatrix} a & b & c \\ b & c & a \\ c & a & b \end{vmatrix}^2 \quad \text{...(i)}$$

For $a = 1, b = x$ and $c = x^2$

$$\begin{vmatrix} x^3 - 1 & 0 & x - x^4 \\ 0 & x - x^4 & x^3 - 1 \\ x - x^4 & x^3 - 1 & 0 \end{vmatrix} = \begin{vmatrix} 1 & x & x^2 \\ x & x^2 & 1 \\ x^2 & 1 & x \end{vmatrix}^2$$

$\therefore \quad \Delta = 5^2 = 25$

49. $\because \Delta^2 = (25)^2 = 625$

Sum of digits of $\Delta^2 = 6 + 2 + 5 = 13$

50. From Eq. (i), we get

$$\begin{vmatrix} A & B & C \\ B & C & A \\ C & A & B \end{vmatrix} = \begin{vmatrix} a & b & c \\ b & c & a \\ c & a & b \end{vmatrix}^2$$

$$\Rightarrow \quad 49 = \begin{vmatrix} a & b & c \\ b & c & a \\ c & a & b \end{vmatrix}^2$$

$$\Rightarrow \quad q \begin{vmatrix} a & b & c \\ b & c & a \\ c & a & b \end{vmatrix} = \pm 7$$

$\Rightarrow -(a^3 + b^3 + c^3 - 3abc) = \pm 7$

$\Rightarrow \quad a^3 + b^3 + c^3 - 3abc = \mp 7$

$\therefore \quad a^3 + b^3 + c^3 - 3abc = 7 \quad [\because a + b + c > 0]$

51. $\because aA + bB + cC = \begin{vmatrix} a & b & c \\ b & c & a \\ c & a & b \end{vmatrix} = -(a^3 + b^3 + c^3 - 3abc)$

$$= -(-3) = 3$$

Sol. (Q. Nos. 52 to 54)

$\because \alpha + \beta + \gamma = -2, \alpha\beta + \beta\gamma + \gamma\alpha = -1$ and $\alpha\beta\gamma = 3$

52. $\begin{vmatrix} \alpha & \beta & \gamma \\ \gamma & \alpha & \beta \\ \beta & \gamma & \alpha \end{vmatrix} = -\begin{vmatrix} \alpha & \beta & \gamma \\ \beta & \gamma & \alpha \\ \gamma & \alpha & \beta \end{vmatrix} = \alpha^3 + \beta^3 + \gamma^3 - 3\alpha\beta\gamma$

$$= (\alpha + \beta + \gamma)(\alpha^2 + \beta^2 + \gamma^2 - \alpha\beta - \beta\gamma - \gamma\alpha)$$

$$= (\alpha + \beta + \gamma)[(\alpha + \beta + \gamma)^2 - 3(\alpha\beta + \beta\gamma + \gamma\alpha)]$$

$$= (-2)(4 - 9) = 10$$

53. Let $x = \dfrac{\alpha - 1}{\alpha + 2} \Rightarrow \alpha = \dfrac{2x + 1}{1 - x}$

$\because \quad \alpha$ is a root of $x^3 + 2x^2 - x - 3 = 0$

$\Rightarrow \quad \alpha^3 + 2\alpha^2 - \alpha - 3 = 0$

$$\Rightarrow \left(\frac{2x+1}{1-x}\right)^3 + 2\left(\frac{2x+1}{1-x}\right)^2 - \left(\frac{2x+1}{1-x}\right) - 3 = 0$$

$$\Rightarrow \quad x^3 + 6x^2 + 21x - 1 = 0 \quad \text{...(i)}$$

Hence, $\dfrac{\alpha-1}{\alpha+2}, \dfrac{\beta-1}{\beta+2}$ and $\dfrac{\gamma-1}{\gamma+2}$ are the roots of Eq. (i), then

$$\frac{\alpha-1}{\alpha+2} + \frac{\beta-1}{\beta+2} + \frac{\gamma-1}{\gamma+2} = -6$$

$$\therefore \quad \left|\frac{\alpha-1}{\alpha+2} + \frac{\beta-1}{\beta+1} + \frac{\gamma-1}{\gamma+2}\right| = \frac{6}{1} = \frac{m}{n}$$

$$\Rightarrow \quad m = 6 \text{ and } n = 1,$$

then $\begin{vmatrix} m & n^2 \\ m-n & m+n \end{vmatrix} = \begin{vmatrix} 6 & 1 \\ 5 & 7 \end{vmatrix} = 42 - 5 = 37$

54. $\because \begin{vmatrix} a & b & b \\ b & a & b \\ b & b & a \end{vmatrix} = \begin{vmatrix} \alpha & \beta & \gamma \\ \beta & \gamma & \alpha \\ \gamma & \alpha & \beta \end{vmatrix}^2 = (\alpha^3 + \beta^3 + \gamma^3 - 3\alpha\beta\gamma)^2$

$$= (\alpha+\beta+\gamma)^2[(\alpha+\beta+\gamma)^2 - 3(\alpha\beta+\beta\gamma+\gamma\alpha)]^2$$

$$= (-2)^2[(-2)^2 + 3]^2 = 4 \times 49 = 196$$

Sol. (Q. Nos. 55 to 57)

$$\because \; f'(x) = \begin{vmatrix} 2ax & 2ax-1 & 2ax+b+1 \\ b & b+1 & -1 \\ 2(ax+b) & 2ax+2b+1 & 2ax+b \end{vmatrix}$$

Applying $C_2 \to C_2 - C_1$ and $C_3 \to C_3 - C_1$, then

$$f'(x) = \begin{vmatrix} 2ax & -1 & b+1 \\ b & 1 & -1-b \\ 2ax+2b & 1 & -b \end{vmatrix}$$

Applying $R_3 \to R_3 - R_1$, then

$$f'(x) = \begin{vmatrix} 2ax & -1 & b+1 \\ b & 1 & -1-b \\ 2b & 2 & -2b-1 \end{vmatrix}$$

Applying $R_3 \to R_3 - 2R_2$, then

$$f'(x) = \begin{vmatrix} 2ax & -1 & b+1 \\ & & \vdots \\ b & 1 & -1-b \\ & & \vdots \\ 0 \;\cdots & 0 \;\cdots & 1 \end{vmatrix}$$

$$\Rightarrow \quad f'(x) = (2ax + b)$$

$$\therefore \quad f(x) = ax^2 + bx + c$$

$$f(0) = 2 \Rightarrow c = 2 \quad \text{...(i)}$$

and $f(1) = 1 \Rightarrow a + b + 2 = 1 \Rightarrow a + b = -1$ ...(ii)

Also, $f'\left(\dfrac{5}{2}\right) = 0 \Rightarrow 5a + b = 0$ ...(iii)

From Eqs. (ii) and (iii), we get

$$a = \frac{1}{4} \text{ and } b = -\frac{5}{4}$$

$$\therefore \quad f(x) = \frac{x^2}{4} - \frac{5x}{4} + 2$$

55. $\because f(2) + f(3) = \left(\dfrac{4}{4} - \dfrac{10}{4} + 2\right) + \left(\dfrac{9}{4} - \dfrac{15}{4} + 2\right) = 1$

56. $\because f(x) + 1 = 0 \Rightarrow \dfrac{x^2}{4} - \dfrac{5x}{4} + 3 = 0$

$$\because \quad D = \frac{25}{16} - 3 = -\frac{23}{16} < 0$$

$\therefore$ Number of solutions $= 0$

57. Minimum value of $f(x) = -\dfrac{D}{4a} = -\dfrac{-\left(\dfrac{25}{16} - 2\right)}{1} = \dfrac{7}{16}$

Hence, range of $f(x)$ is $\left[\dfrac{7}{16}, \infty\right)$

Sol. (Q. Nos. 58 to 60)

Put $x = 1$ on both sides, we get

$$\begin{vmatrix} 1 & 1 & 0 \\ 1 & 1 & 0 \\ \tan 1 & \sin^2 1 & \cos^2 1 \end{vmatrix} = a_0 \Rightarrow 0 = a_0$$

we observe that

$$a_1 = f'(1)$$

$$\text{where } f(x) = \begin{vmatrix} x & e^{x-1} & (x-1)^3 \\ x - \ln x & \cos(x-1) & (x-1)^2 \\ \tan x & \sin^2 x & \cos^2 x \end{vmatrix}$$

$$f'(x) = \begin{vmatrix} 1 & e^{x-1} & 3(x-1)^2 \\ x - \ln x & \cos(x-1) & (x-1)^2 \\ \tan x & \sin^2 x & \cos^2 x \end{vmatrix} + \begin{vmatrix} x & e^{x-1} & (x-1)^3 \\ 1 - \frac{1}{x} & -\sin(x-1) & 2(x-1) \\ \tan x & \sin^2 x & \cos^2 x \end{vmatrix} + \begin{vmatrix} x & e^{x-1} & (x-1)^3 \\ x - \ln x & \cos(x-1) & (x-1)^2 \\ \sec^2 x & \sin 2x & -\sin 2x \end{vmatrix}$$

$$\Rightarrow \quad f'(1) = \begin{vmatrix} 1 & 1 & 0 \\ 1 & 1 & 0 \\ \tan 1 & \sin^2 1 & \cos^2 1 \end{vmatrix} + \begin{vmatrix} 1 & 1 & 0 \\ 0 & 0 & 0 \\ \tan 1 & \sin^2 1 & \cos^2 1 \end{vmatrix} + \begin{vmatrix} 1 & 1 & 0 \\ 1 & 1 & 0 \\ \sec^2 1 & \sin 2 & -\sin 2 \end{vmatrix}$$

$$= 0 + 0 + 0 = 0$$

$$\therefore \quad a_1 = 0$$

58. $\cos^{-1}(a_1) = \cos^{-1}(0) = \dfrac{\pi}{2}$

59. Let $P = \lim\limits_{x \to a_0} (\sin x)^x = \lim\limits_{x \to 0} (\sin x)^x$

$\therefore \ln p = \lim\limits_{x \to 0} x \ln \sin x$ [form $(0 \times \infty)$]

$$= \lim_{x \to 0} \frac{\ln \sin x}{Yx} = \lim_{x \to 0} \frac{\cot x}{-Yx^2} \quad \text{[by } L' \text{ Hospital's Rule]}$$

$$= -\lim_{x\to 0} \frac{x^2}{\tan x} = -1 \times 0 = 0$$

$\therefore \quad P = e^0 = 1$

60. Required Equation is

$$(x - a_0)(x - a_1) = 0$$

$$\Rightarrow \quad (x-0)(x-0) = 0$$

$$\Rightarrow \quad x^2 = 0$$

Sol. (Q. Nos. 61 to 63)

Multiplying R_1, R_2, R_3 by a, b, c respectively and then taking a, b, c common from C_1, C_2, C_3, we get

$$\Delta = \begin{vmatrix} -bc & ab+ac & ac+ab \\ ab+bc & -ac & bc+ab \\ ac+bc & bc+ac & -ab \end{vmatrix}$$

Applying $C_2 \to C_2 - C_1$ and $C_3 \to C_3 - C_1$ and then taking $(ab+bc+ca)$ from C_2 and C_3, we get

$$\Delta = (ab+bc+ca)^2 \begin{vmatrix} -bc & 1 & 1 \\ ab+bc & -1 & 0 \\ ac+bc & 0 & -1 \end{vmatrix}$$

Applying $R_1 \to R_1 + R_2 + R_3$, we get

$$= (ab+bc+ca)^2 \begin{vmatrix} ab+bc+ca & \cdots & 0 & \cdots & 0 \\ \vdots & & & & \\ ab+bc & & -1 & & 0 \\ \vdots & & & & \\ ac+bc & & 0 & & -1 \end{vmatrix}$$

$$= (ab+bc+ca)^3 \begin{vmatrix} -1 & 0 \\ 0 & -1 \end{vmatrix} = (ab+bc+ca)^3$$

Also, a, b and c are the roots of

$$x^3 - px^2 + qx - r = 0$$

$\because \quad a+b+c = p,\ ab+bc+ca = q,\ abc = r$

$$\Rightarrow \quad \Delta = q^3 \qquad \text{...(i)}$$

61. $\because$ AM $\geq$ GM

$$\Rightarrow \quad \left(\frac{ab+bc+ca}{3}\right) \geq (ab \cdot bc \cdot ca)^{1/3}$$

$$\Rightarrow \quad \frac{q}{3} \geq (r^2)^{1/3} \Rightarrow q^3 \geq 27r^2$$

or $\quad \Delta \geq 27r^2 \qquad$ [from Eq. (i)]

62. $\because$ a, b and c are in GP.

$\therefore \quad mb^2 = ac \Rightarrow b^3 = abc = r \Rightarrow b = r^{1/3}$

and b is a root of $x^3 - px^2 + qx - r = 0$

$$\Rightarrow \quad b^3 - pb^2 + qb - r = 0$$

$$\Rightarrow \quad r - pr^{2/3} + qr^{1/3} - r = 0$$

$$\Rightarrow \quad p^3r^2 = q^3r$$

$$\therefore \quad q^3 = p^3r$$

63. $\because \quad \Delta = 27 \Rightarrow q^3 = 27$

$\therefore \quad q = 3$

or $\quad ab+bc+ca = 3$ and $a^2+b^2+c^2 = 2$

$$\therefore \quad \sum a^2b = a^2b + a^2c + b^2a + b^2c + c^2a + c^2b$$

$$= (a+b+c)(ab+bc+ca) - 3abc$$

$$= 3p - 3r$$

$$= 6\sqrt{2} - 3r$$

$[\because (a+b+c)^2 = a^2+b^2+c^2+2(ab+bc+ca)]$

$$= 3(2\sqrt{2} - r) \qquad [\therefore p^2 = 8 \Rightarrow p = 2\sqrt{2}]$$

Sol. (Q. Nos. 64 to 66)

Taking a, b, c common from R_1, R_2, R_3 respectively and then multiplying by a, b, c is C_1, C_2, C_3 respectively, we get

$$\Delta_n = \begin{vmatrix} a^2+n & b^2 & c^2 \\ a^2 & b^2+n & c^2 \\ a^2 & b^2 & c^2+n \end{vmatrix}$$

Applying $C_1 \to C_1 + C_2 + C_3$, then

$$\Delta_n = \begin{vmatrix} n+a^2+b^2+c^2 & b^2 & c^2 \\ n+a^2+b^2+c^2 & b^2+n & c^2 \\ n+a^2+b^2+c^2 & b^2 & c^2+n \end{vmatrix}$$

Applying $R_2 \to R_2 - R_1$ and $R_3 \to R_3 - R_1$, then

$$\Delta_n = \begin{vmatrix} n+a^2+b^2+c^2 & b^2 & c^2 \\ 0 & n & 0 \\ 0 & 0 & n \end{vmatrix}$$

$$\Delta_n = n^3 + n^2(a^2+b^2+c^2) \qquad \text{...(i)}$$

Also, $a+b+c = \lambda$

$$3b = \lambda \qquad [\because a, b, c \text{ are in AP}]$$

$$\therefore \quad b = \frac{\lambda}{3}$$

Also, b is root of $x^3 - \lambda x^2 + 11x - 6 = 0$

$$\Rightarrow \quad b^3 - \lambda b^2 + 11b - 6 = 0$$

$$\Rightarrow \quad \frac{\lambda^3}{27} - \frac{\lambda^3}{9} + \frac{11\lambda}{3} - 6 = 0$$

$$\Rightarrow \quad 2\lambda^3 - 99\lambda + 162 = 0$$

$$\because \quad \lambda = 6$$

Then, equation becomes $x^3 - 6x^2 + 11x - 6 = 0$

$\therefore \quad x = 1, 2, 3$

Let $\quad a = 1, b = 2$ and $c = 3$

From Eq. (i), we get

$$\Delta_n = n^3 + 14n^2$$

$$\therefore \quad \sum_{n=1}^{n} \Delta_n = \frac{n(n+1)(3n^2+59n+28)}{12}$$

64. $\displaystyle\sum_{r=1}^{7} \Delta_r = \frac{7 \cdot 8(147 + 59 \cdot 7 + 28)}{12} = (14)^3$

65. $\dfrac{\Delta_{2n}}{\Delta_n} = \dfrac{8(n+7)}{(n+14)} < 8$

$$\therefore \quad \frac{\Delta_{2n}}{\Delta_n} < 8$$

66. $\because$ $$\Delta_r = r^3 + 14r^2$$

$\therefore$ $$\frac{27\Delta_r - \Delta_{3r}}{27r^2} = \frac{28}{3}$$

$\Rightarrow$ $$\sum_{r=1}^{30}\left(\frac{27\Delta_r - \Delta_{3r}}{27r^2}\right) = \frac{28}{3} \times 30 = 280$$

67. We have, $$\begin{vmatrix} 3^2 + k & 4^2 & 3^2 + 3 + k \\ 4^2 + k & 5^2 & 4^2 + 4 + k \\ 5^2 + k & 6^2 & 5^2 + 5 + k \end{vmatrix} = 0$$

Applying $C_3 \to C_3 - C_1$, then

$$\begin{vmatrix} 3^2 + k & 4^2 & 3 \\ 4^2 + k & 5^2 & 4 \\ 5^2 + k & 6^2 & 5 \end{vmatrix} = 0$$

Applying $R_2 \to R_2 - R_1$ and $R_3 \to R_3 - R_1$, then

$$\begin{vmatrix} 9 + k & 16 & 3 \\ 7 & 9 & 1 \\ 16 & 20 & 2 \end{vmatrix} = 0$$

$\Rightarrow$ $(9 + k)(18 - 20) - 16(14 - 16) + 3(140 - 144) = 0$

$\Rightarrow$ $-18 - 2k + 32 - 12 = 0 \Rightarrow 2k = 2$

$\therefore$ $k = 1$

Now, $\sqrt{2^k\sqrt{2^k\sqrt{2^k}}\ldots\infty} = (2^k)^{\frac{1}{2}+\frac{1}{4}+\frac{1}{8}+\ldots+\infty}$

$$= (2^k)^{\frac{\frac{1}{2}}{1-\frac{1}{2}}} = 2^k = 2^1 = 2$$

68. We have, $$\begin{vmatrix} x - 1 & -6 & 2 \\ -6 & x - 2 & -4 \\ 2 & -4 & x - 6 \end{vmatrix} = 0$$

Applying $C_2 \to C_2 + 3C_3$, then

$$\begin{vmatrix} x - 1 & 0 & 2 \\ -6 & x - 14 & -4 \\ 2 & 3x - 22 & x - 6 \end{vmatrix} = 0$$

Expanding along R_1, then

$(x - 1)\{(x - 14)(x - 6) + 4(3x - 22)\} - 0 + 2$

$\{-18x + 132 - 2x + 2\} = 0$

$\Rightarrow$ $(x - 1)(x^2 - 8x - 4) + 2(-20x + 160) = 0$

$\Rightarrow$ $x^3 - 9x^2 - 36x + 324 = 0$

$\Rightarrow$ $(x - 9)(x - 6)(x + 6) = 0$

$\therefore$ $x = 9$ or 6 or -6

Now, let $\alpha = 9, \beta = 6, \gamma = -6$

$\therefore$ $$\frac{1}{\alpha} + \frac{1}{\beta} + \frac{1}{\gamma} = \frac{1}{9} + \frac{1}{6} - \frac{1}{6} = \frac{1}{9}$$

$\therefore$ $$\left(\frac{1}{\alpha} + \frac{1}{\beta} + \frac{1}{\gamma}\right)^{-1} = 9$$

69. We have, $$\begin{vmatrix} x & e^{x-1} & (x-1)^3 \\ x - \ln x & \cos(x-1) & (x-1)^2 \\ \tan x & \sin^2 x & \cos^2 x \end{vmatrix}$$

$$= a_0 + a_1(x-1) + a_2(x-1)^2 + \ldots + a_n(x-1)^n \quad \ldots(i)$$

On putting $x = 1$ in Eq. (i), we get

$$\begin{vmatrix} 1 & 1 & 0 \\ 1 & 1 & 0 \\ \tan 1 & \sin^2 1 & \cos^2 1 \end{vmatrix} = a_0 + 0 + 0 + \ldots$$

$\therefore$ $a_0 = 0$ [$\because R_1$ and R_2 an identical]

On differentiating Eq. (i) both sides w.r.t. x, then

$$\begin{vmatrix} 1 & e^{x-1} & 3(x-1)^2 \\ x - \ln x & \cos(x-1) & (x-1)^2 \\ \tan x & \sin^2 x & \cos^2 x \end{vmatrix} + \begin{vmatrix} x & e^{x-1} & (x-1)^3 \\ \left(1 - \frac{1}{x}\right) & -\sin(x-1) & 2(x-1) \\ \tan x & \sin^2 x & \cos^2 x \end{vmatrix} + \begin{vmatrix} x & e^{x-1} & (x-1)^3 \\ x - \ln x & \cos(x-1) & (x-1)^2 \\ \sec^2 x & \sin 2x & -\sin 2x \end{vmatrix}$$

$$= 0 + a_1 + 2a_2(x-1) + 3a_3(x-1)^2 + \ldots + na_n(x-1)^{n-1}$$

Now, on putting $x = 1$, we get

$$\begin{vmatrix} 1 & 1 & 0 \\ 1 & 1 & 0 \\ \tan 1 & \sin^2 1 & \cos^2 1 \end{vmatrix} + \begin{vmatrix} 1 & 1 & 0 \\ 0 & 0 & 0 \\ \tan 1 & \sin^2 1 & \cos^2 1 \end{vmatrix} + \begin{vmatrix} 1 & 1 & 0 \\ 1 & 1 & 0 \\ \sec^2 1 & \sin 2 & -\sin 2 \end{vmatrix}$$

$$= a_1 + 0 + 0 + \ldots + 0$$

$\therefore a_1 = 0 + 0 + 0 = 0$

Hence, $(2^{a_0} + 3^{a_1})^{a_1 + 1} = (2^0 + 3^0)^{0+1} = (1 + 1)^1 = 2^1 = 2$

70. Given, $$\begin{vmatrix} 1 & \cos\alpha & \cos\beta \\ \cos\alpha & 1 & \cos\gamma \\ \cos\beta & \cos\gamma & 1 \end{vmatrix} = \begin{vmatrix} 0 & \cos\alpha & \cos\beta \\ \cos\alpha & 0 & \cos\gamma \\ \cos\beta & \cos\gamma & 0 \end{vmatrix}$$

$\Rightarrow$ $1(1 - \cos^2\gamma) - \cos\alpha(\cos\alpha - \cos\beta\cos\gamma)$

$+ \cos\beta(\cos\gamma\cos\alpha - \cos\beta)$

$= 0 - \cos\alpha(0 - \cos\beta\cos\gamma) + \cos\beta(\cos\gamma\cos\alpha - 0)$

$\Rightarrow$ $1 - \cos^2\alpha - \cos^2\beta - \cos^2\gamma$

$+ 2\cos\alpha\cos\beta\cos\gamma = 2\cos\alpha\cos\beta\cos\gamma$

$\Rightarrow$ $1 - \cos^2\alpha - \cos^2\beta - \cos^2\gamma = 0$

Hence, $\cos^2\alpha + \cos^2\beta + \cos^2\gamma = 1$

71. $\because$ $$f(a, b, c) = \begin{vmatrix} (b + c)^2 & a^2 & a^2 \\ b^2 & (c + a)^2 & b^2 \\ c^2 & c^2 & (a + b)^2 \end{vmatrix}$$

Applying $C_2 \to C_2 - C_1$ and $C_3 \to C_3 - C_1$, then

$$f(a,b,c) = \begin{vmatrix} (b+c)^2 & a^2-(b+c)^2 & a^2-(b+c)^2 \\ b^2 & (c+a)^2-b^2 & 0 \\ c^2 & 0 & (a+b)^2-c^2 \end{vmatrix}$$

$$= \begin{vmatrix} (b+c)^2 & (a+b+c)(a-b-c) & (a+b+c)(a-b-c) \\ b^2 & (c+a+b)(c+a-b) & 0 \\ c^2 & 0 & (a+b+c)(a+b-c) \end{vmatrix}$$

$$= (a+b+c)^2 \begin{vmatrix} (b+c)^2 & a-b-c & a-b-c \\ b^2 & c+a-b & 0 \\ c^2 & 0 & a+b-c \end{vmatrix}$$

Applying $R_1 \to R_1 - (R_2 + R_3)$, then

$$f(a,b,c) = (a+b+c)^2 \begin{vmatrix} 2bc & -2c & -2b \\ b^2 & c+a-b & 0 \\ c^2 & 0 & a+b-c \end{vmatrix}$$

Applying $C_2 \to C_2 + \frac{1}{b} C_1$ and $C_3 \to C_3 + \frac{1}{c} C_1$, then

$$f(a,b,c) = (a+b+c)^2 \begin{vmatrix} 2bc & 0 & 0 \\ b^2 & c+a & \frac{b^2}{c} \\ c^2 & \frac{c^2}{b} & a+b \end{vmatrix}$$

Expanding along R_1, then

$$f(a,b,c) = (a+b+c)^2 [2bc\,\{(c+a)(a+b) - bc\}]$$
$$= (a+b+c)^2 \{2bc\,(ac+bc+a^2+ab-bc)\}$$
$$= 2bc\,(a+b+c)^2\, a\,(a+b+c)$$
$$= 2abc\,(a+b+c)^3$$

We get, greatest integer $n \in N$ such that $(a+b+c)^n$ divides $f(a,b,c)$ is 3.

72. The system of equations has a non-trivial solution, then

$$\begin{vmatrix} 1 & -\sin\theta & -\cos\theta \\ -\cos\theta & 1 & -1 \\ -\sin\theta & -1 & 1 \end{vmatrix} = 0$$

Applying $C_3 \to C_3 + C_2$, then

$$\begin{vmatrix} 1 & -\sin\theta & -\sin\theta-\cos\theta \\ -\cos\theta & 1 & 0 \\ -\sin\theta & -1 & 0 \end{vmatrix} = 0$$

Expanding along C_3, then

$$(-\sin\theta - \cos\theta)(\cos\theta + \sin\theta) = 0$$
$$\Rightarrow \quad (\sin\theta + \cos\theta)^2 = 0$$
$$\Rightarrow \quad \sin\theta + \cos\theta = 0$$
$$\Rightarrow \quad \sin\theta = -\cos\theta$$
$$\therefore \quad \tan\theta = -1$$

$$\Rightarrow \quad \theta = \frac{3\pi}{4} \qquad [\because \theta \in [0, \pi$$

Hence, $\dfrac{8\theta}{\pi} = 6$

73. Let
$$\Delta = \begin{vmatrix} 1 & 1 & 1 & 1 \\ 1 & 2 & 3 & 4 \\ 1 & 3 & 6 & 10 \\ 1 & 4 & 10 & 20 \end{vmatrix}$$

Applying $R_2 \to R_2 - R_1$, $R_3 \to R_3 - R_1$ and $R_4 \to R_4 - R_1$, then

$$\Delta = \begin{vmatrix} 1 & 1 & 1 & 1 \\ 0 & 1 & 2 & 3 \\ 0 & 2 & 5 & 9 \\ 0 & 3 & 9 & 19 \end{vmatrix}$$

Expanding along C_1, then $\Delta = \begin{vmatrix} 1 & 2 & 3 \\ 2 & 5 & 9 \\ 3 & 9 & 19 \end{vmatrix}$

Applying $R_2 \to R_2 - 2R_1$ and $R_3 \to R_3 - R_1$, then $= \begin{vmatrix} 1 & 2 & 3 \\ 0 & 1 & 3 \\ 0 & 3 & 10 \end{vmatrix}$

Expanding along C_1, we get $\Delta = 1 \begin{vmatrix} 1 & 3 \\ 3 & 10 \end{vmatrix} = 10 - 9 = 1$

74. Let $\Delta = \begin{vmatrix} 1+a & 1 & 1 & 1 \\ 1 & 1+b & 1 & 1 \\ 1 & 1 & 1+c & 1 \\ 1 & 1 & 1 & 1+d \end{vmatrix}$

Taking a, b, c, d common from R_1, R_2, R_3 and R_4 respectively then

$$\Delta = abcd \begin{vmatrix} 1+\frac{1}{a} & \frac{1}{a} & \frac{1}{a} & \frac{1}{a} \\ \frac{1}{b} & 1+\frac{1}{b} & \frac{1}{b} & \frac{1}{b} \\ \frac{1}{c} & \frac{1}{c} & 1+\frac{1}{c} & \frac{1}{c} \\ \frac{1}{d} & \frac{1}{d} & \frac{1}{d} & 1+\frac{1}{d} \end{vmatrix}$$

Applying $R_1 \to R_1 + R_2 + R_3 + R_4$ and taking $\left(1 + \frac{1}{a} + \frac{1}{b} + \frac{1}{c} + \frac{1}{d}\right)$ common, we get

$$\Delta = abcd\left(1 + \frac{1}{a} + \frac{1}{b} + \frac{1}{c} + \frac{1}{d}\right) \begin{vmatrix} 1 & 1 & 1 & 1 \\ \frac{1}{b} & 1+\frac{1}{b} & \frac{1}{b} & \frac{1}{b} \\ \frac{1}{c} & \frac{1}{c} & 1+\frac{1}{c} & \frac{1}{c} \\ \frac{1}{d} & \frac{1}{d} & \frac{1}{d} & 1+\frac{1}{d} \end{vmatrix}$$

Applying $C_2 \to C_2 - C_1$, $C_3 \to C_3 - C_1$ and $C_4 \to C_4 - C_1$, then

$$\Delta = abcd\left(1+\frac{1}{a}+\frac{1}{b}+\frac{1}{c}+\frac{1}{d}\right)\begin{vmatrix} 1 & 0 & 0 & 0 \\ \frac{1}{b} & 1 & 0 & 0 \\ \frac{1}{c} & 0 & 1 & 0 \\ \frac{1}{d} & 0 & 0 & 1 \end{vmatrix}$$

$$= abcd\left(1+\frac{1}{a}+\frac{1}{b}+\frac{1}{c}+\frac{1}{d}\right)1\cdot 1\cdot 1$$

$$= abcd + (bcd + acd + abd + abc) = \sigma_4 + \sigma_3$$

$$= \frac{16}{1} + \left(-\frac{8}{1}\right) = 8$$

75. Given, $\begin{vmatrix} 1+a & 1 & 1 \\ 1+b & 1+2b & 1 \\ 1+c & 1+c & 1+3c \end{vmatrix} = 0$

Taking a, b, c common from R_1, R_2 and R_3 respectively, then

$$abc\begin{vmatrix} 1+\frac{1}{a} & \frac{1}{a} & \frac{1}{a} \\ 1+\frac{1}{b} & 2+\frac{1}{b} & \frac{1}{b} \\ 1+\frac{1}{c} & 1+\frac{1}{c} & 3+\frac{1}{c} \end{vmatrix} = 0$$

Applying $R_1 \to R_1 + R_2 + R_3$ and taking $\left(3+\frac{1}{a}+\frac{1}{b}+\frac{1}{c}\right)$ common, we get

$$abc\left(3+\frac{1}{a}+\frac{1}{b}+\frac{1}{c}\right)\begin{vmatrix} 1 & 1 & 1 \\ 1+\frac{1}{b} & 2+\frac{1}{b} & \frac{1}{b} \\ 1+\frac{1}{c} & 1+\frac{1}{c} & 3+\frac{1}{c} \end{vmatrix} = 0$$

Applying $C_2 \to C_2 - C_1$ and $C_3 \to C_3 - C_1$, then

$$abc\left(3+\frac{1}{a}+\frac{1}{b}+\frac{1}{c}\right)\begin{vmatrix} 1 & 0 & 0 \\ 1+\frac{1}{2} & 1 & -1 \\ 1+\frac{1}{c} & 0 & 2 \end{vmatrix} = 0$$

Expanding along R_1, we get

$$2\,abc\left(3+\frac{1}{a}+\frac{1}{b}+\frac{1}{c}\right) = 0$$

$\because \quad a \neq 0, b \neq 0, c \neq 0$

$\therefore \quad \frac{1}{a}+\frac{1}{b}+\frac{1}{c} = -3$ or $|a^{-1}+b^{-1}+c^{-1}| = 3$

76. Given equations

$$ax + hy + g = 0, \quad \text{...(i)}$$

$$hx + by + f = 0 \quad \text{...(ii)}$$

and $ax^2 + 2hxy + by^2 + 2gx + 2fy + c + \lambda = 0$ ...(iii)

Eq. (iii), can be written as

$$x(ax + hy + g) + y(hx + by + f) + gx + fy + c + \lambda = 0$$

$\Rightarrow \quad x \cdot 0 + y \cdot 0 + gx + fy + c + \lambda = 0$ [from Eqs. (i) and (ii)]

$\Rightarrow \quad gx + fy + c + \lambda = 0$ ...(iv)

According to the question Eqs. (i), (ii) and (iii) has unique solution. So, Eqs. (i), (ii) and (iv) has unique solution,

then $\begin{vmatrix} a & h & g \\ h & b & f \\ g & f & c+\lambda \end{vmatrix} = 0$

$\Rightarrow \quad a(bc + b\lambda - f^2) - h(ch + h\lambda - fg) + g(hf - bg)$

$\Rightarrow \quad (abc + 2fgh - af^2 - bg^2 - ch^2) = \lambda(h^2 - ab)$

or $\quad \frac{abc + 2fgh - af^2 - bg^2 - ch^2}{h^2 - ab} = \lambda$

According to the question, $\lambda = 8$

77. (A) → (p, r); (B) → (p, r); (C) → (p, q, s, t)

(A) Using $a^2 + b^2 + c^2 = 0$, we get

$$\Delta = \begin{vmatrix} b^2+c^2 & ab & ac \\ ab & c^2+a^2 & bc \\ ac & bc & a^2+b^2 \end{vmatrix} = \begin{vmatrix} -a^2 & ab & ac \\ ab & -b^2 & bc \\ ac & bc & -c^2 \end{vmatrix}$$

$$= abc\begin{vmatrix} -a & a & a \\ b & -b & b \\ c & c & -c \end{vmatrix}$$

[taking a, b, c common from C_1, C_2, C_3 respectively]

Applying $C_2 \to C_2 + C_1$ and $C_3 \to C_3 + C_1$, then

$$\Delta = abc\begin{vmatrix} -a & 0 & 0 \\ b & 0 & 2b \\ c & 2c & 0 \end{vmatrix}$$

$$= (abc)(-a)(-4bc) = 4a^2b^2c^2$$

$\therefore \quad \lambda = 4$

(B) Let $\quad \Delta = \begin{vmatrix} a & a+b & a+b+c \\ 2a & 5a+2b & 7a+5b+2c \\ 3a & 7a+3b & 9a+7b+3c \end{vmatrix}$

Applying $R_2 \to R_2 - 2R_1$ and $R_3 \to R_3 - 3R_1$, then

$$\Delta = \begin{vmatrix} a & a+b & a+b+c \\ 0 & 3a & 5a+3b \\ 0 & 4a & 6a+4b \end{vmatrix}$$

$$= a\begin{vmatrix} 3a & 5a+3b \\ 4a & 6a+4b \end{vmatrix}$$

$$= a(18a^2 + 12ab - 20a^2 - 12ab)$$

$$= -2a^3 = -1024 \quad \text{[given]}$$

$\Rightarrow \quad a^3 = 512 = 8^3$

$\therefore \quad a = 8$

(C) Let $\Delta(x)=\begin{vmatrix} x-1 & 2x^2-5 & x^3-1 \\ 2x^2+5 & 2x+2 & x^3+3 \\ x^3-1 & x+1 & 3x^2-2 \end{vmatrix}$ ...(i)

According to the question,

$\Delta(x)=(x^2-1)\,P(x)+ax+b$ ...(ii)

$\therefore\ \Delta(1)=a+b$ and $\Delta(-1)=-a+b$

From Eq. (i), we get

$$\Delta(1)=\begin{vmatrix} 0 & 3 & 0 \\ 7 & 4 & 4 \\ 0 & 2 & 1 \end{vmatrix}=3(7-0)=21$$

$$\text{and } \Delta(-1)=\begin{vmatrix} -2 & -3 & 2 \\ 7 & 0 & 2 \\ -2 & 0 & 1 \end{vmatrix}=3(7+4)=33$$

From Eq. (ii), $a+b=21$ and $-a+b=33$,

we get $a=-6,\ b=27$

$\therefore\ \ 4a+2b=-24+54=30$

78. (A) → (p, s, t); (B) → (r, t); (C) → (p, q)

(A) $\because\ \Delta=\begin{vmatrix} 1 & 1 & 1 \\ f_1(x_1) & f_1(x_2) & f_1(x_3) \\ f_2(x_1) & f_2(x_2) & f_2(x_3) \end{vmatrix}=\begin{vmatrix} 1 & 1 & 1 \\ f_1(2) & f_1(3) & f_1(5) \\ f_2(2) & f_2(3) & f_2(5) \end{vmatrix}$

$$=\begin{vmatrix} 1 & 1 & 1 \\ 2+a_1 & 3+a_1 & 5+a_1 \\ 4+2b_1+b_2 & 9+3b_1+b_2 & 25+5b_1+b_2 \end{vmatrix}$$

Applying $C_2\to C_2-C_1$ and $C_3\to C_3-C_1$, then

$$\Delta=\begin{vmatrix} 1 & 0 & 0 \\ 2+a_1 & 1 & 3 \\ 4+2b_1+b_2 & 5+b_1 & 21+3b_1 \end{vmatrix}$$

$$=\begin{vmatrix} 1 & 3 \\ 5+b_1 & 21+3b_1 \end{vmatrix}$$

$=21+3b_1-15-3b_1=6$

(B) $\because\ f(x)=\begin{vmatrix} 1 & b_1 & a_1 \\ 1 & b_1 & 2a_1-x \\ 1 & 2b_1-x & a_1 \end{vmatrix}$

Applying $R_2\to R_2-R_1$ and $R_3\to R_3-R_1$, then

$$f(x)=\begin{vmatrix} 1 & b_1 & a_1 \\ 0 & 0 & a_1-x \\ 0 & b_1-x & 0 \end{vmatrix}$$

$=-(a_1-x)(b_1-x)=-x^2+(a_1+b_1)x-a_1\,b_1$

Minimum value of $f(x)=-\dfrac{D}{4a}=-\dfrac{(a_1+b_1)^2-4a_1b_1}{4(-1)}$

$=\dfrac{(a_1-b_1)^2}{4}=\dfrac{36}{4}=9$

(C) $\because\ f(x)$ is a polynomial of degree atmost 6 in x.

If $f(x)=a_0+a_1x+a_2x^2+a_3x^3+a_4x^4+a_5x^5+a_6x^6$

$\Rightarrow \lambda=a_1=f'(0)$

$$=\begin{vmatrix} 1 & 1 & 0 \\ 1 & 0 & 1 \\ 1 & 1 & 8 \end{vmatrix}+\begin{vmatrix} -2 & -2 & 0 \\ -1 & 0 & 1 \\ 0 & 2 & 8 \end{vmatrix}+\begin{vmatrix} -2 & 1 & 0 \\ -1 & 0 & 3 \\ 0 & 1 & 12 \end{vmatrix}$$

$=-8-12+18=-2$

$\therefore\ \ |\lambda|=2$

79. (A) → (r); (B) → (r, t); (C) → (p, q, s)

(A) Let $f(x)=\begin{vmatrix} x^2+3x & x-1 & x+3 \\ x^2+1 & 2+3x & x-3 \\ x^2-3 & x+4 & 3x \end{vmatrix}$

$f(x)=ax^4+bx^3+cx^2+dx+e$ ...(i)

$$\therefore\ \ e=f(0)=\begin{vmatrix} 0 & -1 & 3 \\ 1 & 2 & -3 \\ -3 & 4 & 0 \end{vmatrix}=0+1(0-9)+3(4+6)=21$$

Dividing both sides of Eq. (i) by x^4 i.e., C_1 by x^2, C_2 by x and C_3 by x and then taking $\lim\limits_{x\to\infty}$, we get

$$a=\begin{vmatrix} 1 & 1 & 1 \\ 1 & 3 & 1 \\ 1 & 1 & 3 \end{vmatrix}=1(8)-1(2)+1(-2)=4$$

Hence, $e+a=25$

(B) Let $f(x)=\begin{vmatrix} x-1 & 5x & 7 \\ x^2-1 & x-1 & 8 \\ 2x & 3x & 0 \end{vmatrix}=ax^3+bx^2+cx+d$ ...(i)

$$\therefore\ \ c=f'(0)=\begin{vmatrix} 1 & 0 & 7 \\ 0 & -1 & 8 \\ 2 & 0 & 0 \end{vmatrix}+\begin{vmatrix} -1 & 5 & 7 \\ -1 & 1 & 8 \\ 0 & 3 & 0 \end{vmatrix}+\begin{vmatrix} -1 & 0 & 0 \\ -1 & -1 & 0 \\ 0 & 0 & 0 \end{vmatrix}$$

$=2(0+7)-3(-8+7)+0=17$

Dividing both sides of Eq. (i) by x^3 i.e., c_1 by x^2, c_2 by x and taking $\lim\limits_{x\to\infty}$, we get

$$a=\begin{vmatrix} 0 & 5 & 7 \\ 1 & 1 & 8 \\ 0 & 3 & 0 \end{vmatrix}=-1(0-21)=21$$

Hence, $c+a-3=35$

(C) Let $g(x)=\begin{vmatrix} x^3+4x & x+3 & x-2 \\ x-2 & 5x & x-1 \\ x-3 & x+2 & 4x \end{vmatrix}$

$=ax^5+bx^4+cx^3+dx^2+ex+f$

$$\therefore\ f = g(0) = \begin{vmatrix} 0 & 3 & -2 \\ -2 & 0 & -1 \\ -3 & 2 & 0 \end{vmatrix} = 0 - 3(0-3) - 2(-4-0) = 17$$

$$\text{and } e = g'(0) = \begin{vmatrix} 4 & 3 & -2 \\ 1 & 0 & -1 \\ 1 & 2 & 0 \end{vmatrix} + \begin{vmatrix} 0 & 1 & -2 \\ -2 & 5 & -1 \\ -3 & 1 & 0 \end{vmatrix} + \begin{vmatrix} 0 & 3 & 1 \\ -2 & 0 & 1 \\ -3 & 2 & 4 \end{vmatrix}$$

$$= 1 - 23 + 11 = -11$$

Hence, $f + e = 17 - 11 = 6$

80. (A) → (p, q, r); (B) → (p, q, r, s, t); (C) → (p, q, r, s, t)

(A) Taking common a, b, c from R_1, R_2 and R_3 respectively and then multiplying in C_1, C_2 and C_3 by a, b, c respectively, then

$$\Delta = \begin{vmatrix} a+(b^2+c^2)d & b^2(1-d) & c^2(1-d) \\ a^2(1-d) & b^2+(c^2+a^2)d & c^2(1-d) \\ a^2(1-d) & b^2(1-d) & c^2+(a^2+b^2)d \end{vmatrix}$$

Applying $C_1 \to C_1 + C_2 + C_3$, then

$$\Delta = \begin{vmatrix} 1 & b^2(1-d) & c^2(1-d) \\ 1 & b^2+(c^2+a^2)d & c^2(1-d) \\ 1 & b^2(1-d) & c^2+(a^2+b^2)d \end{vmatrix}$$

$[\because a^2 + b^2 + c^2 = 1]$

Applying $R_2 \to R_2 - R_1$ and $R_3 \to R_3 - R_1$, then

$$\Delta = \begin{vmatrix} 1 & b^2(1-d) & c^2(1-d) \\ 0 & d & 0 \\ 0 & 0 & d \end{vmatrix} = d^2$$

$[\because a^2 + b^2 + c^2 = 1]$

(B) Multiplying C_1 by a, C_2 by b and C_3 by c, then

$$\Delta = \frac{1}{abc}\begin{vmatrix} \frac{a}{c} & \frac{b}{c} & -\frac{(a+b)}{c} \\ -\frac{(b+c)}{a} & \frac{b}{a} & \frac{c}{a} \\ -\frac{bd(b+c)}{ac} & \frac{bd(a+2b+c)}{ac} & -\frac{(a+b)bd}{ac} \end{vmatrix}$$

Applying $C_1 \to C_1 + C_2 + C_3$, then

$$\Delta = \frac{1}{abc}\begin{vmatrix} 0 & \frac{b}{c} & -\frac{(a+b)}{c} \\ 0 & \frac{b}{a} & \frac{c}{a} \\ 0 & \frac{bd(a+2b+c)}{ac} & -\frac{(a+b)bd}{ac} \end{vmatrix} = 0$$

(C) Applying $C_3 \to C_3 - \cos d\, C_1 - \sin d\, C_2$, then

$$\Delta = \begin{vmatrix} \sin a & \cos a & 0 \\ \sin b & \cos b & 0 \\ \sin c & \cos c & 0 \end{vmatrix} = 0$$

81. (A) → (p, r); (B) → (p, q, r, t); (C) → (p, r, s)

(A) Possible values are −2 , −1, 0, 1, 2 and numbering determinant $= 3^4 = 81$

i.e., $\begin{vmatrix} 1 & 0 \\ -1 & 1 \end{vmatrix} = 1, \begin{vmatrix} 1 & -1 \\ 0 & 0 \end{vmatrix} = 0, \begin{vmatrix} 0 & 1 \\ 1 & -1 \end{vmatrix} = -1, \begin{vmatrix} 1 & -1 \\ 1 & 1 \end{vmatrix} = 2,$

$\begin{vmatrix} -1 & 1 \\ 1 & 1 \end{vmatrix} = -2 \quad \therefore n = 5 \Rightarrow (n-1)^2 = 16$

(B) There are only three determinants of second order with negative value

$$\begin{vmatrix} 0 & 1 \\ 1 & 0 \end{vmatrix}, \begin{vmatrix} 1 & 1 \\ 1 & 0 \end{vmatrix}, \begin{vmatrix} 0 & 1 \\ 1 & 1 \end{vmatrix}$$

Number of possible determinants with elements 0 and 1 are $2^4 = 16$. Therefore, number of determinants with non-negative values is 13.

$\therefore \quad n = 13$

$\Rightarrow \quad (n-1) = 12$

(C) There are only four determinants of second order with negative value

$$\begin{vmatrix} -1 & 1 \\ 1 & 1 \end{vmatrix}, \begin{vmatrix} 1 & 1 \\ 1 & -1 \end{vmatrix}, \begin{vmatrix} -1 & -1 \\ -1 & 1 \end{vmatrix}, \begin{vmatrix} 1 & -1 \\ -1 & -1 \end{vmatrix}$$

$\therefore \quad n = 4 \Rightarrow n(n+1) = 20$

82. Statement-1

$$\Delta(r) = \begin{vmatrix} r & r+1 \\ r+3 & r+4 \end{vmatrix} = r(r+4) - (r+1)(r+3)$$

$$= (r^2 + 4r) - (r^2 + 4r + 3) = -3$$

$$\therefore \quad \sum_{r=1}^{n} \Delta(r) = \sum_{r=1}^{n} (-3)$$

$$= \underbrace{(-3) + (-3) + (-3) + \dots + (-3)}_{n \text{ times}} = -3n$$

⇒ Statement-1 is true.

Statement-2

$$\Delta(r) = \begin{vmatrix} f_1(r) & f_2(r) \\ f_3(r) & f_4(r) \end{vmatrix} = f_1(r) f_4(r) - f_2(r) f_3(r)$$

$$\therefore \quad \sum_{r=1}^{n} \Delta(r) = \sum_{r=1}^{n} [f_1(r) f_4(r) - f_2(r) f_3(r)]$$

$$= \sum_{r=1}^{n} [f_1(r) f_4(r)] - \sum_{r=1}^{n} [f_2(r) f_3(r)] \quad \text{...(i)}$$

and
$$\begin{vmatrix} \sum_{r=1}^{n} f_1(r) & \sum_{r=1}^{n} f_2(r) \\ \sum_{r=1}^{n} f_3(r) & \sum_{r=1}^{n} f_4(r) \end{vmatrix}$$

$$= \left(\sum_{r=1}^{n} f_1(r)\right)\left(\sum_{r=1}^{n} f_4(r)\right) - \left(\sum_{r=1}^{n} f_2(r)\right)\left(\sum_{r=1}^{n} f_3(r)\right) \quad \text{...(ii)}$$

From Eqs. (i) and (ii), we get $\sum_{r=1}^{n} \Delta(r) \neq \begin{vmatrix} \sum_{r=1}^{n} f_1(r) & \sum_{r=1}^{n} f_2(r) \\ \sum_{r=1}^{n} f_3(r) & \sum_{r=1}^{n} f_4(r) \end{vmatrix}$

∴ Statement-2 is false.

Hence, Statement-1 is true and Statement-2 is false.

83. $\because$ $\Delta = \begin{vmatrix} a_1 + b_1x^2 & a_1x^2 + b_1 & c_1 \\ a_2 + b_2x^2 & a_2x^2 + b_2 & c_2 \\ a_3 + b_3x^2 & a_3x^2 + b_3 & c_3 \end{vmatrix}$

$$= \begin{vmatrix} a_1 & b_1 & c_1 \\ a_2 & b_2 & c_2 \\ a_3 & b_3 & c_3 \end{vmatrix} \times \begin{vmatrix} 1 & x^2 & 0 \\ x^2 & 1 & 0 \\ 0 & 0 & 1 \end{vmatrix} \quad \text{...(i)}$$

Statement-1 If $\Delta = 0$, then

$$\begin{vmatrix} a_1 & b_1 & c_1 \\ a_2 & b_2 & c_2 \\ a_3 & b_3 & c_3 \end{vmatrix} \times \begin{vmatrix} 1 & x^2 & 0 \\ x^2 & 1 & 0 \\ 0 & 0 & 1 \end{vmatrix} = 0$$

$$\Rightarrow \begin{vmatrix} 1 & x^2 & 0 \\ x^2 & 1 & 0 \\ 0 & 0 & 1 \end{vmatrix} = 0 \Rightarrow 1 - x^4 = 0 \text{ or } x^4 = 1$$

$[\because x^2 \neq -1]$

Statement-1 is true

Now, if $\begin{vmatrix} a_1 & b_1 & c_1 \\ a_2 & b_2 & c_2 \\ a_3 & b_3 & c_3 \end{vmatrix} = 0$, then

$\Delta = 0$ [from Eq. (i)]

Statement-2 is also true.

Hence, both the statements are true but Statement-2 is not a correct explanation of Statement-1.

84. Statement-2 is always true for Statement-1

$$\cos\left(x + \frac{\pi}{4}\right) = \cos\left(\frac{\pi}{2} - \left(\frac{\pi}{4} - x\right)\right) = \sin\left(\frac{\pi}{4} - x\right)$$

$$= -\sin\left(x - \frac{\pi}{4}\right)$$

$$\cot\left(\frac{\pi}{4} + x\right) = \cot\left(\frac{\pi}{2} - \left(\frac{\pi}{4} - x\right)\right) = \tan\left(\frac{\pi}{4} - x\right)$$

$$= -\tan\left(x - \frac{\pi}{4}\right)$$

Also, $\ln\left(\frac{y}{x}\right) = -\ln\left(\frac{x}{y}\right)$

Therefore, determinant given in Statement-1 is skew-symmetric and hence its value is zero. Hence, both statements are true and Statement-2 is a correct explanation of Statement-1.

85. $\begin{vmatrix} (1+x)^{11} & (1+x)^{12} & (1+x)^{13} \\ (1+x)^{21} & (1+x)^{22} & (1+x)^{23} \\ (1+x)^{31} & (1+x)^{32} & (1+x)^{33} \end{vmatrix} = A_0 + A_1x + A_2x^2 + \dots$ [let]

On differentiating both sides w.r.t.x and then put $x = 0$, we get

$$\begin{vmatrix} 11 & 12 & 13 \\ 1 & 1 & 1 \\ 1 & 1 & 1 \end{vmatrix} + \begin{vmatrix} 1 & 1 & 1 \\ 21 & 22 & 23 \\ 1 & 1 & 1 \end{vmatrix} + \begin{vmatrix} 1 & 1 & 1 \\ 1 & 1 & 1 \\ 31 & 32 & 33 \end{vmatrix} = 0 + A_1 + 0 + 0 + \dots$$

$$\Rightarrow \quad 0 + 0 + 0 = A_1 \quad \therefore A_1 = 0$$

$\therefore$ Coefficient of x in $f(x) = 0$

Both statements are true, Statement-2 is a correct explanation of Statement-1.

86. Here, $\Delta = \begin{vmatrix} 2 & 3 \\ b & 4 \end{vmatrix} = 8 - 3b$,

$$\Delta_1 = \begin{vmatrix} a & 3 \\ 5 & 4 \end{vmatrix} = 4a - 15$$

and $\Delta_2 = \begin{vmatrix} 2 & a \\ b & 5 \end{vmatrix} = 10 - ab$

For infinite solutions, $\Delta = \Delta_1 = \Delta_2 = 0$

We get, $a = \frac{15}{4}$ and $b = \frac{8}{3}$

$\therefore$ Statement-1 is true and if lines $a_1x + b_1y + c_1 = 0$ and $a_2x + b_2y + c_2 = 0$ are parallel, then

$$\frac{a_1}{a_2} = \frac{b_1}{b_2} \neq \frac{c_1}{c_2}$$

$\therefore$ Statement-2 is true, but in Statement-1

$$\frac{2}{b} = \frac{3}{4} = \frac{a}{5}$$

$$\Rightarrow \quad \frac{3}{4} = \frac{3}{4} = \frac{3}{4}$$

[both equation are identical]

$\therefore$ Statement-2 is not a correct explanation for Statement-1.

87. $\because \begin{vmatrix} 1 & 2 & 3 \\ 4 & 5 & 6 \\ 7 & 8 & 0 \end{vmatrix} = 1(0 - 48) - 2(0 - 42) + 3(32 - 35)$

$$= -48 + 84 - 9$$
$$= 84 - 57 = 27 \neq 0$$

$\therefore$ Statement-1 is true.

Also, in given determinant neither two rows or columns are identical, Statement-2 is true, Statement-2 is not a correct explanation for Statement-1.

88. $\because$ $A88, 6B8, 86C$ are divisible by 72, then $A88 = 72\lambda$, $6B8 = 72\mu$ and $86C = 72\upsilon$, where $\lambda, \mu, \upsilon \in N$.

$$\because \begin{vmatrix} A & 6 & 8 \\ 8 & B & 6 \\ 8 & 8 & C \end{vmatrix}$$

Applying $R_3 \to R_3 + 10R_2 + 100R_1$, then

$$\begin{vmatrix} A & 6 & 8 \\ 8 & B & 6 \\ 100A + 80 + 8 & 600 + 10B + 8 & 800 + 60 + c \end{vmatrix}$$

$$= \begin{vmatrix} A & 6 & 8 \\ 8 & B & 6 \\ 72\lambda & 72\mu & 72\upsilon \end{vmatrix} = 72 \begin{vmatrix} A & 6 & 8 \\ 8 & B & 6 \\ \lambda & \mu & \upsilon \end{vmatrix} \quad \text{...(i)}$$

Now, $A88$ is also divisible by 9, then

$A + 8 + 8 = A + 16$ is divisible by 9

$\therefore$ $A = 2$

and $6B8$ is also divisible by 9, then $6 + B + 8 = B + 14$ is divisible by 9

$\therefore$ $B = 4$

From Eq. (i), we get

$$=72\begin{vmatrix} 2 & 6 & 8 \\ 8 & 2 & 6 \\ \lambda & \mu & \upsilon \end{vmatrix}=288\begin{vmatrix} 1 & 3 & 4 \\ 4 & 1 & 3 \\ \lambda & \mu & \upsilon \end{vmatrix}=288 \qquad \text{[integer]}$$

Statement-1 is true and Statement-2 is false.

89. Let $\Delta=\begin{vmatrix} b+c & c & b \\ c & c+a & a \\ b & a & a+b \end{vmatrix}$

Applying $R_1 \to R_1 - (R_2 + R_3)$, then

$$\therefore \quad \Delta=\begin{vmatrix} 0 & -2a & -2a \\ c & c+a & a \\ b & a & a+b \end{vmatrix}$$

Taking $(-2a)$ common from R_1, then

$$\Delta=(-2a)\begin{vmatrix} 0 & 1 & 1 \\ c & c+a & a \\ b & a & a+b \end{vmatrix}$$

Applying $C_2 \to C_2 - C_3$, then

$$\therefore \quad \Delta=(-2a)\begin{vmatrix} 0 & 0 & 1 \\ c & c & a \\ b & -b & a+b \end{vmatrix}$$

Expanding along R_1, we get

$$\Delta=(-2a)\cdot 1\cdot\begin{vmatrix} c & c \\ b & -b \end{vmatrix}=(-2a)(-2bc)$$

Hence, $\Delta = 4abc$

90. Let $\Delta=\begin{vmatrix} a-b-c & 2a & 2a \\ 2b & b-c-a & 2b \\ 2c & 2c & c-a-b \end{vmatrix}$

Since, the answer is $(a+b+c)^3$, we shall try to get $(a+b+c)$.

Applying $R_1 \to R_1 + R_2 + R_3$, then

$$\Delta=\begin{vmatrix} a+b+c & a+b+c & a+b+c \\ 2b & b-c-a & 2b \\ 2c & 2c & c-a-b \end{vmatrix}$$

Taking $(a+b+c)$ common from R_1, we get

$$\Delta=(a+b+c)\begin{vmatrix} 1 & 1 & 1 \\ 2b & b-c-a & 2b \\ 2c & 2c & c-a-b \end{vmatrix}$$

Applying $C_1 \to C_2 - C_1$ and $C_3 \to C_3 - C_1$

$$\therefore \quad \Delta=(a+b+c)\begin{vmatrix} 1 & 0 & 0 \\ 2b & -a-b-c & 0 \\ 2c & 0 & -c-a-b \end{vmatrix}$$

[by property, since all elements above leading diagonal are zero]

$$=(a+b+c)\cdot 1\cdot(-a-b-c)\cdot(-c-a-b)$$

Hence, $\Delta=(a+b+c)^3$

91. Let $\Delta=\begin{vmatrix} \sqrt{13}+\sqrt{3} & 2\sqrt{5} & \sqrt{5} \\ \sqrt{15}+\sqrt{26} & 5 & \sqrt{10} \\ 3+\sqrt{65} & \sqrt{15} & 5 \end{vmatrix}$

$$=\begin{vmatrix} \sqrt{3} & 2\sqrt{5} & \sqrt{5} \\ \sqrt{15} & 5 & \sqrt{10} \\ 3 & \sqrt{15} & 5 \end{vmatrix}+\begin{vmatrix} \sqrt{13} & 2\sqrt{5} & \sqrt{5} \\ \sqrt{26} & 5 & \sqrt{10} \\ \sqrt{65} & \sqrt{15} & 5 \end{vmatrix}$$

Taking common from 1st determinant $\sqrt{3}$, $\sqrt{5}$ and $\sqrt{5}$ from C_1, C_2 and C_3 respectively and taking common from 2nd determinant $\sqrt{13}$, $\sqrt{5}$ and $\sqrt{5}$ from C_1, C_3 and C_3 respectively, we get

$$=\sqrt{3}\times\sqrt{5}\times\sqrt{5}\begin{vmatrix} 1 & 2 & 1 \\ \sqrt{5} & \sqrt{5} & \sqrt{2} \\ \sqrt{3} & \sqrt{3} & \sqrt{5} \end{vmatrix}+\sqrt{13}\times\sqrt{5}\times\sqrt{5}\begin{vmatrix} 1 & 2 & 1 \\ \sqrt{2} & \sqrt{5} & \sqrt{2} \\ \sqrt{5} & \sqrt{3} & \sqrt{5} \end{vmatrix}$$

$$=\sqrt{3}\times 5\begin{vmatrix} 1 & 2 & 1 \\ \sqrt{5} & \sqrt{5} & \sqrt{2} \\ \sqrt{3} & \sqrt{3} & \sqrt{5} \end{vmatrix}+0 \qquad [\because C_1 \text{ and } C_3 \text{ are identical}]$$

$$=5\sqrt{3}\begin{vmatrix} 1 & 2 & 1 \\ \sqrt{5} & \sqrt{5} & \sqrt{2} \\ \sqrt{3} & \sqrt{3} & \sqrt{5} \end{vmatrix}$$

Applying $C_2 \to C_2 - C_1$,

then $\Delta=5\sqrt{3}\begin{vmatrix} 1 & 1 & 1 \\ \sqrt{5} & 0 & \sqrt{2} \\ \sqrt{3} & 0 & \sqrt{5} \end{vmatrix}$

Expanding along C_2, then

$$\Delta=5\sqrt{3}\cdot(-1)\begin{vmatrix} \sqrt{5} & \sqrt{2} \\ \sqrt{3} & \sqrt{5} \end{vmatrix}=-5\sqrt{3}(5-\sqrt{6})$$

$$=-25\sqrt{3}+15\sqrt{2}$$

$$=15\sqrt{2}-25\sqrt{3}$$

92. Given that, a, b and c are p th, q th and r th terms of HP $\Rightarrow \frac{1}{a}, \frac{1}{b}$ and $\frac{1}{c}$ are p th, q th and r th terms of an AP. Let A and D are the first term and common difference of AP, then

$$\frac{1}{a}=A+(p-1)D \qquad \text{...(i)}$$

$$\frac{1}{b}=A+(q-1)D \qquad \text{...(ii)}$$

$$\frac{1}{c}=A+(r-1)D \qquad \text{...(iii)}$$

Now, given determinant is

$$\Delta=\begin{vmatrix} bc & ca & ab \\ p & q & r \\ 1 & 1 & 1 \end{vmatrix}=abc\begin{vmatrix} \frac{1}{a} & \frac{1}{b} & \frac{1}{c} \\ p & q & r \\ 1 & 1 & 1 \end{vmatrix}$$

On substituting the values of $\frac{1}{a}, \frac{1}{b}$ and $\frac{1}{c}$ from Eqs. (i), (ii) and (iii) in Δ, then

$$\Delta = abc \begin{vmatrix} A+(p-1)D & A+(q-1)D & A+(r-1)D \\ p & q & r \\ 1 & 1 & 1 \end{vmatrix}$$

Applying $R_1 \to R_1 - (A-D)R_3 - DR_2$, then

$$\Delta = abc \begin{vmatrix} 0 & 0 & 0 \\ p & q & r \\ 1 & 1 & 1 \end{vmatrix} = 0$$

93. Let
$$z = \begin{vmatrix} -5 & 3+5i & \frac{3}{2}-4i \\ 3-5i & 8 & 4+5i \\ \frac{3}{2}+4i & 4-5i & 9 \end{vmatrix}$$

Then,
$$\bar{z} = \begin{vmatrix} -5 & 3-5i & \frac{3}{2}+4i \\ 3+5i & 8 & 4-5i \\ \frac{3}{2}-4i & 4+5i & 9 \end{vmatrix} \quad \text{[i.e., conjugate of } z]$$

$$= \begin{vmatrix} -5 & 3+5i & \frac{3}{2}-4i \\ 3-5i & 8 & 4+5i \\ \frac{3}{2}+4i & 4-5i & 9 \end{vmatrix}$$

[interchanging rows into columns]

$\Rightarrow \quad \bar{z} = z$

Hence, z is purely real.

94. LHS
$$= \begin{vmatrix} ah+bg & g & ab+ch \\ bf+ba & f & hb+bc \\ af+bc & c & bg+fc \end{vmatrix}$$

$$= b\begin{vmatrix} ah+bg & g & a \\ bf+ba & f & h \\ af+bc & c & g \end{vmatrix} + c\begin{vmatrix} ah+bg & g & h \\ bf+ba & f & b \\ af+bc & c & f \end{vmatrix}$$

In second determinant, applying $C_1 \to C_1 - bC_2 - aC_3$, then

$$= \begin{vmatrix} ah+bg & bg & a \\ bf+ba & bf & h \\ af+bc & bc & g \end{vmatrix} + c\begin{vmatrix} 0 & g & h \\ 0 & f & b \\ 0 & c & f \end{vmatrix}$$

In first determinant, applying $C_2 \to C_2 - C_1$, then

$$= \begin{vmatrix} ah+bg & -ah & a \\ bf+ba & -ba & h \\ af+bc & -af & q \end{vmatrix} + 0 = a\begin{vmatrix} ah+bg & a & h \\ bf+ba & h & b \\ af+bc & g & f \end{vmatrix} = \text{RHS}$$

95. Let
$$\Delta = \begin{vmatrix} 1 & 1 & 1 \\ 1+\sin A & 1+\sin B & 1+\sin C \\ \sin A+\sin^2 A & \sin B+\sin^2 B & \sin C+\sin^2 C \end{vmatrix}$$

Applying $C_2 \to C_2 - C_1$ and $C_3 \to C_3 - C_1$, then

$$\Delta = \begin{vmatrix} 1 & 0 & 0 \\ 1+\sin A & \sin B - \sin A & \sin C - \sin A \\ \sin A + \sin^2 A & (\sin B - \sin A)(\sin B + \sin A + 1) & (\sin C - \sin A)(\sin C + \sin A + 1) \end{vmatrix}$$

Expanding along R_1, then

$$\Delta = \begin{vmatrix} \sin B - \sin A & \sin C - \sin A \\ (\sin B - \sin A)(\sin B + \sin A + 1) & (\sin C - \sin A)(\sin C + \sin A + 1) \end{vmatrix}$$

$$= (\sin B - \sin A)(\sin C - \sin A)\begin{vmatrix} 1 & 1 \\ \sin B + \sin A + 1 & \sin C + \sin A + 1 \end{vmatrix}$$

$$= (\sin B - \sin A)(\sin C - \sin A)(\sin C - \sin B)$$

But, given $\Delta = 0$

$\therefore \quad (\sin B - \sin A)(\sin C - \sin A)(\sin C - \sin B) = 0$

$\therefore \quad \sin B - \sin A = 0$ or $\sin C - \sin A = 0$

or $\quad \sin C - \sin B = 0$

$\Rightarrow \quad \sin B = \sin A$ or $\sin C = \sin A$ or $\sin C = \sin B$

$B = A$ or $C = A$ or $C = B$

In all the three cases, we will have an isosceles triangle.

96. Let
$$\Delta = \begin{vmatrix} \beta\gamma & \beta\gamma' + \beta'\gamma & \beta'\gamma' \\ \gamma'\alpha & \gamma'\alpha' + \gamma'\alpha & \gamma'\alpha' \\ \alpha\beta & \alpha\beta' + \alpha'\beta & \alpha'\beta' \end{vmatrix}$$

Taking $\beta'\gamma', \gamma'\alpha'$ and $\alpha'\beta'$ common from R_1, R_2 and R_3 respectively, then

$$\Delta = (\beta'\gamma')(\gamma'\alpha')(\alpha'\beta')\begin{vmatrix} \frac{\beta}{\beta'}\frac{\gamma}{\gamma'} & \frac{\beta}{\beta'}+\frac{\gamma}{\gamma'} & 1 \\ \frac{\gamma}{\gamma'}\frac{\alpha}{\alpha'} & \frac{\gamma}{\gamma'}+\frac{\alpha}{\alpha'} & 1 \\ \frac{\alpha}{\alpha'}\frac{\beta}{\beta'} & \frac{\alpha}{\alpha'}+\frac{\beta}{\beta'} & 1 \end{vmatrix}$$

Applying $R_2 \to R_2 - R_1$ and $R_3 \to R_3 - R_1$

Then,
$$\Delta = (\alpha'\beta'\gamma')^2 \begin{vmatrix} \frac{\beta}{\beta'}\frac{\gamma}{\gamma'} & \frac{\beta}{\beta'}+\frac{\gamma}{\gamma'} & 1 \\ \frac{\gamma}{\gamma'}\left(\frac{\alpha}{\alpha'}-\frac{\beta}{\beta'}\right) & \left(\frac{\alpha}{\alpha'}-\frac{\beta}{\beta'}\right) & 0 \\ \frac{\beta}{\beta'}\left(\frac{\alpha}{\alpha'}-\frac{\gamma}{\gamma'}\right) & \left(\frac{\alpha}{\alpha'}-\frac{\gamma}{\gamma'}\right) & 0 \end{vmatrix}$$

$$= (\alpha'\beta'\gamma')^2\left(\frac{\alpha}{\alpha'}-\frac{\beta}{\beta'}\right)\left(\frac{\alpha}{\alpha'}-\frac{\gamma}{\gamma'}\right)\begin{vmatrix} \frac{\beta}{\beta'}\frac{\gamma}{\gamma'} & \frac{\beta}{\beta'}+\frac{\gamma}{\gamma'} & 1 \\ \frac{\gamma}{\gamma'} & 1 & 0 \\ \frac{\beta}{\beta'} & 1 & 0 \end{vmatrix}$$

Expanding along C_3, then

$$\Delta = (\alpha'\beta'\gamma')^2\left(\frac{\alpha}{\alpha'}-\frac{\beta}{\beta'}\right)\left(\frac{\alpha}{\alpha'}-\frac{\gamma}{\gamma'}\right)\left(\frac{\gamma}{\gamma'}-\frac{\beta}{\beta'}\right)$$

$$= (\alpha'\beta'\gamma')^2\left(\frac{\alpha}{\alpha'}-\frac{\beta}{\beta'}\right)\left(\frac{\beta}{\beta'}-\frac{\gamma}{\gamma'}\right)\left(\frac{\gamma}{\gamma'}-\frac{\alpha}{\alpha'}\right)$$

$$= (\alpha'\beta'\gamma')^2 \frac{(\alpha\beta' - \alpha'\beta)(\beta\gamma' - \beta'\gamma)(\gamma\alpha' - \gamma'\alpha)}{(\alpha'\beta'\gamma')^2}$$

Hence, $\Delta = (\alpha\beta' - \alpha'\beta)(\beta\gamma' - \beta'\gamma)(\gamma\alpha' - \gamma'\alpha)$

97. Since, $y = \dfrac{u}{v}$

$$\therefore \quad \frac{dy}{dx} = \frac{v\dfrac{du}{dx} - u\dfrac{dv}{dx}}{v^2} = \frac{vu' - uv'}{v^2}$$

$$\Rightarrow \quad v^2 \frac{dy}{dx} = vu' - uv' \qquad \text{...(i)}$$

On differentiating both sides w.r.t. x, we get

$$v^2 \frac{d^2y}{dx^2} + \frac{dy}{dx}\cdot 2vv' = (vu'' + u'v') - (uv'' + v'u')$$

$$\Rightarrow \quad v^2 \frac{d^2y}{dx^2} + 2vv'\frac{dy}{dx} = vu'' - uv''$$

On multiplying both sides by v, then

$$v^3 \frac{d^2y}{dx^2} + 2v'\left(v^2 \frac{dy}{dx}\right) = v^2u'' - uvv''$$

$$\Rightarrow \quad v^3 \frac{d^2y}{dx^2} + 2v'(vu' - uv') = v^2u'' - uvv'' \qquad \text{[from Eq. (i)]}$$

$$\Rightarrow \quad v^3 \frac{d^2y}{dx^2} = 2uv^2 - uvv'' - 2vu'v' + v^2u'' \qquad \text{...(ii)}$$

and
$$\begin{vmatrix} v & v & 0 \\ v' & v' & v \\ v'' & v'' & 2v'' \end{vmatrix} = u(2v'^2 - vu'') - v(2u'v' - u''v)$$

$$= 2uv'^2 - 4vv'' - 2vu'v' + v^2u'' \qquad \text{...(iii)}$$

From Eqs. (ii) and (iii), we get

$$v^3 \frac{d^2y}{dx^2} = \begin{vmatrix} u & v & 0 \\ u' & v' & v \\ u' & v'' & 2v' \end{vmatrix}$$

98. Here, we have to prove that $\Delta(x)$ is independent of x. So, it is sufficient to prove that $\Delta'(x) = 0$

$$\text{Now, } \Delta(x) = \begin{vmatrix} \sin(x+\alpha) & \cos(x+\alpha) & a + x\sin\alpha \\ \sin(x+\beta) & \cos(x+\beta) & b + x\sin\beta \\ \sin(x+\gamma) & \cos(x+\gamma) & c + x\sin\gamma \end{vmatrix}$$

On differentiating w.r.t. x, we get

$$\Delta'(x) = \begin{vmatrix} \cos(x+\alpha) & \cos(x+\alpha) & a + x\sin\alpha \\ \cos(x+\beta) & \cos(x+\beta) & b + x\sin\beta \\ \cos(x+\gamma) & \cos(x+\gamma) & c + x\sin\gamma \end{vmatrix}$$

$$+ \begin{vmatrix} \sin(x+\alpha) & -\sin(x+\alpha) & a + x\sin\alpha \\ \sin(x+\beta) & -\sin(x+\beta) & b + x\sin\beta \\ \sin(x+\gamma) & -\sin(x+\gamma) & c + x\sin\gamma \end{vmatrix}$$

$$+ \begin{vmatrix} \sin(x+\alpha) & \cos(x+\alpha) & \sin\alpha \\ \sin(x+\beta) & \cos(x+\beta) & \sin\beta \\ \sin(x+\gamma) & \cos(x+\gamma) & \sin\gamma \end{vmatrix}$$

$$= 0 - 0 + \begin{vmatrix} \sin(x+\alpha) & \cos(x+\alpha) & \sin\alpha \\ \sin(x+\beta) & \cos(x+\beta) & \sin\beta \\ \sin(x+\gamma) & \cos(x+\gamma) & \sin\gamma \end{vmatrix}$$

$$= \begin{vmatrix} \sin(x+\alpha) & \cos(x+\alpha) & \sin\alpha \\ \sin(x+\beta) & \cos(x+\beta) & \sin\beta \\ \sin(x+\gamma) & \cos(x+\gamma) & \sin\gamma \end{vmatrix}$$

Applying $C_1 \to C_1 - (\cos x)C_3$ and $C_2 \to C_2 + (\sin x)C_3$, we get

$$\Delta'(x) = \begin{vmatrix} \sin x\cos\alpha & \cos x\cos\alpha & \sin\alpha \\ \sin x\cos\beta & \cos x\cos\beta & \sin\beta \\ \sin x\cos\gamma & \cos x\cos\gamma & \sin\gamma \end{vmatrix}$$

$$= \sin x\cdot\cos x \begin{vmatrix} \cos\alpha & \cos\alpha & \sin\alpha \\ \cos\beta & \cos\beta & \sin\beta \\ \cos\gamma & \cos\gamma & \sin\gamma \end{vmatrix}$$

$$= \sin x\cdot\cos x \times 0 \qquad [\because C_1 \text{ and } C_2 \text{ are identical}]$$

$$= 0$$

Thus, $\Delta(x)$ is independent of x.

99. Let
$$\Delta = \begin{vmatrix} {}^xC_1 & {}^xC_2 & {}^xC_3 \\ {}^yC_1 & {}^yC_2 & {}^yC_3 \\ {}^zC_1 & {}^zC_2 & {}^zC_3 \end{vmatrix} = \begin{vmatrix} x & \dfrac{x(x-1)}{1\cdot2} & \dfrac{x(x-1)(x-2)}{1\cdot2\cdot3} \\ y & \dfrac{y(y-1)}{1\cdot2} & \dfrac{y(y-1)(y-2)}{1\cdot2\cdot3} \\ z & \dfrac{z(z-1)}{1\cdot2} & \dfrac{z(z-1)(z-2)}{1\cdot2\cdot3} \end{vmatrix}$$

$$= \frac{xyz}{12}\begin{vmatrix} 1 & x-1 & x^2-3x+2 \\ 1 & y-1 & y^2-3y+2 \\ 1 & z-1 & z^2-3z+2 \end{vmatrix}$$

Applying $C_2 \to C_2 + C_1$, then

$$\Delta = \frac{xyz}{12}\begin{vmatrix} 1 & x & x^2-3x+2 \\ 1 & y & y^2-3y+2 \\ 1 & z & z^2-3z+2 \end{vmatrix}$$

Applying $C_3 \to C_3 + 3C_2 - 2C_1$, then

$$\Delta = \frac{xyz}{12}\begin{vmatrix} 1 & x & x^2 \\ 1 & y & y^2 \\ 1 & z & z^2 \end{vmatrix} = \frac{1}{12}xyz(x-y)(y-z)(z-x)$$

100. (i) $\because$
$$f(x) = \begin{vmatrix} 1+\sin^2 x & \cos^2 x & 4\sin 2x \\ \sin^2 x & 1+\cos^2 x & 4\sin 2x \\ \sin^2 x & \cos^2 x & 1+4\sin 2x \end{vmatrix}$$

Applying $R_2 \to R_2 - R_1$ and $R_3 \to R_3 - R_1$, then

$$f(x) = \begin{vmatrix} 1+\sin^2 x & \cos^2 x & 4\sin 2x \\ -1 & 1 & 0 \\ -1 & 0 & 1 \end{vmatrix}$$

Applying $C_2 \to C_2 + C_1$, then

$$f(x) = \begin{vmatrix} 1+\sin^2 x & 2 & 4\sin 2x \\ \vdots & & \\ -1 & \dots\ 0\ \dots & 0 \\ \vdots & & \\ -1 & -1 & 1 \end{vmatrix}$$

Expanding along R_2, then

$$f(x) = \begin{vmatrix} 2 & 4\sin 2x \\ -1 & 1 \end{vmatrix} = 2 + 4\sin 2x$$

$\therefore$ Maximum value of

$$f(x) = 2 + 4(1) = 6$$

(ii) $\because$ $\Delta = \begin{vmatrix} \sin^2 A & \sin A \cos A & \cos^2 A \\ \sin^2 B & \sin B \cos B & \cos^2 B \\ \sin^2 C & \sin C \cos C & \cos^2 C \end{vmatrix}$

$$= \cos^2 A \cos^2 B \cos^2 C \begin{vmatrix} \tan^2 A & \tan A & 1 \\ \tan^2 B & \tan B & 1 \\ \tan^2 C & \tan C & 1 \end{vmatrix}$$

$$= -\cos^2 A \cos^2 B \cos^2 C \begin{vmatrix} 1 & \tan A & \tan^2 A \\ 1 & \tan B & \tan^2 B \\ 1 & \tan C & \tan^2 C \end{vmatrix}$$

$$= -\cos^2 A \cos^2 B \cos^2 C (\tan A - \tan B)(\tan B - \tan C)(\tan C - \tan A)$$

$$= -\sin(A - B)\sin(B - C)\sin(C - A)$$

$$= \sin(A - B)\sin(B - C)\sin(A - C) \geq 0 \quad [\because A \geq B \geq C]$$

$\therefore$ $\Delta \geq 0$

Hence, minimum value of Δ is 0.

101. Let $f(x) = \begin{vmatrix} x^2 - 4x + 6 & 2x^2 + 4x + 10 & 3x^2 - 2x + 16 \\ x - 2 & 2x + 2 & 3x - 1 \\ 1 & 2 & 3 \end{vmatrix}$

On differentiating w.r.t. x, we get

$$f'(x) = \begin{vmatrix} 2x - 4 & 4x + 4 & 6x - 2 \\ x - 2 & 2x + 2 & 3x - 1 \\ 1 & 2 & 3 \end{vmatrix} + \begin{vmatrix} x^2 - 4x + 6 & 2x^2 + 4x + 10 & 3x^2 - 2x + 16 \\ 1 & 2 & 3 \\ 1 & 2 & 3 \end{vmatrix} + \begin{vmatrix} x^2 - 4x + 6 & 2x^2 + 4x + 10 & 3x^2 - 2x + 16 \\ x - 2 & 2x + 2 & 3x - 1 \\ 0 & 0 & 0 \end{vmatrix}$$

$f'(x) = 0, \forall x \in R$ and $f(x) =$ Constant

As, $f(0) = \begin{vmatrix} 6 & 10 & 16 \\ -2 & 2 & -1 \\ 1 & 2 & 3 \end{vmatrix} = 2 \therefore f(x) = 2$

Now, $I = \int_{-3}^{3} \frac{x^2 \sin x}{1 + x^6} f(x)\, dx = 2 \int_{-3}^{3} \frac{x^2 \sin x}{1 + x^6} dx$

Let $g(x) = \frac{x^2 \sin x}{1 + x^6}$

$\therefore$ $g(-x) = \frac{-x^2 \sin x}{1 + x^6} = -g(x)$

Hence, g is an odd function.

$\therefore$ $I = 0$

102. Since, $Y = X$ and $Z = tX$

$$Y_1 = sX_1 + Xs_1 \quad \text{...(i)}$$

$$Y_2 = sX_2 + Xs_2 + 2X_1 s_1 \quad \text{...(ii)}$$

$$Z_1 = tX_1 + Xt_1 \quad \text{...(i}$$

and $Z_2 = tX_2 + Xt_2 + 2X_1 t_1$ ...(i

$$\text{LHS} = \begin{vmatrix} X & Y & Z \\ X_1 & Y_1 & Z_1 \\ X_2 & Y_2 & Z_2 \end{vmatrix}$$

$$= \begin{vmatrix} X & sX & tX \\ X_1 & sX_1 + Xs_1 & tX_1 + Xt_1 \\ X_2 & sX_2 + Xs_2 + 2X_1 s_1 & tX_2 + Xt_2 + 2X_1 t_1 \end{vmatrix}$$

[using Eqs. (i), (ii), (iii) and (iv)]

Applying $C_2 \to C_2 - sC_1$ and $C_3 \to C_3 - tC_1$, then

$$= \begin{vmatrix} X & 0 & 0 \\ X_1 & Xs_1 & Xt_1 \\ X_2 & Xs_2 + 2X_1 s_1 & Xt_2 + 2X_1 t_1 \end{vmatrix}$$

Expanding w.r.t. R_1, then

$$= X^2 \begin{vmatrix} s_1 & t_1 \\ Xs_2 + 2X_1 s_1 & Xt_2 + 2X_1 t_1 \end{vmatrix}$$

Applying $R_2 \to R_2 - 2X_1 R_1$, then

$$= X^2 \begin{vmatrix} s_1 & t_1 \\ Xs_2 & Xt_2 \end{vmatrix} = X^3 \begin{vmatrix} s_1 & t_1 \\ s_2 & t_2 \end{vmatrix} = \text{RHS}$$

103. Given determinant may be expressed as

$$\Delta = \begin{vmatrix} f & g & h \\ xf' + f & xg' + g & xh' + h \\ (x^2 f'' + 4xf' + 2f) & (x^2 g'' + 4xg' + 2g) & (x^2 h'' + 4xh' + 2h) \end{vmatrix}$$

Now, applying $R_3 \to R_3 - 4R_2 + 2R_1$, then

$$\Delta = \begin{vmatrix} f & g & h \\ xf' + f & xg' + g & xh' + h \\ x^2 f'' & x^2 g'' & x^2 h'' \end{vmatrix}$$

Applying $R_2 \to R_2 - R_1$, then $\Delta = \begin{vmatrix} f & g & h \\ xf' & xg' & xh' \\ x^2 f'' & x^2 g'' & x^2 h'' \end{vmatrix}$

$$\Rightarrow \quad \Delta = x \begin{vmatrix} f & g & h \\ f' & g' & h' \\ x^2 f'' & x^2 g'' & x^2 h'' \end{vmatrix}$$

$$\Rightarrow \quad \Delta = \begin{vmatrix} f & g & h \\ f' & g' & h' \\ x^3 f'' & x^3 g'' & x^3 h'' \end{vmatrix}$$

$$\therefore \quad \Delta' = \begin{vmatrix} f' & g & h' \\ f' & g' & h' \\ x^3 f'' & x^3 g'' & x^3 h'' \end{vmatrix} + \begin{vmatrix} f & g & h \\ f'' & g'' & h'' \\ x^3 f'' & x^3 g'' & x^3 h'' \end{vmatrix} + \begin{vmatrix} f & g & h \\ f' & g' & h' \\ (x^3 f'')' & (x^3 g'')' & (x^3 h'')' \end{vmatrix}$$

$$= 0 + 0 + \begin{vmatrix} f & g & h \\ f' & g' & h' \\ (x^3 f'')' & (x^3 g'')' & (x^3 h'')' \end{vmatrix}$$

Hence, $\Delta' = \begin{vmatrix} f & g & h \\ f' & g' & h' \\ (x^3 f'')' & (x^3 g'')' & (x^3 h'')' \end{vmatrix}$

104. Let the given determinant be equal to zero. Then, there exist x, y and z not all zero, such that

$$a_1 x + a_2 y + a_3 z = 0,\ b_1 x + b_2 y + b_3 z = 0$$

and $c_1 x + c_2 y + c_3 z = 0$

Assume that, $|x| \ge |y| \ge |z|$ and $x \ne 0$. Then, from $a_1 x = (-a_2 y) + (-a_3 z)$

$\therefore$ $|a_1 x| = |-a_2 y - a_3 z| \le |a_2 y| + |a_3 z|$

$\Rightarrow$ $|a_1|\,|x| \le |a_2|\,|y| + |a_3|\,|z|$

But $x \ne 0$ i.e. $|a_1| \le |a_2| + |a_3|$

Similarly, $|b_2| \le |b_1| + |b_3|$

$|c_3| \le |c_1| + |c_2|$

which is contradiction. Hence, the assumption that the determinant is zero must be wrong.

105. $\text{LHS} = \begin{vmatrix} (a-a_1)^{-2} & (a-a_1)^{-1} & a_1^{-1} \\ (a-a_2)^{-2} & (a-a_2)^{-1} & a_2^{-1} \\ (a-a_3)^{-2} & (a-a_3)^{-1} & a_3^{-1} \end{vmatrix}$

$$= (a-a_1)^{-2}(a-a_2)^{-2}(a-a_3)^{-2} \begin{vmatrix} 1 & (a-a_1) & a_1^{-1}(a-a_1)^2 \\ 1 & (a-a_2) & a_2^{-1}(a-a_2)^2 \\ 1 & (a-a_3) & a_3^{-1}(a-a_3)^2 \end{vmatrix}$$

Applying $R_2 \to R_2 - R_1$ and $R_3 \to -R_3 - R_1$, then

$$\text{LHS} = \frac{1}{\prod (a-a_i)^2} \begin{vmatrix} 1 & (a-a_1) & a_1^{-1}(a-a_1)^2 \\ 0 & (a_1-a_2) & \dfrac{(a^2-a_1a_2)(a_1-a_2)}{a_1a_2} \\ 0 & (a_1-a_3) & \dfrac{(a^2-a_1a_3)(a_1-a_3)}{a_1a_3} \end{vmatrix}$$

Expanding w.r.t. 1st column, then

$$\text{LHS} = \frac{1}{\prod (a-a_i)^2} \begin{vmatrix} (a_1-a_2) & \dfrac{(a^2-a_1a_2)(a_1-a_2)}{a_1a_2} \\ (a_1-a_3) & \dfrac{(a^2-a_1a_3)(a_1-a_3)}{a_1a_3} \end{vmatrix}$$

$$= \frac{(a_1-a_2)(a_1-a_3)}{\prod (a-a_i)^2} \begin{vmatrix} 1 & \dfrac{a^2-a_1a_2}{a_1a_2} \\ 1 & \dfrac{a^2-a_1a_3}{a_1a_3} \end{vmatrix}$$

$$= \frac{(a_1-a_2)(a_1-a_3)\,a^2(a_2-a_3)}{a_1a_2a_3 \prod (a-a_i)^2} = \frac{-a^2 \prod (a_i - a_j)}{\prod a_i \prod (a-a_i)^2}$$

Numerator $= -a^2(a_1-a_2)(a_2-a_3)(a_3-a_1)$

The resulting expression has negative sign.

106. The given system of equation will have a non-trivial solution in the determinant of coefficients.

$$\therefore \quad \Delta = \begin{vmatrix} a-t & b & c \\ b & c-t & a \\ c & a & b-t \end{vmatrix}$$

$\Delta = 0$ is a cubic equation in t.

So, it has in general three solutions t_1, t_2 and t_3.

Let $\Delta = a_0 t^3 + a_1 t^2 + a_2 t + a_3$

Clearly, $a_0 =$ Coefficient of $t^3 = -1$,

so $t_1 t_2 t_3 = -\dfrac{a_3}{a_0} = -\dfrac{a_3}{-1} = a_3 =$ Constant term in the expansion of Δ. i.e. Δ (at $t = 0$)

$$\therefore \quad t_1 t_2 t_3 = a_3 = \begin{vmatrix} a & b & c \\ b & c & a \\ c & a & b \end{vmatrix}$$

107. (i) Eliminating a, b and c from given equations, we obtain

$$\begin{vmatrix} -1 & \dfrac{y}{z} & \dfrac{z}{y} \\ -1 & \dfrac{z}{x} & \dfrac{x}{z} \\ -1 & \dfrac{x}{y} & \dfrac{y}{z} \end{vmatrix} = 0$$

Applying $R_2 \to R_2 - R_1$ and $R_3 \to R_3 - R_1$, then

$$\begin{vmatrix} -1 & \dfrac{y}{z} & \dfrac{z}{y} \\ 0 & \dfrac{z}{x} - \dfrac{y}{z} & \dfrac{x}{z} - \dfrac{z}{y} \\ 0 & \dfrac{x}{y} - \dfrac{y}{z} & \dfrac{y}{x} - \dfrac{z}{y} \end{vmatrix} = 0$$

Expanding along C_1, then

$$-\left(\frac{z}{x} - \frac{y}{x}\right)\left(\frac{y}{x} - \frac{z}{y}\right) + \left(\frac{x}{y} - \frac{y}{z}\right)\left(\frac{x}{z} - \frac{z}{y}\right) = 0$$

$$\Rightarrow \quad \frac{yz}{x^2} + \frac{zx}{y^2} + \frac{xy}{z^2} + 1 = 0$$

(ii) To eliminate x, y and z.

Let $\alpha = \dfrac{y}{z}$, $\beta = \dfrac{z}{x}$ and $\gamma = \dfrac{x}{y}$ in the given equations,

$$b\alpha + \frac{c}{\alpha} = a, \quad \text{...(i)}$$

$$c\beta + \frac{a}{\beta} = b \quad \text{...(ii)}$$

and $$a\gamma + \frac{b}{\gamma} = c \quad \text{...(iii)}$$

Also, $\alpha\beta\gamma = 1$

From Eqs. (i), (ii) and (iii), we get

$$\left(b\alpha + \frac{c}{\alpha}\right)\left(c\beta + \frac{a}{\beta}\right)\left(a\gamma + \frac{b}{\gamma}\right) = abc$$

$$\Rightarrow 2abc + ac^2 \frac{\beta\gamma}{\alpha} + a^2 b \frac{\alpha\gamma}{\beta} + b^2 c \frac{\alpha\beta}{\gamma} + a^2 c \frac{\gamma}{\alpha\beta} + bc^2 \frac{\beta}{\gamma\alpha} + ab^2 \frac{\alpha}{\beta\gamma} = abc$$

$$\Rightarrow \quad ac^2 \frac{1}{\alpha^2} + a^2 b \frac{1}{\beta^2} + b^2 c \frac{1}{\gamma^2} + a^2 c \gamma^2 + bc^2 \beta^2 + ab^2 \alpha^2 = -abc \quad [\because \alpha\beta\gamma = 1]$$

$$\Rightarrow a\left(\frac{c^2}{\alpha^2} + b^2\alpha^2\right) + b\left(\frac{a^2}{\beta^2} + \beta^2 c^2\right) + c\left(\frac{b^2}{\gamma^2} + a^2\gamma^2\right) = -abc \quad \text{...(iv)}$$

On squaring Eqs. (i), (ii) and (iii), we get

$$b^2\alpha^2 + \frac{c^2}{\alpha^2} = a^2 - 2bc, c^2\beta^2 + \frac{a^2}{\beta^2} = b^2 - 2ca \text{ and}$$

$$a^2\gamma^2 + \frac{b^2}{\gamma^2} = c^2 - 2ab$$

On putting these values in Eq. (iv), we get

$$a(a^2 - 2bc) + b(b^2 - 2ca) + c(c^2 - 2ab) = -abc$$

$$a^3 + b^3 + c^3 = 5abc$$

108. Here, $\Delta = \begin{vmatrix} a & b & c \\ b & c & a \\ c & a & b \end{vmatrix}$. According to the question, x, y and z not all zero. Hence, the given system of equations has non-trivial solution.

$$\Delta = 0$$

$$\begin{vmatrix} a & b & c \\ b & c & a \\ c & a & b \end{vmatrix} = 0$$

$$\Rightarrow \frac{1}{2}(a + b + c)[(a - b)^2 + (b - c)^2 + (c - a)^2] = 0$$

$\therefore$ $$a + b + c = 0$$

or $$(a - b)^2 + (b - c)^2 + (c - a)^2 = 0$$

***Case* I** If $a + b + c = 0$

From first two equations,

$$ax + by - (a + b)z = 0$$

$$bx - (a + b)y + ax = 0$$

[by cross-multiplication law]

$$\therefore \frac{x}{ab - (a + b)^2} = \frac{y}{-b(a + b) - a^2} = \frac{z}{-a(a + b) - b^2}$$

$$\Rightarrow \frac{x}{-(a^2 + ab + b^2)} = \frac{y}{-(a^2 + ab + b^2)} = \frac{z}{-(a^2 + ab + b^2)}$$

$$\therefore x : y : z = 1 : 1 : 1$$

***Case* II** If $(a - b)^2 + (b - c)^2 + (c - a)^2 = 0$

It is possible only, when

$$a - b = 0, b - c = 0 \text{ and } c - a = 0$$

Then, $$a = b = c$$

In this case all the three equations reduce in the forms

$$x + y + z = 0 \quad \text{...(i)}$$

Then, Eq. (i) will be satisfied, if

$$x = k, y = k\omega, z = k\omega^2$$

or $$x = k, y = k\omega^2, z = k\omega$$

where ω is the cube root of unity.

Then, $x : y : z = 1 : \omega : \omega^2$ or $1 : \omega^2 : \omega$

Hence, combined both cases, we get

$$x : y : z = 1 : 1 : 1$$

or $1 : \omega : \omega^2$

or $1 : \omega^2 : \omega$

109. Applying $C_1 \to C_1 + C_2 + C_3$, then

$$f(x) = \begin{vmatrix} 1 & (1 + b^2)x & (1 + c^2)x \\ 1 & 1 + b^2x & (1 + c^2)x \\ 1 & (1 + b^2)x & 1 + c^2x \end{vmatrix} \quad [\because a^2 + b^2 + c^2 + 2 = 0]$$

Applying $R_2 \to R_2 - R_1$ and $R_3 \to R_3 - R_1$, then

$$= \begin{vmatrix} 1 & (1 + b^2)x & (1 + c^2)x \\ 0 & 1 - x & 0 \\ 0 & 0 & 1 - x \end{vmatrix} = (1 - x^2)$$

Hence, degree of $f(x) = 2$

110. For no solution or infinitely many solutions

$$\begin{vmatrix} \alpha & 1 & 1 \\ 1 & \alpha & 1 \\ 1 & 1 & \alpha \end{vmatrix} = 0$$

Applying $C_1 \to C_1 + C_2 + C_3$, then

$$\begin{vmatrix} \alpha + 2 & 1 & 1 \\ \alpha + 2 & \alpha & 1 \\ \alpha + 2 & 1 & \alpha \end{vmatrix} = 0$$

Applying $R_1 \to R_2 - R_1$ and $R_3 \to R_3 - R_1$, then

$$\begin{vmatrix} \alpha + 2 & 1 & 1 \\ 0 & \alpha - 1 & 0 \\ 0 & 0 & \alpha - 1 \end{vmatrix} = 0 \Rightarrow (\alpha - 1)^2(\alpha + 2) = 0$$

$$\therefore \alpha = 1, -2$$

For $\alpha = 1$, clearly there an infinitely many solutions and when we put $\alpha = -2$ in given system of equations and adding them together LHS $\neq$ RHS. i.e., no solution.

111. $\because a_1, a_2, a_3, \ldots$ are in GP.

$\therefore$ Using $a_n = a_1 r^{n-1}$, we get the given determinant, as

$$\begin{vmatrix} \log(a_1 r^{n-1}) & \log(a_1 r^n) & \log(a_1 r^{n+1}) \\ \log(a_1 r^{n+2}) & \log(a_1 r^{n+3}) & \log(a_1 r^{n+4}) \\ \log(a_1 r^{n+5}) & \log(a_1 r^{n+6}) & \log(a_1 r^{n+7}) \end{vmatrix}$$

Applying $C_2 \to C_2 - C_1$ and $C_3 \to C_3 - C_1$ and using $\log m - \log n = \log\left(\frac{m}{n}\right)$, we get

$$\begin{vmatrix} \log(a_1 r^{n-1}) & \log r & 2\log r \\ \log(a_1 r^{n+2}) & \log r & 2\log r \\ \log(a_1 r^{n+5}) & \log r & 2\log r \end{vmatrix} = 0$$

[$\because C_2$ and C_3 are proportional]

112. Applying $R_2 \to R_2 - R_1$ and $R_3 \to R_3 - R_1$, then

$$D = \begin{vmatrix} 1 & 1 & 1 \\ 0 & x & 0 \\ 0 & 0 & y \end{vmatrix} = xy$$

113. $\because$ $$D = \begin{vmatrix} 1 & -2 & 3 \\ -1 & 1 & -2 \\ 1 & -3 & 4 \end{vmatrix} = 0$$

and $$D_1 = \begin{vmatrix} -1 & -2 & 3 \\ k & 1 & -2 \\ 1 & -3 & 4 \end{vmatrix} = (3 - k) = 0, \text{ if } k = 3$$

$$D_2 = \begin{vmatrix} 1 & -1 & 3 \\ -1 & k & -2 \\ 1 & -3 & 4 \end{vmatrix} = (k - 3) = 0, \text{ if } k = 3$$

$$D_3 = \begin{vmatrix} -1 & -2 & 3 \\ k & 1 & -2 \\ 1 & -3 & 4 \end{vmatrix} = (k = 3) = 0, \text{ if } k = 3$$

$\therefore$ System of equations has no solution for $k \neq 3$.

114. The system of equations

$x - cy - bz = 0,\ -cx + y - az = 0$ and $-bx - ay + z = 0$

have non-trivial solution, if

$$\begin{vmatrix} 1 & -c & -b \\ -c & 1 & -a \\ -b & -a & 1 \end{vmatrix} = 0$$

$$\Rightarrow \quad 1 + 2(-a)(-b)(-c) - a^2 - b^2 - c^2 = 0$$

or $$a^2 + b^2 + c^2 + 2abc = 1$$

115. $$\begin{vmatrix} a & a+1 & a-1 \\ -b & b+1 & b-1 \\ c & c-1 & c+1 \end{vmatrix} + (-1)^n \begin{vmatrix} a+1 & b+1 & c-1 \\ a-1 & b-1 & c+1 \\ a & -b & c \end{vmatrix} = 0$$

$$\Rightarrow \begin{vmatrix} a & a+1 & a-1 \\ -b & b+1 & b-1 \\ c & c-1 & c+1 \end{vmatrix} + (-1)^n \begin{vmatrix} a+1 & a-1 & a \\ b+1 & b-1 & -b \\ c-1 & c+1 & c \end{vmatrix} = 0$$

[by property]

$$\Rightarrow \begin{vmatrix} a & a+1 & a-1 \\ -b & b+1 & b-1 \\ c & c-1 & c+1 \end{vmatrix} + (-1)^{n+2} \begin{vmatrix} a & a+1 & a-1 \\ -b & b+1 & b-1 \\ c & c-1 & c+1 \end{vmatrix} = 0$$

116. Applying $R_1 \to R_1 + R_3$, then

$$f(\theta) = \begin{vmatrix} \theta & \cdots & 0 & \cdots & 2 \\ & & & & \vdots \\ -\tan\theta & & 1 & & \tan\theta \\ & & & & \vdots \\ -1 & & -\tan\theta & & 1 \end{vmatrix}$$

$$= 2(1 + \tan^2\theta) = 2\sec^2\theta \geq 2$$

$\therefore f(\theta) \in [2, \infty)$

117. Non-zero solution means non-trivial solution.

For non-trivial solution of the given system of linear equations

$$\begin{vmatrix} 4 & k & 2 \\ k & 4 & 1 \\ 2 & 2 & 1 \end{vmatrix} = 0$$

$$\Rightarrow \quad 4(4-2) - k(k-2) + (2k-8) = 0$$

$$\Rightarrow \quad -k^2 + 6k - 8 = 0$$

$$\Rightarrow \quad k^2 - 6k + 8 = 0$$

$$\Rightarrow \quad (k-2)(k-4) = 0$$

$$\therefore \quad k = 2, 4$$

Clearly, there exist values of k.

118. For trivial solution $\begin{vmatrix} 1 & -k & 1 \\ k & 3 & -k \\ 3 & 1 & -1 \end{vmatrix} \neq 0$

$$\Rightarrow 1(-3+k) + k(-k+3k) + 1(k-9) \neq 0$$

$$\Rightarrow \quad 2k^2 + 2k - 12 \neq 0$$

$$\Rightarrow \quad k^2 + k - 6 \neq 0$$

$$\Rightarrow \quad (k+3)(k-2) \neq 0$$

$$\Rightarrow \quad k \neq 2, -3$$

or $$k \in R - \{2, -3\}$$

119. $$\Delta = \begin{vmatrix} k+1 & 8 \\ k & k=3 \end{vmatrix} = (k+1)(k+3) - 8k = k^2 - 4k + 3$$

$$\therefore \quad \Delta = (k-1)(k-3)$$

$$\Delta_1 = \begin{vmatrix} 4k & 8 \\ 3k-1 & k+3 \end{vmatrix} = 4k^2 + 12k - 24k + 8 = 4k^2 - 12k + 8$$

$$\Delta_1 = 4(k-1)(k-2)$$

and $$\Delta_2 = \begin{vmatrix} k+1 & 4k \\ k & 3k-1 \end{vmatrix} = (k+1)(3k-1) - 4k^2 = -k^2 + 2k + 1$$

$$\therefore \quad \Delta_2 = -(k-1)^2$$

As given no solutions

$$\Rightarrow \quad \Delta_1 \text{ and } \Delta_2 \neq 0$$

but $$\Delta = 0$$

$$k = 3$$

120. $$\because \begin{vmatrix} 3 & 1+f(1) & 1+f(2) \\ 1+f(1) & 1+f(2) & 1+f(3) \\ 1+f(2) & 1+f(3) & 1+f(4) \end{vmatrix}$$

$$= \begin{vmatrix} 1+1+1 & 1+\alpha+\beta & 1+\alpha^2+\beta^2 \\ 1+\alpha+\beta & 1+\alpha^2+\beta^2 & 1+\alpha^3+\beta^3 \\ 1+\alpha^2+\beta^2 & 1+\alpha^3+\beta^3 & 1+\alpha^4+\beta^4 \end{vmatrix}$$

$$= \begin{vmatrix} 1 & 1 & 1 \\ 1 & \alpha & \beta \\ 1 & \alpha^2 & \beta^2 \end{vmatrix} \times \begin{vmatrix} 1 & 1 & 1 \\ 1 & \alpha & \beta \\ 1 & \alpha^2 & \beta^2 \end{vmatrix} = \begin{vmatrix} 1 & 1 & 1 \\ 1 & \alpha & \beta \\ 1 & \alpha^2 & \beta^2 \end{vmatrix}^2$$

$$= \{(1-\alpha)(1-\beta)(\alpha-\beta)\}^2$$

$$= (1-\alpha)^2(1-\beta)^2(\alpha-\beta)^2$$

So, $k = 1$.

121. The given system can be written as

$$(2-\lambda)x_1 - 2x_2 + x_3 = 0$$

$$2x_1 - (3+\lambda)x_2 + 2x_3 = 0$$

$$-x_1 + 2x_2 - \lambda x_3 = 0$$

For non-trivial solutions, $\Delta = 0$

$$\begin{vmatrix} 2-\lambda & -2 & 1 \\ 2 & -(3+\lambda) & 2 \\ -1 & 2 & -\lambda \end{vmatrix} = 0$$

$$\Rightarrow (2-\lambda)(\lambda^2 + 3\lambda - 4) + 2(-2\lambda + 2) + 1(4 - 3 - \lambda) = 0$$

$$\Rightarrow \quad \lambda^3 + \lambda^2 - 5\lambda + 3 = 0$$

$$\Rightarrow \quad \lambda = 1, 1, -3$$

Hence, λ has two values.

122. Applying $R_2 \to R_2 - R_1$ and $R_3 \to R_3 - R_1$, then

$$\begin{vmatrix} (1+\alpha)^2 & (1+2\alpha)^2 & (1+3\alpha)^2 \\ 2\alpha+3 & 4\alpha+3 & 6\alpha+3 \\ 4\alpha+8 & 8\alpha+8 & 12\alpha+8 \end{vmatrix} = -648\alpha$$

Applying $R_3 \to R_3 - 2R_2$, then

$$\begin{vmatrix} (1+\alpha)^2 & (1+2\alpha)^2 & (1+3\alpha)^2 \\ 2\alpha+3 & 4\alpha+3 & 6\alpha+3 \\ 2 & 2 & 2 \end{vmatrix} = -648\alpha$$

Applying $C_2 \to C_2 - \frac{1}{2}(C_1 + C_3)$, then

$$\begin{vmatrix} (1+\alpha)^2 & -\alpha^2 & (1+3\alpha)^2 \\ 2\alpha+3 & 4\alpha+3 & 6\alpha+3 \\ 2 & 0 & 2 \end{vmatrix} = -648\alpha$$

$$\Rightarrow \quad \alpha^2(4\alpha + 6 - 12\alpha - 6) = -648\alpha$$

$$\Rightarrow \quad -8\alpha^3 = -648\alpha$$

$$\Rightarrow \quad \alpha^3 - 81\alpha = 0$$

$$\therefore \quad \alpha = 0, 9, -9$$

123. For non-trivial solution

$$\begin{bmatrix} 1 & \lambda & -1 \\ \lambda & -1 & -1 \\ 1 & 1 & -\lambda \end{bmatrix} = 0$$

$$\Rightarrow \quad 1(\lambda+1) - \lambda(-\lambda^2+1) - 1(\lambda+1) = 0$$

$$\Rightarrow \quad \lambda(\lambda^2 - 1) = 0$$

$$\Rightarrow \quad \lambda = 0, \ \pm 1$$

124.

$$x^3 \begin{bmatrix} 1 & 1 & 1+x^3 \\ 2 & 4 & 1+8x^3 \\ 3 & 9 & 1+27x^3 \end{bmatrix} = 10$$

$$\Rightarrow \quad x^3 \begin{bmatrix} 1 & 1 & 1 \\ 2 & 4 & 1 \\ 3 & 9 & 1 \end{bmatrix} + x^6 \begin{bmatrix} 1 & 1 & 1 \\ 2 & 4 & 8 \\ 3 & 9 & 27 \end{bmatrix} = 10$$

Applying $C_2 \to C_2 - C_1$ and $C_3 \to C_3 - C_1$, then

$$x^3 \begin{bmatrix} 1 & 0 & 0 \\ 2 & 2 & -1 \\ 3 & 6 & -2 \end{bmatrix} + x^6 \begin{bmatrix} 1 & 0 & 0 \\ 2 & 2 & 6 \\ 3 & 6 & 24 \end{bmatrix} = 10$$

$$\Rightarrow \quad 2x^3 + 12x^6 = 10 \text{ or } 6x^6 + x^3 - 5 = 0$$

or
$$(6x^3 - 5)(x^3 + 1) = 0$$

$$\Rightarrow \quad x^3 = \frac{5}{6} \text{ or } x^3 = -1$$

$$\therefore \quad x = \left(\frac{5}{6}\right)^{1/3}, -1$$

i.e. Two distinct values of x.

125.

$$\Delta = \begin{vmatrix} a & 2 \\ 3 & -2 \end{vmatrix} = -2a - 6,$$

$$\Delta_1 = \begin{vmatrix} \lambda & 2 \\ \mu & -2 \end{vmatrix} = -2(\lambda + \mu)$$

or
$$\Delta_2 = \begin{vmatrix} a & \lambda \\ 3 & \mu \end{vmatrix} = \alpha\mu - 3\lambda$$

System has unique solution for $\Delta \neq 0$

$\therefore$ $a \neq -3$ for all values λ and μ

System has infinitely many solution for

$$\Delta = \Delta_1 = \Delta_2 = 0$$

$\therefore$ $a = -3$, $\lambda + \mu = 0$, $a\mu - 3\lambda = 0$

and system has no solution

$$\Delta = 0 \Rightarrow a = -3$$

and
$$\lambda + \mu \neq 0$$

126. $\because$
$$\Delta = \begin{bmatrix} 1 & 1 & 1 \\ 1 & a & 1 \\ a & b & 1 \end{bmatrix} = 1(a-b) - 1(1-a) + 1(b-a^2) = -(a-1)^2$$

$$\Delta_1 = \begin{bmatrix} 1 & 1 & 1 \\ 1 & a & 1 \\ 0 & b & 1 \end{bmatrix} = 1(a-b) - 1(1) + 1(b) = (a-1)$$

$$\Delta_2 = \begin{bmatrix} 1 & 1 & 1 \\ 1 & 1 & 1 \\ a & 0 & 1 \end{bmatrix} = 1(1) - 1(1-a) + 1(0-a) = 0$$

and
$$\Delta_3 = \begin{bmatrix} 1 & 1 & 1 \\ 1 & a & 1 \\ a & b & 0 \end{bmatrix} = 1(-b) - 1(-a) + 1(b-a^2) = -a(a-1)$$

For $a = 1$, $\Delta = \Delta_1 = \Delta_2 = \Delta_3 = 0$

and for $b = 1$ only

$$x + y + z = 1$$
$$x + y + z = 1$$
$$x + y + z = 0$$

i.e. no solution ($\because$ RHS are not equal)

Hence, for no solution $b = 1$ only.

CHAPTER

08

Matrices

Learning Part

Session 1

- Definition
- Types of Matrices
- Difference Between a Matrix and a Determinant
- Equal Matrices
- Operations of Matrices
- Various Kinds of Matrices

Session 2

- Transpose of a Matrix
- Symmetric Matrix
- Orthogonal Matrix
- Complex Conjugate (or Conjugate) of a Matrix
- Hermitian Matrix
- Unitary Matrix
- Determinant of a Matrix
- Singular and Non-Singular Matrices

Session 3

- Adjoint of a Matrix
- Elementary Row Operations
- Matrix Polynomial
- Inverse of a Matrix
- Equivalent Matrices
- Use of Mathematical Induction

Session 4

- Solutions of Linear Simultaneous Equations Using Matrix Method

Practice Part

- JEE Type Examples
- Chapter Exercises

J. J. Sylvester was the first to use the word "Matrix" in 1850 and later on in 1858 Arthur Cayley developed the theory of matrices in a systematic way. 'Matrices' is a powerful tool in mathematics and its study is becoming important day by day due to its wide applications in almost every branch of science. This mathematical tool is not only used in certain branches of sciences but also in genetics, economics, sociology, modern psychology and industrial management.

Session 1

Definition, Types of Matrices, Difference Between a Matrix and a Determinant, Equal Matrices, Operations of Matrices, Various Kinds of Matrices

Definition

A set of mn numbers (real or complex) arranged in the form of a rectangular array having m rows and n columns is called a matrix of order $m \times n$ or an $m \times n$ matrix (which is read as m by n matrix).

An $m \times n$ matrix is usually written as

$$\begin{bmatrix} a_{11} & a_{12} & a_{13} & \dots & a_{1n} \\ a_{21} & a_{22} & a_{23} & \dots & a_{2n} \\ a_{31} & a_{32} & a_{33} & \dots & a_{3n} \\ \dots & \dots & \dots & \dots & \dots \\ \dots & \dots & \dots & \dots & \dots \\ a_{m_1} & a_{m_2} & a_{m_3} & \dots & a_{mn} \end{bmatrix}$$

In a compact form the above matrix is represented by $[a_{ij}]$, $i = 1, 2, 3, \dots, m$, $j = 1, 2, 3, \dots, n$ or simply by $[a_{ij}]_{m \times n}$, where the symbols a_{ij} represent any numbers (a_{ij} lies in the ith row (from top) and jth column (from left)).

Notations A matrix is denoted by capital letter such as $A, B, C, \dots, X, Y, Z$.

Note

1. A matrix may be represented by the symbols $[a_{ij}], (a_{ij}), \| a_{ij} \|$ or by a single capital letter A (say)
$$A = [a_{ij}]_{m \times n} \text{ or } (a_{ij})_{m \times n} \text{ or } \| a_{ij} \|$$
Generally, the first system is adopted.
2. The numbers $a_{11}, a_{12}, \dots$, etc., of rectangular array are called the elements or entries of the matrix.
3. A matrix is essentially an arrangement of elements and has no value.
4. The plural of 'matrix' is 'matrices'.

| Example 1. If a matrix has 12 elements, what are the possible orders it can have? What will be the possible orders if it has 7 elements?

Sol. We know that, if a matrix is of order $m \times n$, it has mn elements. Thus, to find all possible orders of a matrix with 12 elements, we will find all ordered pairs of natural numbers, whose product is 12.

Thus, all possible ordered pairs are (1, 12), (12, 1), (2, 6), (6, 2), (3, 4), (4, 3).

Hence, possible orders are 1×12, 12×1, 2×6, 6×2, 3×4 and 4×3.

If the matrix has 7 elements, then the possible orders will be 1×7 and 7×1.

| Example 2. Construct a 2×3 matrix $A = [a_{ij}]$, whose elements are given by

(i) $a_{ij} = \dfrac{(i+2j)^2}{2}$. (ii) $a_{ij} = \dfrac{1}{2}|2i - 3j|$.

(iii) $a_{ij} = \begin{cases} i - j, i \ge j \\ i + j, i < j \end{cases}$

(iv) $a_{ij} = \left[\dfrac{i}{j}\right]$,

where [.] denotes the greatest integer function.

(v) $a_{ij} = \left\{\dfrac{2i}{3j}\right\}$,

where {.} denotes the fractional part function.

(vi) $a_{ij} = \left(\dfrac{3i + 4j}{2}\right)$

where (.) denotes the least integer function.

Sol. We have, $A=\begin{bmatrix} a_{11} & a_{12} & a_{13} \\ a_{21} & a_{22} & a_{23} \end{bmatrix}_{2\times 3}$

(i) Since, $a_{ij}=\dfrac{(i+2j)^2}{2}$, therefore

$$a_{11}=\frac{(1+2)^2}{2}=\frac{9}{2}, a_{12}=\frac{(1+4)^2}{2}=\frac{25}{2},$$

$$a_{13}=\frac{(1+6)^2}{2}=\frac{49}{2}, a_{21}=\frac{(2+2)^2}{2}=8,$$

$$a_{22}=\frac{(2+4)^2}{2}=18 \text{ and } a_{23}=\frac{(2+6)^2}{2}=32$$

Hence, the required matrix is $A=\begin{bmatrix} \frac{9}{2} & \frac{25}{2} & \frac{49}{2} \\ 8 & 18 & 32 \end{bmatrix}$.

(ii) Since, $a_{ij}=\dfrac{1}{2}|2i-3j|$, therefore

$$a_{11}=\frac{1}{2}|2-3|=\frac{1}{2}|-1|=\frac{1}{2},$$

$$a_{12}=\frac{1}{2}|2-6|=\frac{1}{2}|-4|=\frac{4}{2}=2,$$

$$a_{13}=\frac{1}{2}|2-9|=\frac{1}{2}|-7|=\frac{7}{2},$$

$$a_{21}=\frac{1}{2}|2-3|=\frac{1}{2}|-1|=\frac{1}{2},$$

$$a_{22}=\frac{1}{2}|2-6|=\frac{1}{2}|-4|=\frac{4}{2}=2$$

and $a_{23}=\dfrac{1}{2}|4-9|=\dfrac{1}{2}|-5|=\dfrac{5}{2}$

Hence, the required matrix is $A=\begin{bmatrix} \frac{1}{2} & 2 & \frac{7}{2} \\ \frac{1}{2} & 2 & \frac{5}{2} \end{bmatrix}$.

(iii) Since, $a_{ij}=\begin{cases} i-j, & i\geq j \\ i+j, & i<j \end{cases}$, therefore

$$a_{11}=1-1=0, a_{12}=1+2=3, a_{13}=1+3=4,$$

$$a_{21}=2-1=1, a_{22}=2-2=0 \text{ and } a_{23}=2+3=5$$

Hence, the required matrix is

$$A=\begin{bmatrix} 0 & 3 & 4 \\ 1 & 0 & 5 \end{bmatrix}$$

(iv) Since, $a_{ij}=\left[\dfrac{i}{j}\right]$, therefore $[\because [x]\leq x]$

$$a_{11}=\left[\frac{1}{1}\right]=[1]=1, a_{12}=\left[\frac{1}{2}\right]=[0.5]=0,$$

$$a_{13}=\left[\frac{1}{3}\right]=[0.33]=0, a_{21}=\left[\frac{2}{1}\right]=[2]=2$$

and $a_{22}=\left[\dfrac{2}{2}\right]=[1]=1$ and $a_{23}=\left[\dfrac{2}{3}\right]=[0.67]=0$

Hence, the required matrix is $A=\begin{bmatrix} 1 & 0 & 0 \\ 2 & 1 & 0 \end{bmatrix}$

(v) Since, $a_{ij}=\left\{\dfrac{2i}{3j}\right\}$, therefore $[\because 0\leq \{x\}<1]$

$$a_{11}=\left\{\frac{2}{3}\right\}=\frac{2}{3}, a_{12}=\left\{\frac{2}{6}\right\}=\left\{\frac{1}{3}\right\}=\frac{1}{3},$$

$$a_{13}=\left\{\frac{2}{9}\right\}=\frac{2}{9}, a_{21}=\left\{\frac{4}{3}\right\}=\left\{1+\frac{1}{3}\right\}=\frac{1}{3},$$

$$a_{22}=\left\{\frac{4}{6}\right\}=\left\{\frac{2}{3}\right\}=\frac{2}{3} \text{ and } a_{23}=\left\{\frac{4}{9}\right\}=\frac{4}{9}$$

Hence, the required matrix is $A=\begin{bmatrix} \frac{2}{3} & \frac{1}{3} & \frac{2}{9} \\ \frac{1}{3} & \frac{2}{3} & \frac{4}{9} \end{bmatrix}$.

(vi) Since, $a_{ij}=\left(\dfrac{3i+4j}{2}\right)$, therefore $[\because (x)\geq x]$

$$a_{11}=\left(\frac{3+4}{2}\right)=\left(\frac{7}{2}\right)=(3.5)=4,$$

$$a_{12}=\left(\frac{3+8}{2}\right)=\left(\frac{11}{2}\right)=(5.5)=6,$$

$$a_{13}=\left(\frac{3+12}{2}\right)=\left(\frac{15}{2}\right)=(7.5)=8,$$

$$a_{21}=\left(\frac{6+4}{2}\right)=\left(\frac{10}{2}\right)=(5)=5,$$

$$a_{22}=\left(\frac{6+8}{2}\right)=\left(\frac{14}{2}\right)=(7)=7$$

and $a_{23}=\left(\dfrac{6+12}{2}\right)=\left(\dfrac{18}{2}\right)=(9)=9$

Hence, the required matrix is

$$A=\begin{bmatrix} 4 & 6 & 8 \\ 5 & 7 & 9 \end{bmatrix}$$

Types of Matrices

1. Row Matrix or Row Vector

A matrix is said to be row matrix or row vector, if it contains only one row, i.e. a matrix $A=[a_{ij}]_{m\times n}$ is said to be row matrix, if $m=1$.

For example,

(i) $A=[a_{11} \quad a_{12} \quad a_{13} \quad \dots \quad a_{1n}]_{1\times n}$

(ii) $B=[3 \quad 5 \quad -7 \quad 9]_{1\times 4}$

are called row matrices.

2. Column Matrix or Column Vector

A matrix is said to be column matrix or column vector, if it contains only one column, i.e., a matrix $A=[a_{ij}]_{m\times n}$ is said to be column matrix, if $n=1$. *For example,*

(i) $A=\begin{bmatrix} a_{11} \\ a_{21} \\ a_{31} \\ \vdots \\ a_{mn} \end{bmatrix}_{m \times 1}$ (ii) $B=\begin{bmatrix} 7 \\ 0 \\ -8 \\ 2 \\ 1 \end{bmatrix}_{5 \times 1}$

are called column matrices.

3. Rectangular Matrix

A matrix is said to be rectangular matrix, if the number of rows and the number of columns are not equal i.e., a matrix $A=[a_{ij}]_{m \times n}$ is called a rectangular matrix, iff $m \neq n$. *For example,*

(i) $A=\begin{bmatrix} 1 & 3 & 4 & 5 \\ 2 & 0 & -3 & 8 \\ 7 & 4 & 2 & 5 \end{bmatrix}_{3 \times 4}$ (ii) $B=\begin{bmatrix} 2 & -3 \\ 3 & 0 \\ 4 & 8 \end{bmatrix}_{3 \times 2}$

are called rectangular matrices.

4. Square Matrix

A matrix is said to be a square matrix, if the number of rows and the number of columns are equal i.e., a matrix $A=[a_{ij}]_{m \times n}$ is called a square matrix, iff $m=n$.

For example,

(i) $A=\begin{bmatrix} a_{11} & a_{12} & a_{13} \\ a_{21} & a_{22} & a_{23} \\ a_{31} & a_{32} & a_{33} \end{bmatrix}_{3 \times 3}$ (ii) $B=\begin{bmatrix} a & b \\ c & d \end{bmatrix}_{2 \times 2}$

are called square matrices.

Remark

If $A=[a_{ij}]$ is a square matrix of order n, then elements (entries) $a_{11}, a_{22}, a_{33}, \ldots, a_{nn}$ are said to constitute the *diagonal* of the matrix A. The line along which the diagonal elements lie is called principal or leading diagonal. Thus, if $A=\begin{bmatrix} 1 & 4 & 0 \\ 8 & 3 & -2 \\ 9 & 2 & 5 \end{bmatrix}$, then the elements of the diagonal of A are 1, 3, 5.

5. Diagonal Matrix

A square matrix is said to be a diagonal matrix, if all its non-diagonal elements are zero. Thus, $A=[a_{ij}]_{n \times n}$ is called a diagonal matrix, if $a_{ij}=0$, when $i \neq j$.

For example,

(i) $A=[2]$ (ii) $B=\begin{bmatrix} -1 & 0 \\ 0 & 2 \end{bmatrix}$ (iii) $C=\begin{bmatrix} 3 & 0 & 0 \\ 0 & 5 & 0 \\ 0 & 0 & 7 \end{bmatrix}$

are diagonal matrices of order 1, 2 and 3, respectively. A diagonal matrix of order n having $d_1, d_2, d_3, \ldots, d_n$ as diagonal elements may be denoted by diag $(d_1, d_2, d_3, .., d_n)$.

Thus, $A=$ diag (2), $B=$ diag $(-1, 2)$ and $C=$ diag (3, 5, 7).

Remark

(i) No element of principal diagonal in a diagonal matrix is zero.

(ii) Minimum number of zero in a diagonal matrix is given by $n(n-1)$, where n is order of matrix.

6. Scalar Matrix

A diagonal matrix is said to be a scalar matrix, if its diagonal elements are equal. Thus, $A=[a_{ij}]_{n \times n}$ is called scalar matrix, if

$$a_{ij}=\begin{cases} 0, \text{ if } i \neq j \\ k, \text{ if } i=j \end{cases}, \text{ where } k \text{ is scalar.}$$

For example,

(i) [7] (ii) $\begin{bmatrix} 2 & 0 \\ 0 & 2 \end{bmatrix}$ (iii) $\begin{bmatrix} 5 & 0 & 0 \\ 0 & 5 & 0 \\ 0 & 0 & 5 \end{bmatrix}$

are scalar matrices of order 1, 2 and 3, respectively. They can be written as diag (7), diag (2, 2) and diag (5, 5, 5), respectively.

7. Unit or Identity Matrix

A diagonal matrix is said to be an identity matrix, if its diagonal elements are equal to 1.

Thus, $A=[a_{ij}]_{n \times n}$ is called unit or identity matrix, if

$$a_{ij}=\begin{cases} 0, \text{ if } i \neq j \\ 1, \text{ if } i=j \end{cases}$$

A unit matrix of order n is denoted by I_n or I. *For example,*

(i) $I_1=[1]$ (ii) $I_2=\begin{bmatrix} 1 & 0 \\ 0 & 1 \end{bmatrix}$ (iii) $I_3=\begin{bmatrix} 1 & 0 & 0 \\ 0 & 1 & 0 \\ 0 & 0 & 1 \end{bmatrix}$

are identity matrices of order 1, 2 and 3, respectively.

8. Singleton Matrix

A matrix is said to be singleton matrix, if it has only one element i.e. a matrix $A=[a_{ij}]_{m \times n}$ is said to be singleton matrix, if $m=n=1$.

For example, $[3], [k], [-2]$ are singleton matrices.

9. Triangular Matrix

A square matrix is called a triangular matrix, if its each element above or below the principal diagonal is zero. It is of two types:

(a) **Upper Triangular Matrix** A square matrix in which all elements below the principal diagonal are zero is called an upper triangular matrix i.e., a matrix $A=[a_{ij}]_{n \times n}$ is said to be an upper triangular matrix, if $a_{ij}=0$, when $i>j$.

For example,

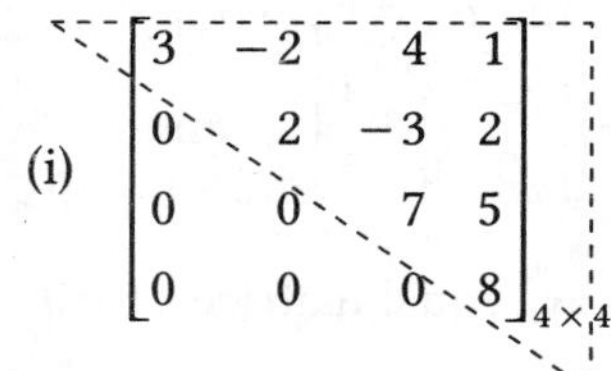

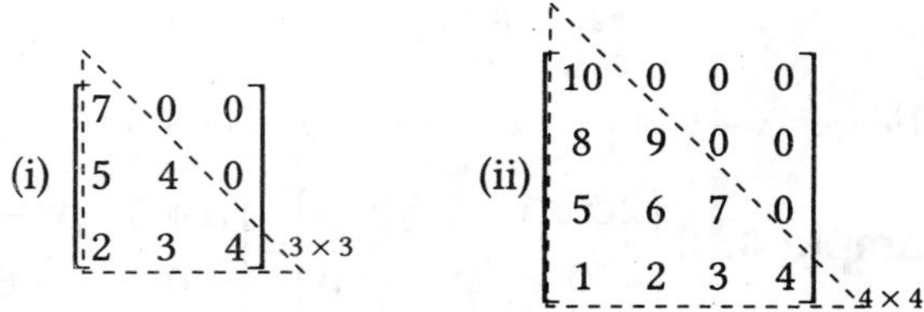

are upper triangular matrices.

(b) **Lower Triangular Matrix** A square matrix in which all elements above the principal diagonal are zero is called a lower triangular matrix i.e., a matrix $A=[a_{ij}]_{n\times n}$ is said to be a lower triangular matrix, if $a_{ij}=0$, when $i<j$. *For example,*

(i) $\begin{bmatrix} 7 & 0 & 0 \\ 5 & 4 & 0 \\ 2 & 3 & 4 \end{bmatrix}_{3\times 3}$ (ii) $\begin{bmatrix} 10 & 0 & 0 & 0 \\ 8 & 9 & 0 & 0 \\ 5 & 6 & 7 & 0 \\ 1 & 2 & 3 & 4 \end{bmatrix}_{4\times 4}$

are lower triangular matrices.

Note

Minimum number of zeroes in a triangular matrix is given by $\frac{n(n-1)}{2}$, where n is order of matrix.

10. Horizontal Matrix

A matrix is said to be horizontal matrix, if the number of rows is less than the number of columns i.e., a matrix $A=[a_{ij}]_{m\times n}$ is said to horizontal matrix, iff $m<n$.

For example, $A=\begin{bmatrix} 2 & 3 & 4 & 5 \\ 8 & 9 & 7 & -2 \\ 2 & -2 & -3 & 4 \end{bmatrix}_{3\times 4}$ is a horizontal matrix. [$\because$ number of rows (3) < number of columns (4)]

11. Vertical Matrix

A matrix is said to be vertical matrix, if the number of rows is greater than the number of columns i.e., a matrix $A=[a_{ij}]_{m\times n}$ is said to vertical matrix, iff $m>n$.

For example, $A=\begin{bmatrix} 2 & 3 & 4 \\ 0 & -1 & 7 \\ 3 & 5 & 4 \\ 2 & 7 & 9 \\ -1 & 2 & -5 \end{bmatrix}_{5\times 3}$ is a vertical matrix.

[$\because$ number of rows (5) > number of columns (3)]

12. Null Matrix or Zero Matrix

A matrix is said to be null matrix or zero matrix, if all elements are zero i.e., a matrix $A=[a_{ij}]_{m\times n}$ is said to be a zero or null matrix, iff $a_{ij}=0, \forall i, j$. It is denoted by O.

For example,

(i) $O_{2\times 3}=\begin{bmatrix} 0 & 0 & 0 \\ 0 & 0 & 0 \end{bmatrix}$ (ii) $O_{3\times 3}=\begin{bmatrix} 0 & 0 & 0 \\ 0 & 0 & 0 \\ 0 & 0 & 0 \end{bmatrix}$

are called the null matrices.

13. Sub-Matrix

A matrix which is obtained from a given matrix by deleting any number of rows and number of columns is called a sub-matrix of the given matrix.

For example, $\begin{bmatrix} 3 & 4 \\ -2 & 5 \end{bmatrix}$ is a sub-matrix of $\begin{bmatrix} 8 & 9 & 5 \\ 2 & 3 & 4 \\ 3 & -2 & 5 \end{bmatrix}$.

14. Trace of a Matrix

The sum of all diagonal elements of a square matrix $A=[a_{ij}]_{n\times n}$ (say) is called the **trace** of a matrix A and is denoted by Tr (A).

Thus, $$\text{Tr}(A)=\sum_{i=1}^{n} a_{ii}$$

For example, If $A=\begin{bmatrix} 2 & -7 & 9 \\ 0 & 3 & 2 \\ 8 & 9 & 4 \end{bmatrix}$, then

$$\text{Tr}(A)=2+3+4=9$$

Properties of Trace of a Matrix

Let $A=[a_{ij}]_{n\times n}$, $B=[b_{ij}]_{n\times n}$ and k is a scalar, then

(i) $\text{Tr}(kA)=k\cdot\text{Tr}(A)$
(ii) $\text{Tr}(A\pm B)=\text{Tr}(A)\pm\text{Tr}(B)$
(iii) $\text{Tr}(AB)=\text{Tr}(BA)$
(iv) $\text{Tr}(A)=\text{Tr}(A')$
(v) $\text{Tr}(I_n)=n$
(vi) $\text{Tr}(AB)\neq\text{Tr}(A)\,\text{Tr}(B)$
(vii) $\text{Tr}(A)=\text{Tr}(CAC^{-1})$, where C is a non-singular square matrix of order n.

15. Determinant of Square Matrix

Let $A=[a_{ij}]_{n\times n}$ be a matrix. The determinant formed by the elements of A is said to be the determinant of matrix A. This is denoted by $|A|$.

For example,

If $A=\begin{bmatrix}3 & 4 & 5\\ 6 & 7 & 8\\ 2 & -3 & 5\end{bmatrix}$, then $|A|=\begin{vmatrix}3 & 4 & 5\\ 6 & 7 & 8\\ 2 & -3 & 5\end{vmatrix}=-39.$

Remark

1. If $A_1, A_2, A_3, \ldots, A_n$ are square matrices of the same order, then $|A_1A_2A_3\ldots A_n|=|A_1||A_2||A_3|\cdots|A_n|$.
2. If k is a scalar and A is a square matrix of order n, then $|kA|=k^n|A|$

16. Comparable Matrices

Two matrices $A=[a_{ij}]_{m\times n}$ and $B=[b_{ij}]_{p\times q}$ are said to be comparable, if $m=p$ and $n=q$.

For example,

The matrices $\begin{bmatrix}a & b & c\\ d & e & f\end{bmatrix}$ and $\begin{bmatrix}p & q & r\\ s & t & u\end{bmatrix}$ are comparable

but the matrices $\begin{bmatrix}1 & 2\\ 4 & 8\end{bmatrix}$ and $\begin{bmatrix}2 & 4 & 6\\ 5 & 3 & 1\end{bmatrix}$ are not comparable.

Difference Between a Matrix and a Determinant

(i) A matrix cannot be reduced to a number but determinant can be reduced to a number.

(ii) The number of rows may or may not be equal to the number of columns in matrices but in determinant the number of rows is equal to the number of columns.

(iii) On interchanging the rows and columns, a different matrix is formed but in determinant it does not change the value.

(iv) A square matrix A such that $|A|\neq 0$, is called a non-singular matrix. If $|A|=0$, then the matrix A is called a singular matrix.

(v) Matrices represented by [ ], ( ), ‖ ‖ but determinant is represented by | |.

Equal Matrices

Two matrices are said to be equal, if

(i) they are of the same order i.e., if they have same number of rows and columns.

(ii) the elements in the corresponding positions of the two matrices are equal.

Thus, if $A=[a_{ij}]_{m\times n}$, $B=[b_{ij}]_{p\times q}$, then $A=B$, iff

(i) $m=p, n=q$ (ii) $a_{ij}=b_{ij}, \forall\, i, j$

For example, If $A=\begin{bmatrix}-1 & 2 & 4\\ 3 & 0 & 5\end{bmatrix}_{2\times 3}$ and

$B=\begin{bmatrix}a & b & c\\ d & e & f\end{bmatrix}_{2\times 3}$ are equal matrices, then

$a=-1, b=2, c=4 d=3, e=0, f=5$

| Example 3. If $\begin{bmatrix}x+3 & 2y+x\\ z-1 & 4w-8\end{bmatrix}=\begin{bmatrix}-x-1 & 0\\ 3 & 2w\end{bmatrix}$, then find the value of $|x+y|+|z+w|$.

Sol. As the given matrices are equal so their corresponding elements are equal.

$$x+3=-x-1 \Rightarrow 2x=-4 \quad \ldots\text{(i)}$$
$$\therefore \quad x=-2$$
$$2y+x=0$$
$$\Rightarrow \quad 2y-2=0 \quad \text{[from Eq. (i)]}$$
$$\Rightarrow \quad y=1 \quad \ldots\text{(ii)}$$
$$z-1=3$$
$$\Rightarrow \quad z=4 \quad \ldots\text{(iii)}$$
$$4w-8=2w$$
$$\Rightarrow \quad 2w=8$$
$$\therefore \quad w=4 \quad \ldots\text{(iv)}$$

Hence, $|x+y|+|z+w|=|-2+1|+|4+4|=1+8=9$

| Example 4. If $\begin{bmatrix}2\alpha+1 & 3\beta\\ 0 & \beta^2-5\beta\end{bmatrix}=\begin{bmatrix}\alpha+3 & \beta^2+2\\ 0 & -6\end{bmatrix}$, find the equation whose roots are α and β.

Sol. The given matrices will be equal, iff

$$2\alpha+1=\alpha+3 \Rightarrow \alpha=2$$
$$3\beta=\beta^2+2 \Rightarrow \beta^2-3\beta+2=0$$
$$\therefore \quad \beta=1, 2 \text{ and } \beta^2-5\beta=-6 \quad \ldots\text{(i)}$$
$$\Rightarrow \quad \beta^2-5\beta+6=0$$
$$\therefore \quad \beta=2, 3 \quad \ldots\text{(ii)}$$

From Eqs. (i) and (ii), we get $\beta=2$

$$\Rightarrow \quad \alpha=2, \beta=2$$

$\therefore$ Required equation is $x^2-(2+2)x+2\cdot 2=0$

$$\Rightarrow \quad x^2-4x+4=0$$

Operations of Matrices

Addition of Matrices

Let A, B be two matrices, each of order $m\times n$. Then, their sum $A+B$ is a matrix of order $m\times n$ and is obtained by adding the corresponding elements of A and B.

Thus, if $A=[a_{ij}]_{m\times n}$ and $B=[b_{ij}]_{m\times n}$, then $A+B=[a_{ij}+b_{ij}]_{m\times n}, \forall\, i, j$

Example 5. Given, $A=\begin{bmatrix}1 & 3 & 5\\ -2 & 0 & 2\\ 0 & 4 & -3\end{bmatrix}, B=\begin{bmatrix}0 & 3\\ -2 & 0\\ 0 & -4\end{bmatrix}$

and $C=\begin{bmatrix}4 & 1 & -2\\ 3 & 2 & 1\\ 2 & -1 & 7\end{bmatrix}$. Find (whichever defined)

(i) $A+B$. (ii) $A+C$.

Sol. (i) Given, A is a matrix of the type 3×3 and B is a matrix of the type 3×2.
Since, A and B are not of the same type.
$\therefore$ Sum $A+B$ is not defined.

(ii) As A and C are two matrices of the same type, therefore the sum $A+C$ is defined.

$$\therefore\ A+C=\begin{bmatrix}1 & 3 & 5\\ -2 & 0 & 2\\ 0 & 4 & -3\end{bmatrix}+\begin{bmatrix}4 & 1 & -2\\ 3 & 2 & 1\\ 2 & -1 & 7\end{bmatrix}$$

$$=\begin{bmatrix}1+4 & 3+1 & 5-2\\ -2+3 & 0+2 & 2+1\\ 0+2 & 4-1 & -3+7\end{bmatrix}=\begin{bmatrix}5 & 4 & 3\\ 1 & 2 & 3\\ 2 & 3 & 4\end{bmatrix}$$

Example 6. If $a, b; b, c$ and c, a are the roots of $x^2-4x+3=0$, $x^2-8x+15=0$ and $x^2-6x+5=0$, respectively. Compute $\begin{bmatrix}a^2+c^2 & a^2+b^2\\ b^2+c^2 & a^2+c^2\end{bmatrix}+\begin{bmatrix}2ac & -2ab\\ -2bc & -2ac\end{bmatrix}$.

Sol. $\because$ $x^2-4x+3=0$

$\Rightarrow$ $(x-1)(x-3)=0$ $\therefore$ $x=1, 3$

$x^2-8x+15=0$

$\Rightarrow$ $(x-3)(x-5)=0$ $\therefore$ $x=3, 5$

and $x^2-6x+5=0$

$\Rightarrow$ $(x-5)(x-1)=0$ $\therefore$ $x=5, 1$

It is clear that $a=1$, $b=3$ and $c=5$

Now, $\begin{bmatrix}a^2+c^2 & a^2+b^2\\ b^2+c^2 & a^2+c^2\end{bmatrix}+\begin{bmatrix}2ac & -2ab\\ -2bc & -2ac\end{bmatrix}$

$$=\begin{bmatrix}a^2+c^2+2ac & a^2+b^2-2ab\\ b^2+c^2-2bc & a^2+c^2-2ac\end{bmatrix}=\begin{bmatrix}(a+c)^2 & (a-b)^2\\ (b-c)^2 & (a-c)^2\end{bmatrix}$$

$$=\begin{bmatrix}(1+5)^2 & (1-3)^2\\ (3-5)^2 & (1-5)^2\end{bmatrix}=\begin{bmatrix}36 & 4\\ 4 & 16\end{bmatrix}$$

Properties of Matrix Addition

Property 1 Addition of matrices is commutative,

i.e. $A+B=B+A$

where A and B are any two $m\times n$ matrices, i.e. matrices of the same order.

Property 2 Addition of matrices is associative

i.e. $(A+B)+C=A+(B+C)$

where A, B and C are any three matrices of the same order $m\times n$ (say).

Property 3 Existence of additive identity

i.e. $A+O=A=O+A$

where A be any $m\times n$ matrix and O be the $m\times n$ null matrix. The null matrix O is the identity element for matrix addition.

Property 4 Existence of additive inverse

If A be any $m\times n$ matrix, then there exists another $m\times n$ matrix B, such that $A+B=O=B+A$

where O is the $m\times n$ null matrix.

Here, the matrix B is called the additive inverse of the matrix A or the negative of A.

Property 5 Cancellation laws

If A, B and C are matrices of the same order $m\times n$ (say), then $A+B=A+C\Rightarrow B=C$ [left cancellation law]

and $B+A=C+A\Rightarrow B=C$ [right cancellation law]

Scalar Multiplication

Let $A=[a_{ij}]_{m\times n}$ be a matrix and k be any number called a scalar. Then, the matrix obtained by multiplying every element of A by k is called the scalar multiple of A by k and is denoted by kA.

Thus, $kA=[ka_{ij}]_{m\times n}$

Properties of Scalar Multiplication

If $A=[a_{ij}]_{m\times n}$, $B=[b_{ij}]_{m\times n}$ are two matrices and k, l are scalars , then

(i) $k(A+B)=kA+kB$ (ii) $(k+l)A=kA+lA$

(iii) $(kl)A=k(lA)=l(kA)$

(iv) $(-k)A=-(kA)=k(-A)$

(v) $1A=A, (-1)A=-A$

Example 7. Determine the matrix A,

when $A=4\begin{bmatrix}1 & 2 & 3\\ -1 & -2 & -3\\ 4 & 2 & 6\end{bmatrix}+2\begin{bmatrix}5 & 4 & 1\\ 3 & 2 & 4\\ 3 & 8 & 2\end{bmatrix}$.

Sol. $A = \begin{bmatrix} 4 & 8 & 12 \\ -4 & -8 & -12 \\ 16 & 8 & 24 \end{bmatrix} + \begin{bmatrix} 10 & 8 & 2 \\ 6 & 4 & 8 \\ 6 & 16 & 4 \end{bmatrix}$

$= \begin{bmatrix} 4+10 & 8+8 & 12+2 \\ -4+6 & -8+4 & -12+8 \\ 16+6 & 8+16 & 24+4 \end{bmatrix} = \begin{bmatrix} 14 & 16 & 14 \\ 2 & -4 & -4 \\ 22 & 24 & 28 \end{bmatrix}$

| Example 8. If $A = \begin{bmatrix} 0 & 2 \\ 3 & -4 \end{bmatrix}$ and $kA = \begin{bmatrix} 0 & 3a \\ 2b & 24 \end{bmatrix}$, then find the value of $b - a - k$.

Sol. We have, $A = \begin{bmatrix} 0 & 2 \\ 3 & -4 \end{bmatrix} \Rightarrow kA = \begin{bmatrix} 0 & 2k \\ 3k & -4k \end{bmatrix}$

But $kA = \begin{bmatrix} 0 & 3a \\ 2b & 24 \end{bmatrix}$

$\therefore \begin{bmatrix} 0 & 2k \\ 3k & -4k \end{bmatrix} = \begin{bmatrix} 0 & 3a \\ 2b & 24 \end{bmatrix}$

$\Rightarrow 2k = 3a, 3k = 2b, -4k = 24$

$\Rightarrow k = -6, a = -4, b = -9$

Hence, $b - a - k = -9 - (-4) - (-6) = -9 + 4 + 6 = 1$

Subtraction of Matrices

Let A, B be two matrices, each of order $m \times n$. Then, their subtraction $A - B$ is a matrix of order $m \times n$ and is obtained by subtracting the corresponding elements of A and B. Thus, if $A = [a_{ij}]_{m \times n}$ and $B = [b_{ij}]_{m \times n}$,

then $A - B = [a_{ij} - b_{ij}]_{m \times n}, \forall\, i, j$

For example, If $A = \begin{bmatrix} 2 & 3 \\ 4 & 5 \\ 6 & 7 \end{bmatrix}$ and $B = \begin{bmatrix} a & b \\ c & d \\ e & f \end{bmatrix}$

then $A - B = \begin{bmatrix} 2 & 3 \\ 4 & 5 \\ 6 & 7 \end{bmatrix} - \begin{bmatrix} a & b \\ c & d \\ e & f \end{bmatrix} = \begin{bmatrix} 2-a & 3-b \\ 4-c & 5-d \\ 6-e & 7-f \end{bmatrix}$

| Example 9. Given, $A = \begin{bmatrix} 1 & 2 & -3 \\ 5 & 0 & 2 \\ 1 & -1 & 1 \end{bmatrix}$ and $B = \begin{bmatrix} 3 & -1 & 2 \\ 4 & 2 & 5 \\ 2 & 0 & 3 \end{bmatrix}$. Find the matrix C such that $A + 2C = B$.

Sol. Given, $A + 2C = B$

$2C = B - A = \begin{bmatrix} 3 & -1 & 2 \\ 4 & 2 & 5 \\ 2 & 0 & 3 \end{bmatrix} - \begin{bmatrix} 1 & 2 & -3 \\ 5 & 0 & 2 \\ 1 & -1 & 1 \end{bmatrix}$

$= \begin{bmatrix} 3-1 & -1-2 & 2+3 \\ 4-5 & 2-0 & 5-2 \\ 2-1 & 0+1 & 3-1 \end{bmatrix}$

$\therefore 2C = \begin{bmatrix} 2 & -3 & 5 \\ -1 & 2 & 3 \\ 1 & 1 & 2 \end{bmatrix} \Rightarrow C = \frac{1}{2}\begin{bmatrix} 2 & -3 & 5 \\ -1 & 2 & 3 \\ 1 & 1 & 2 \end{bmatrix}$

$= \begin{bmatrix} 1 & -3/2 & 5/2 \\ -1/2 & 1 & 3/2 \\ 1/2 & 1/2 & 1 \end{bmatrix}$

| Example 10. Solve the following equations for X and Y. $2X - Y = \begin{bmatrix} 3 & -3 & 0 \\ 3 & 3 & 2 \end{bmatrix}, 2Y + X = \begin{bmatrix} 4 & 1 & 5 \\ -1 & 4 & -4 \end{bmatrix}$

Sol. Given, $2X - Y = \begin{bmatrix} 3 & -3 & 0 \\ 3 & 3 & 2 \end{bmatrix}$

On multiplying both sides by 2, we get

$4X - 2Y = 2\begin{bmatrix} 3 & -3 & 0 \\ 3 & 3 & 2 \end{bmatrix}; \ 4X - 2Y = \begin{bmatrix} 6 & -6 & 0 \\ 6 & 6 & 4 \end{bmatrix}$ ...(i)

also given $X + 2Y = \begin{bmatrix} 4 & 1 & 5 \\ -1 & 4 & -4 \end{bmatrix}$ ...(ii)

Adding Eqs. (i) and (ii), we get

$5X = \begin{bmatrix} 6 & -6 & 0 \\ 6 & 6 & 4 \end{bmatrix} + \begin{bmatrix} 4 & 1 & 5 \\ -1 & 4 & -4 \end{bmatrix}$

$= \begin{bmatrix} 6+4 & -6+1 & 0+5 \\ 6-1 & 6+4 & 4-4 \end{bmatrix} = \begin{bmatrix} 10 & -5 & 5 \\ 5 & 10 & 0 \end{bmatrix}$

$\therefore X = \frac{1}{5}\begin{bmatrix} 10 & -5 & 5 \\ 5 & 10 & 0 \end{bmatrix} \Rightarrow X = \begin{bmatrix} 2 & -1 & 1 \\ 1 & 2 & 0 \end{bmatrix}$

Putting the value of X in Eq. (ii), we get

$\begin{bmatrix} 2 & -1 & 1 \\ 1 & 2 & 0 \end{bmatrix} + 2Y = \begin{bmatrix} 4 & 1 & 5 \\ -1 & 4 & -4 \end{bmatrix}$

$\Rightarrow 2Y = \begin{bmatrix} 4 & 1 & 5 \\ -1 & 4 & -4 \end{bmatrix} - \begin{bmatrix} 2 & -1 & 1 \\ 1 & 2 & 0 \end{bmatrix}$

$= \begin{bmatrix} 4-2 & 1+1 & 5-1 \\ -1-1 & 4-2 & -4-0 \end{bmatrix} = \begin{bmatrix} 2 & 2 & 4 \\ -2 & 2 & -4 \end{bmatrix}$

$\therefore Y = \begin{bmatrix} 1 & 1 & 2 \\ -1 & 1 & -2 \end{bmatrix}$

Hence, $X = \begin{bmatrix} 2 & -1 & 1 \\ 1 & 2 & 0 \end{bmatrix}$ and $Y = \begin{bmatrix} 1 & 1 & 2 \\ -1 & 1 & -2 \end{bmatrix}$

Remark

If two matrices A and B are of the same order, then only their addition and subtraction is possible and these matrices are said to be conformable for addition or subtraction. On the other hand, if the matrices A and B are of different orders, then their addition and subtraction is not possible and these matrices are called non-conformable for addition and subtraction.

Multiplication

Conformable for Multiplication

If A and B be two matrices which are said to be conformable for the product AB. If the number of columns in A (called the pre-factor) is equal to the number of rows in B (called the post-factor) otherwise non-conformable for multiplication. Thus,

(i) AB is defined, if number of columns in A = number of rows in B.

(ii) BA is defined, if number of columns in B = number of rows in A.

Multiplication of Matrices

Let $A=[a_{ij}]_{m\times n}$ and $B=[b_{ij}]_{n\times p}$ be two matrices, then the product AB is defined as the matrix $C=[C_{ij}]_{m\times p}$,

where $C_{ij}=\sum_{j=1}^{n} a_{ij}\, b_{jk}, 1\le i\le m, 1\le k\le p$

$$=a_{i1}\,b_{1k}+a_{i2}\,b_{2k}+a_{i3}\,b_{3k}+\ldots+a_{in}\,b_{nk}$$

i.e., (i, k) th entry of the product AB is the sum of the product of the corresponding elements of the ith row of A (pre-factor) and kth column of B (post-factor).

Note

In the product AB, $\begin{cases} A = \text{Pre-factor} \\ B = \text{Post-factor}\end{cases}$

Example 11. If $A=\begin{bmatrix}0&1&2\\1&2&3\\2&3&4\end{bmatrix}$ and $B=\begin{bmatrix}1&-2\\-1&0\\2&-1\end{bmatrix}$,

obtain the product AB and explain why BA is not defined?

Sol. Here, the number of columns in $A=3$ = the number of rows in B. Therefore, the product AB is defined.

$$AB=\begin{bmatrix}0&1&2\\1&2&3\\2&3&4\end{bmatrix}\begin{matrix}R_1\\R_2\\R_3\end{matrix}\times\overset{\begin{matrix}C_1 & C_2\end{matrix}}{\begin{bmatrix}1&-2\\-1&0\\2&-1\end{bmatrix}}$$

R_1, R_2, R_3 are rows of A and C_1, C_2 are columns of B.

$$\therefore \quad AB=\begin{bmatrix}R_1C_1 & R_1C_2\\R_2C_1 & R_2C_2\\R_3C_1 & R_3C_2\end{bmatrix}_{3\times 2}$$

$$\begin{bmatrix}\boxed{0\ 1\ 2}\begin{bmatrix}1\\-1\\2\end{bmatrix} & \boxed{0\ 1\ 2}\begin{bmatrix}-2\\0\\-1\end{bmatrix}\\ \boxed{1\ 2\ 3}\begin{bmatrix}1\\-1\\2\end{bmatrix} & \boxed{1\ 2\ 3}\begin{bmatrix}-2\\0\\-1\end{bmatrix}\\ \boxed{2\ 3\ 4}\begin{bmatrix}1\\-1\\2\end{bmatrix} & \boxed{2\ 3\ 4}\begin{bmatrix}-2\\0\\-1\end{bmatrix}\end{bmatrix}_{3\times 2}$$

For convenience of multiplication we write columns in horizontal rectangles.

$$\begin{bmatrix}\left\{\begin{matrix}\boxed{0\ \ 1\ \ 2}\\\boxed{1\ -1\ \ 2}\end{matrix}\right\} & \left\{\begin{matrix}\boxed{0\ \ 1\ \ 2}\\\boxed{-2\ \ 0\ -1}\end{matrix}\right\}\\ \left\{\begin{matrix}\boxed{1\ \ 2\ \ 3}\\\boxed{1\ -1\ \ 2}\end{matrix}\right\} & \left\{\begin{matrix}\boxed{1\ \ 2\ \ 3}\\\boxed{-2\ \ 0\ -1}\end{matrix}\right\}\\ \left\{\begin{matrix}\boxed{2\ \ 3\ \ 4}\\\boxed{1\ -1\ \ 2}\end{matrix}\right\} & \left\{\begin{matrix}\boxed{2\ \ 3\ \ 4}\\\boxed{-2\ \ 0\ -1}\end{matrix}\right\}\end{bmatrix}$$

$$=\begin{bmatrix}0\times1+1\times(-1)+2\times2 & 0\times(-2)+1\times0+2\times(-1)\\1\times1+2\times(-1)+3\times2 & 1\times(-2)+2\times0+3\times(-1)\\2\times1+3\times(-1)+4\times2 & 2\times(-2)+3\times0+4\times(-1)\end{bmatrix}_{3\times 2}$$

$$=\begin{bmatrix}0-1+4 & 0+0-2\\1-2+6 & -2+0-3\\2-3+8 & -4+0-4\end{bmatrix}_{3\times 2}=\begin{bmatrix}3&-2\\5&-5\\7&-8\end{bmatrix}_{3\times 2}$$

Since, the number of columns of B is 2 and the number of rows of A is 3, BA is not defined ($\because 2\ne 3$).

Remark

Verification for the product to be correct.

From above example

$$\begin{bmatrix}0&1&2\\1&2&3\\2&3&4\end{bmatrix}\times\begin{bmatrix}1&-2\\-1&0\\2&-1\end{bmatrix}=\begin{bmatrix}3&-2\\5&-5\\7&-8\end{bmatrix}$$

Sum $\underline{3\quad 6\quad 9}$ $\qquad\qquad$ $\underline{15\ -15}$

Now, $\boxed{3\,6\,9}\ \begin{bmatrix}1\\-1\\2\end{bmatrix}$ $=3\times1+6\times(-1)+9\times2$ $=3-6+18$ $=15$

and $\boxed{3\,6\,9}\ \begin{bmatrix}-2\\0\\-1\end{bmatrix}$ $=3(-2)+6\times0+9\times(-1)$ $=-6+0-9$ $=-15$

Example 12. If $A=\begin{bmatrix}0 & -\tan(\alpha/2)\\ \tan(\alpha/2) & 0\end{bmatrix}$ and I is a 2×2 unit matrix, prove that

$$I+A=(I-A)\begin{bmatrix}\cos\alpha & -\sin\alpha\\ \sin\alpha & \cos\alpha\end{bmatrix}.$$

Sol. Since, $I=\begin{bmatrix}1&0\\0&1\end{bmatrix}$ and given $A=\begin{bmatrix}0 & -\tan(\alpha/2)\\ \tan(\alpha/2) & 0\end{bmatrix}$

$$\therefore \quad I+A=\begin{bmatrix}1 & -\tan(\alpha/2)\\ \tan(\alpha/2) & 1\end{bmatrix} \quad \ldots(i)$$

$$\text{RHS}=(I-A)\begin{bmatrix}\cos\alpha & -\sin\alpha\\ \sin\alpha & \cos\alpha\end{bmatrix}$$

$$=\begin{bmatrix}1 & \tan(\alpha/2)\\ -\tan(\alpha/2) & 1\end{bmatrix}\begin{bmatrix}\cos\alpha & -\sin\alpha\\ \sin\alpha & \cos\alpha\end{bmatrix}$$

$$= \begin{bmatrix} 1 & \tan(\alpha/2) \\ -\tan(\alpha/2) & 1 \end{bmatrix} \begin{bmatrix} \frac{1-\tan^2(\alpha/2)}{1+\tan^2(\alpha/2)} & \frac{-2\tan(\alpha/2)}{1+\tan^2(\alpha/2)} \\ \frac{2\tan(\alpha/2)}{1+\tan^2(\alpha/2)} & \frac{1-\tan^2(\alpha/2)}{1+\tan^2(\alpha/2)} \end{bmatrix}$$

Let $\tan(\alpha/2) = \lambda$, then

$$\text{RHS} = \begin{bmatrix} 1 & \lambda \\ -\lambda & 1 \end{bmatrix} \begin{bmatrix} \frac{1-\lambda^2}{1+\lambda^2} & \frac{-2\lambda}{1+\lambda^2} \\ \frac{2\lambda}{1+\lambda^2} & \frac{1-\lambda^2}{1+\lambda^2} \end{bmatrix}$$

$$= \begin{bmatrix} \frac{1-\lambda^2+2\lambda^2}{1+\lambda^2} & \frac{-2\lambda+\lambda(1-\lambda^2)}{1+\lambda^2} \\ \frac{-\lambda(1-\lambda^2)+2\lambda}{1+\lambda^2} & \frac{2\lambda^2+1-\lambda^2}{1+\lambda^2} \end{bmatrix}$$

$$= \begin{bmatrix} \frac{1+\lambda^2}{1+\lambda^2} & \frac{-\lambda(1+\lambda^2)}{1+\lambda^2} \\ \frac{\lambda(1+\lambda^2)}{1+\lambda^2} & \frac{1+\lambda^2}{1+\lambda^2} \end{bmatrix} = \begin{bmatrix} 1 & -\lambda \\ \lambda & 1 \end{bmatrix}$$

$$= \begin{bmatrix} 1 & -\tan(\alpha/2) \\ \tan(\alpha/2) & 1 \end{bmatrix} \quad [\because \lambda = \tan(\alpha/2)]$$

$= I + A$ [from Eq. (i)]

$=$ LHS

Pre-multiplication and Post-multiplication of Matrices

The matrix AB is the matrix B pre-multiplied by A and the matrix BA is the matrix B post-multiplied by A.

Properties of Multiplication of Matrices

Property 1 Multiplication of matrices is not commutative i.e.

$$AB \neq BA$$

Note

1. If $AB = -BA$, then A and B are said to anti-commute.
2. If $A = \begin{bmatrix} 1 & 0 \\ 0 & 2 \end{bmatrix}$ and $B = \begin{bmatrix} 3 & 0 \\ 0 & 4 \end{bmatrix}$, then $AB = BA = \begin{bmatrix} 3 & 0 \\ 0 & 8 \end{bmatrix}$.

Observe that multiplication of diagonal matrices of same order will be commutative.

Property 2 Matrix multiplication associative if conformability assumed.

i.e. $A(BC) = (AB)C$

Property 3 Matrix multiplication is distributive with respect to addition. i.e. $A(B+C) = AB + AC$, whenever both sides of equality are defined.

Property 4 If A is an $m \times n$ matrix, then $I_m A = A = A I_n$.

Property 5 If product of two matrices is a zero matrix, it is not necessary that one of the matrices is a zero matrix.

For example,

(i) $\begin{bmatrix} 1 & 1 \\ 2 & 2 \end{bmatrix} \times \begin{bmatrix} -1 & 1 \\ 1 & -1 \end{bmatrix} = \begin{bmatrix} 1(-1)+1.1 & 1\cdot1+1\cdot(-1) \\ 2\cdot(-1)+2.1 & 2\cdot1+2\cdot(-1) \end{bmatrix} = \begin{bmatrix} 0 & 0 \\ 0 & 0 \end{bmatrix} = O$

(ii) $\begin{bmatrix} 0 & 0 \\ 1 & 0 \end{bmatrix} \times \begin{bmatrix} 0 & 0 \\ 0 & 1 \end{bmatrix} = \begin{bmatrix} 0\cdot0+0\cdot0 & 0\cdot0+0\cdot1 \\ 1\cdot0+0\cdot0 & 1\cdot0+0\cdot1 \end{bmatrix} = \begin{bmatrix} 0 & 0 \\ 0 & 0 \end{bmatrix} = O$

None of the matrices on the LHS is a null matrix whereas their product is a null matrix.

Note If A and B are two non-zero matrices such that $AB = 0$, then A and B are called the divisors of zero. Also, if

$AB = 0 \Rightarrow |AB| = 0 \Rightarrow |A||B| = 0$

$\Rightarrow$ $|A| = 0$ or $|B| = 0$ but not the converse.

Property 6 Multiplication of a matrix A by a null matrix conformable with A for multiplication.

For example, If $A = \begin{bmatrix} 3 & 4 \\ 5 & 6 \\ 7 & 8 \end{bmatrix}_{3\times2}$ and $O = \begin{bmatrix} 0 & 0 & 0 \\ 0 & 0 & 0 \end{bmatrix}_{2\times3}$,

then $AO = \begin{bmatrix} 0 & 0 & 0 \\ 0 & 0 & 0 \\ 0 & 0 & 0 \end{bmatrix}_{3\times3}$, which is a 3×3 null matrix.

Property 7 Multiplication of a matrix by itself

The product of $A\,A\,A \ldots m$ times $= A^m$ and $(A^m)^n = A^{mn}$

Note

1. If I be unit matrix, then $I^2 = I^3 = \ldots = I^m = I \ (m \in I_+)$
2. If A and B are two matrices of the same order, then
   (i) $(A+B)^2 = A^2 + AB + BA + B^2$
   (ii) $(A-B)^2 = A^2 - AB - BA + B^2$
   (iii) $(A-B)(A+B) = A^2 + AB - BA + B^2$
   (iv) $(A+B)(A-B) = A^2 - AB + BA - B^2$
   (v) $A(-B) = (-A)(B) = -AB$

Example 13. If $A = \begin{bmatrix} 1 & 2 \\ -2 & 3 \end{bmatrix}$, $B = \begin{bmatrix} 2 & 1 \\ 2 & 3 \end{bmatrix}$ and $C = \begin{bmatrix} -3 & 1 \\ 2 & 0 \end{bmatrix}$, verify that $(AB)C = A(BC)$ and $A(B+C) = AB + AC$.

Sol. We have, $AB = \begin{bmatrix} 1 & 2 \\ -2 & 3 \end{bmatrix} \times \begin{bmatrix} 2 & 1 \\ 2 & 3 \end{bmatrix}$

$$= \begin{bmatrix} 1\cdot2+2\cdot2 & 1\cdot1+2\cdot3 \\ (-2)\cdot2+3\cdot2 & (-2)\cdot1+3\cdot3 \end{bmatrix} = \begin{bmatrix} 6 & 7 \\ 2 & 7 \end{bmatrix}$$

$$BC = \begin{bmatrix} 2 & 1 \\ 2 & 3 \end{bmatrix} \times \begin{bmatrix} -3 & 1 \\ 2 & 0 \end{bmatrix} = \begin{bmatrix} 2\cdot(-3)+1\cdot 2 & 2\cdot 1+1\cdot 0 \\ 2\cdot(-3)+3\cdot 2 & 2\cdot 1+3\cdot 0 \end{bmatrix}$$

$$= \begin{bmatrix} -6+2 & 2+0 \\ -6+6 & 2+0 \end{bmatrix} = \begin{bmatrix} -4 & 2 \\ 0 & 2 \end{bmatrix}$$

$$AC = \begin{bmatrix} 1 & 2 \\ -2 & 3 \end{bmatrix} \times \begin{bmatrix} -3 & 1 \\ 2 & 0 \end{bmatrix} = \begin{bmatrix} 1\cdot(-3)+2\cdot 2 & 1\cdot 1+2\cdot 0 \\ (-2)\cdot(-3)+3\cdot 2 & (-2)\cdot 1+3\cdot 0 \end{bmatrix}$$

$$= \begin{bmatrix} -3+4 & 1+0 \\ 6+6 & -2+0 \end{bmatrix} = \begin{bmatrix} 1 & 1 \\ 12 & -2 \end{bmatrix}$$

$$B+C = \begin{bmatrix} 2 & 1 \\ 2 & 3 \end{bmatrix} + \begin{bmatrix} -3 & 1 \\ 2 & 0 \end{bmatrix} = \begin{bmatrix} 2-3 & 1+1 \\ 2+2 & 3+0 \end{bmatrix} = \begin{bmatrix} -1 & 2 \\ 4 & 3 \end{bmatrix}$$

Now, $(AB)C = \begin{bmatrix} 6 & 7 \\ 2 & 7 \end{bmatrix} \times \begin{bmatrix} -3 & 1 \\ 2 & 0 \end{bmatrix} = \begin{bmatrix} -18+14 & 6+0 \\ -6+14 & 2+0 \end{bmatrix}$

$$= \begin{bmatrix} -4 & 6 \\ 8 & 2 \end{bmatrix} \quad \text{...(i)}$$

$$A(BC) = \begin{bmatrix} 1 & 2 \\ -2 & 3 \end{bmatrix} \times \begin{bmatrix} -4 & 2 \\ 0 & 2 \end{bmatrix}$$

$$= \begin{bmatrix} -4+0 & 2+4 \\ 8+0 & -4+6 \end{bmatrix} = \begin{bmatrix} -4 & 6 \\ 8 & 2 \end{bmatrix} \quad \text{...(ii)}$$

Thus, from Eqs. (i) and (ii), we get, $(AB)C = A(BC)$

Now, $A(B+C) = \begin{bmatrix} 1 & 2 \\ -2 & 3 \end{bmatrix} \times \begin{bmatrix} -1 & 2 \\ 4 & 3 \end{bmatrix} = \begin{bmatrix} -1+8 & 2+6 \\ 2+12 & -4+9 \end{bmatrix}$

$$= \begin{bmatrix} 7 & 8 \\ 14 & 5 \end{bmatrix} \quad \text{...(iii)}$$

and $AB + AC = \begin{bmatrix} 6 & 7 \\ 2 & 7 \end{bmatrix} + \begin{bmatrix} 1 & 1 \\ 12 & -2 \end{bmatrix} = \begin{bmatrix} 6+1 & 7+1 \\ 2+12 & 7-2 \end{bmatrix}$

$$= \begin{bmatrix} 7 & 8 \\ 14 & 5 \end{bmatrix} \quad \text{...(iv)}$$

Thus, from Eqs. (iii) and (iv), we get

$$A(B+C) = AB + AC$$

Example 14. If $A = \begin{bmatrix} 0 & 1 & 0 \\ 0 & 0 & 1 \\ p & q & r \end{bmatrix}$, show that $A^3 = pI + qA + rA^2$.

Sol. We have, $A^2 = A \cdot A$

$$= \begin{bmatrix} 0 & 1 & 0 \\ 0 & 0 & 1 \\ p & q & r \end{bmatrix} \times \begin{bmatrix} 0 & 1 & 0 \\ 0 & 0 & 1 \\ p & q & r \end{bmatrix}$$

$$= \begin{bmatrix} 0 & 0 & 1 \\ p & q & r \\ pr & p+qr & q+r^2 \end{bmatrix}$$

$$\therefore \quad A^3 = A^2 \cdot A = \begin{bmatrix} 0 & 0 & 1 \\ p & q & r \\ pr & p+qr & q+r^2 \end{bmatrix} \times \begin{bmatrix} 0 & 1 & 0 \\ 0 & 0 & 1 \\ p & q & r \end{bmatrix}$$

$$= \begin{bmatrix} p & q & r \\ pr & p+qr & q+r^2 \\ pq+r^2p & pr+q^2+qr^2 & p+2qr+r^3 \end{bmatrix} \quad \text{...(i)}$$

and $pI + qA + rA^2 = p\begin{bmatrix} 1 & 0 & 0 \\ 0 & 1 & 0 \\ 0 & 0 & 1 \end{bmatrix} + q\begin{bmatrix} 0 & 1 & 0 \\ 0 & 0 & 1 \\ p & q & r \end{bmatrix}$

$$+ r\begin{bmatrix} 0 & 0 & 1 \\ p & q & r \\ pr & p+qr & q+r^2 \end{bmatrix}$$

$$= \begin{bmatrix} p & 0 & 0 \\ 0 & p & 0 \\ 0 & 0 & p \end{bmatrix} + \begin{bmatrix} 0 & q & 0 \\ 0 & 0 & q \\ pq & q^2 & qr \end{bmatrix} + \begin{bmatrix} 0 & 0 & r \\ pr & qr & r^2 \\ pr^2 & pr+qr^2 & qr+r^3 \end{bmatrix}$$

$$= \begin{bmatrix} p+0+0 & 0+q+0 & 0+0+r \\ 0+0+pr & p+0+qr & 0+q+r^2 \\ 0+pq+pr^2 & 0+q^2+pr+qr^2 & p+qr+qr+r^3 \end{bmatrix}$$

$$= \begin{bmatrix} p & q & r \\ pr & p+qr & q+r^2 \\ pq+pr^2 & q^2+pr+qr^2 & p+2qr+r^3 \end{bmatrix} \quad \text{...(ii)}$$

Thus, from Eqs. (i) and (ii), we get $A^3 = pI + qA + rA^2$

Example 15. Find x, so that $[1 \;\; x \;\; 1]\begin{bmatrix} 1 & 3 & 2 \\ 0 & 5 & 1 \\ 0 & 3 & 2 \end{bmatrix}\begin{bmatrix} 1 \\ 1 \\ x \end{bmatrix} = O$.

Sol. We have, $[1 \;\; x \;\; 1]\begin{bmatrix} 1 & 3 & 2 \\ 0 & 5 & 1 \\ 0 & 3 & 2 \end{bmatrix}\begin{bmatrix} 1 \\ 1 \\ x \end{bmatrix} = O$

$$\Rightarrow \quad [1 \;\; 5x+6 \;\; x+4]\begin{bmatrix} 1 \\ 1 \\ x \end{bmatrix} = O$$

$$\Rightarrow \quad [1+5x+6+x^2+4x] = O$$

or $\quad x^2 + 9x + 7 = 0$

$$\therefore \quad x = \frac{-9 \pm \sqrt{(81-28)}}{2} \Rightarrow x = \frac{-9 \pm \sqrt{53}}{2}$$

Various Kinds of Matrices

Idempotent Matrix

A square matrix A is called idempotent provided it satisfies the relation $A^2 = A$.

Note

$A^n = A, \forall n \geq 2, n \in N$.

Example 16. Show that the matrix

$$A = \begin{bmatrix} 2 & -2 & -4 \\ -1 & 3 & 4 \\ 1 & -2 & -3 \end{bmatrix}$$ is idempotent.

Sol. $$A^2 = A \cdot A = \begin{bmatrix} 2 & -2 & -4 \\ -1 & 3 & 4 \\ 1 & -2 & -3 \end{bmatrix} \times \begin{bmatrix} 2 & -2 & -4 \\ -1 & 3 & 4 \\ 1 & -2 & -3 \end{bmatrix}$$

$$= \begin{bmatrix} 2\cdot 2 + (-2)\cdot(-1) + (-4)\cdot 1 & 2\cdot(-2) + (-2)\cdot 3 + (-4)\cdot(-2) & 2\cdot(-4) + (-2)\cdot 4 + (-4)\cdot(-3) \\ (-1)\cdot 2 + 3\cdot(-1) + 4\cdot 1 & (-1)\cdot(-2) + 3\cdot 3 + 4\cdot(-2) & (-1)\cdot(-4) + 3\cdot 4 + 4\cdot(-3) \\ 1\cdot 2 + (-2)\cdot(-1) + (-3)\cdot 1 & 1\cdot(-2) + (-2)\cdot 3 + (-3)\cdot(-2) & 1\cdot(-4) + (-2)\cdot 4 + (-3)\cdot(-3) \end{bmatrix}$$

$$= \begin{bmatrix} 2 & -2 & -4 \\ -1 & 3 & 4 \\ 1 & -2 & -3 \end{bmatrix} = A$$

Hence, the matrix A is idempotent.

Periodic Matrix

A square matrix A is called periodic, if $A^{k+1} = A$, where k is a positive integer. If k is the least positive integer for which $A^{k+1} = A$, then k is said to be **period** of A. For $k = 1$, we get $A^2 = A$ and we called it to be **idempotent matrix.**

Note

Period of an idempotent matrix is 1.

Nilpotent Matrix

A square matrix A is called nilpotent matrix of order m provided it satisfies the relation $A^k = O$ and $A^{k-1} \neq O$, where k is positive integer and O is null matrix and k is the order of the nilpotent matrix A.

Example 17. Show that $\begin{bmatrix} 1 & 1 & 3 \\ 5 & 2 & 6 \\ -2 & -1 & -3 \end{bmatrix}$ is nilpotent matrix of order 3.

Sol. Let $A = \begin{bmatrix} 1 & 1 & 3 \\ 5 & 2 & 6 \\ -2 & -1 & -3 \end{bmatrix}$

$$\therefore A^2 = A \cdot A = \begin{bmatrix} 1 & 1 & 3 \\ 5 & 2 & 6 \\ -2 & -1 & -3 \end{bmatrix} \times \begin{bmatrix} 1 & 1 & 3 \\ 5 & 2 & 6 \\ -2 & -1 & -3 \end{bmatrix}$$

$$= \begin{bmatrix} 1+5-6 & 1+2-3 & 3+6-9 \\ 5+10-12 & 5+4-6 & 15+12-18 \\ -2-5+6 & -2-2+3 & -6-6+9 \end{bmatrix}$$

$$= \begin{bmatrix} 0 & 0 & 0 \\ 3 & 3 & 9 \\ -1 & -1 & -3 \end{bmatrix}$$

$$\therefore A^3 = A^2 \cdot A = \begin{bmatrix} 0 & 0 & 0 \\ 3 & 3 & 9 \\ -1 & -1 & -3 \end{bmatrix} \times \begin{bmatrix} 1 & 1 & 3 \\ 5 & 2 & 6 \\ -2 & -1 & -3 \end{bmatrix}$$

$$= \begin{bmatrix} 0+0+0 & 0+0+0 & 0+0+0 \\ 3+15-18 & 3+6-9 & 9+18-27 \\ -1-5+6 & -1-2+3 & -3-6+9 \end{bmatrix} = \begin{bmatrix} 0 & 0 & 0 \\ 0 & 0 & 0 \\ 0 & 0 & 0 \end{bmatrix} = O$$

$\therefore$ $A^3 = O$ i.e., $A^k = O$

Here, $k = 3$

Hence, the matrix A is nilpotent of order 3.

Involutory Matrix

A square matrix A is called involutory provided it satisfies the relation $A^2 = I$, where I is identity matrix.

Note $A = A^{-1}$ for an involutory matrix.

Example 18. Show that the matrix

$$A = \begin{bmatrix} -5 & -8 & 0 \\ 3 & 5 & 0 \\ 1 & 2 & -1 \end{bmatrix}$$ is involutory.

Sol. $$A^2 = A \cdot A = \begin{bmatrix} -5 & -8 & 0 \\ 3 & 5 & 0 \\ 1 & 2 & -1 \end{bmatrix} \times \begin{bmatrix} -5 & -8 & 0 \\ 3 & 5 & 0 \\ 1 & 2 & -1 \end{bmatrix}$$

$$= \begin{bmatrix} 25-24+0 & 40-40+0 & 0+0+0 \\ -15+15+0 & -24+25+0 & 0+0+0 \\ -5+6-1 & -8+10-2 & 0+0+1 \end{bmatrix} = \begin{bmatrix} 1 & 0 & 0 \\ 0 & 1 & 0 \\ 0 & 0 & 1 \end{bmatrix} = I$$

Hence, the given matrix A is involutory.

Exercise for Session 1

1. If $A=\begin{bmatrix}\alpha & 2\\ 2 & \alpha\end{bmatrix}$ and $|A^3|=125$, α is equal to
   (a) ± 2 (b) ± 3
   (c) ± 5 (d) 0

2. If $A=\begin{bmatrix}1 & -1\\ 2 & -1\end{bmatrix}$, $B=\begin{bmatrix}a & 1\\ b & -1\end{bmatrix}$ and $(A+B)^2=A^2+B^2$, the value of $a+b$ is
   (a) 4 (b) 5
   (c) 6 (d) 7

3. If $A=\begin{bmatrix}1 & 2\\ 2 & 3\end{bmatrix}$ and $A^2-\lambda A-I_2=O$, then λ is equal to
   (a) -4 (b) -2
   (c) 2 (d) 4

4. Let $A=\begin{bmatrix}0 & \alpha\\ 0 & 0\end{bmatrix}$ and $(A+I)^{50}-50A=\begin{bmatrix}a & b\\ c & d\end{bmatrix}$, the value of $a+b+c+d$, is
   (a) 1 (b) 2
   (c) 4 (d) None of these

5. If $A=\begin{bmatrix}\cos\theta & \sin\theta\\ -\sin\theta & \cos\theta\end{bmatrix}$, then $A^2=I$ is true for
   (a) $\theta=0$ (b) $\theta=\frac{\pi}{4}$
   (c) $\theta=\frac{\pi}{2}$ (d) None of these

6. If $\begin{bmatrix}\alpha & \beta\\ \gamma & -\alpha\end{bmatrix}$ is to be the square root of two rowed unit matrix, then α, β and γ should satisfy the relation
   (a) $1-\alpha^2+\beta\gamma=0$ (b) $\alpha^2+\beta\gamma-1=0$
   (c) $1+\alpha^2+\beta\gamma=0$ (d) $1-\alpha^2-\beta\gamma=0$

7. If $A=\begin{bmatrix}1 & 0\\ 1/2 & 1\end{bmatrix}$, then A^{100} is equal to
   (a) $\begin{bmatrix}1 & 0\\ 25 & 0\end{bmatrix}$ (b) $\begin{bmatrix}1 & 0\\ 50 & 1\end{bmatrix}$
   (c) $\begin{bmatrix}1 & 0\\ (1/2)^{100} & 1\end{bmatrix}$ (d) None of these

8. If the product of n matrices $\begin{bmatrix}1 & 1\\ 0 & 1\end{bmatrix}\begin{bmatrix}1 & 2\\ 0 & 1\end{bmatrix}\begin{bmatrix}1 & 3\\ 0 & 1\end{bmatrix}\cdots\begin{bmatrix}1 & n\\ 0 & 1\end{bmatrix}$ is equal to the matrix $\begin{bmatrix}1 & 378\\ 0 & 1\end{bmatrix}$, the value of n is equal to
   (a) 26 (b) 27
   (c) 377 (d) 378

9. If A and B are two matrices such that $AB=B$ and $BA=A$, then A^2+B^2 is equal to
   (a) $2AB$ (b) $2BA$
   (c) $A+B$ (d) AB

Session 2

Transpose of a Matrix, Symmetric Matrix, Orthogonal Matrix, Complex Conjugate (or Conjugate) of a Matrix, Hermitian Matrix, Unitary Matrix, Determinant of a Matrix, Singular and Non-Singular Matrices,

Transpose of a Matrix

Let $A \quad a_{ij\ m \times n}$ be any given matrix, then the matrix obtained by interchanging the rows and columns of A is called the transpose of A. Transpose of the matrix A is denoted by A' or A^T or A^t. In other words, if $A \quad a_{ij\ m\times n}$, then $A' = [a_{ji}]_{n \times m}$.

For example,

$$\text{If} \qquad A = \begin{bmatrix} 2 & 3 & 4 & 5 \\ -2 & -1 & 4 & 8 \\ 7 & 5 & 3 & 1 \end{bmatrix}_{3\times 4},$$

$$\text{then} \qquad A' = \begin{bmatrix} 2 & -2 & 7 \\ 3 & -1 & 5 \\ 4 & 4 & 3 \\ 5 & 8 & 1 \end{bmatrix}_{4\times 3}$$

Properties of Transpose Matrices

If A' and B' denote the transpose of A and B respectively, then

(i) $A')' = A$

(ii) $A \pm B\ ' = A' \pm B'$; A and B are conformable for matrix addition.

(iii) $kA\ ' = kA'$; k is a scalar.

(iv) $AB\ ' = B'A'$; A and B are conformable for matrix product AB.

In general, $A\ A\ A\ \ldots A_{n-}\ A_n)' = A'_n\ A'_{n-1}$ $A'_3\ A'_2\ A'_1$ (reversal law for transpose).

Remark

$I' = I$, where I is an identity matrix.

| Example 19. If $A \quad \begin{bmatrix} \theta & -\sin\theta \\ \sin\theta & \cos\theta \end{bmatrix}$, find the values of θ satisfying the equation $A^T + A \quad I_2$.

Sol. We have, $A^T \quad A \quad I_2$

$$\Rightarrow \begin{bmatrix} \cos\theta & \sin\theta \\ -\sin\theta & \cos\theta \end{bmatrix} + \begin{bmatrix} \cos\theta & -\sin\theta \\ \sin\theta & \cos\theta \end{bmatrix} = \begin{bmatrix} 1 & 0 \\ 0 & 1 \end{bmatrix}$$

$$\Rightarrow \begin{bmatrix} 2\cos\theta & 0 \\ 0 & 2\cos\theta \end{bmatrix} = \begin{bmatrix} 1 & 0 \\ 0 & 1 \end{bmatrix}$$

$$\Rightarrow \cos\theta = \frac{1}{2} = \cos\left(\frac{\pi}{3}\right) \Rightarrow \theta = 2n\pi \pm \frac{\pi}{3}, n \in$$

Symmetric Matrix

A square matrix $A \quad a_{ij\ n\times n}$ is said to be symmetric, if $A' = A$ i.e., $a_{ij} = a_{ji}, \forall\ i, j$.

For example,

$$\text{If } A \quad \begin{bmatrix} a & h & g \\ h & b & f \\ g & f & c \end{bmatrix}, \text{ then } A' = \begin{bmatrix} a & h & g \\ h & b & f \\ g & f & c \end{bmatrix}$$

Here, A is symmetric matrix as $A' = A$.

Note

1. Maximum number of distinct entries in any symmetric matrix of order n is $\frac{n(n+1)}{2}$.
2. For any square matrix A with real number entries, then $A + A'$ is a symmetric matrix.

Proof $(A + A')' = A' + (A')' = A' + A = A + A'$

Skew-Symmetric Matrix

A square matrix $A = [a_{ij}]_{n\times n}$ is said to be skew-symmetric matrix, if $A' = -A$, i.e. $a_{ij} = -a_{ji}, \forall\ i, j$. (the pair of conjugate elements are additive inverse of each other)

Now, if we put $i = j$, we have $a_{ii} = -a_{ii}$.

Therefore, $2a_{ii} = 0$ or $a_{ii} = 0, \forall\ i$'s.

This means that all the diagonal elements of a skew-symmetric matrix are zero, but not the converse.

For example,

If $A = \begin{bmatrix} 0 & h & g \\ -h & 0 & f \\ -g & -f & 0 \end{bmatrix}$, then

$$A' = \begin{bmatrix} 0 & -h & -g \\ h & 0 & -f \\ g & f & 0 \end{bmatrix} = - \begin{bmatrix} 0 & h & g \\ -h & 0 & f \\ -g & -f & 0 \end{bmatrix} = -A$$

Here, A is skew-symmetric matrix as $A' = -A$.

Note

1. Trace of a skew-symmetric matrix is always 0.
2. For any square matrix A with real number entries, then $A - A'$ is a skew-symmetric matrix.

   Proof $(A - A')' = A' - (A')' = A' - A = -(A - A')$
3. Every square matrix can be uniquely expressed as the sum of a symmetric and a skew-symmetric matrix.

   i.e. If A is a square matrix, then we can write

   $$A = \frac{1}{2}(A + A') + \frac{1}{2}(A - A')$$

Example 20. The square matrix $A = [a_{ij}]_{m \times m}$ given by $a_{ij} = (i - j)^n$, show that A is symmetric and skew-symmetric matrices according as n is even or odd, respectively.

Sol. $\because a_{ij} = (i - j)^n = (-1)^n (j - i)^n$

$$= (-1)^n a_{ji} = \begin{cases} a_{ji}, & n \text{ is even integer} \\ -a_{ji}, & n \text{ is odd integer} \end{cases}$$

Hence, A is symmetric if n is even and skew-symmetric if n is odd integer.

Example 21. Express A as the sum of a symmetric and a skew-symmetric matrix, where $A = \begin{bmatrix} 3 & 5 \\ -1 & 2 \end{bmatrix}$.

Sol. We have,

$$A = \begin{bmatrix} 3 & 5 \\ -1 & 2 \end{bmatrix}, \text{ then } A' = \begin{bmatrix} 3 & -1 \\ 5 & 2 \end{bmatrix}$$

Let $P = \frac{1}{2}(A + A') = \frac{1}{2}\begin{bmatrix} 6 & 4 \\ 4 & 4 \end{bmatrix} = \begin{bmatrix} 3 & 2 \\ 2 & 2 \end{bmatrix} = P'$

Thus, $P = \frac{1}{2}(A + A')$ is a symmetric matrix.

Also, let $Q = \frac{1}{2}(A - A') = \frac{1}{2}\begin{bmatrix} 0 & 6 \\ -6 & 0 \end{bmatrix} = \begin{bmatrix} 0 & 3 \\ -3 & 0 \end{bmatrix}$

Then, $Q' = \begin{bmatrix} 0 & -3 \\ 3 & 0 \end{bmatrix} = -\begin{bmatrix} 0 & 3 \\ -3 & 0 \end{bmatrix} = -Q$

Thus, $Q = \frac{1}{2}(A - A')$ is a skew-symmetric matrix.

Now, $P + Q = \begin{bmatrix} 3 & 2 \\ 2 & 2 \end{bmatrix} + \begin{bmatrix} 0 & 3 \\ -3 & 0 \end{bmatrix} = \begin{bmatrix} 3 & 5 \\ -1 & 2 \end{bmatrix} = A$

Hence, A is represented as the sum of a symmetric and a skew-symmetric matrix.

Properties of Symmetric and Skew-Symmetric Matrices

(i) If A be a square matrix, then AA' and $A'A$ are symmetric matrices.

(ii) All positive integral powers of a symmetric matrix are symmetric, because

$$(A^n)' = (A')^n$$

(iii) All positive odd integral powers of a skew-symmetric matrix are skew-symmetric and positive even integral powers of a skew-symmetric matrix are symmetric, because $(A^n)' = (A')^n$

(iv) If A be a symmetric matrix and B be a square matrix of order that of A, then $-A, kA, A', A^{-1}, A^n$ and $B'AB$ are also symmetric matrices, where $n \in N$ and k is a scalar.

(v) If A be a skew-symmetric matrix, then
- (a) A^{2n} is a symmetric matrix for $n \in N$.
- (b) A^{2n+1} is a skew-symmetric matrix for $n \in N$.
- (c) kA is a skew-symmetric matrix, where k is scalar.
- (d) $B'AB$ is also skew-symmetric matrix, where B is a square matrix of order that of A.

(vi) If A and B are two symmetric matrices, then
- (a) $A \pm B$, $AB + BA$ are symmetric matrices.
- (b) $AB - BA$ is a skew-symmetric matrix
- (c) AB is a symmetric matrix, iff $AB = BA$

(where A and B are square matrices of same order)

(vii) If A and B are two skew-symmetric matrices, then
- (a) $A \pm B$, $AB - BA$ are skew-symmetric matrices.
- (b) $AB + BA$ is a symmetric matrix.

(where A and B are square matrices of same order)

(viii) If A be a skew-symmetric matrix and C is a column matrix, then $C'AC$ is a zero matrix, where $C'AC$ is conformable.

Orthogonal Matrix

A square matrix A is said to be orthogonal matrix, iff $AA' = I$, where I is an identity matrix.

Note

1. If $AA' = I$, then $A^{-1} = A$
2. If A and B are orthogonal, then AB is also orthogonal.
3. If A is orthogonal, then A^{-1} and A' are also orthogonal.

| Example 22. If $\begin{bmatrix} 0 & 2\beta & \gamma \\ \alpha & \beta & -\gamma \\ \alpha & -\beta & \gamma \end{bmatrix}$ is orthogonal, then find the value of $2\alpha^2 + 6\beta^2 + 3\gamma^2$.

Sol. Let $A = \begin{bmatrix} 0 & 2\beta & \gamma \\ \alpha & \beta & -\gamma \\ \alpha & -\beta & \gamma \end{bmatrix}$, then $A' = \begin{bmatrix} 0 & \alpha & \alpha \\ 2\beta & \beta & -\beta \\ \gamma & -\gamma & \gamma \end{bmatrix}$

Since, A is orthogonal.

$\therefore \quad AA' = I$

$$\Rightarrow \begin{bmatrix} 0 & 2\beta & \gamma \\ \alpha & \beta & -\gamma \\ \alpha & -\beta & \gamma \end{bmatrix} \begin{bmatrix} 0 & \alpha & \alpha \\ 2\beta & \beta & -\beta \\ \gamma & -\gamma & \gamma \end{bmatrix} = \begin{bmatrix} 1 & 0 & 0 \\ 0 & 1 & 0 \\ 0 & 0 & 1 \end{bmatrix}$$

$$\Rightarrow \begin{bmatrix} 4\beta^2 + \gamma^2 & 2\beta^2 - \gamma^2 & -2\beta^2 + \gamma^2 \\ 2\beta^2 - \gamma^2 & \alpha^2 + \beta^2 + \gamma^2 & \alpha^2 - \beta^2 - \gamma^2 \\ -2\beta^2 + \gamma^2 & \alpha^2 - \beta^2 - \gamma^2 & \alpha^2 + \beta^2 + \gamma^2 \end{bmatrix} = \begin{bmatrix} 1 & 0 & 0 \\ 0 & 1 & 0 \\ 0 & 0 & 1 \end{bmatrix}$$

Equating the corresponding elements, we get

$$4\beta^2 + \gamma^2 = 1 \quad \text{...(i)}$$

$$2\beta^2 - \gamma^2 = 0 \quad \text{...(ii)}$$

and $$\alpha^2 + \beta^2 + \gamma^2 = 1 \quad \text{...(iii)}$$

From Eqs. (i) and (ii), we get

$$\beta^2 = \frac{1}{6} \text{ and } \gamma^2 = \frac{1}{3}$$

From Eq. (iii),

$$\alpha^2 = 1 - \beta^2 - \gamma^2 = 1 - \frac{1}{6} - \frac{1}{3} = \frac{1}{2}$$

Hence, $2\alpha^2 + 6\beta^2 + 3\gamma^2 = 2 \times \frac{1}{2} + 6 \times \frac{1}{6} + 3 \times \frac{1}{3} = 3$

Aliter

The rows of matrix A are unit orthogonal vectors

$$\vec{R_1} \cdot \vec{R_2} = 0 \Rightarrow 2\beta^2 - \gamma^2 = 0 \Rightarrow 2\beta^2 = \gamma^2 \quad \text{...(i)}$$

$$\vec{R_2} \cdot \vec{R_3} = 0 \Rightarrow \alpha^2 - \beta^2 - \gamma^2 = 0 \Rightarrow \beta^2 + \gamma^2 = \alpha^2 \quad \text{...(ii)}$$

and $$\vec{R_3} \cdot \vec{R_3} = 1 \Rightarrow \alpha^2 + \beta^2 + \gamma^2 = 1 \quad \text{...(iii)}$$

From Eqs. (i), (ii) and (iii), we get

$$\alpha^2 = \frac{1}{2}, \beta^2 = \frac{1}{6} \text{ and } \gamma^2 = \frac{1}{3}$$

$$\therefore \quad 2\alpha^2 + 6\beta^2 + 3\gamma^2 = 3$$

| Example 23. If $A = \begin{bmatrix} 1 & 2 & 2 \\ 2 & 1 & -2 \\ a & 2 & b \end{bmatrix}$ is a matrix satisfying $AA' = 9I_3$, find the value of $|a| + |b|$.

Sol. Since, $AA' = 9I_3$

$$\Rightarrow \begin{bmatrix} 1 & 2 & 2 \\ 2 & 1 & -2 \\ a & 2 & b \end{bmatrix} \begin{bmatrix} 1 & 2 & a \\ 2 & 1 & 2 \\ 2 & -2 & b \end{bmatrix} = 9 \begin{bmatrix} 1 & 0 & 0 \\ 0 & 1 & 0 \\ 0 & 0 & 1 \end{bmatrix}$$

$$\Rightarrow \begin{bmatrix} 9 & 0 & a + 2b + 4 \\ 0 & 9 & 2a - 2b + 2 \\ a + 2b + 4 & 2a - 2b + 2 & a^2 + b^2 + 4 \end{bmatrix} = \begin{bmatrix} 9 & 0 & 0 \\ 0 & 9 & 0 \\ 0 & 0 & 9 \end{bmatrix}$$

Equating the corresponding elements, we get

$$a + 2b + 4 = 0 \quad \text{...(i)}$$

$$2a - 2b + 2 = 0 \quad \text{...(ii)}$$

and $$a^2 + b^2 + 4 = 9 \quad \text{...(iii)}$$

From Eqs. (i) and (ii), we get

$$a = -2 \text{ and } b = -1$$

Hence, $|a| + |b| = |-2| + |-1| = 2 + 1 = 3$

Complex Conjugate (or Conjugate) of a Matrix

If a matrix A is having complex numbers as its elements, the matrix obtained from A by replacing each element of A by its conjugate ($\overline{a \pm ib} = a \mp ib$, where $i = \sqrt{-1}$) is called the conjugate of matrix A and is denoted by $\overline{A}$.

For example, If $A = \begin{bmatrix} 2+5i & 3-i & 7 \\ -2i & 6+i & 7-5i \\ 1-i & 3 & 6i \end{bmatrix}$, where $i = \sqrt{-1}$,

then $$\overline{A} = \begin{bmatrix} 2-5i & 3+i & 7 \\ 2i & 6-i & 7+5i \\ 1+i & 3 & -6i \end{bmatrix}$$

Note

If all elements of A are real, then $\overline{A} = A$.

Properties of Complex Conjugate of a Matrix

If A and B are two matrices of same order, then

(i) $(\overline{\overline{A}}) = A$

(ii) $(\overline{A + B}) = \overline{A} + \overline{B}$, where A and B being conformable for addition.

(iii) $(\overline{kA}) = k\,\overline{A}$, where k is real.

(iv) $(\overline{AB}) = \overline{A}\,\overline{B}$, where A and B being conformable for multiplication.

Conjugate Transpose of a Matrix

The conjugate of the transpose of a matrix A is called the conjugate transpose of A and is denoted by A^θ i.e. A^θ = Conjugate of $A' = (\overline{A'})$

For example,

If $A = \begin{bmatrix} 2+4i & 3 & 5-9i \\ 4 & 5+2i & 3i \\ 2 & -5 & 4-i \end{bmatrix}$, where $i = \sqrt{-1}$,

then $A^\theta = (\overline{A'}) = \begin{bmatrix} 2-4i & 4 & 2 \\ 3 & 5-2i & -5 \\ 5+9i & -3i & 4+i \end{bmatrix}$

Properties of Transpose Conjugate Matrix

If A and B are two matrices of same order, then

(i) $(\overline{A})' = (\overline{A'})$ (ii) $(A^\theta)^\theta = A$

(iii) $(A+B)^\theta = A^\theta + B^\theta$, where A and B being conformable for addition.

(iv) $(kA)^\theta = k\,A^\theta$, where k is real.

(v) $(AB)^\theta = B^\theta A^\theta$, where A and B being conformable for multiplication

Hermitian Matrix

A square matrix $A = [a_{ij}]_{n\times n}$ is said to be hermitian, if $A^\theta = A$ i.e., $a_{ij} = \overline{a}_{ji}$, $\forall\, i, j$. If we put $j = i$, we have $a_{ii} = \overline{a}_{ii}$ $\Rightarrow a_{ii}$ is purely real for all i's.

This means that all the diagonal elements of a hermitian matrix must be purely real.

For example,

If $A = \begin{bmatrix} \alpha & \lambda + i\mu & \theta + i\phi \\ \lambda - i\mu & \beta & x+iy \\ \theta - i\phi & x - iy & \gamma \end{bmatrix}$

where $\alpha, \beta, \gamma, \lambda, \mu, \theta, \phi, x, y \in R$ and $i = \sqrt{-1}$, then

$$A' = \begin{bmatrix} \alpha & \lambda - i\mu & \theta - i\phi \\ \lambda + i\mu & \beta & x-iy \\ \theta + i\phi & x + iy & \gamma \end{bmatrix}$$

$$\therefore A^\theta = (\overline{A'}) = \begin{bmatrix} \alpha & \lambda + i\mu & \theta + i\phi \\ \lambda - i\mu & \beta & x+iy \\ \theta - i\phi & x - iy & \gamma \end{bmatrix} = A$$

Here, A is hermitian matrix as $A^\theta = A$.

Note

For any square matrix A with complex number entries, then $A + A^\theta$ is a Hermitian matrix.

Proof $(A + A^\theta)^\theta = A^\theta + (A^\theta)^\theta = A^\theta + A = A + A^\theta$

Skew-Hermitian Matrix

A square matrix $A = [a_{ij}]_{n\times n}$ is said to be skew-hermitian matrix. If $A^\theta = -A$, i.e. $a_{ij} = -\overline{a}_{ij}$, $\forall\, i, j$. If we put $j = i$, we have $a_{ii} = -\overline{a}_{ii} \Rightarrow a_{ii} + \overline{a}_{ii} = 0 \Rightarrow a_{ii}$ is purely imaginary for all i's. This means that all the diagonal elements of a skew-hermitian matrix must be purely imaginary or zero.

For example,

If $A = \begin{bmatrix} 2i & -2-3i & -2+i \\ 2-3i & -i & 3i \\ 2+i & 3i & 0 \end{bmatrix}$, where $i = \sqrt{-1}$,

then $A' = \begin{bmatrix} 2i & 2-3i & 2+i \\ -2-3i & -i & 3i \\ -2+i & 3i & 0 \end{bmatrix}$

$$\therefore A^\theta = (\overline{A'}) = \begin{bmatrix} -2i & 2+3i & 2-i \\ -2+3i & i & -3i \\ -2-i & -3i & 0 \end{bmatrix}$$

$$= -\begin{bmatrix} 2i & -2-3i & -2+i \\ 2-3i & -i & 3i \\ 2+i & 3i & 0 \end{bmatrix} = -A$$

Hence, A is skew-hermitian matrix.

Note

1. For any square matrix A with complex number entries, then $A - A^\theta$ is a skew-hermitian matrix.
   Proof $(A - A^\theta)^\theta = (A^\theta) - (A^\theta)^\theta = A^\theta - A = -(A - A^\theta)$
2. Every square matrix (with complex elements) can be uniquely expressed as the sum of a hermitian and a skew-hermitian matrix i.e.
   If A is a square matrix, then we can write
   $$A = \frac{1}{2}(A + A^\theta) + \frac{1}{2}(A - A^\theta)$$

| Example 24. Express A as the sum of a hermitian and a skew-hermitian matrix, where $A = \begin{bmatrix} 2+3i & 7 \\ 1-i & 2i \end{bmatrix}$, $i = \sqrt{-1}$.

Sol. We have, $A = \begin{bmatrix} 2+3i & 7 \\ 1-i & 2i \end{bmatrix}$, then $A^\theta = (\overline{A'}) = \begin{bmatrix} 2-3i & 1+i \\ 7 & -2i \end{bmatrix}$

$$\text{Let } P = \frac{1}{2}(A + A^\theta) = \frac{1}{2}\begin{bmatrix} 4 & 8+i \\ 8-i & 0 \end{bmatrix} = \begin{bmatrix} 2 & 4+\frac{i}{2} \\ 4-\frac{i}{2} & 0 \end{bmatrix} = P^\theta$$

Thus, $P = \frac{1}{2}(A + A^\theta)$ is a hermitian matrix.

Also, let $Q = \frac{1}{2}(A - A^\theta) = \frac{1}{2}\begin{bmatrix} 6i & 6-i \\ -6-i & 4i \end{bmatrix}$

$$= \begin{bmatrix} 3i & 3-\frac{i}{2} \\ -3-\frac{i}{2} & 2i \end{bmatrix} = -\begin{bmatrix} -3i & -3+\frac{i}{2} \\ 3+\frac{i}{2} & -2i \end{bmatrix} = -Q^\theta$$

Thus, $Q = \frac{1}{2}(A - A^\theta)$ is a skew-hermitian matrix.

Now, $P + Q = \begin{bmatrix} 2 & 4+\frac{i}{2} \\ 4-\frac{i}{2} & 0 \end{bmatrix} + \begin{bmatrix} 3i & 3-\frac{i}{2} \\ -3-\frac{i}{2} & 2i \end{bmatrix}$

$$= \begin{bmatrix} 2+3i & 7 \\ 1-i & 2i \end{bmatrix} = A$$

Hence, A is represented as the sum of a hermitian and a skew-hermitian matrix.

Properties of Hermitian and Skew-Hermitian Matrices

(i) If A be a square matrix, then AA^θ and $A^\theta A$ are hermitian matrices.

(ii) If A is a hermitian matrix, then
- (a) iA is skew-hermitian matrix, where $i = \sqrt{-1}$.
- (b) iff $\bar{A}$ is hermitian matrix.
- (c) kA is hermitian matrix, where $k \in R$.

(iii) If A is a skew-hermitian matrix, then
- (a) iA is hermitian matrix, where $i = \sqrt{-1}$.
- (b) iff $\bar{A}$ is skew-hermitian matrix.
- (c) kA is skew-hermitian matrix, where $k \in R$.

(iv) If A and B are hermitian matrices of same order, then
- (a) $k_1 A + k_2 B$ is also hermitian, where $k_1, k_2 \in R$.
- (b) AB is also hermitian, if $AB = BA$.
- (c) $AB + BA$ is a hermitian matrix.
- (d) $AB - BA$ is a skew-hermitian matrix.

(v) If A and B are skew-hermitian matrices of same order, then $k_1 A + k_2 B$ is also skew-hermitian matrix.

Unitary Matrix

A square matrix A is said to be unitary matrix iff $AA^\theta = I$, where I is an identity matrix.

Note

1. If $AA^\theta = I$, then $A^{-1} = A^\theta$
2. If A and B are unitary, then AB is also unitary.
3. If A is unitary, then A^{-1} and A' are also unitary.

| Example 25. Verify that the matrix $\frac{1}{\sqrt{3}}\begin{bmatrix} 1 & 1+i \\ 1-i & -1 \end{bmatrix}$ is unitary, where $i = \sqrt{-1}$.

Sol. Let $A = \frac{1}{\sqrt{3}}\begin{bmatrix} 1 & 1+i \\ 1-i & -1 \end{bmatrix}$, then $A^\theta = (\bar{A'}) = \frac{1}{\sqrt{3}}\begin{bmatrix} 1 & 1+i \\ 1-i & -1 \end{bmatrix}$

$$\therefore \quad AA^\theta = \frac{1}{\sqrt{3}}\begin{bmatrix} 1 & 1+i \\ 1-i & -1 \end{bmatrix} \times \frac{1}{\sqrt{3}}\begin{bmatrix} 1 & 1+i \\ 1-i & -1 \end{bmatrix}$$

$$= \frac{1}{3}\begin{bmatrix} 3 & 0 \\ 0 & 3 \end{bmatrix} = \begin{bmatrix} 1 & 0 \\ 0 & 1 \end{bmatrix} = I$$

Hence, A is unitary matrix.

Determinant of a Matrix

Let A be a square matrix, then the determinant formed by the elements of A without changing their respective positions is called the determinant of A and is denoted by det A or $|A|$.

i.e., If $A = \begin{bmatrix} a_1 & a_2 & a_3 \\ b_1 & b_2 & b_3 \\ c_1 & c_2 & c_3 \end{bmatrix}$, then $|A| = \begin{vmatrix} a_1 & a_2 & a_3 \\ b_1 & b_2 & b_3 \\ c_1 & c_2 & c_3 \end{vmatrix}$.

Properties of the Determinant of a Matrix

If A and B are square matrices of same order, then

(i) $|A|$ exists $\Leftrightarrow$ A is a square matrix.

(ii) $|A'| = |A|$

(iii) $|AB| = |A||B|$ and $|AB| = |BA|$

(iv) If A is orthogonal matrix, then $|A| = \pm 1$

(v) If A is skew-symmetric matrix of odd order, then $|A| = 0$

(vi) If A is skew-symmetric matrix of even order, then $|A|$ is a perfect square.

(vii) $|kA| = k^n |A|$, where n is order of A and k is scalar.

(viii) $|A^n| = |A|^n$, where $n \in N$

(ix) If $A = (a_1, a_2, a_3, \ldots, a_n)$, then $|A| = a_1 \cdot a_2 \cdot a_3 \ldots a_n$

| Example 26. If A, B and C are square matrices of order n and $\det(A) = 2$, $\det(B) = 3$ and $\det(C) = 5$, then find the value of $10\det(A^3 B^2 C^{-1})$.

Sol. Given, $|A| = 2$, $|B| = 3$ and $|C| = 5$.

Now, $10\det(A^3 B^2 C^{-1}) = 10 \times |A^3 B^2 C^{-1}|$

$$= 10 \times |A^3| \times |B^2| \times |C^{-1}| = 10 \times |A|^3 \times |B|^2 \times |C|^{-1}$$

$$= \frac{10 \times |A|^3 \times |B^2|}{|C|} = \frac{10 \times 2^3 \times 3^2}{5} = 144$$

Example 27. If $A = \begin{bmatrix} a & b & c \\ b & c & a \\ c & a & b \end{bmatrix}$, $abc = 1$, $A^T A = I$, then find the value of $a^3 + b^3 + c^3$.

Sol. $\because \quad A^T A = I$

$\Rightarrow \quad |A^T A| = |I| \Rightarrow |A^T||A| = 1$

$\Rightarrow \quad |A||A| = 1 \quad [\because |A^T| = |A|]$

$\Rightarrow \quad |A| = \pm 1$

$\Rightarrow \quad \begin{vmatrix} a & b & c \\ b & c & a \\ c & a & b \end{vmatrix} = \pm 1$

$\Rightarrow \quad 3abc - (a^3 + b^3 + c^3) = \pm 1$

or $\quad 3 - (a^3 + b^3 + c^3) = \pm 1 \quad [\because abc = 1]$

or $\quad a^3 + b^3 + c^3 = 3 \pm 1 = 2 \text{ or } 4$

Singular and Non-Singular Matrices

A square matrix A is said to be a singular, if $|A| = 0$ and a square matrix A is said to be non-singular, if $|A| \neq 0$.

For example,

(i) $A = \begin{bmatrix} 1 & 2 & 3 \\ -1 & 0 & 2 \\ 2 & 4 & 6 \end{bmatrix}$ is a singular matrix.

Since, $|A| = 0$.

(ii) $A = \begin{bmatrix} 2 & 3 \\ 4 & 5 \end{bmatrix}$ is a non-singular matrix.

Since, $|A| = 10 - 12 = -2 \neq 0$

Example 28. If $\omega \neq 1$ is a complex cube root of unity, then prove that

$$\begin{bmatrix} 1+2\omega^{2017}+\omega^{2018} & \omega^{2018} & 1 \\ 1 & 1+\omega^{2018}+2\omega^{2017} & \omega^{2017} \\ \omega^{2017} & \omega^{2018} & 2+\omega^{2017}+2\omega^{2018} \end{bmatrix}$$ is singular.

Sol. Let $A = \begin{bmatrix} 1+2\omega^{2017}+\omega^{2018} & \omega^{2018} & 1 \\ 1 & 1+\omega^{2018}+2\omega^{2017} & \omega^{2017} \\ \omega^{2017} & \omega^{2018} & 2+\omega^{2017}+2\omega^{2018} \end{bmatrix}$

$\because \quad \omega^3 = 1 \Rightarrow \omega^{2017} = \omega$

and $\quad \omega^{2018} = \omega^2$, then

$$A = \begin{bmatrix} 1+2\omega+\omega^2 & \omega^2 & 1 \\ 1 & 1+\omega^2+2\omega & \omega \\ \omega & \omega^2 & 2+\omega+2\omega^2 \end{bmatrix}$$

$$= \begin{bmatrix} \omega & \omega^2 & 1 \\ 1 & \omega & \omega \\ \omega & \omega^2 & -\omega \end{bmatrix} \quad [\because 1+\omega+\omega^2 = 0]$$

Now, $|A| = \begin{vmatrix} \omega & \omega^2 & 1 \\ 1 & \omega & \omega \\ \omega & \omega^2 & -\omega \end{vmatrix} = \omega \begin{vmatrix} \omega & \omega & 1 \\ 1 & 1 & \omega \\ \omega & \omega & -\omega \end{vmatrix} = 0 \quad [\because C_1 = C_2]$

Thus, $|A| = 0$.

Hence, A is singular matrix.

Example 29. Find the real values of x for which the matrix $\begin{bmatrix} x+1 & 3 & 5 \\ 1 & x+3 & 5 \\ 1 & 3 & x+5 \end{bmatrix}$ is non-singular.

Sol. Let $A = \begin{bmatrix} x+1 & 3 & 5 \\ 1 & x+3 & 5 \\ 1 & 3 & x+5 \end{bmatrix}$

$\therefore \quad |A| = \begin{vmatrix} x+1 & 3 & 5 \\ 1 & x+3 & 5 \\ 1 & 3 & x+5 \end{vmatrix}$

Applying $C_1 \to C_1 + C_2 + C_3$, then

$$|A| = \begin{vmatrix} x+9 & 3 & 5 \\ x+9 & x+3 & 5 \\ x+9 & 3 & x+5 \end{vmatrix}$$

Applying $R_2 \to R_2 - R_1$ and $R_3 \to R_3 - R_1$, then

$$|A| = \begin{vmatrix} x+9 & 3 & 5 \\ 0 & x & 0 \\ 0 & 0 & x \end{vmatrix} = x^2(x+9)$$

$\because \quad A$ is non-singular.

$\therefore \quad |A| \neq 0 \Rightarrow x^2(x+9) \neq 0$

$\therefore \quad x \neq 0, -9$

Hence, $x \in R - \{0, -9\}$.

Exercise for Session 2

1 If $A = \begin{bmatrix} 4 & x+2 \\ 2x-3 & x+1 \end{bmatrix}$ is symmetric, then x is equal to

(a) 2 (b) 3
(c) 4 (d) 5

2 If A and B are symmetric matrices, then ABA is

(a) symmetric matrix (b) skew-symmetric matrix
(c) diagonal matrix (d) scalar matrix

3 If A and B are symmetric matrices of the same order and $P = AB + BA$ and $Q = AB - BA$, then $(PQ)'$ is equal to

(a) PQ (b) QP
(c) $-QP$ (d) None of these

4 If A is a skew-symmetric matrix and n is odd positive integer, then A^n is

(a) a skew-symmetric matrix (b) a symmetric matrix
(c) a diagonal matrix (d) None of these

5 If A is symmetric as well as skew-symmetric matrix, then A is

(a) diagonal matrix (b) null matrix
(c) triangular matrix (d) None of these

6 If A is square matrix order 3, then $|(A - A')^{2015}|$ is

(a) $|A|$ (b) $|A'|$
(c) 0 (d) None of these

7 The maximum number of different elements required to form a symmetric matrix of order 6 is

(a) 15 (b) 17
(c) 19 (d) 21

8 If A and B are square matrices of order 3×3 such that A is an orthogonal matrix and B is a skew-symmetric matrix, then which of the following statement is true?

(a) $|AB| = 1$ (b) $|AB| = 0$
(c) $|AB| = -1$ (d) None of these

9 The matrix $A = \begin{bmatrix} i & 1-2i \\ -1-2i & 0 \end{bmatrix}$, where $i = \sqrt{-1}$, is

(a) symmetric (b) skew-symmetric
(c) hermitian (d) skew-hermitian

10 If A and B are square matrices of same order such that $A^* = A$ and $B^* = B$, where A^* denotes the conjugate transpose of A, then $(AB - BA)^*$ is equal to

(a) null matrix (b) $AB - BA$
(c) $BA - AB$ (d) None of these

11 If matrix $A = \frac{1}{\sqrt{2}}\begin{bmatrix} 1 & i \\ -i & a \end{bmatrix}$, $i = \sqrt{-1}$ is unitary matrix, a is equal to

(a) 2 (b) -1
(c) 0 (d) 1

12 If A is a 3×3 matrix and $\det(3A) = k\{\det(A)\}$, k is equal to

(a) 9 (b) 6
(c) 1 (d) 27

13 If A and B are square matrices of order 3 such that $|A| = -1$, $|B| = 3$, then $|3AB|$ is equal to

(a) -9 (b) -81
(c) -27 (d) 81

14 If A is a square matrix such that $A^2 = A$, then $\det(A)$ is equal to

(a) 0 or 1
(b) -2 or 2
(c) -3 or 3
(d) None of these

15 If I is a unit matrix of order 10, the determinant of I is equal to

(a) 10
(b) 1
(c) $\frac{1}{10}$
(d) 9

16 If $A_i = \begin{bmatrix} 2^{-i} & 3^{-i} \\ 3^{-i} & 2^{-i} \end{bmatrix}$, then $\sum_{i=1}^{\infty} \det(A_i)$ is equal to

(a) $\frac{3}{4}$
(b) $\frac{5}{24}$
(c) $\frac{5}{4}$
(d) $\frac{7}{144}$

17 The number of values of x for which the matrix $A = \begin{bmatrix} 3-x & 2 & 2 \\ 2 & 4-x & 1 \\ -2 & -4 & -1-x \end{bmatrix}$ is singular, is

(a) 0
(b) 1
(c) 2
(d) 3

18 The number of values of x in the closed interval $[-4, -1]$, the matrix $\begin{bmatrix} 3 & -1+x & 2 \\ 3 & -1 & x+2 \\ x+3 & -1 & 2 \end{bmatrix}$ is singular, is

(a) 0
(b) 1
(c) 2
(d) 3

19 The values of x for which the given matrix $\begin{bmatrix} -x & x & 2 \\ 2 & x & -x \\ x & -2 & -x \end{bmatrix}$ will be non-singular are

(a) $-2 \le x \le 2$
(b) for all x other than 2 and -2
(c) $x \ge 2$
(d) $x \le -2$

Session 3

Adjoint of a Matrix, Inverse of a Matrix (Reciprocal Matrix), Elementary Row Operations (Transformations), Equivalent Matrices, Matrix Polynomial, Use of Mathematical Induction,

Adjoint of a Matrix

Let $A = [a_{ij}]$ be a square matrix of order n and let C_{ij} be cofactor of a_{ij} in A. Then, the transpose of the matrix of cofactors of elements of A is called the adjoint of A and is denoted by adj (A).

Thus, $\text{adj}(A) = [C_{ij}]'$

$\Rightarrow \quad (\text{adj } A)_{ij} = C_{ji} = \text{Cofactor of } a_{ji} \text{ in } A$

i.e. if $A = \begin{bmatrix} a_{11} & a_{12} & a_{13} \\ a_{21} & a_{22} & a_{23} \\ a_{31} & a_{32} & a_{33} \end{bmatrix}$, then

$$\text{adj } A = \begin{bmatrix} C_{11} & C_{12} & C_{13} \\ C_{21} & C_{22} & C_{23} \\ C_{31} & C_{32} & C_{33} \end{bmatrix}' = \begin{bmatrix} C_{11} & C_{21} & C_{31} \\ C_{12} & C_{22} & C_{32} \\ C_{13} & C_{23} & C_{33} \end{bmatrix}$$

where C_{ij} denotes the cofactor of a_{ij} in A.

Here, $C_{11} = \begin{vmatrix} a_{22} & a_{23} \\ a_{32} & a_{33} \end{vmatrix} = a_{22}a_{33} - a_{23}a_{32}$,

$C_{12} = -\begin{vmatrix} a_{21} & a_{23} \\ a_{31} & a_{33} \end{vmatrix} = a_{31}a_{23} - a_{33}a_{21}$,

$C_{13} = \begin{vmatrix} a_{21} & a_{22} \\ a_{31} & a_{32} \end{vmatrix} = a_{21}a_{32} - a_{31}a_{22}$,

$C_{21} = -\begin{vmatrix} a_{12} & a_{13} \\ a_{32} & a_{33} \end{vmatrix} = a_{13}a_{32} - a_{12}a_{33}$,

$C_{22} = \begin{vmatrix} a_{11} & a_{13} \\ a_{31} & a_{33} \end{vmatrix} = a_{11}a_{33} - a_{31}a_{13}$,

$C_{23} = -\begin{vmatrix} a_{11} & a_{12} \\ a_{31} & a_{32} \end{vmatrix} = a_{12}a_{31} - a_{11}a_{32}$,

$C_{31} = \begin{vmatrix} a_{12} & a_{13} \\ a_{22} & a_{23} \end{vmatrix} = a_{12}a_{23} - a_{22}a_{13}$,

$C_{32} = -\begin{vmatrix} a_{11} & a_{13} \\ a_{21} & a_{23} \end{vmatrix} = a_{13}a_{21} - a_{11}a_{23}$

and $C_{33} = \begin{vmatrix} a_{11} & a_{12} \\ a_{21} & a_{22} \end{vmatrix} = a_{11}a_{22} - a_{21}a_{12}$

Rule to Write Cofactors of an Element a_{ij}

Cross the row and column intersection at the element a_{ij} and the determinant which is left be denoted by D, then

$$\text{Cofactors of } a_{ij} = \begin{cases} D, & \text{if } i + j = \text{even integer} \\ -D, & \text{if } i + j = \text{odd integer} \end{cases}$$

| Example 30. Find the cofactor of a_{23} in $\begin{bmatrix} 3 & 1 & 4 \\ 0 & 2 & -1 \\ 1 & -3 & 5 \end{bmatrix}$.

Sol. Let $A = \begin{bmatrix} 3 & 1 & 4 \\ 0 & \cdots 2 & \cdots -1 \\ 1 & -3 & 5 \end{bmatrix}$

$\therefore$ Cofactor of $a_{23} = -D$ $\quad [\because 2 + 3 = \text{odd}]$

where $D = \begin{vmatrix} 3 & 1 \\ 1 & -3 \end{vmatrix}$

[after crossing the 2nd row and 3rd column]

$= -9 - 1 = -10$

Hence, cofactor of $a_{23} = -(-10) = 10$

> ***Note***
>
> The adjoint of a square matrix of order 2 is obtained by interchanging the diagonal elements and changing signs of off-diagonal elements.
>
> If $A = \begin{bmatrix} a & b \\ c & d \end{bmatrix}$, then
>
> $(\text{adj } A) = \begin{bmatrix} d & -b \\ -c & a \end{bmatrix}$

| Example 31. Find the adjoint of the matrix

$$A = \begin{bmatrix} 1 & 2 & 3 \\ 0 & 5 & 0 \\ 2 & 4 & 3 \end{bmatrix}.$$

Sol. If C be the matrix of cofactors of the element in $|A|$, then

$$C = \begin{bmatrix} C_{11} & C_{12} & C_{13} \\ C_{21} & C_{22} & C_{23} \\ C_{31} & C_{32} & C_{33} \end{bmatrix}$$

$$= \begin{bmatrix} \begin{vmatrix} 5 & 0 \\ 4 & 3 \end{vmatrix} & -\begin{vmatrix} 0 & 0 \\ 2 & 3 \end{vmatrix} & \begin{vmatrix} 0 & 5 \\ 2 & 4 \end{vmatrix} \\ -\begin{vmatrix} 2 & 3 \\ 4 & 3 \end{vmatrix} & \begin{vmatrix} 1 & 3 \\ 2 & 3 \end{vmatrix} & -\begin{vmatrix} 1 & 2 \\ 2 & 4 \end{vmatrix} \\ \begin{vmatrix} 2 & 3 \\ 5 & 0 \end{vmatrix} & -\begin{vmatrix} 1 & 3 \\ 0 & 0 \end{vmatrix} & \begin{vmatrix} 1 & 2 \\ 0 & 5 \end{vmatrix} \end{bmatrix} = \begin{bmatrix} 12 & 0 & -10 \\ 6 & -3 & 0 \\ -15 & 0 & 5 \end{bmatrix}$$

$$\Rightarrow \text{adj}A = C' = \begin{bmatrix} 12 & 6 & -15 \\ 0 & -3 & 0 \\ -10 & 0 & 5 \end{bmatrix}$$

Maha Shortcut for Adjoint

(Goyal's Method)

This method applied only for third order square matrix.

Method : Let $A = \begin{bmatrix} 1 & 2 & 3 \\ 0 & 5 & 0 \\ 2 & 4 & 3 \end{bmatrix}$

Step I Write down the three rows of A and rewrite first two rows.

i.e.

$$\begin{matrix} 1 & 2 & 3 \\ 0 & 5 & 0 \\ 2 & 4 & 3 \\ 1 & 2 & 3 \\ 0 & 5 & 0 \end{matrix}$$

Step II After Step I, rewrite first two columns.

i.e.

$$\begin{matrix} 1 & 2 & 3 & 1 & 2 \\ 0 & 5 & 0 & 0 & 5 \\ 2 & 4 & 3 & 2 & 4 \\ 1 & 2 & 3 & 1 & 2 \\ 0 & 5 & 0 & 0 & 5 \end{matrix}$$

Step III After Step II, deleting first row and first column, then we get all elements of adj A i.e.,

```
1 ··· 2 ··· 3 ··· 1 ··· 2
⋮
0     5     0     0     5
⋮        ⤨     ⤨     ⤨        ⇒ 15   0  −10   first column of adj A
2     4     3     2     4
⋮        ⤨     ⤨     ⤨        ⇒ 6   −3   0    second column of adj A
1     2     3     1     2
⋮        ⤨     ⤨     ⤨        ⇒ −15  0   5    third column of adj A
0     5     0     0     5
```

$$\text{or} \quad \text{adj } A = \begin{bmatrix} 15 & 6 & -15 \\ 0 & -3 & 0 \\ -10 & 0 & 5 \end{bmatrix}$$

Properties of Adjoint Matrix

Property 1 If A be a square matrix order n, then

$$A(\text{adj } A) = (\text{adj } A)A = |A| I_n$$

i.e., the product of a matrix and its adjoint is commutative.

Deductions of Property 1

Deduction 1 If A be a square singular matrix of order n, then $A(\text{adj } A) = (\text{adj } A)\, A = O$ [null matrix]

Since, for singular matrix, $|A| = 0$.

Deduction 2 If A be a square non-singular matrix of order n, then $|\text{adj } A| = |A|^{n-1}$

Since, for non-singular matrix, $|A| \neq 0$.

Proof ∵ $A(\text{adj } A) = |A| I_n$

Taking determinant on both sides, then

$$|A(\text{adj } A)| = ||A| I_n|$$

$$\Rightarrow |A||\text{adj } A| = |A|^n |I_n| = |A|^n \quad [\because |I_n| = 1]$$

$$\Rightarrow |\text{adj } A| = |A|^{n-1} \quad [\because |A| \neq 0]$$

> **Note**
> In general $\underbrace{|\text{adj}(\text{adj}(\text{adj} \ldots (\text{adj } A)))|}_{\text{adj repeat } m \text{ times}} = |A|^{(n-1)^m}$

Property 2 If A and B are square matrices of order n, then

$$\text{adj}(AB) = (\text{adj } B)(\text{adj } A)$$

Property 3 If A is a square matrix of order n, then

$$(\text{adj } A)' = \text{adj } A'$$

Property 4 If A be a square non-singular matrix of order n, then $\text{adj}(\text{adj} A) = |A|^{n-2} A$

Proof ∵ $A(\text{adj } A) = |A| I_n$ ...(i)

Replace A by adj A, then

$$(\text{adj } A)(\text{adj}(\text{adj } A)) = |\text{adj } A| I_n$$

$$= |A|^{n-1} I_n \quad [\because |\text{adj } A| = |A|^{n-1}]$$

$$= I_n |A|^{n-1}$$

Pre-multiplying both sides by matrix A, then

$$A(\text{adj } A)(\text{adj}(\text{adj } A)) = A I_n |A|^{n-1} = A|A|^{n-1}$$

$$\Rightarrow |A| I_n(\text{adj}(\text{adj} A)) = A|A|^{n-1}$$

$$\Rightarrow (\text{adj}(\text{adj } A)) = A|A|^{n-2}$$

$$\text{or} \quad \text{adj}(\text{adj} A) = |A|^{n-2} A$$

Property 5 If A be a square non-singular matrix of order n, then

$$|\text{adj}(\text{adj } A)| = |A|^{(n-1)^2}$$

Proof ∵ $\text{adj adj } A = |A|^{n-2} A$

Taking determinant on both sides, then

$$|\text{adj}(\text{adj } A)| = ||A|^{n-2} A|$$

$$= |A|^{n(n-2)}|A| \quad [\because |kA| = k^n |A|]$$
$$= |A|^{n^2-2n+1} = |A|^{(n-1)^2}$$

Note

In general, $|\underbrace{\text{adj (adj (adj} \ldots \text{(adj } A)))}_{\text{adj } m \text{ times}}| = |A|^{(n-1)^m}$

Property 6 If A be a square matrix of order n and k is a scalar, then

$$\text{adj}(kA) = k^{n-1} \cdot (\text{adj } A)$$

Proof $\because \quad A(\text{adj } A) = |A| I_n \quad \ldots(\text{i})$

Replace A by kA, then

$$kA(\text{adj}(kA)) = |kA| I_n = k^n |A| I_n$$
$$\Rightarrow \quad A(\text{adj}(kA)) = k^{n-1}|A| I_n$$
$$= k^{n-1} A(\text{adj } A) \quad [\text{from Eq. (i)}]$$

Hence, $\quad \text{adj}(kA) = k^{n-1}(\text{adj } A)$

Property 7 If A be a square matrix of order n and $m \in N$, then $\quad (\text{adj } A^m) = (\text{adj } A)^m$

Property 8 If A and B be two square matrices of order n such that B is the adjoint of A and k is a scalar, then

$$|AB + kI_n| = (|A| + k)^n$$

Proof $\because \quad B = \text{adj } A$

$$\therefore \quad AB = A(\text{adj } A) = |A| I_n$$
$$\text{LHS} = |AB + kI_n| = ||A| I_n + kI_n| = |(|A| + k) I_n|$$
$$= (|A| + k)^n |I_n| = (|A| + k)^n = \text{RHS}$$

Property 9 Adjoint of a diagonal matrix is a diagonal matrix.

i.e. If $A = \begin{bmatrix} a & 0 & 0 \\ 0 & b & 0 \\ 0 & 0 & c \end{bmatrix}$, then $\text{adj } A = \begin{bmatrix} bc & 0 & 0 \\ 0 & ca & 0 \\ 0 & 0 & ab \end{bmatrix}$

Note

$\text{adj}(I_n) = I_n$.

Example 32. If $A = \begin{bmatrix} -1 & 1 & 1 \\ 1 & -1 & 1 \\ 1 & 1 & -1 \end{bmatrix}$, find the values of

(i) $|A||\text{adj } A|$ (ii) $|\text{adj}(\text{adj } (\text{adj } A))|$
(iii) $|\text{adj } (3A)|$ (iv) adj adj A

Sol. $\because \quad A = \begin{bmatrix} -1 & 1 & 1 \\ 1 & -1 & 1 \\ 1 & 1 & -1 \end{bmatrix}$

$\therefore |A| = (-1)(1-1) - (1)(-1-1) + (1)(1+1) = 4 \neq 0$

$\Rightarrow$ A is non-singular.

(i) $|A||\text{adj } A| = |A||A|^2 \quad [\because n = 3]$
$= |A|^3 = 4^3 = 64$

(ii) $|\text{adj}(\text{adj}(\text{adj } A))| = |A|^{(3-1)^3} = |A|^8 = 4^8 = 2^{16}$

(iii) $|\text{adj}(3A)| = |3^2 \text{ adj } A| = (3^2)^3 |\text{adj } A|$
$= 3^6 |A|^2 = 729 \times 4^2 = 11664$

(iv) $\text{adj}(\text{adj} A) = |A|^2 A = 16A$

Example 33. If $A = \begin{bmatrix} 3 & -3 & 4 \\ 2 & -3 & 4 \\ 0 & -1 & 1 \end{bmatrix}$ and B is the adjoint of A, find the value of $|AB + 2I|$, where I is the identity matrix of order 3.

Sol. $\because \quad A = \begin{bmatrix} 3 & -3 & 4 \\ 2 & -3 & 4 \\ 0 & -1 & 1 \end{bmatrix}$

$$\therefore \quad |A| = \begin{vmatrix} 3 & -3 & 4 \\ 2 & -3 & 4 \\ 0 & -1 & 1 \end{vmatrix}$$
$$= 3(-3+4) + 3(2-0) + 4(-2-0) = 1 \neq 0$$

$$\therefore |AB + 2I| = (|A| + 2)^3 \quad [\text{by property 8}]$$
$$= (1+2)^3 = 3^3 = 27$$

Inverse of a Matrix
(Reciprocal Matrix)

A square matrix A (non-singular) of order n is said to be invertible, if there exists a square matrix B of the same order such that $AB = I_n = BA$,

then B is called the inverse (reciprocal) of A and is denoted by A^{-1}. Thus, $\quad A^{-1} = B \Leftrightarrow AB = I_n = BA$

We have, $\quad A(\text{adj } A) = |A| I_n$

$$\Rightarrow \quad A^{-1} A(\text{adj } A) = A^{-1} I_n |A|$$
$$\Rightarrow \quad I_n(\text{adj } A) = A^{-1}|A| I_n$$
$$\therefore \quad A^{-1} = \frac{\text{adj } A}{|A|}; \text{ provided } |A| \neq 0$$

Note The necessary and sufficient condition for a square matrix A to be invertible is that $|A| \neq 0$.

Properties of Inverse of a Matrix

Property 1 (Uniqueness of inverse) Every invertible matrix possesses a unique inverse.

Proof Let A be an invertible matrix of order $n \times n$. Let B and C be two inverses of A. Then,

$$AB = BA = I_n \quad \ldots(\text{i})$$

and $AC = CA = I_n$ ...(ii)

Now, $AB = I_n$

$\Rightarrow C(AB) = CI_n$ [pre-multiplying by C]

$\Rightarrow (CA)B = CI_n$ [by associativity]

$\Rightarrow I_n B = CI_n$ [$\because CA = I_n$ by Eq. (ii)]

$\Rightarrow B = C$

Hence, an invertible matrix possesses a unique inverse.

Property 2 (Reversal law) If A and B are invertible matrices of order $n \times n$, then AB is invertible and $(AB)^{-1} = B^{-1}A^{-1}$.

Proof It is given that A and B are invertible matrices.

$$|A| \neq 0 \text{ and } |B| \neq 0 \Rightarrow |A||B| \neq 0$$

$\Rightarrow |AB| \neq 0$

Hence, AB is an invertible matrix.

Now, $(AB)(B^{-1}A^{-1}) = A(BB^{-1})A^{-1}$ [by associativity]

$= (AI_n)A^{-1}$ [$\because BB^{-1} = I_n$]

$= AA^{-1}$ [$\because AI_n = A$]

$= I_n$ [$\because AA^{-1} = I_n$]

Also, $(B^{-1}A^{-1})(AB) = B^{-1}(A^{-1}A)B$ [by associativity]

$= B^{-1}(I_n B)$ [$\because A^{-1}A = I_n$]

$= B^{-1}B$ [$\because I_n B = B$]

$= I_n$ [$\because B^{-1}B = I_n$]

Thus, $(AB)(B^{-1}A^{-1}) = I_n = (B^{-1}A^{-1})(AB)$

Hence, $(AB)^{-1} = B^{-1}A^{-1}$

Note

If $A, B, C, \ldots, Y, Z$ are invertible matrices, then

$(ABC \ldots YZ)^{-1} = Z^{-1}Y^{-1} \ldots C^{-1}B^{-1}A^{-1}$ [reversal law]

Property 3 Let A be an invertible matrix of order n, then A' is also invertible and $(A')^{-1} = (A^{-1})'$.

Proof $\because A$ is invertible matrix

$\therefore |A| \neq 0 \Rightarrow |A'| \neq 0$ [$\because |A| = |A'|$]

Hence, A^{-1} is also invertible.

Now, $AA^{-1} = I_n = A^{-1}A$

$\Rightarrow (AA^{-1})' = (I_n)' = (A^{-1}A)'$

$\Rightarrow (A^{-1})'A' = I_n = A'(A^{-1})'$

[by reversal law for transpose]

$\Rightarrow (A')^{-1} = (A^{-1})'$ [by definition of inverse]

Property 4 Let A be an invertible matrix of order n and $k \in N$, then

$$(A^k)^{-1} = (A^{-1})^k = A^{-k}$$

Proof We have,

$$(A^k)^{-1} = (\underbrace{A \times A \times A \times \ldots \times A}_{\text{repeat } k \text{ times}})^{-1}$$

$$= \underbrace{A^{-1} \times A^{-1} \times A^{-1} \times \ldots \times A^{-1}}_{\text{repeat } k \text{ times}}$$

[by reversal law for inverse]

$$= (A^{-1})^k = A^{-k}$$

Property 5 Let A be an invertible matrix of order n, then $(A^{-1})^{-1} = A$.

Proof We have, $A^{-1}A = I_n$

$\therefore$ Inverse of $A^{-1} = A \Rightarrow (A^{-1})^{-1} = A$

Note

$I_n^{-1} = I_n$ as $I_n^{-1} I_n = I_n$

Property 6 Let A be an invertible matrix of order n, then $|A^{-1}| = \dfrac{1}{|A|}$.

Proof $\because A$ is invertible, then $|A| \neq 0$.

Now, $AA^{-1} = I_n = A^{-1}A$

$\Rightarrow |AA^{-1}| = |I_n|$

$\Rightarrow |A||A^{-1}| = 1$

[$\because |AB| = |A||B|$ and $|I_n| = 1$]

$\Rightarrow |A^{-1}| = \dfrac{1}{|A|}$ [$\because |A| \neq 0$]

Property 7 Inverse of a non-singular diagonal matrix is a diagonal matrix.

i.e. If $A = \begin{bmatrix} a & 0 & 0 \\ 0 & b & 0 \\ 0 & 0 & c \end{bmatrix}$ and $|A| \neq 0$, then

$$A^{-1} = \begin{bmatrix} \frac{1}{a} & 0 & 0 \\ 0 & \frac{1}{b} & 0 \\ 0 & 0 & \frac{1}{c} \end{bmatrix}$$

Note

The inverse of a non-singular square matrix A of order 2 is obtained by interchanging the diagonal elements and changing signs of off-diagonal elements and dividing by $|A|$.

For example,

If $A = \begin{bmatrix} a & b \\ c & d \end{bmatrix}$ and $|A| = (ad - bc) \neq 0$, then

$$A^{-1} = \frac{1}{(ad - bc)}\begin{bmatrix} d & -b \\ -c & a \end{bmatrix}$$

Example 34. Compute the inverse of the matrix $A=\begin{bmatrix}0&1&2\\1&2&3\\3&1&1\end{bmatrix}$.

Sol. We have, $A=\begin{bmatrix}0&1&2\\1&2&3\\3&1&1\end{bmatrix}$

Then, $|A|=\begin{vmatrix}0&1&2\\1&2&3\\3&1&1\end{vmatrix}=0\cdot(2-3)-1(1-9)+2(1-6)$

$=-2\neq 0$

$\therefore$ A^{-1} exists.

Now, cofactors along $R_1=-1, 8, -5$

cofactors along $R_2=1, -6, 3$

cofactors along $R_3=-1, 2, -1$

Let C is a matrix of cofactors of the elements in $|A|$

$$\therefore \quad C=\begin{bmatrix}-1&8&-5\\1&-6&3\\-1&2&-1\end{bmatrix}$$

$$\therefore \quad \text{adj } A=C'=\begin{bmatrix}-1&1&-1\\8&-6&2\\-5&3&-1\end{bmatrix}$$

Hence, $A^{-1}=\dfrac{\text{adj } A}{|A|}=-\dfrac{1}{2}\begin{bmatrix}-1&1&-1\\8&-6&2\\-5&3&-1\end{bmatrix}$

$$=\begin{bmatrix}\frac{1}{2}&-\frac{1}{2}&\frac{1}{2}\\-4&3&-1\\\frac{5}{2}&-\frac{3}{2}&\frac{1}{2}\end{bmatrix}$$

Example 35. If A and B are symmetric non-singular matrices of same order, $AB=BA$ and $A^{-1}B^{-1}$ exist, prove that $A^{-1}B^{-1}$ is symmetric.

Sol. $\because$ $A'=A,\ B'=B$ and $|A|\neq 0, |B|'\neq 0$

$\therefore$ $(A^{-1}B^{-1})'=(B^{-1})'(A^{-1})'$ [by reversal law of transpose]

$=(B')^{-1}(A')^{-1}$ [by property 3]

$=B^{-1}A^{-1}$ [$\because A'=A$ and $B'=B$]

$=(AB)^{-1}$ [by reversal law of inverse]

$=(BA)^{-1}$ [$\because AB=BA$]

$=A^{-1}B^{-1}$ [by reversal law of inverse]

Hence, $A^{-1}B^{-1}$ is symmetric.

Example 36. Matrices A and B satisfy $AB=B^{-1}$, where $B=\begin{bmatrix}2&-2\\-1&0\end{bmatrix}$, find the value of λ for which $\lambda A-2B^{-1}+I=O$, without finding B^{-1}.

Sol. $\because$ $AB=B^{-1}$ or $AB^2=I$

Now, $\lambda A-2B^{-1}+I=O$

$\Rightarrow$ $\lambda AB-2B^{-1}B+IB=O$ [post-multiplying by B]

$\Rightarrow$ $\lambda AB-2I+B=O$

$\Rightarrow$ $\lambda AB^2-2IB+B^2=O$ [again post-multiplying by B]

$\Rightarrow$ $\lambda AB^2-2B+B^2=O$

$\Rightarrow$ $\lambda I-2B+B^2=O$ [$\because AB^2=I$]

$$\Rightarrow \lambda\begin{bmatrix}1&0\\0&1\end{bmatrix}-2\begin{bmatrix}2&-2\\-1&0\end{bmatrix}+\begin{bmatrix}2&-2\\-1&0\end{bmatrix}\begin{bmatrix}2&-2\\-1&0\end{bmatrix}=\begin{bmatrix}0&0\\0&0\end{bmatrix}$$

$$\Rightarrow \begin{bmatrix}\lambda&0\\0&\lambda\end{bmatrix}-\begin{bmatrix}4&-4\\-2&0\end{bmatrix}+\begin{bmatrix}6&-4\\-2&2\end{bmatrix}=\begin{bmatrix}0&0\\0&0\end{bmatrix}$$

$$\Rightarrow \begin{bmatrix}\lambda+2&0\\0&\lambda+2\end{bmatrix}=\begin{bmatrix}0&0\\0&0\end{bmatrix}$$

$\Rightarrow$ $\lambda+2=0$

$\therefore$ $\lambda=-2$

Example 37. If A, B and C are three non-singular square matrices of order 3 satisfying the equation $A^2=A^{-1}$ and let $B=A^8$ and $C=A^2$, find the value of det $(B-C)$.

Sol. $\because$ $B=A^8=(A^2)^4=(A^{-1})^4$ [$\because A^{-1}=A^2$]

$=(A^4)^{-1}=(A^{2\cdot 2})^{-1}$

$=((A^2)^2)^{-1}=((A^2)^{-1})^2$

$=((A^{-1})^{-1})^2=A^2=C$

So, $B=C\Rightarrow B-C=0$

$\therefore$ $\det(B-C)=0$

Elementary Row Operations (Transformations)

The following three types of operations (transformations) on the rows of a given matrix are known as elementary row operation (transformations).

(i) The interchange of ith and jth rows is denoted by $R_i\leftrightarrow R_j$ or R_{ij}.

(ii) The multiplication of the ith row by a constant $k(k\neq 0)$ is denoted by $R_i\to kR_i$ or $R_i(k)$

(iii) The addition of the ith row to the elements of the jth row multiplied by constant $k(k \neq 0)$ is denoted by $R_i \to R_i + kR_j$ or $R_{ij}(k)$.

Note

Similarly, we can define the three column operations, $C_{ij}(C_i \leftrightarrow C_j)$, $C_i(k)(C_i \to kC_i)$ and $C_{ij}(k)(C_i \to C_i + kC_j)$.

Equivalent Matrices

Two matrices are said to be equivalent if one is obtained from the other by elementary operations (transformations). The symbol ~ is used for equivalence.

Properties of Equivalent Matrices

(i) If A and B are equivalent matrices, there exist non-singular matrices P and Q such that $B = PAQ$

(ii) If A and B are equivalent matrices such that $B = PAQ$, then $P^{-1}BQ^{-1} = A$

(iii) Every non-singular square matrix can be expressed as the product of elementary matrices.

Example 38. Transform $\begin{bmatrix} 1 & 3 & 3 \\ 2 & 4 & 10 \\ 3 & 8 & 4 \end{bmatrix}$ into a unit matrix.

Sol. Let $$A = \begin{bmatrix} 1 & 3 & 3 \\ 2 & 4 & 10 \\ 3 & 8 & 4 \end{bmatrix}$$

Applying $R_2 \to R_2 - 2R_1$ and $R_3 \to R_3 - 3R_1$, we get

$$A \sim \begin{bmatrix} 1 & 3 & 3 \\ 0 & -2 & 4 \\ 0 & -1 & -5 \end{bmatrix}$$

Applying $R_2 \to \left(-\frac{1}{2}\right)R_2$ and $R_2 \to (-1)R_2$, we get

$$A \sim \begin{bmatrix} 1 & 3 & 3 \\ 0 & 1 & -2 \\ 0 & 1 & 5 \end{bmatrix}$$

Applying $R_1 \to R_1 - 3R_2$ and $R_3 \to R_3 - R_2$, we get

$$A \sim \begin{bmatrix} 1 & 0 & 9 \\ 0 & 1 & -2 \\ 0 & 0 & 7 \end{bmatrix}$$

Applying $R_3 \to \left(\frac{1}{7}\right)R_3$, we get

$$A \sim \begin{bmatrix} 1 & 0 & 9 \\ 0 & 1 & -2 \\ 0 & 0 & 1 \end{bmatrix}$$

Applying $R_1 \to R_1 - 9R_3$ and $R_2 \to R_2 + 2R_3$, we get

$$A \sim \begin{bmatrix} 1 & 0 & 0 \\ 0 & 1 & 0 \\ 0 & 0 & 1 \end{bmatrix}$$

Hence, $A \sim I$

Example 39. Given $A = \begin{bmatrix} 1 & 1 & 1 \\ 2 & 4 & 1 \\ 2 & 3 & 1 \end{bmatrix}$, $B = \begin{bmatrix} 2 & 3 \\ 3 & 4 \end{bmatrix}$. Find P such that $BPA = \begin{bmatrix} 1 & 0 & 1 \\ 0 & 1 & 0 \end{bmatrix}$

Sol. Given, $$BPA = \begin{bmatrix} 1 & 0 & 1 \\ 0 & 1 & 0 \end{bmatrix}$$

$$\therefore \quad P = B^{-1}\begin{bmatrix} 1 & 0 & 1 \\ 0 & 1 & 0 \end{bmatrix}A^{-1} \quad \text{...(i) [by property]}$$

$$\because \quad B = \begin{bmatrix} 2 & 3 \\ 3 & 4 \end{bmatrix} \Rightarrow B^{-1} = \frac{1}{(-1)}\begin{bmatrix} 4 & -3 \\ -3 & 2 \end{bmatrix} = \begin{bmatrix} -4 & 3 \\ 3 & -2 \end{bmatrix}$$

$$\therefore \quad B^{-1} = \begin{bmatrix} -4 & 3 \\ 3 & -2 \end{bmatrix} \quad \text{...(ii)}$$

and $$A = \begin{bmatrix} 1 & 1 & 1 \\ 2 & 4 & 1 \\ 2 & 3 & 1 \end{bmatrix}$$

$\therefore \quad |A| = 1(4-3) - 1(2-2) + 1(6-8) = -1 \neq 0$

$\Rightarrow A^{-1}$ exists.

Now, $$\text{adj } A = \begin{bmatrix} 1 & 2 & -3 \\ 0 & -1 & 1 \\ -2 & -1 & 2 \end{bmatrix} \quad \text{[by shortcut method]}$$

$$\therefore \quad A^{-1} = \frac{\text{adj } A}{|A|} = \begin{bmatrix} -1 & -2 & 3 \\ 0 & 1 & -1 \\ 2 & 1 & -2 \end{bmatrix} \quad \text{...(iii)}$$

Substituting the values of A^{-1} and B^{-1} from Eqs. (ii) and (iii) in Eq. (i), then

$$P = \begin{bmatrix} -4 & 3 \\ 3 & -2 \end{bmatrix}\begin{bmatrix} 1 & 0 & 1 \\ 0 & 1 & 0 \end{bmatrix}\begin{bmatrix} -1 & -2 & 3 \\ 0 & 1 & -1 \\ 2 & 1 & -2 \end{bmatrix}$$

$$= \begin{bmatrix} -4 & 3 \\ 3 & -2 \end{bmatrix}\begin{bmatrix} 1 & -1 & 1 \\ 0 & 1 & -1 \end{bmatrix} = \begin{bmatrix} -4 & 7 & -7 \\ 3 & -5 & 5 \end{bmatrix}$$

To Compute the Inverse of a Non-Singular Matrix by Elementary Operations

(Gauss-Jordan Method)

If A be a non-singular matrix of order n, then write $A = I_n A$.

If A is reduced to I_n by elementary operations (LHS), then suppose I_n is reduced to P(RHS) and not change A in RHS, then after elementary operations, we get

$$I_n = PA,$$

then P is the inverse of A

$$\therefore \quad P = A^{-1}$$

| Example 40. Find the inverse of the matrix $\begin{bmatrix} 1 & 2 & 5 \\ 2 & 3 & 1 \\ -1 & 1 & 1 \end{bmatrix}$, using elementary row operations.

Sol. Let $A = \begin{bmatrix} 1 & 2 & 5 \\ 2 & 3 & 1 \\ -1 & 1 & 1 \end{bmatrix}$

$$\therefore \quad |A| = \begin{vmatrix} 1 & 2 & 5 \\ 2 & 3 & 1 \\ -1 & 1 & 1 \end{vmatrix} = 1(3-1) - 2(2+1) + 5(2+3) = 21 \neq 0$$

$\therefore \quad A^{-1}$ exists.

We write $A = IA$

$$\Rightarrow \quad \begin{bmatrix} 1 & 2 & 5 \\ 2 & 3 & 1 \\ -1 & 1 & 1 \end{bmatrix} = \begin{bmatrix} 1 & 0 & 0 \\ 0 & 1 & 0 \\ 0 & 0 & 1 \end{bmatrix} A$$

Applying $R_2 \to R_2 - 2R_1$ and $R_3 \to R_3 + R_1$, we get

$$\begin{bmatrix} 1 & 2 & 5 \\ 0 & -1 & -9 \\ 0 & 3 & 6 \end{bmatrix} = \begin{bmatrix} 1 & 0 & 0 \\ -2 & 1 & 0 \\ 1 & 0 & 1 \end{bmatrix} A$$

Applying $R_2 \to (-1)R_2$ and $R_3 \to \left(\frac{1}{3}\right)R_3$, we get

$$\begin{bmatrix} 1 & 2 & 5 \\ 0 & 1 & 9 \\ 0 & 1 & 2 \end{bmatrix} = \begin{bmatrix} 1 & 0 & 0 \\ 2 & -1 & 0 \\ \frac{1}{3} & 0 & \frac{1}{3} \end{bmatrix} A$$

Applying $R_1 \to R_1 - 2R_2$ and $R_3 \to R_3 - R_2$, we get

$$\begin{bmatrix} 1 & 0 & -13 \\ 0 & 1 & 9 \\ 0 & 0 & -7 \end{bmatrix} = \begin{bmatrix} -3 & 2 & 0 \\ 2 & -1 & 0 \\ -\frac{5}{3} & 1 & \frac{1}{3} \end{bmatrix} A$$

Applying $R_3 \to \left(-\frac{1}{7}\right)R_3$, we get

$$\begin{bmatrix} 1 & 0 & -13 \\ 0 & 1 & 9 \\ 0 & 0 & 1 \end{bmatrix} = \begin{bmatrix} -3 & 2 & 0 \\ 2 & -1 & 0 \\ \frac{5}{21} & -\frac{1}{7} & -\frac{1}{21} \end{bmatrix} A$$

Applying $R_2 \to R_2 - 9R_3$ and $R_1 \to R_1 + 13R_3$, we get

$$\begin{bmatrix} 1 & 0 & 0 \\ 0 & 1 & 0 \\ 0 & 0 & 1 \end{bmatrix} = \begin{bmatrix} \frac{2}{21} & \frac{1}{7} & -\frac{13}{21} \\ -\frac{1}{7} & \frac{2}{7} & \frac{3}{7} \\ \frac{5}{21} & -\frac{1}{7} & -\frac{1}{21} \end{bmatrix} A$$

Hence, $$A^{-1} = \begin{bmatrix} \frac{2}{21} & \frac{1}{7} & -\frac{13}{21} \\ -\frac{1}{7} & \frac{2}{7} & \frac{3}{7} \\ \frac{5}{21} & -\frac{1}{7} & -\frac{1}{21} \end{bmatrix}$$

Matrix Polynomial

Let $f(x) = a_0 x^m + a_1 x^{m-1} + a_2 x^{m-2} + \ldots + a_{m-1} x + a_m$ be a polynomial in x and let $A = [a_{ij}]_{n \times n}$, then expression of the form

$f(A) = a_0 A^m + a_1 A^{m-1} + a_2 A^{m-2} + \ldots + a_{m-1} A + a_m I_n$ is called a matrix polynomial.

Thus, to obtain $f(A)$ replace x by A in $f(x)$ and the constant term is multiplied by the identity matrix of order equal to that of A.

For example, If $f(x) = x^2 - 7x + 32$ is a polynomial in x and A is a square matrix of order 3, then $f(A) = A^2 - 7A + 32 I_3$ is a matrix polynomial.

Note

1. The polynomial equation $f(x) = 0$ is satisfied by the matrix $A = [a_{ij}]_{n \times n}$, then $f(A) = 0$.
2. Let $A = [a_{ij}]_{n \times n}$ satisfies the equation $a_0 + a_1 x + a_2 x^2 + \ldots + a_r x^r = 0$, then A is invertible of $a_0 \neq 0, |A| = 0$ and its inverse is given by $A^{-1} = \frac{1}{a_0}(a_1 I_n + a_2 A + \ldots + a_r A^{r-1})$.

| Example 41. If $A = \begin{bmatrix} k & l \\ m & n \end{bmatrix}$ and $kn \neq lm$, show that $A^2 - (k+n)A + (kn - lm) I = O$. Hence, find A^{-1}.

Sol. We have, $A = \begin{bmatrix} k & l \\ m & n \end{bmatrix}$, then $|A| = \begin{vmatrix} k & l \\ m & n \end{vmatrix}$

$= kn - ml \neq 0$ [given]

$\therefore$ A^{-1} exists.

Now, $A^2 = A \cdot A = \begin{bmatrix} k & l \\ m & n \end{bmatrix}\begin{bmatrix} k & l \\ m & n \end{bmatrix} = \begin{bmatrix} k^2 + lm & kl + ln \\ mk + nm & ml + n^2 \end{bmatrix}$

$\therefore$ $A^2 - (k+n)A + (kn - lm)I$

$$= \begin{bmatrix} k^2 + lm & kl + ln \\ mk + nm & ml + n^2 \end{bmatrix} - (k+n)\begin{bmatrix} k & l \\ m & n \end{bmatrix} + (kn - lm)\begin{bmatrix} 1 & 0 \\ 0 & 1 \end{bmatrix}$$

$$= \begin{bmatrix} k^2 + lm & kl + ln \\ mk + nm & ml + n^2 \end{bmatrix} - \begin{bmatrix} k^2 + nk & kl + nl \\ km + nm & kn + n^2 \end{bmatrix} + \begin{bmatrix} kn - lm & 0 \\ 0 & kn - lm \end{bmatrix}$$

$$= \begin{bmatrix} k^2 + lm - k^2 - nk + kn - lm & kl + ln - kl - ln \\ mk + nm - km - nm & ml + n^2 - kn - n^2 + kn - lm \end{bmatrix}$$

$$= \begin{bmatrix} 0 & 0 \\ 0 & 0 \end{bmatrix} = O$$

As $A^2 - (k+n)A + (kn - lm)I = O$

$\Rightarrow$ $(kn - lm)I = (k+n)A - A^2$

$\Rightarrow$ $(kn - lm)IA^{-1} = ((k+n)A - A^2)A^{-1}$

$\Rightarrow$ $(kn - lm)A^{-1} = (k+n)AA^{-1} - A(AA^{-1})$

$= (k+n)I - AI$ $[\because AA^{-1} = I]$

$= (k+n)I - A$

$= (k+n)\begin{bmatrix} 1 & 0 \\ 0 & 1 \end{bmatrix} - \begin{bmatrix} k & l \\ m & n \end{bmatrix}$

$= \begin{bmatrix} k+n & 0 \\ 0 & k+n \end{bmatrix} - \begin{bmatrix} k & l \\ m & n \end{bmatrix}$

$\Rightarrow$ $(kn - lm)A^{-1} = \begin{bmatrix} n & -l \\ -m & k \end{bmatrix}$

Hence, $A^{-1} = \dfrac{1}{(kn - lm)}\begin{bmatrix} n & -l \\ -m & k \end{bmatrix}$

Example 42. If $A = \begin{bmatrix} 3 & 1 \\ 2 & 1 \end{bmatrix}$, find the value of $|a| + |b|$ such that $A^2 + aA + bI = O$. Hence, find A^{-1}.

Sol. We have, $A = \begin{bmatrix} 3 & 1 \\ 2 & 1 \end{bmatrix}$, then $|A| = \begin{vmatrix} 3 & 1 \\ 2 & 1 \end{vmatrix} = 3 - 2 = 1 \neq 0$

$\therefore$ A^{-1} exists.

Now, $A^2 = A \cdot A = \begin{bmatrix} 3 & 1 \\ 2 & 1 \end{bmatrix}\begin{bmatrix} 3 & 1 \\ 2 & 1 \end{bmatrix} = \begin{bmatrix} 11 & 4 \\ 8 & 3 \end{bmatrix}$

Since, $A^2 + aA + bI = O$

$\Rightarrow$ $\begin{bmatrix} 11 & 4 \\ 8 & 3 \end{bmatrix} + a\begin{bmatrix} 3 & 1 \\ 2 & 1 \end{bmatrix} + b\begin{bmatrix} 1 & 0 \\ 0 & 1 \end{bmatrix} = \begin{bmatrix} 0 & 0 \\ 0 & 0 \end{bmatrix}$

$\Rightarrow$ $\begin{bmatrix} 11 + 3a + b & 4 + a \\ 8 + 2a & 3 + a + b \end{bmatrix} = \begin{bmatrix} 0 & 0 \\ 0 & 0 \end{bmatrix}$

Equating the corresponding elements, we get

$11 + 3a + b = 0$ ...(i)

$4 + a = 0$ ...(ii)

$8 + 2a = 0$ ...(iii)

$3 + a + b = 0$ ...(iv)

From Eqs. (ii) and (iv), we get $a = -4$ and $b = 1$

$\therefore$ $|a| + |b| = |-4| + |1| = 4 + 1 = 5$

As $A^2 + aA + bI = O$

$\Rightarrow$ $A^2 - 4A + I = O \Rightarrow I = 4A - A^2$

$\Rightarrow$ $IA^{-1} = (4A - A^2)A^{-1}$

$\Rightarrow$ $A^{-1} = 4(AA^{-1}) - A(AA^{-1})$

$= 4I - AI = 4I - A$

$= 4\begin{bmatrix} 1 & 0 \\ 0 & 1 \end{bmatrix} - \begin{bmatrix} 3 & 1 \\ 2 & 1 \end{bmatrix} = \begin{bmatrix} 4 & 0 \\ 0 & 4 \end{bmatrix} - \begin{bmatrix} 3 & 1 \\ 2 & 1 \end{bmatrix}$

$\therefore$ $A^{-1} = \begin{bmatrix} 1 & -1 \\ -2 & 3 \end{bmatrix}$

Use of Mathematical Induction

Example 43. Let $A = \begin{bmatrix} 0 & 1 \\ 0 & 0 \end{bmatrix}$, show that

$$(aI + bA)^n = a^n I + na^{n-1} bA, \forall n \in N.$$

Sol. Let $P(n): (aI + bA)^n = a^n I + na^{n-1}bA$

Step I For $n = 1$,

LHS $= (aI + bA)^1 = aI + bA$

and RHS $= a^1 I + 1 \cdot a^0 bA = aI + bA$

LHS = RHS

Therefore, $P(1)$ is true.

Step II Assume that $P(k)$ is true, then

$P(k): (aI + bA)^k = a^k I + ka^{k-1} bA$

Step III For $n = k + 1$, we have to prove that

$P(k+1): (aI + bA)^{k+1} = a^{k+1} I + (k+1) a^k bA$

LHS $= (aI + bA)^{k+1} = (aI + bA)^k (aI + bA)$

$= (a^k I + ka^{k-1}bA)(aI + bA)$ [from step II]

$= a^{k+1} I^2 + a^k b(IA) + ka^k b(AI) + k a^{k-1} b^2 A^2$

$= a^{k+1} I + (k+1)a^k b A + 0$

$[\because AI = A, A^2 = 0 \text{ and } I^2 = I]$

$= a^{k+1} I + (k+1)a^k bA =$ RHS

Therefore, $P(k+1)$ is true.

Hence, by the principal of mathematical2 induction $P(n)$ is true for all $n \in N$.

Example 44. If $A = \begin{bmatrix} 3 & -4 \\ 1 & -1 \end{bmatrix}$, use mathematical induction to show that $A^n = \begin{bmatrix} 1+2n & -4n \\ n & 1-2n \end{bmatrix}$, $\forall\, n \in N$.

Sol. Let $P(n) : A^n = \begin{bmatrix} 1+2n & -4n \\ n & 1-2n \end{bmatrix}$

Step I For $n = 1$,

$\text{LHS} = A^1 = A$

and $\text{RHS} = \begin{bmatrix} 1+2 & -4 \\ 1 & 1-2 \end{bmatrix} = \begin{bmatrix} 3 & -4 \\ 1 & -1 \end{bmatrix} = A$

$\Rightarrow$ LHS = RHS

Therefore, $P(1)$ is true.

Step II Assume that $P(k)$ is true, then

$$P(k) : A^k = \begin{bmatrix} 1+2k & -4k \\ k & 1-2k \end{bmatrix}$$

Step III For $n = k + 1$, we have to prove that

$$P(k+1) : A^{k+1} = \begin{bmatrix} 3+2k & -4(k+1) \\ k+1 & -1-2k \end{bmatrix}$$

$$\text{LHS} = A^{k+1} = A^k \cdot A$$

$$= \begin{bmatrix} 1+2k & -4k \\ k & 1-2k \end{bmatrix} \begin{bmatrix} 3 & -4 \\ 1 & -1 \end{bmatrix} \quad \text{[from step II]}$$

$$= \begin{bmatrix} 3(1+2k) - 4k & -4(1+2k) + 4k \\ 3k + 1(1-2k) & -4k - 1(1-2k) \end{bmatrix}$$

$$= \begin{bmatrix} 3+2k & -4(k+1) \\ k+1 & -1-2k \end{bmatrix} = \text{RHS}$$

Therefore, $P(k+1)$ is true.

Hence, by the principal of mathematical induction $P(n)$ is true for all $n \in N$.

Exercise for Session 3

1 If $A = \begin{bmatrix} -1 & -2 & -2 \\ 2 & 1 & -2 \\ 2 & -2 & 1 \end{bmatrix}$, then adj A equals to

(a) A (b) A^T (c) $3A$ (d) $3A^T$

2 If A is a 3×3 matrix and B is its adjoint such that $|B| = 64$, then $|A|$ is equal to

(a) 64 (b) $\pm$ 64 (c) $\pm$ 8 (d) 18

3 For any 2×2 matrix A, if $A\,(\text{adj } A) = \begin{bmatrix} 10 & 0 \\ 0 & 10 \end{bmatrix}$, then $|A|$ is equal to

(a) 0 (b) 10 (c) 20 (d) 100

4 If A is a singular matrix, then adj A is

(a) singular (b) non-singular (c) symmetric (d) not defined

5 If $A = \begin{bmatrix} 1 & 2 & -1 \\ -1 & 1 & 2 \\ 2 & -1 & 1 \end{bmatrix}$, then det (adj (adj A)) is

(a) 14^4 (b) 14^3 (c) 14^2 (d) 14

6 If $k \in R_0$, then det adj $(k I_n)$) is equal to

(a) k^{n-1} (b) $k^{n(n-1)}$ (c) k^n (d) k

7 With $1, \omega, \omega^2$ as cube roots of unity, inverse of which of the following matrices exists?

(a) $\begin{bmatrix} 1 & \omega \\ \omega & \omega^2 \end{bmatrix}$ (b) $\begin{bmatrix} \omega^2 & 1 \\ 1 & \omega \end{bmatrix}$

(c) $\begin{bmatrix} \omega & \omega^2 \\ \omega^2 & 1 \end{bmatrix}$ (d) None of these

8 If the matrix A is such that $A\begin{bmatrix}-1 & 2\\ 3 & 1\end{bmatrix}=\begin{bmatrix}-4 & 1\\ 7 & 7\end{bmatrix}$, then A is equal to

(a) $\begin{bmatrix}1 & 1\\ 2 & -3\end{bmatrix}$ (b) $\begin{bmatrix}1 & 1\\ -2 & 3\end{bmatrix}$ (c) $\begin{bmatrix}1 & -1\\ 2 & 3\end{bmatrix}$ (d) $\begin{bmatrix}-1 & 1\\ 2 & 3\end{bmatrix}$

9 If $A=\begin{bmatrix}\cos x & \sin x & 0\\ -\sin x & \cos x & 0\\ 0 & 0 & 1\end{bmatrix}=f(x)$, then A^{-1} is equal to

(a) $f(-x)$ (b) $f(x)$
(c) $-f(x)$ (d) $-f(-x)$

10 The element in the first row and third column of the inverse of the matrix $\begin{bmatrix}1 & 2 & -3\\ 0 & 1 & 2\\ 0 & 0 & 1\end{bmatrix}$, is

(a) -2 (b) 0 (c) 1 (d) None of these

11 If $A=\begin{bmatrix}0 & 1 & -1\\ 2 & 1 & 3\\ 3 & 2 & 1\end{bmatrix}$, then $(A(\text{adj } A)\, A^{-1})\, A$ is equal to

(a) $\begin{bmatrix}-6 & 0 & 0\\ 0 & -6 & 0\\ 0 & 0 & -6\end{bmatrix}$ (b) $\begin{bmatrix}0 & \frac{1}{6} & -\frac{1}{6}\\ \frac{1}{3} & \frac{1}{6} & \frac{1}{2}\\ \frac{1}{2} & \frac{1}{3} & \frac{1}{6}\end{bmatrix}$ (c) $2\begin{bmatrix}3 & 0 & 0\\ 0 & 3 & 0\\ 0 & 0 & 3\end{bmatrix}$ (d) $2\begin{bmatrix}1 & 0 & 0\\ 0 & 1 & 0\\ 0 & 0 & 1\end{bmatrix}$

12 A is an involutory matrix given by $A=\begin{bmatrix}0 & 1 & -1\\ 4 & -3 & 4\\ 3 & -3 & 4\end{bmatrix}$, then the inverse of $\frac{A}{2}$ will be

(a) $2A$ (b) $\frac{A^{-1}}{2}$
(c) $\frac{A}{2}$ (d) A^2

13 If A satisfies the equation $x^3-5x^2+4x+\lambda=0$, then A^{-1} exists, if

(a) $\lambda\neq 1$ (b) $\lambda\neq 2$
(c) $\lambda\neq -1$ (d) $\lambda\neq 0$

14 A square non-singular matrix A satisfies the equation $x^2-x+2=0$, then A^{-1} is equal to

(a) $I-A$ (b) $(I-A)/2$
(c) $I+A$ (d) $(I+A)/2$

15 Matrix A is such that $A^2=2A-I$, where I is the identity matrix, then for $n\geq 2$, A^n is equal to

(a) $nA-(n-1)I$ (b) $nA-I$
(c) $2^{n-1}A-(n-1)I$ (d) $2^{n-1}A-I$

16 If $X=\begin{bmatrix}3 & -4\\ 1 & -1\end{bmatrix}$, the value of X^n is

(a) $\begin{bmatrix}3n & -4n\\ n & -n\end{bmatrix}$ (b) $\begin{bmatrix}2n+n & 5-n\\ n & -n\end{bmatrix}$

(c) $\begin{bmatrix}3^n & (-4)^n\\ 1^n & (-1)^n\end{bmatrix}$ (d) None of these

Session 4

Solutions of Linear Simultaneous Equations Using Matrix Method

Solutions of Linear Simultaneous Equations Using Matrix Method

Let us consider a system of n linear equations in n unknowns say $x_1, x_2, x_3, ..., x_n$ given as below

$$\left.\begin{array}{l} a_{11}x_1 + a_{12}x_2 + a_{13}x_3 + \ldots + a_{1n}x_n = b_1 \\ a_{21}x_1 + a_{22}x_2 + a_{23}x_3 + \ldots + a_{2n}x_n = b_2 \\ a_{31}x_1 + a_{32}x_2 + a_{33}x_3 + \ldots + a_{3n}x_n = b_3 \\ \ldots \quad \ldots \quad \ldots \quad \ldots \quad \ldots \\ \ldots \quad \ldots \quad \ldots \quad \ldots \quad \ldots \\ a_{n1}x_1 + a_{n2}x_2 + a_{n3}x_3 + \ldots + a_{nn}x_n = b_n \end{array}\right\} \quad \ldots \text{(i)}$$

If $b_1 = b_2 = b_3 = \ldots = b_n = 0$, then the system of Eq.(i) is called a system of homogeneous linear equations and if atleast one of $b_1, b_2, b_3, ..., b_n$ is non-zero, then it is called a system of non-homogeneous linear equation. We write the above system of Eq. (i) in the matrix form as

$$\begin{bmatrix} a_{11} & a_{12} & a_{13} & \cdots & a_{1n} \\ a_{21} & a_{22} & a_{23} & \cdots & a_{2n} \\ a_{31} & a_{32} & a_{33} & \cdots & a_{3n} \\ \cdots & \cdots & \cdots & \cdots & \cdots \\ \cdots & \cdots & \cdots & \cdots & \cdots \\ a_{n1} & a_{n2} & a_{n3} & \cdots & a_{nn} \end{bmatrix} \begin{bmatrix} x_1 \\ x_2 \\ x_3 \\ \cdots \\ \cdots \\ x_n \end{bmatrix} = \begin{bmatrix} b_1 \\ b_2 \\ b_3 \\ \cdots \\ \cdots \\ b_n \end{bmatrix}$$

$$\Rightarrow \quad AX = B \quad \ldots \text{(ii)}$$

where $A = \begin{bmatrix} a_{11} & a_{12} & a_{13} & \cdots & a_{1n} \\ a_{21} & a_{22} & a_{23} & \cdots & a_{2n} \\ a_{31} & a_{32} & a_{33} & \cdots & a_{3n} \\ \cdots & \cdots & \cdots & \cdots & \cdots \\ \cdots & \cdots & \cdots & \cdots & \cdots \\ a_{n1} & a_{n2} & a_{n3} & \cdots & a_{nn} \end{bmatrix}$,

$X = \begin{bmatrix} x_1 \\ x_2 \\ x_3 \\ \cdots \\ \cdots \\ x_n \end{bmatrix}$ and $B = \begin{bmatrix} b_1 \\ b_2 \\ b_3 \\ \cdots \\ \cdots \\ b_n \end{bmatrix}$

Pre-multiplying Eq. (ii) by A^{-1}, we get

$$A^{-1}(AX) = A^{-1}B \Rightarrow (A^{-1}A)X = A^{-1}B$$

$$\Rightarrow \quad IX = A^{-1}B$$

$$\Rightarrow \quad X = A^{-1}B = \frac{(\text{adj } A)B}{|A|}$$

Types of Equations

(1) **When system of equations is non-homogeneous**

(i) If $|A| \neq 0$, then the system of equations is consistent and has a unique solution given by $X = A^{-1}B$.

(ii) If $|A| = 0$ and $(\text{adj}A) \cdot B \neq 0$, then the system of equations is inconsistent and has no solution.

(iii) If $|A| = 0$ and $(\text{adj}A) \cdot B = O$, then the system of equations is consistent and has an infinite number of solutions.

(2) **When system of equations is homogeneous**

(i) If $|A| \neq 0$, then the system of equations has only trivial solution and it has one solution.

(ii) If $|A| = 0$, then the system of equations has non-trivial solution and it has infinite solutions.

(iii) If number of equations < number of unknowns, then it has non-trivial solution.

Note

Non-homogeneous linear equations can also be solved by Cramer's rule, this method has been discussed in the chapter on determinants.

| Example 45. Solve the system of equations $x + 2y + 3z = 1$, $2x + 3y + 2z = 2$ and $3x + 3y + 4z = 1$ with the help of matrix inversion.

Sol. We have,

$$x + 2y + 3z = 1,\ 2x + 3y + 2z = 2 \text{ and } 3x + 3y + 4z = 1$$

The given system of equations in the matrix form are written as below.

$$\begin{bmatrix} 1 & 2 & 3 \\ 2 & 3 & 2 \\ 3 & 3 & 4 \end{bmatrix} \begin{bmatrix} x \\ y \\ z \end{bmatrix} = \begin{bmatrix} 1 \\ 2 \\ 1 \end{bmatrix}$$

$$AX = B$$

$$\Rightarrow \quad X = A^{-1}B \quad \text{...(i)}$$

where $A = \begin{bmatrix} 1 & 2 & 3 \\ 2 & 3 & 2 \\ 3 & 3 & 4 \end{bmatrix}, X = \begin{bmatrix} x \\ y \\ z \end{bmatrix}$ and $B = \begin{bmatrix} 1 \\ 2 \\ 1 \end{bmatrix}$

$$|A| = 1(12-6) - 2(8-6) + 3(6-9)$$
$$= 6 - 4 - 9 = -7 \neq 0$$

$\therefore$ A^{-1} exists and has unique solution.

Let C be the matrix of cofactors of elements in $|A|$.

Now, cofactors along $R_1 = 6, -2, -3$

cofactors along $R_2 = 1, -5, 3$

and cofactors along $R_3 = -5, 4, -1$

$$\therefore \quad C = \begin{bmatrix} 6 & -2 & -3 \\ 1 & -5 & 3 \\ -5 & 4 & -1 \end{bmatrix}$$

$$\therefore \quad \text{adj } A = C^T$$

$$\Rightarrow \quad \text{adj } A = \begin{bmatrix} 6 & -2 & -3 \\ 1 & -5 & 3 \\ -5 & 4 & -1 \end{bmatrix}^T = \begin{bmatrix} 6 & 1 & -5 \\ -2 & -5 & 4 \\ -3 & 3 & -1 \end{bmatrix}$$

$$\Rightarrow \quad A^{-1} = \frac{\text{adj } A}{|A|} = -\frac{1}{7}\begin{bmatrix} 6 & 1 & -5 \\ -2 & -5 & 4 \\ -3 & 3 & -1 \end{bmatrix}$$

$$= \begin{bmatrix} -\frac{6}{7} & -\frac{1}{7} & \frac{5}{7} \\ \frac{2}{7} & \frac{5}{7} & -\frac{4}{7} \\ \frac{3}{7} & -\frac{3}{7} & \frac{1}{7} \end{bmatrix}$$

From Eq. (i), $X = A^{-1}B$

$$\Rightarrow \quad \begin{bmatrix} x \\ y \\ z \end{bmatrix} = \begin{bmatrix} -\frac{6}{7} & -\frac{1}{7} & \frac{5}{7} \\ \frac{2}{7} & \frac{5}{7} & -\frac{4}{7} \\ \frac{3}{7} & -\frac{3}{7} & \frac{1}{7} \end{bmatrix}\begin{bmatrix} 1 \\ 2 \\ 1 \end{bmatrix} = \begin{bmatrix} -\frac{3}{7} \\ \frac{8}{7} \\ -\frac{2}{7} \end{bmatrix}$$

Hence, $x = -\frac{3}{7}, y = \frac{8}{7}$ and $z = -\frac{2}{7}$ is the required solution.

| Example 46. Solve the system of equations $x + y + z = 6$, $x + 2y + 3z = 14$ and $x + 4y + 7z = 30$ with the help of matrix method.

Sol. We have, $x + y + z = 6,$

$$x + 2y + 3z = 14$$

and $x + 4y + 7z = 30$

The given system of equations in the matrix form are written as below :

$$\begin{bmatrix} 1 & 1 & 1 \\ 1 & 2 & 3 \\ 1 & 4 & 7 \end{bmatrix}\begin{bmatrix} x \\ y \\ z \end{bmatrix} = \begin{bmatrix} 6 \\ 14 \\ 30 \end{bmatrix}$$

$$AX = B \quad \text{...(i)}$$

where, $A = \begin{bmatrix} 1 & 1 & 1 \\ 1 & 2 & 3 \\ 1 & 4 & 7 \end{bmatrix}, X = \begin{bmatrix} x \\ y \\ z \end{bmatrix}$ and $B = \begin{bmatrix} 6 \\ 14 \\ 30 \end{bmatrix}$

$$|A| = 1(14-12) - 1(7-3) + 1(4-2) = 2 - 4 + 2 = 0$$

$\therefore$ The equation either has no solution or an infinite number of solutions. To decide about this, we proceed to find
(adj A) B.

Let C be the matrix of cofactors of elements in $|A|$.

Now, cofactors along $R_1 = 2, -4, 2$

cofactors along $R_2 = -3, 6, -3$

and cofactors along $R_3 = 1, -2, 1$

$$\therefore \quad C = \begin{bmatrix} 2 & -4 & 2 \\ -3 & 6 & -3 \\ 1 & -2 & 1 \end{bmatrix}$$

$$\Rightarrow \quad \text{adj} = C^T = \begin{bmatrix} 2 & -3 & 1 \\ -4 & 6 & -2 \\ 2 & -3 & 1 \end{bmatrix},$$

then $\quad (\text{adj} A)\, B = \begin{bmatrix} 2 & -3 & 1 \\ -4 & 6 & -2 \\ 2 & -3 & 1 \end{bmatrix}\begin{bmatrix} 6 \\ 14 \\ 30 \end{bmatrix} = \begin{bmatrix} 0 \\ 0 \\ 0 \end{bmatrix} = O$

Hence, both conditions $|A| = 0$ and $(\text{adj } A)\, B = O$ are satisfied, then the system of equations is consistent and has an infinite number of solutions.

Proceed as follows :

$$[A : B] = \begin{bmatrix} 1 & 1 & 1 & \vdots & 6 \\ 1 & 2 & 3 & \vdots & 14 \\ 1 & 4 & 7 & \vdots & 30 \end{bmatrix}$$

Applying $R_2 \to R_2 - R_1$ and $R_3 \to R_3 - R_1$, then

$$[A : B] = \begin{bmatrix} 1 & 1 & 1 & \vdots & 6 \\ 0 & 1 & 2 & \vdots & 8 \\ 0 & 2 & 4 & \vdots & 16 \end{bmatrix}$$

Applying $R_3 \to R_3 - 2R_2$, then

$$[A : B] = \begin{bmatrix} 1 & 1 & 1 & \vdots & 6 \\ 0 & 1 & 2 & \vdots & 8 \\ 0 & 0 & 0 & \vdots & 0 \end{bmatrix}$$

Then, Eq. (i) reduces to

$$\begin{bmatrix} 1 & 1 & 1 \\ 0 & 1 & 2 \\ 0 & 0 & 0 \end{bmatrix}\begin{bmatrix} x \\ y \\ z \end{bmatrix} = \begin{bmatrix} 6 \\ 8 \\ 0 \end{bmatrix} \Rightarrow \begin{bmatrix} x + y + z \\ y + 2z \\ 0 \end{bmatrix} = \begin{bmatrix} 6 \\ 8 \\ 0 \end{bmatrix}$$

On comparing $x+y+z=6$ and $y+2z=8$

Taking $z=k \in R$, then $y=8-2k$ and $x=k-2$.

Since, k is arbitrary, hence the number of solutions is infinite.

| Example 47. Solve the system of equations $x+3y-2z=0$, $2x-y+4z=0$ and $x-11y+14z=0$.

Sol. We have,

$$x+3y-2z=0$$
$$2x-y+4z=0$$
$$x-11y+14z=0$$

The given system of equations in the matrix form are written as below.

$$\begin{bmatrix} 1 & 3 & -2 \\ 2 & -1 & 4 \\ 1 & -11 & 14 \end{bmatrix}\begin{bmatrix} x \\ y \\ z \end{bmatrix}=\begin{bmatrix} 0 \\ 0 \\ 0 \end{bmatrix}$$

$$AX=O \quad \ldots(\text{i})$$

where $A=\begin{bmatrix} 1 & 3 & -2 \\ 2 & -1 & 4 \\ 1 & -11 & 14 \end{bmatrix}$, $X=\begin{bmatrix} x \\ y \\ z \end{bmatrix}$ and $O=\begin{bmatrix} 0 \\ 0 \\ 0 \end{bmatrix}$

$$\therefore \quad |A|=1(-14+44)-3(28-4)-2(-22+1)$$
$$=30-72+42=0$$

and therefore the system has a non-trivial solution. Now, we may write first two of the given equations

$$x+3y=2z \text{ and } 2x-y=-4z$$

Solving these equations in terms of z, we get

$$x=-\frac{10}{7}z \text{ and } y=\frac{8}{7}z$$

Putting $x=-\frac{10}{7}z$ and $y=\frac{8}{7}z$ in third equation of the given system,

we get, LHS $=-\frac{10}{7}z-\frac{88}{7}z+14z=0=$ RHS

Now, if $z=7k$, then $x=-10k$ and $y=8k$.

Hence, $x=-10k$, $y=8k$ and $z=7k$ (where k is arbitrary) are the required solutions.

| Example 48. Solve the system of equations

$$2x+3y-3z=0,$$
$$3x-3y+z=0$$

and

$$3x-2y-3z=0$$

Sol. We have,

$$2x+3y-3z=0$$
$$3x-3y+z=0$$
$$3x-2y-3z=0$$

The given system of equations in the matrix form are written as below.

$$\begin{bmatrix} 2 & 3 & -3 \\ 3 & -3 & 1 \\ 3 & -2 & -3 \end{bmatrix}\begin{bmatrix} x \\ y \\ z \end{bmatrix}=\begin{bmatrix} 0 \\ 0 \\ 0 \end{bmatrix}$$

$$AX=O \quad \ldots(\text{i})$$

where $A=\begin{bmatrix} 2 & 3 & -3 \\ 3 & -3 & 1 \\ 3 & -2 & -3 \end{bmatrix}$, $X=\begin{bmatrix} x \\ y \\ z \end{bmatrix}$ and $O=\begin{bmatrix} 0 \\ 0 \\ 0 \end{bmatrix}$

$$\therefore \quad |A|=2(9+2)-3(-9-3)-3(-6+9)$$
$$=22+36-9=49 \neq 0$$

Hence, the equations have a unique trivial solution $x=0$, $y=0$ and $z=0$ only.

Echelon Form of a Matrix

A matrix A is said to be in echelon form, if

(i) The first non-zero element in each row is 1.

(ii) Every non-zero row in A precedes every zero-row.

(iii) The number of zeroes before the first non-zero element in 1st, 2nd, 3rd, ... rows should be in increasing order.

For example,

(i) $\begin{bmatrix} 1 & 2 & 3 \\ 0 & 1 & 4 \\ 0 & 0 & 1 \end{bmatrix}$ (ii) $\begin{bmatrix} 1 & 2 & 3 & 4 \\ 0 & 1 & 4 & 5 \\ 0 & 0 & 1 & 9 \\ 0 & 0 & 0 & 1 \end{bmatrix}$

(iii) $\begin{bmatrix} 1 & 2 & 3 & 4 & 5 \\ 0 & 1 & 2 & 4 & 3 \\ 0 & 0 & 1 & 2 & 5 \\ 0 & 0 & 0 & 0 & 0 \end{bmatrix}$

Rank of Matrix

The rank of a matrix is said to be r, if

(i) It has atleast minors of order r is different from zero.

(ii) All minors of A of order higher than r are zero.

The rank of A is denoted by $\rho(A)$.

Note

1. The rank of a zero matrix is zero and the rank of an identity matrix of order n is n.
2. The rank of a matrix in echelon form is equal to the number of non-zero rows of the matrix.
3. The rank of a non-singular matrix ($|A| \neq 0$) of order n is n.

Properties of Rank of Matrices

(i) If $A=[a_{ij}]_{m \times n}$ and $B=[b_{ij}]_{m \times n}$, then

$$\rho(A+B) \leq \rho(A)+\rho(B)$$

(ii) If $A=[a_{ij}]_{m \times n}$ and $B=[b_{ij}]_{n \times p}$, then

$$\rho(AB) \leq \rho(A) \text{ and } \rho(AB) \leq \rho(B)$$

(iii) If $A=[a_{ij}]_{n \times n}$, then $\rho(A)=\rho(A')$

Example 49. Find the rank of $\begin{bmatrix} 3 & -1 & 2 \\ -3 & 1 & 2 \\ -6 & 2 & 4 \end{bmatrix}$.

Sol. We have,

Let $A = \begin{bmatrix} 3 & -1 & 2 \\ -3 & 1 & 2 \\ -6 & 2 & 4 \end{bmatrix}$

Applying $R_2 \to R_2 + R_1$ and $R_3 \to R_3 + 2R_1$, we get

$$A = \begin{bmatrix} 3 & -1 & 2 \\ 0 & 0 & 4 \\ 0 & 0 & 8 \end{bmatrix}$$

Applying $R_3 \to R_3 - 2R_2$, we get

$$A = \begin{bmatrix} 3 & -1 & 2 \\ 0 & 0 & 4 \\ 0 & 0 & 0 \end{bmatrix}$$

Applying $R_1 \to \left(\frac{1}{3}\right) R_1$ and $R_2 \to \left(\frac{1}{4}\right) R_2$, then

$$A = \begin{bmatrix} 1 & -\frac{1}{3} & \frac{2}{3} \\ 0 & 0 & 1 \\ 0 & 0 & 0 \end{bmatrix}$$

This is Echelon form of matrix A.

$\therefore$ Rank = Number of non-zero rows $\Rightarrow \rho(A) = 2$

Aliter $|A| = \begin{vmatrix} 3 & -1 & 2 \\ -3 & 1 & 2 \\ -6 & 2 & 4 \end{vmatrix}$

$$= 3(4 - 4) + 1(-12 + 12) + 2(-6 + 6) = 0$$

$\therefore$ Rank of $A \neq 3$ but less than 3.

There will be ${}^3C_2 \times {}^3C_2 = 9$ square minors of order 2. Now, we consider of there minors.

(i) $\begin{vmatrix} 1 & 2 \\ 2 & 4 \end{vmatrix} = 0$ (ii) $\begin{vmatrix} 3 & 2 \\ -6 & 4 \end{vmatrix} = 24 \neq 0$

Hence, all minors are not zero.

Hence, rank of A is 2. $\Rightarrow \rho(A) = 2$

Solutions of Linear Simultaneous Equations Using Rank Method

Let us consider a system of n linear equations in n unknowns say $x_1, x_2, x_3, \ldots, x_n$ given as below.

$$\left.\begin{array}{l} a_{11}x_1 + a_{12}x_2 + a_{13}x_3 + \ldots + a_{1n}x_n = b_1 \\ a_{21}x_1 + a_{22}x_2 + a_{23}x_3 + \ldots + a_{2n}x_n = b_2 \\ a_{31}x_1 + a_{32}x_2 + a_{33}x_3 + \ldots + a_{3n}x_n = b_3 \\ \ldots \quad \ldots \ldots \ldots \ldots \ldots \quad \ldots \ldots \\ \ldots \quad \ldots \ldots \ldots \ldots \ldots \quad \ldots \ldots \\ a_{m1}x_1 + a_{m2}x_2 + a_{m3}x_3 + \ldots + a_{mn}x_n = b_m \end{array}\right\} \quad \ldots(i)$$

We write the above system of Eq. (i) in the matrix form as

$$\begin{bmatrix} a_{11} & a_{12} & a_{13} & \ldots & \ldots & a_{1n} \\ a_{21} & a_{22} & a_{23} & \ldots & \ldots & a_{2n} \\ a_{31} & a_{32} & a_{33} & \ldots & \ldots & a_{3n} \\ \ldots & \ldots & \ldots & \ldots & \ldots & \ldots \\ \ldots & \ldots & \ldots & \ldots & \ldots & \ldots \\ a_{m1} & a_{m2} & a_{m3} & \ldots & \ldots & a_{mn} \end{bmatrix} \begin{bmatrix} x_1 \\ x_2 \\ x_3 \\ \ldots \\ \ldots \\ x_n \end{bmatrix} = \begin{bmatrix} b_1 \\ b_2 \\ b_3 \\ \ldots \\ \ldots \\ b_m \end{bmatrix}$$

$$\Rightarrow \qquad AX = B \qquad \ldots(ii)$$

where $A = \begin{bmatrix} a_{11} & a_{12} & a_{13} & \ldots & \ldots & a_{1n} \\ a_{21} & a_{22} & a_{23} & \ldots & \ldots & a_{2n} \\ a_{31} & a_{32} & a_{33} & \ldots & \ldots & a_{3n} \\ \ldots & \ldots & \ldots & \ldots & \ldots & \ldots \\ \ldots & \ldots & \ldots & \ldots & \ldots & \ldots \\ a_{m1} & a_{m2} & a_{m3} & \ldots & \ldots & a_{mn} \end{bmatrix}$

$$X = \begin{bmatrix} x_1 \\ x_2 \\ x_3 \\ \ldots \\ \ldots \\ x_n \end{bmatrix} \text{ and } B = \begin{bmatrix} b_1 \\ b_2 \\ b_3 \\ \ldots \\ \ldots \\ b_m \end{bmatrix}$$

The matrix A is called the coefficient matrix and the matrix

$$C = [A : B] = \left[\begin{array}{cccccc:c} a_{11} & a_{12} & a_{13} & \ldots & \ldots & a_{1n} & b_1 \\ a_{21} & a_{22} & a_{23} & \ldots & \ldots & a_{2n} & b_2 \\ a_{31} & a_{32} & a_{33} & \ldots & \ldots & a_{3n} & b_3 \\ \ldots & \ldots & \ldots & \ldots & \ldots & \ldots & \ldots \\ \ldots & \ldots & \ldots & \ldots & \ldots & \ldots & \ldots \\ a_{m1} & a_{m2} & a_{m3} & \ldots & \ldots & a_{mn} & b_m \end{array}\right]$$

is called the augmented matrix of the given system of equations.

Types of Equations

1. **Consistent Equation** If $\rho(A) = \rho(C)$
   (i) **Unique Solution** If $\rho(A) = \rho(C) = n$, where n = number of knowns.
   (ii) **Infinite Solution** If $\rho(A) = \rho(C) = r$, where $r < n$.
2. **Inconsistent Equation** If $\rho(A) \neq \rho(C)$, then no solution.

Example 50. Determine for what values of λ and μ the following system of equations

$$x + y + z = 6,$$
$$x + 2y + 3z = 10$$

and $\quad x+2y+\lambda z=\mu$
have (i) no solution? (ii) a unique solution?
(iii) an infinite number of solutions?

Sol. We can write the above system of equations in the matrix form

$$\begin{bmatrix}1 & 1 & 1\\ 1 & 2 & 3\\ 1 & 2 & \lambda\end{bmatrix}\begin{bmatrix}x\\ y\\ z\end{bmatrix}=\begin{bmatrix}6\\ 10\\ \mu\end{bmatrix}$$

$\Rightarrow \quad AX=B$

where $\quad A=\begin{bmatrix}1 & 1 & 1\\ 1 & 2 & 3\\ 1 & 2 & \lambda\end{bmatrix}, \quad X=\begin{bmatrix}x\\ y\\ z\end{bmatrix}$ and $B=\begin{bmatrix}6\\ 10\\ \mu\end{bmatrix}$

$\therefore$ The augmented matrix

$$C=[A:B]=\begin{bmatrix}1 & 1 & 1 & : & 6\\ 1 & 2 & 3 & : & 10\\ 1 & 2 & \lambda & : & \mu\end{bmatrix}$$

Applying $R_2 \to R_2-R_1$ and $R_3 \to R_3-R_1$, we get

$$C=\begin{bmatrix}1 & 1 & 1 & : & 6\\ 0 & 1 & 2 & : & 4\\ 0 & 1 & \lambda-1 & : & \mu-6\end{bmatrix}$$

Applying $R_3 \to R_3-R_2$, we get

$$C=\begin{bmatrix}1 & 1 & 1 & : & 6\\ 0 & 1 & 2 & : & 4\\ 0 & 0 & \lambda-3 & : & \mu-10\end{bmatrix}$$

(i) No solution $\rho(A)\neq\rho(C)$
i.e. $\lambda-3=0$ and $\mu-10\neq 0$
$\therefore \quad \lambda=3$ and $\mu\neq 10$

(ii) A unique solution $\rho(A)=\rho(C)=3$
i.e., $\quad \lambda-3\neq 0$ and $\mu\in R$
$\therefore \quad \lambda\neq 3$ and $\mu\in R$

(iii) Infinite number of solutions
$\rho(A)=\rho(C)\,(\angle 3)$
i.e. $\lambda-3=0$ and $\mu-10=0$
$\therefore \quad \lambda=3$ and $\mu=10$

Reflection Matrix

(i) Reflection in the X-axis

Let $P(x,y)$ be any point and $P'(x_1,y_1)$ be its image after reflection in the X-axis, then

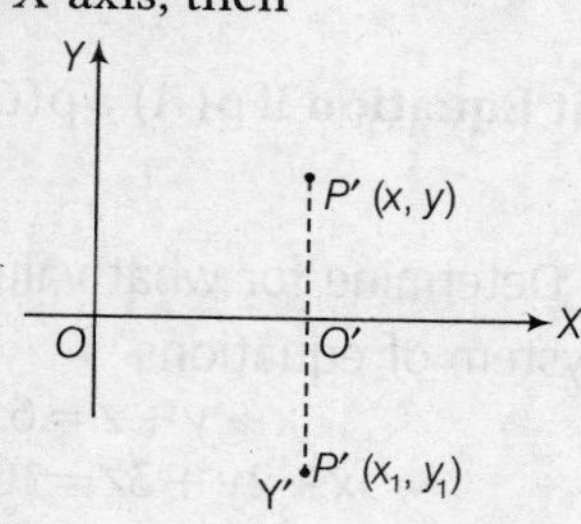

$$\begin{cases}x_1=x\\ y_1=-y\end{cases} \quad [O' \text{ is the mid-point of } P \text{ and } P'$$

These may be rewritten as

$$\begin{cases}x_1=1\cdot x+0\cdot y\\ y_1=0\cdot x+(-1)\cdot y\end{cases}$$

These system of equations in the matrix form are written as below.

$$\begin{bmatrix}x_1\\ y_1\end{bmatrix}=\begin{bmatrix}1 & 0\\ 0 & -1\end{bmatrix}\begin{bmatrix}x\\ y\end{bmatrix}$$

Thus, **the matrix** $\begin{bmatrix}1 & 0\\ 0 & -1\end{bmatrix}$ **describes the reflection of a point $P(x,y)$ in the X-axis.**

(ii) Reflection in the Y-axis

Let $P(x,y)$ be any point and $P'(x_1,y_1)$ be its image after reflection in the Y-axis, then

$$\begin{cases}x_1=-x\\ y_1=y\end{cases} \quad [O' \text{ is the mid-point of } P \text{ and } P'$$

These may be written as

$$\begin{cases}x_1=(-1)\cdot x+0\cdot y\\ y_1=\;\;0\cdot x+1\cdot y\end{cases}$$

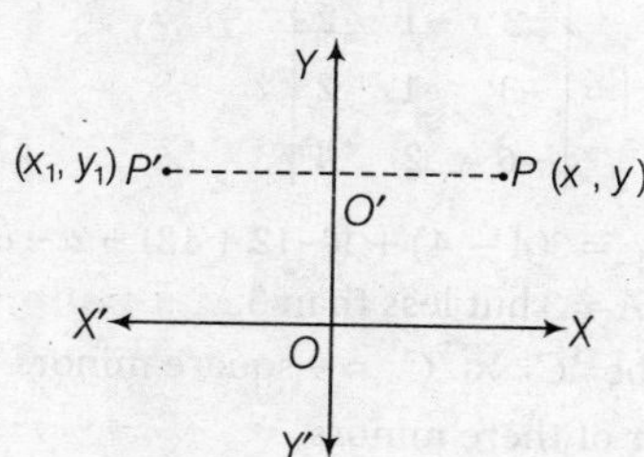

These system of equations in the matrix form are written as below.

$$\begin{bmatrix}x_1\\ y_1\end{bmatrix}=\begin{bmatrix}-1 & 0\\ 0 & 1\end{bmatrix}\begin{bmatrix}x\\ y\end{bmatrix}$$

Thus, **the matrix** $\begin{bmatrix}-1 & 0\\ 0 & 1\end{bmatrix}$ **describes the reflection of a point $P(x,y)$ in the Y-axis.**

(iii) Reflection through the origin

Let $P(x,y)$ be any point and $P'(x_1,y_1)$ be its image after reflection through the origin, then

$$\begin{cases}x_1=-x\\ y_1=-y\end{cases} \quad [O' \text{ is the mid-point of } P \text{ and } P']$$

These may be written as

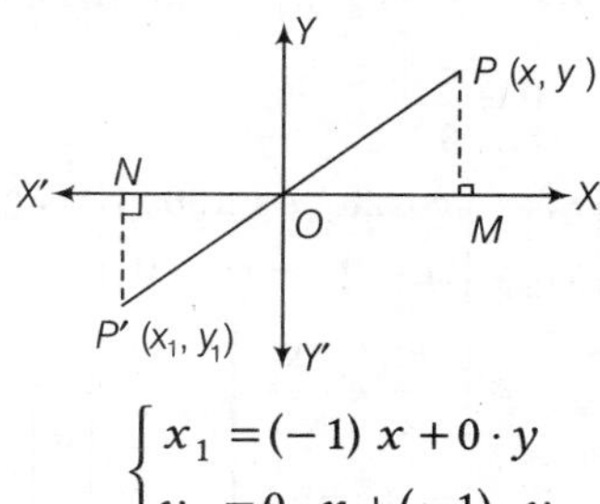

$$\begin{cases} x_1 = (-1)\,x + 0 \cdot y \\ y_1 = 0 \cdot x + (-1) \cdot y \end{cases}$$

These system of equations in the matrix form are written as below.

$$\begin{bmatrix} x_1 \\ y_1 \end{bmatrix} = \begin{bmatrix} -1 & 0 \\ 0 & -1 \end{bmatrix} \begin{bmatrix} x \\ y \end{bmatrix}$$

Thus, **the matrix** $\begin{bmatrix} -1 & 0 \\ 0 & -1 \end{bmatrix}$ **describes the reflection of a point $P(x, y)$ through the origin.**

(iv) Reflection in the line y = x

Let $P(x, y)$ be any point and $P'(x_1, y_1)$ be its image after reflection in the line $y = x$, then

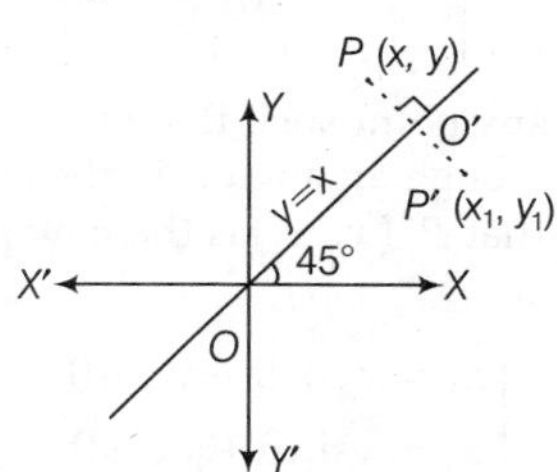

$$\begin{cases} x_1 = y \\ y_1 = x \end{cases} \quad [O' \text{ is the mid-point of } P \text{ and } P']$$

These may be written as

$$\begin{cases} x_1 = 0 \cdot x + 1 \cdot y \\ y_1 = 1 \cdot x + 0 \cdot y \end{cases}$$

These system of equations in the matrix form are written as below.

$$\begin{bmatrix} x_1 \\ y_1 \end{bmatrix} = \begin{bmatrix} 0 & 1 \\ 1 & 0 \end{bmatrix} \begin{bmatrix} x \\ y \end{bmatrix}$$

Thus, **the matrix** $\begin{bmatrix} 0 & 1 \\ 1 & 0 \end{bmatrix}$ **describes the reflection of a point $P(x, y)$ in the line $y = x$.**

(v) Reflection in the line y = x tan θ

Let $P(x, y)$ be any point and $P'(x_1, y_1)$ be its image after reflection in the line $y = x\tan\theta$, then

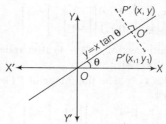

$$\begin{cases} x_1 = x\cos 2\theta + y\sin 2\theta \\ y_1 = x\sin 2\theta - y\cos 2\theta \end{cases}$$

[O' is the mid-point of P and P']

These may be written as

$$\begin{cases} x_1 = x \cdot \cos 2\theta + y \cdot \sin 2\theta \\ y_1 = x \cdot \sin 2\theta + y \cdot (-\cos 2\theta) \end{cases}$$

These system of equations in the matrix form are written as below.

$$\begin{bmatrix} x_1 \\ y_1 \end{bmatrix} = \begin{bmatrix} \cos 2\theta & \sin 2\theta \\ \sin 2\theta & -\cos 2\theta \end{bmatrix} \begin{bmatrix} x \\ y \end{bmatrix}$$

Thus, the matrix $\begin{bmatrix} \cos 2\theta & \sin 2\theta \\ \sin 2\theta & -\cos 2\theta \end{bmatrix}$ describes the reflection of a point $P(x, y)$ in the line $y = x\tan\theta$.

Note

By putting $\theta = 0, \frac{\pi}{2}, \frac{\pi}{4}$, we can get the reflection matrices in the X-axis, Y-axis and the line $y = x$, respectively.

| Example 51. The point $P(3, 4)$ undergoes a reflection in the X-axis followed by a reflection in the Y-axis. Show that their combined effect is the same as the single reflection of $P(3, 4)$ in the origin.

Sol. Let $P_1(x_1, y_1)$ be the image of $P(3, 4)$ after reflection in the X-axis. Then,

$$\begin{bmatrix} x_1 \\ y_1 \end{bmatrix} = \begin{bmatrix} 1 & 0 \\ 0 & -1 \end{bmatrix} \begin{bmatrix} 3 \\ 4 \end{bmatrix} = \begin{bmatrix} 3 \\ -4 \end{bmatrix}$$

Therefore, the image of $P(3, 4)$ after reflection in the X-axis is $P_1(3, -4)$.

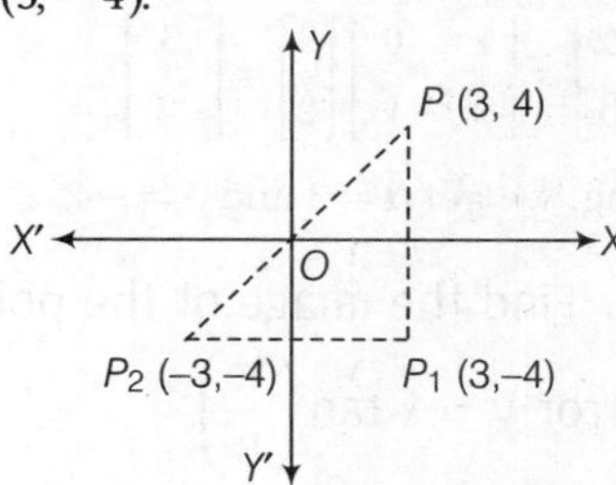

Now, let $P_2(x_2, y_2)$ be the image of $P_1(3, -4)$ after reflection in the Y-axis, then

$$\begin{bmatrix} x_2 \\ y_2 \end{bmatrix} = \begin{bmatrix} -1 & 0 \\ 0 & 1 \end{bmatrix} \begin{bmatrix} 3 \\ -4 \end{bmatrix} = \begin{bmatrix} -3 \\ -4 \end{bmatrix}$$

Therefore, the image of P_1 (3, – 4) after reflection in the Y-axis is P_2 (– 3, – 4).

Further, let P_3 (x_3, y_3) be the image of P (3, 4) in the origin O. Then,

$$\begin{bmatrix} x_3 \\ y_3 \end{bmatrix} = \begin{bmatrix} -1 & 0 \\ 0 & -1 \end{bmatrix} \begin{bmatrix} 3 \\ 4 \end{bmatrix} = \begin{bmatrix} -3 \\ -4 \end{bmatrix}$$

Therefore, the image of P (3, 4) after reflection in the origin is P_3 (– 3, – 4) . It is clear that $P_2 = P_3$

Hence, the image of P_2 of P often successive reflections in their X-axis and Y-axis is the same as P_3, which is single reflection of P in the origin.

| Example 52. Find the image of the point (– 2, – 7) under the transformations $(x, y) \to (x - 2y, -3x + y)$.

Sol. Let (x_1, y_1) be the image of the point (x, y) under the given transormations, then

$$\begin{cases} x_1 = x - 2y = 1 \cdot x + (-2) \cdot y \\ y_1 = -3x + y = (-3) \cdot x + 1 \cdot y \end{cases}$$

$$\Rightarrow \begin{bmatrix} x_1 \\ y_1 \end{bmatrix} = \begin{bmatrix} 1 & -2 \\ -3 & 1 \end{bmatrix} \begin{bmatrix} x \\ y \end{bmatrix}$$

$$= \begin{bmatrix} 1 & -2 \\ -3 & 1 \end{bmatrix} \begin{bmatrix} -2 \\ -7 \end{bmatrix} = \begin{bmatrix} -2+14 \\ 6-7 \end{bmatrix} = \begin{bmatrix} 12 \\ -1 \end{bmatrix}$$

Therefore, the required image is (12, – 1).

| Example 53. The image of the point A(2, 3) by the line mirror $y = x$ is the point B and the image of B by the line mirror $y = 0$ is the point (α, β). Find α and β.

Sol. Let $B\,(x_1, y_1)$ be the image of the point A(2,3) about the line $y = x$, then

$$\begin{bmatrix} x_1 \\ y_1 \end{bmatrix} = \begin{bmatrix} 0 & 1 \\ 1 & 0 \end{bmatrix} \begin{bmatrix} 2 \\ 3 \end{bmatrix} = \begin{bmatrix} 3 \\ 2 \end{bmatrix}$$

Therefore, the image of A (2, 3) by the line mirror $y = x$ is B (3, 2).

Given, image of B by the line mirror $y = 0$ (X-axis) is (α, β), then

$$\begin{bmatrix} \alpha \\ \beta \end{bmatrix} = \begin{bmatrix} 1 & 0 \\ 0 & -1 \end{bmatrix} \begin{bmatrix} 3 \\ 2 \end{bmatrix} = \begin{bmatrix} 3 \\ -2 \end{bmatrix}$$

On comparing, we get $\alpha = 3$ and $\beta = -2$.

| Example 54. Find the image of the point $(-\sqrt{2}, \sqrt{2})$ by the line mirror $y = x \tan\left(\frac{\pi}{8}\right)$.

Sol. Let (x_1, y_1) be the image of $(-\sqrt{2}, \sqrt{2})$ about the line $y = x \tan\left(\frac{\pi}{8}\right)$.

On comparing $y = x \tan\left(\frac{\pi}{8}\right)$ by $y = x \tan\theta$

$$\therefore \quad \theta = \frac{\pi}{8}$$

Now,
$$\begin{bmatrix} x_1 \\ y_1 \end{bmatrix} = \begin{bmatrix} \cos 2\theta & \sin 2\theta \\ \sin 2\theta & -\cos 2\theta \end{bmatrix} \begin{bmatrix} -\sqrt{2} \\ \sqrt{2} \end{bmatrix}$$

$$= \begin{bmatrix} \frac{1}{\sqrt{2}} & \frac{1}{\sqrt{2}} \\ \frac{1}{\sqrt{2}} & -\frac{1}{\sqrt{2}} \end{bmatrix} \begin{bmatrix} -\sqrt{2} \\ \sqrt{2} \end{bmatrix} = \begin{bmatrix} 0 \\ -2 \end{bmatrix}$$

On comparing $x_1 = 0$ and $y_1 = -2$.

Therefore, the required image is (0, – 2).

Rotation Through an Angle θ

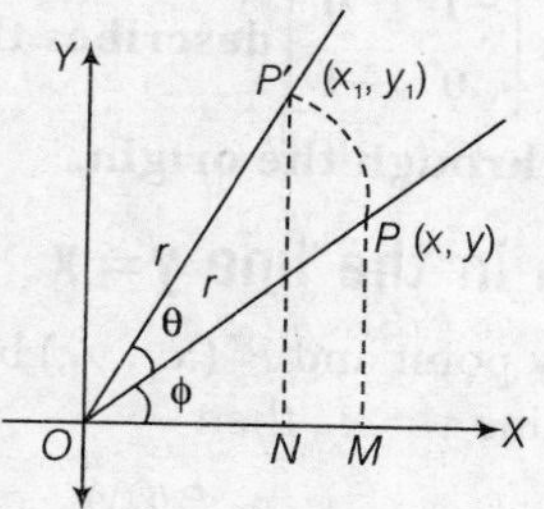

Let $P\,(x, y)$ be any point such that $OP = r$ and $\angle POX = \phi$. Let OP rotate through an angle θ in the anti-clockwise direction such that $P'(x_1, y_1)$ is the new position.

$$\therefore \quad OP' = r, \qquad [\because OP = OP']$$

then
$$\begin{cases} x_1 = x\cos\theta - y\sin\theta \\ x_1 = x\sin\theta + y\cos\theta \end{cases}$$

These system of equations in the matrix form are written as below.

$$\begin{bmatrix} x_1 \\ y_1 \end{bmatrix} = \begin{bmatrix} \cos\theta & -\sin\theta \\ \sin\theta & \cos\theta \end{bmatrix} \begin{bmatrix} x \\ y \end{bmatrix}$$

Thus, the matrix $\begin{bmatrix} \cos\theta & -\sin\theta \\ \sin\theta & \cos\theta \end{bmatrix}$ describes a rotation of a line segment through an angle θ.

Remember Use of complex number

$$OP' = OP\, e^{i\theta}, i = \sqrt{-1}$$

$$(x_1 + iy_1) = (x + iy)(\cos\theta + i\sin\theta)$$

$$= (x\cos\theta - y\sin\theta) + i(x\sin\theta + y\cos\theta)$$

$$\therefore \quad x_1 = x\cos\theta - y\sin\theta$$

and
$$y_1 = x\sin\theta + y\cos\theta$$

| Example 55. Find the matrices of transformation T_1T_2 and T_2T_1 when T_1 is rotation through an angle 60° and T_2 is the reflection in the Y-axis. Also, verify that $T_1T_2 \neq T_2T_1$.

Sol. $T_1 = \begin{bmatrix} \cos 60^\circ & -\sin 60^\circ \\ \sin 60^\circ & \cos 60^\circ \end{bmatrix} = \begin{bmatrix} \frac{1}{2} & \frac{\sqrt{3}}{2} \\ \frac{\sqrt{3}}{2} & \frac{1}{2} \end{bmatrix} = \frac{1}{2}\begin{bmatrix} 1 & -\sqrt{3} \\ \sqrt{3} & 1 \end{bmatrix}$

and $T_2 = \begin{bmatrix} -1 & 0 \\ 0 & 1 \end{bmatrix}$

$\therefore \quad T_1 T_2 = \frac{1}{2}\begin{bmatrix} 1 & -\sqrt{3} \\ \sqrt{3} & 1 \end{bmatrix} \times \begin{bmatrix} -1 & 0 \\ 0 & 1 \end{bmatrix} = \frac{1}{2}\begin{bmatrix} -1+0 & 0-\sqrt{3} \\ -\sqrt{3}+0 & 0+1 \end{bmatrix}$

$$= \frac{1}{2}\begin{bmatrix} -1 & -\sqrt{3} \\ -\sqrt{3} & 1 \end{bmatrix} = \begin{bmatrix} -\frac{1}{2} & -\frac{\sqrt{3}}{2} \\ -\frac{\sqrt{3}}{2} & \frac{1}{2} \end{bmatrix} \quad \text{...(i)}$$

and $T_2 T_1 = \begin{bmatrix} -1 & 0 \\ 0 & 1 \end{bmatrix} \times \frac{1}{2}\begin{bmatrix} 1 & -\sqrt{3} \\ \sqrt{3} & 1 \end{bmatrix} = \frac{1}{2}\begin{bmatrix} -1+0 & \sqrt{3}+0 \\ 0+\sqrt{3} & 0+1 \end{bmatrix}$

$$= \frac{1}{2}\begin{bmatrix} -1 & \sqrt{3} \\ \sqrt{3} & 1 \end{bmatrix} = \begin{bmatrix} -\frac{1}{2} & \frac{\sqrt{3}}{2} \\ \frac{\sqrt{3}}{2} & \frac{1}{2} \end{bmatrix} \quad \text{...(ii)}$$

It is clear from Eqs.(i) and (ii), then

$$T_1 T_2 \neq T_2 T_1$$

Example 56. Write down 2×2 matrix A which corresponds to a counterclockwise rotation of 60° about the origin. In the diagram the square $OABC$ has its diagonal OB of $2\sqrt{2}$ units in length. The square is rotated counterclockwise about O through 60°. Find the coordiates of the vertices of the square after rotating.

Sol. The matrix describes a rotation through an angle 60° in counterclockwise direction is

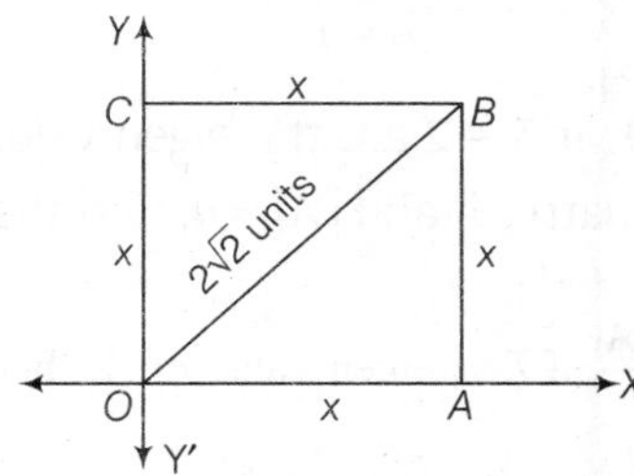

$$\begin{bmatrix} \cos 60^\circ & -\sin 60^\circ \\ \sin 60^\circ & \cos 60^\circ \end{bmatrix} = \begin{bmatrix} \frac{1}{2} & -\frac{\sqrt{3}}{2} \\ \frac{\sqrt{3}}{2} & \frac{1}{2} \end{bmatrix} = \frac{1}{2}\begin{bmatrix} 1 & -\sqrt{3} \\ \sqrt{3} & 1 \end{bmatrix}$$

Since, each side of the square be x,

then $\quad x^2 + x^2 = (2\sqrt{2})^2$

$\Rightarrow \quad 2x^2 = 8 \Rightarrow x^2 = 4$

$\therefore \quad x = 2$ units

Therefore, the coordinates of the vertices O, A, B and C are (0, 0), (2, 0), (2, 2) and (0, 2), respectively. Let after rotation A map into A', B map into B', C map into C' but the O map into itself.

If coordinates of A', B' and C' are (x', y'), (x'', y'') and (x''', y'''), respectively.

$\therefore \quad \begin{bmatrix} x' \\ y' \end{bmatrix} = \frac{1}{2}\begin{bmatrix} 1 & -\sqrt{3} \\ \sqrt{3} & 1 \end{bmatrix}\begin{bmatrix} 2 \\ 0 \end{bmatrix} = \frac{1}{2}\begin{bmatrix} 2 \\ 2\sqrt{3} \end{bmatrix} = \begin{bmatrix} 1 \\ \sqrt{3} \end{bmatrix}$

$\therefore \quad x' = 1, y' = \sqrt{3} \Rightarrow A(2, 0) \to A'(1, \sqrt{3})$

and $\begin{bmatrix} x'' \\ y'' \end{bmatrix} = \frac{1}{2}\begin{bmatrix} 1 & -\sqrt{3} \\ \sqrt{3} & 1 \end{bmatrix}\begin{bmatrix} 2 \\ 2 \end{bmatrix} = \frac{1}{2}\begin{bmatrix} 2-2\sqrt{3} \\ 2\sqrt{3}+2 \end{bmatrix} = \begin{bmatrix} 1-\sqrt{3} \\ \sqrt{3}+1 \end{bmatrix}$

$\therefore \quad x'' = 1 - \sqrt{3}, y'' = \sqrt{3} + 1$

$\Rightarrow \quad B(2, 2) \to B'(1 - \sqrt{3}, \sqrt{3} + 1)$

$$\begin{bmatrix} x''' \\ y''' \end{bmatrix} = \frac{1}{2}\begin{bmatrix} 1 & -\sqrt{3} \\ \sqrt{3} & 1 \end{bmatrix}\begin{bmatrix} 0 \\ 2 \end{bmatrix} = \frac{1}{2}\begin{bmatrix} -2\sqrt{3} \\ 2 \end{bmatrix} = \begin{bmatrix} -\sqrt{3} \\ 1 \end{bmatrix}$$

$\therefore \quad x''' = -\sqrt{3}, y''' = 1$

$\Rightarrow \quad C(0, 2) \to C'(-\sqrt{3}, 1)$

Eigen Values or Characteristic roots and Characteristic Vectors of a square matrix

Let X be any non-zero vector satisfying

$$AX = \lambda X \quad \text{...(i)}$$

where λ is any scalar, then λ is said to be eigen value or characteristic root of square matrix A and the vector X is called eigen vector or characteristic vector of matrix A.

Now, from Eq. (i), we have

$$(A - \lambda I) X = O$$

Since, $X \neq O$, we deduce that the matrix $(A - \lambda I)$ is singular, so that its determinant is 0

i.e.

$$|A - \lambda I| = 0 \quad \text{...(ii)}$$

is called characteristic equation of matrix A.

If A be $n \times n$ matrix, then equation $|A - \lambda I| = 0$ reduces to polynomial equation of nth from degree in λ, which given n values of λ i.e., matrix A will have n characteristic roots or eigen values.

Important Properties of Eigen Values

(i) Any square matrix A and its transpose A^T have the same eigen values.

(ii) The sum of the eigen values of a matrix is equal to the trace of the matrix.

(iii) The product the eigen values of a matrix A is equal to the determinant of A.

(iv) If $\lambda_1, \lambda_2, \lambda_3, \lambda_4, \ldots, \lambda_n$ are the eigen values of A, then the eigen values of

(a) kA are $k\lambda_1, k\lambda_2, k\lambda_3, k\lambda_4, \ldots, k\lambda_n$.

(b) A^m are $\lambda_1^m, \lambda_2^m, \lambda_3^m, \lambda_4^m, \ldots, \lambda_n^m$

(c) A^{-1} are $\dfrac{1}{\lambda_1}, \dfrac{1}{\lambda_2}, \dfrac{1}{\lambda_3}, \dfrac{1}{\lambda_4}, \ldots, \dfrac{1}{\lambda_n}$.

Remark

1. All the eigen values of a real symmetric matrix are real and the eigen vectors corresponding to two distinct eigen values are orthogonal.
2. All the eigen values of a real skew-symmetric matrix are purely imaginary or zero. An odd order skew-symmetric matrix is singular and hence has zero as an eigen value.

Example 57. Let matrix $A = \begin{bmatrix} 4 & 6 & 6 \\ 1 & 3 & 2 \\ -1 & -4 & -3 \end{bmatrix}$, find the non-zero column vector X such that $AX = \lambda X$ for some scalar λ.

Sol. The characteristic equation is $|A - \lambda I| = 0$

$$\Rightarrow \begin{bmatrix} 4-\lambda & 6 & 6 \\ 1 & 3-\lambda & 2 \\ -1 & -4 & -3-\lambda \end{bmatrix} = 0$$

$$\Rightarrow \lambda^3 - 4\lambda^2 - \lambda + 4 = 0$$

or $$(\lambda + 1)(\lambda - 1)(\lambda - 4) = 0$$

The eigen values are $\lambda = -1, 1, 4$

If $\lambda = -1$, we get $5x + 6y + 6z = 0$, $x + 4y + 2z = 0$

and $-x - 4y - 2z = 0$

Giving $$\frac{x}{6} = \frac{y}{2} = \frac{z}{-7}, X = \begin{bmatrix} 6 \\ 2 \\ -7 \end{bmatrix}$$

If $\lambda = 1$, we get $3x + 6y + 6z = 0$, $x + 2y + 2z = 0$

and $-x - 4y - 4z = 0$

Giving, $$\frac{x}{0} = \frac{y}{1} = \frac{z}{-1}, X = \begin{bmatrix} 0 \\ 1 \\ -1 \end{bmatrix}$$

If $\lambda = 4$, we get $0 \cdot x + 6y + 6z = 0$, $x - y + 2z = 0$

and $-x - 4y - 7z = 0$

Giving, $$\frac{x}{3} = \frac{y}{1} = \frac{3}{-1}, x = \begin{bmatrix} 3 \\ 1 \\ -1 \end{bmatrix}$$

Hence, vector are $X = \begin{bmatrix} 6 \\ 2 \\ -7 \end{bmatrix}, \begin{bmatrix} 0 \\ 1 \\ -1 \end{bmatrix}, \begin{bmatrix} 3 \\ 1 \\ -1 \end{bmatrix}$.

Example 58. If A and P are the square matrices of the same order and if P be invertible, show that the matrices A and $P^{-1}AP$ have the same characteristic roots.

Sol. Let $P^{-1}AP = B$

$$\begin{aligned} \therefore \quad |B - \lambda I| &= |P^{-1}AP - \lambda I| \\ &= |P^{-1}AP - P^{-1}\lambda P| \quad [\because P^{-1}P = I] \\ &= |P^{-1}(A - \lambda I)P| \\ &= |P^{-1}||A - \lambda I||P| \\ &= \frac{1}{|P|}|A - \lambda I||P| = |A - \lambda I| \end{aligned}$$

Example 59. Show that the characteristic roots of an idempotent matrix are either zero or unity.

Sol. Let A be an idempotent matrix, then

$$A^2 = A \quad \ldots(i)$$

If λ be an eigen value of the matrix A corresponding to eigen vector X, so that

$$AX = \lambda X \quad \ldots(ii)$$

where $X \neq 0$

From Eq. (ii), $A(AX) = A(\lambda X)$

$\Rightarrow (AA)X = \lambda(AX)$

$\Rightarrow A^2X = \lambda(\lambda X)$ [from Eq. (ii)]

$\Rightarrow AX = \lambda^2 X$ [from Eq. (i)]

$\Rightarrow \lambda X = \lambda^2 X$ [from Eq. (ii)]

$\Rightarrow (\lambda - \lambda^2)X = 0$

$\Rightarrow \lambda - \lambda^2 = 0$ [$\because X \neq 0$]

$\therefore \lambda = 0$

or $\lambda = 1$

Example 60. If $3, -2$ are the eigen values of a non-singular matrix A and $|A| = 4$, find the eigen values of adj (A).

Sol. $\because A^{-1} = \dfrac{\text{adj } A}{|A|}$, if λ is eigen value of A, then λ^{-1} is eigen value of A^{-1}.

Thus, for adj $(A)X = (A^{-1}X)|A| = |A|\lambda^{-1}I$

Thus, eigen value corresponding to $\lambda = 3$ is $\dfrac{4}{3}$ and corresponding to $\lambda = -2$ is $\dfrac{4}{-2} = -2$

Cayley-Hamilton Theorem

Every square matrix A satisfies its characteristic equation $|A - \lambda I| = 0$

i.e., $$a_0\lambda^n + a_1\lambda^{n-1} + a_2\lambda^{n-2} + \ldots + a_n = 0$$

By Cayley-Hamilton theorem

$$a_0A^n + a_1A^{n-1} + a_2A^{n-2} + \dots + a_nI = O$$

$$\Rightarrow A^{-1} = -\left\{\frac{a_0}{a_n}A^{n-1} + \frac{a_1}{a_n}A^{n-2} + \frac{a_2}{a_n}A^{n-3} + \dots + \frac{a_{n-1}}{a_n}I\right\}$$

Example 61. Find the characteristic equation of the matrix $A = \begin{bmatrix} 2 & 1 \\ 3 & 2 \end{bmatrix}$ and hence find its inverse using Cayley-hamilton theorem.

Sol. Characteristic equation is

$$|A - \lambda I| = 0 \Rightarrow \begin{bmatrix} 2-\lambda & 1 \\ 3 & 2-\lambda \end{bmatrix} = 0$$

$$\Rightarrow \quad (2-\lambda)^2 - 3 = 0$$

$$\Rightarrow \quad \lambda^2 - 4\lambda + 1 = 0$$

∴ By Cayley-hamilton theorem,

$$A^2 - 4A + I = O \text{ or } I = 4A - A^2$$

Multiplying by A^{-1}, we get

$$A^{-1} = 4A^{-1}A - A^{-1}AA$$

$$= 4I - IA = 4I - A$$

$$= 4\begin{bmatrix} 1 & 0 \\ 0 & 1 \end{bmatrix} - \begin{bmatrix} 2 & 1 \\ 3 & 2 \end{bmatrix}$$

$$= \begin{bmatrix} 2 & -1 \\ -3 & 2 \end{bmatrix}$$

Exercise for Session 4

1 If the system of equations $ax + y = 1, x + 2y = 3, 2x + 3y = 5$ are consistent, then a is given by

(a) 0 (b) 1 (c) 2 (d) None of these

2 The system of equations $x + y + z = 2, 2x + y - z = 3, 3x + 2y + \lambda z = 4$ has unique solution if

(a) $\lambda \neq 0$ (b) $-1 < \lambda < 1$ (c) $\lambda = 0$ (d) $-2 < \lambda < 2$

3 The value of a for which the following system of equations $a^3x + (a+1)^3y + (a+2)^3z = 0$, $ax + (a+1)y + (a+2)z = 0, x + y + z = 0$ has a non-trivial solution is equal to

(a) 2 (b) 1 (c) 0 (d) -1

4 The number of solutions of the set of equations

$$\frac{2x^2}{a^2} - \frac{y^2}{b^2} - \frac{z^2}{c^2} = 0, -\frac{x^2}{a^2} + \frac{2y^2}{b^2} - \frac{z^2}{c^2} = 0, -\frac{x^2}{a^2} - \frac{y^2}{b^2} + \frac{2z^2}{c^2} = 0 \text{ is}$$

(a) 6 (b) 7 (c) 8 (d) 9

5 The matrix $\begin{bmatrix} 0 & 1 \\ 1 & 0 \end{bmatrix}$ is the matrix reflection in the line

(a) $x = 1$ (b) $x + y = 1$ (c) $y = 1$ (d) $x = y$

6 The matrix S is rotation through an angle 45° and G is the reflection about the line $y = 2x$, then $(SG)^2$ is equal to

(a) $7I$ (b) $5I$ (c) $3I$ (d) I

7 If $A = \begin{bmatrix} -2 & 3 \\ -1 & 1 \end{bmatrix}$, then A^3 is equal to

(a) $2A$ (b) A (c) $2I$. (d) I

8 If $A = \begin{bmatrix} 2 & 2 & 1 \\ 1 & 3 & 1 \\ 1 & 2 & 2 \end{bmatrix}$ and the sum of eigen values of A is m and product of eigen values of A is n, then $m + n$ is equal to

(a) 10 (b) 12 (c) 14 (d) 16

9 If $A = \begin{bmatrix} 1 & 2 \\ -1 & 4 \end{bmatrix}$ and θ be the angle between the two non-zero column vectors X such that $AX = \lambda X$ for some scalar λ, then $9\sec^2\theta$ is equal to

(a) 13 (b) 12 (c) 11 (d) 10

Shortcuts And Important Results To Remember

1 $|A|$ exists $\Leftrightarrow A$ is square matrix.

2 No element of principal diagonal in a diagonal matrix is zero.

3 If A is a diagonal matrix of order n, then

(a) Number of zeroes in A is $n(n-1)$

(b) If $d_1, d_2, d_3, \dots, d_n$ are diagonal elements, then

$$A = \text{diag}\{d_1, d_2, d_3, \dots, d_n\}$$

and $$|A| = d_1 d_2 d_3 \dots d_n$$

$$A^{-1} = \text{diag}(d_1^{-1}, d_2^{-1}, d_3^{-1}, \dots, d_n^{-1})$$

(c) Diagonal matrix is both upper and lower triangular.

(d) $\text{diag}\{a_1, a_2, a_3, \dots, a_n\} \times \text{diag}\{b_1, b_2, b_3, \dots, b_n\} = \text{diag}\{a_1b_1, a_2b_2, a_3b_3, \dots, a_nb_n\}$

4 If $A = \begin{bmatrix} 1 & 1 \\ 0 & 1 \end{bmatrix}$ and $B = \begin{bmatrix} 1 & 0 \\ 1 & 1 \end{bmatrix}$, then $A^k = \begin{bmatrix} 1 & k \\ 0 & 1 \end{bmatrix}$ and $B^k = \begin{bmatrix} 1 & 0 \\ k & 1 \end{bmatrix}$, $\forall\, k \in N$.

5 If A and B are square matrices of order n, then

(a) $|kA| = k^n |A|$, k is scalar

(b) $|AB| = |A||B|$

(c) $|kAB| = k^n |A||B|$, k is scalar

(d) $|AB| = |BA|$

(e) $|A^T| = |A| = |A^\theta|$, where A^θ is conjugate transpose matrix of A

(f) $|A|^m = |A^m|$, $m \in N$

6 Minimum number of zeroes in a triangular matrix is given by $\dfrac{n(n-1)}{2}$, where n is order of matrix.

7 If A is a skew-symmetric matrix of odd order, then $|A| = 0$ and of even order is a non-zero perfect square.

8 If A is involutory matrix, then

(a) $|A| = \pm 1$

(b) $\frac{1}{2}(I + A)$ and $\frac{1}{2}(I - A)$ are idempotent and $\frac{1}{2}(I + A) \cdot \frac{1}{2}(I - A) = 0$

9 If A is orthogonal matrix, then $|A| = \pm 1$

10 To obtain an orthogonal matrix B from a skew-symmetric matrix A, then $B = (I - A)^{-1}(I + A)$ or $B = (I - A)(I + A)^{-1}$

11 The sum of two orthogonal matrices is not orthogonal while the sum of two symmetric (skew-symmetric) matrices is symmetric (skew-symmetric)

12 The product of two orthogonal matrices is orthogonal while the product of two symmetric (skew-symmetric) matrices need not be symmetric (skew-symmetric)

13 The adjoint of a square matrix of order 2 can be easily obtained by interchanging the principal diagonal elements and changing the sign of the other diagonal.

i.e., If $A = \begin{bmatrix} a & b \\ c & d \end{bmatrix}$, then $\text{adj}(A) = \begin{bmatrix} d & -b \\ -c & a \end{bmatrix}$

14 If $|A| \neq 0$, then $|A^{-1}| = \dfrac{1}{|A|}$.

15 If A and B are invertible matrices such that $AB = C$, then $|B| = \dfrac{|C|}{|A|}$.

16 Commutative law does not necessarily hold for matrices.

17 If $AB = -BA$, then matrices A and B are called anti-commutative matrices.

18 If $AB = O$, it is not necessary that atleast one of the matrix should be zero matrix.

For example, If $A = \begin{bmatrix} 0 & 2 \\ 0 & 0 \end{bmatrix}$ and $B = \begin{bmatrix} 3 & 0 \\ 0 & 0 \end{bmatrix}$, then $AB = \begin{bmatrix} 0 & 0 \\ 0 & 0 \end{bmatrix}$ while neither A nor B is the null matrix.

19 If A, B and C are invertible matrices, then

(a) $(AB)^{-1} = B^{-1}A^{-1}$

(b) $(ABC)^{-1} = C^{-1}B^{-1}A^{-1}$

20 If B is a non-singular matrix and A is any square matrix, then $\det(B^{-1}AB) = \det(A)$

21 If A is a non-singular square matrix of order n, then $\text{adj}(\text{adj } A) = |A|^{n-2} A$

22 If A is a non-singular square matrix of order n, then

$$|\underbrace{\text{adj}(\text{adj}(\text{adj} \dots (\text{adj}(\text{adj } A))))}_{m \text{ times}}| = |A|^{(n-1)^m}$$

23 If $A = \begin{bmatrix} 0 & \alpha \\ 0 & 0 \end{bmatrix}$; $A^m = O, \forall\, m \geq 2$

$\therefore \quad (A + I)^n = I + nA$

24 If A and B are two symmetric matrices, then $A \pm B$, $AB + BA$ are symmetric matrices and $AB - BA$ is a skew-symmetric matrix.

25 If A and B are two square matrices of order n and λ be a scalar, then

(i) $\text{Tr}(\lambda A) = \lambda \text{Tr}(A)$

(ii) $\text{Tr}(A \pm B) = \text{Tr}(A) \pm \text{Tr}(B)$

(iii) $\text{Tr}(AB) = \text{Tr}(BA)$

(iv) $\text{Tr}(A) = \text{Tr}(A')$

(v) $\text{Tr}(I_n) = n$

(vi) $\text{Tr}(O) = 0$

(vii) $\text{Tr}(AB) \neq \text{Tr}(A) \cdot \text{tr}(B)$

contd...

26 If rank of a matrix A is denoted by $\rho(A)$, then

(i) $\rho(A) = 0$, if A is zero matrix.

(ii) $\rho(A) = 1$, if every element of A is same.

(iii) If A and B are square matrices of order n each and $\rho(A) = \rho(B) = n$, then $\rho(AB) = n$

(iv) If A is a square matrix of order n and $\rho(A) = n - 1$, then $\rho(\text{adj } A) = 1$ and if $\rho(A) < n - 1$, then $\rho(\text{adj } A) = 0$

27 System of planes

$$a_{11}x + a_{12}y + a_{13}z = b_1,$$
$$a_{21}x + a_{22}y + a_{23}z = b_2$$
and
$$a_{31}x + a_{32}y + a_{33}z = b_3$$

Augmented matrix $C = [A : B]$ and if Rank of $A = r$ and Rank of $C = s$, then

(i) If $r = s = 1$, then planes are coincident

(ii) If $r = 1, s = 2$, then planes are parallel

(iii) If $r = s = 2$, then planes intersect along a single straight line

(iv) If $r = 2, s = 3$, then planes form a triangular prism

(v) If $r = s = 3$, then planes meet at a single point

28 If P is an orthogonal matrix, then $\det(P) = \pm 1$

(i) P represents a reflection about a line, then $\det(P) = -1$.

(ii) P represents a rotation about a point, then $\det(P) = 1$.

29 **Cayley-Hamilton Theorem** : Every matrix satisfies its characteristic equation.

For Example, Let A be a square matrix, then $|A - \lambda I| = 0$ is the characteristic equation for A.

If $\lambda^3 - 6\lambda^2 + 11\lambda - 6 = 0$ is the characteristic equation for A, then $A^3 - 6A^2 + 11A - 6I = O$. Roots of characteristic equation for A are called eigen values of A or characteristic roots of A or latent roots of A. If λ is a characteristic root of A, then λ^{-1} is characteristic root of A^{-1}.

JEE Type Solved Examples : Single Option Correct Type Questions

- This section contains **10 multiple choice examples.** Each example has four choices (a), (b), (c) and (d) out of which **ONLY ONE** is correct.

● ***Ex. 1*** *If A is a square matrix of order 2 such that* $A\begin{bmatrix}1\\-1\end{bmatrix}=\begin{bmatrix}-1\\2\end{bmatrix}$ *and* $A^2\begin{bmatrix}1\\-1\end{bmatrix}=\begin{bmatrix}1\\0\end{bmatrix}$. *The sum of elements and product of elements of A are S and P, then S + P is*

(a) −1 (b) 2 (c) 4 (d) 5

Sol. (*d*) Let $A=\begin{bmatrix}a & b\\c & d\end{bmatrix}$

From first part, $A\begin{bmatrix}1\\-1\end{bmatrix}=\begin{bmatrix}-1\\2\end{bmatrix}$ ...(i)

$\Rightarrow \begin{bmatrix}a & b\\c & d\end{bmatrix}\begin{bmatrix}1\\-1\end{bmatrix}=\begin{bmatrix}-1\\2\end{bmatrix}$

or $a-b=-1$ ...(ii)

and $c-d=2$ ...(iii)

From second part,

$$A^2\begin{bmatrix}1\\-1\end{bmatrix}=\begin{bmatrix}1\\0\end{bmatrix} \Rightarrow A\left(A\begin{bmatrix}1\\-1\end{bmatrix}\right)=\begin{bmatrix}1\\0\end{bmatrix}$$

From Eq. (i), we get

$$A\begin{bmatrix}-1\\2\end{bmatrix}=\begin{bmatrix}1\\0\end{bmatrix} \Rightarrow \begin{bmatrix}a & b\\c & d\end{bmatrix}\begin{bmatrix}-1\\2\end{bmatrix}=\begin{bmatrix}1\\0\end{bmatrix}$$

or $-a+2b=1$ ...(iv)

and $-c+2d=0$ ...(v)

From Eqs. (ii) and (iv), we get

$$a=-1, b=0$$

and from Eqs. (iii) and (v), we get

$$c=4, d=2$$

∴ $S=a+b+c+d=5$

and $P=abcd=0$

Hence, $S+P=5$

● ***Ex. 2*** *If P is an orthogonal matrix and* $Q=PAP^T$ *and* $B=P^TQ^{1000}P$, *then* B^{-1} *is, where A is involutory matrix*

(a) A (b) A^{1000} (c) I (d) None of these

Sol. (*c*) Given, *P* is orthogonal

∴ $P^TP=I$ ...(i)

and $Q=PAP^T$ ...(ii)

Now, $B=P^TQ^{1000}P=P^T(PAP^T)^{1000}P$ [from Eq. (ii)]

$=P^TPAP^T(PAP^T)^{999}P$

$=IAP^T\cdot PAP^T(PAP^T)^{998}P$

$=AIAP^T(PAP^T)^{998}P$

$=A^2P^TPAP^T(PAP^T)^{997}P$

$=A^2IAP^T(PAP^T)^{997}P$

$=A^3P^T(PAP^T)^{997}P$

... ...

$=A^{1000}P^TP=A^{1000}=I$ [∵ *A* is involutory]

Hence, $B^{-1}=I^{-1}=I$

● ***Ex. 3*** *If A is a diagonal matrix of order* 3×3 *is commutative with every square matrix of order* 3×3 *under multiplication and trace* $(A)=12$, *then*

(a) $|A|=64$ (b) $|A|=16$

(c) $|A|=12$ (d) $|A|=4$

Sol. (*a*) A diagonal matrix is commutative with every square matrix, if it is scalar matrix so every diagonal element is 4.

$$\therefore \quad A=\begin{bmatrix}4 & 0 & 0\\0 & 4 & 0\\0 & 0 & 4\end{bmatrix}$$

$$\Rightarrow \quad |A|=4\cdot4\cdot4=64$$

● ***Ex. 4*** *If* $A=[a_{ij}]_{4\times4}$, *such that* $a_{ij}=\begin{cases}2, & \text{when } i=j\\0, & \text{when } i\neq j\end{cases}$, *then* $\left\{\dfrac{\det(\text{adj}(\text{adj } A))}{7}\right\}$ *is [when {·} represents fractional part function]*

(a) $\frac{1}{7}$ (b) $\frac{2}{7}$ (c) $\frac{3}{7}$ (d) $\frac{4}{7}$

Sol. (*a*) ∵ $A=\begin{bmatrix}2 & 0 & 0 & 0\\0 & 2 & 0 & 0\\0 & 0 & 2 & 0\\0 & 0 & 0 & 2\end{bmatrix}$

$$\therefore \quad |A|=\begin{vmatrix}2 & 0 & 0 & 0\\0 & 2 & 0 & 0\\0 & 0 & 2 & 0\\0 & 0 & 0 & 2\end{vmatrix}=2^4=16$$

$$\because \det(\text{adj}(\text{adj } A))=|\text{adj}(\text{adj } A)|=|A|^{3^2}=|A|^9$$

$$=(2^4)^9=2^{36}=(2^3)^{12}=(1+7)^{12}$$

$$=1+{}^{12}C_1(7)+{}^{12}C_2(7)^2+\ldots$$

$$\frac{\det(\text{adj}(\text{adj } A))}{7}=\frac{1}{7}+\text{Positive integer}$$

$$\therefore \quad \left\{\frac{\det(\text{adj}(\text{adj } A))}{7}\right\}=\frac{1}{7}$$

● **Ex. 5** *If* $A=\begin{bmatrix}1&1\\1&1\end{bmatrix}$ *and* $\det(A^n-I)=1-\lambda^n, n\in N$, *then the value of* λ, *is*

(a) 1 (b) 2 (c) 3 (d) 4

Sol. (*b*) $\because$ $A=\begin{bmatrix}1&1\\1&1\end{bmatrix}$

$$\therefore \quad A^2=\begin{bmatrix}2&2\\2&2\end{bmatrix}=2\begin{bmatrix}1&1\\1&1\end{bmatrix}=2A$$

$$\Rightarrow \quad A^3=A^2\cdot A=2A^2=2^2A$$

Similarly, $A^n=2^{n-1}A$

$$\therefore \quad A^n-I=\begin{bmatrix}2^{n-1}&2^{n-1}\\2^{n-1}&2^{n-1}\end{bmatrix}-\begin{bmatrix}1&0\\0&1\end{bmatrix}$$

$$=\begin{bmatrix}2^{n-1}-1&2^{n-1}\\2^{n-1}&2^{n-1}-1\end{bmatrix}$$

$$\Rightarrow \quad \det(A^n-I)=(2^{n-1}-1)^2-(2^{n-1})^2$$

$$=1-2^n=1-\lambda^n \quad \text{[given]}$$

$$\therefore \quad \lambda=2$$

● **Ex. 6** *If* $A=\begin{bmatrix}1&2\\2&1\end{bmatrix}$ *and* $f(x)=\dfrac{1+x}{1-x}$, *then* $f(A)$ *is*

(a) $\begin{bmatrix}1&1\\1&1\end{bmatrix}$ (b) $\begin{bmatrix}2&2\\2&2\end{bmatrix}$

(c) $\begin{bmatrix}-1&-1\\-1&-1\end{bmatrix}$ (d) None of these

Sol. (*c*) $\because$ $f(x)=\dfrac{1+x}{1-x}$

$$\Rightarrow \quad (1-x)f(x)=1+x$$

$$\Rightarrow \quad (I-A)f(A)=(I+A)$$

$$\Rightarrow \quad f(A)=(I-A)^{-1}(I+A)$$

$$=\left(\begin{bmatrix}1&0\\0&1\end{bmatrix}-\begin{bmatrix}1&2\\2&1\end{bmatrix}\right)^{-1}\left(\begin{bmatrix}1&0\\0&1\end{bmatrix}+\begin{bmatrix}1&2\\2&1\end{bmatrix}\right)$$

$$=\begin{bmatrix}0&-2\\-2&0\end{bmatrix}^{-1}\begin{bmatrix}2&2\\2&2\end{bmatrix}=-\frac{1}{4}\begin{bmatrix}0&2\\2&0\end{bmatrix}\begin{bmatrix}2&2\\2&2\end{bmatrix}$$

$$=-\frac{1}{4}\begin{bmatrix}4&4\\4&4\end{bmatrix}=\begin{bmatrix}-1&-1\\-1&-1\end{bmatrix}$$

● **Ex. 7** *The number of solutions of the matrix equation* $X^2=\begin{bmatrix}1&1\\2&3\end{bmatrix}$ *is*

(a) more than 2 (b) 2

(c) 0 (d) 1

Sol. (*a*) Let $X=\begin{bmatrix}a&b\\c&d\end{bmatrix}$

$$\therefore \quad X^2=\begin{bmatrix}a^2+bc&b(a+d)\\c(a+d)&bc+d^2\end{bmatrix}=\begin{bmatrix}1&1\\2&3\end{bmatrix} \quad \text{[given]}$$

$$\Rightarrow \quad a^2+bc=1, b(a+d)=1,$$

$$c(a+d)=2 \text{ and } bc+d^2=3$$

$$\Rightarrow \quad d^2-a^2=2$$

$$\Rightarrow \quad d-a=\frac{2}{d+a}=2b \text{ and } d+a=\frac{1}{b}$$

$$\therefore \quad 2d=2b+\frac{1}{b} \text{ and } 2a=\frac{1}{b}-2b$$

Also, $c=2b$

Now, from $bc+d^2=3$

$$\Rightarrow \quad 2b^2+\left(b+\frac{1}{2b}\right)^2=3 \Rightarrow 3b^2+\frac{1}{4b^2}-2=0$$

$$\Rightarrow \quad 12b^4-8b^2+1=0$$

or $(6b^2-1)(2b^2-1)=0$

$$\Rightarrow \quad b=\pm\frac{1}{\sqrt{6}} \text{ or } b=\pm\frac{1}{\sqrt{2}}$$

Therefore, matrices are

$$\begin{bmatrix}0&\frac{1}{\sqrt{2}}\\\sqrt{2}&\sqrt{2}\end{bmatrix},\begin{bmatrix}0&-\frac{1}{\sqrt{2}}\\-\sqrt{2}&-\sqrt{2}\end{bmatrix},\begin{bmatrix}\frac{2}{\sqrt{6}}&\frac{1}{\sqrt{6}}\\\frac{2}{\sqrt{6}}&\frac{4}{\sqrt{6}}\end{bmatrix} \text{ and } \begin{bmatrix}-\frac{2}{\sqrt{6}}&-\frac{1}{\sqrt{6}}\\-\frac{2}{\sqrt{6}}&-\frac{4}{\sqrt{6}}\end{bmatrix}.$$

● **Ex. 8** *For a matrix* $A=\begin{bmatrix}1&2r-1\\0&1\end{bmatrix}$, *the value of* $\prod_{r=1}^{50}\begin{bmatrix}1&2r-1\\0&1\end{bmatrix}$ *is equal to*

(a) $\begin{bmatrix}1&100\\0&1\end{bmatrix}$ (b) $\begin{bmatrix}1&4950\\0&1\end{bmatrix}$ (c) $\begin{bmatrix}1&5050\\0&1\end{bmatrix}$ (d) $\begin{bmatrix}1&2500\\0&1\end{bmatrix}$

Sol. (*d*) $\prod_{r=1}^{50}\begin{bmatrix}1&2r-1\\0&1\end{bmatrix}=\begin{bmatrix}1&1+3+5+\ldots+99\\0&1\end{bmatrix}$

$$=\begin{bmatrix}1&(50)^2\\0&1\end{bmatrix}=\begin{bmatrix}1&2500\\0&1\end{bmatrix}$$

● **Ex. 9** *If* $A_1, A_2, A_3, \ldots, A_{2n-1}$ *are n skew-symmetric matrices of same order, then* $B=\sum_{r=1}^{n}(2r-1)(A_{2r-1})^{2r-1}$ *will be*

(a) symmetric
(b) skew-symmetric
(c) neither symmetric nor skew-symmetric
(d) data not adequate

Sol. (b) $\because\ B = A_1 + 3A_3^3 + 5A_5^5 + \ldots + (2n-1)(A_{2n-1})^{2n-1}$

$$\therefore\ B^T = (A_1 + 3A_3^3 + 5A_5^5 + \ldots + (2n-1)(A_{2n-1})^{2n-1})^T$$
$$= A_1^T + 3(A_3^T)^3 + 5(A_5^T)^5 + \ldots + (2n-1)(A_{2n-1}^T)^{2n-1}$$
$$= -A_1 + 3(-A_3)^3 + 5(-A_5)^5 + \ldots + (2n-1)(-A_{2n-1})^{2n-1}$$
$$= -(A_1 + 3A_3^3 + 5A_5^5 + \ldots + (2n-1)A_{2n-1}^{2n-1})$$
$$= -B$$

Hence, B is skew-symmetric.

● **Ex. 10** *Elements of a matrix A of order 10×10 are defined as $a_{ij} = \omega^{i+j}$ (where ω is cube root of unity), then trace (A) of the matrix is*

(a) 0 (b) 1 (c) 3 (d) None of these

Sol. (d) $\operatorname{tr}(A) = \sum_{i=j=1}^{10} a_{ij} = \sum_{i=j=1}^{10} \omega^{i+j} = \sum_{i=1}^{10} \omega^{2i}$

$$= \omega^2 + \omega^4 + \omega^6 + \omega^8 + \ldots + \omega^{20}$$
$$= (\omega^2 + \omega + 1) + (\omega^2 + \omega + 1) + (\omega^2 + \omega + 1) + \omega^{20}$$
$$= 0 + 0 + 0 + \omega^2 = \omega^2$$

JEE Type Solved Examples : More than One Correct Option Type Questions

- This section contains **5 multiple choice examples.** Each example has four choices (a), (b), (c) and (d) out of **which more than one** may be correct.

● **Ex. 11** *If $A = \begin{bmatrix} a & b \\ c & d \end{bmatrix}$ (where $bc \neq 0$) satisfies the equations $x^2 + k = 0$, then*

(a) $a + d = 0$ (b) $k = -|A|$
(c) $k = |A|$ (d) None of these

Sol. (a, c) We have, $A^2 = \begin{bmatrix} a & b \\ c & d \end{bmatrix}\begin{bmatrix} a & b \\ c & d \end{bmatrix} = \begin{bmatrix} a^2 + bc & ab + bd \\ ac + cd & bc + d^2 \end{bmatrix}$

As A satisfies $x^2 + k = 0$, therefore

$$A^2 + kI = 0$$

$$\Rightarrow \begin{bmatrix} a^2 + bc + k & (a+d)b \\ (a+d)c & bc + d^2 + k \end{bmatrix} = \begin{bmatrix} 0 & 0 \\ 0 & 0 \end{bmatrix}$$

$$\Rightarrow a^2 + bc + k = 0, (a+d)b = 0,$$
$$(a+d)c = 0 \text{ and } bc + d^2 + k = 0$$

As $bc \neq 0 \Rightarrow b \neq 0, c \neq 0$

So, $a + d = 0 \Rightarrow a = -d$

Also, $k = -(a^2 + bc) = -(-ad + bc) = (ad - bc) = |A|$

● **Ex. 12** *If $A = [a_{ij}]_{n \times n}$ and f is a function, we define $f(A) = [f(a_{ij})]_{n \times n}$. Let $A = \begin{bmatrix} \frac{\pi}{2} - \theta & \theta \\ -\theta & \frac{\pi}{2} - \theta \end{bmatrix}$, then*

(a) $\sin A$ is invertible (b) $\sin A = \cos A$
(c) $\sin A$ is orthogonal (d) $\sin 2A = 2 \sin A \cos A$

Sol. (a, c) $\sin A = \begin{bmatrix} \cos\theta & \sin\theta \\ -\sin\theta & \cos\theta \end{bmatrix}$ and $\cos\theta = \begin{bmatrix} \sin\theta & \cos\theta \\ \cos\theta & \sin\theta \end{bmatrix}$

$$\therefore\ |\sin A| = \cos^2\theta + \sin^2\theta = 1 \neq 0$$

Hence, $\sin A$ is invertible.

Also, $(\sin A)(\sin A)^T = \begin{bmatrix} \cos\theta & \sin\theta \\ -\sin\theta & \cos\theta \end{bmatrix}\begin{bmatrix} \cos\theta & -\sin\theta \\ \sin\theta & \cos\theta \end{bmatrix}$

$$= \begin{bmatrix} 1 & 0 \\ 0 & 1 \end{bmatrix} = I$$

Hence, $\sin A$ is orthogonal.

Also, $2 \sin A \cos A = 2\begin{bmatrix} \cos\theta & \sin\theta \\ -\sin\theta & \cos\theta \end{bmatrix}\begin{bmatrix} \sin\theta & \cos\theta \\ \cos\theta & \sin\theta \end{bmatrix}$

$$= 2\begin{bmatrix} \sin 2\theta & 1 \\ \cos 2\theta & 0 \end{bmatrix} \neq \sin 2A$$

● **Ex. 13** *Let A and B are two square idempotent matrices such that $AB \pm BA$ is a null matrix, the value of $\det(A - B)$ can be equal*

(a) -1 (b) 0
(c) 1 (d) 2

Sol. (a, b, c)

$$\because (A - B)^2 = A^2 - AB - BA + B^2$$
$$= A + B \quad [\because AB + BA = 0 \text{ and } A^2 = A, B^2 = B]$$
$$\therefore\ |A - B|^2 = |A + B| \quad \ldots(i)$$

and $(A + B)^2 = A^2 + AB + BA + B^2$

$$= A + B \quad [\because AB + BA = 0 \text{ and } A^2 = A, B^2 = B]$$
$$\Rightarrow |A + B|^2 = |A + B|$$
$$\Rightarrow |A + B|(|A + B| - 1) = 0$$
$$\therefore\ |A + B| = 0, 1$$

From Eq. (i),

$$|A-B|^2 = 0, 1 \Rightarrow |A-B| = 0, \pm 1$$

or $\det(A-B) = 0, -1, 1$

Ex. 14 *If $AB = A$ and $BA = B$, then*

(a) $A^2B = A^2$ (b) $B^2A = B^2$

(c) $ABA = A$ (d) $BAB = B$

Sol. (*a, b, c, d*)

We have, $A^2B = A(AB) = A \cdot A = A^2$,

$B^2A = B(BA) = BB = B^2$,

$ABA = A(BA) = AB = A$, $BAB = B(AB) = BA = B$

Ex. 15 *If A is a square matrix of order 3 and I is an Identity matrix of order 3 such that $A^3 - 2A^2 - A + 2I = 0$, then A is equal to*

(a) I (b) $2I$ (c) $\begin{bmatrix} 2 & -1 & 2 \\ 1 & 0 & 0 \\ 0 & 1 & 0 \end{bmatrix}$ (d) $\begin{bmatrix} 2 & 1 & -2 \\ 1 & 0 & 0 \\ 0 & 1 & 0 \end{bmatrix}$

Sol. (*a, b, d*) It is clear that $A = I$ and $A = 2I$ satisfy the given equaion $A^3 - 2A^2 - A + 2I = 0$ and the characteristic equation of the matrix in (c) is

$$\begin{vmatrix} 2-\lambda & -1 & 2 \\ 1 & -\lambda & 0 \\ 0 & 1 & -\lambda \end{vmatrix} = 0$$

$\Rightarrow$ $\lambda^3 - 2\lambda^2 + \lambda - 2 = 0,$

giving $A^3 - 2A^2 + A - 2I = 0$

$\neq A^3 - 2A^2 - A + 2I = 0$

and the characteristic equation of the matrix in (d) is

$$\begin{vmatrix} 2-\lambda & 1 & -2 \\ 1 & -\lambda & 0 \\ 0 & 1 & -\lambda \end{vmatrix} = 0$$

$\Rightarrow$ $\lambda^3 - 2\lambda^2 - \lambda + 2 = 0,$

giving $A^3 - 2A^2 - A + 2I = 0$

JEE Type Solved Examples : Passage Based Questions

- This section contains **2 solved passages**. Base upon each of the passage **3 multiple choice question** have to be answered. Each of these question has four choices (a), (b), (c) and (d) out of which **ONLY ONE** is correct.

Passage I

(Ex. Nos. 16 to 18)

If $A_0 = \begin{bmatrix} 2 & -2 & -4 \\ -1 & 3 & 4 \\ 1 & -2 & -3 \end{bmatrix}$ and $B_0 = \begin{bmatrix} -4 & -3 & -3 \\ 1 & 0 & 1 \\ 4 & 4 & 3 \end{bmatrix}$ and

$B_n = \text{adj}(B_{n-1}), n \in N$ and I is an identity matrix of order 3.

16. $\det(A_0 + A_0^2 B_0^2 + A_0^3 + A_0^4 B_0^4 + \dots$ upto 12 terms) is equal to

(a) 1200 (b) −960

(c) 0 (d) −9600

17. $B_2 + B_3 + B_4 + \dots + B_{50}$ is equal to

(a) B_0 (b) $7B_0$

(c) $49B_0$ (d) $49I$

18. For a variable matrix X, the equation $A_0 X = B_0$ will have

(a) unique solution

(b) infinite solution

(c) finitely many solution

(d) no solution

Sol. (Ex. Nos 16 to 18)

$\because$ $A_0 = \begin{bmatrix} 2 & -2 & -4 \\ -1 & 3 & 4 \\ 1 & -2 & -3 \end{bmatrix} \Rightarrow |A_0| = 0$

and $\text{adj } B_0 = \begin{bmatrix} -4 & 1 & 4 \\ -3 & 0 & 4 \\ -3 & 1 & 3 \end{bmatrix}^T = \begin{bmatrix} -4 & -3 & -3 \\ 1 & 0 & 1 \\ 4 & 4 & 3 \end{bmatrix} = B_0$

$\because$ $B_n = \text{adj}(B_{n-1}), n \in N$

$\therefore$ $B_1 = \text{adj}(B_0) = B_0$

$\Rightarrow$ $B_2 = \text{adj}(B_1) = \text{adj}(B_0) = B_0,$

Similarly $B_3 = B_0, B_4 = B_0, \dots$

$\therefore$ $B_n = B_0 \ \forall \ n \in N$

16. (c) $\det(A_0 + A_0^2 B_0^2 + A_0^3 + A_0^4 B_0^4 + \dots$ upto 12 terms) = det $\{A_0 (I + A_0 B_0^2 + A_0^2 + A_0^3 B_0^4 + \dots \text{upto 12 terms})\}$

$= |A_0|(I + A_0 B_0^2 + A_0^2 + A_0^3 B_0^4 + \dots$ upto 12 terms)

$= 0$ $[\because |A_0| = 0]$

17. (c) $B_2 + B_3 + B_4 + \dots + B_{50} = B_0 + B_0 + B_0 + \dots + B_0 = 49B_0$

18. (d) $\because |A_0| = 0$

$\Rightarrow A_0^{-1}$ is not possible.

Hence, system of equation $A_0 X = B_0$ has no Sol.

Passage II

(Ex. Nos. 19 to 21)

Let $A = \begin{bmatrix} 1 & 0 & 0 \\ 1 & 0 & 1 \\ 0 & 1 & 0 \end{bmatrix}$ satisfies $A^n = A^{n-2} + A^2 - I$ for $n \geq 3$ and consider a matrix $\underset{3\times 3}{U}$ with its columns as U_1, U_2, U_3, such that

$$A^{50}U_1 = \begin{bmatrix} 1 \\ 25 \\ 25 \end{bmatrix}, A^{50}U_2 = \begin{bmatrix} 0 \\ 1 \\ 0 \end{bmatrix} \text{ and } A^{50}U_3 = \begin{bmatrix} 0 \\ 0 \\ 1 \end{bmatrix}$$

19. The value of $|A^{50}|$ equals

(a) −1 (b) 0 (c) 1 (d) 25

20. Trace of A^{50} equals

(a) 0 (b) 1 (c) 2 (d) 3

21. The value of $|U|$ equals

(a) −1 (b) 0 (c) 1 (d) 2

Sol. (Ex. Nos. 19 to 21)

$$\because \quad A^n = A^{n-2} + A^2 - I \Rightarrow A^{50} = A^{48} + A^2 - I$$

Further, $A^{48} = A^{46} + A^2 - I$

$$A^{46} = A^{44} + A^2 - I$$

$$\vdots \quad \vdots \quad \vdots \quad \vdots$$

$$A^4 = A^2 + A^2 - I^4$$

On adding all, we get

$$A^{50} = 25A^2 - 24I \quad \text{...(i)}$$

19. (c) $|A^{50}| = |A|^{50} = \begin{vmatrix} 1 & 0 & 0 \\ 1 & 0 & 1 \\ 0 & 1 & 0 \end{vmatrix}^{50} = (-1)^{50} = 1$

20. (d) $\because A^2 = \begin{bmatrix} 1 & 0 & 0 \\ 1 & 0 & 1 \\ 0 & 1 & 0 \end{bmatrix}\begin{bmatrix} 1 & 0 & 0 \\ 1 & 0 & 1 \\ 0 & 1 & 0 \end{bmatrix} = \begin{bmatrix} 1 & 0 & 0 \\ 1 & 1 & 0 \\ 1 & 0 & 1 \end{bmatrix}$

$$\therefore A^{50} = 25A^2 - 24I = \begin{bmatrix} 25 & 0 & 0 \\ 25 & 25 & 0 \\ 25 & 0 & 25 \end{bmatrix} - \begin{bmatrix} 24 & 0 & 0 \\ 0 & 24 & 0 \\ 0 & 0 & 24 \end{bmatrix}$$

[from Eq. (i)]

$$= \begin{bmatrix} 1 & 0 & 0 \\ 25 & 1 & 0 \\ 25 & 0 & 1 \end{bmatrix} \quad \text{...(ii)}$$

Hence, trace of $A^{50} = 1 + 1 + 1 = 3$

21. (c) Let $U_1 = \begin{bmatrix} x \\ y \\ z \end{bmatrix}$

Given, $A^{50}U_1 = \begin{bmatrix} 1 \\ 25 \\ 25 \end{bmatrix} \Rightarrow \begin{bmatrix} 1 & 0 & 0 \\ 25 & 1 & 0 \\ 25 & 0 & 1 \end{bmatrix}\begin{bmatrix} x \\ y \\ z \end{bmatrix} = \begin{bmatrix} 1 \\ 25 \\ 25 \end{bmatrix}$ [from Eq. (ii)]

$\Rightarrow \begin{bmatrix} x \\ 25x + y \\ 25x + z \end{bmatrix} = \begin{bmatrix} 1 \\ 25 \\ 25 \end{bmatrix}$, we get $x = 1, y = 20$ and $z = 0$

$\therefore \quad U_1 = \begin{bmatrix} 1 \\ 0 \\ 0 \end{bmatrix}$, similarly $U_2 = \begin{bmatrix} 0 \\ 1 \\ 0 \end{bmatrix}$

and $\quad U_3 = \begin{bmatrix} 0 \\ 0 \\ 1 \end{bmatrix} \Rightarrow U = \begin{bmatrix} 1 & 0 & 0 \\ 0 & 1 & 0 \\ 0 & 0 & 1 \end{bmatrix} = I$

$\therefore \quad |U| = 1$

JEE Type Solved Examples : Single Integer Answer Type Questions

- This section contains **2 examples.** The answer to each example is a **single digit integer** ranging from **0** to **9** (both inclusive).

● **Ex. 22** *Let A be a* 3×3 *diagonal matrix which commutes with every* 3×3 *matrix. If* $\det(A) = 8$*, then tr A is*

Sol. (6) Let $A = \begin{bmatrix} \alpha & 0 & 0 \\ 0 & \beta & 0 \\ 0 & 0 & \gamma \end{bmatrix}$

$$\therefore \begin{bmatrix} \alpha & 0 & 0 \\ 0 & \beta & 0 \\ 0 & 0 & \gamma \end{bmatrix}\begin{bmatrix} a & h & g \\ h & b & f \\ g & f & c \end{bmatrix} = \begin{bmatrix} a & h & g \\ h & b & f \\ g & f & c \end{bmatrix}\begin{bmatrix} \alpha & 0 & 0 \\ 0 & \beta & 0 \\ 0 & 0 & \gamma \end{bmatrix}$$

$$\Rightarrow \quad \alpha = \beta = \gamma$$

$$\therefore \quad A = \begin{bmatrix} \alpha & 0 & 0 \\ 0 & \alpha & 0 \\ 0 & 0 & \alpha \end{bmatrix}$$

$$\Rightarrow \quad \det(A) = \alpha^3 = 8 \quad \text{[given]}$$

$$\therefore \quad \alpha = 2$$

$$\therefore \quad A = \begin{bmatrix} 2 & 0 & 0 \\ 0 & 2 & 0 \\ 0 & 0 & 2 \end{bmatrix}$$

$$\Rightarrow \quad \text{tr } A = 2 + 2 + 2 = 6$$

● ***Ex. 23*** *Let A and B be two non-singular matrices such that $A \neq I$, $B^3 = I$ and $AB = BA^2$, where I is the identity matrix, the least value of k such that $A^k = I$ is*

Sol. (7) Given, $AB = BA^2 \Rightarrow B = A^{-1}BA^2 \Rightarrow B^3 = I$

$$\Rightarrow (A^{-1}BAA)(A^{-1}BAA)(A^{-1}BAA) = I$$

$$\Rightarrow (A^{-1}BA)(BA)(BAA) = I \quad [\because A^{-1}A = I]$$

$$\Rightarrow A^{-1}B(AB)(AB)AA = I$$

$$\Rightarrow A^{-1}B(BA^2)(BA^2)AA = I \quad [\because AB = BA^2]$$

$$\Rightarrow A^{-1}BBA(AB)A^4 = I$$

$$\Rightarrow A^{-1}BBA(BA^2)A^4 = I \quad [\because AB = BA^2]$$

$$\Rightarrow A^{-1}BB(AB)A^6 = I$$

$$\Rightarrow A^{-1}BB(BA^2)A^6 = I \quad [\because AB = BA^2]$$

$$\Rightarrow A^{-1}B^3A^8 = I$$

$$\Rightarrow (A^{-1}I)A^8 = I \quad [\because B^3 = I]$$

$$\Rightarrow A^{-1}A^8 = I$$

$$\Rightarrow A^7 = I = A^k \quad [\because A^k = I]$$

$$\Rightarrow A^k = A^7$$

∴ Least value of k is 7.

JEE Type Solved Examples : Matching Type Questions

- This section contains **2 examples.** Example 24 have three statements (A, B and C) given in **Column I** and four statements (p, q, r and s) in **Column II** and example 25 have three statements (A, B and C) given in **Column I** and five statements (p, q, r, s and t). In **Column II** any given statement in **Column I** can have correct matching with one or more statement(s) given in **Column II.**

● ***Ex. 24***

	Column I		Column II
(A)	If A is a square matrix of order 3 and det $(A) = 3$, then det $(6A^{-1})$ is divisible by	(p)	3
(B)	If A is a square matrix of order 3 and det $(A) = \frac{1}{4}$, then det [adj (adj (2A))] is divisible by	(q)	4
(C)	If A and B are square matrices of odd order and $(A+B)^2 = A^2 + B^2$, if det $(A) = 2$, then det(B) is divisible by	(r)	5
		(s)	6

Sol. (A) → (p, q, s); (B) →(q); (C) →(p, q, r, s)

(A) $\det(6A^{-1}) = 6^3 \det(A^{-1}) = \dfrac{216}{\det(A)} = \dfrac{216}{3} = 72$

(B) $\det[\text{adj}(\text{adj}(2A))] = [\det(2A)]^4 = [2^3 \det(A)]^4$

$$= 2^{12}[\det(A)]^4$$

$$= 2^{12}\left(\frac{1}{4}\right)^4 = 2^4 = 16$$

(C) ∵ $(A+B)^2 = A^2 + AB + BA + B^2$

$$\Rightarrow A^2 + B^2 = A^2 + AB + BA + B^2$$

$$[\because (A+B)^2 = A^2 + B^2]$$

$$\Rightarrow AB + BA = O \Rightarrow AB = -BA$$

$$\therefore \det(AB) = \det(-BA) = -\det(BA)$$

$$\Rightarrow \det(A)\cdot\det(B) = -\det B \cdot \det(A)$$

$$\Rightarrow 2\det(A)\cdot\det(B) = 0 \Rightarrow 4\det(B) = 0 \quad [\because \det(A) = 2]$$

$$\therefore \det(B) = 0$$

● ***Ex. 25***

	Column I		Column II
(A)	If $\begin{bmatrix} 1 & 2 & a \\ 0 & 1 & 4 \\ 0 & 0 & 1 \end{bmatrix}^n = \begin{bmatrix} 1 & 18 & 2007 \\ 0 & 1 & 36 \\ 0 & 0 & 1 \end{bmatrix}$, then $(n+a)$ is divisible by	(p)	4
(B)	If A is a square matrix of order 3 such that $\|A\| = a$, $B = \text{adj}(A)$ and $\|B\| = b$, then $(ab^2 + a^2b + 1)\lambda$ is divisible by, where $\frac{1}{2}\lambda = \frac{a}{b} + \frac{a^2}{b^3} + \frac{a^3}{b^5} + \ldots$ upto ∞ and $a = 3$	(q)	6
(C)	Let $A = \begin{bmatrix} a & b & c \\ p & q & r \\ 1 & 1 & 1 \end{bmatrix}$ and $B = A^2$. If $(a-b)^2 + (p-q)^2 = 25$, $(b-c)^2 + (q-r)^2 = 36$ and $(c-a)^2 + (r-p)^2 = 49$, then det $\left(\frac{B}{2}\right)$ is divisible by	(r)	10
		(s)	12
		(t)	15

Sol. (A) → (p, r); (B) →(t); (C) → (q, s)

(A) ∵ $A = \begin{bmatrix} 1 & 2 & a \\ 0 & 1 & 4 \\ 0 & 0 & 1 \end{bmatrix}$

$$\therefore A^2 = \begin{bmatrix} 1 & 2 & a \\ 0 & 1 & 4 \\ 0 & 0 & 1 \end{bmatrix}\begin{bmatrix} 1 & 2 & a \\ 0 & 1 & 4 \\ 0 & 0 & 1 \end{bmatrix} = \begin{bmatrix} 1 & 4 & 2a+8 \\ 0 & 1 & 8 \\ 0 & 0 & 1 \end{bmatrix}$$

$$\Rightarrow \quad A^3 = \begin{bmatrix} 1 & 4 & 2a+8 \\ 0 & 1 & 8 \\ 0 & 0 & 1 \end{bmatrix} \begin{bmatrix} 1 & 2 & a \\ 0 & 1 & 4 \\ 0 & 0 & 1 \end{bmatrix} = \begin{bmatrix} 1 & 6 & 3a+24 \\ 0 & 1 & 12 \\ 0 & 0 & 1 \end{bmatrix}$$

Similarly, we get

$$A^n = \begin{bmatrix} 1 & 2n & na + 8\sum_{r=0}^{n-1} r \\ 0 & 1 & 4n \\ 0 & 0 & 1 \end{bmatrix} = \begin{bmatrix} 1 & 18 & 2007 \\ 0 & 1 & 36 \\ 0 & 0 & 1 \end{bmatrix} \text{ [given]}$$

$$\Rightarrow \quad 2n = 18 \Rightarrow n = 9$$

$$\therefore \quad na + 8\sum_{r=0}^{n-1} r = 2007 \Rightarrow 9a + 8\sum_{r=0}^{8} r = 2007$$

$$\Rightarrow \quad 9a + 8 \cdot \left(\frac{8 \times 9}{2}\right) = 2007 \Rightarrow 9a = 2007 - 288 = 1719$$

$$\therefore \quad a = 191$$

Hence, $n + a = 9 + 191 = 200$

(B) $B = \text{adj } A$

$$\Rightarrow \quad b = |B| = |\text{adj } A| = |A|^2 = a^2 = 9 \Rightarrow a = 3, b = 9$$

and $\frac{1}{2}\lambda = \frac{3}{9} + \frac{3^2}{9^3} + \frac{3^3}{9^5} + \ldots + \infty$

$$= \frac{1}{3} + \frac{1}{81} + \frac{1}{27 \times 81} + \ldots + \infty = \frac{\frac{1}{3}}{1 - \frac{1}{27}} = \frac{9}{26}$$

$$\Rightarrow \quad \lambda = \frac{9}{13}$$

Now, $(ab^2 + a^2b + 1)\lambda = (3 \times 81 + 9 \times 9 + 1) \times \frac{9}{13} = 225$

(C) $\det(A) = \begin{vmatrix} a & b & c \\ p & q & r \\ 1 & 1 & 1 \end{vmatrix} = \begin{vmatrix} a & p & 1 \\ b & q & 1 \\ c & r & 1 \end{vmatrix} = 2 \times \frac{1}{2} \begin{vmatrix} a & p & 1 \\ b & q & 1 \\ c & r & 1 \end{vmatrix}$

$= 2 \times$ Area of the triangle with vertices $(a, p), (b, q)$ and (c, r) with sides 5, 6, 7

$$= 2 \times \sqrt{s(s-a)(s-b)(s-c)} = 2 \times 6\sqrt{6} = 12\sqrt{6}$$

Hence, $\det\left(\frac{B}{2}\right) = \left(\frac{1}{2}\right)^3 \det(B) = \frac{1}{8}\det(A^2)$

$$= \frac{1}{8}(\det A)^2 = \frac{1}{8}(12\sqrt{6})^2 = 108$$

JEE Type Solved Examples : Statement I and II Type Questions

- **Direction** example numbers 26 and 27 are Assertion-Reason type examples. Each of these examples contains two statements:

Statement-1 (Assertion) and **Statement-2** (Reason)

Each of these examples also has four alternative choices, **ONLY ONE** of which is the correct answer. You have to select the correct choice as given below.

(a) Statement-1 is true, Statement-2 is true; Statement-2 is correct explanation for Statement-1

(b) Statement-1 is true, Statement-2 is true; Statement-2 is not a correct explanation for Statement-1

(c) Statement-1 is true, Statement-2 is false

(d) Statement-1 is false, Statement-2 is true

- ***Ex. 26*** **Statement-1** *A is singular matrix of order* $n \times n$, *then adj A is singular.*

Statement-2 $|\text{adj } A| = |A|^{n-1}$

Sol. (*d*) If A is non-singular matrix of order $n \times n$, then

$$|\text{adj } A| = |A|^{n-1}$$

Hence, Statement-1 is false and Statement-2 is true.

- ***Ex. 27*** **Statement-1** *If A and B are two matrices such that* $AB = B$, $BA = A$, *then* $A^2 + B^2 = A + B$.

Statement-2 *A and B are idempotent matrices, then* $A^2 = A$, $B^2 = B$.

Sol. (*b*) $\because AB = B$

$\Rightarrow \quad B(AB) = B \cdot B$

$\Rightarrow \quad (BA)B = B^2$ [by associative law]

$\Rightarrow \quad AB = B^2$ [$\because BA = A$]

$\Rightarrow \quad B = B^2$ [$\because AB = B$]

and $\quad BA = A$

$\Rightarrow \quad A(BA) = A \cdot A$

$\Rightarrow \quad (AB)A = A^2$ [by associative law]

$\Rightarrow \quad BA = A^2$ [$\because AB = B$]

$\Rightarrow \quad A = A^2$ [$\because BA = A$]

Hence, $\therefore \quad A^2 + B^2 = A + B$

Here, both statements are true and Statement-2 is not a correct explanation for Statement-1.

Subjective Type Examples

- In this section, there are **12 subjective** solved examples.

- ***Ex. 28*** *If $A^n = 0$, then evaluate*

(i) $I + A + A^2 + A^3 + \ldots + A^{n-1}$

(ii) $I - A + A^2 - A^3 + \ldots + (-1)^{n-1}A^{n-1}$ for odd 'n', where I is the identity matrix having the same order of A.

Sol. (i) $A^n = 0 \Rightarrow A^n - I = -I$

$$\Rightarrow A^n - I^n = -I \Rightarrow I^n - A^n = I$$
$$\Rightarrow (I - A)(I + A + A^2 + A^3 + \ldots + A^{n-1}) = I$$
$$\Rightarrow (I + A + A^2 + A^3 + \ldots + A^{n-1}) = (I - A)^{-1}I = (I - A)^{-1}$$

(ii) $A^n = 0 \Rightarrow A^n + I = I$

$$\Rightarrow A^n + I^n = I$$
$$\Rightarrow I^n + A^n = I$$
$$\Rightarrow (I + A)(I - A + A^2 - A^3 + \ldots + A^{n-1}) = I \quad [\because n \text{ is odd}]$$
$$\Rightarrow I - A + A^2 - A^3 + \ldots + A^{n-1} = (I + A)^{-1}I = (I + A)^{-1}$$

- ***Ex. 29*** *If A is idempotent matrix, then show that $(A + I)^n = I + (2^n - 1)A, \forall n \in N$, where I is the identity matrix having the same order of A.*

Sol. $\because$ A is idempotent matrix

$\therefore$ $A^2 = A$,

similarly $A = A^2 = A^3 = A^4 = \ldots = A^n$ ...(i)

Now, $(A + I)^n = (I + A)^n$

$$= I + {}^nC_1A + {}^nC_2A^2 + {}^nC_3A^3 + \ldots + {}^nC_nA^n$$
$$= I + ({}^nC_1 + {}^nC_2 + {}^nC_3 + \ldots + {}^nC_n)A \quad [\text{from Eq. (i)}]$$
$$= I + (2^n - 1)A$$

Hence, $(A + I)^n = I + (2^n - 1)A, \forall n \in N$.

- ***Ex. 30*** *If the matrices $A = \begin{bmatrix} 1 & 2 \\ 3 & 4 \end{bmatrix}$ and $B = \begin{bmatrix} a & b \\ c & d \end{bmatrix}$ (a, b, c, d not all simultaneously zero) commute, find the value of $\dfrac{d - b}{a + c - b}$. Also, show that the matrix which commutes with A is of the form $\begin{bmatrix} \alpha - \beta & \frac{2\beta}{3} \\ \beta & \alpha \end{bmatrix}$.*

Sol. Given, $AB = BA$

$$\begin{bmatrix} 1 & 2 \\ 3 & 4 \end{bmatrix}\begin{bmatrix} a & b \\ c & d \end{bmatrix} = \begin{bmatrix} a & b \\ c & d \end{bmatrix}\begin{bmatrix} 1 & 2 \\ 3 & 4 \end{bmatrix}$$
$$\Rightarrow \begin{bmatrix} a + 2c & b + 2d \\ 3a + 4c & 3b + 4d \end{bmatrix} = \begin{bmatrix} a + 3b & 2a + 4b \\ c + 3d & 2c + 4d \end{bmatrix}$$

On comparing, we get

$$a + 2c = a + 3b$$
$$\Rightarrow b = \frac{2c}{3} \quad \text{...(i)}$$
$$b + 2d = 2a + 4b$$
$$\Rightarrow d = a + \frac{3b}{2} \quad \text{...(ii)}$$
$$\Rightarrow 3a + 4c = c + 3d$$
$$d = a + c \quad \text{...(iii)}$$
and
$$3b + 4d = 2c + 4d$$
$$\Rightarrow b = \frac{2c}{3} \quad \text{...(iv)}$$
$$\Rightarrow \frac{d - b}{a + c - b} = \frac{d - b}{d - b} = 1 \quad [\text{from Eq. (iii)}]$$

Now, $B = \begin{bmatrix} a & b \\ c & d \end{bmatrix} = \begin{bmatrix} d - c & \frac{2c}{3} \\ c & d \end{bmatrix}$

If $c = \beta$ and $d = \alpha$, then $B = \begin{bmatrix} \alpha - \beta & \frac{2\beta}{3} \\ \beta & \alpha \end{bmatrix}$

- ***Ex. 31*** *Given the matrix $A = \begin{bmatrix} -1 & 3 & 5 \\ 1 & -3 & -5 \\ -1 & 3 & 5 \end{bmatrix}$ and X be the solution set of the equation $A^x = A$, where $x \in N - \{1\}$. Evaluate $\prod\left(\dfrac{x^3 + 1}{x^3 - 1}\right)$, where the continued extends for all $x \in X$.*

Sol. $\because$ $A^2 = \begin{bmatrix} -1 & 3 & 5 \\ 1 & -3 & -5 \\ -1 & 3 & 5 \end{bmatrix}\begin{bmatrix} -1 & 3 & 5 \\ 1 & -3 & -5 \\ -1 & 3 & 5 \end{bmatrix} = \begin{bmatrix} -1 & 3 & 5 \\ 1 & -3 & -5 \\ -1 & 3 & 5 \end{bmatrix}$

$= A$

$\therefore$ $A^2 = A^3 = A^4 = A^5 = \ldots = A$

but given $A^x = A$

$\Rightarrow$ $x = 2, 3, 4, 5, \ldots$ $[\because x \neq 1, \text{given}]$

$$\therefore \prod\left(\frac{x^3 + 1}{x^3 - 1}\right) = \prod\left(\frac{x + 1}{x - 1}\right)\prod\left(\frac{x^2 - x + 1}{x^2 + x + 1}\right)$$

On putting $x = 2, 3, 4, 5, \ldots$

$$\prod\left(\frac{x^3+1}{x^3-1}\right) = \lim_{n\to\infty}\prod_{x=2}^{n}\left(\frac{x+1}{x-1}\right)\prod_{x=2}^{n}\left(\frac{x^2-x+1}{x^2+x+1}\right)$$

$$= \lim_{n\to\infty}\left(\frac{3\cdot 4\cdot 5\ldots(n-1)n(n+1)}{1\cdot 2\cdot 3\ldots(n-3)(n-2)(n-1)}\right)$$

$$\times \lim_{n\to\infty}\left(\frac{3\cdot 7\ldots(n^2-n+1)}{7\cdot 13\ldots(n^2-n+1)(n^2+n+1)}\right)$$

$$= \lim_{n\to\infty}\frac{n(n+1)}{2}\times\frac{3}{(n^2+n+1)}$$

$$= \frac{3}{2}\lim_{n\to\infty}\frac{\left(1+\frac{1}{n}\right)}{\left(1+\frac{1}{n}+\frac{1}{n^2}\right)} = \frac{3}{2}\cdot\frac{(1+0)}{(1+0+0)} = \frac{3}{2}$$

● ***Ex. 32*** *If P is a non-singular matrix, with (P^{-1}) in terms of 'P', then show that* $\operatorname{adj}(Q^{-1}BP^{-1}) = PAQ$. *Given that,* $(B) = A$ *and* $|P| = |Q| = 1$.

Sol. $\because \operatorname{adj}(P^{-1}) = |P|(P^{-1})^{-1} = |P|P = P$ $\quad [\because |P| = 1]$

and $\operatorname{adj}(Q^{-1}BP^{-1}) = \operatorname{adj}(P^{-1})\cdot\operatorname{adj}B\cdot\operatorname{adj}(Q^{-1})$

$$= \frac{P}{|P|}A\cdot\frac{Q}{|Q|} = PAQ \qquad [\because |P| = |Q| = 1]$$

● ***Ex. 33*** *Let A and B be matrices of order n. Prove that if $(I - AB)$ is invertible, $(I - BA)$ is also invertible and $(I - BA)^{-1} = I + B(I - AB)^{-1}A$, where I be the identity matrix of order n.*

Sol. Here, $I - BA = BIB^{-1} - BABB^{-1} = B(I - AB)B^{-1}$ $\quad$ ...(i)

Hence, $|I - BA| = |B||I - AB||B^{-1}| = |B||I - AB|\dfrac{1}{|B|}$

$= |I - AB|$

If $|I - AB| \neq 0$, then $|I - BA| \neq 0$

i.e. if $(I - AB)$ is invertible, then $(I - BA)$ is also invertible.

Now, $(I - BA)[I + B(I - AB)^{-1}A]$

$= (I - BA) + (I - BA)B(I - AB)^{-1}A$ $\quad$ [using Eq. (i)]

$= (I - BA) + B(I - AB)B^{-1}B(I - AB)^{-1}A$

$= (I - BA) + B(I - AB)(I - AB^{-1})A$

$= (I - BA) + BA = I$

Hence, $(I - BA)^{-1} = I + B(I - AB)^{-1}A$.

● ***Ex. 34*** *Prove that the inverse of* $\begin{bmatrix} A & O \\ B & C \end{bmatrix}$ *is* $\begin{bmatrix} A^{-1} & O \\ -C^{-1}BA^{-1} & C^{-1} \end{bmatrix}$, *where A, C are non-singular matrices and O is null matrix and find the inverse* $\begin{bmatrix} 1 & 0 & 0 & 0 \\ 1 & 1 & 0 & 0 \\ 1 & 1 & 1 & 0 \\ 1 & 1 & 1 & 1 \end{bmatrix}$

Sol. We have, First part $\begin{bmatrix} A & O \\ B & C \end{bmatrix}\begin{bmatrix} A^{-1} & O \\ -C^{-1}BA^{-1} & C^{-1} \end{bmatrix}$

$$= \begin{bmatrix} AA^{-1} & O \\ BA^{-1} - CC^{-1}BA^{-1} & CC^{-1} \end{bmatrix}$$

$$= \begin{bmatrix} I & O \\ BA^{-1} - BA^{-1} & I \end{bmatrix} = \begin{bmatrix} I & O \\ 0 & I \end{bmatrix}$$

Hence, $\begin{bmatrix} A^{-1} & O \\ -C^{-1}BA^{-1} & C^{-1} \end{bmatrix}$ is the inverse of $\begin{bmatrix} A & O \\ B & C \end{bmatrix}$.

Second part $\begin{bmatrix} 1 & 0 & 0 & 0 \\ 1 & 1 & 0 & 0 \\ 1 & 1 & 1 & 0 \\ 1 & 1 & 1 & 1 \end{bmatrix} = \begin{bmatrix} A & O \\ B & C \end{bmatrix}$

where $A = \begin{bmatrix} 1 & 0 \\ 1 & 1 \end{bmatrix}, B = \begin{bmatrix} 1 & 1 \\ 1 & 1 \end{bmatrix}, C = \begin{bmatrix} 1 & 0 \\ 1 & 1 \end{bmatrix}$ and $O = \begin{bmatrix} 0 & 0 \\ 0 & 0 \end{bmatrix}$

and $A^{-1} = \begin{bmatrix} 1 & 0 \\ -1 & 1 \end{bmatrix}, C^{-1} = \begin{bmatrix} 1 & 0 \\ -1 & 1 \end{bmatrix}$

Now, $C^{-1}BA^{-1} = \begin{bmatrix} 1 & 0 \\ -1 & 1 \end{bmatrix}\begin{bmatrix} 1 & 1 \\ 1 & 1 \end{bmatrix}\begin{bmatrix} 1 & 0 \\ -1 & 1 \end{bmatrix} = \begin{bmatrix} 0 & 1 \\ 0 & 0 \end{bmatrix}$

$\therefore$ Inverse of $\begin{bmatrix} 1 & 0 & 0 & 0 \\ 1 & 1 & 0 & 0 \\ 1 & 1 & 1 & 0 \\ 1 & 1 & 1 & 1 \end{bmatrix}$ is $\begin{bmatrix} 1 & 0 & 0 & 0 \\ -1 & 1 & 0 & 0 \\ 0 & -1 & 1 & 0 \\ 0 & 0 & -1 & 1 \end{bmatrix}$

● ***Ex. 35*** *Let* $A = \begin{bmatrix} 3 & a & -1 \\ 2 & 5 & c \\ b & 8 & 2 \end{bmatrix}$ *is symmetric and* $B = \begin{bmatrix} d & 3 & a \\ b-a & e & -2b-c \\ -2 & 6 & -f \end{bmatrix}$ *is skew-symmetric, find AB. If AB is symmetric or skew-symmetric or neither of them. Justify your answer.*

Sol. $\because$ A is symmetric

$\therefore \quad c = 8, b = -1$ and $a = 2$ $\quad$ ...(i)

and B is skew-symmetric

$\therefore \quad d = e = f = 0$ and $2b + c = 6, a = 2, b - a = -3$ $\quad$ ...(ii)

From Eqs. (i) and (ii), we get

$$a = 2, b = -1, c = 8, d = 0, e = 0, f = 0$$

$$\therefore \quad A = \begin{bmatrix} 3 & 2 & -1 \\ 2 & 5 & 8 \\ -1 & 8 & 2 \end{bmatrix} \text{ and } B = \begin{bmatrix} 0 & 3 & 2 \\ -3 & 0 & -6 \\ -2 & 6 & 0 \end{bmatrix}$$

$$\Rightarrow \quad AB = \begin{bmatrix} -4 & 3 & -6 \\ -31 & 54 & -26 \\ -28 & 9 & -50 \end{bmatrix}$$

which neither symmetric nor skew-symmetric.

• **Ex. 36** *If B, C are square matrices of order n and if $A=B+C$, $BC=CB$, $C^2=0$, show that for any positive integer p, $A^{p+1}=B^p[B+(p+1)C]$.*

Sol. $\because$ $A=B+C \Rightarrow A^{p+1}=(B+C)^{p+1}$

$$= {}^{p+1}C_0B^{p+1}+{}^{p+1}C_1B^pC+{}^{p+1}C_2B^{p-1}C^2+\dots+{}^{p+1}C_{p+1}C^{p+1}$$

$$=B^{p+1}+{}^{p+1}C_1B^pC+0+0+\dots \quad [\because C^2=0\Rightarrow C^2=C^3=\dots=0]$$

$$=B^p[B+(p+1)C]$$

Hence, $A^{p+1}=B^p[B+(p+1)C]$

• **Ex. 37** *If there an three square matrices A, B, C of same order satisfying the equation $A^2=A^{-1}$ and let $B=A^{2^n}$ and $C=A^{2^{(n-2)}}$, prove that $\det(B-C)=0$.*

Sol. $\because$ $B=A^{2^n}=A^{2\cdot 2^{n-1}}=(A^2)^{2^{n-1}}=(A^{-1})^{2^{n-1}} \quad [\because A^2=A^{-1}]$

$$=(A^{2^{n-1}})^{-1}=(A^{2\cdot 2^{n-2}})^{-1}=[(A^2)^{2^{n-2}}]^{-1}$$

$$=[(A^{-1})^{2^{n-2}}]^{-1}=((A^{-1})^{-1})^{2^{n-2}}=A^{2^{n-2}}=C$$

$$\Rightarrow B-C=0\Rightarrow \det(B-C)=0$$

• **Ex. 38** *Construct an orthogonal matrix using the skew-symmetric matrix $A=\begin{bmatrix}0&2\\-2&0\end{bmatrix}$.*

Sol. $\because$ $A=\begin{bmatrix}0&2\\-2&0\end{bmatrix}\Rightarrow I-A=\begin{bmatrix}1&-2\\2&1\end{bmatrix}$

$$\Rightarrow (I-A)^{-1}=\frac{1}{5}\begin{bmatrix}1&2\\-2&1\end{bmatrix} \text{ and } (I+A)=\begin{bmatrix}1&2\\-2&1\end{bmatrix}$$

Let B be the orthogonal matrix from a skew-symmetric matrix A, then $B=(I-A)^{-1}(I+A)$

$$=\frac{1}{5}\begin{bmatrix}1&2\\-2&1\end{bmatrix}\begin{bmatrix}1&2\\-2&1\end{bmatrix}=\frac{1}{5}\begin{bmatrix}-3&4\\-4&-3\end{bmatrix}=\begin{bmatrix}-\frac{3}{5}&\frac{4}{5}\\-\frac{4}{5}&-\frac{3}{5}\end{bmatrix}$$

• **Ex. 39** *If $A=\begin{bmatrix}3&2&2\\2&4&1\\-2&-4&-1\end{bmatrix}$ and X, Y are two non-zero column vectors such that $AX=\lambda X$, $AY=\mu Y$, $\lambda\neq\mu$, find angle between X and Y.*

Sol. $\because$ $AX=\lambda X\Rightarrow (A-\lambda I)X=0$

$\because$ $X\neq 0$

$\therefore$ $\det(A-\lambda I)=0$

$$\Rightarrow \begin{vmatrix}3-\lambda&2&2\\2&4-\lambda&1\\-2&-4&-1-\lambda\end{vmatrix}=0$$

Applying $R_3\to R_3+R_2$, then

$$\begin{vmatrix}3-\lambda&2&2\\2&4-\lambda&1\\0&-\lambda&-\lambda\end{vmatrix}=0$$

Applying $C_2\to C_2-C_3$, then

$$\Rightarrow \begin{vmatrix}3-\lambda&0&2\\2&3-\lambda&1\\0&0&-\lambda\end{vmatrix}=0$$

$$\Rightarrow -\lambda(3-\lambda)^2=0$$

$$\Rightarrow \lambda=0,3$$

It is clear that $\lambda=0,\mu=3$

For $\lambda=0$, $AX=0\Rightarrow \begin{bmatrix}3&2&2\\2&4&1\\-2&-4&-1\end{bmatrix}\begin{bmatrix}x\\y\\z\end{bmatrix}=\begin{bmatrix}0\\0\\0\end{bmatrix}$

$$\Rightarrow 3x+2y+2z=0 \text{ and } 2x+4y+z=0$$

$$\therefore \frac{x}{-6}=\frac{y}{1}=\frac{z}{8}$$

So, $X=\begin{bmatrix}-6\\1\\8\end{bmatrix}$

For $\mu=3$, $(A-3I)Y=0$

$$\Rightarrow \begin{bmatrix}0&2&2\\2&1&1\\-2&-4&-4\end{bmatrix}\begin{bmatrix}\alpha\\\beta\\\gamma\end{bmatrix}=\begin{bmatrix}0\\0\\0\end{bmatrix}$$

$$\Rightarrow 0\cdot\alpha+2\beta+2\gamma=0 \text{ and } 2\alpha+\beta+\gamma=0$$

$$\therefore \frac{\alpha}{0}=\frac{\beta}{4}=\frac{\gamma}{-4}$$

$$\Rightarrow \frac{\alpha}{0}=\frac{\beta}{-1}=\frac{\gamma}{1}$$

So, $Y=\begin{bmatrix}0\\-1\\1\end{bmatrix}$

If θ be the angle between X and Y, then

$$\cos\theta=\frac{0\cdot(-6)+(-1)\cdot 1+1\cdot 8}{\sqrt{(0+1+1)}\sqrt{36+1+64}}=\frac{7}{\sqrt{202}}$$

$$\therefore \theta=\cos^{-1}\left(\frac{7}{\sqrt{202}}\right)$$

Matrices Exercise 1 :
Single Option Correct Type Questions

- This section contains **30 multiple choice questions.** Each question has four choices (a), (b), (c) and (d) out of which **ONLY ONE** is correct

1. If $A^5 = O$ such that $A^n \neq I$ for $1 \leq n \leq 4$, then $(I - A)^{-1}$ is equal to
(a) A^4 (b) A^3
(c) $I + A$ (d) None of these

2. Let $A = \begin{bmatrix} a & b & c \\ p & q & r \\ x & y & z \end{bmatrix}$ and suppose that det $(A) = 2$, then det (B) equals, where $B = \begin{bmatrix} 4x & 2a & -p \\ 4y & 2b & -q \\ 4z & 2c & -r \end{bmatrix}$
(a) −2 (b) −8 (c) −16 (d) 8

3. If both $A - \frac{1}{2}I$ and $A + \frac{1}{2}I$ are orthogonal matrices, then
(a) A is orthogonal
(b) A is skew-symmetric matrix of even order
(c) $A^2 = \frac{3}{4}I$
(d) None of the above

4. Let $a = \lim_{x \to 1}\left(\frac{x}{\ln x} - \frac{1}{x \ln x}\right)$, $b = \lim_{x \to 0}\left(\frac{x^3 - 16x}{4x + x^2}\right)$
$c = \lim_{x \to 0}\left(\frac{\ln(1 + \sin x)}{x}\right)$ and
$d = \lim_{x \to -1}\frac{(x+1)^3}{3[\sin(x+1) - (x+1)]}$, then $\begin{bmatrix} a & b \\ c & d \end{bmatrix}$ is
(a) idempotent (b) involutory
(c) non-singular (d) nilpotent

5. Let $A = \begin{bmatrix} 1 & 4 \\ 3 & 2 \end{bmatrix}$. If θ is the angle between the two non-zero column vectors X such that $AX = \lambda X$ for some scalar λ, then $\tan\theta$ is equal to
(a) 3 (b) 5
(c) 7 (d) 9

6. If a square matrix A is involutory, then A^{2n+1} is equal to
(a) I (b) A
(c) A^2 (d) $(2n + 1)A$

7. If $A = \begin{bmatrix} \cos\theta & \sin\theta \\ -\sin\theta & \cos\theta \end{bmatrix}$, then $\lim_{n \to \infty}\frac{A^n}{n}$ is (where $\theta \in R$)
(a) a zero matrix (b) an identity matrix
(c) $\begin{bmatrix} 0 & 1 \\ -1 & 0 \end{bmatrix}$ (d) $\begin{bmatrix} 0 & 1 \\ 0 & -1 \end{bmatrix}$

8. The rank of the matrix $\begin{bmatrix} -1 & 2 & 5 \\ 2 & -4 & a-4 \\ 1 & -2 & a+1 \end{bmatrix}$ is (where $a = -6$)
(a) 1 (b) 2 (c) 3 (d) 4

9. A is an involutory matrix given by $A = \begin{bmatrix} 0 & 1 & -1 \\ 4 & -3 & 4 \\ 3 & -3 & 4 \end{bmatrix}$, the inverse of $\frac{A}{2}$ will be
(a) $2A$ (b) $\frac{A^{-1}}{2}$ (c) $\frac{A}{2}$ (d) A^2

10. Let A be a nth order square matrix and B be its adjoint, then $|AB + kI_n|$, is (where k is a scalar quantity)
(a) $(|A| + k)^{n-2}$ (b) $(|A| + k)^n$
(c) $(|A| + k)^{n-1}$ (d) $(|A| + k)^{n+1}$

11. If A and B are two square matrices such that $B = -A^{-1}BA$, then $(A + B)^2$ is equal to
(a) O (b) $A^2 + B^2$
(c) $A^2 + 2AB + B^2$ (d) $A + B$

12. If matrix $A = [a_{ij}]_{3 \times 3}$, matrix $B = [b_{ij}]_{3 \times 3}$, where $a_{ij} + a_{ji} = 0$ and $b_{ij} - b_{ji} = 0$, then $A^4 \cdot B^3$ is
(a) skew-symmetric matrix (b) singular
(c) symmetric (d) zero matrix

13. Let A be a $n \times n$ matrix such that $A^n = \alpha A$, where α is a real number different from 1 and −1. The matrix $A + I_n$ is
(a) singular (b) invertible
(c) scalar matrix (d) None of these

14. If $A = \begin{bmatrix} \frac{-1 + i\sqrt{3}}{2i} & \frac{-1 - i\sqrt{3}}{2i} \\ \frac{1 + i\sqrt{3}}{2i} & \frac{1 - i\sqrt{3}}{2i} \end{bmatrix}$, $i = \sqrt{-1}$ and $f(x) = x^2 + 2$, then $f(A)$ equals to
(a) $\begin{bmatrix} 1 & 0 \\ 0 & 1 \end{bmatrix}$ (b) $\left(\frac{3 - i\sqrt{3}}{2}\right)\begin{bmatrix} 1 & 0 \\ 0 & 1 \end{bmatrix}$
(c) $\left(\frac{5 - i\sqrt{3}}{2}\right)\begin{bmatrix} 1 & 0 \\ 0 & 1 \end{bmatrix}$ (d) $(2 + i\sqrt{3})\begin{bmatrix} 1 & 0 \\ 0 & 1 \end{bmatrix}$

15. The number of solutions of the matrix equation $X^2 = I$ other than I is
(a) 0 (b) 1
(c) 2 (d) more than 2

16. If A and B are square matrices such that $A^{2006}=0$ and $AB=A+B$, then det (B) equals to

(a) -1 (b) 0
(c) 1 (d) None of these

17. If $P=\begin{bmatrix}\cos\frac{\pi}{6} & \sin\frac{\pi}{6}\\ -\sin\frac{\pi}{6} & \cos\frac{\pi}{6}\end{bmatrix}, A=\begin{bmatrix}1 & 1\\ 0 & 1\end{bmatrix}$ and $Q=PAP^T$, then $P^TQ^{2007}P$ is equal to

(a) $\begin{bmatrix}1 & \sqrt{3}/2\\ 0 & 2007\end{bmatrix}$ (b) $\begin{bmatrix}1 & 2007\\ 0 & 1\end{bmatrix}$
(c) $\begin{bmatrix}\sqrt{3}/2 & 2007\\ 0 & 1\end{bmatrix}$ (d) $\begin{bmatrix}\sqrt{3}/2 & -1/2\\ 1 & 2007\end{bmatrix}$

18. There are two possible values of A in the solution of the matrix equation $\begin{bmatrix}2A+1 & -5\\ -4 & A\end{bmatrix}^{-1}\begin{bmatrix}A-5 & B\\ 2A-2 & C\end{bmatrix}=\begin{bmatrix}14 & D\\ E & F\end{bmatrix}$, where A, B, C, D, E, F are real numbers. The absolute value of the difference of these two solutions, is

(a) $\frac{8}{3}$ (b) $\frac{11}{3}$ (c) $\frac{1}{3}$ (d) $\frac{19}{3}$

19. If $f(\theta)=\begin{bmatrix}\cos^2\theta & \cos\theta\sin\theta & -\sin\theta\\ \cos\theta\sin\theta & \sin^2\theta & \cos\theta\\ \sin\theta & -\cos\theta & 0\end{bmatrix}$, then $f\left(\frac{\pi}{7}\right)$ is

(a) symmetric (b) skew-symmetric
(c) singular (d) non-singular

20. In a square matrix A of order 3 the elements a_{ii}'s are the sum of the roots of the equation $x^2-(a+b)x+ab=0$; $a_{i,i+1}$'s are the product of the roots, $a_{i,i-1}$'s are all unity and the rest of the elements are all zero.

The value of the det (A) is equal to

(a) 0 (b) $(a+b)^3$
(c) a^3-b^3 (d) $(a^2+b^2)(a+b)$

21. If A and B are two non-singular matrices of the same order such that $B^r=I$ for some positive integer $r>1$. Then $A^{-1}B^{r-1}A-A^{-1}B^{-1}A$ is equal to

(a) I (b) $2I$ (c) 0 (d) $-I$

22. If $A=\begin{bmatrix}\cos\theta & \sin\theta\\ \sin\theta & -\cos\theta\end{bmatrix}, B=\begin{bmatrix}1 & 0\\ -1 & 1\end{bmatrix}, C=ABA^T$, then $A^TC^nA, n\in I^+$ equals to

(a) $\begin{bmatrix}-n & 1\\ 1 & 0\end{bmatrix}$ (b) $\begin{bmatrix}1 & -n\\ 0 & 1\end{bmatrix}$ (c) $\begin{bmatrix}0 & 1\\ 1 & -n\end{bmatrix}$ (d) $\begin{bmatrix}1 & 0\\ -n & 1\end{bmatrix}$

23. If A is a square matrix of order 3 such that $|A|=2$, then $|(\text{adj } A^{-1})^{-1}|$ is

(a) 1 (b) 2 (c) 4 (d) 8

24. If A and B are different matrices satisfying $A^3=B^3$ and $A^2B=B^2A$, then

(a) det (A^2+B^2) must be zero
(b) det $(A-B)$ must be zero
(c) det (A^2+B^2) as well as det $(A-B)$ must be zero
(d) atleast one of det (A^2+B^2) or det $(A-B)$ must be zero

25. If A is a skew-symmetric matrix of order 2 and B, C are matrices $\begin{bmatrix}1 & 4\\ 2 & 9\end{bmatrix}, \begin{bmatrix}9 & -4\\ -2 & 1\end{bmatrix}$ respectively, then

$A^3(BC)+A^5(B^2C^2)+A^7(B^3C^3)+\ldots$
$+A^{2n+1}(B^nC^n)$, is

(a) a symmetric matrix (b) a skew-symmetric matrix
(c) an identity matrix (d) None of these

26. If $A=\begin{bmatrix}a & b & c\\ x & y & z\\ p & q & r\end{bmatrix}, B=\begin{bmatrix}q & -b & y\\ -p & a & -x\\ r & -c & z\end{bmatrix}$ and if A is invertible, then which of the following is not true?

(a) $|A|=|B|$
(b) $|A|=-|B|$
(c) $|\text{adj } A|=|\text{adj } B|$
(d) A is invertible $\Leftrightarrow B$ is invertible

27. Let three matrices $A=\begin{bmatrix}2 & 1\\ 4 & 1\end{bmatrix}, B=\begin{bmatrix}3 & 4\\ 2 & 3\end{bmatrix}$ and $C=\begin{bmatrix}3 & -4\\ -2 & 3\end{bmatrix}$, then tr $(A)+\text{tr}\left(\frac{ABC}{2}\right)+\text{tr}\left(\frac{A(BC)^2}{4}\right)$ $+\text{tr}\left(\frac{A(BC)^3}{8}\right)+\ldots+\infty$ equals to

(a) 4 (b) 9 (c) 12 (d) 6

28. If A is non-singular and $(A-2I)(A-4I)=O$, then $\frac{1}{6}A+\frac{4}{3}A^{-1}$ is equal to

(a) O (b) I
(c) $2I$ (d) $6I$

29. If $A=\begin{bmatrix}0 & 1 & 2\\ 1 & 2 & 3\\ 3 & a & 1\end{bmatrix}$ and $A^{-1}=\begin{bmatrix}1/2 & -1/2 & 1/2\\ -4 & 3 & b\\ 5/2 & -3/2 & 1/2\end{bmatrix}$, then

(a) $a=1, b=-1$ (b) $a=2, b=-\frac{1}{2}$
(c) $a=-1, b=1$ (d) $a=\frac{1}{2}, b=\frac{1}{2}$

30. Given the matrix $A=\begin{bmatrix}x & 3 & 2\\ 1 & y & 4\\ 2 & 2 & z\end{bmatrix}$. If $xyz=60$ and $8x+4y+3z=20$, then $A(\text{adj } A)$ is equal to

(a) $64I$ (b) $88I$ (c) $68I$ (d) $34I$

Matrices Exercise 2 : More than One Correct Option Type Questions

- This section contains **15 multiple choice questions.** Each question has four choices (a), (b), (c) and (d) out of which **MORE THAN ONE** may be correct.

31. If $A = \begin{bmatrix} 1 & 1 & 1 \\ 1 & 1 & 1 \\ 1 & 1 & 1 \end{bmatrix}$, then

(a) $A^3 = 9A$ (b) $A^3 = 27A$
(c) $A + A = A^2$ (d) A^{-1} does not exist

32. A square matrix A with elements from the set of real numbers is said to be orthogonal if $A' = A^{-1}$. If A is an orthogonal matrix, then

(a) A' is orthogonal (b) A^{-1} is orthogonal
(c) adj $A = A'$ (d) $|A^{-1}| = 1$

33. Let $A = \begin{bmatrix} 1 & 2 & 2 \\ 2 & 1 & 2 \\ 2 & 2 & 1 \end{bmatrix}$, then

(a) $A^2 - 4A - 5I_3 = O$ (b) $A^{-1} = \frac{1}{5}(A - 4I_3)$
(c) A^3 is not invertible (d) A^2 is invertible

34. D is a 3×3 diagonal matrix. Which of the following statements are not true?

(a) $D^T = D$
(b) $AD = DA$ for every matrix A of order 3×3
(c) D^{-1} if exists is a scalar matrix
(d) None of the above

35. The rank of the matrix $\begin{bmatrix} -1 & 2 & 5 \\ 2 & -4 & a-4 \\ 1 & -2 & a+1 \end{bmatrix}$, is

(a) 2, if $a = -6$ (b) 2, if $a = 1$
(c) 1, if $a = 2$ (d) 1, if $a = -6$

36. If $A = \begin{bmatrix} 3 & -3 & 4 \\ 2 & -3 & 4 \\ 0 & -1 & 1 \end{bmatrix}$, then

(a) adj (adj A) = A (b) $|$ adj (adj (A)) $| = 1$
(c) $|$ adj (A) $| = 1$ (d) None of these

37. If B is an idempotent matrix and $A = I - B$, then

(a) $A^2 = A$ (b) $A^2 = I$
(c) $AB = O$ (d) $BA = O$

38. If A is a non-singular matrix, then

(a) A^{-1} is symmetric if A is symmetric
(b) A^{-1} is skew-symmetric if A is symmetric
(c) $|A^{-1}| = |A|$
(d) $|A^{-1}| = |A|^{-1}$

39. Let A and B are two matrices such that $AB = BA$, then for every $n \in N$

(a) $A^n B = BA^n$
(b) $(AB)^n = A^n B^n$
(c) $(A + B)^n = {}^nC_0 A^n + {}^nC_1 A^{n-1} B + \dots + {}^nC_n B^n$
(d) $A^{2n} - B^{2n} = (A^n - B^n)(A^n + B^n)$

40. If A and B are 3×3 matrices and $|A| \neq 0$, which of the following are true?

(a) $|AB| = 0 \Rightarrow |B| = 0$
(b) $|AB| = 0 \Rightarrow B = 0$
(c) $|A^{-1}| = |A|^{-1}$
(d) $|A + A| = 2|A|$

41. If A is a matrix of order $m \times m$ such that $A^2 + A + 2I = O$, then

(a) A is non-singular (b) A is symmetric
(c) $|A| \neq 0$ (d) $A^{-1} = -\frac{1}{2}(A + I)$

42. If $A^2 - 3A + 2I = 0$, then A is equal to

(a) I (b) $2I$
(c) $\begin{bmatrix} 3 & -2 \\ 1 & 0 \end{bmatrix}$ (d) $\begin{bmatrix} 3 & 1 \\ -2 & 0 \end{bmatrix}$

43. If A and B are two matrices such that their product AB is a null matrix, then

(a) det $A \neq 0 \Rightarrow B$ must be a null matrix
(b) det $B \neq 0 \Rightarrow A$ must be a null matrix
(c) atleast one of the two matrices must be singular
(d) if neither det A nor det B is zero, then the given statement is not possible

44. If D_1 and D_2 are two 3×3 diagonal matrices where none of the diagonal elements is zero, then

(a) $D_1 D_2$ is a diagonal matrix
(b) $D_1 D_2 = D_2 D_1$
(c) $D_1^2 + D_2^2$ is a diagonal matrix
(d) None of the above

45. Let, $C_k = {}^nC_k$ for $0 \leq k \leq n$ and $A_k = \begin{bmatrix} C_{k-1}^2 & 0 \\ 0 & C_k^2 \end{bmatrix}$ for $k \geq 1$ and

$A_1 + A_2 + A_3 + \dots + A_n = \begin{bmatrix} k_1 & 0 \\ 0 & k_2 \end{bmatrix}$, then

(a) $k_1 = k_2$ (b) $k_1 + k_2 = 2$
(c) $k_1 = {}^{2n}C_n - 1$ (d) $k_2 = {}^{2n}C_{n+1}$

Matrices Exercise 3 : Passage Based Questions

This section contains **6 passages.** Based upon each of the passage **3 multiple choice questions** have to be answered. Each of these questions has four choices (a), (b), (c) and (d) out of which **ONLY ONE** is correct.

Passage I (Q. Nos. 46 to 48)

uppose A and B be two non-singular matrices such that $AB = BA^m$, $B^n = I$ and $A^p = I$, where I is an identity matrix.

46. If $m = 2$ and $n = 5$, then p equals to

(a) 30 (b) 31
(c) 33 (d) 81

47. The relation between m, n and p, is

(a) $p = mn^2$ (b) $p = m^n - 1$
(c) $p = n^m - 1$ (d) $p = m^{n-1}$

48. Which of the following ordered triplet (m, n, p) is false?

(a) (3, 4, 80) (b) (6, 3, 215)
(c) (8, 3, 510) (d) (2, 8, 255)

Passage II (Q. Nos. 49 to 51)

et $A = \begin{bmatrix} a & b & c \\ b & c & a \\ c & a & b \end{bmatrix}$ is an orthogonal matrix and $abc = \lambda (< 0)$.

49. The value of $a^2b^2 + b^2c^2 + c^2a^2$, is

(a) 2λ (b) -2λ
(c) λ^2 (d) $-\lambda$

50. The value of $a^3 + b^3 + c^3$, is

(a) λ (b) 2λ
(c) 3λ (d) None of these

51. The equation whose roots are a, b, c, is

(a) $x^3 - 2x^2 + \lambda = 0$ (b) $x^3 - \lambda x^2 + \lambda x + \lambda = 0$
(c) $x^3 - 2x^2 + 2\lambda x + \lambda = 0$ (d) $x^3 \pm x^2 - \lambda = 0$

Passage III (Q. Nos. 52 to 53)

et $A = [a_{ij}]_{3 \times 3}$. If tr is arithmetic mean of elements of rth row nd $a_{ij} + a_{jk} + a_{ki} = 0$ holds for all $1 \le i, j, k \le 3$.

52. $\sum_{1 \le i} \sum_{j \le 3} a_{ij}$ is not equal to

(a) $t_1 + t_2 + t_3$ (b) zero
(c) $(\det(A))^2$ (d) $t_1t_2t_3$

53. Matrix A is

(a) non-singular
(b) symmetric
(c) skew-symmetric
(d) neither symmetric nor skew-symmetric

Passage IV (Q. Nos. 54 to 56)

Let $A = \begin{bmatrix} 1 & 0 & 0 \\ 2 & 1 & 0 \\ 3 & 2 & 1 \end{bmatrix}$ be a square matrix and C_1, C_2, C_3 be three column matrices satisfying $AC_1 = \begin{bmatrix} 1 \\ 0 \\ 0 \end{bmatrix}$, $AC_2 = \begin{bmatrix} 2 \\ 3 \\ 0 \end{bmatrix}$ and $AC_3 = \begin{bmatrix} 2 \\ 3 \\ 1 \end{bmatrix}$ of matrix B. If the matrix $C = \frac{1}{3}(A \cdot B)$.

54. The value of $\det(B^{-1})$, is

(a) 2 (b) $\frac{1}{2}$ (c) 3 (d) $\frac{1}{3}$

55. The ratio of the trace of the matrix B to the matrix C, is

(a) $-\frac{9}{5}$ (b) $-\frac{5}{9}$ (c) $-\frac{2}{3}$ (d) $-\frac{3}{2}$

56. The value of $\sin^{-1}(\det A) + \tan^{-1}(9 \det C)$, is

(a) $\frac{\pi}{4}$ (b) $\frac{\pi}{2}$ (c) $\frac{3\pi}{4}$ (d) π

Passage V (Q. Nos. 57 to 59)

If A is symmetric and B skew-symmetric matrix and $A + B$ is non-singular and $C = (A + B)^{-1}(A - B)$.

57. $C^T(A + B)C$ equals to

(a) $A + B$ (b) $A - B$
(c) A (d) B

58. $C^T(A - B)C$ equals to

(a) $A + B$ (b) $A - B$ (c) A (d) B

59. C^TAC equals to

(a) $A + B$ (b) $A - B$
(c) A (d) B

Passage VI (Q. Nos. 60 to 61)

Let A be a square matrix of order 3 satisfies the matrix equation $A^3 - 6A^2 + 7A - 8I = O$ and $B = A - 2I$. Also, $\det A = 8$.

60. The value of $\det(\operatorname{adj}(I - 2A^{-1}))$ is equal to

(a) $\frac{25}{16}$ (b) $\frac{125}{64}$
(c) $\frac{64}{125}$ (d) $\frac{16}{25}$

61. If $\operatorname{adj}\left(\left(\frac{B}{2}\right)^{-1}\right) = \left(\frac{p}{q}\right)B$, where $p, q \in N$, the least value of $(p + q)$ is equal to

(a) 7 (b) 9 (c) 29 (d) 41

Matrices Exercise 4 :
Single Integer Answer Type Questions

- This section contains **10 questions**. The answer to each question is a **single digit integer**, ranging from 0 to 9 (both inclusive).

62. Let A, B, C, D be (not necessarily) real matrices such that $A^T = BCD; B^T = CDA; C^T = DAB$ and $D^T = ABC$ for the matrix $S = ABCD$, the least value of k such that $S^k = S$ is

63. If $A = \begin{bmatrix} 1 & \tan x \\ -\tan x & 1 \end{bmatrix}$ and a function $f(x)$ is defined as $f(x) = \det(A^T A^{-1})$ and if $f(f(f(f \ldots f(x))))$ is $(n \geq 2)$ λ, the value of 2^λ is

64. If the matrix $A = \begin{bmatrix} \lambda_1^2 & \lambda_1\lambda_2 & \lambda_1\lambda_3 \\ \lambda_2\lambda_1 & \lambda_2^2 & \lambda_2\lambda_3 \\ \lambda_3\lambda_1 & \lambda_3\lambda_2 & \lambda_3^2 \end{bmatrix}$ is idempotent, the value of $\lambda_1^2 + \lambda_2^2 + \lambda_3^2$ is

65. Let A be a 3×3 matrix given by $A = [a_{ij}]$. If for every column vector X, $X^T AX = O$ and $a_{23} = -1008$, the sum of the digits of a_{32} is

66. Let X be the solution set of the equation $A^x = I$, where $A = \begin{bmatrix} 0 & 1 & -1 \\ 4 & -3 & 4 \\ 3 & -3 & 4 \end{bmatrix}$ and I is the corresponding unit matrix and $x \subseteq N$, the minimum value of $\Sigma(\cos^x \theta + \sin^x \theta)$, $\theta \in R - \left\{\frac{n\pi}{2}, n \in I\right\}$ is

67. If A is an idempotent matrix and I is an identity matrix of the same order, then the value of n, such that $(A+I)^n = I + 127\,A$ is

68. Suppose $a, b, c \in R$ and $abc = 1$, if $A = \begin{bmatrix} 3a & b & c \\ b & 3c & a \\ c & a & 3b \end{bmatrix}$ is such that $A^T A = 4^{1/3}\ I$ and $|A| > 0$, the value of $a^3 + b^3 + c^3$ is

69. If $A = \begin{bmatrix} 0 & 1 \\ 3 & 0 \end{bmatrix}$ and $(A^8 + A^6 + A^4 + A^2 + I)\,V = \begin{bmatrix} 0 \\ 11 \end{bmatrix}$, where V is a vertical vector and I is the 2×2 identity matrix and if λ is sum of all elements of vertical vector V, the value of 11λ is

70. Let the matrix A and B be defined as $A = \begin{bmatrix} 3 & 2 \\ 2 & 1 \end{bmatrix}$ and $B = \begin{bmatrix} 3 & 1 \\ 7 & 3 \end{bmatrix}$, then the absolute value of $\det(2A^9\,B^{-1})$ is

71. Let $A = \begin{bmatrix} 0 & \alpha \\ 0 & 0 \end{bmatrix}$ and $(A+I)^{70} - 70A = \begin{bmatrix} a-1 & b-1 \\ c-1 & d-1 \end{bmatrix}$, the value of $a + b + c + d$ is

Matrices Exercise 5 :
Matching Type Questions

- This section contains **4 questions**. Question 72 has four statements (A, B, C and D) given in **Column I** and four statements (p, q, r and s) in **Column II** and questions 73 to 75 have four statements (A, B, C and D) given in **Column I** and five statements (p, q, r, s and t) in **Column II**. Any given statement in **Column I** can have correct matching with one or more statement(s) given in **Column II**.

72. Suppose a, b, c are three distinct real numbers and $f(x)$ is a real quadratic polynomial such that

$$\begin{bmatrix} 4a^2 & 4a & 1 \\ 4b^2 & 4b & 1 \\ 4c^2 & 4c & 1 \end{bmatrix} \begin{bmatrix} f(-1) \\ f(1) \\ f(2) \end{bmatrix} = \begin{bmatrix} 3a^2 + 3a \\ 3b^2 + 3b \\ 3c^2 + 3c \end{bmatrix}.$$

	Column I		Column II
(A)	x-coordinate(s) of the point of intersection of $y = f(x)$ with the X-axis is	(p)	-2
(B)	Area (in sq units) bounded by $y = \frac{3}{2} f(x)$ and the X-axis is	(q)	1
(C)	Maximum value of $f(x)$ is	(r)	2
(D)	Length (in unit) of the intercept made by $y = f(x)$ on the X-axis is	(s)	4

73. If A is non-singular matrix of order $n \times n$,

	Column I		Column II
(A)	adj (A^{-1}) is	(p)	$A\,(\det A)^{n-2}$
(B)	det (adj (A^{-1})) is	(q)	$(\det A)^{n-1}$ (adj A)
(C)	adj (adj A) is	(r)	$\dfrac{\text{adj (adj } A)}{(\det A)^{n-1}}$
(D)	adj (A det (A)) is	(s)	$(\det A)^{1-n}$
		(t)	$\dfrac{A}{(\det A)}$

74.

	Column I		Column II
(A)	If A is a diagonal matrix of order 3×3 is commutative with every square matrix of order 3×3 under multiplication and tr $(A) = 12$, then $\|A\|$ is divisible by	(p)	3
		(q)	4
(B)	Let $a, b, c \in R^+$ and the system of equations $(1-a)x + y + z = 0$, $x + (1-b)y + z = 0$, $x + y + (1-c)z = 0$ has infinitely many solutions. If λ be the minimum value of $a\,b\,c$, then λ is divisible by	(r)	6
(C)	Let $A = [a_{ij}]_{3\times 3}$ be a matrix whose elements are distinct integers from 1, 2, 3, ..., 9. The matrix is formed so that the sum of the numbers is every row, column and each diagonal is a multiple of 9. If number of all such possible matrices is λ, then λ is divisible by	(s)	8

	Column I		Column II
(D)	If the equations $x + y = 1$, $(c+2)x + (c+4)y = 6$, $(c+2)^2 x + (c+4)^2 y = 36$ are consistent and c_1, c_2 $(c_1 > c_2)$ are two values of c, then $c_1\,c_2$ is divisible by	(t)	9

75.

	Column I		Column II
(A)	If C is skew-symmetric matrix of order n and X is $n \times 1$ column matrix, then $X^T C X$ is	(p)	invertible
(B)	If A is skew - symmetric, then $I - A$ is, where I is an identity matrix of order A.	(q)	singular
(C)	If $S = \begin{bmatrix} 0 & 1 & 1 \\ 1 & 0 & 1 \\ 1 & 1 & 0 \end{bmatrix}$ and $A = \begin{bmatrix} b+c & c-a & b-a \\ c-b & c+a & a-b \\ b-c & a-c & a+b \end{bmatrix}$ $(a, b, c \neq 0)$, then SAS^{-1} is	(r)	symmetric
(D)	If A, B, C are the angles of a triangle, then the matrix $A = \begin{bmatrix} \sin 2A & \sin C & \sin B \\ \sin C & \sin 2B & \sin A \\ \sin B & \sin A & \sin 2C \end{bmatrix}$ is	(s)	non-singular
		(t)	non-invertible

Matrices Exercise 6 : Statement I and II Type Questions

- **Directions** (Q. Nos. 76 to 85) are Assertion-Reason type questions. Each of these questions contains two statements:
Statement-1 (Assertion) and **Statement-2** (Reason)
Each of these questions also has four alternative choices, only one of which is the correct answer. You have to select the correct choice as given below.
  (a) Statement-1 is true, Statement-2 is true; Statement-2 is a correct explanation for Statement-1
  (b) Statement-1 is true, Statement-2 is true; Statement-2 is not a correct explanation for Statement-1
  (c) Statement1 is true, Statement-2 is false
  (d) Statement-1 is false, Statement-2 is true

76. **Statement-1** If matrix $A = [a_{ij}]_{3\times 3}$, $B = [b_{ij}]_{3\times 3}$, where $a_{ij} + a_{ji} = 0$ and $b_{ij} - b_{ji} = 0$, then $A^4 B^5$ is non-singular matrix.
Statement-2 If A is non-singular matrix, then $|A| \neq 0$.

77. **Statement-1** If A and B are two square matrices of order $n \times n$ which satisfy $AB = A$ and $BA = B$, then $(A + B)^7 = 2^6\,(A + B)$.
Statement-2 A and B are unit matrices.

78. **Statement-1** For a singular matrix A, if $AB = AC \Rightarrow B = C$
Statement-2 If $|A| = 0$, then A^{-1} does not exist.

79. **Statement-1** If A is skew-symmetric matrix of order 3, then its determinant should be zero.
Statement-2 If A is square matrix, $\det(A) = \det(A') = \det(-A')$.

80. Let A be a skew-symmetric matrix, $B = (I - A)(I + A)^{-1}$ and X and Y be column vectors conformable for multiplication with B.
Statement-1 $(BX)^T\,(BY) = X^T Y$
Statement-2 If A is skew-symmetric, then $(I + A)$ is non-singular.

81. **Statement-1** Let a 2×2 matrix A has determinant 2. If $B = 9A^2$, the determinant of B^T is equal to 36.

Statement-2 If A, B and C are three square matrices such that $C = AB$, then $|C| = |A||B|$.

82. **Statement-1** If $A = \begin{bmatrix} 1 & -1 & -1 \\ 1 & -1 & 0 \\ 1 & 0 & -1 \end{bmatrix}$, then $A^3 + A^2 + A = I$.

Statement-2 If $\det(A - \lambda I) = C_0\lambda^3 + C_1\lambda^2 + C_2\lambda + C_3 = 0$, then $C_0A^3 + C_1A^2 + C_3A + C_3I = O$.

83. **Statement-1** $A = [a_{ij}]$ be a matrix of order 3×3, where $a_{ij} = \dfrac{i-j}{i+2j}$ cannot be expressed as a sum of symmetric and skew-symmetric matrix.

Statement-2 Matrix $A = [a_{ij}]_{n \times n}$, $a_{ij} = \dfrac{i-j}{i+2j}$ is neither symmetric nor skew-symmetric.

84. **Statement-1** If A, B, C are matrices such that $|A_{3\times 3}| = 3$, $|B_{3\times 3}| = -1$ and $|C_{2\times 2}| = 2$, $|2ABC| = -12$.

Statement-2 For matrices A, B, C of the same order $|ABC| = |A||B||C|$.

85. **Statement-1** The determinant of a matrix $A = [a_{ij}]_{n\times n}$, where $a_{ij} + a_{ji} = 0$ for all i and j is zero.

Statement-2 The determinant of a skew-symmetric matrix of odd order is zero.

Matrices Exercise 7 : Subjective Type Questions

- In this section, there are **12 subjective** questions.

86. If S is a real skew-symmetric matrix, the show that $I - S$ is non-singular and matrix $A = (I+S)(I-S)^{-1} = (I-S)^{-1}(I+S)$ is orthogonal.

87. If M is a 3×3 matrix, where $\det M = I$ and $MM^T = I$, where I is an identity matrix, prove that $\det(M - I) = 0$.

88. If $A = \begin{bmatrix} \cos\alpha & -\sin\alpha \\ \sin\alpha & \cos\alpha \end{bmatrix}$, $B = \begin{bmatrix} \cos 2\beta & \sin 2\beta \\ \sin 2\beta & -\cos 2\beta \end{bmatrix}$, where $0 < \beta < \dfrac{\pi}{2}$, then prove that $BAB = A^{-1}$. Also, find the least value of α for which $BA^4B = A^{-1}$.

89. Find the product of two matrices

$$A = \begin{bmatrix} \cos^2\theta & \cos\theta\sin\theta \\ \cos\theta\sin\theta & \sin^2\theta \end{bmatrix} B = \begin{bmatrix} \cos^2\phi & \cos\phi\sin\phi \\ \cos\phi\sin\phi & \sin^2\phi \end{bmatrix}$$

Show that, AB is the zero matrix if θ and ϕ differ by an odd multiple of $\dfrac{\pi}{2}$.

90. Show that the matrix $\begin{bmatrix} l_1 & m_1 & n_1 \\ l_2 & m_2 & n_2 \\ l_3 & m_3 & n_3 \end{bmatrix}$ is orthogonal, if $l_1^2 + m_1^2 + n_1^2 = \Sigma l_1^2 = 1 = \Sigma l_2^2 = \Sigma l_3^2$ and $l_1l_2 + m_1m_2 + n_1n_2 = \Sigma l_1l_2 = 0 = \Sigma l_2l_3 = \Sigma l_3l_1$.

91. A finance company has offices located in every division, every district and every taluka in a certain state in India. Assume that there are five divisions, thirty districts and 200 talukas in the state. Each office has one head clerk, one cashier, one clerk and one peon. A divisional office has, in addition, one office superintendent, two clerks, one typist and one poen. A district office, has in addition, one clerk and one peon. The basic monthly salaries are as follows:

Office superintendent ₹ 500, Head clerk ₹ 200, cashier ₹ 175, clerks and typist ₹ 150 and peon ₹ 100. Using matrix notation find

(i) the total number of posts of each kind in all the offices taken together,

(ii) the total basic monthly salary bill of each kind of office

(iii) the total basic monthly salary bill of all the offices taken together.

92. In a development plan of a city, a contractor has taken a contract to construct certain houses for which he needs building materials like stones, sand etc. There are three firms A, B, C that can supply him these materials. At one time these firms A, B, C supplied him 40, 35 and 25 truck loads of stones and 10, 5 and 8 truck loads of stone and sand, respectively. If the cost of one truck load of stone and sand are ₹ 1200 and 500 respectively, find the total amount paid by the contractor to each of these firms A, B, C separately.

93. Show that the matrix $A = \begin{bmatrix} 1 & a & \alpha & a\alpha \\ 1 & b & \beta & b\beta \\ 1 & c & \gamma & c\gamma \end{bmatrix}$ is of rank 3 provided no two of a, b, c are equal and no two of α, β, γ are equal.

94. By the method of matrix inversion, solve the system.

$$\begin{bmatrix} 1 & 1 & 1 \\ 2 & 5 & 7 \\ 2 & 1 & -1 \end{bmatrix}\begin{bmatrix} x & u \\ y & v \\ z & w \end{bmatrix} = \begin{bmatrix} 9 & 2 \\ 52 & 15 \\ 0 & -1 \end{bmatrix}$$

95. If $x_1 = 3y_1 + 2y_2 - y_3$, $y_1 = z_1 - z_2 + z_3$
$x_2 = -y_1 + 4y_2 + 5y_3$, $y_2 = z_2 + 3z_3$
$x_3 = y_1 - y_2 + 3y_3$, $y_3 = 2z_1 + z_2$
express x_1, x_2, x_3 in terms of z_1, z_2, z_3.

96. For what values of k the set of equations $2x-3y+6z-5t=3, y-4z+t=1,$ $4x-5y+8z-9t=k$ has
(i) no solution? (ii) infinite number of solutions?

97. Let A, B, U, V and X be the matrices defined as follows.

$$A=\begin{bmatrix} a & 1 & 0 \\ 1 & b & d \\ 1 & b & c \end{bmatrix}, B=\begin{bmatrix} a & 1 & 1 \\ 0 & d & c \\ f & g & h \end{bmatrix}, U=\begin{bmatrix} f \\ g \\ h \end{bmatrix}, V=\begin{bmatrix} a^2 \\ 0 \\ 0 \end{bmatrix}, X=\begin{bmatrix} x \\ y \\ z \end{bmatrix}$$

If $AX=U$ has infinitely many solutions, show that $BX=V$ cannot have a unique solution. If $afd \neq 0$, show that $BX=V$ has no solution.

Matrices Exercise 8 :
Questions Asked in Previous 13 Year's Exam

- This section contains questions asked in **IIT-JEE, AIEEE, JEE Main & JEE Advanced** from year **2005** to year **2017**.

98. $A=\begin{bmatrix} 1 & 0 & 0 \\ 0 & 1 & 1 \\ 0 & -2 & 4 \end{bmatrix}; I=\begin{bmatrix} 1 & 0 & 0 \\ 0 & 1 & 0 \\ 0 & 0 & 1 \end{bmatrix}$ and

$A^{-1}=\frac{1}{6}[A^2+cA+dI]$ where $c, d \in R$, the pair of values (c, d) **[IIT- JEE 2005, 3M]**

(a) (6, 11) (b) (6, − 11) (c) (− 6, 11) (d) (− 6, − 11)

99. If $P=\begin{bmatrix} \frac{\sqrt{3}}{2} & \frac{1}{2} \\ -\frac{1}{2} & \frac{\sqrt{3}}{2} \end{bmatrix}, A=\begin{bmatrix} 1 & 1 \\ 0 & 1 \end{bmatrix}$ and $Q=PAP^T$, the $P(Q^{2005})P^T$ equal to **[IIT- JEE 2005, 3M]**

(a) $\begin{bmatrix} 1 & 2005 \\ 0 & 1 \end{bmatrix}$ (b) $\begin{bmatrix} \sqrt{3}/1 & 2005 \\ 1 & 0 \end{bmatrix}$

(c) $\begin{bmatrix} 1 & 2005 \\ \sqrt{3}/2 & 1 \end{bmatrix}$ (d) $\begin{bmatrix} 1 & \sqrt{3}/2 \\ 0 & 2005 \end{bmatrix}$

100. If $A=\begin{bmatrix} 1 & 0 \\ 1 & 1 \end{bmatrix}$ and $I=\begin{bmatrix} 1 & 0 \\ 0 & 1 \end{bmatrix}$, which one of the following holds for all $n \geq 1$, (by the principal of mathematical induction) **[AIEEE 2005, 3M]**

(a) $A^n=nA+(n-1)I$ (b) $A^n=2^{n-1}A+(n-1)I$
(c) $A^n=nA-(n-1)I$ (d) $A^n=2^{n-1}A-(n-1)I$

101. If $A^2-A+I=0$, then A^{-1} is equal to **[AIEEE 2005, 3M]**

(a) A^{-2} (b) $A+I$ (c) $I-A$ (d) $A-I$

102. If $A=\begin{pmatrix} 1 & 0 & 0 \\ 2 & 1 & 0 \\ 3 & 2 & 1 \end{pmatrix}$, U_1, U_2 and U_3 are column matrices satisfying $AU_1=\begin{pmatrix} 1 \\ 0 \\ 0 \end{pmatrix}, AU_2=\begin{pmatrix} 2 \\ 3 \\ 0 \end{pmatrix}$ and $AU_3=\begin{pmatrix} 2 \\ 3 \\ 1 \end{pmatrix}$ and U is 3×3 matrix when columns are U_1, U_2, U_3, then answer the following questions

(i) The value of $|U|$ is
(a) 3 (b) − 3 (c) 3/2 (d) 2

(ii) The sum of the elements of U^{-1} is
(a) − 1 (b) 0 (c) 1 (d) 3

(iii) The value of $(3\ 2\ 0)\,U\begin{pmatrix} 3 \\ 2 \\ 0 \end{pmatrix}$ is **[IIT- JEE 2006, 5+5+5M]**
(a) 5 (b) 5/2 (c) 4 (d) 3/2

103. Let $A=\begin{pmatrix} 1 & 2 \\ 3 & 4 \end{pmatrix}$ and $B=\begin{pmatrix} a & 0 \\ 0 & b \end{pmatrix}, a, b \in N$. Then, **[AIEEE 2006, 4½M]**

(a) there cannot exist any B such that $AB=BA$
(b) there exist more than one but finite number of B's such that $AB=BA$
(c) there exists exactly one B such that $AB=BA$
(d) there exist infinitely among B's such that $AB=BA$

104. If A and B are square matrices of size $n \times n$ such that $A^2-B^2=(A-B)(A+B)$, which of the following will be always true? **[AIEEE 2006, 3M]**

(a) $A=B$ (b) $AB=BA$
(c) Either of A or B is a zero matrix
(d) Either of A or B is identity matrix

105. Let $A=\begin{bmatrix} 5 & 5\alpha & \alpha \\ 0 & \alpha & 5\alpha \\ 0 & 0 & 5 \end{bmatrix}$. If $|A^2|=25$, then $|\alpha|$ equals to **[AIEEE 2007, 3M]**

(a) 5^2 (b) 1 (c) 1/5 (d) 5

106. Let A and B be 3×3 matrices of real numbers, where A is symmetric, B is skew-symmetric and $(A+B)(A-B)=(A-B)(A+B)$. If $(AB)^t=(-1)^k AB$, where $(AB)^t$ is the transpose of matrix AB, the value of k is **[IIT- JEE 2008, 1½M]**

(a) 0 (b) 1 (c) 2 (d) 3

107. Let A be a square matrix all of whose entries are integers. Which one of the following is true? **[AIEEE 2008, 3M]**

(a) If det $A \neq \pm 1$, then A^{-1} exists and all its entries are non-integers
(b) If det $A=\pm 1$, then A^{-1} exists and all its entries are integers
(c) If det $A=\pm 1$, then A^{-1} need not exist
(d) If det $A=\pm 1$, then A^{-1} exists but all its entries are not necessarily integers

108. Let A be a 2×2 matrix with real entries. Let I be the 2×2 identity matrix. Denote by $\text{tr}(A)$, the sum of diagonal entries of A. Assume that $A^2 = I$. **[AIEEE 2008, 3M]**

Statement-1 If $A \neq I$ and $A \neq -I$, then $\det A = -1$.

Statement-2 If $A \neq I$ and $A \neq -1$, then $\text{tr}(A) \neq 0$.

(a) Statement-1 is true, Statement-2 is true; Statement-2 is a correct explanation for Statement-1
(b) Statement-1 is true, Statement-2 is true; Statement-2 is not a correct explanation for Statement-1
(c) Statement-1 is true, Statement-2 is false
(d) Statement-1 is false, Statement-2 is true

109. Let A be the set of all 3×3 symmetric matrices all of whose entries are either 0 or 1. Five of these entries are 1 and four of them are 0. **[IIT- JEE 2009, 4+4+4M]**

(i) The number of matrices in A is
(a) 12 (b) 6
(c) 9 (d) 3

(ii) The number of matrices A for which the system of linear equations $A\begin{bmatrix} x \\ y \\ z \end{bmatrix} = \begin{bmatrix} 1 \\ 0 \\ 0 \end{bmatrix}$ has a unique solution, is
(a) less than 4 (b) atleast 4 but less than 7
(c) atleast 7 but less than 10
(d) atleast 10

(iii) The number of matrices A in which the system of linear equations $A\begin{bmatrix} x \\ y \\ z \end{bmatrix} = \begin{bmatrix} 1 \\ 0 \\ 0 \end{bmatrix}$ is inconsistent is
(a) 0 (b) more than 2
(c) 2 (d) 1

110. Let A be a 2×2 matrix

Statement-1 $\text{adj}(\text{adj}\, A) = A$

Statement-2 $|\text{adj}\, A| = |A|$ **[AIEEE 2009, 4M]**

(a) Statement-1 is true, Statement-2 is true; Statement-2 is a correct explanation for Statement-1
(b) Statement-1 is true, Statement-2 is true; Statement-2 is not a correct explanation for Statement-1
(c) Statement-1 is true, Statement-2 is false
(d) Statement-1 is false, Statement-2 is true

111. The number of 3×3 matrices A whose are either 0 or 1 and for which the system $A\begin{bmatrix} x \\ y \\ z \end{bmatrix} = \begin{bmatrix} 1 \\ 0 \\ 0 \end{bmatrix}$ has exactly two distinct solutions, is **[IIT- JEE 2010, 3M]**
(a) 0 (b) $2^9 - 1$
(c) 168 (d) 2

112. Let p be an odd prime number and T_p be the following set of 2×2 matrices.

$$T_p = \left\{ A = \begin{bmatrix} a & b \\ c & a \end{bmatrix};\ a, b, c, \in \{0, 1, 2, \ldots, p-1\} \right\}$$

[IIT- JEE 2010, 3+3+3M]

(i) The number of A in T_p such that A is either symmetric or skew-symmetric or both and $\det(A)$ divisible by p, is
(a) $(p-1)^2$ (b) $2(p-1)$
(c) $(p-1)^2 + 1$ (d) $2p - 1$

(ii) The number of A in T_p such that the trace of A is not divisible by p but $\det(A)$ is divisible by p, is
[**Note** The trace of a matrix is the sum of its diagonal entries]
(a) $(p-1)(p^2 - p + 1)$ (b) $p^3 - (p-1)^2$
(c) $(p-1)^2$ (d) $(p-1)(p^2 - 2)$

(iii) The number of A in T_p such that $\det(A)$ is not divisible by p, is
(a) $2p^2$ (b) $p^3 - 5p$ (c) $p^3 - 3p$ (d) $p^3 - p^2$

113. Let k be a positive real number and let

$$A = \begin{bmatrix} 2k-1 & 2\sqrt{k} & 2\sqrt{k} \\ 2\sqrt{k} & 1 & -2k \\ -2\sqrt{k} & 2k & -1 \end{bmatrix} \text{ and } \begin{bmatrix} 0 & 2k-1 & \sqrt{k} \\ 1-2k & 0 & 2\sqrt{k} \\ -\sqrt{k} & -2\sqrt{k} & 0 \end{bmatrix}.$$

If $\det(\text{adj}\, A) + \det(\text{adj}\, B) = 10^6$, then $[k]$ is equal to **[IIT- JEE 2010, 3M]**

Note adj M denotes the adjoint of a square matrix M and $[k]$ denotes the largest integer less than or equal to k}.

114. The number of 3×3 non-singular matrices, with four entries as 1 and all other entries as 0, is **[AIEEE 2010, 8M]**
(a) 5 (b) 6
(c) atleast 7 (d) less than 4

115. Let A be a 2×2 matrix with non-zero entries and let $A^2 = I$, where I is 2×2 identity matrix. Define $\text{Tr}(A) =$ sum of diagonal elements of A and $|A| =$ determinant of matrix A.

Statement-1 $\text{Tr}(A) = 0$

Statement-2 $|A| = 1$ **[AIEEE 2010, 4M]**

(a) Statement-1 is true, Statement-2 is true; Statement-2 is not a correct explanation for Statement-1.
(b) Statement-1 is true, Statement-2 is false.
(c) Statement-1 is false, Statement-2 is true.
(d) Statement-1 is true, Statement-2 is true; Statement-2 is a correct explanation for Statement-1.

116. Let M and N be two 3×3 non-singular skew-symmetric matrices such that $MN = NM$. If P^T denotes the transpose of P, then $M^2 N^2 (M^T N)^{-1} (MN^{-1})^T$ is equal to **[IIT- JEE 2011, 4M]**
(a) M^2 (b) $-N^2$ (c) $-M^2$ (d) MN

117. Let a, b and c be three real numbers satisfying

$$[a\ b\ c]\begin{bmatrix}1 & 9 & 7\\ 8 & 2 & 7\\ 7 & 3 & 7\end{bmatrix}=[0\ 0\ 0]. \quad \ldots(E)$$

(i) If the point $P(a, b, c)$, with reference to (E), lies on the plane $2x + y + z = 1$, then the value of $7a + b + c$ is

(a) 0 (b) 12 (c) 7 (d) 6

(ii) Let ω be a solution of $x^3 - 1 = 0$ with $\text{Im}(\omega) > 0$. If $a = 2$ with b and c satisfying (E), the value of $\frac{3}{\omega^a}+\frac{1}{\omega^b}+\frac{3}{\omega^c}$ is equal to

(a) -2 (b) 2 (c) 3 (d) -3

(iii) Let $b = 6$ with a and c satisfying (E). If α and β are the roots of the quadratic equation $ax^2 + bx + c = 0$, then $\sum_{n=0}^{\infty}\left(\frac{1}{\alpha}+\frac{1}{\beta}\right)^n$ is **[IIT- JEE 2011, 3+3+3M]**

(a) 6 (b) 7
(c) $\frac{6}{7}$ (d) ∞

118. Let $\omega \neq 1$ be a cube root of unity and S be the set of all non-singular matrices of the form $\begin{bmatrix}1 & a & b\\ \omega & 1 & c\\ \omega^2 & \omega & 1\end{bmatrix}$, where each of a, b and c is either ω or ω^2. The number of distinct matrices in the set S is **[IIT- JEE 2011, 3M]**

(a) 2 (b) 6
(c) 4 (d) 8

119. Let M be a 3×3 matrix satisfying $M\begin{bmatrix}0\\1\\0\end{bmatrix}=\begin{bmatrix}-1\\2\\3\end{bmatrix}$,

$M\begin{bmatrix}1\\-1\\0\end{bmatrix}=\begin{bmatrix}1\\1\\-1\end{bmatrix}$ and $M\begin{bmatrix}1\\1\\1\end{bmatrix}=\begin{bmatrix}0\\0\\12\end{bmatrix}$.

The sum of the diagonal entries of M is **[IIT- JEE 2011, 4M]**

120. Let A and B are symmetric matrices of order 3.

Statement-1 $A(BA)$ and $(AB)A$ are symmetric matrices.

Statement-2 AB is symmetric matrix, if matrix multiplication of A with B is commutative.

(a) Statement-1 is true, Statement-2 is true; Statement-2 is not a correct explanation for Statement-1
(b) Statement-1 is true, Statement-2 is false
(c) Statement-1 is false, Statement-2 is true
(d) Statement-1 is true, Statement-2 is true; Statement-2 is a correct explanation for Statement-1 **[AIEEE 2011, 4M]**

121. Let $P = [a_{ij}]$ be a 3×3 matrix and $Q = [b_{ij}]$, where $b_{ij} = 2^{i+j}a_{ij}$ for $1 \le i, j \le 3$. If the determinant of P is 2, the determinant of the matrix Q is **[IIT- JEE 2012, 3M]**

(a) 2^{11} (b) 2^{12}
(c) 2^{13} (d) 2^{10}

122. If P is a 3×3 matrix such that $P^T = 2P + I$, where P^T is the transpose of P and I is the 3×3 identity matrix, then there exists a column matrix $X = \begin{bmatrix}x\\y\\z\end{bmatrix} \neq \begin{bmatrix}0\\0\\0\end{bmatrix}$ such that **[IIT- JEE 2012, 3M]**

(a) $PX = \begin{bmatrix}0\\0\\0\end{bmatrix}$ (b) $PX = X$ (c) $PX = 2X$ (d) $PX = -X$

123. If the adjoint of a 3×3 matrix P is $\begin{bmatrix}1 & 4 & 4\\ 2 & 1 & 7\\ 1 & 1 & 3\end{bmatrix}$, then the possible value(s) of the determinant of P is (are) **[IIT- JEE 2012, 4M]**

(a) -2 (b) -1 (c) 1 (d) 2

124. If $A = \begin{pmatrix}1 & 0 & 0\\ 2 & 1 & 0\\ 3 & 2 & 1\end{pmatrix}$, u_1 and u_2 are the column matrices such that $Au_1 = \begin{pmatrix}1\\0\\0\end{pmatrix}$ and $Au_2 = \begin{pmatrix}0\\1\\0\end{pmatrix}$, then $u_1 + u_2$ is equal to **[AIEEE 2012, 4M]**

(a) $\begin{pmatrix}-1\\-1\\0\end{pmatrix}$ (b) $\begin{pmatrix}1\\-1\\-1\end{pmatrix}$ (c) $\begin{pmatrix}-1\\1\\0\end{pmatrix}$ (d) $\begin{pmatrix}-1\\1\\-1\end{pmatrix}$

125. Let P and Q be 3×3 matrices with $P \neq Q$. If $P^3 = Q^3$ and $P^2Q = Q^2P$, the determinant of $(P^2 + Q^2)$ is equal to **[AIEEE 2012, 4M]**

(a) 0 (b) -1 (c) -2 (d) 1

126. If $P = \begin{bmatrix}1 & \alpha & 3\\ 1 & 3 & 3\\ 2 & 4 & 4\end{bmatrix}$ is the adjoint of a 3×3 matrix A and $|A| = 4$, then α is equal to **[JEE Main 2013, 4M]**

(a) 11 (b) 5 (c) 0 (d) 4

127. For 3×3 matrices M and N, which of the following statement(s) is (are) **not** correct?

(a) N^TMN is symmetric or skew-symmetric, according as M is symmetric or skew-symmetric
(b) $MN - NM$ is skew-symmetric for all symmetric matrices M and N
(c) MN is symmetric for all symmetric matrices M and N
(d) (adj M) (adj N) = adj (MN) for all invertible matrices M and N **[JEE Advanced 2013, 4M]**

128. Let ω be a complex cube root of unity with $\omega \neq 1$ and $P = [p_{ij}]$ be a $n \times n$ matrix with $p_{ij} = \omega^{i+j}$. Then, $p^2 \neq 0$, when n is equal to **[JEE Advanced 2013, 3M]**
(a) 55 (b) 56 (c) 57 (d) 58

129. If A is a 3×3 non-singular matrix such that $AA' = A'A$ and $B = A^{-1}A'$, then BB' equals to **[JEE Main 2014, 4M]**
(a) B^{-1} (b) $(B^{-1})'$ (c) $I + B$ (d) I

130. Let M be a 2×2 symmetric matrix with integer entries. Then, M is invertible, if
(a) the first column of M is the transpose of the second row of M
(b) the second row of M is the transpose of the first column of M
(c) m is a diagonal matrix with non-zero entries in the main diagonal
(d) the product of entries in the main diagonal of M is not the square of an integer **[JEE Advanced 2014, 3M]**

131. Let M and N be two 3×3 matrices such that $MN = NM$. Further, if $M \neq N^2$ and $M^2 = N^4$, then
(a) determinant of $(M^2 + MN^2)$ is 0
(b) there is a 3×3 non-zero matrix U such that $(M^2 + MN^2)U$ is the zero matrix
(c) determinant of $(M^2 + MN^2) \geq 1$
(d) for a 3×3 matrix U, if $(M^2 + MN^2)U$ equals the zero matrix, then U is the zero matrix
[JEE Advanced 2014, 3M]

132. If $A = \begin{bmatrix} 1 & 2 & 2 \\ 2 & 1 & -2 \\ a & 2 & b \end{bmatrix}$ is a matrix satisfying the equation $AA^T = 9I$, where I is 3×3 identity matrix, then the ordered pair (a, b) is equal to **[JEE Main 2015, 4M]**
(a) $(2, 1)$ (b) $(-2, -1)$ (c) $(2, -1)$ (d) $(-2, 1)$

133. Let X and Y be two arbitrary 3×3 non-zero, skew-symmetric matrices and Z be an arbitrary 3×3 non-zero, symmetric matrix. Then, which of the following matrices is (are) skew-symmetric?
[JEE Advanced 2015, 4M]
(a) $Y^3Z^4 - Z^4Y^3$ (b) $X^{44} + Y^{44}$
(c) $X^4Z^3 - Z^3X^4$ (d) $X^{23} + Y^{23}$

134. If $A = \begin{bmatrix} 5a & -b \\ 3 & 2 \end{bmatrix}$ and $A\,\text{adj}A = AA^T$, then $5a + b$ is equal to **[JEE Main 2016, 4M]**
(a) 5 (b) 13
(c) 4 (d) -1

135. Let $P = \begin{bmatrix} 3 & -1 & -2 \\ 2 & 0 & \alpha \\ 3 & -5 & 0 \end{bmatrix}$, where $\alpha \in R$. Suppose $Q = [q_{ij}]$ is a matrix such that $PQ = kI$, where $k \in R, k \neq 0$ and I is the identity matrix of order 3. If $q_{23} = -\frac{k}{8}$ and det. $(Q) = \frac{k^2}{2}$, then **[JEE Advanced 2016, 4M]**
(a) $\alpha = 0, k = 8$ (b) $4\alpha - k + 8 = 0$
(c) det $(P\text{adj}(Q)) = 2^9$ (d) det $(Q \text{ adj}(P)) = 2^{13}$

136. Let $z = \frac{-1+\sqrt{3}i}{2}$, where $i = \sqrt{-1}$, and $r, s = \{1,2,3\}$. Let $P = \begin{bmatrix} (-z)^r & z^{2s} \\ z^{2s} & z^r \end{bmatrix}$ and I be the identity matrix of oreder 2. Then the total number of ordered pairs (r, s) for which $p^2 = -I$ is **[JEE Advanced 2016, 3M]**
(a) $\frac{1}{2}|\mathbf{a} - \mathbf{b}|$ (b) $\frac{1}{2}|\mathbf{a} + \mathbf{b}|$
(c) $|\mathbf{a} - \mathbf{b}|$ (d) $|\mathbf{a} + \mathbf{b}|$

137. Let $P = \begin{bmatrix} 1 & 0 & 0 \\ 4 & 1 & 0 \\ 16 & 4 & 1 \end{bmatrix}$ and I be the identity matrix of order 3. If $Q = [q_{ij}]$ is a matrix such that $P^{50} - Q = I$, then $\frac{q_{31} + q_{32}}{q_{21}}$ equals **[JEE Advanced 2016, 3M]**
(a) 52 (b) 103
(c) 201 (d) 205

138. If $A = \begin{bmatrix} 2 & -3 \\ -4 & 1 \end{bmatrix}$, then adj $(3A^2 + 12A)$ is equal to **[JEE Main 2017, 4M]**
(a) $\begin{bmatrix} 72 & -63 \\ -84 & 51 \end{bmatrix}$ (b) $\begin{bmatrix} 72 & -84 \\ -63 & 51 \end{bmatrix}$
(c) $\begin{bmatrix} 51 & 63 \\ 84 & 72 \end{bmatrix}$ (d) $\begin{bmatrix} 51 & 84 \\ 63 & 72 \end{bmatrix}$

Answers

Exercise for Session 1

1. (b) 2. (b) 3. (d) 4. (b) 5. (a) 6. (b)
7. (b) 8. (b) 9. (c)

Exercise for Session 2

1. (d) 2. (a) 3. (c) 4. (a) 5. (b) 6. (c)
7. (d) 8. (b) 9. (d) 10. (c) 11. (b) 12. (d)
13. (b) 14. (a) 15. (b) 16. (b) 17. (c) 18. (b)
19. (b)

Exercise for Session 3

1. (d) 2. (c) 3. (b) 4. (d) 5. (a) 6. (b)
7. (d) 8. (c) 9. (a) 10. (d) 11. (c) 12. (a)
13. (d) 14. (b) 15. (a) 16. (d)

Exercise for Session 4

1. (a) 2. (a) 3. (d) 4. (d) 5. (d) 6. (d)
7. (d) 8. (b) 9. (d)

Chapter Exercises

1. (d) 2. (c) 3. (b) 4. (d) 5. (c) 6. (b)
7. (a) 8. (a) 9. (a) 10. (b) 11. (b) 12. (b)
13. (b) 14. (d) 15. (d) 16. (b) 17. (b) 18. (d)
19. (d) 20. (d) 21. (c) 22. (d) 23. (c) 24. (d)
25. (b) 26. (a) 27. (d) 28. (b) 29. (a) 30. (c)
31. (a, d) 32. (a, b, d) 33. (a, b, d) 34. (b, c)
35. (b, d) 36. (a, b, c) 37. (a, c, d) 38. (a, d)
39. (a,c,d) 40. (a, c) 41. (a, c, d) 42. (a,b,c,d)
43. (c, d) 44. (a, b, c) 45. (a, c)
46. (b) 47. (b) 48. (c) 49. (b) 50. (d) 51. (d)
52. (d) 53. (c) 54. (d) 55. (a) 56. (c) 57. (a)
58. (b) 59. (c) 60. (a) 61. (a)
62. (3) 63. (2) 64. (1) 65. (9) 66. (2) 67. (7)
68. (9) 69. (1) 70. (2) 71. (6)
72. (A) $\rightarrow$ (p, r); (B) $\rightarrow$ (s); (C) $\rightarrow$ (q); (D) $\rightarrow$ (s)
73. (A) $\rightarrow$ (r, t); (B) $\rightarrow$ (s); (C) $\rightarrow$ (p); (D) $\rightarrow$ (q)
74. (A) $\rightarrow$ (q, s); (B) $\rightarrow$ (p, t); (C) $\rightarrow$ (p, q, r, s); (D) $\rightarrow$ (q, s)
75. (A) $\rightarrow$ (q, t); (B) $\rightarrow$ (p, s); (C) $\rightarrow$ (p, r, s); (D) $\rightarrow$ (q, r, t)
76. (d) 77. (c) 78. (d) 79. (c) 80. (a) 81. (d)
82. (d) 83. (d) 84. (d) 85. (a)
88. $\alpha = \frac{2\pi}{3}$ 89. $\begin{bmatrix} \cos\theta\cos\phi\cos(\theta \sim \phi) & \cos\theta\sin\phi\cos(\theta \sim \phi) \\ \sin\theta\cos\phi\cos(\theta \sim \phi) & \sin\theta\sin\phi\cos(\theta \sim \phi) \end{bmatrix}$

91. (i) Number of posts in all the offices taken together are 5 office superintendents; 235 head clerks; 235 cashiers; 275 clerks; 5 typists and 270 peons.
(ii) Total basic monthly salary bill of each division or district and taluka offices an ₹1675, ₹875 and ₹625, respectively.
(iii) Total basic monthly salary bill of all the offices taken together is ₹ 159625.

92. ₹53000; ₹44500; ₹34000, respectively
94. $x = 1,\ u = -1,\ y = 3,\ v = 2,\ z = 5,\ w = 1$
95. $x_1 = z_1 - 2z_2 + 9z_3, x_2 = 9z_1 + 10z_2 + 11z_3, x_3 = 7z_1 + z_2 - 2z_3$
96. (i) $k \neq 7$ (ii) $k = 7$
98. (c) 99. (a) 100. (c)
101. (c) 102. (i) (a), (ii) (b), (iii) (a) 103. (b) 104. (b)
105. (c) 106. (b,d) 107. (d) 108. (c)
109. (i) (a), (ii) (b), (iii) (b)
110. (b) 111. (a)
112. (i) (d), (ii) (c), (iii) (d) 113. (4) 114. (c)
115. (b) 116. (c)
117. (i) (d), (ii) (a), (iii) (b)
118. (a) 119. (9) 120. (a) 121. (c)
122. (d) 123. (a, d) 124. (b) 125. (a) 126. (a) 127. (c,d)
128. (a,b,d) 129. (d) 130. (c, d) 131. (a, b) 132. (b) 133. (c, d)
134. (a) 135. (b,c) 136. (1) 137. (b) 138. (c)

Solutions

1. $\because \quad A^4(I-A) = A^4 I - A^5 = A^4 - 0 = A^4 \neq I$

$A^3(I-A) = A^3 I - A^4 = A^3 - A^4 \neq I$

$(I+A)(I-A) = I^2 - A^2 = I - A^2 \neq I$

2. $\because \det(B) = \begin{vmatrix} 4x & 2a & -p \\ 4y & 2b & -q \\ 4z & 2c & -r \end{vmatrix} = -8 \begin{vmatrix} x & a & p \\ y & b & q \\ z & c & r \end{vmatrix}$

$= -8 \begin{vmatrix} x & y & z \\ a & b & c \\ p & q & r \end{vmatrix} = 8 \begin{vmatrix} a & b & c \\ x & y & z \\ p & q & r \end{vmatrix}$ [by property]

$= -8 \begin{vmatrix} a & b & c \\ p & q & r \\ x & y & z \end{vmatrix} = -8 \det(A) = -16$

3. $\because \quad \left(A - \frac{1}{2}I\right)\left(A - \frac{1}{2}I\right)^T = I$ ...(i)

and $\left(A + \frac{1}{2}I\right)\left(A + \frac{1}{2}I\right)^T = I$ ...(ii)

$\Rightarrow \left(A - \frac{1}{2}I\right)\left(A^T - \frac{I}{2}\right) = I$

and $\left(A + \frac{1}{2}I\right)\left(A^T + \frac{1}{2}I\right) = I$

$\Rightarrow \quad A + A^T = 0$ [subtracting the two results]

$\Rightarrow \quad A^T = -A$

$\therefore$ A is skew-symmetric matrix.

From first result, we get

$AA^T = \frac{3}{4}I$

$\Rightarrow \quad A^2 = -\frac{3}{4}I$

$\therefore \quad |A^2| = \left|-\frac{3}{4}I\right|$

$\therefore \quad |A|^2 = \left(-\frac{3}{4}\right)^n$

$\Rightarrow$ n is even.

4. $\because \quad a = \lim_{x \to 1}\left(\frac{x}{\ln x} - \frac{1}{x \ln x}\right) = \lim_{x \to 1}\left(\frac{x^2-1}{x \ln x}\right)$

$= \lim_{x \to 1}\left(\frac{2x}{1+\ln x}\right)$ [by L'Hospital's Rule]

$b = \lim_{x \to 0}\left(\frac{x^3 - 16x}{4x + x^2}\right)$

$= \lim_{x \to 0}\left(\frac{x(x+4)(x-4)}{x(x+4)}\right) = \lim_{x \to 0}(x-4) = -4$

$c = \lim_{x \to 0} \frac{\ln(1+\sin x)}{x}$

$= \lim_{x \to 0} \frac{\ln(1+\sin x)}{\sin x} \cdot \lim_{x \to 0} \frac{\sin x}{x} = 1 \cdot 1 = 1$

$d = \lim_{x \to -1} \frac{(x+1)^3}{3[\sin(x+1) - (x+1)]}$

$= \lim_{x \to -1} \frac{3(x+1)^2}{3[\cos(x+1) - 1]}$ [using L'Hospital's Rule]

$= -\lim_{x \to -1} \frac{1}{\frac{[1-\cos(x+1)]}{(x+1)^2}} = -2$

Let, $A = \begin{bmatrix} 2 & -4 \\ 1 & -2 \end{bmatrix} \Rightarrow A^2 = 0$

5. $\because \quad (A - \lambda I)X = 0$

$\therefore \quad |A - \lambda I| = 0$

$\Rightarrow \quad \begin{vmatrix} 1-\lambda & 4 \\ 3 & 2-\lambda \end{vmatrix} = 0$

$\Rightarrow \quad \lambda^2 - 3\lambda - 10 = 0$

$\therefore \quad \lambda = -2, 5$

For $\lambda = -2 \Rightarrow \begin{bmatrix} x \\ y \end{bmatrix} = \begin{bmatrix} 4 \\ -3 \end{bmatrix}$

For $\lambda = 5 \Rightarrow \begin{bmatrix} x \\ y \end{bmatrix} = \begin{bmatrix} 1 \\ 1 \end{bmatrix}$

$\therefore \cos\theta = \frac{4 \cdot 1 + (-3) \cdot 1}{\sqrt{(16+9)}\sqrt{(1+1)}} = \frac{1}{5\sqrt{2}}$

$\therefore \tan\theta = \sqrt{(\sec^2\theta - 1)} = \sqrt{49} = 7$

6. $\because A^{2n+1} = (A^2)^n \cdot A = (I)^n \cdot A = IA = A$

7. $\because \quad A = \begin{bmatrix} \cos\theta & \sin\theta \\ -\sin\theta & \cos\theta \end{bmatrix}$

$\therefore \quad A^n = \begin{bmatrix} \cos n\theta & \sin n\theta \\ -\sin n\theta & \cos n\theta \end{bmatrix}$

$\Rightarrow \lim_{n \to \infty} \frac{A^n}{n} = \begin{bmatrix} \lim_{n \to \infty} \frac{\cos n\theta}{n} & \lim_{n \to \infty} \frac{\sin n\theta}{n} \\ -\lim_{n \to \infty} \frac{\sin n\theta}{n} & \lim_{n \to \infty} \frac{\cos n\theta}{n} \end{bmatrix} = \begin{bmatrix} 0 & 0 \\ 0 & 0 \end{bmatrix}$

= a zero matrix [$\because -1 < \sin\infty < 1$ and $-1 < \cos\infty < 1$]

8. Let $A = \begin{bmatrix} -1 & 2 & 5 \\ 2 & -4 & -10 \\ 1 & -2 & -5 \end{bmatrix}$ [$\because a = -6$]

Applying $R_2 \to R_2 + 2R_1$ and $R_3 \to R_3 + R_1$, then

$A = \begin{bmatrix} -1 & 2 & 5 \\ 0 & 0 & 0 \\ 0 & 0 & 0 \end{bmatrix} \Rightarrow \rho(A) = 1$

9. $\because$ A is involutory

$\therefore \quad A^2 = I \Rightarrow A = A^{-1}$

$\therefore \quad \left(\frac{A}{2}\right)^{-1} = 2A^{-1} = 2A$

10. $\because \quad B = \text{adj } A$

$\Rightarrow \quad AB = A(\text{adj } A) = |A| I_n$

$\therefore \quad AB + kI_n = |A| I_n + kI_n = (|A| + k) I_n$

$\Rightarrow \quad |AB + kI_n| = |(|A| + k) I_n| = (|A| + k)^n$

11. $\because \quad B = -A^{-1}BA$

$\Rightarrow \quad AB = -BA$

$\Rightarrow \quad AB + BA = 0$

Now, $(A+B)^2 = (A+B)(A+B)$

$= A^2 + AB + BA + B^2$

$= A^2 + 0 + B^2$

$= A^2 + B^2$

12. Since, A is skew-symmetric.

$\therefore \quad |A| = 0$

$\Rightarrow \quad |A^4B^3| = |A^4||B^3| = |A|^4 |B|^3 = 0$

13. Let $\quad B = A + I_n$

$\therefore \quad A = B - I_n$

Given, $\quad A^n = \alpha A$

$\Rightarrow \quad (B - I_n)^n = \alpha(B - I_n)$

$\Rightarrow \quad B^n - {}^nC_1B^{n-1} + {}^nC_2B^{n-2} + \ldots + (-1)^n I_n$

$= \alpha B - \alpha I_n$

$\Rightarrow B(B^{n-1} - {}^nC_1B^{n-2} + {}^nC_2B^{n-3} + \ldots + (-1)^{n-1} I_n - \alpha I_n)$

$= [(-1)^{n+1} - \alpha] I_n \neq 0 \quad [\because \alpha \neq \pm 1]$

Hence, B is invertible.

14. $\because \omega = \dfrac{-1 + i\sqrt{3}}{2}$ and $\omega^2 = \dfrac{-1 - i\sqrt{3}}{2}$

Also, $\omega^3 = 1$ and $\omega + \omega^2 = -1$

Thus, $A = \begin{bmatrix} -i\omega & -i\omega^2 \\ i\omega^2 & i\omega \end{bmatrix}$

$\therefore \quad A^2 = \begin{bmatrix} -i\omega & -i\omega^2 \\ i\omega^2 & i\omega \end{bmatrix}\begin{bmatrix} -i\omega & -i\omega^2 \\ i\omega^2 & i\omega \end{bmatrix} = \begin{bmatrix} -\omega^2 + \omega & 0 \\ 0 & -\omega^2 + \omega \end{bmatrix}$

Now, $f(A) = A^2 + 2I = \begin{bmatrix} -\omega^2 + \omega & 0 \\ 0 & -\omega^2 + \omega \end{bmatrix} + \begin{bmatrix} 2 & 0 \\ 0 & 2 \end{bmatrix}$

$= \begin{bmatrix} -\omega^2 + \omega + 2 & 0 \\ 0 & -\omega^2 + \omega + 2 \end{bmatrix}$

$= (-\omega^2 + \omega + 2)\begin{bmatrix} 1 & 0 \\ 0 & 1 \end{bmatrix} = (2 + i\sqrt{3})\begin{bmatrix} 1 & 0 \\ 0 & 1 \end{bmatrix}$

15. $\because \quad X^2 = I \Rightarrow (X^{-1}X)X = X^{-1}I$

$\Rightarrow \quad IX = X^{-1}$

$\Rightarrow \quad X = X^{-1}$

which is self invertible involutory matrix.

There are many such matrices which are inverse of their own.

16. $\because \quad AB = A + B$

$\Rightarrow \quad B = AB - A = A(B - I)$

$\Rightarrow \quad \det(B) = \det(A) \cdot \det(B - I) = 0$

$[\because A^{2006} = 0 \Rightarrow \det A^{2006} = 0]\ [\therefore \det A = 0]$

17. We have, $\quad P^T = P^{-1} \quad [\because PP^T = I]$

Now, $\quad Q = PAP^T = PAP^{-1}$

$\therefore \quad Q^{2007} = PA^{2007}P^{-1}$

$\therefore \quad P^TQ^{2007}P = P^{-1}(PA^{2007}P^{-1})P$

$= A^{2007} = \begin{bmatrix} 1 & 2007 \\ 0 & 1 \end{bmatrix}$

$\left[\because A^2 = \begin{bmatrix} 1 & 2 \\ 0 & 1 \end{bmatrix}, A^3 = \begin{bmatrix} 1 & 3 \\ 0 & 1 \end{bmatrix} \ldots\right]$

18. $\because \begin{bmatrix} A-5 & B \\ 2A-2 & C \end{bmatrix} = \begin{bmatrix} 2A+1 & -5 \\ -4 & A \end{bmatrix}\begin{bmatrix} 14 & D \\ E & F \end{bmatrix}$

$\Rightarrow \quad A - 5 = 28A + 14 - 5E$

$\Rightarrow \quad 5E = 27A + 19 \quad \ldots(\text{i})$

$2A - 2 = -56 + AE$

$\Rightarrow \quad AE = 2A + 54 \quad \ldots(\text{ii})$

From Eq. (i), we get

$5AE = 27A^2 + 19A$

$\Rightarrow \quad 5(2A + 54) = 27A^2 + 19A \quad$ [from Eq. (ii)]

$\Rightarrow \quad 27A^2 + 9A - 270 = 0$

$\Rightarrow \quad 9(A - 3)(3A + 10) = 0$

$\therefore \quad A = 3, A = -\dfrac{10}{3}$

$\therefore$ Absolute value of difference

$= \left|3 + \dfrac{10}{3}\right| = \dfrac{19}{3}$

19. $\because |f(\theta)| = \begin{vmatrix} \cos^2\theta & \cos\theta\sin\theta & -\sin\theta \\ \cos\theta\sin\theta & \sin^2\theta & \cos\theta \\ \sin\theta & -\cos\theta & 0 \end{vmatrix}$

On multiplying in R_3 by $\cos\theta$ and then take common $\cos\theta$ from C_1, then

$|f(\theta)| = \begin{vmatrix} \cos\theta & \cos\theta\sin\theta & -\sin\theta \\ \sin\theta & \sin^2\theta & \cos\theta \\ \sin\theta & -\cos^2\theta & 0 \end{vmatrix}$

Applying $R_2 \to R_2 - R_3$, we get

$|f(\theta)| = \begin{vmatrix} \cos\theta & \cos\theta\sin\theta & -\sin\theta \\ 0 & 1 & \cos\theta \\ \sin\theta & -\cos^2\theta & 0 \end{vmatrix} = 1$

Applying $C_2 \to C_2 - \sin\theta\, C_1$, then

$|f(\theta)| = \begin{vmatrix} \cos\theta & 0 & -\sin\theta \\ 0 & 1 & \cos\theta \\ \sin\theta & -1 & 0 \end{vmatrix} = 1$

$\therefore \quad f\left(\dfrac{\pi}{7}\right)$ is non-singular matrix.

20. $\because\ a_{11} = a_{22} = a_{33} = a + b,$

$a_{12} = a_{23} = ab, a_{21} = a_{32} = 1, a_{13} = a_{31} = 0$

$$\therefore \quad A = \begin{bmatrix} a+b & ab & 0 \\ 1 & a+b & ab \\ 0 & 1 & a+b \end{bmatrix}$$

$$\Rightarrow |A| = \begin{vmatrix} a+b & ab & 0 \\ 1 & a+b & ab \\ 0 & 1 & a+b \end{vmatrix}$$

$$= (a+b)[(a+b)^2 - ab] - ab(a+b) = (a+b)(a^2+b^2)$$

21. Given, $B^r = I \Rightarrow B^r B^{-1} = IB^{-1}$

$\Rightarrow \quad B^{r-1} = B^{-1}$

$\therefore \quad A^{-1}B^{r-1}A = A^{-1}B^{-1}A$

$\Rightarrow \quad A^{-1}B^{r-1}A - A^{-1}B^{-1}A = 0$

22. Here, $A = \begin{bmatrix} \cos\theta & \sin\theta \\ \sin\theta & -\cos\theta \end{bmatrix}$

$\Rightarrow \quad AA^T = I$

$\because \quad C = ABA^T \Rightarrow A^TC = BA^T$

Now, $A^TC^nA = A^TC \cdot C^{n-1}A$

$= BA^TC^{n-1}A = BA^TC\,C^{n-2}A$

$= B^2A^TC^{n-2}A$

... ...

$= B^{n-1}A^TCA = B^{n-1}(BA^T)A$

$= B^nA^TA = B^nI = B^n = \begin{bmatrix} 1 & 0 \\ -n & 1 \end{bmatrix}$

23. $\because\ |\text{adj } A^{-1}| = |A^{-1}|^2 = \dfrac{1}{|A|^2}$

$\therefore\ |(\text{adj } A^{-1})^{-1}| = \dfrac{1}{|\text{adj } A^{-1}|} = |A|^2 = 2^2 = 4$

24. $\because\ A^3 - A^2B = B^3 - B^2A$

$\Rightarrow \quad A^2(A - B) = B^2(B - A)$

or $\quad (A^2 + B^2)(A - B) = 0$

or $\det(A^2 + B^2) \cdot \det(A - B) = 0$

Either $\det(A^2 + B^2) = 0$ or $\det(A - B) = 0$

25. Let, $A = \begin{bmatrix} 0 & a \\ -a & 0 \end{bmatrix}$

$$BC = \begin{bmatrix} 1 & 4 \\ 2 & 9 \end{bmatrix}\begin{bmatrix} 9 & -4 \\ -2 & 1 \end{bmatrix} = \begin{bmatrix} 1 & 0 \\ 0 & 1 \end{bmatrix} = I$$

$\therefore\ B^2C^2 = (BC)^2 = I^2 = I$

Similarly, $B^2C^2 = B^3C^3 = \ldots = B^nC^n = I$

Let, $\quad D = A^3(BC) + A^5(B^2C^2) + A^7(B^3C^3) + \ldots + A^{2n+1}(B^nC^n)$

$= A^3 + A^5 + A^7 + \ldots + A^{2n+1}$

$= A(A^2 + A^4 + A^6 + \ldots + A^{2n})$

Let, $\quad A = \begin{bmatrix} 0 & a \\ -a & 0 \end{bmatrix}$

$\Rightarrow \quad A^2 = \begin{bmatrix} -a^2 & 0 \\ 0 & -a^2 \end{bmatrix} = -a^2I$

$\therefore \quad D = IA(-a^2 + a^4 - a^6 + \ldots + (-1)^n a^{2n}) \quad [a > 0]$

$= A(-a^2 + a^4 - a^6 + \ldots + (-1)^n a^{2n})$

Hence, D is skew-symmetric.

26. $\because\ |B| = \begin{vmatrix} q & -b & y \\ -p & a & -x \\ r & -c & z \end{vmatrix}$

Applying $R_2 \to (-1)R_2$, then

$$|B| = \begin{vmatrix} q & -b & y \\ p & -a & x \\ r & -c & z \end{vmatrix}$$

Applying $C_2 \to (-1)C_2$, then

$$|B| = \begin{vmatrix} q & b & y \\ p & a & x \\ r & c & z \end{vmatrix} = |B^T| = \begin{vmatrix} q & p & r \\ b & a & c \\ y & x & z \end{vmatrix}$$

$$= -\begin{vmatrix} b & a & c \\ q & p & r \\ y & x & z \end{vmatrix} \quad [R_1 \leftrightarrow R_2]$$

$$= \begin{vmatrix} b & a & c \\ y & x & z \\ q & p & r \end{vmatrix} \quad [R_2 \leftrightarrow R_3 0]$$

$$= -\begin{vmatrix} a & b & c \\ x & y & z \\ p & q & r \end{vmatrix} = -|A|$$

$\Rightarrow \quad |B| = -|A|$

Also, $|\text{adj } B| = |B|^2$

$= |A|^2 = |\text{adj } A| \quad [\because |A| \neq 0, \text{then } |B| \neq 0]$

27. $\because\ BC = \begin{bmatrix} 3 & 4 \\ 2 & 3 \end{bmatrix}\begin{bmatrix} 3 & -4 \\ -2 & 3 \end{bmatrix} = \begin{bmatrix} 1 & 0 \\ 0 & 1 \end{bmatrix} = I$

$$\therefore \quad \text{tr}(A) + \text{tr}\left(\frac{ABC}{2}\right) + \text{tr}\left(\frac{A(BC)^2}{4}\right) + \text{tr}\left(\frac{A(BC)^3}{8}\right) + \ldots$$

$$= \text{tr}(A) + \text{tr}\left(\frac{A}{2}\right) + \text{tr}\left(\frac{A}{2^2}\right) + \text{tr}\left(\frac{A}{2^3}\right) + \ldots \text{ upto } \infty$$

$$= \text{tr}(A) + \frac{1}{2}\text{tr}(A) + \frac{1}{2^2}\text{tr}(A) + \ldots \text{ upto } \infty$$

$$= \frac{\text{tr}(A)}{1 - \left(\frac{1}{2}\right)} = 2\,\text{tr}(A) = 2(2+1) = 6$$

28. We have, $\quad (A - 2I)(A - 4I) = 0$

$\Rightarrow \quad A^2 - 4A - 2A + 8I^2 = 0$

$$\Rightarrow \quad A^2 - 6A + 8I = 0$$

$$\Rightarrow \quad A^{-1}(A^2 - 6A + 8I) = A^{-1}0$$

$$\Rightarrow \quad A - 6I + 8A^{-1} = 0$$

$$\Rightarrow \quad \frac{1}{6}A + \frac{4}{3}A^{-1} = I$$

29. We have, $\quad AA^{-1} = I$

$$\Rightarrow \begin{bmatrix} 0 & 1 & 2 \\ 1 & 2 & 3 \\ 3 & a & 1 \end{bmatrix} \begin{bmatrix} \frac{1}{2} & -\frac{1}{2} & \frac{1}{2} \\ -4 & 3 & 6 \\ \frac{5}{2} & -\frac{3}{2} & \frac{1}{2} \end{bmatrix} = \begin{bmatrix} 1 & 0 & 0 \\ 0 & 1 & 0 \\ 0 & 0 & 1 \end{bmatrix}$$

$$\Rightarrow \begin{bmatrix} 1 & 0 & b+1 \\ 0 & 1 & 2(b+1) \\ 4(1-a) & 3(a-1) & ab+2 \end{bmatrix} = \begin{bmatrix} 1 & 0 & 0 \\ 0 & 1 & 0 \\ 0 & 0 & 1 \end{bmatrix}$$

On comparing, we get

$$b + 1 = 0, ab + 2 = 1, a - 1 = 0$$

$$\therefore \quad a = 1, b = -1$$

30. $\because \quad A\,(\text{adj } A) = |A|\, I \quad \text{...(i)}$

Now, $\quad |A| = \begin{vmatrix} x & 3 & 2 \\ 1 & y & 4 \\ 2 & 2 & z \end{vmatrix}$

$$= x(yz - 8) - 3(z - 8) + 2(2 - 2y)$$

$$= xyz - (8x + 4y + 3z) + 28$$

$$= 60 - 20 + 28 = 68$$

From Eq. (i), $A\,(\text{adj } A) = 68I$

31. Here, $|A| = 0$

$\therefore A^{-1}$ does not exist.

Now, $A^2 = \begin{bmatrix} 1 & 1 & 1 \\ 1 & 1 & 1 \\ 1 & 1 & 1 \end{bmatrix} \begin{bmatrix} 1 & 1 & 1 \\ 1 & 1 & 1 \\ 1 & 1 & 1 \end{bmatrix} = \begin{bmatrix} 3 & 3 & 3 \\ 3 & 3 & 3 \\ 3 & 3 & 3 \end{bmatrix} = 3A$

$$\therefore \quad A^3 = A^2 \cdot 2 = 3A \cdot A = 3A^2 = 3(3A) = 9A$$

32. $\because \quad A' = A^{-1} \Rightarrow AA' = I \quad \text{...(i)}$

Now, $\quad (A')' A' = I$

$\therefore A'$ is orthogonal

From Eq. (i), $\quad (AA')^{-1} = I^{-1}$

$$\Rightarrow \quad (A')^{-1} A^{-1} = I$$

$$\Rightarrow \quad (A^{-1})' (A^{-1}) = I$$

$\therefore A^{-1}$ is orthogonal

Since, $\quad \text{adj } A = A^{-1} |A| \neq A'$

and $\quad |A^{-1}| = \frac{1}{|A|} = \pm 1 \quad$ [for orthogonal $|A| = \pm 1$]

33. $\because A^2 = \begin{bmatrix} 1 & 2 & 2 \\ 2 & 1 & 2 \\ 2 & 2 & 1 \end{bmatrix} \begin{bmatrix} 1 & 2 & 2 \\ 2 & 1 & 2 \\ 2 & 2 & 1 \end{bmatrix} = \begin{bmatrix} 9 & 8 & 8 \\ 8 & 9 & 8 \\ 8 & 8 & 9 \end{bmatrix}$

We have, $A^2 - 4A - 5I_3$

$$= \begin{bmatrix} 9 & 8 & 8 \\ 8 & 9 & 8 \\ 8 & 8 & 9 \end{bmatrix} - 4\begin{bmatrix} 1 & 2 & 2 \\ 2 & 1 & 2 \\ 2 & 2 & 1 \end{bmatrix} - 5\begin{bmatrix} 1 & 0 & 0 \\ 0 & 1 & 0 \\ 0 & 0 & 1 \end{bmatrix}$$

$$= \begin{bmatrix} 0 & 0 & 0 \\ 0 & 0 & 0 \\ 0 & 0 & 0 \end{bmatrix} = 0$$

$$\Rightarrow \quad 5I_3 = A^2 - 4A = A(A - 4I_3)$$

$$\Rightarrow \quad I_3 = \frac{1}{5}A(A - 4I_3)$$

$$\therefore \quad A^{-1} = \frac{1}{5}(A - 4I_3)$$

Since, $\quad |A| = 5$

$$\therefore \quad |A^3| = |A|^3 = 125 \neq 0$$

$\Rightarrow A^3$ is invertible

Similarly, A^2 is invertible.

34. Let, $D = \begin{bmatrix} a & 0 & 0 \\ 0 & b & 0 \\ 0 & 0 & c \end{bmatrix} = D^T$ and let $A = \begin{bmatrix} a_1 & a_2 & a_3 \\ b_1 & b_2 & b_3 \\ c_1 & c_2 & c_3 \end{bmatrix}$

$$\therefore \quad DA = \begin{bmatrix} a & 0 & 0 \\ 0 & b & 0 \\ 0 & 0 & c \end{bmatrix} \begin{bmatrix} a_1 & a_2 & a_3 \\ b_1 & b_2 & b_3 \\ c_1 & c_2 & c_3 \end{bmatrix} = \begin{bmatrix} aa_1 & aa_2 & aa_3 \\ bb_1 & bb_2 & bb_3 \\ cc_1 & cc_2 & cc_3 \end{bmatrix}$$

$$AD = \begin{bmatrix} a_1 & a_2 & a_3 \\ b_1 & b_2 & b_3 \\ c_1 & c_2 & c_3 \end{bmatrix} \begin{bmatrix} a & 0 & 0 \\ 0 & b & 0 \\ 0 & 0 & c \end{bmatrix} = \begin{bmatrix} a_1a & a_2b & a_3c \\ b_1a & b_2b & b_3c \\ c_1a & c_2b & c_3c \end{bmatrix} \neq DA$$

and $D^{-1} = \begin{bmatrix} \frac{1}{a} & 0 & 0 \\ 0 & \frac{1}{b} & 0 \\ 0 & 0 & \frac{1}{c} \end{bmatrix}$

$$|D^{-1}| = \frac{1}{abc} \neq 0 \quad [\because a \neq 0, b \neq 0, c \neq 0]$$

35. Let $\quad A = \begin{bmatrix} -1 & 2 & 5 \\ 2 & -4 & a-4 \\ 1 & -2 & a+1 \end{bmatrix}$

Applying $R_2 \to R_2 + 2R_1$ and $R_3 \to R_3 + R_1$, then

$$A = \begin{bmatrix} -1 & 2 & 5 \\ 0 & 0 & a+6 \\ 0 & 0 & a+6 \end{bmatrix}$$

Applying $R_3 \to R_3 - R_2$, then

$$A = \begin{bmatrix} -1 & 2 & 5 \\ 0 & 0 & a+6 \\ 0 & 0 & 0 \end{bmatrix}$$

For $a = -6$, $\rho(A) = 1$

For $a = 1, 2$, $\rho(A) = 2$

36. Here, $|A| = \begin{vmatrix} 3 & -3 & 4 \\ 2 & -3 & 4 \\ 0 & -1 & 1 \end{vmatrix}$

$= 3(-3+4) + 3(2-0) + 4(-2+0) = 1 \neq 0$

$\because \quad \text{adj}(\text{adj}\, A) = |A|^{3-2} A = A$ ...(i)

and $\quad |\text{adj}(A)| = |A|^{3-1} = |A|^2 = 1^2 = 1$

Also, $|\text{adj}(\text{adj}(A))| = |A| = 1$ [from Eq. (i)]

37. $\because \quad A = I - B$

$\Rightarrow \quad A^2 = I^2 + B^2 - 2B = I - B = A$ [$\because B$ is idempotent]

and $\quad AB = B - B^2 = B - B = 0$ [null matrix]

and $\quad BA = B - B^2 = B - B = 0$ [null matrix]

38. $\because \quad |A| \neq 0 \Rightarrow A^{-1}$ is also symmetric, if A is symmetric

and $|A^{-1}| = \dfrac{1}{|A|} = |A|^{-1}$

39. $\because \; A^2B = A(AB) = A(BA) = (AB)A = (BA)A = BA^2$

Similarly, $A^3B = BA^3$

In general, $A^nB = BA^n, \; \forall \, n \geq 1$

and $\quad (A+B)^n = {}^nC_0A^n + {}^nC_1A^{n-1}B + {}^nC_2A^{n-2}B^2 + \dots + {}^nC_nB^n$

Also, $(A^n - B^n)(A^n + B^n) = A^nA^n + A^nB^n - B^nA^n - B^nB^n$

$= A^{2n} - B^{2n}$ [$\because AB = BA$]

40. $|AB| = 0 \Rightarrow |A||B| = 0$

$\therefore \quad |B| = 0$ as $|A| \neq 0$

Also, $\quad |A^{-1}| = |A|^{-1}$

41. Here, $A(A+I) = -2I$ ...(i)

$\Rightarrow \quad |A(A+I)| = |-2I| = (-2)^m \neq 0$

Thus, $\quad |A| \neq 0,$

also, $\quad I = -\dfrac{1}{2}A(A+I)$ [from Eq. (i)]

$\therefore \quad A^{-1} = -\dfrac{1}{2}(A+I)$

42. $\because \quad A^2 - 3A + 2I = 0$ ...(i)

$\Rightarrow \quad A^2 - 3AI + 2I^2 = 0$

$\Rightarrow \quad (A-I)(A-2I) = 0$

$\therefore \quad A = I$ or $A = 2I$

Characteristic Eq. (i) is

$\lambda^2 - 3\lambda + 2 = 0 \Rightarrow \lambda = 1, 2$

It is clear that alternate (c) and (d) have the characteristic equation $\lambda^2 - 3\lambda + 2 = 0$.

43. $\because \quad AB = 0$

$\Rightarrow \quad |AB| = 0 \Rightarrow |A||B| = 0$

or $\quad (\det A)(\det B) = 0$

$\Rightarrow$ Either $\det A = 0$ or $\det B = 0$

Hence, atleast one of the two matrices must be singular otherwise this statement is not possible.

44. Let $D_1 = \begin{bmatrix} d_1 & 0 & 0 \\ 0 & d_2 & 0 \\ 0 & 0 & d_3 \end{bmatrix}$ and $D_2 = \begin{bmatrix} d_4 & 0 & 0 \\ 0 & d_5 & 0 \\ 0 & 0 & d_6 \end{bmatrix}$

$\therefore \; D_1D_2 = \begin{bmatrix} d_1d_4 & 0 & 0 \\ 0 & d_2d_5 & 0 \\ 0 & 0 & d_3d_6 \end{bmatrix} = D_2D_1$

and $\; D_1^2 + D_2^2 = \begin{bmatrix} d_1^2 & 0 & 0 \\ 0 & d_2^2 & 0 \\ 0 & 0 & d_3^2 \end{bmatrix} + \begin{bmatrix} d_4^2 & 0 & 0 \\ 0 & d_5^2 & 0 \\ 0 & 0 & d_6^2 \end{bmatrix}$

$= \begin{bmatrix} d_1^2 + d_4^2 & 0 & 0 \\ 0 & d_2^2 + d_5^2 & 0 \\ 0 & 0 & d_3^2 + d_6^2 \end{bmatrix}$

45. $A_1 + A_2 + A_3 + \dots + A_n = \begin{bmatrix} C_0^2 & 0 \\ 0 & C_1^2 \end{bmatrix} + \begin{bmatrix} C_1^2 & 0 \\ 0 & C_2^2 \end{bmatrix} + \begin{bmatrix} C_2^2 & 0 \\ 0 & C_3^2 \end{bmatrix} + \dots + \begin{bmatrix} C_{n-1}^2 & 0 \\ 0 & C_n^2 \end{bmatrix}$

$= \begin{bmatrix} C_0^2 + C_1^2 + C_2^2 + \dots + C_{n-1}^2 & 0 \\ 0 & C_1^2 + C_2^2 + C_3^2 + \dots + C_n^2 \end{bmatrix}$

$= \begin{bmatrix} {}^{2n}C_n - 1 & 0 \\ 0 & {}^{2n}C_n - 1 \end{bmatrix} = \begin{bmatrix} k_1 & 0 \\ 0 & k_2 \end{bmatrix}$ [given]

$\therefore \quad k_1 = k_2 = {}^{2n}C_n - 1$

Passage (Q. Nos. 46 to 48)

$\because \quad AB = BA^m$

$\Rightarrow \quad B = A^{-1}BA^m$

$\therefore \quad B^n = \underbrace{(A^{-1}BA^m)(A^{-1}BA^m)\dots(A^{-1}BA^m)}_{n \text{ times}}$

$= A^{-1}\underbrace{BA^{m-1}BA^{m-1}\dots BA^{m-1}BA^{m-1}}_{n \text{ times}}A$ ...(i)

Given, $\quad AB = BA^m$

$\Rightarrow \quad AAB = ABA^m = BA^{2m} \Rightarrow AAAB = BA^{3m}$

Similarly, $\quad A^xB = BA^{mx} \; \forall \, m \in N$

From Eq. (i), we get

$B^n = A^{-1}BA^{m-1}\underbrace{BA^{m-1}BA^{m-1}\dots BA^{m-1}BA^{m-1}}_{(n-1) \text{ times}}A$

$= A^{-1}B(A^{m-1}B)A^{m-1}\underbrace{BA^{m-1}\dots BA^{m-1}BA^{m-1}}_{(n-2) \text{ times}}A$

$= A^{-1}BBA^{(m-1)m}A^{m-1}\underbrace{BA^{m-1}\dots BA^{m-1}BA^{m-1}}_{(n-2) \text{ times}}A$

$= A^{-1}B^2A^{(m^2-1)}\underbrace{BA^{m-1}\dots BA^{m-1}BA^{m-1}}_{(n-2) \text{ times}}A$

... ...

$= A^{-1}B^m(A)^{(m^n-1)}A$

$I = A^{-1}IA^{(m^n-1)}A$ [$\because B^n = I$]

$I = A^{-1}A^{(m^n-1)}A = A^{-1}A^{m^n}$

$\Rightarrow \quad I = A^{(m^n-1)}$

$\therefore \quad p = m^n - 1$ ...(ii) [$\because A^p = I$]

46. Put $m = 2, n = 5$ in Eq. (ii), we get

$$p = 2^5 - 1 = 31$$

47. From Eq. (ii), we get

$$p = m^n - 1$$

48. From Eq. (ii), we get

$$510 \neq 8^3 - 1$$

Passage (Q. Nos. 49 to 51)

$\because$ A is an orthogonal matrix

$$\therefore \quad AA^T = I$$

$$\begin{bmatrix} a & b & c \\ b & c & a \\ c & a & b \end{bmatrix}\begin{bmatrix} a & b & c \\ b & c & a \\ c & a & b \end{bmatrix} = 1\begin{bmatrix} 1 & 0 & 0 \\ 0 & 1 & 0 \\ 0 & 0 & 1 \end{bmatrix}$$

$$\begin{bmatrix} a^2+b^2+c^2 & ab+bc+ca & ab+bc+ca \\ ab+bc+ca & a^2+b^2+c^2 & ab+bc+ca \\ ab+bc+ca & ab+bc+ca & a^2+b^2+c^2 \end{bmatrix} = \begin{bmatrix} 1 & 0 & 0 \\ 0 & 1 & 0 \\ 0 & 0 & 1 \end{bmatrix}$$

By equality of matrices, we get

$$a^2 + b^2 + c^2 = 1 \quad \text{...(i)}$$

$$ab + bc + ca = 0 \quad \text{...(ii)}$$

$$(a+b+c)^2 + a^2 = b^2 + c^2 + 2(ab+bc+ca)$$

$$= 1 + 0 = 1$$

$$\therefore \quad a + b + c = \pm 1 \quad \text{...(iii)}$$

49. $\because a^2b^2 + b^2c^2 + c^2a^2 = (ab+bc+ca)^2 - 2abc(a+b+c)$

$$= 0 - 2abc(\pm 1) = \mp 2\lambda \quad [\because abc = \lambda]$$

$$= -2\lambda \quad [\because \lambda < 0]$$

50. $\because a^3 + b^3 + c^3 - 3abc = (a+b+c)(a^2+b^2+c^2-ab-bc-ca)$

$$\Rightarrow a^3 + b^3 + c^3 - 3\lambda = (\pm 1)(1-0)$$

[from Eqs. (i), (ii) and (iii) and $abc = \lambda$]

$$\Rightarrow a^3 + b^3 + c^3 = 3\lambda \pm 1$$

51. Equation whose roots are a, b, c is

$$x^3 - (a+b+c)x^2 + (ab+bc+ca)x - abc = 0$$

$$\Rightarrow x^3 - (\pm 1)x^2 + 0 - \lambda = 0$$

$$\therefore x^3 \pm x^2 - \lambda = 0$$

Passage (Q. Nos. 52 to 53)

$$\therefore \quad A = \begin{bmatrix} a_{11} & a_{12} & a_{13} \\ a_{21} & a_{22} & a_{23} \\ a_{31} & a_{32} & a_{33} \end{bmatrix}$$

$$\Rightarrow t_1 = \frac{a_{11} + a_{12} + a_{13}}{3} = 0, \quad [\because a_{ij} + a_{jk} + a_{ki} = 0]$$

$$t_2 = \frac{a_{21} + a_{22} + a_{23}}{3} = 0$$

and
$$t_3 = \frac{a_{31} + a_{32} + a_{33}}{3} = 0$$

52. $\sum_{1 \le i,} \sum_{j \le 3} a_{ij} = 3(t_1 + t_2 + t_3) = 0 = t_1 + t_2 + t_3$

$$\neq t_1 t_2 t_3 \quad [\because t_1 = 0, t_2 = 0, t_3 = 0]$$

and
$$\det A = \begin{vmatrix} a_{11} & a_{12} & a_{13} \\ a_{21} & a_{22} & a_{23} \\ a_{31} & a_{32} & a_{33} \end{vmatrix}$$

Applying $C_1 \to C_1 + C_2 + C_3$, we get

$$= \begin{vmatrix} 0 & a_{12} & a_{13} \\ 0 & a_{22} & a_{23} \\ 0 & a_{32} & a_{33} \end{vmatrix} = 0$$

$$\therefore \quad (\det A)^2 = 0$$

53. $\because$ $a_{11} + a_{11} + a_{11} = 0, a_{11} + a_{12} + a_{21} = 0,$

$a_{11} + a_{13} + a_{31} = 0, a_{22} + a_{22} + a_{22} = 0,$

$a_{22} + a_{12} + a_{21} = 0, a_{22} + a_{23} + a_{32} = 0,$

$a_{33} + a_{13} + a_{31} = 0, a_{33} + a_{23} + a_{32} = 0$

and $a_{33} + a_{12} + a_{21} = 0$, we get

$a_{11} = a_{22} = a_{33} = 0$

and $a_{12} = -a_{21}, a_{23} = -a_{32}, a_{13} = -a_{31}$

Hence, A is skew-symmetric matrix.

Passage (Q. Nos. 54 to 56)

Let
$$B = \begin{bmatrix} \alpha_1 & \beta_1 & \gamma_1 \\ \alpha_2 & \beta_2 & \gamma_2 \\ \alpha_3 & \beta_3 & \gamma_3 \end{bmatrix}$$

$$\therefore \quad C_1 = \begin{bmatrix} \alpha_1 \\ \alpha_2 \\ \alpha_3 \end{bmatrix}, C_2 = \begin{bmatrix} \beta_1 \\ \beta_2 \\ \beta_3 \end{bmatrix} \text{ and } C_3 = \begin{bmatrix} \gamma_1 \\ \gamma_2 \\ \gamma_3 \end{bmatrix}$$

$$\Rightarrow \quad AC_1 = \begin{bmatrix} \alpha_1 \\ 2\alpha_1 + \alpha_2 \\ 3\alpha_1 + 2\alpha_2 + \alpha_3 \end{bmatrix} = \begin{bmatrix} 1 \\ 0 \\ 0 \end{bmatrix}$$

$$\Rightarrow \quad \alpha_1 = 1, \alpha_2 = -2, \alpha_3 = 1$$

$$\Rightarrow \quad AC_2 = \begin{bmatrix} \beta_1 \\ 2\beta_1 + \beta_2 \\ 3\beta_1 + 2\beta_2 + \beta_3 \end{bmatrix} = \begin{bmatrix} 2 \\ 3 \\ 0 \end{bmatrix}$$

$$\Rightarrow \quad \beta_1 = 2, \beta_2 = -1, \beta_3 = -4$$

and
$$AC_3 = \begin{bmatrix} \gamma_1 \\ 2\gamma_1 + \gamma_2 \\ 3\gamma_1 + 2\gamma_2 + \gamma_3 \end{bmatrix} = \begin{bmatrix} 2 \\ 3 \\ 1 \end{bmatrix}$$

$$\Rightarrow \quad \gamma_1 = 2, \gamma_2 = -1, \gamma_3 = -3$$

$$\therefore \quad B = \begin{bmatrix} 1 & 2 & 2 \\ -2 & -1 & -1 \\ 1 & -4 & -3 \end{bmatrix}$$

$$\Rightarrow \quad \det B = \begin{vmatrix} 1 & 2 & 2 \\ -2 & -1 & -1 \\ 1 & -4 & -3 \end{vmatrix}$$

$$= 1(3-4) - 2(6+1) + 2(8+1) = 3$$

and
$$C = \frac{1}{3}\begin{bmatrix} 1 & 0 & 0 \\ 2 & 1 & 0 \\ 3 & 2 & 1 \end{bmatrix}\begin{bmatrix} 1 & 2 & 2 \\ -2 & -1 & -1 \\ 1 & -4 & -3 \end{bmatrix}$$

$$= \frac{1}{3}\begin{bmatrix} 1 & 2 & 2 \\ 0 & 3 & 3 \\ 0 & 0 & 1 \end{bmatrix}$$

$$\therefore \quad \det C = \begin{vmatrix} \frac{1}{3} & \frac{2}{3} & \frac{2}{3} \\ 0 & 1 & 1 \\ 0 & 0 & \frac{1}{3} \end{vmatrix} = \frac{1}{9}$$

54. $\det(B^{-1}) = \dfrac{1}{\det B} = \dfrac{1}{3}$

55. $\dfrac{\text{Trace of } B}{\text{Trace of } C} = \dfrac{(-3)}{\left(\frac{5}{3}\right)} = -\dfrac{9}{5}$

56. $\sin^{-1}(\det A) + \tan^{-1}(9\det C) = \sin^{-1}(1) + \tan^{-1}(1)$

$$= \frac{\pi}{2} + \frac{\pi}{4} = \frac{3\pi}{4}$$

Passage (Q. Nos. 57 to 59)

Given, $A^T = A,\ B^T = -B,\ \det(A + B) \neq 0$

and $\quad C = (A + B)^{-1}(A - B)$

$\Rightarrow \quad (A + B)C = A - B \quad$ ...(i)

Also, $\quad (A + B)^T = A - B \quad$ ...(ii)

and $\quad (A - B)^T = A + B \quad$ ...(iii)

57. $C^T(A + B)C = C^T[(A + B)C]$

$= C^T(A - B) \quad$ [from Eq. (i)]

$= C^T(A + B)^T \quad$ [from Eq. (ii)]

$= [(A + B)C]^T$

$= (A - B)^T \quad$ [from Eq. (i)]

$= A + B \quad$ [from Eq. (iii)]

58. $C^T(A - B)C = [C^T(A + B)^T]C \quad$ [from Eq. (ii)]

$= [(A + B)C]^T C$

$= (A - B)^T C \quad$ [from Eq. (i)]

$= (A + B)C \quad$ [from Eq. (iii)]

$= A - B \quad$ [from Eq. (i)]

59. $C^T AC = C^T\left(\dfrac{A + B + A - B}{2}\right)C$

$= \dfrac{1}{2}C^T(A + B)C + \dfrac{1}{2}C^T(A - B)C$

$= \dfrac{1}{2}(A + B) + \dfrac{1}{2}(A - B) \quad$ [from Q13 and Q15]

$= A$

Passage (Q. Nos. 60 to 61)

$\because \quad B = A - 2I$

$\therefore \quad A^{-1}B = I - 2A^{-1} \quad$ ...(i)

60. $\det[\text{adj}(I - 2A^{-1})] = \det[\text{adj}(A^{-1}B)] \quad$ [from Eq. (i)]

$= |\text{adj}(A^{-1}B)|$

$= |A^{-1}B|^2 = (|A^{-1}||B|)^2 = \left(\dfrac{|B|}{|A|}\right)^2 \quad$ ...(ii)

From Eq. (i), we get $B = A - 2I$

$\therefore \quad B^3 = (A - 2I)^3 = A^3 - 6A^2 + 12A - 8I$

$= 5A \quad [\because A^3 - 6A^2 + 7A - 8I = 0]$

$\Rightarrow \quad |B^3| = |5A|$

$\Rightarrow \quad |B|^3 = 5^3|A|$

$\Rightarrow \quad |B|^3 = 5^3 \times 8$

$\Rightarrow \quad |B|^3 = (10)^3$

$\therefore \quad |B| = 10$

From Eq. (ii), we get

$$\det[\text{adj}(I - 2A^{-1})] = \left(\frac{|B|}{|A|}\right)^2 = \left(\frac{10}{8}\right)^2 = \frac{25}{16}$$

61. $\text{adj}\left[\left(\dfrac{B}{2}\right)^{-1}\right] = \dfrac{\frac{B}{2}}{\left|\frac{B}{2}\right|} = \dfrac{\frac{B}{2}}{\frac{1}{8}|B|} = \dfrac{4B}{|B|} = \dfrac{4}{10}B \quad [\because |B| = 10]$

$= \dfrac{2}{5}B = \dfrac{p}{q}B \quad$ [given]

$\therefore \quad p = 2$ and $q = 5$

Hence, $\quad p + q = 7$

62. $S = ABCD = A(BCD) = AA^T \quad$ ...(i)

$\therefore \quad S^3 = (ABCD)(ABCD)(ABCD)$

$= (ABC)(DAB)(CDA)(BCD)$

$= D^T C^T B^T A^T = (BCD)^T A^T$

$= (A^T)^T A^T = AA^T = S$

$\Rightarrow \quad S^3 = S$

Hence, least value of k is 3.

63. $\because \quad A = \begin{bmatrix} 1 & \tan x \\ -\tan x & 1 \end{bmatrix}$

$\therefore \quad \det A = \begin{vmatrix} 1 & \tan x \\ -\tan x & 1 \end{vmatrix} = (1 + \tan^2 x) = {}^2 x$

$\Rightarrow \quad \det A^T = \det A = \sec^2 x$

Now, $\quad f(x) = \det(A^T A^{-1}) = (\det A^T)(\det A^{-1})$

$= (\det A^T)(\det A)^{-1} = \dfrac{\det A^T}{\det A} = 1$

$\therefore \quad \lambda = \underbrace{f(f(f(f \ldots f(x))))}_{n \text{ times}} = 1 \quad [\because f(x) = 1]$

Hence, $\quad 2^\lambda = 2^1 = 2$

64. $\because A^2 = A \cdot A = \begin{bmatrix} \lambda_1^2 & \lambda_1\lambda_2 & \lambda_1\lambda_3 \\ \lambda_2\lambda_1 & \lambda_2^2 & \lambda_2\lambda_3 \\ \lambda_3\lambda_1 & \lambda_3\lambda_2 & \lambda_3^2 \end{bmatrix}\begin{bmatrix} \lambda_1^2 & \lambda_1\lambda_2 & \lambda_1\lambda_3 \\ \lambda_2\lambda_1 & \lambda_2^2 & \lambda_2\lambda_3 \\ \lambda_3\lambda_1 & \lambda_3\lambda_2 & \lambda_3^2 \end{bmatrix}$

$$= \begin{bmatrix} \lambda_1^2(\lambda_1^2 + \lambda_2^2 + \lambda_3^2) & \lambda_1\lambda_2(\lambda_1^2 + \lambda_2^2 + \lambda_3^2) & \lambda_1\lambda_3(\lambda_1^2 + \lambda_2^2 + \lambda_3^2) \\ \lambda_1\lambda_2(\lambda_1^2 + \lambda_2^2 + \lambda_3^2) & \lambda_2^2(\lambda_1^2 + \lambda_2^2 + \lambda_3^2) & \lambda_2\lambda_3(\lambda_1^2 + \lambda_2^2 + \lambda_3^2) \\ \lambda_1\lambda_3(\lambda_1^2 + \lambda_2^2 + \lambda_3^2) & \lambda_3\lambda_2(\lambda_1^2 + \lambda_2^2 + \lambda_3^2) & \lambda_3^2(\lambda_1^2 + \lambda_2^2 + \lambda_3^2) \end{bmatrix}$$

$$= (\lambda_1^2 + \lambda_2^2 + \lambda_3^2) A$$

Given, A is idempotent

$\Rightarrow \quad A^2 = A$

$\therefore \quad \lambda_1^2 + \lambda_2^2 + \lambda_3^2 = 1$

65. Let $X = \begin{bmatrix} x_1 \\ x_2 \\ x_3 \end{bmatrix}$ and given $X^T AX = O$

$$\Rightarrow \quad [x_1\ x_2\ x_3] \begin{bmatrix} a_{11} & a_{12} & a_{13} \\ a_{21} & a_{22} & a_{23} \\ a_{31} & a_{32} & a_{33} \end{bmatrix} \begin{bmatrix} x_1 \\ x_2 \\ x_3 \end{bmatrix} = O$$

$$\Rightarrow \quad [x_1\ x_2\ x_3] \begin{bmatrix} a_{11}x_1 + a_{12}x_2 + a_{13}x_3 \\ a_{21}x_1 + a_{22}x_2 + a_{23}x_3 \\ a_{31}x_1 + a_{32}x_2 + a_{33}x_3 \end{bmatrix} = O$$

$$\Rightarrow a_{11}x_1^2 + a_{12}x_1x_2 + a_{13}x_1x_3 + a_{21}x_1x_2 + a_{22}x_2^2 + a_{23}x_2x_3 + a_{31}x_1x_3 + a_{32}x_2x_3 + a_{33}x_3^2 = 0$$

$$\Rightarrow a_{11}x_1^2 + a_{22}x_2^2 + a_{33}x_3^2 + (a_{12} + a_{21})x_1x_2 + (a_{23} + a_{32})x_2x_3 + (a_{31} + a_{13})x_3x_1 = 0$$

it is true for every x_1, x_2, x_3, then

$$a_{11} = a_{22} = a_{33} = 0 \text{ and } a_{12} = -a_{21}, a_{23} = -a_{32}, a_{13} = -a_{31}$$

Now, as $a_{23} = -1008 \Rightarrow a_{32} = 1008$

$\therefore$ Sum of digits $= 1 + 0 + 0 + 8 = 9$

66. $\because A = \begin{bmatrix} 0 & 1 & -1 \\ 4 & -3 & 4 \\ 3 & -3 & 4 \end{bmatrix}$

$$\therefore \quad A^2 = A \cdot A = \begin{bmatrix} 0 & 1 & -1 \\ 4 & -3 & 4 \\ 3 & -3 & 4 \end{bmatrix} \begin{bmatrix} 0 & 1 & -1 \\ 4 & -3 & 4 \\ 3 & -3 & 4 \end{bmatrix} = \begin{bmatrix} 1 & 0 & 0 \\ 0 & 1 & 0 \\ 0 & 0 & 1 \end{bmatrix} = I$$

$\Rightarrow A^2 = I \Rightarrow A^4 = A^6 = A^8 = \ldots = I$

Now, $\quad A^x = I$

$\Rightarrow \quad x = 2, 4, 6, 8, \ldots$

$$\therefore \sum (\cos^x \theta + \sin^x \theta) = (\cos^2 \theta + \sin^2 \theta) + (\cos^4 \theta + \sin^4 \theta) + (\cos^6 \theta + \sin^6 \theta) + \ldots$$

$$= (\cos^2 \theta + \cos^4 \theta + \cos^6 \theta + \ldots) + (\sin^2 \theta + \sin^4 \theta + \sin^6 \theta + \ldots)$$

$$= \frac{\cos^2 \theta}{1 - \cos^2 \theta} + \frac{\sin^2 \theta}{1 - \sin^2 \theta}$$

$$= \cot^2 \theta + \tan^2 \theta \geq 2$$

Hence, minimum value of $\sum (\cos^x \theta + \sin^x \theta)$ is 2.

67. $\because A$ is idempotent matrix

$\therefore \quad A^2 = A$

$\Rightarrow \quad A = A^2 = A^3 = A^4 = A^5 = \ldots \quad \ldots$(i)

Now, $(A + I)^n = (I + A)^n$

$$= I + {}^nC_1 A + {}^nC_2 A^2 + {}^nC_3 A^3 + \ldots + {}^nC_n A^n$$

$$= I + ({}^nC_1 + {}^nC_2 + {}^nC_3 + \ldots + {}^nC_n) A$$

[from Eq.(i)]

$\Rightarrow \quad (A + I)^n = I + (2^n - 1)A \quad \ldots$(ii)

Given, we get

$(A + I)^n = I + 127 A \quad \ldots$(iii)

From Eqs (ii) and (iii), we get

$2^n - 1 = 127$

$\Rightarrow \quad 2^n = 128 = 2^7$

$\therefore \quad n = 7$

68. $\because \quad A = \begin{bmatrix} 3a & b & c \\ b & 3c & a \\ c & a & 3b \end{bmatrix}$

$$\therefore \det(A) = \begin{vmatrix} 3a & b & c \\ b & 3c & a \\ c & a & 3b \end{vmatrix} = 29abc - 3(a^3 + b^3 + c^3)$$

Or

$|A| = 29abc - 3(a^3 + b^3 + c^3) \quad \ldots$(i)

Given, $\quad A^T A = 4^{1/3} I$

$\Rightarrow \quad |A^T A| = |4^{1/3} I|$

$\Rightarrow \quad |A^T||A| = (4^{1/3})^3 |I|$

$\Rightarrow \quad |A||A| = 4 \cdot 1$

$\Rightarrow \quad |A|^2 = 4$

$\therefore \quad |A| = 2 \quad [\because |A| > 0]$

From Eq.(i), we get

$2 = 29abc - 3(a^3 + b^3 + c^3)$

$\Rightarrow \quad 2 = 29 - 3(a^3 + b^3 + c^3) \quad [\because abc = 1]$

$\therefore \quad a^3 + b^3 + c^3 = 9$

69. $\because \quad A = \begin{bmatrix} 0 & 1 \\ 3 & 0 \end{bmatrix}$

$$\therefore A^2 = A \cdot A = \begin{bmatrix} 0 & 1 \\ 3 & 0 \end{bmatrix} \begin{bmatrix} 0 & 1 \\ 3 & 0 \end{bmatrix} = \begin{bmatrix} 3 & 0 \\ 0 & 3 \end{bmatrix} = 3I$$

$\Rightarrow \quad A^4 = (A^2)^2 = 9I, A^6 = 27I, A^8 = 81I$

Now, $(A^8 + A^6 + A^4 + A^2 + I)V = (121)IV = (121)V \quad \ldots$(i)

Given, $(A^8 + A^6 + A^4 + A^2 + I)V = \begin{bmatrix} 0 \\ 11 \end{bmatrix} \quad \ldots$(ii)

From Eqs.(i) and (ii), $(121)V = \begin{bmatrix} 0 \\ 11 \end{bmatrix} \Rightarrow V = \begin{bmatrix} 0 \\ \frac{1}{11} \end{bmatrix}$

$\therefore$ Sum of elements of $V = 0 + \frac{1}{11} = \frac{1}{11} = \lambda \quad$ [given]

$\therefore \quad 11\lambda = 1$

70. $\because A = \begin{bmatrix} 3 & 2 \\ 2 & 1 \end{bmatrix}$ and $B = \begin{bmatrix} 3 & 1 \\ 7 & 3 \end{bmatrix}$

$\therefore \quad \det A = -1$ and $\det B = 2$

Now, $\det(2A^9 B^{-1}) = 2^2 \cdot \det(A^9) \cdot \det(B^{-1})$

$$= 2^2 \cdot (\det A)^9 \cdot (\det B)^{-1}$$

$$= 2^2 \cdot (-1)^9 \cdot (2)^{-1} = -2$$

Hence, absolute value of $\det(2A^9B^{-1}) = 2$

71. $\because$ $$A=\begin{bmatrix}0 & \alpha\\ 0 & 0\end{bmatrix}$$

$\therefore$ $$A^2 = A\cdot A=\begin{bmatrix}0 & \alpha\\ 0 & 0\end{bmatrix}\begin{bmatrix}0 & \alpha\\ 0 & 0\end{bmatrix}=\begin{bmatrix}0 & 0\\ 0 & 0\end{bmatrix}=0$$

$\Rightarrow$ $$A^2 = A^3 = A^4 = A^5 = \dots = 0$$

Now, $(A+I)^{70} = (I+A)^{70}$

$$= I + {}^{70}C_1\, A + {}^{70}C_2\, A^2 + {}^{70}C_3\, A^3 + \dots + {}^{70}C_{70}\, A^{70}$$

$$= I + 70\,A + 0 + 0 + \dots = I + 70A$$

$\Rightarrow (A+I)^{70} - 70A = I = \begin{bmatrix}1 & 0\\ 0 & 1\end{bmatrix} = \begin{bmatrix}a-1 & b-1\\ c-1 & d-1\end{bmatrix}$ [given]

$\therefore$ $a-1=1, b-1=0, c-1=0, d-1=1$

$\Rightarrow$ $a=2, b=1, c=1, d=2$

Hence, $a+b+c+d=6$

72. (A) $\to$ (p, r); (B) $\to$ (s); (C) $\to$ (q); (D) $\to$ (s)

On comparing, we get

$$\{4f(-1)-3\}a^2 + \{4f(1)-3\}a + f(2) = 0$$

$$\{4f(-1)-3\}b^2 + \{4f(1)-3\}b + f(2) = 0,$$

and $$\{4f(-1)-3\}c^2 + \{4f(1)-3\}C + f(2) = 0$$

It is clear that a, b, c are the roots of

$$\{4f(-1)-3\}x^2 + \{4f(1)-3\}x + f(2) = 0, \text{ then}$$

$$4f(-1)-3=0, 4f(1)-3=0, f(2)=0$$

$\Rightarrow$ $$f(-1)=\frac{3}{4}, f(1)=\frac{3}{4}, f(2)=0$$

Let $f(x)=(x-2)(ax+b)$

Now, $f(-1)=\frac{3}{4} \Rightarrow (-3)(-a+b)=\frac{3}{4} \Rightarrow a-b=\frac{1}{4}$

$f(1)=\frac{3}{4} \Rightarrow (-1)(a+b)=\frac{3}{4} \Rightarrow a+b=-\frac{3}{4}$

$\therefore$ $a=-\frac{1}{4}, b=-\frac{1}{2}$

$\Rightarrow$ $f(x)=\frac{1}{4}(4-x^2)$

Graph of $y=f(x)$

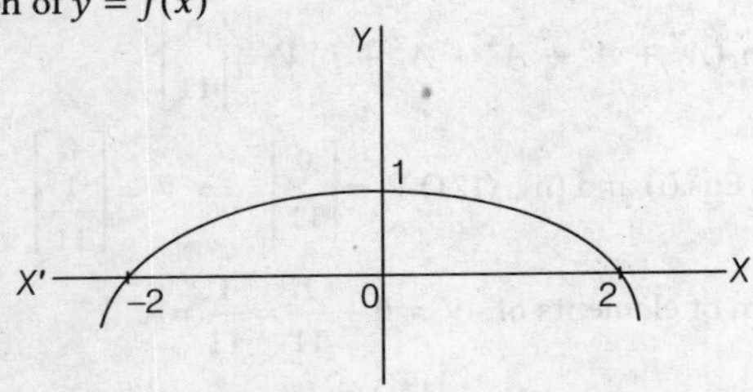

(A) x-coordinates of the point intersection of $y=f(x)$ with the X-axis are -2 and 2.

(B) Area $=\frac{3}{2}\int_{-2}^{2}\frac{1}{4}(4-x^2)dx=\frac{3}{4}\int_0^2(4-x^2)dx$

$$=\frac{3}{4}\left[4x-\frac{x^3}{3}\right]_0^2=\frac{3}{4}\times\frac{16}{3}=4$$

(C) Maximum value of $f(x)$ is 1.

(D) Length of intercept on the X-axis is 4.

73. (A) $\to$ (r, t); (B) $\to$ (s); (C) $\to$ (p); (D) $\to$ (q)

(A) $\text{adj}(A^{-1}) = (A^{-1})^{-1}\det(A^{-1}) = \frac{A}{\det(A)}$

Also, $$\frac{\text{adj adj } A}{(\text{adj } A)^{n-1}} = \frac{A[\det(A)]^{n-2}}{(\det A)^{n-1}} = \frac{A}{\det(A)}$$

(B) $\det(\text{adj } A^{-1})) = (\det A^{-1})^{n-1}$

$$= \frac{1}{(\det A)^{n-1}} = (\det A)^{1-n}$$

(C) $\text{adj}[\text{adj } A] = A(\det A)^{n-2}$

(D) $\text{adj}(A\det A) = (\det A)^{n-1}(\text{adj } A)$

74. (A)$\to$(q, s); (B)$\to$(p, t); (C)$\to$(p, q, r, s); (D)$\to$(q, s)

(A) A diagonal matrix is commutative with every square matrix, if it is scalar matrix, so every diagonal element is 4.

Therefore, $|A| = \begin{vmatrix}4 & 0 & 0\\ 0 & 4 & 0\\ 0 & 0 & 4\end{vmatrix} = 64$

(B) $$\begin{vmatrix}1-a & 1 & 1\\ 1 & 1-b & 1\\ 1 & 1 & 1-c\end{vmatrix} = 0$$

Applying $R_1 \to R_1 - R_3$ and $R_2 \to R_2 - R_3$, then

$$\begin{vmatrix}-a & 0 & c\\ 0 & -b & c\\ 1 & 1 & 1-c\end{vmatrix} = 0$$

$\Rightarrow$ $-a(-b+bc-c) - 0 + c(b) = 0$

$$ab+bc+ca = abc \quad \text{...(i)}$$

Now, $AM \ge GM$

$\Rightarrow$ $\frac{ab+bc+ca}{3} \ge (ab\cdot bc\cdot ca)^{\frac{1}{3}}$

$\Rightarrow$ $\frac{abc}{3} \ge (abc)^{\frac{2}{3}}$ [from Eq. (i)]

$\Rightarrow$ $(abc)^{\frac{1}{3}} \ge 3$

$\therefore$ $abc \ge 27$

Hence, $\lambda = 27$

(C) $\because$ $$A = \begin{bmatrix}a_{11} & a_{12} & a_{13}\\ a_{21} & a_{22} & a_{23}\\ a_{31} & a_{32} & a_{33}\end{bmatrix}$$

Given, $\sum_{k=1}^{3} a_{ik} = 9\lambda_i, \forall\, i \in \{1, 2, 3\}$;

$\sum_{k=1}^{3} a_{kj} = 9\mu_j\ \forall\, j \in \{1, 2, 3\}$ and

$a_{11} + a_{22} + a_{33} = 9\upsilon$; where $\lambda_i, \mu_j, v \in \{1, 2\}$

Following types of matrices are possible:

$$A = \begin{bmatrix}1 & & \\ & 3 & \\ & & 5\end{bmatrix}; B = \begin{bmatrix}2 & & \\ & 3 & \\ & & 4\end{bmatrix}; C = \begin{bmatrix}7 & & \\ & 3 & \\ & & 8\end{bmatrix};$$

$$D = \begin{bmatrix}6 & & \\ & 3 & \\ & & 9\end{bmatrix}; E = \begin{bmatrix}1 & & \\ & 6 & \\ & & 2\end{bmatrix}; F = \begin{bmatrix}3 & & \\ & 6 & \\ & & 9\end{bmatrix};$$

$$G=\begin{bmatrix}4&&\\&6&\\&&8\end{bmatrix}; H=\begin{bmatrix}5&&\\&6&\\&&7\end{bmatrix}; I=\begin{bmatrix}1&&\\&9&\\&&8\end{bmatrix};$$

$$J=\begin{bmatrix}2&&\\&9&\\&&7\end{bmatrix}; K=\begin{bmatrix}3&&\\&9&\\&&6\end{bmatrix}; L=\begin{bmatrix}4&&\\&9&\\&&5\end{bmatrix}$$

Now, if we interchange 1 and 5 to obtain

$$A_1=\begin{bmatrix}5&4&9\\7&3&8\\6&2&1\end{bmatrix}$$

Also, $$A^T=\begin{bmatrix}1&8&9\\2&3&4\\6&7&5\end{bmatrix}$$

and $$A_1^T=\begin{bmatrix}5&7&6\\4&3&2\\9&8&1\end{bmatrix}$$

Then, from A we get four matrices A, A_1, A^T, A_1^T.

Similarly, from $B, C, D, \ldots, K, L$ we get 4 matrices.

Thus, total $12 \times 4 = 48$ matrices. Hence, $\lambda = 48$.

(D) For consistent, $\begin{vmatrix}1&1&1\\c+2&c+4&6\\(c+2)^2&(c+4)^2&36\end{vmatrix}=0$

Applying $C_2 \to C_2 - C_1$, we get

$$\begin{vmatrix}1&0&1\\c+2&2&6\\(c+2)^2&4c+12&36\end{vmatrix}=0$$

$$\Rightarrow \quad 2\begin{vmatrix}1&0&1\\c+2&1&6\\(c+2)^2&2c+6&36\end{vmatrix}=0$$

$$\Rightarrow \quad -12c-0+1[(c+2)(2c+6)-(c+2)^2]=0$$

$$\Rightarrow \quad c^2-6c+8=0$$

$$\Rightarrow \quad c=2, 4$$

$$\therefore \quad c_1=4, c_2=2$$

$$\Rightarrow \quad c_1^{c_2}=4^2=16$$

75. (A)→(q, t); (B)→(p, s); (C)→(p, r, s); (D)→(q, r, t)

(A) Here, X is a $n \times 1$ matrix, C is $n \times n$ matrix and X^T is a $1 \times n$ matrix.

Hence, X^TCX is a 1×1 matrix.

Let $X^TCX = [\lambda]$, then

$$(X^TCX)^T = X^TC^T(X^T)^T = X^T(-C)X = -X^TCX$$

$$\therefore \quad [\lambda]=-[\lambda]$$

$$\Rightarrow \quad \lambda = 0$$

$$\Rightarrow \quad X^TCX = O$$

i.e., X^TCX is null matrix.

(B) Consider the homogeneous system

$$(I-A)X=O$$

$$\Rightarrow \quad AX = IX = X \qquad \ldots \text{(i)}$$

Now, $\quad (AX)^T = X^TA^T \Rightarrow X^T = -X^TA$

$$\Rightarrow \quad X^TX = -X^TAX = -X^TX \qquad \text{[from Eq. (i)]}$$

$$\Rightarrow \quad 2X^TX = O \Rightarrow |X| = O$$

$(I-A)X = O$ has only trivial solution

$\therefore$ $I-A$ is non-singular

$\Rightarrow$ $(I-A)$ is invertible

(C) $\because$ $$S=\begin{bmatrix}0&1&1\\1&0&1\\1&1&0\end{bmatrix}$$

$$\Rightarrow \quad S^{-1}=\frac{1}{2}\begin{bmatrix}-1&1&1\\1&-1&1\\1&1&-1\end{bmatrix}$$

We have, $$SA=\begin{bmatrix}0&1&1\\1&0&1\\1&1&0\end{bmatrix}\begin{bmatrix}b+c&c-a&b-a\\c-b&c+a&a-b\\b-c&a-c&a+b\end{bmatrix}$$

$$=\begin{bmatrix}0&2a&2a\\2b&0&2b\\2c&2c&0\end{bmatrix}$$

$$\therefore \quad SAS^{-1}=\begin{bmatrix}0&2a&2a\\2b&0&2b\\2c&2c&0\end{bmatrix}\frac{1}{2}\begin{bmatrix}-1&1&1\\1&-1&1\\1&1&-1\end{bmatrix}$$

$$=\begin{bmatrix}0&a&a\\b&0&b\\c&c&0\end{bmatrix}\begin{bmatrix}-1&1&1\\1&-1&1\\1&1&-1\end{bmatrix}=\begin{bmatrix}2a&0&0\\0&2b&0\\0&0&2c\end{bmatrix}$$

$$\therefore \quad |SAS^{-1}| = 8abc \neq 0$$

(D) $\because$ $$A=\begin{bmatrix}\sin 2A&\sin C&\sin B\\\sin C&\sin 2B&\sin A\\\sin B&\sin A&\sin 2C\end{bmatrix}$$

$$|A|=\begin{vmatrix}2ak\cos A&ck&bk\\ck&2bk\cos B&ak\\bk&ak&2ck\cos C\end{vmatrix}$$

$$=k^3\begin{vmatrix}a\cos A+a\cos A&a\cos B+b\cos A&a\cos C+c\cos A\\a\cos B+b\cos A&b\cos B+b\cos B&b\cos C+c\cos B\\a\cos C+c\cos A&b\cos C+c\cos B&c\cos C+c\cos C\end{vmatrix}$$

$$=k^3\begin{vmatrix}a&\cos A&0\\b&\cos B&0\\c&\cos C&0\end{vmatrix}\times\begin{vmatrix}\cos A&a&0\\\cos B&b&0\\\cos C&c&0\end{vmatrix}=k^3\cdot 0\cdot 0=0$$

76. Since, matrix A is skew-symmetric

$$\therefore \quad |A|=0$$

$$\therefore \quad |A^4B^5|=0$$

$\Rightarrow A^4B^5$ is singular matrix.

Statement-1 is false and Statement-2 is true.

77. $\because \quad AB = A, BA = B \Rightarrow A^2 = A$ and $B^2 = B$

$\therefore \quad (A+B)^2 = A^2 + B^2 + AB + BA = A + B + A + B$

$= 2(A+B)$

$(A+B)^3 = (A+B)^2 . (A+B)$

$= 2(A+B)^2 = 2^2 (A+B)$

$\therefore \quad (A+B)^7 = 2^6 (A+B)$

Statement-1 is true and Statement-2 is false.

78. A^{-1} exists only for non-singular matrix

$$AB = AC \Rightarrow A^{-1}(AB) = A^{-1}(AC)$$

$\Rightarrow \quad (A^{-1} A) B = (A^{-1} A) C$

$\Rightarrow \quad IB = IC$

$\Rightarrow \quad B = C$, if A^{-1} exist

$\therefore \quad |A| \neq 0$

Statement-1 is false and Statement-2 is true.

79. Statement-2 is false

$\because \quad \det(A^{-1}) \neq \det(-A')$

$[\because \det(-A') = (-1)^3 \det(A') = -\det(A')]$

but in Statement-1

$$A' = -A \Rightarrow A = -A'$$

$\therefore \quad \det(A) = \det(-A')$

$= -\det A' = -\det(A)$

$\Rightarrow \quad 2\det(A) = 0$

$\therefore \quad \det(A) = 0$

Then, Statement-1 is true.

80. $\because (BX)^T (BY) = \{(I-A)(I+A)^{-1} X\}^T (I-A)(I+A)^{-1} Y$

$= X^T \{(I+A)^{-1}\}^T (I-A)^T (I-A)(I+A)^{-1} Y$

$= X^T (I+A^T)^{-1} (I-A^T)(I-A)(I+A)^{-1} Y$

$= X^T (I-A)^{-1} (I+A)(I-A)(I+A)^{-1} Y$

$= X^T (I-A)^{-1} (I-A)(I+A)(I+A)^{-1} Y$

$[\because A^T = -A$ and $(I-A)(I+A) = (I+A)(I-A)]$

$= X^T \cdot I \cdot I \cdot Y = X^T Y$

Both Statements are true; Statement-2 is correct explanation for Statement-1.

81. $\because \quad |A| = 2$

and $\quad B = 9A^2$ (given)

$\therefore \quad |B| = |9A^2| = 9^2 |A|^2$

$= 81 \times 4 = 324 \Rightarrow |B^T| = |B| = 324$

Hence, Statement-1 is false but Statement-2 is true.

82. $\therefore \det(A - \lambda I) = \begin{vmatrix} 1-\lambda & -1 & -1 \\ 1 & -1-\lambda & 0 \\ 1 & 0 & -1-\lambda \end{vmatrix} = 0$

$\Rightarrow \quad (1-\lambda)(1+\lambda)^2 - 1 - \lambda - 1 - \lambda = 0$

$\Rightarrow \quad \lambda^3 + \lambda^2 + \lambda + 1 = 0$

$\Rightarrow \quad A^3 + A^2 + A + I = 0$

$\Rightarrow \quad A^3 + A^2 + A = -I$

Statement-1 is false but Statement-2 is true.

83. $A = \begin{bmatrix} 0 & -\frac{1}{5} & -\frac{2}{7} \\ \frac{1}{4} & 0 & -\frac{1}{8} \\ \frac{2}{5} & \frac{1}{7} & 0 \end{bmatrix}$

which is neither symmetric nor skew-symmetric. Infact every square matrix can be expressed as a sum of symmetric and skew-symmetric matrix. Hence, Statement-1 is false and Statement-2 is true.

84. ABC is not defined, as order of A, B and C are such that they are not conformable for multiplication.

Hence, Statement-1 is false and Statement-2 is true.

85. $\because \quad A^T = -A$

$\Rightarrow \quad |A^T| = |-A|$

$= (-1)^5 |A| = -|A|$

$\Rightarrow \quad |A| = -|A|$

$\Rightarrow \quad 2|A| = 0$

$\therefore \quad |A| = 0$

Both Statements are true but Statement-2 is a correct explanation of Statement-1.

86. $\because S$ is skew-symmetric matrix

$\therefore \quad S^T = -S$ ...(i)

First we will show that $I - S$ is non-singular. The equality $|I - S| = 0 \Rightarrow I$ is a characteristic root of the matrix S but this is not possible, for a real skew-symmetric matrix can have zero or purely imaginary numbers as its characteristic roots. Thus, $|I - S| \neq 0$ i.e., $I - S$ is non-singular.

We have,

$A^T = \{(I+S)(I-S)^{-1}\}^T = \{(I-S)^{-1}(I+S)\}^T$

$= ((I-S)^{-1})^T (I+S)^T = (I+S)^T \{(I-S)^{-1}\}^T$

$= ((I-S)^T)^{-1} (I+S)^T = (I+S)^T ((I-S)^T)^{-1}$

$= (I^T - S^T)^{-1} (I^T + S^T) = (I^T + S^T)(I^T - S^T)^{-1}$

$= (I+S)^{-1}(I-S) = (I-S)(I+S)^{-1}$ [from Eq. (i)]

$\therefore \quad A^T A = (I+S)^{-1}(I-S)(I+S)(I-S)^{-1}$

$= (I-S)(I+S)^{-1}(I-S)^{-1}(I+S)$

$= (I+S)^{-1}(I+S)(I-S)(I-S)^{-1}$

$= (I-S)(I-S)^{-1}(I+S)^{-1}(I+S)$

$= I \cdot I = I \cdot I = I = I$

Hence, A is orthogonal.

87. $\because \quad MM^T = I$ ...(i)

Let $\quad B = M - I$ ...(ii)

$\therefore \quad B^T = M^T - I^T = M^T - M^T M$ [from Eq. (i)]

$= M^T (I - M) = -M^T B$ [from Eq. (ii)]

Now, $\det(B^T) = \det(-M^T B)$

$= (-1)^3 \det(M^T) \det(B) = -\det(M^T) \det(B)$

$\Rightarrow \quad \det(B) = -\det(M)\det(B) = -\det(B)$

$\therefore \quad \det(B) = 0$

$\Rightarrow \quad \det(M - I) = 0$

88. $\because \quad BAB = A^{-1}$

$\Rightarrow \quad ABAB = I$

$\Rightarrow \quad (AB)^2 = I$

Now, $AB = \begin{bmatrix} \cos(\alpha + 2\beta) & \sin(\alpha + 2\beta) \\ \sin(\alpha + 2\beta) & -\cos(\alpha + 2\beta) \end{bmatrix}$

and $(AB)^2 = (AB)(AB) = \begin{bmatrix} 1 & 0 \\ 0 & 1 \end{bmatrix} = I \quad [\because (AB)(AB) = I]$

Also, $BA^4B = A^{-1}$

or $A^4B = B^{-1}A^{-1} = (AB)^{-1} = AB$

or $A^4 = A$ ...(i)

Now, $A^2 = \begin{bmatrix} \cos\alpha & -\sin\alpha \\ \sin\alpha & \cos\alpha \end{bmatrix}\begin{bmatrix} \cos\alpha & -\sin\alpha \\ \sin\alpha & \cos\alpha \end{bmatrix}$

$= \begin{bmatrix} \cos 2\alpha & -\sin 2\alpha \\ \sin 2\alpha & \cos 2\alpha \end{bmatrix}$

Similarly, $A^4 = \begin{bmatrix} \cos 4\alpha & -\sin 4\alpha \\ \sin 4\alpha & \cos 4\alpha \end{bmatrix}$

Hence, from Eq. (i)

$\begin{bmatrix} \cos 4\alpha & -\sin 4\alpha \\ \sin 4\alpha & \cos 4\alpha \end{bmatrix} = \begin{bmatrix} \cos\alpha & -\sin\alpha \\ \sin\alpha & \cos\alpha \end{bmatrix}$

or $4\alpha = 2\pi + \alpha$

$\therefore \quad \alpha = \dfrac{2\pi}{3}$

89. $AB = \begin{bmatrix} \cos^2\theta & \cos\theta\sin\theta \\ \cos\theta\sin\theta & \sin^2\theta \end{bmatrix}\begin{bmatrix} \cos^2\phi & \cos\phi\sin\phi \\ \cos\phi\sin\phi & \sin^2\phi \end{bmatrix}$

$= \begin{bmatrix} \cos^2\theta\cos^2\phi + \cos\theta\cos\phi\sin\theta\sin\phi & \cos^2\theta\cos\phi\sin\phi + \sin^2\phi\sin\theta\cos\theta \\ \cos^2\phi\cos\theta\sin\theta + \sin^2\theta\sin\phi\cos\phi & \cos\theta\cos\phi\sin\theta\sin\phi + \sin^2\theta\sin^2\phi \end{bmatrix}$

$= \begin{bmatrix} \cos\theta\cos\phi(\cos\theta\cos\phi + \sin\theta\sin\phi) & \cos\phi\sin\phi(\cos\theta\cos\phi + \sin\theta\sin\phi) \\ \sin\theta\cos\phi(\cos\theta\cos\phi + \sin\theta\sin\phi) & \sin\theta\sin\phi(\cos\theta\cos\phi + \sin\theta\sin\phi) \end{bmatrix}$

$= \begin{bmatrix} \cos\theta\cos\phi\cos(\theta - \phi) & \cos\theta\sin\phi\cos(\theta - \phi) \\ \sin\theta\cos\phi\cos(\theta - \phi) & \sin\theta\sin\phi\cos(\theta - \phi) \end{bmatrix}$

Clearly, AB is the zero matrix, if $\cos(\theta \sim \phi) = 0$ i.e., $\theta - \phi$ is an odd multiple of $\dfrac{\pi}{2}$.

90. Let $A = \begin{bmatrix} l_1 & m_1 & n_1 \\ l_2 & m_2 & n_2 \\ l_3 & m_3 & n_3 \end{bmatrix}$

$\therefore \quad A^T = \begin{bmatrix} l_1 & l_2 & l_3 \\ m_1 & m_2 & m_3 \\ n_1 & n_2 & n_3 \end{bmatrix}$

Now, $AA^T = \begin{bmatrix} l_1 & m_1 & n_1 \\ l_2 & m_2 & n_2 \\ l_3 & m_3 & n_3 \end{bmatrix} \times \begin{bmatrix} l_1 & l_2 & l_3 \\ m_1 & m_2 & m_3 \\ n_1 & n_2 & n_3 \end{bmatrix}$

$= \begin{bmatrix} \Sigma l_1^2 & \Sigma l_1 l_2 & \Sigma l_3 l_1 \\ \Sigma l_1 l_2 & \Sigma l_2^2 & \Sigma l_2 l_3 \\ \Sigma l_3 l_1 & \Sigma l_2 l_3 & \Sigma l_3^2 \end{bmatrix} = \begin{bmatrix} 1 & 0 & 0 \\ 0 & 1 & 0 \\ 0 & 0 & 1 \end{bmatrix} = I$

Hence, matrix A is orthogonal.

91. Let us use the symbols Div, Dis, Tal for division, district, taluka respectively and O, H, C, Cl, T and P for office superintendent, Head clerk, Cashier, Clerk, Typist and Peon respectively.

Then, the number of offices can be arranged as elements of a row matrix A and the composition of staff in various offices can be arranged in a 3×6 matrix B (say).

$\therefore \quad A = \begin{matrix} \text{Div} & \text{Dis} & \text{Tal} \\ [5 & 30 & 200] \end{matrix}$

and $B = \begin{bmatrix} 1 & 1 & 1 & 2+1 & 1 & 1+1 \\ 0 & 1 & 1 & 1+1 & 0 & 1+1 \\ 0 & 1 & 1 & 1 & 0 & 1 \end{bmatrix}$

or $B = \begin{bmatrix} 1 & 1 & 1 & 3 & 1 & 2 \\ 0 & 1 & 1 & 2 & 0 & 2 \\ 0 & 1 & 1 & 1 & 0 & 1 \end{bmatrix}$

The basic monthly salaries of various types of employees of these offices correspond to the elements of the column matrix C.

$\therefore \quad C = \begin{matrix} \text{O} \\ \text{H} \\ \text{C} \\ \text{Cl} \\ \text{T} \\ \text{P} \end{matrix}\begin{bmatrix} 500 \\ 200 \\ 175 \\ 150 \\ 150 \\ 100 \end{bmatrix}$

(i) Total number of Posts = AB

$= \begin{matrix} \text{Div} & \text{Dis} & \text{Tal} \\ [5 & 30 & 200] \end{matrix} \times \begin{bmatrix} \text{O} & \text{H} & \text{C} & \text{Cl} & \text{T} & \text{P} \\ 1 & 1 & 1 & 3 & 1 & 2 \\ 0 & 1 & 1 & 2 & 0 & 2 \\ 0 & 1 & 1 & 1 & 0 & 1 \end{bmatrix}$

$= \begin{matrix} \text{O} & \text{H} & \text{C} & \text{Cl} & \text{T} & \text{P} \\ [5 & 235 & 235 & 275 & 5 & 270] \end{matrix}$

i.e., Required number of posts in all the offices taken together are 5 office Suprintendents, 235 Head Clerks, 235 Cashiers, 275 Clerks, 5 Typists and 270 Peons.

(ii) The total basic monthly salary bill of each kind of office = BC

$= \begin{bmatrix} \text{O} & \text{H} & \text{C} & \text{Cl} & \text{T} & \text{P} \\ 1 & 1 & 1 & 3 & 1 & 2 \\ 0 & 1 & 1 & 2 & 0 & 2 \\ 0 & 1 & 1 & 1 & 0 & 1 \end{bmatrix} \times \begin{bmatrix} 500 \\ 200 \\ 175 \\ 150 \\ 150 \\ 100 \end{bmatrix}\begin{matrix} \text{O} \\ \text{H} \\ \text{C} \\ \text{Cl} \\ \text{T} \\ \text{P} \end{matrix}$

$$= \begin{bmatrix} 500 + 200 + 175 + 3 \times 150 + 1 \times 150 + 2 \times 100 \\ 0 + 1 \times 200 + 1 \times 175 + 2 \times 150 + 0 + 2 \times 100 \\ 0 + 1 \times 200 + 1 \times 175 + 1 \times 150 + 0 + 1 \times 100 \end{bmatrix}$$

$$= \begin{bmatrix} 1675 \\ 875 \\ 625 \end{bmatrix}$$

i.e., The total basic monthly salary bill of each divisional, district and taluka offices are ₹ 1675, ₹ 875 and ₹ 625, respectively.

(iii) The total basic monthly salary bill of all the offices taken together

$$= ABC = A(BC)$$

$$= [5 \quad 30 \quad 200] \times \begin{bmatrix} 1675 \\ 875 \\ 625 \end{bmatrix}$$

$$= [5 \times 1675 + 30 \times 875 + 200 \times 625]$$

$$= [159625]$$

Hence, total basic monthly salary bill of all the offices taken together is ₹ 159625.

92. The total load of stone and sand supplied by A can be represented by row matrix X_1 and cost of one truck load of stone and sand can be represented by column matrix Y_1.

$$\therefore \quad X_1 = [40 \quad 10], Y_1 = \begin{bmatrix} 1200 \\ 500 \end{bmatrix}$$

Total amount paid by contractor to $A = X_1 Y_1$

$$= [40 \quad 10] \begin{bmatrix} 1200 \\ 500 \end{bmatrix}$$

$$= [48000 + 5000]$$

$$= [53000]$$

$\therefore$ Amount paid by contractor to A is ₹ 53000.

Similarly for B, $X_2 = [35 \quad 5]$, $Y_2 = \begin{bmatrix} 1200 \\ 500 \end{bmatrix}$

Total amount paid by contractor to $B = X_2 Y_2$

$$= [35 \quad 5] \begin{bmatrix} 1200 \\ 500 \end{bmatrix} = [42000 + 2500]$$

$$= [44500]$$

$\therefore$ Amount paid by contractor to B is ₹ 44500.

Similarly for C,

$$X_3 = [25 \quad 8], Y_3 = \begin{bmatrix} 1200 \\ 500 \end{bmatrix}$$

Total amount paid by contractor to $C = X_3 Y_3$

$$= [25 \quad 8] \begin{bmatrix} 1200 \\ 500 \end{bmatrix}$$

$$= [30000 + 4000] = [34000]$$

$\therefore$ Amount paid by contractor to C is ₹ 34000.

93. We have, $A = \begin{bmatrix} 1 & a & \alpha & a\alpha \\ 1 & b & \beta & b\beta \\ 1 & c & \gamma & c\gamma \end{bmatrix}$

Applying $R_2 \to R_2 - R_1$ and $R_3 \to R_3 - R_1$, we get

$$A = \begin{bmatrix} 1 & a & \alpha & a\alpha \\ 0 & b-a & \beta-\alpha & b\beta - a\alpha \\ 0 & c-a & \gamma-\alpha & c\gamma - a\alpha \end{bmatrix}$$

Applying $C_2 \to C_2 - aC_1$, $C_3 \to C_3 - \alpha C_1$ and $C_4 \to C_4 - a\alpha C_1$, we get

$$A = \begin{bmatrix} 1 & 0 & 0 & 0 \\ 0 & b-a & \beta-\alpha & b\beta - a\alpha \\ 0 & c-a & \gamma-\alpha & c\gamma - a\alpha \end{bmatrix}$$

Applying $C_4 \to C_4 - \alpha C_2 - bC_3$, we get

$$A = \begin{bmatrix} 1 & 0 & 0 & 0 \\ 0 & b-a & \beta-\alpha & 0 \\ 0 & c-a & \gamma-\alpha & (c-b)(\gamma-\alpha) \end{bmatrix}$$

For $\rho(A) = 3$

$$c - a \neq 0, \gamma - \alpha \neq 0, c - b \neq 0, b - a \neq 0, \beta - \alpha \neq 0$$

i.e., $a \neq b, b \neq c, c \neq a$ and $\alpha \neq \beta, \beta \neq \gamma, \gamma \neq \alpha$

94. We have, $\begin{bmatrix} 1 & 1 & 1 \\ 2 & 5 & 7 \\ 2 & 1 & -1 \end{bmatrix} \begin{bmatrix} x & u \\ y & v \\ z & w \end{bmatrix} = \begin{bmatrix} 9 & 2 \\ 52 & 15 \\ 0 & -1 \end{bmatrix}$

or $\quad AX = B$

or $\quad X = A^{-1}B \quad$ ...(i)

Where, $A = \begin{bmatrix} 1 & 1 & 1 \\ 2 & 5 & 7 \\ 2 & 1 & -1 \end{bmatrix}$, $X = \begin{bmatrix} x & u \\ y & v \\ z & \omega \end{bmatrix}$ and $B = \begin{bmatrix} 9 & 2 \\ 52 & 15 \\ 0 & -1 \end{bmatrix}$

$$\therefore \quad |A| = 1(-5-7) - 1(-2-14) + 1(2-10)$$

$$= -12 + 16 - 8 = -4 \neq 0$$

Let C be the matrix of cofactors of elements of $|A|$.

$$\therefore \quad C = \begin{bmatrix} C_{11} & C_{12} & C_{13} \\ C_{21} & C_{22} & C_{23} \\ C_{31} & C_{32} & C_{33} \end{bmatrix}$$

$$= \begin{bmatrix} \begin{vmatrix} 5 & 7 \\ 1 & -1 \end{vmatrix} & -\begin{vmatrix} 2 & 7 \\ 2 & -1 \end{vmatrix} & \begin{vmatrix} 2 & 5 \\ 2 & 1 \end{vmatrix} \\ -\begin{vmatrix} 1 & 1 \\ 1 & -1 \end{vmatrix} & \begin{vmatrix} 1 & 1 \\ 2 & -1 \end{vmatrix} & -\begin{vmatrix} 1 & 1 \\ 2 & 1 \end{vmatrix} \\ \begin{vmatrix} 1 & 1 \\ 5 & 7 \end{vmatrix} & -\begin{vmatrix} 1 & 1 \\ 2 & 7 \end{vmatrix} & \begin{vmatrix} 1 & 1 \\ 2 & 5 \end{vmatrix} \end{bmatrix}$$

$$= \begin{bmatrix} -12 & 16 & -8 \\ 2 & -3 & 1 \\ 2 & -5 & 3 \end{bmatrix}$$

$$\therefore \quad \text{adj } A = C' = \begin{bmatrix} -12 & 2 & 2 \\ 16 & -3 & -5 \\ -8 & 1 & 3 \end{bmatrix}$$

$$\therefore \quad A^{-1} = \frac{\text{adj } A}{|A|} = -\frac{1}{4} \begin{bmatrix} -12 & 2 & 2 \\ 16 & -3 & -5 \\ -8 & 1 & 3 \end{bmatrix}$$

Now, $A^{-1}B = -\frac{1}{4} \begin{bmatrix} -12 & 2 & 2 \\ 16 & -3 & -5 \\ -8 & 1 & 3 \end{bmatrix} \times \begin{bmatrix} 9 & 2 \\ 52 & 15 \\ 0 & -1 \end{bmatrix}$

$$= -\frac{1}{4}\begin{bmatrix} -4 & 4 \\ -12 & -8 \\ -20 & -4 \end{bmatrix} = \begin{bmatrix} 1 & -1 \\ 3 & 2 \\ 5 & 1 \end{bmatrix}$$

From Eq. (i) $\quad X = A^{-1}B$

$$\Rightarrow \quad \begin{bmatrix} x & u \\ y & v \\ z & w \end{bmatrix} = \begin{bmatrix} 1 & -1 \\ 3 & 2 \\ 5 & 1 \end{bmatrix}$$

On equating the corresponding elements, we have

$$x = 1, u = -1$$
$$y = 3, v = 2$$
$$z = 5, w = 1$$

95. Since, $x_1 = 3y_1 + 2y_2 - y_3$

$$\Rightarrow \quad [x_1] = [3 \quad 2 \quad -1]\begin{bmatrix} y_1 \\ y_2 \\ y_3 \end{bmatrix}$$

Putting the values of y_1, y_2, y_3, we get

$$[x_1] = [3 \quad 2 \quad -1]\begin{bmatrix} z_1 - z_2 + z_3 \\ 0 + z_2 + 3z_3 \\ 2z_1 + z_2 + 0 \end{bmatrix}$$

$$= [3 \quad 2 \quad -1]\begin{bmatrix} 1 & -1 & 1 \\ 0 & 1 & 3 \\ 2 & 1 & 0 \end{bmatrix}\begin{bmatrix} z_1 \\ z_2 \\ z_3 \end{bmatrix}$$

$$= [3 + 0 - 2 \quad -3 + 2 - 1 \quad 3 + 6 + 0]\begin{bmatrix} z_1 \\ z_2 \\ z_3 \end{bmatrix}$$

$$= [1 \quad -2 \quad 9]\begin{bmatrix} z_1 \\ z_2 \\ z_3 \end{bmatrix}$$

$$[x_1] = [z_1 - 2z_2 + 9z_3]$$

$$\therefore \quad x_1 = z_1 - 2z_2 + 9z_3 \quad \text{...(i)}$$

Further, $\quad x_2 = -y_1 + 4y_2 + 5y_3$

$$\Rightarrow \quad [x_2] = [-1 \quad 4 \quad 5]\begin{bmatrix} y_1 \\ y_2 \\ y_3 \end{bmatrix}$$

Putting the values of y_1, y_2, y_3, we get

$$[x_2] = [-1 \quad 4 \quad 5]\begin{bmatrix} z_1 - z_2 + z_3 \\ 0 + z_2 + 3z_3 \\ 2z_1 + z_2 + 0 \end{bmatrix}$$

$$= [-1 \quad 4 \quad 5]\begin{bmatrix} 1 & -1 & 1 \\ 0 & 1 & 3 \\ 2 & 1 & 0 \end{bmatrix}\begin{bmatrix} z_1 \\ z_2 \\ z_3 \end{bmatrix}$$

$$= [-1 + 0 + 10 \quad 1 + 4 + 5 \quad -1 + 12 + 0]\begin{bmatrix} z_1 \\ z_2 \\ z_3 \end{bmatrix}$$

$$= [9 \quad 10 \quad 11]\begin{bmatrix} z_1 \\ z_2 \\ z_3 \end{bmatrix} = [9z_1 + 10z_2 + 11z_3]$$

Hence, $\quad x_2 = 9z_1 + 10z_2 + 11z_3 \quad$ ...(ii)

Further, $\quad x_3 = y_1 - y_2 + 3y_3$

$$\therefore \quad [x_3] = [1 \quad -1 \quad 3]\begin{bmatrix} y_1 \\ y_2 \\ y_3 \end{bmatrix}$$

Putting the values of y_1, y_2, y_3, we get

$$\Rightarrow \quad [x_3] = [1 \quad -1 \quad 3]\begin{bmatrix} z_1 - z_2 + z_3 \\ 0 + z_2 + 3z_3 \\ 2z_1 + z_2 + 0 \end{bmatrix}$$

$$= [1 \quad -1 \quad 3]\begin{bmatrix} 1 & -1 & 1 \\ 0 & 1 & 3 \\ 2 & 1 & 0 \end{bmatrix}\begin{bmatrix} z_1 \\ z_2 \\ z_3 \end{bmatrix}$$

$$= [1 - 0 + 6 \quad -1 - 1 + 3 \quad 1 - 3 + 0]\begin{bmatrix} z_1 \\ z_2 \\ z_3 \end{bmatrix}$$

$$= [7 \quad 1 \quad -2]\begin{bmatrix} z_1 \\ z_2 \\ z_3 \end{bmatrix} = [7z_1 + z_2 - 2z_3]$$

$$\therefore \quad x_3 = 7z_1 + z_2 - 2z_3 \quad \text{...(iii)}$$

Hence, from Eqs. (i), (ii) and (iii), we get

$x_1 = z_1 - 2z_2 + 9z_3$, $x_2 = 9z_1 + 10z_2 + 11z_3$, $x_3 = 7z_1 + z_2 - 2z_3$

96. Given equations can be written as,

$$2x - 3y + 6z = 5t + 3$$
$$y - 4z = 1 - t$$
$$4x - 5y + 8z = 9t + k$$

which is of the form $AX = B$.

Let C be the augmented matrix, then

$$C = [A : B] = \left[\begin{array}{ccc:c} 2 & -3 & 6 & 5t + 3 \\ 0 & 1 & -4 & 1 - t \\ 4 & -5 & 8 & 9t + k \end{array}\right]$$

Applying $R_3 \to R_3 - 2R_1$, then

$$C = \left[\begin{array}{ccc:c} 2 & -3 & 6 & 5t + 3 \\ 0 & 1 & -4 & 1 - t \\ 0 & 1 & -4 & -t + k - 6 \end{array}\right]$$

Applying $R_3 \to R_3 - R_2$, then

$$C = \left[\begin{array}{ccc:c} 2 & -3 & 6 & 5t + 3 \\ 0 & 1 & -4 & 1 - t \\ 0 & 0 & 0 & k - 7 \end{array}\right]$$

(i) For no solution

$$R_A \neq R_C$$
$$\therefore \quad k \neq 7$$

(ii) For infinite number of solutions

$$R_A = R_C$$
$$\therefore \quad k = 7$$

97. $AX = U$ has infinite many solutions

$$\Rightarrow \quad |A| = 0 = |A_1| = |A_2| = |A_3|$$

Now, $\quad |A| = 0$

$$\Rightarrow \quad \begin{vmatrix} a & 1 & 0 \\ 1 & b & d \\ 1 & b & c \end{vmatrix} = 0 \Rightarrow (ab - 1)(c - d) = 0$$

$$\Rightarrow \quad ab = 1 \text{ or } c = d \quad \text{...(i)}$$

and $|A_1| = 0$

$$\Rightarrow \begin{vmatrix} f & 1 & 0 \\ g & b & d \\ h & b & c \end{vmatrix} = 0$$

$$\Rightarrow fb(c-d) - gc + hd = 0$$

$$\Rightarrow fb(c-d) = gc - hd \quad \text{...(ii)}$$

$$\Rightarrow |A_2| = 0$$

$$\Rightarrow \begin{vmatrix} a & f & 0 \\ 1 & g & d \\ 1 & h & c \end{vmatrix} = 0$$

$$\Rightarrow a(gc - dh) - f(c-d) = 0$$

$$\Rightarrow a(gc - dh) = f(c-d) \quad \text{...(iii)}$$

$$|A_3| = 0$$

$$\Rightarrow \begin{vmatrix} a & 1 & f \\ 1 & b & g \\ 1 & b & h \end{vmatrix} = 0$$

$$\Rightarrow (h-g)(ab-1) = 0$$

$$\Rightarrow h = g \text{ or } ab = 1 \quad \text{...(iv)}$$

Taking $c = d \Rightarrow h = g$ and $ab \neq 1$ (from Eqs. (i), (ii) and (iv))

Now, taking $BX = V$,

Then, $$|B| = \begin{vmatrix} a & 1 & 1 \\ 0 & d & c \\ f & g & h \end{vmatrix} = 0$$

[$\because$ In view of $c = d$ and $g = h$, c_2 and c_3 are identical]

$\Rightarrow$ $BX = V$ has no unique solution.

and $$|B_1| = \begin{vmatrix} a^2 & 1 & 1 \\ 0 & d & c \\ 0 & g & h \end{vmatrix} = 0 \quad [\because c = d, g = h]$$

$$|B_2| = \begin{vmatrix} a & a^2 & 1 \\ 0 & 0 & c \\ f & 0 & h \end{vmatrix} = a^2 fc = a^2 df \quad [\because c = d]$$

and $$|B_3| = \begin{vmatrix} a & 1 & a^2 \\ 0 & d & 0 \\ f & g & 0 \end{vmatrix} = -a^2 df$$

If $a^2 df \neq 0$, then $|B_2| = |B_3| \neq 0$

Hence, no solution exist.

98. Given, $A = \begin{bmatrix} 1 & 0 & 0 \\ 0 & 1 & 1 \\ 0 & -2 & 4 \end{bmatrix}$, $A^{-1} = \frac{1}{6}\begin{bmatrix} 6 & 0 & 0 \\ 0 & 4 & -1 \\ 0 & 2 & 1 \end{bmatrix}$

$$A^2 = \begin{bmatrix} 1 & 0 & 0 \\ 0 & 1 & 1 \\ 0 & -2 & 4 \end{bmatrix}\begin{bmatrix} 1 & 0 & 0 \\ 0 & 1 & 1 \\ 0 & -2 & 4 \end{bmatrix} = \begin{bmatrix} 1 & 0 & 0 \\ 0 & -1 & 5 \\ 0 & -10 & 14 \end{bmatrix}$$

$$cA = \begin{bmatrix} c & 0 & 0 \\ 0 & c & c \\ 0 & -2c & 4c \end{bmatrix}; dI = \begin{bmatrix} d & 0 & 0 \\ 0 & d & 0 \\ 0 & 0 & d \end{bmatrix}$$

$\therefore$ By $A^{-1} = \frac{1}{6}[A^2 + cA + dI]$

$\Rightarrow$ $6 = 1 + c + d$ [By equality of matrice

$\therefore (-6, 11)$ satisfy the relation.

99. If $Q = PAP^T$

then $P^TQ = AP^T$ [$\because PP^T =$

$$\Rightarrow P^TQ^{2005}P = AP^TQ^{2004}P$$

$$= A^2P^TQ^{2003}P = A^3P^TQ^{2002}P$$

$$= A^{2004}P^T(QP)$$

$$= A^{2004}P^T(PA) \quad [Q = PAP^T \Rightarrow QP = P\text{/}$$

$$= A^{2005}$$

$$\therefore A^{2005} = \begin{bmatrix} 1 & 2005 \\ 0 & 1 \end{bmatrix}$$

100. $$A^2 = \begin{bmatrix} 1 & 0 \\ 1 & 1 \end{bmatrix}\begin{bmatrix} 1 & 0 \\ 1 & 1 \end{bmatrix} = \begin{bmatrix} 1 & 0 \\ 2 & 1 \end{bmatrix}$$

$$A^3 = \begin{bmatrix} 1 & 0 \\ 2 & 1 \end{bmatrix}\begin{bmatrix} 1 & 0 \\ 1 & 1 \end{bmatrix} = \begin{bmatrix} 1 & 0 \\ 3 & 1 \end{bmatrix}$$

$$\therefore A^n = \begin{bmatrix} 1 & 0 \\ n & 1 \end{bmatrix}$$

$$nA = \begin{bmatrix} n & 0 \\ n & n \end{bmatrix}, (n-1)I = \begin{bmatrix} n-1 & 0 \\ 0 & n-1 \end{bmatrix}$$

$$nA - (n-1)I = \begin{bmatrix} 1 & 0 \\ n & 1 \end{bmatrix} = A^n$$

101. $$A^2 - A + I = 0$$

$$\Rightarrow I = A - A^2 \Rightarrow I = A(I - A)$$

$$\Rightarrow A^{-1}I = A^{-1}(A(I-A)) \Rightarrow A^{-1} = I - A$$

102. (i) Let U_1 be $\begin{pmatrix} x \\ y \\ z \end{pmatrix}$ so that $\begin{pmatrix} 1 & 0 & 0 \\ 2 & 1 & 0 \\ 3 & 2 & 1 \end{pmatrix}\begin{pmatrix} x \\ y \\ z \end{pmatrix} = \begin{pmatrix} 1 \\ 0 \\ 0 \end{pmatrix}$

$$\Rightarrow \begin{pmatrix} x \\ y \\ z \end{pmatrix} = \begin{pmatrix} 1 \\ -2 \\ 1 \end{pmatrix}$$

Similarly, $$U_2 = \begin{pmatrix} 2 \\ -1 \\ -4 \end{pmatrix}, U_3 = \begin{pmatrix} 2 \\ -1 \\ -3 \end{pmatrix}$$

Hence, $$U = \begin{pmatrix} 1 & 2 & 2 \\ -2 & -1 & -1 \\ 1 & -4 & -3 \end{pmatrix}$$

$$\therefore |U| = 3$$

(ii) $\because$ $\text{Adj}U = \begin{pmatrix} -1 & -2 & 0 \\ -7 & -5 & -3 \\ 9 & -6 & 3 \end{pmatrix}$

$\therefore \quad U^{-1} = \frac{\text{Adj}U}{|U|} = \frac{\text{Adj}U}{3}$

$\Rightarrow$ sum of the elements of

$U^{-1} = \frac{1}{3}(-1-2+0-7-5-3+9+6+3) = 0$

(iii) The value of

$(3\ 2\ 0)\,U\begin{pmatrix}3\\2\\0\end{pmatrix} = (3\ 2\ 0)\begin{pmatrix} 1 & 2 & 2 \\ -2 & -1 & -1 \\ 1 & -6 & -3 \end{pmatrix}\begin{pmatrix}3\\2\\0\end{pmatrix}$

$= (-1\ 4\ 4)\begin{pmatrix}3\\2\\0\end{pmatrix}$

$= (-3+8+0) = 5$

103. $A = \begin{pmatrix} 1 & 2 \\ 3 & 4 \end{pmatrix}, B = \begin{pmatrix} a & 0 \\ 0 & b \end{pmatrix}$

$\Rightarrow \quad AB = \begin{pmatrix} a & 2b \\ 3a & 4b \end{pmatrix}$

and $\quad BA = \begin{pmatrix} a & 0 \\ 0 & b \end{pmatrix}\begin{pmatrix} 1 & 2 \\ 3 & 4 \end{pmatrix} = \begin{pmatrix} a & 2a \\ 3b & 4b \end{pmatrix}$

Hence, $AB = BA$ only when $a = b$.

104. $A^2 - B^2 = (A-B)(A+B)$

$\Rightarrow \quad A^2 - B^2 = A^2 + AB - BA - B^2$

$\Rightarrow \quad AB = BA$

105. $A = \begin{bmatrix} 5 & 5\alpha & \alpha \\ 0 & \alpha & 5\alpha \\ 0 & 0 & 5 \end{bmatrix} \Rightarrow |A \cdot A| = |A||A| = (25\alpha)^2 = 25$

$\Rightarrow \quad \alpha^2 = \frac{1}{25}$

$\Rightarrow \quad \alpha = \pm\frac{1}{5}$

106. $\because \quad A^t = A, B^t = -B$

Given, $\quad (A+B)(A-B) = (A-B)(A+B)$

$\Rightarrow \quad A^2 - AB + BA - B^2 = A^2 + AB - BA - B^2$

$\Rightarrow \quad AB = BA$

Also, given $\quad (AB)^t = (-1)^k AB$

$\Rightarrow \quad B^t A^t = (-1)^k AB$

$\Rightarrow \quad -BA = (-1)^k AB$

$\Rightarrow \quad (-1) = (-1)^k \qquad [\because AB = BA]$

$\therefore \quad k = 1, 3, 5, \ldots$

107. Let $A = \begin{bmatrix} 2 & 1 \\ 0 & 1/2 \end{bmatrix}$

$\det A = \begin{vmatrix} 2 & 1 \\ 0 & 1/2 \end{vmatrix} = 1$

and $\quad A^{-1} = \begin{bmatrix} 1/2 & -1 \\ 0 & 2 \end{bmatrix}$

and let $\quad A = \begin{bmatrix} 3 & 0 \\ -3 & -1/3 \end{bmatrix}$,

$\det A = \begin{vmatrix} 3 & 0 \\ -3 & -1/3 \end{vmatrix} = -1$

and $\quad A^{-1} = \begin{bmatrix} 1/3 & 0 \\ -3 & -3 \end{bmatrix}$

108. Let $A = \begin{bmatrix} 1 & 0 \\ 0 & -1 \end{bmatrix}$ or $\begin{bmatrix} -1 & 0 \\ 0 & 1 \end{bmatrix}$

Then, $A^2 = I$

$\therefore \quad \det A = \begin{vmatrix} 1 & 0 \\ 0 & -1 \end{vmatrix} = -1$ and $\text{tr}(A) = 0$

109. (i) If two zero's are the entries in the diagonal, then

$^3C_2 \times {}^3C_1 = 9$

If the entries in the principal diagonal is1, then

$^3C_1 = 3$

$\Rightarrow$ Total matrix $= 9 + 3 = 12$

(ii) $\begin{bmatrix} 0 & a & b \\ a & 0 & c \\ b & c & 1 \end{bmatrix}$ either $b = 0$ or $c = 0 \Rightarrow |A| \neq 0$

$\Rightarrow$ 2 matrices

$\begin{bmatrix} 0 & a & b \\ a & 1 & c \\ b & c & 0 \end{bmatrix}$ either $a = 0$ or $c = 0 \Rightarrow |A| \neq 0$

$\Rightarrow$ 2 matrices

$\begin{bmatrix} 1 & a & b \\ a & 0 & c \\ b & c & 0 \end{bmatrix}$ either $a = 0$ or $b = 0 \Rightarrow |A| \neq 0$

$\Rightarrow$ 2 matrices

$\begin{bmatrix} 1 & a & b \\ a & 1 & c \\ b & c & 1 \end{bmatrix}$

If $a = b = 0 \Rightarrow |A| = 0$

If $a = c = 0 \Rightarrow |A| = 0$

If $b = c = 0 \Rightarrow |A| = 0$

$\Rightarrow$ There will be only 6 matrices.

(iii) The six matrix A for which $|A| = 0$ are

$\begin{bmatrix} 0 & 0 & 1 \\ 0 & 0 & 1 \\ 1 & 1 & 1 \end{bmatrix} \Rightarrow$ inconsistent

$\begin{bmatrix} 0 & 1 & 0 \\ 1 & 1 & 1 \\ 0 & 1 & 0 \end{bmatrix} \Rightarrow$ inconsistent

$\begin{bmatrix} 1 & 1 & 1 \\ 1 & 0 & 0 \\ 1 & 0 & 0 \end{bmatrix} \Rightarrow$ infinite solutions

$\begin{bmatrix}1&1&0\\1&1&0\\0&0&1\end{bmatrix} \Rightarrow$ inconsistent

$\begin{bmatrix}1&0&1\\0&1&0\\1&0&1\end{bmatrix} \Rightarrow$ inconsistent

$\begin{bmatrix}1&0&0\\0&1&1\\0&1&1\end{bmatrix} \Rightarrow$ infinite solutions

110. $|\text{adj } A| = |A|^{n-1} = |A|^{2-1} = |A|$

$\text{adj}(\text{adj } A) = |A|^{n-2} A$

$= |A|^{2-2} A = |A|^0 A = A$

111. Three planes cannot meet only at two distinct points.

Hence, number of matrices = 0

112. If A is symmetric matrix, then $b = c$

$\therefore \det(A) = \begin{vmatrix} a & b \\ b & a \end{vmatrix} = a^2 - b^2 = (a+b)(a-b)$

$a, b, c \in \{0, 1, 2, 3, \dots, p-1\}$

Number of numbers of type

$np = 1$

$np + 1 = 1$

$np + 2 = 1$

....

....

$np + (p-1) = 1 \ \forall\ n \in I$

(i) as $\det(A)$ is divisible by $p \Rightarrow$ either $a + b$ divisible by p corresponding number of ways $= (p-1)$ [excluding zero] or $(a-b)$ is divisible by p corresponding number of ways $= p$
Total Number of ways $= 2p - 1$

(ii) as $\text{Tr}(A)$ not divisible by $p \Rightarrow a \neq 0$
$\det(A)$ is divisible by $p \Rightarrow a^2 - bc$ divisible by p
Number of ways of selection of a, b, c
$= (p-1)[(p-1) \times 1] = (p-1)^2$

(iii) Total number of $A = p \times p \times p = p^3$
Number of A such that $\det(A)$ divisible by p
$= (p-1)^2 +$ number of A in which $a = 0$
$= (p-1)^2 + p + p - 1 = p^2$
Required number $= p^3 - p^2$

113. $|A| = (2k-1)(-1+4k^2) + 2\sqrt{k}\,(2\sqrt{k} + 4k\sqrt{k})$

$+ 2\sqrt{k}\,(4k\sqrt{k} + 2\sqrt{k})(2k-1)(4k^2-1)$

$+ 4k + 8k^2 + 8k^2 + 4k$

$= (2k-1)(4k^2-1) + 8k + 16k^2$

$= 8k^3 - 4k^2 - 2k + 1 + 8k + 16k^2$

$= 8k^3 + 12k^2 + 6k + 1$

$|B| = 0$ as B is skew-symmetric matrix of odd order.

$\Rightarrow (8k^3 + 12k^2 + 6k + 1)^2 = (10^3)^2$

$\Rightarrow (2k+1)^3 = 10^3$

$\Rightarrow 2k + 1 = 10$

$\Rightarrow k = 4.5$

$\Rightarrow [k] = 4$

114. First row with exactly one zero

$\therefore$ Total number of cases = 6

First row 2 zeroes, we get more cases.

$\therefore$ Total we get more than 7.

115. Let $A = \begin{pmatrix} a & b \\ c & d \end{pmatrix}$, $abcd \neq 0$

$A^2 = \begin{pmatrix} a & b \\ c & d \end{pmatrix} \cdot \begin{pmatrix} a & b \\ c & d \end{pmatrix}$

$\Rightarrow A^2 = \begin{pmatrix} a^2 + bc & ab + bd \\ ac + cd & bc + d^2 \end{pmatrix}$

$\Rightarrow a^2 + bc = 1,\ bc + d^2 = 1$

$ab + bd = ac + cd = 0$

$c \neq 0$ and $b \neq 0$

and $a + d = 0$

Trace $A = a + d = 0$

$|A| = ad - bc = -a^2 - bc = 1$

116. $MN = NM$

$M^2N^2 (M^TN)^{-1} (MN^{-1})^T M^2N^2N^{-1} (M^T)^{-1} (N^{-1})^T \cdot M^T$

$= M^2N \cdot (M^T)^{-1} (N^{-1})^T M^T = -M^2 \cdot N (M)^{-1} (N^T)^{-1} M^T$

$= +M^2NM^{-1}N^{-1}M^T = -M \cdot NMM^{-1}N^{-1} M$

$= -MNN^{-1}M = -M^2$

Note

A skew-symmetric matrix of order 3 cannot be non-singular hence the question is wrong.

117. (i) $a + 8b + 7c = 0;\ 9a + 2b + 3c = 0$

$7a + 7b + 7c = 0$

Solving these equations, we get

$b = 6a$

$\Rightarrow c = -7a$

Now, $2x + y + z = 0$

$\Rightarrow 2a + 6a + (-7a) = 1$

$\Rightarrow a = 1, b = 6, c = -7$

$\therefore 7a + b + c = 7 + 6 - 7 = 6$

(ii) $\because a = 2$ with b and c satisfying (E)

$\therefore 2 + 8b + 7c = 0,\ 18 + 2b + 3c = 0$

and $2 + b + c = 0$

we get $b = 12$ and $c = -14$

Hence, $\dfrac{3}{\omega^a} + \dfrac{1}{\omega^b} + \dfrac{3}{\omega^c} = \dfrac{3}{\omega^2} + \dfrac{1}{\omega^{12}} + \dfrac{3}{\omega^{-14}}$

$= \dfrac{3\omega}{\omega^3} + \dfrac{1}{1} + 3\omega^{14}$

$= 3\omega + 1 + 3\omega^2$

$= 1 + 3(\omega + \omega^2)$

$= 1 + 3(-1) = -2$

(iii) $\because b = 6$, with a and c satisfying (E)

$\therefore \quad a + 48 + 7c = 0, 9a + 12 + 3c = 0, a + 6 + c = 0$

we get $\quad a = 1, c = -7$

Given, α, β are the roots of $ax^2 + bx + c = 0$

$$\therefore \quad \alpha + \beta = -\frac{b}{a} = -6,$$

$$\alpha\beta = \frac{c}{a} = -7$$

$$\text{Now, } \frac{1}{\alpha} + \frac{1}{\beta} = \frac{\alpha + \beta}{\alpha\beta} = \frac{-6}{-7} = \frac{6}{7}$$

$$\therefore \quad \sum_{n=0}^{\infty}\left(\frac{1}{\alpha} + \frac{1}{\beta}\right)^n = \sum_{n=0}^{\infty}\left(\frac{6}{7}\right)^n$$

$$= 1 + \left(\frac{6}{7}\right) + \left(\frac{6}{7}\right)^2 + \dots \infty$$

$$= \frac{1}{1 - 6/7} = 7$$

118. For the given matrix to be non singular

$$\therefore \quad \begin{vmatrix} 1 & a & b \\ \omega & 1 & c \\ \omega^2 & \omega & 1 \end{vmatrix} \neq 0$$

$$\Rightarrow \quad 1 - (a + c)\omega + ac\omega^2 \neq 0$$

$$\Rightarrow \quad (1 - a\omega)(1 - c\omega) \neq 0$$

$$\Rightarrow \quad a \neq \omega^2 \text{ and } c \neq \omega^2$$

$\because a, b$ and c are complex cube roots of unity.

$\therefore a$ and c can take only one value i.e., ω while b can take two values i.e., ω and ω^2.

$\therefore$ Total number of distinct $= 2$

119. Let $M = \begin{bmatrix} a & b & c \\ d & e & f \\ g & h & i \end{bmatrix}$

$$M\begin{bmatrix} 0 \\ 1 \\ 0 \end{bmatrix} = \begin{bmatrix} -1 \\ 2 \\ 3 \end{bmatrix} \Rightarrow b = -1, e = 2, h = 3$$

$$M\begin{bmatrix} 1 \\ -1 \\ 0 \end{bmatrix} = \begin{bmatrix} 1 \\ 1 \\ -1 \end{bmatrix} \Rightarrow a = 0, d = 3, g = 2$$

$$M\begin{bmatrix} 1 \\ 1 \\ 1 \end{bmatrix} = \begin{bmatrix} 0 \\ 0 \\ 12 \end{bmatrix} \Rightarrow g + h + i = 12 \Rightarrow i = 7$$

$\therefore$ Sum of diagonal elements $= a + e + i = 0 + 2 + 7 = 9$

120. Since, A and B are symmetric matrices

$$\therefore \quad A' = A \text{ and } B' = B$$

Statement-1 Let $P = A(BA)$

$$\therefore \quad P' = (A(BA))' = (BA)'A'$$

$$= (A'B')A'$$

$$= (AB)A \qquad [\because A' = A, B' = B]$$

$$= A(BA) \qquad \text{[By associative law]}$$

$$= P$$

$\Rightarrow A(BA)$ is symmetric

Now, let $\quad Q = (AB)A$

$$Q' = ((AB)A)'$$

$$= A'(AB)' = A'(B'A')$$

$$= A(BA) \qquad [\because A' = A, B' = B]$$

$$= (AB)A \qquad \text{[By associative law]}$$

$$= Q$$

$\Rightarrow (AB)A$ is symmetric.

$\therefore$ Statement-1 is true.

Statement - 2 $(AB)' = B'A' = BA \qquad [\because A' = A, B' = B]$

$= AB \qquad [\because AB = BA]$

$\Rightarrow AB$ is symmetric matrix

$\therefore$ Statement-2 is true.

Hence, both Statements are true, Statement-2 is not a correct explanation for Statement-1.

121. We have, $|Q| = \begin{vmatrix} 2^2a_{11} & 2^3a_{12} & 2^4a_{13} \\ 2^3a_{21} & 2^4a_{22} & 2^5a_{23} \\ 2^4a_{31} & 2^5a_{32} & 2^6a_{33} \end{vmatrix}$

$$= 2^2 \cdot 2^3 \cdot 2^4 \begin{vmatrix} a_{11} & a_{12} & a_{13} \\ 2a_{21} & 2a_{22} & 2a_{23} \\ 2^2a_{31} & 2^2a_{32} & 2^2a_{33} \end{vmatrix}$$

$$= 2^9 \cdot 2 \cdot 2^2 \begin{vmatrix} a_{11} & a_{12} & a_{13} \\ a_{21} & a_{22} & a_{23} \\ a_{31} & a_{32} & a_{33} \end{vmatrix} = 2^{12}|P|$$

$$\therefore \quad |Q| = 2^{12} \times 2 = 2^{13}$$

122. $\because \quad P^T = 2P + I \qquad \dots \text{(i)}$

$\therefore \quad (P^T)^T = (2P + I)^T$

$\Rightarrow \quad P = 2P^T + I \qquad \dots \text{(ii)}$

From Eqs. (i) and (ii), we get

$$P = 2(2P + I) + I$$

$$\Rightarrow \quad P = -I$$

$$\therefore \quad PX = -IX = -X$$

123. Given, $\text{adj } P = \begin{bmatrix} 1 & 4 & 4 \\ 2 & 1 & 7 \\ 1 & 1 & 3 \end{bmatrix}$

$$\Rightarrow \quad |\text{adj} P| = \begin{vmatrix} 1 & 4 & 4 \\ 2 & 1 & 7 \\ 1 & 1 & 3 \end{vmatrix}$$

$$= 1(-4) - 4(-1) + 4(1) = 4$$

$$\Rightarrow \quad |P|^{3-1} = 4$$

$$\Rightarrow \quad |P| = \pm 2$$

124. Let $u_1 + u_2 = \begin{pmatrix} x \\ y \\ z \end{pmatrix}$

Now, $\quad Au_1 + Au_2 = \begin{pmatrix} 1 \\ 1 \\ 0 \end{pmatrix}$

$$\Rightarrow \quad A(u_1 + u_2) = \begin{pmatrix} 1 \\ 1 \\ 0 \end{pmatrix}$$

$$\Rightarrow \begin{pmatrix} 1 & 0 & 0 \\ 2 & 1 & 0 \\ 3 & 2 & 1 \end{pmatrix} \begin{pmatrix} x \\ y \\ z \end{pmatrix} = \begin{pmatrix} 1 \\ 1 \\ 0 \end{pmatrix}$$

$$\Rightarrow \begin{pmatrix} x \\ 2x + y \\ 3x + 2y + z \end{pmatrix} = \begin{pmatrix} 1 \\ 1 \\ 0 \end{pmatrix}$$

$\therefore \quad x = 1, 2x + y = 1$

and $\quad 3x + 2y + z = 0$

$\Rightarrow \quad x = 1, y = -1, z = -1$

Hence, $u_1 + u_2 = \begin{pmatrix} 1 \\ -1 \\ -1 \end{pmatrix}$.

125. Given, $P^3 = Q^3$ ...(i)

and $P^2Q = Q^2P$ ... (ii)

Subtracting Eq. (i) and (ii), we get

$$P^3 - P^2Q = Q^3 - Q^2P$$

$$P^2 (P - Q) = - Q^2 (P - Q)$$

$$\Rightarrow \quad (P^2 + Q^2)(P - Q) = O$$

$$\Rightarrow \quad |(P^2 + Q^2)(P - Q)| = |O|$$

$$\Rightarrow \quad |P^2 + Q^2||P - Q| = 0$$

$$\therefore \quad |P^2 + Q^2| = 0 \quad [\because P \neq Q]$$

126. Given, adj $A = P$

$$\therefore \quad |\text{adj } A| = |P|$$

$$\Rightarrow \quad |A|^{3-1} = |P| \quad [\because |A| = 4]$$

$$\Rightarrow \quad 16 = |P|$$

$$\Rightarrow \quad 16 = \begin{vmatrix} 1 & \alpha & 3 \\ 1 & 3 & 3 \\ 2 & 4 & 4 \end{vmatrix}$$

$$\Rightarrow \quad 16 = 1(0) - \alpha (4 - 6) + 3(4 - 6)$$

$$\Rightarrow \quad 16 = 2\alpha - 6$$

$$\Rightarrow \quad 2\alpha = 22$$

$$\therefore \quad \alpha = 11$$

127. (a) $(N^TMN)^T = N^TM^T(N^T)^T = N^TM^TN = N^TMN$ or $-N^TMN$ According as M is symmetric or skew-symmetric.

$\therefore$ Correct.

(b) $(MN - NM)^T = (MN)^T - (NM)^T = N^TM^T - M^TN^T$

$= NM - MN$ $\quad [\because M, N \text{ are symmetric}]$

$= -(MN - NM)$

$\therefore$ correct

(c) $(MN)^T = N^TM^T = NM \neq MN$ $\quad [\because M, N \text{ are symmetric}]$

$\therefore$ Incorrect.

(d) $(\text{adj} M)(\text{adj} N) = \text{adj}(NM) \neq \text{adj}(MN)$

$\therefore$ Incorrect.

128. $P = [p_{ij}]_{n \times n} = [\omega^{i+j}]_{n \times n} = \begin{bmatrix} \omega^2 & \omega^3 & \omega^4 & \dots \omega^{1+n} \\ \omega^3 & \omega^4 & \omega^5 & \dots \omega^{2+n} \\ \omega^4 & \omega^5 & \omega^6 & \dots \omega^{3+n} \\ \vdots & \vdots & \vdots & \vdots \\ \omega^{n+1} & \omega^{n+2} & \omega^{n+3} & \dots \omega^{2n} \end{bmatrix}$

$$\therefore \quad P^2 = \begin{bmatrix} 0 & 0 & 0 & \dots 0 \\ 0 & 0 & 0 & \dots 0 \\ 0 & 0 & 0 & \dots 0 \\ \vdots & \vdots & \vdots & \vdots \\ 0 & 0 & 0 & \dots 0 \end{bmatrix} = 0$$

If n is multiple of 3, so for $P^2 \neq 0$, n should not be a multiple of 3, i.e. n can take values 55, 56 and 58.

129. $B = A^{-1} A'$

$$B' = (A^{-1} A')' = A(A^{-1})'$$

Now, $BB' = (A^{-1}A') A (A^{-1})' = A^{-1} (A' A) (A^{-1})'$

$= A^{-1} (AA') (A^{-1})'$ $\quad [\because A' A = AA']$

$= (A^{-1}A) A' (A^{-1})'$

$= (IA') (A^{-1})' = A' (A^{-1})' = (A^{-1} A)' = I' = I$

130. Let $M = \begin{bmatrix} a & b \\ b & c \end{bmatrix}$, where $a, b, c \in I$

M is invertible if $\begin{vmatrix} a & b \\ b & c \end{vmatrix} \neq 0 \Rightarrow ac - b^2 \neq 0$

(a) $\begin{bmatrix} a \\ b \end{bmatrix} = \begin{bmatrix} b \\ c \end{bmatrix} \Rightarrow a = b = c \Rightarrow ac - b^2 = 0$

$\therefore$ Option (a) is incorrect

(b) $[b \ c] = [a \ b] \Rightarrow a = b = c \Rightarrow ac - b^2 = 0$

$\therefore$ Option (b) is incorrect

(c) $M = \begin{bmatrix} a & 0 \\ 0 & c \end{bmatrix}$, then $|M| = ac \neq 0$

$\therefore$ M is invertible

$\therefore$ Option (c) is correct.

(d) As $ac \neq$ (Integer ^{2} $\Rightarrow ac \neq b^2$

$\therefore$ Option (d) is correct.

131. Given, $MN = NM$, $M \neq N^2$ and $M^2 = N^4$

Then, $\quad M^2 = N^4$

$$\Rightarrow \quad (M + N^2)(M - N^2) = 0$$

$$\therefore \quad M + N^2 = 0 \quad [\because M \neq N^2]$$

$$\Rightarrow \quad |M + N^2| = 0$$

(a) $|M^2 + MN^2| = |M||M + N^2| = 0$

$\therefore$ Option (a) is correct.

(b) $(M^2 + MN^2) U = M(M + N^2) U = 0$

$\therefore$ Option (b) is correct.

(c) $\because |M^2 + MN^2| = 0$ from option (a)

$\therefore \quad |M^2 + MN^2| \not\geq 1$

$\therefore$ Option (c) is incorrect.

(d) If $AX = 0$ and $|A| = 0$, then X can be non-zero.

(c) $\because$ $|M^2 + MN^2| = 0$ from option (a)

$\therefore \quad |M^2 + MN^2| \not\geq 1$

$\therefore$ Option (c) is incorrect.

(d) If $AX = 0$ and $|A| = 0$, then X can be non-zero.

132. $\because \; AA^T = 9I$

$$\begin{bmatrix} 1 & 2 & 2 \\ 2 & 1 & -2 \\ a & 2 & b \end{bmatrix}\begin{bmatrix} 1 & 2 & a \\ 2 & 1 & 2 \\ 2 & -2 & b \end{bmatrix} = 9\begin{bmatrix} 1 & 0 & 0 \\ 0 & 1 & 0 \\ 0 & 0 & 1 \end{bmatrix}$$

$$\Rightarrow \begin{bmatrix} 9 & 0 & a+4+2b \\ 0 & 9 & 2a+2-2b \\ a+4+2b & 2a+2-2b & a^2+4+b^2 \end{bmatrix} = \begin{bmatrix} 9 & 0 & 0 \\ 0 & 9 & 0 \\ 0 & 0 & 9 \end{bmatrix}$$

On comparing, we get

$$a + 2b + 4 = 0 \qquad \text{... (i)}$$
$$2a - 2b + 2 = 0 \qquad \text{... (ii)}$$

From Eqs. (i) and (ii), we get

$$a = -2,$$
$$b = -1$$

$\therefore$ Ordered pair is $(-2, -1)$.

133. $\because \; X^T = -X, Y^T = -Y, Z^T = Z$

(a) $(Y^3 Z^4 - Z^4 Y^3)^T = (Y^3 Z^4)^T - (Z^4 Y^3)^T$

$$= (Z^4)^T (Y^3)^T - (Y^3)^T (Z^4)^T$$
$$= (Z^T)^4 (Y^T)^3 - (Y^T)^3 (Z^T)^4$$
$$= -Z^4Y^3 + Y^3 Z^4$$
$$= Y^3Z^4 - Z^4Y^3$$

Option (a) is incorrect.

(b) $X^{44} + Y^{44}$ is symmetric matrix. Option b is incorrect.

(c) $(X^4 Z^3 - Z^3X^4)^T = (X^4Z^3)^T - (Z^3 X^4)^T$

$$= (Z^3)^T (X^4)^T - (X^4)^T (Z^3)^T$$
$$= (Z^T)^3 (X^T)^4 - (X^T)^4 (Z^T)^3$$
$$= Z^3X^4 - X^4Z^3$$
$$= -(X^4Z^3 - Z^3X^4)$$

$\therefore$ Option (c) is correct.

(d) $X^{23} + Y^{23}$ is skew-symmetric matrix. Option (d) is correct.

134. $\because$

$$A \text{ adj } A = AA^T$$
$$\Rightarrow \quad A^{-1}(A \text{ adj } A) = A^{-1}(AA^T)$$
$$\Rightarrow \quad (A^{-1}A) \text{ adj } A = (A^{-1}A)A^T$$
$$\Rightarrow \quad I(\text{adj } A) = IA^T$$

or $\quad \text{adj } A = A^T$

or $\quad \begin{bmatrix} 2 & b \\ -3 & 5a \end{bmatrix} = \begin{bmatrix} 5a & 3 \\ -b & 2 \end{bmatrix}$

$\Rightarrow \quad 5a = 2$ and $b = 3$

$\therefore \quad 5a + b = 5$

135. $\because \; PQ = kI \Rightarrow \dfrac{P.Q}{k} = I \Rightarrow P^{-1} = \dfrac{Q}{k}$ ...(i)

Also $\quad |P| = 12\alpha + 20$ ...(ii)

and $\quad$ given $q_{23} = \dfrac{-k}{8}$

Comparing the third element of 2nd row on both sides,

we get $\quad \dfrac{1}{(12\alpha+20)}(-(3\alpha+4)) = \dfrac{1}{k} \times \dfrac{-k}{8}$

$\Rightarrow \quad 24\alpha + 32 = 12\alpha + 20$

$\quad \alpha = -1$ ...(iii)

From (ii), $\quad |P| = 8$ ...(iv)

Also $\quad PQ = kI$

$\Rightarrow \quad |PQ| = |kI|$

$\Rightarrow \quad |P||Q| = k^3$

$\Rightarrow \quad 8 \times \dfrac{k^2}{2} = k^3 \qquad \left(\because |P| = 8, |Q| = \dfrac{k^2}{2}\right)$

$\therefore \quad k = 4$ ...(v)

(b) $4\alpha - k + 8 = -4 - 4 + 8 = 0$

(c) $\det(P \text{ adj}(Q)) = |P|\,|\text{adj } Q| = |P||Q|^2 = 8 \times 8^2 = 2^9$

(d) $\det(Q \text{ adj}(P)) = |Q|\,|\text{adj } P| = |Q||P|^2 = 8 \times 8^2 = 2^9$

136. $\because \; Z = \dfrac{-1+\sqrt{3}i}{2} = \omega$ ...(i)

$\Rightarrow \quad \omega^3 = 1$ and $1 + \omega + \omega^2 = 0$

Now, $\quad P = \begin{bmatrix} (-\omega)^r & \omega^{2s} \\ \omega^{2s} & \omega^r \end{bmatrix}$

$$\therefore \quad P^2 = \begin{bmatrix} (-\omega)^r & \omega^{2s} \\ \omega^{2s} & \omega^r \end{bmatrix}\begin{bmatrix} (-\omega)^r & \omega^{2s} \\ \omega^{2s} & \omega^r \end{bmatrix}$$

$$= \begin{bmatrix} \omega^{2r} + \omega^{4s} & \omega^{2r}((-\omega)^r + \omega^r) \\ \omega^{2s}((-\omega)^r + \omega^r) & \omega^{4s} + \omega^{2r} \end{bmatrix}$$

$$= \begin{bmatrix} \omega^{2r} + \omega^{s} & \omega^{2s}((-\omega)^r + \omega^r) \\ \omega^{2s}((-\omega)^r + \omega^s) & \omega^{s} + \omega^{2r} \end{bmatrix} \quad (\because \omega^3 = 1)$$

$$\because \quad P^2 = -I = \begin{bmatrix} -1 & 0 \\ 0 & -1 \end{bmatrix} \qquad \text{...(ii)}$$

Form Eqs. (i) and (ii), we get

$$\omega^{2r} + \omega^s = -1$$

and $\quad \omega^{2s}((-\omega)^r + \omega^r) = 0$

$\Rightarrow r$ is odd and $s = r$ but not a multiple of 3. Which is possible when $r = s = 1$

$\therefore$ Only one pair is there.

137. $P=\begin{bmatrix}1&0&0\\4&1&0\\16&4&1\end{bmatrix}=I+\begin{bmatrix}0&0&0\\4&0&0\\16&4&0\end{bmatrix}=I+A$

Let $A=\begin{bmatrix}0&0&0\\4&0&0\\16&4&0\end{bmatrix}$

$\Rightarrow \quad A^2=\begin{bmatrix}0&0&0\\0&0&0\\16&0&0\end{bmatrix}$ and $A^3=\begin{bmatrix}0&0&0\\0&0&0\\0&0&0\end{bmatrix}$

$\Rightarrow A^n$ is a null matrix $\forall n \geq 3$

$\therefore \quad P^{50}=(I+A)^{50}=I+50A+\dfrac{50\times 49}{2}A^2$

$\Rightarrow \quad Q+\mathcal{J}=I+50A+25\times 49A^2$

or $\quad Q=50A+25\times 49A^2$

$$=\begin{bmatrix}0&0&0\\200&0&0\\800&200&0\end{bmatrix}+\begin{bmatrix}0&0&0\\0&0&0\\19600&0&0\end{bmatrix}$$

$\therefore \quad \begin{bmatrix}q_{11}&q_{12}&q_{13}\\q_{21}&q_{22}&q_{23}\\q_{31}&q_{32}&q_{33}\end{bmatrix}=\begin{bmatrix}0&0&0\\200&0&0\\20400&200&0\end{bmatrix}$

On comparing, we get

$$q_{21}=q_{32}=200,\ q_{31}=20400$$

$$\therefore \quad \frac{q_{31}+q_{32}}{q_{21}}=\frac{20400+200}{200}$$

$$=102+1=103$$

138. $\because A^2=\begin{bmatrix}2&-3\\-4&1\end{bmatrix}\begin{bmatrix}2&-3\\-4&1\end{bmatrix}=\begin{bmatrix}16&-9\\-12&13\end{bmatrix}$

$\therefore \quad 3A^2+12A=3\begin{bmatrix}16&-9\\-12&13\end{bmatrix}+12\begin{bmatrix}2&-3\\-4&1\end{bmatrix}$

$$=\begin{bmatrix}72&-63\\-84&51\end{bmatrix}$$

$\Rightarrow \quad \text{adj}\,(3A^2+12A)=\begin{bmatrix}51&63\\84&72\end{bmatrix}$

CHAPTER

09

Probability

Learning Part

Session 1

- Some Basic Definitions
- Mathematical or Priori or Classical Definition of Probability
- Odds in Favour and Odds Against the Event

Sesstion 2

- Some Important Symbols
- Conditional Probability

Sesstion 3

- Total Probability Theorem
- Baye's Theorem or Inverse Probability

Sesstion 4

- Binomial Theorem on Probability
- Poisson Distribution
- Expectation
- Multinomial Theorem
- Uncountable Uniform Spaces

Practice Part

- JEE Type Examples
- Chapter Exercises

Arihant on Your Mobile !

Exercises with the symbol can be practised on your mobile. See inside cover page to activate for free.

Session 1

Some Basic Definitions, Mathematical or Priori or Classical Definition of Probability, Odds in Favour and Odds Against the Event

Some Basic Definitions

1. Random Experiment

An experiment whose outcome cannot be predicted with certainty, is called a random experiment.

Or

If in each trial of an experiment, which when repeated under identical conditions, the outcome is not unique but the outcome in a trial is one of the several possible outcomes, then such an experiment is known as a random experiment.

For example,

(i) "Throwing an unbiased die" is a random experiment because when a die is thrown, we cannot say with certainty which one of the numbers 1, 2, 3, 4, 5 and 6 will come up.

(ii) "Tossing of a fair coin" is a random experiment because when a coin is tossed, we cannot say with certainty whether either a head or a tail will come up.

(iii) "Drawing a card from a well-shuffled pack of cards" is a random experiment.

Remark

1. A die is a solid cube which has six faces and numbers 1, 2, 3, 4, 5 and 6 marked on the faces, respectively. In throwing or rolling a die, then any one number can be on the uppermost face.
2. (i) A pack of cards consists of 52 cards in 4 suits, i.e (a) Spades (♠) (b) Clubs (♣) (c) Hearts (♥) (d) Diamonds (♦). Each suit consists of 13 cards. Out of these, spades and clubs are black faced cards, while hearts and diamonds are red faced cards. The King, Queen, Jack (or Knave) are called face cards or honour cards.
   (ii) **Game of bridge** It is played by 4 players, each player is given 13 cards.
   (iii) **Game of whist** It is played by two pairs of persons.

2. Sample Space

The set of all possible results of a random experiment is called the sample space of that experiment and it is generally denoted by S.

Each element of a sample space is called a **sample point.**

For example,

(i) If we toss a coin, there are two possible results, namely a head (H) or a tail (T).
So, the sample space in this experiment is given by
$$S = \{H, T\}.$$

(ii) When two coins are tossed, the sample space
$$S = \{HH, HT, TH, TT\}$$o
where, HH denotes the head on the first coin and head on the second coin. Similarly, HT denotes the head on the first coin and tail on the second coin.

(iii) When we throw a die, then any one of the numbers 1 2, 3, 4, 5 and 6 will come up. So, the sample space
$$S = \{1, 2, 3, 4, 5, 6\}.$$

3. Elementary Event

An event having only a single sample point is called an elementary or simple event.

For example, When two coins are tossed, the sample space $S = \{HH, HT, TH, TT\}$, then the event, $E_1 = \{HH\}$ of getting both the heads is a simple event.

4. Mixed Event or Compound Event or Composite Event

An event other than elementary or simple event is called mixed event.

For example,

(i) When two coins are tossed, the sample space
$$S = \{HH, HT, TH, TT\}$$
Then, the event $E = \{HH, HT, TH\}$ of getting atleast one head, is a mixed event.

(ii) When a die is thrown, the sample space
$$S = \{1, 2, 3, 4, 5, 6\}$$
Let $A = \{2, 4, 6\}$ = the event of occurrence of an even number
and $B = \{3, 6\}$ = the event of occurrence of a number divisible by 3.
Here, A and B are mixed events.

Equally likely Events

e given events are said to be equally likely, if none of ·m is expected to occur in preference to the other.

· example,

i) When an unbiased coin is tossed, then occurrence of head or tail are equally likely cases and there is no reason to expect a 'head' or a 'tail' in preference to the other.

i) When an unbiased die is thrown, all the six faces 1, 2, 3, 4, 5 and 6 are equally likely to come up. There is no reason to expect 1 or 2 or 3 or 4 or 5 or 6 in preference to the other.

Independent Events

vo events are said to be independent, if the occurrence one does not depend on the occurrence of the other.

r example, When an unbiased die is thrown, then the mple space $S = \{1, 2, 3, 4, 5, 6\}$

t $E_1 = \{1, 3, 5\}$ = the event of occurrence of an odd mber and $E_2 = \{2, 4, 6\}$ = the event of occurrence of an en number. Clearly, the occurrence of odd number does t depend on the occurrence of even number. So, E_1 and are independent events.

. Complementary Event

t E be an event and S be the sample space for a random periment, then complement of E is denoted by E' or E^c $\bar{E}$. Clearly, E' means E does not occur.

ıus, E' occurs $\Leftrightarrow E$ does not occur.

r example, When an unbiased die is thrown, then the mple space $S = \{1, 2, 3, 4, 5, 6\}$.

$$E = \{1, 4, 6\}, \text{ then } E' = \{2, 3, 5\}$$

. Mutually Exclusive Events

set of events is said to be mutually exclusive, if currence of one of them precludes the occurrence of any the remaining events. If a set of events $E_1, E_2, \ldots, E_n$ r mutually exclusive events.

hen, $$E_1 \cap E_2 \cap \ldots \cap E_n = \phi$$

r example, If we thrown an unbiased die, then the mple space $S = \{1, 2, 3, 4, 5, 6\}$ in which

$_1 = \{1, 2, 3\}$ = the event of occurrence of a number less ıan 4 and $E_2 = \{5, 6\}$ = the event of occurrence of a umber greater than 4. Clearly, $E_1 \cap E_2 = \phi$

o, E_1 and E_2 are mutually exclusive.

. Exhaustive Events

set of events is said to be exhaustive, if the performance f the experiment results in the occurrence of atleast one of ıem. If a set of events $E_1, E_2, \ldots, E_n$ for exhaustive events.

Then, $$E_1 \cup E_2 \cup \ldots \cup E_n = S$$

For example, If we thrown an unbiased die, then sample space $S = \{1, 2, 3, 4, 5, 6\}$ in which

$E_1 = \{1, 2, 3, 4\}$ = the event of occurrence of a number less than 5 and $E_2 = \{3, 4, 5, 6\}$ = the event of occurrence of a number greater than 2.

Then, $E_1 \cup E_2 = \{1, 2, 3, 4, 5, 6\}$ and $E_1 \cap E_2 = \{3, 4\}$

So, $E_1 \cup E_2 = S$ and $E_1 \cap E_2 \neq \phi$

Hence, E_1 and E_2 are exhaustive events.

10. Mutually Exclusive and Exhaustive Events

A set of events is said to be mutually exclusive and exhaustive, if above two conditions are satisfied. If a set of events $E_1, E_2, \ldots, E_n$ for mutually exclusive and exhaustive events.

Then, $E_1 \cup E_2 \cup \ldots \cup E_n = S$ and $E_1 \cap E_2 \cap \ldots \cap E_n = \phi$

For example, If we thrown an unbiased die, then sample space

$S = \{1,2,3,4,5,6\}$ in which

$E_1 = \{1,3,5\}$ = the event of occurrence of an odd number and $E_2 = \{2,4,6\}$ = the event of occurrence of an even number.

Then, $E_1 \cup E_2 = \{1,2,3,4,5,6\}$ and $E_1 \cap E_2 = \phi$

So, $E_1 \cup E_2 = S$ and $E_1 \cap E_2 = \phi$.

Hence, E_1 and E_2 are mutually exclusive and exhaustive events.

Mathematical or Priori or Classical Definition of Probability

The probability of an event E to occur is the ratio of the number of cases in its favour to the total number of cases (equally likely).

$$\therefore \quad P(E) = \frac{n(E)}{n(S)} = \frac{\text{Number of cases favourable to event E}}{\text{Total number of cases}}$$

Range of Value of $P(E)$

Probability of occurrence of an event is a number lying between 0 and 1.

Proof Let S be the sample space and E be an event. Then,

$$E \subseteq S \quad \ldots \text{(i)}$$

Also, $$\phi \subseteq S \quad \ldots \text{(ii)}$$

where ϕ is a null set. From Eqs. (i) and (ii), we get

$$\phi \subseteq S \supseteq E \Rightarrow n(\phi) \leq n(E) \leq n(S)$$

$$\Rightarrow \quad 0 \leq \frac{n(E)}{n(S)} \leq 1 \quad [\because n(\phi) = 0]$$

$$\Rightarrow \quad 0 \leq P(E) \leq 1$$

Remark

1. For impossible event ϕ; $P(\phi) = 0$
2. For sure event S, $P(S) = 1$

Relationship between $P(E)$ and $P(E')$

If E is any event and E' be the complement of event E, then
$$P(E) + P(E') = 1$$

Proof Let S be the sample space, then
$$E' = S - E$$
$$\Rightarrow \quad n(E') = n(S) - n(E)$$
$$\Rightarrow \quad \frac{n(E')}{n(S)} = 1 - \frac{n(E)}{n(S)}$$
$$\Rightarrow \quad P(E') = 1 - P(E)$$
i.e. $\quad P(E) + P(E') = 1$

Odds in Favour and Odds Against the Event

Let S be the sample space. If a is the number of cases favourable to the event E, b is the number of cases favourable to the event E', the **odds in favour** of E are defined by $a:b$ and **odds against** of E are $b:a$.

i.e. odds in favour of event E is

$$\frac{a}{b} = \frac{n(E)}{n(E')} = \frac{\frac{n(E)}{n(S)}}{\frac{n(E')}{n(S)}} = \frac{P(E)}{P(E')} \Rightarrow \frac{P(E')}{P(E)} = \frac{b}{a}$$

$$\Rightarrow \quad \frac{P(E') + P(E)}{P(E)} = \frac{b+a}{a}$$

$$\Rightarrow \quad \frac{1}{P(E)} = \frac{b+a}{a}$$

$$\Rightarrow \quad P(E) = \frac{a}{a+b} \text{ and } P(E') = \frac{b}{a+b}$$

Remark

We use the sign '+' for the operation 'or' and '×' for the operation 'and' in order to solve the problems on definition of probability.

| Example 1. If three coins are tossed, represent the sample space and the event of getting atleast two heads, then find the number of elements in them.

Sol. Let S be the sample space and E be the event of occurrence of atleast two heads and let H denote the occurrence of head and T denote the occurrence of tail, when one coin is tossed.

Then, $\quad S = \{H, T\} \times \{H, T\} \times \{H, T\}$

$S = \{(H, H, H), (H, H, T), (H, T, H), (T, H, H), (T, T, H), (T, H, T), (H, T, T), (T, T, T)\}$

and $\quad E = \{(H, H, H), (H, H, T), (H, T, H), (T, H, H)\}$

Also, $n(S) = 8$ and $n(E) = 4$

| Example 2. One ticket is drawn at random from a bag containing 24 tickets numbered 1 to 24. Represent the sample space and the event of drawing a ticket containing number which is a prime. Also, find the number of elements in them.

Sol. Let S be the sample space and E be the event of occurrence a prime number.

Then, $\quad S = \{1, 2, 3, 4, 5, \dots, 24\}$

and $\quad E = \{2, 3, 5, 7, 11, 13, 17, 19, 23\}$

Also, $\quad n(S) = 24$ and $n(E) = 9$

| Example 3. Two dice are thrown simultaneously. What is the probability obtaining a total score less than 11?

Sol. Let S be the sample space and E be the event of obtaining a total less than 11.

Then, $S = \{1, 2, 3, 4, 5, 6\} \times \{1, 2, 3, 4, 5, 6\} \Rightarrow n(S) = 6 \times 6 = 36$

Let E' be the event of obtaining a total score greater than or equal to 11.

Also, $\quad E' = \{(5, 6), (6, 5), (6, 6)\}; \ \therefore n(E') = 3$

Then, probability of obtaining a total score greater than or equal to 11,

$$P(E') = \frac{n(E')}{n(S)} = \frac{3}{36} = \frac{1}{12}$$

$$\therefore \quad P(E) = 1 - P(E') = 1 - \frac{1}{12} = \frac{11}{12}$$

Hence, required probability is $\frac{11}{12}$.

| Example 4. If a leap-leap year is selected at random then what is the chance it will contain 53 Sunday?

Sol. A leap-leap year has 367 days i.e., 52 complete week and three days more. These three days will be three consecutive days of a week. A leap-leap year will have 53 Sundays, if out of the three consecutive days of a week selected at random one is a Sunday.

Let be the sample space and E be the event that out of the three consecutive days of a week one is Sunday, then

$S =$ {(Sunday, Monday, Tuesday), (Monday, Tuesday, Wednesday), (Tuesday, Wednesday, Thursday), (Wednesday, Thursday, Friday), (Thursday, Friday, Saturday), (Friday, Saturday, Sunday), (Saturday, Sunday, Monday)}; $n(S) = 7$

and $\quad E =$ {(Sunday, Monday, Tuesday), (Friday, Saturday, Sunday), (Saturday, Sunday, Monday)}

$\therefore \quad n(E) = 3$

Now, required probability, $P(E) = \frac{n(E)}{n(S)} = \frac{3}{7}$

| Example 5. From a pack of 52 playing cards, three cards are drawn at random. Find the probability of drawing a King, a Queen and a Knave.

Sol. Let S be the sample space and E be the event that out of the three cards drawn one is a King, one is a Queen and one is a Knave.

$\therefore n(S)$ = Total number of selecting 3 cards out of 52 cards $= {}^{52}C_3$

and $n(E)$ = Number of selecting 3 cards out of one is King, one is Queen and one is Knave $= {}^4C_1 \cdot {}^4C_1 \cdot {}^4C_1 = 64$

$\therefore$ Required probability, $P(E) = \dfrac{n(E)}{n(S)} = \dfrac{64}{{}^{52}C_3} = \dfrac{64}{\dfrac{52 \cdot 51 \cdot 50}{1 \cdot 2 \cdot 3}} = \dfrac{16}{5525}$

| Example 6. A bag contains 8 red and 5 white balls. Three balls are drawn at random. Find the probability that

(i) all the three balls are white.
(ii) all the three balls are red.
(iii) one ball is red and two balls are white.

Sol. Let S be the sample space, E_1 be the event of getting 3 white balls, E_2 be the event of getting 3 red balls and E_3 be the event of getting one red ball and two white balls.

$\therefore n(S)$ = Number of ways of selecting 3 balls out of $13(8+5) = {}^{13}C_3 = \dfrac{13 \cdot 12 \cdot 11}{1 \cdot 2 \cdot 3} = 286$

(i) $n(E_1)$ = Number of ways of selecting 3 white balls out of 5

$= {}^5C_3 = {}^5C_2 = \dfrac{5 \cdot 4}{1 \cdot 2} = 10$

$\therefore P$ (getting 3 white balls) $= \dfrac{n(E_1)}{n(S)} = \dfrac{10}{286} = \dfrac{5}{143}$

(ii) $n(E_2)$ = Number of ways of selecting 3 red balls out of 8

$= {}^8C_3 = \dfrac{8 \cdot 7 \cdot 6}{1 \cdot 2 \cdot 3} = 56$

$\therefore P$ (getting 3 red balls) $= \dfrac{n(E_2)}{n(S)}$

$= \dfrac{56}{286} = \dfrac{28}{143}$

(iii) $n(E_3)$ = Number of ways of selecting 1 red ball out of 8 and 2 black balls out of $5 = {}^8C_1 \cdot {}^5C_2 = 8 \cdot 10 = 80$

$\therefore P$ (getting 1 red and 2 black balls)

$= \dfrac{n(E_3)}{n(S)} = \dfrac{80}{286} = \dfrac{40}{143}$

Exercise for Session 1

1. A problem in mathematics is given to three students and their respective probabilities of solving the problem are $\frac{1}{2}, \frac{1}{3}$ and $\frac{1}{4}$. The probability that the problem is solved, is

(a) $\frac{3}{4}$ (b) $\frac{1}{2}$ (c) $\frac{2}{3}$ (d) $\frac{1}{3}$

2. A dice is thrown 3 times and the sum of the 3 numbers thrown is 15. The probability that the first throw was a four, is

(a) $\frac{1}{5}$ (b) $\frac{1}{4}$ (c) $\frac{1}{6}$ (d) $\frac{2}{5}$

3. Three faces of a fair dice are yellow, two faces red and one blue. The dice is tossed three times. The probability that the colours yellow, red and blue appear in the first, second and third toss respectively, is

(a) $\frac{1}{6}$ (b) $\frac{1}{12}$ (c) $\frac{1}{24}$ (d) $\frac{1}{36}$

4. *A* speaks truth in 75% of cases and *B* in 80% of cases. The percentage of cases they are likely to contradict each other in stating the same fact, is

(a) 30% (b) 35% (c) 45% (d) 25%

5. An unbiased dice with faces marked 1, 2, 3, 4, 5, 6 is rolled four times. Out of four face values obtained the probability that the minimum face value is not less than 2 and the maximum face value is not greater than 5, is

(a) $\frac{16}{81}$ (b) $\frac{1}{81}$ (c) $\frac{80}{81}$ (d) $\frac{65}{81}$

6. Three numbers are chosen at random without replacement from {1, 2, 3, ..., 10}. The probability that the minimum of the chosen number is 3 or their maximum is 7, is

(a) $\frac{11}{20}$ (b) $\frac{7}{20}$ (c) $\frac{11}{40}$ (d) $\frac{7}{40}$

7. Seven white balls and three black balls are randomly placed in a row. The probability that no two black balls are placed adjacently, is

(a) $\frac{1}{2}$ (b) $\frac{7}{15}$ (c) $\frac{2}{15}$ (d) $\frac{1}{3}$

8. Two numbers are selected randomly from the set $S = \{1, 2, 3, 4, 5, 6\}$ without replacement. The probability that minimum of the two numbers is less than 4, is

(a) $\frac{1}{15}$ (b) $\frac{14}{15}$ (c) $\frac{1}{5}$ (d) $\frac{4}{5}$

9. If $\frac{1+3p}{3}$, $\frac{1-p}{4}$ and $\frac{1-2p}{2}$ are the probabilities of the three mutually exclusive events, then $p \in$

(a) $[0, 1]$ (b) $\left[0, \frac{1}{2}\right]$ (c) $\left[\frac{1}{3}, 1\right]$ (d) $\left[\frac{1}{3}, \frac{1}{2}\right]$

10. Three identical dice are rolled once. The probability that the same number will appear on each of them, is

(a) $\frac{1}{6}$ (b) $\frac{1}{36}$ (c) $\frac{1}{18}$ (d) $\frac{3}{28}$

11. If the letters of the word ASSASSIN are written down in a row, the probability that no two S's occur together, is

(a) $\frac{1}{35}$ (b) $\frac{1}{21}$ (c) $\frac{1}{14}$ (d) $\frac{1}{28}$

12. A box contains 2 black, 4 white and 3 red balls. One ball is drawn at random from the box and kept aside. From the remaining balls in the box another ball is drawn and kept beside the first. This process is repeated till all the balls are drawn from the box. The probability that the balls drawn from the box are in the sequence 2 black, 4 white and 3 red, is

(a) $\frac{1}{126}$ (b) $\frac{1}{630}$ (c) $\frac{1}{1260}$ (d) $\frac{1}{2520}$

13. If three distinct numbers are chosen randomly from the first 100 natural numbers, then the probability that all three of them are divisible by both 2 and 3, is

(a) $\frac{4}{55}$ (b) $\frac{4}{35}$ (c) $\frac{4}{33}$ (d) $\frac{4}{1155}$

14. There are 2 vans each having numbered seats, 3 in the front and 4 at the back. There are 3 girls and 9 boys to be seated in the vans. The probability of 3 girls sitting together in a back row on adjacent seats, is

(a) $\frac{1}{13}$ (b) $\frac{1}{39}$ (c) $\frac{1}{65}$ (d) $\frac{1}{91}$

15. A and B stand in a ring along with 10 other persons. If the arrangement is at random, then the probability that there are exactly 3 persons between A and B, is

(a) $\frac{1}{11}$ (b) $\frac{2}{11}$ (c) $\frac{3}{11}$ (d) $\frac{4}{11}$

16. The first 12 letters of English alphabet are written down at random in a row. The probability that there are exactly 4 letters between A and B, is

(a) $\frac{7}{33}$ (b) $\frac{7}{66}$ (c) $\frac{7}{99}$ (d) $\frac{5}{33}$

17. Six boys and six girls sit in a row randomly. The probability that the six girls sit together or the boys and girls sit alternately, is

(a) $\frac{3}{308}$ (b) $\frac{1}{100}$ (c) $\frac{2}{205}$ (d) $\frac{4}{407}$

18. If from each of three boxes containing 3 white and 1 black, 2 white and 2 black, 1 white and 3 black balls, one ball is drawn, the probability of drawing 2 white and 1 black ball, is

(a) $\frac{13}{32}$ (b) $\frac{1}{4}$ (c) $\frac{1}{32}$ (d) $\frac{3}{16}$

19. The probability that a year chosen at random has 53 Sundays, is

(a) $\frac{5}{7}$ (b) $\frac{3}{7}$ (c) $\frac{5}{28}$ (d) $\frac{3}{28}$

20. If the letters of the word MATHEMATICS are arranged arbitrarily, the probability that C comes before E, E before H, H before I and I before S, is

(a) $\frac{3}{10}$ (b) $\frac{1}{20}$ (c) $\frac{1}{120}$ (d) $\frac{1}{720}$

Session 2

Some Important Symbols, Conditional Probability

Some Important Symbols

If A, B and C are any three events, then

(i) $A \cap B$ or AB denotes the event of simultaneous occurrence of both the events A and B.

(ii) $A \cup B$ or $A + B$ denotes the event of occurrence of atleast one of the events A or B.

(iii) $A - B$ denotes the occurrence of event A but not B.

(iv) $\overline{A}$ denotes the not occurrence of event A.

(v) $A \cap \overline{B}$ denotes the occurrence of event A but not B.

(vi) $\overline{A} \cap \overline{B} = \overline{(A \cup B)}$ denotes the occurrence of neither A nor B.

(vii) $A \cup B \cup C$ denotes the occurrence of atleast one event A, B or C.

(viii) $(A \cap \overline{B}) \cup (\overline{A} \cap B)$ denotes the occurrence of exactly one of A and B.

(ix) $A \cap B \cap C$ denotes the occurrence of all three A, B and C.

(x) $(A \cap B \cap \overline{C}) \cup (A \cap \overline{B} \cap C) \cup (\overline{A} \cap B \cap C)$ denotes the occurrence of exactly two of A, B and C.

Remark

Remember with the help of figures

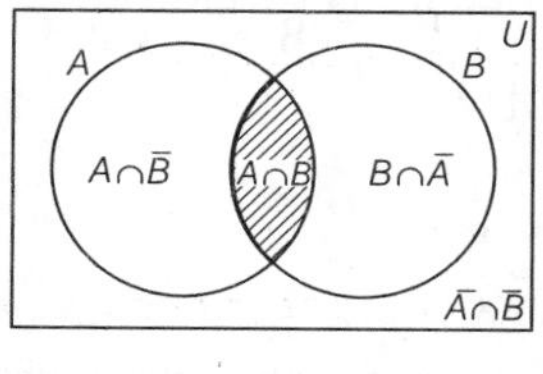

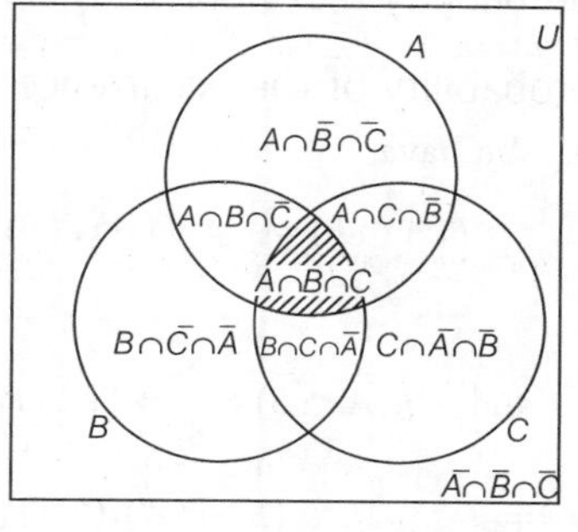

Important Results

1. If A and B are arbitrary events, then

(a) $P(A \cup B) = P(A) + P(B) - P(A \cap B)$

Proof Let S be the sample space. Since, we know that

$$n(A \cup B) = n(A) + n(B) - n(A \cap B)$$

$$\Rightarrow \frac{n(A \cup B)}{n(S)} = \frac{n(A)}{n(S)} + \frac{n(B)}{n(S)} - \frac{n(A \cap B)}{n(S)}$$

$$\Rightarrow P(A \cup B) = P(A) + P(B) - P(A \cap B)$$

Remark

If A and B are mutually exclusive events, then $A \cap B = \phi$. Hence, $P(A \cap B) = 0$.

$\therefore P(A \cup B) = P(A) + P(B)$

(b) P (exactly one of A, B occurs)

$$= P(A \cap \overline{B}) + P(\overline{A} \cap B)$$
$$= P(A) - P(A \cap B) + P(B) - P(A \cap B)$$
$$= P(A) + P(B) - 2P(A \cap B)$$
$$= P(A \cup B) - P(A \cap B)$$

(c) P (neither A nor B)

$$= P(\overline{A} \cap \overline{B}) = P(\overline{A \cup B}) = 1 - P(A \cup B)$$

Remark

$P(\overline{A} \cup \overline{B}) = 1 - P(A \cap B)$

2. If A, B and C are three events, then

(a) $P(A \cup B \cup C) = P(A) + P(B) + P(C) - P(A \cap B) - P(B \cap C) - P(C \cap A) + P(A \cap B \cap C)$

Remark

If A, B and C are mutually exclusive events, then

$$A \cap B = \phi,\ B \cap C = \phi,\ C \cap A = \phi,\ A \cap B \cap C = \phi$$

$\Rightarrow P(A \cap B) = 0, P(B \cap C) = 0, P(C \cap A) = 0, P(A \cap B \cap C) = 0$

$\therefore \quad P(A \cup B \cup C) = P(A) + P(B) + P(C)$

General form of Addition Theorem of Probability

$$P(A_1 \cup A_2 \cup \ldots \cup A_n) = \sum_{i=1}^{n} P(A_i) - \sum_{i<j} P(A_i \cap A_j) + \sum_{i<j<k} P(A_i \cap A_j \cap A_k) - \ldots + (-1)^{n-1} P(A_1 \cap A_2 \cap \ldots \cap A_n)$$

Remark

If $A_1, A_2, \ldots, A_n$ are mutually exclusive events, then

$\sum_{i<j} P(A_i \cap A_j) = 0, \ \sum_{i<j<k} P(A_i \cap A_j \cap A_k) = 0$

and $\quad P(A_1 \cap A_2 \cap \ldots \cap A_n) = 0$

$\therefore \quad P(A_1 \cup A_2 \cup \ldots \cup A_n) = \sum_{i=1}^{n} P(A_i)$

(b) P (atleast two of A, B, C occur)
$= P(A \cap B) + P(B \cap C) + P(C \cap A) - 2P(A \cap B \cap C)$

(c) P (exactly two of A, B, C occur)
$= P(A \cap B) + P(B \cap C) + P(C \cap A) - 3P(A \cap B \cap C)$

(d) P (exactly one of A, B, C occur)
$= P(A) + P(B) + P(C) - 2P(A \cap B) - 2P(B \cap C) - 2P(C \cap A) + 3P(A \cap B \cap C)$

3. (a) If $A_1, A_2, \ldots, A_n$ are independent events, then
$P(A_1 \cap A_2 \cap \ldots \cap A_n) = P(A_1)P(A_2)\ldots P(A_n)$

(b) If $A_1, A_2, \ldots, A_n$ are mutually exclusive events, then
$P(A_1 \cup A_2 \cup \ldots \cup A_n) = P(A_1) + P(A_2) + \ldots + P(A_n)$

(c) If $A_1, A_2, \ldots, A_n$ are exhaustive events, then
$P(A_1 \cup A_2 \cup \ldots \cup A_n) = 1$

(d) If $A_1, A_2, \ldots, A_n$ are mutually exclusive and exhaustive events, then
$P(A_1 \cup A_2 \cap \ldots \cap A_n) = P(A_1) + P(A_2) + \ldots + P(A_n) = 1$

4. If $A_1, A_2, \ldots, A_n$ are n events, then

(a) $P(A_1 \cup A_2 \cup \ldots \cup A_n) \le P(A_1) + P(A_2) + \ldots + P(A_n)$

(b) $P(A_1 \cap A_2 \cap \ldots \cap A_n) \ge 1 - P(\overline{A}_1) - P(\overline{A}_2) - \ldots - P(\overline{A}_n)$

Important Result

If E_1 and E_2 are independent events, then

(a) E_1 and $\overline{E}_2$ are independent events.

(b) $\overline{E}_1$ and E_2 are independent events.

(c) $\overline{E}_1$ and $\overline{E}_2$ are independent events.

Proof Given, E_1 and E_2 are independent events, then
$P(E_1 \cap E_2) = P(E_1) \cdot P(E_2)$

(a) $P(E_1 \cap \overline{E}_2) = P(E_1) - P(E_1 \cap E_2)$
$= P(E_1) - P(E_1) \cdot P(E_2)$
$= P(E_1)[1 - P(E_2)] = P(E_1) \cdot P(\overline{E}_2)$

So, E_1 and $\overline{E}_2$ are independent events.

(b) Same as in part (i).

(c) $P(\overline{E}_1 \cap \overline{E}_2) = P(\overline{E_1 \cup E_2})$
$= 1 - P(E_1 \cup E_2) = 1 - [P(E_1) + P(E_2) - P(E_1 \cap E_2)]$
$= 1 - P(E_1) - P(E_2) + P(E_1) \cdot P(E_2)$
$= P(\overline{E}_1) - P(E_2)[1 - P(E_1)]$
$= P(\overline{E}_1) - P(E_2) \cdot P(\overline{E}_1) = P(\overline{E}_1)[1 - P(E_2)]$
$= P(\overline{E}_1) P(\overline{E}_2)$

Remark

If $E_1, E_2, \ldots, E_n$ are independent events, then $P(E_1 \cup E_2 \cup \ldots \cup E_n)$
$= 1 - P(E_1 \cup E_2 \cup \ldots \cup E_n)' = 1 - P(E_1' \cap E_2' \cap \ldots \cap E_n')$
$= 1 - P(E_1') \cdot P(E_2') \ldots P(E_n')$

Example 7. For a post, three persons A, B and C appear in the interiew. The probability of A being selected is twice that of B and the probability of B being selected is thrice that of C. What are the individual probabilities of A, B and C being selected?

Sol. Let E_1, E_2 and E_3 be the events of selection of A, B and C respectively.

Let $P(E_3) = x$.

Then, $P(E_2) = 3P(E_3) = 3x$ and $P(E_1) = 2P(E_2) = 6x$

Since, E_1, E_2 and E_3 are mutually exclusive and exhaustive events.

$\therefore \quad P(E_1 \cup E_2 \cup E_3) = P(E_1) + P(E_2) + P(E_3) = 1$

$\therefore \quad P(E_1) + P(E_2) + P(E_3) = 1$

$\Rightarrow \quad 6x + 3x + x = 1$

$\therefore \quad x = \frac{1}{10}$

Hence, $P(E_1) = 6x = \frac{6}{10} = \frac{3}{5}$

$P(E_2) = 3x = \frac{3}{10}$ and $P(E_3) = x = \frac{1}{10}$

Example 8. If A and B are independent events, the probability that both A and B occur is $\frac{1}{8}$ and the probability that none of them occurs is $\frac{3}{8}$. Find the probability of the occurrence of A.

Sol. We have,

$P(A \cap B) = \frac{1}{8} \Rightarrow P(A)P(B) = \frac{1}{8}$ ...(i)

[$\because$ A and B are independent]

and $P(\overline{A} \cap \overline{B}) = \frac{3}{8} \Rightarrow P(\overline{A})P(\overline{B}) = \frac{3}{8}$

$\Rightarrow \quad (1 - P(A))(1 - P(B)) = \frac{3}{8}$

$\Rightarrow \quad 1 - P(A) - P(B) + \frac{1}{8} = \frac{3}{8}$ [from Eq. (i)]

$\Rightarrow \quad P(A) + P(B) = \frac{3}{4}$ ...(ii)

The quadratic equation whose roots are $P(A)$ and $P(B)$ is

$x^2 - [P(A) + P(B)]x + P(A) \cdot P(B) = 0$

$\Rightarrow \quad x^2 - \frac{3}{4}x + \frac{1}{8} = 0$ [from Eqs. (i) and (ii)] or $8x^2 - 6x + 1 = 0$ or $x = \frac{1}{2}, \frac{1}{4}$

Hence, $P(A) = \frac{1}{2}$ or $\frac{1}{4}$

Example 9. A and B are two candidates seeking admission in IIT. The probability that A is selected is 0.5 and the probability that both A and B are selected is atmost 0.3. Is it possible that the probability of B getting selected is 0.9?

Sol. Let E_1 and E_2 are the events of A and B selected, respectively.

Given, $P(E_1 \cap E_2) \le 0.3$ and $P(E_1) = 0.5$

Since, $P(E_1 \cup E_2) = P(E_1) + P(E_2) - P(E_1 \cap E_2)$

$\because \quad P(E_1 \cup E_2) \le 1$

$\therefore \quad P(E_1) + P(E_2) - P(E_1 \cap E_2) \le 1$

$\Rightarrow \quad P(E_1) + P(E_2) \le 1 + P(E_1 \cap E_2)$

$\Rightarrow \quad 0.5 + P(E_2) \le 1 + 0.3 \Rightarrow P(E_2) \le 0.8$

Hence, $P(E_2) \ne 0.9$

Example 10. Let A, B and C be three events. If the probability of occurring exactly one event out of A and B is $1 - a$, out of B and C is $1 - 2a$, out of C and A is $1 - a$ and that of occurring three events simultaneously is a^2, then prove that the probability that atleast one out of A, B and C will occur is greater than $\frac{1}{2}$.

Sol. Given,

$$P(A) + P(B) - 2P(A \cap B) = 1 - a \quad \text{...(i)}$$

$$P(B) + P(C) - 2P(B \cap C) = 1 - 2a \quad \text{...(ii)}$$

and $$P(C) + P(A) - 2P(C \cap A) = 1 - a \quad \text{...(iii)}$$

$\therefore$ $$P(A \cap B \cap C) = a^2 \quad \text{...(iv)}$$

$\therefore P(A \cup B \cup C) = P(A) + P(B) + P(C) - P(A \cap B) - P(B \cap C) - P(C \cap A) + P(A \cap B \cap C)$

$= \frac{1}{2}\{P(A) + P(B) - 2P(A \cap B) + P(B) + P(C) - 2P(B \cap C) + P(C) + P(A) - 2P(C \cap A)\} + P(A \cap B \cap C)$

$= \frac{1}{2}\{1 - a + 1 - 2a + 1 - a\} + a^2$ [from Eqs. (i), (ii), (iii) and (iv)]

$= \frac{3}{2} - 2a + a^2 = (a - 1)^2 + \frac{1}{2} > \frac{1}{2}$ $\quad [\because a \ne 1]$

Example 11. If A, B and C are three events, such that $P(A) = 0.3$, $P(B) = 0.4$, $P(C) = 0.8$, $P(AB) = 0.08$, $P(AC) = 0.28$, $P(ABC) = 0.09$. If $P(A \cup B \cup C) \ge 0.75$, then show that $P(BC)$ lies in the interval $0.23 \le x \le 0.48$.

Sol. Let $P(BC) = x$

Since, $P(A \cup B \cup C) = P(A) + P(B) + P(C) - P(AB) - P(BC) - P(CA) + P(ABC)$

$\therefore \quad = 0.3 + 0.4 + 0.8 - 0.08 - x - 0.28 + 0.09 = 1.23 - x$

But given that, $P(A \cup B \cup C) \ge 0.75$ and $P(A \cup B \cup C) \le 1$

$\therefore \quad 0.75 \le 1.23 - x \le 1 \Rightarrow -0.75 \ge -1.23 + x \ge -1$

or $\quad 1.23 - 0.75 \ge x \ge 1.23 - 1$ or $0.23 \le x \le 0.48$

Conditional Probability

The probability of occurrence of an event E_1, given that E_2 has already occurred is called the conditional probability of occurrence of E_1 on the condition that E_2 has already occurred, it is denoted by $P\left(\frac{E_1}{E_2}\right)$.

Thus, $$P\left(\frac{E_1}{E_2}\right) = \frac{P(E_1 \cap E_2)}{P(E_2)}, E_2 \ne \phi = \frac{\frac{n(E_1 \cap E_2)}{n(S)}}{\frac{n(E_2)}{n(S)}}$$

$$\Rightarrow \quad = \frac{n(E_1 \cap E_2)}{n(E_2)}$$

Remark

1. If E_1 and E_2 are independent events, then $P\left(\frac{E_2}{E_1}\right) = P(E_2)$
2. If E_1 and E_2 are two events such that $E_2 \ne \phi$, then $P\left(\frac{E_1}{E_2}\right) + P\left(\frac{\overline{E}_1}{E_2}\right) = 1$
3. If $E_1, E_2, E_3, \ldots, E_4$ are independent events, then $P(E_1 \cup E_2 \cup E_3 \cup \ldots \cup E_n) = 1 - P(\overline{E}_1) \cdot P(\overline{E}_2) \cdot P(\overline{E}_3) \ldots P(\overline{E}_n)$
4. If E_1, E_2 and E_3 are three events such that $E_1 \ne \phi$, $E_1E_2 \ne \phi$, then $P(E_1 \cap E_2 \cap E_3) = P(E_1) \cdot P\left(\frac{E_2}{E_1}\right) \cdot P\left(\frac{E_3}{E_1 E_2}\right)$

Generalised form

If $E_1, E_2, E_3, \ldots, E_n$ are n events such that $E_1 \ne \phi$, $E_1 E_2 \ne \phi$, $E_1 E_2 E_3 \ne \phi$, ..., $E_1 E_2 E_3 \ldots E_{n-1} \ne \phi$, then $P(E_1 \cap E_2 \cap E_3 \cap \ldots \cap E_n)$

$$= P(E_1) \cdot P\left(\frac{E_2}{E_1}\right) \cdot P\left(\frac{E_3}{E_1 E_2}\right) \cdot P\left(\frac{E_4}{E_1 E_2 E_3}\right) \ldots P\left(\frac{E_n}{E_1 E_2 E_3 \ldots E_{n-1}}\right)$$

Example 12. Two dice are thrown. Find the probability that the sum of the numbers coming up on them is 9, if it is known that the number 5 always occurs on the first dice.

Sol. Let S be the sample space

$\therefore \quad S = \{1, 2, 3, 4, 5, 6\} \times \{1, 2, 3, 4, 5, 6\}$

$\therefore \quad n(S) = 36$

and let $E_1 \equiv$ The event that the sum of the numbers coming up is 9.

and $\quad E_2 \equiv$ The event of occurrence of 5 on the first dice.

$\therefore \quad E_1 \equiv \{(3, 6), (6, 3), (4, 5), (5, 4)\}$

$\therefore \quad n(E_1) = 4$

and $E_2 = \{(5,1),(5,2),(5,3),(5,4),(5,5),(5,6)\}$

$\therefore$ $n(E_2) = 6$

$E_1 \cap E_2 = \{(5,4)\}$

$\therefore$ $n(E_1 \cap E_2) = 1$

Now, $P(E_1 \cap E_2) = \dfrac{n(E_1 \cap E_2)}{n(S)} = \dfrac{1}{36}$

and $P(E_2) = \dfrac{n(E_2)}{n(S)} = \dfrac{6}{36} = \dfrac{1}{6}$

$\therefore$ Required probability,

$$P\left(\frac{E_1}{E_2}\right) = \frac{P(E_1 \cap E_2)}{P(E_2)} = \frac{\frac{1}{36}}{\frac{1}{6}} = \frac{1}{6}$$

Aliter $P\left(\dfrac{E_1}{E_2}\right) = \dfrac{n(E_1 \cap E_2)}{n(E_2)} = \dfrac{1}{6}$

| Example 13. In a class, 30% students fail in English; 20% students fail in Hindi and 10% students fail in English and Hindi both. A student is chosen at random, then what is the probability that he will fail in English, if he has failed in Hindi?

Sol. Let S be the sample space.

If $n(S) = 100$, then

$E_1 \equiv$ The event that the student chosen fail in English

$\therefore n(E_1) = 30$

and $E_2 \equiv$ The event that the student chosen fail in Hindi

$\therefore$ $n(E_2) = 20$ and $n(E_1 \cap E_2) = 10$

$\therefore$ $P(E_2) = \dfrac{n(E_2)}{n(S)}$

$= \dfrac{20}{100} = \dfrac{1}{5}$

and $P(E_1 \cap E_2) = \dfrac{n(E_1 \cap E_2)}{n(S)} = \dfrac{10}{100} = \dfrac{1}{10}$

$\therefore$ Required probability, $P\left(\dfrac{E_1}{E_2}\right) = \dfrac{P(E_1 \cap E_2)}{P(E_2)} = \dfrac{\frac{1}{10}}{\frac{1}{5}} = \dfrac{1}{2}$

Aliter $P\left(\dfrac{E_1}{E_2}\right) = \dfrac{n(E_1 \cap E_2)}{n(E_2)}$

$= \dfrac{10}{20} = \dfrac{1}{2}$

Exercise for Session 2

1 If $P(A) = 0\cdot 8$, $P(B) = 0\cdot 5$, then $P(A \cap B)$ lies in the interval

(a) $[0\cdot 2, 0\cdot 5]$ (b) $[0\cdot 2, 0\cdot 3]$ (c) $[0\cdot 3, 0\cdot 5]$ (d) $[0\cdot 1, 0\cdot 5]$

2 If $P(A) = \dfrac{1}{4}$, $P(B) = \dfrac{1}{13}$ and $P(A \cap B) = \dfrac{1}{52}$, then the value of $P(\overline{A} \cap \overline{B})$, is

(a) $\dfrac{3}{13}$ (b) $\dfrac{5}{13}$ (c) $\dfrac{7}{13}$ (d) $\dfrac{9}{13}$

3 If A and B are independent events such that $P(\overline{A} \cap B) = \dfrac{2}{15}$ and $P(A \cap \overline{B}) = \dfrac{1}{6}$, then $P(B)$ is

(a) $\dfrac{1}{5}$ (b) $\dfrac{1}{6}$ (c) $\dfrac{4}{5}$ (d) $\dfrac{5}{6}$

4 If A and B are two events such that $P(A \cup B) = \dfrac{5}{6}$, $P(A) = \dfrac{1}{3}$, $P(B) = \dfrac{3}{4}$, then A and B are

(a) mutually exclusive (b) dependent (c) independent (d) None of these

5 If A, B and C are mutually exclusive and exhaustive events associated with a random experiment. If $P(B) = \dfrac{3}{2}P(A)$ and $P(C) = \dfrac{1}{2}P(B)$, then $P(A)$ is equal to

(a) $\dfrac{2}{13}$ (b) $\dfrac{4}{13}$ (c) $\dfrac{6}{13}$ (d) $\dfrac{8}{13}$

6 If A and B are two events, then $P(A) + P(B) = 2P(A \cap B)$ if and only if

(a) $P(A) + P(B) = 1$ (b) $P(A) = P(B)$ (c) $P(A) + P(B) > 1$ (d) None of these

7 If A and B are two events such that $P(A \cap B) = \dfrac{1}{4}$, $P(\overline{A} \cap \overline{B}) = \dfrac{1}{5}$ and $P(A) = P(B) = p$, then p is equal to

(a) $\dfrac{17}{40}$ (b) $\dfrac{19}{40}$ (c) $\dfrac{21}{40}$ (d) $\dfrac{23}{40}$

8 If A and B are two events such that $P(A\cup B)=\frac{3}{4}$, $P(A\cap B)=\frac{1}{4}$, $P(\bar{A})=\frac{2}{3}$. Then $(\bar{A}\cap B)$ is equal to

(a) $\frac{5}{12}$ (b) $\frac{3}{8}$ (c) $\frac{5}{8}$ (d) $\frac{1}{4}$

9 If $P(B)=\frac{3}{4}$, $P(A\cap B\cap \bar{C})=\frac{1}{3}$ and $P(\bar{A}\cap B\cap \bar{C})=\frac{1}{3}$, then $P(B\cap C)$ is equal to

(a) $\frac{1}{12}$ (b) $\frac{1}{6}$ (c) $\frac{1}{15}$ (d) $\frac{1}{9}$

10 If A and B are two events such that $P(A)>0$ and $P(B)\neq 1$, then $P\left(\frac{\bar{A}}{\bar{B}}\right)$ is equal to

(a) $1-P\left(\frac{A}{B}\right)$ (b) $1-P\left(\frac{A}{\bar{B}}\right)$ (c) $\frac{1-P(A\cup B)}{P(B)}$ (d) $\frac{P(\bar{A})}{P(B)}$

11 If $P(A)=\frac{3}{8}$, $P(B)=\frac{5}{8}$ and $P(A\cup B)=\frac{3}{4}$, then $P\left(\frac{\bar{A}}{\bar{B}}\right)$ is equal to

(a) $\frac{1}{4}$ (b) $\frac{1}{3}$ (c) $\frac{2}{3}$ (d) $\frac{3}{4}$

12 If two events A and B are such that $P(\bar{A})=0\cdot 3$, $P(B)=0\cdot 4$ and $P(A\cap\bar{B})=0\cdot 5$, then $P\left(\frac{B}{A\cup\bar{B}}\right)$ is equal to

(a) $\frac{1}{4}$ (b) $\frac{1}{5}$ (c) $\frac{2}{5}$ (d) $\frac{3}{5}$

13 Two dice are thrown. The probability that the number appeared have a sum of 8. If it is known that the second die always exhibits 4, is

(a) $\frac{5}{6}$ (b) $\frac{1}{6}$ (c) $\frac{2}{3}$ (d) $\frac{1}{3}$

14 A is targetting to B, B and C are targetting to A. The probability of hitting the target by A, B and C are $\frac{2}{3},\frac{1}{2},\frac{1}{3}$ respectively. If A is hit, the probability that B hits the target and C does not, is

(a) $\frac{1}{3}$ (b) $\frac{1}{2}$ (c) $\frac{2}{3}$ (d) $\frac{3}{4}$

15 If A and B are two events such that $A\cap B\not\supset\phi$, $P\left(\frac{A}{B}\right)=P\left(\frac{B}{A}\right)$. Then,

(a) $A=B$ (b) $P(A)=P(B)$
(c) A and B are independent (d) All of these

Session 3

Total Probability Theorem, Baye's Theorem or Inverse Probability

Total Probability Theorem

Let $E_1, E_2, \ldots, E_n$ be n mutually exclusive and exhaustive events i.e., $E_i \cap E_j = \phi$ for $i \neq j$ and $\bigcup_{i=1}^{n} E_i = S$.

Suppose that, $P(E_i) > 0, \forall\ 1 \le i \le n$

Then for any event E

$$P(E) = \sum_{i=1}^{n} P(E_i) \cdot P\left(\frac{E}{E_i}\right)$$

Proof Since, $E_1, E_2, \ldots, E_n$ are disjoint

$\therefore E \cap E_1, E \cap E_2, \ldots, E \cap E_n$ are also disjoint.

Now, $$E = E \cap S = E \cap \left(\bigcup_{i=1}^{n} E_i\right) = \bigcup_{i=1}^{n} (E \cap E_i)$$

$$\therefore \quad P(E) = \sum_{i=1}^{n} P(E \cap E_i) = \sum_{i=1}^{n} P(E_i) \cdot P\left(\frac{E}{E_i}\right)$$

| Example 14. The probability that certain electronic component fails, when first used is 0.10. If it does not fail immediately, then the probability that it lasts for one year is 0.99. What is the probability that a new component will last for one year?

Sol. Given probability of electronic component fails, when first used $= 0.10$

i.e., $$P(F) = 0.10$$

$$\therefore \quad P(\overline{F}) = 1 - P(F) = 0.90$$

and let $P(Y) =$ Probability of new component to last for one year

$$\because \quad P(F) + P(\overline{F}) = 1$$

Obviously, the two events are mutually exclusive and exhaustive

$$\therefore \quad P\left(\frac{Y}{F}\right) = 0 \text{ and } P\left(\frac{Y}{\overline{F}}\right) = 0.99$$

$$\therefore \quad P(Y) = P(F) \cdot P\left(\frac{Y}{F}\right) + P(\overline{F}) . P\left(\frac{Y}{\overline{F}}\right)$$

$$= 0.10 \times 0 + 0.90 \times 0.99$$

$$= 0 + (0.9)(0.99) = 0.891$$

| Example 15. Three groups A, B and C are contesting for positions on the Board of Directors of a company. The probabilities of their winning are 0.5, 0.3 and 0.2, respectively. If the group A wins, then the probability of introducing a new product is 0.7 and the corresponding probabilities for groups B and C are 0.6 and 0.5, respectively. Find the probability that the new product will be introduced.

Sol. Given, $P(A) = 0.5$, $P(B) = 0.3$ and $P(C) = 0.2$

$$\therefore \quad P(A) + P(B) + P(C) = 1$$

Then, events A, B, C are exhaustive.

If $P(E) =$ Probability of introducing a new product, then as given

$$P\left(\frac{E}{A}\right) = 0.7,\ P\left(\frac{E}{B}\right) = 0.6 \text{ and } P\left(\frac{E}{C}\right) = 0.5$$

$$P(E) = P(A) \cdot P\left(\frac{E}{A}\right) + P(B) \cdot P\left(\frac{E}{B}\right) + P(C) \cdot P\left(\frac{E}{C}\right)$$

$$= 0.5 \times 0.7 + 0.3 \times 0.6 + 0.2 \times 0.5$$

$$= 0.35 + 0.18 + 0.10 = 0.63$$

| Example 16. An urn contains 2 white and 2 black balls. A ball is drawn at random. If it is white, it is not replace into urn, otherwise it is replaced along with another ball of the same colour. The process is repeated, find the probability that the third ball drawn is black.

Sol. For the first two draw, the balls taken out may be

Let $E_1 =$ White and White; $E_2 =$ White and Black

$E_3 =$ Black and White; $E_4 =$ Black and Black

$$\therefore \quad P(E_1) = P(W) \cdot P\left(\frac{W}{W}\right) = \frac{2}{4} \cdot \frac{1}{3} = \frac{1}{6}$$

$$P(E_2) = P(W) \cdot P\left(\frac{B}{W}\right) = \frac{2}{4} \cdot \frac{2}{3} = \frac{1}{3}$$

$$P(E_3) = P(B) \cdot P\left(\frac{W}{B}\right) = \frac{2}{4} \cdot \frac{2}{5} = \frac{1}{5}$$

$$\text{and } P(E_4) = P(B) \cdot P\left(\frac{B}{B}\right) = \frac{2}{4} \cdot \frac{3}{5} = \frac{3}{10}$$

$$\therefore P(E_1)+P(E_2)+P(E_3)+P(E_4)=\frac{1}{6}+\frac{1}{3}+\frac{1}{5}+\frac{3}{10}$$
$$=\frac{10+20+12+18}{60}=1$$

Then, events E_1, E_2, E_3 and E_4 are exhaustive. Obviously, these events are mutually exclusive, then

$$P\left(\frac{B}{E_1}\right)=\frac{2}{2}=1;\ P\left(\frac{B}{E_2}\right)=\frac{3}{4}$$
$$P\left(\frac{B}{E_3}\right)=\frac{3}{4}\text{ and }P\left(\frac{B}{E_4}\right)=\frac{4}{6}=\frac{2}{3}$$

$\therefore$ Required probability,

$$P(B)=P(E_1)\cdot P\left(\frac{B}{E_1}\right)+P(E_2)\cdot P\left(\frac{B}{E_2}\right)+P(E_3)\cdot P\left(\frac{B}{E_3}\right)+P(E_4)\cdot P\left(\frac{B}{E_4}\right)$$
$$=\frac{1}{6}\times 1+\frac{1}{3}\times\frac{3}{4}+\frac{1}{5}\times\frac{3}{4}+\frac{3}{10}\times\frac{2}{3}$$
$$=\frac{1}{6}+\frac{1}{4}+\frac{3}{20}+\frac{1}{5}$$
$$=\frac{10+15+9+12}{60}=\frac{46}{60}=\frac{23}{30}$$

Baye's Theorem or Inverse Probability

If an event E can occur only with one of the n mutually exclusive and exhaustive events $E_1, E_2, E_3, \ldots, E_n$ and the probabilities $P(E/E_1), P(E/E_2), \ldots, P(E/E_n)$ are known, then

$$P\left(\frac{E_k}{E}\right)=\frac{P(E_k)\cdot P\left(\frac{E}{E_k}\right)}{\sum_{k=1}^{n}P(E_k)\cdot P\left(\frac{E}{E_k}\right)}$$

Proof The event E occurs with one of the n mutually exclusive and exhaustive events $E_1, E_2, E_3, \ldots, E_n$, then

$$E=EE_1+EE_2+EE_3+\ldots+EE_n$$
$$\Rightarrow P(E)=P(EE_1)+P(EE_2)+P(EE_3)+\ldots+P(EE_n)$$
$$=\sum_{k=1}^{n}P(EE_k)=\sum_{k=1}^{n}P(E_k)\cdot P\left(\frac{E}{E_k}\right)$$
$$\therefore P\left(\frac{E_k}{E}\right)=\frac{P(E_k\,E)}{P(E)}=\frac{P(E_k)\cdot P\left(\frac{E}{E_k}\right)}{\sum_{k=1}^{n}P(E_k)\cdot P\left(\frac{E}{E_k}\right)}$$

Remark

The probabilities $P(E_k)$ and $P\left(\frac{E_k}{E}\right)$ are known as **priori** and **posteriori** probabilities, respectively.

Remarks We can visualise a tree structure here

$$P(A)=p,\ P(B)=q$$
$$P\left(\frac{R}{A}\right)=p_1,\ P\left(\frac{T}{A}\right)=q_1$$
$$P\left(\frac{R}{B}\right)=p_2,\ P\left(\frac{T}{B}\right)=q_2$$

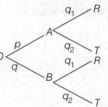

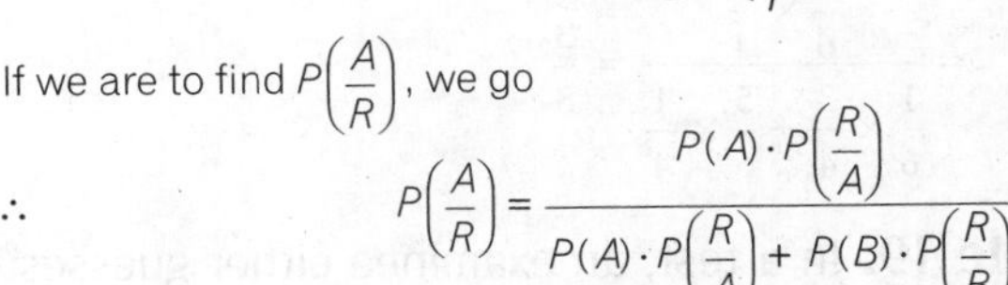

If we are to find $P\left(\frac{A}{R}\right)$, we go

$$\therefore P\left(\frac{A}{R}\right)=\frac{P(A)\cdot P\left(\frac{R}{A}\right)}{P(A)\cdot P\left(\frac{R}{A}\right)+P(B)\cdot P\left(\frac{R}{B}\right)}$$

Example 17. A bag A contains 2 white and 3 red balls and a bag B contains 4 white and 5 red balls. One ball is drawn at random from one of the bags and it is found to be red. Then, find the probability that it was drawn from the bag B.

Sol. Let $E_1 \equiv$ The event of ball being drawn from bag A.
$E_2 \equiv$ The event of ball being drawn from bag B.
and $E \equiv$ The event of ball being red.
Since, both the bag are equally likely to be selected, therefore

$$P(E_1)=P(E_2)=\frac{1}{2}\text{ and }P\left(\frac{E}{E_1}\right)=\frac{3}{5}\text{ and }P\left(\frac{E}{E_2}\right)=\frac{5}{9}$$

$\therefore$ Required probability,

$$P\left(\frac{E_2}{E}\right)=\frac{P(E_2)\cdot P\left(\frac{E}{E_2}\right)}{P(E_1)\cdot P\left(\frac{E}{E_1}\right)+P(E_2)\cdot P\left(\frac{E}{E_2}\right)}$$
$$=\frac{\frac{1}{2}\times\frac{5}{9}}{\frac{1}{2}\times\frac{3}{5}+\frac{1}{2}\times\frac{5}{9}}=\frac{\frac{5}{9}}{\frac{3}{5}+\frac{5}{9}}=\frac{25}{52}$$

Example 18. A man is known to speak the truth 3 out of 4 times. He throws a die and reports that it is a six. Find the probability that it is actually a six.

Sol. Let E_1 be the event that the man reports that it is a six and E be the event that a six occurs.

Then, $P(E) = \frac{1}{6}$

$\therefore \quad P(\overline{E}) = 1 - P(E) = 1 - \frac{1}{6} = \frac{5}{6}$

$\therefore \quad P\left(\frac{E_1}{E}\right) = P$ (man speaking the truth) $= \frac{3}{4}$

and $P\left(\frac{E_1}{\overline{E}}\right) = P$ (man not speaking the truth) $= 1 - \frac{3}{4} = \frac{1}{4}$

Clearly, $\left(\frac{E}{E_1}\right)$ is the event that it is actually a six, when it is known that the man reports a six.

$$P\left(\frac{E}{E_1}\right) = \frac{P(E)\cdot P\left(\frac{E_1}{E}\right)}{P(E)\cdot P\left(\frac{E_1}{E}\right) + P(\overline{E})\cdot P\left(\frac{E_1}{\overline{E}}\right)}$$

$$= \frac{\frac{1}{6}\times\frac{3}{4}}{\frac{1}{6}\times\frac{3}{4}+\frac{5}{6}\times\frac{1}{4}} = \frac{3}{8}$$

Example 19. In a test, an examinee either guesses or copies or knows the answer to a multiple choice question with four choices. The probability that he makes a guess is $\frac{1}{3}$ and the probability that he copies the answer is $\frac{1}{6}$. The probability that his answer is correct given that he copied it is $\frac{1}{8}$. Find the probability that he knew the answer to the question given that he correctly answered it.

Sol. Lest E_1 be the event that the answer is guessed, E_2 be the event that the answer is copied, E_3 be the event that the examinee knows the answer and E be the event that the examinee answers correctly.

Given, $P(E_1) = \frac{1}{3}$, $P(E_2) = \frac{1}{6}$

Assume that events E_1, E_2 and E_3 are exhaustive

$\therefore \quad P(E_1) + P(E_2) + P(E_3) = 1$

$\therefore \quad P(E_3) = 1 - P(E_1) - P(E_2) = 1 - \frac{1}{3} - \frac{1}{6} = \frac{1}{2}$

Now, $P\left(\frac{E}{E_1}\right)$

$\equiv$ Probability of getting correct answer by guessing

$= \frac{1}{4}$ [since 4 alternatives]

$P\left(\frac{E}{E_2}\right) \equiv$ Probability of answering correctly by copying $= \frac{1}{8}$

and $P\left(\frac{E}{E_3}\right) \equiv$ Probability of answering correctly by knowing $= 1$

Clearly, $\left(\frac{E_3}{E}\right)$ is the event he knew the answer to the question, given that he correctly answered it.

$$\therefore \quad P\left(\frac{E_3}{E}\right) = \frac{P(E_3)\cdot P\left(\frac{E}{E_3}\right)}{P(E_1)\cdot P\left(\frac{E}{E_1}\right) + P(E_2)\cdot P\left(\frac{E}{E_2}\right) + P(E_2)\cdot P\left(\frac{E}{E_3}\right)}$$

$$= \frac{\frac{1}{2}\times 1}{\frac{1}{3}\times\frac{1}{4}+\frac{1}{6}\times\frac{1}{8}+\frac{1}{2}\times 1} = \frac{24}{29}$$

Example 20. A and B are two independent witnesses (i.e., there is no collusion between them) in a case. The probability that A will speak the truth is x and the probability that B will speak the truth is y. A and B agree in a certain statements. Show that the probability that the statements is true, is $\frac{xy}{1-x-y+2xy}$.

Sol. Let E_1 be the event that both A and B speak the truth, E_2 be the event that both A and B tell a lie and E be the event that A and B agree in a certain statements.

And also, let C be the event that A speak the truth and D be the event that B speaks the truth.

$\therefore \quad E_1 = C \cap D$

[$\because C$ and D are independent events]

and $\quad E_2 = \overline{C} \cap \overline{D}$

then, $\quad P(E_1) = (C \cap D) = P(C)\cdot P(D) = xy$

and $\quad P(E_2) = P(\overline{C} \cap \overline{D}) = P(\overline{C})\, P(\overline{D})$

$= \{1 - P(C)\}\{1 - P(D)\} = (1 - x)(1 - y)$

$= 1 - x - y - xy$

Now, $P\left(\frac{E}{E_1}\right) \equiv$ Probability that A and B will agree, when both of them speak the truth $= 1$

and $P\left(\frac{E}{E_2}\right) =$ Probability that A and B will agree, when both of them tell a lie $= 1$

Clearly, $\left(\frac{E_1}{E}\right)$ be the event that the statement is true

$$\therefore \quad P\left(\frac{E_1}{E}\right) = \frac{P(E_1)\cdot P\left(\frac{E}{E_1}\right)}{P(E_1)\cdot P\left(\frac{E}{E_1}\right) + P(E_2)\cdot P\left(\frac{E}{E_2}\right)}$$

$$= \frac{xy\cdot 1}{xy\cdot 1 + (1 - x - y + xy)\cdot 1} = \frac{xy}{1 - x - y + 2xy}$$

Exercise for Session 3

1. A bag A contains 3 white and 2 black balls and another bag B contains 2 white and 4 black balls. A bag and a ball out of it are picked at random. The probability that the ball is white, is

(a) $\frac{2}{7}$ (b) $\frac{7}{9}$ (c) $\frac{4}{15}$ (d) $\frac{7}{15}$

2. There are two bags, one of which contains 3 black and 4 white balls, while the other contains 4 black and 3 white balls. A die is cast. If the face 1 or 3 turns up a ball is taken out from the first bag and if any other face turns up, a ball is taken from the second bag. The probability of choosing a black ball, is

(a) $\frac{7}{15}$ (b) $\frac{8}{15}$ (c) $\frac{10}{21}$ (d) $\frac{11}{21}$

3. There are two groups of subjects, one of which consists of 5 Science subjects and 3 Engineering subjects and the other consists of 3 Science and 5 Engineering subjects. An unbiased die is cast. If number 3 or 5 turns up, a subject from group I is selected, otherwise a subject is selected from group II. The probability that an Engineering subject is selected ultimately, is

(a) $\frac{7}{13}$ (b) $\frac{9}{17}$ (c) $\frac{13}{24}$ (d) $\frac{11}{20}$

4. Urn A contains 6 red and 4 white balls and urn B contains 4 red and 6 white balls. One ball is drawn at random from urn A and placed in urn B. Then a ball is drawn from urn B and placed in urn A. Now, if one ball is drawn from urn A, the probability that it is red, is

(a) $\frac{6}{11}$ (b) $\frac{17}{50}$ (c) $\frac{16}{55}$ (d) $\frac{32}{55}$

5. A box contains N coins, of which m are fair and the rest are biased. The probability of getting head when a fair coin is tossed is $\frac{1}{2}$, while it $\frac{2}{3}$ when a biased coin is tossed. A coin is drawn from the box at random and is tossed twice. The first time it shows head and the second time it shows tail. The probability that the coin drawn is fair, is

(a) $\frac{5m}{m+8N}$ (b) $\frac{3m}{m+8N}$ (c) $\frac{7m}{m+8N}$ (d) $\frac{9m}{m+8N}$

6. A pack of playing cards was found to contain only 51 cards. If the first 13 cards which are examined are all red, then the probability that the missing card is black, is

(a) $\frac{1}{3}$ (b) $\frac{2}{3}$ (c) $\frac{15}{26}$ (d) $\frac{16}{39}$

7. A purse contains n coins of unknown values. A coin is drawn from it at random and is found to be a rupee. Then the chance that it is the only rupee coin in the purse, is

(a) $\frac{1}{n}$ (b) $\frac{2}{n+1}$ (c) $\frac{1}{n(n+1)}$ (d) $\frac{2}{n(n+1)}$

8. A card is lost from a pack of 52 playing cards. From the remainder of the pack, one card is drawn and is found to be a spade. The probability that the missing card is a spade, is

(a) $\frac{2}{17}$ (b) $\frac{3}{17}$ (c) $\frac{4}{17}$ (d) $\frac{5}{17}$

9. A person is known to speak the truth 4 times out of 5. He throws a die and reports that it is an ace. The probability that it is actually an ace, is

(a) $\frac{1}{3}$ (b) $\frac{2}{9}$ (c) $\frac{4}{9}$ (d) $\frac{5}{9}$

10. Each of the n urns contains 4 white and 6 black balls, the $(n+1)$ th urn contains 5 white and 5 black balls. Out of $(n+1)$ urns an urn is chosen at random and two balls are drawn from it without replacement. Both the balls are found to be black. If the probability that the $(n+1)$th urn was chosen to drawn the balls is $\frac{1}{16}$, the value of n, is

(a) 10 (b) 11 (c) 12 (d) 13

Session 4

Binomial Theorem on Probability, Poisson Distribution, Expectation, Multinomial Theorem, Uncountable Uniform Spaces (Geometrical Problems)

Binomial Theorem on Probability

Suppose, a binomial experiment has probability of success p and that of failure q (i.e., $p+q=1$). If E be an event and let $X=$ number of successes i.e., number of times event E occurs in n trials. Then, the probability of occurrence of event E exactly r times in n trials is denoted by $P(X=r)$ or $P(r)$ and is given by $P(X=r)$

or $\quad P(r) = {}^nC_r\, p^r q^{n-r}$

$\quad = (r+1)$ th terms in the expansion of $(q+p)^n$

where, $r = 0, 1, 2, 3, \ldots, n$.

Remark

1. The probability of getting atleast k success is

$$P(r \ge k) = \sum_{r=k}^{n} {}^nC_r p^r q^{n-r}.$$

2. The probability of getting atmost k success is

$$P(0 \le r \le k) = \sum_{r=0}^{k} {}^nC_r p^r q^{n-r}.$$

3. The probability distribution of the random variable X is as given below

X	0	1	2	...	r	...	n
$P(X)$	q^n	${}^nC_1\, pq^{n-1}$	${}^nC_2\, p^2 q^{n-2}$	...	${}^nC_r\, p^r q^{n-r}$		p^n

4. The mean, the variance and the standard deviation of binomial distribution are np, npq, $\sqrt{npq}$.

5. Mode of binomial distribution Mode of Binomial distribution is the value of r when $P(X=r)$ is maximum.

$$(n+1)\,p - 1 \le r \le (n+1)p$$

Example 21. If on an average, out of 10 ships, one is drowned, then what is the probability that out of 5 ships, atleast 4 reach safely?

Sol. Let p be the probability that a ship reaches safely.

$$\therefore \quad p = \frac{9}{10}$$

$$\therefore \quad q = \text{Probability that a ship is drowned} = 1 - p = 1 - \frac{9}{10}$$

$$\therefore \quad q = \frac{1}{10}$$

Let X be the random variable, showing the number of ships reaching safely.

Then, P (atleast 4 reaching safely) $= P(X=4 \text{ or } X=5)$

$$= P(X=4) + P(X=5)$$

$$= {}^5C_4\left(\frac{9}{10}\right)^4\left(\frac{1}{10}\right)^{5-4} + {}^5C_5\left(\frac{9}{10}\right)^5\left(\frac{1}{10}\right)^{5-5}$$

$$= \frac{5\times 9^4}{10^5} + \frac{9^5}{10^5} = \frac{9^4\times 14}{10^5}$$

Example 22. Numbers are selected at random one at a time, from the numbers 00, 01, 02, ..., 99 with replacement. An event E occurs, if and only if the product of the two digits of a selected number is 18. If four numbers are selected, then find the probability that E occurs atleast 3 times.

Sol. Out of the numbers 00, 01, 02, ..., 99, those numbers the product of whose digits is 18 are 29, 36, 63, 92 i.e., only 4.

$$p = P(E) = \frac{4}{100} = \frac{1}{25},\; q = P(\overline{E}) = 1 - \frac{1}{25} = \frac{24}{25}$$

Let X be the random variable, showing the number of times E occurs in 4 selections.

Then, $P(E$ occurs atleast 3 times$) = P(X=3 \text{ or } X=4)$

$$= P(X=3) + P(X=4) = {}^4C_3\, p^3 q^1 + {}^4C_4\, p^4 q^0$$

$$= 4p^3 q + p^4 = 4\times\left(\frac{1}{25}\right)^3 \times \frac{24}{25} + \left(\frac{1}{25}\right)^4$$

$$= \frac{97}{390625}$$

Example 23. A man takes a step forward with probability 0.4 and backward with probability 0.6. Then, find the probability that at the end of eleven steps he is one step away from the starting point.

Sol. Since, the man is one step away from starting point mean that either

(i) man has taken 6 steps forward and 5 steps backward.

(ii) man has taken 5 steps forward and 6 steps backward.

Taking, movement 1 step forward as success and 1 step backward as failure.

$\therefore$ p = Probability of success = 0.4

and q = Probability of failure = 0.6

$\therefore$ Required probability = $P(X = 6 \text{ or } X = 5)$

$$= P(X = 6) + P(X = 5) = {}^{11}C_6\, p^6 q^5 + {}^{11}C_5\, p^5 q^6$$

$$= {}^{11}C_5 (p^6 q^5 + p^5 q^6)$$

$$= \frac{11\cdot 10\cdot 9\cdot 8\cdot 7}{1\cdot 2\cdot 3\cdot 4\cdot 5}\{(0\cdot 4)^6 (0\cdot 6)^5 + (0\cdot 4)^5 (0\cdot 6)^6\}$$

$$= \frac{11\cdot 10\cdot 9\cdot 8\cdot 7}{1\cdot 2\cdot 3\cdot 4\cdot 5}(0\cdot 24)^5 = 0\cdot 37$$

Hence, the required probability is 0·37.

Example 24. Find the minimum number of tosses of a pair of dice, so that the probability of getting the sum of the digits on the dice equal to 7 on atleast one toss, is greater than 0.95. (Given, $\log_{10} 2 = 0\cdot 3010$, $\log_{10} 3 = 0\cdot 4771$)

Sol. The sample space,

$$S = \{1, 2, 3, 4, 5, 6\} \times \{1, 2, 3, 4, 5, 6\}$$

$\therefore$ $n(S) = 36$ and let E be the event getting the sum of digits on the dice equal to 7, then

$$E = \{(1, 6), (6, 1), (2, 5), (5, 2), (3, 4), (4, 3)\}$$

$\therefore$ $n(E) = 6$

p = Probability of getting the sum 7

$$p = \frac{6}{36} = \frac{1}{6} \quad \therefore \quad q = 1 - p = 1 - \frac{1}{6} = \frac{5}{6}$$

$\because$ Probability of not throwing the sum 7 in first m trials = q^m

$\therefore$ P (atleast one 7 in m throws) $= 1 - q^m = 1 - \left(\frac{5}{6}\right)^m$

According to the question, $1 - \left(\frac{5}{6}\right)^m > 0\cdot 95$

$$\Rightarrow \left(\frac{5}{6}\right)^m < 1 - 0\cdot 95 \Rightarrow \left(\frac{5}{6}\right)^m < 0.05$$

$$\Rightarrow \left(\frac{5}{6}\right)^m < \frac{1}{20}$$

Taking logarithm,

$$\Rightarrow m\{\log_{10} 5 - \log_{10} 6\} < \log_{10} 1 - \log_{10} 20$$

$$\Rightarrow m\{1 - \log_{10} 2 - \log_{10} 2 - \log_{10} 3\} < 0 - \log_{10} 2 - \log_{10} 10$$

$$\Rightarrow m\{1 - 2\log_{10} 2 - \log_{10} 3\} < -\log_{10} 2 - 1$$

$$\Rightarrow m\{1 - 0.6020 - 0.4771\} < -0.3010 - 1$$

$$\Rightarrow -0.079\, m < -1.3010$$

$$\Rightarrow m > \frac{1.3010}{0.079} = 16.44$$

$$\therefore \quad m > 16.44$$

Hence, the least number of trials is 17.

Example 25. Write probability distribution, when three coins are tossed.

Sol. Let X be a random variable denoting the number of heads occurred, then $P(X = 0)$ = Probability of occurrence of zero head

$$= P(TTT) = \frac{1}{2}\cdot\frac{1}{2}\cdot\frac{1}{2} = \frac{1}{8}$$

$P(X = 1)$ = Probability of occurrence of one head

$$= P(HTT) + P(THT) + P(TTH)$$

$$= \frac{1}{2}\cdot\frac{1}{2}\cdot\frac{1}{2} + \frac{1}{2}\cdot\frac{1}{2}\cdot\frac{1}{2} + \frac{1}{2}\cdot\frac{1}{2}\cdot\frac{1}{2} = \frac{3}{8}$$

$P(X = 2)$ = Probability of occurrence of two heads

$$= P(HHT) + P(HTH) + P(THH)$$

$$= \frac{1}{2}\cdot\frac{1}{2}\cdot\frac{1}{2} + \frac{1}{2}\cdot\frac{1}{2}\cdot\frac{1}{2} + \frac{1}{2}\cdot\frac{1}{2}\cdot\frac{1}{2} = \frac{3}{8}$$

$P(X = 3)$ = Probability of occurrence of three heads

$$= P(HHH) = \frac{1}{2}\cdot\frac{1}{2}\cdot\frac{1}{2} = \frac{1}{8}$$

Thus, the probability distribution when three coins are tossed is as given below

X	0	1	2	3
$P(X)$	$\frac{1}{8}$	$\frac{3}{8}$	$\frac{3}{8}$	$\frac{1}{8}$

another form,

$$\begin{pmatrix} X & : & 0 & 1 & 2 & 3 \\ P(X) & : & \frac{1}{8} & \frac{3}{8} & \frac{3}{8} & \frac{1}{8} \end{pmatrix}$$

Example 26. The mean and variance of a binomial variable X are 2 and 1, respectively. Find the probability that X takes values greater than 1.

Sol. Given, mean, $np = 2$ ...(i)

and variance, $npq = 1$ ...(ii)

On dividing Eq. (ii) by Eq. (i), we get $q = \frac{1}{2}$

$$\therefore \quad p = 1 - q = \frac{1}{2}$$

From Eq. (i), $n \times \frac{1}{2} = 2 \therefore n = 4$

The binomial distribution is $\left(\frac{1}{2} + \frac{1}{2}\right)^4$

Now, $P(X > 1) = P(X = 2) + P(X = 3) + P(X = 4)$

$$= {}^4C_2\left(\frac{1}{2}\right)^2\left(\frac{1}{2}\right)^2 + {}^4C_4\left(\frac{1}{2}\right)^1\left(\frac{1}{2}\right)^3 + {}^4C_4\left(\frac{1}{2}\right)^4$$

$$= \frac{6 + 4 + 1}{16} = \frac{11}{16}$$

Aliter $P(X > 1) = 1 - \{P(X = 0) + P(X = 1)\}$

$$= 1 - \left\{{}^4C_0\left(\frac{1}{2}\right)^0\left(\frac{1}{2}\right)^4 + {}^4C_3\left(\frac{1}{2}\right)\left(\frac{1}{2}\right)^3\right\} = 1 - \left(\frac{1 + 4}{16}\right) = \frac{11}{16}$$

Poisson Distribution

It is the limiting case of binomial distribution under the following conditions :

(i) Number of trails are very large i.e. $n \to \infty$

(ii) $p \to 0$

(iii) $nq \to \lambda$, a finite quantity (λ is called parameter)

(a) Probability of r success for poisson distribution is given by $P(X=r)=\dfrac{e^{-\lambda}\lambda^r}{r!}$, $r=0, 1, 2, \ldots$

(b) Recurrence formula for poisson distribution is given by $P(r+1)=\dfrac{\lambda}{(r+1)}P(r)$

Remark

1. For poisson distribution, mean = variance = $\lambda = np$
2. If X and Y are independent poisson variates with parameters λ_1 and λ_2, then $X+Y$ has poisson distribution with parameter $\lambda_1+\lambda_2$.

Expectation

If p be the probability of success of a person in any venture and m be the sum of money which he will receive in case of success, the sum of money denoted by pm is called his expectation.

| Example 27. A random variable X has Poisson's distribution with mean 3. Then find the value of $P(X > 2.5)$

Sol. $P(X>2.5)=1-P(X=0)-P(X=1)-P(X=2)$

$\because \quad P(X=k)=e^{-\lambda}\cdot\dfrac{\lambda^k}{k!}$

$$\therefore \quad P(X>2.5)=1-\frac{e^{-\lambda}}{0!}-\frac{e^{-\lambda}\cdot\lambda^1}{1!}-\frac{e^{-\lambda}\cdot\lambda^2}{2!}$$

$$=1-e^{-\lambda}\left(1+\lambda+\frac{\lambda^2}{2}\right)$$

$$=1-e^{-3}\left(1+3+\frac{9}{2}\right) \quad (\because \lambda = np = 3)$$

$$=1-\frac{17}{2e^3}$$

| Example 28. A and B throw with one die for a stake of ₹ 11 which is to be won by the player who first throw 6. If A has the first throw, then what are their respective expectations?

Sol. Since, A can win the game at the 1st, 3rd, 5th,..., trials.

If p be the probability of success and q be the probability of fail, then

$$p=\frac{1}{6} \text{ and } q=\frac{5}{6}$$

$$P(A \text{ wins at the first trial})=\frac{1}{6}$$

$$P(A \text{ wins at the 3rd trials})=\frac{5}{6}\cdot\frac{5}{6}\cdot\frac{1}{6}$$

$$P(A \text{ wins at the 5th trials})=\frac{5}{6}\cdot\frac{5}{6}\cdot\frac{5}{6}\cdot\frac{5}{6}\cdot\frac{1}{6} \text{ and so on.}$$

$$\text{Therefore, } P(A \text{ wins})=\frac{1}{6}+\left(\frac{5}{6}\right)^2\frac{1}{6}+\left(\frac{5}{6}\right)^4\cdot\frac{1}{6}+\ldots\infty$$

$$=\frac{\frac{1}{6}}{1-\left(\frac{5}{6}\right)^2}=\frac{6}{11}$$

$$\text{Similarly, } P(B \text{ wins})=\frac{5}{6}\cdot\frac{1}{6}+\left(\frac{5}{6}\right)^3\frac{1}{6}+\left(\frac{5}{6}\right)^5\frac{1}{6}+\ldots\infty$$

$$=\frac{\frac{5}{6}\cdot\frac{1}{6}}{1-\left(\frac{5}{6}\right)^2}=\frac{5}{11}$$

Hence, expectations of A and B are ₹ $\dfrac{6}{11}\times 11$ and ₹ $\dfrac{5}{11}\times 11$, respectively. i.e. Expectations of A and B are ₹ 6 and ₹ 5, respectively.

Multinomial Theorem

If a dice has m faces marked 1, 2, 3,..., m and if such n dice are thrown, then the probability that the sum of the numbers of the upper faces is equal to r is given by the coefficient of x^r in $\dfrac{(x+x^2+\ldots+x^m)^n}{m^n}$.

| Example 29. A person throws two dice, one the common cube and the other a regular tetrahedron, the number on the lowest face being taken in the case of the tetrahedron, then find the probability that the sum of the numbers appearing on the dice is 6.

Sol. Let S be the sample space, then

$$S=\{1, 2, 3, 4\}\times\{1, 2, 3, 4, 5, 6\}$$

$$\therefore \quad n(S)=24$$

If E be the event that the sum of the numbers on dice is 6.

Then, $n(E)$ = Coefficient of x^6 in

$$(x^1+x^2+x^3+x^4)\times(x^1+x^2+x^3+x^4+x^5+x^6)$$

$$=1+1+1+1=4$$

$$\therefore \text{Required probability, } P(E)=\frac{n(E)}{n(S)}=\frac{4}{24}=\frac{1}{6}$$

| Example 30. Five ordinary dice are rolled at random and the sum of the numbers shown on them is 16. What is the probability that the numbers shown on each is any one from 2, 3, 4 or 5?

Sol. If the integers x_1, x_2, x_3, x_4 and x_5 are shown on the dice, then $x_1 + x_2 + x_3 + x_4 + x_5 = 16$

where, $1 \le x_i \le 6$ $(i = 1, 2, 3, 4, 5)$

The number of total solutions of this equation.

$= \text{Coefficient of } x^{16} \text{ in } (x^1 + x^2 + x^3 + x^4 + x^5 + x^6)^5$

$= \text{Coefficient of } x^{16} \text{ in } x^5 (1 + x + x^2 + x^3 + x^4 + x^5)^5$

$= \text{Coefficient of } x^{11} \text{ in } (1 + x + x^2 + x^3 + x^4 + x^5)^5$

$= \text{Coefficient of } x^{11} \text{ in } \left\{\left(\frac{1 - x^6}{1 - x}\right)^5\right\}$

$= \text{Coefficient of } x^{11} \text{ in } (1 - x^6)^5 (1 - x)^{-5}$

$= \text{Coefficient of } x^{11}$ in

$(1 - 5x^6 + \dots)(1 + {}^5C_1 x + {}^6C_2 x^2 + \dots + {}^9C_{C_5} x^5 + \dots + {}^{15}C_{11} x^{11} + \dots)$

$= {}^{15}C_{11} - 5 \cdot {}^9C_5$

$= {}^{15}C_4 - 5 \cdot {}^9C_4 = \frac{15 \cdot 14 \cdot 13 \cdot 12}{1 \cdot 2 \cdot 3 \cdot 4} - 5 \cdot \frac{9 \cdot 8 \cdot 7 \cdot 6}{1 \cdot 2 \cdot 3 \cdot 4} = 735$

If S be the sample space

$\therefore \quad n(S) = 735$

Let E be the occurrence event, then

$n(E) =$ The number of integral solutions of

$x_1 + x_2 + x_3 + x_4 + x_5 = 16,$

where $2 \le x_i \le 5$ $(i = 1, 2, 3, 4, 5)$

$= \text{Coefficient of } x^{16} \text{ in } (x^2 + x^3 + x^4 + x^5)^5$

$= \text{Coefficient of } x^{16} \text{ in } x^{10} (1 + x + x^2 + x^3)^5$

$= \text{Coefficient of } x^6 \text{ in } (1 + x + x^2 + x^3)^5$

$= \text{Coefficient of } x^6 \text{ in } \left\{\left(\frac{1 - x^4}{1 - x}\right)^5\right\}$

$= \text{Coefficient of } x^6 \text{ in } (1 - x^4)^5 (1 - x)^{-5}$

$= \text{Coefficient of } x^6$ in

$(1 - 5x^4 + \dots)(1 + {}^5C_1 x + {}^6C_2 x^2 + \dots + {}^{10}C_6 x^6 + \dots)$

$= {}^{10}C_6 - 5 \cdot {}^6C_2 = {}^{10}C_4 - 5 \cdot {}^6C_2$

$= \frac{10 \cdot 9 \cdot 8 \cdot 7}{1 \cdot 2 \cdot 3 \cdot 4} - 5 \cdot \frac{6 \cdot 5}{1 \cdot 2} = 210 - 75 = 135$

$\therefore$ The required probability, $P(E) = \frac{n(E)}{n(S)} = \frac{135}{735} = \frac{9}{49}$

Uncountable Uniform Spaces

(Geometrical Problems)

Example 31. Two persons A and B agree to meet at a place between 11 to 12 noon. The first one to arrive waits for 20 min and then leave. If the time of their arrival be independent and at random, then what is the probability that A and B meet?

Sol. Let A and B arrive at the place of their meeting x minutes and y minutes after 11 noon.

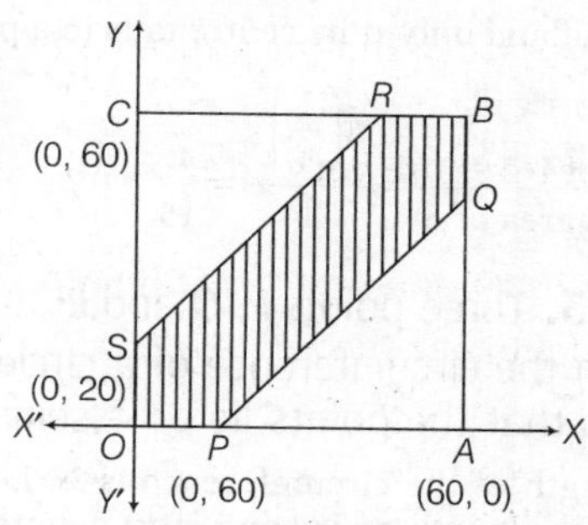

The given condition $\Rightarrow$ their meeting is possible only if

$$|x - y| \le 20 \qquad \dots(i)$$

$OABC$ is a square, where $A \equiv (60, 0)$ and $C \equiv (0, 60)$

Considering the equality part of Eq. (i)

i.e., $|x - y| = 20$

$\therefore$ The area representing the favourable cases

$= \text{Area } OPQBRSO$

$= \text{Area of square } OABC - \text{Area of } \Delta PAQ - \text{Area of } \Delta SRC$

$= (60)(60) - \frac{1}{2}(40)(40) - \frac{1}{2}(40)(40)$

$= 3600 - 1600 = 2000$ sq units

Total way = Area of square $OABC = (60)(60) = 3600$ sq units

Required probability $= \frac{2000}{3600} = \frac{5}{9}$

Example 32. Consider the cartesian plane R^2 and let X denote the subset of points for which both coordinates are integers. A coin of diameter $\frac{1}{2}$ is tossed randomly onto the plane. Find the probability p that the coin covers a point of X.

Sol. Let S denote the set of points inside a square with corners $(a, b), (a, b + 1), (a + 1, b), (a + 1, b + 1) \in X$

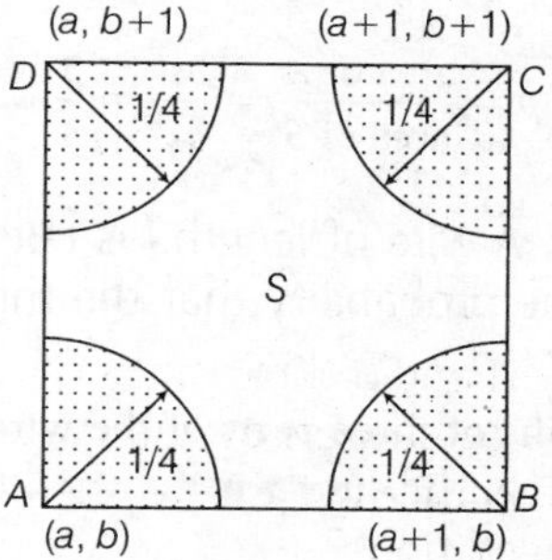

Let P denotes the set of points in S with distance less than $\frac{1}{4}$ from any corner point. (observe that the area of P is equal to the area inside a circle of

radius $\frac{1}{4}$). Thus a coin, whose centre falls in S, will cover a point of X if and only if its centre falls in a point of P.

$$\text{Hence, } p = \frac{\text{area of } P}{\text{area of } S} = \frac{\pi\left(\frac{1}{4}\right)^2}{1} = \frac{\pi}{15} \approx 0.2$$

Example 33. Three points P, Q and R are selected at random from the circumference of a circle. Find the probability p that the points lie on a semi-circle.

Sol. Let the length of the circumference is $2s$. Let x denote the clockwise arc length of PQ and let y denote the clockwise arc length of PR.

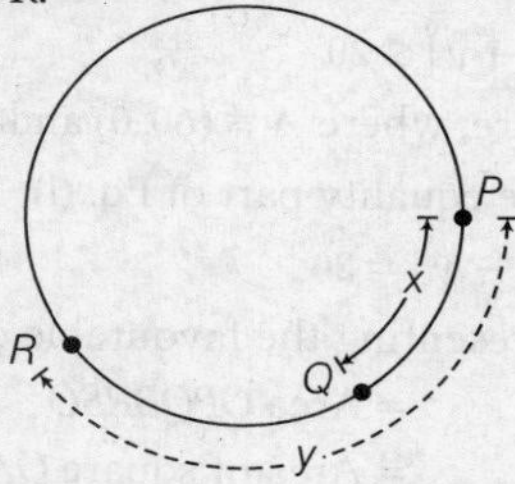

Thus, $0 < x < 2s$ and $0 < y < 2s$

Let A denotes the subset of S for which any of the following conditions holds:

(i) $x, y < s$ (ii) $x < s$ and $y - x > s$

(iii) $x, y > s$ (iv) $y < s$ and $x - y > s$

Then, A consists of those points for which P, Q and R lie on a semi-circle. Thus,

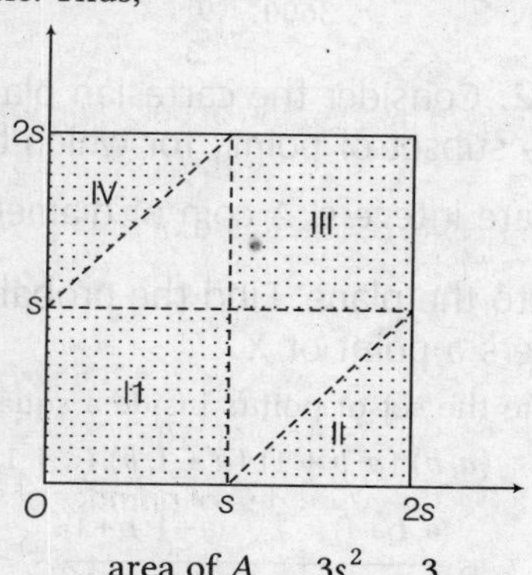

$$p = \frac{\text{area of } A}{\text{area of } S} = \frac{3s^2}{4s^2} = \frac{3}{4}$$

Example 34. A wire of length l is cut into three pieces. Find the probability that the three pieces form a triangle.

Sol. Let the lengths of three parts of the wire be x, y and $l - (x + y)$. Then, $x > 0$, $y > 0$

and $l - (x + y) > 0$

i.e., $x + y < l$ or $y < l - x$

Since, in a triangle, the sum of any two sides is greater than third side, so

$$x + y > l - (x + y) \Rightarrow y > \frac{l}{2} - x$$

and $x + l - (x + y) > y \Rightarrow y < \frac{l}{2}$

and $y + l - (x + y) > x \Rightarrow x < \frac{l}{2}$

$$\Rightarrow \frac{l}{2} - x < y < \frac{l}{2} \text{ and } 0 < x < \frac{l}{2}$$

$$\text{So, required probability} = \frac{\int_0^{l/2}\int_{l/2-x}^{l/2} dy\,dx}{\int_0^{l}\int_0^{l-x} dy\,dx}$$

$$= \frac{\int_0^{l/2}\left\{\frac{l}{2} - \left(\frac{l}{2} - x\right)\right\}dx}{\int_0^{l}(l-x)dx} = \frac{\int_0^{l/2} x\,dx}{\int_0^{l}(l-x)\,dx} = \frac{l^2/8}{l^2/2} = \frac{1}{4}$$

Aliter

The elementary event w is characterised by two parameters x and y [since $z = l - (x + y)$]. We depict the event by a point on x, y plane. The conditions $x > 0$, $y > 0$, $x + y < l$ are imposed on the quantities x and y, the sample space is the interior of a right angled triangle with unit legs i.e. $S_\Omega = \frac{1}{2}$.

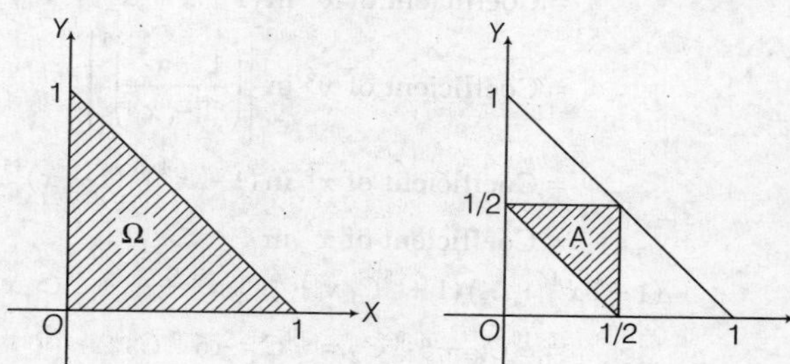

The condition A requiring that a triangle could be formed from the segments x, y, $l - (x + y)$ reduces to the following two conditions: (1) The sum of any two sides is larger than the third side, (2) The difference between any two sides is smaller than the third side. This condition is associated with the triangular domain A with area.

$$S_A = \left(\frac{1}{2}\right)\left(\frac{1}{4}\right) = \frac{1}{8} \therefore P(A) = \frac{S_A}{S_\Omega} = \frac{\left(\frac{1}{8}\right)}{\left(\frac{1}{2}\right)} = \frac{1}{4}$$

Exercise for Session 4

1 A coin is tossed three times. The probability of getting exactly 2 heads is

(a) $\frac{1}{4}$ (b) $\frac{1}{8}$ (c) $\frac{3}{8}$ (d) $\frac{5}{8}$

2 A coin is tossed 4 times. The probability that atleast one head turns up is

(a) $\frac{1}{16}$ (b) $\frac{1}{8}$ (c) $\frac{7}{8}$ (d) $\frac{15}{16}$

3 The following is the probability distribution of a random variable X.

X	1	2	3	4	5
$P(X)$	0.1	0.2	k	0.3	$2k$

The value of k is

(a) $\frac{4}{15}$ (b) $\frac{1}{15}$ (c) $\frac{1}{5}$ (d) $\frac{2}{15}$

4 A random variable X has the distribution

X	2	3	4
$P(X=x)$	0.3	0.4	0.3

Then, variance of the distribution, is

(a) 0.6 (b) 0.7 (c) 0.77 (d) 1.55

5. In a box containing 100 bulbs, 10 bulbs are defective. Probability that out of a sample of 5 bulbs, none is defective, is

(a) 10^{-5} (b) 2^{-5} (c) $(0.9)^5$ (d) 0.9

6. A pair of dice is rolled together till a sum of either 5 or 7 is obtained. The probability that 5 comes before 7, is

(a) $\frac{2}{5}$ (b) $\frac{2}{7}$ (c) $\frac{3}{7}$ (d) None of these

7. If X follows the binomial distribution with parameters $n=6$ and p and $9P(X=4)=P(X=2)$, then p is

(a) $\frac{1}{4}$ (b) $\frac{1}{3}$ (c) $\frac{1}{2}$ (d) $\frac{2}{3}$

8. If probability of a defective bolt is 0.1, then mean and standard deviation of distribution of bolts in a total of 400, are

(a) 30, 3 (b) 40, 5 (c) 30, 4 (d) 40, 6

9. The mean and variance of a binomial distribution are $\frac{5}{4}$ and $\frac{15}{16}$ respectively, then value of p, is

(a) $\frac{1}{2}$ (b) $\frac{15}{16}$ (c) $\frac{1}{4}$ (d) $\frac{3}{4}$

10. The mean and variance of a binomial distribution are 6 and 4, then n is

(a) 9 (b) 12 (c) 18 (d) 10

11. A die is thrown 100 times. Getting an even number is considered a success. Variance of number of successes, is

(a) 10 (b) 20 (c) 25 (d) 50

12. 10% of tools produced by a certain manufacturing process turn out to be defective. Assuming binomial distribution, the probability of 2 defective in sample of 10 tools chosen at random, is

(a) 0.368 (b) 0.194 (c) 0.271 (d) None of these

13. If X follows a binomial distribution with parameters $n=100$ and $p=\frac{1}{3}$, then $P(X=r)$ is maximum, when r equals

(a) 16 (b) 32 (c) 33 (d) None of these

14. The expected value of the number of points, obtained in a single throw of die, is

(a) $\frac{3}{2}$ (b) $\frac{5}{2}$ (c) $\frac{7}{2}$ (d) $\frac{9}{2}$

15. Two points P and Q are taken at random on a line segment OA of length a. The probability that $PQ>b$, where $0<b<a$, is

(a) $\frac{b}{a}$ (b) $\frac{b^2}{a^2}$ (c) $\left(\frac{a-b}{a}\right)^2$ (d) $\left(\frac{a-2b}{a-b}\right)^2$

Shortcuts and Important Results to Remember

1 If n letters corresponding to n envelopes are placed in the envelopes at random, then

(i) probability that all letters are in right envelopes $= \frac{1}{n!}$.

(ii) probability that all letters are not in right envelopes $= 1 - \frac{1}{n!}$.

(iii) probability that no letter is in right envelopes $= \frac{1}{2!} - \frac{1}{3!} + \frac{1}{4!} - \dots + (-1)^n \frac{1}{n!}$.

(iv) probability that exactly r letters are in right envelopes $= \frac{1}{r!}\left[\frac{1}{2!} - \frac{1}{3!} + \frac{1}{4!} - \dots + (-1)^{n-r} \frac{1}{(n-r)!}\right]$.

2 When two dice are thrown, the probability of getting a total r (sum of numbers on upper faces), is

(i) $\frac{(r-1)}{36}$, if $2 \le r \le 7$ (ii) $\frac{(13-r)}{36}$, if $8 \le r \le 12$

3 When three dice are thrown, the probability of getting a total r (sum of numbers on upper faces), is

(i) $\frac{^{r-1}C_2}{216}$, if $3 \le r \le 8$ (ii) $\frac{25}{216}$, if $r = 9$

(iii) $\frac{27}{216}$, if $r = 10, 11$ (iv) $\frac{25}{216}$, if $r = 12$

(v) $\frac{^{(20-r)}C_2}{216}$, if $13 \le r \le 18$

4 If A and B are two finite sets (Let $n(A) = n$ and $n(B) = m$) and if a mapping is selected at random from the set of all mappings from A to B, the probability that the mapping is

(i) a one-one function is $\frac{^mP_n}{m^n}$.

(ii) a one-one onto function is $\frac{n!}{m^n}$.

(iii) a many one function is $1 - \frac{^mP_n}{m^n}$.

5 If r squares are selected from a chess board of size 8×8, then the probability that they lie on a diagonal line, is $\frac{4(^7C_r + {}^6C_r + {}^5C_r + \dots + {}^rC_r) + 2(^8C_r)}{^{64}C_r}$ for $1 \le r \le 7$.

6 If n objects are distributed among n persons, then the probability that atleast one of them will not get anything, is $\frac{n^n - n!}{n^n}$.

7 Points about coin, dice and playing cards:

(a) **Coin** If 'one' coin is tossed n times 'n' coins are tossed once, then number of simple events (or simple points) in the space of the experiment is 2^n. All these events are equally likely.

(b) **Dice** If 'one' die is thrown 'n' times or 'n' dice are thrown once, then number of simple events (or simple points) in the space of the experiment is 6^n (here dice is cubical). All events are equally likely.

(c) **Playing Cards** A pack of playing cards has 52 cards. There are four suits Spade (♠ black face), Heart (♥ red face), Diamond (♦ red face) and Club (♣ black face) each having 13 cards. In 13 cards of each suit, there are 3 face (or court) cards namely King, Queen and Jack (or knave), so there are in all 12 face cards King, 4 Queen and 4 Jacks (or knaves). 4 of each suit namely Ace (or Ekka), King, Queen and Jack (or knave).

(i) **Game of bridge** It is played by 4 players, each player is given 13 cards.

(ii) **Game of whist** It is played by two pairs of persons.

(iii) If two cards (one after the other) can be drawn out of a well-shuffled pack of 52 cards, then number of ways; (x) With replacement is $52 \times 52 = (52)^2 = 2704$ (β) Without replacement is $52 \times 51 = 2652$.

(iv) Two cards (simultaneously) can be drawn out of a well-shuffled pack of 52 cards, then number of ways is $^{52}C_2 = \frac{52 \times 51}{2} = 1326$.

8 Out of $(2n+1)$ tickets consecutively numbered, three are drawn at random, then the probability that the numbers on them are in AP, is $\frac{3n}{4n^2 - 1}$.

9 Out of $3n$ consecutive integers, three are selected at random, then the probability that their sum is divided by 3, is $\frac{(3n^2 - 3n + 2)}{(3n-1)(3n-2)}$.

10 Two numbers a and b are chosen at random from the set $\{1, 2, 3, \dots, 5n\}$, the probability that $a^4 - b^4$ is divisible by 5, is $\frac{17n - 5}{5(5n-1)}$.

11 Two numbers a and b are chosen at random from the set $\{1, 2, 3, \dots, 3n\}$ the probability that $a^2 - b^2$ is divisible by 3, is $\frac{(5n-3)}{3(3n-1)}$.

12 Two numbers a and b are chosen at random from the set $\{1, 2, 3, \dots, 3n\}$, the probability that $a^3 + b^3$ is divisible by 3, is $\frac{1}{3}$.

13 There are n stations between two cities A and B. A train is to stop at three of these n stations. The probability that no two of these three stations are consecutive, is $\frac{(n-3)(n-4)}{n(n-1)}$.

JEE Type Solved Examples : Single Option Correct Type Questions

- This section contains **10 multiple choice examples.** Each example has four choices (a), (b), (c) and (d) out of which **ONLY ONE** is correct.

• Ex. 1 *The probability that in a year of 22nd century chosen at random, there will be 53 Sundays, is*

(a) $\frac{3}{28}$ (b) $\frac{2}{28}$ (c) $\frac{7}{28}$ (d) $\frac{5}{28}$

Sol. (d) In the 22nd century, there are 25 leap years viz. 2100, 2104, 2108,..., 2196 and 75 non-leap years.

Consider the following events:

E_1 = Selecting a leap year from 22nd century

E_2 = Selecting a non-leap year from 22nd century

E = There are 53 Sundays in a year of 22nd century

We have,

$$P(E_1)=\frac{25}{100},\ P(E_2)=\frac{75}{100},\ P\left(\frac{E}{E_1}\right)=\frac{2}{7}\text{ and }P\left(\frac{E}{E_2}\right)=\frac{1}{7}$$

Required probability $= P(E) = P((E\cap E_1)\cup(E\cap E_2))$

$$= P(E\cap E_1)+P(E\cap E_2)$$

$$= P(E_1).P\left(\frac{E}{E_1}\right)+P(E_2).P\left(\frac{E}{E_2}\right)$$

$$= \frac{25}{100}\times\frac{2}{7}+\frac{75}{100}\times\frac{1}{7}=\frac{5}{28}$$

• Ex. 2 *In a convex hexagon two diagonals are drawn at random. The probability that the diagonals intersect at an interior point of the hexagon, is*

(a) $\frac{5}{12}$ (b) $\frac{7}{12}$ (c) $\frac{2}{5}$ (d) $\frac{3}{5}$

Sol. (a) We have,

Number of diagonals of a hexagon $= {}^6C_2 - 6 = 9$

$\therefore$ $n(s)$ = Total number of selections of two diagonals $= {}^9C_2 = 36$

and $n(E)$ = The number of selections of two diagonals which intersect at an interior point

= The number of selections of four vertices $= {}^6C_4 = 15$

Hence, required probability $=\frac{n(E)}{n(S)}=\frac{15}{36}=\frac{5}{12}$

• Ex. 3 *If three integers are chosen at random from the set of first 20 natural numbers, the chance that their product is a multiple of 3, is*

(a) $\frac{1}{57}$ (b) $\frac{13}{19}$

(c) $\frac{2}{19}$ (d) $\frac{194}{285}$

Sol. (d) $n(S)$ = Total number of ways of selecting 3 integers from 20 natural numbers $= {}^{20}C_3 = 1140.$

Their product is multiple of 3 means atleast one number is divisible by 3. The number which are divisible by 3 are 3, 6, 9, 12, 15 and 16.

$\therefore n(E)$ = The number of ways of selecting atleast one of them multiple of 3

$$= {}^6C_1\times{}^{14}C_2+{}^6C_2\times{}^{14}C_1\times{}^6C_3=776$$

$\therefore$ Required probability $=\frac{n(E)}{n(S)}$

$$=\frac{776}{1140}=\frac{194}{285}$$

• Ex. 4 *If three numbers are selected from the set of the first 20 natural numbers, the probability that they are in GP, is*

(a) $\frac{1}{285}$ (b) $\frac{4}{285}$

(c) $\frac{11}{1140}$ (d) $\frac{1}{71}$

Sol. (c) $n(S)$ = Total number of ways of selecting 3 numbers from first 20 natural numbers $= {}^{20}C_3 = 1140$

Three numbers are in GP, the favourable cases are 1, 2, 4; 1, 3, 9; 1, 4, 16; 2, 4, 8; 2, 6, 18; 3, 6, 12; 4, 8, 16; 5, 10, 20; 4, 6, 9; 8, 12, 18; 9, 12, 16

$\therefore n(E)$ = The number of favourable cases = 11

$\therefore$ Required probability $=\frac{n(E)}{n(S)}=\frac{11}{1140}$

• Ex. 5 *Two numbers b and c are chosen at random with replacement from the numbers 1, 2, 3, 4, 5, 6, 7, 8 and 9. The probability that $x^2+bx+c>0$ for all $x\in R$, is*

(a) $\frac{17}{123}$ (b) $\frac{32}{81}$

(c) $\frac{82}{125}$ (d) $\frac{45}{143}$

Sol. (b) Here, $x^2+bx+c>0, \forall\ x\in R$

$\therefore$ $D<0$

$\Rightarrow$ $b^2<4c$

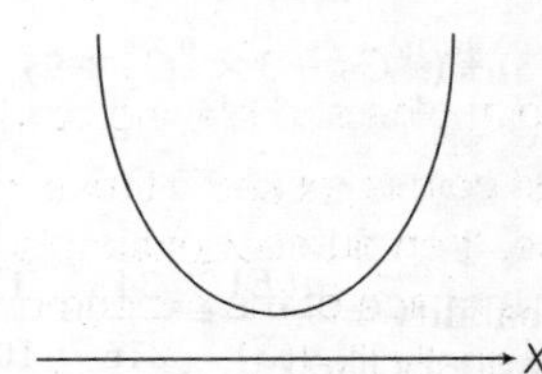

Value of b	Possible values of c		
1	$1 < 4c$	$\Rightarrow c > \frac{1}{4} \Rightarrow$	{1, 2, 3, 4, 5, 6, 7, 8, 9}
2	$4 < 4c$	$\Rightarrow c > 1 \Rightarrow$	{2, 3, 4, 5, 6, 7, 8, 9}
3	$9 < 4c$	$\Rightarrow c > \frac{9}{4} \Rightarrow$	{3, 4, 5, 6, 7, 8, 9}
4	$16 < 4c$	$\Rightarrow c > 4 \Rightarrow$	{5, 6, 7, 8, 9}
5	$25 < 4c$	$\Rightarrow c > 6.25 \Rightarrow$	{7, 8, 9}
6	$36 < 4c$	$\Rightarrow c > 9 \Rightarrow$	Impossible
7	Impossible		
8	Impossible		
9	Impossible		

$n(E)$ = Number of favourable cases $= 9 + 8 + 7 + 5 + 3 = 32$

$n(S)$ = Total ways $= 9 \times 9 = 81$

$\therefore$ Required probability $= \frac{n(E)}{n(S)} = \frac{32}{81}$

• **Ex. 6** *Three dice are thrown. The probability of getting a sum which is a perfect square, is*

(a) $\frac{2}{5}$ (b) $\frac{9}{20}$

(c) $\frac{1}{4}$ (d) None of these

Sol. (d) $n(S)$ = Total number of ways $= 6 \times 6 \times 6 = 216$

The sum of the numbers on three dice varies from 3 to 18 and among these 4, 9 and 16 are perfect squares.

$\therefore n(E)$ = Number of favourable ways

= Coefficient of x^4 in $(x + x^2 + \ldots + x^6)^3$ + Coefficient of x^9 in $(x + x^2 + \ldots + x^6)^3$ + Coefficient of x^{16} in $(x + x^2 + \ldots + x^6)^3$

= Coefficient of x in $(1 + x + \ldots + x^5)^3$ + Coefficient of x^6 in $(1 + x + x^2 + \ldots + x^5)^3$ + Coefficient of x^{13} in $(1 + x + x^2 + \ldots + x^5)^3$

= Coefficient of x in $(1 - x^6)^3(1 - x)^{-3}$ + Coefficient of x^6 in $(1 - x^6)^3(1 - x)^{-3}$ + Coefficient of x^{13} in $(1 - x^6)^3(1 - x)^{-3}$

= Coefficient of x in $(1)(1 + {}^3C_1 x + \ldots)$ + Coefficient of x^6 in $(1 - 3x^6)(1 + {}^3C_1 x + \ldots)$ + Coefficient of x^{13} in $(1 - 3x^6 + 3x^{12} + \ldots); (1 + {}^3C_1 x + \ldots)$

$= {}^3C_1 + ({}^8C_6 - 3) + ({}^{15}C_{13} - 3 \times {}^9C_7 + 9)$

$= {}^3C_1 + ({}^8C_2 - 3) + ({}^{15}C_2 - 3 \times {}^9C_2 + 9)$

$= 3 + 25 + 6$

$= 34$

$\therefore$ Required probability $= \frac{n(E)}{n(S)} = \frac{34}{216} = \frac{17}{108}$

• **Ex. 7** *A quadratic equation is chosen from the set of all quadratic equations which are unchanged by squaring their roots. The chance that the chosen equation has equal roots,*

(a) $\frac{1}{2}$ (b) $\frac{1}{3}$

(c) $\frac{1}{4}$ (d) None of these

Sol. (a) Let α and β be the roots of the quadratic equation. According to question,

$\alpha + \beta = \alpha^2 + \beta^2$ and $\alpha\beta = \alpha^2\beta^2 \Rightarrow \alpha\beta(\alpha\beta - 1) = 0$

$\Rightarrow \alpha\beta = 1$ or $\alpha\beta = 0$

$\Rightarrow \alpha = 1, \beta = 1; \alpha = \omega, \beta = \omega^2$ [cube roots and unity

$\alpha = 1, \beta = 0; \alpha = 0, \beta = 0$

$\therefore n(S)$ = Number of quadratic equations which are unchanged by squaring their roots = 4

and $n(E)$ = Number of quadratic equations have equal root. = 2

$\therefore$ Required probability $= \frac{n(E)}{n(S)} = \frac{2}{4} = \frac{1}{2}$

• **Ex. 8** *Three-digit numbers are formed using the digits 0, 1, 2, 3, 4, 5 without repetition of digits. If a number is choser at random, then the probability that the digits either increas or decrease, is*

(a) $\frac{1}{10}$ (b) $\frac{2}{11}$ (c) $\frac{3}{10}$ (d) $\frac{4}{11}$

Sol. (c) $n(S)$ = Total number of three digit numbers

$= {}^6P_3 - {}^5P_2 = 120 - 20 = 100$

$n(E)$ = Number of numbers with digits either increase or decrease

= Number of numbers with increasing digits + Number of numbers with decreasing digits

$= {}^5C_3 + {}^6C_3 = 10 + 20 = 30$

$\therefore$ Required probability $= \frac{n(E)}{n(S)} = \frac{30}{100} = \frac{3}{10}$

• **Ex. 9** *If X follows a binomial distribution with parameters $n = 8$ and $p = \frac{1}{2}$, then $p(|x - 4| \le 2)$ is equal to*

(a) $\frac{121}{128}$ (b) $\frac{119}{128}$ (c) $\frac{117}{128}$ (d) $\frac{115}{128}$

Sol. (b) Here, $p = \frac{1}{2}, n = 8$

$\therefore \quad q = 1 - p = 1 - \frac{1}{2} = \frac{1}{2}$

$\therefore$ The binomial distribution is $\left(\frac{1}{2} + \frac{1}{2}\right)^8$

Also, $|x - 4| \le 2$

$\Rightarrow \quad -2 \le x - 4 \le 2 \Rightarrow 2 \le x \le 6$

$\therefore\ p(|x-4|\le 2) = p(x=2)+p(x=3)+p(x=4) + p(x=5)+p(x=6)$

$$= {}^8C_2\left(\frac{1}{2}\right)^2\left(\frac{1}{2}\right)^6 + {}^8C_3\left(\frac{1}{2}\right)^3\left(\frac{1}{2}\right)^5 + {}^8C_4\left(\frac{1}{2}\right)^4\left(\frac{1}{2}\right)^4 + {}^8C_5\left(\frac{1}{2}\right)^5\left(\frac{1}{2}\right)^3 + {}^8C_6\left(\frac{1}{2}\right)^6\left(\frac{1}{2}\right)^2$$

$$= \frac{{}^8C_2 + {}^8C_3 + {}^8C_4 + {}^8C_5 + {}^8C_6}{2^8}$$

$$= \frac{238}{256} = \frac{119}{128}$$

● **Ex. 10** *A doctor is called to see a sick child. The doctor knows (prior to the visit) that 90% of the sick children in that neighbourhood are sick with the flue, denoted by F, while 10% are sick with the measles, denoted by M. A well-known symptom of measles is a rash, denoted by R. The probability of having a rash for a child sick with the measles is 0.95. However, occasionally children with the flue also develop a rash with conditional probability 0.08. Upon examination the child, the doctor finds a rash, then the probability that the child has the measles, is*

(a) $\frac{89}{167}$ (b) $\frac{91}{167}$ (c) $\frac{93}{167}$ (d) $\frac{95}{167}$

Sol. (d) $\because P(F) = 0\cdot 90,\ P(M) = 0\cdot 10,$

$$P\left(\frac{R}{F}\right) = 0\cdot 08,\ P\left(\frac{R}{M}\right) = 0\cdot 95$$

$$\therefore\quad P\left(\frac{M}{R}\right) = \frac{P(M)\cdot P\left(\frac{R}{M}\right)}{P(M)\cdot P\left(\frac{R}{M}\right) + P(F)\cdot P\left(\frac{R}{F}\right)}$$

$$= \frac{0\cdot 10\times 0\cdot 95}{0\cdot 10\times 0\cdot 95 + 0\cdot 90\times 0\cdot 08} = \frac{0\cdot 095}{0\cdot 167} = \frac{95}{167}$$

JEE Type Solved Examples : More than One Correct Option Type Questions

- This section contains **5 multiple choice examples.** Each example has four choices (a), (b), (c) and (d) out of **which more than one** may be correct.

● **Ex. 11** *Let p_n denote the probability of getting n heads, when a fair coin is tossed m times. If p_4, p_5, p_6 are in AP, then values of m can be*

(a) 5 (b) 7 (c) 10 (d) 14

Sol. (b, d) $\because p_4 = {}^mC_4\left(\frac{1}{2}\right)^4\left(\frac{1}{2}\right)^{m-4} = {}^mC_4\left(\frac{1}{2}\right)^m$

$$p_5 = {}^mC_5\left(\frac{1}{2}\right)^5\left(\frac{1}{2}\right)^{m-5} = {}^mC_5\left(\frac{1}{2}\right)^m$$

and $\quad p_6 = {}^mC_6\left(\frac{1}{2}\right)^6\left(\frac{1}{2}\right)^{m-6} = {}^mC_6\left(\frac{1}{2}\right)^m$

According to the question, p_4, p_5, p_6 are in AP

$\therefore\quad 2p_5 = p_4 + p_6$

$\Rightarrow\quad 2\times {}^mC_5\left(\frac{1}{2}\right)^m = {}^mC_4\left(\frac{1}{2}\right)^m + {}^mC_6\left(\frac{1}{2}\right)^m$

or $\quad 2\times {}^mC_5 = {}^mC_4 + {}^mC_6$

or $\quad 2 = \frac{{}^mC_4}{{}^mC_5} + \frac{{}^mC_6}{{}^mC_5} \Rightarrow 2 = \frac{5}{m-5+1} + \frac{m-6+1}{6}$

$\Rightarrow\quad 2 = \frac{5}{m-4} + \frac{m-5}{6} \Rightarrow (m^2-2)\,m + 98 = 0$

$\Rightarrow\quad (m-14)(m-7) = 0$

$\Rightarrow\quad m = 7$ or 14

● **Ex. 12** *A random variable X follows binomial distribution with mean a and variance b. Then,*

(a) $a > b > 0$ (b) $\frac{a}{b} > 1$

(c) $\frac{a^2}{a-b}$ is an integer (d) $\frac{a^2}{a+b}$ is an integer

Sol. (a, b, c) Suppose, $X \sim B(n, p)$ i.e. $(q+p)^n$

Here, $np = a$ and $npq = b$

$\therefore\quad q = \frac{b}{a}$, then $p = 1 - q = 1 - \frac{b}{a}$

Now, $0 < q < 1 \Rightarrow 0 < \frac{b}{a} < 1 \Rightarrow a > b > 0$ [alternate (a)]

and $\frac{a}{b} > 1$ [alternate (b)]

Also, $\frac{a^2}{a-b} = \frac{(np)^2}{np - npq} = \frac{np}{1-q} = \frac{np}{p} = n =$ Integer [alternate (c)]

● **Ex. 13** *If $A_1, A_2, \ldots, A_n$ are n independent events, such that $P(A_i) = \frac{1}{i+1}, i = 1, 2, \ldots, n$, then the probability that none of $A_1, A_2, A_3, \ldots, A_n$ occur, is*

(a) $\frac{n}{n+1}$ (b) $\frac{1}{n+1}$

(c) less than $\frac{1}{n}$ (d) greater than $\frac{1}{n+2}$

Sol. (b, c, d) $\because A_1, A_2, A_3, \ldots, A_n$ are n independent, then

Required probability $= P(A_1' \cap A_2' \cap A_3' \cap \ldots \cap A_n')$

$= P(A_1').P(A_2').P(A_3') \ldots P(A_n')$

$= (1 - P(A_1))(1 - P(A_2))(1 - P(A_3)) \ldots (1 - P(A_n))$

$= \left(1 - \frac{1}{2}\right)\left(1 - \frac{1}{3}\right)\left(1 - \frac{1}{4}\right) \ldots \left(1 - \frac{1}{n+1}\right)$

$= \frac{1}{2} \times \frac{2}{3} \times \frac{3}{4} \times \ldots \times \frac{n}{n+1} = \frac{1}{n+1}$

$\because n + 2 > n + 1 > n; \therefore \quad \frac{1}{n+2} < \frac{1}{n+1} < \frac{1}{n}$

• **Ex. 14** *A and B are two events, such that $P(A \cup B) \geq \frac{3}{4}$ and $\frac{1}{8} \leq P(A \cap B) \leq \frac{3}{8}$, then*

(a) $P(A) + P(B) \leq \frac{11}{8}$ (b) $P(A) \cdot P(B) \leq \frac{3}{8}$

(c) $P(A) + P(B) \geq \frac{7}{8}$ (d) None of these

Sol. (a, c) $\because \frac{3}{4} \leq P(A \cup B) \leq 1$

$\Rightarrow \frac{3}{4} \leq P(A) + P(B) - P(A \cap B) \leq 1$

As the minimum value of $P(A \cap B) = \frac{1}{8}$, we get

$P(A) + P(B) - \frac{1}{8} \geq \frac{3}{4} \Rightarrow P(A) + P(B) \geq \frac{7}{8}$ [alternate (c)]

As the maximum value of $P(A \cap B) = \frac{3}{8}$, we get

$P(A) + P(B) - \frac{3}{8} \leq 1 \Rightarrow P(A) + P(B) \leq \frac{11}{8}$ [alternate (a)]

• **Ex. 15** *A, B, C and D cut a pack of 52 cards successively in the order given. If the person who cuts a spade first receives ₹ 350, then the expectations of*

(a) B is ₹ 96 (b) D is ₹ 54

(c) $(A + C)$ is ₹ 200 (d) $(B - D)$ is ₹ 56

Sol. (a, b, c) Let E be the event of any one cutting a spade in one cut and let S be the sample space, then

$n(E) = {}^{13}C_1 = 13$ and $n(S) = {}^{52}C_1 = 52$

$\therefore \quad p = P(E) = \frac{n(E)}{n(S)} = \frac{1}{4}$ and $q = p(\bar{E}) = 1 - p = \frac{3}{4}$

The probability of A winning (when A starts the game)

$= p + q^4 p + q^8 p + \ldots \infty = \frac{p}{1 - q^4} = \frac{\frac{1}{4}}{1 - \left(\frac{3}{4}\right)^4} = \frac{64}{175}$

$\therefore \quad E(A) = ₹\ 350 \times \frac{64}{175} = ₹\ 128$

$E(B) = ₹128 \times q = ₹128 \times \frac{3}{4} = ₹\ 96$

$E(C) = ₹96 \times q = ₹96 \times \frac{3}{4} = ₹\ 72$

and $E(D) = ₹72 \times q = ₹72 \times \frac{3}{4} = ₹\ 54$

$\therefore E(A + C) = ₹\ 200$ and $E(B - D) = ₹\ 42$.

JEE Type Solved Examples : Passage Based Questions

- This section contains **3 solved passages** based upon each of the passage **3 multiple choice** examples have to be answered. Each of these examples has four choices (a), (b), (c) and (d) out of which **ONLY ONE** is correct.

Passage I

(Ex. Nos. 16 to 18)

Each coefficient in the equation $ax^2 + bx + c = 0$ is determined by throwing an ordinary die.

16. *The probability that roots of quadratic are real and distinct, is*

(a) $\frac{5}{216}$ (b) $\frac{19}{108}$ (c) $\frac{173}{216}$ (d) $\frac{17}{108}$

Sol. (b) For roots of $ax^2 + bx + c = 0$ to be real and distinct,

$$b^2 - 4ac > 0$$

Value of b	Possible values of a and c
1, 2	No values of a and c
3	(1, 1), (1, 2), (2, 1)
4	(1, 1), (1, 2), (2, 1), (1, 3), (3, 1)
5	(1, 1), (1, 2), (2, 1), (1, 3), (3, 1), (2, 2), (1, 4), (4, 1), (1, 5), (5, 1), (2, 3), (3, 2), (1, 6), (6, 1)
6	(1, 1), (1, 2), (2, 1), (1, 3), (3, 1), (2, 2), (1, 4), (4, 1), (1, 5), (5, 1), (2, 3), (3, 2), (1, 6), (6, 1), (2, 4), (4, 2)

If E be the event of favourable cases, then $n(E) = 38$

Total ways, $n(S) = 6 \times 6 \times 6 = 216$

Hence, the required probability, $p_1 = \frac{n(E)}{n(S)} = \frac{38}{216} = \frac{19}{108}$

17. *The probability that roots of quadratic are equal, is*

(a) $\frac{5}{216}$ (b) $\frac{7}{216}$ (c) $\frac{11}{216}$ (d) $\frac{17}{216}$

Sol. (a) For roots of $ax^2 + bx + c = 0$ to be equal $b^2 = 4ac$

i.e. b^2 must be even.

Value of b	Possible values of a and c
2	(1, 1)
4	(2, 2), (1, 4), (4, 1)
6	(3, 3)

If E be the event of favourable cases, then $n(E) = 5$

Total ways, $n(S) = 6 \times 6 \times 6 = 216$

Hence, the required probability, $p_2 = \dfrac{n(E)}{n(S)} = \dfrac{5}{216}$

18. *The probability that roots of quadratic are imaginary, is*

(a) $\dfrac{103}{216}$ (b) $\dfrac{133}{216}$ (c) $\dfrac{157}{216}$ (d) $\dfrac{173}{216}$

Sol. (d) Let p_3 = Probability that roots of $ax^2 + bx + c = 0$ are imaginary

$= 1 -$ (Probability that roots of $ax^2 + bx + c = 0$ are real)

$= 1 - (p_1 + p_2)$ [from above]

$= 1 - \dfrac{43}{216} = \dfrac{173}{216}$

Passage II

(Ex. Nos. 19 to 21)

A box contains n coins. Let $P(E_i)$ be the probability that exactly i out of n coins are biased. If $P(E_i)$ is directly proportional to $i(i+1); 1 \le i \le n$.

19. *Proportionality constant k is equal to*

(a) $\dfrac{3}{n(n^2+1)}$ (b) $\dfrac{1}{(n^2+1)(n+2)}$

(c) $\dfrac{3}{n(n+1)(n+2)}$ (d) $\dfrac{1}{(n+1)(n+2)(n+3)}$

Sol. (c) $\because P(E_i) \propto i(i+1)$

$\Rightarrow P(E_i) = k\, i(i+1)$, where k is proportionality constant.

We have, $P(E_1) + P(E_2) + P(E_3) + \ldots + P(E_n) = 1$

($\because E_1, E_2, \ldots, E_n$ are mutually exclusive and exhaustive events)

$$\Rightarrow \sum_{i=1}^{n} P(E_i) = 1$$

$$\Rightarrow k \sum_{i=1}^{n} (i^2 + i) = 1$$

$$\Rightarrow k\left[\sum n^2 + \sum n\right] = 1$$

$$\Rightarrow k\left[\frac{n(n+1)(2n+1)}{6} + \frac{n(n+1)}{2}\right] = 1$$

$$\therefore \quad k = \frac{3}{n(n+1)(n+2)} \quad \ldots\text{(i)}$$

20. *If P be the probability that a coin selected at random is biased, then $\lim_{x \to \infty} P$ is*

(a) $\dfrac{1}{4}$ (b) $\dfrac{3}{4}$ (c) $\dfrac{3}{5}$ (d) $\dfrac{7}{8}$

Sol. (b) $\because P = P(E) = \sum_{i=1}^{n} \cdot P(E_i)\, P\left(\dfrac{E}{E_i}\right)$ ...(ii)

$$= \sum_{i=1}^{n} k\, i(i+1) \cdot \frac{i}{n}$$

$$= \frac{k}{n} \sum_{i=1}^{n} (i^3 + i^2) = \frac{k}{n}\left[\sum n^3 + \sum n^2\right]$$

$$= \frac{k}{n}\left[\left(\frac{n(n+1)}{2}\right)^2 + \frac{n(n+1)(2n+1)}{6}\right]$$

$$= \frac{k(n+1)(n+2)(3n+1)}{12}$$

$$= \frac{3}{n(n+1)(n+2)} \cdot \frac{(n+1)(n+2)(3n+1)}{12} \quad \text{[from Eq. (i)]}$$

$$= \frac{3n+1}{4n} = \frac{3}{4} + \frac{1}{4n}$$

$$\therefore \lim_{n \to \infty} P = \lim_{n \to \infty}\left[\frac{3}{4} + \frac{1}{3n}\right] = \frac{3}{4} + 0 = \frac{3}{4}$$

21. *If a coin is selected at random is found to be biased, the probability that it is the only biased coin the box, is*

(a) $\dfrac{1}{(n+1)(n+2)(n+3)(n+4)}$ (b) $\dfrac{12}{n(n+1)(n+2)(3n+1)}$

(c) $\dfrac{24}{n(n+1)(n+2)(2n+1)}$ (d) $\dfrac{24}{n(n+1)(n+2)(3n+1)}$

Sol. (d) $P\left(\dfrac{E_1}{E}\right) = \dfrac{P(E_1) \cdot P\left(\dfrac{E}{E_1}\right)}{\sum_{i=1}^{n} P(E_i) \cdot P\left(\dfrac{E}{E_i}\right)} = \dfrac{2k \times \dfrac{1}{n}}{P(E)}$ [from Eq. (ii)]

$$= \frac{\dfrac{2k}{n}}{\left(\dfrac{3n+1}{4n}\right)} = \frac{8k}{(3n+1)}$$

$$= \frac{24}{n(n+1)(n+2)(3n+1)} \quad \text{[from Eq. (i)]}$$

Passage III

(Ex. Nos. 22 to 24)

Let S be the set of the first 21 natural numbers, then the probability of

22. *Choosing $\{x, y\} \subseteq S$, such that $x^3 + y^3$ is divisible by 3, is*

(a) $\dfrac{1}{6}$ (b) $\dfrac{1}{5}$ (c) $\dfrac{1}{4}$ (d) $\dfrac{1}{3}$

Sol. (d) $\because S = \{1, 2, 3, 4, 5, \ldots, 21\}$

Total number of ways choosing x and y is

$$^{21}C_2 = \frac{21 \cdot 20}{1 \cdot 2} = 210$$

Now, arrange the given numbers as below:

1	4	7	10	13	16	19
2	5	8	11	14	17	20
3	6	9	12	15	18	21

We see that, $x^3 + y^3 = (x + y)(x^2 - xy + y^2)$ will be divisible by 3 in the following cases:

One of two numbers belongs to the first row and one of the two numbers belongs to the second row or both numbers occurs in third row.

$\therefore$ Number of favourable cases $= ({}^7C_1)({}^7C_1) + {}^7C_2 = 70$

$\therefore$ Required probability $= \dfrac{70}{210} = \dfrac{1}{3}$

23. *Choosing $\{x, y, z\} \subseteq S$, such that x, y, z are in AP, is*

(a) $\dfrac{5}{133}$ (b) $\dfrac{10}{133}$ (c) $\dfrac{3}{133}$ (d) $\dfrac{2}{133}$

Sol. (b) Given, x, y, z are in AP

$\therefore$ $2y = x + z$

It is clear that sum of x and z is even.

$\therefore$ x and z both are even or odd out of set S.

i.e., 11 numbers (1, 3, 5,..., 21) are odd and 10 numbers (2, 4, 6,..., 20) are even.

$\therefore$ Number of favourable cases

$$= {}^{21}C_2 + {}^{10}C_2 = \frac{11\cdot 10}{1\cdot 2} + \frac{10\cdot 9}{1\cdot 2} = 100$$

and total number of ways choosing x, y and z is

$${}^{21}C_3 = \frac{21\cdot 20\cdot 19}{1\cdot 2\cdot 3} = 1330$$

$\therefore$ Required probability $= \dfrac{100}{1330} = \dfrac{10}{133}$

24. *Choosing $\{x, y, z\} \subseteq S$, such that x, y, z are not consecutive, is*

(a) $\dfrac{17}{70}$ (b) $\dfrac{34}{70}$ (c) $\dfrac{51}{70}$ (d) $\dfrac{34}{35}$

Sol. (c) Given, x, y and z are not consecutive.

$\therefore$ Number of favourable ways $= {}^{21-3+1}C_3$

$$= {}^{19}C_3 = \frac{19\cdot 18\cdot 17}{1\cdot 2\cdot 3} = 969$$

and total number of ways $= {}^{21}C_3 = \dfrac{21\cdot 20\cdot 19}{1\cdot 2\cdot 3} = 1330$

$\therefore$ Required probability $= \dfrac{969}{1330} = \dfrac{51}{70}$

JEE Type Solved Examples : Single Integer Answer Type Questions

- This section contains **2 examples.** The answer to each example is a **single digit integer** ranging from **0** to **9** (both inclusive).

• **Ex. 25** *The altitude through A of ΔABC meets BC at D and the circumscribed circle at E. If $D \equiv (2, 3)$, $E \equiv (5, 5)$, the ordinate of the orthocentre being a natural number. If the probability that the orthocentre lies on the lines $y = 1$; $y = 2$; $y = 3$...... $y = 10$ is $\dfrac{m}{n}$, where m and n are relative primes, the value of $m + n$ is*

Sol. (8) Let the orthocentre be $O(x, y)$.

It is clear from the OE is perpendicular bisector of line BC.

$\therefore$ $OD = DE$

$\Rightarrow \sqrt{(x-2)^2 + (y-3)^2} = \sqrt{(5-2)^2 + (5-3)^2}$

$\Rightarrow (x-2)^2 + (y-3)^2 = (5-2)^2 + (5-3)^2$

$\Rightarrow x^2 + y^2 - 4x - 6y = 0 \Rightarrow x = 2 \pm \sqrt{13 - (y-3)^2}$

$\Rightarrow y$ can take the values as 1, 2, 3, 4, 5, 6

$\therefore$ Required probability $= \dfrac{6}{10} = \dfrac{3}{5} = \dfrac{m}{n}$ [given]

$\Rightarrow$ $m = 3$ and $n = 5$

$\therefore$ $m + n = 8$

• **Ex. 26** *The digits 1, 2, 3, 4, 5, 6, 7, 8 and 9 are written in random order to form a nine digit number. Let p be the probability that this number is divisible by 36, the value of 9p is*

Sol. (2) $\because$ $1 + 2 + 3 + 4 + 5 + 6 + 7 + 8 + 9 = 45$, a number consisting all these digits will be divisible by 9. Thus, the number will be divisible by 36, if and only if it is divisible by 4. The number formed by its last two digits must be divisible by 4. The possible values of the last pair to the following:

12, 16, 24, 28, 32, 36, 48, 52, 56, 64, 68, 72, 76, 84, 92, 96.

i.e., There are 16 ways of choosing last two digits.

The remaining digits can be arranged in ${}^7P_7 = 7!$ ways.

Therefore, number of favourable ways $= 16 \times 7!$

and number of total ways $= 9!$

$\therefore$ Required probability, $p = \dfrac{16 \times 7!}{9!} = \dfrac{16}{9 \times 8} = \dfrac{2}{9}$

$\Rightarrow$ $9p = 2$

JEE Type Solved Examples : Matching Type Questions

- This section contains **2 examples.** Examples 27 and 28 have four statements (A, B, C and D) given in **Column I** and four statements (p, q, r and s) in **Column II.** Any given statement in **Column I** can have correct matching with one or more statement(s) given in **Column II.**

• Ex. 27 *If n positive integers taken at random are multiplied together.*

	Column I		Column II
(A)	The probability that the last digit is 1, 3, 7 or 9 is $P(n)$, then 100 $P(2)$ is divisible by	(p)	3
(B)	The probability that the last digit is 2, 4, 6 or 8 is $Q(n)$, then 100 $Q(2)$ is divisible by	(q)	4
(C)	The probability that the last digit is 5 is $R(n)$, then 100 $R(2)$ is divisible by	(r)	6
(D)	The probability that the last digit is zero is $S(n)$, then 100 $S(2)$ is divisible by	(s)	9

Sol. A → (q); B → (p, q, r); C → (p, s); D → (p, s)

Let n positive integers be $x_1, x_2, x_3, \ldots, x_n$

Let $a = x_1 \cdot x_2 \cdot x_3 \ldots x_n$

Since, the last digit in each of the numbers $x_1, x_2, \ldots, x_n$ can be any one of the digits

0, 1, 2,..., 9 (total 10)

$\therefore \quad n(S) = 10^n$

Let E_1, E_2, E_3 and E_4 are the events given in A, B, C and D, respectively.

(A) $n(E_1) = 4^n \Rightarrow P(E_1) = \left(\frac{4}{10}\right)^n = P(n)$ [given]

$\therefore \quad 100\,P(2) = 16$

(B) $n(E_2) = n$ (last digit is 1 or 2 or 3 or 4 or 6 or 7 or 8 or 9) $- n(E_1) = 8^n - 4^n$

$\Rightarrow \quad P(E_2) = \frac{8^n - 4^n}{10^n} = Q(n)$ [given]

$\therefore \quad 100\,Q(2) = 64 - 16 = 48$

(C) $n(E_3) = n$ (last digit is 1 or 3 or 5 or 7 or 9) $- n(E_1)$

$= 5^n - 4^n$

$\Rightarrow \quad P(E_3) = \frac{5^n - 4^n}{10^n} = R(n)$ [given]

$\therefore$ 100 $R(2) = 25 - 16 = 9$

(D) $n(E_4) = n(S) - n$ (last digit is 1 or 2 or 3 or 4 or 6 or 7 or 8 or 9)$- n(E_3) = 10^n - 8^n - (5^n - 4^n)$

$\therefore \quad P(E_4) = \frac{10^n - 8^n - 5^n + 4^n}{10^n} = S(n)$ [given]

$\therefore \quad 100\,S(2) = 27$

• Ex. 28 *If A and B are two independent events, such that $P(A) = \frac{1}{3}$ and $P(B) = \frac{1}{4}$.*

	Column I		Column II
(A)	If $P\left(\frac{A}{B}\right) = \lambda_1$, then $12\lambda_1$ is	(p)	a prime number
(B)	If $P\left(\frac{A}{A \cup B}\right) = \lambda_2$, then $9\lambda_2$ is	(q)	a composite number
(C)	If $P[(A \cap \overline{B}) \cup (\overline{A} \cap B)] = \lambda_3$, then $12\lambda_3$ is	(r)	a natural number
(D)	If $P(\overline{A} \cup B) = \lambda_4$, then $12\lambda_4$ is	(s)	a perfect number

Sol. A → (q, r); B (q, r, s); C → (p, r); D → (q, r)

$\because$ *A* and *B* are independent events.

$\therefore \quad P(A \cap B) = P(A) \cdot P(B) = \frac{1}{12},$

$P(A \cap \overline{B}) = P(A) \cdot P(\overline{B}) = \frac{1}{3} \times \left(1 - \frac{1}{4}\right) = \frac{1}{4},$

$P(\overline{A} \cap B) = P(\overline{A}) \cdot P(B) = \left(1 - \frac{1}{3}\right) \cdot \frac{1}{4} = \frac{1}{6}$

(A) $P\left(\frac{A}{B}\right) = \frac{P(A \cap B)}{P(B)} = \frac{\frac{1}{12}}{\frac{1}{4}} = \frac{1}{3} = \lambda_1$ [given]

$\therefore \quad 12\lambda_1 = 4$ [natural number and composite number]

(B) $P\left(\frac{A}{A \cup B}\right) = \frac{P(A \cap (A \cup B))}{P(A \cup B)}$

$= \frac{P(A)}{P(A \cup B)} = \frac{P(A)}{P(A) + P(B) - P(A \cap B)}$

$= \frac{\frac{1}{3}}{\frac{1}{3} + \frac{1}{4} - \frac{1}{12}} = \frac{2}{3} = \lambda_2$ [given]

$\therefore \quad 9\lambda_2 = 6$

[natural number, composite number and perfect number]

(C) $P(A \cap \overline{B}) \cup (\overline{A} \cap B)) = P(A \cap \overline{B}) + P(\overline{A} \cap B)$

$= \frac{1}{4} + \frac{1}{6} = \frac{5}{12} = \lambda_3$ [given]

$\therefore \quad 12\lambda_3 = 5$ [prime number and natural number]

(D) $P(\overline{A} \cup B) = P(\overline{A}) + P(B) - P(\overline{A} \cap B)$

$= \left(1 - \frac{1}{3}\right) + \frac{1}{4} - \frac{1}{6} = \frac{3}{4} = \lambda_4$ [given]

$\therefore \quad 12\lambda_4 = 9$ [natural number and composite number]

JEE Type Solved Examples : Statement I and II Type Questions

- **Directions** Example numbers 29 and 30 are Assertion-Reason type examples. Each of these examples contains two statements:

Statement-1 (Assertion) and **Statement-2** (Reason)
Each of these examples also has four alternative choices, only one of which is the correct answer. You have to select the correct choice as given below.

(a) Statement-1 is true, Statement-2 is true; Statement-2 is a correct explanation for Statement-1
(b) Statement-1 is true, Statement-2 is true; Statement-2 is not a correct explanation for Statement-1
(c) Statement-1 is true, Statement-2 is false
(d) Statement-1 is false, Statement-2 is true

- ***Ex. 29.*** *A man P speaks truth with probability p and another man Q speaks truth with probability 2p.*

Statement-1 *If P and Q contradict each other with probability $\frac{1}{2}$, then there are two values of p.*

Statement-2 *A quadratic equation with real coefficients has two real roots.*

Sol. (c) Let E_1 be the event that P speaks the truth, then $P(E_1) = p$ and let E_2 be the event that Q speaks the truth, then $P(E_2) = 2p$.

Statement-1 If P and Q contradict each other with probability $\frac{1}{2}$, then $P(E_1)\cdot P(E_2') + P(E_1')\cdot P(E_2) = \frac{1}{2}$

$$\Rightarrow p\cdot(1-2p) + (1-p)\cdot 2p = \frac{1}{2} \Rightarrow 8p^2 - 6p + 1 = 0$$

$$\Rightarrow \quad (2p-1)(4p-1) = 0 \Rightarrow p = \frac{1}{2} \text{ and } p = \frac{1}{4}$$

$\therefore$ Statement-1 is true.

Statement-2 Let quadratic equation
$ax^2 + bx + c = 0$, where $a, b, c \in R$
If $\quad b^2 - 4ac < 0$
then, roots are imaginary.
$\therefore$ Statement-2 is false.

- ***Ex. 30*** *A fair die thrown twice. Let (a, b) denote the outcome in which the first throw shows a and the second shows b. Let A and B be the following two events:*
$A = \{(a, b) | a \text{ is even}\}$, $B = \{(a, b) | b \text{ is even}\}$

Statement-1 If $C = \{(a, b) | a + b \text{ is odd}\}$, then $P(A \cap B \cap C) = \frac{1}{8}$.

Statement-2 If $D = \{(a, b) | a + b \text{ is even}\}$, then
$$P[(A \cap B \cap D) | (A \cup B)] = \frac{1}{3}$$

Sol. (c) If a and b are both even, then $a + b$ is even, therefore $P(A \cap B \cap C) = 0$

$\therefore$ Statement-1 is false.

Also, $P(A) = \frac{1}{2}$, $P(B) = \frac{1}{2}$, $P(A \cap B) = \frac{1}{2} \times \frac{1}{2} = \frac{1}{4}$

$$\therefore P(A \cup B) = P(A) + P(B) - P(A \cap B)$$
$$= \frac{1}{2} + \frac{1}{2} - \frac{1}{4} = \frac{3}{4}$$

$$\therefore P[(A \cap B \cap D) | (A \cup B)] = \frac{P((A \cap B \cap D) \cap (A \cup B))}{P(A \cup B)}$$

$$= \frac{P(A \cap B)}{P(A \cup B)} = \frac{\frac{1}{4}}{\frac{3}{4}} = \frac{1}{3} \quad [\because A \cap B \subseteq D]$$

$\therefore$ Statement-2 is true.

Subjective Type Examples

- In this section, there are **24 subjective** solved examples.

- ***Ex. 31*** *Three critics review a book. Odds in favour of the book are 5 : 2, 4 : 3 and 3 : 4 respectively for the three critics. Find the probability that majority are in favour of the book.*

Sol. Let the critics be E_1, E_2 and E_3. Let $P(E_1)$, $P(E_2)$ and $P(E_3)$ denotes the probabilities of the critics E_1, E_2 and E_3 to be in favour of the book. Since, the odds in favour of the book for the critics E_1, E_2 and E_3 are 5 : 2, 4 : 3 and 3 : 4, respectively.

$$\therefore \quad P(E_1) = \frac{5}{5+2} = \frac{5}{7}, P(E_2) = \frac{4}{4+3} = \frac{4}{7}$$

and $\quad P(E_3) = \frac{3}{3+4} = \frac{3}{7}$

Clearly, the event of majority being in favour = the event of atleast two critics being in favour

$\therefore$ The required probability

$$= P(E_1 E_2 \overline{E}_3) + P(\overline{E}_1 E_2 E_3) + P(E_1 \overline{E}_2 E_3) + P(E_1 E_2 E_3)$$
$$= P(E_1)\cdot P(E_2)\cdot P(\overline{E}_3) + P(\overline{E}_1)\cdot P(E_2)\cdot P(E_3)$$
$$+ P(E_1)\cdot P(\overline{E}_2)\cdot P(E_3) + P(E_1)\cdot P(E_2)\cdot P(E_3$$

$[\because E_1, E_2 \text{ and } E_3 \text{ are independent}]$

$$= \frac{5}{7}\cdot\frac{4}{7}\cdot\left(1-\frac{3}{7}\right)+\left(1-\frac{5}{7}\right)\cdot\frac{4}{7}\cdot\frac{3}{7}+\frac{5}{7}\cdot\left(1-\frac{4}{7}\right)\cdot\frac{3}{7}+\frac{5}{7}\cdot\frac{4}{7}\cdot\frac{3}{7}$$

$$= \frac{1}{7^3}[80+24+45+60] = \frac{209}{343}$$

Ex. 32 *A has 3 shares is a lottery containing 3 prizes and 9 blanks; B has 2 shares in a lottery containing 2 prizes and 6 blanks. Compare their chances of success.*

Sol. Let E_1 and E_2 be the events of success of A and B, respectively. Therefore, E'_1 and E'_2 are the events of unsuccess of A and B, respectively.

Since, A has 3 shares in a lottery containing 3 prizes and 9 blanks, therefore A will draw 3 tickets out of 12 tickets (3 prizes + 9 blanks). Then, A will get success if he draws atleast one prize out of 3 draws. Similarly, B will get success if he draws atleast one prize out of 2 draws.

$$\therefore \quad P(E'_1) = \frac{{}^9C_3}{{}^{12}C_3} = \frac{\dfrac{9\cdot8\cdot7}{1\cdot2\cdot3}}{\dfrac{12\cdot11\cdot10}{1\cdot2\cdot3}} = \frac{21}{55}$$

$$\therefore \quad P(E_1) = 1 - P(E'_1) = 1 - \frac{21}{55} = \frac{34}{55}$$

$$\text{Again,} \quad P(E'_2) = \frac{{}^6C_2}{{}^8C_2} = \frac{\dfrac{6\cdot5}{1\cdot2}}{\dfrac{8\cdot7}{1\cdot2}} = \frac{15}{28}$$

$$\therefore \quad P(E_2) = 1 - P(E'_2) = 1 - \frac{15}{28} = \frac{13}{28}$$

$$\text{Hence,} \quad \frac{P(E_1)}{P(E_2)} = \frac{\dfrac{34}{55}}{\dfrac{13}{28}} = \frac{952}{715}$$

$$\therefore \quad P(E_1):P(E_2) = 952:715$$

Ex. 33 *A bag contains a white and b black balls. Two players A and B alternately draw a ball from the bag, replacing the ball each time after the draw till one of them draws a white ball and wins the game. If A begins the game and the probability of A winning the game is three times that of B, show that a : b = 2 : 1.*

Sol. Let E_1 denote the event of drawing a white ball at any draw and E_2 that for a black ball and let E be the event for A winning the game

$$\therefore P(E_1) = \frac{a}{a+b} \text{ and } P(E_2) = \frac{b}{a+b}$$

$$\therefore P(E) = P(E_1 \text{ or } E_2E_2E_1 \text{ or } E_2E_2E_2E_2E_1 \text{ or } \ldots)$$

$$= P(E_1) + P(E_2E_2E_1) + P(E_2E_2E_2E_2E_1) + \ldots$$

$$= P(E_1) + P(E_2)\,P(E_2)\,P(E_1) + P(E_2)\,P(E_2)\,P(E_2)\,P(E_2)\,P(E_1) + \ldots$$

[$\because E_1$ and E_2 are independent]

$$= \frac{P(E_1)}{1-\{P(E_2)\}^2} \quad \text{[sum of infinite GP]}$$

$$= \frac{\dfrac{a}{a+b}}{1-\left(\dfrac{b}{a+b}\right)^2} = \frac{a(a+b)}{a^2+2ab} \quad \therefore P(E) = \frac{a+b}{a+2b}$$

Then, $P(E')$ is the probability for B winning the game

$$\therefore P(E') = 1 - P(E) = 1 - \frac{a+b}{a+2b} = \frac{b}{a+2b}$$

According to the problem, $P(E) = 3P(E')$

$$\Rightarrow \quad \frac{a+b}{a+2b} = \frac{3b}{a+2b} \Rightarrow \alpha + \beta = 3\beta \Rightarrow \alpha = 2\beta$$

$$\therefore \quad \frac{a}{b} = \frac{2}{1} \quad \Rightarrow \alpha:\beta = 2:1$$

Ex. 34 *Five persons entered the lift cabin on the ground floor of an 8 floors house. Suppose that each of them, independently and with equal probability can leave the cabin at any floor beginning with the first. Find out the probability of all five persons leaving at different floors.*

Sol. Let S be the sample space and E be the event that the five persons get down at different floors.

Total number of floors excluding the ground floor = 7

Since, each of the 5 persons can get down at any one of the 7 floors in 7 ways.

$\therefore n(S)$ = Total number of ways in which the 5 persons can get down = 7^5

and $n(E)$ = number of ways in which the 5 persons can get down at 5 different floors out of 7 floors = ${}^7P_5$

$$\therefore \text{Required probability, } P(E) = \frac{n(E)}{n(S)} = \frac{{}^7P_5}{7^5}$$

Ex. 35 *Let X be a set containing n elements. Two subsets A and B of X are chosen at random. Find the probability that $A \cup B = X$.*

Sol. Let $X = \{x_1, x_2, \ldots, x_n\}$

For each $x_i \in X$ $(1 \le i \le n)$, we have the following four choices

(i) $x_i \in A$ and $x_i \in B$ (ii) $x_i \in A$ and $x_i \notin B$

(iii) $x_i \notin A$ and $x_i \in B$ (iv) $x_i \notin A$ and $x_i \notin B$

Let S be the sample space and E be the event favourable for the occurrence of $A \cup B = X$.

$$\therefore \quad n(S) = 4^n$$

$$\text{and} \quad n(E) = 3^n \quad [\because \text{case (iv)} \notin X]$$

Hence, the required probability,

$$P(E) = \frac{n(E)}{n(S)} \Rightarrow = \frac{3^n}{4^n} = \left(\frac{3}{4}\right)^n$$

Ex. 36 *Two persons each makes a single throw with a pair of dice. Find the probability that the throws are unequal.*

Sol. Let E be the event that the throws of the two persons are unequal. Then, E' be the event that the throws of the two persons are equal.

$\therefore$ The total number of cases for E' is $(36)^2$

i.e., $n(S) = (36)^2$ [$\because$ S be the sample space]

We now proceed to find out the number of favourable cases for E'. Suppose

$$(x + x^2 + x^3 + \ldots + x^6)^2 = a_2 x^2 + a_3 x^3 + \ldots + a_{12} x^{12}$$

The number of favourable ways of $E' = a_2^2 + a_3^2 + \ldots + a_{12}^2$

$\therefore$ $n(E')$ = coefficient of constant term in

$$(a_2 x^2 + a_3 x^3 + \ldots + a_{12} x^{12}) \times \left(\frac{a_2}{x^2} + \frac{a_3}{x^3} + \ldots + \frac{a_{12}}{x^{12}}\right)$$

$$= \text{coefficient of constant term in } \frac{(1 - x^6)^2}{(1 - x)^2} \times \frac{\left(1 - \frac{1}{x^6}\right)^2}{\left(1 - \frac{1}{x}\right)^2}$$

$$= \text{coefficient of } x^{10} \text{ in } (1 - x^6)^4 (1 - x)^{-4}$$

$$= \text{coefficient of } x^{10} \text{ in } (1 - 4x^6 + \ldots)$$
$$(1 + {}^4C_1 x + {}^5C_2 x^2 + \ldots + {}^{13}C_{10} x^{10} + \ldots)$$

$$= {}^{13}C_{10} - 4 \cdot {}^7C_4$$

$$= {}^{13}C_3 - 4 \cdot {}^7C_3 = \frac{13 \cdot 12 \cdot 11}{1 \cdot 2 \cdot 3} - 4 \cdot \frac{7 \cdot 6 \cdot 5}{1 \cdot 2 \cdot 3} = 146$$

$$\therefore \quad P(E') = \frac{n(E')}{n(S)} = \frac{146}{(36)^2} = \frac{73}{648}$$

Hence, required probability,

$$P(E) = 1 - P(E') = 1 - \frac{73}{648} = \frac{575}{648}$$

Ex. 37 *If X and Y are independent binomial variates B (5, 1/2) and B (7, 1/2), find the value of P(X + Y = 3).*

Sol. We have,

$$P(X + Y = 3) = P(X = 0, Y = 3) + P(X = 1, Y = 2) + P(X = 2, Y = 1) + P(X = 3, Y = 0)$$

$$= P(X = 0)\,P(Y = 3) + P(X = 1)\,P(Y = 2) + P(X = 2)\,P(Y = 1) + P(X = 3)\,P(Y = 0)$$

[$\because$ X and Y are independent]

$$= {}^5C_0 \left(\frac{1}{2}\right)^5 \cdot {}^7C_3 \left(\frac{1}{2}\right)^7 + {}^5C_1 \left(\frac{1}{2}\right)^5 \cdot {}^7C_2 \left(\frac{1}{2}\right)^7 + {}^5C_2 \left(\frac{1}{2}\right)^5 \cdot {}^7C_1 \left(\frac{1}{2}\right)^7 + {}^5C_3 \left(\frac{1}{2}\right)^5 \cdot {}^7C_0 \left(\frac{1}{2}\right)^7$$

$$= \left(\frac{1}{2}\right)^{12} [(1)(35) + (5)(21) + (10)(7) + (10)(1)]$$

$$= \frac{220}{2^{12}} = \frac{55}{1024}$$

Ex. 38 *If $a \in [-20, 0]$, find the probability that the graph of the function $y = 16x^2 + 8(a + 5)x - 7a - 5$ is strictly above the X-axis.*

Sol. Since, the graph $y = 16x^2 + 8(a + 5)x - 7a - 5$ is strictly above the X-axis, therefore $y > 0$ for all x

$$\Rightarrow \quad 16x^2 + 8(a + 5)x - 7a - 5 > 0, \forall x$$

$\therefore$ Discriminant < 0

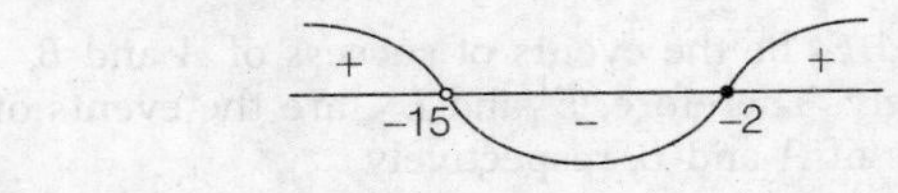

$$\Rightarrow \quad 64(a + 5)^2 - 4 \cdot 16(-7a - 5) < 0$$

$$\Rightarrow a^2 + 17a + 30 < 0 \Rightarrow (a + 15)(a + 2) < 0$$

$$\Rightarrow \quad -15 < a < -2$$

$$\therefore \text{Required probability} = \frac{\int_{-15}^{-2} dx}{\int_{-20}^{0} dx} = \frac{13}{20}$$

Ex. 39 *3 distinct integers are selected at random from 1, 2, 3,..., 20. Find out the probability that the sum is divisible by 5.*

Sol. The number of wayds choosing 3 distinct integers from 1, 2, 3, ..., 20 is

$${}^{20}C_3 = \frac{20 \cdot 19 \cdot 18}{1 \cdot 2 \cdot 3} = 20 \times 57 = 1140$$

Now, arrange the given numbers as below:

1	6	11	16
2	7	12	17
3	8	13	18
4	9	14	19
5	10	15	20

We see that the sum of three digits divisible by 5 in the following cases :

Two number from 1st row and one number from 3rd row or one number from 2nd row and two numbers from 4th row or three numbers from 5th row or one number from each (1st row, 4th row, 5th row) or one number from each (2nd row, 3rd row, 5th row).

Then, the number of favourable ways

$$= {}^4C_2 \times {}^4C_1 + {}^4C_1 \times {}^4C_2 + {}^4C_3 + {}^4C_1 \times {}^4C_1 \times {}^4C_1 + {}^4C_1 \times {}^4C_1 \times {}^4C_1$$

$$= 24 + 24 + 4 + 64 + 64 = 180$$

Hence, the required probability $= \dfrac{180}{1140} = \dfrac{3}{19}$

Note

If divisible by 4, then take four rows and if divisible by 3, then take three rows, etc.

Ex. 40 *5 girls and 10 boys sit at random in a row having chairs numbered as 1 to 15. Find the probability that end seats are occupied by the girls and between any two girls odd number of boys sit.*

Sol. There are four gaps in between the girls where the boys can sit. Let the number of boys in these gaps be $2a + 1$, $2b + 1$, $2c + 1$, $2d + 1$, then

$$2a + 1 + 2b + 1 + 2c + 1 + 2d + 1 = 10$$

or $$a + b + c + d = 3$$

The number of solutions of above equation

$$= \text{coefficient of } x^3 \text{ in } (1 - x)^{-4} = {}^6C_3 = 20$$

Thus, boys and girls can sit in $20 \times 10! \times 5!$ ways. Total ways $= 15!$

Hence, the required probability $= \dfrac{20 \times 10! \times 5!}{15!}$

Ex. 41 *A four digit number (numbered from 0000 to 9999) is said to be lucky if sum of its first two digits is equal to the sum of its last two digits. If a four-digit number is picked up at random, find the probability that it is lucky number.*

Sol. The total number of ways of choosing a four digit number is $10^4 = 10000$. Let a_k denote the number of distinct non-negative integral solutions of the equation $x + y = k$ $(0 \le k \le 18)$

$\therefore$ The number of favourable cases $= a_0^2 + a_1^2 + \dots + a_{18}^2$

Suppose, $(1 + x + x^2 + \dots + x^9)^2$

$$= a_0 + a_1 x + a_2 x^2 + \dots + a_{18} x^{18}$$

Thus, $a_0^2 + a_1^2 + \dots + a_{18}^2 =$ coefficient of constant term in

$$(a_0 + a_1 x + \dots + a_{18} x^{18}) \times \left(a_0 + \frac{a_1}{x} + \dots + \frac{a_{18}}{x^{18}} \right)$$

$=$ coefficient of constant term in

$$(1 + x + x^2 + \dots + x^9)^2 \times \left(1 + \frac{1}{x} + \frac{1}{x^2} + \dots + \frac{1}{x^9} \right)^2$$

$= \text{coefficient of } x^{18} \text{ in } (1 + x + x^2 + \dots + x^9)^4$

$= \text{coefficient of } x^{18} \text{ in } (1 - x^{10})^4 (1 - x)^{-4}$

$= \text{coefficient of } x^{18} \text{ in } (1 - 4x^{10})(1 + {}^4C_1 x + {}^5C_2 x^2 + \dots)$

$= {}^{21}C_{18} - 4 \cdot {}^{11}C_8 = 1330 - 660 = 670$

Hence, the required probability $= \dfrac{670}{10000} = 0.067$

Ex. 42

(i) If four squares are chosen at random on a chess board, find the probability that they lie on a diagonal line.

(ii) If two squares are chosen at random on a chess board, what is the probability that they have exactly one corner in common?

(iii) If nine squares are chosen at random on a chess board, what is the probability that they form a square of size 3×3?

Sol. (i) Total number of ways $= {}^{64}C_4$

The chess board can be divided into two parts by a diagonal line BD. Now, if we begin to select four squares from the diagonal P_1Q_1, P_2Q_2, …, BD, then we can find number of squares selected

$$= 2({}^4C_4 + {}^5C_4 + {}^6C_4 + {}^7C_4) = 112$$

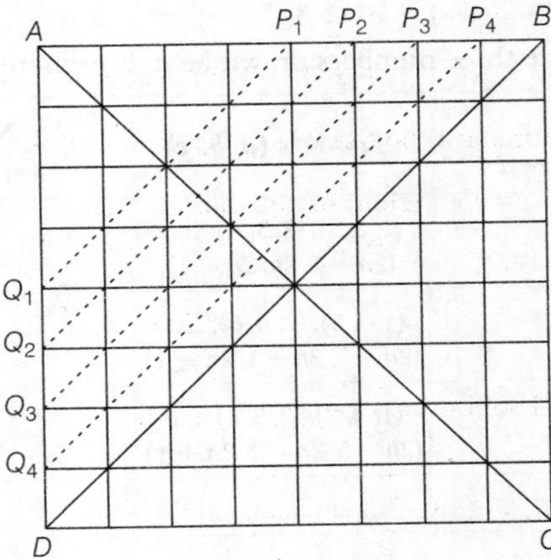

Similarly, number of squares for the diagonals chosen parallel to $AC = 112$

$\therefore$ Total favourable ways $= 364$

$\therefore$ Required probability $= \dfrac{364}{{}^{64}C_4}$.

(ii) Total ways $= 64 \times 63$

Now, if first square is in one of the four corners, then the second square can be chosen in just one way $= (4)(1) = 4$

If the first square is one of the 24 non-corner squares along the sides of the chess board, the second square can be chosen in two ways $= (24)(2) = 48$.

Now, if the first square is any of the 36 remaining squares, the second square can be chosen in four ways $= (36)(4) = 144$

$\therefore$ Favourable ways $= 4 + 48 + 144 = 196$

$\therefore$ Required probability $= \dfrac{196}{64 \times 63} = \dfrac{7}{144}$.

(iii) Total ways $= {}^{64}C_9$

A chess board has 9 horizontal and 9 vertical lines. We see that a square of size 3×3 can be formed by choosing four consecutive horizontal and vertical lines.

Hence, favourable ways $= ({}^6C_1)({}^6C_1) = 36$

$\therefore$ Required probability $= \dfrac{36}{{}^{64}C_9}$.

● Ex. 43 *Out of $(2n+1)$ tickets consecutively numbered, three are drawn at random. Find the chance that the numbers on them are in AP.*

Sol. Let us consider first $(2n+1)$ natural numbers as $(2n+1)$ consecutive numbers.

Let S be the sample space and E be the event of favourable cases.

$$\therefore \quad n(S) = {}^{2n+1}C_3$$

$$= \frac{(2n+1)\,2n(2n-1)}{1\cdot 2\cdot 3} = \frac{n(4n^2-1)}{3}$$

Let the three numbers drawn be a, b, c where $a < b < c$.

Common difference d	Triplets (a, b, c)	Number of Triplets
1	$(1, 2, 3), (2, 3, 4), \ldots, (2n-1, 2n, 2n+1)$	$2n-1$
2	$(1, 3, 5), (2, 4, 6), \ldots, (2n-3, 2n-1, 2n+1)$	$2n-3$
3	$(1, 4, 7), (2, 5, 8), \ldots, (2n-5, 2n-2, 2n+1)$	$2n-5$
...	....	...
...	....	...
...	....	...
$n-1$	$(1, n, 2n-1), (2, n+1, 2n), (3, n+2, 2n+1)$	3
n	$(1, n+1, 2n+1)$	1

$$\therefore \quad n(E) = 1 + 3 + \ldots + (2n-5) + (2n-3) + (2n-1)$$

$$= \frac{n}{2}\{1 + 2n - 1\} = n^2$$

$$\therefore \text{ Required probability, } P(E) = \frac{n(E)}{n(S)}$$

$$= \frac{n^2}{\frac{n(4n^2-1)}{3}} = \frac{3n}{4n^2-1}$$

Aliter Let S be the sample space and E be the event of favourable cases.

$$\therefore \quad n(S) = {}^{2n+1}C_3 = \frac{(2n+1)\,2n(2n-1)}{1\cdot 2\cdot 3} = \frac{n(4n^2-1)}{3}$$

Let the three numbers a, b, c are drawn where $a < b < c$ and given a, b, c are in AP.

$$\therefore \quad b = \frac{a+c}{2} \text{ or } 2b = a + c \qquad \ldots\text{(i)}$$

It is clear from Eq. (i), a and c are both odd or both even. Out of $(2n+1)$ tickets consecutively numbers either $(n+1)$ of them will be odd and n of them will be even (if the numbers begin with an odd number) or $(n+1)$ of them will be even and n of them will be odd (if the number begin with an even number).

$$\therefore \quad n(E) = {}^{n+1}C_2 + {}^{n}C_2$$

$$= \frac{(n+1)\,n}{2} + \frac{n(n-1)}{2} = n^2$$

$\therefore$ Required probability,

$$P(E) = \frac{n(E)}{n(S)} = \frac{n^2}{\frac{n(4n^2-1)}{3}} = \frac{3n}{4n^2-1}$$

● Ex. 44 *Out of $3n$ consecutive integers, three are selected at random. Find the chance that their sum is divisible by 3.*

Sol. Let $3n$ consecutive integers (start with the integer m) are

$$m, m+1, m+2, \ldots, m+3n-1$$

Now, we write these $3n$ numbers in 3 rows as follows :

$$m, m+3, m+6, \ldots, m+3n-3$$
$$m+1, m+4, m+7, \ldots, m+3n-2$$
$$m+2, m+5, m+8, \ldots, m+3n-1$$

The total number of ways of choosing 3 integers out of $3n$ is

$${}^{3n}C_3 = \frac{3n(3n-1)(3n-2)}{1\cdot 2\cdot 3}$$

$$= \frac{n(3n-1)(3n-2)}{2}$$

The sum of the three numbers shall be divisible by 3 if and only if either all the three numbers are from the same row or all the three numbers are from different rows.

Therefore, the number of favourable ways are

$$3({}^{n}C_3) + ({}^{n}C_1)({}^{n}C_1)({}^{n}C_1)$$

$$= \frac{3n(n-1)(n-2)}{1\cdot 2\cdot 3} + n^3 = \frac{3n^3 - 3n^2 + 2n}{2}$$

$\therefore$ The required probability

$$= \frac{\text{Favourable ways}}{\text{Total ways}}$$

$$= \frac{\frac{3n^3 - 3n^2 + 2n}{2}}{\frac{n(3n-1)(3n-2)}{2}}$$

$$= \frac{3n^2 - 3n + 2}{(3n-1)(3n-2)}$$

Ex. 45 *If 6n tickets numbered 0, 1, 2, ..., 6n − 1 are placed in a bag and three are drawn out, show that the chance that the sum of the numbers on them is equal to 6n is* $\dfrac{3n}{(6n-1)(6n-2)}$.

Sol. Total number of ways to selecting 3 tickets from $6n$ tickets

$$= {}^{6n}C_3 = n(6n-1)(6n-2) \quad \text{...(i)}$$

For the sum of these tickets of be $6n$, we have the following pattern :

Lowest number	Numbers	Ways
0	$(0, 1, 6n-1), (0, 2, 6n-2) \dots (0, 3n-1, 3n+1)$	$(3n-1)$
1	$(1, 2, 6n-3), (1, 3, 6n-4) \dots (1, 3n-1, 3n)$	$(3n-2)$
2	$(2, 3, 6n-5), (2, 4, 6n-6) \dots (2, 3n-2, 3n)$	$(3n-4)$
3	$(3, 4, 6n-7), (3, 5, 6n-8) \dots (3, 3n-2, 3n-1)$	$(3n-5)$
4		
5		
:		
$(2n-2)$	$(2n-2, 2n-1, 2n+3), (2n-2, 2n, 2n+2)$	2
$(2n-1)$	$(2n-1, 2n, 2n+1)$	1

Lowest number cannot be greater than $(2n-1)$ as their sum will become $> 6n$.

$\therefore$ Favourable ways $= 1 + 2 + \dots + (3n-5) + (3n-4) + (3n-2) + (3n-1)$

Adding Ist with last, 2nd with last one, respectively

$$= [1 + 3n - 1] + [2 + 3n - 2] + \dots \text{upto } n \text{ terms}$$

$$= 3n + 3n + \dots n \text{ terms}$$

$$= 3n(n) = 3n^2$$

Hence, $\quad$ probability $= \dfrac{3n^2}{n(6n-1)(6n-2)}$

$$= \frac{3n}{(6n-1)(6n-2)}$$

Probability Exercise 1 : Single Option Correct Type Questions

- This section contains **30 multiple choice questions.** Each question has four choices (a), (b), (c) and (d) out of which **ONLY ONE** is correct

1. There are two vans each having numbered seats, 3 in the front and 4 at the back. There are 3 girls and 9 boys to be seated in the vans. The probability of 3 girls sitting together in a back row on adjacent seats, is

(a) $\frac{1}{13}$ (b) $\frac{1}{39}$ (c) $\frac{1}{65}$ (d) $\frac{1}{91}$

2. The probability that a year chosen at random has 53 Sundays, is

(a) $\frac{1}{7}$ (b) $\frac{2}{7}$ (c) $\frac{3}{28}$ (d) $\frac{5}{28}$

3. The probability that a leap year selected at random contains either 53 Sundays or 53 Mondays, is

(a) $\frac{1}{7}$ (b) $\frac{2}{7}$ (c) $\frac{3}{7}$ (d) $\frac{4}{7}$

4. A positive integer N is selected so as to be $100 < N < 200$. Then, the probability that it is divisible by 4 or 7, is

(a) $\frac{7}{33}$ (b) $\frac{17}{33}$ (c) $\frac{32}{99}$ (d) $\frac{34}{99}$

5. Two numbers a and b are selected at random from 1, 2, 3, ..., 100 and are multiplied. Then, the probability that the product ab is divisible by 3, is

(a) $\frac{67}{150}$ (b) $\frac{83}{150}$ (c) $\frac{67}{75}$ (d) $\frac{8}{75}$

6. Three different numbers are selected at random from the set $A = \{1, 2, 3, \ldots, 10\}$. The probability that the product of two of the numbers is equal to third, is

(a) $\frac{3}{4}$ (b) $\frac{1}{40}$ (c) $\frac{1}{8}$ (d) $\frac{39}{40}$

7. The numbers $1, 2, 3, \ldots, n$ are arranged in a random order. Then, the probability that the digits $1, 2, 3, \ldots, k (k < n)$ appears as neighbours in that order, is

(a) $\frac{1}{n!}$ (b) $\frac{k!}{n!}$ (c) $\frac{(n-k)!}{n!}$ (d) $\frac{(n-k+1)!}{n!}$

8. The numbers $1, 2, 3, \ldots, n$ are arranged in a random order. Then, the probability that the digits $1, 2, 3, \ldots, k (k < n)$ appears as neighbours, is

(a) $\frac{(n-k)!}{n!}$ (b) $\frac{(n-k+1)}{{}^nC_k}$

(c) $\frac{(n-k)}{{}^nC_k}$ (d) $\frac{k!}{n!}$

9. Four identical dice are rolled once. The probability that atleast three different numbers appear on them, is

(a) $\frac{13}{42}$ (b) $\frac{17}{42}$ (c) $\frac{23}{42}$ (d) $\frac{25}{42}$

10. Three of the six vertices of a regular hexagon are chosen at random. The probability that the triangle formed by these vertices is equilateral, is

(a) $\frac{1}{2}$ (b) $\frac{1}{3}$ (c) $\frac{1}{10}$ (d) $\frac{1}{20}$

11. Two small squares on a chess board are chosen at random. Then, the probability that they have a common side, is

(a) $\frac{1}{3}$ (b) $\frac{1}{9}$ (c) $\frac{1}{18}$ (d) $\frac{5}{18}$

12. A letter is known to have come from CHENNAI, JAIPUR, NAINITAL, DUBAI and MUMBAI. On the post mark only two consecutive letters AI are legible. Then the probability that it come from MUMBAI, is

(a) $\frac{42}{319}$ (b) $\frac{84}{403}$ (c) $\frac{39}{331}$ (d) $\frac{42}{331}$

13. Let a die is loaded in such a way that prime number faces are twice as likely to occur as a non-prime number faces. Then, the probability that an odd number will be show up when the die is tossed, is

(a) $\frac{1}{3}$ (b) $\frac{2}{3}$ (c) $\frac{4}{9}$ (d) $\frac{5}{9}$

14. One ticket is selected at random from 100 tickets numbered 00, 01, 02, .., 99.

Suppose, X and Y are the sum and product of the digit found on the ticket $P(X = 7 / Y = 0)$ is given by

(a) $\frac{2}{3}$ (b) $\frac{2}{19}$ (c) $\frac{1}{50}$ (d) None of these

15. All the spades are taken out from a pack of cards. From these cards, cards are drawn one by one without replacement till the ace of spades comes. The probability that the ace comes in the 4th draw, is

(a) $\frac{1}{13}$ (b) $\frac{12}{13}$

(c) $\frac{4}{13}$ (d) None of these

16. A number is selected at random from the first twenty-five natural numbers. If it is a composite number, then it is divided by 5. But if it is not a composite number, then it is divided by 2. The probability that there will be no remainder in the division, is

(a) $\frac{11}{30}$ (b) 0.4

(c) 0.2 (d) None of these

17. If a bag contains 50 tickets, numbered 1, 2, 3, ..., 50 of which five are drawn at random and arranged in ascending order of magnitude $(x_1 < x_2 < x_3 < x_4 < x_5)$. The probability that $x_3 = 30$, is

(a) $\frac{^{20}C_2 \times {}^{29}C_2}{^{50}C_5}$ (b) $\frac{^{20}C_2}{^{50}C_5}$

(c) $\frac{^{29}C_2}{^{50}C_5}$ (d) None of these

18. India play two matches each with West Indies and Australia. In any match the probabilities of India getting points 0, 1 and 2 are 0.45, 0.05 and 0.50, respectively. Assuming that the outcomes are independent, then the probability of India getting atleast 7 points, is

(a) 0.8750 (b) 0.0875 (c) 0.0625 (d) 0.0250

19. Three six faced dice are tossed together, then the probability that exactly two of the three numbers are equal, is

(a) $\frac{165}{216}$ (b) $\frac{177}{216}$ (c) $\frac{51}{216}$ (d) $\frac{90}{216}$

20. Three six-faced fair dice are thrown together. The probability that the sum of the numbers appearing on the dice is $k(3 \le k \le 8)$, is

(a) $\frac{(k-1)(k-2)}{432}$ (b) $\frac{k(k-1)}{432}$

(c) $\frac{k^2}{432}$ (d) None of these

21. A book contains 1000 pages. A page is chosen at random. The probability that the sum of the digits of the marked number on the page is equal to 9, is

(a) $\frac{23}{500}$ (b) $\frac{11}{200}$

(c) $\frac{7}{100}$ (d) None of these

22. A bag contains four tickets numbered 00, 01, 10 and 11. Four tickets are chosen at random with replacement, then the probability that sum of the numbers on the tickets is 23, is

(a) $\frac{3}{32}$ (b) $\frac{1}{64}$ (c) $\frac{5}{256}$ (d) $\frac{7}{256}$

23. Fifteen coupons are numbered 1 to 15. Seven coupons are selected at random, one at a time with replacement. Then, the probability that the largest number appearing on a selected coupon be 9, is

(a) $\left(\frac{1}{15}\right)^7$ (b) $\left(\frac{8}{15}\right)^7$

(c) $\left(\frac{3}{5}\right)^7$ (d) None of these

24. A box contains tickets numbered 1 to 20. 3 tickets are drawn from the box with replacement. The probability that the largest number on the tickets is 7, is

(a) $\frac{7}{20}$ (b) $1-\left(\frac{7}{20}\right)^3$

(c) $\frac{2}{19}$ (d) None of these

25. An unbiased die with faces marked 1, 2, 3, 4, 5 and 6 is rolled four times. Out of four face values obtained, then the probability that the minimum face value is not less than 2 and the maximum face value is not greater than 5, is

(a) $\frac{16}{81}$ (b) $\frac{1}{81}$ (c) $\frac{80}{81}$ (d) $\frac{65}{81}$

26. A bag contains four tickets marked with numbers 112, 121, 211 and 222. One ticket is drawn at random from the bag. Let $E_i (i = 1, 2, 3)$ denote the event that ith digit on the ticket is 2. Then, which of the following is not true?

(a) E_1 and E_2 are independent
(b) E_2 and E_3 are independent
(c) E_3 and E_1 are independent
(d) E_1, E_2 and E_3 are not independent

27. Two non-negative integers are chosen at random. The probability that the sum of the square is divisible by 10, is

(a) $\frac{17}{100}$ (b) $\frac{9}{50}$ (c) $\frac{7}{50}$ (d) $\frac{9}{16}$

28. Two positive real numbers x and y satisfying $x \le 1$ and $y \le 1$ are chosen at random. The probability that $x + y \le 1$, given that $x^2 + y^2 \le 1/4$, is

(a) $\frac{8-\pi}{16-\pi}$ (b) $\frac{4-\pi}{16-\pi}$

(c) $\frac{4-\pi}{8-\pi}$ (d) None of these

29. If the sides of a triangle are decided by the throw of a single dice thrice, the probability that triangle is of maximum area given that it is an isosceles triangle, is

(a) $\frac{1}{7}$ (b) $\frac{1}{27}$

(c) $\frac{1}{14}$ (d) None of these

30. A and B are persons standing in corner square as shown in the figure. They start to move on same time with equal speed, if A can move only in East or South direction and B can move only in North or West direction. If in each step they reach in next square and their choice of direction are equality. If it is given that A and B meet in shaded region, then the probability that they have met in the top most shaded square, is

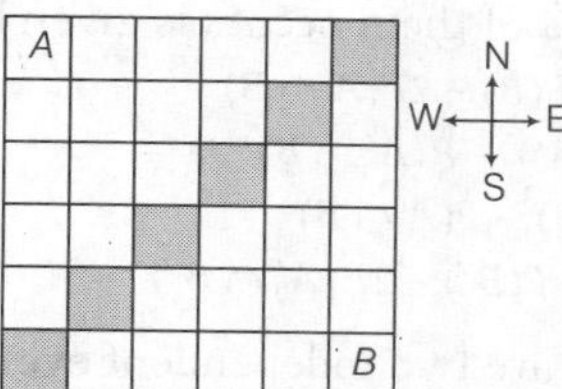

(a) $\frac{1}{6}$ (b) $\frac{^5C_2}{^{10}C_3}$ (c) $\frac{1}{^{10}C_5}$ (d) $\frac{1}{2^5 \times 6}$

Probability Exercise 2 :
More than One Correct Option Type Questions

- This section contains **15 multiple choice questions.** Each question has four choices (a), (b), (c) and (d) out of which **MORE THAN ONE** may be correct.

31. For two given events A and B, $P(A \cap B)$ is

(a) not less than $P(A) + P(B) - 1$
(b) not greater than $P(A) + P(B)$
(c) equal to $P(A) + P(B) - P(A \cup B)$
(d) equal to $P(A) + P(B) + P(A \cup B)$

32. If E and F are independent events such that $0 < P(E) < 1$ and $0 < P(F) < 1$, then

(a) E and F are mutually exclusive
(b) E and $\overline{F}$ (complement of the event F) are independent
(c) $\overline{E}$ and $\overline{F}$ are independent
(d) $P(E / F) + P(\overline{E} / F) = 1$

33. For any two events A and B in a sample space:

(a) $P\left(\frac{A}{B}\right) \geq \frac{P(A) + P(B) - 1}{P(B)}$, $P(B) \neq 0$, is always true
(b) $P(A \cap \overline{B}) = P(A) - P(A \cap B)$, does not hold
(c) $P(A \cup B) = 1 - P(\overline{A})\, P(\overline{B})$, if A and B are independent
(d) $P(A \cup B) = 1 - P(\overline{A})\, P(\overline{B})$, if A and B are disjoint

34. Let E and F be two independent events. Then, the probability that both E and F happens is $\frac{1}{12}$ and the probability that neither E nor F happens is $\frac{1}{2}$. Then,

(a) $P(E) = 1/3, P(F) = 1/4$ (b) $P(E) = 1/2, P(F) = 1/6$
(c) $P(E) = 1/6, P(F) = 1/2$ (d) $P(E) = 1/4, P(F) = 1/3$

35. If $\overline{E}$ and $\overline{F}$ are the complementary events of events E and F, respectively and if $0 < P(F) < 1$, then

(a) $P(\overline{E} / F) + P(\overline{E} / F) = 1$ (b) $P(E / F) + P(E / \overline{F}) = 1$
(c) $P(\overline{E} / F) + P(E / \overline{F}) = 1$ (d) $P(E / \overline{F}) + P(\overline{E} / \overline{F}) = 1$

36. Let $0 < P(A) < 1, 0 < P(B) < 1$ and $P(A \cup B) = P(A) + P(B) - P(A)\, P(B)$. Then,

(a) $P(B - A) = P(B) - P(A)$ (b) $P(A' \cup B') = P(A') + P(B')$
(c) $P((A \cup B)') = P(A')\, P(B')$ (d) $P(A / B) = P(A)$

37. If A and B are two events, then the probability that exactly one of them occurs is given by

(a) $P(A) + P(B) - 2P(A \cap B)$
(b) $P(A \cap B') + P(A' \cap B)$
(c) $P(A \cup B) - P(A \cap B)$
(d) $P(A') + P(B') - 2P(A' \cap B')$

38. If A and B are two independent events such that $P(A) = 1/2$ and $P(B) = 1/5$. Then,

(a) $P(A \cup B) = 3/5$ (b) $P(A / B) = 1/2$
(c) $P(A / A \cup B) = 5/6$ (d) $P(A \cap B) / (A' \cup B') = 0$

39. A student appears for tests I, II and III. The student is successful if he passes either in tests I and II or tests I and III. The probabilities of the student passing in tests I, II and III are p, q and $1/2$, respectively. If the probability that the student is successful is $1/2$, then

(a) $p = 1, q = 0$ (b) $p = 2/3, q = 1/2$
(c) $p = 3/5, q = 2/3$ (d) infinitely values of p and q

40. Let X be a set containing n elements. If two subsets A and B of X are picked at random, then the probability that A and B have same number of elements, is

(a) $\frac{{}^{2n}C_n}{2^{2n}}$ (b) $\frac{1}{{}^{2n}C_n}$ (c) $\frac{1 \cdot 3 \cdot 5 \dots (2n-1)}{2^n \cdot (n!)}$ (d) $\frac{3^n}{4^n}$

41. Suppose m boys and m girls take their seats randomly around a circle. The probability of their sitting is $({}^{2m-1}C_m)^{-1}$, when

(a) no two boys sit together (b) no two girls sit together
(c) boys and girls sit alternatively
(d) all the boys sit together

42. The probabilities that a student passes in Mathematics, Physics and Chemistry are m, p and c, respectively. In these subjects, the student has a 75% chance of passing in atleast one, a 50% chance of passing in atleast two and a 40% chance of passing in exactly two. Which of the following relations are true?

(a) $p + m + c = 19/20$ (b) $p + m + c = 27/20$
(c) $pmc = 1/10$ (d) $pmc = 1/4$

43. $(n \geq 5)$ persons are sitting in a row. Three of these are selected at random, the probability that no two of the selected persons are sit together, is

(a) $\frac{{}^{n-3}P_2}{{}^nP_2}$ (b) $\frac{{}^{n-3}C_2}{{}^nC_2}$ (c) $\frac{(n-3)(n-4)}{n(n-1)}$ (d) $\frac{{}^{n-3}C_2}{{}^nP_2}$

44. Given that $x \in [0, 1]$ and $y \in [0, 1]$. Let A be the event of (x, y) satisfying $y^2 \leq x$ and B be the event of (x, y) satisfying $x^2 \leq y$, then not true, is

(a) $P(A \cap B) = \frac{1}{3}$
(b) A and B are exhaustive
(c) A and B are mutually exclusive
(d) A and B are independent

45. If the probability of chosing an integer 'k' out of $2n$ integers $1, 2, 3, \dots, 2n$ is inversely proportional to $k^4 (1 \leq k \leq n)$. If α is the probability that chosen number is odd and β is the probability that chosen number is even, then

(a) $\alpha > \frac{1}{2}$ (b) $\alpha > \frac{2}{3}$ (c) $\beta < \frac{1}{2}$ (d) $\beta < \frac{2}{3}$

Probability Exercise 3 :
Passage Based Questions

This section contains **9 passages**. Based upon each of the passage **3 multiple choice questions** have to be answered. Each of these questions has four choices (a), (b), (c) and (d) out of which **ONLY ONE** is correct.

Passage I
(Q. Nos. 46 to 48)

If p and q are chosen randomly from the set {1, 2, 3, 4, 5, 6, 7, 8, 9, 10} with replacement.

46. The probability that roots of $x^2 + px + q = 0$ are real and distinct, is
(a) 0.38 (b) 0.03 (c) 0.59 (d) 0.89

47. The probability that roots of $x^2 + px + q = 0$ are equal, is
(a) 0.58 (b) 0.55 (c) 0.38 (d) 0.03

48. The probability that roots of $x^2 + px + q = 0$ are imaginary, is
(a) 0.62 (b) 0.38 (c) 0.59 (d) 0.89

Passage II
(Q. Nos. 49 to 51)

A chess game between two grandmasters X and Y is won by whoever first wins a total of two games. X 's chances of winning, drawing or loosing any particular game are a, b and c, respectively. The games are independent and $a + b + c = 1$

49. The probability that X wins the match after $(n + 1)$ th game $(n \geq 1)$, is
(a) $na^2 b^{n-1}$ (b) $na^2 b^{n-2}(b + (n-1)c)$
(c) $na^2 bc^{n-1}$ (d) $na\, b^{n-1}(b + nc)$

50. The probability that Y wins the match after the 4th game, is
(a) $abc(2a + 3b)$ (b) $bc^2(a + 3b)$
(c) $2ac^2(b + c)$ (d) $3bc^2(2a + b)$

51. The probability that X wins the match, is
(a) $\frac{a^2(a + 2c)}{(a + c)^3}$ (b) $\frac{a^3}{(a + c)^3}$ (c) $\frac{a^2(a + 3c)}{(a + c)^3}$ (d) $\frac{c^3}{(a + c)^3}$

Passage III
(Q. Nos. 52 to 54)

There are n students in a class. Let $P(E_\lambda)$ be the probability that exactly λ out of n pass the examination. If $P(E_\lambda)$ is directly proportional to λ^2 $(0 \leq \lambda \leq n)$.

52. Proportionality constant k is equal to
(a) $\frac{1}{\Sigma n}$ (b) $\frac{1}{\Sigma n^2}$ (c) $\frac{1}{\Sigma n^3}$ (d) $\frac{1}{\Sigma n^4}$

53. If $P(A)$ be the probability that a student selected at random has passed the examination, then $\lim_{x \to \infty} P(A)$, is
(a) 0.25 (b) 0.50
(c) 0.75 (d) 0.35

54. If a selected student has been found to pass the examination, then the probability that he is the only student to have passed the examination, is
(a) $\frac{1}{\Sigma n}$ (b) $\frac{1}{\Sigma n^2}$
(c) $\frac{1}{\Sigma n^3}$ (d) $\frac{1}{\Sigma n^4}$

Passage IV
(Q. Nos. 55 to 57)

A cube having all of its sides painted is cut to be two horizontal, two vertical and other two planes, so as to form 27 cubes all having the same dimensions of these cubes, a cube is selected at random.

55. If P_1 be the probability that the cube selected having atleast one of its sides painted, then the value of $27P_1$, is
(a) 14 (b) 18 (c) 22 (d) 26

56. If P_2 be the probability that the cube selected has two sides painted, then the value of $27P_2$, is
(a) 3 (b) 8 (c) 12 (d) 17

57. If P_3 be the probability that the cube selected has none of its sides painted, then the value of $27P_3$, is
(a) 1 (b) 2
(c) 3 (d) 5

Passage V
(Q. Nos. 58 to 60)

A JEE aspirant estimates that she will be successful with an 80% chance, if she studies 10 h per day with a 60% chance, if she studies 7 h per day and with a 40% chance if she studies 4 h per day. She further believes that she will study 10 h, 7 h and 4 h per day with probabilities 0.1, 0.2, and 0.7, respectively.

58. The probability that she will be successful, is
(a) 0.28 (b) 0.38 (c) 0.48 (d) 0.58

59. Given that she is successful, the chances that she studied for 4 h, is
(a) $\frac{1}{12}$ (b) $\frac{5}{12}$
(c) $\frac{7}{12}$ (d) $\frac{11}{12}$

60. Given that she does not achieve success, the chance that she studied for 4 h, is

(a) $\frac{15}{26}$ (b) $\frac{17}{26}$ (c) $\frac{19}{26}$ (d) $\frac{21}{26}$

Passage VI
(Q. Nos. 61 to 63)

Suppose E_1, E_2 and E_3 be three mutually exclusive events such that $P(E_i) = p_i$ for $i = 1, 2, 3$.

61. If p_1, p_2 and p_3 are the roots of $27x^3 - 27x^2 + ax - 1 = 0$, the value of a is

(a) 3 (b) 6 (c) 9 (d) 12

62. P (none of E_1, E_2, E_3) equals

(a) 0
(b) $p_1 + p_2 + p_3$
(c) $(1 - p_1)(1 - p_2)(1 - p_3)$
(d) None of the above

63. $P(E_1 \cap \overline{E}_2) + P(E_2 \cap \overline{E}_3) + P(E_3 \cap \overline{E}_1)$ equals

(a) $p_1(1 - p_2) + p_2(1 - p_3) + p_3(1 - p_1)$
(b) $p_1p_2 + p_2p_3 + p_3p_1$
(c) $p_1 + p_2 + p_3$
(d) None of the above

Passage VII
(Q. Nos. 64 to 66)

Let $A = \{1, 2, 3\}$ and $B = \{-2, -1, 0, 1, 2, 3\}$.

64. The probability of increasing functions from A to B, is

(a) $\frac{1}{27}$ (b) $\frac{1}{18}$ (c) $\frac{5}{54}$ (d) $\frac{7}{54}$

65. The probability of non-decreasing functions from A to B, is

(a) $\frac{5}{27}$ (b) $\frac{7}{27}$
(c) $\frac{1}{3}$ (d) $\frac{11}{27}$

66. The probability of onto functions from B to B, such that $f(i) \neq i, i = -2, -1, 0, 1, 2, 3$, is

(a) $\frac{53}{144}$ (b) $\frac{35}{144}$ (c) $\frac{29}{72}$ (d) $\frac{25}{72}$

Passage VIII
(Q. Nos. 67 to 69)

A random variable X takes values 0, 1, 2, 3, ... with probability proportional to $(x+1)\left(\frac{1}{5}\right)^x$.

67. $P(X = 0)$ equals

(a) $\frac{2}{25}$ (b) $\frac{4}{25}$ (c) $\frac{9}{25}$ (d) $\frac{16}{25}$

68. $P(X \geq 2)$ equals

(a) $\frac{11}{25}$ (b) $\frac{13}{25}$ (c) $\frac{11}{125}$ (d) $\frac{13}{125}$

69. The expectation of X i.e., $E(X)$ is equal to

(a) $\frac{1}{4}$ (b) 2 (c) $\frac{1}{2}$ (d) 4

Passage IX
(Q. Nos. 70 to 72)

Let $n = 10\lambda + r$, where $\lambda, r \in N, 0 \leq r \leq 9$. A number a is chosen at random from the set $\{1, 2, 3, \ldots, n\}$ and let p_n denote the probability that $(a^2 - 1)$ is divisible by 10.

70. If $r = 0$, then np_n equals

(a) 2λ (b) $(\lambda + 1)$
(c) $(2\lambda + 1)$ (d) λ

71. If $r = 9$, then np_n equals

(a) 2λ (b) $2(\lambda + 1)$
(c) $(2\lambda + 1)$ (d) λ

72. If $1 \leq r \leq 8$, then np_n equals

(a) $(2\lambda - 1)$ (b) 2λ
(c) $(2\lambda + 1)$ (d) λ

Probability Exercise 4 :
Single Integer Answer Type Questions

- This section contains **10 questions**. The answer to each question is a **single digit integer**, ranging from **0 to 9** (both inclusive).

73. A bag contains $(n + 1)$ coins. It is known that one of these coins shows heads on both sides, whereas the other coins are fair. One coin is selected at random and tossed. If the probability that the toss result in heads is $\frac{7}{12}$, then the value of n is

74. A determinant of the second order is made with the elements 0 and 1. If $\frac{m}{n}$ be the probability that the determinant made is non-negative, where m and n are relative primes, then the value of $n - m$ is

75. Three students appear in an examination of Mathematics. The probabilities of their success are $\frac{1}{3}, \frac{1}{4}$ and $\frac{1}{5}$, respectively. If the probability of success of atleast two is $\frac{\lambda}{12}$, then the value of λ is

76. A die is rolled three times, if p be the probability of getting a large number than the previous number, then the value of $54p$ is

77. In a multiple choice question, there are five alternative answers of which one or more than one are correct. A candidate will get marks on the question, if he ticks all the correct answers. If he decides to tick answers at random, then the least number of choices should he be allowed, so that the probability of his getting marks on the question exceeds $\frac{1}{8}$ is

78. There are n different objects $1, 2, 3, \ldots, n$ distributed at random in n places marked $1, 2, 3, \ldots, n$. If p be the probability that atleast three of the objects occupy places corresponding to their number, then the value of $6p$ is

79. A sum of money is rounded off to the nearest rupee, if $\left(\frac{m}{n}\right)^2$ be the probability that the round off error is atleast ten paise, where m and n are positive relative primes, then the value of $(n - m)$ is

80. A special die is so constructed that the probabilities of throwing 1, 2, 3, 4, 5 and 6 are $(1-k)/6, (1+2k)/6, (1-k)/6, (1+k)/6, (1-2k)/6$ and $(1+k)/6$, respectively. If two such dice are thrown and the probability of getting a sum equal to lies between $\frac{1}{9}$ and $\frac{2}{9}$, then the integral value of k is

81. Seven digits from the numbers 1, 2, 3, 4, 5, 6, 7, 8 and 9 are written in random order. If the probability that this seven-digit number divisible by 9 is p, then the value of $18p$ is

82. 8 players $P_1, P_2, P_3, \ldots, P_8$ play a knock out tournament. It is known that all the players are of equal strength. The tournament is held in three rounds where the players are paired at random in each round. If it is given that P_1 wins in the third round. If p be the probability that P_2 loses in the second round, then the value of $7p$ is

Probability Exercise 5 : Matching Type Questions

- This section contains **6 questions**. Questions 83 to 88 have four statements (A, B C and D) given in **Column I** and four statements (p, q, r and s) in **Column II**. Any given statement in **Column I** can have correct matching with one or more statement(s) given in **Column II**.

83.

	Column I		Column II
(A)	If $P(\overline{A}) = 0.3$, $P(B) = 0.4$ and $P(A\overline{B}) = 0.5$ and $P[B/(A \cup \overline{B})] = \lambda_1$, then $\frac{1}{\lambda_1}$ is	(p)	A prime number
(B)	The coefficient of a quadratic equation $ax^2 + bx + c = 10 (a \neq b \neq c)$ are chosen from first three prime numbers, then the probability that roots of the equation are real is λ_2, then $\frac{1}{\lambda_2}$ is	(q)	A composite number
(C)	A fair coin is tossed repeatedly. If tail appears on first four tosses, then the probability of head appearing on the fifth toss is λ_3, then $\frac{1}{\lambda_3}$ is	(r)	A natural number
(D)	Three persons A, B and C are to speak at a function along with 6 other persons. If the persons speak in random order, then the probability that A speaks before B and B speaks before C is λ_4, then $\frac{1}{\lambda_4}$ is	(s)	A perfect number

84. A and B are two events, such that $P(A)=\dfrac{3}{5}$ and $P(B)=\dfrac{2}{3}$

	Column I		Column II
(A)	$P(A\cap B)\in$	(p)	$\left[\dfrac{2}{3},1\right]$
(B)	$P(A\cup B)\in$	(q)	$\left[\dfrac{4}{9},1\right]$
(C)	$P(A/B)\in$	(r)	$\left[\dfrac{2}{5},\dfrac{9}{10}\right]$
(D)	$P(B/A)\in$	(s)	$\left[\dfrac{4}{15},\dfrac{3}{5}\right]$

85. Three players A, B and C alternatively throw a die in that order, the first player to throw a 6 being deemed the winner. A's die is fair whereas B and C throw dice with probabilities p_1 and p_2 respectively, of throwing a 6.

	Column I		Column II
(A)	If $p_1=\dfrac{1}{5}$, $p_2=\dfrac{1}{4}$ and probability that A wins the game is $\dfrac{1}{\lambda_1}$, then λ_1 is divisor of	(p)	6
(B)	If $p_1=\dfrac{1}{5}$, $p_2=\dfrac{1}{4}$ and probability that C wins the game is $\dfrac{1}{\lambda_2}$, then λ_2 is divisor of	(q)	8
(C)	If P(A wins) = P(B wins) and $\dfrac{1}{p_1}=\lambda_3$, then λ_3 is divisor of	(r)	12
(D)	If game is equiprobable to all the three players and $\dfrac{1}{p_1}=\lambda_4$, then λ_4 is divisor of	(s)	15

86. Two numbers a and b are chosen at random from the set {1, 2, 3, 4,.., 9} with replacement. The probability that the equation $x^2+\sqrt{2}(a-b)x+b=0$ has

	Column I		Column II
(A)	Real and distinct roots is p_1, then the value of $[9p_1]$, where [·] denotes the greatest integer function, is	(p)	2
(B)	Imaginary roots is p_2, then the value of $[9p_2]$, where [·] denotes the greatest integer function, is	(q)	3
(C)	Equal roots is p_3, then the value of $[81p_3]$, where [·] denotes the greatest integer function, is	(r)	4
(D)	Real roots is p_4, then the value of $[9p_4]$, where [·] denotes the greatest integer function, is	(s)	5

87. Three numbers are chosen at random without replacement from the set $\{x \mid 1\le x\le 10, x\in N\}$

	Column I		Column II
(A)	Let p_1 be the probability that the minimum of the chosen numbers is 3 and maximum is 7, then the value of $\dfrac{2}{5p_1}$, is	(p)	10
(B)	Let p_2 be the probability that the minimum of the chosen numbers is 4 or their maximum is 8, then the value of $80p_2$, is	(q)	14
(C)	Let p_3 be the probability that their minimum is 3, given that their maximum is 7, then the value of $\dfrac{2}{p_3}$, is	(r)	16
(D)	Let p_4 be the probability that their minimum is 4, given that their maximum is 8, then the value of $\dfrac{2}{p_4}$, is	(s)	22

88.

	Column I		Column II
(A)	If the integers m and n are chosen at random between 1 and 100, then the probability that a number of the form 7^m+7^n is divisible by 5, is	(p)	$\dfrac{1}{7}$
(B)	A second order determinant is written down at random using the numbers 1, −1 as elements. The probability that the value of the determinant is non-zero, is	(q)	$\dfrac{1}{5}$
(C)	The probability of a number n showing in a throw of a die marked 1 to 6 is proportional to n. Then, the probability of the number 3 showing in a throw, is	(r)	$\dfrac{2}{5}$
(D)	A pair of dice is rolled together till a sum of either 5 or 7 is obtained. Then, the probability that 5 comes before 7, is	(s)	$\dfrac{1}{2}$

Probability Exercise 6 : Statement I and II Type Questions

- **Directions** (Q. Nos. 89 to 100) are Assertion-Reason type questions. Each of these questions contains two statements:
Statement-1 (Assertion) and
Statement-2 (Reason) Each of these questions also has four alternative choices, only one of which is the correct answer. You have to select the correct choice as given below.
(a) Statement-1 is true, Statement-2 is true; Statement-2 is a correct explanation for Statement-1
(b) Statement-1 is true, Statement-2 is true; Statement-2 is not a correct explanation for Statement-1
(c) Statement1 is true, Statement-2 is false
(d) Statement-1 is false, Statement-2 is true

89. **Statement-1** If 10 coins are thrown simultaneously, then the probability of appearing exactly four heads is equal to probability of appearing exactly six heads.

Statement-2 ${}^nC_r = {}^nC_s \Rightarrow$ either $r = s$ or $r + s = n$ and $P(H) = P(T)$ in a single trial.

90. **Statement-1** If A is any event and $P(B) = 1$, then A and B are independent.

Statement-2 $P(A \cap B) = P(A) \cdot P(B)$, if A and B are independent.

91. **Statement-1** If A and B be the events in a sample space, such that $P(A) = 0.3$ and $P(B) = 0.2$, then $P(A \cap \overline{B})$ cannot be found.
Statement-2 $P(A \cap \overline{B}) = P(A) - P(A \cap B)$

92. **Statement-1** Let A and B be two events, such that $P(A \cup B) = P(A \cap B)$, then

$$P(A \cap B') = P(A' \cap B) = 0$$

Statement-2 Let A and B be two events, such that $P(A \cup B) = P(A \cap B)$, then $P(A) + P(B) = 1$

93. A fair die is rolled once.
Statement-1 The probability of getting a composite number is $\frac{1}{3}$, is

Statement-2 There are three possibilities for the obtained number.
(i) The number is prime number.
(ii) The number is a composite number and
(iii) The number is 1.

Hence, probabilities of getting a prime number is $\frac{1}{3}$.

94. From a well shuffled pack of 52 playing cards, a card is drawn at random. Two events A and B are defined as
A : Red card is drawn
B: Card drawn is either a Diamond or Heart
Statement-1 $P(A + B) = P(AB)$
Statement-2 $A \subseteq B$ and $B \subseteq A$

95. **Statement-1** The probability that A and B can solve a problem is $\frac{1}{2}$ and $\frac{1}{3}$ respectively, then the probability that problem will be solved is $\frac{5}{6}$.

Statement-2 Above mentioned events are independent events.

96. **Statement-1** Out of 21 tickets with numbers 1 to 21, 3 tickets are drawn at random, the chance that the numbers on them are in AP is $\frac{10}{133}$.

Statement-2 Out of $(2n + 1)$ tickets consecutively numbered three are drawn at random, the chance that the numbers on them are in AP is $(4n - 10)/(4n^2 - 1)$.

97. **Statement-1** If A and B are two events, such that $0 < P(A)$, $P(B) < 1$, then $P\left(\frac{A}{\overline{B}}\right) + P\left(\frac{\overline{A}}{\overline{B}}\right) = \frac{3}{2}$

Statement-2 If A and B are two events, such that $0 < P(A)$, $P(B) < 1$, then

$$P(A / B) = \frac{P(A \cap B)}{P(B)} \text{ and } P(\overline{B}) = P(A \cap \overline{B}) + P(\overline{A} \cap \overline{B})$$

98. In a T-20 tournament, there are five teams. Each team plays one match against every other team.
Each team has 50% chance of winning any game it plays. No match ends in a tie.
Statement-1 The probability that there is an undefeated team in the tournament is $\frac{5}{16}$.

Statement-2 The probability that there is a winless team in the tournament is $\frac{3}{16}$.

99. **Statement-1** If p is chosen at random in the closed interval $[0, 5]$, then the probability that the equation $x^2 + px + \frac{1}{4}(p + 2) = 0$ has real is $\frac{3}{5}$.

Statement-2 If discriminant ≥ 0, then roots of the quadratic equation are always real.

100. Let a sample space S contains n elements. Two events A and B are defined on S and $B \neq \phi$.

Statement-1 The conditional probability of the event A given B, is the ratio of the number of elements in AB divided by the number of elements in B.

Statement-2 The conditional probability model given B, is equally likely model on B.

Probability Exercise 7 : Subjective Type Questions

- In this section, there are **24 subjective** questions.

101. A five digit number is formed by the digits 1, 2, 3, 4 and 5 without repetition. Find the probability that the number formed is divisible by 4.

102. A dice is rolled three times, then find the probability of getting a large number than the previous number.

103. A car is parked among N cars standing in a row but not at either end. On his return, the owner finds that exactly r of the N places are still occupied. What is the probability that both the places neighbouring his car are empty?

104. Two teams A and B play a tournament. The first one to win $(n+1)$ games win the series. The probability that A wins a game is p and that B wins a game is q (no ties). Find the probability that A wins the series. Hence or otherwise prove that $\sum_{r=0}^{n} {}^{n+1}C_r \cdot \frac{1}{2^{n+r}} = 1$.

105. An artillery target may be either at point I with probability $\frac{8}{9}$ or at point II with probability $\frac{1}{9}$. We have 21 shells each of which can be fired either at point I or II. Each shell may hit the target independently of the other shell with probability $\frac{1}{2}$.

How many shells must be fired at point I to hit the target with maximum probability?

106. There are 6 red and 8 green balls in a bag. 5 balls are drawn at random and placed in a red box. The remaining balls are placed in a green box. What is the probability that the number of red balls in the green box plus the number of green balls in the red box is not a prime number?

107. An urn contains 'a' green and 'b' pink balls $k\ (< a, b)$ balls are drawn and laid a side, their colour being ignored. Then, one more ball is drawn. Find the probability that it is green.

108. A fair coin is tossed 12 times. Find the probability that two heads do not occur consecutively.

109. Given that $x + y = 2a$, where a is constant and that all values of x between 0 and $2a$ are equally likely, then show that the chance that $xy > \frac{3}{4}a^2$, is $\frac{1}{2}$.

110. A chess game between Kamsky and Anand is won by whoever first wins a out of 2 games. Kamsky's chance of winning, drawing or loosing a particular game are 2. The games are independent and $p + q + r = 1$. Prove that the probability that Kamsky wins the match is $\frac{p^2(p+3r)}{(p+r)^3}$.

111. Of three independent events, the chance that only the first occurs is a, the other that only the second occurs is b and the chance of only third occurs is c. Show that the cases of three events are respectively $a/(a+x)$, $b/(b+x)$, $c/(c+x)$, where x is a root of the equation $(a+x)(b+x)(c+x) = x^2$.

112. A is a set containing n elements. A subset P of A is chosen at random and the set A is reconstructed by replacing the elements of P. Another subset Q of A is now chosen at random. Find the probability that $P \cup Q$ contains exactly r elements, with $1 \le r \le n$.

113. An electric component manufactured by 'RASU electronics' is tested for its defectiveness by a sophisticated testing device. Let A denote the even "the device is defective" and B the event "the testing device reveals the component to be defective." Suppose, $P(A) = \alpha$ and $P(B/A) = P(B'/A') = 1 - \alpha$, where $0 < \alpha < 1$. Show that the probability that the component is not defective, given that the testing device reveals it to be defective is independent of α.

114. A bag contains n white and n red balls. Pairs of balls are drawn without replacement until the bag is empty. Show that the probability that each pair consists of one white and one red ball is $2^n / ({}^{2n}C_n)$.

115. If m things are distributed among 'a' men and 'b' women, then show that the probability that the number of things received by men is odd, is $\frac{1}{2}\frac{\{(b+a)^m - (b-a)^m\}}{(b+a)^m}$.

Probability Exercise 8 :
Questions Asked in Previous 13 Year's Exam

- This section contains questions asked in **IIT-JEE, AIEEE, JEE Main & JEE Advanced** from year **2005** to year **2017**.

116. A person goes to office either by car, scooter, bus or train. The probability of which being $\frac{1}{7}, \frac{3}{7}, \frac{2}{7}$ and $\frac{1}{7}$, respectively. Probability that he reaches office late, if he takes car, scooter, bus or train is $\frac{2}{9}, \frac{1}{9}, \frac{4}{9}$ and $\frac{1}{9}$, respectively. Given that he reached office in time, then what is the probability that he travelled by a car. **[IIT-JEE 2005, 2M]**

117. A six faced fair die is thrown until 1 comes. Then, the probability that 1 comes in even number of trials, is **[IIT-JEE 2005, 3M]**

(a) $\frac{5}{11}$ (b) $\frac{5}{6}$ (c) $\frac{6}{11}$ (d) $\frac{1}{6}$

118. Let A and B be two events such that $P(\overline{A \cup B}) = \frac{1}{6}$, $P(A \cap B) = \frac{1}{4}$ and $P(\overline{A}) = \frac{1}{4}$, where $\overline{A}$ stands for complement of event A. Then, events A and B are **[IIT-JEE 2005, 3M]**

(a) independent but not equally likely
(b) mutually exclusive and independent
(c) equally likely and mutually exclusive
(d) equally likely but not independent

119. Three houses are available in a locality. Three persons apply for the houses. Each applies for one house without consulting others. The probability that all the three apply for the same house, is **[AIEEE 2005, 3M]**

(a) $\frac{8}{9}$ (b) $\frac{7}{9}$ (c) $\frac{2}{9}$ (d) $\frac{1}{9}$

120. A random variable X has Poisson's distribution with mean 2. Then, $P(X > 1.5)$ is equal to **[AIEEE 2005, 3M]**

(a) $1 - \frac{3}{e^2}$ (b) $\frac{3}{e^2}$ (c) $\frac{2}{e^2}$ (d) 0

121. There are n urns each containing $(n + 1)$ balls such that the ith urn contains i white balls and $(n + 1 - i)$ red balls. Let u_i be the event of selecting ith urn, $i = 1, 2, 3, \ldots, n$ and w denotes the event of getting a white ball. **[IIT-JEE 2006, 5+5+5M]**

(i) If $P(u_i) \propto i$, where $i = 1, 2, 3, \ldots, n$, then $\lim_{n \to \infty} P(w)$, is

(a) 1 (b) $\frac{2}{3}$ (c) $\frac{3}{4}$ (d) $\frac{1}{4}$

(ii) If $P(u_i) = c$, where c is a constant, then $P\left(\frac{u_n}{w}\right)$, is

(a) $\frac{2}{n+1}$ (b) $\frac{1}{n+1}$ (c) $\frac{n}{n+1}$ (d) $\frac{1}{2}$

(iii) If n is even and E denotes the event of choosing even numbered urn $\left(P(u_i) = \frac{1}{n}\right)$, then the value of $P\left(\frac{w}{E}\right)$, is

(a) $\frac{n+2}{2n+1}$ (b) $\frac{n+2}{2(n+1)}$ (c) $\frac{n}{n+1}$ (d) $\frac{1}{n+1}$

122. At a telephone enquiry system, the number of phone calls regarding relevant enquiry follow Poisson's distribution with an average of 5 phone calls during 10 min time interval. The probability that there is atmost one phone call during a 10 min time period, is **[AIEEE 2006, 4, 5M]**

(a) $\frac{6}{5^e}$ (b) $\frac{5}{6}$ (c) $\frac{6}{55}$ (d) $\frac{6}{e^5}$

123. One Indian and four American men and their wives are to be seated randomly around a circular table. Then, the conditional probability that the Indian man is seated adjacent to his wife given that each American man is seated adjacent to his wife, is **[IIT-JEE 2007, 3M]**

(a) $\frac{1}{2}$ (b) $\frac{1}{3}$ (c) $\frac{2}{5}$ (d) $\frac{1}{5}$

124. Let $H_1, H_2, \ldots, H_n$ be mutually exclusive events with $P(H_i) > 0, i = 1, 2, \ldots, n$. Let E be any other event with $0 < P(E) < 1$.

Statement-1 $P(H_i / E) > P(E / H_i)\, P(H_i)$, for $i = 1, 2, \ldots, n$.

Statement-2 $\sum_{i=1}^{n} P(H_i) = 1$ **[IIT-JEE 2007, 3M]**

(a) Statement-1 is true, Statement-2 is true; Statement-2 is a correct explanation for Statement-1
(b) Statement-1 is true, Statement-2 is true; Statement-2 is not a correct explanation for Statement-1
(c) Statement-1 is true, Statement-2 is false
(d) Statement-1 is false, Statement-2 is true

125. Let E^c denote the complement of an event E. Let E, F and G be pairwise independent events with $P(G) > 0$ and $P(E \cap F \cap G) = 0$, then $P(E^c \cap F^c / G)$, is **[IIT-JEE 2007, 3M]**

(a) $P(E^c) + P(F^c)$ (b) $P(E^c) - P(F^c)$
(c) $P(E^c) - P(F)$ (d) $P(E) - P(F^c)$

126. A pair of fair dice is thrown independently three times. Then, the probability of getting a score of exactly 9 twice, is **[AIEEE 2007, 3M]**

(a) $\frac{1}{729}$ (b) $\frac{8}{9}$ (c) $\frac{8}{729}$ (d) $\frac{8}{243}$

127. Two aeroplanes I and II bomb a target in successions. The probabilities of I and II scoring a hit correctly are 0.3 and 0.2, respectively. The second plane will bomb only if the first misses the target. The probability that the target is hit by the second plane, is **[AIEEE 2007, 3M]**

(a) 0.06 (b) 0.14 (c) 0.2 (d) 0.7

128. An experiment has 10 equally likely outcomes. Let A and B be two non-empty events of the experiment. If A consists of 4 outcomes, then the number of outcomes that B must have, so that A and B are independent, is **[IIT-JEE 2008, 3M]**

(a) 2, 4 or 8 (b) 3, 6 or 9 (c) 4 or 8 (d) 5 or 10

129. Consider the system of equations $ax + by = 0$ and $cx + dy = 0$, where $a, b, c, d \in \{0, 1\}$.

Statement-1 The probability that the system of equations has a unique solution is 3/8 and **[IIT-JEE 2008, 3M]**

Statement-2 The probability that the system of equations has a solution is 1.

(a) Statement-1 is true, Statement-2 is true; Statement-2 is a correct explanation for Statement-1.

(b) Statement-1 is true, Statement-2 is true; Statement-2 is not a correct explanation for Statement-1.

(c) Statement-1 is true, Statement-2 is false.

(d) Statement-1 is false, Statement-2 is true.

130. A die is thrown. Let A be the event that the number obtained is greater than 3. Let B be the event that the number obtained is less than 5. Then $P(A \cup B)$ is **[AIEEE 2008, 3M]**

(a) 0 (b) 1 (c) $\frac{2}{5}$ (d) $\frac{3}{5}$

131. It is given that the events A and B are such that $P(A) = \frac{1}{4}, P\left(\frac{A}{B}\right) = \frac{1}{2}$ and $P\left(\frac{B}{A}\right) = \frac{2}{3}$. Then $P(B)$ is **[AIEEE 2008, 3M]**

(a) $\frac{1}{3}$ (b) $\frac{2}{3}$ (c) $\frac{1}{2}$ (d) $\frac{1}{6}$

▪ **Passage for Question Nos. 132 to 134**

A fair die is tossed repeatedly until a six is obtained. Let X denote the number of tosses required.

132. The probability that $X = 3$ is

(a) $\frac{25}{216}$ (b) $\frac{25}{36}$ (c) $\frac{5}{36}$ (d) $\frac{125}{216}$

133. The probability that $X \geq 3$ is

(a) $\frac{125}{216}$ (b) $\frac{25}{36}$ (c) $\frac{5}{36}$ (d) $\frac{25}{216}$

134. The conditional probability that $X \geq 6$ given $X > 3$, is

(a) $\frac{125}{216}$ (b) $\frac{25}{216}$ (c) $\frac{5}{36}$ (d) $\frac{25}{36}$

[IIT-JEE 2009, 4+4+4M]

135. In a binomial distribution $B\left(n, p = \frac{1}{4}\right)$, if the probability of atleast one success is greater than or equal to $\frac{9}{10}$, then n is greater than **[AIEEE 2009, 4M]**

(a) $\frac{4}{\log_{10} 4 - \log_{10} 3}$ (b) $\frac{1}{\log_{10} 4 - \log_{10} 3}$

(c) $\frac{1}{\log_{10} 4 + \log_{10} 3}$ (d) $\frac{9}{\log_{10} 4 - \log_{10} 3}$

136. One ticket is selected at random from 50 tickets numbered 00, 01, 02, ..., 49. Then, the probability that the sum of the digits on the selected ticket is 8, given that the product of these digits is zero, is **[AIEEE 2009, 4M]**

(a) $\frac{1}{50}$ (b) $\frac{1}{14}$

(c) $\frac{1}{7}$ (d) $\frac{5}{14}$

137. Let ω be a complex cube root of unity with $\omega \neq 1$. A fair die is thrown three times. If r_1, r_2 and r_3 are the numbers obtained on the die, then the probability that $\omega^{r_1} + \omega^{r_2} + \omega^{r_3} = 0$, is **[IIT-JEE 2010, 3M]**

(a) $\frac{1}{18}$ (b) $\frac{1}{9}$ (c) $\frac{2}{9}$ (d) $\frac{1}{36}$

138. A signal which can be green or red with probability $\frac{4}{5}$ and $\frac{1}{5}$ respectively, is received by station A and then transmitted to station B. The probability of each station receiving the signal correctly is $\frac{3}{4}$. If the signal received at station B is green, then the probability that the original signal was green, is **[IIT-JEE 2010, 5M]**

(a) $\frac{3}{5}$ (b) $\frac{6}{7}$ (c) $\frac{20}{23}$ (d) $\frac{9}{20}$

139. Four numbers are chosen at random (without replacement) from the set $\{1, 2, 3, \ldots, 20\}$.

Statement-1 The probability that the chosen numbers, when arranged in some order will form an AP is $\frac{1}{85}$.

Statement-2 If the four chosen number form an AP, then the set of all possible values of common difference is $\{\pm 1, \pm 2, \pm 3, \pm 4, \pm 5\}$. **[AIEEE 2010, 8M]**

(a) Statement-1 is true, Statement-2 is true; Statement-2 is a correct explanation for Statement-1

(b) Statement-1 is true, Statement-2 is false

(c) Statement-1 is false, Statement-2 is true

(d) Statement-1 is true, Statement-2 is true; Statement-2 is not a correct explanation for Statement-1

140. An urn contains nine balls of which three are red, four are blue and two are green. Three balls are drawn at random without replacement from the urn. The probability that the three balls have different colour, is **[AIEEE 2010, 4M]**

(a) $\frac{2}{7}$ (b) $\frac{1}{21}$ (c) $\frac{2}{23}$ (d) $\frac{1}{3}$

■ **Passage for Question Nos. 141 and 142**

Let U_1 and U_2 be two urns such that U_1 contains 3 white balls and 2 red balls and U_2 contains only 1 white ball. A fair coin is tossed. If head appears, then 1 ball is drawn at random from U_1 and put into U_2. However, if tail appears, then 2 balls are drawn at random from U_1 and put into U_2. Now, 1 ball is drawn at random from U_2.

141. The probability of the drawn ball from U_2 being white, is

(a) $\frac{13}{30}$ (b) $\frac{23}{30}$ (c) $\frac{19}{30}$ (d) $\frac{11}{30}$

142. Given that the drawn ball from U_2 is white, then the probability that head appeared on the coin, is **[IIT-JEE 2011, 3+3M]**

(a) $\frac{17}{23}$ (b) $\frac{11}{23}$ (c) $\frac{15}{23}$ (d) $\frac{12}{23}$

143. Let E and F be two independent events. The probability that exactly one of them occurs is $\frac{11}{25}$ and the probability of none of them occurring is $\frac{2}{25}$. If $P(T)$ denotes the probability of occurrence of the event T, then **[IIT-JEE 2011, 4M]**

(a) $P(E)=\frac{4}{5}, P(F)=\frac{3}{5}$ (b) $P(E)=\frac{1}{5}, P(F)=\frac{2}{5}$

(c) $P(E)=\frac{2}{5}, P(F)=\frac{1}{5}$ (d) $P(E)=\frac{3}{5}, P(F)=\frac{4}{5}$

144. Consider 5 independent Bernoulli's trials each with probability of success P. If the probability of atleast one failure is greater than or equal to $\frac{31}{32}$, then P lies in the interval **[AIEEE 2011, 4M]**

(a) $\left(\frac{3}{4}, \frac{11}{12}\right]$ (b) $\left[0, \frac{1}{2}\right]$ (c) $\left(\frac{11}{12}, 1\right]$ (d) $\left(\frac{1}{2}, \frac{3}{4}\right]$

145. If C and D are two events, such that $C \subset D$ and $P(D) \neq 0$, then the correct statement among the following, is **[AIEEE 2011, 4M]**

(a) $P\left(\frac{C}{D}\right) \geq P(C)$ (b) $P\left(\frac{C}{D}\right) < P(C)$

(c) $P\left(\frac{C}{D}\right) = \frac{P(D)}{P(C)}$ (d) $P\left(\frac{C}{D}\right) = P(C)$

146. Let A, B and C are pairwise independent events with $P(C) > 0$ and $P(A \cap B \cap C) = 0$. Then, $P\left(\frac{(A^c \cap B^c)}{C}\right)$ is

(a) $P(A^c) - P(B)$ (b) $P(A) - P(B^c)$

(c) $P(A^c) + P(B^c)$ (d) $P(A^c) - P(B^c)$

147. A ship is fitted with three engines E_1, E_2 and E_3. The engines function independently of each other with respective probabilities $\frac{1}{2}, \frac{1}{4}$ and $\frac{1}{4}$, respectively. For the ship to be operational atleast two of its engines must function. Let X denote the event that the ship is operational and let X_1, X_2 and X_3 denote respectively the events that the engines E_1, E_2 and E_3 are functioning. Which of the following is (are) true? **[IIT-JEE 2012, 4M]**

(a) $P[X_1^c / X] = \frac{3}{16}$

(b) P [exactly two engines of the ship are functioning $/X] = \frac{7}{8}$

(c) $P[X / X_2] = \frac{5}{16}$

(d) $P[X / X_1] = \frac{7}{16}$

148. Four fair dice D_1, D_2, D_3 and D_4 each having six faces numbered 1, 2, 3, 4, 5 and 6 are rolled simultaneously. The probability that D_4 shows a number appearing on one of D_1, D_2 and D_3, is **[IIT-JEE 2012, 3M]**

(a) $\frac{91}{216}$ (b) $\frac{108}{216}$ (c) $\frac{25}{216}$ (d) $\frac{127}{216}$

149. Let X and Y be two events, such that $P(X/Y) = \frac{1}{2}$, $P(Y/X) = \frac{1}{3}$ and $P(X \cap Y) = \frac{1}{6}$. Which of the following is (are) correct? **[IIT-JEE 2012, 4M]**

(a) $P(X \cup Y) = \frac{2}{3}$ (b) X and Y are independent

(c) X and Y are not independent

(d) $P(X^c \cap Y) = \frac{1}{3}$

150. Three numbers are chosen at random without replacement from $\{1, 2, 3, \ldots, 8\}$. The probability that their minimum is 3, given that their maximum is 6, is **[AIEEE 2012, 4M]**

(a) $\frac{1}{4}$ (b) $\frac{2}{5}$ (c) $\frac{3}{8}$ (d) $\frac{1}{5}$

151. A multiple choice examination has 5 questions. Each question has three alternative answers of which exactly one is correct. The probability that a student will get 4 or more correct answers just by guessing, is **[JEE Main 2013, 4M]**

(a) $\frac{13}{3^5}$ (b) $\frac{11}{3^5}$ (c) $\frac{10}{3^5}$ (d) $\frac{17}{3^5}$

152. Four persons independently solve a certain problem correctly with probabilities $\frac{1}{2}, \frac{3}{4}, \frac{1}{4}$ and $\frac{1}{8}$. Then, the probability that the problem is solved correctly by atleast one of them, is **[JEE Advanced 2013, 2M]**

(a) $\frac{235}{256}$ (b) $\frac{21}{256}$ (c) $\frac{3}{256}$ (d) $\frac{253}{256}$

153. Of the three independent events E_1, E_2 and E_3, the probability that only E_1 occurs α, only E_2 occurs is β and only E_3 occurs is γ. Let the probability p that none of events E_1, E_2 or E_3 occurs satisfy the equation $(\alpha - 2\beta)p = \alpha\beta$ and $(\beta - 3\gamma)p = 2\beta\gamma$. All the given probabilities are assumed to lie in the interval (0, 1).

Then, $\dfrac{\text{Probability of occurrence of } E_1}{\text{Probability of occurrence of } E_3}$ is

[JEE Advanced 2013, 4M]

Passage for Question Nos. 154 and 155

A box B_1 contains 1 white ball, 3 red balls and 2 black balls. Another box B_2 contains 2 white balls, 3 red balls and 4 black balls. A third box B_3 contains 3 white balls, 4 red balls and 5 black balls.

154. If 2 balls are drawn (without replacement) from a randomly selected box and one of the balls is white and the other ball is red, then the probability that these 2 balls are drawn from box B_2, is

(a) $\frac{116}{181}$ (b) $\frac{126}{181}$ (c) $\frac{65}{181}$ (d) $\frac{55}{181}$

155. If 1 ball is drawn from each of the boxes B_1, B_2 and B_3, then the probability that all 3 drawn balls are of the same colour, is **[JEE Advanced 2013, 3+3M]**

(a) $\frac{82}{648}$ (b) $\frac{90}{648}$ (c) $\frac{558}{648}$ (d) $\frac{566}{648}$

156. Let A and B be two events, such that $P(\overline{A \cup B}) = \frac{1}{6}$, $P(A \cap B) = \frac{1}{4}$ and $P(\overline{A}) = \frac{1}{4}$, where $\overline{A}$ stands for the complement of the event A. Then, the events A and B are

(a) independent but not equally likely **[JEE Main 2014, 4M]**
(b) independent and equally likely
(c) mutually exclusive and independent
(d) equally likely but not independent

157. Three boys and two girls stand in a queue. The probability that the number of boys ahead of every girl is atleast one more than the number of girls ahead of her, is **[JEE Advanced 2014, 3M]**

(a) $\frac{1}{2}$ (b) $\frac{1}{3}$ (c) $\frac{2}{3}$ (d) $\frac{3}{4}$

Passage for Question Nos. 158 and 159

Box 1 contains three cards bearing numbers 1, 2, 3, box 2 contains five cards bearing numbers 1, 2, 3, 4, 5 and box 3 contains seven cards bearing numbers 1, 2, 3, 4, 5, 6, 7. A card is drawn from each of the boxes. Let x_i be the number on the card drawn from the ith box, $i = 1, 2, 3$.

158. The probability that $x_1 + x_2 + x_3$ is odd, is

(a) $\frac{29}{105}$ (b) $\frac{53}{105}$ (c) $\frac{57}{105}$ (d) $\frac{1}{2}$

159. The probability that x_1, x_2 and x_3 are in arithmetic progression, is **[JEE Advanced 2014, 3+3M]**

(a) $\frac{9}{105}$ (b) $\frac{10}{105}$ (c) $\frac{11}{105}$ (d) $\frac{7}{105}$

160. If 12 identical balls are to be placed in 3 identical boxes, then the probability that one of the boxes contains exactly 3 balls, is **[JEE Main 2015, 4M]**

(a) $220\left(\frac{1}{3}\right)^{12}$ (b) $22\left(\frac{1}{3}\right)^{11}$ (c) $\frac{55}{3}\left(\frac{2}{3}\right)^{11}$ (d) $55\left(\frac{2}{3}\right)^{10}$

161. The minimum number of times a fair coin needs to be tossed, so that the probability of getting atleast two heads is atleast 0.96, is **[JEE Advanced 2015, 4M]**

Passage for Question Nos. 162 and 163

Let n_1 and n_2 be the number of red and black balls respectively, in box I. Let n_3 and n_4 be the number of red and black balls respectively, in box II.

162. One of the two boxes, box I and box II, was selected at random and a ball was drawn randomly out of this box. The ball was found to be red. If the probability that this red ball was drawn from box II is 1/3, then the correct option(s) with the possible values of n_1, n_2, n_3 and n_4 is (are)

(a) $n_1 = 3, n_2 = 3, n_3 = 5, n_4 = 15$ (b) $n_1 = 3, n_2 = 6, n_3 = 10, n_4 = 50$
(c) $n_1 = 8, n_2 = 6, n_3 = 5, n_4 = 20$ (d) $n_1 = 6, n_2 = 12, n_3 = 5, n_4 = 20$

163. A ball is drawn at random from box I and transferred to box II. If the probability of drawing a red ball from box I, after this transfer is $\frac{1}{3}$, then correct option(s) with possible values of n_1 and n_2 is (are) **[JEE Advanced 2015, 4+4M]**

(a) $n_1 = 4$ and $n_2 = 6$ (b) $n_1 = 2$ and $n_2 = 3$
(c) $n_1 = 10$ and $n_2 = 20$ (d) $n_1 = 3$ and $n_2 = 6$

164. Let two fair six-faced dice A and B be thrown simultaneously. If E_1 is the event that die A shows up four, E_2 is the event that die B shows up two and E_3 is the event that the sum of numbers on both dice is odd, then which of the following statements is NOT true? **[JEE Main 2016, 4M]**

(a) E_2 and E_3 are independent (b) E_1 and E_3 are independent
(c) E_1, E_2 and E_3 are independent (d) E_1 and E_2 are independent

165. A computer producing factory has only two plants T_1 and T_2. Plant T_1 produces 20% and plant T_2 produces 80% of the total computers produced 7% of computers produced in the factory turn out to be defective. It is known that P (computer terms out to be defective given that it is produced in plant T_1) = $10P$ (computer terms out to be defective given that it is produced in plant T_2), when $P(E)$ denotes the probability of an event E. A computer produced in the factory is randomly selected and it does not turn out to be defective. Then, the probability that it is produced in plant T_2 is

[JEE Advanced 2016, 3M]

(a) $\frac{36}{73}$ (b) $\frac{47}{79}$ (c) $\frac{78}{93}$ (d) $\frac{75}{83}$

Passage for Question Nos. 166 and 167

ootball teams T_1 and T_2 have to play two games against ach other. It is assumed that the outcomes of the two ames are independent. The probabilities of T_1 winning, rawing and losing a game against T_2 are $\frac{1}{2}, \frac{1}{6}$ and $\frac{1}{3}$ espectively. Each team gets 3 points for a win, 1 point for draw and 0 point for a loss in a game. Let X and Y enote the total points scored by teams T_1 and T_2 espectively, after two games. **[JEE Advanced 2016, 3+3M]**

(a) $\frac{1}{4}$ (b) $\frac{5}{12}$ (c) $\frac{1}{2}$ (d) $\frac{7}{12}$

67. $P(X = Y)$ is

(a) $\frac{11}{36}$ (b) $\frac{1}{3}$ (c) $\frac{13}{36}$ (d) $\frac{1}{2}$

68. A box contains 15 green and 10 yellow balls. If 10 balls are randomly drawn, one-by-one with replacement, then the variance of the number of green balls drawn is **[JEE Main 2017, 4M]**

(a) $\frac{6}{25}$ (b) $\frac{12}{5}$ (c) 6 (d) 4

169. If two different numbers are taken from the set {0, 1, 2, 3, ..., 10}, then the probability that their sum as well as absolute difference are both multiple of 4, is **[JEE Main 2017, 4M]**

(a) $\frac{7}{55}$ (b) $\frac{6}{55}$ (c) $\frac{12}{55}$ (d) $\frac{14}{45}$

170. For three events A, B and C.

P(Exactly one of A or B or C occurs)

$= P$(Exactly one of B or C occurs)

$= P$(Exactly one of C or A occurs) $= \frac{1}{4}$

and P (All the three events occur simultaneously) $= \frac{1}{16}$,

Then the probability that atleast one of the events occurs, is **[JEE Main 2017, 4M]**

(a) $\frac{3}{16}$ (b) $\frac{7}{32}$

(c) $\frac{7}{16}$ (d) $\frac{7}{64}$

Answers

Exercise for Session 1

1. (a) 2. (a) 3. (d) 4. (b) 5. (a) 6. (c)
7. (b) 8. (d) 9. (d) 10. (d) 11. (c) 12. (c)
13. (d) 14. (d) 15. (b) 16. (b) 17. (a) 18. (a)
19. (c) 20. (c)

Exercise for Session 2

1. (c) 2. (d) 3. (b) 4. (c) 5. (b) 6. (b)
7. (c) 8. (a) 9. (a) 10. (b) 11. (c) 12. (a)
13. (b) 14. (b) 15. (b)

Exercise for Session 3

1. (d) 2. (d) 3. (c) 4. (d) 5. (d) 6. (b)
7. (d) 8. (c) 9. (c) 10. (a)

Exercise for Session 4

1. (c) 2. (d) 3. (d) 4. (a) 5. (c) 6. (a)
7. (a) 8. (d) 9. (c) 10. (c) 11. (c) 12. (b)
13. (c) 14. (c) 15. (a)

Chapter Exercise

1. (d) 2. (d) 3. (c) 4. (d) 5. (b) 6. (b)
7. (d) 8. (b) 9. (d) 10. (c) 11. (c) 12. (b)
13. (d) 14. (b) 15. (a) 16. (c) 17. (a) 18. (b)
19. (d) 20. (a) 21. (b) 22. (a) 23. (c) 24. (d)
25. (a) 26. (d) 27. (b) 28. (a) 29. (b) 30. (c)
31. (a,b,c) 32. (b,c,d) 33. (a,c) 34. (a,d) 35. (a,b) 36. (c, d)
37. (a,b,c,d) 38. (a,b,c,d) 39. (a,b,c) 40. (a,c)
41. (a,b,c) 42. (b,c) 43. (a,b,c,d) 44. (b,c,d)
45. (a,c) 46. (c) 47. (d) 48. (b) 49. (b) 50. (d)
51. (c) 52. (b) 53. (c) 54. (c) 55. (d) 56. (c)
57. (a) 58. (c) 59. (c) 60. (d) 61. (c) 62. (a)
63. (c) 64. (c) 65. (b) 66. (a) 67. (d) 68. (d)
69. (c) 70. (a) 71. (b) 72. (c) 73. (5) 74. (3)
75. (2) 76. (5) 77. (4)
78. (1) 79. (1) 80. (0) 81. (2) 82. (2)
83. (A) → (q,r); (B) → (p,r); (C) → (p,r); (D) → (q,r,s)
84. (A) → (s); (B) → (p); (C) → (r); (D) → (q)
85. (A) → (p,r,s); (B) → (p,r,s); (C) → (s); (D) → (q,r)
86. (A) → (q); (B) → (r); (C) → (p); (D) → (s)
87. (A) → (r); (B) → (s); (C) → (p); (D) → (q)
88. (A) → (q); (B) → (s); (C) → (p); (D) → (r)
89. (a) 90. (a) 91. (a) 92. (c) 93. (c)
94. (a) 95. (d) 96. (c) 97. (d) 98. (c)
99. (a) 100. (a)
101. $\left(\frac{1}{5}\right)$ 102. $\left(\frac{5}{54}\right)$ 103. $\left(\frac{(N-r)(N-r-1)}{(N-1)(N-2)}\right)$
105. (12) 106. $\left(\frac{213}{1001}\right)$ 107. $\left(\frac{a}{a+b}\right)$
108. $\left(\frac{377}{4096}\right)$ 109. $\left(\frac{1}{2}\right)$ 112. $\left(\frac{{}^nC_r 3^r}{4^n}\right)$
116. $\frac{1}{7}$ 117. (a) 118. (a) 119. (d) 120. (a)
121. (i) (b), (ii) (a), (iii) (b) 122. (d) 123. (c) 124. (d)
125. (c) 126. (d) 127. (b) 128. (d) 129. (b) 130. (b)
131. (a) 132. (a) 133. (b) 134. (d) 135. (b) 136. (b)
137. (c) 138. (c) 139. (b) 140. (a) 141. (b) 142. (d)
143. (a, d) 144. (b) 145. (a) 146. (a) 147. (b,d) 148. (a)
149. (a,b) 150. (d) 151. (b) 152. (a) 153. (b) 154. (d)
155. (a) 156. (a) 157. (a) 158. (b) 159. (b) 160. (c)
161. (8) 162. (a,b) 163. (c,d) 164. (c) 165. (c) 166. (b)
167. (c) 168. (b) 169. (c) 170. (c)

Solutions

1.

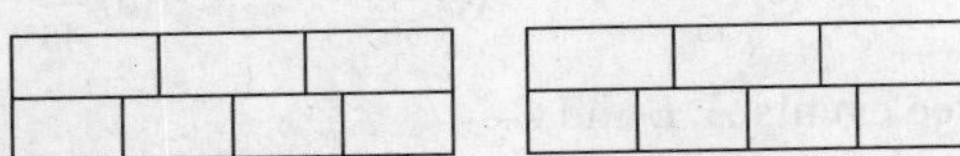

$n(S)$ = Number of total ways $= {}^{14}P_{12} = \frac{14!}{2!} = 7 \times 13!$

The girls can be seated together in the back seats leaving a corner seat in $4 \times 3! = 24$ ways and the boys can be seated in the remaining 11 seats in

${}^{11}P_9 = \frac{11!}{2!} = \frac{1}{2} \times 11!$ ways

$\therefore n(E)$ = Number of favourable ways $= 24 \times \frac{1}{2} \times 11! = 12!$

The required probability $= \frac{n(E)}{n(S)} = \frac{12!}{7 \times 13!} = \frac{1}{91}$

2. For non-leap year

The probability of 53 Sundays $= \frac{1}{7}$

For leap year

The probability of 53 Sundays $= \frac{2}{7}$

$\therefore$ Required probability $= \frac{3}{4} \times \frac{1}{7} + \frac{1}{4} \times \frac{2}{7} = \frac{5}{28}$

3. Let us consider two events:

A : The leap year contains 53 Sundays.

B : The leap year contains 53 Mondays. We have,

$P(A) = \frac{2}{7}, P(B) = \frac{2}{7}$ and $P(A \cap B) = \frac{1}{7}$

$\therefore$ Required probability $= P(A \cup B)$

$= P(A) + P(B) - P(A \cap B)$

$= \frac{2}{7} + \frac{2}{7} - \frac{1}{7} = \frac{3}{7}$

4. Let us consider two events:

A : Numbers divisible by 4.

B : Numbers divisible by 7.

We have, $A = \{104, 108, \ldots, 196\}$

$\Rightarrow n(A) = 24$

$B = \{105, 112, \ldots, 196\}$

$n(B) = 14$ and $A \cap B = \{112, 140, 168, 196\}$

$\Rightarrow n(A \cap B) = 4$

$n(E)$ = Number of favourable ways $n(A \cup B)$

$= n(A) + n(B) - n(A \cap B) = 34$

$n(S)$ = Total number of ways $= 99$

$\therefore$ Required probability $= \frac{n(E)}{n(S)} = \frac{34}{99}$

5. $n(S)$ = Total number of ways $= {}^{100}C_2 = 50 \times 99$

The product is divisible by 3, if atleast one of the two numbers is divisible by 3.

Let $n(E)$ = Number of ways, if atleast one of the two numbers is divisible by 3.

and $n(\overline{E})$ = Number of ways, if none of the two numbers chosen is divisible by 3.

$= {}^{67}C_2 = \frac{67 \times 66}{1 \times 2} = 67 \times 33$

$\therefore$ Required probability $= \frac{n(E)}{n(S)} = \frac{n(S) - n(\overline{E})}{n(S)}$

$= 1 - \frac{67 \times 33}{50 \times 99} = \frac{83}{150}$

6. $n(S)$ = Total number of ways $= {}^{10}C_3 = \frac{10 \cdot 9 \cdot 8}{1 \cdot 2 \cdot 3} = 120$

The product of two numbers is equal to third number, the favourable cases are 2, 3, 6; 2, 4, 8; 2, 5, 10

$\therefore n(E)$ = The number of favourable cases = 3

$\therefore$ Required probability $= \frac{n(E)}{n(S)} = \frac{3}{120} = \frac{1}{40}$

7. $n(S)$ = Total number of ways $= {}^nP_n = n!$

Considering digits 1, 2, 3, 4, ..., k as one digit, we have $(n - k + 1)$ digits which can be arranged $= (n - k + 1)!$

$\therefore n(E)$ = Number of favourable ways $= (n - k + 1)!$

Hence, required probability $= \frac{n(E)}{n(S)} = \frac{(n - k + 1)!}{n!}$

8. $n(S)$ = Total number of ways $= {}^nP_n = n!$

The number of ways in which the digits 1, 2, 3, 4, ..., k $(k < n)$ occur together $= k!(n - k + 1)!$

Hence, required probability $= \frac{n(E)}{n(S)} = \frac{k!(n - k + 1)!}{n!} = \frac{(n - k + 1)}{{}^nC_k}$

9. Let a, b, c and d are four different numbers out of $\{1, 2, 3, 4, 5, 6\}$.

$\Rightarrow$ (a, a, a, a) can appear in ${}^6C_1 = 6$ ways

$\Rightarrow$ (a, a, a, b) can appear in $2 \times {}^6C_2 = 30$ ways

$\Rightarrow$ (a, a, b, b) can appear in ${}^6C_2 = 15$ ways

$\Rightarrow$ (a, a, b, c) can appear in $3 \times {}^6C_3 = 60$ ways

$\Rightarrow$ (a, b, c, d) can appear in ${}^6C_4 = 15$ ways

$\therefore$ Required probability $= \frac{60 + 15}{6 + 30 + 15 + 60 + 15} = \frac{75}{126} = \frac{25}{42}$

10. Let $ABCDEF$ be the regular hexagon.

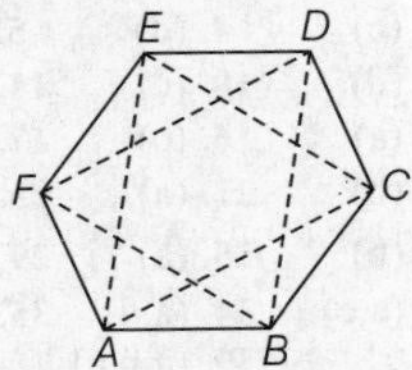

Number of total triangles $= {}^6C_3 = 20$ ways

For the favourable event, the vertices should be either A, C, E or B, D, F

$\therefore$ The required probability $= \dfrac{\text{Favourable ways}}{\text{Total ways}} = \dfrac{2}{20} = \dfrac{1}{10}$

11. Total number of ways to choose two squares

$$= {}^{64}C_2 = \frac{64 \cdot 63}{2} = 32 \cdot 63$$

For favourable ways we must chosen two consecutive small squares for any row or any columns.

$\therefore$ Number of favourable ways $= 7 \cdot 8 + 8 \cdot 7 = 2 \cdot 8 \cdot 7$

$\therefore$ Required probability $= \dfrac{2 \cdot 8 \cdot 7}{32 \cdot 63} = \dfrac{1}{18}$

12. In the word MUMBAI, there are 5 adjacent pairs of letters of which only one gives AI.

$$\therefore \text{ Required probability} = \frac{\frac{1}{5}}{\frac{1}{6} + \frac{1}{5} + \frac{1}{7} + \frac{1}{4} + \frac{1}{5}} = \frac{84}{403}$$

13. Numbers on die are 1, 2, 3, 4, 5, 6.

Prime numbers are 2, 3, 5 and non-prime numbers are 1, 4, 6.

Now, let weight assigned to non-prime numbers is λ, then weight assigned to prime number is 2λ.

$\therefore \lambda + 2\lambda + 2\lambda + \lambda + 2\lambda + \lambda = 1$

$\Rightarrow \qquad \lambda = \dfrac{1}{9}$

$\therefore$ Probability that an odd number will be show up when the die is tossed 1 or 3 or 5.

$$\lambda + 2\lambda + 2\lambda = 5\lambda = \frac{5}{9}$$

14. We have,

$(X = 7) = \{07, 16, 25, 34, 43, 52, 61, 70\}$

and $\quad (Y = 0) = \{00, 01, 02, \ldots, 10, 20, 30, \ldots, 90\}$

Thus, $\quad (X = 7) \cap (Y = 0) = \{07, 70\}$

$$\therefore \quad P\left(\frac{X = 7}{Y = 0}\right) = \frac{P\{(X = 7) \cap (Y = 0)\}}{P(Y = 0)} = \frac{2}{19}$$

15. The probability of not drawing the ace in the first draw, in the second draw and in the third draw are (here all spades i.e., 13 cards) $\dfrac{12}{13}, \dfrac{11}{12}, \dfrac{10}{11}$, respectively.

Probability of drawing ace of spades in the 4th draw

$= \dfrac{1}{10}$ (only one ace and remaining cards = 10)

$\therefore$ Required probability $= \dfrac{12}{13} \times \dfrac{11}{12} \times \dfrac{10}{11} \times \dfrac{1}{10} = \dfrac{1}{13}$

16. $n(S) =$ Total number of ways $= {}^{25}C_1 = 25$

Set of composite numbers = {4, 6, 8, 9, 10, 12, 14, 15, 16, 18, 20, 21, 22, 24, 25} and set of non-composite numbers = {1, 2, 3, 5, 7, 11, 13, 17, 19, 23}

Now, set of composite numbers of the form $5k (k \in N)$ = {10, 15, 20, 25}

and set of non-composite numbers of the form $2k (k \in N) = \{2\}$

$\therefore$ Required prabability $= \dfrac{{}^4C_1 + {}^1C_1}{{}^{25}C_1} = \dfrac{5}{25} = 0.2$

17. $n(S) =$ Total number of ways $= {}^{50}C_5$

Now, x_3 is fixed to be 30 and x_1, x_2 (two numbers) are to be chosen from first 29 numbers and x_4, x_5 (two numbers) from last 20 numbers are to be chosen.

$\therefore$ $n(E) =$ Number of favourable ways $= {}^{29}C_2 \times {}^{20}C_2$

Hence, required probability $= \dfrac{n(E)}{n(S)} = \dfrac{{}^{29}C_2 \times {}^{20}C_2}{{}^{50}C_5}$

18. The points are 2, 2, 2, 2 or 2, 2, 2, 1

$\therefore$ Required probability

$= (0.5)^4 + {}^4C_1 \times (0.5)^3 \times (0.05)^1 = 0.0875$

19. $n(S) =$ Total number of ways $= 6^3 = 216$

$n(E) =$ Number of favourable ways $= 2 \times {}^6C_2 \times \dfrac{3!}{2!} = 90$

$\therefore$ Required probability $= \dfrac{n(E)}{n(S)} = \dfrac{90}{216}$

20. $n(S) =$ Total number of ways $= 6 \times 6 \times 6 = 216$

$n(E) =$ Number of favourable cases

$= \text{Coefficient of } x^k \text{ in } (x + x^2 + x^3 + x^4 + x^5 + x^6)^3$

$= \text{Coefficient of } x^{k-3} \text{ in } (1 + x + x^2 + x^3 + x^4 + x^5)^3$

$= \text{Coefficient of } x^{k-3} \text{ in } (1 - x^6)^3 (1 - x)^{-3}$

$= \text{Coefficient of } x^{k-3} \text{ in } (1 - x)^{-3} \qquad [\because 0 \le k - 3 \le 5]$

$= \text{Coefficient of } x^{k-3} \text{ in } (1 + {}^3C_1 x + \ldots)$

$= {}^{k-1}C_{k-3} = {}^{k-1}C_2 = \dfrac{(k-1)(k-2)}{2}$

$\therefore$ Required probability $= \dfrac{n(E)}{n(S)} = \dfrac{(k-1)(k-2)}{432}$

21. $n(S) =$ Total number of ways $= 1000$

The favourable cases that the sum of the digits of the marked number on the page is equal to 9 are one digit number or two digits numbers or three digits numbers, if three digit number is abc. Then, $a + b + c = 9$; $0 \le a, b, c \le 9$

$\therefore \qquad n(E) =$ Number of favourable ways

$=$ Number of solutions of the equation

$= {}^{9+3-1}C_{3-1} = {}^{11}C_2 = 55$

$\therefore$ Required probability $= \dfrac{n(E)}{n(S)} = \dfrac{55}{1000} = \dfrac{11}{200}$

22. $n(S) =$ The total number of ways of choosing the tickets

$= 4 \times 4 \times 4 \times 4 = 256$

$n(E) =$ The number of ways in which the sum can be 23

$= \text{Coefficient of } x^{23} \text{ in } (1 + x + x^{10} + x^{11})^4$

$= \text{Coefficient of } x^{23} \text{ in } (1 + x^4) + (1 + x^{10})^4$

$= \text{Coefficient of } x^{23} \text{ in } (1 + 4x + 6x^2 + 4x^3 + x^4)$

$\times (1 + 4x^{10} + 6x^{20})$

$= 4 \times 6 = 24$

The probability of required event $= \dfrac{n(E)}{n(S)} = \dfrac{24}{256} = \dfrac{3}{32}$

23. Total coupons = 15

$1 \le$ selected coupon number ≤ 9 i.e., 1, 2, 3, 4, 5, 6, 7, 8, 9

$\therefore$ Probability of one selected coupon $= \frac{9}{15} = \frac{3}{5}$

Hence, the required probability

$$= \left(\frac{3}{5}\right) \times \left(\frac{3}{5}\right) \times \ldots \times 7 \text{ times} = \left(\frac{3}{5}\right)^7$$

24. Let X denote the largest number on the 3 tickets drawn.

We have, $P(X \le 7) = \left(\frac{7}{20}\right)^3$ and $P(X \le 6) = \left(\frac{6}{20}\right)^3$

Thus, $P(X = 7) = P(X \le 7) - P(X \le 6) = \left(\frac{7}{20}\right)^3 - \left(\frac{6}{20}\right)^3$

25. Total number = 6 (i.e., 1, 2, 3, 4, 5, 6)

Favourable number = 2, 3, 4, 5 = 4

Probability of favourable number in one draw $= \frac{4}{6} = \frac{2}{3}$

$\therefore$ Required probability $= \left(\frac{2}{3}\right)^4 = \frac{16}{81}$

26. We have, $P(E_i) = \frac{2}{4} = \frac{1}{2}$ for $i = 1, 2, 3$

Also, for $i \ne j$, $P(E_i \cap E_j) = \frac{1}{4} = P(E_i)\, P(E_j)$

Therefore, E_i and E_j are independent for $i \ne j$.

Also, $P(E_1 \cap E_2 \cap E_3) = \frac{1}{4} \ne P(E_1) P(E_2) P(E_3)$

$\therefore$ E_1, E_2 and E_3 are not independent.

27. Let x and y are two non-negative integers are chosen such that $x^2 + y^2$ is divisible by 10.

By the division algorithm, there exist integers x_1, y_1, a_1 and b_1 such that $x = 10x_1 + a_1$ and $y = 10y_1 + b_1$ with $0 \le a, b_1 \le 9$.

Thus, we can write

$x^2 + y^2 = 100(x_1^2 + y_1^2) + 20(a_1x_1 + b_1y_1) + (a_1^2 + b_1^2)$

We see that $x^2 + y^2$ will be divisible by 10 if and only if $a_1^2 + b_1^2$ is divisible by 10. Now, there are 10 choices each for a_1 and b_1, so that there are $10 \times 10 = 100$ ways of choosing them. The pairs (a_1, b_1) for which $a_1^2 + b_1^2$ is divisible by 10 are follows:

(0, 0), (1, 3), (1, 7), (2, 4), (2, 6), (3, 1), (3, 9), (4, 2), (4, 8), (5, 5), (6, 2), (6, 8), (7, 1), (7, 9), (8, 4), (8, 6), (9, 3), (9, 7)

Therefore, 18 distinct ways.

$\therefore$ Required probability $= \frac{18}{100} = \frac{9}{50}$

28. Required probability $= \frac{\text{Area of strips region}}{\text{Area of dotted region}}$

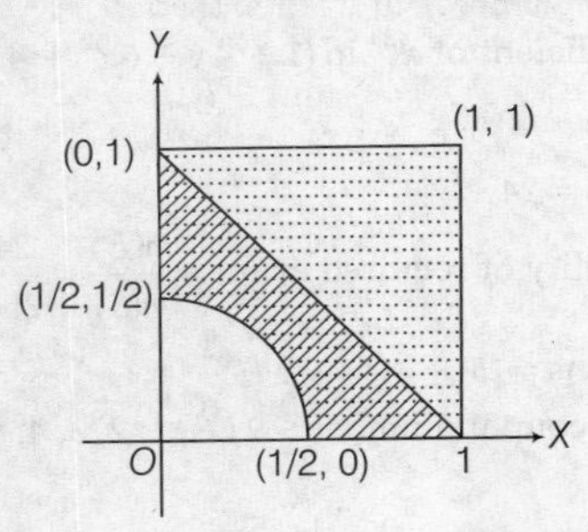

$$= \frac{\frac{1}{2} \times 1 \times 1 - \frac{1}{4} \times \pi \left(\frac{1}{2}\right)^2}{1 \times 1 - \frac{1}{4} \times \pi \left(\frac{1}{2}\right)^2} = \frac{8 - \pi}{16 - \pi}$$

29. When the two equal sides are 1 each, then third side could be only 1.

When the two equal sides are 2 each, then third side can take values 1, 2, 3.

When two equal sides are 3 each, then third side can take values 1, 2, 3, 4, 5. When the two equal sides are 4 each, then third side can take values 1, 2, 3, 4, 5, 6 same in the case when two equal sides are 5 and 6.

$\therefore$ Total number of triangles = 1 + 3 + 5 + 6 + 6 + 6 = 27

Required probability $= \frac{1}{27}$

30. Required probability

$$= \frac{\left(\frac{1}{2}\right)^5 \times \left(\frac{1}{2}\right)^5}{\left(\sum_{r=0}^{5} {}^5C_r \left(\frac{1}{2}\right)^r \left(\frac{1}{2}\right)^{5-r}\right)^2} = \frac{1}{\left(\sum_{r=0}^{5} {}^5C_r\right)^2} = \frac{1}{{}^{10}C_5}$$

31. $P(A \cup B) = P(A) + P(B) - P(A \cap B)$

$P(A \cap B) = P(A) + P(B) - P(A \cup B)$

$\therefore 0 \le P(A \cup B) \le 1 - 1 \le -P(A \cup B) \le 0$

$P(A) + P(B) - 1 \le P(A) + P(B) - P(A \cup B) \le P(A) + P(B)$

32. E and F are independent events. Then,

$$P(E \cap F) = P(E) \cdot P(F) \quad \text{...(i)}$$

Option (a) is obviously not true. So, check for options (b), (c) and (d)

$$\begin{aligned} P(E \cap \bar{F}) &= P(E) - P(E \cap F) \\ &= P(E) - P(E) \cdot P(F) \quad \text{[from Eq. (i)]} \\ &= P(E)[1 - P(F)] \\ &= P(E) \cdot P(\bar{F}) \end{aligned}$$

$\therefore$ E and $\bar{F}$ are independent events.

Now,
$$\begin{aligned} P(\bar{E} \cap \bar{F}) &= P(\overline{E \cup F}) \\ &= 1 - P(E \cup F) \\ &= 1 - [P(E) + P(F) - P(E \cap F)] \\ &= [1 - P(E)] - P(F) + P(E) \cdot P(F) \\ &= P(\bar{E}) - P(F)[1 - P(E)] \\ &= P(\bar{E})\,[1 - P(F)] \\ &= P(\bar{E}) \cdot P(\bar{F}) \end{aligned}$$

$\therefore$ $\bar{E}$ and $\bar{F}$ are independent events.

Again,
$$\begin{aligned} P\left(\frac{E}{F}\right) + P\left(\frac{\bar{E}}{F}\right) &= \frac{P(E \cap F)}{P(F)} + \frac{P(\bar{E} \cap F)}{P(F)} \\ &= \frac{P(E) \cdot P(F)}{P(F)} + \frac{P(\bar{E}) \cdot P(F)}{P(F)} \\ &= P(E) + P(\bar{E}) = 1 \end{aligned}$$

33. We know that, $P(A \cap B) \ge P(A) + P(B) - 1$ ...(i)

$$P\left(\frac{A}{B}\right) = \frac{P(A \cap B)}{P(B)} \quad [P(B) \ne 0]$$

$\Rightarrow \quad P\left(\frac{A}{B}\right) \geq \frac{P(A) + P(B) - 1}{P(B)}$ [from Eq. (i)]

Option (a) is true.

$$P(A \cap \overline{B}) = P(A) - P(A \cap B)$$

Option (b) is not true.

$$P(A \cup B) = P(A) + P(B) - P(A \cap B)$$

If A and B are independent events, then $P(A \cap B) = P(A) \cdot P(B)$.

Then, $P(A \cup B) = P(A) + P(B) - P(A) \cdot P(B)$

$$= P(A) + P(B)[1 - P(A)] + 1 - 1$$

$$= 1 + P(B) P(\overline{A}) - P(\overline{A}) \quad [\because P(\overline{A}) = 1 - P(A)]$$

$$= 1 + P(\overline{A})[P(B) - 1] = 1 - P(\overline{A}) \cdot P(\overline{B})$$

Option (c) is true.

If A and B are disjoint, then $P(A \cap B) = 0$.

Then, $P(A \cup B) = 1 - P(\overline{A}) P(\overline{B})$ does not hold.

34. E and F are two independent events

$$P(E \cap F) = P(E) \cdot P(F) \quad \text{...(i)}$$

$$P(E \cap F) = \frac{1}{12} \quad \text{...(ii)}$$

$$P(\overline{E} \cap \overline{F}) = \frac{1}{2}$$

$\Rightarrow \quad 1 - P(E \cup F) = \frac{1}{2}$

$\Rightarrow \quad P(E) + P(F) - P(E \cap F) = \frac{1}{2}$

$\Rightarrow \quad P(E) + P(F) - \frac{1}{12} = \frac{1}{2}$

$\Rightarrow \quad P(E) + P(F) = \frac{1}{2} + \frac{1}{12}$

$\Rightarrow \quad P(E) + P(F) = \frac{7}{12} \quad \text{...(iii)}$

From Eqs. (i) and (ii), we get,

$$P(E) \cdot P(F) = \frac{1}{12}$$

$$P(E) = \frac{1}{12P(F)}$$

Put this value in Eq. (iii) we get

$$P(F) + \frac{1}{12P(F)} = \frac{7}{12}$$

Let $\quad P(F) = x$

Then, $\quad x + \frac{1}{12x} = \frac{7}{12}$

$\Rightarrow \quad \frac{12x^2 + 1}{12x} = \frac{7}{12} \Rightarrow 12x^2 - 7x + 1 = 0$

$$12x^2 - 4x - 3x + 1 = 0$$

$\Rightarrow \quad 4x(3x - 1) - 1(3x - 1) = 0$

$$(3x - 1)(4x - 1) = 0 \Rightarrow x = \frac{1}{3} \text{ or } \frac{1}{4}$$

$\therefore \quad P(E) = \frac{1}{4}, P(F) = \frac{1}{3}$

or $\quad P(E) = \frac{1}{3}, P(F) = \frac{1}{4}$

35. $P\left(\frac{E}{F}\right) + P\left(\frac{\overline{E}}{F}\right) = \frac{P(E \cap F)}{P(F)} + \frac{P(\overline{E} \cap F)}{P(F)}$

$$= \frac{P(E \cap F) + P(\overline{E} \cap F)}{P(F)} = \frac{P(E \cap F) + P(F) - P(E \cap F)}{P(F)}$$

$$= \frac{P(F)}{P(F)} = 1$$

and $P\left(\frac{E}{\overline{F}}\right) + P\left(\frac{\overline{E}}{\overline{F}}\right) = \frac{P(E \cap \overline{F})}{P(\overline{F})} + \frac{P(\overline{E} \cap \overline{F})}{P(\overline{F})}$

$$= \frac{[P(E) - P(E \cap F)] + [1 - P(E \cup F)]}{P(\overline{F})}$$

$$= \frac{[P(E \cup F) - P(F)] + [1 - P(E \cup F)]}{P(\overline{F})}$$

$$= \frac{1 - P(F)}{P(\overline{F})} = \frac{P(\overline{F})}{P(\overline{F})} = 1$$

36. $P(B - A) = P(B \cap \overline{A}) = P(B) - P(A \cap B)$

Option (a) is not correct.

$P(A' \cup B') = 1 - P(A \cap B) = 1 - P(A) \cdot P(B)$ [by given condition]

$P(A') + P(B') = 1 - P(A) + 1 - P(B) = 2 - [P(A) + P(B)]$

Option (b) is not correct $P[(A \cup B)'] = 1 - P(A \cup B)$

$$= 1 - [P(A) + P(B) - P(A) \cdot P(B)] \quad \text{[by given condition]}$$

$$= 1 - P(A) - P(B)[1 - P(A)]$$

$$= P(\overline{A}) - P(B) \cdot P(\overline{A}) = P(\overline{A}) \cdot P(\overline{B})$$

Option (c) is correct.

$$P\left(\frac{A}{B}\right) = \frac{P(A \cap B)}{P(B)} = \frac{P(A) \cdot P(B)}{P(B)} = P(A)$$

37. Required probability $= P(A - B) + P(B - A)$

$$= P(A \cap \overline{B}) + P(B \cap \overline{A})$$

$$= P(A) - P(A \cap B) + P(B) - P(A \cap B)$$

$$= P(A) + P(B) - 2P(A \cap B)$$

So, options (a) and (b) are true.

$P(A - B) + P(B - A) = P(A \cup B) - P(A \cap B)$ [by venn diagram]

So, option (c) is also true.

$$P(A') + P(B') - 2P(A' \cap B') = 1 - P(A) + 1 - P(B) - 2 + 2P(A \cup B)$$

$$= 2P(A \cup B) - P(A) - P(B)$$

$$= 2P(A) + 2P(B) - 2P(A \cap B) - P(A) - P(B)$$

$$= P(A) + P(B) - 2P(A \cap B)$$

$\therefore$ Option (d) is also true.

38. A and B are independent events, then $P(A \cap B) = P(A) \cdot P(B)$

$$P(A) = \frac{1}{2} \text{ and } P(B) = \frac{1}{5}$$

$$P(A \cap B) = \frac{1}{10}$$

$$P(A \cup B) = P(A) + P(B) - P(A \cap B)$$

$$= \frac{1}{2} + \frac{1}{5} - \frac{1}{10} = \frac{5 + 2 - 1}{10} = \frac{6}{10} = \frac{3}{5}$$

$$P\left(\frac{A}{B}\right) = P(A) = \frac{1}{2}$$

$$P\left(\frac{A}{A \cup B}\right) = \frac{P[A \cap (A \cup B)]}{P(A \cup B)} = \frac{P(A)}{P(A \cup B)} = \frac{\frac{1}{2}}{\frac{3}{5}} = \frac{5}{6}$$

$$P\left(\frac{A \cap B}{A' \cup B'}\right) = P\left(\frac{A \cap B}{(A \cap B)'}\right) = \frac{P[(A \cap B) \cap (A \cap B)']}{P(A \cap B)'} = 0$$

39. Let A, B and C be the event that the student is successful in tests I, II and III, respectively.

P (the student is successful)

$= P(A \cap B \cap C') + P(A \cap B' \cap C) + P(A \cap B \cap C)$

$= P(A) \cdot P(B) \cdot P(C') + P(A) \cdot P(B') \cdot P(C) + P(A) \cdot P(B) \cdot P(C)$

$\therefore$ A, B and C are independent events.

$= pq\left(1 - \frac{1}{2}\right) + p(1-q)\left(\frac{1}{2}\right) + pq\frac{1}{2}$

$= \frac{1}{2}[pq + p(1-q) + pq] = \frac{1}{2}p(1+q)$

$\therefore \quad \frac{1}{2} = \frac{1}{2}p(1+q) \Rightarrow p(1+q) = 1$

which is satisfied for all pairs of values in (a), (b) and (c). Also, it is satisfied for infinitely many values as p and q. For instance, when $p = \frac{n}{n+1}$ and $q = \frac{1}{n}$, where n is any positive integer.

40. Total number of subset of set contain n elements $= 2^n$

Number of ways choosing A and $B = 2^n \cdot 2^n = 2^{2n}$.

The number of subset of x which contains exactly r elements $= {}^nC_r$

$\therefore$ The number of ways of choosing A and B, so that they have the same number of elements

$$= ({}^nC_0)^2 + ({}^nC_1)^2 + \ldots + ({}^nC_n)^2 = {}^{2n}C_n$$

$$= \frac{1 \cdot 2 \cdot 3 \ldots (2n-1)(2n)}{n!\,n!} = \frac{2^n(1 \cdot 3 \cdot 5 \ldots (2n-1))}{n!}$$

41. The number of ways in which m boys and m girls can take their seats around a circle is $(2m-1)!$

(a) We make the girls sit first around the circle. This can be done in $(m-1)!$ ways, after this boys can take their seats in $(m!)$ ways.

$\therefore$ Favourable number of ways $= m!(m-1)!$

Required probability $= \frac{m!(m-1)!}{(2m-1)!} = \frac{1}{{}^{2m-1}C_m}$

(b) Similarly as (a)

(c) Similarly as (a)

(d) Required probability $= \frac{m!m!}{(2m-1)!} \neq \frac{1}{{}^{2m-1}C_m}$

42. According to the question,

$$(m + p + c) - mp - mc - pc + mpc = \frac{3}{4} \quad \ldots\text{(i)}$$

$$mp(1-c) + mc(1-p) + pc(1-m) = \frac{2}{5}$$

or
$$mp + mc + pc - 3mpc = \frac{2}{5} \quad \ldots\text{(ii)}$$

Also,
$$mp + pc + mc - 2mpc = \frac{1}{2} \quad \ldots\text{(iii)}$$

From Eqs. (ii) and (iii), we get

$$mpc = \frac{1}{2} - \frac{2}{5} = \frac{1}{10}$$

$$\therefore \quad mp + mc + pc = \frac{2}{5} + \frac{3}{10} = \frac{7}{10}$$

$$m + p + c = \frac{3}{4} + \frac{7}{10} - \frac{1}{10} = \frac{27}{20}$$

43. Favourable number of cases $= {}^{n-3}P_2$

Total number of cases $= {}^nP_2$

$\therefore$ Required probability $= \frac{{}^{n-3}P_2}{{}^nP_2} = \frac{{}^{n-3}C_2 \times 2!}{{}^nC_2 \times 2!} = \frac{{}^{n-3}C_2}{{}^nC_2}$

$$= \frac{\frac{(n-3)(n-4)}{2 \times 1}}{\frac{n(n-1)}{2 \times 1}} = \frac{(n-3)(n-4)}{n(n-1)}$$

44. $A =$ The event of (x, y) belonging to the area $OEBAO$

$B =$ The event of (x, y) belonging to the area $ODBCO$

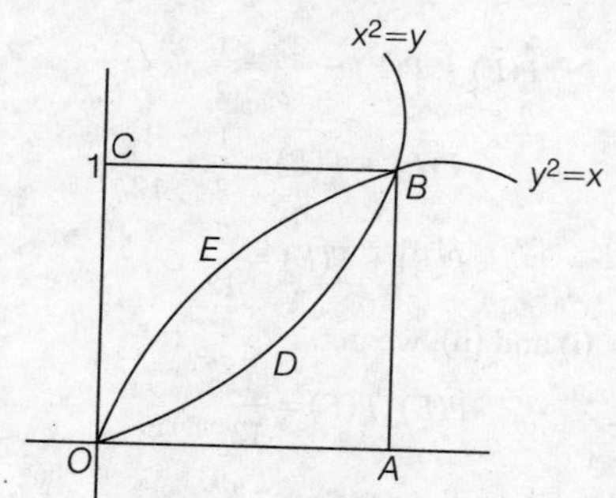

$$\therefore \quad P(A) = \frac{\text{area of } OEBAO}{\text{area of } OABCO} = \frac{\int_0^1 \sqrt{x}\,dx}{1 \times 1} = \frac{2}{3}$$

and
$$P(B) = \frac{\text{area of } ODBCO}{\text{area of } OABCO} = \frac{\int_0^1 \sqrt{y}\,dy}{1 \times 1} = \frac{2}{3}$$

and
$$P(A \cap B) = \frac{\text{area of } ODBEO}{\text{area of } OABCO} = \frac{\int_0^1 \sqrt{x}\,dx - \int_0^1 x^2 dx}{1 \times 1} = \frac{1}{3}$$

$\therefore \; P(A) + P(B) = \frac{2}{3} + \frac{2}{3} \neq 1.$

So, A and B are not exhaustive,

$$P(A) \cdot P(B) = \frac{2}{3} \cdot \frac{2}{3} \neq \frac{1}{3}.$$

So, A and B are not independent and $P(A \cup B) = 1$, $P(A) + P(B) \neq P(A \cup B)$.

So, A and B are not mutually exclusive.

45. Let $P(k) \propto \frac{1}{k^4} \Rightarrow P(k) = \frac{\lambda}{k^4}$

where λ is proportionality constant

Then $\sum_{k=1}^{2n} \frac{\lambda}{k^4} = 1 \Rightarrow \lambda \sum_{k=1}^{2n} \frac{1}{k^4} = 1$

$$\therefore \quad \alpha = \sum_{k=1}^{n} P(2k-1) = \lambda \sum_{k=1}^{n} \frac{1}{(2k-1)^4}$$

and $$\beta = \sum_{k=1}^{n} P(2k) = \lambda \sum_{k=1}^{n} \frac{1}{(2k)^4} < \lambda \sum_{k=1}^{n} \frac{1}{(2k-1)^4}$$

$\Rightarrow \quad \beta < \alpha$ and $\alpha + \beta = 1$

Then, $1 - \alpha < \alpha$ and $\beta < 1 - \beta$

$\therefore \quad \alpha > \frac{1}{2}$ and $\beta < \frac{1}{2}$

46. Roots of $x^2 + px + q = 0$ are real and distinct, if $p^2 > 4q$.

Value of p	Possible values of q
1	No value
2	No value
3	1, 2
4	1, 2, 3
5	1, 2, 3, 4, 5, 6
6	1, 2, 3,..., 8
7	1, 2, 3,..., 10
8	1, 2, 3,..., 10
9	1, 2, 3,..., 10
10	1, 2, 3,..., 10

$\therefore$ Number of favourable ways
$= 2 + 3 + 6 + 8 + 10 + 10 + 10 + 10 = 59$
and total ways $= 10 \times 10 = 100$

Hence, the required probability $= \frac{59}{100} = 0.59$

47. Roots of $x^2 + px + q = 0$ are equal, if $p^2 = 4q$
i.e., p^2 must be even.

Value of p	Possible values of q
2	1
4	4
6	9
8	No value
10	No value

$\therefore$ Number of favourable ways $= 1 + 1 + 1 = 3$
and total ways $= 10 \times 10 = 100$

Hence, the required probability $= \frac{3}{100} = 0.03$

48. Roots of $x^2 + px + q = 0$ are imaginary, if $p^2 < 4q$

Hence, the required probability $= 1 -$(Probability that roots of $x^2 + px + q = 0$ are real) $= 1 - (0.59 - 0.03) = 1 - 0.62$
$= 0.38$

49. X can win after the $(n+1)$ th game in the following two mutually exclusive ways.

(i) X wins exactly one of the first n games draws $(n-1)$ games and wins the $(n+1)$th game.

$\therefore$ Probability, $P_1 = ({}^nP_1 ab^{n-1})a = na^2b^{n-1}$

(ii) X losses exactly one of the first n games, wins exactly one of the first n games and draws $(n-2)$ games and wins the $(n+1)$ th game.

$\therefore$ Probability, $P_2 = ({}^nP_2(ac)b^{n-2})a = n(n-1)a^2b^{n-2}c$

Hence, the probability that X wins two match after $(n+1)$th game.

$$P_n = P_1 + P_2 = na^2b^{n-2}[b + (n-1)c]$$

50. Put $n = 3$ in solution of question 4 and interchange a and c, then required probability $= 3c^2 \cdot b^1(b + 2a) = 3bc^2(2a + b)$

51. The probability that X wins the match

$$= \sum_{n=1}^{\infty} Pn = \sum_{n=1}^{\infty} na^2b^{n-1} + \sum_{n=1}^{\infty} n(n-1)a^2b^{n-2}c$$

$$= \frac{a^2}{b} \sum_{n=1}^{\infty} nb^n + \frac{a^2c}{b^2} \sum_{n=1}^{\infty} n(n-1)b^n$$

$$= \frac{a^2}{b} \cdot \frac{b}{(1-b)^2} + \frac{a^2c}{b^2} \cdot \frac{2b^2}{(1-b)^3}$$

[sum of infinite AGS]

$$= \frac{a^2(1 - b + 2c)}{(1-b)^3} = \frac{a^2(a + 3c)}{(a+c)^3} \quad \left| \begin{array}{l} \because a + b + c = 1 \\ \because 1 - b = a + c \end{array} \right.$$

52. $\because P(E_\lambda) \propto \lambda^2$

$\Rightarrow P(E_\lambda) = k\lambda^2$, where k is proportionality constant.

$\because E_0, E_1, E_2, \ldots, E_n$ are mutually exclusive and exhaustive events

We have, $P(E_0) + P(E_1) + P(E_2) + \ldots + P(E_n) = 1$

$$0 + k(1)^1 + k(2)^2 + \ldots + k(n)^2 = 1$$

$$\Rightarrow \quad k\left(\sum n^2\right) = 1$$

$$\therefore \quad k = \frac{1}{\sum n^2} \quad \ldots(i)$$

53. $P(A) = \sum_{\lambda=0}^{n} P(E_\lambda) \cdot P\left(\frac{A}{E_\lambda}\right)$

$$= \sum_{\lambda=0}^{n} \left(k\lambda^2 \times \frac{\lambda}{n}\right) = \frac{k}{n} \sum_{\lambda=1}^{n} \lambda^3 = \frac{k}{n} \sum_{\lambda=0}^{n} \lambda^3$$

$$= \frac{k}{n} \sum n^3 = \frac{1}{n} \times \frac{1}{\sum n^2} \times \sum n^3 \quad \text{[from Eq. (i)]}$$

$$= \frac{\left(\frac{n(n+1)}{2}\right)^2}{n \cdot \frac{n(n+1)(2n+1)}{6}} = \frac{3}{2} \cdot \left(\frac{n+1}{2n+1}\right) = \frac{3}{4} \cdot \frac{\left(1 + \frac{1}{n}\right)}{\left(1 + \frac{1}{2n}\right)}$$

$$\therefore \lim_{n \to \infty} P(A) = \frac{3}{4} \lim_{n \to \infty} \left(\frac{1 + \frac{1}{n}}{1 + \frac{1}{2n}} \right) = \frac{3}{4} \cdot \left(\frac{1+0}{1+0} \right) = \frac{3}{4} = 0.75$$

54. $P\left(\frac{E_1}{A}\right) = \frac{P(E_1) \cdot P\left(\frac{A}{E_1}\right)}{\sum_{\lambda=0}^{n} P(E_\lambda) \cdot P\left(\frac{A}{E_\lambda}\right)} = \frac{P(E_1) \cdot P\left(\frac{A}{E_1}\right)}{P(A)}$

$$= \frac{\frac{6}{n(n+1)(2n+1)} \times \frac{1}{n}}{\frac{3n(n+1)}{2(2n+1)}} = \frac{4}{[n(n+1)]^2} = \frac{1}{\sum n^3}$$

55. The number of cubes having atleast one side painted is

$9 + 9 + 3 + 3 + 1 + 1 = 26$ and total cubes $= 27$

$\therefore$ Required probability, $P_1 = \frac{26}{27} \Rightarrow 27P_1 = 26$

56. The number of cubes having two sides painted is

$4 + 4 + 1 + 1 + 1 + 1 = 12$ and total cubes $= 27$

$\therefore$ Required probability, $P_2 = \frac{12}{27} \Rightarrow 27P_2 = 12$

57. Required probability, $P_3 = 1 - p_1 = 1 - \frac{26}{27} = \frac{1}{27} \Rightarrow 27P_3 = 1$

58. A : She gets a success

E_1 : She studies 10 h

$\therefore \quad P(E_1) = 0.1$

E_2 : She studies 7 h

$\therefore \quad P(E_2) = 0.2$

and E_3: She studies 4h

$\therefore \quad P(E_3) = 0.7$

and $P\left(\frac{A}{E_1}\right) = 0.80$, $P\left(\frac{A}{E_2}\right) = 0.60$ and $P\left(\frac{A}{E_3}\right) = 0.40$

$\therefore \quad P(A) = P(E_1) \cdot P\left(\frac{A}{E_1}\right) + P(E_2) \cdot P\left(\frac{A}{E_2}\right) + P(E_3) \cdot P\left(\frac{A}{E_3}\right)$

$= 0.1 \times 0.80 + 0.2 \times 0.60 + 0.7 \times 0.40 = 0.48$

59. $P\left(\frac{E_3}{A}\right) = \frac{P(E_3 \cap A)}{P(A)} = \frac{P(E_3) \cdot P\left(\frac{A}{E_3}\right)}{P(A)} = \frac{0.7 \times 0.40}{0.48} = \frac{7}{12}$

60. $P\left(\frac{E_3}{\overline{A}}\right) = \frac{P(E_3 \cap \overline{A})}{P(\overline{A})} = \frac{P(E_3) - P(E_3 \cap A)}{1 - P(A)}$

$$= \frac{0.7 - 0.28}{1 - 0.48} = \frac{0.42}{0.52} = \frac{21}{26}$$

61. $\because p_1, p_2$ and p_3 are mutually exclusive events.

$\therefore \quad p_1 + p_2 + p_3 = 1$

Also, p_1, p_2 and p_3 are the roots of

$27x^3 - 27x^2 + ax - 1 = 0$

$\therefore \quad p_1 + p_2 + p_3 = 1$ ...(i)

$p_1p_2 + p_2p_3 + p_3p_1 = \frac{a}{27}$ ...(ii)

and $\quad p_1p_2p_3 = \frac{1}{27}$

Now, $\quad$ AM of $p_1, p_2, p_3 = \frac{p_1 + p_2 + p_3}{3} = \frac{1}{3}$

and GM of $p_1, p_2, p_3 = (p_1p_2p_3)^{1/3} = \left(\frac{1}{27}\right)^{1/3} = \frac{1}{3}$

Here, $\quad$ AM = GM

$\therefore \quad p_1 = p_2 = p_3 = \frac{1}{3}$

From Eq. (ii), we get

$$\frac{1}{3} \cdot \frac{1}{3} + \frac{1}{3} \cdot \frac{1}{3} + \frac{1}{3} \cdot \frac{1}{3} = \frac{a}{27} \Rightarrow a = 9$$

62. P (none of E_1, E_2, E_3) $= 1 - P(E_1 \cup E_2 \cup E_3)$

$= 1 - [P(E_1) + P(E_2) + P(E_3)]$

$= 1 - (p_1 + p_2 + p_3) = 0$

[$\because E_1, E_2$ and E_3 are mutually exclusive]

63. $P(E_1 \cup \overline{E}_2) + P(E_2 \cap \overline{E}_3) + P(E_3 \cap \overline{E}_1)$

$= P(E_1) - P(E_1 \cap E_2) + P(E_2) - P(E_2 \cap E_3) + P(E_3) - P(E_3 \cap E_1)$

$= P(E_1) - 0 + P(E_2) - 0 + P(E_3) - 0$

$= p_1 + p_2 + p_3$ [$\because E_1, E_2$ and E_3 are mutually exclusive]

64. The number of increasing functions $= {}^6C_3 = 20$

and the number of total functions $= 6^3 = 216$

$\therefore \quad$ Required probability $= \frac{20}{216} = \frac{5}{54}$

65. The number of non-decreasing functions $= {}^{6+3-1}C_3 = {}^8C_3 = 56$

the number of total functions $= 6^3 = 216$

$\therefore$ Required probability $= \frac{56}{216} = \frac{7}{27}$

66. The number of onto functions such that $f(i) \neq i$ is

$$6!\left(1 - \frac{1}{1!} + \frac{1}{2!} - \frac{1}{3!} + \frac{1}{4!} - \frac{1}{5!} + \frac{1}{6!}\right) = 265$$

and number of total functions $= 6! = 720$

$\therefore \quad$ Required probability $= \frac{265}{720} = \frac{53}{144}$

67. $\because P(X = x) \propto (x + 1)\left(\frac{1}{5}\right)^x$

$P(X = x) = k(x + 1)\left(\frac{1}{5}\right)^x$

We have, $k\left[1 + 2\left(\frac{1}{5}\right) + 3\left(\frac{1}{5}\right)^2 + \ldots\right] = 1$

$\Rightarrow \quad k\left[\frac{1}{\left(1 - \frac{1}{5}\right)^2}\right] = 1 \Rightarrow k = \frac{16}{25}$

Now, $\quad P(X = 0) = k(1)\left(\frac{1}{5}\right)^0 = k = \frac{16}{25}$

68. $P(X \geq 2) = 1 - [P(X = 0) + P(X = 1)]$

$$= 1 - k\left[1 + \frac{2}{5}\right] = 1 - \frac{7k}{5} = 1 - \frac{7}{5} \times \frac{16}{25} = \frac{13}{125}$$

69. $E(X) = \sum_{x=0}^{\infty} x\, P(X = x) = k \sum_{x=0}^{\infty} x(x+1)\left(\frac{1}{5}\right)^x$

$$= k\left[(1)(2)\left(\frac{1}{5}\right)^1 + (2)(3)\left(\frac{1}{5}\right)^2 + (3)(4)\left(\frac{1}{5}\right)^3 + \ldots + \infty\right]$$

$$E(X) = k\left[\frac{2}{5} + \frac{6}{25} + \frac{12}{125} + \ldots + \infty\right] \quad \ldots\text{(i)}$$

$$\text{and} \frac{1}{5}E(X) = k\left[\frac{2}{25} + \frac{6}{125} + \frac{12}{625} + \ldots + \infty\right] \quad \ldots\text{(ii)}$$

On subtracting Eq. (ii) from Eq. (i), we get

$$\frac{4}{5}E(X) = k\left[\frac{2}{5} + \frac{4}{25} + \frac{6}{125} + \ldots + \infty\right] \quad \ldots\text{(iii)}$$

On multiplying both sides by $\frac{1}{5}$ in Eq. (i), we get

$$\frac{4}{25}E(X) = k\left[\frac{2}{25} + \frac{4}{125} + \frac{6}{625} + \ldots + \infty\right] \quad \ldots\text{(iv)}$$

On subtracting Eq. (iv) from Eq. (iii), we get

$$\frac{16}{25}E(X) = k\left[\frac{2}{5} + \frac{2}{25} + \frac{2}{125} + \ldots + \infty\right]$$

$$= k\left[\frac{\frac{2}{5}}{1 - \frac{1}{5}}\right] = \frac{k}{2} = \frac{16}{25} \times \frac{1}{2} \quad \left[\because k = \frac{16}{25}\right]$$

$$\therefore \quad E(x) = \frac{1}{2}$$

70. $\because (a^2 - 1)$ is divisible by 10, if and only if last digit of a is 1 or 9.

If $r = 0$, then there are 2λ ways to choose a.

$$\therefore \quad p_n = \frac{2\lambda}{n} \Rightarrow n p_n = 2\lambda$$

71. If $r = 9$, then there are $2(\lambda + 1)$ ways to choose a.

$$\therefore \quad p_n = \frac{2(\lambda + 1)}{n}$$

$$\Rightarrow \quad n p_n = 2(\lambda + 1)$$

72. If $1 \leq r \leq 8$, then there are $2(\lambda + 1)$ ways to choose a.

$$\therefore \quad p_n = \frac{2(\lambda + 1)}{n}$$

$$\Rightarrow \quad x p_n = 2(\lambda + 1)$$

73. $$\frac{7}{12} = \frac{1}{(n+1)} \cdot 1 + \frac{n}{(n+1)} \cdot \frac{1}{2}$$

$$\Rightarrow \frac{7}{6} = \frac{(n+2)}{(n+1)} \Rightarrow n = 5$$

74. Let S be the sample space, then

$n(S)$ = Total number of determinants that can be made with 0 and 1 $= 2 \times 2 \times 2 \times 2 = 16$

$\because \begin{vmatrix} a & b \\ c & d \end{vmatrix}$, each element can be replaced by two types

i.e., 0 and 1

and let E be the event that the determinant made is non-negative.

Also, E' be the event that the determinant is negative.

$$\therefore \quad E' = \left\{\begin{vmatrix} 1 & 1 \\ 1 & 0 \end{vmatrix}, \begin{vmatrix} 0 & 1 \\ 1 & 1 \end{vmatrix}, \begin{vmatrix} 0 & 1 \\ 1 & 0 \end{vmatrix}\right\}$$

$$\therefore \quad P(E') = 3$$

then $P(E') = \frac{n(E')}{n(S)} = \frac{3}{16}$

Hence, the required probability,

$$P(E) = 1 - P(E')$$

$$= 1 - \frac{3}{16} = \frac{13}{16} = \frac{m}{n} \quad \text{[given]}$$

$$\Rightarrow \quad m = 13 \text{ and } n = 16, \text{ then } n - m = 3$$

75. Let E_1, E_2 and E_3 be the events that first, second and third student get success. Then,

$$P(E_1) = \frac{1}{3}, P(E_2) = \frac{1}{4} \text{ and } P(E_3) = \frac{1}{5}$$

Given, probability of success of atleast two $= \frac{\lambda}{12}$

$$\Rightarrow P(E_1 \cap E_2 \cap \bar{E}_3) + P(\bar{E}_1 \cap E_2 \cap E_3) + P(E_1 \cap \bar{E}_2 \cap E_3) + P(E_1 \cap E_2 \cap E_3) = \frac{\lambda}{12}$$

$$\Rightarrow P(E_1) \cdot P(E_2) \cdot P(\bar{E}_3) + P(\bar{E}_1) \cdot P(E_2) \cdot P(E_3) + P(E_1) \cdot P(\bar{E}_2) \cdot P(E_3) + P(E_1) \cdot P(E_2) \cdot P(E_3) = \frac{\lambda}{12}$$

$$\Rightarrow \frac{1}{3} \cdot \frac{1}{4} \cdot \frac{4}{5} + \frac{2}{3} \cdot \frac{1}{4} \cdot \frac{1}{5} + \frac{1}{3} \cdot \frac{3}{4} \cdot \frac{1}{5} + \frac{1}{3} \cdot \frac{1}{4} \cdot \frac{1}{5} = \frac{\lambda}{12}$$

$$\Rightarrow \frac{10}{60} = \frac{\lambda}{12}$$

$$\therefore \quad \lambda = 2$$

76. Let S be the sample space and E be the event of getting a large number than the previous number.

$\therefore \quad n(S) = 6 \times 6 \times 6 = 216$

Now, we count the number of favourable ways. Obviously, the second number has to be greater than 1. If the second number is $i (i > 1)$, then the number of favourable ways $= (i - 1) \times (6 - i)$

$\therefore \quad n(E)$ = Total number of favourable ways

$$= \sum_{i=1}^{6} (i - 1) \times (6 - i)$$

$$= 0 + 1 \times 4 + 2 \times 3 + 3 \times 2 + 4 \times 1 + 5 \times 0$$

$$= 4 + 6 + 6 + 4 = 20$$

Therefore, the required probability, $P(E) = \frac{n(E)}{n(S)} = \frac{20}{216}$

$$= \frac{5}{54} = p \quad \text{[given]}$$

$$\therefore \quad 54p = 5$$

77. The number of ways to answer a question $= 2^5 - 1 = 31$.

i.e., In 31 ways only one correct.

Let number of choices $= n$

Now, according to the question $\frac{n}{31} > \frac{1}{8}$

$\Rightarrow \quad n > \frac{31}{8} \Rightarrow n > 3.8$

$\therefore$ Least value of $n = 4$

78. Let E_i denote the event that the ith object goes to the ith place, we have

$$P(E_i \cap E_j \cap E_k) = \frac{(n-3)!}{n!} \text{ for } i < j < k$$

Since, we can choose 3 places out of n is ${}^nC_3$ ways, the probability of the required event is

$$p = {}^nC_3 \cdot \frac{(n-3)!}{n!} = \frac{n!}{3!(n-3)!} \cdot \frac{(n-3)!}{n!} = \frac{1}{6}$$

$\therefore \quad 6p = 1$

79. The sample space is

$S = \{-0.50, -0.49, -0.48, \ldots, -0.01, 0.00, 0.01, \ldots, 0.49\}$

Let E be the event that the round off error is atleast 10 paise, then E' is the event that the round off error is atmost a paise.

$\therefore \quad E' = \{-0.09, -0.08, \ldots, -0.01, 0.00, 0.01, \ldots, 0.09\}$

$\therefore \quad n(E') = 19$ and $n(S) = 100$

$\therefore \; P(E') = \frac{n(E')}{n(S)} = \frac{19}{100}$

$\therefore$ Required probability, $P(E) = 1 - P(E') = 1 - \frac{19}{100}$

$$= \frac{81}{100} = \left(\frac{m}{n}\right)^2$$

$\therefore \quad m = 9$ and $n = 10$

$\Rightarrow \quad n - m = 1$

80. Let E_1, E_2, E_3, E_4, E_5 and E_6 be the events of occurrence of 1, 2, 3, 4, 5 and 6 on the dice respectively and let E be the event of getting a sum of numbers equal to 9.

$\therefore \; P(E_1) = \frac{1-k}{6}; P(E_2) = \frac{1+2k}{6}; P(E_3) = \frac{1-k}{6};$

$P(E_4) = \frac{1+k}{6}; P(E_5) = \frac{1-2k}{6}; P(E_6) = \frac{1+k}{6}$

and $\frac{1}{9} \le P(E) \le \frac{2}{9}$

Then, $E \equiv \{(3, 6), (6, 3), (4, 5), (5, 4)\}$

Hence, $P(E) = P(E_3E_6) + P(E_6E_3) + P(E_4E_5) + P(E_5E_4)$

$= P(E_3)P(E_6) + P(E_6)P(E_3) + P(E_4)P(E_5) + P(E_5)P(E_4)$

$= 2P(E_3)P(E_6) + 2P(E_4)P(E_5)$

[since E_1, E_2, E_3, E_4, E_5 and E_6 are independent]

$$= 2\left(\frac{1-k}{6}\right)\left(\frac{1+k}{6}\right) + 2\left(\frac{1+k}{6}\right)\left(\frac{1-2k}{6}\right)$$

$$= \frac{1}{18}[2 - k - 3k^2]$$

Since, $\frac{1}{9} \le P(E) \le \frac{2}{9}$

$\Rightarrow \quad \frac{1}{9} \le \frac{1}{18}[2 - k - 3k^2] \le \frac{2}{9}$

$\Rightarrow \quad 2 \le 2 - k - 3k^2 \le 4$

$\Rightarrow \quad 2 \le 2 - k - 3k^2$ and $2 - k - 3k^2 \le 4$

$\Rightarrow \quad 3k\left(k + \frac{1}{3}\right) \le 0$ and $3k^2 + k + 2 \ge 0$

$\Rightarrow \quad -\frac{1}{3} \le k \le 0$ and $k \in R$

$\therefore \quad -\frac{1}{3} \le k \le 0$

Hence, integral value of k is 0.

81. Let $a_1, a_2, a_3, a_4, a_5, a_6$ and a_7 be the seven digits and the remaining two be a_8 and a_9.

Let $a_1 + a_2 + a_3 + a_4 + a_5 + a_6 + a_7 = 9k, k \in I$ ...(i)

Also, $a_1 + a_2 + a_3 + a_4 + \ldots + a_9 = 1 + 2 + 3 + 4 + \ldots + 9$

$$= \frac{9 \times 10}{2} = 45 \quad \text{...(ii)}$$

On subtracting Eq. (i) from Eq. (ii), we get

$$a_8 + a_9 = 45 - 9k \quad \text{...(iii)}$$

Since, $a_1 + a_2 + a_3 + a_4 + \ldots + a_9$ and $a_1 + a_2 + \ldots + a_7$ are divisible by 9, if and only if $a_8 + a_9$ is divisible by 9. Let S be the sample space and E be the event that the sum of the digits a_8 and a_9 is divisible by 9.

$\because \quad a_8 + a_9 = 45 - 9k$

Maximum value of $a_8 + a_9 = 17$ and minimum value of $a_8 + a_9 = 3$

$\therefore \quad 3 \le 45 - 9k \le 17$

$\Rightarrow \quad -42 \le -9k \le -28 \Rightarrow \frac{42}{9} \le k \ge \frac{28}{9}$

or $\quad \frac{28}{9} \le k \ge \frac{42}{9}$

Hence, $k = 4$ [$\because k$ is positive integer]

$\therefore$ From Eq. (iii), we get

$a_8 + a_9 = 45 - 9 \times 4$

$\therefore \quad a_8 + a_9 = 9$

Now, possible pair of (a_8, a_9) can be $\{(1, 8), (2, 7), (3, 6), (4, 5)\}$

$\therefore \quad E = \{(1, 8), (2, 7), (3, 6), (4, 5)\}$

$n(E) = 4$ and $n(S) = {}^9C_2 = 36$

$\therefore$ Required probability, $P(E) = \frac{n(E)}{n(S)} = \frac{4}{36} = \frac{1}{9} = p$ [given]

$\therefore \quad 18p = 2$

82. Let A be the event of P_1 winning in third round and B be the event of P_2 winning in first round but loosing in second round.

We have, $P(A) = \frac{1}{{}^8C_1} = \frac{1}{8}$

$P(B \cap A)$ = Probability of both P_1 and P_2 winning in first round $\times$ Probability of P_1 winning and P_2 loosing in second round $\times$ Probability of P_1 winning in third round

$$= \frac{{}^{8-2}C_{4-2}}{{}^8C_4} \times \frac{{}^{4-2}C_{2-1}}{{}^4C_2} \times \frac{{}^{2-1}C_{1-1}}{{}^2C_1}$$

$$= \frac{{}^6C_2}{{}^8C_4} \times \frac{{}^2C_1}{{}^4C_2} \times \frac{{}^1C_0}{{}^2C_1} = \frac{1}{28}$$

Hence, $P\left(\frac{B}{A}\right) = \frac{P(B \cap A)}{P(A)} = \frac{\frac{1}{28}}{\frac{1}{8}} = \frac{2}{7} = p$ [given]

$\therefore \quad 7p = 2$

83. (A) → (q,r); (B) → (p,r); (C) → (p,r); (D) → (q,r,s)

(A) $P(\bar{A}) = 0.3 \Rightarrow P(A) = 1 - P(\bar{A}) = 0.7,\ P(B) = 0.4,$

$\Rightarrow \quad 0.5 = 0.7 - P(AB)$

$\therefore \quad P(AB) = 0.2$

$\Rightarrow P\left[\frac{B}{(A \cup \bar{B})}\right] = \frac{P[B \cap (A \cup \bar{B})]}{P(A \cup \bar{B})} = \frac{P(A \cap B)}{P(A) + P(\bar{B}) - P(A\bar{B})}$

$= \frac{0.2}{0.7 + 0.6 - 0.5} = \frac{1}{4} = \lambda_1$ [given]

$\therefore \quad \frac{1}{\lambda_1} = 4$ [composite number and natural number]

(B) First three prime numbers are 2, 3 and 5.

For roots to be real $D \ge 0$

Thus, real roots are obtained by $b = 5, a = 2, c = 3$

and $b = 5, a = 3, c = 2$

i.e., two ways.

Total ways of choosing $a, b, c = 3 \times 2 \times 1 = 6$

$\therefore$ Required probability $= \frac{2}{6} = \frac{1}{3} = \lambda_2$ [given]

$\therefore \quad \frac{1}{\lambda_2} = 3$

[prime number and natural number]

(C) Here, tossing of the coin is an independent event. Thus, the result of 5th trial is independent of outcome of previous trials.

$\therefore \quad \lambda_3 = \frac{1}{2} \Rightarrow \frac{1}{\lambda_3} = 2$

[prime number and natural number]

(D) Clearly, $n(S) = {}^9P_9 = 9!$

Now, 3 positions out of 9 positions can be chosen in ${}^9C_3$ ways and at these positions A, B and C can speak in required order, further remaining 6 persons can speak in 6! ways.

$\therefore$ Required probability $= \frac{{}^9C_3 \times 6!}{9!}$

$= \frac{9! \times 6!}{3! \times 6! \times 9!} = \frac{1}{6} = \lambda_4$ [given]

$\therefore \quad \frac{1}{\lambda_4} = 6$

[a composite number, a natural number and a perfect number]

84. (A) → (s); (B) → (p); (C) → (r); (D) → (q)

(A) $\frac{3}{5} \ge P(A \cap B) \ge P(A) + P(B) - 1 = \frac{3}{5} + \frac{2}{3} - 1 = \frac{4}{15}$

$\therefore \quad \frac{3}{5} \ge P(A \cap B) \ge \frac{4}{15}$

$\Rightarrow \quad P(A \cap B) \in \left[\frac{4}{15}, \frac{3}{5}\right]$

(B) $\because P(A \cup B) = P(A) + P(B) - P(A \cap B)$

$= \frac{3}{5} + \frac{2}{3} - P(A \cap B) = \frac{19}{15} - P(A \cap B)$

$\Rightarrow \quad \frac{2}{3} \le P(A \cup B) \le 1 \quad \left[\because P(A \cap B) \in \left[\frac{4}{15}, \frac{3}{5}\right]\right]$

$\therefore \quad P(A \cup B) \in \left[\frac{2}{3}, 1\right]$

(C) $P\left(\frac{A}{B}\right) = \frac{P(A \cap B)}{P(B)} = \frac{3}{2} P(A \cap B)$

$\Rightarrow \quad \frac{2}{5} \le P\left(\frac{A}{B}\right) \le \frac{9}{10} \left[\because P(A \cap B) \in \left[\frac{4}{15}, \frac{3}{5}\right]\right]$

$\therefore \quad P\left(\frac{A}{B}\right) \in \left[\frac{2}{5}, \frac{9}{10}\right]$

(D) $P\left(\frac{B}{A}\right) = \frac{P(B \cap A)}{P(A)} = \frac{5}{3} P(A \cap B)$

$\Rightarrow \quad \frac{4}{9} \le P\left(\frac{B}{A}\right) \le 1 \quad \left[\because P(A \cap B) \in \left[\frac{4}{15}, \frac{3}{5}\right]\right]$

$\therefore \quad P\left(\frac{B}{A}\right) \in \left[\frac{4}{9}, 1\right]$

85. (A) → (p,r,s) ; (B) → (p,r,s); (C) → (s); (D) → (q,r)

Let $q_1 = 1 - p_1$ and $q_2 = 1 - p_2$

(A) $\because$ A can win the game at the 1st, 4th, 7th,... trials.

$\therefore P(A \text{ wins}) = \frac{1}{6} + \frac{5}{6}(q_1)(q_2)\left(\frac{1}{6}\right) + \left(\frac{5}{6}\right)^2 (q_1)^2(q_2)^2\left(\frac{1}{6}\right) + \ldots$

$= \frac{\frac{1}{6}}{1 - \frac{5}{6}q_1q_2} = \frac{1}{6 - 5q_1q_2} = \frac{1}{6 - 5\left(\frac{4}{5}\right)\left(\frac{3}{4}\right)} = \frac{1}{\lambda_1}$ [given]

$\therefore \quad \lambda_1 = 3$

(B) $P(C \text{ wins}) = \frac{5}{6} \cdot q_1 \cdot p_2 + \left(\frac{5}{6}\right)^2 \cdot q_1^2 \cdot q_2 p_2 + \ldots$

$= \frac{\frac{5}{6}q_1 \cdot p_2}{1 - \frac{5}{6}q_1q_2} = \frac{5q_1p_2}{6 - 5q_1q_2} = \frac{5 \times \frac{4}{5} \times \frac{1}{4}}{6 - 5 \times \frac{4}{5} \times \frac{3}{4}} = \frac{1}{3}$

$= \frac{1}{\lambda_2}$ [given]

$\therefore \quad \lambda_2 = 3$

(C) $\because$ P (A wins) $= P$ (B wins)

$\Rightarrow \quad \frac{1}{6 - 5q_1q_2} = \frac{5p_1}{6 - 5q_1q_2}$

$\therefore \quad p_1 = \frac{1}{5} = \frac{1}{\lambda_3}$ [given]

$\therefore \quad \lambda_3 = 5$

(D) $P(A \text{ wins}) = P(B \text{ wins}) = P(C \text{ wins})$

$$\Rightarrow \quad \frac{1}{6-5q_1q_2} = \frac{5p_1}{6-5q_1q_2} = \frac{5q_1p_2}{6-5q_1q_2}$$

$$\Rightarrow \quad 1 = 5p_1 = 5q_1p_2$$

$$\Rightarrow \quad p_1 = \frac{1}{5}, \frac{1}{p_2} = 5q_1 = 5\left(1-\frac{1}{5}\right) = 4 = \lambda_4 \quad \text{[given]}$$

$\therefore \quad \lambda_4 = 4$

86. (A) → (q); (B) → (r); (C) → (p); (D) → (s)

(A) $\because a, b \in \{1, 2, 3, \ldots, 9\}$

For real and distinct roots $D > 0$

i.e., $2(a-b)^2 > 4b \Rightarrow (a-b)^2 > 2b$

The possible pairs are

b	a	Total pairs of a and b
1	3, 4, 5, ..., 9	7
2	5, 6, ..., 9	5
3	6, 7, 8, 9	4
4	1, 7, 8, 9	4
5	1, 9	2
6	1, 2	2
7	1, 2, 3	3
8	1, 2, 3	3
9	1, 2, 3, 4	4
		34

$n(S) = 9 \times 9 = 81$ and $n(E) = 34$

$$\therefore \quad p_1 = \frac{34}{81} \Rightarrow 9p_1 = \frac{34}{9}$$

$$\therefore \quad [9p_1] = \left[\frac{34}{9}\right] = 3$$

(B) For imaginary roots,

$$p_2 = 1 - p_4 = 1 - \frac{5}{9} = \frac{4}{9}$$

$\therefore \quad [9p_2] = 4$

(C) For equal roots, there are only 2 possible pairs are

$b = 2, a = 4$ and $b = 8, a = 4$

$\therefore \quad n(S) = 81, n(E) = 2$

$$\therefore \quad p_3 = \frac{2}{81}$$

$\Rightarrow \quad [81p_3] = 2$

(D) For real roots,

$$p_4 = 1 - (p_1 + p_3) = 1 - \left(\frac{34}{81} + \frac{2}{81}\right)$$

$$= 1 - \frac{36}{81} = 1 - \frac{4}{9} = \frac{5}{9}$$

$\therefore \quad [9p_4] = 5$

87. (A) → (r); B → (s); (C) → (p); D → (q)

(A) $n(S) = {}^{10}C_3 = 120$ and $n(E) = {}^3C_1 = 3$, because on selection 3 and 7, we have to select one from 4, 5 and 6.

$$\therefore \quad P(E) = \frac{n(E)}{n(S)} = \frac{3}{120} = \frac{1}{40} = p_1 \quad \text{[given]}$$

$$\Rightarrow \quad \frac{2}{5p_1} = 16$$

(B) The probability of 4 being the minimum number

$$= \frac{{}^6C_2}{{}^{10}C_3} = \frac{1}{8}$$ [because after selecting 4 any two can be selected from 5, 6, 7, 8, 9, 10]

and the probability of being the maximum number

$$= \frac{{}^7C_2}{{}^{10}C_3} = \frac{7}{40}$$ [because after selecting 8 any two can be selected from 1, 2, 3, 4, 5, 6, 7]

and the probability of 4 being the minimum number and 8 being the maximum number

$$= \frac{{}^3C_1}{{}^{10}C_3} = \frac{1}{40}$$ [because on selecting 4, 8 and we have to select one from 5, 6, 7]

$\therefore$ Required probability

$$= P(A \cup B) = P(A) + P(B) - P(A \cap B)$$

$$= \frac{1}{8} + \frac{7}{40} - \frac{1}{40} = \frac{11}{40} = p_2 \quad \text{[given]}$$

$\therefore \quad 80p_2 = 22$

(C) Let $A = \{\text{maximum of three numbers is 7}\}$

$\therefore \quad A = \{1, 2, 3, 4, 5, 6, 7\}$

and $B = \{\text{minimum of three numbers is 3}\}$

$\therefore \quad B = \{3, 4, 5, 6, 7, 8, 9, 10\}$

and $A \cap B = \{3, 4, 5, 6, 7\}$

$$\therefore \quad P\left(\frac{B}{A}\right) = \frac{P(B \cap A)}{P(A)} = \frac{{}^3C_1}{{}^6C_2} = \frac{1}{5} = p_3 \quad \text{[given]}$$

$$\therefore \quad \frac{2}{p_3} = 10$$

(D) Let $A = \{\text{ maximum of three numbers is 8 }\}$

$\therefore \quad A = \{1, 2, 3, 4, 5, 6, 7, 8\}$

and $B = \{\text{ minimum of three numbers is 4 }\}$

$\therefore \quad B = \{4, 5, 6, 7, 8, 9, 10\}$ and $A \cap B = \{4, 5, 6, 7, 8\}$

$$\therefore \quad P\left(\frac{B}{A}\right) = \frac{P(B \cap A)}{P(A)} = \frac{{}^3C_1}{{}^7C_2} = \frac{1}{7} = p_4 \quad \text{[given]}$$

$$\therefore \quad \frac{2}{p_4} = 14$$

88. (A) → (q); (B) → (s); C → (p); (D) → (r)

(A) We know that $7^\lambda, \lambda \in N$ has 1, 3, 7, 9 at the unit's place for $\lambda = 4k, 4k-1, 4k-2, 4k-3$ respectively, when $k = 1, 2, 3, \ldots$

Clearly, $7^m + 7^n$ will be divisible by 5, if 7^m has 3 or 7 in the unit's place and 7^n has 7 or 3 in the unit's place or 7^m has 1 or 9 in the unit's place and 7^n has 9 or 1 in the unit's place.

$\therefore$ For any choice of m, n the digit in the unit's place of $7^m + 7^n$ is 2, 4, 6, 8, 0

It is divisible by 5 only when this digit is 0.

$\therefore$ Required probability $= \frac{1}{5}$

(B) $n(S) = 2 \times 2 \times 2 \times 2 = 16$

[because each of the four places in determinant can be filled in 2 ways]

The zero determinants are

$$\begin{vmatrix} 1 & 1 \\ 1 & 1 \end{vmatrix}, \begin{vmatrix} -1 & -1 \\ -1 & -1 \end{vmatrix}, \begin{vmatrix} 1 & 1 \\ -1 & -1 \end{vmatrix}, \begin{vmatrix} -1 & -1 \\ 1 & 1 \end{vmatrix}, \begin{vmatrix} 1 & -1 \\ -1 & 1 \end{vmatrix},$$

$$\begin{vmatrix} 1 & -1 \\ 1 & -1 \end{vmatrix}, \begin{vmatrix} -1 & 1 \\ -1 & 1 \end{vmatrix}, \begin{vmatrix} -1 & 1 \\ 1 & -1 \end{vmatrix}$$

Number of zero determinants = 8, number of non-zero determinants

$$= 16 - 8 = 8 = n(E) \quad \text{[say]}$$

$\therefore$ Required probability $= \frac{n(E)}{n(S)} = \frac{8}{16} = \frac{1}{2}$

(C) $\because P(E_n) \propto n$

$\Rightarrow P(E_n) = kn$, where k is proportionality constant.

Clearly,

$P(E_1) + P(E_2) + P(E_3) + P(E_4) + P(E_5) + P(E_6) = 1$

$\Rightarrow \quad k(1 + 2 + 3 + 4 + 5 + 6) = 1 \Rightarrow k = \frac{1}{21}$

$\therefore$ Required probability $= P(E_3) = 3k = 3 \times \frac{1}{21} = \frac{1}{7}$

(D) 5 can be thrown in 4 ways and 7 can be thrown in 6 ways in a single throw of two dice.

Number of ways of throwing neither 5 nor 7

$$= 36 - (4 + 6) = 26$$

Probability of throwing a sum of 5 in a throw $= \frac{4}{36} = \frac{1}{9}$

and probability of throwing neither 5 nor 7 $= \frac{26}{36} = \frac{13}{18}$

$\therefore$ Required probability

$$= \frac{1}{9} + \frac{13}{18}\left(\frac{1}{9}\right) + \left(\frac{13}{18}\right)^2\left(\frac{1}{9}\right) + \ldots = \frac{\frac{1}{9}}{1 - \frac{13}{18}} = \frac{2}{5}$$

89. In $\left(\frac{1}{2} + \frac{1}{2}\right)^{10}$

Probability of appearing exactly four heads

$$= {}^{10}C_4\left(\frac{1}{2}\right)^4\left(\frac{1}{2}\right)^6 = {}^{10}C_{10-4}\left(\frac{1}{2}\right)^6\left(\frac{1}{2}\right)^4$$

$$= {}^{10}C_6\left(\frac{1}{2}\right)^6\left(\frac{1}{2}\right)^4$$

= Probability of appearing exactly six heads. Both statements are true,

Statement-2 is a correct explanation for Statement-1.

90. If A and B are independent, then

$$P(A \cap B) = P(A) \cdot P(B) = P(A) \quad [\because P(B) = 1] \ldots\text{(i)}$$

and $\quad P(A \cup B) = P(A) + P(B) - P(A \cap B)$

$$= P(A) + P(B) - P(A) \quad \text{[from Eq. (i)]}$$

$$= P(B) = 1 \text{ which is true.}$$

Hence, both statements are true and Statement-2 is a correct explanation for Statement-1.

91. $\because \quad P(A \cap \overline{B}) = P(A) - P(A \cap B)$

$\Rightarrow \quad P(A \cap \overline{B}) = 0.3 - P(A \cap B)$

$\therefore P(A \cap \overline{B})$ cannot be found. Hence, both statements are true and Statement-2 is a correct explanation for Statement-1.

92. $\because P(A \cup B) = P(A \cap B)$

$\Rightarrow P(A) + P(B) - P(A \cap B) = P(A \cap B)$

$\Rightarrow (P(A) - P(A \cap B)) + (P(B) - P(A \cap B)) = 0$

$\Rightarrow \quad P(A \cap B') + P(A' \cap B) = 0 \quad \ldots\text{(i)}$

$\because \quad A \cap B \subseteq A$ and $A \cap B \subseteq B$

$\Rightarrow \quad P(A \cap B) \leq P(A)$ and $P(A \cap B) \leq P(B)$

$\Rightarrow P(A) - P(A \cap B) \geq 0$ and $P(B) - P(A \cap B) \geq 0$

$\Rightarrow \quad P(A \cap B') \geq 0 \quad \ldots\text{(ii)}$

and $\quad P(A' \cap B) \geq 0 \quad \ldots\text{(iii)}$

From Eqs. (i), (ii) and (iii), we get

$P(A \cap B') = 0$ and $P(A' \cap B) = 0$

or $\quad P(A \cap B') = P(A' \cap B) = 0$

$\Rightarrow$ Statement-1 is true and Statement-2 is false.

93. Statement-1 There are six equally likely possibilities of which only 2 are favourable (4 and 6)

$\therefore$ Probability that the obtained number is composite $= \frac{2}{6} = \frac{1}{3}$

$\therefore$ Statement-1 is true.

Statement-2 As the given 3 possibilities are not equally likely.

$\therefore$ Statement-2 is false.

94. Total cards = 52 = 26 Red + 26 Black

(26 Red →) 13 Diamond, 13 Heart

Given A : Red card is drawn

B : Card drawn is either a diamond or heart

It is clear that $A \subseteq B$ and $B \subseteq A$

$\therefore$ Statement-2 is true.

and $P(A + B) = P(A \cup B) = P(A \cup A) = P(A)$

$[\because A \subseteq B \text{ and } B \subseteq A]$

and $\quad P(AB) = P(A \cap B) = P(A \cap A) = P(A)$

$[\because A \subseteq B \text{ and } B \subseteq A]$

$\therefore \quad P(A + B) = P(AB)$

Statement-1 is true.

Hence, both statements are true and Statement-2 is a correct explanation for Statement-1.

95. Required probability = 1 – Problem will not be solved

$= 1 - P(\overline{A} \cap \overline{B}) = 1 - P(\overline{A})P(\overline{B}) = 1 - (1 - P(A))(1 - P(B))$

$= 1 - \left(1 - \frac{1}{2}\right)\left(1 - \frac{1}{3}\right) = 1 - \frac{1}{2} \times \frac{2}{3} = 1 - \frac{1}{3} = \frac{2}{3}$

$\therefore$ Statement-1 is false and Statement-2 is true.

96. Total ways $= {}^{2n+1}C_3 = \dfrac{(2n+1).2n.(2n-1)}{1\cdot 2\cdot 3} = \dfrac{n(4n^2-1)}{3}$

Let the three numbers a, b, c are drawn, where $a < b < c$ and given a, b and c are in AP.

$\therefore \quad 2b = a + c$...(i)

It is clear from Eq. (i) that a and c both are odd or both are even.

$\therefore$ Favourable ways $= {}^{n+1}C_2 + {}^nC_2$

$$= \frac{(n+1)n}{1\cdot 2} + \frac{n(n-1)}{1\cdot 2} = n^2$$

$\therefore$ Required probability $= \dfrac{n^2}{\dfrac{n(4n^2-1)}{3}} = \dfrac{3n}{(4n^2-1)}$

$\Rightarrow$ Statement-2 is false.

In Statement-1, $2n + 1 = 21$

$\Rightarrow \quad n = 10$

$\because$ Required probability $= \dfrac{3 \times 10}{4(10)^2 - 1} = \dfrac{30}{399} = \dfrac{10}{133}$

$\therefore$ Statement-1 is true.

97. In Statement-2 $P\left(\dfrac{A}{B}\right) = \dfrac{P(A \cap B)}{P(B)}$ [by definition]

$$P(\overline{B}) = P((A \cup \overline{A}) \cap \overline{B}) = P((A \cap \overline{B}) \cup (\overline{A} \cap \overline{B}))$$
$$= P(A \cap \overline{B}) + P(\overline{A} \cap \overline{B}) \quad \text{...(i)}$$

$\therefore$ Statement-2 is true.

In Statement-1

$$P\left(\frac{A}{\overline{B}}\right) + P\left(\frac{\overline{A}}{\overline{B}}\right) = \frac{P(A \cap \overline{B})}{P(\overline{B})} + \frac{P(\overline{A} \cap \overline{B})}{P(\overline{B})}$$

$$= \frac{P(A \cap \overline{B}) + P(\overline{A} \cap \overline{B})}{P(\overline{B})} = \frac{P(\overline{B})}{P(\overline{B})} = 1 \quad \text{[From Eq. (i)]}$$

$\therefore$ Statement-1 is false.

98. The total number of matches played in the tournament

$$= {}^5C_2 = 10$$

The probability that a particular team (say A) wins all its 4 matches $= \left(\dfrac{1}{2}\right)^4 = \dfrac{1}{16}$

$\therefore$ Probability that team is undefeated in the tournament

$$= {}^5C_1\left(\frac{1}{2}\right)^4 = \frac{5}{16}$$

$\Rightarrow$ Statement-1 is true.

Similarly, the probability that there is an winless team $= \dfrac{5}{16}$

$\Rightarrow$ Statement-2 is false.

99. For real roots, $D \geq 0$

$\Rightarrow \quad p^2 - 4\cdot 1\cdot \dfrac{1}{4}(p+2) \geq 0$

$\Rightarrow \quad p^2 - p - 2 \geq 0$

$\Rightarrow \quad (p-2)(p+1) \geq 0$

$\Rightarrow \quad p \leq -1$ or $p \geq 2$

But $\quad p \in [0, 5]$.

So, $\quad E = [2, 5]$

$n(E)$ = length of the interval $[2, 5] = 3$

and $\quad n(S)$ = length of the interval $[0, 5] = 5$

$\therefore \quad$ Required probability $= \dfrac{n(E)}{n(S)} = \dfrac{3}{5}$

Hence, both statements are true and Statement-2 is a correct explanation for Statement-1

100. $P\left(\dfrac{A}{B}\right) = \dfrac{P(A \cap B)}{P(B)} = \dfrac{\dfrac{n(A \cap B)}{n(S)}}{\dfrac{n(B)}{n(S)}} = \dfrac{n(A \cap B)}{n(B)} = \dfrac{n(AB)}{n(B)}$

Hence, both statements are true and Statement-2 is a correct explanation for Statement-1.

101. Let S be the sample space, then

$n(S)$ = Total number of numbers of five digits formed with the digits 1, 2, 3, 4 and 5 without repetition $= {}^5P_5 = 5! = 120$

We know that, a number is divisible by 4 if the last two digits of the number is divisible by 4.

Then, for divisible by 4, last two digits 12 or 24 or 32 or 52.

Let E be the event that the number formed is divisible by 4.

$\therefore \quad n(E) = 3! \times 4 = 24$

$\therefore$ Required probability, $P(E) = \dfrac{n(E)}{n(S)} = \dfrac{24}{120} = \dfrac{1}{5}$

102. Let S be the sample space and E be the event of getting a large number than the previous number.

$\therefore \quad n(S) = 6 \times 6 \times 6 = 216$

Now, we count the number of favourable ways. Obviously, the second number has to be greater than 1. If the second number is $i(i > 1)$, then the number of favourable ways $= (i-1) \times (6-i)$

$\therefore n(E)$ = Total number of favourable ways

$$= \sum_{i=1}^{6}(i-1) \times (6-i)$$
$$= 0 + 1 \times 4 + 2 \times 3 + 3 \times 2 + 4 \times 1 + 5 \times 0$$
$$= 4 + 6 + 6 + 4 = 20$$

Therefore, the required probability,

$$P(E) = \frac{n(E)}{n(S)} = \frac{20}{216} = \frac{5}{54}$$

103. Finding r cars in N places, there are $(r-1)$ cars other than his own in $(N-1)$ places.

$\therefore \quad$ Total number of ways $= {}^{N-1}C_{r-1} = \dfrac{(n-1)!}{(r-1)!\,(N-r)!}$

Now, the $(r-1)$ cars must be parked in $N-3$ places (because neighbouring slots are empty).

$\therefore$ Number of favourable ways $= {}^{N-3}C_{r-1}$

$$= \frac{(N-3)!}{(r-1)!\,(N-r-2)!}$$

$\therefore$ Required probability $= \dfrac{\text{Favourable ways}}{\text{Total ways}}$

$$= \frac{(N-3)!}{(r-1)!\,(N-r-2)!} \times \frac{(r-1)!\,(N-r)!}{(N-1)!}$$
$$= \frac{(N-r)\,(N-r-1)}{(N-1)\,(N-2)}$$

104. A wins the series in $(n+r+1)$ games (say). He wins the $(n+r+1)$ th game and n out of the first $(n+r)$ games.

$$\therefore \quad P(A) = \sum_{r=0}^{n} ({}^{n+r}C_n)\, q^r p^{n+1} \qquad [\text{where } p+q=1]$$

Similarly, $$P(B) = \sum_{r=0}^{n} ({}^{n+r}C_n)\, q^{n+1} p^r$$

Now, $P(A) + P(B) = 1$

$$\therefore \quad \sum_{r=0}^{n} [q^r p^{n+1} + q^{n+1} p^r]\, {}^{n+r}C_n = 1$$

Now, put $p = q = \dfrac{1}{2}$

$$\therefore \quad \sum_{r=0}^{n} {}^{n+r}C_n \left[\frac{1}{2^{n+r+1}} + \frac{1}{2^{n+r+1}}\right] = 1$$

$$\Rightarrow \quad \sum_{r=0}^{n} ({}^{n+r}C_n)\frac{1}{2^{n+r}} = 1$$

105. Let A denotes the event that the target is hit when x shells are fired at point I.

Let $E_1(E_2)$ denote the event.

We have, $P(E_1) = \dfrac{8}{9}$, $P(E_2) = \dfrac{1}{9}$

$$\Rightarrow \quad P\left(\frac{A}{E_1}\right) = 1 - \left(\frac{1}{2}\right)^x \text{ and } P\left(\frac{A}{E_2}\right) = 1 - \left(\frac{1}{2}\right)^{21-x}$$

Now, $$P(A) = \frac{8}{9}\left[1 - \left(\frac{1}{2}\right)^x\right] + \frac{1}{9}\left[1 - \left(\frac{1}{2}\right)^{21-x}\right]$$

$$\Rightarrow \quad \frac{dP(A)}{dx} = \frac{8}{9}\left[\left(\frac{1}{2}\right)^x \log 2\right] + \frac{1}{9}\left[-\left(\frac{1}{2}\right)^{21-x} \log 2\right]$$

Now, we must have $\dfrac{dP(A)}{dx} = 0 \Rightarrow \quad x = 12$, also $\dfrac{d^2P(A)}{dx^2} < 0$

Hence, $P(A)$ is maximum where $x = 12$.

106. The composition of the balls in the red box and in the green box; and the sum suggested in the problem may be one of the following:

Red box		Green box		Sum of Green in Red and Red in Green
Red	**Green**	**Green**	**Red**	
0	5	3	6	11
1	4	4	5	9
2	3	5	4	7
3	2	6	3	5
4	1	7	2	3
5	0	8	1	1

Of these the 2nd and the last correspond to the sum being NOT a prime number. Hence, the required probability

$$= \frac{{}^6C_1 \times {}^8C_4 \times {}^6C_5 \times {}^8C_0}{{}^{14}C_5} = \frac{420+6}{2002} = \frac{213}{1001}$$

107. Let E_i denote the event that out of the first k balls drawn, i balls are green. Let A denote the event that $(k+1)$th ball drawn is also green. We have, now $P(E_i) = \dfrac{{}^aC_i \times {}^bC_{k-i}}{{}^{a+b}C_k}$

Here, $0 \le i \le k$ and $P\left(\dfrac{A}{E_i}\right) = \dfrac{a-i}{a+b-k}$

Now, $$P(A) = \sum_{j=0}^{k} \frac{{}^aC_j \times {}^bC_{k-j}}{{}^{a+b}C_k} \times \frac{a-j}{a+b-k}$$

Also, $(1+x)^{a-1}(1+x)^b$

$$= [{}^{a-1}C_0 + {}^{a-1}C_1 x + \ldots + {}^{a-1}C_{a-1}x^{a-1}] \times [{}^bC_0 + {}^bC_1 x + \ldots + {}^bC_b x^b]$$

$$\Rightarrow \quad \sum_{j=0}^{n} ({}^{a-1}C_j)({}^bC_{k-j}) = \text{coefficient of } x^k$$

Hence, $$P(A) = \frac{a}{a+b}$$

108. Total number of outcomes $= 2 \times 2 \times 2 \ldots 12$ times $= 4096$

Let a_n denote the number of outcomes in which two consecutive heads do not occur when the fair coin is tossed n times.

$$\Rightarrow \quad a_1 = 2,\ a_2 = 3$$

For $n \ge 3$, if the last outcome is T, then we cannot have two consecutive heads in the first $(n-1)$ tosses. This can happen in a_{n-1} ways. If the last outcome is H, we must have T the $(n-1)$th toss and we cannot have two consecutive heads in the first $(n-2)$ tosses. This can happen in a_{n-2} ways.

$$\Rightarrow \quad a_n = a_{n-1} + a_{n-2} \text{ for } n \ge 3$$

$$\Rightarrow \quad a_{10} = 144,\ a_{11} = 233$$

$$\Rightarrow \quad a_{12} = 377$$

Hence, the required probability is $\dfrac{377}{4096}$.

109. Let PQ be a diameter of a circle with centre O and radius a. Take a point A at random in PQ.

Let, $AP = x$, $AQ = y$, then $x + y = 2a$ and all values of x between 0 and $2a$ are equally likely.

Draw the ordinate AB, then $AB^2 = AP$, $AQ = xy$

If P', Q' are the mid-points of OP, OQ, the ordinates at these points are equal to $a\sqrt{\dfrac{3}{4}}$.

Hence, $AB > a\sqrt{\dfrac{3}{4}}$ if and only if, A lies in $P'Q'$.

Hence, the chance that $xy > \dfrac{3}{4}a^2$ is $\dfrac{A'B'}{AB}$ i.e., $\dfrac{1}{2}$.

110. (i) Kamsky wins one of the first n games and draws the remaining $[(n-1)$ or

(ii) Kamsky wins exactly one of the first n games and draws the remaining$]$ $n-2$. We have,

$$P(i) = {}^nP_1 pq^{n-1}$$

and $$P(ii) = {}^nP_2\, pq^{n-2} r$$

$\Rightarrow$ The probability that Kamsky wins this match is

$$\sum_{n=1}^{\infty} p^2[nq^{n-1} + n(n-1)\, rq^{n-2}]$$

$$= p^2 \sum_{n=1}^{\infty} nq^{n-1} + p^2 r \sum_{n=1}^{\infty} n(n-1)\, q^{n-2}$$

Differentiating both sides w.r.t. q, we get

$$\sum_{n=1}^{\infty} nq^{n-1} = \frac{1}{(1-q)^2} \text{ and } \sum_{n=1}^{\infty} n(n-1)\, q^{n-2} = \frac{2}{(1-q)^3}$$

Thus, the probability that Kamsky wins the match is

$$\frac{p^2}{(1-q)^2} + \frac{2p^2 r}{(1-q)^3} = \frac{p^2(p+3r)}{(p+r)^3}$$

because $p + q + r = 1$.

111. Let A, B and C be three independent events having probabilities p, q and r, respectively.

Then, according to the question, we have

P (only the first occurs) $= P(A \cap \overline{B} \cap \overline{C})$ [$\because$ A, B, C are independent]

$$= P(A) \cdot P(\overline{B}) \cdot P(\overline{C})$$
$$= p(1-q)(1-r) = a \quad \text{...(i)}$$

P (only the second occurs) $= P(\overline{A} \cap B \cap \overline{C})$

$$= P(\overline{A}) \cdot P(B) \cdot P(\overline{C})$$
$$= (1-p)\, q(1-r) = b \quad \text{...(ii)}$$

and P (only the third occurs) $= P(\overline{A} \cap \overline{B} \cap C)$

$$= P(\overline{A}) \cdot P(\overline{B}) \cdot P(C)$$
$$= (1-p)(1-q)\, r = c \quad \text{...(iii)}$$

Multiplying Eqs. (i), (ii) and (iii), then

$$pqr\, \{(1-p)(1-q)(1-r)\}^2 = abc$$

or $$\frac{abc}{pqr} = [(1-p)(1-q)(1-r)]^2 = x^2 \quad \text{[say] ...(iv)}$$

$$(1-p)(1-q)(1-r) = x \quad \text{...(v)}$$

Dividing Eq. (i) by Eq. (v), then

$$\frac{p}{1-p} = \frac{a}{x} \text{ or } px = a - ap$$

$$\therefore \quad p = \frac{a}{(a+x)}$$

Similarly, $q = \dfrac{b}{b+x}$ and $r = \dfrac{c}{c+x}$

Replacing the values of p, q and r in Eq. (iv), then

$$\left\{\left(1 - \frac{a}{a+x}\right)\left(1 - \frac{b}{b+x}\right)\left(1 - \frac{c}{c+x}\right)\right\}^2 = x^2$$

$$\Rightarrow \quad \frac{(x^3)^2}{(a+x)^2 (b+x)^2 (c+x)^2} = x^2$$

$$\Rightarrow \quad \frac{x^3}{(a+x)(b+x)(c+x)} = x$$

or $$(a+x)(b+x)(c+x) = x^2$$

Hence, x is a root of the equation $(a+x)(b+x)(c+x) = x^2$

112. Let $A = \{a_1, a_2, \ldots, a_n\}$

For each $a_i \in A$ $(1 \le i \le n)$, we have the following choices.

(i) $a_i \in P$ and $a_i \in Q$ (ii) $a_i \in P$ and $a_i \notin Q$

(iii) $a_i \notin P$ and $a_i \in Q$ (iv) $a_i \notin P$ and $a_i \notin Q$

Therefore, for one element a_i of A, total number of cases is 4.

Let S be the sample space

$$\therefore \quad n(S) = 4^n$$

and number of cases in which $a_i \in P \cup Q$ is 3, since case $4 \notin P \cup Q$ and let E be the event of favourable cases, then

$n(E)$ = number of ways in which exactly r elements of A will belong to $P \cup Q$

$$= {}^nC_r (3)^r\, 1^{n-r} = {}^nC_r 3^r$$

$$\therefore \text{ Required probability, } P(E) = \frac{n(E)}{n(S)} = \frac{{}^nC_r 3^r}{4^n}$$

113. Given that $P(A) = \alpha$, $P(B/A) = P(B'/A') = 1 - \alpha$

Thus, $P(A') = 1 - P(A) = 1 - \alpha$

and $P(B/A') = 1 - P(B'/A') = 1 - (1-\alpha) = \alpha$ ...(i)

$$\therefore \quad P(A'/B) = \frac{P(A' \cap B)}{P(B)}$$

$$= \frac{P(B) - P(A \cap B)}{P(B)} = \frac{P(B) - P(A) \cdot P(B/A)}{P(B)}$$

$$\left[\because P\left(\frac{B}{A}\right) = \frac{P(A \cap B)}{P(A)}\right]$$

$$= \frac{P(B) - \alpha(1-\alpha)}{P(B)} \quad \text{...(ii)}$$

But $P(B) = P(A) \cdot P(B/A) + P(A') \cdot P(B/A')$

$$= \alpha(1-\alpha) + (1-\alpha) \cdot \alpha \quad \text{[from Eq. (i)]}$$
$$= 2\alpha(1-\alpha) \quad \text{...(3)}$$

Putting the value of $P(B)$ from Eq. (iii) in Eq. (ii), then

$$P\left(\frac{A'}{B}\right) = \frac{2\alpha(1-\alpha) - \alpha(1-\alpha)}{2\alpha(1-\alpha)} = \frac{\alpha(1-\alpha)}{2\alpha(1-\alpha)} = \frac{1}{2}$$

which is independent of α.

114. Let S be the sample space and E be the event that each of the n pairs of balls drawn consists of one white and one red ball.

$$\therefore \quad n(S) = ({}^{2n}C_2)({}^{2n-2}C_2)({}^{2n-4}C_2) \ldots ({}^4C_2)({}^2C_2)$$

$$= \left\{\frac{(2n)(2n-1)}{1 \cdot 2}\right\}\left\{\frac{(2n-2)(2n-3)}{1 \cdot 2}\right\}\left\{\frac{(2n-4)(2n-5)}{1 \cdot 2}\right\} \ldots \left\{\frac{4 \cdot 3}{1 \cdot 2}\right\}\left\{\frac{2 \cdot 1}{1 \cdot 2}\right\}$$

$$= \frac{1 \cdot 2 \cdot 3 \cdot 4 \ldots (2n-1)\, 2n}{2^n} = \frac{2n!}{2^n}$$

and $n(E) = ({}^nC_1\, {}^nC_1)({}^{n-1}C_1\, {}^{n-1}C_1)({}^{n-2}C_1\, {}^{n-2}C_1) \ldots ({}^2C_1 \cdot {}^2C_1)({}^1C_1 \cdot {}^1C_1)$

$$= n^2 \cdot (n-1)^2 \cdot (n-2)^2 \ldots 2^2 \cdot 1^2 = [1 \cdot 2 \cdot 3 \ldots (n-1)\, n]^2 = (n!)^2$$

$\therefore$ Required probability,

$$P(E) = \frac{n(E)}{n(S)} = \frac{(n!)^2}{(2n)!/2^n} = \frac{2^n}{\dfrac{2n!}{(n!)^2}} = \frac{2^n}{{}^{2n}C_n}$$

115. Let p be the probability that any one thing is received by a men and q be the probability that any one thing is received by a women.

$$\therefore \quad p = \frac{a}{a+b} \text{ and } q = \frac{b}{a+b}$$

Clearly, $p + q = 1$ i.e., $q = 1 - p$

Out of m things, if r are received by a men, then the rest $(m-r)$ will be received by women.

The probability for this to happen is given by

$$P(r) = {}^mC_r p^r q^{m-r} \quad [r = 0, 1, \ldots, m]$$

The probability P that odd number of things are received by men is given by

$$P = P(1) + P(3) + P(5) + \ldots$$

$$= {}^mC_1 pq^{m-1} + {}^mC_3 p^3 q^{m-3} + {}^mC_5 p^5 q^{m-5} + \ldots \quad \ldots\text{(i)}$$

We know that,

$$(q+p)^m = q^m + {}^mC_1 q^{m-1} p + {}^mC_2 q^{m-2} p^2 + \ldots + p^m \quad \ldots\text{(ii)}$$

and $(q-p)^m = q^m - {}^mC_1 q^{m-1} p + {}^mC_2 q^{m-2} p^2 - \ldots + (-1)^m p^m$ ...(iii)

Subtracting Eq.(iii) from Eq. (ii), then

$$(q+p)^m - (q-p)^m = 2\{{}^mC_1 q^{m-1} p + {}^mC_3 q^{m-3} p^3 + \ldots\}$$

$$= 2P \quad \text{[from Eq. (i)]}$$

$$\therefore \quad P = \frac{1}{2}\{(q+p)^m - (q-p)^m\}$$

$$= \frac{1}{2}\left\{1 - \left(\frac{b-a}{b+a}\right)^m\right\} = \frac{1}{2}\left\{\frac{(b+a)^m - (b-a)^m}{(b+a)^m}\right\}$$

116. $\because P(C) = \frac{1}{7}, P(S) = \frac{3}{7}, P(B) = \frac{2}{7}, P(T) = \frac{1}{7}$

Let E be the event that person reaches late

$$\therefore P\left(\frac{E}{C}\right) = \frac{2}{9}, P\left(\frac{E}{S}\right) = \frac{1}{9}, P\left(\frac{E}{B}\right) = \frac{4}{9}, P\left(\frac{E}{T}\right) = \frac{1}{9}$$

To find $P\left(\frac{C}{E}\right)$ [$\because$ reaches in time = not late]

Using Baye's Theorem

$$P\left(\frac{C}{E}\right) = \frac{P(C).P\left(\frac{\overline{E}}{C}\right)}{P(C).P\left(\frac{\overline{E}}{C}\right) + P(S).P\left(\frac{\overline{E}}{S}\right) + P(B).P\left(\frac{\overline{E}}{B}\right) + P(T).P\left(\frac{\overline{E}}{T}\right)}$$

$$= \frac{\frac{1}{7}\times\left(1-\frac{2}{9}\right)}{\frac{1}{7}\times\left(1-\frac{2}{9}\right) + \frac{3}{7}\times\left(1-\frac{1}{9}\right) + \frac{2}{7}\times\left(1-\frac{4}{9}\right) + \frac{1}{7}\times\left(1-\frac{1}{9}\right)}$$

$$= \frac{7}{7 + 3\times 8 + 2\times 5 + 8} = \frac{7}{49} = \frac{1}{7}$$

117. Probability of getting 1 is $\frac{1}{6}$ and probability of not getting 1 is $\frac{5}{6}$.

Then, getting 1 in even number of chances = getting 1 in 2nd chance or in 4th chance or in 6th chance and so on.

$\therefore$ Required probability

$$= \frac{5}{6}\times\frac{1}{6} + \left(\frac{5}{6}\right)^3 \times\frac{1}{6} + \left(\frac{5}{6}\right)^6 \times\frac{1}{6} + \ldots\infty$$

$$= \frac{\frac{5}{36}}{1-\frac{25}{36}} = \frac{5}{11}$$

118. $P(\overline{A\cup B}) = \frac{1}{6}; P(A\cap B) = \frac{1}{4}$,

$$P(\overline{A}) = \frac{1}{4} \Rightarrow P(A) = \frac{3}{4},$$

$$P(\overline{A\cup B}) = 1 - P(A\cup B)$$

$$= 1 - P(A) - P(B) + P(A\cap B)$$

$$\Rightarrow \quad \frac{1}{6} = \frac{1}{4} - P(B) + \frac{1}{4}$$

$$\Rightarrow \quad P(B) = \frac{1}{3}$$

Since, $P(A\cap B) = P(A)\cdot P(B)$ and $P(A) \neq P(B)$

$\therefore$ A and B are independent but not equally likely.

119. For a particular house being selected, probability $= \frac{1}{3}$

Probability (all the persons apply for the same house)

$$= \left(\frac{1}{3}\times\frac{1}{3}\times\frac{1}{3}\right)3 = \frac{1}{9}$$

120. $P(X > 1.5) = 1 - P(X=0) - P(X=1)$

$$P(X=k) = e^{-\lambda}\frac{\lambda^k}{k!}$$

$$\therefore \quad P(x > 1.5) = 1 - \frac{1}{e^2} - \frac{2}{e^2} = 1 - \frac{3}{e^2} \quad [\because \lambda = np = 2]$$

121. (i) $P(u_i) = ki, \Sigma P(u_i) = 1 \Rightarrow k = \frac{2}{n(n+1)}$

$$\lim_{n\to\infty} P(w) = \lim_{n\to\infty}\sum_{i=1}^{\infty}\frac{2i^2}{n(n+1)^2}$$

$$= \lim_{n\to\infty}\frac{2n(n+1)(2n+1)}{n(n+1)^2 6} = \frac{2}{3}$$

(ii) $$P\left(\frac{u_n}{w}\right) = \frac{P(u_n\cap w)}{P(w)} = \frac{P(u_n)\cdot P\left(\frac{w}{u_n}\right)}{\sum_{i=1}^{n} P(u_n)\cdot P\left(\frac{w}{u_i}\right)}$$

$$\frac{c\frac{n}{n+1}}{c\sum_{i=1}^{n}\frac{i}{(n+1)}} = \frac{n.2}{n(n+1)} = \frac{2}{n+1}$$

(iii) $$E = u_2 \cup u_4 \cup u_6 \cup \ldots \cup u_n$$

$$P(E) = P(u_2) + P(u_4) + \ldots + P(u_n)$$

$$= \frac{1}{n} + \frac{1}{n} + \ldots + \frac{1}{n} = \frac{1}{n}\frac{n}{2} = \frac{1}{2}$$

$$P\left(\frac{w}{E}\right) = \frac{P(w\cap E)}{P(E)}$$

$$= \frac{P(w\cap u_2) + P(w\cap u_4) + \ldots + P(w\cap u_n)}{\frac{1}{2}}$$

$$= 2\left[\frac{1}{n}\cdot\frac{2}{n+1} + \frac{1}{n}\cdot\frac{4}{n+1} + \ldots + \frac{1}{n}\cdot\frac{n}{n+1}\right]$$

$$= \frac{2}{n}\cdot\frac{\frac{n}{4}(2+n)}{n+1} = \frac{n+2}{2(n+1)}$$

122. $P(X = r) = \dfrac{e^{-m} m^r}{r!}$

$= P(X \le 1) = P(X = 0) + P(X = 1)$

$= e^{-5} + 5 \times e^{-5} = \dfrac{6}{e^5}$ $[\because m = \text{mean} = 5]$

123. Let E be the event when each American man is seated adjacent to his wife and A be the event when Indian man is seated adjacent to his wife.

Now, $n(A \cap E) = (4!) \times (2!)^5$ and $n(E) = (5!) \times (2!)^4$

$\Rightarrow P\left(\dfrac{A}{E}\right) = \dfrac{P(A \cap E)}{P(E)} = \dfrac{n(A \cap E)}{n(E)} = \dfrac{(4!) \times (2!)^5}{(5!) \times (2!)^4} = \dfrac{2}{5}$

124. Statement-1 If $P(H_i \cap E) = 0$ for some i, then

$$P\left(\frac{H_i}{E}\right) = P\left(\frac{E}{H_i}\right) = 0$$

If $P(H_i \cap E) \ne 0$, $\forall\ i = 1, 2, 3, \ldots, n$, then

$P\left(\dfrac{H_i}{E}\right) = \dfrac{P(H_i \cap E)}{P(E)} = \dfrac{P(H_i \cap E)}{P(H_i)} \times \dfrac{P(H_i)}{P(E)}$

$= P\left(\dfrac{E}{H_i}\right) \times \dfrac{P(H_i)}{P(E)} > P\left(\dfrac{E}{H_i}\right) . P(H_i)$ [as $0 < P(E) < 1$]

Hence, Statement-1 may not always be true.

Statement -2 Clearly, $H_1 \cup H_2 \cup \ldots \cup H_n = S$ (Sample space)

$\Rightarrow P(H_1) + P(H_2) + \ldots + P(H_n) = 1$

125. $P\left(\dfrac{E^c \cap F^c}{G}\right) = \dfrac{P(E^c \cap F^c \cap G)}{P(G)}$

$= \dfrac{P(G) - P(E \cap G) - P(F \cap G)}{P(G)}$

$= \dfrac{P(G) - P(E) \cdot P(G) - P(F) \cdot P(G)}{P(G)}$

$= 1 - P(E) - P(F) = P(E^c) - P(F)$

126. Probability of getting sum of nine in a single thrown $= \dfrac{1}{9}$

$\therefore$ Probability of getting sum nine exactly two times out of three draws $= {}^3C_2 \left(\dfrac{1}{9}\right)^2 \left(\dfrac{8}{9}\right) = \dfrac{8}{243}$

127. $P(I) = 0.3$, $P(II) = 0.2$

$\therefore$ Required probability

$= P(\bar{I}) P(II) = (1 - P(I)) P(II) = (1 - 0.3) \times 0.2 = 0.7 \times 0.2 = 0.14$

128. Since, $P(A) = \dfrac{2}{5}$

For independent events,

$$P(A \cap B) = P(A) P(B) \Rightarrow P(A \cap B) \le \frac{2}{5}$$

$$\Rightarrow P(A \cap B) = \frac{1}{10}, \frac{2}{10}, \frac{3}{10}, \frac{4}{10}$$

[maximum 4 outcomes may be in $A \cap B$]

(i) Now, $P(A \cap B) = \dfrac{1}{10}$

$\Rightarrow P(A) \cdot P(B) = \dfrac{1}{10}$

$\Rightarrow P(B) = \dfrac{1}{10} \times \dfrac{5}{2} = \dfrac{1}{4}$, not possible

(ii) Now, $P(A \cap B) = \dfrac{2}{10} \Rightarrow \dfrac{2}{5} \times P(B) = \dfrac{2}{10}$

$\Rightarrow P(B) = \dfrac{5}{10}$, outcomes of $B = 5$

(iii) Now, $P(A \cap B) = \dfrac{3}{10}$

$\Rightarrow P(A) P(B) = \dfrac{3}{10} \Rightarrow \dfrac{2}{5} \times P(B) = \dfrac{3}{10}$

$P(B) = \dfrac{3}{4}$, not possible

(iv) Now, $P(A \cap B) = \dfrac{4}{10} \Rightarrow P(A) \cdot P(B) = \dfrac{4}{10}$

$\Rightarrow P(B) = 1$, outcomes of $B = 10$.

129. For unique solution $\begin{vmatrix} a & b \\ c & d \end{vmatrix} \ne 0$,

where $a, b, c, d \in \{0, 1\}$. Total cases $= 16$

Favourable cases $= 6$ (Either $ad = 1$, $bc = 0$ or $ad = 0$, $bc = 1$)

Probability that system of equations has unique solution is $\dfrac{6}{16} = \dfrac{3}{8}$ and system of equations has either unique solution or infinite solutions, so that probability for system to have a solution is 1.

130. $A = \{4, 5, 6\}$, $B = \{1, 2, 3, 4\}$

$\therefore A \cup B = \{1, 2, 3, 4, 5, 6\}$

$\Rightarrow n(A \cup B) = 6$ and total ways $= 6$

$\therefore P(A \cup B) = \dfrac{6}{6} = 1$

131. $\because P\left(\dfrac{A}{B}\right) = \dfrac{1}{2} \Rightarrow \dfrac{P(A \cap B)}{P(B)} = \dfrac{1}{2}$ ...(i)

and $P\left(\dfrac{B}{A}\right) = \dfrac{2}{3} \Rightarrow \dfrac{P(A \cap B)}{P(A)} = \dfrac{2}{3}$ ...(ii)

On dividing Eq. (i) by Eq. (ii), we get

$$\frac{P(A)}{P(B)} = \frac{3}{4} \Rightarrow P(B) = \frac{4}{3} P(A)$$

$$= \frac{4}{3} \times \frac{1}{4} = \frac{1}{3} \quad \left[\because P(A) = \frac{1}{4}\right]$$

132. $P(X = 3) = \left(\dfrac{5}{6}\right)\left(\dfrac{5}{6}\right)\dfrac{1}{6} = \dfrac{25}{216}$

133. $P(X \ge 3) = 1 - P(X \le 2) = 1 - \left\{\dfrac{1}{6} + \dfrac{5}{6} \times \dfrac{1}{6}\right\} = 1 - \dfrac{11}{36} = \dfrac{25}{36}$

134. $P(X \ge 6) = \dfrac{5^5}{6^6} + \dfrac{5^6}{6^7} + \ldots \infty = \dfrac{\frac{5^5}{6^6}}{1 - \frac{5}{6}} = \left(\dfrac{5}{6}\right)^5$

and $P(X > 3) = \dfrac{5^3}{6^4} + \dfrac{5^4}{6^5} + \dfrac{5^5}{6^6} + \ldots \infty = \dfrac{\frac{5^3}{6^4}}{1 - \frac{5}{6}} = \left(\dfrac{5}{6}\right)^3$

Hence, the conditional probability $= \dfrac{\left(\frac{5}{6}\right)^5}{\left(\frac{5}{6}\right)^3} = \dfrac{25}{36}$

135. $1 - q^n \geq \frac{9}{10} \Rightarrow q^n \leq \frac{1}{10} \Rightarrow \left(\frac{3}{4}\right)^n \leq \frac{1}{10}$

$\Rightarrow n(\log_{10} 3 - \log_{10} 4) \leq 0 - 1 \Rightarrow n \geq \frac{1}{(\log_{10} 4 - \log_{10} 3)}$

136. $S = \{00, 01, 02, ..., 49\}$

Let A be the event that sum of the digits on the selected ticket is 8, then $A = \{08, 17, 26, 26, 35, 44\}$

and let B be the event that the product of the digits is zero, then

$B = \{00, 01, 02, ..., 09, 10, 20, 30, 40\}$

$\therefore \quad A \cap B = \{08\}$

$\therefore$ Required probability $= P\left(\frac{A}{B}\right) = \frac{P(A \cap B)}{P(B)} = \frac{\frac{1}{50}}{\frac{14}{50}} = \frac{1}{14}$

137. Required probability $= \frac{2 \times 2 \times 2(3!)}{6^3} = \frac{2}{9}$

138. Let E_1 denote original signal is green, E_2 denote original signal is red and E denote signal received at station B is green.

$$\therefore \quad P\left(\frac{E_1}{E}\right) = \frac{P(E_1) \cdot P\left(\frac{E}{E_1}\right)}{P(E_1) \cdot P\left(\frac{E}{E_1}\right) + P(E_2) \cdot P\left(\frac{E}{E_2}\right)}$$

$$= \frac{\frac{4}{5}\left[\left(\frac{3}{4}\right)^2 + \left(\frac{1}{4}\right)^2\right]}{\frac{4}{5}\left[\left(\frac{3}{4}\right)^2 + \left(\frac{1}{4}\right)^2\right] + \frac{1}{5}\left[\frac{3}{4} \times \frac{1}{4} + \frac{1}{4} \times \frac{3}{4}\right]} = \frac{40}{46} = \frac{20}{23}$$

139. Total ways $= {}^{20}C_4 = \frac{20 \,.\, 19 \,.\, 18 \,.\, 17}{1 \,.\, 2 \,.\, 3 \,.\, 4} = 4845$

Statement-1

Common difference (d)	Number of cases
1	17
2	14
3	11
4	8
5	5
6	2

$\therefore$ Number of favourable cases $= 17 + 14 + 11 + 8 + 5 + 2$
$= 57$

$\therefore$ Required probability $= \frac{57}{4845} = \frac{1}{85}$

Statement-1 is true and Statement-2 is false.

140. Total ways, ${}^9C_3 = \frac{9 \cdot 8 \cdot 7}{1 \cdot 2 \cdot 3} = 84$

Favourable ways $= {}^3C_1 \times {}^4C_1 \times {}^2C_1 = 24$

$\therefore$ Required probability $= \frac{24}{84} = \frac{2}{7}$

141. $H \to 1$ ball from U_1 to U_2

$T \to 2$ balls from U_1 to U_2

E : 1 ball drawn from U_2

$$\therefore P(W \text{ from } U_2) = \frac{1}{2} \times \left(\frac{3}{5} \times 1\right) + \frac{1}{2} \times \left(\frac{2}{5} \times \frac{1}{2}\right)$$

$$+ \frac{1}{2} \times \left(\frac{{}^3C_2}{{}^5C_2} \times \frac{1}{3}\right) + \frac{1}{2} \times \left(\frac{{}^3C_1 \cdot {}^2C_1}{{}^5C_2} \times \frac{2}{3}\right) = \frac{23}{30}$$

142. $$P\left(\frac{H}{W}\right) = \frac{P(H) \times P\left(\frac{W}{H}\right)}{P(H) \times P\left(\frac{W}{H}\right) + P(T) \times P\left(\frac{W}{T}\right)} = \frac{\frac{1}{2}\left(\frac{3}{2} \times 1 + \frac{2}{5} \times \frac{1}{2}\right)}{\frac{23}{30}}$$

$$= \frac{12}{23}$$

143. Let $P(E) = e$ and $P(F) = f$

$\Rightarrow \quad P(E \cup F) - P(E \cap F) = \frac{11}{25}$

$\Rightarrow \quad P(E) + P(F) - 2P(E \cap F) = \frac{11}{25}$

$\Rightarrow \quad e + f - 2ef = \frac{11}{25}$ ...(i)

$P(\overline{E} \cap \overline{F}) = \frac{2}{25} \Rightarrow P(\overline{E}).\, P(\overline{F}) = \frac{2}{25} \Rightarrow (1 - e)(1 - f) = \frac{2}{25}$

$\Rightarrow \quad e + f - ef = \frac{23}{25}$ ...(ii)

From Eqs. (i) and (ii), we get $ef = \frac{12}{25}$ and $e + f = \frac{7}{5}$

On solving, we get $e = \frac{4}{5}, f = \frac{3}{5}$ or $e = \frac{3}{5}, f = \frac{4}{5}$

144. Given probability of atleast one failure $\geq \frac{31}{32}$

$\Rightarrow \quad 1 - P(X = 0) \geq \frac{31}{32}$

$\Rightarrow 1 - {}^5C_0 \cdot Q^0 \cdot P^5 \geq \frac{31}{32}$ $\quad [\because (P + Q)^5]$

$\Rightarrow \quad P^5 \leq \frac{1}{32}$

$\therefore \quad P \leq \frac{1}{2}$ and $P \geq 0 \Rightarrow P \in \left[0, \frac{1}{2}\right]$

145. We have, $C \subset D \Rightarrow C \cap D = C$

$\Rightarrow P\left(\frac{C}{D}\right) = \frac{P(C \cap D)}{P(D)} = \frac{P(C)}{P(D)} \geq P(C)$ $\quad [\because 0 < P(D) \leq 1]$

146. $$P\left(\frac{A^c \cap B^c}{C}\right) = \frac{P(A^c \cap B^c \cap C)}{P(C)}$$

$$= \frac{P(C) - P(A \cap C) - P(B \cap C) + P(A \cap B \cap C)}{P(C)}$$

$$= \frac{P(C) - P(A) \cdot P(C) - P(B) \cdot P(C) + 0}{P(C)}$$

[$\because$ A, B, C are pairwise independent]

$= 1 - P(A) - P(B) = P(A^c) - P(B)$

147. $P(X) = P(X_1 \cap X_2 \cap X_3) + P(\overline{X}_1 \cap X_2 \cap X_3) + P(X_1 \cap \overline{X}_2 \cap X_3) + P(X_1 \cap X_2 \cap \overline{X}_3)$

$$= \frac{1}{2}\cdot\frac{1}{4}\cdot\frac{1}{4} + \frac{1}{2}\cdot\frac{1}{4}\cdot\frac{1}{4} + \frac{1}{2}\cdot\frac{3}{4}\cdot\frac{1}{4} + \frac{1}{2}\cdot\frac{1}{4}\cdot\frac{3}{4} = \frac{1}{4}$$

(a) $P\left(\frac{X_1}{X}\right) = \frac{\frac{1}{2}\cdot\frac{1}{4}\cdot\frac{1}{4}}{\frac{1}{4}} = \frac{1}{8}$

(b) P (exactly two engines of the ship are functioning / X)

$$= \frac{\frac{1}{2}\cdot\frac{1}{4}\cdot\frac{1}{4} + \frac{1}{2}\cdot\frac{3}{4}\cdot\frac{1}{4} + \frac{1}{2}\cdot\frac{1}{4}\cdot\frac{3}{4}}{1/4} = \frac{7}{8}$$

(c) $P\left(\frac{X}{X_2}\right)$ = Probability that X occurs given that engine E_2 has started

$$\frac{P(X_1 \cap X_2 \cap X_3) + P(\overline{X}_1 \cap X_2 \cap X_3) + P(X_1 \cap X_2 \cap \overline{X}_3)}{P(X_1 \cap X_2 \cap X_3) + P(\overline{X}_1 \cap X_2 \cap X_3) + P(X_1 \cap X_2 \cap \overline{X}_3) + P(\overline{X}_1 \cap X_2 \cap \overline{X}_3)} = \frac{5}{8}$$

(d) $P\left(\frac{X}{X_1}\right)$ = Probability that X occurs given that engine E_1 has started

$$\frac{P(X_1 \cap X_2 \cap X_3) + P(X_1 \cap \overline{X}_2 \cap X_3) + P(X_1 \cap X_2 \cap \overline{X}_3)}{P(X_1 \cap X_2 \cap X_3) + P(X_1 \cap \overline{X}_2 \cap X_3) + P(X_1 \cap X_2 \cap \overline{X}_3) + P(X_1 \cap \overline{X}_2 \cap \overline{X}_3)} = \frac{7}{16}$$

148. ***Case* I** When D_1, D_2, D_3 all show different number and one of the number is shown by D_4, $P(E_1) = \frac{{}^6C_3 \times 3!}{216} \times \frac{3}{6} = \frac{60}{216}$

***Case* II** When D_1, D_2, D_3 all show same number and that number is shown by D_4, $P(E_2) = 6 \times \left(\frac{1}{6}\right)^4 = \frac{1}{216}$

***Case* III** When two numbers shown by D_1, D_2, D_3 are same and one is different and one of the number is shown by D_4,

$$P(E_3) = \frac{{}^6C_1 \times {}^5C_1}{216} \times \frac{3!}{2!} \times \frac{2}{6} = \frac{30}{216}$$

$\therefore$ Required probability $= P(E_1) + P(E_2) + P(E_3) = \frac{91}{216}$

149. $P\left(\frac{X}{Y}\right) = \frac{P(X \cap Y)}{P(Y)} = \frac{1}{2} \Rightarrow P(Y) = \frac{1}{3}$

$P\left(\frac{Y}{X}\right) = \frac{P(X \cap Y)}{P(X)} = \frac{1}{3} \Rightarrow P(X) = \frac{1}{2}$

(a) $P(X \cup Y) = P(X) + P(Y) - P(X \cap Y) = \frac{2}{3}$

(b) $\because P(X \cap Y) = P(X) \cdot P(Y)$, they are independent. Also, X^c and Y will be independent

Now, $P(X^c \cap Y) = \frac{1}{2} \times \frac{1}{3} = \frac{1}{6} \neq \frac{1}{3}$.

150. $\because S = \{1, 2, 3, \ldots, 8\}$

Let A : Maximum of three numbers is 6

$\therefore A = \{1, 2, 3, 4, 5, 6\}$

and B : Maximum of three numbers is 3

$\therefore B = \{3, 4, 5, 6, 7, 8\}$ and $A \cap B = \{3, 4, 5, 6\}$

$$\Rightarrow P\left(\frac{B}{A}\right) = \frac{P(A \cap B)}{P(A)} = \frac{\frac{n(A \cap B)}{n(S)}}{\frac{n(B)}{n(S)}} = \frac{n(A \cap B)}{n(B)} = \frac{{}^2C_1}{{}^5C_2} = \frac{1}{5}$$

151. Here, $p = \frac{1}{3}$ and $q = 1 - \frac{1}{3} = \frac{2}{3}$

$\therefore$ Required probability $= P(X = 4) + P(X = 5)$ $\left[\because \left(\frac{2}{3} + 1\right)^5\right]$

$$= {}^5C_4\left(\frac{1}{3}\right)^4\left(\frac{2}{3}\right) + {}^5C_5\left(\frac{1}{3}\right)^5 = \frac{11}{3^5}$$

152. Probability of solving the problem correctly by atleast one of them $= 1 - \left(\left(1 - \frac{1}{2}\right)\left(1 - \frac{3}{4}\right)\left(1 - \frac{1}{4}\right)\left(1 - \frac{1}{8}\right)\right) = \frac{235}{256}$

153. Let x, y and z be the probability of occurrence of E_1, E_2 and E_3, respectively.

Then, $\alpha = x(1 - y)(1 - z) = \frac{px}{(1 - x)}$ $[\because p = (1 - x)(1 - y)(1 - z)]$

Similarly, $\beta = \frac{py}{(1 - y)}$ and $\gamma = \frac{pz}{(1 - z)}$

Now, $(\alpha - 2\beta)\, p = \alpha\beta$

$\Rightarrow \frac{p}{\beta} - \frac{2p}{\alpha} = 1$

$\Rightarrow \frac{(1 - y)}{y} - \frac{2(1 - x)}{x} = 1$

$\Rightarrow x = 2y$ ...(i)

and $(\beta - 3\gamma)\, p = 2\beta$

$\Rightarrow \frac{p}{\gamma} - \frac{3p}{\beta} = 2$

$\Rightarrow \frac{(1 - z)}{z} - \frac{3(1 - y)}{y} = 2$

$\Rightarrow y = 3z$ ...(ii)

From Eqs. (i) and (ii), we get $x = 6z$ $\therefore \frac{x}{z} = 6$

154. Let E = Event that one ball is white and the other ball is red.

Then, $$P\left(\frac{B_2}{E}\right) = \frac{\frac{{}^2C_1 \times {}^3C_1}{{}^9C_2}}{\frac{{}^1C_1 \times {}^3C_1}{{}^6C_2} + \frac{{}^2C_1 \times {}^3C_1}{{}^9C_2} + \frac{{}^3C_1 \times {}^4C_1}{{}^{12}C_2}} = \frac{55}{181}$$

155. Required probability $= \prod_{i=1}^{3} P(W_i) + \prod_{i=1}^{3} P(R_i) + \prod_{i=1}^{3} P(B_i)$

$$= \frac{1}{6} \times \frac{2}{9} \times \frac{3}{12} + \frac{3}{6} \times \frac{3}{9} \times \frac{4}{12} + \frac{2}{6} \times \frac{4}{9} \times \frac{5}{12}$$

$$= \frac{82}{648}$$

156. $\because P(A \cup B) = 1 - P(\overline{A \cup B}) = 1 - \frac{1}{6} = \frac{5}{6}$

$$P(A) = 1 - P(\overline{A}) = 1 - \frac{1}{4} = \frac{3}{4}$$

and $P(B) = P(A \cup B) - P(A) + P(A \cap B)$

$$= \frac{5}{6} - \frac{3}{4} + \frac{1}{4} = \frac{1}{3}$$

$\Rightarrow A$ and B are not equally likely.

Also, $P(A \cap B) = \frac{1}{4} = \frac{3}{4} \times \frac{1}{3} = P(A) \,.\, P(B)$

$\therefore$ A and B are independent.

Hence, A and B are independent but not equally likely.

157. $n(S) = 5! = 120$ and possible favourable cases are

$(B, G, G, B, B), (G, G, B, B, B), (G, B, G, B, B),$
$(G, B, B, G, B), (B, G, B, G, B)$

$\therefore$ Number of favourable cases $= n(E) = 5 \times 12 = 60$

$\therefore$ Required probability,

$$P(E) = \frac{n(E)}{n(S)} = \frac{60}{120} = \frac{1}{2}$$

158. $n(S) = 3 \times 5 \times 7 = 105$; $x_1 + x_2 + x_3 =$ odd

***Case* I** All three odd $= 2 \times 3 \times 4 = 24$

***Case* II** Two even and one odd

$= 1 \times 2 \times 4 + 1 \times 3 \times 3 + 2 \times 2 \times 3 = 29 \therefore n(E) = 24 + 29 = 53$

Required probability, $P(E) = \frac{n(E)}{n(S)} = \frac{53}{105}$

159. x_1, x_2, x_3 are in AP.

AP with common difference = 1, (1, 2, 3) (2, 3, 4) (3, 4, 5)

AP with common difference = 2, (1, 3, 5), (2, 4, 6), (3, 5, 7)

AP with common difference = 3, (1, 4, 7)

AP with common difference = 0, (1, 1, 1), (2, 2, 2) (3, 3, 3)

$\therefore$ $n(E) = 10$

$\therefore$ Required probability, $P(E) = \frac{n(E)}{n(S)} = \frac{10}{105}$

160. We have mentioned that boxes are different and one particular box has 3 balls.

Then number of ways $= \frac{{}^{12}C_3 \times 2^9}{3^{12}} = \frac{55}{3}\left(\frac{2}{3}\right)^{11}$

161. Using Binomial distribution

$$P(X \geq 2) = 1 - P(X = 0) - P(X = 1)$$

$$= 1 - \left(\frac{1}{2}\right)^n - \left[{}^nC_1 \cdot \left(\frac{1}{2}\right) \cdot \left(\frac{1}{2}\right)^{n-1}\right]$$

$$= 1 - \frac{1}{2^n} - {}^nC_1 \cdot \frac{1}{2^n} = 1 - \left(\frac{1+n}{2^n}\right)$$

Given, $P(X \geq 2) \geq 0.96$

$$1 - \frac{(n+1)}{2^n} \geq \frac{24}{25}$$

$$\Rightarrow \quad \frac{(n+1)}{2^n} \leq \frac{1}{25}$$

$$\Rightarrow \quad n = 8$$

162.

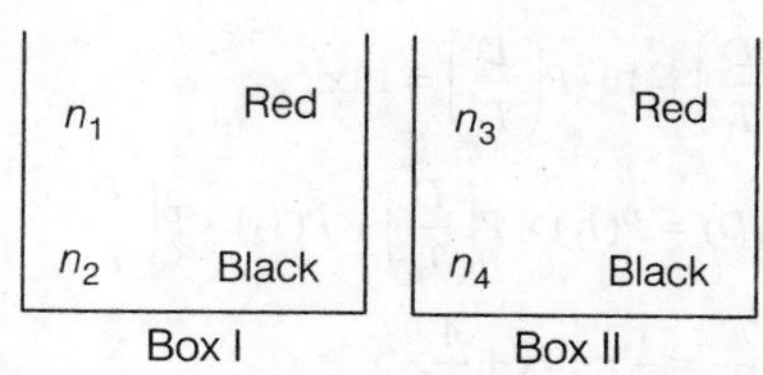

Let A = Drawing red ball

$\therefore$ $P(A) = P(B_1) \cdot P(A / B_1) + P(B_2) \cdot P(A / B_2)$

$$= \frac{1}{2}\left(\frac{n_1}{n_1 + n_2}\right) + \frac{1}{2}\left(\frac{n_3}{n_3 + n_4}\right)$$

Given, $P(B_2 / A) = \frac{1}{3} \Rightarrow \frac{P(B_2) \cdot P(B_2 \cap A)}{P(A)} = \frac{1}{3}$

$$\Rightarrow \quad \frac{\frac{1}{2}\left(\frac{n_3}{n_3 + n_4}\right)}{\frac{1}{2}\left(\frac{n_1}{n_1 + n_2}\right) + \frac{1}{2}\left(\frac{n_3}{n_3 + n_4}\right)} = \frac{1}{3}$$

$$\Rightarrow \quad \frac{n_3(n_1 + n_2)}{n_1(n_3 + n_4) + n_3(n_1 + n_2)} = \frac{1}{3}$$

Now, check options, then clearly options (a) and (b) satisfy.

163.

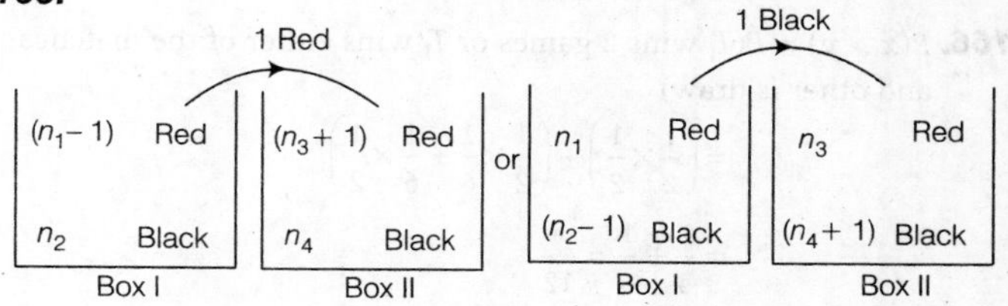

$\therefore P$ (drawing red ball from B_1) $= \frac{1}{3}$

$$\Rightarrow \left(\frac{n_1 - 1}{n_1 + n_2 - 1}\right)\left(\frac{n_1}{n_1 + n_2}\right) + \left(\frac{n_2}{n_1 + n_2}\right)\left(\frac{n_1}{n_1 + n_2 - 1}\right) = \frac{1}{3}$$

$$\Rightarrow \quad \frac{n_1^2 + n_1 n_2 - n_1}{(n_1 + n_2)(n_1 + n_2 - 1)} = \frac{1}{3}$$

Clearly, options (c) and (d) satisfy.

164. $\because$ $P(E_1) = \frac{1}{6}, P(E_2) = \frac{1}{6},$

$$P(E_3) = \frac{2 + 4 + 6 + 4 + 2}{36} = \frac{1}{2}$$

Also, $P(E_1 \cap E_2) = \frac{1}{36},$

$$P(E_1 \cap E_3) = \frac{1}{12}, P(E_3 \cap E_1) = \frac{1}{12}$$

and $P(E_1 \cap E_2 \cap E_3) = 0 \neq P(E_1) . P(E_2) . P(E_3)$

Hence, E_1, E_2, E_3 are not independent

165. $P(T_1) = \frac{200}{100} = \frac{1}{5}, P(T_2) = \frac{80}{100} = \frac{4}{5},$

$P(D) = \frac{7}{100}$. Let $P\left(\frac{D}{T_2}\right) = x$, then

$$P\left(\frac{D}{T_1}\right) = 10 \cdot P\left(\frac{D}{T_2}\right) = 10x$$

$\because$ $$P(D) = P(T_1) \times P\left(\frac{D}{T_1}\right) + P(T_2) \times P\left(\frac{D}{T_2}\right)$$

$\Rightarrow$ $$\frac{7}{100} = \frac{1}{5} \times 10x + \frac{4}{5} \times x$$

$\therefore$ $$x = \frac{1}{40}$$

$\therefore$ $$P\left(\frac{T_2}{\overline{D}}\right) = \frac{P(T_2) \times P\left(\frac{\overline{D}}{T_2}\right)}{P(T_1) \times P\left(\frac{\overline{D}}{T_1}\right) + P(T_2) \times P\left(\frac{\overline{D}}{T_2}\right)}$$

$$= \frac{P(T_2) \times P\left(\frac{\overline{D}}{T_2}\right)}{P(\overline{D})}$$

$$= \frac{\frac{4}{5} \times \frac{39}{40}}{\frac{93}{100}}$$

$$= \frac{78}{93}$$

166. $P(x > y) = P(T_1$ wins 2 games or T_1 wins either of the matches and other is draw)

$$= \left(\frac{1}{2} \times \frac{1}{2}\right) + \left(\frac{1}{2} \times \frac{1}{6} + \frac{1}{6} \times \frac{1}{2}\right)$$

$$= \frac{1}{4} + \frac{1}{6} = \frac{5}{12}$$

167. $P(x = y) = P(T_1$ and T_2 win alternately)

$+P$ (Both matches are draws)

$$= \left(\frac{1}{2} \times \frac{1}{3} + \frac{1}{3} \times \frac{1}{2}\right) + \left(\frac{1}{6} \times \frac{1}{6}\right)$$

$$= \frac{1}{3} + \frac{1}{36} = \frac{13}{36}$$

168. $P = \frac{15}{25} = \frac{3}{5}, Q = 1 - P = 1 - \frac{3}{5} = \frac{2}{5}$

and $n = 10$

$\therefore$ Variance $= nPQ = 10 \times \frac{3}{5} \times \frac{2}{5} = \frac{12}{5}$

169. Cases: (0, 4), (0, 8), (2, 6), (2, 10), (4, 8), (6, 10)

$\therefore$ Required probability $= \frac{6}{{}^{11}C_2} = \frac{6}{55}$

170. $\because$ $$P(A) + P(B) - 2P(A \cap B) = \frac{1}{4} \quad \text{...(i)}$$

$$P(B) + P(C) - 2P(B \cap C) = \frac{1}{4} \quad \text{...(ii)}$$

$$P(C) + P(A) - 2P(C \cap A) = \frac{1}{4} \quad \text{...(iii)}$$

and $$P(A \cap B \cap C) = \frac{1}{16} \quad \text{...(iv)}$$

Now, adding Eqs. (i), (ii) and (iii), then

$$P(A) + P(B) + P(C) - P(A \cap B) - P(B \cap C) - P(C \cap A) = \frac{3}{8} \quad \text{...(v)}$$

On adding Eqs. (iv) and (v), we get

$$P(A) + P(B) + P(C) - P(A \cap B) - P(B \cap C) - P(C \cap A) + P(A \cap B \cap C) = \frac{3}{8} + \frac{1}{16}$$

or $$P(A \cup B \cup C) = \frac{7}{16}$$

CHAPTER

10

Mathematical Induction

Learning Part

- Introduction
- Statement
- Mathematical Statement

Practice Part

- JEE Type Examples
- Chapter Exercises

Arihant on Your Mobile !
Exercises with the symbol can be practised on your mobile. See inside cover page to activate for free.

Introduction

There are two basic processes of reasoning which are commonly used to draw mathematical or scientific conclusions. Reasoning or drawing conclusions can be classified in two categories:

(i) Inductive reasoning
(ii) Deductive reasoning

(i) **Inductive reasoning** This is the process of reasoning from particular to general.

The numbers 324, 576, 603, 732 are all divisible by 3. From these particular results, we can hope to have a general result that all numbers of 3-digits are divisible by 3. But this is not true, because 692 is not divisible by 3.

If at all this conjuctive were true, we would have to establish its validity either by verifying the conjuctive for all possible 3-digit numbers or by using some mathematical process. The process of reasoning a valid general result from particular results is called inductive reasoning.

(ii) **Deductive reasoning** This is the process of reasoning from general to particular.

The sum of first n natural numbers is $\frac{n(n+1)}{2}$. This is a general result. From this, we can deduce that the sum of first 100 natural numbers is $5050 \left(= \frac{100(100+1)}{2} \right)$. This process of reasoning a valid particular result from general result is called deductive reasoning.

The principle of mathematical induction is a mathematical process which is used to establish the validity of a general result involving **natural numbers.**

Statement

A sentence or description which is either definitely true or definitely false is called a **statement.** *For example,*

1. Mumbai is the capital of Maharashtra is a true statement.
2. There are 30 days in February is a false statement.
3. Umang is a good boy is not a statement (as it is not a definite sentence. One day whose name is Umang may be a good boy while the other boy whose name is also Umang may not be a good boy. Also, the word 'good' is not well-defined).

Mathematical Statement

A statement involving mathematical relation or relations is called **mathematical statement.**

A statement concerning the natural number 'n' is generally denoted by $P(n)$.

For example, If $P(n)$ denotes the statement "$n(n+1)$ is divisible by 2",

then $P(3)$: "$3(3+1) = 12$ is divisible by 2"

and $P(8)$: "$8(8+1) = 72$ is divisible by 2", etc.

Here, $P(3)$ and $P(8)$ are both true.

First Principle of Mathematical Induction

To prove that $P(n)$ is true for all natural numbers $n \geq i$, we proceed as follows:

***Step* I** (*Verification Step*) : Verify $P(n)$ for $n = i$.

***Step* II** (*Assumption Step*) : Assume $P(n)$ is true for $n = k > i$.

***Step* III** (*Induction Step*) : Using results in Step I and Step II, prove that $P(k+1)$ is true.

Remark

If $P(n)$ is true for $n = 1$ (i.e., for $i =$).

Second Principle of Mathematical Induction

Sometimes the above procedure will not work. Then, we consider the alternative principle called the second principle of mathematical induction, which consists of the following steps:

***Step* I** (*Verification Step*) : Verify $P(n)$ for $n = i$.

***Step* II** (*Assumption Step*) : Assume $P(n)$ is true for $i < n \leq k$.

***Step* III** (*Induction Step*) : Prove $P(n)$ for $n = k+1$.

Remark

The second principle of mathematical induction is useful to prove recurrence relations which involve three successive terms,

For example, statements of the type

$$pT_{n+1} = qT_n + rT_{n-1}$$

Different Types of Problems of Mathematical Induction

Type I These problems are of the **Identity Type.** Examples of this type are as follows:

Example 1. Prove by mathematical induction that $1^3 + 2^3 + 3^3 + \dots + n^3 = \left[\frac{n(n+1)}{2}\right]^2$ for every natural number n.

Sol. Let $P(n): 1^3 + 2^3 + 3^3 + \dots + n^3 = \left[\frac{n(n+1)}{2}\right]^2$ ...(i)

Step I For $n = 1$, LHS of Eq. (i) $= 1^3 = 1$

and RHS of Eq. (i) $= \left[\frac{1(1+1)}{2}\right]^2 = 1^2 = 1$

$\therefore$ LHS = RHS

Therefore, $P(1)$ is true.

Step II Assume $P(k)$ is true, then

$$P(k): 1^3 + 2^3 + 3^3 + \dots + k^3 = \left[\frac{k(k+1)}{2}\right]^2$$

Step III For $n = k + 1$,

$$P(k+1): 1^3 + 2^3 + 3^3 + \dots + k^3 + (k+1)^3 = \left[\frac{(k+1)(k+2)}{2}\right]^2$$

$$\text{LHS} = 1^3 + 2^3 + 3^3 + \dots + k^3 + (k+1)^3$$

$$= \left[\frac{k(k+1)}{2}\right]^2 + (k+1)^3$$

[by assumption step]

$$= \frac{(k+1)^2}{4}[k^2 + 4(k+1)]$$

$$= \frac{(k+1)^2(k^2 + 4k + 4)}{4}$$

$$= \frac{(k+1)^2(k+2)^2}{4}$$

$$= \left[\frac{(k+1)(k+2)}{2}\right]^2 = \text{RHS}$$

Therefore, $P(k+1)$ is true. Hence, by the principle of mathematical induction, $P(n)$ is true for all $n \in N$.

Example 2. Prove by mathematical induction that $1\cdot2\cdot3 + 2\cdot3\cdot4 + \dots + n(n+1)(n+2) = \frac{n(n+1)(n+2)(n+3)}{4}$ for every natural number.

Sol. Let $P(n): 1\cdot2\cdot3 + 2\cdot3\cdot4 + \dots + n(n+1)(n+2)$

$$= \frac{n(n+1)(n+2)(n+3)}{4} \quad \text{...(i)}$$

Step I For $n = 1$, LHS of Eq. (i) $= 1\cdot2\cdot3 = 6$

and RHS of Eq. (i) $= \frac{1\cdot(1+1)(1+2)(1+3)}{4} = 6$

$\therefore$ LHS = RHS

Therefore, $P(1)$ is true.

Step II Assume that $P(k)$ is true, then

$$P(k): 1\cdot2\cdot3 + 2\cdot3\cdot4 + \dots + k(k+1)(k+2) = \frac{k(k+1)(k+2)(k+3)}{4}$$

Step III For $n = k + 1$

$$P(k+1): 1\cdot2\cdot3 + 2\cdot3\cdot4 + \dots + k(k+1)(k+2) + (k+1)(k+2)(k+3) = \frac{(k+1)(k+2)(k+3)(k+4)}{4}$$

$$\therefore \text{LHS} = 1\cdot2\cdot3 + 2\cdot3\cdot4 + \dots + k(k+1)(k+2) + (k+1)(k+2)(k+3)$$

$$= \frac{k(k+1)(k+2)(k+3)}{4} + (k+1)(k+2)(k+3)$$

[by assumption step]

$$= \frac{(k+1)(k+2)(k+3)}{4}(k+4)$$

$$= \frac{(k+1)(k+2)(k+3)(k+4)}{4} = \text{RHS}$$

Therefore, $P(k+1)$ is true. Hence, by the principle of mathematical induction $P(n)$ is true for all $n \in N$.

Example 3. Prove by mathematical induction that $\frac{1}{1\cdot2\cdot3} + \frac{1}{2\cdot3\cdot4} + \dots + \frac{1}{n(n+1)(n+2)} = \frac{n(n+3)}{4(n+1)(n+2)}$, $\forall n \in N$.

Sol. Let $P(n): \frac{1}{1\cdot2\cdot3} + \frac{1}{2\cdot3\cdot4} + \dots + \frac{1}{n(n+1)(n+2)}$

$$= \frac{n(n+3)}{4(n+1)(n+2)} \quad \text{...(i)}$$

Step I For $n = 1$,

LHS of Eq. (i) $= \frac{1}{1\cdot2\cdot3} = \frac{1}{6}$

and RHS of Eq. (i) $= \frac{1\cdot(1+3)}{4(1+1)(1+2)} = \frac{1}{6}$

Therefore, $P(1)$ is true.

Step II Assume that $P(k)$ is true, then

$$P(k): \frac{1}{1\cdot2\cdot3}+\frac{1}{2\cdot3\cdot4}+\ldots+\frac{1}{k(k+1)(k+2)} = \frac{k(k+3)}{4(k+1)(k+2)}$$

Step III For $n = k+1$,

$$P(k+1): \frac{1}{1\cdot2\cdot3}+\frac{1}{2\cdot3\cdot4}+\ldots+\frac{1}{k(k+1)(k+2)} + \frac{1}{(k+1)(k+2)(k+3)} = \frac{(k+1)(k+4)}{4(k+2)(k+3)}$$

$$\therefore \text{LHS} = \frac{1}{1\cdot2\cdot3}+\frac{1}{2\cdot3\cdot4}+\ldots+\frac{1}{k(k+1)(k+2)} + \frac{1}{(k+1)(k+2)(k+3)}$$

$$= \frac{k(k+3)}{4(k+1)(k+2)}+\frac{1}{(k+1)(k+2)(k+3)} \quad \text{[by assumption step]}$$

$$= \frac{k(k+3)^2+4}{4(k+1)(k+2)(k+3)}$$

$$= \frac{k^3+6k^2+9k+4}{4(k+1)(k+2)(k+3)}$$

$$= \frac{(k+1)^2(k+4)}{4(k+1)(k+2)(k+3)}$$

$$= \frac{(k+1)(k+4)}{4(k+2)(k+3)} = \text{RHS}$$

Therefore, $P(k+1)$ is true. Hence, by the principle of mathematical induction $P(n)$ is true for all $n \in N$.

Example 4. Prove by mathematical induction that $\sum_{r=0}^{n} r\,{}^nC_r = n\cdot 2^{n-1}$, $\forall\, n \in N$.

Sol. Let $P(n): \sum_{r=0}^{n} r\,{}^nC_r = n\cdot2^{n-1}$

Step I For $n = 1$,

$$\text{LHS of Eq. (i)} = \sum_{r=0}^{1} r\cdot{}^1C_r = 0 + 1\cdot{}^1C_1 = 1$$

and RHS of Eq. (i) $= 1\cdot 2^{1-1} = 2^0 = 1$

Therefore, $P(1)$ is true.

Step II Assume that $P(k)$ is true, then $P(k)$

$$: \sum_{r=0}^{k} r\cdot{}^kC_r = k\cdot2^{k-1}$$

Step III For $n = k+1$

$$P(k+1): \sum_{r=0}^{k+1} r\cdot{}^{k+1}C_r = (k+1)\cdot2^k$$

$$\therefore \text{LHS} = \sum_{r=0}^{k+1} r\cdot{}^{k+1}C_r = 0 + \sum_{r=1}^{k+1} r\cdot{}^{k+1}C_r$$

$$= \sum_{r=1}^{k+1} r\cdot{}^{k+1}C_r = \sum_{r=1}^{k} r\cdot{}^{k+1}C_r + (k+1)\,{}^{k+1}C_{k+1}$$

$$= \sum_{r=1}^{k} r\,({}^kC_r + {}^kC_{r-1}) + (k+1)$$

$$= \sum_{r=1}^{k} r\cdot{}^kC_r + \sum_{r=1}^{k} r\cdot{}^kC_{r-1} + (k+1)$$

$$= \sum_{r=0}^{k} r\cdot{}^kC_r + \sum_{r=0}^{k} r\cdot{}^kC_{r-1} + (k+1)$$

$$= \sum_{r=0}^{k} r\cdot{}^kC_r + \sum_{r=0}^{k+1} r\cdot{}^kC_{r-1}$$

$$= \sum_{r=0}^{k} r\cdot{}^kC_r + \sum_{r=0}^{k} (r+1)\cdot{}^kC_r$$

$$= \sum_{r=0}^{k} r\cdot{}^kC_r + \sum_{r=0}^{k} r\cdot{}^kC_r + \sum_{r=0}^{k} {}^kC_r$$

$$= P(k) + P(k) + 2^k \quad \text{[by assumption step]}$$

$$= k\cdot2^{k-1} + k\cdot2^{k-1} + 2^k = 2\cdot k\cdot2^{k-1} + 2^k$$

$$= k\cdot2^k + 2^k = (k+1)\cdot2^k = \text{RHS}$$

Therefore, $P(k+1)$ is true. Hence, by the principle of mathematical induction $P(n)$ is true for all $n \in N$.

Type II These problems are of the **Divisibility Type**. Examples of this type are as follows:

Example 5. Use the principle of mathematical induction to show that $5^{2n+1}+3^{n+2}\cdot2^{n-1}$ divisible by 19 for all natural numbers n.

Sol. Let $P(n) = 5^{2n+1} + 3^{n+2}\cdot2^{n-1}$

Step I For $n = 1$, $P(1) = 5^{2+1} + 3^{1+2}\cdot2^{1-1}$

$= 125 + 27 = 152$, which is divisible by 19.

Therefore, the result is true for $n = 1$.

Step II Assume that the result is true for $n = k$, i.e.,

$P(k) = 5^{2k+1} + 3^{k+2}\cdot2^{k-1}$ is divisible by 19.

$\Rightarrow P(k) = 19r$, where r is an integer.

Step III For $n = k+1$,

$$P(k+1) = 5^{2(k+1)+1} + 3^{k+1+2}\cdot2^{k+1-1}$$

$$= 5^{2k+3} + 3^{k+3}\cdot2^k$$

$$= 25\cdot5^{2k+1} + 3\cdot3^{k+2}\cdot2\cdot2^{k-1}$$

$$= 25\cdot5^{2k+1} + 6\cdot3^{k+2}\cdot2^{k-1}$$

Now, $5^{2k+1} + 3^{k+2}\cdot2^{k-1}\;\big)\;25\cdot5^{2k+1} + 6\cdot3^{k+2}\cdot2^{k-1}\;\big(25$

$\;25\cdot5^{2k+1} + 25\cdot3^{k+2}\cdot2^{k-1}$

$\;\;\underline{-}\qquad\quad \underline{-}$

$\;\;-19\cdot3^{k+2}\cdot2^{k-1}$

$\therefore \quad 25\cdot5^{2k+1} + 6\cdot3^{k+2}\cdot2^{k-1}$

$= 25\cdot(5^{2k+1} + 3^{k-2}\cdot2^{k-2}) - 19\cdot3^{k+2}\cdot2^{k-1}$

i.e., $P(k+1) = 25\,P(k) - 19\cdot3^{k+2}\cdot2^{k-1}$

But we know that $P(k)$ is divisible by 19. Also, $19\cdot3^{k+2}\cdot2^{k-1}$ is clearly divisible by 19.

Therefore, $P(k+1)$ is divisible by 19. This shows that the result is true for $n = k+1$.

Hence, by the principle of mathematical induction, the result is true for all $n \in N$.

Example 6. Use the principle of mathematical induction to show that $a^n - b^n$ is divisible by $a - b$ for all natural numbers n.

Sol. Let $P(n) = a^n - b^n$

***Step* I** For $n = 1$,

$P(1) = a - b$, which is divisible by $a - b$.

Therefore, the result is true for $n = 1$.

***Step* II** Assume that the result is true for $n = k$,

i.e., $P(k) = a^k - b^k$ is divisible by $a - b$.

$\Rightarrow \quad P(k) = (a-b)\,r$, where r is an integer.

***Step* III** For $n = k+1$,

$\therefore \quad P(k+1) = a^{k+1} - b^{k+1}$

Now, $a^k - b^k \,\big)\, a^{k+1} - b^{k+1} \,\big(\, a$

$\underline{-a^{k+1} \mp ab^k}$

$ab^k - b^{k+1} = b^k(a-b)$

$\therefore \quad a^{k+1} - b^{k+1} = a(a^k - b^k) + b^k(a-b)$

i.e., $\quad P(k+1) = a\,P(k) + b^k\,(a-b)$

But we know that $P(k)$ is divisible by $a - b$. Also, $b^k\,(a-b)$ is clearly divisible by $a - b$.

Therefore, $P(k+1)$ is divisible by $a - b$.

This shows that the result is true for $n = k+1$.

Hence, by the principle of mathematical induction, the result is true for all $n \in N$.

Type III These problems are of the **Inequality Type**. Examples of this type are as follows:

Example 7. Using mathematical induction, show that $\tan n\alpha > n\tan\alpha$, where $0 < \alpha < \dfrac{\pi}{4(n-1)}$, $\forall\, n \in N$ and $n > 1$.

Sol. Let $P(n): \tan n\alpha > n\tan\alpha$

***Step* I** For $n = 2$, $\quad \tan 2\alpha > 2\tan\alpha$

$$\Rightarrow \quad \frac{2\tan\alpha}{1-\tan^2\alpha} - 2\tan\alpha > 0$$

$$\Rightarrow \quad 2\tan\alpha\left(\frac{1-(1-\tan^2\alpha)}{1-\tan^2\alpha}\right) > 0$$

$$\Rightarrow \quad \tan^2\alpha\cdot\tan2\alpha > 0 \quad \left[\because 0 < \alpha < \frac{\pi}{4} \text{ for } n = 2\right]$$

$$\Rightarrow \quad \tan2\alpha > 0 \quad \left[\because 0 < 2\alpha < \frac{\pi}{2}\right]$$

which is true ($\because$ in first quadrant, $\tan2\alpha$ is positive)

Therefore, $P(2)$ is true.

***Step* II** Assume that $P(k)$ is true, then $P(k)$: $\tan k\alpha > k\tan\alpha$

***Step* III** For $n = k+1$, we shall prove that $\tan(k+1)\alpha > (k+1)\tan\alpha$

$$\because \quad \tan(k+1)\alpha = \frac{\tan k\alpha + \tan\alpha}{1 - \tan k\alpha\tan\alpha} \quad \text{...(i)}$$

when $0 < \alpha < \dfrac{\pi}{4k}$ or $0 < k\alpha < \dfrac{\pi}{4}$

i.e. $\quad 0 < \tan k\alpha < 1$, also $0 < \tan\alpha < 1$

$\therefore \quad \tan k\alpha\tan\alpha < 1$

$1 - \tan k\alpha\tan\alpha > 0$ and $1 - \tan k\alpha\tan\alpha < 1$ ...(ii)

From Eqs. (i) and (ii), we get

$$\tan(k+1)\alpha > \frac{\tan k\alpha + \tan\alpha}{1}$$

$$> \tan k\alpha + \tan\alpha > k\tan\alpha + \tan\alpha$$

[by assumption step]

$\therefore \quad \tan(k+1)\alpha > (k+1)\tan\alpha$

Therefore, $P(k+1)$ is true. Hence by the principle of mathematical induction $P(n)$ is true for all $n \in N$.

Example 8. Show using mathematical induction that $n! < \left(\dfrac{n+1}{2}\right)^n$, where $n \in N$ and $n > 1$.

Sol. Let $P(n): n! < \left(\dfrac{n+1}{2}\right)^n$

***Step* I** For $n = 2$, $2! < \left(\dfrac{2+1}{2}\right)^2 \Rightarrow 2 < \dfrac{9}{4}$

$\Rightarrow \quad 2 < 2\cdot25$, which is true.

Therefore, $P(2)$ is true.

***Step* II** Assume that $P(k)$ is true, then

$$P(k): k! < \left(\frac{k+1}{2}\right)^k$$

***Step* III** For $n = k+1$, we shall prove that

$$P(k+1): (k+1)! < \left(\frac{k+2}{2}\right)^{k+1}$$

From assumption step $k! < \dfrac{(k+1)^k}{2^k}$

$$\Rightarrow \quad (k+1)k! < \frac{(k+1)^{k+1}}{2^k}$$

$$\Rightarrow \quad (k+1)! < \frac{(k+1)^{k+1}}{2^k} \quad \text{...(i)}$$

Let us assume, $\frac{(k+1)^{k+1}}{2^k} < \left(\frac{k+2}{2}\right)^{k+1}$ ...(ii)

$$\Rightarrow \quad \left(\frac{k+2}{k+1}\right)^{k+1} > 2 \Rightarrow \left(1+\frac{1}{k+1}\right)^{k+1} > 2$$

$$\Rightarrow \quad 1+(k+1)\cdot\frac{1}{(k+1)} + {}^{k+1}C_2\left(\frac{1}{k+1}\right)^2 + \ldots > 2$$

$$\Rightarrow \quad 1+1+{}^{k+1}C_2\left(\frac{1}{k+1}\right)^2 + \ldots > 2$$

which is true, hence Eq. (ii) is true.

From Eqs. (i) and (ii), we get

$$(k+1)! < \frac{(k+1)^{k+1}}{2^k} < \left(\frac{k+2}{2}\right)^{k+1}$$

$$\Rightarrow (k+1)! < \left(\frac{k+2}{2}\right)^{k+1}$$

Therefore, $P(k+1)$ is true. Hence, by the principle of mathematical induction $P(n)$ is true for all $n \in N$.

Type IV These problems are of the **Second principle of induction**. Examples of this type are as follows:

Example 9. If $a+b=c+d$ and $a^2+b^2=c^2+d^2$, then show by mathematical induction

$$a^n+b^n=c^n+d^n$$

Sol. $P(n): a^n+b^n=c^n+d^n$

Step I For $n=1$ and $n=2$,

$P(1): a+b=c+d$ and $P(2): a^2+b^2=c^2+d^2$

which are true (from given conditions).

Therefore, $P(1)$ and $P(2)$ are true.

Step II Assume $P(k-1)$ and $P(k)$ to be true

$$\therefore \quad a^{k-1}+b^{k-1}=c^{k-1}+d^{k-1} \quad \text{...(i)}$$

$$\text{and} \quad a^k+b^k=c^k+d^k \quad \text{...(ii)}$$

Step III For $n=k+1$,

$P(k+1): a^{k+1}+b^{k+1}=c^{k+1}+d^{k+1}$

$$\therefore \quad \text{LHS} = a^{k+1}+b^{k+1}$$

$$= (a+b)(a^k+b^k) - ab^k - ba^k$$

$$= (a+b)(a^k+b^k) - ab(a^{k-1}+b^{k-1})$$

[given $a+b=c+d$ and $a^2+b^2=c^2+d^2$, then $ab=cd$]

$$= (c+d)(c^k+d^k) - cd(c^{k-1}+d^{k-1})$$

[from Eqs. (i) and (ii)]

$$= c^{k+1}+d^{k+1} = \text{RHS}$$

Therefore, $P(k+1)$ is true. Hence, by the principle of mathematical induction $P(n)$ is true for all $n \in N$.

Example 10. Let $I_m = \int_0^\pi \left(\frac{1-\cos mx}{1-\cos x}\right) dx$ use mathematical induction to prove that $I_m = m\pi$, $m=0,1,2,\ldots$

Sol. $\because \quad I_m = \int_0^\pi \left(\frac{1-\cos mx}{1-\cos x}\right) dx$

Step I For $m=1$, $I_1 = \int_0^\pi \left(\frac{1-\cos x}{1-\cos x}\right) dx$

$\therefore \quad I_1 = \pi$ and for $m=2$,

$$I_2 = \int_0^\pi \left(\frac{1-\cos 2x}{1-\cos x}\right) dx$$

$$= \int_0^\pi \frac{2\sin^2 x(1+\cos x)}{(1-\cos x)(1+\cos x)} dx$$

$$= \int_0^\pi \frac{2\sin^2 x(1+\cos x)}{\sin^2 x} dx = 2\int_0^\pi (1+\cos x) dx$$

$$= 2[x+\sin x]_0^\pi = 2[(\pi+0)-(0+0)] = 2\pi$$

which are true, therefore I_1 and I_2 are true.

Step II Assume I_{k-1} and I_k to be true

$$\therefore \quad I_{k-1} = (k-1)\pi \quad \text{...(i)}$$

$$\text{and} \quad I_k = k\pi \quad \text{...(ii)}$$

Step III For $m=k+1$,

$$I_{k+1} = \int_0^\pi \frac{1-\cos(k+1)x}{1-\cos x} dx$$

$$\therefore \quad I_{k+1} - I_k = \int_0^\pi \frac{\cos kx - \cos(k+1)x}{1-\cos x} dx$$

$$= \int_0^\pi \frac{2\sin\left(\frac{2k+1}{2}\right)x \cdot \sin\left(\frac{x}{2}\right)}{2\sin^2\left(\frac{x}{2}\right)} dx$$

$$= \int_0^\pi \frac{\sin\left(\frac{2k+1}{2}\right)x}{\sin\left(\frac{x}{2}\right)} dx \quad \text{...(iii)}$$

Similarly, $I_k - I_{k-1} = \int_0^\pi \frac{\sin\left(\frac{2k-1}{2}\right)x}{\sin\left(\frac{x}{2}\right)} dx$ ...(iv)

On subtracting Eq. (iv) from Eq. (iii), we get

$$I_{k+1} - 2I_k + I_{k-1} = \int_0^{\pi} \frac{\sin\left(\frac{2k+1}{2}\right)x - \sin\left(\frac{2k-1}{2}\right)x}{\sin\left(\frac{x}{2}\right)} dx$$

$$= \int_0^{\pi} \frac{2\cos(kx)\sin\left(\frac{x}{2}\right)}{\sin\left(\frac{x}{2}\right)} dx = 2\int_0^{\pi} \cos kx \, dx = 2\left[\frac{\sin kx}{k}\right]_0^{\pi} = 0$$

$$\Rightarrow \quad I_{k+1} = 2I_k - I_{k-1} = 2k\pi - (k-1)\pi$$

[by assumption step]

$$= k\pi + \pi = (k+1)\pi$$

This shows that the result is true for $m = k + 1$. Hence, by the principle of mathematical induction the result is true for all $m \in N$.

Type V These problems are of the **Recursion Type**. Examples of this type are as follows:

| Example 11. Given $u_{n+1} = 3u_n - 2u_{n-1}$ and $u_0 = 2$, $u_1 = 3$. Prove that $u_n = 2^n + 1, \forall n \in N$.

Sol. $\because u_{n+1} = 3u_n - 2u_{n-1}$ ...(i)

***Step* I** Given, $u_1 = 3 = 2 + 1 = 2^1 + 1$ which is true for $n = 1$.

Putting $n = 1$ in Eq. (i), we get

$$u_{1+1} = 3u_1 - 2u_{1-1}$$

$$\Rightarrow \quad u_2 = 3u_1 - 2u_0 = 3\cdot 3 - 2\cdot 2 = 5 = 2^2 + 1$$

which is true for $n = 2$.

Therefore, the result is true for $n = 1$ and $n = 2$.

***Step* II** Assume it is true for $n = k$, then it is also true for $n = k - 1$.

Then, $u_k = 2^k + 1$ ...(ii)

and $u_{k-1} = 2^{k-1} + 1$ ...(iii)

***Step* III** Putting $n = k$ in Eq. (i), we get

$$u_{k+1} = 3u_k - 2u_{k-1}$$

$$= 3(2^k + 1) - 2(2^{k-1} + 1)$$

[from Eqs. (ii) and (iii)]

$$= 3\cdot 2^k + 3 - 2\cdot 2^{k-1} - 2 = 3\cdot 2^k + 3 - 2^k - 2$$

$$= (3-1)2^k + 1 = 2\cdot 2^k + 1 = 2^{k+1} + 1$$

This shows that the result is true for $n = k + 1$. Hence, by the principle of mathematical induction the result is true for all $n \in N$.

| Example 12. Let $u_1 = 1, u_2 = 2, u_3 = \frac{7}{2}$ and $u_{n+3} = 3u_{n+2} - \left(\frac{3}{2}\right)u_{n+1} - u_n$. Use the principle of mathematical induction to show that $u_n = \frac{1}{3}\left[2^n + \left(\frac{1+\sqrt{3}}{2}\right)^n + \left(\frac{1-\sqrt{3}}{2}\right)^n\right] \forall n \geq 1$.

Sol. $\because \quad u_n = \frac{1}{3}\left[2^n + \left(\frac{1+\sqrt{3}}{2}\right)^n + \left(\frac{1-\sqrt{3}}{2}\right)^n\right]$ ...(i)

***Step* I** For $n = 1$, $u_1 = \frac{1}{3}\left[2^1 + \left(\frac{1+\sqrt{3}}{2}\right)^1 + \left(\frac{1-\sqrt{3}}{2}\right)^1\right]$

$$= \frac{1}{3}[2 + 1] = 1$$

which is true for $n = 1$ and for $n = 2$,

$$u_2 = \frac{1}{3}\left[2^2 + \left(\frac{1+\sqrt{3}}{2}\right)^2 + \left(\frac{1-\sqrt{3}}{2}\right)^2\right]$$

$$= \frac{1}{3}\left[4 + \left(\frac{4+2\sqrt{3}}{4}\right) + \left(\frac{4-2\sqrt{3}}{4}\right)\right] = \frac{1}{3}[6] = 2$$

which is true for $n = 2$.

Therefore, the result is true for $n = 1$ and $n = 2$.

***Step* II** Assume it is true for $n = k$, then it is also true for $n = k - 1, k - 2$

$$\therefore \quad u_k = \frac{1}{3}\left[2^k + \left(\frac{1+\sqrt{3}}{2}\right)^k + \left(\frac{1-\sqrt{3}}{2}\right)^k\right] \quad \text{...(ii)}$$

$$u_{k-1} = \frac{1}{3}\left[2^{k-1} + \left(\frac{1+\sqrt{3}}{2}\right)^{k-1} + \left(\frac{1-\sqrt{3}}{2}\right)^{k-1}\right] \quad \text{...(iii)}$$

$$u_{k-2} = \frac{1}{3}\left[2^{k-2} + \left(\frac{1+\sqrt{3}}{2}\right)^{k-2} + \left(\frac{1-\sqrt{3}}{2}\right)^{k-2}\right] \quad \text{...(iv)}$$

***Step* III** Given that, $u_{n+3} = 3u_{n+2} - \left(\frac{3}{2}\right)u_{n+1} - u_n$

Replace n by $k - 2$

Then, $u_{k+1} = 3u_k - \frac{3}{2}u_{k-1} - u_{k-2}$

$$= \frac{1}{3}\left[3\cdot 2^k + 3\left(\frac{1+\sqrt{3}}{2}\right)^k + 3\left(\frac{1-\sqrt{3}}{2}\right)^k\right]$$
$$+ \frac{1}{3}\left[-\frac{3}{2}\cdot 2^{k-1} - \frac{3}{2}\left(\frac{1+\sqrt{3}}{2}\right)^{k-1} - \frac{3}{2}\left(\frac{1-\sqrt{3}}{2}\right)^{k-1}\right]$$
$$+ \frac{1}{3}\left[-2^{k-2} - \left(\frac{1+\sqrt{3}}{2}\right)^{k-2} - \left(\frac{1-\sqrt{3}}{2}\right)^{k-2}\right]$$

$$= \frac{1}{3}\left[3\cdot 2^k - 3\cdot 2^{k-2} - 2^{k-2} + \left(\frac{1+\sqrt{3}}{2}\right)^k - \frac{3}{2}\left(\frac{1+\sqrt{3}}{2}\right)^{k-1} - \left(\frac{1+\sqrt{3}}{2}\right)^{k-2} + 3\left(\frac{1-\sqrt{3}}{2}\right)^k - \frac{3}{2}\left(\frac{1-\sqrt{3}}{2}\right)^{k-1} - \left(\frac{1-\sqrt{3}}{2}\right)^{k-2}\right]$$

$$= \frac{1}{3}\left[2^{k-2}(3\cdot 4 - 3 - 1) + \left(\frac{1+\sqrt{3}}{2}\right)^{k-2}\left[3\left(\frac{1+\sqrt{3}}{2}\right)^2 - \frac{3}{2}\left(\frac{1+\sqrt{3}}{2}\right) - 1\right] + \left(\frac{1-\sqrt{3}}{2}\right)^{k-2}\left[3\left(\frac{1-\sqrt{3}}{2}\right)^2 - \frac{3}{2}\left(\frac{1-\sqrt{3}}{2}\right) - 1\right]\right]$$

$$= \frac{1}{3}\left[2^{k-2}\cdot 8 + \left(\frac{1+\sqrt{3}}{2}\right)^{k-2}\left[\frac{3(1+\sqrt{3})^2 - 3(1+\sqrt{3}) - 4}{4}\right] + \left(\frac{1-\sqrt{3}}{2}\right)^{k-2}\left[\frac{3(1-\sqrt{3})^2 - 3(1-\sqrt{3}) - 4}{4}\right]\right]$$

$$= \frac{1}{3}\left[2^{k+1} + \left(\frac{1+\sqrt{3}}{2}\right)^{k-2}\left[\frac{10+6\sqrt{3}}{8}\right] + \left(\frac{1-\sqrt{3}}{2}\right)^{k-2}\left[\frac{10-6\sqrt{3}}{8}\right]\right]$$

$$= \frac{1}{3}\left[2^{k+1} + \left(\frac{1+\sqrt{3}}{2}\right)^{k-2}\left(\frac{1+\sqrt{3}}{2}\right)^3 + \left(\frac{1-\sqrt{3}}{2}\right)^{k-2}\left(\frac{1-\sqrt{3}}{2}\right)^3\right]$$

$$= \frac{1}{3}\left[2^{k+1} + \left(\frac{1+\sqrt{3}}{2}\right)^{k+1} + \left(\frac{1-\sqrt{3}}{2}\right)^{k+1}\right]$$

This shows that the result is true for $n = k + 1$. Hence, by the principle of mathematical induction the result is true for all $n \in N$.

Shortcuts and Important Results to Remember

1 Principle of mathematical induction is widely used in proving identities, theorems, divisibility of an expression by a number or by another expression, inequalities, etc.

2 Principle of mathematical induction can only help in verifying an established result. It cannot discover a new formula.

3 If $f(k)$ is divisible by a number p and it is to be proved that $f(k+1)$ is divisible by p, sometimes it is easier to show that $f(k+1) - f(k)$ is divisible by p.

4 $\underbrace{aaaaa\ldots a}_{m \text{ times}} = a(1 + 10 + 10^2 + 10^3 + \ldots + 10^{m-1})$

$$= \frac{a(10^m - 1)}{9}, \forall 1 \le a \le 9 \text{ and } a \in N.$$

JEE Type Solved Examples :
Single Option Correct Type Questions

- This section contains **5 multiple choice examples**. Each example has four choices (a), (b), (c) and (d), out of which **ONLY ONE** is correct.

Ex. 1 *When P is a natural number, then $P^{n+1} + (P+1)^{2n-1}$ is divisible by*

(a) P (b) $P^2 + P$ (c) $P^2 + P + 1$ (d) $P^2 - 1$

Sol. (c) For $n = 1$, we get

$$P^{n+1} + (P+1)^{2n-1} = P^2 + (P+1)^1 = P^2 + P + 1,$$

which is divisible by $P^2 + P + 1$, so result is true for $n = 1$.

Let us assume that the given result is true for $n = m \in N$.

i.e., $P^{m+1} + (P+1)^{2m-1}$ is divisible by $P^2 + P + 1$.

i.e., $P^{m+1} + (P+1)^{2m-1} = k(P^2 + P + 1), \forall k \in N$ ...(i)

Now, $P^{(m+1)+1} + (P+1)^{2(m+1)-1}$

$$= P^{m+2} + (P+1)^{2m+1}$$

$$= P^{m+2} + (P+1)^2 (P+1)^{2m-1}$$

$$= P^{m+2} + (P+1)^2 [k(P^2 + P + 1) - P^{m+1}]$$

[by using Eq. (i)]

$$= P^{m+2} + (P+1)^2 \cdot k(P^2 + P + 1) - (P+1)^2 (P)^{m+1}$$

$$= P^{m+1} [P - (P+1)^2] + (P+1)^2 \cdot k(P^2 + P + 1)$$

$$= P^{m+1} [P - P^2 - 2P - 1] + (P+1)^2 \cdot k(P^2 + P + 1)$$

$$= -P^{m+1} [P^2 + P + 1] + (P+1)^2 \cdot k(P^2 + P + 1)$$

$$= (P^2 + P + 1)[k \cdot (P+1)^2 - P^{m+1}]$$

which is divisible by $P^2 + P + 1$, so the result is true for $n = m + 1$. Therefore, the given result is true for all $n \in N$ by induction.

Ex. 2 *Let P(n) denote the statement that $n^2 + n$ is odd. It is seen that $P(n) \Rightarrow P(n+1)$, $P(n)$ is true for all*

(a) $n > 1$ (b) n
(c) $n > 2$ (d) None of these

Sol. (d) $P(n) = n^2 + n$. It is always odd (statement) but square of any odd number is always odd and also, sum of two odd numbers is always even. So, for no any 'n' for which this statement is true.

Ex. 3 *For a positive integer n, let $a(n) = 1 + \frac{1}{2} + \frac{1}{3} + \frac{1}{4} + \ldots + \frac{1}{2^n - 1}$. Then*

(a) $a(100) > 100$
(b) $a(100) < 200$
(c) $a(200) \le 100$
(d) $a(200) > 100$

Sol. (d) It can be proved with the help of mathematical induction that

$$\frac{n}{2} < a(n) \le n$$

$$\Rightarrow \quad \frac{200}{2} < a(200)$$

$$\Rightarrow \quad a(200) > 100$$

Ex. 4 *Let $S(k) = 1 + 3 + 5 + \ldots + (2k-1) = 3 + k^2$. Which of the following is true?*

(a) Principle of mathematical induction can be used to prove the formula
(b) $S(k) \Rightarrow S(k+1)$
(c) $S(k) \not\Rightarrow S(k+1)$
(d) $S(1)$ is correct

Sol. (c) We have, $S(k) = 1 + 3 + 5 + \ldots + (2k - 1) = 3 + k^2$,

$S(1) \Rightarrow 1 = 4$, which is not true

and $S(2) \Rightarrow 4 = 7$, which is not true.

Hence, induction cannot be applied and $S(k) \ne S(k+1)$.

Ex. 5 *$10^n + 3(4^{n+2}) + 5$ is divisible by $(n \in N)$*

(a) 7 (b) 5
(c) 9 (d) 17

Sol. (c) $10^n + 3(4^{n+2}) + 5$

Taking $n = 2$,

$$10^2 + 3 \times 4^4 + 5 = 100 + 768 + 5 = 873$$

Therefore, this is divisible by 9.

JEE Type Solved Examples : Statement I and II Type Questions

- **Directions** Example numbers 6 and 7 are Assertion-Reason type Examples. Each of these Examples contains two statements :

Statement-1 (Assertion) and
Statement-2 (Reason)
Each of these examples also has four alternative choices, only one of which is the correct answer. You have to select the correct choice as given below:

(a) Statement-1 is true, Statement-2 is true Statement-2 is correct explanation for Statement-1
(b) Statement-1 is true, Statement-2 is true, Statement-2 is not the correct explanation for Statement-1
(c) Statement-1 is true, Statement-2 is false
(d) Statement-1 is false, Statement-2 is true

Ex. 6 Statement-1 *For all natural number n,*

$$1+2+\dots+n<(2n+1)^2$$

Statement-2 *For all natural numbers,* $(2n+3)^2<7(n+1)$

Sol. (b) Let $P(n): 1+2+3+\dots+n<(2n+1)^2$

Step I For $n=1$,

$P(1): 1<(2+1)^2 \Rightarrow 1<9$

which is true.

Step II Assume $P(n)$ is true for $n=k$, then

$P(k): 1+2+\dots+k<(2k+1)^2$

Step III For $n=k+1$, we shall prove that

$P(k+1): 1+2+3+\dots+k+(k+1)<(2k+3)^2$

From assumption step

$$1+2+3+\dots+k+(k+1)<(2k+1)^2+k+1$$
$$=4k^2+5k+2$$
$$=(2k+3)^2-7(k+1)<(2k+3)^2 \qquad [\because 7(k+1)>0]$$

$\therefore$ $P(k+1)$ is true.

Here, both Statements are true but Statement-2 is not correct explanation of Statement-1.

Ex. 7 Statement-1 *For all natural numbers n,*

$$7+77+777+\dots\underbrace{777\dots7}_{n\text{ digits}}=\frac{7}{81}(10^{n+1}-9n-10)$$

Statement-2 *For all natural numbers,*

$$\underbrace{777\dots7}_{n\text{ digits}}=7+7\times10+7\times10^2+\dots+7\times10^n$$

Sol. (c) $\because$ $\underbrace{777\dots7}_{n\text{ digits}}=7(\underbrace{111\dots1}_{n\text{ digits}})$

$$=7(1+10+10^2+\dots+10^{n-1})$$
$$=7+7\times10+7\times10^2+\dots+7\times10^{n-1}$$
$$\neq 7+7\times10+7\times10^2+\dots+7\times10^n$$

$\therefore$ Statement-2 is false.

Now, let $P(n): 7+77+777+\dots+\underbrace{777\dots7}_{n\text{ digits}}=\frac{7}{81}(10^{n+1}-9n-10)$

Step I For $n=1$,

LHS $=7$ and RHS $=\frac{7}{81}(10^2-9-10)=7$

$\therefore$ LHS = RHS

which is true for $n=1$.

Step II Assume $P(n)$ is true for $n=k$, then

$$P(k): 7+77+777+\dots+\underbrace{777\dots7}_{k\text{ digits}}=\frac{7}{81}(10^{k+1}-9k-10)$$

Step III For $n=k+1$,

$$P(k+1): 7+77+777+\dots+\underbrace{777\dots7}_{k\text{ digits}}+\underbrace{777\dots7}_{(k+1)\text{ digits}}=\frac{7}{81}[10^{k+2}-9(k+1)-10]$$

$$\text{LHS}=7+77+777+\dots+\underbrace{777\dots7}_{k\text{ digits}}+\underbrace{777\dots7}_{(k+1)\text{ digits}}$$

$$=\frac{7}{81}(10^{k+1}-9k-10)+7(1+10+10^2+\dots+10^k)$$

[from assumption step]

$$=\frac{7}{81}(10^{k+1}-9k-10)+\frac{7(10^{k+1}-1)}{10-1}$$
$$=\frac{7}{81}(10^{k+1}-9k-10+9\cdot10^{k+1}-9)$$
$$=\frac{7}{81}[10^{k+1}(1+9)-9(k+1)-10]$$
$$=\frac{7}{81}[10^{k+2}-9(k+1)-10]$$
$$=\text{RHS}$$

Therefore, $P(k+1)$ is true. Hence, by mathematical induction $P(n)$ is true for all natural numbers.

Hence, Statement-1 is true and Statement-2 is false.

Subjective Type Examples

- In this section, there are **8 subjective** solved examples.

● **Ex. 8** *Prove by induction that the integer next greater than $(3+\sqrt{5})^n$ is divisible by 2^n for all $n \in N$.*

Sol. Let $\alpha = 3+\sqrt{5}$ and $\beta = 3-\sqrt{5}$

$\therefore \quad 0 < \beta^n < 1, \forall n \in N$

$\Rightarrow \quad \alpha+\beta = 6, \alpha\beta = 4 \quad$ ...(i)

Then, α and β are the roots of

$$x^2 - 6x + 4 = 0$$

$\Rightarrow \quad \left.\begin{array}{l}\alpha^2 = 6\alpha - 4\\ \beta^2 = 6\beta - 4\end{array}\right] \quad$ ...(ii)

$\therefore \quad \alpha^2+\beta^2 = 6(\alpha+\beta) - 8 = 28 \quad$ ...(iii)

$\therefore \quad \alpha^n + \beta^n = (3+\sqrt{5})^n + (3-\sqrt{5})^n$

$= 2[3^n + {}^nC_2 3^{n-2}\cdot 5 + {}^nC_4 3^{n-4}\cdot 5^2 + \dots]$

= Even integer.

As, $0 < \beta^n < 1, \alpha^n + \beta^n$ is the even integer next greater than α^n.

***Step* I** For $n = 1$,

$\alpha + \beta = 6 \quad$ [from Eq. (i)]

divisible by 2^1

and for $n = 2, \alpha^2+\beta^2 = 28 \quad$ [from Eq. (iii)]

divisible by 2^2

which is true for $n = 1, 2$.

***Step* II** Assume it is true for $n = k$.

i.e., $\alpha^k + \beta^k$ is divisible by 2^k.

***Step* III** For $n = k+1$,

the integer next greater than α^{k+1} is $\alpha^{k+1}+\beta^{k+1}$

$= \alpha^2\cdot\alpha^{k-1} + \beta^2\cdot\beta^{k-1}$

$= (6\alpha - 4)\cdot\alpha^{k-1} + (6\beta-4)\cdot\beta^{k-1} \quad$ [from Eq. (ii)]

$= 6(\alpha^k+\beta^k) - 4(\alpha^{k-1}+\beta^{k-1})$

$= 3$ (divisible by 2^{k+1}) – (divisible by 2^{k+1})

= Divisible by 2^{k+1}

This shows that the result is true for $n = k+1$. Hence, the integer next greater than α^{k+1} is divisible by 2^{k+1}.

● **Ex. 9** *Using mathematical induction, show that*

$$\left(1-\frac{1}{2^2}\right)\left(1-\frac{1}{3^2}\right)\left(1-\frac{1}{4^2}\right)\dots\left(1-\frac{1}{(n+1)^2}\right) = \frac{n+2}{2(n+1)}, \forall n \in N.$$

Sol. Let $P(n): \left(1-\frac{1}{2^2}\right)\left(1-\frac{1}{3^2}\right)\left(1-\frac{1}{4^2}\right)\dots\left(1-\frac{1}{(n+1)^2}\right)$

$= \frac{n+2}{2(n+1)} \quad$ ...(i)

***Step* I** For $n = 1$,

LHS of Eq. (i) $= 1 - \frac{1}{2^2} = \frac{3}{4}$ and RHS of Eq. (i)

$= \frac{3}{2\cdot 2} = \frac{3}{4}$.

Therefore, $P(1)$ is true.

***Step* II** Assume it is true for $n = k$, then

$P(k): \left(1-\frac{1}{2^2}\right)\left(1-\frac{1}{3^2}\right)\left(1-\frac{1}{4^2}\right)\dots\left(1-\frac{1}{(k+1)^2}\right)$

$= \frac{k+2}{2(k+1)}$

***Step* III** For $n = k+1$,

$P(k+1): \left(1-\frac{1}{2^2}\right)\left(1-\frac{1}{3^2}\right)\left(1-\frac{1}{4^2}\right)\dots$

$\left(1-\frac{1}{(k+1)^2}\right)\left(1-\frac{1}{(k+2)^2}\right) = \frac{k+3}{2(k+2)}$

$\therefore \quad$ LHS $= \left(1-\frac{1}{2^2}\right)\left(1-\frac{1}{3^2}\right)\left(1-\frac{1}{4^2}\right)\dots$

$\left(1-\frac{1}{(k+1)^2}\right)\left(1-\frac{1}{(k+2)^2}\right)$

$= \frac{k+2}{2(k+1)}\left(1-\frac{1}{(k+2)^2}\right) \quad$ [by assumption step]

$= \frac{(k+2)}{2(k+1)}\cdot\frac{[(k+2)^2-1)]}{(k+2)^2} = \frac{k^2+4k+3}{2(k+1)(k+2)}$

$= \frac{(k+1)(k+3)}{2(k+1)(k+2)} = \frac{(k+3)}{2(k+2)} =$ RHS

This shows that the result is true for $n = k+1$. Hence, by the principle of mathematical induction, the result is true for all $n \in N$.

● **Ex. 10** *Using the principle of mathematical induction to show that*

$$\tan^{-1}\left(\frac{x}{1+1\cdot 2\cdot x^2}\right) + \tan^{-1}\left(\frac{x}{1+2\cdot 3\cdot x^2}\right) + \dots + \tan^{-1}\left(\frac{x}{1+n(n+1)x^2}\right) = \tan^{-1}(n+1)x - \tan^{-1}x, \forall x \in N.$$

Sol. Let $P(n): \tan^{-1}\left(\frac{x}{1+1\cdot 2\cdot x^2}\right)+\tan^{-1}\left(\frac{x}{1+2\cdot 3\cdot x^2}\right)$
$+\ldots+\tan^{-1}\left(\frac{x}{1+n(n+1)x^2}\right)$
$=\tan^{-1}(n+1)x-\tan^{-1}x$ ...(i)

Step I For $n=1$,

LHS of Eq. (i) $=\tan^{-1}\left(\frac{x}{1+1\cdot 2\cdot x^2}\right)$

$=\tan^{-1}\left(\frac{2x-x}{1+2x\cdot x}\right)=\tan^{-1}2x-\tan^{-1}x$

= RHS of Eq. (i)

Therefore, $P(1)$ is true.

Step II Assume it is true for $n=k$.

$P(k): \tan^{-1}\left(\frac{x}{1+1\cdot 2x^2}\right)+\tan^{-1}\left(\frac{x}{1+2\cdot 3x^2}\right)+\ldots$
$+\tan^{-1}\left(\frac{x}{[1+k(k+1)x^2]}\right)$
$=\tan^{-1}(k+1)x-\tan^{-1}x$

Step III For $n=k+1$,

$P(k+1): \tan^{-1}\left(\frac{x}{1+1\cdot 2\cdot x^2}\right)+\tan^{-1}\left(\frac{x}{1+2\cdot 3\cdot x^2}\right)$
$+\ldots+\tan^{-1}\left(\frac{x}{1+k(k+1)x^2}\right)$
$+\tan^{-1}\left(\frac{x}{1+(k+1)(k+2)x^2}\right)$
$=\tan^{-1}(k+2)x-\tan^{-1}x$

$\therefore$ LHS $=\tan^{-1}\left(\frac{x}{1+1\cdot 2\cdot x^2}\right)$
$+\tan^{-1}\left(\frac{x}{1+2\cdot 3\cdot x^2}\right)+\ldots+\tan^{-1}\left(\frac{x}{1+k(k+1)x^2}\right)$
$+\tan^{-1}\left(\frac{x}{1+(k+1)(k+2)x^2}\right)$
$=\tan^{-1}(k+1)x-\tan^{-1}x$
$+\tan^{-1}\left(\frac{x}{1+(k+1)(k+2)x^2}\right)$
[by assumption step]
$=\tan^{-1}(k+1)x-\tan^{-1}x$
$+\tan^{-1}\left(\frac{(k+2)x-(k+1)x}{1+(k+2)x(k+1)x}\right)$
$=\tan^{-1}(k+1)x-\tan^{-1}x+\tan^{-1}(k+2)x$
$-\tan^{-1}(k+1)x$
$=\tan^{-1}(k+2)x-\tan^{-1}x=$ RHS

This shows that the result is true for $n=k+1$. Hence, by the principle of mathematical induction, the result is true for all $n\in N$.

● ***Ex. 11** Use the principle of mathematical induction to prove that for all $n\in N$.*

$$\sqrt{2+\sqrt{2+\sqrt{2+\ldots+\ldots+\sqrt{2}}}}=2\cos\left(\frac{\pi}{2^{n+1}}\right)$$

when the LHS contains n radical sign.

Sol. Let $P(n)=\sqrt{2+\sqrt{2+\sqrt{2+\ldots+\ldots+\sqrt{2}}}}$
$=2\cos\left(\frac{\pi}{2^{n+1}}\right)$ ...(i)

Step I For $n=1$,

LHS of Eq. (i) $=\sqrt{2}$ and RHS Eq. (i) $=2\cos\left(\frac{\pi}{2^2}\right)$

$=2\cos\left(\frac{\pi}{4}\right)=2\cdot\frac{1}{\sqrt{2}}=\sqrt{2}$

Therefore, $P(1)$ is true.

Step II Assume it is true for $n=k$,

$P(k)=\underbrace{\sqrt{2+\sqrt{2+\sqrt{2+\ldots+\ldots+\sqrt{2}}}}}_{k \text{ radical sign}}=2\cos\left(\frac{\pi}{2^{k+1}}\right)$

Step III For $n=k+1$,

$\therefore P(k+1)=\underbrace{\sqrt{2+\sqrt{2+\sqrt{2+\ldots+\ldots+\sqrt{2}}}}}_{(k+1)\text{ radical sign}}$

$=\sqrt{\{2+P(k)\}}$

$=\sqrt{2+2\cos\left(\frac{\pi}{2^{k+1}}\right)}$ [by assumption step]

$=\sqrt{2\left(1+\cos\left(\frac{\pi}{2^{k+1}}\right)\right)}$

$=\sqrt{2\left(1+2\cos^2\left(\frac{\pi}{2^{k+2}}\right)-1\right)}$

$=\sqrt{4\cos^2\left(\frac{\pi}{2^{k+2}}\right)}=2\cos\left(\frac{\pi}{2^{k+2}}\right)$

This shows that the result is true for $n=k+1$. Hence, by the principle of mathematical induction, the result is true for all $n\in N$.

● ***Ex. 12** Prove by mathematical induction that*

$$\frac{1}{1+x}+\frac{2}{1+x^2}+\frac{4}{1+x^4}+\ldots+\frac{2^n}{1+x^{2^n}}=\frac{1}{x-1}+\frac{2^{n+1}}{1-x^{2^{n+1}}}$$

where, $|x|\neq 1$ and n is non-negative integer.

Sol. Let $P(n): \frac{1}{1+x}+\frac{2}{1+x^2}+\frac{4}{1+x^4}+\ldots+\frac{2^n}{1+x^{2^n}}$
$=\frac{1}{x-1}+\frac{2^{n+1}}{1-x^{2^{n+1}}}$ ...(i)

***Step* I** For $n = 1$,

$$\text{LHS of Eq. (i)} = \frac{1}{1+x} + \frac{2}{1+x^2}$$

$$= \frac{1}{x-1} - \frac{1}{x-1} + \frac{1}{1+x} + \frac{2}{1+x^2}$$

$$= \frac{1}{x-1} + \left(\frac{1}{1-x} + \frac{1}{1+x}\right) + \frac{2}{1+x^2}$$

$$= \frac{1}{x-1} + \frac{2}{1-x^2} + \frac{2}{1+x^2}$$

$$= \frac{1}{x-1} + 2\left(\frac{2}{(1-x^2)(1+x^2)}\right) = \frac{1}{x-1} + \frac{2^2}{1-x^2}$$

= RHS of Eq. (i)

***Step* II** Assume it is true for $n = k$, then

$$P(k): \frac{1}{1+x} + \frac{2}{1+x^2} + \frac{4}{1+x^4} + \dots + \frac{2^k}{1+x^{2^k}}$$

$$= \frac{1}{x-1} + \frac{2^{k+1}}{1-x^{2^{k+1}}}$$

***Step* III** For $n = k+1$,

$$P(k+1): \frac{1}{1+x} + \frac{2}{1+x^2} + \frac{4}{1+x^4} + \dots + \frac{2^k}{1+x^{2^k}} + \frac{2^{k+1}}{1+x^{2^{k+1}}}$$

$$= \frac{1}{x-1} + \frac{2^{k+2}}{1-x^{2^{k+1}}}$$

$$\text{LHS} = \frac{1}{1+x} + \frac{2}{1+x^2} + \frac{4}{1+x^4} + \dots + \frac{2k}{1+x^{2^k}} + \frac{2^{k+1}}{1+x^{2^{k+1}}}$$

$$= \frac{1}{x-1} + \frac{2^{k+1}}{1-x^{2^{k+1}}} + \frac{2^{k+1}}{1+x^{2^{k+1}}}$$

[by assumption step]

$$= \frac{1}{x-1} + 2^{k+1}\left(\frac{2}{(1-x^{2^{k+1}})(1+x^{2^{k+1}})}\right)$$

$$= \frac{1}{x-1} + \frac{2^{k+2}}{1-x^{2^{k+2}}} = \text{RHS}$$

This shows that the result is true for $n = k+1$. Hence, by the principle of mathematical induction, the result is true for all $n \in N$.

• *Ex. 13* *Using the principle of mathematical induction to prove that* $\int_0^{\pi/2} \frac{\sin^2 nx}{\sin x}\,dx = 1 + \frac{1}{3} + \frac{1}{5} + \dots + \frac{1}{2n-1}$

Sol. Let $P(n): \int_0^{\pi/2} \frac{\sin^2 nx}{\sin x}\,dx = 1 + \frac{1}{3} + \frac{1}{5} + \dots + \frac{1}{2n-1}$ ...(i)

***Step* I** For $n = 1$,

$$\text{LHS of Eq. (i)} = \int_0^{\pi/2} \frac{\sin^2 x}{\sin x}\,dx = \int_0^{\pi/2} \sin x\,dx$$

$$= -[\cos x]_0^{\pi/2} = -(0-1) = 1$$

and RHS of Eq. (i) = 1

Therefore, $P(1)$ is true.

***Step* II** Assume it is true for $n = k$, then

$$P(k): \int_0^{\pi/2} \frac{\sin^2 kx}{\sin x}\,dx = 1 + \frac{1}{3} + \frac{1}{5} + \dots + \frac{1}{2k-1}$$

***Step* III** For $n = k+1$,

$$P(k+1): \int_0^{\pi/2} \frac{\sin^2 (k+1)x}{\sin x}\,dx = 1 + \frac{1}{3} + \frac{1}{5} + \dots + \frac{1}{2k-1} + \frac{1}{2k+1}$$

$$\text{LHS} = \int_0^{\pi/2} \frac{\sin^2 (k+1)x}{\sin x}\,dx$$

$$= \int_0^{\pi/2} \frac{\sin^2 (k+1)x - \sin^2 kx + \sin^2 kx}{\sin x}\,dx$$

$$= \int_0^{\pi/2} \frac{\sin^2 (k+1)x - \sin^2 kx}{\sin x}\,dx + \int_0^{\pi/2} \frac{\sin^2 kx}{\sin x}\,dx$$

$$= \int_0^{\pi/2} \frac{\sin (2k+1)x \sin x}{\sin x}\,dx + P(k)$$

[by assumption step]

$$= \int_0^{\pi/2} \sin (2k+1)x\,dx + P(k)$$

$$= -\left[\frac{\cos (2k+1)x}{2k+1}\right]_0^{\pi/2} + P(k)$$

$$= -\frac{1}{(2k+1)}\left[\cos\left(\pi k + \frac{\pi}{2}\right) - 1\right] + P(k)$$

$$= -\frac{1}{(2k+1)}[-\sin \pi k - 1] + P(k)$$

$$= -\frac{1}{2k+1}[-0-1] + P(k)$$

$$= \frac{1}{(2k+1)} + 1 + \frac{1}{3} + \frac{1}{5} + \dots + \frac{1}{(2k-1)}$$

[by assumption step]

$$= 1 + \frac{1}{3} + \frac{1}{5} + \dots + \frac{1}{(2k-1)} + \frac{1}{(2k+1)}$$

= RHS

This shows that the result is true for $n = k+1$. Hence, by the principle of mathematical induction, the result is true for all $n \in N$.

- **Ex. 14** *Use induction to show that for all $n \in N$.*

$$\sqrt{a+\sqrt{a+\sqrt{a+\ldots+\sqrt{a}}}} < \frac{1+\sqrt{(4a+1)}}{2}$$

where 'a' is fixed positive number and n radical signs are taken on LHS.

Sol. Let $P(n): \sqrt{a+\sqrt{a+\sqrt{a+\ldots+\sqrt{a}}}} < 1+\sqrt{\frac{(4a+1)}{2}}$

Step I For $n=1$, then $\sqrt{a} < \frac{1+\sqrt{(4a+1)}}{2}$

$\Rightarrow \quad 2\sqrt{a} < 1+\sqrt{(4a+1)}$

$\Rightarrow \quad 4a < 1+4a+1+2\sqrt{(4a+1)}$

$\Rightarrow \quad 2\sqrt{(4a+1)}+2>0$ which is true.

Therefore, $P(1)$ is true.

Step II Assume it is true for $n=k$,

$$P(k): \underbrace{\sqrt{a+\sqrt{a+\sqrt{a+\ldots+\sqrt{a}}}}}_{k \text{ radical signs}} < \frac{1+\sqrt{(4a+1)}}{2}$$

Step III For $n=k+1$,

$$P(k+1): \underbrace{\sqrt{a+\sqrt{a+\sqrt{a+\ldots+\sqrt{a}}}}}_{(k+1) \text{ radical signs}} < \frac{1+\sqrt{(4a+1)}}{2}$$

From assumption step

$$\underbrace{\sqrt{a+\sqrt{a+\sqrt{a+\ldots+\sqrt{a}}}}}_{k \text{ radical signs}} < \frac{1+\sqrt{4a+1}}{2}$$

$$a+\underbrace{\sqrt{a+\sqrt{a+\sqrt{a+\ldots+\sqrt{a}}}}}_{k \text{ radical signs}} < a+\frac{1+\sqrt{(4a+1)}}{2}$$

$$\Rightarrow \underbrace{\sqrt{a+\sqrt{a+\sqrt{a+\sqrt{a+\ldots+\sqrt{a}}}}}}_{(k+1) \text{ radical signs}} < \sqrt{a+\frac{1+\sqrt{(4a+1)}}{2}}$$

$$= \sqrt{\frac{2a+1+\sqrt{(4a+1)}}{2}} = \sqrt{\frac{4a+2+2\sqrt{(4a+1)}}{4}}$$

$$= \sqrt{\frac{(\sqrt{(4a+1)})^2+1+2\sqrt{(4a+1)}}{4}}$$

$$= \sqrt{\left(\frac{1+\sqrt{(4a+1)}}{2}\right)^2} = \frac{1+\sqrt{(4a+1)}}{2}$$

$$\therefore \underbrace{\sqrt{a+\sqrt{a+\sqrt{a+\sqrt{a+\ldots+\sqrt{a}}}}}}_{(k+1) \text{ radical signs}} < \frac{1+\sqrt{(4a+1)}}{2}$$

which is true for $n=k+1$.

Hence, by the principle of mathematical induction, the result is true for all $n \in N$.

- **Ex. 15** *Prove by induction that*

$$\left\{\prod_{r=0}^{n} f_r(x)\right\}' = \sum_{i=1}^{n}\{f_1(x)f_2(x)\ldots f_i'(x)\ldots f_n(x)\},$$

where dash denotes derivative with respect to x.

Sol. Let $P(n): \left\{\prod_{r=0}^{n} f_r(x)\right\}' = \sum_{i=1}^{n}\{f_1(x)f_2(x)\ldots f_i'(x)\ldots f_n(x)\}$ ...(i)

Step I For $n=1$,

LHS of Eq. (i) $= \left\{\prod_{r=1}^{1} f_r(x)\right\}' = \{f_1(x)\}' = f_1'(x)$

RHS of Eq. (i) $= \sum_{i=1}^{1}\{f_1(x)f_2(x)\ldots f_i'(x)\ldots f_1(x)\}$

$= f_1'(x)$

which is true for $n=1$.

Step II Assume it is true for $n=k$, then

$$P(k): \left\{\prod_{r=1}^{k} f_r(x)\right\}' = \sum_{i=1}^{k}\{f_1(x)f_2(x)\ldots f_i'(x)\ldots f_k(x)\}$$

Step III For $n=k+1$,

$$P(k+1): \left\{\prod_{r=1}^{k+1} f_r(x)\right\}' = \sum_{i=1}^{k+1}\{f_1(x)f_2(x)\ldots f_i'(x)\ldots f_k(x)\}$$

$$\text{LHS} = \left\{\prod_{r=1}^{(k+1)} f_r(x)\right\}' = \left\{\prod_{r=1}^{k} f_r(x)\cdot f_{k+1}(x)\right\}'$$

$$= \prod_{r=1}^{k} f_r(x)\cdot f'_{k+1}(x) + f_{k+1}(x)\left\{\prod_{r=1}^{k} f_r(x)\right\}'$$

$$= \prod_{r=1}^{k} f_r(x)\cdot f'_{k+1}(x) + f_{k+1}(x) \sum_{i=1}^{k}\{f_1(x)\cdot f_2(x)\ldots f_i'(x)\ldots f_k(x)\}$$

[by assumption step]

$$= \{f_1(x)f_2(x)\ldots f_k(x)\}f'_{k+1}(x) + f_{k+1}(x)\sum_{i=1}^{k}\{f_1(x)f_2(x)\ldots f_i'(x)\ldots f_k(x)\}$$

$$= \sum_{i=1}^{k+1}\{f_1(x)f_2(x)\ldots f_i'(x)\ldots f_{k+1}(x)\}$$

$=$ RHS

This shows that the result is true for $n=k+1$. Hence, by the principle of mathematical induction, the result is true for all $n \in N$.

Mathematical Induction Exercise 1 :
Single Option Correct Type Questions

- This section contains 3 **multiple choice questions**. Each question has four choices (a), (b), (c) and (d), out of which **ONLY ONE** is correct.

1. If $a_n = \sqrt{7 + \sqrt{7 + \sqrt{7 + \dots}}}$ having n radical signs. Then, by mathematical induction which one is true?
(a) $a_n > 7, \forall\ n \geq 1$
(b) $a_n > 3, \forall\ n \geq 1$
(c) $a_n < 4, \forall\ n \geq 1$
(d) $a_n < 3, \forall\ n \geq 1$

2. If $P(n) = 2 + 4 + 6 + \dots + 2n, n \in N$, then $P(k) = k(k+1) + 2$ $\Rightarrow P(k+1) = (k+1)(k+2) + 2, \forall\ k \in N$. So, we can conclude that $P(n) = n(n+1) + 2$ for
(a) all $n \in N$
(b) $n > 1$
(c) $n > 2$
(d) Nothing can be said

3. The value of the natural number n such that the inequality $2^n > 2n + 1$ is valid, is
(a) for $n \geq 3$ (b) for $n < 3$ (c) for all n (d) for mn

Mathematical Induction Exercise 2 :
Statement I and II Type Questions

- **Directions** Question Number 4 to 6 Assertion-Reason type questions. Each of these questions contains two statements.
Statement-1 (Assertion) and
Statement-2 (Reason)
Each of these questions also four alternative choices, only one of which is the correct answer. You have to select the correct choice as given below:
(a) Statement-1 is true, Statement-2 is true; Statement-2 is correct explanation for Statement-1
(b) Statement-1 is true, Statement-2 is true; Statement-2 is not correct explanation for Statement-1
(c) Statement-1 is true, Statement-2 is false
(d) Statement-1 is false, Statement-2 is true

4. Statement-1 If $a_1 = 1, a_2 = 5$, then $a_n = 3^n - 2^n, \forall\ n \in N$ and $n \geq 1$.
Statement-2 $a_{n+2} = 5a_{n+1} - 6a_n, n \geq 1$.

5. Statement-1 For all natural numbers n, $2 \cdot 7^n + 3 \cdot 5^n - 5$ is divisible by 24.
Statement-2 If $f(x)$ is divisible by x, then $f(x+1) - f(x)$ is divisible by $x + 1, \forall\ x \in N$.

6. Statement-1 For all natural numbers n, $0 \cdot 5 + 0 \cdot 55 + 0 \cdot 555 + \dots$ upto n terms$= \frac{5}{9}\left\{n - \frac{1}{9}\left(1 - \frac{1}{10^n}\right)\right\}$
Statement-2 $a + ar + ar^2 + \dots + ar^{n-1} = \frac{a(1 - r^n)}{(1 - r)}$, for $0 < r < 1$.

Mathematical Induction Exercise 3 :
Subjective Type Questions

- In this section, there are **10 subjective** questions.

7. Prove the following by using induction for all $n \in N$.
(i) $11^{n+2} + 12^{2n+1}$ is divisible by 133.
(ii) $n^7 - n$ is divisible by 42.
(iii) $3^{2n} + 24n - 1$ is divisible by 32.
(iv) $n(n+1)(n+5)$ is divisible by 6.
(v) $(25)^{n+1} - 24n + 5735$ is divisible by $(24)^2$.
(vi) $x^{2n} - y^{2n}$ is divisible by $x + y$.

8. Prove by induction that if n is a positive integer not divisible by 3, then $3^{2n} + 3^n + 1$ is divisible by 13.

9. Prove by induction that the product of three consecutive positive integers is divisible by 6.

10. Prove by induction that the sum of three successive natural numbers is divisible by 9.

11. Prove by induction that the even power of every odd integer when divided by 8 leaves the remainder 1.

12. Prove the following by using induction for all $n \in N$:

(i) $1+2+3+\ldots+n=\dfrac{n(n+1)}{2}$

(ii) $1^2+2^2+3^2+\ldots+n^2=\dfrac{n(n+1)(2n+1)}{6}$

(iii) $1\cdot 3+3\cdot 5+5\cdot 7+\ldots+(2n-1)(2n+1)$
$=\dfrac{n(4n^2+6n-1)}{3}$

(iv) $\dfrac{1}{2\cdot 5}+\dfrac{1}{5\cdot 8}+\dfrac{1}{8\cdot 11}+\ldots+\dfrac{1}{(3n-1)(3n+2)}=\dfrac{n}{6n+4}$

(v) $1\cdot 4\cdot 7+2\cdot 5\cdot 8+3\cdot 6\cdot 9+\ldots$ upto n terms
$=\dfrac{n}{4}(n+1)(n+6)(n+7)$

(vi) $\dfrac{1^2}{1\cdot 3}+\dfrac{2^2}{3\cdot 5}+\ldots+\dfrac{n^2}{(2n-1)(2n+1)}=\dfrac{n(n+1)}{2(2n+1)}$

13. Let $a_0=2, a_1=5$ and for $n\ge 2, a_n=5a_{n-1}-6a_{n-2}$, then prove by induction that $a_n=2^n+3^n, \forall\, n\ge 0, n\in N$.

14. If $a_1=1, a_{n+1}=\dfrac{1}{n+1}a_n, n\ge 1$, then prove by induction that $a_{n+1}=\dfrac{1}{(n+1)!}, n\in N$.

15. If a, b, c, d, e and f are six real numbers such that
$$a+b+c=d+e+f$$
$$a^2+b^2+c^2=d^2+e^2+f^2$$
and $a^3+b^3+c^3=d^3+e^3+f^3$, prove by mathematical induction that
$$a^n+b^n+c^n=d^n+e^n+f^n, \forall\, n\in N.$$

16. Using mathematical induction, prove that
$$\tan^{-1}\left(\frac{1}{3}\right)+\tan^{-1}\left(\frac{1}{7}\right)+\ldots+\tan^{-1}\left(\frac{1}{n^2+n+1}\right)=\tan^{-1}\left(\frac{n}{n+2}\right).$$

Mathematical Induction Exercise 4 : Questions Asked in Previous 13 Year's Exam

- This section contains questions asked in **IIT-JEE, AIEEE, JEE Main & JEE Advanced** from year **2005** to year **2017**.

17. Statement-1 For every natural number $n\ge 2\;\dfrac{1}{\sqrt{1}}+\dfrac{1}{\sqrt{2}}+\ldots+\dfrac{1}{n}>\sqrt{n}$,

Statement-2 For every natural number $n\ge 2\;\sqrt{n(n+1)}<n+1$

(a) Statement-1 is true, Statement-2 is true; Statement-2 is correct explanation for Statement-1
(b) Statement-1 is true, Statement-2 is true; Statement-2 is not a correct explanation for Statement-1
(c) Statement-1 is true, Statement-2 is false
(d) Statement-1 is false, Statement-2 is true

[AIEEE 2008, 3M]

18. Statement-1 For each natural number n, $(n+1)^7-n^7-1$ is divisible by 7.

Statement-2 For each natural number n, n^7-n is divisible by 7.

(a) Statement-1 is false, Statement-2 is true
(b) Statement-1 is true, Statement-2 is true; Statement-2 is correct explanation for Statement-1
(c) Statement-1 is true, Statement-2 is true; Statement-2 is not a correct explanation for Statement-1
(d) Statement-1 is true, Statement-2 is false

[AIEEE 2011, 4M]

Answers

Chapter Exercise

1. (c) 2. (d) 3. (a) 4. (a) 5. (c) 6. (b) 17. (b) 18. (b)

Solutions

1. Let $P(n): a_n = \sqrt{7+\sqrt{7+\sqrt{7+\dots}}}$ (n radical sign)

***Step* I** For $n = 1$,

$$P(1): a_1 = \sqrt{7} < 4$$

***Step* II** Assume that $a_k < 4$ for all natural number, $n = k$

***Step* III** For $n = k+1$,

$$P(k+1): a_{k+1} = \sqrt{7+\sqrt{7+\sqrt{7+\dots}}}$$

[$(k+1)$ radical sign]

$$= \sqrt{7 + a_k} < \sqrt{7+4} \quad [\because a_k < 4]$$

$$< 4 \quad \text{[by assumption]}$$

This shows that, $a_{k+1} < 4$, i.e. the result is true for $n = k+1$. Hence, by the principle of mathematical induction

$$a_n < 4, \forall n \geq 1$$

2. It is obvious.

3. Check through options, the condition $2^n > 2n + 1$ is valid for $n \geq 3$.

4. Let $P(n): a_n = 3^n - 2^n$

***Step* I** For $n = 1$,

$$\text{LHS} = a_1 = 1 \quad \text{[given]}$$

and $\text{RHS} = 3^1 - 2^1 = 1$

$\therefore$ LHS = RHS

Hence, $P(1)$ is true.

For $n = 2$,

$$\text{LHS} = a_2 = 5 \quad \text{[given]}$$

and $\text{RHS} = 3^2 - 2^2 = 5$

$\therefore$ LHS = RHS

Hence, $P(2)$ is also true.

Thus, $P(1)$ and $P(2)$ are true.

***Step* II** Let $P(k)$ and $P(k-1)$ are true

$\therefore \quad a_k = 3^k - 2^k$ and $a_{k-1} = 3^{k-1} - 2^{k-1}$

***Step* III** For $n = k+1$,

$$a_{k+1} = 5a_k - 6a_{k-1} \quad \text{[from Statement-2]}$$

$$= 5(3^k - 2^k) - 6(3^{k-1} - 2^{k-1})$$

$$= 5 \cdot 3^k - 5 \cdot 2^k - 2 \cdot 3^k + 3 \cdot 2^k$$

$$= 3 \cdot 3^k - 2 \cdot 2^k = 3^{k+1} - 2^{k+1}$$

which is true for $n = k+1$.

Hence, both statements are true and Statement-2 is a correct explanation of Statement-1.

5. Let $P(n): 2 \cdot 7^n + 3 \cdot 5^n - 5$

***Step* I** For $n = 1$,

$$P(1): 2 \cdot 7^1 + 3 \cdot 5^1 - 5$$

: 24 is divisible by 24.

***Step* II** Assume $P(k)$ is divisible by 24, then

$P(k): 2 \cdot 7^k + 3 \cdot 5^k - 5 = 24\lambda$, λ is positive integer.

***Step* III** For $n = k+1$,

$$P(k+1) - P(k) = (2 \cdot 7^{k+1} + 3 \cdot 5^{k+1} - 5) - (2 \cdot 7^k + 3 \cdot 5^k - 5)$$

$$= 2 \cdot 7^k(7-1) + 3 \cdot 5^k(5-1)$$

$$= 12(7^k + 5^k)$$

$$= \text{divisible by } 24$$

$$= 24\mu, \forall \mu \in I$$

$[\because 7^k + 5^k$ is always divisible by 24$]$

$$\therefore \quad P(k+1) = P(k) + 24\mu = 24\lambda + 24\mu$$

$$= 24(\lambda + \mu)$$

Hence, $P(k+1)$ is divisible by 24.

Hence, Statement-1 is true and Statement-2 is false.

6. ***Step* I** For $n = 1$,

$$\text{LHS} = 0.5 \text{ and RHS} = \frac{5}{9}\left\{1 - \frac{1}{9}\left(1 - \frac{1}{10}\right)\right\} = \frac{5}{9}\left(1 - \frac{1}{10}\right) = \frac{5}{10} = 0.5$$

$\therefore$ LHS = RHS

which is true for $n = 1$.

***Step* II** Assume it is true for $n = k$, then $0.5 + 0.55 + 0.555 + \dots$ + upto k terms

$$= \frac{5}{9}\left\{k - \frac{1}{9}\left(1 - \frac{1}{10^k}\right)\right\}$$

***Step* III** For $n = k+1$,

$$\text{LHS} = 0.5 + 0.55 + 0.555 + \dots + \text{upto } (k+1) \text{ terms}$$

$$= \frac{5}{9}\left\{k - \frac{1}{9}\left(1 - \frac{1}{10^k}\right)\right\} + (k+1)\text{ th terms}$$

$$= \frac{5}{9}\left\{k - \frac{1}{9}\left(1 - \frac{1}{10^k}\right)\right\} + \underbrace{0.555\dots5}_{(k+1)\text{ times}}$$

$$= \frac{5}{9}\left\{k - \frac{1}{9}\left(1 - \frac{1}{10^k}\right)\right\} + \frac{1}{10^{k+1}}\left(\underbrace{555\dots5}_{(k+1)\text{ times}}\right)$$

$$= \frac{5}{9}\left\{k - \frac{1}{9}\left(1 - \frac{1}{10^k}\right)\right\} + \frac{5}{10^{k+1}}(1 + 10 + 10^2 + \dots + 10^k)$$

$$= \frac{5}{9}\left\{k - \frac{1}{9}\left(1 - \frac{1}{10^k}\right)\right\} + \frac{5 \cdot (10^{k+1} - 1)}{10^{k+1} \cdot (10 - 1)}$$

$$= \frac{5}{9}\left\{k - \frac{1}{9}\left(1 - \frac{1}{10^k}\right) + \frac{10^{k+1} - 1}{10^{k+1}}\right\}$$

$$= \frac{5}{9}\left\{(k+1) - \frac{1}{9} + \frac{1}{9 \cdot 10^k} - \frac{1}{10^{k+1}}\right\}$$

$$= \frac{5}{9}\left\{(k+1) - \frac{1}{9} + \frac{(10-9)}{9 \cdot 10^{k+1}}\right\}$$

$$= \frac{5}{9}\left\{(k+1) - \frac{1}{9}\left(1 - \frac{1}{10^{k+1}}\right)\right\} = \text{RHS}$$

which is true for $n = k+1$.

Hence, both statements are true but Statement-2 is not a correct explanation for Statement-1.

7. (i) Let $P(n) = 11^{n+2} + 12^{2n+1}$

***Step* I** For $n = 1$,

$$P(1) = 11^{1+2} + 12^{2\times1+1} = 11^3 + 12^3$$
$$= (11 + 12)(11^2 - 11 \times 12 + 12^2)$$
$$= 23 \times 133 \text{, which is divisible by 133.}$$

Therefore, the result is true for $n = 1$.

***Step* II** Assume that the result is true for $n = k$, then

$$P(k) = 11^{k+2} + 12^{2k+1} \text{ is divisible by 133.}$$

$\Rightarrow$ $P(k) = 133r$, where r is an integer.

***Step* III** For $n = k + 1$,

$$\therefore P(k+1) = 11^{(k+1)+2} + 12^{2(k+1)+1} = 11^{k+3} + 12^{2k+3}$$
$$= 11^{(k+1)+1} \cdot 11 + 12^{2k+1} \cdot 12^2$$
$$= 11 \cdot 11^{k+2} + 144 \cdot 12^{2k+1}$$

Now, $11^{k+2} + 12^{2k+1} \overline{)\,11\cdot 11^{k+2} + 144\cdot 12^{2k+1}\,(}\ 11$

$$11 \cdot 11^{k+2} + 11 \cdot 12^{2k+1}$$
$$- \quad -$$
$$133 \cdot 12^{2k+1}$$

$$\therefore \quad 11 \cdot 11^{(k+2)} + 144 \cdot 12^{2k+1}$$
$$= 11(11^{k+2} + 12^{2k+1}) + 133 \cdot 12^{2k+1}$$

i.e. $P(k+1) = 11\,P(k) + 133 \cdot 12^{2k+1}$

But we know that, $P(k)$ is divisible by 133. Also, $133 \cdot 12^{2k+1}$ is divisible by 133.

Hence, $P(k + 1)$ is divisible by 133. This shows that, the result is true for $n = k + 1$.

Hence, by the principle of mathematical induction, the result is true for all $n \in N$.

(ii) Let $P(n) = n^7 - n$

***Step* I** For $n = 1$,

$$P(1) = 1^7 - 1 = 0, \text{ which is divisible by 42.}$$

Therefore, the result is true for $n = 1$.

***Step* II** Assume that the result is true for $n = k$. Then,

$$P(k) = k^7 - k \text{ is divisible by 42.}$$

$\Rightarrow$ $P(k) = 42r$, where r is an integer.

***Step* III** For $n = k + 1$,

$$P(k+1) = (k+1)^7 - (k+1)$$
$$= (1+k)^7 - (k+1)$$
$$= 1 + {}^7C_1 k + {}^7C_2 k^2 + {}^7C_3 k^3 + {}^7C_4 k^4 + {}^7C_5 k^5 + {}^7C_6 k^6 + {}^7C_7 k^7 - (k+1)$$
$$= (k^7 - k) + ({}^7C_1 k + {}^7C_2 k^2 + {}^7C_3 k^3 + {}^7C_4 k^4 + {}^7C_5 k^5 + {}^7C_6 k^6)$$

But by assumption $k^7 - k$ is divisible by 42.

Also, ${}^7C_1 k + {}^7C_2 k^2 + {}^7C_3 k^3 + {}^7C_4 k^4 + {}^7C_5 k^5 + {}^7C_6 k^6$ is divisible by 42. $[\because {}^7C_r, 1 \le r \le 6 \text{ is divisible by } 7]$

Hence, $P(k + 1)$ is divisible by 42. This shows that, the result is true for $n = k + 1$.

$\therefore$ By the principle of mathematical induction, the result is true for all $n \in N$.

(iii) Let $P(n) = 3^{2n} + 24n - 1$

***Step* I** For $n = 1$,

$$P(1) = 3^{2\times1} + 24 \times 1 - 1 = 3^2 + 24 - 1 = 9 + 24 - 1$$
$$= 32, \text{ which is divisible by 32.}$$

Therefore, the result is true for $n = 1$.

***Step* II** Assume that the result is true for $n = k$. Then,

$$P(k) = 3^{2k} + 24k - 1 \text{ is divisible by 32.}$$

$\Rightarrow$ $P(k) = 32r$, where r is an integer.

***Step* III** For $n = k + 1$,

$$P(k+1) = 3^{2(k+1)} + 24(k+1) - 1$$
$$= 3^{2k+2} + 24k + 24 - 1$$
$$= 3^2 \cdot 3^{2k} + 24k + 23$$
$$= 9 \cdot 3^{2k} + 24k + 23$$

Now, $3^{2k} + 24k - 1 \overline{)\,9\times 3^{2k} + 24k + 23\,(}\ 9$

$$9 \cdot 3^{2k} + 216k - 9$$
$$- \quad - \quad +$$
$$-192k + 32$$

$$\therefore \quad P(k+1) = 9(3^{2k} + 24k - 1) - 32(6k - 1)$$
$$= 9\,P(k) - 32(6k - 1)$$

$\therefore$ $P(k+1) = 9(32r) - 32(6k - 1)$ [by assumption step]

$$= 32(9r - 6k + 1),$$

which is divisible by 32, as $9r - 6k + 1$ is an integer.

Therefore, $P(k + 1)$ is divisible by 32. Hence, by the principle of mathematical induction $P(n)$ is divisible by 32, $\forall\, n \in N$.

(iv) Let $P(n) = n(n + 1)(n + 5)$

***Step* I** For $n = 1$,

$$P(1) = 1 \cdot (1 + 1)(1 + 5) = 1 \cdot 2 \cdot 6$$
$$= 12, \text{ which is divisible by 6.}$$

Therefore, the result is true for $n = 1$.

Step II Assume that the result is true for $n = k$. Then,

$\Rightarrow$ $\left.\begin{array}{l} P(k) = k(k+1)(k+5) \text{ is divisible by } 6. \\ P(k) = 6r, r \text{ is an integer.}\end{array}\right\}$

Step III For $n = k + 1$,

$$P(k+1) = (k+1)(k+1+1)(k+1+5)$$
$$= (k+1)(k+2)(k+6)$$

Now, $P(k+1) - P(k) = (k+1)(k+2)(k+6) - k(k+1)(k+5)$

$$= (k+1)\{k^2 + 8k + 12 - k^2 - 5k\}$$
$$= (k+1)(3k+12)$$
$$= 3(k+1)(k+4)$$

$\Rightarrow$ $P(k+1) = P(k) + 3(k+1)(k+4)$

which is divisible by 6 as $P(k)$ is divisible by 6 [by assumption step]

and clearly $3(k + 1)(k + 4)$ is divisible by 6, $\forall\, k \in N$.

Hence, the result is true for $n = k + 1$.

Therefore, by the principle of mathematical induction, the result is true for all $n \in N$.

(v) Let $P(n) = (25)^{n+1} - 24n + 5735$

***Step* I** For $n = 1$,

$$P(1) = (25)^2 - 24 + 5735 = 625 - 24 + 5735 = 6336$$
$$= 11 \times (24)^2, \text{ which is divisible by } (24)^2.$$

Therefore, the result is true for $n = 1$.

***Step* II** Assume that the result is true for $n = k$. Then,

$$P(k) = (25)^{k+1} - 24k + 5735 \text{ is divisible by } (24)^2.$$

$\Rightarrow$ $P(k) = (24)^2 r$, where r is an integer.

***Step* III** For $n = k + 1$,

$$P(k+1) = (25)^{(k+1)+1} - 24(k+1) + 5735$$
$$= (25)^{k+2} - 24k + 5711$$
$$= (25)(25)^{k+1} - 24k + 5711$$

Now, $P(k+1) - P(k)$

$$= \{(25)(25)^{k+1} - 24k + 5711\} - \{(25)^{k+1} - 24k + 5735\}$$
$$= (24)(25)^{k+1} - 24$$
$$= 24\{(25)^{k+1} - 1\}$$

$\Rightarrow$ $P(k+1) = P(k) + 24\{(25)^{k+1} - 1\}$

But by assumption $P(k)$ is divisible by $(24)^2$. Also, $24\{(25)^{k+1} - 1\}$ is clearly divisible by $(24)^2$, $\forall\ k \in N$. This shows that, the result is true for $n = k + 1$.

Hence, by the principle of mathematical induction, result is true for all $n \in N$.

(vi) Let $P(n) = x^{2n} - y^{2n}$

***Step* I** For $n = 1$,

$$P(1) = x^2 - y^2$$
$$= (x - y)(x + y) \text{ which is divisible by } (x + y).$$

Therefore, the result is true for $n = 1$.

***Step* II** Assume that the result is true for $n = k$. Then,

$$P(k) = x^{2k} - y^{2k} \text{ is divisible by } x + y.$$

$\Rightarrow$ $P(k) = (x + y)r$, where r is an integer.

***Step* III** For $n = k + 1$,

$$= x^2 \cdot x^{2k} - y^2 \cdot y^{2k}$$
$$= x^2x^{2k} - x^2y^{2k} + x^2y^{2k} - y^2y^{2k}$$
$$= x^2(x^{2k} - y^{2k}) + y^{2k}(x^2 - y^2)$$
$$= x^2(x + y)r + y^{2k}(x - y)(x + y)$$

[by assumption step]

$$= (x + y)\{x^2r + y^{2k}(x - y)\}$$

which is divisible by $(x + y)$ as $x^2r + y^{2k}(x - y)$ is an integer.

This shows that the result is true for $n = k + 1$. Hence, by the principle of mathematical induction, the result is true for all $n \in N$.

8. Let $P(n) = 3^{2n} + 3^n + 1$, $\forall\ n$ is a positive integer not divisible by 3.

***Step* I** For $n = 1$,

$$P(1) = 3^2 + 3 + 1 = 9 + 3 + 1$$
$$= 13, \text{ which is divisible by 13.}$$

Therefore, $P(1)$ is true.

***Step* II** Assume $P(n)$ is true for $n = k$, k is a positive integer not divisible by 3, then

$$P(k) = 3^{2k} + 3^k + 1, \text{ is divisible by 13.}$$

$\Rightarrow$ $P(k) = 13r$, where r is an integer.

***Step* III** For $n = k + 1$,

$$P(k+1) = 3^{2(k+1)} + 3^{k+1} + 1$$
$$= 3^2 \cdot 3^{2k} + 3 \cdot 3^k + 1$$

Now, $3^{2k} + 3^k + 1 \overline{)\ 3^2 \cdot 3^{2k} + 3 \cdot 3^k + 1\ (}\ 3^2$

$$3^2 \cdot 3^{2k} + 3^2 \cdot 3^k + 3^2$$
$$- \quad - \quad -$$
$$-6 \cdot 3^k - 8$$

$\Rightarrow$ $P(k+1) = 3^2(3^{2k} + 3^k + 1) - 6 \cdot 3^k - 8$

$$= 9\,P(k) - 2(3^{k+1} + 4)$$
$$= 9(13r) - 2(3^{k+1} + 4) \quad \text{[by assumption step]}$$

which is divisible by 13 as $3^{k+1} + 4$ is also divisible by 13, $\forall\ k \in N$ and not divisible by 3. This shows that the result is true for $n = k + 1$. Hence, by the principle of mathematical induction, the result is true for all natural numbers not divisible by 3.

9. Let $P(n) = n(n+1)(n+2)$, where n is a positive integer.

***Step* I** For $n = 1$,

$$P(1) = 1(1+1)(1+2) = 1 \cdot 2 \cdot 3$$
$$= 6, \text{ which is divisible by 6.}$$

Therefore, the result is true for $n = 1$.

***Step* II** Let us assume that the result is true for $n = k$, where k is a positive integer.

Then, $P(k) = k(k+1)(k+2)$ is divisible by 6.

$\Rightarrow$ $P(k) = 6r$, where r is an integer.

$\overline{)\ a^2\ a^k + b^2\ b^k\ (}\ a^2$ [infact positive integer]

***Step* III** For $n = k + 1$, where k is a positive integer.

$$P(k+1) = (k+1)(k+1+1)(k+2+1)$$
$$= (k+1)(k+2)(k+3)$$

Now, $P(k+1) - P(k) = (k+1)(k+2)(k+3) - k(k+1)(k+2)$

$$= (k+1)(k+2)(k+3-k)$$
$$= 3(k+1)(k+2)$$

$\Rightarrow$ $P(k+1) = P(k) + 3(k+1)(k+2)$

But we know that, $P(k)$ is divisible by 6. Also, $3(k+1)(k+2)$ is divisible by 6 for all positive integer. This shows that the result is true for $n = k + 1$. Hence, by the principle of mathematical induction, the result is true for all positive integer.

10. Let $P(n) = n^3 + (n+1)^3 + (n+2)^3$, where $n \in N$.

***Step* I** For $n = 1$,

$$P(1) = 1^3 + 2^3 + 3^3 = 1 + 8 + 27$$
$$= 36, \text{ which is divisible by 9.}$$

***Step* II** Assume that $P(n)$ is true for $n = k$, then

$$P(k) = k^3 + (k+1)^3 + (k+2)^3, \text{ where } k \in N.$$

$\Rightarrow$ $P(k) = 9r$, where r is a positive integer.

***Step* III** For $n = k + 1$,

$$P(k+1) = (k+1)^3 + (k+2)^3 + (k+3)^3$$

Now, $P(k+1) - P(k) = (k+1)^3 + (k+2)^3 + (k+3)^3 - \{k^3 + (k+1)^3 + (k+2)^3\}$

$$= (k+3)^3 - k^3$$
$$= k^3 + 9k^2 + 27k + 27 - k^3$$
$$= 9(k^2 + 3k + 3)$$

$\Rightarrow \quad P(k+1) = P(k) + 9(k^2 + 3k + 3)$

$$= 9r + 9(k^2 + 3k + 3)$$
$$= 9(r + k^2 + 3k + 3)$$

which is divisible by 9 as $(r + k^2 + 3k + 3)$ is a positive integer. Hence, by the principle mathematical induction, $P(n)$ is divisible by 9 for all $n \in N$.

11. Let $P(n) : (2r+1)^{2n}$, $\forall\ n \in N$ and $r \in I$.

***Step* I** For $n = 1$,

$$P(1) : (2r+1)^2 = 4r^2 + 4r + 1$$
$$= 4r(r+1) + 1 = 8p + 1,\ p \in I$$

[$\because r(r+1)$ is an even integer]

Therefore, $P(1)$ is true.

***Step* II** Assume $P(n)$ is true for $n = k$, then

$P(k) : (2r+1)^{2k}$ is divisible by 8 leaves remainder 1.

$\Rightarrow \quad P(k) = 8m + 1,\ n \in I$, where m is a positive integer.

***Step* III** For $n = k + 1$,

$\therefore \quad P(k+1) = (2r+1)2(k+1)$

$$= (2r+1)^{2k}(2r+1)^2$$
$$= (8m+1)(8p+1) \quad \text{[from Steps I and II]}$$
$$= 64\ mp + 8\ (m + p) + 1$$
$$= 8\ (8mp + m + p) + 1$$

which is true for $n = k + 1$ as $8mp + m + p$ is an integer. Hence, by the principle of mathematical induction, when $P(n)$ is divided by 8 leaves the remainder 1 for all $n \in N$.

12. (i) Let $P(n) : 1 + 2 + 3 + \ldots + n = \dfrac{n(n+1)}{2}$ ...(i)

***Step* I** For $n = 1$,

LHS of Eq. (i) = 1

RHS of Eq. (i) $= \dfrac{1(1+1)}{2} = 1$

LHS = RHS

Therefore, $P(1)$ is true.

***Step* II** Let us assume that the result is true for $n = k$. Then,

$$P(k) : 1 + 2 + 3 + \ldots + k = \frac{k(k+1)}{2}$$

***Step* III** For $n = k + 1$, we have to prove that

$$P(k+1) = 1 + 2 + 3 + \ldots + k + (k+1) = \frac{(k+1)(k+2)}{2}$$

$$\text{LHS} = 1 + 2 + 3 + \ldots + k + (k+1)$$
$$= \frac{k(k+1)}{2} + k + 1 \quad \text{[by assumption step]}$$
$$= (k+1)\left(\frac{k}{2} + 1\right) = (k+1)\left(\frac{k+2}{2}\right)$$
$$= \frac{(k+1)(k+2)}{2}$$
$$= \text{RHS}$$

This shows that the result is true for $n = k + 1$. Therefore, by the principle of mathematical induction, the result is true for all $n \in N$.

(ii) Let $P(n) : 1^2 + 2^2 + 3^2 + \ldots + n^2 = \dfrac{(n+1)(2n+1)}{6}$ ...(i)

***Step* I** For $n = 1$,

LHS of Eq. (i) $= 1^2 = 1$

RHS of Eq. (i) $= \dfrac{1(1+1)(2 \times 1 + 1)}{6}$

$$= \frac{1 \cdot 2 \cdot 3}{6} = 1$$

LHS = RHS

Therefore, $P(1)$ is true.

***Step* II** Let us assume that the result is true for $n = k$. Then,

$$P(k) : 1^2 + 2^2 + 3^2 + \ldots + k^2 = \frac{k(k+1)(2k+1)}{6}$$

***Step* III** For $n = k + 1$, we have to prove that

$$P(k+1) : 1^2 + 2^2 + 3^2 + \ldots + k^2 + (k+1)^2 = \frac{(k+1)(k+2)(2k+3)}{6}$$

$$\text{LHS} = 1^2 + 2^2 + 3^2 + \ldots + k^2 + (k+1)^2$$
$$= \frac{k(k+1)(2k+1)}{6} + (k+1)^2 \quad \text{[by assumption step]}$$
$$= (k+1)\left\{\frac{k(2k+1)}{6} + (k+1)\right\}$$
$$= (k+1)\left\{\frac{2k^2 + 7k + 6}{6}\right\}$$
$$= (k+1)\left\{\frac{(k+2)(2k+3)}{6}\right\} = \frac{(k+1)(k+2)(2k+3)}{6}$$
$$= \text{RHS}$$

This shows that the result is true for $n = k + 1$. Therefore, by the principle of mathematical induction, the result is true for all $n \in N$.

(iii) Let $P(n) : 1 \cdot 3 + 3 \cdot 5 + 5 \cdot 7 + \ldots + (2n-1)(2n+1)$

$$= \frac{n(4n^2 + 6n - 1)}{3} \quad \text{...(i)}$$

***Step* I** For $n = 1$,

LHS of Eq. (i) $= 1 \cdot 3 = 3$

RHS of Eq. (i) $= \dfrac{1(4 \times 1^2 + 6 \times 1 - 1)}{3} = \dfrac{4 + 6 - 1}{3} = 3$

$\therefore$ LHS = RHS

Therefore, $P(1)$ is true.

***Step* II** Assume that the result is true for $n = k$. Then,

$$P(k) : 1 \cdot 3 + 3 \cdot 5 + 5 \cdot 7 + \ldots + (2k-1)(2k+1) = \frac{k(4k^2 + 6k - 1)}{3}$$

***Step* III** For $n = k + 1$, we have to prove that

$$P(k+1): 1\cdot 3 + 3\cdot 5 + 5\cdot 7 + \dots + (2k-1)(2k+1) + (2k+1)(2k+3)$$

$$= \frac{(k+1)[4(k+1)^2 + 6(k+1) - 1]}{3}$$

$$= \frac{(k+1)(4k^2 + 14k + 9)}{3}$$

$$\text{LHS} = 1\cdot 3 + 3\cdot 5 + 5\cdot 7 + \dots + (2k-1)(2k+1) + (2k+1)(2k+3)$$

$$= \frac{k(4k^2 + 6k - 1)}{3} + (2k+1)(2k+3) \quad \text{[by assumption step]}$$

$$= \frac{4k^3 + 6k^2 - k}{3} + (4k^2 + 8k + 3)$$

$$= \frac{4k^3 + 18k^2 + 23k + 9}{3}$$

$$= \frac{(k+1)(4k^2 + 14k + 9)}{3} = \text{RHS}$$

This shows that the result is true for $n = k + 1$. Therefore, by the principle of mathematical induction, the result is true for all $n \in N$.

(iv) Let $P(n): \frac{1}{2\cdot 5} + \frac{1}{5\cdot 8} + \frac{1}{8\cdot 11} + \dots + \frac{1}{(3n-1)(3n+2)}$

$$= \frac{n}{6n+4} \quad \text{...(i)}$$

***Step* I** For $n = 1$,

$$\text{LHS of Eq. (i)} = \frac{1}{2\cdot 5} = \frac{1}{10}$$

$$\text{RHS of Eq. (i)} = \frac{1}{6\times 1 + 4} = \frac{1}{10}$$

LHS = RHS

Therefore, $P(1)$ is true.

***Step* II** Let us assume that the result is true for $n = k$. Then,

$$P(k): \frac{1}{2\cdot 5} + \frac{1}{5\cdot 8} + \frac{1}{8\cdot 11} + \dots + \frac{1}{(3k-1)(3k+2)} = \frac{k}{6k+4}$$

***Step* III** For $n = k + 1$, we have to prove that

$$P(k+1): \frac{1}{2\cdot 5} + \frac{1}{5\cdot 8} + \frac{1}{8\cdot 11} + \dots + \frac{1}{(3k-1)(3k+2)} + \frac{1}{(3k+2)(3k+5)}$$

$$= \frac{(k+1)}{6(k+1)+4} = \frac{(k+1)}{6k+10}$$

$$\text{LHS} = \frac{1}{2\cdot 5} + \frac{1}{5\cdot 8} + \frac{1}{8\cdot 11} + \dots + \frac{1}{(3k-1)(3k+2)} + \frac{1}{(3k+2)(3k+5)}$$

$$= \frac{k}{6k+4} + \frac{1}{(3k+2)(3k+5)} \quad \text{[by assumption step]}$$

$$= \frac{k(3k+5)+2}{2(3k+2)(3k+5)} = \frac{3k^2 + 5k + 2}{2(3k+2)(3k+5)}$$

$$= \frac{(k+1)(3k+2)}{2(3k+2)(3k+5)} = \frac{k+1}{6k+10}$$

= RHS

This shows that the result is true for $n = k + 1$. Therefore, by the principle of mathematical induction, the result is true for all $n \in N$.

(v) Let $P(n): 1\cdot 4\cdot 7 + 2\cdot 5\cdot 8 + 3\cdot 6\cdot 9 + \dots$ + upto n terms

$$= \frac{n}{4}(n+1)(n+6)(n+7)$$

i.e., $P(n): 1\cdot 4\cdot 7 + 2\cdot 5\cdot 8 + 3\cdot 6\cdot 9 + \dots + n(n+3)(n+6)$

$$= \frac{n}{4}(n+1)(n+6)(n+7) \quad \text{...(i)}$$

***Step* I** For $n = 1$,

LHS of Eq. (i) $= 1\cdot 4\cdot 7 = 28$

$$\text{RHS of Eq. (i)} = \frac{1}{4}(1+1)(1+6)(1+7) = \frac{2\cdot 7\cdot 8}{4} = 28$$

LHS = RHS

Therefore, $P(1)$ is true.

***Step* II** Let us assume that the result is true for $n = k$. Then,

$$P(k): 1\cdot 4\cdot 7 + 2\cdot 5\cdot 8 + 3\cdot 6\cdot 9 + \dots + k(k+3)(k+6) = \frac{k}{4}(k+1)(k+6)(k+7)$$

***Step* III** For $n = k + 1$, we have to prove that

$$P(k+1): 1\cdot 4\cdot 7 + 2\cdot 5\cdot 8 + 3\cdot 6\cdot 9 + \dots + k(k+3)(k+6) + (k+1)(k+4)(k+7)$$

$$= \frac{(k+1)}{4}(k+2)(k+7)(k+8)$$

$$\text{LHS} = 1\cdot 4\cdot 7 + 2\cdot 5\cdot 8 + 3\cdot 6\cdot 9 + \dots + k(k+3)(k+6) + (k+1)(k+4)(k+7)$$

$$= \frac{k}{4}(k+1)(k+6)(k+7) + (k+1)(k+4)(k+7) \quad \text{[by assumption step]}$$

$$= (k+1)(k+7)\left\{\frac{k}{4}(k+6) + (k+4)\right\}$$

$$= (k+1)(k+7)\left\{\frac{k^2 + 6k + 4k + 16}{4}\right\}$$

$$= (k+1)(k+7)\left\{\frac{k^2 + 10k + 16}{4}\right\}$$

$$= (k+1)(k+7)\left\{\frac{(k+2)(k+8)}{4}\right\}$$

$$= \frac{(k+1)}{4}(k+2)(k+7)(k+8) = \text{RHS}$$

This shows that the result is true for $n = k + 1$. Hence, by the principle of mathematical induction, the result is true for all $n \in N$.

(vi) Let $P(n): \frac{1^2}{1\cdot 3} + \frac{2^2}{3\cdot 5} + \dots + \frac{n^2}{(2n-1)(2n+1)}$

$$= \frac{n(n+1)}{2(2n+1)} \quad \text{...(i)}$$

***Step* I** For $n = 1$,

LHS of Eq. (i) $= \dfrac{1^2}{1 \cdot 3} = \dfrac{1}{3}$

RHS of Eq. (i) $= \dfrac{1(1+1)}{2(2 \times 1 + 1)} = \dfrac{2}{2(3)} = \dfrac{1}{3}$

$$\text{LHS} = \text{RHS}$$

Therefore, $P(1)$ is true.

***Step* II** Let us assume that the result is true for $n = k$, then

$$P(k) = \frac{1^2}{1 \cdot 3} + \frac{2^2}{3 \cdot 5} + \ldots + \frac{k^2}{(2k-1)(2k+1)} = \frac{k(k+1)}{2(2k+1)}$$

***Step* III** For $n = k + 1$, we have to prove that

$$P(k+1): \frac{1^2}{1 \cdot 3} + \frac{2^2}{3 \cdot 5} + \ldots + \frac{k^2}{(2k-1)(2k+1)} + \frac{(k+1)^2}{(2k+1)(2k+3)} = \frac{(k+1)(k+2)}{2(2k+3)}$$

$$\text{LHS} = \frac{1^2}{1 \cdot 3} + \frac{2^2}{3 \cdot 5} + \ldots + \frac{k^2}{(2k-1)(2k+1)} + \frac{(k+1)^2}{(2k+1)(2k+3)}$$

$$= \frac{k(k+1)}{2(2k+1)} + \frac{(k+1)^2}{(2k+1)(2k+3)} \quad \text{[by assumption step]}$$

$$= \frac{(k+1)}{(2k+1)}\left\{\frac{k}{2} + \frac{k+1}{(2k+3)}\right\} = \frac{(k+1)}{(2k+1)}\left\{\frac{2k^2+5k+2}{2(2k+3)}\right\}$$

$$= \frac{(k+1)}{(2k+1)} \cdot \frac{(k+2)(2k+1)}{2(2k+3)} = \frac{(k+1)(k+2)}{2(2k+3)}$$

$$= \text{RHS}$$

This shows that, the result is true for $n = k + 1$. Therefore, by the principle of mathematical induction the result is true for all $n \in N$.

13. Let $P(n): a_n = 2^n + 3^n, \forall n \geq 0, n \in N$

and $a_0 = 2, a_1 = 5$ and for $n \geq 2$; $a_n = 5a_{n-1} - 6a_n - 2$

***Step* I** For $n = 0$,

$$a_0 = 2^0 + 3^0 = 1 + 10 = 2$$

which is true as $a_0 = 2$. [given]

Also, for $n = 1$, $\quad a_1 = 2^1 + 3^1 = 2 + 3 = 5$

which is also true as $a_1 = 5$. [given]

Hence, $P(0)$ and $P(1)$ are true.

***Step* II** Assume that $P(k-1)$ and $P(k)$ are true. Then,

$$a_{k-1} = 2^{k-1} + 3^{k-1} \quad \ldots\text{(i)}$$

where $\quad a_{k-1} = 5a_{k-2} - 6a_{k-3}$ and $a_k = 2^k + 3^k \quad \ldots$(ii)

where $\quad a_k = 5a_{k-1} - 6a_{k-2}$

***Step* III** For $n = k + 1$,

$$P(k+1): a_{k+1} = 2^{k+1} + 3^{k+1}, \forall k \geq 0, k \in N.$$

where $\quad a_{k+1} = 5a_k - 6a_{k-1}$

Now, $\quad a_{k+1} = 5a_k - 6a_{k-1}$

$$= 5(2^k + 3^k) - 6(2^{k-1} + 3^{k-1})$$

[by using Eqs. (i) and (ii)]

$$= 5 \cdot 2^k + 5 \cdot 3^k - 6 \cdot 2^{k-1} - 6 \cdot 3^{k-1}$$

$$= 2^{k-1}(5 \cdot 2 - 6) + 3^{k-1}(5 \cdot 3 - 6)$$

$$= 2^{k-1} \cdot 4 + 3^{k-1} \cdot 9 = 2^{k+1} + 3^{k+1}$$

$$\Rightarrow \quad a_{k+1} = 2^{k+1} + 3^{k+1}$$

where $\quad a_{k+1} = 5a_k - 6a_{k-1}$

This shows that the result is true for $n = k + 1$. Hence, by the second principle of mathematical induction, the result is true for $n \in N, n \geq 0$.

14. Let $P(n): a_{n+1} = \dfrac{1}{(n+1)!}, n \in N \quad \ldots$(i)

where $a_1 = 1$ and $a_{n+1} = \dfrac{1}{(n+1)} a_n, n \geq 1 \quad \ldots$(ii)

***Step* I** For $n = 1$, from Eq. (i), we get

$$a_2 = \frac{1}{(1+1)!} = \frac{1}{2!}$$

But from Eq. (ii), we get $a_2 = \dfrac{1}{(1+1)}, a_1 = \dfrac{1}{2}(1) = \dfrac{1}{2}$

which is true.

Also, for $n = 2$ from Eq. (i), we get

$$a_3 = \frac{1}{3!} = \frac{1}{6}$$

But from Eq. (ii), we get $a_3 = \dfrac{1}{3}, a_2 = \dfrac{1}{3} \cdot \dfrac{1}{2} = \dfrac{1}{6}$

which is also true.

Hence, $P(1)$ and $P(2)$ are true.

***Step* II** Assume that $P(k-1)$ and $P(k)$ are true. Then,

$$P(k-1): a_k = \frac{1}{k!} \quad \ldots\text{(iii)}$$

where, $a_k = \dfrac{1}{k} a_{k-1}, \quad k \geq 1 \quad \ldots$(iv)

and $\quad P(k): a_{k+1} = \dfrac{1}{(k+1)!} \quad \ldots$(v)

where $\quad a_{k+1} = \dfrac{1}{k+1} a_k, k \geq 1 \quad \ldots$(vi)

***Step* III** For $n = k + 1$,

$$P(k+1): a_{k+2} = \frac{1}{(k+2)!} \quad \ldots\text{(vii)}$$

where $\quad a_{k+2} = \dfrac{1}{(k+2)} a_{k+1} \quad \ldots$(viii)

Now, LHS of Eq. (vii) $= a_{k+2}$

$$= \frac{1}{(k+2)} a_{k+1} \quad \text{[using Eq. (viii)]}$$

$$= \frac{1}{(k+2)} \cdot \frac{1}{(k+1)} a_k \quad \text{[using Eq. (vi)]}$$

$$= \frac{1}{k+2} \cdot \frac{1}{k+1} \cdot \frac{1}{k} a_{k-1} \quad \text{[using Eq. (iv)]}$$

$$= \frac{1}{k+2} \cdot \frac{1}{k+1} \cdot \frac{1}{k} \cdot \frac{1}{k!} \quad \text{[using Eq. (iii)]}$$

$$= \frac{1}{(k+2)!} = \text{RHS of Eq. (vii)}$$

This shows that the result is true for $n = k + 1$. Hence, by the second principle of mathematical induction, the result is true for all $n \geq 1, n \in N$.

5. Let $P(n): a^n + b^n + c^n = d^n + e^n + f^n, \forall\, n \in N$ ...(i)

where $a + b + c = d + e + f$ ...(ii)

$a^2 + b^2 + c^2 = d^2 + e^2 + f^2$ ...(iii)

and $a^3 + b^3 + c^3 = d^3 + e^3 + f^3$ ...(iv)

***Step* I** For $n = 1$ from Eq. (i), we get

$P(1): a + b + c = d + e + f$ [given]

Hence, the result is true for $n = 1$.

Also, for $n = 2$ from Eq. (i), we get

$P(2): a^2 + b^2 + c^2 = d^2 + e^2 + f^2$ [given]

Hence, the result is true for $n = 2$.

Also, for $x = 3$, from Eq. (i), we get

$P(3): a^3 + b^3 + c^3 = d^3 + e^3 + f^3$ [given]

Hence, the result is true for $n = 3$.

Therefore, $P(1)$, $P(2)$ and $P(3)$ are true.

***Step* II** Assume that $P(k-2)$, $P(k-1)$ and $P(k)$ are true, then

$P(k-2): a^{k-2} + b^{k-2} + c^{k-2} = d^{k-2} + e^{k-2} + f^{k-2}$ ...(v)

$P(k-1): a^{k-1} + b^{k-1} + c^{k-1} = d^{k-1} + e^{k-1} + f^{k-1}$ ...(vi)

and $P(k): a^k + b^k + c^k = d^k + e^k + f^k$ ...(vii)

***Step* III** For $xn = k + 1$, we shall to prove that

$P(k+1): a^{k+1} + b^{k+1} + c^{k+1} = d^{k+1} + e^{k+1} + f^{k+1}$

$$\text{LHS} = a^{k+1} + b^{k+1} + c^{k+1}$$
$$= (a^k + b^k + c^k)(a + b + c) - (a^{k-1} + b^{k-1} + c^{k-1})$$
$$(ab + bc + ca) + abc\,(a^{k-2} + b^{k-2} + c^{k-2})$$
$$= (d^k + e^k + f^k)(d + e + f) - (d^{k-1} + e^{k-1} + f^{k-1})$$
$$(de + ef + fd) + def(d^{k-2} + e^{k-2} + f^{k-2})$$

[using Eqs. (ii), (iii), (iv), (v), (vi), (vii)]

$$\therefore \quad (a + b + c)^2 = (d + e + f)^2$$
$$\Rightarrow \quad a^2 + b^2 + c^2 + 2(ab + bc + ca) = d^2 + e^2 + f^2 + 2(de + ef + fd)$$
$$\Rightarrow \quad ab + bc + ca = de + ef + fd \quad [\because a^2 + b^2 + c^2 = d^2 + e^2 + f^2]$$

and
$$a^3 + b^3 + c^3 - 3abc = (d + e + f)(d^2 + e^2 + f^2 - de - ef - fd)$$
$$= d^3 + e^3 + f^3 - 3def$$
$$\Rightarrow \quad abc = def \quad [\because a^3 + b^3 + c^3 = d^3 + e^3 + f^3]$$
$$= d^{k+1} + e^{k+1} + f^{k+1} = \text{RHS}$$

This shows that the result is true for $n = k + 1$. Hence, by second principle of mathematical induction, the result is true for all $n \in N$.

16. Let $P(n): \tan^{-1}\left(\frac{1}{3}\right) + \tan^{-1}\left(\frac{1}{7}\right) + \ldots + \tan^{-1}\left(\frac{1}{n^2+n+1}\right)$

$$= \tan^{-1}\left(\frac{n}{n+2}\right) \quad \text{...(i)}$$

***Step* I** For $n = 1$,

$$\text{LHS of Eq. (i)} = \tan^{-1}\left(\frac{1}{3}\right) = \tan^{-1}\left(\frac{1}{1+2}\right) = \text{RHS of Eq. (i)}$$

Therefore, $P(1)$ is true.

***Step* II** Assume that $P(k)$ is true. Then,

$$P(k): \tan^{-1}\left(\frac{1}{3}\right) + \tan^{-1}\left(\frac{1}{7}\right) + \ldots + \tan^{-1}\left(\frac{1}{k^2+k+1}\right) = \tan^{-1}\left(\frac{k}{k+2}\right)$$

***Step* III** For $n = k + 1$,

$$P(k+1): \tan^{-1}\left(\frac{1}{3}\right) + \tan^{-1}\left(\frac{1}{7}\right) + \ldots + \tan^{-1}\left(\frac{1}{k^2+k+1}\right) + \tan^{-1}\left(\frac{1}{(k+1)^2 + (k+1) + 1}\right)$$
$$= \tan^{-1}\left(\frac{k+1}{k+3}\right) \quad \text{...(ii)}$$

LHS of Eq. (ii)

$$= \tan^{-1}\left(\frac{1}{3}\right) + \tan^{-1}\left(\frac{1}{7}\right) + \ldots + \tan^{-1}\left(\frac{1}{k^2+k+1}\right) + \tan^{-1}\left(\frac{1}{(k+1)^2 + (k+1) + 1}\right)$$
$$= \tan^{-1}\left(\frac{k}{k+2}\right) + \tan^{-1}\left(\frac{1}{(k+1)^2 + (k+1) + 1}\right)$$

[by assumption step]

$$= \tan^{-1}\left(\frac{k}{1 + (k+1)}\right) + \tan^{-1}\left(\frac{1}{k^2 + 3k + 3}\right)$$
$$= \tan^{-1}\left(\frac{k}{1 + (k+1)}\right) + \tan^{-1}\left(\frac{1}{1 + (k+1)(k+2)}\right)$$
$$= \tan^{-1}\left(\frac{(k+1) - 1}{1 + (k+1)\cdot 1}\right) + \tan^{-1}\left(\frac{(k+2) - (k+1)}{1 + (k+2)(k+1)}\right)$$
$$= \tan^{-1}(k+1) - \tan^{-1}1 + \tan^{-1}(k+2) - \tan^{-1}(k+1)$$
$$= \tan^{-1}(k+2) - \tan^{-1}1$$
$$= \tan^{-1}\left(\frac{k+2-1}{1 + (k+2)\cdot 1}\right) = \tan^{-1}\left(\frac{k+1}{k+3}\right) = \text{RHS of Eq. (ii)}$$

This shows that the result is true for $n = k + 1$. Hence, by the principle of mathematical induction, the result is true for all $n \in N$.

17. Let $P(n) = \frac{1}{\sqrt{1}} + \frac{1}{\sqrt{2}} + \ldots + \frac{1}{\sqrt{n}}$

$$\therefore \quad P(2) = \frac{1}{\sqrt{1}} + \frac{1}{\sqrt{2}} = 1.707 > \sqrt{2}$$

Let us assume that

$$P(k) = \frac{1}{\sqrt{1}} + \frac{1}{\sqrt{2}} + \ldots + \frac{1}{\sqrt{k}} > \sqrt{k} \text{ is true for } n = k + 1.$$

$$\text{LHS} = \frac{1}{\sqrt{1}} + \frac{1}{\sqrt{2}} + \ldots + \frac{1}{\sqrt{k}} + \frac{1}{\sqrt{k+1}}$$

$$> \sqrt{k} + \frac{1}{\sqrt{k+1}} = \frac{\sqrt{k(k+1)}+1}{\sqrt{(k+1)}} > \frac{k+1}{\sqrt{(k+1)}}$$

$$[\because \sqrt{k(k+1)} + 1 > k, \forall k \ge 0]$$

$$\therefore \quad P(k+1) > \sqrt{(k+1)}$$

By mathematical induction Statement-1 is true, $\forall n \ge 2$.

Now, let $\alpha(n) = \sqrt{n(n+1)}$

$$\therefore \quad \alpha(2) = \sqrt{2(2+1)} = \sqrt{6} < 3$$

Let us assume that

$$\alpha(k) = \sqrt{k(k+1)} < (k+1) \text{ is true}$$

for $\quad n = k + 1$

$$\text{LHS} = \sqrt{(k+1)(k+2)} < (k+2)$$

$$[\because (k+1) < (k+2)]$$

By mathematical induction Statement-2 is true but Statement-2 is not a correct explanation for Statement-1.

18. Let $P(n) = n^7 - n$

By mathematical induction for $n = 1$, $P(1) = 0$, which is divisib by 7

for $\quad n = k, P(k) = k^7 - k$

Assume $P(k)$ is divisible by 7

$$\therefore \quad k^7 - k = 7\lambda, \lambda \in I$$

For $n = k + 1$,

$$P(k+1) = (k+1)^7 - (k+1)$$

$$= ({}^7C_0 k^7 + {}^7C_1 k^6 + {}^7C_2 k^5 + {}^7C_3 k^4 + \ldots + {}^7C_6 k + {}^7C_7) - (k+1)$$

$$= (k^7 - k) + 7(k^6 + 3k^5 + \ldots + k)$$

$$= 7\lambda + 7(k^6 + 3k^5 + \ldots + k) = \text{Divisible by } 7$$

$\therefore$ Statement-2 is true.

Also, let $F(n) = (n+1)^7 - n^7 - 1$

$$= \{(n+1)^7 - (n+1)\} - (n^7 - n)$$

$$= \text{Divisible by 7 from Statement-2}$$

Hence, both statements are true and Statement-2 is correct explanation of Statement-1.

CHAPTER

11

Sets, Relations and Functions

Learning Part

Session 1

- Definition of Set
- Representation of Set
- Different Types of Sets
- Laws and Theorems
- Venn Diagrams (Euler-Venn Diagrams)

Session 2

- Ordered Pair
- Definition of Relation
- Ordered Relation
- Composition of Two Relations

Session 3

- Definition of Functions
- Domain, Codomain and Range
- Composition of Mapping
- Equivalence Classes
- Partition of Set
- Congruences

Practice Part

- JEE Type Examples
- Chapter Exercises

Session 1

Definition of Set, Representation of Set, Different Types of Sets, Laws and Theorems, Venn Diagram (Euler-Venn Diagrams)

Introduction

The concept of set is fundamental in modern Mathematics. Today this concept is being used in different branches of Mathematics and widely used in the foundation of relations and functions. The theory of sets was developed by German Mathematician **Georg Cantor** (1845-1918).

Definition of Set

A set is well-defined collection of distinct objects. Sets are usually denoted by capital letters $A, B, C, X, Y, Z, \ldots$.

Examples of sets

(i) The set of all complex numbers.

(ii) The set of vowels in the alphabets of English language.

(iii) The set of all natural numbers.

(iv) The set of all triangles in a plane.

(v) The set of all states in India.

(vi) The set of all months in year which has 30 days.

(vii) The set of all stars in space.

Elements of the Set

The elements of the set are denoted by small letters in the alphabets of English language, i.e. $a, b, c, x, y, z, \ldots$. If x is an element of a set A, we write $x \in A$ (read as 'x belongs to A').

If x is not an element of A, then we write $x \notin A$ (read as 'x does not belong to A').

For example,

If $A = \{1, 2, 3, 4, 5\}$, then $3 \in A$, $6 \notin A$.

Representation of a Set

There are two methods for representing a set.

1. Tabulation or Roster or Enumeration Method

Under this method, the elements are enclosed in curly brackets or braces { } after separating them by commas.

Remark

1. The order of writing the elements of a set is immaterial, so $\{a, b, c\}$, $\{b, a, c\}$, $\{c, a, b\}$ all denote the same set.
2. An element of a set is not written more than once, i.e. the set {1, 2, 3, 4, 3, 3, 2, 1, 2, 1, 4} is identical with the set {1, 2, 3, 4}.

For example,

1. If A is the set of prime numbers less than 10, then
$$A = \{2, 3, 5, 7\}$$
2. If A is the set of all even numbers lying between 2 and 20, then
$$A = \{4, 6, 8, 10, 12, 14, 16, 18\}$$

2. Set Builder Method

Under this method, the stating properties which its elements are to satisfy, then we write

$$A = \{x\ P(x)\} \quad \text{or} \quad A = \{x : P(x)\}$$

and read as 'A is the set of elements x, such that x has the property P'.

Remark

1. " : " or " | " means 'such that'.
2. The other names of this method are property method, rule method and symbolic method.

For example,

1. If $A = \{1, 2, 3, 4, 5, 6, 7, 8\}$, then we can write
$$A = \{x \in N : x \le 8\}.$$
2. A is the set of all odd integers lying between 2 and 51, then
$$A = \{x : 2 < x < 51, x \text{ is odd}\}.$$

ome Standard Sets

N denotes set of all natural numbers $= \{1, 2, 3, \dots\}$.

Z or I denotes set of all integers $= \{\dots, -3, -2, -1, 0, 1, 2, 3, \dots\}$.

Z_0 or I_0 denotes set of all integers excluding zero $= \{\dots, -3, -2, -1, 1, 2, 3, \dots\}$.

Z^+ or I^+ denotes set of all positive integers $= \{1, 2, 3, \dots\} = N$.

E denotes set of all even integers $= \{\dots, -6, -4, -2, 0, 2, 4, 6, \dots\}$.

O denotes set of all odd integers $= \{\dots, -5, -3, -1, 1, 3, 5, \dots\}$.

W denotes set of all whole numbers $= \{0, 1, 2, 3, \dots\}$.

Q denotes set of all rational numbers $= \{x : x = p/q$, where p and q are integers and $q \neq 0\}$.

Q_0 denotes set of all non-zero rational numbers $\{x : x = p/q$, where p and q are integers and $p \neq 0$ and $q \neq 0\}$.

Q^+ denotes set of all positive rational numbers $= \{x : x = p/q$, where p and q are both positive or negative integers$\}$

R denotes set of all real numbers.

R_0 denotes set of all non-zero real numbers.

R^+ denotes set of all positive real numbers.

$R - Q$ denotes set of all irrational numbers.

C denotes set of all complex numbers $= \{a + ib : a, b \in R$ and $i = \sqrt{-1}\}$.

C_0 denotes set of all non-zero complex numbers $= \{a + ib : a, b \in R_0$ and $i = \sqrt{-1}\}$.

N_a denotes set of all natural numbers which are less than or equal to a, where a is positive integer $= \{1, 2, 3, \dots, a\}$.

Different Types of Sets

1. Null Set or Empty Set or Void Set

A set having no element is called a null set or empty set or void set. It is denoted by ϕ or $\{\ \}$.

Remark

1. ϕ is called the null set.
2. ϕ is unique.
3. ϕ is a subset of every set.
4. ϕ is never written within braces i.e., $\{\phi\}$ is not the null set.
5. $\{0\}$ is not an empty set as it contains the element 0 (zero).

For example,

1. $\{x : x \in N, 4 < x < 5\} = \phi$
2. $\{x : x \in R, x^2 + 1 = 0\} = \phi$
3. $\{x : x^2 = 25, x$ is even number$\} = \phi$

2. Singleton or Unit Set

A set having one and only one element is called singleton or unit set.

For example, $\{x : x - 3 = 4\}$ is a singleton set.

Since, $x - 3 = 4 \Rightarrow x = 7$

$\therefore \{x : x - 3 = 4\} = \{7\}$

3. Subset

If every element of a set A is also an element of a set B, then A is called the subset of B, we write $A \subseteq B$ (read as A is subset of B or A is contained in B).

Thus, $A \subseteq B \Leftrightarrow [x \in A \Rightarrow x \in B]$

Remark

1. Every set is a subset of itself i.e., $A \subseteq A$.
2. If $A \subseteq B$, $B \subseteq C$, then $A \subseteq C$.

For example,

1. If $A = \{2, 3, 4\}$ and $B = \{5, 4, 2, 3, 1\}$, then $A \subseteq B$.
2. The sets $\{a\}, \{b\}, \{a, b\}, \{b, c\}$ are the subsets of the set $\{a, b, c\}$.

4. Total Number of Subsets

If a set A has n elements, then the number of subsets of $A = 2^n$.

Example 1. Write the letters of the word ALLAHABAD in set form and find the number of subsets in it and write all subsets.

Sol. There are 5 different letters in the word ALLAHABAD i.e., A, L, H, B, D, then set is {A, B, D, H, L}, then number of subsets $= 2^5 = 32$ and all subsets are

ϕ, {A}, {B}, {D}, {H}, {L}, {A, B}, {A, D}, {A, H}, {A, L}, {B, D}, {B, H}, {B, L}, {D, H}, {D, L}, {H, L}, {A, B, D}, {A, B, H}, {A, B, L}, {A, D, H}, {A, D, L}, {A, H, L}, {B, D, H}, {B, D, L}, {B, H, L}, {D, H, L}, {A, B, D, H}, {A, B, D, L}, {B, D, H, L}, {A, D, H, L}, {A, B, H, L}, {A, B, D, H, L}.

5. Equal Sets

Two sets A and B are said to be equal, if every element of A is an element of B, and every element of B is an element of A. If A and B are equal, we write $A = B$.

It is clear that $A \subseteq B$ and $B \subseteq A \Leftrightarrow A = B$.

For example,

1. The sets {1, 2, 5} and {5, 2, 1} are equal.
2. $\{1, 2, 3\} = \{x : x^3 - 6x^2 + 11x - 6 = 0\}$

6. Power Set

The set of all the subsets of a given set A is said to be the power set A and is denoted by $P(A)$ or 2^A.

Symbolically, $P(A) = \{x : x \subseteq A\}$

Thus, $x \in P(A) \Leftrightarrow x \subseteq A$.

Remark

1. ϕ and A are both elements of $P(A)$.
2. If $A = \phi$, then $P(\phi) = \{\phi\}$, a singleton but ϕ is a null set.
3. If $A = \{a\}$, then $P(A) = \{\phi, \{a\}\}$

   For example, If $A = \{a, b, c\}$, then

   $P(A)$ or $2^A = \{\phi, \{a\}, \{b\}, \{c\}, \{a, b\}, \{b, c\}, \{c, a\}, \{a, b, c\}\}$

   Also, $n(P(A))$ or $n(2^A) = 2^3 = 8$
4. Since, $P(\phi) = \{\phi\}$

   $\therefore$ $P(P(\phi)) = \{\phi, \{\phi\}\}$

   and $P(P(P(\phi))) = \{\phi, \{\phi\}, \{\{\phi\}\}, \{\phi, \{\phi\}\}\}$
5. If A has n elements, then $P(A)$ has 2^n elements.

7. Super Set

The statement $A \subseteq B$ can be rewritten as $B \supseteq A$, then B is called the super set of A and is written as $B \supset A$.

8. Proper Subset

A set A is said to be proper subset of a set B, if every element of A is an element of B and B has atleast one element which is not an element of A and is denoted by $A \subset B$ (read as "A is a proper subset of B").

For example,

1. If $A = \{1, 2, 4\}$ and $B = \{5, 1, 2, 4, 3\}$, then $A \subset B$

   Since, $3, 5 \notin A$.
2. If $A = \{a, b, c\}$ and $B = \{c, b, a\}$, then $A \not\subset B$ (since, B does not contain any element which is not in A).
3. $N \subset I \subset Q \subset R \subset C$

9. Finite and Infinite Sets

A set in which the process of counting of elements comes to an end is called a finite set, otherwise it is called an infinite set.

For example,

1. Each one of the following sets is a finite set.
   (i) Set of universities in India.
   (ii) Set of Gold Medalist students in Civil Branch, sec A in A.M.I.E. (India).
   (iii) Set of natural numbers less than 500.
2. Each one of the following is an infinite set.
   (i) Set of all integers.
   (ii) Set of all points in a plane.
   (iii) $\{x : x \in R, 1 < x < 2\}$
   (iv) Set of all concentric circles with centre as origin

10. Cardinal Number of a Finite Set

The number of distinct elements in a finite set A is called cardinal number and the cardinal number of a set A is denoted by $n(A)$.

For example,

If $A = \{-3, -1, 8, 9, 13, 17\}$, then $n(A) = 6$.

11. Comparability of Sets

Two sets A and B are said to be comparable, if either $A \subset B$ or $B \subset A$ or $A = B$, otherwise A and B are said to be incomparable.

For example,

1. The sets $A = \{1,2,3\}$ and $B = \{1,2,4,6\}$ are incomparable (since $A \not\subset B$ or $B \not\subset A$ or $A \neq B$)
2. The sets $A = \{1, 2, 4\}$ and $B = \{1, 4\}$ are comparable (since $B \subset A$).

12. Universal Set

All the sets under consideration are likely to be subsets of a set is called the universal set and is denoted by Ω or S or U.

For example,

1. The set of all letters in alphabet of English language $U = \{a, b, c, \ldots, x, y, z\}$ is the universal set of vowels in alphabet of English language.

   i.e., $A = \{a, e, i, o, u\}$.
2. The set of all integers $I = \{0, \pm 1, \pm 2, \pm 3, \ldots\}$ is the universal set of all even integers

   i.e., $\{0, \pm 2, \pm 4, \pm 6, \ldots\}$

13. Union of Sets

The union of two sets A and B is the set of all those elements which are either in A or in B or in both. This set is denoted by $A \cup B$ or $A + B$ (read as 'A union B' or 'A cup B' or 'A join B').

Symbolically, $A \cup B = \{x : x \in A \text{ or } x \in B\}$

or $A \cup B = \{x : x \in A \vee x \in B\}$

Clearly, $x \in A \cup B \Leftrightarrow x \in A$ or $x \in B$

r example,

1. If $A=\{1,2,3,4\}$ and $B=\{4,5,6\}$, then $A\cup B=\{1,2,3,4,4,5,6\}=\{1,2,3,4,5,6\}$
2. If $A=\{1,2,3\}$, $B=\{2,3,4,5\}$, $C=\{7,8\}$, then $A\cup B\cup C=\{1,2,3,4,5,7,8\}$

Remark

The union of a finite number of sets $A_1, A_2, A_3, \ldots, A_n$ is represented by $A_1\cup A_2\cup A_3\cup\ldots\cup A_n$ or $\bigcup_{i=1}^{n} A_i$.

Symbolically, $\bigcup_{i=1}^{n} A_i=\{x : x\in A_i \text{ for atleast one } i\}$

4. Intersection of Sets

he intersection of two sets A and B is the set of all ements which are common in A and B. This set is enoted by $A\cap B$ or AB (read as 'A intersection B' or 'A ap B' or 'A meet B').

ymbolically, $A\cap B=\{x : x\in A \text{ and } x\in B\}$

r $\qquad A\cap B=\{x : x\in A\wedge x\in B\}$

learly, $x\in A\cap B \Leftrightarrow x\in A$ and $x\in B$

or example,

1. If $A=\{1,2,3\}$ and $B=\{3,4,5,6\}$, then $A\cap B=\{3\}$.
2. If $A=\{1,2,3\}$, $B=\{2,3,4\}$ and $C=\{3,4,5\}$, then $A\cap B\cap C=\{3\}$

Remark

The intersection of a finite number of sets $A_1, A_2, A_3, \ldots, A_n$ represented by

$$A_1\cap A_2\cap A_3\cap\ldots\cap A_n \quad \text{or} \quad \bigcap_{i=1}^{n} A_i.$$

Symbolically, $\bigcap_{i=1}^{n} A_i=\{x : x\in A_i \text{ for all } i\}$

15. Disjoint Sets

f the two sets A and B have no common element.

.e., $A\cap B=\phi$, then the two sets A and B are called disjoint r mutually exclusive events.

or example, If $A=\{a,b,c\}$ and $B=\{1,2,3\}$, then $A\cap B=\phi$

Hence, A and B are disjoint sets.

Remark

If $S=\{a_1, a_2, a_3, \ldots, a_n\}$, so

number of ordered pairs of disjoint sets of S is $\frac{3^n+1}{2}$.

($\because$ each element in either (A) or (B) or neither

$\therefore$ Total ways $=3^n$ i.e., $A=B$, iff $A=B=\phi$ (1 case) otherwise A and B are interchangeable.

$\therefore$ Number of ordered pairs of disjoint sets of $S=1+\frac{3^n-1}{2}=\frac{3^n+1}{2}$)

16. Difference of Sets

If A and B be two given sets, then the set of all those elements of A which do not belong to B is called difference of sets A and B. It is written as $A-B$. It is also denoted by $A\sim B$ or $A\backslash B$ or $C_A B$ (complement of B in A).

Symbolically, $A-B=\{x : x\in A \text{ and } x\notin B\}$

Clearly, $x\in A-B \Leftrightarrow x\in A$ and $x\notin B$.

Remark

1. $A-B\neq B-A$
2. The sets $A-B$, $B-A$ and $A\cap B$ are disjoint sets.
3. $A-B\subseteq A$ and $B-A\subseteq B$
4. $A-\phi=A$ and $A-A=\phi$

For example,

If $A=\{1,2,3,4\}$ and $B=\{4,5,6,7\}$, then $A-B=\{1,2,3\}$.

17. Symmetric Difference of Two Sets

Let A and B be two sets. The symmetric difference of sets A and B is the set $(A-B)\cup(B-A)$ or $(A\cup B)-(A\cap B)$ and is denoted by $A\,\Delta\, B$ or $A\oplus B$ (A direct sum B).

i.e., $\quad A\oplus B$ or $A\,\Delta\, B=(A-B)\cup(B-A)$

and $\quad A\oplus B$ or $A\,\Delta\, B=(A\cup B)-(A\cap B)$

Remark

1. $A\,\Delta\, B=\{x : x\in A \text{ and } x\notin B\}$
   or $\quad A\,\Delta\, B=\{x : x\in B \text{ and } x\notin A\}$
2. $A\,\Delta\, B=B\,\Delta\, A$ (commutative)

For example,

Let $\qquad A=\{1,2,3,4,5\}$ and $B=\{1,3,5,7\}$,

then $A-B=\{2,4\}$, $B-A=\{7\}$

$\therefore \qquad A\,\Delta\, B=(A-B)\cup(B-A)=\{2,4,7\}$

18. Complement Set

Let U be the universal set and A be a set, such that $A\subset U$. Then, the complement of A with respect to U is denoted by A' or A^c or $C(A)$ or $U-A$.

Symbolically, A' or A^c or $C(A)=\{x : x\in U \text{ and } x\notin A\}$.

Clearly, $\quad x\in A' \Leftrightarrow x\notin A$.

Remark

1. $U'=\phi$ and $\phi'=U$
2. $A\cup A'=U$ and $A\cap A'=\phi$

For example,

Let $U=\{1,2,3,4,5,6,7\}$ and $A=\{1,3,5,7\}$.

Then, $A'=U-A=\{2,4,6\}$

Laws and Theorems

1. **Idempotent Laws**

For **any set** A,

(i) $A \cup A = A$ (ii) $A \cap A = A$

Proof

(i) Let $x \in A \cup A \Leftrightarrow x \in A$ or $x \in A$

$\Leftrightarrow x \in A$

Hence, $A \cup A = A$

(ii) Let $x \in A \cap A \Leftrightarrow x \in A$ and $x \in A$

$\Leftrightarrow x \in A$

Hence, $A \cap A = A$

2. **Identity Laws**

For **any set** A,

(i) $A \cup \phi = A$ (ii) $A \cap \phi = \phi$

(iii) $A \cup U = U$ (iv) $A \cap U = A$

Proof

(i) Let $x \in A \cup \phi \Leftrightarrow x \in A$ and $x \in \phi$

$\Leftrightarrow x \in A$

Hence, $A \cup \phi = A$

(ii) Let $x \in A \cap \phi \Leftrightarrow x \in A$ and $x \in \phi$

$\Leftrightarrow x \in \phi$

Hence, $A \cap \phi = \phi$

(iii) Let $x \in A \cup U \Leftrightarrow x \in A$ or $x \in U$

$\Leftrightarrow x \in U$

Hence, $A \cup U = U$

(iv) Let $x \in A \cap U \Leftrightarrow x \in A$ and $x \in U$

$\Leftrightarrow x \in A$

Hence, $A \cap U = A$

3. **Commutative Laws**

For any two sets A and B, we have

(i) $A \cup B = B \cup A$ (ii) $A \cap B = B \cap A$

Proof

(i) Let $x \in A \cup B \Leftrightarrow x \in A$ or $x \in B$

$\Leftrightarrow x \in B$ or $x \in A$

$\Leftrightarrow x \in B \cup A$

$\therefore x \in A \cup B \Leftrightarrow x \in B \cup A$

Hence, $A \cup B = B \cup A$

(ii) Let $x \in A \cap B \Leftrightarrow x \in A$ and $x \in B$

$\Leftrightarrow x \in B$ and $x \in A$

$\Leftrightarrow x \in B \cap A$

$\therefore x \in A \cap B \Leftrightarrow x \in B \cap A$

Hence, $A \cap B = B \cap A$.

4. **Associative Laws**

For any three sets A, B and C, we have

(i) $A \cup (B \cup C) = (A \cup B) \cup C$

(ii) $A \cap (B \cap C) = (A \cap B) \cap C$

Proof

(i) Let $x \in A \cup (B \cup C) \Leftrightarrow x \in A$ or $x \in B \cup C$

$\Leftrightarrow x \in A$ or ($x \in B$ or $x \in$

$\Leftrightarrow$ ($x \in A$ or $x \in B$) or $x \in$

$\Leftrightarrow x \in A \cup B$ or $x \in C$

$\Leftrightarrow x \in (A \cup B) \cup C$

$\therefore x \in A \cup (B \cup C) \Leftrightarrow x \in (A \cup B) \cup C$

Hence, $A \cup (B \cup C) = (A \cup B) \cup C$.

(ii) Let $x \in A \cap (B \cap C) \Leftrightarrow x \in A$ and $x \in B \cap C$

$\Leftrightarrow x \in A$ and ($x \in B$ and $x \in C$)

$\Leftrightarrow$ ($x \in A$ and $x \in B$) and $x \in C$

$\Leftrightarrow x \in A \cap B$ and $x \in C$

$\Leftrightarrow x \in (A \cap B) \cap C$

Hence, $A \cap (B \cap C) = (A \cap B) \cap C$.

5. **Distributive Laws**

For any three sets A, B and C, we have

(i) $A \cup (B \cap C) = (A \cup B) \cap (A \cup C)$

(ii) $A \cap (B \cup C) = (A \cap B) \cup (A \cap C)$

Proof

(i) Let $x \in A \cup (B \cap C) \Leftrightarrow x \in A$ or $x \in B \cap C$

$\Leftrightarrow x \in A$ or ($x \in B$ and $x \in C$)

$\Leftrightarrow$ ($x \in A$ or $x \in B$) and ($x \in A$ or $x \in C$)

$\Leftrightarrow x \in A \cup B$ and $x \in A \cup C$

$\Leftrightarrow x \in [(A \cup B) \cap (A \cup C)]$

$\therefore x \in A \cup (B \cap C) \Leftrightarrow x \in (A \cup B) \cap (A \cup C)$

Hence, $A \cup (B \cap C) = (A \cup B) \cap (A \cup C)$.

(ii) Let $x \in A \cap (B \cup C) \Leftrightarrow x \in A$ and $x \in B \cup C$

$\Leftrightarrow x \in A$ and ($x \in B$ or $x \in C$)

$\Leftrightarrow$ ($x \in A$ and $x \in B$) or ($x \in A$ and $x \in C$)

$\Leftrightarrow x \in A \cap B$ or $x \in A \cap C$

$\Leftrightarrow x \in (A \cap B) \cup (A \cap C)$

$\therefore x \in A \cap (B \cup C) \Leftrightarrow x \in (A \cap B) \cup (A \cap C)$

Hence, $A \cap (B \cup C) = (A \cap B) \cup (A \cap C)$.

6. **For any two sets A and B, we have**

(i) $P(A) \cap P(B) = P(A \cap B)$

(ii) $P(A) \cup P(B) \subseteq P(A \cup B)$

where, $P(A)$ is the power set of A.

Proof

(i) Let $x \in P(A) \cap P(B) \Leftrightarrow x \in P(A)$ or $x \in P(B)$

$\Leftrightarrow x \subseteq A$ or $x \subseteq B$

$\Leftrightarrow x \subseteq A \cap B$

$\Leftrightarrow x \in P(A \cap B)$

Hence, $P(A) \cap P(B) = P(A \cap B)$

(ii) Let $x \in P(A) \cup P(B) \Leftrightarrow x \in P(A)$ or $x \in P(B)$

$\Leftrightarrow x \subseteq A$ or $x \subseteq B$

$\Leftrightarrow x \subseteq A \cup B$

$\Leftrightarrow x \in P(A \cup B)$

Hence, $P(A) \cup P(B) \subseteq P(A \cup B)$

7. If A is any set, then $\mathbf{(A')' = A}$

Proof Let $x \in (A')' \Leftrightarrow x \notin A' \Leftrightarrow x \in A$

Hence, $(A')' = A$

8. **De-Morgan's Laws**

For any three sets A, B and C, we have

(i) $\mathbf{(A \cup B)' = A' \cap B'}$

(ii) $\mathbf{(A \cap B)' = A' \cup B'}$

(iii) $\mathbf{A - (B \cup C) = (A - B) \cap (A - C)}$

(iv) $\mathbf{A - (B \cap C) = (A - B) \cup (A - C)}$

Proof

(i) Let $x \in (A \cup B)' \Leftrightarrow x \notin A \cup B$

$\Leftrightarrow x \notin A$ and $x \notin B$

$\Leftrightarrow x \in A'$ and $x \in B'$

$\Leftrightarrow x \in A' \cap B'$

$\therefore \quad x \in (A \cup B)' \Leftrightarrow x \in A' \cap B'$

Hence, $(A \cup B)' = A' \cap B'$.

(ii) Let $x \in (A \cap B)' \Leftrightarrow x \notin A \cap B$

$\Leftrightarrow x \notin A$ or $x \notin B$

$\Leftrightarrow x \in A'$ or $x \in B'$

$\Leftrightarrow x \in A' \cup B'$

$\therefore \quad x \in (A \cap B)' \Leftrightarrow x \in A' \cup B'$

Hence, $(A \cap B)' = A' \cup B'$.

(iii) Let $x \in A - (B \cup C) \Leftrightarrow x \in A$ and $x \notin B \cup C$

$\Leftrightarrow x \in A$ and $(x \notin B$ and $x \notin C)$

$\Leftrightarrow (x \in A$ and $x \notin B)$ and $(x \in A$ and $x \notin C)$

$\Leftrightarrow x \in (A - B)$ and $x \in (A - C)$

$\Leftrightarrow x \in (A - B) \cap (A - C)$

Hence, $A - (B \cup C) = (A - B) \cap (A - C)$.

(iv) Let $x \in A - (B \cap C) \Leftrightarrow x \in A$ and $x \notin (B \cap C)$

$\Leftrightarrow x \in A$ and $(x \notin B$ or $x \notin C)$

$\Leftrightarrow (x \in A$ and $x \notin B)$ or $(x \in A$ and $x \notin C)$

$\Leftrightarrow x \in (A - B)$ or $x \in (A - C)$

$\Leftrightarrow x \in (A - B) \cup (A - C)$

Hence, $A - (B \cap C) = (A - B) \cup (A - C)$.

Aliter

$$A - (B \cap C) = A \cap (B \cap C)' \quad [\because A - B = A \cap B']$$
$$= A \cap (B' \cap C)'$$
$$= (A \cap B') \cup (A \cap C')$$
$$= (A - B) \cup (A - C)$$

More Results on Operations on Sets

For any two sets A and B, we have

1. $\mathbf{A \subseteq A \cup B, B \subseteq A \cup B, A \cap B \subseteq A, A \cap B \subseteq B}$

2. $\mathbf{A - B = A \cap B'}$

Proof

Let $x \in A - B \Leftrightarrow x \in A$ and $x \notin B$

$\Leftrightarrow x \in A$ and $x \in B'$

$\Leftrightarrow x \in A \cap B'$

Hence, $A - B = A \cap B'$

3. $\mathbf{(A - B) \cup B = A \cup B}$

Proof $(A - B) \cup B = (A \cap B') \cup B$

$= (A \cup B) \cap (B' \cup B)$ [from distributive law]

$= (A \cup B) \cap U$

$= A \cup B$

Hence, $(A - B) \cup B = A \cup B$

4. $\mathbf{(A - B) \cap B = \phi}$

Proof $(A - B) \cap B = (A \cap B') \cap B$

$= A \cap (B' \cap B)$ [from associative law]

$= A \cap \phi = \phi$

Hence, $(A - B) \cap B = \phi$

5. $\mathbf{A \subseteq B \Leftrightarrow B' \subseteq A'}$

Proof **Only if part** Let $A \subseteq B$ ...(i)

To prove $B' \subseteq A'$

Let $x \in B' \Rightarrow x \notin B$

$\Rightarrow x \notin A$ $[\because A \subseteq B]$

$\Rightarrow x \in A'$

Thus, $x \in B' \Rightarrow x \in A'$ $[\because B \subseteq A]$

Hence, $B' \subseteq A'$ ...(ii)

If part Let $B' \subseteq A'$ ...(iii)

To prove $A \subseteq B$

Let $x \in A \Rightarrow x \notin A'$

$\Rightarrow x \notin B'$ [from Eq.(iii)]

$\Rightarrow x \in B$

Hence, $A \subseteq B$ ...(iv)

From Eqs. (ii) and (iv), we get $A \subseteq B \Leftrightarrow B' \subseteq A'$

6. $\mathbf{A - B = B' - A'}$

Proof $A - B = (A \cap B')$

$= B' \cap A = B' \cap (A')' = B' - A'$

Hence, $A - B = B' - A'$

7. $\mathbf{(A \cup B) \cap (A \cup B') = A}$

Proof $(A \cup B) \cap (A \cup B') = A \cup (B \cap B')$ [by distributive law]

$= A \cup \phi = A$

Hence, $(A \cup B) \cap (A \cup B') = A$

8. $\mathbf{A \cup B = (A - B) \cup (B - A) \cup (A \cap B)}$

Proof $(A - B) \cup (B - A) \cup (A \cap B)$

$= [(A \cup B) - (A \cap B)] \cup (A \cap B)$

$=[(A\cup B)\cap(A\cap B)']\cup(A\cap B)$
$=[(A\cup B)\cup(A\cap B)]\cap[(A\cap B)'\cup(A\cap B)]$
$=(A\cup B)\cap U=A\cup B$

Hence, $A\cup B=(A-B)\cup(B-A)\cup(A\cap B)$

9. $A-(A-B)=A\cap B$

Proof $A-(A-B)=A-(A\cap B')$
$=A\cap(A\cap B')'$
$=A\cap(A'\cup B)$
$=(A\cap A')\cup(A\cap B)$
$=\phi\cup(A\cap B)=A\cap B$

Hence, $A-(A-B)=A\cap B$

10. $A-B=B-A\Leftrightarrow A=B$

Proof Only if part Let $A-B=B-A$ ...(i)

To prove $A=B$

Let $x\in A\Leftrightarrow(x\in A$ and $x\notin B)$ or $(x\in A$ and $x\in B)$
$\Leftrightarrow x\in(A-B)$ or $x\in(A\cap B)$
$\Leftrightarrow x\in(B-A)$
or $x\in A\cap B$ [from Eq. (i)]
$\Leftrightarrow(x\in B$ and $x\notin A)$ or $(x\in B$ and $x\in A)$
$\Leftrightarrow x\in B$

Hence, $A=B$

If part Let $A=B$

To prove $A-B=B-A$

Now, $A-B=A-A=\phi$ $[\because B=A]$
and $B-A=A-A=\phi$ $[\because B=A]$
$\therefore$ $A-B=B-A$
Hence, $A=B\Rightarrow A-B=B-A$

11. $A\cup B=A\cap B\Leftrightarrow A=B$

Proof Only if part Let $A\cup B=A\cap B$

Now, $x\in A\Rightarrow x\in A\cup B$
$\Rightarrow$ $x\in A\cap B$ $[\because A\cup B=A\cap B]$
$\Rightarrow$ $x\in B$
Thus, $A\subseteq B$ ...(i)
Again, $y\in B\Rightarrow y\in A\cup B$
$\Rightarrow$ $y\in A\cap B$ $[\because A\cup B=A\cap B]$
$\Rightarrow$ $y\in A$
Thus, $B\subseteq A$ ...(ii)

From Eqs. (i) and (ii), we have $A=B$

Thus, $A\cup B=A\cap B\Rightarrow A=B$.

If part Let $A=B$ ...(iii)

To prove $A\cup B=A\cap B$

Now, $A\cup B=A\cup A=A$ $[\because B=A]$ ...(iv)
and $A\cap B=A\cap A=A$ $[\because B=A]$ ...(v)

From Eqs. (iv) and (v), we have $A\cup B=A\cap B$

Hence, $A\cup B=A\cap B\Leftrightarrow A=B$

Example 2. Let A, B and C be three sets such that $A\cup B=A\cup C$ and $A\cap B=A\cap C$. Show that $B=C$.

Sol. Given, $A\cup B=A\cup C$ ...(i)
and $A\cap B=A\cap C$ ...(ii)

To prove $B=C$.

From Eq. (i), $(A\cup B)\cap C=(A\cup C)\cap C$
$\Rightarrow$ $(A\cap C)\cup(B\cap C)=(A\cap C)\cup(C\cup C)$
$\Rightarrow$ $(A\cap B)\cup(B\cap C)=(A\cap C)\cup C$ $[\because A\cap C=A\cap B]$
$\Rightarrow$ $(A\cap B)\cup(B\cap C)=C$ $[\because A\cap C\subseteq C]$
Thus, $C=(A\cap B)\cup(B\cap C)$ ...(iii)

Again, from Eq. (i), $(A\cup B)\cap B=(A\cup C)\cap B$
$\Rightarrow$ $(A\cap B)\cup(B\cap B)=(A\cap B)\cup(C\cap B)$
$\Rightarrow$ $(A\cap B)\cup B=(A\cap B)\cup(B\cap C)$
$\Rightarrow$ $B=(A\cap B)\cup(B\cap C)$ $[\because A\cap B\subseteq B]$
Thus, $B=(A\cap B)\cup(B\cap C)$ ...(iv)

From Eqs. (iii) and (iv), we have $B=C$.

Example 3. Let A and B be any two sets. If for some set X, $A\cap X=B\cap X=\phi$ and $A\cup X=B\cup X$, prove that $A=B$.

Sol. Given, $A\cap X=B\cap X=\phi$ ...(i)
and $A\cup X=B\cup X$ ...(ii)

From Eq. (ii), $A\cap(A\cup X)=A\cap(B\cup X)$
$\Rightarrow$ $A=(A\cap B)\cup(A\cap X)$ $[\because A\subseteq A\cup X\ \therefore A\cap(A\cup X)=A]$
$\Rightarrow$ $A=(A\cap B)\cup\phi$ $[\because A\cap X=\phi]$
$\Rightarrow$ $A=(A\cap B)$
$\Rightarrow$ $A\subseteq B$ ...(iii)

Again, $A\cup X=B\cup X$
$\Rightarrow$ $B\cap(A\cup X)=B\cap(B\cup X)$
$\Rightarrow$ $(B\cap A)\cup(B\cap X)=B.$ $[\because B\subseteq B\cup X\ \therefore B\cap(B\cup X)=B]$
$\Rightarrow$ $(B\cap A)\cup\phi=B$ $[\because B\cap X=\phi]$
$\Rightarrow$ $B\cap A=B$
$\Rightarrow$ $B\subseteq A$ ...(iv)

From Eqs. (iii) and (iv), we have $A=B$.

Example 4. If A and B are any two sets, prove that $P(A)=P(B)\Rightarrow A=B$.

Sol. Given, $P(A)=P(B)$ ...(i)

To prove $A=B$

Let $x\in A\Rightarrow$ there exists a subset X of A such that $x\in X$.

Now, $X\subseteq A\Rightarrow X\in P(A)$

$\Rightarrow \quad X \subseteq B$

$\Rightarrow \quad x \in B \quad [\because x \in X]$

Thus, $\quad x \in A \Rightarrow x \in B$

$\therefore \quad A \subseteq B \quad \text{...(ii)}$

Let $y \in B \Rightarrow$ there exists a subset Y of B such that $y \in Y$.

Now, $\quad Y \subseteq B \Rightarrow Y \in P(B)$

$\Rightarrow \quad Y \in P(A) \quad [\because P(B) = P(A)]$

$\Rightarrow \quad Y \subseteq A$

$\Rightarrow \quad y \in A \quad [\because y \in Y]$

Thus, $\quad y \in B \Rightarrow y \in A$

$\therefore \quad B \subseteq A \quad \text{...(iii)}$

From Eqs. (ii) and (iii), we have $A = B$

Use of Sets in Logical Problems

M = Set of students which have Mathematics.

P = Set of students which have Physics.

C = Set of students which have Chemistry.

Applying the different operations on the above sets, then we get following important results.

M' = Set of students which have no Mathematics.

P' = Set of students which have no Physics.

C' = Set of students which have no Chemistry.

$M \cup P$ = Set of students which have atleast one subject Mathematics or Physics.

$P \cup C$ = Set of students which have atleast one subject Physics or Chemistry.

$C \cup M$ = Set of students which have atleast one subject Chemistry or Mathematics.

$M \cap P$ = Set of students which have both subjects Mathematics and Physics.

$P \cap C$ = Set of students which have both subjects Physics and Chemistry.

$C \cap M$ = Set of students which have both subjects Chemistry and Mathematics.

$M \cap P'$ = Set of students which have Mathematics but not Physics.

$P \cap C'$ = Set of students which have Physics but not Chemistry.

$C \cap M'$ = Set of students which have Chemistry but not Mathematics.

$(M \cup P)'$ = Set of students which have not both subjects Mathematics and Physics.

$(P \cup C)'$ = Set of students which have not both subjects Physics and Chemistry.

$(C \cup M)'$ = Set of students which have not both subjects Chemistry and Mathematics.

$(M \cap P \cap C)$ = Set of students which have all three subjects Mathematics, Physics and Chemistry.

$(M \cup P \cup C)$ = Set of all students which have three subjects.

Cardinal Number of Some Sets

If A, B and C are finite sets and U be the finite universal set, then

(i) $n(A') = n(U) - n(A)$

(ii) $n(A \cup B) = n(A) + n(B) - n(A \cap B)$

(iii) $n(A \cup B) = n(A) + n(B)$, if A and B are disjoint non-void sets.

(iv) $n(A \cap B') = n(A) - n(A \cap B)$

(v) $n(A' \cap B') = n(A \cup B)' = n(U) - n(A \cup B)$

(vi) $n(A' \cup B') = n(A \cap B)' = n(U) - n(A \cap B)$

(vii) $n(A - B) = n(A) - n(A \cap B)$

(viii) $n(A \cap B) = n(A \cup B) - n(A \cap B') - n(A' \cap B)$

(ix) $n(A \cup B \cup C) = n(A) + n(B) + n(C) - n(A \cap B) - n(B \cap C) - n(C \cap A) + n(A \cap B \cap C)$

(x) If $A_1, A_2, A_3, \ldots, A_n$ are disjoint sets, then $n(A_1 \cup A_2 \cup A_3 \cup \ldots \cup A_n) = n(A_1) + n(A_2) + n(A_3) + \ldots + n(A_n)$

Example 5. If A and B be two sets containing 6 and 3 elements respectively, what can be the minimum number of elements in $A \cup B$? Also, find the maximum number of elements in $A \cup B$.

Sol. We have, $\quad n(A \cup B) = n(A) + n(B) - n(A \cap B)$,

$n(A \cup B)$ is minimum or maximum according as $n(A \cap B)$ is maximum or minimum, respectively.

***Case* I** If $n(A \cap B)$ is minimum i.e., $n(A \cap B) = 0$ such that

$$A = \{a, b, c, d, e, f\} \text{ and } B = \{g, h, i\}$$

$$\therefore \quad n(A \cup B) = n(A) + n(B) = 6 + 3 = 9$$

***Case* II** If $n(A \cap B)$ is maximum i.e., $n(A \cap B) = 3$, such that

$$A = \{a, b, c, d, e, f\} \text{ and } B = \{d, a, c\}$$

$$\therefore n(A \cup B) = n(A) + n(B) - n(A \cap B) = 6 + 3 - 3 = 6$$

Example 6. Suppose $A_1, A_2, \ldots, A_{30}$ are thirty sets each with five elements and $B_1, B_2, \ldots, B_n$ are n sets each with three elements.

Let $\quad \bigcup_{i=1}^{30} A_i = \bigcup_{j=1}^{n} B_j = S$

Assume that each element of S belongs to exactly ten of the A_i's and exactly to nine of the B_j's. Find n.

Sol. Given, A's are thirty sets with five elements each, so

$$\sum_{i=1}^{30} n(A_i) = 5 \times 30 = 150 \qquad \text{...(i)}$$

If the m distinct elements in S and each element of S belongs to exactly 10 of the A_i's, so we have

$$\sum_{i=1}^{30} n(A_i) = 10m \qquad \text{...(ii)}$$

$\therefore$ From Eqs. (i) and (ii), we get $10m = 150$

$\therefore \quad m = 15 \qquad$ ...(iii)

Similarly, $\sum_{j=1}^{n} n(B_j) = 3n$ and $\sum_{j=1}^{n} n(B_j) = 9m$

$\therefore \quad 3n = 9m \Rightarrow n = \frac{9m}{3} = 3m$

$= 3 \times 15 = 45 \qquad$ [from Eq. (iii)]

Hence, $\quad n = 45$

Example 7. In a group of 1000 people, there are 750 who can speak Hindi and 400 who can speak Bengali. How many can speak Hindi only? How many can speak Bengali only? How many can speak both Hindi and Bengali?

Sol. Let H and B be the set of those people who can speak Hindi and Bengali respectively, then according to the problem, we have

$$n(H \cup B) = 1000,$$
$$n(H) = 750, n(B) = 400$$

We know that,

$$n(H \cup B) = n(H) + n(B) - n(H \cap B)$$
$$1000 = 750 + 400 - n(H \cap B)$$
$$\therefore \quad n(H \cap B) = 150$$

$\therefore$ Number of people speaking Hindi and Bengali both is 150.

Also, $\quad n(H \cap B') = n(H) - n(H \cap B)$

$= 750 - 150$

$= 600$

Thus, number of people speaking Hindi only is 600.

Again, $\quad n(B \cap H') = n(B) - n(B \cap H) = 400 - 150 = 250$

Thus, number of people speaking Bengali only is 250.

Example 8. A survey of 500 television watchers produced the following information, 285 watch football, 195 watch hockey, 115 watch basketball, 45 watch football and basketball, 70 watch football and hockey, 50 watch hockey and basketball, 50 do not watch any of the three games. How many watch all the three games? How many watch exactly one of the three games?

Sol. Let F, H and B be the sets of television watchers who watch Football, Hockey and Basketball, respectively.

Then, according to the problem, we have

$$n(U) = 500, \ n(F) = 285, n(H) = 195,$$
$$n(B) = 115, \ n(F \cap B) = 45,$$
$$n(F \cap H) = 70, n(H \cap B) = 50$$

and $\quad n(F' \cup H' \cup B') = 50,$

where U is the set of all the television watchers.

Since, $\quad n(F' \cup H' \cup B') = n(U) - n(F \cup H \cup B)$

$\Rightarrow \quad 50 = 500 - n(F \cup H \cup B)$

$\Rightarrow \quad n(F \cup H \cup B) = 450$

We know that,

$$n(F \cup H \cup B) = n(F) + n(H) + n(B) - n(F \cap H) - n(H \cap B) - n(B \cap F) + n(F \cap H \cap B)$$

$\Rightarrow \quad 450 = 285 + 195 + 115 - 70 - 50 - 45 + n(F \cap H \cap B)$

$\therefore \quad n(F \cap H \cap B) = 20$

which is the number of those who watch all the three games. Also, number of persons who watch football only

$= n(F \cap H' \cap B')$

$= n(F) - n(F \cap H) - n(F \cap B) + n(F \cap H \cap B)$

$= 285 - 70 - 45 + 20 = 190$

The number of persons who watch hockey only

$= n(H \cap F' \cap B')$

$= n(H) - n(H \cap F) - n(H \cap B) + n(H \cap F \cap B)$

$= 195 - 70 - 50 + 20 = 95$

and the number of persons who watch basketball only

$= n(B \cap H' \cap F')$

$= n(B) - n(B \cap H) - n(B \cap F) + n(H \cap F \cap B)$

$= 115 - 50 - 45 + 20 = 40$

Hence, required number of those who watch exactly one of the three games

$= 190 + 95 + 40 = 325$

Venn Diagrams

(Euler-Venn Diagrams)

The diagram drawn to represent sets are called Venn diagrams or Euler Venn diagrams. Here, we represent the universal set U by points within rectangle and the subset A of the set U is represented by the interior of a circle. If a set A is a subset of a set B, then the circle representing A is drawn inside the circle representing B. If A and B are not equal but they have some common elements, then to represent A and B by two intersecting circles.

Venn Diagrams in Different Situations

1. Subset

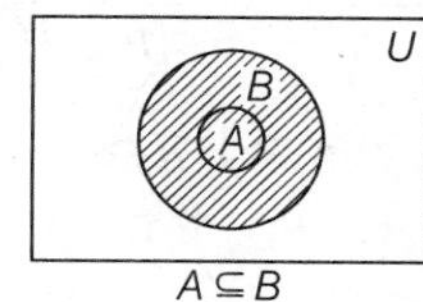

$A \subseteq B$

2. Union of sets

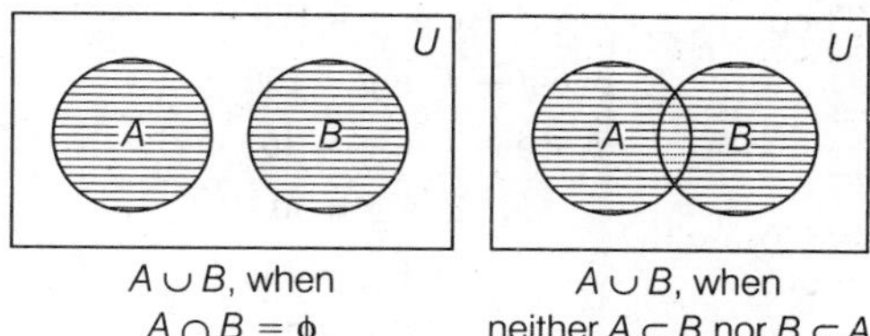

$A \cup B$, when $A \cap B = \phi$

$A \cup B$, when neither $A \subseteq B$ nor $B \subseteq A$

3. Intersection of sets

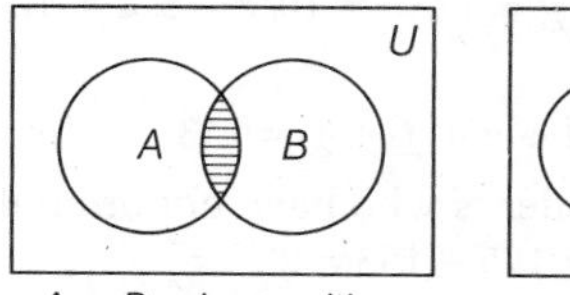

$A \cap B$, when neither $A \subseteq B$ nor $B \subseteq A$

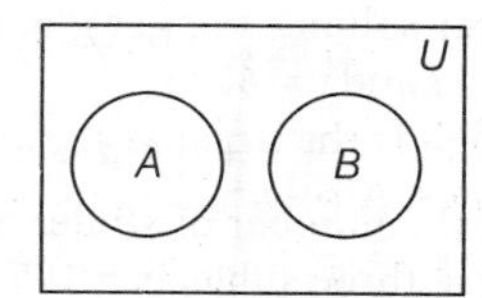

$A \cap B$, when $A \cap B = \phi$ (no shaded one)

4. Difference of sets

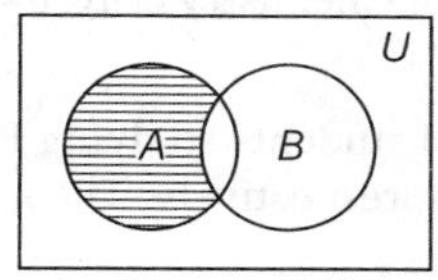

$A - B$, when neither $A \subseteq B$ nor $B \subseteq A$

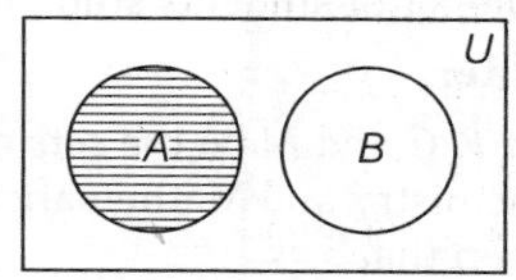

$A - B$, when $A - B = \phi$

5. Complement set

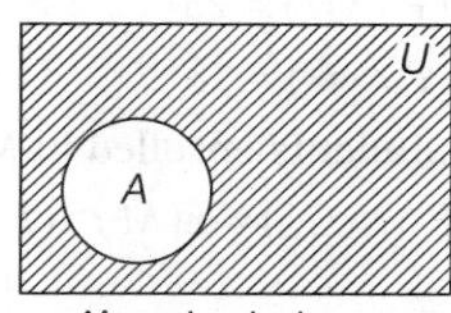

A' = shaded one

6. $A \cup (B \cup C)$ and $(A \cup B) \cup C$

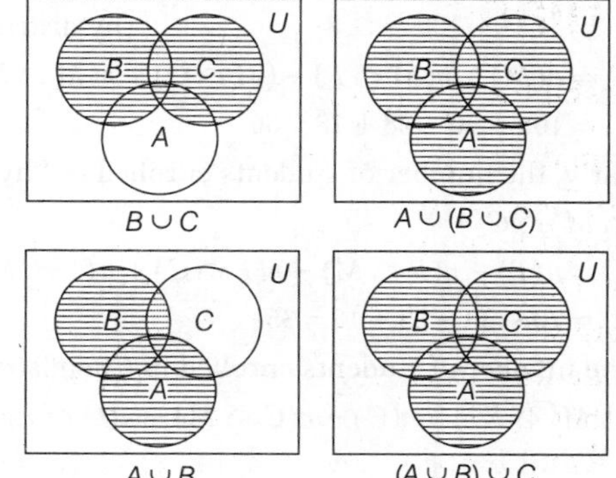

$B \cup C$ $\quad$ $A \cup (B \cup C)$

$A \cup B$ $\quad$ $(A \cup B) \cup C$

Hence, $A \cup (B \cup C) = (A \cup B) \cup C$ which is associative law for union.

7. $A \cap (B \cap C)$ and $(A \cap B) \cap C$

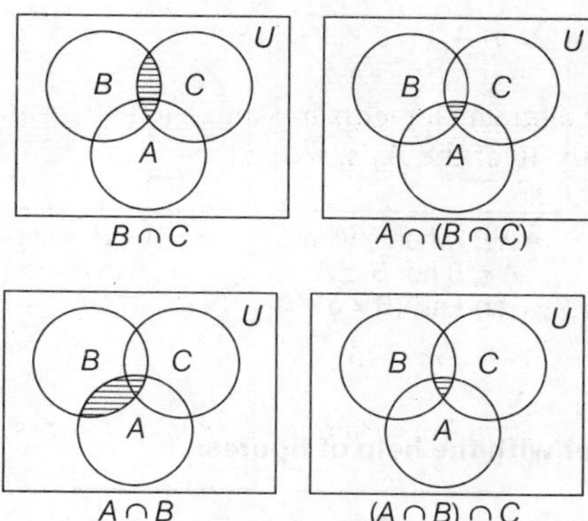

$B \cap C$ $\quad$ $A \cap (B \cap C)$

$A \cap B$ $\quad$ $(A \cap B) \cap C$

Hence, $A \cap (B \cap C) = (A \cap B) \cap C$ which is associative law for intersection.

8. Distributive law

(i) $A \cup (B \cap C) = (A \cup B) \cap (A \cup C)$

(ii) $A \cap (B \cup C) = (A \cap B) \cup (A \cap C)$

(i)

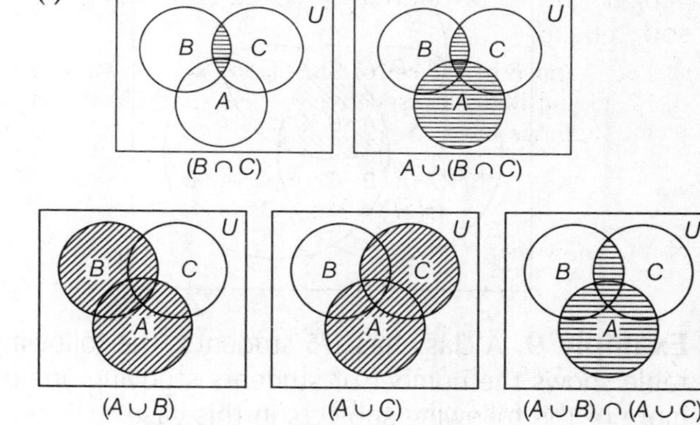

$(B \cap C)$ $\quad$ $A \cup (B \cap C)$

$(A \cup B)$ $\quad$ $(A \cup C)$ $\quad$ $(A \cup B) \cap (A \cup C)$

It is clear from diagrams that

$$A \cup (B \cap C) = (A \cup B) \cap (A \cup C)$$

(ii)

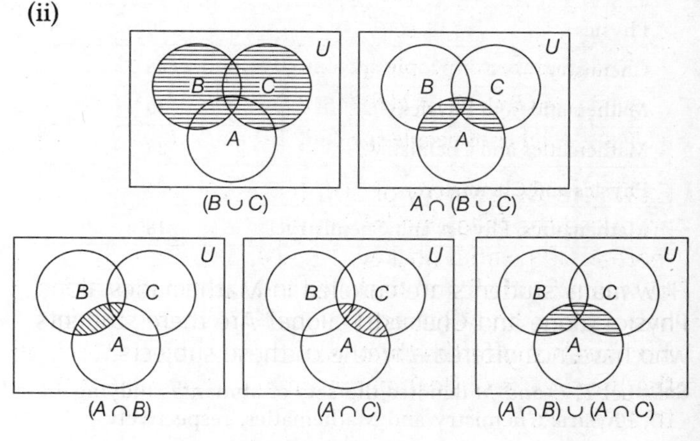

$(B \cup C)$ $\quad$ $A \cap (B \cup C)$

$(A \cap B)$ $\quad$ $(A \cap C)$ $\quad$ $(A \cap B) \cup (A \cap C)$

It is clear from diagrams that

$$A \cap (B \cup C) = (A \cap B) \cup (A \cap C)$$

9. Symmetric difference

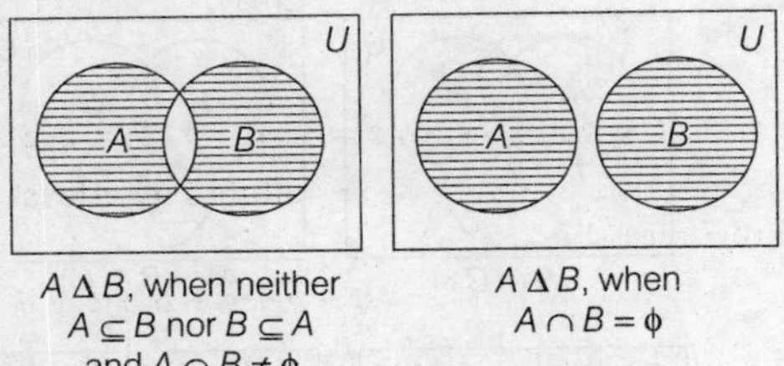

$A \Delta B$, when neither $A \subseteq B$ nor $B \subseteq A$ and $A \cap B \neq \phi$

$A \Delta B$, when $A \cap B = \phi$

Remark

Remember with the help of figures.

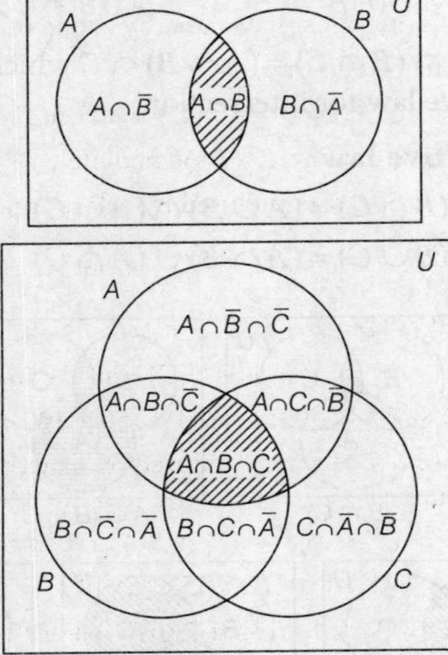

Example 9. A class has 175 students. The following table shows the number of students studying one or more of the following subjects in this case.

Subjects	Number of students
Mathematics	100
Physics	70
Chemistry	46
Mathematics and Physics	30
Mathematics and Chemistry	28
Physics and Chemistry	23
Mathematics, Physics and Chemistry	18

How many students are enrolled in Mathematics alone, Physics alone and Chemistry alone? Are there students who have not offered any one of these subjects?

Sol. Let P, C and M denotes the sets of students studying Physics, Chemistry and Mathematics, respectively.

Let a, b, c, d, e, f, g denote the elements (students) contained in the bounded region as shown in the diagram.

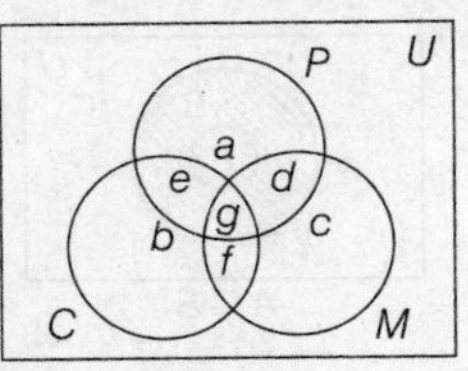

Then,
$$a + d + e + g = 170$$
$$c + d + f + g = 100$$
$$b + e + f + g = 46$$
$$d + g = 30$$
$$e + g = 23$$
$$f + g = 28$$
$$g = 18$$

After solving, we get $g = 18$, $f = 10$, $e = 5$, $d = 12$, $a = 35$, $b = 13$ and $c = 60$

$$\therefore \quad a + b + c + d + e + f + g = 153$$

So, the number of students who have not offered any of these three subjects $= 175 - 153 = 22$

Number of students studying Mathematics only, $c = 60$

Number of students studying Physics only, $a = 35$

Number of students studying Chemistry only, $b = 13$

Aliter

Let P, C and M be the sets of students studying Physics, Chemistry and Mathematics, respectively. Then, we are given that

$$n(P) = 70, n(C) = 46, n(M) = 100$$
$$n(M \cap P) = 30, n(M \cap C) = 28$$
$$n(P \cap C) = 23$$
and
$$n(M \cap P \cap C) = 18$$

$\therefore$ The number of students enrolled in Mathematics only

$$= n(M \cap P' \cap C') = n(M \cap (P \cup C)')$$ [by De-Morgan's law]
$$= n(M) - n(M \cap (P \cup C))$$
$$= n(M) - \{n[(M \cap P) \cup (M \cap C)]\}$$ [by distributive law]
$$= n(M) - n(M \cap P) - (M \cap C) + n(M \cap P \cap C)$$
$$= 100 - 30 - 28 + 18 = 60$$

Similarly, the number of students enrolled in Physics only,

$n(P \cap M' \cap C')$
$$= n(P) - n(P \cap M) - n(P \cap C) + n(P \cap M \cap C)$$
$$= 70 - 30 - 23 + 18 = 35$$

and the number of students enrolled in Chemistry only,

$$n(C \cap M' \cap P') = n(C) - n(C \cap M) - n(C \cap P) + n(C \cap M \cap P)$$

$= 46 - 28 - 23 + 18 = 13$

and the number of students who have not offered any of the three subjects,

$n(M' \cap P' \cap C') = n(M \cap P \cap C)'$ [by De-Morgan's law]

$$= n(U) - n(M \cup P \cup C)$$
$$= n(U) - \{n(M) + n(P) + n(C) - n(M \cap P) - n(M \cap C) - n(P \cap C) + n(P \cap C \cap M)\}$$
$$= 175 - \{100 + 70 + 46 - 30 - 28 - 23 + 8\}$$
$$= 175 - 153 = 22$$

Example 10. In a pollution study of 1500 Indian rivers the following data were reported. 520 were polluted by sulphur compounds, 335 were polluted by phosphates, 425 were polluted by crude oil, 100 were polluted by both crude oil and sulphur compounds, 180 were polluted by both sulphur compounds and phosphates, 150 were polluted by both phosphates and crude oil and 28 were polluted by sulphur compounds, phosphates and crude oil. How many of the rivers were polluted by atleast one of the three impurities?
How many of the rivers were polluted by exactly one of the three impurities?

Sol. Let S, P and C denote the sets of rivers polluted by sulphur compounds, by phosphates and by crude oil respectively, and let a, b, c, d, e, f, g denote the elements (impurities) contained in the bounded region as shown in the diagram.

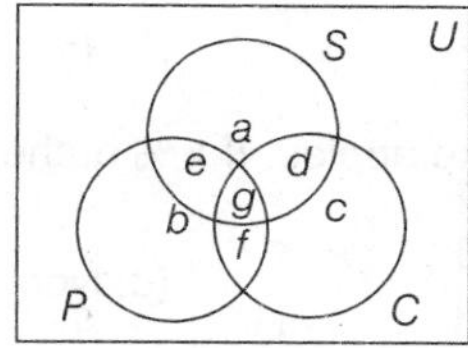

Then, $a + d + e + g = 520$

$c + d + f + g = 425$

$b + e + f + g = 335 \Rightarrow d + g = 100$

$e + g = 180 \Rightarrow f + g = 150$

$g = 28$

After solving, we get

$g = 28, f = 122, e = 152, b = 33, d = 72, c = 203$ and $a = 268$

The number of rivers were polluted by atleast one of the three impurities

$$= (a + b + c + d + e + f + g) = 878$$

and the number of rivers were polluted by exactly one of the three impurities,

$$a + b + c = 268 + 33 + 203 = 504$$

Aliter

Let S, P and C denote the sets of rivers polluted by sulphur compounds, by phosphates and by crude oil, respectively.

Then, we are given that

$n(S) = 520, n(P) = 335, n(C) = 425, n(C \cap S) = 100,$
$n(S \cap P) = 180, n(P \cap C) = 150$ and $n(S \cap P \cap C) = 28.$

The number of rivers polluted by atleast one of the three impurities,

$$n(S \cup P \cup C) = n(S) + n(P) + n(C) - n(S \cap P) - n(P \cap C) - n(C \cap S) + n(S \cap P \cap C)$$
$$= 520 + 335 + 425 - 180 - 150 - 100 + 28 = 878$$

and the number of rivers polluted by exactly one of the three impurities,

$$n\{(S \cap P' \cap C') \cup (P \cap C' \cap S') \cup (C \cap P' \cap S')\}$$
$$= n\{(S \cap (P \cup C)'\} \cup \{P \cap (C \cup S)'\} \cup \{C \cap P \cup S)'\}$$
$$= n(S \cap (P \cup C)') + n(P \cap (C \cup S)') + n(C \cap (P \cup S)')$$
$$= n(S) - n(S \cap P) - n(S \cap C) + n(S \cap P \cap C) + n(P) - n(P \cap C) - n(P \cap S) + n(S \cap P \cap C) + n(C) - n(C \cap P) - n(C \cap S) + n(S \cap P \cap C)$$
$$= n(S) + n(P) + n(C) - 2n(S \cap P) - 2n(S \cap C) - 2n(P \cap C) + 3n(S \cap P \cap C)$$
$$= 520 + 335 + 425 - 360 - 200 - 300 + 84 = 504$$

Exercise for Session 1

1. If $X = \{4^n - 3n - 1 : n \in N\}$ and $y = \{9(n-1) : n \in N\}$, then $X \cup Y$ equals

(a) X (b) Y (c) N (d) None of these

2. If $N_a = \{an : n \in N\}$, then $N_5 \cap N_7$ equals

(a) N (b) N_5 (c) N_7 (d) N_{35}

3. If A and B are two sets, then $A \cap (A \cup B)'$ equals

(a) A (b) B (c) ϕ (d) None of these

4. If U be the universal set and $A \cup B \cup C = U$, then $[(A - B) \cup (B - C) \cup (C - A)']$ equals

(a) $A \cup B \cup C$ (b) $A \cap B \cap C$ (d) $A \cup (B \cap C)$ (d) $A \cap (B \cup C)$

5. If A and B are two sets, then $(A - B) \cup (B - A) \cup (A \cap B)$ equals

(a) $A \cup B$ (b) $A \cap B$ (c) A (d) B'

6. If $A = \{x : x$ is a multiple of 4$\}$ and $B = \{x : x$ is a multiple of 6$\}$, then $A \subset B$ consists of all multiple of

(a) 4 (b) 8 (c) 12 (d) 16

7. A set contains $2n + 1$ elements. The number of subsets of this set containing more than n elements equals

(a) 2^{n-1} (b) 2^n (c) 2^{n+1} (d) 2^{2n}

8. If $A = \{\phi, \{\phi\}\}$, then the power set of A is

(a) A (b) $\{\phi, \{\phi\}, A\}$

(c) $\{\phi, \{\phi\}, \{\{\phi\}\}, A\}$ (d) None of these

9. Given $n(U) = 20$, $n(A) = 12$, $n(B) = 9$, $n(A \cap B) = 4$, where U is the universal set, A and B are subsets of U, then $n((A \cup B)')$ equals

(a) 3 (b) 9 (c) 11 (d) 17

10. A survey shows that 63% of the Indians like cheese, whereas 76% like apples. If x % of the Indians like both cheese and apples, then x can be

(a) 40 (b) 65 (c) 39 (d) None of these

11. In a class of 55 students, the number of students studying different subjects are 23 in Mathematics, 24 in Physics, 19 in Chemistry, 12 in Mathematics and Physics, 9 in Mathematics and Chemistry, 7 in Physics and Chemistry and 4 in all the three subjects. The number of students who have taken exactly one subject is

(a) 6 (b) 7 (c) 9 (d) 22

Session 2

Ordered Pair, Definition of Relation, Ordered Relation, Composition of Two Relations

Ordered Pair

If A be a set and $a, b \in A$, then the ordered pair of elements a and b in A denoted by (a, b), where a is called the first coordinate and b is called the second coordinate.

Remark

1. Ordered pairs (a, b) and (b, a) are different.
2. Ordered pairs (a, b) and (c, d) are equal iff $a = c$ and $b = d$.

Cartesian Product of Two Sets

The cartesian product to two sets A and B is the set of all those ordered pairs whose first coordinate belongs to A and second coordinate belongs to B. This set is denoted by $A \times B$ (read as 'A cross B' or 'product set of A and B').

Symbolically, $A \times B = \{(a, b) : a \in A \text{ and } b \in B\}$

or $\quad A \times B = \{(a, b) : a \in A \wedge b \in B\}$

Thus, $\quad (a, b) \in A \times B \Leftrightarrow a \in A \wedge b \in B$

Similarly, $\quad B \times A = \{(b, a) : b \in B \wedge a \in A\}$

Remark

1. $A \times B \neq B \times A$
2. If A has p elements and B has q elements, then $A \times B$ has pq elements.
3. If $A = \phi$ and $B = \phi$, then $A \times B = \phi$.
4. Cartesian product of n sets $A_1, A_2, A_3, \ldots, A_n$ is the set of all ordered n-tuples $(a_1, a_2, \ldots, a_n)$ $a_i \in A_i$, $i = 1, 2, 3, \ldots, n$ and is denoted by $A_1 \times A_2 \times \ldots \times A_n$ or $\prod_{i=1}^{n} A_i$.

Example 11. If $A = \{1, 2, 3\}$ and $B = \{4, 5\}$, find $A \times B$, $B \times A$ and show that $A \times B \neq B \times A$.

Sol. $A \times B = \{1, 2, 3\} \times \{4, 5\} = \{(1, 4), (1, 5), (2, 4), (2, 5), (3, 4), (3, 5)\}$

and $B \times A = \{4, 5\} \times \{1, 2, 3\} = \{(4, 1), (4, 2), (4, 3), (5, 1), (5, 2), (5, 3)\}$

It is clear that $A \times B \neq B \times A$.

Example 12. If A and B be two sets and $A \times B = \{(3, 3), (3, 4), (5, 2), (5, 4)\}$, find A and B.

Sol. A = First coordinates of all ordered pairs = $\{3, 5\}$

and B = Second coordinates of all ordered pairs = $\{2, 3, 4\}$

Hence, $A = \{3, 5\}$ and $B = \{2, 3, 4\}$

Important Theorems on Cartesian Product

If A, B and C are three sets, then

(i) $A \times (B \cup C) = (A \times B) \cup (A \times C)$

(ii) $A \times (B \cap C) = (A \times B) \cap (A \times C)$

(iii) $A \times (B - C) = (A \times B) - (A \times C)$

(iv) $(A \times B) \cap (S \times T) = (A \cap S) \times (B \cap T)$, where S and T are two sets.

(v) If $A \subseteq B$, then $(A \times C) \subseteq (B \times C)$

(vi) If $A \subseteq B$, then $(A \times B) \cap (B \times A) = A^2$

(vii) If $A \subseteq B$ and $C \subseteq D$, then $A \times C \subseteq B \times D$

Example 13. If A and B are two sets given in such a way that $A \times B$ consists of 6 elements and if three elements of $A \times B$ are $(1, 5)$, $(2, 3)$ and $(3, 5)$, what are the remaining elements?

Sol. Since, $(1, 5), (2, 3), (3, 5) \in A \times B$, then clearly $1, 2, 3 \in A$ and $3, 5 \in B$.

$A \times B = \{1, 2, 3\} \times (3, 5)$

$= (1, 3), (1, 5), (2, 3), (2, 5), (3, 3), (3, 5)$

Hence, the remaining elements are $(1, 3)$, $(2, 5)$, $(3, 3)$.

Relations

Introduction of Relation

We use sentences depending upon the relationship of an object to the other object in our daily life such as

(i) 'Ram, Laxman, Bharat, Shatrughan' were the sons of Dashrath.
(ii) 'Sita' was the wife of Ram.
(iii) 'Laxman' was the brother of Ram.
(iv) 'Dashrath' was the father of Ram.
(v) 'Kaushaliya' was the mother of Ram.

If Ram, Laxman, Bharat, Shatrughan, Sita, Kaushaliya and Dashrath are represented by a, b, c, d, e, f and y respectively and A represents the set, then

$$A = \{a, b, c, d, e, f, y\}$$

Here, we see that any two elements of set A are related many ways, i.e. a, b, c, d are sons of y. 'a' is the son of y is represented by aRy. Similarly, b is the son of y, c is the son of y and d is also son of y are represented as $b\,R\,y$, $c\,R\,y$ and $d\,R\,y$, respectively.

If we write here $y\,R\,a$ it means that y is the son of a which is impossible, since a is the son of y. Hence, y and a cannot be related like this. Its generally represented as $y \not R a$. Hence, we can say that a and y are in definite order. a comes before R and y after R. Therefore, aRy may be represented as a order pair (a, y). Similarly, bRy, cRy and dRy are represented by (b, y), (c, y) and (d, y), respectively. If all pairs will represented by a set, then we see that first element of each pair is the son of second element. Hence, the set of these pairs may be represented by set R, then

$$R = \{(a, y), (b, y), (c, y), (d, y)\}$$

Symbolically, $R = \{(x, y) : x, y \in A$, where x is son of $y\}$

It is clear that R is subset of $A \times A$

i.e., $R \subseteq A \times A$

Corollary In above example, if $A = \{a, b, c, d\}$ and $B = \{e, f, y\}$, then

$R = \{(x, z) : x \in A, z \in B$, where x is son of $z\}$

It is clear that $R \subseteq A \times B$.

Definition of Relation

A relation (or binary relation) R, from a non-empty set A to another non-empty set B, is a subset of $A \times B$.

i.e., $R \subseteq A \times B$ or $R \subseteq \{(a, b) : a \in A, b \in B\}$

Now, if (a, b) be an element of the relation R, then we write aRb (read as 'a is related to b')

i.e., $(a, b) \in R \Leftrightarrow aRb$

and if (a, b) is not an element of the relation R, then we write $a \not R b$ (read as 'a is not related to b'),

i.e. $(a, b) \notin R \Leftrightarrow a \not R b$.

Remark

1. Any subset of $A \times A$ is said to be a relation on A.
2. If A has m elements and B has n elements, then $A \times B$ has $m \times n$ elements and total number of different relations from A to B is 2^{mn}.
3. If $R = A \times B$, then Domain $R = A$ and Range $R = B$.
4. The domain as well as range of the empty set ϕ is ϕ.
5. If $A =$ Dom R and $B =$ Ran R, then we write $B = R[A]$.

For example,

Let $A = \{1, 2, 3\}$ and $B = \{3, 5, 7\}$, then

$A \times B = \{(1, 3), (1, 5), (1, 7), (2, 3), (2, 5), (2, 7), (3, 3), (3, 5), (3, 7)\}$.

But $R \subseteq A \times B$

i.e., every subset of $A \times B$ is a relation from A to B. If we consider the relation, $R = \{(1, 5), (1, 7), (3, 5), (3, 7)\}$

Then, $1\,R\,5$; $1\,R\,7$; $3\,R\,5$; $3\,R\,7$

Also, $1 \not R 3$; $2 \not R 3$; $2 \not R 5$; $2 \not R 7$; $3 \not R 3$;

Clearly, Domain $R = \{1, 3\}$ and Range $R = \{5, 7\}$

For example,

Let $A = \{1, 2, 3\}$ and $B = \{4, 5\}$, then number of different relations from A to B is $2^{3\times2} = 2^6 = 64$ because A has 3 elements and B has 2 elements.

Types of Relations from One Set to Another Set

1. Empty Relation

A relation R from A to B is called an empty relation or a void relation from A to B if $R = \phi$.

For example,

Let $A = \{2, 4, 6\}$ and $B = \{7, 11\}$

Let $R = \{(a, b) : a \in A, b \in B$ and $a - b$ is even$\}$

As, none of the numbers $2 - 7, 2 - 11, 4 - 7, 4 - 11, 6 - 7, 6 - 11$ is an even number, $R = \phi$.

Hence, R is an empty relation.

2. Universal Relation

A relation R from A to B is said to be the universal relation, if $R = A \times B$.

For example, Let $A = \{1, 2\}$, $B = \{1, 3\}$ and

$$R = \{(1, 1), (1, 3), (2, 1), (2, 3)\}$$

Here, $R = A \times B$

Hence, R is the universal relation from A to B.

Types of Relations on a Set

1. Empty Relation

A relation R on a set A is said to be an empty relation or a void relation, if $R = \phi$.

For example,

Let $A = \{1, 3\}$ and $R = \{(a, b) : a, b \in A$ and $a + b$ is odd$\}$
Hence, R contains no element, therefore R is an empty relation on A.

2. Universal Relation

A relation R on a set A is said to be universal relation on A, if $R = A \times A$.

For example,

Let $A = \{1, 2\}$
and $R = [(1, 1), (1, 2), (2, 1), (2, 2)]$
Here, $R = A \times A$
Hence, R is the universal relation on A.

3. Identity Relation

A relation R on a set A is said to be the identity relation on A, if

$$R = [(a, b) : a \in A, b \in A \text{ and } a = b]$$

Thus, identity relation, $R = [(a, a) : \forall a \in A]$
Identity relation on set A is also denoted by I_A.
Symbolically, $I_A = [(a, a) : a \in A]$

For example,

Let $A = \{1, 2, 3\}$
Then, $I_A = \{(1, 1), (2, 2), (3, 3)\}$

Remark

In an identity relation on A every element of A should be related to itself only.

4. Inverse Relation

If R is a relation from a set A to a set B, then inverse relation of R to be denoted by R^{-1}, is a relation from B to A.

Symbolically, $R^{-1} = \{(b, a) : (a, b) \in R\}$.

Thus, $(a, b) \in R \Leftrightarrow (b, a) \in R^{-1}, \forall a \in A, b \in B$.

Remark

1. Dom (R^{-1}) = Range (R) and Range (R^{-1}) = Dom (R)
2. $(R^{-1})^{-1} = R$

For example,

If $R = \{(1, 2), (3, 4), (5, 6)\}$, then
$R^{-1} = \{(2, 1), (4, 3), (6, 5)\}$
$\therefore (R^{-1})^{-1} = \{(1, 2), (3, 4), (5, 6)\} = R$

Here, dom $(R) = \{1, 3, 5\}$, range $(R) = \{2, 4, 6\}$
and dom $(R^{-1}) = \{2, 4, 6\}$, range $(R^{-1}) = \{1, 3, 5\}$
Clearly, dom (R^{-1}) = range (R)
and range (R^{-1}) = dom (R).

Various Types of Relations

1. Reflexive Relation

A relation R on a set A is said to be reflexive, if $a R a, \forall a \in A$
i.e., if $(a, a) \in R, \forall a \in A$

For example,

Let $A = \{1, 2, 3\}$
$R_1 = \{(1, 1), (2, 2), (3, 3)\}$
$R_2 = \{(1, 1), (2, 2), (3, 3), (1, 2), (2, 1), (1, 3)\}$
and $R_3 = \{(1, 1), (2, 2), (2, 3), (3, 2)\}$

Here, R_1 and R_2 are reflexive relations on A, R_3 is not a reflexive relation on A as $(3, 3) \notin R_3$, i.e. $3 \not R_3\ 3$.

Remark

The identity relation is always a reflexive relation but a reflexive relation may or may not be the identity relation. It is clear in the above example given, R_1 is both reflexive and identity relation on A but R_2 is a reflexive relation on A but not an identity relation on A

2. Symmetric Relation

A relation R on a set A is said to be symmetric relation, if

$$a R b \Rightarrow b R a, \forall a, b \in A$$

i.e., if $(a, b) \in R \Rightarrow (b, a) \in R, \forall a, b \in A$

For example,

Let $A = \{1, 2, 3\}$
$R_1 = \{(1, 2), (2, 1)\}$
$R_2 = \{(1, 2), (2, 1), (1, 3), (3, 1)\}$
and $R_3 = \{(2, 3), (1, 3), (3, 1)\}$

Here, R_1 and R_2 are symmetric relations on A but R_3 is not a symmetric relation on A because $(2, 3) \in R_3$ and $(3, 2) \notin R_3$.

3. Anti-symmetric Relation

A relation R on a set A is said to be anti-symmetric, if $a R b, b R a \Rightarrow a = b, \forall a, b \in A$
i.e., $(a, b) \in R$ and $(b, a) \in R \Rightarrow a = b, \forall a, b \in A$

For example,

Let R be the relation in N (natural number) defined by, "x is divisor of y", then R is anti-symmetric because x divides y and y divides $x \Rightarrow x = y$

4. Transitive Relation

A relation R on a set A is said to be a transitive relation, if $a\,R\,b$ and $b\,R\,c \Rightarrow aRc, \forall\ a, b, c \in A$

i.e., $(a, b) \in R$ and $(b, c) \in R \Rightarrow (a, c) \in R, \forall\ a, b, c \in A$

For example,

Let $A = \{1, 2, 3\}$

$R_1 = \{(1, 2), (2, 3), (1, 3), (3, 2)\}$

$R_2 = \{(2, 3), (3, 1)\}$

$R_3 = \{(1, 3), (3, 2), (1, 2)\}$

Then, R_1 is not transitive relation on A because $(2, 3) \in R_1$ and $(3, 2) \in R_1$ but $(2, 2) \notin R_1$. Again, R_2 is not transitive relation on A because $(2, 3) \in R_2$ and $(3, 1) \in R_2$ but $(2, 1) \notin R_2$. Finally R_3 is a transitive relation.

Example 14. Let $A = \{1, 2, 3\}$ and $R = \{(a, b) : a, b \in A$, a divides b and b divides $a\}$. Show that R is an identity relation on A.

Sol. Given, $A = \{1, 2, 3\}$

$a \in A, b \in B$, a divides b and b divides a.

$\Rightarrow \quad a = b$

$\therefore \quad R = \{(a, a), a \in A\} = \{(1, 1), (2, 2), (3, 3)\}$

Hence, R is the identity relation on A.

Example 15. Let $A = \{3, 5\}$, $B = \{7, 11\}$. Let $R = \{(a, b) : a \in A, b \in B, a - b$ is even$\}$. Show that R is an universal relation from A to B.

Sol. Given, $A = \{3, 5\}$, $B = \{7, 11\}$.

Now, $R = \{(a, b) : a \in A, b \in B$ and $a - b$ is even$\}$

$= \{(3, 7), (3, 11), (5, 7), (5, 11)\}$

Also, $A \times B = \{(3, 7), (3, 11), (5, 7), (5, 11)\}$

Clearly, $R = A \times B$

Hence, R is an universal relation from A to B.

Example 16. Prove that the relation R defined on the set N of natural numbers by $xRy \Leftrightarrow 2x^2 - 3xy + y^2 = 0$ is not symmetric but it is reflexive.

Sol. (i) $2x^2 - 3x \cdot x + x^2 = 0, \forall\ x \in N$.

$\therefore\ x\,R\,x, \forall\ x \in N$, i.e. R is reflexive.

(ii) For $x = 1, y = 2, 2x^2 - 3xy + y^2 = 0$

$\therefore\ 1R2$

But $2 \cdot 2^2 - 3 \cdot 2 \cdot 1 + 1^2 = 3 \neq 0$

So, 2 is not related to 1 i.e., $2\not{R}1$

$\therefore\ R$ is not symmetric.

Example 17. Let N be the set of natural numbers and relation R on N be defined by $xRy \Leftrightarrow x$ divides y, $\forall\ x, y \in N$. Examine whether R is reflexive, symmetric, anti-symmetric or transitive.

Sol. (i) x divides x i.e., $xRx, \forall\ x \in N$

$\therefore\ R$ is reflexive.

(ii) 1 divides 2 i.e., $1\ R\ 2$ but $2 \not{R}\ 1$ as 2 does not divide 1.

(iii) x divides y and y divides $x \Rightarrow x = y$

i.e., xRy and $yRx \Rightarrow x = y$

$\therefore\ R$ is anti-symmetric relation.

(iv) xRy and $yRz \Rightarrow x$ divides y and y divides z.

$\Rightarrow kx = y$ and $k'y = 2$, where k, k' are positive integers.

$\Rightarrow kk'x = z \Rightarrow x$ divides $z \Rightarrow xRz$

$\therefore\ R$ is transitive.

Equivalence Relation

A relation R on a set A is said to be an equivalence relation on A, when R is (i) reflexive (ii) symmetric and (iii) transitive. The equivalence relation denoted by ~.

Example 18. N is the set of natural numbers. The relation R is defined on $N \times N$ as follows

$(a, b)\,R\,(c, d) \Leftrightarrow a + d = b + c$

Prove that R is an equivalence relation.

Sol. (i) $(a, b)\,R\,(a, b) \Rightarrow a + b = b + a$

$\therefore\ R$ is reflexive.

(ii) $(a, b)\,R\,(c, d) \Rightarrow a + d = b + c$

$\Rightarrow \quad c + b = d + a \Rightarrow (c, d)\,R\,(a, b)$

$\therefore\ R$ is symmetric.

(iii) $(a, b)\,R\,(c, d)$ and $(c, d)\,R\,(e, f) \Rightarrow a + d = b + c$ and $c + f = d + e$

$\Rightarrow\ a + d + c + f = b + c + d + e$

$\Rightarrow \quad a + f = b + e \Rightarrow (a, b)\,R\,(e, f)$

$\therefore\ R$ is transitive.

Thus, R is an equivalence relation on $N \times N$.

Example 19. A relation R on the set of complex numbers is defined by $z_1 R z_2 \Leftrightarrow \dfrac{z_1 - z_2}{z_1 + z_2}$ is real, show that R is an equivalence relation.

Sol. (i) $z_1 R z_1 \Rightarrow \dfrac{z_1 - z_1}{z_1 + z_1}, \forall z_1 \in C \Rightarrow 0$ is real

$\therefore\ R$ is reflexive.

(ii) $z_1 R z_2 \Rightarrow \dfrac{z_1 - z_2}{z_1 + z_2}$ is real

$\Rightarrow -\left(\dfrac{z_2 - z_1}{z_1 + z_2}\right)$ is real $\Rightarrow \left(\dfrac{z_2 - z_1}{z_1 + z_2}\right)$ is real

$\Rightarrow z_2 R z_1, \forall z_1, z_2 \in C$

$\therefore$ R is symmetric.

(iii) $\because z_1 R z_2 \Rightarrow \dfrac{z_1 - z_2}{z_1 + z_2}$ is real

$$\Rightarrow \overline{\left(\frac{z_1 - z_2}{z_1 + z_2}\right)} = -\left(\frac{z_1 - z_2}{z_1 + z_2}\right)$$

$$\Rightarrow \left(\frac{\bar{z}_1 - \bar{z}_2}{\bar{z}_1 + \bar{z}_2}\right) + \left(\frac{z_1 - z_2}{z_1 + z_2}\right) = 0$$

$$\Rightarrow 2(z_1\bar{z}_1 - z_2\bar{z}_2) = 0 \Rightarrow |z_1|^2 = |z_2|^2 \quad \text{...(i)}$$

Similarly, $z_2 R z_2 \Rightarrow |z_2|^2 = |z_3|^2$ ...(ii)

From Eqs. (i) and (ii), we get

$$z_1 R z_2, z_2 R z_3$$

$$\Rightarrow |z_1|^2 = |z_3|^2$$

$$\Rightarrow z_1 R z_3$$

$\therefore$ R is transitive.

Hence, R is an equivalence relation.

Ordered Relation

A relation R is called ordered, if R is transitive but not an equivalence relation.

Symbolically, $a R b, b R c \Rightarrow a R c, \forall a, b, c \in A$

For example,

Let $R = \{(1, 2), (2, 1), (2, 3), (3, 2), (1, 3)\}$.

Here, R is symmetric.

Since, $(1, 2) \in R \Rightarrow (2, 1) \in R, (2, 3) \in R \Rightarrow (3, 2) \in R$ and R is transitive.

Since, $(1, 2) \in R, (2, 3) \in R \Rightarrow (1, 3) \in R$

but R is not reflexive.

Since, $(1, 1) \notin R, (2, 2) \notin R, (3, 3) \notin R$

Hence, R is not an equivalence relation.

$\therefore$ R is an ordered relation.

Partial Order Relation

A relation R is called partial order relation, if R is reflexive, transitive and anti-symmetric at the same time.

For example,

Let $R = \{(1, 1), (2, 2), (3, 3), (1, 2), (2, 3), (1, 3)\}$

$\therefore$ $R^{-1} = \{(1, 1), (2, 2), (3, 3), (2, 1), (3, 2), (3, 1)\}$

$R \cap R^{-1} = \{(1, 1), (2, 2), (3, 3)\} =$ Identity

$\therefore$ R is anti-symmetric.

It is clear that R is reflexive.

Since, $(1, 1) \in R, (2, 2) \in R, (3, 3) \in R$ and R is transitive.

Since, $(1, 2) \in R$ and $(2, 3) \in R \Rightarrow (1, 3) \in R$

Hence, R is partial order relation.

Composition of Two Relations

If A, B and C are three sets such that $R \subseteq A \times B$ and $S \subseteq B \times C$, then $(SOR)^{-1} = R^{-1}OS^{-1}$. It is clear that aRb, bSc $\Rightarrow aSORc$.

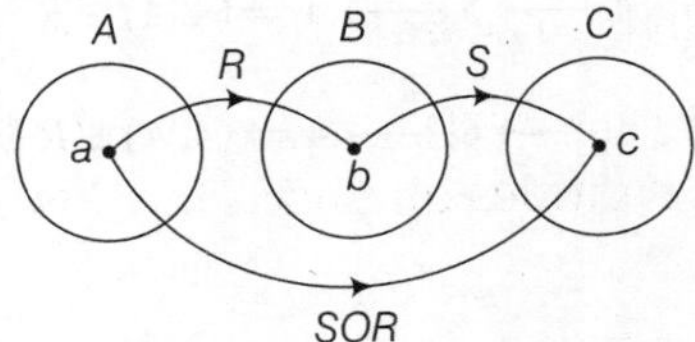

More generally,

$$(R_1 O R_2 O R_3 O \ldots O R_n)^{-1} = R_n^{-1} O \ldots O R_3^{-1} O R_2^{-1} O R_1^{-1}$$

Example 20. Let R be a relation such that $R = \{(1, 4), (3, 7), (4, 5), (4, 6), (7, 6)\}$, find

(i) $R^{-1}OR^{-1}$ and (ii) $(R^{-1}OR)^{-1}$.

Sol. (i) We know that, $(ROR)^{-1} = R^{-1}OR^{-1}$

Dom $(R) = \{1, 3, 4, 7\}$

Range $(R) = \{4, 5, 6, 7\}$

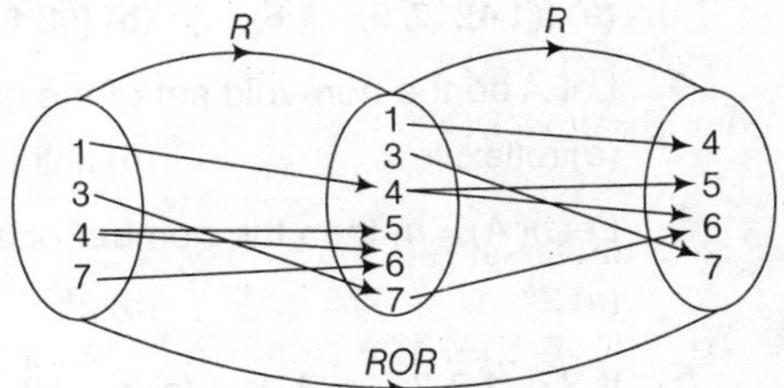

We see that,

$$1 \longrightarrow 4 \longrightarrow 5 \Rightarrow (1, 5) \in ROR$$
$$1 \longrightarrow 4 \longrightarrow 6 \Rightarrow (1, 6) \in ROR$$
$$3 \longrightarrow 7 \longrightarrow 6 \Rightarrow (3, 6) \in ROR$$

$\therefore$ $ROR = \{(1, 5), (1, 6), (3, 6)\}$

Then, $R^{-1}OR^{-1} = (ROR)^{-1}$
$= \{(5, 1), (6, 1), (6, 3)\}$

(ii) We know that, $(R^{-1}OR)^{-1} = R^{-1}O(R^{-1})^{-1} = R^{-1}OR$

Since,

$R = \{(1, 4), (3, 7), (4, 5), (4, 6), (7, 6)\}$

$\therefore$ $R^{-1} = \{(4, 1), (7, 3), (5, 4), (6, 4), (6, 7)\}$

$\therefore$ Dom $(R) = \{1, 3, 4, 7\}$, Range $(R) = \{4, 5, 6, 7\}$

Dom $(R^{-1}) = \{4, 5, 6, 7\}$, Range $(R^{-1}) = \{1, 3, 4, 7\}$

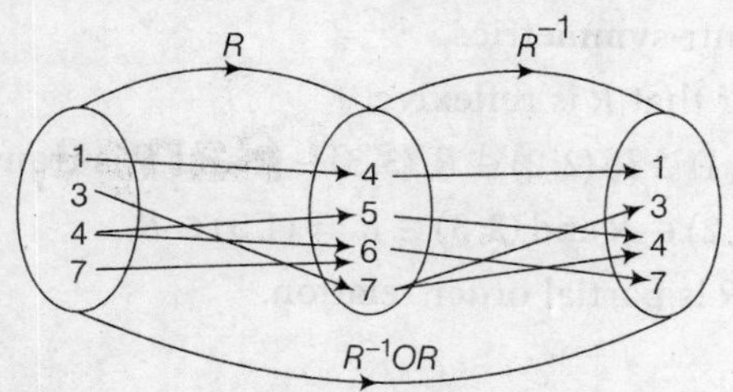

We see that,

$$1 \xrightarrow{R} 4 \xrightarrow{R^{-1}} 1 \Rightarrow (1, 1) \in R^{-1}OR$$

$$3 \xrightarrow{R} 7 \xrightarrow{R^{-1}} 3 \Rightarrow (3, 3) \in R^{-1}OR$$

$$4 \xrightarrow{R} 5 \xrightarrow{R^{-1}} 4 \Rightarrow (4, 4) \in R^{-1}OR$$

$$4 \xrightarrow{R} 6 \xrightarrow{R^{-1}} 4 \Rightarrow (4, 4) \in R^{-1}OR$$

$$4 \xrightarrow{R} 6 \xrightarrow{R^{-1}} 7 \Rightarrow (4, 7) \in R^{-1}OR$$

$$7 \xrightarrow{R} 6 \xrightarrow{R^{-1}} 4 \Rightarrow (7, 4) \in R^{-1}OR$$

$$7 \xrightarrow{R} 6 \xrightarrow{R^{-1}} 7 \Rightarrow (7, 7) \in R^{-1}OR$$

$$\therefore R^{-1}OR = \{(1, 1), (3, 3), (4, 4), (7, 7), (4, 7), (7, 4)\}$$

Hence, $(R^{-1}OR)^{-1} = R^{-1}OR = \{(1, 1), (3, 3)$
$(4, 4), (7, 7), (4, 7), (7, 4)\}$

Theorems on Binary Relations

If R is a relation on a set A, then

(i) R is reflexive $\Rightarrow R^{-1}$ is reflexive.
(ii) R is symmetric $\Rightarrow R^{-1}$ is symmetric.
(iii) R is transitive $\Rightarrow R^{-1}$ is transitive.

Exercise for Session 2

1. If $A = \{2, 3, 5\}$, $B = \{2, 5, 6\}$, then $(A - B) \times (A \cap B)$ is

(a) $\{(3, 2), (3, 3), (3, 5)\}$ (b) $\{(3, 2), (3, 5), (3, 6)\}$
(c) $\{(3, 2), (3, 5)\}$ (d) None of these

2. If $n(A) = 4$, $n(B) = 3$, $n(A \times B \times C) = 24$, then $n(C)$ equals

(a) 1 (b) 2 (c) 17 (d) 288

3. The relation R defined on the set of natural numbers as $\{(a, b) : a$ differs from b by 3$\}$ is given by

(a) $\{(1, 4), (2, 5), (3, 6), \dots\}$ (b) $\{(4, 1), (5, 2), (6, 3), \dots\}$ (c) $\{(1, 3), (2, 6), (3, 9), \dots\}$ (d) None of these

4. Let A be the non-void set of the children in a family. The relation 'x is a brother of y' on A, is

(a) reflexive (b) anti-symmetric (c) transitive (d) equivalence

5. Let $n(A) = n$, then the number of all relations on A, is

(a) 2^n (b) $2^{n!}$ (c) 2^{n^2} (d) None of these

6. If $S = \{1, 2, 3, \dots, 20\}$, $K = \{a, b, c, d\}$, $G = \{b, d, e, f\}$. The number of elements of $(S \times K) \cup (S \times G)$ is

(a) 40 (b) 100 (c) 120 (d) 140

7. The relation R is defined on the set of natural numbers as $\{(a, b) : a = 2b\}$, then R^{-1} is given by

(a) $\{(2, 1) (4, 2) (6, 3), \dots\}$ (b) $\{(1, 2) (2, 4) (3, 6), \dots\}$ (c) R^{-1} is not defined (d) None of these

8. The relation $R = \{(1, 1), (2, 2), (3, 3), (1, 2), (2, 3), (1, 3)\}$ on set $A = \{1, 2, 3\}$ is

(a) reflexive but not symmetric (b) reflexive but not transitive
(c) symmetric and transitive (d) Neither symmetric nor transitive

9. The number of equivalence relations defined in the set $S = \{a, b, c\}$ is

(a) 5 (b) 3! (c) 2^3 (d) 3^3

10. If R be a relation $<$ from $A = \{1, 2, 3, 4\}$ to $B = \{1, 3, 5\}$, i.e. $(a, b) \in R \Leftrightarrow a < b$, then ROR^{-1}, is

(a) $\{(1, 3), (1, 5), (2, 3), (2, 5), (3, 5), (4, 5)\}$ (b) $\{(3, 1), (5, 1), (3, 2), (5, 2), (5, 3), (5, 4)\}$
(c) $\{(3, 3), (3, 5), (5, 3), (5, 5)\}$ (d) $\{(3, 3), (3, 4), (4, 5)\}$

Session 3

Definition of Functions, Domain, Codomain and Range, Composition of Mapping, Equivalence Classes, Partition of Set, Congruences

Functions

Introduction

If two variable quantities x and y according to some law are so related that corresponding to each value of x (considered only real), which belongs to set E, there corresponds one and only one finite value of the quantity y (i.e., unique value of y). Then, y is said to be a function (single valued) of x, defined by $y = f(x)$, where x is the **argument** or **independent variable** and y is the **dependent variable** defined on the set E.

For example, If r is the radius of the circle and A its area, then r and A are related by $A = \pi r^2$ or $A = f(r)$. Then, we say that the area A of the circle is the function of the radius r. **Graphically,**

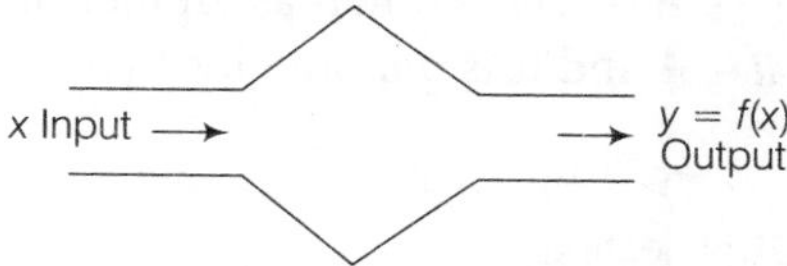

Where, y is the image of x and x is the pre-image of y under f.

Remark

1. If to each value of x, which belongs to set E there corresponds one or more than one values of the quantity y. Then, y is called the multiple valued function of x defined on the set E.
2. The word 'FUNCTION' is used only for single valued function. *For example,* $y = \sqrt{x}$ is single valued functions but $y^2 = x$ is a multiple valued function.
   $\therefore$ $y^2 = x \Rightarrow y = \pm\sqrt{x}$ for one value of x, y gives two values.

Definition of Functions

If A and B be two non-empty sets, then a function from A to B associates to each element x in A, a unique element $f(x)$ in B and is written as

$$f : A \to B \text{ or } A \xrightarrow{f} B$$

which is read as f is a mapping from A to B.

The other terms used for functions are **operators** or **transformations.**

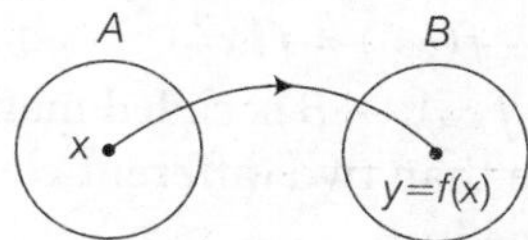

Remark

1. If $x \in A$, $y = [f(x)] \in B$, then $(x, y) \in f$.
2. If $(x_1, y_1) \in f$ and $(x_2, y_2) \in f$, then $y_1 = y_2$.

Domain, Codomain and Range

Domain The set of A is called the domain of f (denoted by D_f).

Codomain The set of B is called the codomain of f (denoted by C_f).

Range The range of f denoted by R_f is the set consisting of all the images of the elements of the domain A.

Range of $f = [f(x) : x \in A]$

The range of f is always a subset of codomain B.

Onto and Into Mappings

In the mapping $f : A \to B$ such

$$f(A) = B$$

i.e., $\quad$ Range = Codomain

Then, the function is **Onto** and if $f(A) \subset B$, i.e. Range $\subset$ Codomain, then the function is **Into**.

Remark

Onto functions is also known as **surjective.**

Method to Test Onto or Into Mapping

Let $f : A \to B$ be a mapping. Let y be an arbitrary element in B and then $y = f(x)$, where $x \in A$. Then, express x in terms of y.

Now, if $x \in A, \forall y \in B$, then f is onto and if $x \notin A, \forall y \in B$, then f is into.

For into mapping Find an element of B which is not f-image of any element of A.

One-one and Many-one Mapping

(i) The mapping $f : A \to B$ is called one-one mapping, if no two different elements of A have the same image in B. Such a mapping is also known as **injective mapping** or an **injection** or **monomorphism.**

Method to Test One-one If $x_1, x_2 \in A$,

then $f(x_1) = f(x_2)$

$\Rightarrow$ $x_1 = x_2$ and $x_1 \neq x_2$

$\Rightarrow$ $f(x_1) \neq f(x_2)$

(ii) The mapping $f : A \to B$ is called many-one mapping, if two or more than two different elements in A have the same image in B.

Method to Test Many-one

If $x_1, x_2 \in A$, then $f(x_1) = f(x_2)$

$\Rightarrow$ $x_1 \neq x_2$

From above classification, we conclude that function is of four types

(i) One-one onto (bijective)

(ii) One-one into

(iii) Many-one onto

(iv) Many-one into

Number of Functions (Mappings) at One Place in a Table

Let $f : A \to B$ be a mapping such that A and B are finite sets having m and n elements respectively, then

Description of mappings
(i) Total number of mappings from A to B
(ii) Total number of one-one mappings from A to B
(iii) Total number of many-one mappings from A to B
(iv) Total number of onto (surjective) mappings from A to B
(v) Total number of one-one onto (bijective) mappings from A to B
(vi) Total number of into mappings from A to B

| Example 21. Let N be the set of all natural numbers. Consider $f : N \to N : f(x) = 2x, \forall x \in N$. Show that f is one-one into.

Sol. Let $x_1, x_2 \in N$, then

$$f(x_1) = f(x_2)$$

$$\Rightarrow \quad 2x_1 = 2x_2 \Rightarrow x_1 = x_2$$

$\therefore$ f is one-one.

Let $y = 2x$, then $x = \frac{y}{2}$

Now, if we put $y = 5$, then $x = \frac{5}{2} \notin N$.

This show that $5 \in N$ has no pre-image in N. So, f is into.

Hence, f is one-one and into.

| Example 22. Show that the mapping $f : R \to R : f(x) = \cos x, \forall x \in R$ is neither one-one nor onto.

Sol. Let $x_1, x_2 \in R$.

Then, $f(x_1) = f(x_2) \Rightarrow \cos x_1 = \cos x_2$

$\Rightarrow$ $x_1 = 2n\pi \pm x_2 \Rightarrow x_1 \neq x_2$

$\therefore$ f is not one-one.

Let $y = \cos x$, but $-1 \leq \cos x \leq 1$

$\therefore$ $y \in [-1, 1]$

$[-1, 1] \subset R$

So, f is into (not onto).

Hence, f is neither one-one nor onto.

Constant Mapping

The mapping $f : A \to B$ is known as a constant mapping, if the range of B has only one element.

For all $x \in A$, $f(x) = a$, where as $a \in B$.

Identity Mapping

The mapping $f : A \to B$ is known as an identity mapping, if $f(a) = a, \forall a \in A$ and it is denoted by I_A.

Remark

I_A is bijective or bijection.

Equal Mapping

Let A and B be two mappings are $f : A \to B$ and $g : A \to B$ such that

$$f(x) = g(x), \forall x \in A$$

Then, the mappings f and g are equal and written as $f = g$.

Inclusion Mapping

The mapping $f : A \to B$ is known as inclusion mapping. If $A \subseteq B$, then $f(a) = a, \forall a \in A$.

Equivalent or Equipotent or Equinumerous Set

The mapping $f : A \to B$ is known as equivalent sets, if A and B are both one-one and onto and written as $A \sim B$ which is read as 'A wiggle B'.

Inverse Mapping

If $f : A \to B$ be one-one and onto mapping, let $b \in B$, then there exist exactly one element $a \in A$ such that $f(a) = b$, so we may define

$$f^{-1} : B \to A : f^{-1}(b) = a$$

$$\Leftrightarrow \qquad f(a) = b$$

The function f^{-1} is called the inverse of f. A functions is invertible iff f is one-one onto.

Remark

1. $f^{-1}(b) \subseteq A$
2. If $f : A \to B$ and $g : B \to A$, then f and g are said to be invertible.

Example 23. Let $f : R \to R$ be defined by $f(x) = \cos(5x + 2)$. Is f invertible? Justify your answer.

Sol. For invertible of f, f must be bijective (i.e., one-one onto).

If $\quad x_1, x_2 \in R,$

then $\quad f(x_1) = f(x_2)$

$\Rightarrow \quad \cos(5x_1 + 2) = \cos(5x_2 + 2)$

$\Rightarrow \quad 5x_1 + 2 = 2n\pi \pm (5x_2 + 2)$

$\Rightarrow \quad x_1 \neq x_2$

$\therefore$ f is not one-one.

But $\quad -1 \le \cos(5x + 2) \le 1$

$\therefore \quad -1 \le f(x) \le 1$

Range $= [-1, 1] \subset R$

$\therefore$ f is into mapping.

Hence, the function $f(x)$ is no bijective and so it is not invertible.

Composition of Mapping

Let A, B and C be three non-empty sets. Let $f : A \to B$ and $g : B \to C$ be two mappings, then $gof : A \to C$. This function is called the product or composite of f and g, given by $(gof)x = g\{f(x)\}, \forall\, x \in A$.

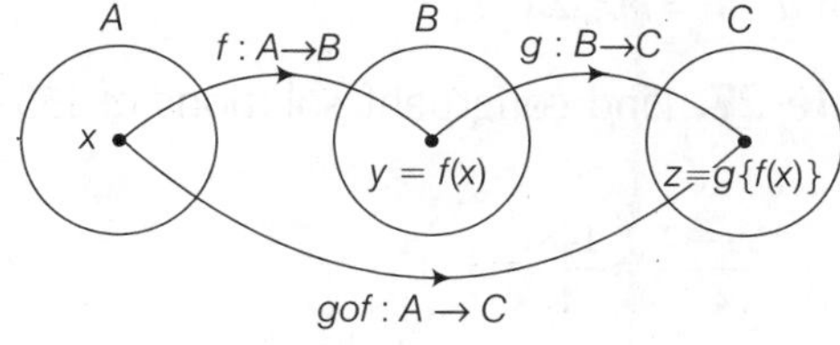

Important Remarks

1. (i) $(fog)x = f\{g(x)\}$ (ii) $(fof)x = f\{f(x)\}$
   (iii) $(gog)x = g\{g(x)\}$ (iv) $(fg)x = f(x)\cdot g(x)$
   (v) $(f \pm g)x = f(x) \pm g(x)$ (vi) $\left(\dfrac{f}{g}\right)x = \dfrac{f(x)}{g(x)}; g(x) \neq 0$
2. Let $h : A \to B$, $g : B \to C$ and $f : C \to D$ be any three functions. Then, $(fog)oh = fo(goh)$.
3. Let $f : A \to B$, $g : B \to C$ be two functions, then
   (i) f and g are injective $\Rightarrow gof$ is injective.
   (ii) f and g are surjective $\Rightarrow gof$ is surjective.
   (iii) f and g are bijective $\Rightarrow gof$ is bijective.
4. An injective mapping from a finite set to itself in bijective.

Example 24. If $f : R \to R$ and $g : R \to R$ be two mapping such that $f(x) = \sin x$ and $g(x) = x^2$, then

(i) prove that $fog \neq gof$.

(ii) find the values of $(fog)\dfrac{\sqrt{\pi}}{2}$ and $(gof)\left(\dfrac{\pi}{3}\right)$.

Sol. (i) Let $x \in R$

$\therefore \quad (fog)x = f\{g(x)\} \qquad [\because g(x) = x^2]$

$= f\{x^2\} = \sin x^2 \qquad$ ...(i)

$[\because f(x) = \sin x]$

and $(gof)x = g\{f(x)\}$

$= g(\sin x) \qquad [\because f(x) = \sin x]$

$= \sin^2 x \qquad$ ...(ii)

$[\because g(x) = x^2]$

From Eqs. (i) and (ii), we get $(fog)x \neq (gof)x, \forall\, x \in R$

Hence, $fog \neq gof$

(ii) From Eq. (i), $(fog)x = \sin x^2$

$\therefore \quad (fog)\dfrac{\sqrt{\pi}}{2} = \sin\dfrac{\pi}{4} = \dfrac{1}{\sqrt{2}}$

and from Eq. (ii), $(gof)x = \sin^2 x$

$\therefore \quad (gof)\dfrac{\pi}{3} = \sin^2\dfrac{\pi}{3} = \left(\dfrac{\sqrt{3}}{2}\right)^2 = \dfrac{3}{4}$

Example 25. If the mapping f and g are given by

$f = \{(1, 2), (3, 5), (4, 1)\}$

and $\quad g = \{(2, 3), (5, 1), (1, 3)\}$,

write down pairs in the mapping fog and gof.

Sol. Domain $f = \{1, 3, 4\}$, Range $f = \{2, 5, 1\}$

Domain $g = \{2, 5, 1\}$, Range $g = \{1, 3\}$

$\because \quad$ Range f = Dom $g = \{(2, 5, 1)\}$

$\therefore$ gof mapping is defined.

Then, gof mapping defined following way

$$\{1, 3, 4\} \xrightarrow{f} \{2, 5, 1\} \xrightarrow{g} \{1, 3\}$$

gof

We see that, $\quad f(1) = 2, f(3) = 5, f(4) = 1$

and $\quad g(2) = 3, g(5) = 1, g(1) = 3$

$\therefore \quad (gof)(1) = g\{f(1)\} = g(2) = 3$

$(gof)(3) = g\{f(3)\} = g(5) = 1$

$$(gof)(4) = g\{f(4)\} = g(1) = 3$$

Hence, $gof = \{(1, 3), (3, 1), (4, 3)\}$

Now, since Range of $f \subset$ Dom f

$\therefore$ fog is defined.

Then, fog mapping defined following way

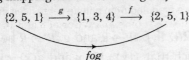

$$\{2, 5, 1\} \xrightarrow{g} \{1, 3, 4\} \xrightarrow{f} \{2, 5, 1\}$$

fog

We see that, $g(2) = 3, g(5) = 1, g(1) = 3$

$f(1) = 2, f(3) = 5, f(4) = 1$

$\therefore$ $(fog)(2) = f\{g(2)\} = f(3) = 5$

$(fog)(5) = f\{g(5)\} = f(1) = 2$

$(fog)(1) = f\{g(1)\} = f(3) = 5$

Hence, $fog = \{(2,5),(5,2),(1,5)\}$

Equivalence Classes

If R be an equivalence relation on a set A, then $[a]$ is equivalence class of a with respect to R.

Symbolically, X_a or $[a] = \{x : x \in X, x\,R\,a\}$.

Remark

1. Square brackets[ ] are used to denote the equivalence classes.
2. $a \in [a]$ and $a \in [b] \Rightarrow [a] = [b]$
3. Either $[a] = [b]$ or $[a] \cap [b] = \phi$
4. Equivalence class of a also denoted by $E(a)$ or $\bar{a}$.
5. If $a \sim b$, $\dfrac{(a-b)}{m} = k$, the total number of equivalence class is m.

Example 26. Let $I = \{0, \pm 1, \pm 2, \pm 3, \pm 4, \ldots\}$ and $R = \{(a,b) : (a-b)/4 = k, k \in I\}$ is an equivalence relation, find equivalence class.

Sol. Given, $\dfrac{a-b}{4} = k$

$\Rightarrow a = 4k + b$, where $0 \le b < 4$

It is clear b has only value in 0, 1, 2, 3.

(i) Equivalence class of $[0] = \{x : x \in I$ and $x \sim 0\}$
$= \{x : x - 0 = 4k\} = \{0, \pm 4, \pm 8, \pm 12, \ldots\}$
where, $k = 0, \pm 1, \pm 2, \pm 3, \ldots$

(ii) Equivalence class of $[1] = \{x : x \in I$ and $x \sim 1\}$
$= \{x : x - 1 = 4k\} = \{x : x = 4k + 1\}$
$= \{\ldots, -11, -7, -3, 1, 5, 9, \ldots\}$

(iii) Equivalence class of $[2] = \{x : x \in I$ and $x \sim 2\}$
$= \{x : x - 2 = 4k\} = \{x : x = 4k + 2\}$
$= \{\ldots, -10, -6, -2, 2, 6, 10, \ldots\}$

(iv) Equivalence class of $[3] = \{x : x \in I$ and $x \sim 3\}$
$= \{x : x - 3 = 4k\} = \{x : x = 4k + 3\}$
$= \{\ldots, -9, -5, -1, 5, 9, 13, \ldots\}$

Continue this process, we see that the equivalence class

$$[4] = [0], [5] = [1], [6] = [2], [7] = [3], [8] = [0]$$

Hence, total equivalence relations are [0], [1], [2], [3] and also clear

(i) $I = [0] \cup [1] \cup [2] \cup [3]$
(ii) every equivalence is a non-empty.
(iii) for any two equivalence classes $[a] \cap [b] = \phi$.

Partition of a Set

If A be a non-empty set, then a partition of A, if

(i) A is a collection of non-empty disjoint subsets of A.
(ii) union of collection of non-empty sets is A.

i.e., If A be a non-empty set and A_1, A_2, A_3, A_4 are subsets of A, then the set $\{A_1, A_2, A_3, A_4\}$ is called partition, if

(i) $A_1 \cup A_2 \cup A_3 \cup A_4 = A$
(ii) $A_1 \cap A_2 \cap A_3 \cap A_4 = \phi$

For example,

If $A = \{0, 1, 2, 3, 4\}$ and $A_1 = \{0\}, A_2 = \{1\}, A_3 = \{4\}$ and $A_4 = \{2, 3\}$, then we see that for $P = \{A_1, A_2, A_3, A_4\}$

(i) all A_1, A_2, A_3, A_4 are non-empty subset of A
(ii) $A_1 \cup A_2 \cup A_3 \cup A_4 = \{0, 1, 2, 3, 4\} = A$ and
(iii) $A_i \cap A_j \neq \phi, \forall\, i \neq j\ (i, j = 1, 2, 3, 4)$

Hence, from definition $P = \{A_1, A_2, A_3, A_4\}$ is partition of A.

Congruences

Let m be a positive integer, then two integers a and b are said to be congruent modulo m, if $a - b$ is divisible by m.

i.e.,
$$m\overline{)\,a-b\,}(\lambda$$
$$\frac{a-b}{\underset{\quad 0}{-\ \ +}}$$

$\therefore$ $a - b = m\lambda$, where λ is a positive integer.

The congruent modulo 'm' is defined on all $a\,b \in I$ by $a \equiv b$ (mod m), if $a - b = m\lambda, \lambda \in I_+$.

Example 27. Find congruent solutions of $155 \equiv 7$ (mod 4).

Sol. Since, $\left(\dfrac{155-7}{4} = \dfrac{148}{4} = 37\right)$

and $a = 155, b = 7, m = 4$

$$\therefore \quad \lambda = \frac{a-b}{4} = \frac{155-7}{4} = \frac{148}{4} \quad [\text{here}, a = 155, b = 7]$$

$= 37$ (integer)

| Example 28. Find all congruent solutions of $8x \equiv 6$ (mod 14).

Sol. Given, $8x \equiv 6 \pmod{14}$

$$\therefore \quad \lambda = \frac{8x-6}{14}, \text{ where } \lambda \in I_+$$

$$\therefore \quad 8x = 14\lambda + 6$$

$$\Rightarrow \quad x = \frac{14\lambda + 6}{8}$$

$$\Rightarrow \quad x = \frac{7\lambda + 3}{4}$$

$$= \frac{4\lambda + 3(\lambda + 1)}{4}$$

$$x = \lambda + \frac{3}{4}(\lambda + 1), \text{ where } \lambda \in I_+$$

and here greatest common divisor of 8 and 14 is 2, so there are two required solutions.

For $\lambda = 3$ and 7, $x = 6$ and 13.

Exercise for Session 3

1. The values of b and c for which the identity $f(x+1) - f(x) = 8x + 3$ is satisfied, where $f(x) = bx^2 + cx + d$, are

(a) $b = 2, c = 1$ (b) $b = 4, c = -1$ (c) $b = -1, c = 4$ (d) $b = -1, c = 1$

2. If $f(x) = \frac{x-1}{x+1}$, then $f(ax)$ in terms of $f(x)$ is equal to

(a) $\frac{f(x)+a}{1+af(x)}$ (b) $\frac{(a-1)f(x)+a+1}{(a+1)f(x)+a-1}$ (c) $\frac{(a+1)f(x)+a-1}{(a-1)f(x)+a+1}$ (d) None of these

3. If f be a function satisfying $f(x+y) = f(x) + f(y)$, $\forall\, x, y \in R$. If $f(1) = k$, then $f(n)$, $n \in N$ is equal to

(a) k^n (b) nk (c) k (d) None of these

4. If $g = \{(1,1), (2,3), (3,5), (4,7)\}$ is a function described by the formula $g(x) = \alpha x + \beta$, what values should be assigned to α and β?

(a) $\alpha = 1, \beta = 1$ (b) $\alpha = 2, \beta = -1$ (c) $\alpha = 1, \beta = -2$ (d) $\alpha = -2, \beta = -1$

5. The values of the parameter α for which the function $f(x) = 1 + \alpha x$, $\alpha \neq 0$ is the inverse of itself, is

(a) -2 (b) -1 (c) 1 (d) 2

6. If $f(x) = (a - x^n)^{1/n}$, where $a > 0$ and $n \in N$, then $fof(x)$ is equal to

(a) a (b) x (c) x^n (d) a^n

7. If $f(x) = (ax^2 + b)^3$, the function g such that $f(g(x)) = g(f(x))$, is given by

(a) $g(x) = \left(\frac{b - x^{1/3}}{a}\right)^{1/2}$ (b) $g(x) = \frac{1}{(ax^2+b)^3}$ (c) $g(x) = (ax^2 + b)^{1/3}$ (d) $g(x) = \left(\frac{x^{1/3} - b}{a}\right)^{1/2}$

8. Which of the following functions from I to itself are bijections?

(a) $f(x) = x^3$ (b) $f(x) = x + 2$ (c) $f(x) = 2x + 1$ (d) $f(x) = x^2 + x$

9. Let $f: R - \{n\} \to R$ be a function defined by $f(x) = \frac{x-m}{x-n}$, where $m \neq n$. Then,

(a) f is one-one onto (b) f is one-one into (c) f is many-one onto (d) f is many-one into

10. If $f(x+2y, x-2y) = xy$, then $f(x, y)$ equals

(a) $\frac{x^2 - y^2}{8}$ (b) $\frac{x^2 - y^2}{4}$ (c) $\frac{x^2 + y^2}{4}$ (d) $\frac{x^2 - y^2}{2}$

Shortcuts and Important Results to Remember

1 Every set is a subset of itself.

2 Null set is a subset of every set.

3 The set $\{0\}$ is not an empty set as it contains one element 0. The set $\{\phi\}$ is not an empty set as it contains one element ϕ.

4 The order of finite set A of n elements is denoted by $O(A)$ or $n(A)$.

5 Number of subsets of a set containing n elements is 2^n.

6 Number of proper subsets of a set containing n elements is $2^n - 1$.

7 If $A = \phi$, then $P(A) = \phi$; $\therefore n(P(A)) = 1$.

8 The order of an infinite set is undefined.

9 A natural number p is a prime number, if p is greater than one and its factors are 1 and p only.

10 Finite sets are equivalent sets only, when they have equal number of elements.

11 Equal sets are equivalent sets but equivalent sets may not be equal sets.

12 If A is any set, then $A \subseteq A$ is true but $A \subset A$ is false.

13 If $A \subseteq B$, then $A \cup B = B$

14 $A \subset B \Leftrightarrow A \subseteq B$ and $A \neq B$

15 $x \notin A \cup B \Leftrightarrow x \notin A$ and $x \notin B$

16 $x \notin A \cap B \Leftrightarrow x \notin A$ or $x \notin B$

17 If $A_1, A_2, \ldots, A_n$ is a finite family of sets, then their union is denoted by $\bigcup_{i=1}^{n} A_i$ or $A_1 \cup A_2 \cup A_3 \cup \ldots \cup A_n$.

18 If $A_1, A_2, A_3, \ldots, A_n$ is a finite family of sets, then their intersection is denoted by $\bigcap_{i=1}^{n} A_i$ or $A_1 \cap A_2 \cap A_3 \cap \ldots \cap A_n$.

19 $R - Q$ is the set of all irrational numbers.

20 Total number of relations from set A to set B is equal to $2^{n(A)n(B)}$.

21 The universal relation on a non-empty set is always reflexive, symmetric and transitive.

22 The identity relation on a non-empty set is always anti-symmetric.

23 The identity relation on a set is also called the diagonal relation on A.

24 For two relations R and S, the composite relations RoS, SoR may be void relations.

25 Every polynomial function $f: R \to R$ of degree odd is ONTO.

26 Every polynomial function $f: R \to R$ of degree even is INTO.

27 (i) The number of onto functions that can be defined from a finite set A containing n elements onto a finite set B containing 2 elements $= 2^n - 2$

(ii) The number of onto functions that can be defined from a finite set A containing n elements onto a finite set B containing 3 elements $= 3^n - 3 \cdot 2^n + 3$

28 If a set A has n elements, then the number of binary relations on $A = n^{n^2}$.

29 If $fog = gof$, then either $f^{-1} = g$ or $g^{-1} = f$.

30 If f and g are bijective functions such that $f: A \to B$ and $g: B \to C$, then $gof: A \to C$ is bijective. Also, $(gof)^{-1} = f^{-1}og^{-1}$.

31 Let $f: A \to B$, $g: B \to C$ be two functions, then

(i) f and g are injective $\Rightarrow gof$ is injective

(ii) f and g are surjective $\Rightarrow gof$ is surjective

(iii) f and g are bijective $\Rightarrow gof$ is bijective

32 Let $f: A \to B$, $g: B \to C$ be two functions, then

(i) $gof: A \to C$ is injective $\Rightarrow f: A \to B$ is injective

(ii) $gof: A \to C$ is surjective $\Rightarrow g: B \to C$ is surjective

(iii) $gof: A \to C$ is injective and $g: B \to C$ is surjective $\Rightarrow$ $g: B \to C$ is injective

(iv) $gof: A \to C$ is surjective and $g: B \to C$ is injective $\Rightarrow$ $f: A \to B$ is surjective

33 An injective mapping from a finite set to itself is bijective.

JEE Type Solved Examples :
Single Option Correct Type Questions

- This section contains **6 multiple choice examples.** Each example has four choices (a), (b), (c) and (d), out of which **ONLY ONE** is correct.

Ex. 1 *Two finite sets have m and n elements. The total number of subsets of the first set is 56 more than the total number of subsets of the second set. The values of m and n are*

(a) 7, 6 (b) 6, 3 (c) 5, 1 (d) 8, 7

Sol. (*b*) Since, $2^m - 2^n = 56 = 8 \times 7 = 2^3 \times 7$

$\Rightarrow \quad 2^n(2^{m-n} - 1) = 2^3 \times 7$

$\Rightarrow \quad n = 3$ and $2^{m-n} = 8 = 2^3 \Rightarrow n = 3$ and $m - n = 3$

$\Rightarrow \quad n = 3$ and $m - 3 = 3 \quad \Rightarrow n = 3$ and $m = 6$

Ex. 2 *If* $aN = \{ax : x \in N\}$ *and* $bN \cap cN = dN$, *where* $b, c \in N$ *are relatively prime, then*

(a) $d = bc$ (b) $c = bd$
(c) $b = cd$ (d) None of these

Sol. (a) bN = The set of positive integral multiples of b
cN = The set of positive integral multiples of c

$\therefore bN \cap cN$ = The set of positive integral multiples of bc
$= bc\,N$ [$\because$ b and c are prime]

$\therefore \quad d = bc$

Ex. 3 *In a town of 10000 families, it was found that 40% families buy newspaper A, 20% families buy newspaper B and 10% families buy newspaper C, 5% families buy newspapers A and B, 3% buy newspapers B and C and 4% buy newspapers A and C. If 2% families buy all the three newspapers, then number of families which buy A only is*

(a) 3100 (b) 3300 (c) 2900 (d) 1400

Sol. (*b*) $n(A) = 40\%$ of $10000 = 4000$

$n(B) = 20\%$ of $10000 = 2000$

$n(C) = 10\%$ of $10000 = 1000$

$n(A \cap B) = 5\%$ of $10000 = 500$

$n(B \cap C) = 3\%$ of $10000 = 300$

$n(C \cap A) = 4\%$ of $10000 = 400$

$n(A \cap B \cap C) = 2\%$ of $10000 = 200$

We want to find $n(A \cap B^c \cap C^c) = n[A \cap (B \cup C)^c]$

$= n(A) - n[A \cap (B \cup C)] = n(A) - n[(A \cap B) \cup (A \cap C)]$

$= n(A) - [n(A \cap B) + n(A \cap C) - n(A \cap B \cap C)]$

$= 4000 - [500 + 400 - 200] = 4000 - 700 = 3300$

Ex. 4 *Let R be the relation on the set R of all real numbers defined by aRb iff* $|a - b| \le 1$. *Then, R is*

(a) reflexive and symmetric (b) symmetric only
(c) transitive only (d) anti-symmetric only

Sol. (a) $\because |a - a| = 0 < 1 \Rightarrow a\,R\,a, \forall\, a \in R$

$\therefore$ R is reflexive.

Again, $aRb \Rightarrow |a - b| \le 1$

$\Rightarrow \quad |b - a| \le 1 \Rightarrow bRa$

$\therefore$ R is symmetric.

Again, $1\,R\,2$ and $2R1$ but $2 \ne 1$

$\therefore$ R is not anti-symmetric.

Further, $1R2$ and $2R\,3$ but $1 \not R 3$ [$\because |1 - 3| = 2 > 1$]

$\therefore$ R is not transitive.

Ex. 5 *The relation R defined on* $A = \{1, 2, 3\}$ *by aRb, if* $|a^2 - b^2| \le 5$. *Which of the following is false?*

(a) $R = \{(1, 1), (2, 2), (3, 3), (2, 1), (1, 2), (2, 3), (3, 2)\}$
(b) $R^{-1} = R$
(c) Domain of $R = \{1, 2, 3\}$
(d) Range of $R = \{5\}$

Sol. (*d*) Let $a = 1$

Then, $|a^2 - b^2| \le 5 \Rightarrow |1 - b^2| \le 5$

$\Rightarrow \quad |b^2 - 1| \le 5 \Rightarrow b = 1, 2$

Let $a = 2$

Then, $|a^2 - b^2| \le 5$

$\Rightarrow \quad |4 - b^2| \le 5 \Rightarrow |b^2 - 4| \le 5$

$\therefore \quad b = 1, 2, 3$

Let $a = 3$

Then, $|a^2 - b^2| \le 5$

$\Rightarrow \quad |9 - b^2| \le 5 \Rightarrow |b^2 - 9| \le 5 \Rightarrow b = 2, 3$

$\therefore \quad R = \{(1, 1), (1, 2), (2, 1), (2, 2), (2, 3), (3, 2), (3, 3)\}$

$R^{-1} = \{(y, x) : (x, y) \in R\}$

$= \{(1, 1), (2, 1), (1, 2), (2, 2), (3, 2), (2, 3), (3, 3)\} = R$

Domain of $R = \{x : (x, y) \in R\} = \{1, 2, 3\}$

Range of $R = \{y : (x, y) \in R\} = \{1, 2, 3\}$

Ex. 6 *If* $f(x) = \dfrac{1}{(1 - x)}$, $g(x) = f\{f(x)\}$ *and* $h(x) = f[f\{f(x)\}]$. *Then the value of* $f(x) \cdot g(x) \cdot h(x)$ *is*

(a) 6 (b) –1 (c) 1 (d) 2

Sol. (*b*) $\because g(x) = f\{f(x)\} = f\left(\dfrac{1}{1 - x}\right) = \dfrac{1}{1 - \dfrac{1}{1 - x}} = \dfrac{x - 1}{x}$

and $h(x) = f[f\{f(x)\}] = f(g(x))$

$$= \frac{1}{1 - g(x)} = \frac{1}{1 - \dfrac{x - 1}{x}} = x$$

$$\therefore \quad f(x) \cdot g(x) \cdot h(x) = \frac{1}{(1 - x)} \cdot \frac{(x - 1)}{x} \cdot x = -1$$

JEE Type Solved Examples : More than One Correct Option Type Questions

- This section contains **3 multiple choice examples.** Each example has four choices (a), (b), (c) and (d) out of which **MORE THAN ONE** may be correct.

• Ex. 7 *If I is the set of integers and if the relation R is defined over I by aRb, iff a − b is an even integer, a, b ∈ I, the relation R is*

(a) reflexive (b) anti-symmetric
(c) symmetric (d) equivalence

Sol. (a, c, d)

$aRb \Leftrightarrow a-b$ is an even integer, $a, b \in I$

$a - a = 0$ (even integer)

$\therefore \quad (a, a) \in R, \ \forall \ a \in I$

$\therefore$ R is reflexive relation.

Let $(a, b) \in R \Rightarrow (a-b)$ is an even integer.

$\Rightarrow \quad -(b-a)$ is an even integer.

$\Rightarrow \quad (b-a)$ is an even integer.

$\Rightarrow \quad (b, a) \in R$

$\therefore$ R is symmetric relation.

Now, let $(a, b) \in R$ and $(b, c) \in R$

Then, $(a-b)$ is an even integer and $(b-c)$ is an even integer.

So, let $\quad a - b = 2x_1, x_1 \in I$

and $\quad b - c = 2x_2, x_2 \in I$

$\therefore \quad (a-b)+(b-c) = 2(x_1+x_2)$

$\Rightarrow \quad (a-c) = 2(x_1+x_2) \Rightarrow a - c = 2x_3$

$\therefore$ $(a-c)$ is an even integer.

$\therefore$ aRb and $bRc \Rightarrow aRc$ So, R is transitive relation.

Hence, R is an equivalence relation.

A relation R on given set A is said to be anti-symmetric iff $(a, b) \in R$ and $(b, a) \in R \Rightarrow a = b, \forall \ a, b \in A$.

$\therefore$ Given relation is not anti-symmetric relation.

• Ex. 8 *If* $f(x) = \dfrac{a-x}{a+x}$, *the domain of* $f^{-1}(x)$ *contains*

(a) $(-\infty, \infty)$ (b) $(-\infty, 1)$
(c) $(-1, \infty)$ (d) $(0, \infty)$

Sol. (b, c, d)

Let $\quad y = f(x) = \dfrac{a-x}{a+x} \Rightarrow ay + xy = a - x$

$\therefore \quad x = \dfrac{a(1-y)}{(1+y)} = f^{-1}(y) \Rightarrow f^{-1}(x) = \dfrac{a(1-x)}{(1+x)}$

$\therefore$ $f^{-1}(x)$ is not defined for $x = -1$.

Domain of $f^{-1}(x)$ belongs to $(-\infty, -1) \cup (-1, \infty)$.

Now, for $a = -1$, given function $f(x) = -1$, which is constant.

Then, $f^{-1}(x)$ is not defined.

$\therefore \quad a \neq -1$

• Ex. 9 *If* $f(x) = \dfrac{\sin([x]\pi)}{x^2+x+1}$, *where* $[\cdot]$ *denotes the greatest integer function, then*

(a) f is one-one
(b) f is not one-one and non-constant
(c) f is constant function (d) f is zero function

Sol. (c, d)

$\because \quad \sin([x]\pi) = 0$

$\therefore \quad f(x) = 0 \quad [\because [x]$ is an integer$]$

$\Rightarrow$ $f(x)$ is a constant function and also $f(x)$ is a zero function.

JEE Type Solved Examples : Passage Based Questions

- This section contains **2 solved passages** based upon each of the passage **3 multiple choice** examples have to be answered. Each of these examples has four choices (a), (b), (c) and (d) out of which **ONLY ONE** is correct.

Passage I
(Ex. Nos. 10 to 12)

If $A = \{x : |x| < 2\}$, $B = \{x : |x-5| \leq 2\}$,
$C = \{x : |x| > x\}$ *and* $D = \{x : |x| < x\}$

• 10. *The number of integral values in* $A \cup B$ *is*

(a) 4 (b) 6
(c) 8 (d) 10

• 11. *The number of integral values in* $A \cap C$ *is*

(a) 1 (b) 2
(c) 3 (d) 0

• 12. *The number of integral values in* $A \cap D$ *is*

(a) 2 (b) 4
(c) 6 (d) 0

Sol. (Ex. Nos. 10 to 12)

$$A = \{x : |x| < 2\} = \{x : -2 < x < 2\} = (-2, 2)$$
$$B = \{x : |x-5| \le 2\} = \{x : -2 \le x - 5 \le 2\}$$
$$= \{x : 3 \le x \le 7\} = [3, 7]$$
$$C = \{x : |x| > x\} = \{x : x < 0\} = (-\infty, 0)$$
and $D = \{x : |x| < x\} = \phi$

10. (*c*) $A \cup B = (-2, 2) \cup [3, 7]$
Integral values in $A \cup B$ are $-1, 0, 1, 3, 4, 5, 6, 7$.
$\therefore$ Number of integral values in $A \cup B$ is 8.

11. (*a*) $A \cap C = (-2, 2) \cap (-\infty, 0) = (-2, 0)$
Integral value in $A \cap C$ is -1.
$\therefore$ Number of integral values in $A \cap C$ is 1.

12. (*d*) $A \cap D = (-2, 2) \cap \phi = \phi$
$\therefore$ Number of integral values in $A \cap D$ is 0.

Passage II
(Ex. Nos. 13 to 15)

If $A = \{x : x^2 - 2x + 2 > 0\}$ *and* $B = \{x : x^2 - 4x + 3 \le 0\}$

● ***13.*** $A \cap B$ *equals*

(a) $[1, \infty)$ (b) $[1, 3]$
(c) $(-\infty, 3]$ (d) $(-\infty, 1) \cup (3, \infty)$

● ***14.*** $A - B$ *equals*

(a) $(-\infty, \infty)$ (b) $(1, 3)$
(c) $(3, \infty)$ (d) $(-\infty, 1) \cup (3, \infty)$

● ***15.*** $A \cup B$ *equals*

(a) $(-\infty, 1)$ (b) $(3, \infty)$
(c) $(-\infty, \infty)$ (d) $(1, 3)$

Sol. (Ex. Nos. 13 to 15)

$$A = \{x : x^2 - 2x + 2 > 0\} = \{x : (x-1)^2 + 1 > 0\} = (-\infty, \infty)$$
$$B = \{x : x^2 - 4x + 3 \le 0\} = \{x : (x-1)(x-3) \le 0\}$$
$$= \{x : 1 \le x \le 3\} = [1, 3]$$

13. (*b*) $A \cap B = (-\infty, \infty) \cap [1, 3] = [1, 3]$

14. (*d*) $A - B = (-\infty, \infty) - [1, 3] = (-\infty, 1) \cup (3, \infty)$

15. (*c*) $A \cup B = (-\infty, \infty) \cup [1, 3] = (-\infty, \infty)$

JEE Type Solved Examples : Single Integer Answer Type Questions

- This section contains **2 examples.** The answer to each example is a **single digit integer** ranging from **0** to **9** (both inclusive).

● ***Ex. 16*** *If* $f : R^+ \to A$, *where* $A = \{x : -5 < x < \infty\}$ *is defined by* $f(x) = x^2 - 5$ *and if* $f^{-1}(13) = \{-\lambda\sqrt{(\lambda - 1)}, \lambda\sqrt{(\lambda - 1)}\}$, *the value of* λ *is*

Sol. (3) $f^{-1}(13) = \{x : f(x) = 13\} = \{x : x^2 - 5 = 13\}$

$$= \{x : x^2 = 18\} = \{x : x = \pm 3\sqrt{2}\}$$
$$= \{-3\sqrt{2}, 3\sqrt{2}\}$$
$$= \{-\lambda\sqrt{(\lambda - 1)}, \lambda\sqrt{(\lambda - 1)}\} \quad \text{[given]}$$

$\therefore \quad \lambda = 3$

● ***Ex. 17*** *If* $A = \{2, 3\}$, $B = \{4, 5\}$ *and* $C = \{5, 6\}$, *then* $n\{(A \times B) \cup (B \times C)\}$ *is*

Sol. (8) $\because A \times B = \{2, 3\} \times \{4, 5\}$

$$= \{(2, 4), (2, 5), (3, 4), (3, 5)\}$$

and $B \times C = \{4, 5\} \times \{5, 6\}$

$$= \{(4, 5), (4, 6), (5, 5), (5, 6)\}$$

$\therefore (A \times B) \cup (B \times C) = \{(2, 4), (2, 5), (3, 4), (3, 5), (4, 5), (4, 6), (5, 5), (5\ 6)\}$

Now, $n\{(A \times B) \cup (B \times C)\} = 8$

JEE Type Solved Examples : Matching Type Questions

- This section contains **1 examples.** Example 18 have three statements (A, B and C) given in Column I and four statements (p, q, r and s) in **Column II.** Any given statement in **Column I** can have correct matching with one or more statement(s) given in **Column II.**

• *Ex. 18*

	Column I		Column II
(A)	$R = \{(x, y) : x < y\,; x, y \in N\}$	(p)	Reflexive
(B)	$S = \{(x, y) : x + y = 10\,; x, y \in N\}$	(q)	Symmetric
(C)	$T = \{(x, y) : x = y$ or $x - y = 1\,; x, y \in N\}$	(r)	Transitive
(D)	$U = \{(x, y) : x^y = y^x; x, y \in N\}$	(s)	Equivalence

Sol. (A) → (r); (B) → (q); (C) → (p); (D) → (p, q, r, s)

(A) $\because \quad R = \{(x, y) : x < y;\, x, y \in N\}$

$x \nless x \ \therefore (x, x) \notin R$

So, R is not reflexive.

Now, $(x, y) \in R \Rightarrow x < y \nRightarrow y < x \Rightarrow (y, x) \notin R$

$\therefore$ R is not symmetric.

Let $(x, y) \in R$ and $(y, z) \in R$

$\Rightarrow \quad x < y$ and $y < z \Rightarrow x < z \Rightarrow (x, z) \in R$

$\therefore R$ is transitive.

(B) $\because S = \{(x, y) : x + y = 10\,; x, y \in N\}$

$\therefore \quad x + x = 10 \Rightarrow 2x = 10 \Rightarrow x = 5$

So, each element of N is not related to itself by the relation $x + y = 10$.

$\therefore$ S is not reflexive.

Now, $(x, y) \in S \Rightarrow x + y = 10 \Rightarrow y + x = 10$

$\Rightarrow \quad (y, x) \in S$

$\therefore$ S is symmetric relation.

Now, let $(3, 7) \in S$ and $(7, 3) \in S \Rightarrow (3, 3) \notin S$

$\therefore$ S is not transitive.

(C) $\because \quad T = \{(x, y) : x = y$ or $x - y = 1;\, x, y \in N\}$

$\therefore \quad x = x$

So, $\quad (x, x) \in T, \forall\, x \in N$

$\therefore \quad T$ is reflexive.

Let $\quad (3, 2) \in T$ and $3 - 2 = 1$

$\nRightarrow \quad 2 - 3 = -1 \Rightarrow (2, 3) \notin T$

$\therefore \quad T$ is not symmetric.

Now, let $\quad (3, 2) \in T$ and $(2, 1) \in T$

$\therefore \quad 3 - 2 = 1$ and $2 - 1 = 1$

Then, $\quad (3, 1) \notin T \qquad [\because 3 - 1 = 2 \neq 1]$

$\therefore \quad T$ is not transitive.

(D) $U = \{(x, y) : x^y = y^x;\, x, y \in N\}$

$\because \quad x^x = x^x$

$\therefore \quad (x, x) \in U$

$\therefore$ U is reflexive.

Now, $(x, y) \in U \Rightarrow x^y = y^x$

$\Rightarrow \quad y^x = x^y \Rightarrow (y, x) \in U$

$\therefore$ U is symmetric.

Now, let $(x, y) \in U$ and $(y, z) \in U$

$\Rightarrow \quad x^y = y^x$ and $y^z = z^y$

Now, $\quad (x^y)^z = (y^x)^z$

$\Rightarrow \quad (x^z)^y = (y^z)^x \Rightarrow (x^z)^y = (z^y)^x$

$\Rightarrow \quad (x^z)^y = (z^x)^y \Rightarrow x^z = z^x \Rightarrow (x, z) \in U$

$\therefore \quad U$ is transitive.

Hence, U is an equivalence relation.

JEE Type Solved Examples : Statement I and II Type Questions

- **Directions** Example numbers 19 and 20 are Assertion-Reason type examples. Each of these examples contains two statements:

Statement-1 (Assertion) and

Statement-2 (Reason)

Each of these examples also has four alternative choices, only one of which is the correct answer. You have to select the correct choice as given below:

(a) Statement-1 is true, Statement-2 is true; Statement-2 is a correct explanation for Statement-1

(b) Statement-1 is true, Statement-2 is true; Statement-2 is not a correct explanation for Statement-1

(c) Statement-1 is true; Statement-2 is false

(d) Statement-1 is false; Statement-2 is true

• *Ex. 19* Statement-1 *If* $A \cup B = A \cup C$ *and* $A \cap B = A \cap C$, *then* $B = C$.

Statement-2 $A \cup (B \cap C) = (A \cup B) \cap (A \cup C)$

Sol. (*a*) We have, $B = B \cup (A \cap B)$

$= B \cup (A \cap C) \qquad [\because A \cap B = A \cap C]$

$= (A \cup C) \cap (B \cup C)$ $[\because A \cup B = A \cup C]$
$= (A \cap B) \cup C$
$= (A \cap C) \cup C$ $[\because A \cap B = A \cap C]$
$= C$

Hence, Statement-1 is true, Statement-2 is true; Statement-2 is a correct explanation of Statement-1.

● **Ex. 20** **Statement-1** *If U is universal set and $B = U - A$, then $n(B) = n(U) - n(A)$.*

Statement-2 *For any three arbitrary sets A, B and C, if $C = A - B$, then $n(C) = n(A) - n(B)$.*

Sol. (c) $\because$ $B = U - A = A'$

$\therefore$ $n(B) = n(A') = n(U) - n(A)$

So, Statement-1 is true.

But for any three arbitrary sets A, B and C, we cannot always have

$$n(C) = n(A) - n(B)$$

if $C = A - B$

As it is not specified A is universal set or not. In case not conclude

$$n(C) = n(A) - n(B)$$

Hence, Statement-2 is false.

Subjective Type Examples

■ In this section, there are **12 subjective** solved examples.

● **Ex. 21.** *If $A = A \cup B$, prove that $B = A \cap B$.*

Sol. $\because A = A \cap B$

$\therefore$ $A \subseteq A \cup B$ and $A \cup B \subseteq A$

Now, let $x \in B \Leftrightarrow x \in A \cup B$ [by definition of union]

$\Leftrightarrow$ $x \in A$ $[\because A \subseteq A \cup B]$

$\Leftrightarrow$ $x \in A \cap B$ $[\because A \subseteq A \cup B,$ then also $A \subseteq A \cap B]$

$\therefore$ $B \subseteq A \cap B$ and $A \cap B \subseteq B$

Hence, $A \cap B = B$ **Hence proved.**

● **Ex. 22** *Find the smallest and largest sets of Y such that $Y \cup \{1, 2\} = \{1, 2, 3, 5, 9\}$.*

Sol. Smallest set of Y has three elements and largest set of Y has five elements, since RHS set has five elements.

$\therefore$ Smallest set of Y is {3, 5, 9}

and largest set of Y is {1, 2, 3, 5, 9}.

● **Ex. 23** *If P, Q and R are the subsets of a set A, then prove that $R \times (P^c \cup Q^c)^c = (R \times P) \cap (R \times Q)$.*

Sol. We know that from De-Morgan's law,

$$A^c \cap B^c = (A \cup B)^c \quad \text{...(i)}$$

Replacing A by P^c and B by Q^c, then Eq. (i) becomes

$$(P^c)^c \cap (Q^c)^c = (P^c \cup Q^c)^c$$

$\Rightarrow$ $P \cap Q = (P^c \cup Q^c)^c$ $[\because (A^c)^c = A]$ ...(ii)

$\therefore R \times (P^c \cup Q^c)^c = R \times (P \cap Q)$ [from Eq. (ii)]

$= (R \times P) \cap (R \times Q)$ [by cartesian product]

Hence, $R \times (P^c \cup Q^c)^c = (R \times P) \cap (R \times Q)$

● **Ex. 24** *Check the following relations R and ρ for reflexive, symmetry and transitivity.*

(i) aRb iff b is divisible by a, where a and b are natural numbers.

(ii) $\alpha \rho \beta$ iff α is perpendicular to β, where α and β are straight lines in a plane.

Sol. (i) The relation R is reflexive, since a is divisible by a, R is not symmetric because b is divisible by a but a is not divisible by b. i.e., $aRb \nRightarrow bRa$

Again, R is transitive, since b is divisible by a and c is divisible by b, then always c is divisible by a.

(ii) The relation ρ is not reflexive as no line can be perpendicular to itself. The relation ρ is symmetric, since a line α is perpendicular to β, then β is perpendicular to α and the relation ρ is not transitive, since a line α is perpendicular to β and if β is perpendicular to γ (new line), then α is not perpendicular to γ (since, α is parallel to γ).

● **Ex. 25** *Let $f:[0,1] \to [0,1]$ be defined by $f(x) = \dfrac{1-x}{1+x}$; $0 \le x \le 1$ and $g:[0,1] \to [0,1]$ be defined by $g(x) = 4x(1-x), 0 \le x \le 1$.*

Determine the functions *fog* and *gof*.

Note that [0,1] stands for the set of all real members x that satisfy the condition $0 \le x \le 1$.

Sol. $(fog)x = f\{g(x)\} = f\{4x(1-x)\}$ $[\because g(x) = 4x(1-x)]$

$$= \frac{1 - 4x(1-x)}{1 + 4x(1-x)} \quad \left[\because f(x) = \frac{1-x}{1+x}\right]$$

$$= \frac{1 - 4x + 4x^2}{1 + 4x - 4x^2} = \frac{(2x-1)^2}{1 + 4x - 4x^2}$$

and $(gof)x = g\{f(x)\} = g\left\{\frac{1-x}{1+x}\right\}$ $\left[\because f(x) = \frac{1-x}{1+x}\right]$

$$= 4\left(\frac{1-x}{1+x}\right)\left(1-\frac{1-x}{1+x}\right) = 4\left(\frac{1-x}{1+x}\right)\left(\frac{2x}{1+x}\right)$$

$$= \frac{8x(1-x)}{(1+x)^2}$$

Ex. 26 *If A, B are two sets, prove that*
$A \cup B = (A - B) \cup (B - A) \cup (A \cap B)$.
Hence or otherwise prove that

$$n(A \cup B) = n(A) + n(B) - n(A \cap B)$$

where, $n(A)$ denotes the number of elements in A.

Sol. Let $x \in A \cup B \Rightarrow x \in A$ or $x \in B$

$\Leftrightarrow (x \in A$ and $x \notin B)$ or $(x \in B$ and $x \notin A)$
or $(x \in A$ and $x \in B)$ [from definition of union]

$\Leftrightarrow$ $x \in (A - B)$ or $x \in (B - A)$ or $x \in A \cap B$

$\Leftrightarrow$ $x \in (A - B) \cup (B - A) \cup (A \cap B)$

$\therefore$ $A \cup B \subseteq (A - B) \cup (B - A) \cup (A \cap B)$

and $(A - B) \cup (B - A) \cup (A \cap B) \subseteq A \cup B$

Hence, $A \cup B = (A - B) \cup (B - A) \cup (A \cap B)$

Let the common elements in A and B are z and only element of A are x (represented by vertical lines in the Venn diagram) and only element of B are y (represented by horizontal lines in the Venn diagram)

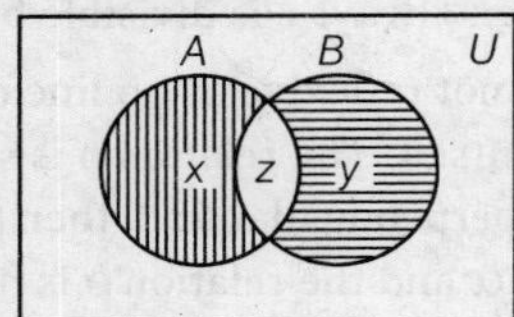

$\therefore$ $n(A) =$ Total elements of $A = x + z$

$n(B) =$ Total elements of $B = y + z$

$n(A \cap B) =$ Common elements in A and $B = z$

Now, $n(A \cup B) =$ Total elements in complete region of A and B

$$= x + y + z$$
$$= (x + z) + (y + z) - z$$
$$= n(A) + n(B) - n(A \cap B)$$

Hence, $n(A \cup B) = n(A) + n(B) - n(A \cap B)$

Ex. 27 *Let $A = \{\theta: 2\cos^2\theta + \sin\theta \le 2\}$ and $B = \{\theta: \pi/2 \le \theta \le 3\pi/2\}$. Then find $A \cap B$.*

Sol. $\because$ $2\cos^2\theta + \sin\theta \le 2$

$\therefore$ $2(1 - \sin^2\theta) + \sin\theta \le 2$

$\Rightarrow$ $2\sin^2\theta - \sin\theta \ge 0$

$\Rightarrow$ $\sin\theta(2\sin\theta - 1) \ge 0$

$\Rightarrow$ $\sin\theta\left(\sin\theta - \frac{1}{2}\right) \ge 0$

$\therefore$ $\sin\theta \le 0$ and $\sin\theta \ge \frac{1}{2}$

Now, the values of θ which lie in the interval $\frac{\pi}{2} \le \theta \le \frac{3\pi}{2}$.

$$\left[\because B = \left\{\theta: \frac{\pi}{2} \le \theta \le \frac{3\pi}{2}\right\}\right]$$

So, θ satisfy $\sin\theta \le 0$ in the interval $\pi \le \theta \le \frac{3\pi}{2}$

and θ satisfy $\sin\theta \ge \frac{1}{2}$ in the interval $\frac{\pi}{2} \le \theta \le \frac{5\pi}{6}$.

$\therefore$ $A \cap B = \left\{\theta: \pi \le \theta \le \frac{3\pi}{2}\right\}$

and $A \cap B = \left\{\theta: \frac{\pi}{2} \le \theta \le \frac{5\pi}{6}\right\}$

Hence, $A \cap B = \left\{\theta: \frac{\pi}{2} \le \theta \le \frac{5\pi}{6} \text{ or } \pi \le \theta \le \frac{3\pi}{2}\right\}$

$$= \left\{\theta: \theta \in \left[\frac{\pi}{2}, \frac{5\pi}{6}\right] \cup \left[\pi, \frac{3\pi}{2}\right]\right\}$$

Ex. 28 *An investigator interviewed 100 students to determine their preferences for the three drinks; milk (M), coffee (C) and tea (T). He reported the following: 10 students has all the three drinks M, C, T; 20 had M and C; 30 had C and T, 25 had M and T; 12 had M only; 5 had C only and 8 had T only. Using a Venn diagram, find how many did not take any of the three drinks?*

Sol. Given, M, C and T are the sets of drinks; milk, coffee and tea, respectively. Let us denote the number of drinks (students) contained in the bounded region as shown in the diagram by a, b, c, d, e, f and g, respectively.

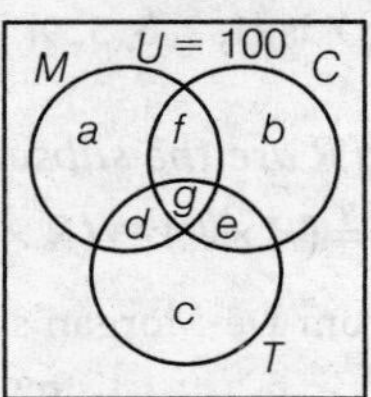

Then, $g = 10$

$g + f = 20 \Rightarrow f = 10$ $[\because g = 10]$

$g + e = 30 \Rightarrow e = 20$

$d + g = 25 \Rightarrow d = 15$

and $a = 12, b = 5, c = 8$

Thus, total number of students taking drinks M or C or T

$$= a + b + c + d + e + f + g$$
$$= 12 + 5 + 8 + 15 + 20 + 10 + 10 = 80$$

Hence, the number of students taking none of them drinks

$$= 100 - 80 = 20$$

● **Ex. 29** *In a certain city, only two newspapers A and B are published. It is known that 25% of the city population reads A and 20% reads B, while 8% reads A and B. It is also known that 30% of those who read A but not B, look into advertisements and 40% of those who read B but not A, look into advertisements while 50% of those who read both A and B, look into advertisements. What per cent of the population read on advertisement?*

Sol. Let C = Set of people who read paper A
and D = Set of people who read paper B

Given, $n(C) = 25, n(D) = 20, n(C \cap D) = 8$

$\therefore \quad n(C \cap D') = n(C) - n(C \cap D)$
$= 25 - 8 = 17$

But total number of people who read A but not B = 30%

$\therefore$ Percentage of people reading A but not B = 30% of 17

$$= \frac{30 \times 17}{100} = \frac{51}{10}$$

and $n(C' \cap D) = n(D) - n(C \cap D) = 20 - 8 = 12$

Also, total number of people who read B but not A = 40%

$\therefore$ Percentage of people reading B but not A = 40% of 12

$$= \frac{40 \times 12}{100} = \frac{24}{5}$$

and given total people who read A and B = 50%

$\therefore$ Total number of people who read A and B = 50% of 8

$$= \frac{50 \times 8}{100} = 4$$

$\therefore$ Percentage of people reading an advertisement

$$= \frac{51}{10} + \frac{24}{5} + 4 = 13.9\%$$

● **Ex. 30** *An analysis of 100 personal injury claims made upon a motor insurance company revealed that loss or injury in respect of an eye, an arm, a leg occurred in 30, 50 and 70 cases, respectively. Claims involving this loss or injury to two of these members numbered 44. How many claims involved loss or injury to all the three, we must assume that one or another of three members was mentioned in each of the 100 claims?*

Sol. Let the set of people having injuries in eyes, arms or legs be denoted by E, A and L, respectively. Then, according to the problem, we have

$$n(E \cup A \cup L) = 30, n(E) = 30$$
$$n(A) = 50, n(L) = 70$$

and $n[(E \cap A \cap L') \cup (E \cap A' \cap L) \cup (E' \cap A \cap L) = 44$

or $n(E \cap A \cap L') + n(E \cap A' \cap L) + n(E' \cap A \cap L) = 44$
[$\because$ each case is mutually exclusive]

or $n(E \cap A) - n(E \cap A \cap L) + n(E \cap L) - n(E \cap A \cap L)$
$+ n(E \cap L) - n(E \cap A \cap L) = 44$

$\Rightarrow \quad n(E \cap A) + n(E \cap L) + n(A \cap L)$
$- 3n(E \cap A \cap L) = 44$ ...(i)

$\because \quad n(E \cup A \cup L) = 100$

$\therefore n(E) + n(A) + n(L) - n(E \cap A) - n(A \cap L) - n(E \cap L)$
$+ n(E \cap A \cap L) = 100$

$\Rightarrow 30 + 50 + 70 - \{44 + 3n(E \cap A \cap L)\}$
$+ n(E \cap A \cap L) = 100$ [from Eq. (i)]

$\Rightarrow \quad 6 - 2n(E \cap A \cap L) = 0$

$\therefore \quad n(E \cap L \cap A) = 3$

Hence, there are three claims involved in loss or injury to all the three.

Aliter

Let E = Set of people having injuries in eyes

$\therefore \quad n(E) = 30$

A = Set of people having injuries in arms

$\therefore \quad n(A) = 50$

and L = Set of people having injuries in legs

$\therefore \quad n(L) = 70$

Let us denote the number of injuries contained in the bounded region as shown in the diagram by a, b, c, d, e, f and g, respectively.

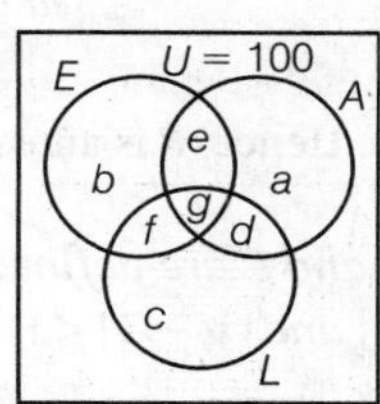

Then, $\quad b + e + f + g = 30$ ...(i)

$a + d + e + g = 50$ ...(ii)

$c + d + f + g = 70$ ...(iii)

$d + e + f = 44$ ...(iv)

and $a + b + c + d + e + f + g = 100$ ...(v)

On adding Eqs. (i), (ii) and (iii), we get

$$a + b + c + 2(d + e + f) + 3g = 150$$

$\Rightarrow 100 - d - e - f - g + 2(d + e + f) + 3g = 150$
[from Eq. (v)]

$\Rightarrow \quad d + e + f + 2g = 50$

$\Rightarrow \quad 44 + 2g = 50$ [from Eq. (iv)]

$\therefore \quad g = 3$

Hence, there are three claims involved loss or injury to all the three.

● **Ex. 31** *N is the set of natural number. The relation R is defined on N × N as follows:*

$$(a, b) R (c, d) \Leftrightarrow ad(b + c) = bc(a + d)$$

Prove that R is an equivalence relation.

Sol. Reflexive

Since, $(a, b) R (a, b) \Leftrightarrow ab(b + a) = ba(a + b), \forall\ a, b \in N$ is true.

Hence, R is reflexive.

Symmetric $(a, b) R (c, d)$

$$\Leftrightarrow \quad ad(b + c) = bc(a + d)$$
$$\Leftrightarrow \quad bc(a + d) = ad(b + c)$$
$$\Leftrightarrow \quad cb(d + a) = da(c + b)$$
$$\Leftrightarrow \quad (c, d) R (a, b)$$

Hence, R is symmetric.

Transitive

Since, $(a, b) R (c, d) \Leftrightarrow ad(b + c) = bc(a + d)$

$$\Leftrightarrow \quad \frac{b + c}{bc} = \frac{a + d}{ad}$$
$$\Leftrightarrow \quad \frac{1}{c} + \frac{1}{b} = \frac{1}{d} + \frac{1}{a}$$
$$\Leftrightarrow \quad \frac{1}{a} - \frac{1}{b} = \frac{1}{c} - \frac{1}{d}$$
$$\therefore \quad (a, b) R (c, d) \Leftrightarrow \frac{1}{a} - \frac{1}{b} = \frac{1}{c} - \frac{1}{d} \quad \text{...(i)}$$

and similarly $(c, d) R (e, f) \Leftrightarrow \frac{1}{c} - \frac{1}{d} = \frac{1}{e} - \frac{1}{f}$ ...(ii)

From Eqs. (i) and (ii),

$$(a,b) R (c,d) \text{ and } (c,d) R (e,f) \Leftrightarrow \frac{1}{a} - \frac{1}{b} = \frac{1}{e} - \frac{1}{f}$$
$$\Leftrightarrow (a, b) R (e, f)$$

So, R is transitive. Hence, R is an equivalence relation.

• ***Ex. 32** The sets S and E are defined as given below:*
$S = \{(x, y): |x - 3| < 1| \text{ and } |y - 3| < 1\}$ and
$E = \{(x, y): 4x^2 + 9y^2 - 32x - 54y + 109 \le 0\}$.
Show that $S \subset E$.

Sol. Graph of S

$\because\ |x - 3| < 1 \Rightarrow -1 < (x - 3) < 1 \Rightarrow 2 < x < 4$

Similarly, $|y - 3| < 1 \Rightarrow 2 < y < 4$

So, S consists of all points inside the square (not on $x \ne 2, 4$ and $y \ne 2, 4$) bounded by the lines $x = 2$, $y = 2$, $x = 4$ and $y = 4$.

Graph of E

$$\because \quad 4x^2 + 9y^2 - 32x - 54y + 109 \le 0$$
$$\Rightarrow \quad 4(x^2 - 8x) + 9(y^2 - 6y) + 109 \le 0$$
$$\Rightarrow \quad 4(x - 4)^2 + 9(y - 3)^2 \le 36$$
$$\Rightarrow \quad \frac{(x - 4)^2}{3^2} + \frac{(y - 3)^2}{2^2} \le 1$$

So, E consists of all points inside and on the ellipse with centre (4, 3) and semi-major and semi-minor axes are 3 and 2, respectively.

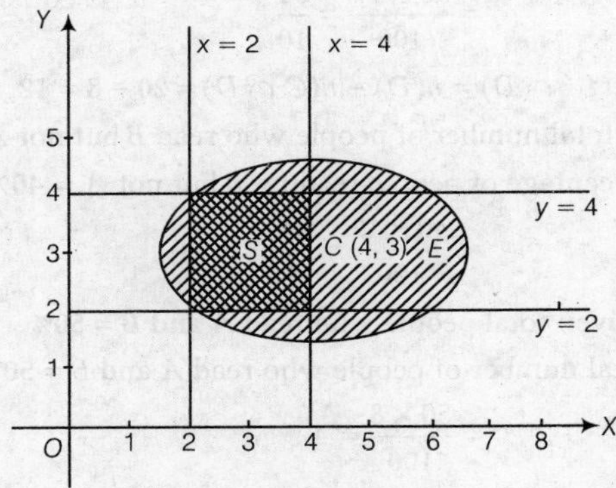

From the above graph, it is evident that the double hatched (which is S) is within the region represented by E. i.e., $S \subset E$

Sets, Relations and Functions Exercise 1 : Single Option Correct Type Questions

- This section contains **39 multiple choice questions.** Each question has four choices (a), (b), (c) and (d) out of which **ONLY ONE** is correct

1. If A and B are two sets, then $A \cap (A \cup B)$ equals
(a) A (b) B
(c) ϕ (d) None of these

2. If R is a relation from a set A to a set B and S is a relation from a set B to set C, then the relation SoR
(a) is from A to C (b) is from C to A
(c) does not exist (d) None of these

3. Let $R = \{(1, 3), (2, 2), (3, 2)\}$ and $S = \{(2, 1), (3, 2), (2, 3)\}$ be two relations on set $A = \{1, 2, 3\}$. Then, RoS is equal
(a) $\{(2, 3), (3, 2), (2, 2)\}$ (b) $\{(1, 3), (2, 2), (3, 2), (2, 1), (2, 3)\}$
(c) $\{(3, 2), (1, 3)\}$ (d) $\{(2, 3) (3, 2)\}$

4. If X and Y are two sets, then $X \cap (Y \cap X)'$ equals
(a) X (b) Y
(c) ϕ (d) None of these

5. For real numbers x and y, we write $x \, R \, y \Leftrightarrow x - y + \sqrt{2}$ is an irrational number. Then, the relation R is
(a) reflexive (b) symmetric
(c) transitive (d) None of these

6. Let $f(x) = (x + 1)^2 - 1, (x \geq -1)$. Then, the set $S = \{x : f(x) = f^{-1}(x)\}$ is
(a) $\left\{0, -1, \dfrac{-3 + i\sqrt{3}}{2}, \dfrac{-3 - i\sqrt{3}}{2}\right\}, i = \sqrt{-1}$
(b) $\{0, 1, -1\}$ (c) $\{0, -1\}$
(d) empty

7. The number of elements of the power set of a set containing n elements is
(a) 2^{n-1} (b) 2^n (c) $2^n - 1$ (d) 2^{n+1}

8. Which one of the following is not true?
(a) $A - B \subseteq A$ (b) $B' - A' \subseteq A$
(c) $A \subseteq A - B$ (d) $A \cap B' \subseteq A$

9. If $A = \{1, 2, 3\}$ and $B = \{3, 8\}$, then $(A \cup B) \times (A \cap B)$ is
(a) $\{(3, 1), (3, 2), (3, 3), (3, 8)\}$ (b) $\{(1, 3), (2, 3), (3, 3), (8, 3)\}$
(c) $\{(1, 2), (2, 2), (3, 3), (8, 8)\}$ (d) $\{(8, 3), (8, 2), (8, 1), (8, 8)\}$

10. Let $A = \{p, q, r\}$. Which of the following is not an equivalence relation on A?
(a) $R_1 = \{(p, q), (q, r), (p, r), (p, p)\}$
(b) $R_2 = \{(r, q), (r, p), (r, r), (q, q)\}$
(c) $R_3 = \{(p, p), (q, q), (r, r), (p, q)\}$
(d) None of the above

11. Let $A = \{x : x$ is a multiple of 3$\}$ and $B = \{x : x$ is a multiple of 5$\}$, then $A \cap B$ is given by
(a) $\{3, 6, 9\}$ (b) $\{5, 10, 15, 20, \ldots\}$
(c) $\{15, 30, 45, \ldots\}$ (d) None of these

12. Let $A = \{1, 2, 3\}$, $B = \{3, 4\}$ and $C = \{4, 5, 6\}$, then $A \cup (B \cap C)$ is
(a) $\{3\}$ (b) $\{1, 2, 3, 4\}$
(c) $\{1, 2, 5, 6\}$ (d) $\{1, 2, 3, 4, 5, 6\}$

13. Let $A = \{x, y, z\}$, $B = \{u, v, w\}$ and $f : A \to B$ be defined by $f(x) = u$, $f(y) = v, f(z) = w$. Then, f is
(a) surjective but not injective
(b) injective but not surjective
(c) bijective
(d) None of the above

14. If $A = \{2, 4\}$ and $B = \{3, 4, 5\}$, then $(A \cap B) \times (A \cup B)$ is
(a) $\{(2, 2), (3, 4), (4, 2), (5, 4)\}$ (b) $\{(2, 3), (4, 3), (4, 5)\}$
(c) $\{(2, 4), (3, 4), (4, 4), (4, 5)\}$ (d) $\{(4, 2), (4, 3), (4, 4), (4, 5)\}$

15. In the set $X = \{a, b, c, d\}$, which of the following functions in X?
(a) $R_1 = \{(b, a) (a, b), (c, d), (a, c)\}$
(b) $R_2 = \{(a, d) (d, c), (b, b), (c, c)\}$
(c) $R_3 = \{(a, b) (b, c), (c, d), (b, d)\}$
(d) $R_4 = \{(a, a) (b, b), (c, c), (a, d)\}$

16. The composite mapping fog of the map $f : R \to R$, $f(x) = \sin x$ and $g : R \to R$, $g(x) = x^2$ is
(a) $x^2 \sin x$ (b) $(\sin x)^2$ (c) $\sin x^2$ (d) $\sin x / x^2$

17. Which of the following is the empty set?
(a) $\{x : x$ is a real number and $x^2 - 1 = 0\}$
(b) $\{x : x$ is a real number and $x^2 + 1 = 0\}$
(c) $\{x : x$ is a real number and $x^2 - 9 = 0\}$
(d) $\{x : x$ is a real number and $x^2 = x + 2\}$

18. In order that a relation R defined on a non-empty set A is an equivalence relation. It is sufficient, if R
(a) is reflexive
(b) is symmetric
(c) is transitive
(d) possesses all the above three properties

19. Let $A = \{p, q, r, s\}$ and $B = \{1, 2, 3\}$. Which of the following relations from A to B is not a function?
(a) $R_1 = \{(p, 1), (q, 2), (r, 1), (s, 2)\}$
(b) $R_2 = \{(p, 1), (q, 2), (r, 1), (s, 1)\}$
(c) $R_3 = \{(p, 1), (q, 2), (r, 2), (r, 2)\}$
(d) $R_4 = \{(p, 2), (q, 3), (r, 2), (s, 2)\}$

20. n/m means that n is factor of m, then the relation f is
(a) reflexive and symmetric
(b) transitive and symmetric
(c) reflexive, transitive and symmetric
(d) reflexive, transitive and not symmetric

21. The solution of $8x \equiv 6 \pmod{14}$ are
(a) [8],[6] (b) [8],[14]
(c) [6],[13] (d) [8],[14],[16]

22. Let A be a set containing 10 distinct elements, the total number of distinct functions from A to A is
(a) 10! (b) 10^{10} (c) 2^{10} (d) $2^{10}-1$

23. Let A and B be two non-empty subsets of set X such that A is not a subset of B, then
(a) A is a subset of the complement of B
(b) B is a subset of A
(c) A and B are disjoint
(d) A and the complement of B are non-disjoint

24. f and h are function from $A \to B$, where $A = \{a, b, c, d\}$ and $B = \{s, t, u\}$ defined as follows
$f(a) = t, f(b) = s, f(c) = s$
$f(d) = u, h(a) = s, h(b) = t$
$h(c) = s, h(a) = u, h(d) = u$
Which one of the following statement is true?
(a) f and h are functions
(b) f is a function and h is not a function
(c) f and h are not functions
(d) None of the above

25. Let I be the set of integer and $f : I \to I$ be defined as $f(x) = x^2, x \in I$, the function is
(a) bijection (b) injection
(c) surjection (d) None of these

26. Which of the four statements given below is different from others?
(a) $f : A \to B$
(b) $f : x \to f(x)$
(c) f is a mapping of A into B
(d) f is a function of A into B

27. The number of surjections from $A = \{1, 2, \dots, n\}, n \ge 2$ onto $B = \{a, b\}$ is
(a) ${}^nP_2$ (b) $2^n - 2$
(c) $2^n - 1$ (d) None of these

28. Let $f : R \to R$ be defined by $f(x) = 3x - 4$, then $f^{-1}(x)$ is
(a) $\frac{1}{3}(x+4)$ (b) $\frac{1}{3}x - 4$
(c) $3x + 4$ (d) not defined

29. $f : R \to R$ is a function defined by $f(x) = 10x - 7$. If $g = f^{-1}$, then $g(x)$ equals
(a) $\frac{1}{10x-7}$ (b) $\frac{1}{10x+7}$ (c) $\frac{x+7}{10}$ (d) $\frac{x-7}{10}$

30. Let R be a relation defined by $R = \{(a, b) : a \ge b\}$, where a and b are real numbers, then R is
(a) reflexive, symmetric and transitive
(b) reflexive, transitive but not symmetric
(c) symmetric, transitive but not reflexive
(d) neither transitive, nor reflexive, not symmetric

31. If sets A and B are defined as
$A = \{(x, y) : y = e^x, x \in R\}$ and $B = \{(x, y) : y = x, x \in R\}$.
(a) $B \subset A$ (b) $A \subset B$
(c) $A \cap B = \phi$ (d) $A \cup B$

32. If $f : A \to B$ is a bijective function, then $f^{-1}of$ is equal to
(a) fof^{-1}
(b) f
(c) f^{-1}
(d) I_A(the identity map of the set A)

33. If $f(y) = \frac{y}{\sqrt{(1-y^2)}}, g(y) = \frac{y}{\sqrt{(1+y^2)}}$, then $(fog)y$ is equal to
(a) $\frac{y}{\sqrt{(1-y^2)}}$ (b) $\frac{y}{\sqrt{(1+y^2)}}$ (c) y (d) $\frac{(1-y^2)}{\sqrt{(1-y^2)}}$

34. If $f : R \to R$ is defined by $f(x) = 2x + |x|$, then $f(3x) - f(-x) - 4x$ equals
(a) $f(x)$ (b) $-f(x)$ (c) $f(-x)$ (d) $2f(x)$

35. Let R and S be two non-void relations on a set A. Which of the following statement is false?
(a) R and S are transitive $\Rightarrow R \cup S$ is transitive.
(b) R and S are transitive $\Rightarrow R \cap S$ is symmetric.
(c) R and S are symmetric $\Rightarrow R \cup S$ is symmetric.
(d) R and S are reflexive $\Rightarrow R \cap S$ is reflexive.

36. Let $f : R \to R, g : R \to R$ be two functions given by $f(x) = 2x - 3, g(x) = x^3 + 5$. Then, $(fog)^{-1}(x)$ is equal to
(a) $\left(\frac{x+7}{2}\right)^{1/3}$ (b) $\left(x - \frac{7}{2}\right)^{1/3}$ (c) $\left(\frac{x-2}{7}\right)^{1/3}$ (d) $\left(\frac{x-7}{2}\right)^{1/3}$

37. If $f(x) = ax + b$ and $g(x) = cx + d$, then $f(g(x)) = g(f(x)) \Leftrightarrow$
(a) $f(a) = g(c)$ (b) $f(b) = g(b)$
(c) $f(d) = g(b)$ (d) $f(c) = g(a)$

38. If $f : R \to R, g : R \to R$ be two given functions, then $f(x) = 2\min(f(x) - g(x), 0)$ equals
(a) $f(x) + g(x) - |g(x) - f(x)|$
(b) $f(x) + g(x) + |g(x) - f(x)|$
(c) $f(x) - g(x) + |g(x) - f(x)|$
(d) $f(x) - g(x) - |g(x) - f(x)|$

39. Let $f : R \to R, g : R \to R$ be two given functions, such that f is injective and g is surjective, then which of the following is injective?
(a) gof (b) fog (c) gog (d) fof

Sets, Relations and Functions Exercise 2 :
More than One Correct Option Type Questions

- This section contains **3 multiple choice questions**. Each question has four choices (a), (b), (c) and (d) out of which **MORE THAN ONE** may be correct.

40. Let L be the set of all straight lines in the Euclidean plane. Two lines l_1 and l_2 are said to be related by the relation R iff l_1 is parallel to l_2. Then, the relation R is

(a) reflexive (b) symmetric
(c) transitive (d) equivalence

41. Let $X = \{1, 2, 3, 4, 5, 6\}$ and $Y = \{1, 3, 5, 7, 9\}$. Which of the following is/are relations from X to Y?

(a) $R_1 = \{(x, y) : y = 2 + x, x \in X, y \in Y\}$
(b) $R_2 = \{(1, 1), (2, 1), (3, 3), (4, 3), (5, 5)\}$
(c) $R_3 = \{(1, 1), (1, 3), (3, 5), (3, 7), (5, 7)\}$
(d) $R_4 = \{(1, 3), (2, 5), (2, 4), (7, 9)\}$

42. Let the function $f : R - \{-b\} \to R - \{1\}$ be defined by $f(x) = \dfrac{x+a}{x+b} (a \neq b)$, then

(a) f is one-one but not onto
(b) f is onto but not one-one
(c) f is both one-one and onto
(d) $f^{-1}(2) = a - 2b$

Sets, Relations and Functions Exercise 3 :
Passage Based Questions

- This section contains **2 passages**. Based upon each of the passage **3 multiple choice questions** have to be answered. Each of these questions has four choices (a), (b), (c) and (d) out of which **ONLY ONE** is correct.

Passage I
(Q. Nos. 43 to 45)

Let f and g be real valued functions defined as

$$f(x) = \begin{cases} 7x^2 + x - 8, & x \le 1 \\ 4x + 5, & 1 < x \le 7 \\ 8x + 3, & x > 7 \end{cases} \quad g(x) = \begin{cases} |x|, & x < -3 \\ 0, & -3 \le x < 2 \\ x^2 + 4, & x \ge 2 \end{cases}$$

43. The value of $(gof)(0) + (fog)(-3)$ is

(a) -8 (b) 0
(c) 8 (d) 16

44. The value of $2(fog)(7) - (gof)(6)$ is

(a) 9 (b) 11
(c) 13 (d) 15

45. The value of $4(gof)(2) - (fog)(9)$ is

(a) 0 (b) 2 (c) 5 (d) 9

Passage II
(Q. Nos. 46 to 48)

R_1 on Z defined by $(a, b) \in R_1$ iff $|a - b| \le 7$, R_2 on Q defined by $(a, b) \in R_2$ iff $ab = 4$ and R_3 on R defined by $(a, b) \in R_3$ iff $a^2 - 4ab + 3ab^2 = 0$.

46. Relation R_1 is

(a) reflexive and symmetric (b) symmetric and transitive
(c) reflexive and transitive (d) equivalence

47. Relation R_2 is

(a) reflexive (b) symmetric
(c) transitive (d) equivalence

48. Relation R_3 is

(a) reflexive (b) symmetric
(c) transitive (d) equivalence

Sets, Relations and Functions Exercise 4 :
Single Integer Answer Type Questions

- This section contains **6 questions**. The answer to each question is a **single digit integer**, ranging from 0 to 9 (both inclusive).

49. In a group of 45 students, 22 can speak Hindi only and 12 can speak English only. If $(2\lambda + 1)$ student can speak both Hindi and English, the value of λ is

50. If $A = \left\{x \mid \cos x > -\dfrac{1}{2} \text{ and } 0 \le x \le \pi\right\}$ and $B = \left\{x \mid \sin x > \dfrac{1}{2} \text{ and } \dfrac{\pi}{3} \le x \le \pi\right\}$ and if $\pi\lambda \le A \cap B < \pi\mu$, the value of $(\lambda + \mu)$ is

51. If $S = R$, $A = \{x : -3 \le x < 7\}$ and $B = \{x : 0 < x < 10\}$, the number of positive integers in $A \Delta B$ is

52. Two finite sets have m and n elements. The total number of subsets of the first set is 48 more than the total number of subsets of the second set. The value of $m - n$ is

53. If two sets A and B are having 99 elements in common, the number of elements common to each of the sets $A \times B$ and $B \times A$ are $121\lambda^2$, the value of λ is

Sets, Relations and Functions Exercise 5 : Matching Type Questions

- This section contains **2 questions**. Questions 54 and 55 have three statements (A, B and C) given in **Column I** and four statements (p, q, r and s) in **Column II** and questions 70 and 71 have four statements (A, B, C and D) given in **Column I** and five statements (p, q, r, s and t) in **Column II**. Any given statement in **Column I** can have correct matching with one or more statement(s) given in **Column II**.

54. The functions defined have domain R.

	Column I		Column II
(A)	$7x + 1$	(p)	onto $[-1, 1]$ but not one-one $[0, \pi]$
(B)	$\cos x$	(q)	one-one on $[0, \pi]$ but not onto R
(C)	$\sin x$	(r)	one-one and onto R
(D)	$1 + \ln x$	(s)	one-one on $(0, \infty)$

55. The domain of the function $f(x)$ is denoted by D_f.

	Column I		Column II
(A)	$f(x) = \sqrt{(3 - x)} + \sin^{-1}\left(\frac{3 - 2x}{5}\right)$, then D_f is	(p)	$\bigcup_{k \in I} [2k\pi, (2k + 1)\pi]$
(B)	$f(x) = \log_{10}(1 - \log_{10}(x^2 - 5x + 16))$, then D_f is	(q)	$[-4, -\pi] \cup [0, \pi]$
(C)	$f(x) = \cos^{-1}\left(\frac{2}{2 + \sin x}\right)$, then D_f is	(r)	$(2, 3)$
(D)	$f(x) = \sqrt{(\sin x)} + \sqrt{(16 - x^2)}$, then D_f is	(s)	$[-1, 3]$

Sets, Relations and Functions Exercise 6 : Statement I and II Type Questions

- **Directions** Question numbers 56 to 59 are Assertion-Reason type questions. Each of these questions contains two statements :
  (a) Statement-1 is true, Statement-2 is true; Statement-2 is a correct explanation for Statement-1.
  (b) Statement-1 is true, Statement-2 is true; Statement-2 is not a correct explanation for Statement-1.
  (c) Statement-1 is true, Statement-2 is false.
  (d) Statement-1 is false, Statement-2 is true.

56. Statement-1 If a set A has n elements, then the number of binary relations on $A = n^{n^2}$.

Statement-2 Number of possible relations from A to $A = 2^{n^2}$.

57. Statement-1 If $A = \{x \mid g(x) = 0\}$ and $B = \{x \mid f(x) = 0\}$, then $A \cap B$ be a root of $\{f(x)\}^2 + \{g(x)\}^2 = 0$.

Statement-2 $x \in A \cap B \Rightarrow x \in A$ or $x \in B$.

58. Statement-1 $P(A) \cap P(B) = P(A \cap B)$, where $P(A)$ is power set of set A.

Statement-2 $P(A) \cup P(B) = P(A \cup B)$

59. Statement-1 If Sets A and B have three and six elements respectively, then the minimum number of elements in $A \cup B$ is 6.

Statement-2 $A \cap B = 3$.

Sets, Relations and Functions Exercise 7 : Subjective Type Questions

- In this section, there are **15 subjective** questions.

60. Let $A = \{x : x \text{ is a natural number}\}$,
$B = \{x : x \text{ is an even natural number}\}$,
$C = \{x : x \text{ is an odd natural number}\}$
and $D = \{x : x \text{ is a prime number}\}$.

Find
(i) $A \cap B$ (ii) $A \cap C$
(iii) $B \cap D$ (iv) $C \cap D$

61. Let U be the set of all people and $M = \{\text{Males}\}$, $S = \{\text{College students}\}$, $T = \{\text{Teenagers}\}$, $W = \{\text{People having height more than five feet}\}$.
Express each of the following in the notation of set theory.
(i) College student having heights more than five feet.
(ii) People who are not teenagers and have their height less five feet.
(iii) All people who are neither males nor teenagers nor college students.

62. The set X consists of all points within and on the unit circle $x^2 + y^2 = 1$, whereas the set Y consists of all points on and inside the rectangular boundary $x = 0$, $x = 1$, $y = -1$ and $y = 1$. Determine $X \cup Y$ and $X \cap Y$. Illustrate your answer by diagrams.

63. In a group of children, 35 play football out of which 20 play football only, 22 play hockey; 25 play cricket out of which 11 play cricket only. Out of these 7 play cricket and football but not hockey, 3 play football and hockey but not cricket and 12 play football and cricket both.
How many play all the three games? How many play cricket and hockey but not football, how many play hockey only? What is the total number of children in the group?

64. Of the members of three athletic team in a certain school, 21 are on the basketball team, 26 on the hockey team and 29 on the football team. 14 play hockey and basketball, 15 play hockey and football, 12 play football and basketball and 8 play all the three games. How many members are there in all?

65. In a survey of 200 students of higher secondary school, it was found that 120 studied Mathematics; 90 studies Physics and 70 studied Chemistry; 40 studied Mathematics and Physics; 3 studied Physics and Chemistry; 50 studied Chemistry and Mathematics and 20 studied none of these subjects. Find the number of students who studied all the three subjects.

66. In a survey of population of 450 people, it is found that 205 can speak English, 210 can speak Hindi and 120 people can speak Tamil. If 100 people can speak both Hindi and English; 80 people can speak both English and Tamil, 35 people can speak Hindi and Tamil and 20 people can speak all the three languages, find the number of people who can speak English but not a Hindi or Tamil. Find also the number of people who can speak neither English nor Hindi nor Tamil.

67. A group of 123 workers went to a canteen for cold drinks, ice-cream and tea, 42 workers took ice-cream, 36 tea and 30 cold drinks. 15 workers purchased ice-cream and tea, 10 ice-cream and cold drinks, and 4 cold drinks and tea but not ice-cream, 11 took ice-cream and tea but not cold drinks. Determine how many workers did not purchase anything?

68. Let n be a fixed positive integer. Define a relation R on I (the set of all integers) as follows:
$a\,R\,b$ iff $n \mid (a - b)$ i.e., iff $(a - b)$ is divisible by n. Show that R is an equivalence relations on I.

69. N is the set of positive integers. The relation R is defined on $N \times N$ as follows:
$$(a, b)\,R\,(c, d) \Leftrightarrow ad = bc$$
Prove that R is an equivalence relation.

70. The following relations are defined on the set of real numbers.
(i) $a\,R\,b \Leftrightarrow |a - b| > 0$
(ii) $a\,R\,b \Leftrightarrow |a| = |b|$
(iii) $a\,R\,b \Leftrightarrow |a| \geq |b|$
(iv) $a\,R\,b \Leftrightarrow 1 + ab > 0$
(v) $a\,R\,b \Leftrightarrow |a| \leq b$
Find whether these relations are reflexive, symmetric or transitive.

71. Let $A = \{x : -1 \leq x \leq 1\} = B$ for each of the following functions from A to B. Find whether it is surjective, injective or bijective
(i) $f(x) = \dfrac{x}{2}$
(ii) $g(x) = |x|$
(iii) $h(x) = x|x|$
(iv) $k(x) = x^2$
(v) $l(x) = \sin \pi x$

72. If the functions f and g defined from the set of real numbers R to R such that $f(x) = e^x$ and $g(x) = 3x - 2$, then find functions fog and gof. Also, find the domain of the functions $(fog)^{-1}$ and $(gof)^{-1}$.

73. If $f(x) = \frac{x^2 - x}{x^2 + 2x}$, then find the domain and range of f. Show that f is one-one. Also, find the function $\frac{d(f^{-1}(x))}{dx}$ and its domain.

74. If the functions f, g and h are defined from the set of real numbers R to R such that

$$f(x) = x^2 - 1,\ g(x) = \sqrt{(x^2 + 1)},$$

$$h(x) = \begin{cases} 0, & \text{if } x \le 0 \\ x, & \text{if } x \ge 0 \end{cases}$$

Then, find the composite function $hofog$ and determine whether the function fog is invertible and h is the identity function.

Sets, Relations and Functions Exercise 8 :
Questions Asked in Previous 13 Year's Exam

- This section contains questions asked in **IIT-JEE, AIEEE, JEE Main & JEE Advanced** from year **2005** to year **2017**.

75. Let $R = \{(3, 3), (6, 6), (9, 9), (12, 12), (6, 12), (3, 9)\}$ be a relation on the set $A = \{3, 6, 9, 12\}$.
The relation is **[AIEEE 2005, 3M]**

(a) an equivalence relation
(b) reflexive and symmetric only
(c) reflexive and transitive only
(d) reflexive only

76. Let W denotes the words in the English dictionary. Define the relation R by $R = \{(x, y) \in W \times W\}$ the words x and y have atleast one letter in common, then R is **[AIEEE 2006, 3M]**

(a) not reflexive, symmetric and transitive
(b) reflexive, symmetric and not transitive
(c) reflexive, symmetric and transitive
(d) reflexive, not symmetric and transitive

77. Let R be the real line, consider the following subsets of the plane $R \times R$ such that **[AIEEE 2008, 3M]**

$S = \{(x, y) : y = x + 1 \text{ and } 0 < x < 2\}$

$T = \{(x, y) : x - y \text{ is an integer}\}$.

Which one of the following is true?

(a) Both S and T are equivalence relations on R
(b) S is an equivalence relation on R but T is not
(c) T is an equivalence relation on R but S is not
(d) Neither S nor T is an equivalence relations on R

78. If A, B and C are three sets such that $A \cap B = A \cap C$ and $A \cup B = A \cup C$, then **[AIEEE 2009, 4M]**

(a) $A \cap B = \phi$ (b) $A = B$
(c) $A = C$ (d) $B = C$

79. Let $S = \{1, 2, 3, 4\}$. The total number of unordered pair of disjoint subsets of S is equal to **[IIT-JEE 2010, 5M]**

(a) 25 (b) 34 (c) 42 (d) 41

80. Consider the following relations.

$R = \{(x, y) \mid x, y$ are real numbers and $x = wy$ for some rational number $w\}$

$S = \left\{\left(\frac{m}{n}, \frac{p}{q}\right) \middle| m, n, p \text{ and } q \text{ are integers such that } n, q \ne 0 \text{ and } qm = pn\right\}$, then **[AIEEE 2010, 4M]**

(a) neither R nor S is an equivalence relation
(b) S is an equivalence relation but R is not an equivalence relation
(c) R and S both are equivalence relations
(d) R is an equivalence relation but S is not an equivalence relation

81. Let $P = \{\theta : \sin\theta - \cos\theta = \sqrt{2}\cos\theta\}$ and $Q = \{\theta : \sin\theta + \cos\theta = \sqrt{2}\sin\theta\}$ be two sets. Then, **[IIT-JEE 2011, 3M]**

(a) $P \subset Q$ and $A - P \ne \phi$ (b) $Q \not\subset P$
(c) $P \not\subset Q$ (d) $P = Q$

82. Let $f(x) = x^2$ and $g(x) = \sin x$ for all $x \in R$. Then, the set of all x satisfying $(fogogof)(x) = (gogof)(x)$, where $(fog)(x) = f(g(x))$ is **[IIT-JEE 2011, 3M]**

(a) $\pm\sqrt{n\pi}, n \in \{0, 1, 2, \ldots\}$
(b) $\pm\sqrt{n\pi}, n \in \{1, 2, 3, \ldots\}$
(c) $\frac{\pi}{2} + 2n\pi, n \in \{\ldots, -2, -1, 0, 1, 2, \ldots\}$
(d) $2n\pi, n \in \{\ldots, -2, -1, 0, 1, 2, \ldots\}$

83. Let R be the set of real numbers.

Statement-1 $A = \{(x, y) \in R \times R : y - x \text{ is an integer}\}$ is an equivalence relation on R.

Statement-2 $B = \{(x, y) \in R \times R : x = \alpha y \text{ for some rational number } \alpha\}$ is an equivalence relation on R. **[AIEEE 2011, 4M]**

(a) Statement-1 is true, Statement-2 is true; Statement-2 is not a correct explanation for Statement-1
(b) Statement-1 is true, Statement-2 is false
(c) Statement-1 is false, Statement-2 is true
(d) Statement-1 is true, Statement-2 is true; Statement-2 is a correct explanation for Statement-1

84. Let A and B be two sets containing 2 elements and 4 elements, respectively. The number of subsets of $A \times B$ having 3 or more elements, is **[JEE Main 2013, 4M]**
(a) 220 (b) 219 (c) 211 (d) 256

85. If $X = \{4^n - 3n - 1 : n \in N\}$ and $Y = \{9(n-1) : n = N\}$, where N is the set of natural numbers, then $X \cup Y$ is equal to **[JEE Main 2014, 4M]**
(a) X (b) Y (c) N (d) $Y - X$

86. Let A and B be two sets containing four and two elements, respectively. Then, the number of subsets of the set $A \times B$, each having atleast three elements is **[JEE Main 2015, 4M]**
(a) 275 (b) 510 (c) 219 (d) 256

Answers

Exercise for Session 1

1. (b) 2. (d) 3. (c) 4. (b) 5. (a) 6. (c)
7. (d) 8. (c) 9. (a) 10. (c) 11. (d)

Exercise for Session 2

1. (c) 2. (b) 3. (b) 4. (c) 5. (c) 6. (c)
7. (b) 8. (a) 9. (a) 10. (c)

Exercise for Session 3

1. (b) 2. (c) 3. (b) 4. (b) 5. (b) 6. (b)
7. (d) 8. (b) 9. (b) 10. (a)

Chapter Exerises

1. (a) 2. (a) 3. (a) 4. (d) 5. (a) 6. (c)
7. (b) 8. (c) 9. (b) 10. (d) 11. (c) 12. (b)
13. (c) 14. (d) 15. (b) 16. (c) 17. (b) 18. (d)
19. (c) 20. (d) 21. (c) 22. (b) 23. (d) 24. (b)
25. (d) 26. (b) 27. (b) 28. (a) 29. (c) 30. (b)
31. (b) 32. (d) 33. (c) 34. (d) 35. (a) 36. (d)
37. (c) 38. (d) 39. (d) 40. (a,b,c,d) 41. (a,b,c)
42. (c,d) 43. (b) 44. (a) 45. (d) 46. (a) 47. (b)
48. (a) 49. (5) 50. (1) 51. (3) 52. (2) 53. (9)
54. (A) → (r); (B) → (q); (C) → (p); (D) → (s)
55. (A) → (s); (B) → (r); (C) → (p); (D) → (q)
56. (b) 57. (c) 58. (c) 59. (a)
60. (i) B (ii) C (iii) $\{2\}$ (iv) $\{x : x$ is an odd prime, natural number$\}$
61. (i) $S \cap W$ (ii) $T' \cap W'$ (iii) $(M \cup T \cup S)'$
62. $X \cup Y = \{(x, y) : x^2 + y^2 \le 1$ or $0 \le x \le 1$ and $-1 \le y \le 1\}$
$X \cap Y = \{(x, y) : x^2 + y^2 \le 1$ and $x \ge 0\}$
63. 5, 2, 12, 60 64. 43 65. 20 66. 45, 110
67. 44
70. (i) Not reflexive, symmetric, not transitive
(ii) Reflexive, symmetric, transitive
(iii) Reflexive, not symmetric, transitive
(iv) Reflexive, symmetric, not transitive
(v) Not reflexive, not symmetric, transitive
71. (i) Injective (ii) Injective
(iii) Bijective (iv) Not injective
(v) Surjective
72. $(fog)x = e^{3x-2}$; $x \in R$ $(gof)x = 3e^x - 2$; $x \in R$
Domain of $(fog)^{-1}(x) = (0, \infty)$.
Domain of $(gof)^{-1}(x) = (-2, \infty)$.
73. $\dfrac{3}{(1-x)^2}$, $R - \{1\}$
$\dfrac{df^{-1}(x)}{dx} = \dfrac{3}{(1-x)^2}$, Domain of $\dfrac{df^{-1}(x)}{dx} = R - \{1\}$
74. $(hofog)\,x = \begin{cases} 0, & x^2 \le 0 \\ x^2, & x^2 \ge 0 \end{cases}$, h is not an identity function and fog is not invertible.
75. (c) 76. (b) 77. (c) 78. (d) 79. (d) 80. (b)
81. (d) 82. (a) 83. (a) 84. (b) 85. (b) 86. (c)

Solutions

1. By Venn diagram,

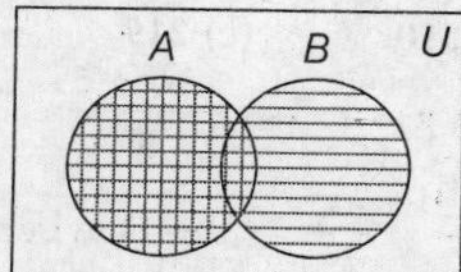

It is clear that $A \cap (A \cup B) = A$

2.

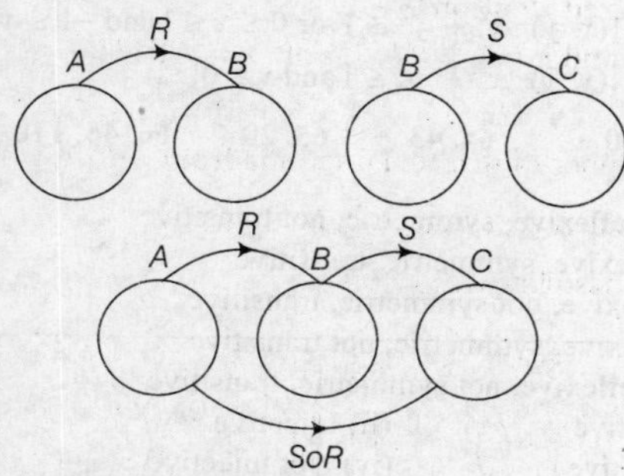

SoR is the relation from A to C.

3. $R = \{(1, 3), (2, 2), (3, 2)\}$

$S = \{(2, 1), (3, 2), (2, 3)\}$

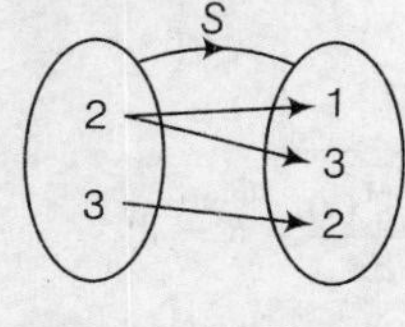

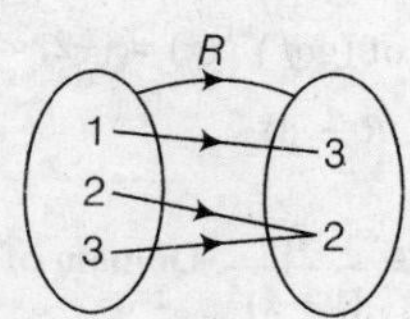

$$RoS = \{(2, 3), (2, 2), (3, 2)\}$$

4. $X \cap (Y \cap X)' = X \cap (Y' \cup X')$

$= (X \cap Y') \cup (X \cap X')$

$= (X \cap Y') \cup \phi = X \cap Y'$

$= X - (X \cap Y)$

5. $xRy \Leftrightarrow (x - y + \sqrt{2})$ is an irrational number.

Let $(x, x) \in R$.

Then, $x - x + \sqrt{2} = \sqrt{2}$ which is an irrational number.

$\therefore \quad x \, R \, x, \forall \, x \in R$

$\therefore$ R is an reflexive relation.

$x \, R \, y \Rightarrow (x - y + \sqrt{2})$ is an irrational number.

$\Rightarrow -(y - x - \sqrt{2})$ is an irrational number.

$\Rightarrow (y - x - \sqrt{2})$ is an irrational number.

$y \, R \, x \Rightarrow (y - x + \sqrt{2})$ is an irrational number.

So, $xRy \not\Rightarrow yRx \therefore R$ is not a symmetric relation.

Let $(1, 2) \in R$, then $(1 - 2 + \sqrt{2})$ is an irrational number.

$\Rightarrow \quad (\sqrt{2} - 1)$ is an irrational number.

and $(2, 3) \in R$, then $(2 \; - 3 + \sqrt{2})$ is an irrational number.

$\Rightarrow \quad (\sqrt{2} - 1)$ is an irrational number.

$(1, 3) \in R \Rightarrow (1 - 3 + \sqrt{2})$ is an irrational number.

$\Rightarrow \quad (\sqrt{2} - 2)$ is an irrational number.

So, $(1, 2) \in R$ and $(2, 3) \in R \not\Rightarrow (1, 3) \in R$ (by any way)

$\therefore$ R is not transitive relation.

6. $f(x) = (x + 1)^2 - 1$ [$\because x \geq 1$

$= x^2 + 1 + 2x - 1 = x^2 + 2x$

$S = \{x : f(x) \equiv f^{-1}(x)\}$

S is the set of point of intersection of $(y = x)$ and tf.

Now, solve $\quad y = x$ and $f(x) = x^2 + 2x$

$x^2 + 2x = x$

$x^2 + x = 0$

$x(x + 1) = 0$

$x = 0$ or $x = -1$

7. Let set A contains n elements.

Power set of A is the set of all subsets.

$\therefore$ Number of subsets of $A = {}^nC_o + {}^nC_1 + {}^nC_2 + \dots + {}^nC_n = 2^n$

$\therefore$ Power set of A contains 2^n elements.

8. By Venn diagram, it is clear that

$A - B \subseteq A$ and $B' - A' \subseteq A$ and $A \cap B' \subseteq A$

but $A \not\subseteq A - B$

9. $A = \{1, 2, 3\}$

$B = \{3, 8\}$

$A \cup B = \{1, 2, 3, 8\}$

$A \cap B = \{3\}$

$(A \cup B) \times (A \cap B) = \{1, 2, 3, 8\} \times \{3\}$

$= \{(1, 3), (2, 3), (3, 3) \; (8, 3)\}$

10. $A = \{p, q, r\}$

$R_1 = \{(p, q), (q, r), (p, r), (p, p)\}$

$(q, q) \notin R_1$, so R_1 is not reflexive relation.

So, R_1 is not an equivalence relation.

$R_2 = \{(r, q), (r, p), (r, r), (q, q)\}$

Here, $(p, p) \notin R_2$, so R_2 is not reflexive relation.

So, R_2 is not an equivalence relation.

$R_3 = \{(p, p), (q, q), (r, r), (p, q)\}$

R_3 is an reflexive relation.

$(p, a) \in R_3$ but $(q, p) \notin R_3$

R_3 is not symmetric relation.

So, R_3 is not equivalence relation.

11. $A = \{x : x$ is a multiple of $3\}$

$A = \{x : x = 3m, m \in N\}$

$B = \{x : x$ is a multiple of $5\}$

$B = \{x : x = 5n, n \in N\}$

$A \cap B = \{x : x$ is a multiple of both 3 and $5\}$

$= \{15, 30, 45, \dots\}$

12. $A = \{1, 2, 3\}, B = \{3, 4\}, C = \{4, 5, 6\}$

$\Rightarrow \quad B \cap C = \{4\}$

and $A \cup (B \cap C) = \{1, 2, 3, 4\}$

13. $A = \{x, y, z\}, B = \{u, v, w\}$

Now, $f : A \to B$

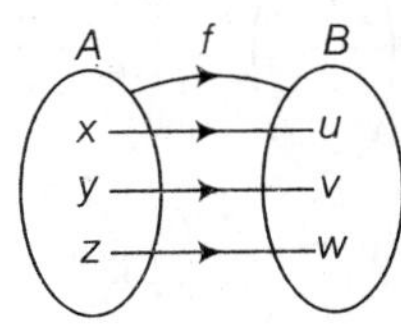

f is one-one and f is onto.

14.
$$A = \{2, 4\}$$
$$B = \{3, 4, 5\}$$
$$A \cap B = \{4\}$$
$$A \cup B = \{2, 3, 4, 5\}$$
$$(A \cap B) \times (A \cup B) = \{(4, 2), (4, 3), (4, 4), (4, 5)\}$$

15. $X = \{a, b, c, d\}$

$$R_1 = \{(b, a), (a, b), (c, d), (a, c)\}$$
$$(a, b) \in R_1 \text{ and } (a, c) \in R,$$

$\therefore R_1$ is not a function.

$$R_2 = \{(a, d), (d, c), (b, b), (c, c)\}$$

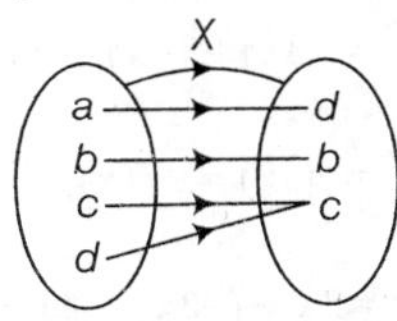

Hence, R_2 is a function.

16. $f : R \to R$

$\Rightarrow \quad f(x) = \sin x$ and $g : R \to R$

$\Rightarrow \quad g(x) = x^2$

Range of g is $R^+ \cup \{0\}$, which is the subset of domain of f.

$\therefore$ Composition of fog is possible.

$$fog = f(g(x)) = f(x^2)$$
$$= \sin x^2$$

17. $x^2 - 1 = 0$

$\Rightarrow \quad x = -1, 1$

$\therefore$ x is real, q $\quad x^2 + 1 = 0$

$\Rightarrow \quad x = \pm i$

$\therefore$ x is not real, $\quad x^2 - 9 = 0$

$\Rightarrow \quad x = \pm 3$

$\therefore$ x is real $\quad x^2 - x - 2 = 0$

$\Rightarrow \quad x = 2, -1$

$\therefore$ x is real.

18. By definition for equivalent relation.

R should be reflexive, symmetric, transitive.

19. $\because$ x - coordinates of two brackets are same.

20. $\frac{n}{m}$ means that n is a factor of m.

So, f is reflexive.

$\because$ A number is a factor of itself.

Now, if n is a factor of m, then m is not a factor of n

$\therefore$ f is not symmetric. Let n is a factor of m and m is a factor of s, then it is true that n is a factor of s.

$\therefore$ f is transitive.

21. $\lambda = \frac{8x - 6}{14}$, where $\lambda \in I_+$

$\therefore \quad 8x = 14\lambda + 6 \Rightarrow x = \frac{14\lambda + 6}{8}$

$\Rightarrow \quad x = \frac{7\lambda + 3}{4} = \lambda + \frac{3}{4}(\lambda + 1)$, when $\lambda \in I$

and here greatest common divisor of 8 and 14 is 2, so there are two required solutions.

for $\lambda = 3$ and $\lambda = 7$, $x = 6, 13$ or $x = [6][13]$

22. $n(A) = 10$

Total number of distinc Functions from A to $A = 10^{10}$.

23. $A \subseteq X$ and $B \subseteq X$ and $A \subseteq B$

In all 3 possible cases,

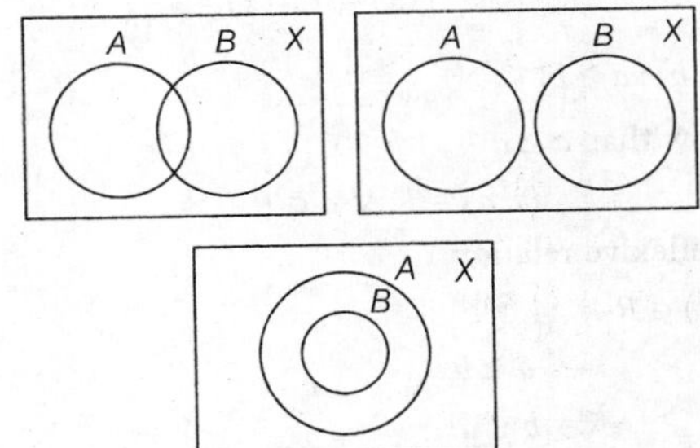

24. $A = \{a, b, c, d\}$

$B = \{s, t, u\}$

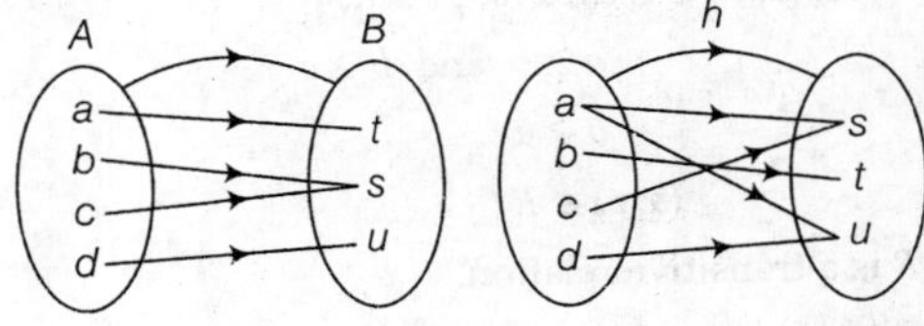

It is clear that f is a function.

But in relation h, a have h image s and u.

So, h is not a function.

25. $f(x) = x^2, x \in Z$

$$f(1) = 1$$
$$f(-1) = 1$$

$\therefore$ f is not one-one

Range of f is set of whole number.

Which is a subset of Z.

$\therefore f$ is not onto.

26. It is obvious.

27. $A = \{1, 2, ..., n\}\ n \geq 2$

$B = \{a, b\}$

Number of into functions from A to $B = 2$

Total Numer of functions from A to $B = [n(B)]^{n(A)} = 2^n$

$\therefore$ Total Number of onto functions from A to $B = 2^n - 2$

28. $f : R \rightarrow R$

$\Rightarrow \quad f(x) = 3x - 4$

f is one-one onto function.

$\therefore$ Let $\quad y = 3x - 4$

$$x = \frac{y+4}{3}$$

Replace x by $y \Rightarrow y = \dfrac{x+4}{3} = f^{-1}(x)$

29. $f : R \rightarrow R$

$\Rightarrow \quad f(x) = 10x - 7$

It is clear that f is one-one and onto.

$\therefore$ Let $\quad y = 10x - 7$

$\therefore \quad x = \dfrac{y+7}{10} = f^{-1}(y)$

$$g(x) = f^{-1}(x) = \frac{x+7}{10}$$

30. $R = \{(a, b) : a \geq b\}$

We know that, $a \geq a$

$\therefore \quad (a, a) \in R, \forall\, a \in R$

R is a reflexive relation.

Let $(a, b) \in R$

$\Rightarrow \quad a \geq b$

$\not\Rightarrow \quad b \leq a$

$\not\Rightarrow \quad (b, a) \in R$

So, R is not symmetric relation.

Now, let $(a, b) \in R$ and $(b, c) \in R$.

$\Rightarrow \quad a \geq b$ and $b \geq c$

$\Rightarrow \quad a \geq c$

$\Rightarrow \quad (a, c) \in R$

$\therefore$ R is a transitive relation.

31. $A = \{(x, y) : y = e^x, x \in R\}$

$B = \{(x, y) : y = x, x \in R\}$

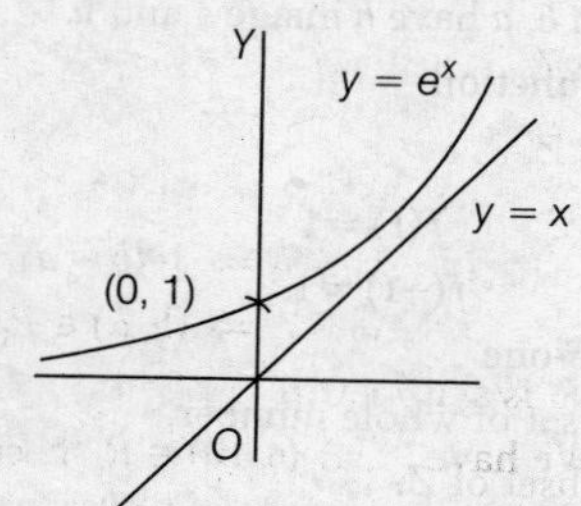

$\therefore \quad A \subset B$

32. $f : A \rightarrow B$

f is a function, then f^{-1} is also a bijective function.

Composite function $(f^{-1} of) = I_A$

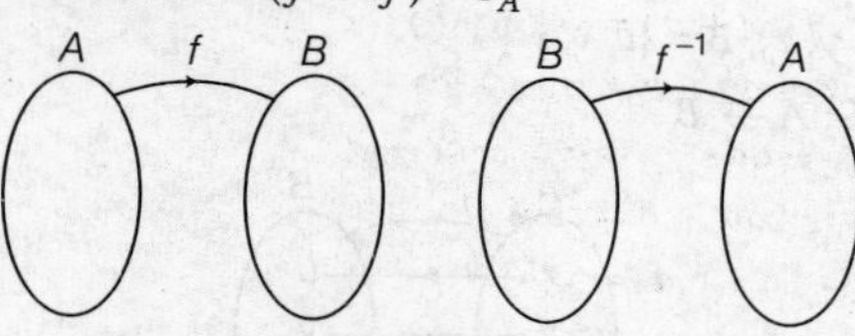

33. $f(y) = \dfrac{y}{\sqrt{(1-y^2)}}, g(y) = \dfrac{y}{\sqrt{(1+y^2)}}$

and $\quad (fog)y = f(g(y)) = f\left(\dfrac{y}{\sqrt{(1+y^2)}}\right)$

$$= \frac{\dfrac{y}{\sqrt{(1+y^2)}}}{\sqrt{1 - \dfrac{y^2}{(1+y^2)}}} = \frac{\dfrac{y}{\sqrt{(1+y^2)}}}{\dfrac{1}{\sqrt{(1+y^2)}}} = y$$

34. $f : R \rightarrow R$

$$f(x) = 2x + |x|$$

When $x \geq 0$, then $f(x) = 2x + x = 3x$

When $x < 0$, then $f(x) = 2x - x = x$

Now, when $x \geq 0$

$f(3x) - f(-x) - 4x = 3(3x) - (-x) - 4x = 9x + x - 4x$

$= 6x \qquad [\because x \geq 0]$

$= 2(3x) = 2f(x) \qquad [\therefore -x \leq 0]$

When $x < 0$,

$f(3x) - f(-x) - 4x = 3x - (-3x) - 4x = 2x = 2f(x)$

35. Let $A = \{1, 2, 3\}, R = \{(1, 1)\ (1, 2)\}$

and $S = \{(2, 2), (2, 3)\}$

be the transitive relation on A.

Then, $R \cup S = \{(1, 1,)\ (1, 2)(2, 2)\ (2, 3)\}$

$R \cup S$ is not transitive, because $(1, 2) \in R \cup S$ and $(2, 3) \in R \cup S$ but $(1, 3) \notin R \cup S$.

36. $f : R \rightarrow R$

$g : R \rightarrow R$

$f(x) = 2x - 3$

$g(x) = x^3 + 5$

$\Rightarrow \quad (fog)(x) = f(g(x)) = f(x^3 + 5) = 2(x^3 + 5) - 3$

$= 2x^3 + 7$

Now, $\quad$ let $y = 2x^3 + 7$

$2x^3 = y - 7$

$$x = \left(\frac{y-7}{2}\right)^{1/3}$$

Replacing x by y, we get

$$y = \left(\frac{x-7}{2}\right)^{1/3}$$

$$\therefore \quad (fog)^{-1}(x) = \left(\frac{x-7}{2}\right)^{1/3}$$

37.
$$f(x) = ax + b$$
$$g(x) = cx + d$$
$$f(g(x)) = g(f(x))$$
$$f(cx + d) = g(ax + b)$$
$$a(cx + d) + b = c(ax + b) + d$$
$$acx + ad + b = acx + bc + d$$
$$ad + b = cb + d$$
$$f(d) = g(b)$$

38. $f : R \to R, g : R \to R$

$f(x) = 2 \min f(x) - g(x), 0)$

Let $f(x) - g(x) > 0$, then

$F(x) = f(x) - g(x) - |f(x) - g(x)|$ and $f(x) - g(x) < 0$, then

$F(x) = 2[f(x) - g(x)] = [f(x) - g(x)] - |f(x) - g(x)|$

39. $f : R \to R$ and $g : R \to R$ such that f is injective and $+g$ is surjective.

Then, g may be one-one or many-one.

If g is one-one, then gof is one-one.

fog is one-one

gog is one-one

But if g is many-one, then *gof* is not one-one.

fog is not one-one.

gog is many-one

Now, *fof* is one-one

40. Relation R on the set of all straight lines in the plane is of parallel line.

A line is parallel to itself. So, R is reflexive.

If l_1 is parallel to l_2, then l_2 is parallel to l_1.

$\therefore R$ is symmetric relation. $[l_1, l_2 \in L]$

Let $l_1, l_2, l_3 \in L$

l_1 is parallel to l_2 and l_2 is parallel to l_3.

Then, l_1 is parallel to l_3.

$\therefore R$ is transitive relation.

So, R is equivalence relation.

41. $X = \{1, 2, 3, 4, 5\}$

$Y = \{1, 3, 5, 7, 9\}$

(a) $R_1 = \{(x, y) : y = 2 + x, x \in X, y \in Y\}$

$x = 1 \quad y = 2$

$x = 2 \quad y = 4$

$x = 3 \quad y = 5$

$x = 4 \quad y = 6$

$x = 5 \quad y = 7$

So, R_1 is a relation from X to Y.

(b) $R_2 = \{(1, 1), (2, 1), (3, 3) (4, 3), (5, 5)\}$

$R_2 \subseteq X \times Y$

(c) $R_3 = \{(1, 1), (1, 3), (3, 5) (5, 7)\}$

$R_3 \subseteq X \times Y$

(d) $R_4 \not\subseteq X \times Y$

42. $f : R - \{-b\} \to R - \{1\}$

$$f(x) = \frac{x + a}{x + b} \quad [a \neq b]$$

Let $x_1, x_2 \in D_f$

$$f(x_1) = f(x_2)$$

$$\Rightarrow \frac{x_1 + a}{x_1 + b} = \frac{x_2 + a}{x_2 + b}$$

$$\Rightarrow x_1x_2 + bx_1 + ax_2 + ab = x_1x_2 + ax_1 + bx_2 + ab$$

$$\Rightarrow b(x_1 - x_2) = a(x_1 - x_2)$$

$$\Rightarrow (x_1 - x_2)(b - a) = 0$$

$$\Rightarrow x_1 = x_2 \quad [\because a \neq b]$$

$\therefore f$ is one-one function.

Now, let $y = \dfrac{x + a}{x + b}$

$$xy + by = x + a$$
$$x(y - 1) = a - by$$
$$x = \frac{a - by}{y - 1} \text{ and } f^{-1}(y) = \frac{a - by}{y - 1}$$

$\because \quad y \in R - \{1\}$

$\therefore \quad x$ is defined, $\forall y \in R - \{1\}$

$$f^{-1}(2) = \frac{a - 2b}{2 - 1} = a - 2b$$

Sol. (Q. Nos. 43 to 45)

43. $(gof)(0) = g(f(0)) = g(7(0)^2 + 0 - 8)$

$= g(-8) = |-8| = 8$

and $(fog)(-3) = f(g(-3)) = f(0) = 7(0)^2 + 0 - 8 = -8$

$\therefore (gof)(0) + (fog)(-3) = -8 + 8 = 0$

44. $(fog)(7) = f(g(7)) = f(7^2 + 4) = f(53)$

$= 8(53) + 3 = 427$

and $(gof)(6) = g(f(6)) = g(4 \times 6 + 5) + g(29)$

$= (29)^2 + 4 = 845$

$\therefore 2(fog)(7) - (gof)(6) = 2 \times 427 - 845 = 9$

45. $(gof)(2) = g(f(2)) = g(4 \times 2 + 5) = g(13)$

$= (13)^2 + 4 = 173$

and $(fog)(g) = f(g(9)) = f(9^2 + 4) = f(85)$

$= 8 \times 85 + 3 = 683$

$\therefore 4(gof)(2) - (fog)(9) = 4 \times 173 - 683 = 9$

Sol. (Q. Nos. 46-48)

46. We have, $(a, b) \in R_1$ iff $|a - b| \leq 7$, where $a, b \in z$

Reflexivity Let $a \in z$

$\Rightarrow \quad a - a = 0$

$\Rightarrow \quad |a - a| \leq 7$

$\Rightarrow \quad 0 \leq 7$

$\Rightarrow \quad (a, a) \in R_1$

$\therefore$ The relation R_1 is reflexive.

Symmetry

$(a, b) \in R_1$

$\Rightarrow \quad |a - b| \leq 7 \Rightarrow |-(b - a)| \leq 7$

$\Rightarrow \quad |b - a| \leq 7 \Rightarrow (b, a) \in R_1$

$\therefore$ The relation R_1 is symmetric.

Transitivity We have $(2, 6), (6, 10) \in R_1$ because

$|2 - 6| = 4 \leq 7$ and $|6 - 10| = 4 \leq 7$

Also, $|2 - 10| = 8 \not\leq 7$

$\therefore \quad (2, 10) \notin R_1$

Hence, the relation R_1 is not transitive.

47. We have $(a, b) \in R_2$ iff $ab = 4$, where $a, b \in Q$

Reflexivity $5 \in Q$ and $(5)(5) = 25 \neq 4$

$\therefore \quad (5, 5) \notin R_2$

The relation R_2 is not reflexive.

Symmetry

$$(a, b) \in R_2$$

$\Rightarrow \quad ab = 4 \Rightarrow ba = 4$

$\Rightarrow \quad (b, a) \in R_2$

$\therefore$ The relation R_2 is symmetric.

Transitivity We have $\left(8, \frac{1}{2}\right), \left(\frac{1}{2}, 8\right) \in R_2$ because

$$8\left(\frac{1}{2}\right) = 4 \text{ and } \left(\frac{1}{2}\right)(8) = 4$$

Also, $\quad 8(8) = 64 \neq 4$

$\therefore \quad (8, 8) \notin R_2$

$\therefore$ The relation R_2 is not transitive.

48. We have, $(a, b) \in R_3$ iff $a^2 - 4ab + 3b^2 = 0$ where $a, b \in R$

Reflexivity

$\therefore \quad a^2 - 4a \cdot a + 3d^2 = 4a^2 - 4a^2 = 0$

$\therefore \quad (a, a) \in R_3$

$\therefore$ The relation R_3 is reflexive.

Symmetry

$$(a, b) \in R_3$$

$\Rightarrow \quad a^2 - 4ab + 3b^2 = 0$, we get $a = b$ and $a = 3b$

and $\quad (b, a) \in R_3$

$\Rightarrow \quad b^2 - 4ab + 3a^2 = 0$

we get $b = a$ and $b = 3a$

$\therefore \quad (a, b) \in R_3 \not\Rightarrow (b, a) \in R_3$

$\therefore$ The relation R_3 is not symmetric.

Transitivity We have $(3, 1), \left(1, \frac{1}{3}\right) \in R_3$

because $(3)^2 - 4(3)(1) + 3(1)^2 = 9 - 12 + 3 = 0$

and $\quad (1)^2 - 4(1)\left(\frac{1}{3}\right) + 3\left(\frac{1}{3}\right)^2 = 1 - \frac{4}{3} + \frac{1}{3} = 0$

Also, $\left(3, \frac{1}{3}\right) \notin R_3$, because

$$(3)^2 - 4 \cdot (3)\left(\frac{1}{3}\right) + 3\left(\frac{1}{3}\right)^2 = 9 - 4 + \frac{1}{3} = \frac{16}{3} \neq 0$$

$\therefore$ The relation R_3 is not transitive.

49. Given, $a = 22$,

$c = 12$

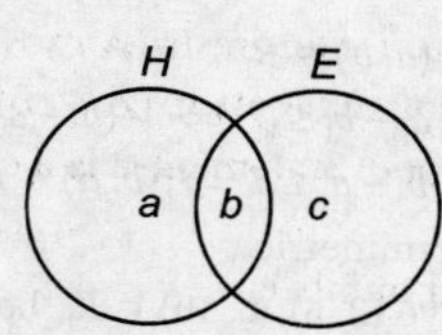

and $\quad a + b + c = 45$

$\Rightarrow \quad 22 + b + 12 = 45$

$\therefore \quad b = 11 = 2\lambda + 1$

$\Rightarrow \quad \lambda = 5$

50. $\therefore \quad \cos x > -\frac{1}{2}$ and $0 \leq x \leq \pi$

$\Rightarrow \quad -\frac{2\pi}{3} < x < \frac{2\pi}{3}$ and $0 \leq x \leq \pi$

$\Rightarrow \quad 0 \leq x < \frac{2\pi}{3}$

$\therefore \quad A = \left[0, \frac{2\pi}{3}\right]$

Again, $\quad \sin x > \frac{1}{2}$ and $\frac{\pi}{3} \leq x \leq \pi$

$\Rightarrow \quad \frac{\pi}{6} < x < \frac{5\pi}{6}$ and $\frac{\pi}{3} \leq x \leq \pi$

$\Rightarrow \quad \frac{\pi}{3} \leq x < \frac{5\pi}{6}$

$$B = \left[\frac{\pi}{3}, \frac{5\pi}{6}\right)$$

Now, $\quad A \cap B = \left[\frac{\pi}{3}, \frac{2\pi}{3}\right)$

$$\frac{\pi}{3} \leq A \cap B < \frac{2\pi}{3}$$

Here $\quad \lambda = \frac{1}{3}$ and $\mu = \frac{2}{3}$

$$\lambda + \mu = 1$$

51. Here, $A = [-3, 7), B = (0, 10)$

and $\quad S = (-\infty, \infty)$

$\therefore \quad A - B = [-3, 0]$ and $B - A = [7, 10)$

$\therefore \quad A \Delta B = (A - B) \cup (B - A) = [-3, 0] \cup [7, 10)$

$\therefore$ Positive integers are 7, 8, 9.

Number of positive integers = 3

52. As $2^m - 2^n = 48 = 16 \times 3 = 2^4 \times 3$

$\Rightarrow \quad 2^n(2^{m-n} - 1) = 2^4(2^2 - 1)$

$\therefore \quad n = 4$ and $m - n = 2$

$n = 4$ and $m = 6$

Now, $\quad m - n = 2$

53. $n((A \times B) \cap (B \times A)) = n((A \cap B) \times (B \cap A))$

$= n(A \cap B) \cdot n(B \cap A)$

$= n(A \cap B) \cdot n(A \cap B)$

$= 99 \times 99 = 121 \times 9^2$

$\therefore \quad \lambda = 9$

54. (A) $y = 7x + 1$

$$f(x) = 7x + 1$$

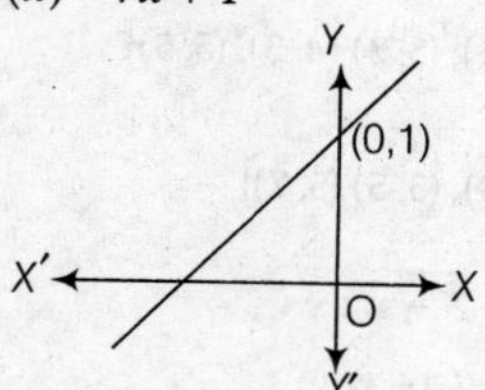

Let $\quad x_1, x_2 \in D_f$,

then $\quad f(x_1) = f(x_2)$

$\Rightarrow \quad 7x_1 + 1 = 7x_2 + 1 \Rightarrow x_1 = x_2$

f is one-one, $\quad \forall x \in R$

Now, $y = 7x + 1 \Rightarrow x = \frac{y-1}{7}$

for each $y \in R$, we get $x \in R$

f is onto function

(B) $y = \cos x$

for $x \in [0, \pi]$, $y \in [-1, 1]$

$\therefore f$ is one-one on $[0\ \pi]$,

$\forall\ x \in R, y \in [-1, 1]$

y is not onto R.

(C) $y = \sin x$ or $f(x) = \sin x$

for $x \in [0, \pi]$, $y \in [0, 1]$

$$f\left(\frac{\pi}{3}\right) = \frac{\sqrt{3}}{2} \text{ and } f\left(\frac{2\pi}{3}\right) = \frac{\sqrt{3}}{2}$$

$\therefore f$ is not one-one on $(0, \pi)$,

$\forall\ x \in R$ and $y \in [-1, 1]$

$\therefore f$ is onto $[-1, 1]$.

(D) $y = 1 + \ln x$ and $f(x) = 1 + \ln x$

y is defined for $x \in (0, \infty)$

Let $x_1, x_2 \in D_f$

then $f(x_1) = f(x_2)$

$\Rightarrow 1 + \ln x_1 = 1 + \ln x_2$

$\Rightarrow x_1 = x_2$

$\therefore$ f is one-one, $\forall\ x \in (0, \infty)$

55. **(A)** Let $y = \sqrt{3 - x} + \sin^{-1}\left(\frac{3 - 2x}{5}\right)$

For y to be defined $3 - x \geq 0$ on $-1 \leq \frac{3-2x}{5} \leq 1$

$x \leq 3$ ...(i)

$-5 \leq 3 - 2x \leq 5$

and $-1 \leq x \leq 4$ ...(ii)

From Eqs. (i) and (ii), we get

$x \in [-1, 3]$

(B) Let $y = \log_{10}\{1 - \log_{10}(x^2 - 5x + 16)\}$ for y to be defined

$x^2 - 5x + 16 > 0$ and $1 - \log_{10}(x^2 - 5x + 16) > 0$

$\left(x - \frac{5}{2}\right)^2 + \frac{39}{4} > 0$ and $\log_{10}(x^2 - 5x + 16) < 1$

which is true, $\forall\ x \in R$ ...(i)

$\Rightarrow x^2 - 5x + 16 < 10$

$\Rightarrow x^2 - 5x + 6 < 0 \Rightarrow (x-3)(x-2) < 0$

$\Rightarrow 2 < x < 3$ ...(ii)

From Eqs. (i) and (ii), $x \in (2, 3)$

(C) Let $y = \cos^{-1}\frac{2}{2 + \sin x}$, for y to be defined

$-1 \leq \frac{2}{2 + \sin x} \leq 1$ $\left[\begin{array}{l}\because -1 < \sin x \leq 1 \\ 1 < 2 + \sin x \leq 3\end{array}\right]$

Multiplying by $(2 + \sin x)$

$-(2 + \sin x) \leq 2 \leq 2 + \sin x$

$\Rightarrow -2 - \sin x \leq 2$ | $2 \leq 2 + \sin x$

$\Rightarrow -\sin x \leq 4$ | $\sin x \geq 0$

$\Rightarrow \sin x \geq -4$ | $2n\pi \leq x \leq (2n+1)\pi, n \in z$ ...(i)

We know that $\sin x \in [-1, 1]$

$\therefore$ $x \in R$ ... (ii)

From Eqs. (i) and (ii); $x \in [2k\pi, (2k+1)\pi]$

Domain $= \bigcup_{k \in I} [2k\pi, (2k + 1\pi)]$

(D) $y = \sqrt{\sin x} + \sqrt{16 - x^2}$ for y to be defined

$\sin x \geq 0$ | $16 - x^2 \geq 0$

$x \in [2k\pi, (2k+1)\pi], k \in I$ ...(i) | $-4 \leq x \leq 4$ ...(ii)

From Eqs. (i) and (ii), we get

$x \in [-4, -\pi] \cup [0, \pi]$

56. Let

$A = \{a_1, a_2, a_3, \ldots, a_n\}$

Then, the number of binary relations on $A = n^{(n \times n)} = n^{n^2}$

and number of relations form A to $A = 2^{n \times n} = 2^{n^2}$

Both statements are true but Statement-2 is not a correct explanation for Statement-1.

57. Let $\alpha \in (A \cap B) \Rightarrow \alpha \in A$ and $\alpha \in B$

$\Rightarrow g(\alpha) = 0$

and $f(\alpha) = 0$

$\Rightarrow \{f(\alpha)\}^2 + \{g(\alpha)\}^2 = 0$

$\Rightarrow \alpha$ is a root of $\{f(x)\}^2 + \{g(x)\}^2 = 0$

Hence, Statement-1 is true and Statement-2 is false.

58. Let $x \in P(A \cap B)$

$\Leftrightarrow x \subseteq (A \cap B)$

$\Leftrightarrow x \subseteq A$ and $x \subseteq B$

$\Leftrightarrow x \in P(A)$ and $x \in P(B)$

$\Leftrightarrow x \in P(A) \cap P(B)$

$\therefore P(A \cap B) \subseteq P(A) \cap P(B)$

and $P(A) \cap P(B) \subseteq P(A \cap B)$

Hence, $P(A) \cap P(B) = P(A \cap B)$

Now, consider sets $A = \{1\}, B = \{2\} \Rightarrow A \cup B = \{1, 2\}$

$\therefore P(A) = \{\phi, \{1\}\}, P(B) = \{\phi, \{2\}\}$.

and $P(A \cup B) = \{\phi\ \{1\}, \{2\}, \{1, 2\} \neq P(A) \cup P(B)\}$

Hence, Statement-1 is true and Statement-2 is false.

59. $n(A \cup B) = n(A) + n(B) - n(A \cap B)$

$= 3 + 6 - n(A \cap B) = 9 - n(A \cap B)$

As maximum number of element in $(A \cap B) = 3$

$\therefore$ Minimum number of elements in $(A \cap B) = 9 - 3 = 6$

Both statements are true; Statement-2 is a correct explanation for Statement-1.

60. $A = \{x : x$ is a natural number$\}$

$B = \{x : x$ is an even natural number$\}$

$C = \{x : x$ is an odd natural number$\}$

$D = \{x : x$ is a prime number$\}$

(i) $A \cap B = \{x : x = 2n, n \in N\} = B$
(ii) $A \cap C = \{x : x \text{ is an odd natural number}\} = C$
(iii) $B \cap D = \{x : x \text{ is prime natural number}\} = \{2\}$
(iv) $C \cap D = \{x : x \text{ is odd prime natural number}\}$

61. U = Set of all people
M = {Males}
S = {College students}
T = {Teenagers}
W = {People having height more than 5 feet}
(i) College students having heights more than 5 feet $= S \cap W$
(ii) People who are not teenagers and having their heights less than 5 feet $= T' \cap W'$
(iii) All people who are neither males nor teenagers nor college students $= (M \cup T \cup S)'$

62. $X = \{(x, y) : x^2 + y^2 \le 1\}$
$Y = \{(x, y) : 0 \le x \le 1, -1 \le y \le 1\}$
$X \cup Y = \{(x, y) : x^2 + y^2 \le 1 \text{ or } 0 \le x \le 1 \text{ and } -1 \le y \le 1\}$
$X \cap Y = \{(x, y) : x^2 + y^2 \le 1 \text{ and } x \ge 0\}$

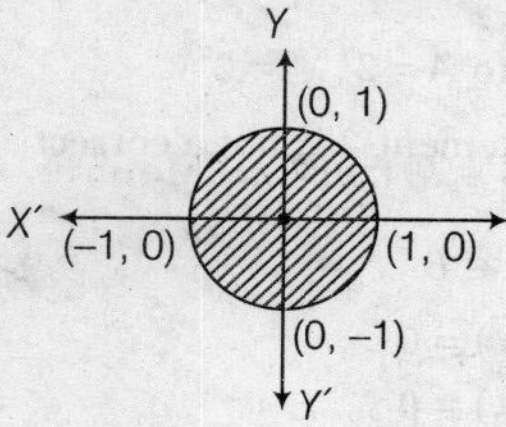

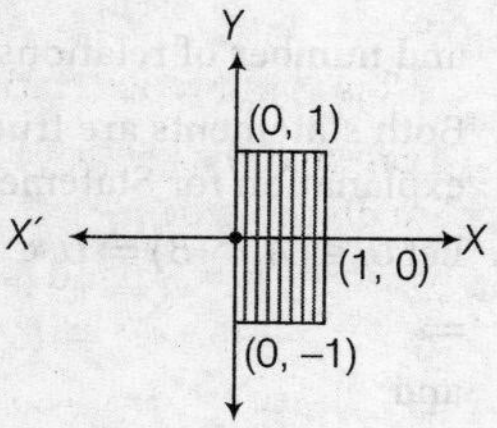

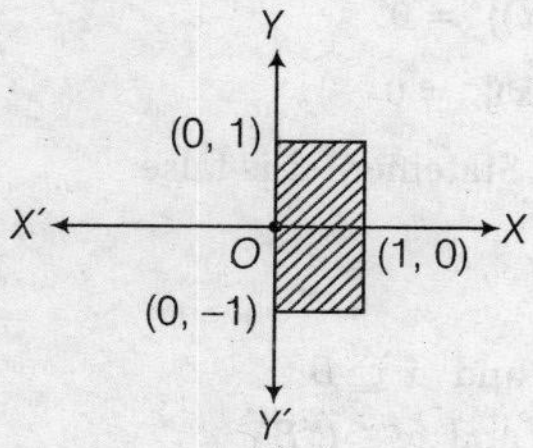

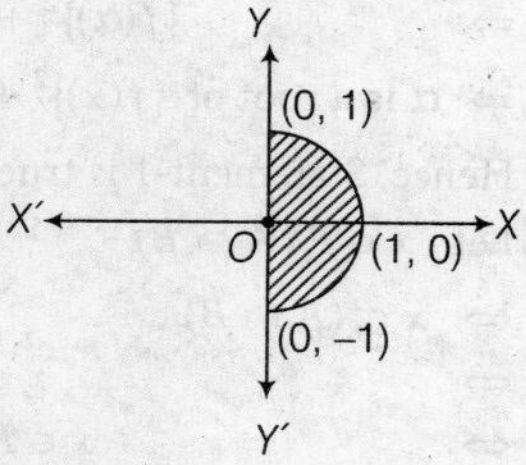

63. Given,
$$a = 20 \quad \text{...(i)}$$
$$e + f + g = 15 \quad \text{...(ii)}$$
$$b + d + f + g = 22 \quad \text{...(iii)}$$
$$c = 11 \quad \text{...(iv)}$$

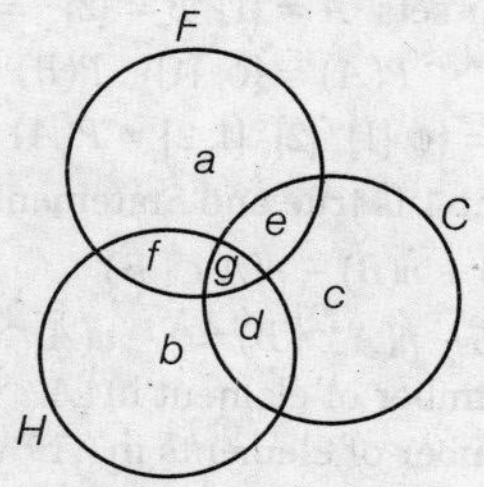

$$c + d + e + g = 25 \quad \text{...(v)}$$
$$\Rightarrow \quad d + e + g = 14 \quad \text{...(vi)}$$
$$e = 7 \quad \text{...(vii)}$$
$$f = 3 \quad \text{...(viii)}$$
From Eqs. (vii), (viii) and (ix),
$$e + g = 12 \quad \text{...(ix)}$$
$$e = 7, f = 3, g = 5$$

From Eq. (vi), $d = 2$
From Eq. (iii) $b + 2 + 3 + 5 = 22$
$\therefore \quad b = 12$
Hence, $\quad a = 20, b = 12, c = 11, d = 2, e = 7, f = 3, g = 5$
Number of children play all the three games $= g = 5$
Number of children play cricket and hockey but not football $= d = 2$
Number of children play hockey only $= b = 12$
Total number of children in the group
$= a + b + c + d + e + f + g = 60$

64. $a + f + e + g = 21$ ...(
$$b + d + f + g = 26 \quad \text{...(i}$$
$$c + d + e + g = 29 \quad \text{...(i}$$
$$f + g = 14 \quad \text{...(i}$$
$$g + d = 15 \quad \text{...(}$$
$$e + g = 12 \quad \text{...(v}$$
$$g = 8 \quad \text{...(v}$$

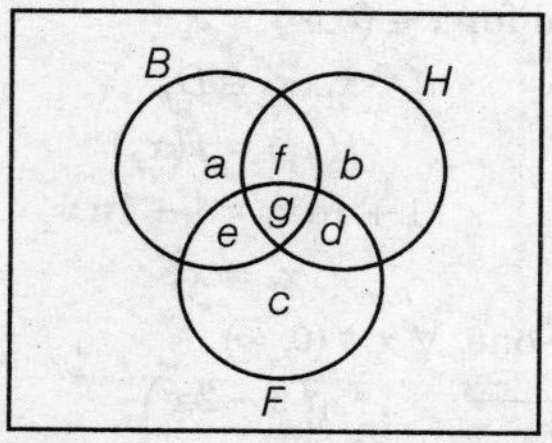

From Eqs. (vii) and (vi), $e = 4$
Form Eqs. (vii) and (v), $d = 7$
From Eqs. (vii) and (iv), $f = 6$
From Eq. (iii), $c + 7 + 4 + 8 = 29 \Rightarrow c = 29 - 19 = 10 = c$
From Eq. (ii), $b + 7 + 6 + 8 = 26 \Rightarrow b = 26 - 21 \Rightarrow b = 5$
From Eq. (i), $a + 6 + 4 + 8 = 21 \Rightarrow a = 21 - 18 \Rightarrow a = 3$
$$n(B) + n(H) + n(F) = a + b + c + d + e + f + g$$
$$= 3 + 5 + 10 + 7 + 4 + 6 + 8 = 43$$

65. $a + e + f + g = 120$ ...(i
$$b + d + f + g = 90 \quad \text{...(ii}$$
$$e + f + c + d = 70 \quad \text{...(iii}$$
$$g + f = 40 \quad \text{...(iv}$$
$$f + d = 30 \quad \text{...(v}$$
$$e + f = 50 \quad \text{...(vi}$$

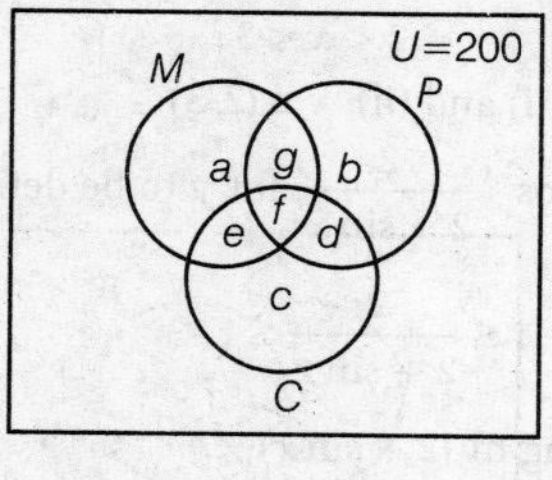

$$U - (a + b + c + d + e + f + g) = 20$$
$$\Rightarrow \quad a + b + c + d + e + f + g = 180 \quad \text{...(vii}$$
From Eqs. (i) and (iv), $\quad a + e = 80$ ...(viii
From Eqs. (ii) and (iv), $\quad b + d = 50$ ...(ix

From Eqs. (iii) and (v), $e + c = 40$ ...(x)

from Eqs (viii), (ix) & (x), $a + b + c + d + e + e = 197$ ...(xi)

from (xi), (vii) and (iv), $197 - e + 40 = 180$

$$170 - e + 40 = 180$$

$$e = 210 - 180 = 30$$

From Eq. (vi), $e + f = 50$

$\Rightarrow$ $30 + f = 50$

$\Rightarrow$ $f = 20$

66. $b + e + f + g = 205$ ...(i)

$a + d + f + g = 210$ ...(ii)

$c + d + e + g = 120$ ...(iii)

$f + g = 100$ ...(iv)

$e + g = 800$ ...(v)

$d + g = 35$ ... (vi)

$g = 20$ ...(vii)

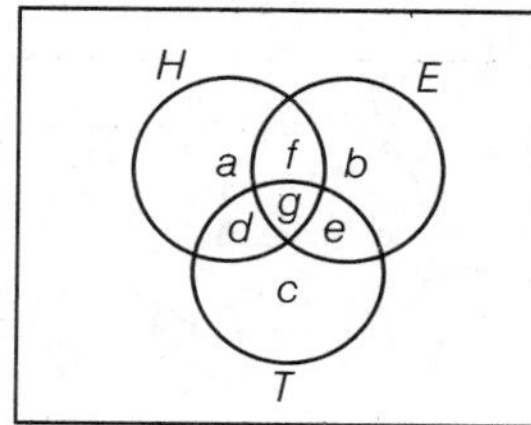

From Eqs. (vi) and (vii), $d = 15$

From Eqs. (vii) and (v), $e = 60$

From Eqs. (vii) and (iv), $f = 80$

From Eq. (i), $b + 60 + 80 + 20 = 205 \Rightarrow b = 205 - 160$

$\Rightarrow b = 45$ = Can speak English but not Hindi or Tamil.

From Eq. (ii) $a + 15 + 80 + 20 = 210$

$\Rightarrow$ $a + 115 = 210 \Rightarrow a = 95$

From Eq. (iii), $c + 15 + 60 + 20 = 120$

$\Rightarrow$ $c = 120 - 95 \Rightarrow c = 25$

People who can speak neither E nor H nor T

$= 450 - (95 + 45 + 25 + 15 + 60 + 80 + 20)$

$= 450 - 340 = 110$

67. $c + f + g + e = 42$ ...(i)

$b + d + g + e = 36$ ...(ii)

$a + f + d + g = 30$ ...(iii)

$g + e = 15$ ...(iv)

$f + g = 10$ ...(v)

$d = 4$ ...(vi)

$e = 11$ ...(vii)

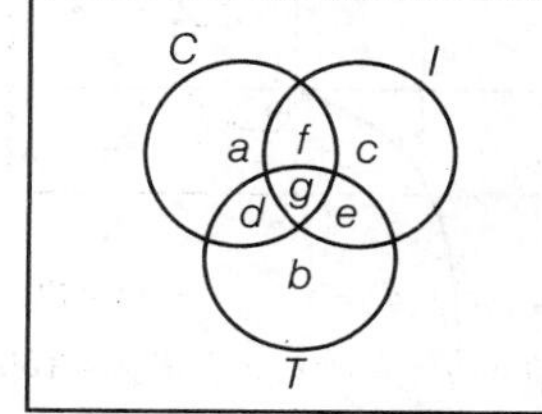

From (iv) and (vii), $g + 11 = 15 \Rightarrow g = 4$ ...(viii)

From (v) and (viii), $f + 4 = 10 \Rightarrow f = 6$ ...(ix)

From (i), $c + 6 + 4 + 11 = 42 \Rightarrow c = 21$ ...(x)

From (ii), $b + 4 + 4 + 11 = 36 \Rightarrow b = 17$ ...(xi)

From (iii), $a + 6 + 4 + 4 = 30 \Rightarrow a = 16$ ...(xii)

Number of required persons

$= 123 - (16 + 17 + 21 + 4 + 11 + 6 + 4)$

$= 123 - 79$

$= 44$

68. aRb iff $n \mid (a - b)$ i.e. $(a - b)$ is divisible by n.

Reflexivity $a - a = 0$ which is divisible by n.

So, $(a, a) \in R, \forall a \in I$

$\therefore$ R is reflexive relation.

Symmetry Let $(a, b) \in R$

Then, $(a, b) \in R \Rightarrow (a - b)$ is divisible by n.

$\Rightarrow$ $-(b - a)$ is divisible by n.

$\Rightarrow$ $(b - a)$ is divisible by n.

$\Rightarrow$ $(b, a) \in R$

$\therefore$ R is symmetric relation.

Transitivity Let $(a, b) \in R, (b, c) \in R$, then $(a - b)$ and $(b - c)$ are divisible by n.

$\Rightarrow$ $a - b = nk_1$ and $b - c = nk_2$ $[k_1, k_2 \in I]$

$\Rightarrow$ $(a - b) + (b - c) = n(k_1 + k_2)$

$\Rightarrow$ $a - c = n(k_1 + k_2)$

$\Rightarrow$ $(a - c)$ is divisible by n.

$\Rightarrow$ $(a, c) \in R$

$\therefore$ R is transitive relation.

$\therefore$ R is an equivalence relation.

69. R defined on $N \times N$ such that

$$(a, b) R (c, d) \Leftrightarrow ad = bc$$

Reflexivity Let $(a, b) \in N \times N$

$\Rightarrow$ $a, b \in N \Rightarrow ab = ba$

$\Rightarrow$ $(a, b) R (a, b)$

$\therefore$ R is reflexive on, $N \times N$.

Symmetry Let $(a, b), (c, d) \in N \times N$,

then $(a, b) R (c, d) \Rightarrow ad = bc$

$\Rightarrow$ $cb = da$

$\Rightarrow$ $(c, d) R (a, b)$

$\therefore$ R is symmetric on $N \times N$.

Transitivity Let $(a, b), (c, d), (e, f) \in N \times N$

Then, $(a, b) R (c, d) \Rightarrow ad = bc$ ...(i)

$(c, d) R (e, f) \Rightarrow cf = de$ ...(ii)

From Eqs. (i) and (ii), $(ad)(cf) = (bc)(de)$

$\Rightarrow$ $af = be$

$\Rightarrow$ $(a, b) R (e, f)$

$\therefore$ R is transitive relation on $N \times N$.

$\therefore$ R is equivalence relation on $N \times N$.

70. (i) $aRb \Leftrightarrow |a-b|>0$

Reflexivity $a-a=0$

$\therefore \quad (a, a) \notin R$

$\therefore$ R is not reflexive

Symmetry $(a, b) \in R \Rightarrow |a-b|>0$

$\Rightarrow \quad |-(b-a)>0|$

$\Rightarrow \quad |b-a|>0$

$\Rightarrow \quad (b, a) \in R$

$\therefore$ R is symmetric relation

Transitivity $(a, b) \in R$ and $(b, c) \in R$

$\Rightarrow \quad |a-b|>0$ and $|b-c|>0$

$\Rightarrow \quad |a-b|+|b-c|>0$ [by addition]

Now, let $a>b$ and $b>c$, then $a>c$

$|a-b|+|b-c|=a-b+b-c=a-c>0$

$\Rightarrow \quad |a-c|>0$

If $a<b$ and $b>c$, then

$|a-b|+|b-c|=-(a-b)+(b-c)=-a+2b-c$

$\not\Rightarrow \quad |a-c|>0$

$\therefore$ R is not transitive relation.

(ii) $aRb \Leftrightarrow |a|=|b|$

Reflexivity We have, $|a|=|a|$

$\Rightarrow \quad aRa \forall a$

$\therefore$ R is reflecxive relation.

Symmetry $aRb \Rightarrow |a|=|b|$

$\Rightarrow \quad |b|=|a|$

$\Rightarrow \quad bRa$

$\therefore$ R is symmetric relation.

Transitivity $(a, b) \in R$ and $(b, c) \in R$

$\Rightarrow \quad |a|=|b|$ and $|b|=|c|$

$\Rightarrow \quad |a|=|c|$

$\Rightarrow \quad (a, c) \in R$

$\therefore$ R is transitive relation.

(iii) $aRb \Leftrightarrow |a| \geq |b|$

Reflexivity For any $a \in R$, we have $|a| \geq |a|$

So, $\quad aRa \ \forall \ a$

$\therefore$ R is reflexive relation.

Symmetry $aRb \Rightarrow |a| \geq |b|$

$\Rightarrow \quad |b| \leq |a|$

$\therefore$ R is not symmetric relation.

Transitivity aRb and $bRc \Rightarrow |a| \geq |b|$ and $|b| \geq |c|$

$\Rightarrow \quad |a| \geq |c|$

$\Rightarrow \quad a \ R \ c$

$\therefore$ R is transitive relation.

(iv) $aRb \Leftrightarrow 1+ab>0, \forall \ a, b \in R$

Reflexivity Let $a \notin R \Rightarrow 1+a \cdot a=1+a^2>0$

$\Rightarrow \quad (a, a) \in R$

$\therefore$ R is reflexive on R.

Symmetry Let $(a, b) \in R$, then $(a, b) \in R$

$\Rightarrow \quad 1+ab>0$

$\Rightarrow \quad 1+ba>0$

$\Rightarrow \quad (b, a) \in R$

$\therefore$ R is symmetric on R.

Transitivity We observe that $\left(1, \frac{1}{2}\right) \in R$ and $\left(\frac{1}{2}, -1\right) \in R$ but $(1, -1) \notin R$ because

$$1+(1)(-1)=0 \not> 0$$

$\therefore$ R is not transitive on R.

(v) $aRb \Leftrightarrow |a| \leq b$

Reflexivity Let $-1 \in R$, then $|-1| \not\leq (-1)$

$\therefore$ R is not reflexive relation

Symmetry Now, let $-3 \, R \, 4$, then $|4| \not\leq -3$

$\Rightarrow \quad 4 \, R -3$

$\therefore R$ is not symmetric relation

Transitivity aRb and $bRc \Rightarrow |a| \leq b$ and $|b| \leq c$

Then, $\quad |a| \leq c \Rightarrow aRc$

$\therefore$ R is transitive relation.

71. $A=\{x: -1 \leq x \leq\}$

$B=\{x: -1 \leq x \leq\}$

(i) $f(x)=\frac{x}{2}$

Let $\quad x_1, x_2 \in A$

$\therefore \quad f(x_1)=f(x_2) \Rightarrow \frac{x_1}{2}=\frac{x_2}{2}$

$\Rightarrow \quad x_1=x_2$

$\therefore$ f is one-one function.

Now, let $\quad y=\frac{x}{2} \Rightarrow x=2y$

$\Rightarrow \quad -1 \leq y \leq 1$

$\Rightarrow \quad -2 \leq 2y \leq 2 \Rightarrow -2 \leq x \leq 2$

Let $\quad x \in [-1, 1]$

$\therefore$ There are some value of y for which x does not exist.

So, f not onto.

(ii) $g(x)=|x|$

For $\quad x=-1, g(-1)=1$

and for $\quad x=1, g(1)=1$

$\therefore$ f is not one-one function

Let $\quad y=|x|$, then $y \geq 0$

$\therefore$ f is not onto.

(iii) $h(x)=x|x|=\begin{cases} x^2, & x \geq 0 \\ -x^2, & x<0 \end{cases}$

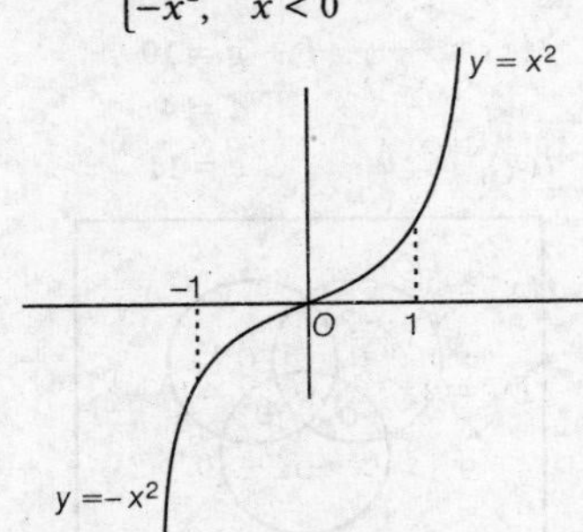

From figure, it is clear tat h is one-one and onto i.e., bijective.

(iv) $k(x) = x^2$

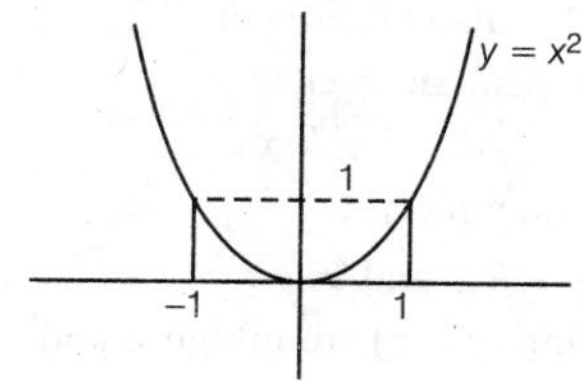

$$k(1) = 1$$

and $k(-1) = 1$

So, k is many-one function.

From figure, $y \in (0, 1)$

$\therefore$ y is not onto function.

(v) $y = l(x) = \sin \pi x$

for $x = 1$, $l(1) = \sin \pi = 0$

for $x = -1$, $l(-1) = \sin(-\pi) = 0$

$\therefore l$ is not one-one.

Now, $-1 \le x \le 1$

$\Rightarrow$ $-\pi \le \pi x \le \pi$

$\Rightarrow$ $-1 \le \sin \pi x \le 1$

$\therefore$ y is onto function.

Hence, l is surjective function.

72. $(fog)x = f(3x - 2) = e^{3x-2}$

and $(gof)x = g(e^x) = 3e^x - 2$

Let $(fog)x = y \Rightarrow e^{3x-2} = y$

$\Rightarrow$ $3x - 2 = \log_e y \Rightarrow x = \dfrac{2 + \log_e y}{3}$

$\Rightarrow (fog)^{-1}(y) = \dfrac{2 + \log_e y}{3}$

$\Rightarrow y > 0$ So, domain of $(fog)^{-1}$ is $(0, \infty)$.

Now, again let $(gof)x = 3e^x - 2$

$\Rightarrow$ $y = 3e^x - 2 \Rightarrow e^x = \dfrac{y+2}{3}$

$\therefore$ $x = \log_e\left(\dfrac{y+2}{3}\right)$

$\Rightarrow$ $(gof)^{-1}(y) = \log_e\left(\dfrac{y+2}{3}\right)$

Clearly, $y + 2 > 0 \Rightarrow y > -2$

$\therefore$ Domain of $(gof)^{-1}$ is $(-2, \infty)$.

73. $f(x) = \dfrac{x^2 - x}{x^2 + 2x}$ ...(i)

$f(x) = \dfrac{x(x-1)}{x(x+2)}$

$f(x) = \dfrac{(x-1)}{(x+2)}, x \ne 0$ ...(ii)

$D_f = \{x : x^2 + 2x \ne 0\}$ [from Eq. (i)]

$= \{x : x \in R - \{0, -2\}\}$

Now, let $y = \dfrac{x-1}{x+2}$

$\Rightarrow$ $yx + 2y = x - 1 \Rightarrow x(y - 1) = -(1 + 2y)$

$\Rightarrow$ $x = \dfrac{1 + 2y}{1 - y}$

Now, for $y = 1$, x is not defined.

Now, $x = 0, f(x) = -\dfrac{1}{2}$

$\therefore$ $R_f = R - \left\{1, -\dfrac{1}{2}\right\}$

Now, let $x_1, x_2 \in D_f$

Then, $f(x_1) = f(x_2) \Rightarrow \dfrac{x_1 - 1}{x_1 + 2} = \dfrac{x_2 - 1}{x_2 + 2}$

$\Rightarrow$ $x_1x_2 + 2x_1 - x_2 - 2 = x_1x_2 - x_1 + 2x_2 - 2$

$\Rightarrow$ $x_1 = x_2$

$\therefore f$ is one-one function.

Now, let $y = \dfrac{x-1}{x+2}$

Then, $x = \dfrac{1+2y}{1-y}$

$\Rightarrow$ $f^{-1}(y) = \dfrac{1+2y}{1-y}$ $[\because f(x) = y \Rightarrow x = f^{-1}(y)]$

Replace y by x, we get $f^{-1}(x) = \dfrac{1+2x}{1-x}$

$\Rightarrow$ $\dfrac{d}{dx}\{f^{-1}(x)\} = \dfrac{(1-x)\,2 - (1+2x)(-1)}{(1-x)^2}$

$= \dfrac{2 - 2x + 1 + 2x}{(1-x)^2}$

$\Rightarrow$ $\dfrac{d}{dx}\{f^{-1}(x)\} = \dfrac{3}{(1-x)^2}$

$\therefore$ Domain of $\dfrac{d}{dx}\{f^{-1}(x)\} = R - \{1\}$

74. $f(x) = x^2 - 1$

$$g(x) = \sqrt{x^2 + 1};\ h(x) = \begin{cases} 0, & \text{if } x \le 0 \\ x, & \text{if } x \ge 0 \end{cases}$$

$\therefore$ $(hofog)(x) = (hof)\{g(x)\}$

$= (hof)\sqrt{x^2 + 1}$

$= h\{f\sqrt{(x^2+1)}\}$

$= h\{\sqrt{(x^2+1)}^2 - 1\} = h(x^2 + 1 - 1)$

$= h(x^2) = x^2$ $[\because x^2 \ge 0]$

and $(fog)(x) = f\{g(x)\}$

$= f(\sqrt{x^2+1}) = \left(\sqrt{x^2+1}\right)^2 - 1 = x^2 + 1 - 1 = x^2$

Let $y = (fog)x = x^2, \forall x \in R$

If $x = 1$, then $y = 1$

If $x = -1$, then $y = 1$

So, fog is not one-one, so it is not invertible $h(x) = \begin{cases} 0, & x \le 0 \\ x, & x \ge 0 \end{cases}$

For $x = -1$, $h(-1) = 0$ and for $x = -2$, $h(-2) = 0$

$\therefore$ h is not identity function.

75. Here, (3, 3), (6, 6), (9, 9), (12, 12) So, it is Reflexive and

(3, 6), (6, 12), (3, 12) So, it is Transitive

Here, reflexive and transitive only.

76. Clearly, $(x, x) \in R, \forall x \in W$

So, R is reflexive.

Let $(x, y) \in R$, then $(y, x) \in R$ as x and y have atleast one letter in common. So, R is symmetric. But R is not transitive.

e.g. Let x = INDIA, y = BOMBAY and z = JUHU

Then, $(x, y) \in R$ and $(y, z) \in R$ but $(x, z) \notin R$

77. $T = \{(x, y) : x - y \in I\}$

As $0 \in I$, so T is a reflexive relation.

If $x - y \in I \Rightarrow y - x \in I$

$\therefore T$ is symmetric also.

If $x - y = I$ and $y - z = I2$

Then, $x - z = (x - y) + (y - z) = I_1 + I_2 \in I$

$\therefore$ T is also transitive.

Hence, T is an equivalence relation. Clearly, $x \neq x + 1 \Rightarrow (x, x) \notin S$

$\therefore S$ is not reflexive.

78. $\because$ $A \cap B = A \cap C \Rightarrow B = C$ and $A \cup B = A \cup C \Rightarrow B = C$

Hence, $B = C$

79. For disoint sets, $A \cap B = \phi$

Each element in either A or B or neither.

$\therefore$ Total ways $= 3^4 = 81$; $A = B$ iff $A = B = \phi$

Otherwise, A and B are interchangable

$\therefore$ Number of unordered pair for disoint subsets of

$$S = \frac{3^4 + 1}{2} = 41$$

80. xRy need not implies yRx.

$S : \frac{m}{n} S \frac{P}{q} \Leftrightarrow qm = pm \Rightarrow \frac{m}{s} S \frac{m}{n}$ is reflexive.

$\frac{m}{n} S \frac{p}{q} \Rightarrow \frac{p}{q} S \frac{m}{n}$ is symmetric.

and $\frac{m}{n} S \frac{p}{q}, \frac{p}{q} S \frac{r}{t} \Rightarrow qm = pn, pt = qr$

$\Rightarrow$ $mt = nr \Rightarrow \frac{m}{n} S \frac{r}{t}$ is transitive.

$\therefore$ S is an equivalence relation.

81. $P : \sin\theta - \cos\theta = \sqrt{2}\cos\theta \Rightarrow \tan\theta = \sqrt{2} + 1$

$Q : \sin\theta + \cos\theta = \sqrt{2}\sin\theta \Rightarrow \tan\theta = \frac{1}{\sqrt{2} - 1} = \sqrt{2} + 1$

$\therefore$ $P = Q$

82. $\because$ $(fogogof)(x) = (gogof)(x)$

$\therefore$ $(\sin\sin x^2)^2 = \sin\sin x^2 \Rightarrow \sin\sin x^2 = 0$ or 1

$\Rightarrow$ $x = +\sqrt{n\pi}, n \in \{0, 1, 2, 3, ...\}$

83. **Statement-1** $A = \{(x, y) \in R \times R : y - x$ is an integer$\}$

(a) **Reflexive** $xRy : (x - x)$ is an integer

which is true.

Hence it is reflexive.

(b) **Symmetric** $xRy : (x - y)$ is an integer.

$\Rightarrow -(y - x)$ is also an integer.

$\therefore$ $(y - x)$ is also an integer.

$\Rightarrow$ $y R x$

Hence, it is symmetric.

(c) **Transitive** $x R y$ and $y R z$

$\Rightarrow (x - y)$ and $(y - z)$ are integere and.

$\Rightarrow (x - y) + (y - z)$ is an integer.

$\Rightarrow (x - z)$ is an integer.

$\Rightarrow x R z$

$\therefore$ It is transitive

Hence, it is equvalence relation.

Statement-2

$B = \{(x, y) \in R \times R : x = \alpha y$ for some reational number $\alpha\}$

If $\alpha = 1$, then

$xRy : x = y$ (To check equivalence)

(a) **Reflexive** $xRx : x = x$ (True)

$\therefore$Reflexive

(b) **Symmetric** $xRy : x = y \Rightarrow y = x \Rightarrow yRx$

$\therefore$ Symmetric

(c) **Transitive** xRy and $yRz \Rightarrow x = y$

and $y = z \Rightarrow x = z \Rightarrow xRz$

$\therefore$ Transitive

Hence, it is equivalence relation.

$\therefore$Both are true but Statement-2 is not correct explanation of Statement-2

84. $\because$ $A \times B$ has 8 elements.

$\therefore$Number of subsets $= 2^8 = 256$

Number of subsets with zero element $= {}^8C_0 = 1$

Number of subsets with one element $= {}^8C_1 = 8$

Number of subsets with one elements $= {}^8C_2 = 28$

Hence, Number of subsets of $A \times B$ having 3 or more elements

$= 256 - (1 + 8 + 28) = 256 - 37 = 219$

85. Since, $4^n - 3n - 1 = (1 + 3)^n - 3n - 1$

$= (1 + {}^nC_1 \cdot 3 + {}^nC_2 \cdot 3^2 + {}^nC_3 \cdot 3^3 + ... + {}^nC_n \cdot 3^n) - 3n - 1$

$= 3^2({}^nC_2 + {}^nC_3 \cdot 3 + ... + {}^nC_n \cdot 3^{n-2})$

$\Rightarrow 4^n - 3n - 1$ is a multiple of 9 for $n \geq 2$

For $n = 1$, $4^n - 3n - 1 = 4 - 3 - 1 = 0$

For $n = 2$, $4^n - 3n - 1 = 16 - 6 - 1 = 9$

$\therefore 4^n - 3n - 1$ is multiple of 9 for all $n \in N$.

It is clear that X contains elements, which are multiples of 9 and Y contains all multiples of 9.

$\therefore$ $X \subseteq Y$ i.e., $X \cup Y = Y$

86. $n(A) = 4, n(B) = 2 \Rightarrow n(A \times B) = 8$

The number of subsets of $A \times B$ having at least three elements

$= {}^8C_3 + {}^8C_4 + {}^8C_5 + ... + {}^8C_8$

$= 2^8 - ({}^8C_0 + {}^8C_1 + {}^8C_2)$

$= 256 - (1 + 8 + 28) = 219$